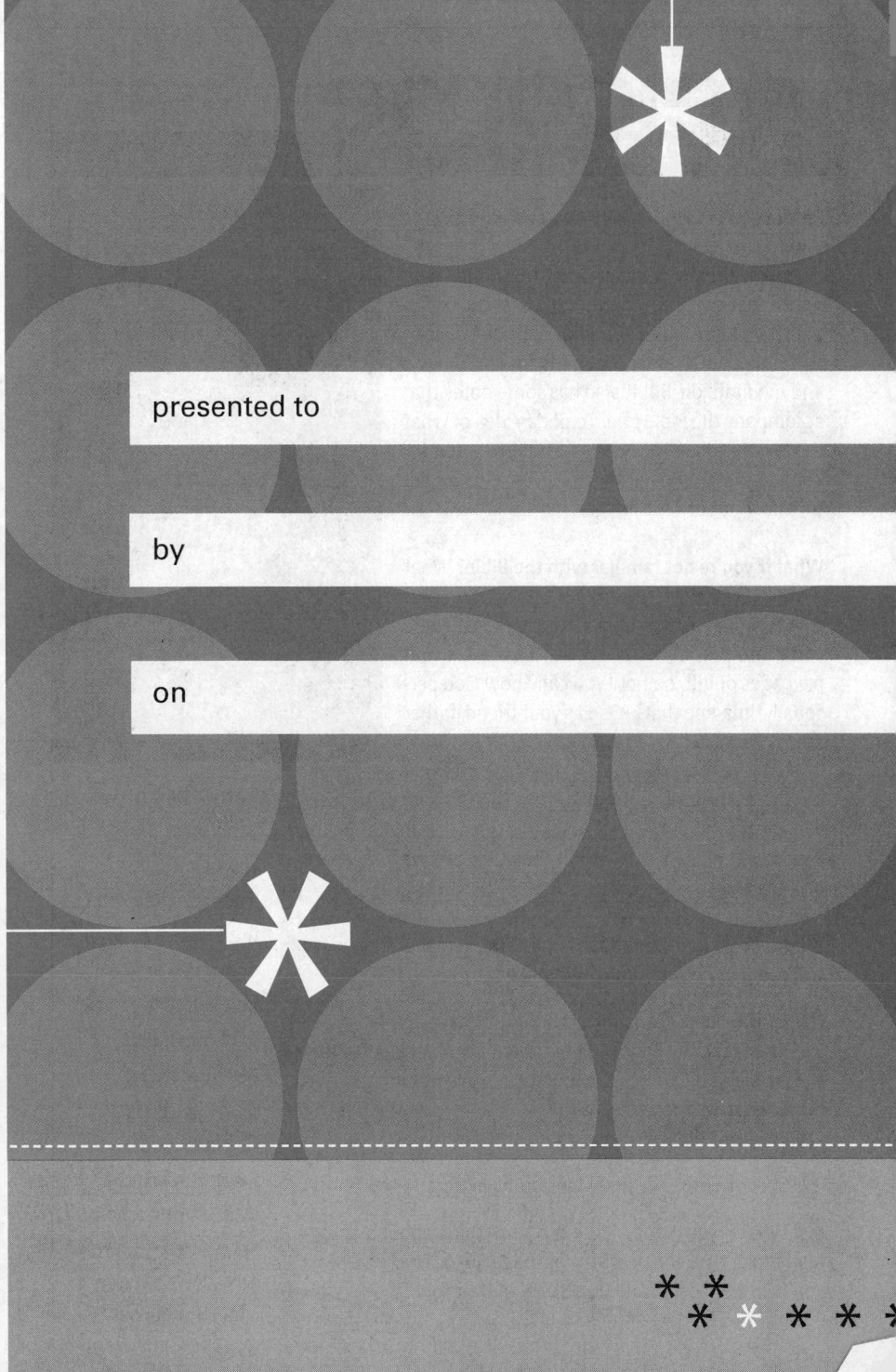

presented to

by

on

welcome

to your new Bible

Before you go any farther, stop and read this.

If you're already familiar with the Bible, then notice that the *True Images Bible* is a little different than other Bibles. It still has all the books of the Bible and all of God's words for you to read and meditate on. But it also has some notes that accompany the Bible text. To get an idea of what those notes are all about, read "An Invitation for You," starting on page vii. That will help you get the most out of *True Images*.

What if you're not familiar with the Bible? What if you're not even sure if you know God? First things first. Run, don't walk, to page 1654. There you'll find the "Christianity 101." It's a short couple pages of info on how you can know God personally. Imagine that—God as your friend, father and savior!

   If you've never owned a Bible before, you might feel a little intimidated by this big book. So after you've checked out "Christianity 101," read "An Invitation for You," page vii, to find out what the notes in *True Images* are designed to do.

Where do you go next? Great question. Here are a few ways you can get into the Word and make sense of it all:

1. Start on page 7 and read the Mirror Images profile about Eve. Then read the Bible passage about Eve. At the bottom of the profile, you'll find out where the next Mirror Images profile is located. There are 52 Mirror Images profiles, one for each week of the year. Try reading one each week.

2. Check out the reading plans on page 1664.

3. What if you want to find out something about a particular topic? The index starts on page 1656. Find the topic you're interested in, and do a study of that topic.

Remember, there are lots of ways to read God's Word. The more you read the Bible, the more comfortable you'll become with it. Talk to other Christians about how they study the Bible. Chances are, they'll have some great ideas for you. Now get started—there's so much waiting for you in the pages ahead!

remember

*true*images

Youth Specialties

YOUTH SPECIALTIES
StudentWare

ZONDERVAN™

GRAND RAPIDS, MICHIGAN 49530 USA

table of contents

feature contents

In Focus Stories

feature contents

feature contents

an invitation

Dear reader,

Have you ever wondered if God's Word relates to your real life? To those things you care about most, like your friendships, future, family, dating, identity and image? Does God have anything to say about those issues?

Yes, he sure does. Although you won't find the word *dating* in the Bible, that doesn't mean God hasn't spoken on the subject. The Bible's a manual for life, and within these pages, God gives you the answers to your toughest questions.

Every day, you are bombarded with messages from the world about how you should look, act, think and talk. You've probably grown so used to these messages that you don't even notice them. Another radio ad. Song lyrics. Air-brushed photos in a fashion magazine. Whether you realize it or not, your mind is receiving those messages. But "they are all false! Their deeds amount to nothing; their images are but wind and confusion" (Isaiah 41:29).

Where are the *true* images, the images that bring life, hope and happiness? Life is all about image—who you are, where you're going, what you're worth. That's why we created *True Images*—to give you a different message, God's message about who you are in his eyes.

The *True Images Bible* combines the timeless truth of God's Word in the easy-to-understand New International Version with features that help you make the connections between Scripture and your life.

Take a look at what's inside.

✳ **120 In Focus Articles.** Maybe you've asked yourself, "How does the Bible relate to my real life? What God says is fine and all, but what does that have to do with the issues I'm facing right now?" Good questions. Check out the 120 "In Focus" articles spread throughout the Bible. These are first-person stories from girls like you on how they've dealt with everyday life issues, such as friendship, body image, popularity, loneliness, devotions, family problems and more. After each story you'll find a short sidebar with tips on how to deal with that issue and a link to the *True Images* website (www.TrueImagesBible.com), where you'll find additional resources on each topic.

✳ **500 Truth or Dare Notes.** Ever opened the Bible and felt like you don't even know where to start? Sometimes all you see is pages and pages of dense black text, and it looks so intimidating. The 500 "Truth or Dare" notes are meant to help you find good places to dive in. These short, sound-byte notes give you a taste of what's in the text and dare you to discover God's truth on a variety of faith-related issues.

✳ **100 Love Notes from God.** When God looks at planet Earth, he doesn't just see a mass of faces. He sees you. And he loves what he sees. The 100 "Love Notes from God" will help you personalize the message of God's very personal love for you. You'll find journaling spaces with each note to help you respond. God's not interested in a soliloquy (him doing all the talking). He's speaking to you, and he'd love to hear back from his daughter.

✳ 300 Genuine Notes. There are a lot of nice-looking bodies walking around on this earth, but if that's all there is to a woman, then she doesn't have true beauty—just a shallow imitation. Believe it or not, God has a lot to say about beauty, and he's not referring to fashion tips or face masks. True beauty begins on the inside, in your heart, and flows out from there. Beauty's all about character, and the 300 "Genuine" notes in the Bible will help you identify what true beauty really looks like. So ask yourself: When God looks at you, does he see a beautiful girl?

✳ 52 Mirror Images Profiles. The Bible was written by a bunch of men and has a lot of male stars in it (Moses, Samson, David, Paul, etc.), but where are all the women?! Where's the girl next door we can relate to (Ruth), the superstar we can look up to (Esther), the female leader we can follow (Deborah)? She's right there! In fact, God features a lot of leading ladies in his Book. The 52 "Mirror Images" profiles highlight both positive and negative role models, identify key personality traits and help you apply the lessons of these women's lives to your life today. You'll get a whole new perspective on the women in the Word.

✳ 66 Book Introductions. Ever crack open your Bible to a book you've never read before and wonder what in the world is going on? Sometimes it helps to have a little background info. You'll find that in the 66 Book Introductions, along with some quick facts on the book and "Life Lessons" to remember. Everything in the Bible is there for a purpose, and when you start discovering God's motives for why he wants you to read each book, you'll be amazed at his master plan and how it all fits together. Rely on the Book Introductions to help prepare you for the time you spend reading God's Word.

✳ 12 Quizzes. How about a little fun . . . or a lot of fun, for that matter? Check out the 12 quizzes located on the glossy tip-in pages in the Bible. What's your image? How well do you know your best friend? Who's your Prince Charming? What are your spiritual gifts? Discover the answers to these questions and more when you take the quizzes inside. While you're there, you can also check out what guys think about specific topics, such as dating and friendship, in the "Reflections from the Other Side" interviews.

✳ Subject Index, "Christianity 101," Reading Plans, Prayer Log. Check out the back of *True Images* for more help in your walk with Christ.

✳ www.TrueImagesBible.com. Well, we ran out of pages. But we didn't want to let that stop us from providing you with extra resources for your walk with Christ. Check out www.TrueImagesBible.com for additional help on life issues, Bible reading plans, info on other Zondervan products and more! Let this site become your online encouragement to carry your commitment to Christ into every area of your life.

As you can tell, we feel strongly about the power of God's Word and what he has to say to you. He loves you so deeply and truly wants what's best for you. We invite you to open *True Images* and discover God's truth for yourself. Go ahead—he's waiting for you inside.

Developed for Zondervan
by the Livingstone
Corporation.

General Editor
Paige Drygas

Development Team
Paige Drygas

Katie E. Gieser

Betsy Todt Schmitt

Graphic Design
Kirk Luttrell

Mark Wainwright

Gayle Raymer

Writers
Emily Barton

Katherine Cloyd

Suzie Cross

Jeanette Dall

Karen Dockrey

Paige Drygas

Katie E. Gieser

Suzanne Keating

Mary Ann Lackland

Mary Larsen

Amber Rae

Betsy Todt Schmitt

Linda Taylor

Linda Washington

contributors

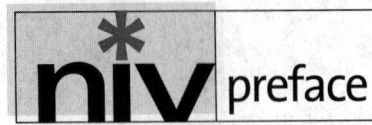 **preface**

THE NEW INTERNATIONAL VERSION is a completely new translation of the Holy Bible made by over a hundred scholars working directly from the best available Hebrew, Aramaic and Greek texts. It had its beginning in 1965 when, after several years of exploratory study by committees from the Christian Reformed Church and the National Association of Evangelicals, a group of scholars met at Palos Heights, Illinois, and concurred in the need for a new translation of the Bible in contemporary English. This group, though not made up of official church representatives, was transdenominational. Its conclusion was endorsed by a large number of leaders from many denominations who met in Chicago in 1966.

Responsibility for the new version was delegated by the Palos Heights group to a self-governing body of fifteen, the Committee on Bible Translation, composed for the most part of biblical scholars from colleges, universities and seminaries. In 1967 the New York Bible Society (now the International Bible Society) generously undertook the financial sponsorship of the project—a sponsorship that made it possible to enlist the help of many distinguished scholars. The fact that participants from the United States, Great Britain, Canada, Australia and New Zealand worked together gave the project its inter-national scope. That they were from many denominations—including Anglican, Assemblies of God, Baptist, Brethren, Christian Reformed, Church of Christ, Evangelical Free, Lutheran, Mennonite, Methodist, Nazarene, Presbyterian, Wesleyan and other churches—helped to safeguard the translation from sectarian bias.

How it was made helps to give the New International Version its distinctiveness. The translation of each book was assigned to a team of scholars. Next, one of the Intermediate Editorial Committees revised the initial translation, with constant reference to the Hebrew, Aramaic or Greek. Their work then went to one of the General Editorial Committees, which checked it in detail and made another thorough revision. This revision in turn was carefully reviewed by the Committee on Bible Translation, which made further changes and then released the final version for publication. In this way the entire Bible underwent three revisions, during each of which the translation was examined for its faithfulness to the original languages and for its English style.

All this involved many thousands of hours of research and discussion regarding the meaning of the texts and the precise way of putting them into English. It may well be that no other translation has been made by a more thorough process of review and revision from committee to committee than this one.

From the beginning of the project, the Committee on Bible Translation held to certain goals for the New International Version: that it would be an accurate translation and one that would have clarity and literary quality and so prove suitable for public and private reading, teaching, preaching, memorizing and liturgical use. The Committee also sought to preserve some measure of continuity with the long tradition of translating the Scriptures into English.

In working toward these goals, the translators were united in their commitment to the authority and infallibility of the Bible as God's Word in written form. They believe that it contains the divine answer to the deepest needs of humanity, that it sheds unique light on our path in a dark world, and that it sets forth the way to our eternal well-being.

The first concern of the translators has been the accuracy of the translation and its fidelity to the thought of the biblical writers. They have weighed the significance of the lexical and grammatical details of the Hebrew, Aramaic and Greek texts. At the same time, they have striven for more than a word-for-word translation. Because thought patterns and syntax differ from language to language, faithful communication of the meaning of the writers of the Bible demands frequent modifications in sentence structure and constant regard for the contextual meanings of words.

A sensitive feeling for style does not always accompany scholarship. Accordingly the Committee on Bible Translation submitted the developing version to a number of stylistic consultants. Two of them read every book of both Old and New Testaments twice—once before and once after the last major revision—and made invaluable suggestions. Samples of the translation were tested for clarity and ease of reading by various kinds of people—young and old, highly educated and less well educated, ministers and laymen.

preface

Concern for clear and natural English—that the New International Version should be idiomatic but not idiosyncratic, contemporary but not dated—motivated the translators and consultants. At the same time, they tried to reflect the differing styles of the biblical writers. In view of the international use of English, the translators sought to avoid obvious Americanisms on the one hand and obvious Anglicisms on the other. A British edition reflects the comparatively few differences of significant idiom and of spelling.

As for the traditional pronouns "thou," "thee" and "thine" in reference to the Deity, the translators judged that to use these archaisms (along with the old verb forms such as "doest," "wouldest" and "hadst") would violate accuracy in translation. Neither Hebrew, Aramaic nor Greek uses special pronouns for the persons of the Godhead. A present-day translation is not enhanced by forms that in the time of the King James Version were used in everyday speech, whether referring to God or man.

For the Old Testament the standard Hebrew text, the Masoretic Text as published in the latest editions of Biblia Hebraica, was used throughout. The Dead Sea Scrolls contain material bearing on an earlier stage of the Hebrew text. They were consulted, as were the Samaritan Pentateuch and the ancient scribal traditions relating to textual changes. Sometimes a variant Hebrew reading in the margin of the Masoretic Text was followed instead of the text itself. Such instances, being variants within the Masoretic tradition, are not specified by footnotes. In rare cases, words in the consonantal text were divided differently from the way they appear in the Masoretic Text. Footnotes indicate this. The translators also consulted the more important early versions—the Septuagint; Aquila, Symmachus and Theodotion; the Vulgate; the Syriac Peshitta; the Targums; and for the Psalms the Juxta Hebraica of Jerome. Readings from these versions were occasionally followed where the Masoretic Text seemed doubtful and where accepted principles of textual criticism showed that one or more of these textual witnesses appeared to provide the correct reading. Such instances are footnoted. Sometimes vowel letters and vowel signs did not, in the judgment of the translators, represent the correct vowels for the original consonantal text. Accordingly some words were read with a different set of vowels. These instances are usually not indicated by footnotes.

The Greek text used in translating the New Testament was an eclectic one. No other piece of ancient literature has such an abundance of manuscript witnesses as does the New Testament. Where existing manuscripts differ, the translators made their choice of readings according to accepted principles of New Testament textual criticism. Footnotes call attention to places where there was uncertainty about what the original text was. The best current printed texts of the Greek New Testament were used.

There is a sense in which the work of translation is never wholly finished. This applies to all great literature and uniquely so to the Bible. In 1973 the New Testament in the New International Version was published. Since then, suggestions for corrections and revisions have been received from various sources. The Committee on Bible Translation carefully considered the suggestions and adopted a number of them. These were incorporated in the first printing of the entire Bible in 1978. Additional revisions were made by the Committee on Bible Translation in 1983 and appear in printings after that date.

As in other ancient documents, the precise meaning of the biblical texts is sometimes uncertain. This is more often the case with the Hebrew and Aramaic texts than with the Greek text. Although archaeological and linguistic discoveries in this century aid in understanding difficult passages, some uncertainties remain. The more significant of these have been called to the reader's attention in the footnotes.

In regard to the divine name YHWH, commonly referred to as the Tetragrammaton, the translators adopted the device used in most English versions of rendering that name as "Lord" in capital letters to distinguish it from Adonai, another Hebrew word rendered "Lord," for which small letters are used. Wherever the two names stand together in the Old Testament as a compound name of God, they are rendered "Sovereign Lord."

Because for most readers today the phrases "the Lord of hosts" and "God of hosts" have little meaning, this version renders them "the Lord Almighty" and "God Almighty." These renderings convey the sense of the Hebrew, namely, "he who is sovereign over all the 'hosts' (powers) in heaven and on earth, especially over the 'hosts' (armies) of Israel." For readers unacquainted with Hebrew this does not make clear the distinction between Sabaoth ("hosts" or "Almighty") and Shaddai (which can also be translated "Almighty"), but the latter occurs infrequently and is always footnoted.

preface

When Adonai and YHWH Sabaoth occur together, they are rendered "the Lord, the Lᴏʀᴅ Almighty."

As for other proper nouns, the familiar spellings of the King James Version are generally retained. Names traditionally spelled with "ch," except where it is final, are usually spelled in this translation with "k" or "c," since the biblical languages do not have the sound that "ch" frequently indicates in English—for example, in chant. For well-known names such as Zechariah, however, the traditional spelling has been retained. Variation in the spelling of names in the original languages has usually not been indicated. Where a person or place has two or more different names in the Hebrew, Aramaic or Greek texts, the more familiar one has generally been used, with footnotes where needed.

To achieve clarity the translators sometimes supplied words not in the original texts but required by the context. If there was uncertainty about such material, it is enclosed in brackets. Also for the sake of clarity or style, nouns, including some proper nouns, are sometimes substituted for pronouns, and vice versa. And though the Hebrew writers often shifted back and forth between first, second and third personal pronouns without change of antecedent, this translation often makes them uniform, in accordance with English style and without the use of footnotes.

Poetical passages are printed as poetry, that is, with indentation of lines and with separate stanzas. These are generally designed to reflect the structure of Hebrew poetry. This poetry is normally characterized by parallelism in balanced lines. Most of the poetry in the Bible is in the Old Testament, and scholars differ regarding the scansion of Hebrew lines. The translators determined the stanza divisions for the most part by analysis of the subject matter. The stanzas therefore serve as poetic paragraphs.

As an aid to the reader, italicized sectional headings are inserted in most of the books. They are not to be regarded as part of the NIV text, are not for oral reading, and are not intended to dictate the interpretation of the sections they head.

The footnotes in this version are of several kinds, most of which need no explanation. Those giving alternative translations begin with "Or" and generally introduce the alternative with the last word preceding it in the text, except when it is a single-word alternative; in poetry quoted in a footnote a slant mark indicates a line division. Footnotes introduced by "Or" do not have uniform significance. In some cases two possible translations were considered to have about equal validity. In other cases, though the translators were convinced that the translation in the text was correct, they judged that another interpretation was possible and of sufficient importance to be represented in a footnote.

In the New Testament, footnotes that refer to uncertainty regarding the original text are introduced by "Some manuscripts" or similar expressions. In the Old Testament, evidence for the reading chosen is given first and evidence for the alternative is added after a semicolon (for example: Septuagint; Hebrew *father*). In such notes the term "Hebrew" refers to the Masoretic Text.

It should be noted that minerals, flora and fauna, architectural details, articles of clothing and jewelry, musical instruments and other articles cannot always be identified with precision. Also measures of capacity in the biblical period are particularly uncertain (see the table of weights and measures following the text).

Like all translations of the Bible, made as they are by imperfect man, this one undoubtedly falls short of its goals. Yet we are grateful to God for the extent to which he has enabled us to realize these goals and for the strength he has given us and our colleagues to complete our task. We offer this version of the Bible to him in whose name and for whose glory it has been made. We pray that it will lead many into a better understanding of the Holy Scriptures and a fuller knowledge of Jesus Christ the incarnate Word, of whom the Scriptures so faithfully testify.

The Committee on Bible Translation

June 1978
(Revised Aug 1983)

Names of the translators and editors may be secured
from the International Bible Society translation sponsors
of the New International Version, 1820 Jet Stream Drive,
Colorado Springs, Colorado 08921-3696 U.S.A

author:	Moses.
date:	During the 1400s B.C., while the Israelites were traveling in the desert.
setting:	The events take place in Mesopotamia, Canaan and Egypt, parts of the region known today as the Middle East.
verse to remember:	I will make you into a great nation and I will bless you; I will make your name great, and you will be a blessing. I will bless those who bless you, and whoever curses you I will curse (12:2–3).
theme to consider:	From the beginning, God has desired a relationship with his creation—you!

unchanging truth

genesis

How do you feel about changes in your life? Maybe you're the adventurous type who gets excited about facing new challenges and meeting new people. Or do you like life to remain the same?

Certainly some changes, such as serious illness or a death in the family, are extremely traumatic and life-altering. But most of the changes in your life evolve over time and are so subtle you hardly notice what's happening.

The book of Genesis is overflowing with changes and relationships. God created a perfect world. Then sin entered and *everything* changed. A flood wiped out all life except those on the ark—more change. Broken family relationships led to murder and slavery. Mended relationships brought forgiveness and reconciliation. But through it all, God never changed, and he never will. God's faithfulness, his love and his forgiveness for his children are a constant throughout this book. At the very heart of Genesis is God's unwavering desire for a loving relationship with his people, as seen in the promise given to Abraham. Ultimately, "all peoples on earth" would have an opportunity for an intimate relationship with God—through the coming of Jesus, our Savior.

Changes are sure to come into your life. Are you ready to face them with joy and confidence? You can, because God's love for you never changes!

life lessons

3

1. God loves his people. You can trust him to keep all his promises (9:12–16).

2. You'll face many temptations to disobey God and "do what everyone else is doing." Pray that God will help you resist these temptations (39:6–10).

3. It's difficult to see God's plan when bad things happen to you. But be assured that God know what's going on and is in control (50:19–20).

The Beginning

1 In the beginning God created the heavens and the earth. ²Now the earth was[a] formless and empty, darkness was over the surface of the deep, and the Spirit of God was hovering over the waters.

³And God said, "Let there be light," and there was light. ⁴God saw that the light was good, and he separated the light from the darkness. ⁵God called the light "day," and the darkness he called "night." And there was evening, and there was morning—the first day.

⁶And God said, "Let there be an expanse between the waters to separate water from water." ⁷So God made the expanse and separated the water under the expanse from the water above it. And it was so. ⁸God called the expanse "sky." And there was evening, and there was morning—the second day.

⁹And God said, "Let the water under the sky be gathered to one place, and let dry ground appear." And it was so. ¹⁰God called the dry ground "land," and the gathered waters he called "seas." And God saw that it was good.

¹¹Then God said, "Let the land produce vegetation: seed-bearing plants and trees on the land that bear fruit with seed in it, according to their various kinds." And it was so. ¹²The land produced vegetation: plants bearing seed according to their kinds and trees bearing fruit with seed in it according to their kinds. And God saw that it was good. ¹³And there was evening, and there was morning—the third day.

¹⁴And God said, "Let there be lights in the expanse of the sky to separate the day from the night, and let them serve as signs to mark seasons and days and years, ¹⁵and let them be lights in the expanse of the sky to give light on the earth." And it was so. ¹⁶God made two great lights—the greater light to govern the day and the lesser light to govern the night. He also made the stars. ¹⁷God set them in the expanse of the sky to give light on the earth, ¹⁸to govern the day and the night, and to separate light from darkness. And God saw that it was good. ¹⁹And there was evening, and there was morning—the fourth day.

²⁰And God said, "Let the water teem with living creatures, and let birds fly above the earth across the expanse of the sky." ²¹So God created the great creatures of the sea and every living and moving thing with which the water teems, according to their kinds, and every winged bird according to its kind. And God saw that it was good. ²²God blessed them and said, "Be fruitful and increase in number and fill the water in the seas, and let the birds increase on the earth." ²³And there was evening, and there was morning—the fifth day.

²⁴And God said, "Let the land produce living creatures according to their kinds: livestock, creatures that move along the ground, and wild animals, each according to its kind." And it was so. ²⁵God made the wild animals according to their kinds, the livestock according to their kinds, and all the creatures that move along the ground according to their kinds. And God saw that it was good.

²⁶Then God said, "Let us make man in our image, in our likeness, and let them rule over the fish of the sea and the birds of the air, over the livestock, over all the earth,[b] and over all the creatures that move along the ground."

²⁷So God created man in his own image,
in the image of God he created him;
male and female he created them.

²⁸God blessed them and said to them, "Be fruitful and increase in number; fill the earth and subdue it. Rule over the fish of the sea and the birds of the air and over every living creature that moves on the ground."

truth or dare

Look around at all the variety on earth. That took some serious creativity. In fact, God created creativity itself! And he used it to make his *good* creation—you.

1:25

---

a 2 Or possibly *became*   b 26 Hebrew; Syriac *all the wild animals*

²⁹Then God said, "I give you every seed-bearing plant on the face of the whole earth and every tree that has fruit with seed in it. They will be yours for food. ³⁰And to all the beasts of the earth and all the birds of the air and all the creatures that move on the ground—everything that has the breath of life in it—I give every green plant for food." And it was so.

³¹God saw all that he had made, and it was very good. And there was evening, and there was morning—the sixth day.

2

Thus the heavens and the earth were completed in all their vast array.

²By the seventh day God had finished the work he had been doing; so on the seventh day he rested^a from all his work. ³And God blessed the seventh day and made it holy, because on it he rested from all the work of creating that he had done.

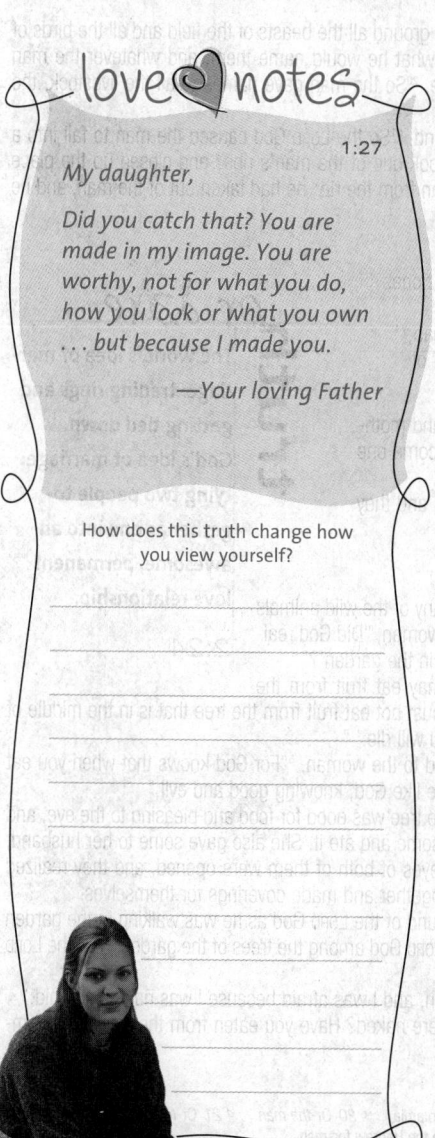

love notes

1:27

My daughter,

Did you catch that? You are made in my image. You are worthy, not for what you do, how you look or what you own . . . but because I made you.

—Your loving Father

How does this truth change how you view yourself?

_____

_____

_____

_____

_____

_____

_____

Adam and Eve

⁴This is the account of the heavens and the earth when they were created.

When the Lᴏʀᴅ God made the earth and the heavens— ⁵and no shrub of the field had yet appeared on the earth^b and no plant of the field had yet sprung up, for the Lᴏʀᴅ God had not sent rain on the earth^b and there was no man to work the ground, ⁶but streams^c came up from the earth and watered the whole surface of the ground— ⁷the Lᴏʀᴅ God formed the man^d from the dust of the ground and breathed into his nostrils the breath of life, and the man became a living being.

⁸Now the Lᴏʀᴅ God had planted a garden in the east, in Eden; and there he put the man he had formed. ⁹And the Lᴏʀᴅ God made all kinds of trees grow out of the ground—trees that were pleasing to the

truth or dare

Feeling a bit frazzled? Taking a break isn't just a good idea; it's a command from God. Even the Creator of the universe took a day off from his work for a little R&R.

2:3

^a 2 Or *ceased*; also in verse 3   ^b 5 Or *land*; also in verse 6   ^c 6 Or *mist*   ^d 7 The Hebrew for *man (adam)* sounds like and may be related to the Hebrew for *ground (adamah)*; it is also the name *Adam* (see Gen. 2:20).

eye and good for food. In the middle of the garden were the tree of life and the tree of the knowledge of good and evil.

[10]A river watering the garden flowed from Eden; from there it was separated into four headwaters. [11]The name of the first is the Pishon; it winds through the entire land of Havilah, where there is gold. [12](The gold of that land is good; aromatic resin[a] and onyx are also there.) [13]The name of the second river is the Gihon; it winds through the entire land of Cush.[b] [14]The name of the third river is the Tigris; it runs along the east side of Asshur. And the fourth river is the Euphrates.

[15]The LORD God took the man and put him in the Garden of Eden to work it and take care of it. [16]And the LORD God commanded the man, "You are free to eat from any tree in the garden; [17]but you must not eat from the tree of the knowledge of good and evil, for when you eat of it you will surely die."

[18]The LORD God said, "It is not good for the man to be alone. I will make a helper suitable for him."

[19]Now the LORD God had formed out of the ground all the beasts of the field and all the birds of the air. He brought them to the man to see what he would name them; and whatever the man called each living creature, that was its name. [20]So the man gave names to all the livestock, the birds of the air and all the beasts of the field.

But for Adam[c] no suitable helper was found. [21]So the LORD God caused the man to fall into a deep sleep; and while he was sleeping, he took one of the man's ribs[d] and closed up the place with flesh. [22]Then the LORD God made a woman from the rib[e] he had taken out of the man, and he brought her to the man.

[23]The man said,

> "This is now bone of my bones
> and flesh of my flesh;
> she shall be called 'woman,'[f]
> for she was taken out of
> man."

[24]For this reason a man will leave his father and mother and be united to his wife, and they will become one flesh.

[25]The man and his wife were both naked, and they felt no shame.

The Fall of Man

3 Now the serpent was more crafty than any of the wild animals the LORD God had made. He said to the woman, "Did God really say, 'You must not eat from any tree in the garden'?" [2]The woman said to the serpent, "We may eat fruit from the trees in the garden, [3]but God did say, 'You must not eat fruit from the tree that is in the middle of the garden, and you must not touch it, or you will die.' "

[4]"You will not surely die," the serpent said to the woman. [5]"For God knows that when you eat of it your eyes will be opened, and you will be like God, knowing good and evil."

[6]When the woman saw that the fruit of the tree was good for food and pleasing to the eye, and also desirable for gaining wisdom, she took some and ate it. She also gave some to her husband, who was with her, and he ate it. [7]Then the eyes of both of them were opened, and they realized they were naked; so they sewed fig leaves together and made coverings for themselves.

[8]Then the man and his wife heard the sound of the LORD God as he was walking in the garden in the cool of the day, and they hid from the LORD God among the trees of the garden. [9]But the LORD God called to the man, "Where are you?"

[10]He answered, "I heard you in the garden, and I was afraid because I was naked; so I hid."

[11]And he said, "Who told you that you were naked? Have you eaten from the tree that I commanded you not to eat from?"

truth or dare

The world's idea of marriage: trading rings and getting tied down. God's idea of marriage: tying two people together as one into an awesome, permanent love relationship.

2:24

---

a 12 Or good; pearls   *b 13 Possibly southeast Mesopotamia*   *c 20 Or the man*   *d 21 Or took part of the man's side*
e 22 Or part   *f 23 The Hebrew for woman sounds like the Hebrew for man.*

¹²The man said, "The woman you put here with me—she gave me some fruit from the tree, and I ate it."

¹³Then the LORD God said to the woman, "What is this you have done?"

The woman said, "The serpent deceived me, and I ate."

¹⁴So the LORD God said to the serpent, "Because you have done this,

> "Cursed are you above all the
> livestock
> and all the wild animals!
> You will crawl on your belly
> and you will eat dust
> all the days of your life.
> ¹⁵And I will put enmity
> between you and the woman,
> and between your offspring ᵃ
> and hers;
> he will crush ᵇ your head,
> and you will strike his heel."

¹⁶To the woman he said,

> "I will greatly increase your pains in
> childbearing;
> with pain you will give birth to children.
> Your desire will be for your husband,
> and he will rule over you."

truth or dare

Who would've thought that Eve's offspring (a.k.a. Jesus) would make an appearance way back in Genesis? Satan did attack Jesus, but in the end, Jesus crushed death and Satan for us!

3:15

¹⁷To Adam he said, "Because you listened to your wife and ate from the tree about which I commanded you, 'You must not eat of it,'

> "Cursed is the ground because of you;
> through painful toil you will eat of it
> all the days of your life.
> ¹⁸It will produce thorns and thistles for you,
> and you will eat the plants of the field.
> ¹⁹By the sweat of your brow
> you will eat your food
> until you return to the ground,
> since from it you were taken;
> for dust you are
> and to dust you will return."

²⁰Adam ᶜ named his wife Eve, ᵈ because she would become the mother of all the living.

²¹The LORD God made garments of skin for Adam and his wife and clothed them. ²²And the LORD God said, "The man has now become like one of us, knowing good and evil. He must not be allowed to reach out his hand and take also from the tree of life and eat, and live forever." ²³So the LORD God banished him from the Garden of Eden to work the ground from which he had been taken. ²⁴After he drove the man out, he placed on the east side ᵉ of the Garden of Eden cherubim and a flaming sword flashing back and forth to guard the way to the tree of life.

Cain and Abel

4 Adam ᶜ lay with his wife Eve, and she became pregnant and gave birth to Cain. ᶠ She said, "With the help of the LORD I have brought forth ᵍ a man." ²Later she gave birth to his brother Abel.

Now Abel kept flocks, and Cain worked the soil. ³In the course of time Cain brought some of the fruits of the soil as an offering to the LORD. ⁴But Abel brought fat portions from some of the first-

---

ᵃ 15 Or *seed*   ᵇ 15 Or *strike*   ᶜ 20,1 Or *The man*   ᵈ 20 *Eve* probably means *living*.   ᵉ 24 Or *placed in front*
ᶠ 1 *Cain* sounds like the Hebrew for *brought forth* or *acquired*.   ᵍ 1 Or *have acquired*

born of his flock. The LORD looked with favor on Abel and his offering, [5]but on Cain and his offering he did not look with favor. So Cain was very angry, and his face was downcast.

[6]Then the LORD said to Cain, "Why are you angry? Why is your face downcast? [7]If you do what is right, will you not be accepted? But if you do not do what is right, sin is crouching at your door; it desires to have you, but you must master it."

[8]Now Cain said to his brother Abel, "Let's go out to the field."[a] And while they were in the field, Cain attacked his brother Abel and killed him.

[9]Then the LORD said to Cain, "Where is your brother Abel?"

"I don't know," he replied. "Am I my brother's keeper?"

[10]The LORD said, "What have you done? Listen! Your brother's blood cries out to me from the ground. [11]Now you are under a curse and driven from the ground, which opened its mouth to receive your brother's blood from your hand. [12]When you work the ground, it will no longer yield its crops for you. You will be a restless wanderer on the earth."

[13]Cain said to the LORD, "My punishment is more than I can bear. [14]Today you are driving me from the land, and I will be hidden from your presence; I will be a restless wanderer on the earth, and whoever finds me will kill me."

[15]But the LORD said to him, "Not so[b]; if anyone kills Cain, he will suffer vengeance seven times over." Then the LORD put a mark on Cain so that no one who found him would kill him. [16]So Cain went out from the LORD's presence and lived in the land of Nod,[c] east of Eden.

[17]Cain lay with his wife, and she became pregnant and gave birth to Enoch. Cain was then building a city, and he named it after his son Enoch. [18]To Enoch was born Irad, and Irad was the father of Mehujael, and Mehujael was the father of Methushael, and Methushael was the father of Lamech.

[19]Lamech married two women, one named Adah and the other Zillah. [20]Adah gave birth to Jabal; he was the father of those who live in tents and raise livestock. [21]His brother's name was Jubal; he was the father of all who play the harp and flute. [22]Zillah also had a son, Tubal-Cain, who forged all kinds of tools out of[d] bronze and iron. Tubal-Cain's sister was Naamah.

[23]Lamech said to his wives,

"Adah and Zillah, listen to me;
　　wives of Lamech, hear my words.
I have killed[e] a man for wounding me,
　　a young man for injuring me.
[24]If Cain is avenged seven times,
　　then Lamech seventy-seven times."

[25]Adam lay with his wife again, and she gave birth to a son and named him Seth,[f] saying, "God has granted me another child in place of Abel, since Cain killed him." [26]Seth also had a son, and he named him Enosh.

At that time men began to call on[g] the name of the LORD.

From Adam to Noah

5 This is the written account of Adam's line.

When God created man, he made him in the likeness of God. [2]He created them male and female and blessed them. And when they were created, he called them "man."[h]

---

a 8 Samaritan Pentateuch, Septuagint, Vulgate and Syriac; Masoretic Text does not have *"Let's go out to the field."*
b 15 Septuagint, Vulgate and Syriac; Hebrew *Very well*　　　c 16 *Nod* means *wandering* (see verses 12 and 14).
d 22 Or *who instructed all who work in*　　e 23 Or *I will kill*　　f 25 *Seth* probably means *granted.*　　g 26 Or *to proclaim*
h 2 Hebrew *adam*

mirror images

When the woman saw that the fruit of the tree was good for food and pleasing to the eye, and also desirable for gaining wisdom, she took some and ate it. Genesis 3:6

Eve—The Girl Who Wants It All

Meet Eve. You probably already know a dozen girls just like her. She's the girl who has it all. She's got a great boyfriend, a great body—a great life. But it doesn't seem like enough to this poor modern "Eve." She can't seem to say no to anything. When her friends tell her smoking pot will make her more popular, she takes a puff. And when they whip out the tarot cards at the Friday night party, she ignores her conscience and joins in. What's worse, "Eve" encourages everyone else to do the wrong thing, too.

In Genesis 3, we see that Eve's poor decisions and inability to say no had very serious, world-changing consequences. When God created Adam and Eve, everything was perfect; they had the beautiful Garden of Eden, God's provision of food and protection, and their love and friendship with each other and with God. Eve gave it all up when she took the only thing God said she couldn't have—forbidden fruit from one particular tree. When Satan promised this delicious fruit would make her wise, Eve bought the lie. Then she got her husband, Adam, to take a bite, too. Sin and pain suddenly entered the world, and it all began with Eve trusting the twisted words of the last person in the world that she should have been listening to.

Thanks a lot, sister, you might think. But sometimes we act a lot like Eve. Sometimes we know what's right, but we think doing the wrong thing will make us happy or popular. Sure, Satan knows the best ways to tempt us, but when it comes to doing the wrong thing, we have only ourselves to blame.

To read the next Mirror Images profile, go to page 21.

Dear Jesus, Eve really blew it. And sometimes I do too. Thanks for still loving me ... and for forgiving me when I confess that I have failed you. And help me to look to you when I need the strength to do the right thing. Amen.

dear Jesus

⟫ Read more about Eve in Genesis 2:18—3:20 (pages 4–5).

³When Adam had lived 130 years, he had a son in his own likeness, in his own image; and he named him Seth. ⁴After Seth was born, Adam lived 800 years and had other sons and daughters. ⁵Altogether, Adam lived 930 years, and then he died.

⁶When Seth had lived 105 years, he became the father*ᵃ* of Enosh. ⁷And after he became the father of Enosh, Seth lived 807 years and had other sons and daughters. ⁸Altogether, Seth lived 912 years, and then he died.

⁹When Enosh had lived 90 years, he became the father of Kenan. ¹⁰And after he became the father of Kenan, Enosh lived 815 years and had other sons and daughters. ¹¹Altogether, Enosh lived 905 years, and then he died.

¹²When Kenan had lived 70 years, he became the father of Mahalalel. ¹³And after he became the father of Mahalalel, Kenan lived 840 years and had other sons and daughters. ¹⁴Altogether, Kenan lived 910 years, and then he died.

¹⁵When Mahalalel had lived 65 years, he became the father of Jared. ¹⁶And after he became the father of Jared, Mahalalel lived 830 years and had other sons and daughters. ¹⁷Altogether, Mahalalel lived 895 years, and then he died.

¹⁸When Jared had lived 162 years, he became the father of Enoch. ¹⁹And after he became the father of Enoch, Jared lived 800 years and had other sons and daughters. ²⁰Altogether, Jared lived 962 years, and then he died.

²¹When Enoch had lived 65 years, he became the father of Methuselah. ²²And after he became the father of Methuselah, Enoch walked with God 300 years and had other sons and daughters. ²³Altogether, Enoch lived 365 years. ²⁴Enoch walked with God; then he was no more, because God took him away.

²⁵When Methuselah had lived 187 years, he became the father of Lamech. ²⁶And after he became the father of Lamech, Methuselah lived 782 years and had other sons and daughters. ²⁷Altogether, Methuselah lived 969 years, and then he died.

²⁸When Lamech had lived 182 years, he had a son. ²⁹He named him Noah*ᵇ* and said, "He will comfort us in the labor and painful toil of our hands caused by the ground the LORD has cursed." ³⁰After Noah was born, Lamech lived 595 years and had other sons and daughters. ³¹Altogether, Lamech lived 777 years, and then he died.

³²After Noah was 500 years old, he became the father of Shem, Ham and Japheth.

The Flood

6 When men began to increase in number on the earth and daughters were born to them, ²the sons of God saw that the daughters of men were beautiful, and they married any of them they chose. ³Then the LORD said, "My Spirit will not contend with*ᶜ* man forever, for he is mortal*ᵈ*; his days will be a hundred and twenty years."

⁴The Nephilim were on the earth in those days—and also afterward—when the sons of God went to the daughters of men and had children by them. They were the heroes of old, men of renown.

⁵The LORD saw how great man's wickedness on the earth had become, and that every inclination of the thoughts of his heart was only evil all the time. ⁶The LORD was grieved that he had

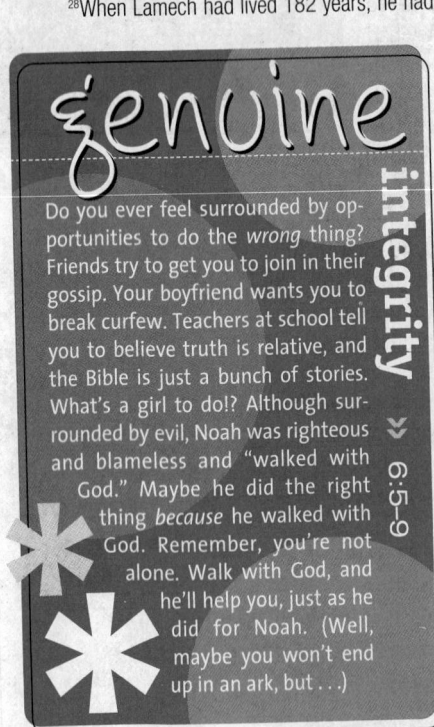

genuine

integrity »» 6:5-9

Do you ever feel surrounded by opportunities to do the *wrong* thing? Friends try to get you to join in their gossip. Your boyfriend wants you to break curfew. Teachers at school tell you to believe truth is relative, and the Bible is just a bunch of stories. What's a girl to do!? Although surrounded by evil, Noah was righteous and blameless and "walked with God." Maybe he did the right thing *because* he walked with God. Remember, you're not alone. Walk with God, and he'll help you, just as he did for Noah. (Well, maybe you won't end up in an ark, but . . .)

ᵃ 6 Father may mean *ancestor*; also in verses 7-26.   *ᵇ 29 Noah* sounds like the Hebrew for *comfort*.   *ᶜ 3 Or My spirit will not remain in*   *ᵈ 3 Or corrupt* made man on the earth, and his heart was filled with pain. ⁷So the LORD said, "I will wipe mankind, whom I have created, from the face of the earth—men and animals, and creatures that move along the ground, and birds of the air—for I am grieved that I have made them." ⁸But Noah found favor in the eyes of the LORD.

⁹This is the account of Noah.

Noah was a righteous man, blameless among the people of his time, and he walked with God. ¹⁰Noah had three sons: Shem, Ham and Japheth.

¹¹Now the earth was corrupt in God's sight and was full of violence. ¹²God saw how corrupt the earth had become, for all the people on earth had corrupted their ways. ¹³So God said to Noah, "I am going to put an end to all people, for the earth is filled with violence because of them. I am surely going to destroy both them and the earth. ¹⁴So make yourself an ark of cypress*ᵃ* wood; make rooms in it and coat it with pitch inside and out. ¹⁵This is how you are to build it: The ark is to be 450 feet long, 75 feet wide and 45 feet high.*ᵇ* ¹⁶Make a roof for it and finish*ᶜ* the ark to within 18 inches*ᵈ* of the top. Put a door in the side of the ark and make lower, middle and upper decks. ¹⁷I am going to bring floodwaters on the earth to destroy all life under the heavens, every creature that has the breath of life in it. Everything on earth will perish. ¹⁸But I will establish my covenant with you, and you will enter the ark—you and your sons and your wife and your sons' wives with you. ¹⁹You are to bring into the ark two of all living creatures, male and female, to keep them alive with you. ²⁰Two of every kind of bird, of every kind of animal and of every kind of creature that moves along the ground will come to you to be kept alive. ²¹You are to take every kind of food that is to be eaten and store it away as food for you and for them."

²²Noah did everything just as God commanded him.

7 The LORD then said to Noah, "Go into the ark, you and your whole family, because I have found you righteous in this generation. ²Take with you seven*ᵉ* of every kind of clean animal, a male and its mate, and two of every kind of unclean animal, a male and its mate, ³and also seven of every kind of bird, male and female, to keep their various kinds alive throughout the earth. ⁴Seven days from now I will send rain on the earth for forty days and forty nights, and I will wipe from the face of the earth every living creature I have made."

⁵And Noah did all that the LORD commanded him.

⁶Noah was six hundred years old when the floodwaters came on the earth. ⁷And Noah and his sons and his wife and his sons' wives entered the ark to escape the waters of the flood. ⁸Pairs of clean and unclean animals, of birds and of all creatures that move along the ground, ⁹male and female, came to Noah and entered the ark, as God had commanded Noah. ¹⁰And after the seven days the floodwaters came on the earth.

¹¹In the six hundredth year of Noah's life, on the seventeenth day of the second month—on that day all the springs of the great deep burst forth, and the floodgates of the heavens were opened. ¹²And rain fell on the earth forty days and forty nights.

¹³On that very day Noah and his sons, Shem, Ham and Japheth, together with his wife and the wives of his three sons, entered the ark. ¹⁴They had with them every wild animal according to its kind, all livestock according to their kinds, every creature that moves along the ground according to its kind and every bird according to its kind, everything with wings. ¹⁵Pairs of all creatures that have the breath of life in them came to Noah and entered the ark. ¹⁶The animals going in were male and female of every living thing, as God had commanded Noah. Then the LORD shut him in.

¹⁷For forty days the flood kept coming on the earth, and as the waters increased they lifted the

truth **or dare**

It's scary to serve God when you don't fully understand his plan, especially when others might make fun of you. Be brave. Take a stand and trust in God.

6:22

a 14 The meaning of the Hebrew for this word is uncertain.   *b 15* Hebrew *300 cubits long, 50 cubits wide and 30 cubits high* (about 140 meters long, 23 meters wide and 13.5 meters high)   *c 16* Or *Make an opening for light by finishing*   *d 16* Hebrew *a cubit* (about 0.5 meter)   *e 2* Or *seven pairs*; also in verse 3

Sisterly Love?

How did my best friend become my worst enemy? We shared the same room until middle school. We borrowed each other's clothes. We told each other our secrets. We were inseparable, best friends from birth.

Now, it feels like a constant competition. If I get a B in school, she gets an A. If I make varsity, guess who's the captain? If I look good in a swimsuit, she looks even better. It's all about who can do or be better than the other. And she always wins.

My mom says I shouldn't compare myself to Kris. How can I *not?* "Your sister is *so* gorgeous!" Believe me, I hear it all the time. My sister—the living Barbie doll. Complete with the Ken-like boyfriend. Why couldn't I at least have a perky name like hers? Even my name sounds boring to me. Madeline—yawn!

Kris got all the looks. The brains. The talent. And what did I get? I got a "good personality" and a cute face. Sometimes I wonder why God didn't even out the gene pool a little bit. Maybe he used all the good stuff on her and saved the scraps for me.

Lately I find myself wishing these horrible things about her. My own sister! But if I didn't constantly think about her, then maybe I would actually enjoy my own life.

For more on the dangers of out-of-control competitiveness, go online at www.TrueImagesBible.com

competition in focus

Competition is part of human nature. In fact, we actually need competition to sharpen our skills. The trouble comes when we constantly compare ourselves to others. Why so?

» When you compete in athletics, you may win or lose. But when you compare yourself to others, you always come up short one way or another.

» Comparison quickly leads to criticism—criticizing others and being critical of yourself. Read how sibling competition can get way out of control in Genesis 4:1–16 (pages 5–6).

» If you're really serious about getting competitiveness under control, pray for your rivals. Yup, that's right—pray. Jesus shows how in Matthew 5:43–44 (page 1297).

For more on this topic, see the index on page 1656.

ark high above the earth. [18]The waters rose and increased greatly on the earth, and the ark floated on the surface of the water. [19]They rose greatly on the earth, and all the high mountains under the entire heavens were covered. [20]The waters rose and covered the mountains to a depth of more than twenty feet. [a,b] [21]Every living thing that moved on the earth perished—birds, livestock, wild animals, all the creatures that swarm over the earth, and all mankind. [22]Everything on dry land that had the breath of life in its nostrils died. [23]Every living thing on the face of the earth was wiped out; men and animals and the creatures that move along the ground and the birds of the air were wiped from the earth. Only Noah was left, and those with him in the ark.

[24]The waters flooded the earth for a hundred and fifty days.

a 20 Hebrew *fifteen cubits* (about 6.9 meters)   *b 20* Or *rose more than twenty feet, and the mountains were covered*

8 But God remembered Noah and all the wild animals and the livestock that were with him in the ark, and he sent a wind over the earth, and the waters receded. ²Now the springs of the deep and the floodgates of the heavens had been closed, and the rain had stopped falling from the sky. ³The water receded steadily from the earth. At the end of the hundred and fifty days the water had gone down, ⁴and on the seventeenth day of the seventh month the ark came to rest on the mountains of Ararat. ⁵The waters continued to recede until the tenth month, and on the first day of the tenth month the tops of the mountains became visible.

⁶After forty days Noah opened the window he had made in the ark ⁷and sent out a raven, and it kept flying back and forth until the water had dried up from the earth. ⁸Then he sent out a dove to see if the water had receded from the surface of the ground. ⁹But the dove could find no place to set its feet because there was water over all the surface of the earth; so it returned to Noah in the ark. He reached out his hand and took the dove and brought it back to himself in the ark. ¹⁰He waited seven more days and again sent out the dove from the ark. ¹¹When the dove returned to him in the evening, there in its beak was a freshly plucked olive leaf! Then Noah knew that the water had receded from the earth. ¹²He waited seven more days and sent the dove out again, but this time it did not return to him.

¹³By the first day of the first month of Noah's six hundred and first year, the water had dried up from the earth. Noah then removed the covering from the ark and saw that the surface of the ground was dry. ¹⁴By the twenty-seventh day of the second month the earth was completely dry.

¹⁵Then God said to Noah, ¹⁶"Come out of the ark, you and your wife and your sons and their wives. ¹⁷Bring out every kind of living creature that is with you—the birds, the animals, and all the creatures that move along the ground—so they can multiply on the earth and be fruitful and increase in number upon it."

¹⁸So Noah came out, together with his sons and his wife and his sons' wives. ¹⁹All the animals and all the creatures that move along the ground and all the birds—everything that moves on the earth—came out of the ark, one kind after another.

²⁰Then Noah built an altar to the LORD and, taking some of all the clean animals and clean birds, he sacrificed burnt offerings on it. ²¹The LORD smelled the pleasing aroma and said in his heart: "Never again will I curse the ground because of man, even though ᵃ every inclination of his heart is evil from childhood. And never again will I destroy all living creatures, as I have done.

²² "As long as the earth endures,
        seedtime and harvest,
        cold and heat,
        summer and winter,
        day and night
        will never cease."

God's Covenant With Noah

9 Then God blessed Noah and his sons, saying to them, "Be fruitful and increase in number and fill the earth. ²The fear and dread of you will fall upon all the beasts of the earth and all the birds of the air, upon every creature that moves along the ground, and upon all the fish of the sea; they are given into your hands. ³Everything that lives and moves will be food for you. Just as I gave you the green plants, I now give you everything.

⁴"But you must not eat meat that has its lifeblood still in it. ⁵And for your lifeblood I will surely demand an accounting. I will demand an accounting from every animal. And from each man, too, I will demand an accounting for the life of his fellow man.

⁶ "Whoever sheds the blood of man,
        by man shall his blood be shed;
    for in the image of God
        has God made man.

⁷As for you, be fruitful and increase in number; multiply on the earth and increase upon it."

⁸Then God said to Noah and to his sons with him: ⁹"I now establish my covenant with you and with your descendants after you ¹⁰and with every living creature that was with you—the birds, the

ᵃ 21 Or man, for

livestock and all the wild animals, all those that came out of the ark with you—every living creature on earth. ¹¹I establish my covenant with you: Never again will all life be cut off by the waters of a flood; never again will there be a flood to destroy the earth."

¹²And God said, "This is the sign of the covenant I am making between me and you and every living creature with you, a covenant for all generations to come: ¹³I have set my rainbow in the clouds, and it will be the sign of the covenant between me and the earth. ¹⁴Whenever I bring clouds over the earth and the rainbow appears in the clouds, ¹⁵I will remember my covenant between me and you and all living creatures of every kind. Never again will the waters become a flood to destroy all life. ¹⁶Whenever the rainbow appears in the clouds, I will see it and remember the everlasting covenant between God and all living creatures of every kind on the earth."

¹⁷So God said to Noah, "This is the sign of the covenant I have established between me and all life on the earth."

love notes

9:12–16

Loved one,

Every time you see a rainbow, it's a promise. It's my promise that as long as the earth remains, I will never destroy all life again, and the seasons will come as expected (see Gen 8:22). It is my sign to you that my word remains true. Forever.

—Your heavenly Father

What promise of God do you need to rely upon today?

_____

_____

_____

_____

_____

_____

_____

_____

The Sons of Noah

¹⁸The sons of Noah who came out of the ark were Shem, Ham and Japheth. (Ham was the father of Canaan.) ¹⁹These were the three sons of Noah, and from them came the people who were scattered over the earth.

²⁰Noah, a man of the soil, proceeded *ᵃ* to plant a vineyard. ²¹When he drank some of its wine, he became drunk and lay uncovered inside his tent. ²²Ham, the father of Canaan, saw his father's nakedness and told his two brothers outside. ²³But Shem and Japheth took a garment and laid it across their shoulders; then they walked in backward and covered their father's nakedness. Their faces were turned the other way so that they would not see their father's nakedness.

²⁴When Noah awoke from his wine and found out what his youngest son had done to him, ²⁵he said,

> "Cursed be Canaan!
>   The lowest of slaves
>   will he be to his brothers."

²⁶He also said,

> "Blessed be the LORD, the God of
>   Shem!
>   May Canaan be the slave of
>   Shem. *ᵇ*
> ²⁷ May God extend the territory of
>   Japheth *ᶜ*;
>   may Japheth live in the tents
>   of Shem,
>   and may Canaan be his *ᵈ*
>   slave."

²⁸After the flood Noah lived 350 years. ²⁹Altogether, Noah lived 950 years, and then he died.

ᵃ 20 Or soil, was the first   ᵇ 26 Or be his slave
ᶜ 27 Japheth sounds like the Hebrew for extend.
ᵈ 27 Or their

The Table of Nations

10 This is the account of Shem, Ham and Japheth, Noah's sons, who themselves had sons after the flood.

The Japhethites

[2] The sons[a] of Japheth:

Gomer, Magog, Madai, Javan, Tubal, Meshech and Tiras.

[3] The sons of Gomer:

Ashkenaz, Riphath and Togarmah.

[4] The sons of Javan:

Elishah, Tarshish, the Kittim and the Rodanim.[b] [5](From these the maritime peoples spread out into their territories by their clans within their nations, each with its own language.)

The Hamites

[6] The sons of Ham:

Cush, Mizraim,[c] Put and Canaan.

[7] The sons of Cush:

Seba, Havilah, Sabtah, Raamah and Sabteca.

The sons of Raamah:

Sheba and Dedan.

[8]Cush was the father[d] of Nimrod, who grew to be a mighty warrior on the earth. [9]He was a mighty hunter before the LORD; that is why it is said, "Like Nimrod, a mighty hunter before the LORD." [10]The first centers of his kingdom were Babylon, Erech, Akkad and Calneh, in[e] Shinar.[f] [11]From that land he went to Assyria, where he built Nineveh, Rehoboth Ir,[g] Calah [12]and Resen, which is between Nineveh and Calah; that is the great city.

[13]Mizraim was the father of

the Ludites, Anamites, Lehabites, Naphtuhites, [14]Pathrusites, Casluhites (from whom the Philistines came) and Caphtorites.

[15]Canaan was the father of

Sidon his firstborn,[h] and of the Hittites, [16]Jebusites, Amorites, Girgashites, [17]Hivites, Arkites, Sinites, [18]Arvadites, Zemarites and Hamathites.

Later the Canaanite clans scattered [19]and the borders of Canaan reached from Sidon toward Gerar as far as Gaza, and then toward Sodom, Gomorrah, Admah and Zeboiim, as far as Lasha.

[20]These are the sons of Ham by their clans and languages, in their territories and nations.

The Semites

[21]Sons were also born to Shem, whose older brother was[i] Japheth; Shem was the ancestor of all the sons of Eber.

[22] The sons of Shem:

Elam, Asshur, Arphaxad, Lud and Aram.

[23] The sons of Aram:

Uz, Hul, Gether and Meshech.[j]

[24] Arphaxad was the father of[k] Shelah,

and Shelah the father of Eber.

[25] Two sons were born to Eber:

---

a 2 Sons may mean *descendants* or *successors* or *nations*; also in verses 3, 4, 6, 7, 20-23, 29 and 31. *b 4* Some manuscripts of the Masoretic Text and Samaritan Pentateuch (see also Septuagint and 1 Chron. 1:7); most manuscripts of the Masoretic Text *Dodanim* *c 6* That is, Egypt; also in verse 13 *d 8 Father* may mean *ancestor* or *predecessor* or *founder*; also in verses 13, 15, 24 and 26. *e 10* Or *Erech and Akkad—all of them in* *f 10* That is, Babylonia *g 11* Or *Nineveh with its city squares* *h 15* Or *of the Sidonians, the foremost* *i 21* Or *Shem, the older brother of* *j 23* See Septuagint and 1 Chron. 1:17; Hebrew *Mash* *k 24* Hebrew; Septuagint *father of Cainan, and Cainan was the father of*

One was named Peleg,[a] because in his time the earth was divided; his brother was named Joktan.

²⁶Joktan was the father of

Almodad, Sheleph, Hazarmaveth, Jerah, ²⁷Hadoram, Uzal, Diklah, ²⁸Obal, Abimael, Sheba, ²⁹Ophir, Havilah and Jobab. All these were sons of Joktan.

³⁰The region where they lived stretched from Mesha toward Sephar, in the eastern hill country. ³¹These are the sons of Shem by their clans and languages, in their territories and nations.

³²These are the clans of Noah's sons, according to their lines of descent, within their nations. From these the nations spread out over the earth after the flood.

The Tower of Babel

11 Now the whole world had one language and a common speech. ²As men moved eastward,[b] they found a plain in Shinar[c] and settled there.

³They said to each other, "Come, let's make bricks and bake them thoroughly." They used brick instead of stone, and tar for mortar. ⁴Then they said, "Come, let us build ourselves a city, with a tower that reaches to the heavens, so that we may make a name for ourselves and not be scattered over the face of the whole earth."

⁵But the LORD came down to see the city and the tower that the men were building. ⁶The LORD said, "If as one people speaking the same language they have begun to do this, then nothing they plan to do will be impossible for them. ⁷Come, let us go down and confuse their language so they will not understand each other."

⁸So the LORD scattered them from there over all the earth, and they stopped building the city. ⁹That is why it was called Babel[d]—because there the LORD confused the language of the whole world. From there the LORD scattered them over the face of the whole earth.

truth or dare

Before you start building up certain things in your life, like your reputation or a relationship, make sure it's for the right reason: to honor God, not yourself.

11:4

From Shem to Abram

¹⁰This is the account of Shem.

Two years after the flood, when Shem was 100 years old, he became the father[e] of Arphaxad. ¹¹And after he became the father of Arphaxad, Shem lived 500 years and had other sons and daughters.

¹²When Arphaxad had lived 35 years, he became the father of Shelah. ¹³And after he became the father of Shelah, Arphaxad lived 403 years and had other sons and daughters.[f]

¹⁴When Shelah had lived 30 years, he became the father of Eber. ¹⁵And after he became the father of Eber, Shelah lived 403 years and had other sons and daughters.

¹⁶When Eber had lived 34 years, he became the father of Peleg. ¹⁷And after he became the father of Peleg, Eber lived 430 years and had other sons and daughters.

¹⁸When Peleg had lived 30 years, he became the father of Reu. ¹⁹And after he became the father of Reu, Peleg lived 209 years and had other sons and daughters.

²⁰When Reu had lived 32 years, he became the father of Serug. ²¹And after he became the father of Serug, Reu lived 207 years and had other sons and daughters.

²²When Serug had lived 30 years, he became the father of Nahor. ²³And after he became the father of Nahor, Serug lived 200 years and had other sons and daughters.

²⁴When Nahor had lived 29 years, he became the father of Terah. ²⁵And after he became the father of Terah, Nahor lived 119 years and had other sons and daughters.

---

a 25 Peleg means division.   b 2 Or from the east; or in the east   c 2 That is, Babylonia   d 9 That is, Babylon; Babel sounds like the Hebrew for confused.   e 10 Father may mean ancestor; also in verses 11-25.   f 12,13 Hebrew; Septuagint (see also Luke 3:35,36 and note at Gen. 10:24) 35 years, he became the father of Cainan. 13And after he became the father of Cainan, Arphaxad lived 430 years and had other sons and daughters, and then he died. When Cainan had lived 130 years, he became the father of Shelah. And after he became the father of Shelah, Cainan lived 330 years and had other sons and daughters

²⁶After Terah had lived 70 years, he became the father of Abram, Nahor and Haran.

²⁷This is the account of Terah.

Terah became the father of Abram, Nahor and Haran. And Haran became the father of Lot. ²⁸While his father Terah was still alive, Haran died in Ur of the Chaldeans, in the land of his birth. ²⁹Abram and Nahor both married. The name of Abram's wife was Sarai, and the name of Nahor's wife was Milcah; she was the daughter of Haran, the father of both Milcah and Iscah. ³⁰Now Sarai was barren; she had no children.

³¹Terah took his son Abram, his grandson Lot son of Haran, and his daughter-in-law Sarai, the wife of his son Abram, and together they set out from Ur of the Chaldeans to go to Canaan. But when they came to Haran, they settled there.

³²Terah lived 205 years, and he died in Haran.

The Call of Abram

12 The LORD had said to Abram, "Leave your country, your people and your father's household and go to the land I will show you.

²"I will make you into a great nation
  and I will bless you;
I will make your name great,
  and you will be a blessing.
³I will bless those who bless you,
  and whoever curses you I will curse;
and all peoples on earth
  will be blessed through you."

⁴So Abram left, as the LORD had told him; and Lot went with him. Abram was seventy-five years old when he set out from Haran. ⁵He took his wife Sarai, his nephew Lot, all the possessions they had accumulated and the people they had acquired in Haran, and they set out for the land of Canaan, and they arrived there.

⁶Abram traveled through the land as far as the site of the great tree of Moreh at Shechem. At that time the Canaanites were in the land. ⁷The LORD appeared to Abram and said, "To your offspring ᵃ I will give this land." So he built an altar there to the LORD, who had appeared to him.

⁸From there he went on toward the hills east of Bethel and pitched his tent, with Bethel on the west and Ai on the east. There he built an altar to the LORD and called on the name of the LORD. ⁹Then Abram set out and continued toward the Negev.

Abram in Egypt

¹⁰Now there was a famine in the land, and Abram went down to Egypt to live there for a while because the famine was severe. ¹¹As he was about to enter Egypt, he said to his wife Sarai, "I know what a beautiful woman you are. ¹²When the Egyptians see you, they will say, 'This is his wife.' Then

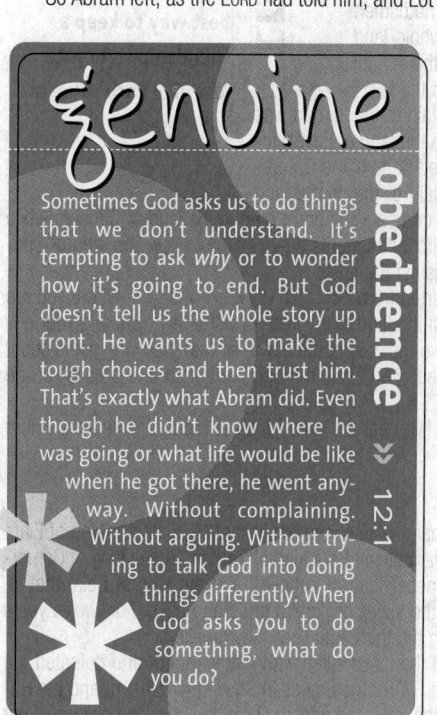

genuine obedience ›› 12:1

Sometimes God asks us to do things that we don't understand. It's tempting to ask *why* or to wonder how it's going to end. But God doesn't tell us the whole story up front. He wants us to make the tough choices and then trust him. That's exactly what Abram did. Even though he didn't know where he was going or what life would be like when he got there, he went anyway. Without complaining. Without arguing. Without trying to talk God into doing things differently. When God asks you to do something, what do you do?

they will kill me but will let you live. [13]Say you are my sister, so that I will be treated well for your sake and my life will be spared because of you."

[14]When Abram came to Egypt, the Egyptians saw that she was a very beautiful woman. [15]And when Pharaoh's officials saw her, they praised her to Pharaoh, and she was taken into his palace. [16]He treated Abram well for her sake, and Abram acquired sheep and cattle, male and female donkeys, menservants and maidservants, and camels.

[17]But the LORD inflicted serious diseases on Pharaoh and his household because of Abram's wife Sarai. [18]So Pharaoh summoned Abram. "What have you done to me?" he said. "Why didn't you tell me she was your wife? [19]Why did you say, 'She is my sister,' so that I took her to be my wife? Now then, here is your wife. Take her and go!" [20]Then Pharaoh gave orders about Abram to his men, and they sent him on his way, with his wife and everything he had.

Abram and Lot Separate

13 So Abram went up from Egypt to the Negev, with his wife and everything he had, and Lot went with him. [2]Abram had become very wealthy in livestock and in silver and gold. [3]From the Negev he went from place to place until he came to Bethel, to the place between Bethel and Ai where his tent had been earlier [4]and where he had first built an altar. There Abram called on the name of the LORD.

[5]Now Lot, who was moving about with Abram, also had flocks and herds and tents. [6]But the land could not support them while they stayed together, for their possessions were so great that they were not able to stay together. [7]And quarreling arose between Abram's herdsmen and the herdsmen of Lot. The Canaanites and Perizzites were also living in the land at that time.

[8]So Abram said to Lot, "Let's not have any quarreling between you and me, or between your herdsmen and mine, for we are brothers. [9]Is not the whole land before you? Let's part company. If you go to the left, I'll go to the right; if you go to the right, I'll go to the left."

[10]Lot looked up and saw that the whole plain of the Jordan was well watered, like the garden of the LORD, like the land of Egypt, toward Zoar. (This was before the LORD destroyed Sodom and Gomorrah.) [11]So Lot chose for himself the whole plain of the Jordan and set out toward the east. The two men parted company: [12]Abram lived in the land of Canaan, while Lot lived among the cities of the plain and pitched his tents near Sodom. [13]Now the men of Sodom were wicked and were sinning greatly against the LORD.

[14]The LORD said to Abram after Lot had parted from him, "Lift up your eyes from where you are and look north and south, east and west. [15]All the land that you see I will give to you and your offspring[a] forever. [16]I will make your offspring like the dust of the earth, so that if anyone could count the dust, then your offspring could be counted. [17]Go, walk through the length and breadth of the land, for I am giving it to you."

[18]So Abram moved his tents and went to live near the great trees of Mamre at Hebron, where he built an altar to the LORD.

Abram Rescues Lot

14 At this time Amraphel king of Shinar,[b] Arioch king of Ellasar, Kedorlaomer king of Elam and Tidal king of Goiim [2]went to war against Bera king of Sodom, Birsha king of Gomorrah, Shinab king of Admah, Shemeber king of Zeboiim, and the king of Bela (that is, Zoar). [3]All these latter kings joined forces in the Valley of Siddim (the Salt Sea[c]). [4]For twelve years they had been subject to Kedorlaomer, but in the thirteenth year they rebelled.

[5]In the fourteenth year, Kedorlaomer and the kings allied with him went out and defeated the Rephaites in Ashteroth Karnaim, the Zuzites in Ham, the Emites in Shaveh Kiriathaim [6]and the Horites in the hill country of Seir, as far as El Paran near the desert. [7]Then they turned back and went

truth or dare

All friendships go through tense times. It's natural! Sometimes the best way to keep a friendship tight is to just give each other a little space.

13:7–9

a 15 Or seed; also in verse 16   b 1 That is, Babylonia; also in verse 9   c 3 That is, the Dead Sea to En Mishpat (that is, Kadesh), and they conquered the whole territory of the Amalekites, as well as the Amorites who were living in Hazazon Tamar.

[8]Then the king of Sodom, the king of Gomorrah, the king of Admah, the king of Zeboiim and the king of Bela (that is, Zoar) marched out and drew up their battle lines in the Valley of Siddim [9]against Kedorlaomer king of Elam, Tidal king of Goiim, Amraphel king of Shinar and Arioch king of Ellasar— four kings against five. [10]Now the Valley of Siddim was full of tar pits, and when the kings of Sodom and Gomorrah fled, some of the men fell into them and the rest fled to the hills. [11]The four kings seized all the goods of Sodom and Gomorrah and all their food; then they went away. [12]They also carried off Abram's nephew Lot and his possessions, since he was living in Sodom.

[13]One who had escaped came and reported this to Abram the Hebrew. Now Abram was living near the great trees of Mamre the Amorite, a brother[a] of Eshcol and Aner, all of whom were allied with Abram. [14]When Abram heard that his relative had been taken captive, he called out the 318 trained men born in his household and went in pursuit as far as Dan. [15]During the night Abram divided his men to attack them and he routed them, pursuing them as far as Hobah, north of Damascus. [16]He recovered all the goods and brought back his relative Lot and his possessions, together with the women and the other people.

[17]After Abram returned from defeating Kedorlaomer and the kings allied with him, the king of Sodom came out to meet him in the Valley of Shaveh (that is, the King's Valley).

[18]Then Melchizedek king of Salem[b] brought out bread and wine. He was priest of God Most High, [19]and he blessed Abram, saying,

"Blessed be Abram by God Most High,
Creator[c] of heaven and earth.
[20]And blessed be[d] God Most High,
who delivered your enemies
into your hand."

Then Abram gave him a tenth of everything.

[21]The king of Sodom said to Abram, "Give me the people and keep the goods for yourself."

[22]But Abram said to the king of Sodom, "I have raised my hand to the LORD, God Most High, Creator of heaven and earth, and have taken an oath [23]that I will accept nothing belonging to you, not even a thread or the thong of a sandal, so that you will never be able to say, 'I made Abram rich.' [24]I will accept nothing but what my men have eaten and the share that belongs to the men who went with me—to Aner, Eshcol and Mamre. Let them have their share."

God's Covenant With Abram

15 After this, the word of the LORD came to Abram in a vision:

"Do not be afraid, Abram.
I am your shield,[e]
your very great reward.[f]"

[2]But Abram said, "O Sovereign LORD, what can you give me since I remain childless and the

---

a 13 Or a relative; or an ally   b 18 That is, Jerusalem   c 19 Or Possessor; also in verse 22   d 20 Or And praise be to   e 1 Or sovereign   f 1 Or shield; / your reward will be very great one who will inherit*a* my estate is Eliezer of Damascus?" ³And Abram said, "You have given me no children; so a servant in my household will be my heir."

⁴Then the word of the Lord came to him: "This man will not be your heir, but a son coming from your own body will be your heir." ⁵He took him outside and said, "Look up at the heavens and count the stars—if indeed you can count them." Then he said to him, "So shall your offspring be."

⁶Abram believed the Lord, and he credited it to him as righteousness.

⁷He also said to him, "I am the Lord, who brought you out of Ur of the Chaldeans to give you this land to take possession of it."

⁸But Abram said, "O Sovereign Lord, how can I know that I will gain possession of it?"

⁹So the Lord said to him, "Bring me a heifer, a goat and a ram, each three years old, along with a dove and a young pigeon."

¹⁰Abram brought all these to him, cut them in two and arranged the halves opposite each other; the birds, however, he did not cut in half. ¹¹Then birds of prey came down on the carcasses, but Abram drove them away.

¹²As the sun was setting, Abram fell into a deep sleep, and a thick and dreadful darkness came over him. ¹³Then the Lord said to him, "Know for certain that your descendants will be strangers in a country not their own, and they will be enslaved and mistreated four hundred years. ¹⁴But I will punish the nation they serve as slaves, and afterward they will come out with great possessions. ¹⁵You, however, will go to your fathers in peace and be buried at a good old age. ¹⁶In the fourth generation your descendants will come back here, for the sin of the Amorites has not yet reached its full measure."

¹⁷When the sun had set and darkness had fallen, a smoking firepot with a blazing torch appeared and passed between the pieces. ¹⁸On that day the Lord made a covenant with Abram and said, "To your descendants I give this land, from the river*b* of Egypt to the great river, the Euphrates— ¹⁹the land of the Kenites, Kenizzites, Kadmonites, ²⁰Hittites, Perizzites, Rephaites, ²¹Amorites, Canaanites, Girgashites and Jebusites."

truth or dare

What are the requirements for being a "good" Christian? It's not so much about what you do; it's about who you believe.

15:6

Hagar and Ishmael

16 Now Sarai, Abram's wife, had borne him no children. But she had an Egyptian maidservant named Hagar; ²so she said to Abram, "The Lord has kept me from having children. Go, sleep with my maidservant; perhaps I can build a family through her."

Abram agreed to what Sarai said. ³So after Abram had been living in Canaan ten years, Sarai his wife took her Egyptian maidservant Hagar and gave her to her husband to be his wife. ⁴He slept with Hagar, and she conceived.

When she knew she was pregnant, she began to despise her mistress. ⁵Then Sarai said to Abram, "You are responsible for the wrong I am suffering. I put my servant in your arms, and now that she knows she is pregnant, she despises me. May the Lord judge between you and me."

⁶"Your servant is in your hands," Abram said. "Do with her whatever you think best." Then Sarai mistreated Hagar; so she fled from her.

⁷The angel of the Lord found Hagar near a spring in the desert; it was the spring that is beside

truth or dare

When facing a problem, it's easy to want to force the situation to change. But cutting corners can lead to an even bigger mess. Have the courage to wait on God's timing.

16:1–3

a 2 The meaning of the Hebrew for this phrase is uncertain.   *b* 18 Or *Wadi* the road to Shur. ⁸And he said, "Hagar, servant of Sarai, where have you come from, and where are you going?"

"I'm running away from my mistress Sarai," she answered.

⁹Then the angel of the Lᴏʀᴅ told her, "Go back to your mistress and submit to her." ¹⁰The angel added, "I will so increase your descendants that they will be too numerous to count."

¹¹The angel of the Lᴏʀᴅ also said to her:

> "You are now with child
> and you will have a son.
> You shall name him Ishmael,ᵃ
> for the Lᴏʀᴅ has heard of your misery.
> ¹²He will be a wild donkey of a man;
> his hand will be against everyone
> and everyone's hand against him,
> and he will live in hostility
> towardᵇ all his brothers."

¹³She gave this name to the Lᴏʀᴅ who spoke to her: "You are the God who sees me," for she said, "I have now seenᶜ the One who sees me." ¹⁴That is why the well was called Beer Lahai Roiᵈ; it is still there, between Kadesh and Bered.

¹⁵So Hagar bore Abram a son, and Abram gave the name Ishmael to the son she had borne. ¹⁶Abram was eighty-six years old when Hagar bore him Ishmael.

The Covenant of Circumcision

17 When Abram was ninety-nine years old, the Lᴏʀᴅ appeared to him and said, "I am God Almightyᵉ; walk before me and be blameless. ²I will confirm my covenant between me and you and will greatly increase your numbers."

love notes

16:7-13

Beloved,

When you are struggling and want to run from your problems, remember Hagar. I am the God who sees you. I know exactly what you are going through, and I am always right beside you.

—The One who sees you

Tell God what problems you are struggling with now. He knows; he can help.

truth or dare

Have you ever told God you'd follow him only after he gave you something? God deserves your obedience just because he's God, not for what he can offer you in return.

17:1

ᵃ 11 *Ishmael* means *God hears.*   ᵇ 12 Or *live to the east / of*   ᶜ 13 Or *seen the back of*   ᵈ 14 *Beer Lahai Roi* means *well of the Living One who sees me.*   ᵉ 1 Hebrew *El-Shaddai*

³Abram fell facedown, and God said to him, ⁴"As for me, this is my covenant with you: You will be the father of many nations. ⁵No longer will you be called Abram ª; your name will be Abraham, ᵇ for I have made you a father of many nations. ⁶I will make you very fruitful; I will make nations of you, and kings will come from you. ⁷I will establish my covenant as an everlasting covenant between me and you and your descendants after you for the generations to come, to be your God and the God of your descendants after you. ⁸The whole land of Canaan, where you are now an alien, I will give as an everlasting possession to you and your descendants after you; and I will be their God."

⁹Then God said to Abraham, "As for you, you must keep my covenant, you and your descendants after you for the generations to come. ¹⁰This is my covenant with you and your descendants after you, the covenant you are to keep: Every male among you shall be circumcised. ¹¹You are to undergo circumcision, and it will be the sign of the covenant between me and you. ¹²For the generations to come every male among you who is eight days old must be circumcised, including those born in your household or bought with money from a foreigner—those who are not your offspring. ¹³Whether born in your household or bought with your money, they must be circumcised. My covenant in your flesh is to be an everlasting covenant. ¹⁴Any uncircumcised male, who has not been circumcised in the flesh, will be cut off from his people; he has broken my covenant."

¹⁵God also said to Abraham, "As for Sarai your wife, you are no longer to call her Sarai; her name will be Sarah. ¹⁶I will bless her and will surely give you a son by her. I will bless her so that she will be the mother of nations; kings of peoples will come from her."

¹⁷Abraham fell facedown; he laughed and said to himself, "Will a son be born to a man a hundred years old? Will Sarah bear a child at the age of ninety?" ¹⁸And Abraham said to God, "If only Ishmael might live under your blessing!"

¹⁹Then God said, "Yes, but your wife Sarah will bear you a son, and you will call him Isaac.ᶜ I will establish my covenant with him as an everlasting covenant for his descendants after him. ²⁰And as for Ishmael, I have heard you: I will surely bless him; I will make him fruitful and will greatly increase his numbers. He will be the father of twelve rulers, and I will make him into a great nation. ²¹But my covenant I will establish with Isaac, whom Sarah will bear to you by this time next year." ²²When he had finished speaking with Abraham, God went up from him.

²³On that very day Abraham took his son Ishmael and all those born in his household or bought with his money, every male in his household, and circumcised them, as God told him. ²⁴Abraham was ninety-nine years old when he was circumcised, ²⁵and his son Ishmael was thirteen; ²⁶Abraham and his son Ishmael were both circumcised on that same day. ²⁷And every male in Abraham's household, including those born in his household or bought from a foreigner, was circumcised with him.

The Three Visitors

18 The LORD appeared to Abraham near the great trees of Mamre while he was sitting at the entrance to his tent in the heat of the day. ²Abraham looked up and saw three men standing nearby. When he saw them, he hurried from the entrance of his tent to meet them and bowed low to the ground.

³He said, "If I have found favor in your eyes, my lord,ᵈ do not pass your servant by. ⁴Let a little water be brought, and then you may all wash your feet and rest under this tree. ⁵Let me get you something to eat, so you can be refreshed and then go on your way—now that you have come to your servant."

"Very well," they answered, "do as you say."

⁶So Abraham hurried into the tent to Sarah. "Quick," he said, "get three seahsᵉ of fine flour and knead it and bake some bread."

⁷Then he ran to the herd and selected a choice, tender calf and gave it to a servant, who hurried to prepare it. ⁸He then brought some curds and milk and the calf that had been prepared, and set these before them. While they ate, he stood near them under a tree.

⁹"Where is your wife Sarah?" they asked him.

"There, in the tent," he said.

¹⁰Then the LORDᶠ said, "I will surely return to you about this time next year, and Sarah your wife will have a son."

ª 5 Abram means exalted father.   ᵇ 5 Abraham means father of many.   ᶜ 19 Isaac means he laughs.
ᵈ 3 Or O Lord   ᵉ 6 That is, probably about 20 quarts (about 22 liters)   ᶠ 10 Hebrew Then he

mirror images

Then the LORD said to Abraham, "Why did Sarah laugh and say, 'Will I really have a child, now that I am old?' " Genesis 18:13

Sarah—God Must Be Joking, Right?

Sarah laughed to herself when she heard God's plans for her. See, God made a promise to Abraham and Sarah that they would have a child in their old age. And get this—the child would make Sarah the birthmother of an entire nation. God's promise to Abraham and Sarah sounded more like a Jerry Springer show: "Senior Citizens in Local Nursing Home Give Birth to Miracle Baby!"

Yet the Bible suggests that Sarah ended up believing God. In fact, she's the first woman listed among the faithful in Hebrews 11 (see Hebrews 11:11). After she got over her fit of laughter, she evidently took God at his word, and he came through for her. Old Sarah became a mother to Isaac—and part of Jesus' family tree.

The world can make us feel like God's call on our life could interest talk show producers. "Meet the Last Virgin on Earth—A Local High School Sophomore Girl!" Sometimes we don't feel like we can pull off what God is calling us to do. We want to believe God, but it's scary. Are you incredibly shy, yet God is calling you to witness for him? God must be joking, right? Are you sitting at home alone on Friday nights, yet God says he will bring a Christian guy into your life some day? It's hard to believe his promise and wait patiently for the results. What if the joke's on you? God's promises are something we could laugh off—except that they're true. They're solid. We can count on each and every one of them.

Sarah evidently turned her doubts into faith. And look what happened. Do you believe God is able to come through for you? Tell him right now you believe his promises. And see what will happen.

To read the next Mirror Images profile, go to page 47.

> Dear God, I know just how Sarah felt—torn between doubt and faith. It's scary, but today I am going to take you at your word and act in faith. Show me your promises are true. Amen.

dear God

» Read more about Sarah in Genesis 18:1–15 (pages 20–22), 21:1–7 (page 24) and Hebrews 11:11–12 (page 1597).

Now Sarah was listening at the entrance to the tent, which was behind him. ¹¹Abraham and Sarah were already old and well advanced in years, and Sarah was past the age of childbearing. ¹²So Sarah laughed to herself as she thought, "After I am worn out and my master*ᵃ* is old, will I now have this pleasure?"

¹³Then the Lord said to Abraham, "Why did Sarah laugh and say, 'Will I really have a child, now that I am old?' ¹⁴Is anything too hard for the Lord? I will return to you at the appointed time next year and Sarah will have a son."

¹⁵Sarah was afraid, so she lied and said, "I did not laugh."

But he said, "Yes, you did laugh."

Abraham Pleads for Sodom

¹⁶When the men got up to leave, they looked down toward Sodom, and Abraham walked along with them to see them on their way. ¹⁷Then the Lord said, "Shall I hide from Abraham what I am about to do? ¹⁸Abraham will surely become a great and powerful nation, and all nations on earth will be blessed through him. ¹⁹For I have chosen him, so that he will direct his children and his household after him to keep the way of the Lord by doing what is right and just, so that the Lord will bring about for Abraham what he has promised him."

²⁰Then the Lord said, "The outcry against Sodom and Gomorrah is so great and their sin so grievous ²¹that I will go down and see if what they have done is as bad as the outcry that has reached me. If not, I will know."

²²The men turned away and went toward Sodom, but Abraham remained standing before the Lord.*ᵇ* ²³Then Abraham approached him and said: "Will you sweep away the righteous with the wicked? ²⁴What if there are fifty righteous people in the city? Will you really sweep it away and not spare*ᶜ* the place for the sake of the fifty righteous people in it? ²⁵Far be it from you to do such a thing—to kill the righteous with the wicked, treating the righteous and the wicked alike. Far be it from you! Will not the Judge*ᵈ* of all the earth do right?"

²⁶The Lord said, "If I find fifty righteous people in the city of Sodom, I will spare the whole place for their sake."

²⁷Then Abraham spoke up again: "Now that I have been so bold as to speak to the Lord, though I am nothing but dust and ashes, ²⁸what if the number of the righteous is five less than fifty? Will you destroy the whole city because of five people?"

"If I find forty-five there," he said, "I will not destroy it."

²⁹Once again he spoke to him, "What if only forty are found there?"

He said, "For the sake of forty, I will not do it."

³⁰Then he said, "May the Lord not be angry, but let me speak. What if only thirty can be found there?"

He answered, "I will not do it if I find thirty there."

³¹Abraham said, "Now that I have been so bold as to speak to the Lord, what if only twenty can be found there?"

He said, "For the sake of twenty, I will not destroy it."

³²Then he said, "May the Lord not be angry, but let me speak just once more. What if only ten can be found there?"

He answered, "For the sake of ten, I will not destroy it."

³³When the Lord had finished speaking with Abraham, he left, and Abraham returned home.

Sodom and Gomorrah Destroyed

19 The two angels arrived at Sodom in the evening, and Lot was sitting in the gateway of the city. When he saw them, he got up to meet them and bowed down with his face to the ground. ²"My lords," he said, "please turn aside to your servant's house. You can wash your feet and spend the night and then go on your way early in the morning."

"No," they answered, "we will spend the night in the square."

³But he insisted so strongly that they did go with him and entered his house. He prepared a meal for them, baking bread without yeast, and they ate. ⁴Before they had gone to bed, all the men

ᵃ 12 Or *husband*   *ᵇ* 22 Masoretic Text; an ancient Hebrew scribal tradition *but the Lord remained standing before Abraham*   *ᶜ* 24 Or *forgive*; also in verse 26   *ᵈ* 25 Or *Ruler* from every part of the city of Sodom—both young and old—surrounded the house. ⁵They called to Lot, "Where are the men who came to you tonight? Bring them out to us so that we can have sex with them."

⁶Lot went outside to meet them and shut the door behind him ⁷and said, "No, my friends. Don't do this wicked thing. ⁸Look, I have two daughters who have never slept with a man. Let me bring them out to you, and you can do what you like with them. But don't do anything to these men, for they have come under the protection of my roof."

⁹"Get out of our way," they replied. And they said, "This fellow came here as an alien, and now he wants to play the judge! We'll treat you worse than them." They kept bringing pressure on Lot and moved forward to break down the door.

¹⁰But the men inside reached out and pulled Lot back into the house and shut the door. ¹¹Then they struck the men who were at the door of the house, young and old, with blindness so that they could not find the door.

¹²The two men said to Lot, "Do you have anyone else here—sons-in-law, sons or daughters, or anyone else in the city who belongs to you? Get them out of here, ¹³because we are going to destroy this place. The outcry to the LORD against its people is so great that he has sent us to destroy it."

¹⁴So Lot went out and spoke to his sons-in-law, who were pledged to marry ᵃ his daughters. He said, "Hurry and get out of this place, because the LORD is about to destroy the city!" But his sons-in-law thought he was joking.

¹⁵With the coming of dawn, the angels urged Lot, saying, "Hurry! Take your wife and your two daughters who are here, or you will be swept away when the city is punished."

¹⁶When he hesitated, the men grasped his hand and the hands of his wife and of his two daughters and led them safely out of the city, for the LORD was merciful to them. ¹⁷As soon as they had brought them out, one of them said, "Flee for your lives! Don't look back, and don't stop anywhere in the plain! Flee to the mountains or you will be swept away!"

¹⁸But Lot said to them, "No, my lords, ᵇ please! ¹⁹Yourᶜ servant has found favor in yourᶜ eyes, and youᶜ have shown great kindness to me in sparing my life. But I can't flee to the mountains; this disaster will overtake me, and I'll die. ²⁰Look, here is a town near enough to run to, and it is small. Let me flee to it—it is very small, isn't it? Then my life will be spared."

²¹He said to him, "Very well, I will grant this request too; I will not overthrow the town you speak of. ²²But flee there quickly, because I cannot do anything until you reach it." (That is why the town was called Zoar.ᵈ)

²³By the time Lot reached Zoar, the sun had risen over the land. ²⁴Then the LORD rained down burning sulfur on Sodom and Gomorrah—from the LORD out of the heavens. ²⁵Thus he overthrew those cities and the entire plain, including all those living in the cities—and also the vegetation in the land. ²⁶But Lot's wife looked back, and she became a pillar of salt.

²⁷Early the next morning Abraham got up and returned to the place where he had stood before the LORD. ²⁸He looked down toward Sodom and Gomorrah, toward all the land of the plain, and he saw dense smoke rising from the land, like smoke from a furnace.

²⁹So when God destroyed the cities of the plain, he remembered Abraham, and he brought Lot out of the catastrophe that overthrew the cities where Lot had lived.

Lot and His Daughters

³⁰Lot and his two daughters left Zoar and settled in the mountains, for he was afraid to stay in Zoar. He and his two daughters lived in a cave. ³¹One day the older daughter said to the younger, "Our father is old, and there is no man around here to lie with us, as is the custom all over the earth. ³²Let's get our father to drink wine and then lie with him and preserve our family line through our father."

³³That night they got their father to drink wine, and the older daughter went in and lay with him. He was not aware of it when she lay down or when she got up.

³⁴The next day the older daughter said to the younger, "Last night I lay with my father. Let's get him to drink wine again tonight, and you go in and lie with him so we can preserve our family line

ᵃ 14 Or were married to   ᵇ 18 Or No, Lord; or No, my lord   ᶜ 19 The Hebrew is singular.   ᵈ 22 Zoar means small.

through our father." 35So they got their father to drink wine that night also, and the younger daughter went and lay with him. Again he was not aware of it when she lay down or when she got up.

36So both of Lot's daughters became pregnant by their father. 37The older daughter had a son, and she named him Moab*a*; he is the father of the Moabites of today. 38The younger daughter also had a son, and she named him Ben-Ammi*b*; he is the father of the Ammonites of today.

Abraham and Abimelech

20 Now Abraham moved on from there into the region of the Negev and lived between Kadesh and Shur. For a while he stayed in Gerar, 2and there Abraham said of his wife Sarah, "She is my sister." Then Abimelech king of Gerar sent for Sarah and took her.

3But God came to Abimelech in a dream one night and said to him, "You are as good as dead because of the woman you have taken; she is a married woman."

4Now Abimelech had not gone near her, so he said, "Lord, will you destroy an innocent nation? 5Did he not say to me, 'She is my sister,' and didn't she also say, 'He is my brother'? I have done this with a clear conscience and clean hands."

6Then God said to him in the dream, "Yes, I know you did this with a clear conscience, and so I have kept you from sinning against me. That is why I did not let you touch her. 7Now return the man's wife, for he is a prophet, and he will pray for you and you will live. But if you do not return her, you may be sure that you and all yours will die."

8Early the next morning Abimelech summoned all his officials, and when he told them all that had happened, they were very much afraid. 9Then Abimelech called Abraham in and said, "What have you done to us? How have I wronged you that you have brought such great guilt upon me and my kingdom? You have done things to me that should not be done." 10And Abimelech asked Abraham, "What was your reason for doing this?"

11Abraham replied, "I said to myself, 'There is surely no fear of God in this place, and they will kill me because of my wife.' 12Besides, she really is my sister, the daughter of my father though not of my mother; and she became my wife. 13And when God had me wander from my father's household, I said to her, 'This is how you can show your love to me: Everywhere we go, say of me, "He is my brother." ' "

14Then Abimelech brought sheep and cattle and male and female slaves and gave them to Abraham, and he returned Sarah his wife to him. 15And Abimelech said, "My land is before you; live wherever you like."

16To Sarah he said, "I am giving your brother a thousand shekels*c* of silver. This is to cover the offense against you before all who are with you; you are completely vindicated."

17Then Abraham prayed to God, and God healed Abimelech, his wife and his slave girls so they could have children again, 18for the Lord had closed up every womb in Abimelech's household because of Abraham's wife Sarah.

truth or dare

What's one of your biggest dreams in life? If you give God control, he will accomplish things in you that will outshine even your wildest imagination!

21:1–7

The Birth of Isaac

21 Now the Lord was gracious to Sarah as he had said, and the Lord did for Sarah what he had promised. 2Sarah became pregnant and bore a son to Abraham in his old age, at the very time God had promised him. 3Abraham gave the name Isaac*d* to the son Sarah bore him. 4When his son Isaac was eight days old, Abraham circumcised him, as God commanded him. 5Abraham was a hundred years old when his son Isaac was born to him.

6Sarah said, "God has brought me laughter, and everyone who hears about this will laugh with me." 7And she added, "Who would have said to Abraham that Sarah would nurse children? Yet I have borne him a son in his old age."

---

a 37 Moab sounds like the Hebrew for *from father.*   *b 38 Ben-Ammi* means *son of my people.*   *c 16* That is, about 25 pounds (about 11.5 kilograms)   *d 3 Isaac* means *he laughs.*

Hagar and Ishmael Sent Away

[8]The child grew and was weaned, and on the day Isaac was weaned Abraham held a great feast. [9]But Sarah saw that the son whom Hagar the Egyptian had borne to Abraham was mocking, [10]and she said to Abraham, "Get rid of that slave woman and her son, for that slave woman's son will never share in the inheritance with my son Isaac."

[11]The matter distressed Abraham greatly because it concerned his son. [12]But God said to him, "Do not be so distressed about the boy and your maidservant. Listen to whatever Sarah tells you, because it is through Isaac that your offspring[a] will be reckoned. [13]I will make the son of the maidservant into a nation also, because he is your offspring."

[14]Early the next morning Abraham took some food and a skin of water and gave them to Hagar. He set them on her shoulders and then sent her off with the boy. She went on her way and wandered in the desert of Beersheba.

[15]When the water in the skin was gone, she put the boy under one of the bushes. [16]Then she went off and sat down nearby, about a bowshot away, for she thought, "I cannot watch the boy die." And as she sat there nearby, she[b] began to sob.

[17]God heard the boy crying, and the angel of God called to Hagar from heaven and said to her, "What is the matter, Hagar? Do not be afraid; God has heard the boy crying as he lies there. [18]Lift the boy up and take him by the hand, for I will make him into a great nation."

[19]Then God opened her eyes and she saw a well of water. So she went and filled the skin with water and gave the boy a drink.

[20]God was with the boy as he grew up. He lived in the desert and became an archer. [21]While he was living in the Desert of Paran, his mother got a wife for him from Egypt.

The Treaty at Beersheba

[22]At that time Abimelech and Phicol the commander of his forces said to Abraham, "God is with you in everything you do. [23]Now swear to me here before God that you will not deal falsely with me or my children or my descendants. Show to me and the country where you are living as an alien the same kindness I have shown to you."

[24]Abraham said, "I swear it."

[25]Then Abraham complained to Abimelech about a well of water that Abimelech's servants had seized. [26]But Abimelech said, "I don't know who has done this. You did not tell me, and I heard about it only today."

[27]So Abraham brought sheep and cattle and gave them to Abimelech, and the two men made a treaty. [28]Abraham set apart seven ewe lambs from the flock, [29]and Abimelech asked Abraham, "What is the meaning of these seven ewe lambs you have set apart by themselves?"

[30]He replied, "Accept these seven lambs from my hand as a witness that I dug this well."

[31]So that place was called Beersheba,[c] because the two men swore an oath there.

[32]After the treaty had been made at Beersheba, Abimelech and Phicol the commander of his forces returned to the land of the Philistines. [33]Abraham planted a tamarisk tree in Beersheba, and there he called upon the name of the Lord, the Eternal God. [34]And Abraham stayed in the land of the Philistines for a long time.

Abraham Tested

22 Some time later God tested Abraham. He said to him, "Abraham!"
"Here I am," he replied.

[2]Then God said, "Take your son, your only son, Isaac, whom you love, and go to the region of Moriah. Sacrifice him there as a burnt offering on one of the mountains I will tell you about."

[3]Early the next morning Abraham got up and saddled his donkey. He took with him two of his servants and his son Isaac. When he had cut enough wood for the burnt offering, he set out for the place God had told him about. [4]On the third day Abraham looked up and saw the place in the distance. [5]He said to his servants, "Stay here with the donkey while I and the boy go over there. We will worship and then we will come back to you."

[6]Abraham took the wood for the burnt offering and placed it on his son Isaac, and he himself

---

a 12 Or seed   b 16 Hebrew; Septuagint the child   c 31 Beersheba can mean well of seven or well of the oath.

carried the fire and the knife. As the two of them went on together, [7]Isaac spoke up and said to his father Abraham, "Father?"

"Yes, my son?" Abraham replied.

"The fire and wood are here," Isaac said, "but where is the lamb for the burnt offering?"

[8]Abraham answered, "God himself will provide the lamb for the burnt offering, my son." And the two of them went on together.

[9]When they reached the place God had told him about, Abraham built an altar there and arranged the wood on it. He bound his son Isaac and laid him on the altar, on top of the wood. [10]Then he reached out his hand and took the knife to slay his son. [11]But the angel of the LORD called out to him from heaven, "Abraham! Abraham!"

"Here I am," he replied.

[12]"Do not lay a hand on the boy," he said. "Do not do anything to him. Now I know that you fear God, because you have not withheld from me your son, your only son."

[13]Abraham looked up and there in a thicket he saw a ram[a] caught by its horns. He went over and took the ram and sacrificed it as a burnt offering instead of his son. [14]So Abraham called that place The LORD Will Provide. And to this day it is said, "On the mountain of the LORD it will be provided."

[15]The angel of the LORD called to Abraham from heaven a second time [16]and said, "I swear by myself, declares the LORD, that because you have done this and have not withheld your son, your only son, [17]I will surely bless you and make your descendants as numerous as the stars in the sky and as the sand on the seashore. Your descendants will take possession of the cities of their enemies, [18]and through your offspring[b] all nations on earth will be blessed, because you have obeyed me."

[19]Then Abraham returned to his servants, and they set off together for Beersheba. And Abraham stayed in Beersheba.

Nahor's Sons

[20]Some time later Abraham was told, "Milcah is also a mother; she has borne sons to your brother Nahor: [21]Uz the firstborn, Buz his brother, Kemuel (the father of Aram), [22]Kesed, Hazo, Pildash, Jidlaph and Bethuel." [23]Bethuel became the father of Rebekah. Milcah bore these eight sons to Abraham's brother Nahor. [24]His concubine, whose name was Reumah, also had sons: Tebah, Gaham, Tahash and Maacah.

The Death of Sarah

23 Sarah lived to be a hundred and twenty-seven years old. [2]She died at Kiriath Arba (that is, Hebron) in the land of Canaan, and Abraham went to mourn for Sarah and to weep over her.

genuine

trust » 22:1-2

What do you value more than anything else? Something you own? Your reputation? Your family? Your friends? A dream for your future? Abraham valued Isaac greatly. He had waited years for God to give him a son. So how could he even consider giving him up? He could do it because—more than anything else—he valued his relationship with God. Every day we have a choice—to hold tightly to things or the stuff we feel is important, or to let go and trust God. If you had to let go of what you value most (other than your relationship with God), could you?

truth or dare

Giving up everything for God directly opposes the world's "me-first" attitude. Dare to offer your whole life to God, and see the great things he can do with an obedient heart!

22:12

---

[a] 13 Many manuscripts of the Masoretic Text, Samaritan Pentateuch, Septuagint and Syriac; most manuscripts of the Masoretic Text *a ram behind him.*   [b] 18 Or *seed*

³Then Abraham rose from beside his dead wife and spoke to the Hittites.ᵃ He said, ⁴"I am an alien and a stranger among you. Sell me some property for a burial site here so I can bury my dead."

⁵The Hittites replied to Abraham, ⁶"Sir, listen to us. You are a mighty prince among us. Bury your dead in the choicest of our tombs. None of us will refuse you his tomb for burying your dead."

⁷Then Abraham rose and bowed down before the people of the land, the Hittites. ⁸He said to them, "If you are willing to let me bury my dead, then listen to me and intercede with Ephron son of Zohar on my behalf ⁹so he will sell me the cave of Machpelah, which belongs to him and is at the end of his field. Ask him to sell it to me for the full price as a burial site among you."

¹⁰Ephron the Hittite was sitting among his people and he replied to Abraham in the hearing of all the Hittites who had come to the gate of his city. ¹¹"No, my lord," he said. "Listen to me; I giveᵇ you the field, and I giveᵇ you the cave that is in it. I giveᵇ it to you in the presence of my people. Bury your dead."

¹²Again Abraham bowed down before the people of the land ¹³and he said to Ephron in their hearing, "Listen to me, if you will. I will pay the price of the field. Accept it from me so I can bury my dead there."

¹⁴Ephron answered Abraham, ¹⁵"Listen to me, my lord; the land is worth four hundred shekelsᶜ of silver, but what is that between me and you? Bury your dead."

¹⁶Abraham agreed to Ephron's terms and weighed out for him the price he had named in the hearing of the Hittites: four hundred shekels of silver, according to the weight current among the merchants.

¹⁷So Ephron's field in Machpelah near Mamre—both the field and the cave in it, and all the trees within the borders of the field—was deeded ¹⁸to Abraham as his property in the presence of all the Hittites who had come to the gate of the city. ¹⁹Afterward Abraham buried his wife Sarah in the cave in the field of Machpelah near Mamre (which is at Hebron) in the land of Canaan. ²⁰So the field and the cave in it were deeded to Abraham by the Hittites as a burial site.

Isaac and Rebekah

24 Abraham was now old and well advanced in years, and the LORD had blessed him in every way. ²He said to the chiefᵈ servant in his household, the one in charge of all that he had, "Put your hand under my thigh. ³I want you to swear by the LORD, the God of heaven and the God of earth, that you will not get a wife for my son from the daughters of the Canaanites, among whom I am living, ⁴but will go to my country and my own relatives and get a wife for my son Isaac."

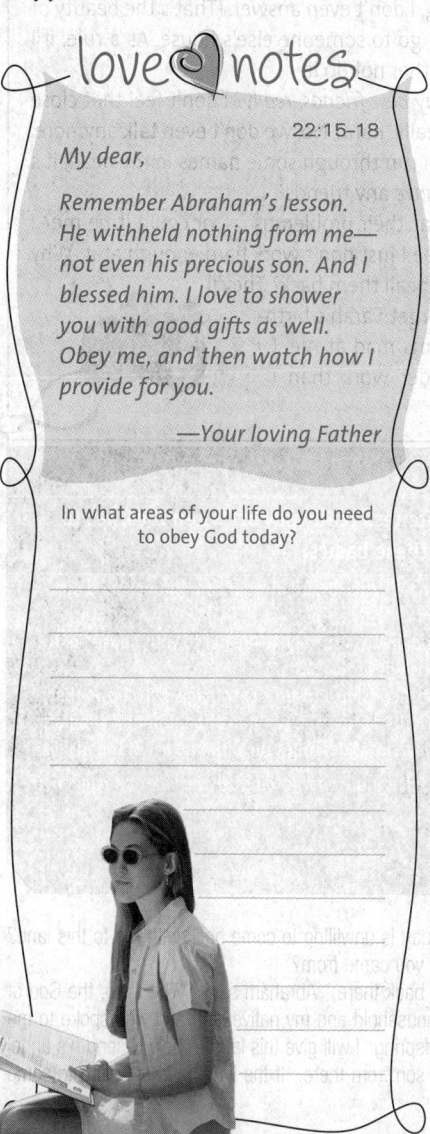

love notes

22:15-18

My dear,

Remember Abraham's lesson. He withheld nothing from me—not even his precious son. And I blessed him. I love to shower you with good gifts as well. Obey me, and then watch how I provide for you.

—Your loving Father

In what areas of your life do you need to obey God today?

ᵃ 3 Or *the sons of Heth*; also in verses 5, 7, 10, 16, 18 and 20 ᵇ 11 Or *sell* ᶜ 15 That is, about 10 pounds (about 4.5 kilograms) ᵈ 2 Or *oldest*

» 27

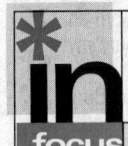

Working on Friendship

focus Profile: **Lori**

My philosophy about cleaning is, "Why make the bed when I'm just going to get back in it again?" Did I hear an Amen? Someday I'm going to invent a remote to find the TV remote so that I won't have to get up and look for it. I'd be rich! I admit it. I'm a little on the lazy side. And proud of it.

When it comes to relationships, I'm pretty laidback. I wait for people to call me first. And if they call when I don't feel like talking, I don't even answer. (That's the beauty of caller I.D.) I never throw parties—I'd rather go to someone else's house. As a rule, if I have to work too much at something, I'd rather not do it.

But lately I've been thinking, *Who are my best friends, really?* I don't feel that close to anyone. Can I talk to Amy? No. Jill? Not really. Kara? No, we don't even talk anymore. Sarah? I don't know what her deal is. After I run through some names in my head, it's like I have a small panic attack—do I even *have* any friends?

That's not a good feeling! I wonder what their problem is . . . or could it be me? I wonder if they think I'm a bad friend. Maybe I just don't work hard enough at it. Why does it matter so much to them that I never call them back? They'll invite me to stuff anyway . . . right? I did forget Sarah's birthday last week—maybe that's why she seems mad at me. I don't know—this friendship thing is harder work than I thought.

friendship in focus

Time, effort and plain ol' politeness really pay off when it comes to long-lasting friendships. Try these basics:

- » Remember your friends' birthdays. Make a card on your computer or send an e-card.
- » Return the favor. When a friend invites you over, invite her to your house next time. Little efforts make friendships grow.
- » The Bible has lots to say about friendship. Proverbs 17:17 (page 828) shows that friendship is a 24/7 thing. Proverbs 27:10 (page 843) talks about not blowing off your friends. And John 15:13 (page 1434) describes the ultimate act of friendship.

For more on this topic, see the index on page 1656.

friendship

⁵The servant asked him, "What if the woman is unwilling to come back with me to this land? Shall I then take your son back to the country you came from?"

⁶"Make sure that you do not take my son back there," Abraham said. ⁷"The LORD, the God of heaven, who brought me out of my father's household and my native land and who spoke to me and promised me on oath, saying, 'To your offspring *a* I will give this land'—he will send his angel before you so that you can get a wife for my son from there. ⁸If the woman is unwilling to come

a 7 Or seed

back with you, then you will be released from this oath of mine. Only do not take my son back there." [9]So the servant put his hand under the thigh of his master Abraham and swore an oath to him concerning this matter.

[10]Then the servant took ten of his master's camels and left, taking with him all kinds of good things from his master. He set out for Aram Naharaim[*a*] and made his way to the town of Nahor. [11]He had the camels kneel down near the well outside the town; it was toward evening, the time the women go out to draw water.

[12]Then he prayed, "O LORD, God of my master Abraham, give me success today, and show kindness to my master Abraham. [13]See, I am standing beside this spring, and the daughters of the townspeople are coming out to draw water. [14]May it be that when I say to a girl, 'Please let down your jar that I may have a drink,' and she says, 'Drink, and I'll water your camels too'—let her be the one you have chosen for your servant Isaac. By this I will know that you have shown kindness to my master."

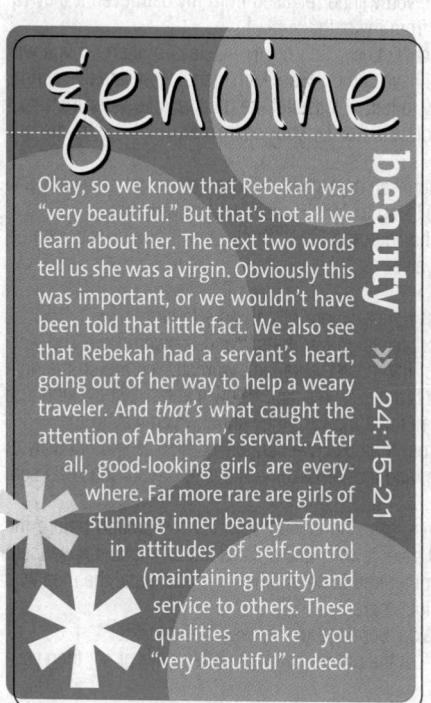

genuine

beauty » 24:15-21

Okay, so we know that Rebekah was "very beautiful." But that's not all we learn about her. The next two words tell us she was a virgin. Obviously this was important, or we wouldn't have been told that little fact. We also see that Rebekah had a servant's heart, going out of her way to help a weary traveler. And *that's* what caught the attention of Abraham's servant. After all, good-looking girls are everywhere. Far more rare are girls of stunning inner beauty—found in attitudes of self-control (maintaining purity) and service to others. These qualities make you "very beautiful" indeed.

[15]Before he had finished praying, Rebekah came out with her jar on her shoulder. She was the daughter of Bethuel son of Milcah, who was the wife of Abraham's brother Nahor. [16]The girl was very beautiful, a virgin; no man had ever lain with her. She went down to the spring, filled her jar and came up again.

[17]The servant hurried to meet her and said, "Please give me a little water from your jar."

[18]"Drink, my lord," she said, and quickly lowered the jar to her hands and gave him a drink.

[19]After she had given him a drink, she said, "I'll draw water for your camels too, until they have finished drinking." [20]So she quickly emptied her jar into the trough, ran back to the well to draw more water, and drew enough for all his camels. [21]Without saying a word, the man watched her closely to learn whether or not the LORD had made his journey successful.

[22]When the camels had finished drinking, the man took out a gold nose ring weighing a beka[*b*] and two gold bracelets weighing ten shekels.[*c*] [23]Then he asked, "Whose daughter are you? Please tell me, is there room in your father's house for us to spend the night?"

[24]She answered him, "I am the daughter of Bethuel, the son that Milcah bore to Nahor." [25]And she added, "We have plenty of straw and fodder, as well as room for you to spend the night."

[26]Then the man bowed down and worshiped the LORD, [27]saying, "Praise be to the LORD, the God of my master Abraham, who has not abandoned his kindness and faithfulness to my master. As for me, the LORD has led me on the journey to the house of my master's relatives."

[28]The girl ran and told her mother's household about these things. [29]Now Rebekah had a brother named Laban, and he hurried out to the man at the spring. [30]As soon as he had seen the nose ring, and the bracelets on his sister's arms, and had heard Rebekah tell what the man said to her, he went out to the man and found him standing by the camels near the spring. [31]"Come, you who are blessed by the LORD," he said. "Why are you standing out here? I have prepared the house and a place for the camels."

[32]So the man went to the house, and the camels were unloaded. Straw and fodder were

---

a 10 That is, Northwest Mesopotamia   *b 22* That is, about 1/5 ounce (about 5.5 grams)   *c 22* That is, about 4 ounces (about 110 grams) brought for the camels, and water for him and his men to wash their feet. ³³Then food was set before him, but he said, "I will not eat until I have told you what I have to say."

"Then tell us," ⌊Laban⌋ said.

³⁴So he said, "I am Abraham's servant. ³⁵The LORD has blessed my master abundantly, and he has become wealthy. He has given him sheep and cattle, silver and gold, menservants and maidservants, and camels and donkeys. ³⁶My master's wife Sarah has borne him a son in her^a old age, and he has given him everything he owns. ³⁷And my master made me swear an oath, and said, 'You must not get a wife for my son from the daughters of the Canaanites, in whose land I live, ³⁸but go to my father's family and to my own clan, and get a wife for my son.'

³⁹"Then I asked my master, 'What if the woman will not come back with me?'

⁴⁰"He replied, 'The LORD, before whom I have walked, will send his angel with you and make your journey a success, so that you can get a wife for my son from my own clan and from my father's family. ⁴¹Then, when you go to my clan, you will be released from my oath even if they refuse to give her to you—you will be released from my oath.'

⁴²"When I came to the spring today, I said, 'O LORD, God of my master Abraham, if you will, please grant success to the journey on which I have come. ⁴³See, I am standing beside this spring; if a maiden comes out to draw water and I say to her, "Please let me drink a little water from your jar," ⁴⁴and if she says to me, "Drink, and I'll draw water for your camels too," let her be the one the LORD has chosen for my master's son.'

⁴⁵"Before I finished praying in my heart, Rebekah came out, with her jar on her shoulder. She went down to the spring and drew water, and I said to her, 'Please give me a drink.'

⁴⁶"She quickly lowered her jar from her shoulder and said, 'Drink, and I'll water your camels too.' So I drank, and she watered the camels also.

⁴⁷"I asked her, 'Whose daughter are you?'

"She said, 'The daughter of Bethuel son of Nahor, whom Milcah bore to him.'

"Then I put the ring in her nose and the bracelets on her arms, ⁴⁸and I bowed down and worshiped the LORD. I praised the LORD, the God of my master Abraham, who had led me on the right road to get the granddaughter of my master's brother for his son. ⁴⁹Now if you will show kindness and faithfulness to my master, tell me; and if not, tell me, so I may know which way to turn."

⁵⁰Laban and Bethuel answered, "This is from the LORD; we can say nothing to you one way or the other. ⁵¹Here is Rebekah; take her and go, and let her become the wife of your master's son, as the LORD has directed."

⁵²When Abraham's servant heard what they said, he bowed down to the ground before the LORD. ⁵³Then the servant brought out gold and silver jewelry and articles of clothing and gave them to Rebekah; he also gave costly gifts to her brother and to her mother. ⁵⁴Then he and the men who were with him ate and drank and spent the night there.

When they got up the next morning, he said, "Send me on my way to my master."

⁵⁵But her brother and her mother replied, "Let the girl remain with us ten days or so; then you^b may go."

⁵⁶But he said to them, "Do not detain me, now that the LORD has granted success to my journey. Send me on my way so I may go to my master."

⁵⁷Then they said, "Let's call the girl and ask her about it." ⁵⁸So they called Rebekah and asked her, "Will you go with this man?"

"I will go," she said.

⁵⁹So they sent their sister Rebekah on her way, along with her nurse and Abraham's servant and his men. ⁶⁰And they blessed Rebekah and said to her,

"Our sister, may you increase
      to thousands upon thousands;
may your offspring possess
      the gates of their enemies."

⁶¹Then Rebekah and her maids got ready and mounted their camels and went back with the man. So the servant took Rebekah and left.

⁶²Now Isaac had come from Beer Lahai Roi, for he was living in the Negev. ⁶³He went out to the

a 36 Or his   b 55 Or she

field one evening to meditate,[a] and as he looked up, he saw camels approaching. [64]Rebekah also looked up and saw Isaac. She got down from her camel [65]and asked the servant, "Who is that man in the field coming to meet us?"

"He is my master," the servant answered. So she took her veil and covered herself.

[66]Then the servant told Isaac all he had done. [67]Isaac brought her into the tent of his mother Sarah, and he married Rebekah. So she became his wife, and he loved her; and Isaac was comforted after his mother's death.

The Death of Abraham

25 Abraham took[b] another wife, whose name was Keturah. [2]She bore him Zimran, Jokshan, Medan, Midian, Ishbak and Shuah. [3]Jokshan was the father of Sheba and Dedan; the descendants of Dedan were the Asshurites, the Letushites and the Leummites. [4]The sons of Midian were Ephah, Epher, Hanoch, Abida and Eldaah. All these were descendants of Keturah.

[5]Abraham left everything he owned to Isaac. [6]But while he was still living, he gave gifts to the sons of his concubines and sent them away from his son Isaac to the land of the east.

[7]Altogether, Abraham lived a hundred and seventy-five years. [8]Then Abraham breathed his last and died at a good old age, an old man and full of years; and he was gathered to his people. [9]His sons Isaac and Ishmael buried him in the cave of Machpelah near Mamre, in the field of Ephron son of Zohar the Hittite, [10]the field Abraham had bought from the Hittites.[c] There Abraham was buried with his wife Sarah. [11]After Abraham's death, God blessed his son Isaac, who then lived near Beer Lahai Roi.

Ishmael's Sons

[12]This is the account of Abraham's son Ishmael, whom Sarah's maidservant, Hagar the Egyptian, bore to Abraham.

[13]These are the names of the sons of Ishmael, listed in the order of their birth: Nebaioth the firstborn of Ishmael, Kedar, Adbeel, Mibsam, [14]Mishma, Dumah, Massa, [15]Hadad, Tema, Jetur, Naphish and Kedemah. [16]These were the sons of Ishmael, and these are the names of the twelve tribal rulers according to their settlements and camps. [17]Altogether, Ishmael lived a hundred and thirty-seven years. He breathed his last and died, and he was gathered to his people. [18]His descendants settled in the area from Havilah to Shur, near the border of Egypt, as you go toward Asshur. And they lived in hostility toward[d] all their brothers.

Jacob and Esau

[19]This is the account of Abraham's son Isaac.

Abraham became the father of Isaac, [20]and Isaac was forty years old when he married Rebekah daughter of Bethuel the Aramean from Paddan Aram[e] and sister of Laban the Aramean.

[21]Isaac prayed to the LORD on behalf of his wife, because she was barren. The LORD answered his prayer, and his wife Rebekah became pregnant. [22]The babies jostled each other within her, and she said, "Why is this happening to me?" So she went to inquire of the LORD.

[23]The LORD said to her,

> "Two nations are in your womb,
>   and two peoples from within you will be separated;
> one people will be stronger than the other,
>   and the older will serve the younger."

[24]When the time came for her to give birth, there were twin boys in her womb. [25]The first to come out was red, and his whole body was like a hairy garment; so they named him Esau.[f] [26]After this, his brother came out, with his hand grasping Esau's heel; so he was named Jacob.[g] Isaac was sixty years old when Rebekah gave birth to them.

[27]The boys grew up, and Esau became a skillful hunter, a man of the open country, while Ja-

---

a 63 The meaning of the Hebrew for this word is uncertain.   b 1 Or had taken   c 10 Or the sons of Heth   d 18 Or lived to the east of   e 20 That is, Northwest Mesopotamia   f 25 Esau may mean hairy; he was also called Edom, which means red.   g 26 Jacob means he grasps the heel (figuratively, he deceives).

» 31

cob was a quiet man, staying among the tents. ²⁸Isaac, who had a taste for wild game, loved Esau, but Rebekah loved Jacob.

²⁹Once when Jacob was cooking some stew, Esau came in from the open country, famished. ³⁰He said to Jacob, "Quick, let me have some of that red stew! I'm famished!" (That is why he was also called Edom.^a)

³¹Jacob replied, "First sell me your birthright."

³²"Look, I am about to die," Esau said. "What good is the birthright to me?"

³³But Jacob said, "Swear to me first." So he swore an oath to him, selling his birthright to Jacob.

³⁴Then Jacob gave Esau some bread and some lentil stew. He ate and drank, and then got up and left.

So Esau despised his birthright.

truth or dare

It's the moment of decision: Do you choose the incredible prize (your relationship with God) or the feel-good, quick fix (like instant popularity)? Don't be a sell-out.

25:32–33

Isaac and Abimelech

26 Now there was a famine in the land—besides the earlier famine of Abraham's time—and Isaac went to Abimelech king of the Philistines in Gerar. ²The LORD appeared to Isaac and said, "Do not go down to Egypt; live in the land where I tell you to live. ³Stay in this land for a while, and I will be with you and will bless you. For to you and your descendants I will give all these lands and will confirm the oath I swore to your father Abraham. ⁴I will make your descendants as numerous as the stars in the sky and will give them all these lands, and through your offspring^b all nations on earth will be blessed, ⁵because Abraham obeyed me and kept my requirements, my commands, my decrees and my laws." ⁶So Isaac stayed in Gerar.

⁷When the men of that place asked him about his wife, he said, "She is my sister," because he was afraid to say, "She is my wife." He thought, "The men of this place might kill me on account of Rebekah, because she is beautiful."

⁸When Isaac had been there a long time, Abimelech king of the Philistines looked down from a window and saw Isaac caressing his wife Rebekah. ⁹So Abimelech summoned Isaac and said, "She is really your wife! Why did you say, 'She is my sister'?"

Isaac answered him, "Because I thought I might lose my life on account of her."

¹⁰Then Abimelech said, "What is this you have done to us? One of the men might well have slept with your wife, and you would have brought guilt upon us."

¹¹So Abimelech gave orders to all the people: "Anyone who molests this man or his wife shall surely be put to death."

truth or dare

It's humbling to give up your own rights just to keep the peace. Are you willing to walk away and make room for people who disagree with you—even when you know you're right?

26:16–22

¹²Isaac planted crops in that land and the same year reaped a hundredfold, because the LORD blessed him. ¹³The man became rich, and his wealth continued to grow until he became very wealthy. ¹⁴He had so many flocks and herds and servants that the Philistines envied him. ¹⁵So all the wells that his father's servants had dug in the time of his father Abraham, the Philistines stopped up, filling them with earth.

¹⁶Then Abimelech said to Isaac, "Move away from us; you have become too powerful for us."

¹⁷So Isaac moved away from there and encamped in the Valley of Gerar and settled there. ¹⁸Isaac reopened the wells that had been dug in the time of his father Abraham, which the Philistines had stopped up after Abraham died, and he gave them the same names his father had given them.

¹⁹Isaac's servants dug in the valley and discovered a well of fresh water there. ²⁰But the herdsmen of Ge-

^a 30 Edom means red.   ^b 4 Or seed

rar quarreled with Isaac's herdsmen and said, "The water is ours!" So he named the well Esek,[a] because they disputed with him. ²¹Then they dug another well, but they quarreled over that one also; so he named it Sitnah.[b] ²²He moved on from there and dug another well, and no one quarreled over it. He named it Rehoboth,[c] saying, "Now the LORD has given us room and we will flourish in the land."

²³From there he went up to Beersheba. ²⁴That night the LORD appeared to him and said, "I am the God of your father Abraham. Do not be afraid, for I am with you; I will bless you and will increase the number of your descendants for the sake of my servant Abraham."

²⁵Isaac built an altar there and called on the name of the LORD. There he pitched his tent, and there his servants dug a well.

²⁶Meanwhile, Abimelech had come to him from Gerar, with Ahuzzath his personal adviser and Phicol the commander of his forces. ²⁷Isaac asked them, "Why have you come to me, since you were hostile to me and sent me away?"

²⁸They answered, "We saw clearly that the LORD was with you; so we said, 'There ought to be a sworn agreement between us'—between us and you. Let us make a treaty with you ²⁹that you will do us no harm, just as we did not molest you but always treated you well and sent you away in peace. And now you are blessed by the LORD."

³⁰Isaac then made a feast for them, and they ate and drank. ³¹Early the next morning the men swore an oath to each other. Then Isaac sent them on their way, and they left him in peace.

³²That day Isaac's servants came and told him about the well they had dug. They said, "We've found water!" ³³He called it Shibah,[d] and to this day the name of the town has been Beersheba.[e]

³⁴When Esau was forty years old, he married Judith daughter of Beeri the Hittite, and also Basemath daughter of Elon the Hittite. ³⁵They were a source of grief to Isaac and Rebekah.

Jacob Gets Isaac's Blessing

27 When Isaac was old and his eyes were so weak that he could no longer see, he called for Esau his older son and said to him, "My son."

"Here I am," he answered.

²Isaac said, "I am now an old man and don't know the day of my death. ³Now then, get your weapons—your quiver and bow—and go out to the open country to hunt some wild game for me. ⁴Prepare me the kind of tasty food I like and bring it to me to eat, so that I may give you my blessing before I die."

⁵Now Rebekah was listening as Isaac spoke to his son Esau. When Esau left for the open country to hunt game and bring it back, ⁶Rebekah said to her son Jacob, "Look, I overheard your father say to your brother Esau, ⁷'Bring me some game and prepare me some tasty food to eat, so that I may give you my blessing in the presence of the LORD before I die.' ⁸Now, my son, listen carefully and do what I tell you: ⁹Go out to the flock and bring me two choice young goats, so I can prepare some tasty food for your father, just the way he likes it. ¹⁰Then take it to your father to eat, so that he may give you his blessing before he dies."

¹¹Jacob said to Rebekah his mother, "But my brother Esau is a hairy man, and I'm a man with smooth skin. ¹²What if my father touches me? I would appear to be tricking him and would bring down a curse on myself rather than a blessing."

¹³His mother said to him, "My son, let the curse fall on me. Just do what I say; go and get them for me."

¹⁴So he went and got them and brought them to his mother, and she prepared some tasty food, just the way his father liked it. ¹⁵Then Rebekah took the best clothes of Esau her older son, which she had in the house, and put them on her younger son Jacob. ¹⁶She also covered his hands and the smooth part of his neck with the goatskins. ¹⁷Then she handed to her son Jacob the tasty food and the bread she had made.

¹⁸He went to his father and said, "My father."

"Yes, my son," he answered. "Who is it?"

¹⁹Jacob said to his father, "I am Esau your firstborn. I have done as you told me. Please sit up and eat some of my game so that you may give me your blessing."

---

[a] 20 Esek means dispute. [b] 21 Sitnah means opposition. [c] 22 Rehoboth means room. [d] 33 Shibah can mean oath or seven. [e] 33 Beersheba can mean well of the oath or well of seven.

Just Call Me Chameleon

focus Profile: **Caroline**

Wanna know a secret? I hate beer. But I can't tell anyone I don't like it. I can just hear their reactions now. "Whaaat? You don't like to drink? Come on!" You'd never guess it if you saw me at a party. I'm the one they count on to make them laugh when I start drinking. They tell me I'm hilarious.

But every time I stumble home, trying not to vomit (or worse, wake up my parents), I wonder why I do this to myself. Every time I wake up with a splitting headache, I wonder who I was with last night.

And while we're on the subject of secrets, here's another one. I really don't like going to church. I mean, I act happy when I'm there, but the only reason I go is my friends. I don't feel close to God at all. Who am I, anyway? When I'm with my party friends, I pretend I like to party. When I'm with my academic friends, I play the part of a serious student. When I'm with my church friends, I act like a good Christian girl.

But which one is the real me? In my effort to fit in everywhere, I've completely lost myself. I never speak my own mind. I just say what I think my friends want to hear. But I'm not really who my friends want me to be. I'm not even the person I want to be. I know the real me is in there somewhere. I just don't know how to set her free. No one has ever met her. What if no one likes her?

identity in focus

God created you to be someone unique. Is it time to set the real you free? It's time to change if . . .

» You are compromising your values to be someone another person will like.
» You know you have to act or look a certain way to please your friends.
» You can't stand the thought of faking it one more day.

There's no better place than the Bible when it comes to finding your true identity. God has a lot to say on the subject, in fact. Check out Psalm 139 (page 791), and read other verses on line.

For more on this topic, see the index on page 1656.

identity

For more to read on the topic of identity, go to www.TrueImageBible.com.

²⁰Isaac asked his son, "How did you find it so quickly, my son?"

"The LORD your God gave me success," he replied.

²¹Then Isaac said to Jacob, "Come near so I can touch you, my son, to know whether you really are my son Esau or not."

²²Jacob went close to his father Isaac, who touched him and said, "The voice is the voice of Jacob, but the hands are the hands of Esau." ²³He did not recognize him, for his hands were hairy like those of his brother Esau; so he blessed him. ²⁴"Are you really my son Esau?" he asked.

"I am," he replied.

²⁵Then he said, "My son, bring me some of your game to eat, so that I may give you my blessing."

Jacob brought it to him and he ate; and he brought some wine and he drank. ²⁶Then his father Isaac said to him, "Come here, my son, and kiss me."

²⁷So he went to him and kissed him. When Isaac caught the smell of his clothes, he blessed him and said,

> "Ah, the smell of my son
> is like the smell of a field
> that the LORD has blessed.
> ²⁸May God give you of heaven's dew
> and of earth's richness—
> an abundance of grain and new wine.
> ²⁹May nations serve you
> and peoples bow down to you.
> Be lord over your brothers,
> and may the sons of your mother bow down to you.
> May those who curse you be cursed
> and those who bless you be blessed."

³⁰After Isaac finished blessing him and Jacob had scarcely left his father's presence, his brother Esau came in from hunting. ³¹He too prepared some tasty food and brought it to his father. Then he said to him, "My father, sit up and eat some of my game, so that you may give me your blessing."

³²His father Isaac asked him, "Who are you?"

"I am your son," he answered, "your firstborn, Esau."

³³Isaac trembled violently and said, "Who was it, then, that hunted game and brought it to me? I ate it just before you came and I blessed him—and indeed he will be blessed!"

³⁴When Esau heard his father's words, he burst out with a loud and bitter cry and said to his father, "Bless me—me too, my father!"

³⁵But he said, "Your brother came deceitfully and took your blessing."

³⁶Esau said, "Isn't he rightly named Jacob^a? He has deceived me these two times: He took my birthright, and now he's taken my blessing!" Then he asked, "Haven't you reserved any blessing for me?"

³⁷Isaac answered Esau, "I have made him lord over you and have made all his relatives his servants, and I have sustained him with grain and new wine. So what can I possibly do for you, my son?"

³⁸Esau said to his father, "Do you have only one blessing, my father? Bless me too, my father!" Then Esau wept aloud.

³⁹His father Isaac answered him,

> "Your dwelling will be
> away from the earth's richness,
> away from the dew of heaven above.
> ⁴⁰You will live by the sword
> and you will serve your brother.
> But when you grow restless,
> you will throw his yoke
> from off your neck."

Jacob Flees to Laban

⁴¹Esau held a grudge against Jacob because of the blessing his father had given him. He said to himself, "The days of mourning for my father are near; then I will kill my brother Jacob."

⁴²When Rebekah was told what her older son Esau had said, she sent for her younger son Jacob and said to him, "Your brother Esau is consoling himself with the thought of killing you. ⁴³Now then, my son, do what I say: Flee at once to my brother Laban in Haran. ⁴⁴Stay with him for a while until your brother's fury subsides. ⁴⁵When your brother is no longer angry with you and forgets what you did to him, I'll send word for you to come back from there. Why should I lose both of you in one day?"

^a 36 Jacob means he grasps the heel (figuratively, he deceives).

[46]Then Rebekah said to Isaac, "I'm disgusted with living because of these Hittite women. If Jacob takes a wife from among the women of this land, from Hittite women like these, my life will not be worth living."

28 So Isaac called for Jacob and blessed[a] him and commanded him: "Do not marry a Canaanite woman. [2]Go at once to Paddan Aram,[b] to the house of your mother's father Bethuel. Take a wife for yourself there, from among the daughters of Laban, your mother's brother. [3]May God Almighty[c] bless you and make you fruitful and increase your numbers until you become a community of peoples. [4]May he give you and your descendants the blessing given to Abraham, so that you may take possession of the land where you now live as an alien, the land God gave to Abraham." [5]Then Isaac sent Jacob on his way, and he went to Paddan Aram, to Laban son of Bethuel the Aramean, the brother of Rebekah, who was the mother of Jacob and Esau.

[6]Now Esau learned that Isaac had blessed Jacob and had sent him to Paddan Aram to take a wife from there, and that when he blessed him he commanded him, "Do not marry a Canaanite woman," [7]and that Jacob had obeyed his father and mother and had gone to Paddan Aram. [8]Esau then realized how displeasing the Canaanite women were to his father Isaac; [9]so he went to Ishmael and married Mahalath, the sister of Nebaioth and daughter of Ishmael son of Abraham, in addition to the wives he already had.

Jacob's Dream at Bethel

[10]Jacob left Beersheba and set out for Haran. [11]When he reached a certain place, he stopped for the night because the sun had set. Taking one of the stones there, he put it under his head and lay down to sleep. [12]He had a dream in which he saw a stairway[d] resting on the earth, with its top reaching to heaven, and the angels of God were ascending and descending on it. [13]There above it[e] stood the LORD, and he said: "I am the LORD, the God of your father Abraham and the God of Isaac. I will give you and your descendants the land on which you are lying. [14]Your descendants will be like the dust of the earth, and you will spread out to the west and to the east, to the north and to the south. All peoples on earth will be blessed through you and your offspring. [15]I am with you and will watch over you wherever you go, and I will bring you back to this land. I will not leave you until I have done what I have promised you."

truth or dare

Your parents' faith record doesn't win or lose you any points with God. He wants a unique relationship with you. It's time to get to know him for yourself.

28:10–15

[16]When Jacob awoke from his sleep, he thought, "Surely the LORD is in this place, and I was not aware of it." [17]He was afraid and said, "How awesome is this place! This is none other than the house of God; this is the gate of heaven."

[18]Early the next morning Jacob took the stone he had placed under his head and set it up as a pillar and poured oil on top of it. [19]He called that place Bethel,[f] though the city used to be called Luz.

[20]Then Jacob made a vow, saying, "If God will be with me and will watch over me on this journey I am taking and will give me food to eat and clothes to wear [21]so that I return safely to my father's house, then the LORD[g] will be my God [22]and[h] this stone that I have set up as a pillar will be God's house, and of all that you give me I will give you a tenth."

Jacob Arrives in Paddan Aram

29 Then Jacob continued on his journey and came to the land of the eastern peoples. [2]There he saw a well in the field, with three flocks of sheep lying near it because the flocks were watered from that well. The stone over the mouth of the well was large. [3]When all the flocks were gathered there, the shepherds would roll the stone away from the well's mouth and water the sheep. Then they would return the stone to its place over the mouth of the well.

---

[a] 1 Or *greeted*   [b] 2 That is, Northwest Mesopotamia; also in verses 5, 6 and 7   [c] 3 Hebrew *El-Shaddai*
[d] 12 Or *ladder*   [e] 13 Or *There beside him*   [f] 19 *Bethel* means *house of God.*   [g] 20,21 Or *Since God . . .*
father's house, the LORD   [h] 21,22 Or *house, and the* LORD *will be my God,* [22]*then*

⁴Jacob asked the shepherds, "My brothers, where are you from?"

"We're from Haran," they replied.

⁵He said to them, "Do you know Laban, Nahor's grandson?"

"Yes, we know him," they answered.

⁶Then Jacob asked them, "Is he well?"

"Yes, he is," they said, "and here comes his daughter Rachel with the sheep."

⁷"Look," he said, "the sun is still high; it is not time for the flocks to be gathered. Water the sheep and take them back to pasture."

⁸"We can't," they replied, "until all the flocks are gathered and the stone has been rolled away from the mouth of the well. Then we will water the sheep."

⁹While he was still talking with them, Rachel came with her father's sheep, for she was a shepherdess. ¹⁰When Jacob saw Rachel daughter of Laban, his mother's brother, and Laban's sheep, he went over and rolled the stone away from the mouth of the well and watered his uncle's sheep. ¹¹Then Jacob kissed Rachel and began to weep aloud. ¹²He had told Rachel that he was a relative of her father and a son of Rebekah. So she ran and told her father.

¹³As soon as Laban heard the news about Jacob, his sister's son, he hurried to meet him. He embraced him and kissed him and brought him to his home, and there Jacob told him all these things. ¹⁴Then Laban said to him, "You are my own flesh and blood."

Jacob Marries Leah and Rachel

After Jacob had stayed with him for a whole month, ¹⁵Laban said to him, "Just because you are a relative of mine, should you work for me for nothing? Tell me what your wages should be."

¹⁶Now Laban had two daughters; the name of the older was Leah, and the name of the younger was Rachel. ¹⁷Leah had weak*ᵃ* eyes, but Rachel was lovely in form, and beautiful. ¹⁸Jacob was in love with Rachel and said, "I'll work for you seven years in return for your younger daughter Rachel."

¹⁹Laban said, "It's better that I give her to you than to some other man. Stay here with me." ²⁰So Jacob served seven years to get Rachel, but they seemed like only a few days to him because of his love for her.

²¹Then Jacob said to Laban, "Give me my wife. My time is completed, and I want to lie with her."

²²So Laban brought together all the people of the place and gave a feast. ²³But when evening came, he took his daughter Leah and gave her to Jacob, and Jacob lay with her. ²⁴And Laban gave his servant girl Zilpah to his daughter as her maidservant.

²⁵When morning came, there was Leah! So Jacob said to Laban, "What is this you have done to me? I served you for Rachel, didn't I? Why have you deceived me?"

²⁶Laban replied, "It is not our custom here to give the younger daughter in marriage before the older one. ²⁷Finish this daughter's bridal week; then we will give you the younger one also, in return for another seven years of work."

²⁸And Jacob did so. He finished the week with Leah, and then Laban gave him his daughter Rachel to be his wife. ²⁹Laban gave his servant girl Bilhah to his daughter Rachel as her maidser-

genuine

persistence » 29:16-20

Imagine wanting something so much that you'd work seven years to get it. (That might be the majority of your life so far!) Don't you think you'd get discouraged after like the fourth year or so? But Jacob kept going. He set his eyes on his goal and never gave up. What kind of goals do you have in life? Getting into a good college? Having a career? Excelling at sports or music? Serving God on the missions field? The key is perseverance—never giving up. Work hard at what God has given you *today*. That's laying the foundation for what's to come in your future.

ᵃ 17 Or delicate

vant. ³⁰Jacob lay with Rachel also, and he loved Rachel more than Leah. And he worked for Laban another seven years.

Jacob's Children

³¹When the LORD saw that Leah was not loved, he opened her womb, but Rachel was barren. ³²Leah became pregnant and gave birth to a son. She named him Reuben,ᵃ for she said, "It is because the LORD has seen my misery. Surely my husband will love me now."

³³She conceived again, and when she gave birth to a son she said, "Because the LORD heard that I am not loved, he gave me this one too." So she named him Simeon.ᵇ

³⁴Again she conceived, and when she gave birth to a son she said, "Now at last my husband will become attached to me, because I have borne him three sons." So he was named Levi.ᶜ

³⁵She conceived again, and when she gave birth to a son she said, "This time I will praise the LORD." So she named him Judah.ᵈ Then she stopped having children.

30 When Rachel saw that she was not bearing Jacob any children, she became jealous of her sister. So she said to Jacob, "Give me children, or I'll die!"

²Jacob became angry with her and said, "Am I in the place of God, who has kept you from having children?"

³Then she said, "Here is Bilhah, my maidservant. Sleep with her so that she can bear children for me and that through her I too can build a family."

⁴So she gave him her servant Bilhah as a wife. Jacob slept with her, ⁵and she became pregnant and bore him a son. ⁶Then Rachel said, "God has vindicated me; he has listened to my plea and given me a son." Because of this she named him Dan.ᵉ

⁷Rachel's servant Bilhah conceived again and bore Jacob a second son. ⁸Then Rachel said, "I have had a great struggle with my sister, and I have won." So she named him Naphtali.ᶠ

⁹When Leah saw that she had stopped having children, she took her maidservant Zilpah and gave her to Jacob as a wife. ¹⁰Leah's servant Zilpah bore Jacob a son. ¹¹Then Leah said, "What good fortune!"ᵍ So she named him Gad.ʰ

¹²Leah's servant Zilpah bore Jacob a second son. ¹³Then Leah said, "How happy I am! The women will call me happy." So she named him Asher.ⁱ

¹⁴During wheat harvest, Reuben went out into the fields and found some mandrake plants, which he brought to his mother Leah. Rachel said to Leah, "Please give me some of your son's mandrakes."

¹⁵But she said to her, "Wasn't it enough that you took away my husband? Will you take my son's mandrakes too?"

"Very well," Rachel said, "he can sleep with you tonight in return for your son's mandrakes."

¹⁶So when Jacob came in from the fields that evening, Leah went out to meet him. "You must sleep with me," she said. "I have hired you with my son's mandrakes." So he slept with her that night.

¹⁷God listened to Leah, and she became pregnant and bore Jacob a fifth son. ¹⁸Then Leah said, "God has rewarded me for giving my maidservant to my husband." So she named him Issachar.ʲ

¹⁹Leah conceived again and bore Jacob a sixth son. ²⁰Then Leah said, "God has presented me with a precious gift. This time my husband will treat me with honor, because I have borne him six sons." So she named him Zebulun.ᵏ

²¹Some time later she gave birth to a daughter and named her Dinah.

²²Then God remembered Rachel; he listened to her and opened her womb. ²³She became pregnant and gave birth to a son and said, "God has taken away my disgrace." ²⁴She named him Joseph,ˡ and said, "May the LORD add to me another son."

Jacob's Flocks Increase

²⁵After Rachel gave birth to Joseph, Jacob said to Laban, "Send me on my way so I can go back to my own homeland. ²⁶Give me my wives and children, for whom I have served you, and I will be on my way. You know how much work I've done for you."

ᵃ 32 Reuben sounds like the Hebrew for he has seen my misery; the name means see, a son.   ᵇ 33 Simeon probably means one who hears.   ᶜ 34 Levi sounds like and may be derived from the Hebrew for attached.   ᵈ 35 Judah sounds like and may be derived from the Hebrew for praise.   ᵉ 6 Dan here means he has vindicated.   ᶠ 8 Naphtali means my struggle.   ᵍ 11 Or "A troop is coming!"   ʰ 11 Gad can mean good fortune or a troop.   ⁱ 13 Asher means happy.   ʲ 18 Issachar sounds like the Hebrew for reward.   ᵏ 20 Zebulun probably means honor.   ˡ 24 Joseph means may he add.

The Truth About Me

I should have guessed the truth at the family reunion. In fact, the thought even flashed through my mind. *I can't believe I'm related to these people!* I remember thinking in disgust as my cousin Mario popped another piece of spaghetti into his mouth and pulled it out his nose. Anything seemed better than knowing that they were actually flesh of my flesh, bone of my bone. Almost anything, that is.

A few nights after the reunion, my parents asked me to sit down for a serious talk. (In our family, that's never a good sign.) I remember feeling frozen in that moment. "Honey, we have been thinking of how to tell you this for quite some time . . ." Their mouths were moving, but I couldn't hear what they were saying. Adopted. I was adopted? I'm 13 years old. How could they not tell me sooner?

It's been a few weeks since I found out the truth. I'm not as angry as I was then. My mom and I have even talked about whether or not I should try to find my birth mother. She will support any decision I make. I believe her. She's always supported me in anything I've ever done. Actually, since I've found out the truth about me, I've also rediscovered the truth about my parents. I am their true child—no matter who gave birth to me. They raised me and loved me as if I were their own. I still have questions. But whatever happens, I have a new, different sense of security. And that's the real truth about me.

adoption in focus

If you are adopted, or you know someone who is, keep these ideas in mind:

» Ask questions. Initially, it may be as awkward for others as it is for you. In time, however, it can bring you closer than ever.
» Journaling is a way of releasing stress and sorting through your own thoughts.
» Many families have found professional Christian counseling helpful for working through questions and emotions.
» Remind yourself that adoption is part of God's special plan. See Jeremiah 29:11 (page 1041) and Ephesians 1:4–5 (page 1543).

For more on this topic, see the index on page 1656.

For more on understanding how adoption can be a special part of God's plan, check out www.TrueImagesBible.com

adoption

[27]But Laban said to him, "If I have found favor in your eyes, please stay. I have learned by divination that*ᵃ* the LORD has blessed me because of you." [28]He added, "Name your wages, and I will pay them."

ᵃ 27 Or possibly *have become rich and*

²⁹Jacob said to him, "You know how I have worked for you and how your livestock has fared under my care. ³⁰The little you had before I came has increased greatly, and the LORD has blessed you wherever I have been. But now, when may I do something for my own household?"

³¹"What shall I give you?" he asked.

"Don't give me anything," Jacob replied. "But if you will do this one thing for me, I will go on tending your flocks and watching over them: ³²Let me go through all your flocks today and remove from them every speckled or spotted sheep, every dark-colored lamb and every spotted or speckled goat. They will be my wages. ³³And my honesty will testify for me in the future, whenever you check on the wages you have paid me. Any goat in my possession that is not speckled or spotted, or any lamb that is not dark-colored, will be considered stolen."

³⁴"Agreed," said Laban. "Let it be as you have said." ³⁵That same day he removed all the male goats that were streaked or spotted, and all the speckled or spotted female goats (all that had white on them) and all the dark-colored lambs, and he placed them in the care of his sons. ³⁶Then he put a three-day journey between himself and Jacob, while Jacob continued to tend the rest of Laban's flocks.

³⁷Jacob, however, took fresh-cut branches from poplar, almond and plane trees and made white stripes on them by peeling the bark and exposing the white inner wood of the branches. ³⁸Then he placed the peeled branches in all the watering troughs, so that they would be directly in front of the flocks when they came to drink. When the flocks were in heat and came to drink, ³⁹they mated in front of the branches. And they bore young that were streaked or speckled or spotted. ⁴⁰Jacob set apart the young of the flock by themselves, but made the rest face the streaked and dark-colored animals that belonged to Laban. Thus he made separate flocks for himself and did not put them with Laban's animals. ⁴¹Whenever the stronger females were in heat, Jacob would place the branches in the troughs in front of the animals so they would mate near the branches, ⁴²but if the animals were weak, he would not place them there. So the weak animals went to Laban and the strong ones to Jacob. ⁴³In this way the man grew exceedingly prosperous and came to own large flocks, and maidservants and menservants, and camels and donkeys.

Jacob Flees From Laban

31 Jacob heard that Laban's sons were saying, "Jacob has taken everything our father owned and has gained all this wealth from what belonged to our father." ²And Jacob noticed that Laban's attitude toward him was not what it had been.

³Then the LORD said to Jacob, "Go back to the land of your fathers and to your relatives, and I will be with you."

⁴So Jacob sent word to Rachel and Leah to come out to the fields where his flocks were. ⁵He said to them, "I see that your father's attitude toward me is not what it was before, but the God of my father has been with me. ⁶You know that I've worked for your father with all my strength, ⁷yet your father has cheated me by changing my wages ten times. However, God has not allowed him to harm me. ⁸If he said, 'The speckled ones will be your wages,' then all the flocks gave birth to speckled young; and if he said, 'The streaked ones will be your wages,' then all the flocks bore streaked young. ⁹So God has taken away your father's livestock and has given them to me.

¹⁰"In breeding season I once had a dream in which I looked up and saw that the male goats mating with the flock were streaked, speckled or spotted. ¹¹The angel of God said to me in the dream, 'Jacob.' I answered, 'Here I am.' ¹²And he said, 'Look up and see that all the male goats mating with the flock are streaked, speckled or spotted, for I have seen all that Laban has been doing to you. ¹³I am the God of Bethel, where you anointed a pillar and where you made a vow to me. Now leave this land at once and go back to your native land.' "

¹⁴Then Rachel and Leah replied, "Do we still have any share in the inheritance of our father's estate? ¹⁵Does he not regard us as foreigners? Not only has he sold us, but he has used up what was paid for us. ¹⁶Surely all the wealth that God took away from our father belongs to us and our children. So do whatever God has told you."

¹⁷Then Jacob put his children and his wives on camels, ¹⁸and he drove all his livestock ahead of him, along with all the goods he had accumulated in Paddan Aram,ᵃ to go to his father Isaac in the land of Canaan.

ᵃ 18 That is, Northwest Mesopotamia

[19] When Laban had gone to shear his sheep, Rachel stole her father's household gods. [20] Moreover, Jacob deceived Laban the Aramean by not telling him he was running away. [21] So he fled with all he had, and crossing the River,[a] he headed for the hill country of Gilead.

Laban Pursues Jacob

[22] On the third day Laban was told that Jacob had fled. [23] Taking his relatives with him, he pursued Jacob for seven days and caught up with him in the hill country of Gilead. [24] Then God came to Laban the Aramean in a dream at night and said to him, "Be careful not to say anything to Jacob, either good or bad."

[25] Jacob had pitched his tent in the hill country of Gilead when Laban overtook him, and Laban and his relatives camped there too. [26] Then Laban said to Jacob, "What have you done? You've deceived me, and you've carried off my daughters like captives in war. [27] Why did you run off secretly and deceive me? Why didn't you tell me, so I could send you away with joy and singing to the music of tambourines and harps? [28] You didn't even let me kiss my grandchildren and my daughters good-by. You have done a foolish thing. [29] I have the power to harm you; but last night the God of your father said to me, 'Be careful not to say anything to Jacob, either good or bad.' [30] Now you have gone off because you longed to return to your father's house. But why did you steal my gods?"

[31] Jacob answered Laban, "I was afraid, because I thought you would take your daughters away from me by force. [32] But if you find anyone who has your gods, he shall not live. In the presence of our relatives, see for yourself whether there is anything of yours here with me; and if so, take it." Now Jacob did not know that Rachel had stolen the gods.

[33] So Laban went into Jacob's tent and into Leah's tent and into the tent of the two maidservants, but he found nothing. After he came out of Leah's tent, he entered Rachel's tent. [34] Now Rachel had taken the household gods and put them inside her camel's saddle and was sitting on them. Laban searched through everything in the tent but found nothing.

[35] Rachel said to her father, "Don't be angry, my lord, that I cannot stand up in your presence; I'm having my period." So he searched but could not find the household gods.

genuine

honor »» 31:38-42

Are you ever guilty of "just getting by"? Do you study just enough to pass your tests? Keep your room just clean enough so that your mom doesn't call in the exterminators? Show just enough respect to your parents? Give God just enough attention each day? What would happen if, like Jacob, you went above and beyond what's expected of you? Your efforts may not get noticed (then again, they might!) What's most important, however, is that God would see your efforts and be pleased.

[36] Jacob was angry and took Laban to task. "What is my crime?" he asked Laban. "What sin have I committed that you hunt me down? [37] Now that you have searched through all my goods, what have you found that belongs to your household? Put it here in front of your relatives and mine, and let them judge between the two of us.

[38] "I have been with you for twenty years now. Your sheep and goats have not miscarried, nor have I eaten rams from your flocks. [39] I did not bring you animals torn by wild beasts; I bore the loss myself. And you demanded payment from me for whatever was stolen by day or night. [40] This was my situation: The heat consumed me in the daytime and the cold at night, and sleep fled from my eyes. [41] It was like this for the twenty years I was in your household. I worked for you fourteen years for your two daughters and six years for your flocks, and you changed my wages ten times. [42] If the God of my father, the God of Abraham and the Fear of Isaac, had not been with me, you would surely have sent me away empty-handed. But God has seen my hardship and the toil of my hands, and last night he rebuked you."

⁴³Laban answered Jacob, "The women are my daughters, the children are my children, and the flocks are my flocks. All you see is mine. Yet what can I do today about these daughters of mine, or about the children they have borne? ⁴⁴Come now, let's make a covenant, you and I, and let it serve as a witness between us."

⁴⁵So Jacob took a stone and set it up as a pillar. ⁴⁶He said to his relatives, "Gather some stones." So they took stones and piled them in a heap, and they ate there by the heap. ⁴⁷Laban called it Jegar Sahadutha, ᵃ and Jacob called it Galeed. ᵇ

⁴⁸Laban said, "This heap is a witness between you and me today." That is why it was called Galeed. ⁴⁹It was also called Mizpah, ᶜ because he said, "May the LORD keep watch between you and me when we are away from each other. ⁵⁰If you mistreat my daughters or if you take any wives besides my daughters, even though no one is with us, remember that God is a witness between you and me."

⁵¹Laban also said to Jacob, "Here is this heap, and here is this pillar I have set up between you and me. ⁵²This heap is a witness, and this pillar is a witness, that I will not go past this heap to your side to harm you and that you will not go past this heap and pillar to my side to harm me. ⁵³May the God of Abraham and the God of Nahor, the God of their father, judge between us."

So Jacob took an oath in the name of the Fear of his father Isaac. ⁵⁴He offered a sacrifice there in the hill country and invited his relatives to a meal. After they had eaten, they spent the night there.

⁵⁵Early the next morning Laban kissed his grandchildren and his daughters and blessed them. Then he left and returned home.

Jacob Prepares to Meet Esau

32 Jacob also went on his way, and the angels of God met him. ²When Jacob saw them, he said, "This is the camp of God!" So he named that place Mahanaim. ᵈ ³Jacob sent messengers ahead of him to his brother Esau in the land of Seir, the country of Edom. ⁴He instructed them: "This is what you are to say to my master Esau: 'Your servant Jacob says, I have been staying with Laban and have remained there till now. ⁵I have cattle and donkeys, sheep and goats, menservants and maidservants. Now I am sending this message to my lord, that I may find favor in your eyes.' "

⁶When the messengers returned to Jacob, they said, "We went to your brother Esau, and now he is coming to meet you, and four hundred men are with him."

⁷In great fear and distress Jacob divided the people who were with him into two groups,ᵉ and the flocks and herds and camels as well. ⁸He thought, "If Esau comes and attacks one group,ᶠ the groupᶠ that is left may escape."

⁹Then Jacob prayed, "O God of my father Abraham, God of my father Isaac, O LORD, who said to me, 'Go back to your country and your relatives, and I will make you prosper,' ¹⁰I am unworthy of all the kindness and faithfulness you have shown your servant. I had only my staff when I crossed this Jordan, but now I have become two groups. ¹¹Save me, I pray, from the hand of my brother Esau, for I am afraid he will come and attack me, and also the mothers with their children. ¹²But you have said, 'I will surely make you prosper and will make your descendants like the sand of the sea, which cannot be counted.' "

¹³He spent the night there, and from what he had with him he selected a gift for his brother Esau: ¹⁴two hundred female goats and twenty male goats, two hundred ewes and twenty rams, ¹⁵thirty female camels with their young, forty cows and ten bulls, and twenty female donkeys and ten male donkeys. ¹⁶He put them in the care of his servants, each herd by itself, and said to his servants, "Go ahead of me, and keep some space between the herds."

¹⁷He instructed the one in the lead: "When my brother Esau meets you and asks, 'To whom do you belong, and where are you going, and who owns all these animals in front of you?' ¹⁸then you are to say, 'They belong to your servant Jacob. They are a gift sent to my lord Esau, and he is coming behind us.' "

¹⁹He also instructed the second, the third and all the others who followed the herds: "You are to say the same thing to Esau when you meet him. ²⁰And be sure to say, 'Your servant Jacob is coming behind us.' " For he thought, "I will pacify him with these gifts I am sending on ahead; lat-

ᵃ 47 The Aramaic *Jegar Sahadutha* means *witness heap.*   ᵇ 47 The Hebrew *Galeed* means *witness heap.*
ᶜ 49 *Mizpah* means *watchtower.*   ᵈ 2 *Mahanaim* means *two camps.*   ᵉ 7 Or *camps*; also in verse 10   ᶠ 8 Or *camp*

er, when I see him, perhaps he will receive me." ²¹So Jacob's gifts went on ahead of him, but he himself spent the night in the camp.

Jacob Wrestles With God

²²That night Jacob got up and took his two wives, his two maidservants and his eleven sons and crossed the ford of the Jabbok. ²³After he had sent them across the stream, he sent over all his possessions. ²⁴So Jacob was left alone, and a man wrestled with him till daybreak. ²⁵When the man saw that he could not overpower him, he touched the socket of Jacob's hip so that his hip was wrenched as he wrestled with the man. ²⁶Then the man said, "Let me go, for it is daybreak."

But Jacob replied, "I will not let you go unless you bless me."

²⁷The man asked him, "What is your name?"

"Jacob," he answered.

²⁸Then the man said, "Your name will no longer be Jacob, but Israel,ᵃ because you have struggled with God and with men and have overcome."

genuine growth »» 32:22-31

Jacob's life had its ups and downs, yet his faith was constantly growing and maturing—even through his mistakes. When he wrestled with God, his life changed forever. Remember that being a Christian is a growing process. You'll make mistakes, but then you have to pick yourself up, learn from them and keep going. When times are tough, that's when you need to hang on tightly to God, without letting him go. Ask him to bless you—even through the tough times. When you hold on to God, you'll discover something amazing: He's holding on to you, too.

²⁹Jacob said, "Please tell me your name."

But he replied, "Why do you ask my name?" Then he blessed him there.

³⁰So Jacob called the place Peniel,ᵇ saying, "It is because I saw God face to face, and yet my life was spared."

³¹The sun rose above him as he passed Peniel,ᶜ and he was limping because of his hip. ³²Therefore to this day the Israelites do not eat the tendon attached to the socket of the hip, because the socket of Jacob's hip was touched near the tendon.

Jacob Meets Esau

33 Jacob looked up and there was Esau, coming with his four hundred men; so he divided the children among Leah, Rachel and the two maidservants. ²He put the maidservants and their children in front, Leah and her children next, and Rachel and Joseph in the rear. ³He himself went on ahead and bowed down to the ground seven times as he approached his brother.

⁴But Esau ran to meet Jacob and embraced him; he threw his arms around his neck and kissed him. And they wept. ⁵Then Esau looked up and saw the women and children. "Who are these with you?" he asked.

Jacob answered, "They are the children God has graciously given your servant."

⁶Then the maidservants and their children approached and bowed down. ⁷Next, Leah and her children came and bowed down. Last of all came Joseph and Rachel, and they too bowed down.

⁸Esau asked, "What do you mean by all these droves I met?"

"To find favor in your eyes, my lord," he said.

⁹But Esau said, "I already have plenty, my brother. Keep what you have for yourself."

¹⁰"No, please!" said Jacob. "If I have found favor in your eyes, accept this gift from me. For to see your face is like seeing the face of God, now that you have received me favorably. ¹¹Please accept the present that was brought to you, for God has been gracious to me and I have all I need." And because Jacob insisted, Esau accepted it.

ᵃ 28 *Israel* means *he struggles with God.*   ᵇ 30 *Peniel* means *face of God.*   ᶜ 31 Hebrew *Penuel,* a variant of *Peniel*

[12]Then Esau said, "Let us be on our way; I'll accompany you."

[13]But Jacob said to him, "My lord knows that the children are tender and that I must care for the ewes and cows that are nursing their young. If they are driven hard just one day, all the animals will die. [14]So let my lord go on ahead of his servant, while I move along slowly at the pace of the droves before me and that of the children, until I come to my lord in Seir."

[15]Esau said, "Then let me leave some of my men with you."

"But why do that?" Jacob asked. "Just let me find favor in the eyes of my lord."

[16]So that day Esau started on his way back to Seir. [17]Jacob, however, went to Succoth, where he built a place for himself and made shelters for his livestock. That is why the place is called Succoth. [a]

[18]After Jacob came from Paddan Aram, [b] he arrived safely at the [c] city of Shechem in Canaan and camped within sight of the city. [19]For a hundred pieces of silver, [d] he bought from the sons of Hamor, the father of Shechem, the plot of ground where he pitched his tent. [20]There he set up an altar and called it El Elohe Israel. [e]

truth or dare

Rape can happen when you least expect it, and it's a high price to pay for being in the wrong place at the wrong time. Don't put yourself in danger.

34:1–4

Dinah and the Shechemites

34 Now Dinah, the daughter Leah had borne to Jacob, went out to visit the women of the land. [2]When Shechem son of Hamor the Hivite, the ruler of that area, saw her, he took her and violated her. [3]His heart was drawn to Dinah daughter of Jacob, and he loved the girl and spoke tenderly to her. [4]And Shechem said to his father Hamor, "Get me this girl as my wife."

[5]When Jacob heard that his daughter Dinah had been defiled, his sons were in the fields with his livestock; so he kept quiet about it until they came home.

[6]Then Shechem's father Hamor went out to talk with Jacob. [7]Now Jacob's sons had come in from the fields as soon as they heard what had happened. They were filled with grief and fury, because Shechem had done a disgraceful thing in [f] Israel by lying with Jacob's daughter—a thing that should not be done.

[8]But Hamor said to them, "My son Shechem has his heart set on your daughter. Please give her to him as his wife. [9]Intermarry with us; give us your daughters and take our daughters for yourselves. [10]You can settle among us; the land is open to you. Live in it, trade [g] in it, and acquire property in it."

[11]Then Shechem said to Dinah's father and brothers, "Let me find favor in your eyes, and I will give you whatever you ask. [12]Make the price for the bride and the gift I am to bring as great as you like, and I'll pay whatever you ask me. Only give me the girl as my wife."

[13]Because their sister Dinah had been defiled, Jacob's sons replied deceitfully as they spoke to Shechem and his father Hamor. [14]They said to them, "We can't do such a thing; we can't give our sister to a man who is not circumcised. That would be a disgrace to us. [15]We will give our consent to you on one condition only: that you become like us by circumcising all your males. [16]Then we will give you our daughters and take your daughters for ourselves. We'll settle among you and become one people with you. [17]But if you will not agree to be circumcised, we'll take our sister [h] and go."

[18]Their proposal seemed good to Hamor and his son Shechem. [19]The young man, who was the most honored of all his father's household, lost no time in doing what they said, because he was delighted with Jacob's daughter. [20]So Hamor and his son Shechem went to the gate of their city to speak to their fellow townsmen. [21]"These men are friendly toward us," they said. "Let them live in our land and trade in it; the land has plenty of room for them. We can marry their daughters and they can marry ours. [22]But the men will consent to live with us as one people only on the condition that our males be circumcised, as they themselves are. [23]Won't their livestock, their property and all their other animals become ours? So let us give our consent to them, and they will settle among us."

---

a 17 Succoth means shelters.   b 18 That is, Northwest Mesopotamia   c 18 Or arrived at Shalem, a   d 19 Hebrew hundred kesitahs; a kesitah was a unit of money of unknown weight and value.   e 20 El Elohe Israel can mean God, the God of Israel or mighty is the God of Israel.   f 7 Or against   g 10 Or move about freely; also in verse 21 h 17 Hebrew daughter

genuine

Did you ever want revenge against someone who hurt you? Dinah's big brothers did. Dinah had been raped, and understandably, they were furious. However, in the case of Simeon and Levi, their anger turned to violence—not only against the man who raped Dinah, but also against his entire city. Their violent revenge affected the future of their own descendants (see 49:5–7.) While it's okay to want justice, it's not okay to seek revenge. God clearly tells us, "It is mine to avenge; I will repay" (Deuteronomy 32:35). Ask God for justice; then have the faith to wait for him to act.

²⁴All the men who went out of the city gate agreed with Hamor and his son Shechem, and every male in the city was circumcised. ²⁵Three days later, while all of them were still in pain, two of Jacob's sons, Simeon and Levi, Dinah's brothers, took their swords and attacked the unsuspecting city, killing every male. ²⁶They put Hamor and his son Shechem to the sword and took Dinah from Shechem's house and left. ²⁷The sons of Jacob came upon the dead bodies and looted the city where ᵃ their sister had been defiled. ²⁸They seized their flocks and herds and donkeys and everything else of theirs in the city and out in the fields. ²⁹They carried off all their wealth and all their women and children, taking as plunder everything in the houses.

³⁰Then Jacob said to Simeon and Levi, "You have brought trouble on me by making me a stench to the Canaanites and Perizzites, the people living in this land. We are few in number, and if they join forces against me and attack me, I and my household will be destroyed."

³¹But they replied, "Should he have treated our sister like a prostitute?"

Jacob Returns to Bethel

35 Then God said to Jacob, "Go up to Bethel and settle there, and build an altar there to God, who appeared to you when you were fleeing from your brother Esau." ²So Jacob said to his household and to all who were with him, "Get rid of the foreign gods you have with you, and purify yourselves and change your clothes. ³Then come, let us go up to Bethel, where I will build an altar to God, who answered me in the day of my distress and who has been with me wherever I have gone." ⁴So they gave Jacob all the foreign gods they had and the rings in their ears, and Jacob buried them under the oak at Shechem. ⁵Then they set out, and the terror of God fell upon the towns all around them so that no one pursued them.

⁶Jacob and all the people with him came to Luz (that is, Bethel) in the land of Canaan. ⁷There he built an altar, and he called the place El Bethel, ᵇ because it was there that God revealed himself to him when he was fleeing from his brother.

⁸Now Deborah, Rebekah's nurse, died and was buried under the oak below Bethel. So it was named Allon Bacuth. ᶜ

⁹After Jacob returned from Paddan Aram, ᵈ God appeared to him again and blessed him. ¹⁰God said to him, "Your name is Jacob, ᵉ but you will no longer be called Jacob; your name will be Israel. ᶠ" So he named him Israel.

¹¹And God said to him, "I am God Almighty ᵍ; be fruitful and increase in number. A nation and a community of nations will come from you, and kings will come from your body. ¹²The land I gave to Abraham and Isaac I also give to you, and I will give this land to your descendants after you." ¹³Then God went up from him at the place where he had talked with him.

¹⁴Jacob set up a stone pillar at the place where God had talked with him, and he poured out a drink offering on it; he also poured oil on it. ¹⁵Jacob called the place where God had talked with him Bethel. ʰ

---

a 27 Or *because*   *b 7 El Bethel* means *God of Bethel.*   *c 8 Allon Bacuth* means *oak of weeping.*   *d 9* That is, Northwest Mesopotamia; also in verse 26   *e 10 Jacob* means *he grasps the heel* (figuratively, *he deceives*). *f 10 Israel* means *he struggles with God.*   *g 11* Hebrew *El-Shaddai*   *h 15 Bethel* means *house of God.*

The Deaths of Rachel and Isaac

[16]Then they moved on from Bethel. While they were still some distance from Ephrath, Rachel began to give birth and had great difficulty. [17]And as she was having great difficulty in childbirth, the midwife said to her, "Don't be afraid, for you have another son." [18]As she breathed her last—for she was dying—she named her son Ben-Oni.[a] But his father named him Benjamin.[b]

[19]So Rachel died and was buried on the way to Ephrath (that is, Bethlehem). [20]Over her tomb Jacob set up a pillar, and to this day that pillar marks Rachel's tomb.

[21]Israel moved on again and pitched his tent beyond Migdal Eder. [22]While Israel was living in that region, Reuben went in and slept with his father's concubine Bilhah, and Israel heard of it.

Jacob had twelve sons:

[23]The sons of Leah:

Reuben the firstborn of Jacob,

Simeon, Levi, Judah, Issachar and Zebulun.

[24]The sons of Rachel:

Joseph and Benjamin.

[25]The sons of Rachel's maidservant Bilhah:

Dan and Naphtali.

[26]The sons of Leah's maidservant Zilpah:

Gad and Asher.

These were the sons of Jacob, who were born to him in Paddan Aram.

[27]Jacob came home to his father Isaac in Mamre, near Kiriath Arba (that is, Hebron), where Abraham and Isaac had stayed. [28]Isaac lived a hundred and eighty years. [29]Then he breathed his last and died and was gathered to his people, old and full of years. And his sons Esau and Jacob buried him.

Esau's Descendants

36
[1]This is the account of Esau (that is, Edom).

[2]Esau took his wives from the women of Canaan: Adah daughter of Elon the Hittite, and Oholibamah daughter of Anah and granddaughter of Zibeon the Hivite— [3]also Basemath daughter of Ishmael and sister of Nebaioth.

[4]Adah bore Eliphaz to Esau, Basemath bore Reuel, [5]and Oholibamah bore Jeush, Jalam and Korah. These were the sons of Esau, who were born to him in Canaan.

[6]Esau took his wives and sons and daughters and all the members of his household, as well as his livestock and all his other animals and all the goods he had acquired in Canaan, and moved to a land some distance from his brother Jacob. [7]Their possessions were too great for them to remain together; the land where they were staying could not support them both because of their livestock. [8]So Esau (that is, Edom) settled in the hill country of Seir.

[9]This is the account of Esau the father of the Edomites in the hill country of Seir.

[10]These are the names of Esau's sons:

Eliphaz, the son of Esau's wife Adah, and Reuel, the son of Esau's wife Basemath.

[11]The sons of Eliphaz:

Teman, Omar, Zepho, Gatam and Kenaz.

[12]Esau's son Eliphaz also had a concubine named Timna, who bore him Amalek. These were grandsons of Esau's wife Adah.

[13]The sons of Reuel:

Nahath, Zerah, Shammah and Mizzah. These were grandsons of Esau's wife Basemath.

[14]The sons of Esau's wife Oholibamah daughter of Anah and granddaughter of Zibeon, whom she bore to Esau:

Jeush, Jalam and Korah.

[15]These were the chiefs among Esau's descendants:

The sons of Eliphaz the firstborn of Esau:

a 18 Ben-Oni means *son of my trouble.*   b 18 Benjamin means *son of my right hand.*

mirror images

Lot's Wife—Leaving the Past Behind

Flee for your lives! Don't look back . . . Translation: get outta town *now!* This was the angels' last warning when Lot's family made their escape from Sin City (otherwise known as Sodom). Because it was so evil, God destroyed this city with burning sulfur raining down from the sky. But he gave Abraham's nephew Lot a chance to escape with his family. Unfortunately, Lot's wife looked back and immediately "became a pillar of salt" as she was covered by the burning sulfur.

"Hullo!" we may say to ourselves. "Why did she turn around?"

It's easy to judge Lot's wife as doing something really stupid. But think about it. Here's Lot's wife—leaving all she ever knew behind her while she's running frantically toward an unknown future. She's leaving everything—Her home. All her stuff—except what she could carry. Her friends. Her whole life was going up in flames behind her. Wouldn't you want to turn around for one last look?

What is God telling you to run from in your life? When God tells you to move on from friendships that are dragging you down, do you go immediately? Or do you find yourself still hanging around your old friends, scared to move on? Or picture this. A break-up. You're devastated—and hoping you'll get back together even though he's not good for you. When you get hung up on "what might have been," it keeps you from seeing "what might be." God has new and better possibilities in the future—if you will only trust him.

Take it from Lot's wife. When it comes to letting go of your past, one look back can be your last.

To read the next Mirror Images profile, go to page 77.

Dear God, thank you for loving me enough to get me out of harmful situations. Help me to leave my past behind so I can enjoy future blessings from you. Amen.

dear God

Read more about Lot's wife in Genesis 19:1–26 on pages 22–23.

47

Chiefs Teman, Omar, Zepho, Kenaz, [16]Korah,[a] Gatam and Amalek. These were the chiefs descended from Eliphaz in Edom; they were grandsons of Adah.

[17] The sons of Esau's son Reuel:

Chiefs Nahath, Zerah, Shammah and Mizzah. These were the chiefs descended from Reuel in Edom; they were grandsons of Esau's wife Basemath.

[18] The sons of Esau's wife Oholibamah:

Chiefs Jeush, Jalam and Korah. These were the chiefs descended from Esau's wife Oholibamah daughter of Anah.

[19]These were the sons of Esau (that is, Edom), and these were their chiefs.

[20]These were the sons of Seir the Horite, who were living in the region:

Lotan, Shobal, Zibeon, Anah, [21]Dishon, Ezer and Dishan. These sons of Seir in Edom were Horite chiefs.

[22] The sons of Lotan:

Hori and Homam.[b] Timna was Lotan's sister.

[23] The sons of Shobal:

Alvan, Manahath, Ebal, Shepho and Onam.

[24] The sons of Zibeon:

Aiah and Anah. This is the Anah who discovered the hot springs[c] in the desert while he was grazing the donkeys of his father Zibeon.

[25] The children of Anah:

Dishon and Oholibamah daughter of Anah.

[26] The sons of Dishon[d]:

Hemdan, Eshban, Ithran and Keran.

[27] The sons of Ezer:

Bilhan, Zaavan and Akan.

[28] The sons of Dishan:

Uz and Aran.

[29] These were the Horite chiefs:

Lotan, Shobal, Zibeon, Anah, [30]Dishon, Ezer and Dishan. These were the Horite chiefs, according to their divisions, in the land of Seir.

The Rulers of Edom

[31]These were the kings who reigned in Edom before any Israelite king reigned[e]:

[32] Bela son of Beor became king of Edom. His city was named Dinhabah.

[33] When Bela died, Jobab son of Zerah from Bozrah succeeded him as king.

[34] When Jobab died, Husham from the land of the Temanites succeeded him as king.

[35] When Husham died, Hadad son of Bedad, who defeated Midian in the country of Moab, succeeded him as king. His city was named Avith.

[36] When Hadad died, Samlah from Masrekah succeeded him as king.

[37] When Samlah died, Shaul from Rehoboth on the river[f] succeeded him as king.

[38] When Shaul died, Baal-Hanan son of Acbor succeeded him as king.

[39] When Baal-Hanan son of Acbor died, Hadad[g] succeeded him as king. His city was named Pau, and his wife's name was Mehetabel daughter of Matred, the daughter of Me-Za-hab.

[40]These were the chiefs descended from Esau, by name, according to their clans and regions:

Timna, Alvah, Jetheth, [41]Oholibamah, Elah, Pinon, [42]Kenaz, Teman, Mibzar, [43]Magdiel and Iram. These were the chiefs of Edom, according to their settlements in the land they occupied.

This was Esau the father of the Edomites.

a 16 Masoretic Text; Samaritan Pentateuch (see also Gen. 36:11 and 1 Chron. 1:36) does not have Korah.   b 22 Hebrew Hemam, a variant of Homam (see 1 Chron. 1:39)   c 24 Vulgate; Syriac discovered water; the meaning of the Hebrew for this word is uncertain.   d 26 Hebrew Dishan, a variant of Dishon   e 31 Or before an Israelite king reigned over them   f 37 Possibly the Euphrates   g 39 Many manuscripts of the Masoretic Text, Samaritan Pentateuch and Syriac (see also 1 Chron. 1:50); most manuscripts of the Masoretic Text Hadar

Joseph's Dreams

37

Jacob lived in the land where his father had stayed, the land of Canaan.

²This is the account of Jacob.

Joseph, a young man of seventeen, was tending the flocks with his brothers, the sons of Bilhah and the sons of Zilpah, his father's wives, and he brought their father a bad report about them. ³Now Israel loved Joseph more than any of his other sons, because he had been born to him in his old age; and he made a richly ornamented*ᵃ* robe for him. ⁴When his brothers saw that their father loved him more than any of them, they hated him and could not speak a kind word to him.

⁵Joseph had a dream, and when he told it to his brothers, they hated him all the more. ⁶He said to them, "Listen to this dream I had: ⁷We were binding sheaves of grain out in the field when suddenly my sheaf rose and stood upright, while your sheaves gathered around mine and bowed down to it."

⁸His brothers said to him, "Do you intend to reign over us? Will you actually rule us?" And they hated him all the more because of his dream and what he had said.

⁹Then he had another dream, and he told it to his brothers. "Listen," he said, "I had another dream, and this time the sun and moon and eleven stars were bowing down to me."

¹⁰When he told his father as well as his brothers, his father rebuked him and said, "What is this dream you had? Will your mother and I and your brothers actually come and bow down to the ground before you?" ¹¹His brothers were jealous of him, but his father kept the matter in mind.

Joseph Sold by His Brothers

¹²Now his brothers had gone to graze their father's flocks near Shechem, ¹³and Israel said to Joseph, "As you know, your brothers are grazing the flocks near Shechem. Come, I am going to send you to them."

"Very well," he replied.

¹⁴So he said to him, "Go and see if all is well with your brothers and with the flocks, and bring word back to me." Then he sent him off from the Valley of Hebron.

When Joseph arrived at Shechem, ¹⁵a man found him wandering around in the fields and asked him, "What are you looking for?"

¹⁶He replied, "I'm looking for my brothers. Can you tell me where they are grazing their flocks?"

¹⁷"They have moved on from here," the man answered. "I heard them say, 'Let's go to Dothan.'"

So Joseph went after his brothers and found them near Dothan. ¹⁸But they saw him in the distance, and before he reached them, they plotted to kill him.

¹⁹"Here comes that dreamer!" they said to each other. ²⁰"Come now, let's kill him and throw him into one of these cisterns and say that a ferocious animal devoured him. Then we'll see what comes of his dreams."

²¹When Reuben heard this, he tried to rescue him from their hands. "Let's not take his life," he said. ²²"Don't shed any blood. Throw him into this cistern here in the desert, but don't lay a hand on him." Reuben said this to rescue him from them and take him back to his father.

²³So when Joseph came to his brothers, they stripped him of his robe—the richly ornamented robe he was wearing— ²⁴and they took him and threw him into the cistern. Now the cistern was empty; there was no water in it.

²⁵As they sat down to eat their meal, they looked up and saw a caravan of Ishmaelites coming from Gilead. Their camels were loaded with spices, balm and myrrh, and they were on their way to take them down to Egypt.

truth or dare

Jealousy, like fire, starts small but quickly grows out of control. What jealous attitudes in your life need to be quickly stamped out before they overwhelm you?

37:18–19

ᵃ 3 The meaning of the Hebrew for *richly ornamented* is uncertain; also in verses 23 and 32.

²⁶Judah said to his brothers, "What will we gain if we kill our brother and cover up his blood? ²⁷Come, let's sell him to the Ishmaelites and not lay our hands on him; after all, he is our brother, our own flesh and blood." His brothers agreed.

²⁸So when the Midianite merchants came by, his brothers pulled Joseph up out of the cistern and sold him for twenty shekels^a of silver to the Ishmaelites, who took him to Egypt.

²⁹When Reuben returned to the cistern and saw that Joseph was not there, he tore his clothes. ³⁰He went back to his brothers and said, "The boy isn't there! Where can I turn now?"

³¹Then they got Joseph's robe, slaughtered a goat and dipped the robe in the blood. ³²They took the ornamented robe back to their father and said, "We found this. Examine it to see whether it is your son's robe."

³³He recognized it and said, "It is my son's robe! Some ferocious animal has devoured him. Joseph has surely been torn to pieces."

³⁴Then Jacob tore his clothes, put on sackcloth and mourned for his son many days. ³⁵All his sons and daughters came to comfort him, but he refused to be comforted. "No," he said, "in mourning will I go down to the grave^b to my son." So his father wept for him.

³⁶Meanwhile, the Midianites^c sold Joseph in Egypt to Potiphar, one of Pharaoh's officials, the captain of the guard.

Judah and Tamar

38 At that time, Judah left his brothers and went down to stay with a man of Adullam named Hirah. ²There Judah met the daughter of a Canaanite man named Shua. He married her and lay with her; ³she became pregnant and gave birth to a son, who was named Er. ⁴She conceived again and gave birth to a son and named him Onan. ⁵She gave birth to still another son and named him Shelah. It was at Kezib that she gave birth to him.

⁶Judah got a wife for Er, his firstborn, and her name was Tamar. ⁷But Er, Judah's firstborn, was wicked in the LORD's sight; so the LORD put him to death.

⁸Then Judah said to Onan, "Lie with your brother's wife and fulfill your duty to her as a brother-in-law to produce offspring for your brother." ⁹But Onan knew that the offspring would not be his; so whenever he lay with his brother's wife, he spilled his semen on the ground to keep from producing offspring for his brother. ¹⁰What he did was wicked in the LORD's sight; so he put him to death also.

¹¹Judah then said to his daughter-in-law Tamar, "Live as a widow in your father's house until my son Shelah grows up." For he thought, "He may die too, just like his brothers." So Tamar went to live in her father's house.

¹²After a long time Judah's wife, the daughter of Shua, died. When Judah had recovered from his grief, he went up to Timnah, to the men who were shearing his sheep, and his friend Hirah the Adullamite went with him.

¹³When Tamar was told, "Your father-in-law is on his way to Timnah to shear his sheep," ¹⁴she took off her widow's clothes, covered herself with a veil to disguise herself, and then sat down at the entrance to Enaim, which is on the road to Timnah. For she saw that, though Shelah had now grown up, she had not been given to him as his wife.

¹⁵When Judah saw her, he thought she was a prostitute, for she had covered her face. ¹⁶Not realizing that she was his daughter-in-law, he went over to her by the roadside and said, "Come now, let me sleep with you."

"And what will you give me to sleep with you?" she asked.

¹⁷"I'll send you a young goat from my flock," he said.

"Will you give me something as a pledge until you send it?" she asked.

¹⁸He said, "What pledge should I give you?"

"Your seal and its cord, and the staff in your hand," she answered. So he gave them to her and slept with her, and she became pregnant by him. ¹⁹After she left, she took off her veil and put on her widow's clothes again.

²⁰Meanwhile Judah sent the young goat by his friend the Adullamite in order to get his pledge

---

^a 28 That is, about 8 ounces (about 0.2 kilogram)   ^b 35 Hebrew *Sheol*   ^c 36 Samaritan Pentateuch, Septuagint, Vulgate and Syriac (see also verse 28); Masoretic Text *Medanites*

back from the woman, but he did not find her. [21]He asked the men who lived there, "Where is the shrine prostitute who was beside the road at Enaim?"

"There hasn't been any shrine prostitute here," they said.

[22]So he went back to Judah and said, "I didn't find her. Besides, the men who lived there said, 'There hasn't been any shrine prostitute here.'"

[23]Then Judah said, "Let her keep what she has, or we will become a laughingstock. After all, I did send her this young goat, but you didn't find her."

[24]About three months later Judah was told, "Your daughter-in-law Tamar is guilty of prostitution, and as a result she is now pregnant."

Judah said, "Bring her out and have her burned to death!"

[25]As she was being brought out, she sent a message to her father-in-law. "I am pregnant by the man who owns these," she said. And she added, "See if you recognize whose seal and cord and staff these are."

[26]Judah recognized them and said, "She is more righteous than I, since I wouldn't give her to my son Shelah." And he did not sleep with her again.

[27]When the time came for her to give birth, there were twin boys in her womb. [28]As she was giving birth, one of them put out his hand; so the midwife took a scarlet thread and tied it on his wrist and said, "This one came out first." [29]But when he drew back his hand, his brother came out, and she said, "So this is how you have broken out!" And he was named Perez. [a] [30]Then his brother, who had the scarlet thread on his wrist, came out and he was given the name Zerah. [b]

Joseph and Potiphar's Wife

39 Now Joseph had been taken down to Egypt. Potiphar, an Egyptian who was one of Pharaoh's officials, the captain of the guard, bought him from the Ishmaelites who had taken him there.

[2]The LORD was with Joseph and he prospered, and he lived in the house of his Egyptian master. [3]When his master saw that the LORD was with him and that the LORD gave him success in everything he did, [4]Joseph found favor in his eyes and became his attendant. Potiphar put him in charge of his household, and he entrusted to his care everything he owned. [5]From the time he put him in charge of his household and of all that he owned, the LORD blessed the household of the Egyptian because of Joseph. The blessing of the LORD was on everything Potiphar had, both in the house and in the field. [6]So he left in Joseph's care everything he had; with Joseph in charge, he did not concern himself with anything except the food he ate.

Now Joseph was well-built and handsome, [7]and after a while his master's wife took notice of Joseph and said, "Come to bed with me!"

[8]But he refused. "With me in charge," he told her, "my master does not concern himself with anything in the house; everything he owns he has entrusted to my care. [9]No one is greater in this house than I am. My master has withheld nothing from me except you, because you are his wife. How then could I do such a wicked thing and sin against God?" [10]And though she spoke to Joseph day after day, he refused to go to bed with her or even be with her.

[11]One day he went into the house to attend to his duties, and none of the household servants was

truth or dare

Often the things that make us most angry with other people are things that we do ourselves! Before pointing out another's faults, examine your own heart.

38:24-26

truth or dare

We usually think that pregnancy is the worst thing that could happen to us if we have sex outside of marriage. Even worse, however, is the fact that we're sinning against God.

39:9

a 29 Perez means breaking out. b 30 Zerah can mean scarlet or brightness.

inside. [12]She caught him by his cloak and said, "Come to bed with me!" But he left his cloak in her hand and ran out of the house.

[13]When she saw that he had left his cloak in her hand and had run out of the house, [14]she called her household servants. "Look," she said to them, "this Hebrew has been brought to us to make sport of us! He came in here to sleep with me, but I screamed. [15]When he heard me scream for help, he left his cloak beside me and ran out of the house."

[16]She kept his cloak beside her until his master came home. [17]Then she told him this story: "That Hebrew slave you brought us came to me to make sport of me. [18]But as soon as I screamed for help, he left his cloak beside me and ran out of the house."

[19]When his master heard the story his wife told him, saying, "This is how your slave treated me," he burned with anger. [20]Joseph's master took him and put him in prison, the place where the king's prisoners were confined.

But while Joseph was there in the prison, [21]the LORD was with him; he showed him kindness and granted him favor in the eyes of the prison warden. [22]So the warden put Joseph in charge of all those held in the prison, and he was made responsible for all that was done there. [23]The warden paid no attention to anything under Joseph's care, because the LORD was with Joseph and gave him success in whatever he did.

genuine persistence

Day after day. Did you catch that? Potiphar's wife tried to seduce Joseph day after day. And *every* time Joseph chose to stay sexually pure. Every day you face the same choice Joseph did. Will *you* dress, talk and act in a way that honors God? Joseph's choice brought him trouble at first—he ended up in prison—and maybe he wondered if it was worth it. But down the road, when he was second in command of Egypt, he could see that his decision to honor God was the right choice.

» 39:10

The Cupbearer and the Baker

40 Some time later, the cupbearer and the baker of the king of Egypt offended their master, the king of Egypt. [2]Pharaoh was angry with his two officials, the chief cupbearer and the chief baker, [3]and put them in custody in the house of the captain of the guard, in the same prison where Joseph was confined. [4]The captain of the guard assigned them to Joseph, and he attended them.

After they had been in custody for some time, [5]each of the two men—the cupbearer and the baker of the king of Egypt, who were being held in prison—had a dream the same night, and each dream had a meaning of its own.

[6]When Joseph came to them the next morning, he saw that they were dejected. [7]So he asked Pharaoh's officials who were in custody with him in his master's house, "Why are your faces so sad today?"

[8]"We both had dreams," they answered, "but there is no one to interpret them."

Then Joseph said to them, "Do not interpretations belong to God? Tell me your dreams."

[9]So the chief cupbearer told Joseph his dream. He said to him, "In my dream I saw a vine in front of me, [10]and on the vine were three branches. As soon as it budded, it blossomed, and its clusters ripened into grapes. [11]Pharaoh's cup was in my hand, and I took the grapes, squeezed them into Pharaoh's cup and put the cup in his hand."

truth or dare

Using your God-given abilities *now* will prepare you for when God puts you in bigger settings. Don't wait! Take advantage of even "small" opportunities to serve God.

40:7–8

¹²"This is what it means," Joseph said to him. "The three branches are three days. ¹³Within three days Pharaoh will lift up your head and restore you to your position, and you will put Pharaoh's cup in his hand, just as you used to do when you were his cupbearer. ¹⁴But when all goes well with you, remember me and show me kindness; mention me to Pharaoh and get me out of this prison. ¹⁵For I was forcibly carried off from the land of the Hebrews, and even here I have done nothing to deserve being put in a dungeon."

¹⁶When the chief baker saw that Joseph had given a favorable interpretation, he said to Joseph, "I too had a dream: On my head were three baskets of bread.ᵃ ¹⁷In the top basket were all kinds of baked goods for Pharaoh, but the birds were eating them out of the basket on my head."

¹⁸"This is what it means," Joseph said. "The three baskets are three days. ¹⁹Within three days Pharaoh will lift off your head and hang you on a tree.ᵇ And the birds will eat away your flesh."

²⁰Now the third day was Pharaoh's birthday, and he gave a feast for all his officials. He lifted up the heads of the chief cupbearer and the chief baker in the presence of his officials: ²¹He restored the chief cupbearer to his position, so that he once again put the cup into Pharaoh's hand, ²²but he hangedᶜ the chief baker, just as Joseph had said to them in his interpretation.

²³The chief cupbearer, however, did not remember Joseph; he forgot him.

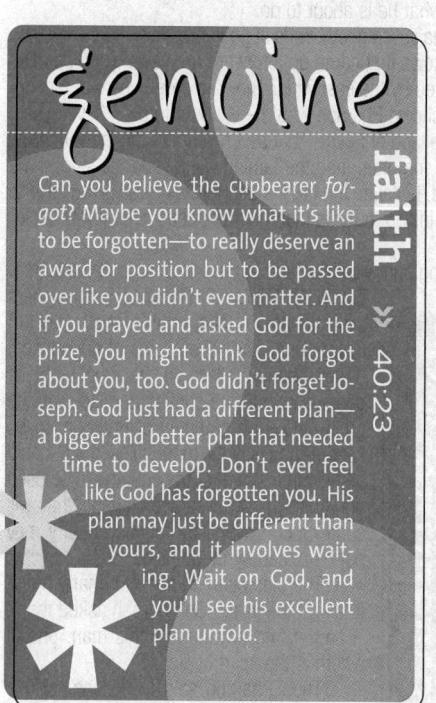

genuine

faith ›› 40:23

Can you believe the cupbearer *forgot*? Maybe you know what it's like to be forgotten—to really deserve an award or position but to be passed over like you didn't even matter. And if you prayed and asked God for the prize, you might think God forgot about you, too. God didn't forget Joseph. God just had a different plan—a bigger and better plan that needed time to develop. Don't ever feel like God has forgotten you. His plan may just be different than yours, and it involves waiting. Wait on God, and you'll see his excellent plan unfold.

Pharaoh's Dreams

41 When two full years had passed, Pharaoh had a dream: He was standing by the Nile, ²when out of the river there came up seven cows, sleek and fat, and they grazed among the reeds. ³After them, seven other cows, ugly and gaunt, came up out of the Nile and stood beside those on the riverbank. ⁴And the cows that were ugly and gaunt ate up the seven sleek, fat cows. Then Pharaoh woke up.

⁵He fell asleep again and had a second dream: Seven heads of grain, healthy and good, were growing on a single stalk. ⁶After them, seven other heads of grain sprouted—thin and scorched by the east wind. ⁷The thin heads of grain swallowed up the seven healthy, full heads. Then Pharaoh woke up; it had been a dream.

⁸In the morning his mind was troubled, so he sent for all the magicians and wise men of Egypt. Pharaoh told them his dreams, but no one could interpret them for him.

⁹Then the chief cupbearer said to Pharaoh, "Today I am reminded of my shortcomings. ¹⁰Pharaoh was once angry with his servants, and he imprisoned me and the chief baker in the house of the captain of the guard. ¹¹Each of us had a dream the same night, and each dream had a meaning of its own. ¹²Now a young Hebrew was there with us, a servant of the captain of the guard. We told him our dreams, and he interpreted them for us, giving each man the interpretation of his dream. ¹³And things turned out exactly as he interpreted them to us: I was restored to my position, and the other man was hanged.ᵈ"

¹⁴So Pharaoh sent for Joseph, and he was quickly brought from the dungeon. When he had shaved and changed his clothes, he came before Pharaoh.

¹⁵Pharaoh said to Joseph, "I had a dream, and no one can interpret it. But I have heard it said of you that when you hear a dream you can interpret it."

¹⁶"I cannot do it," Joseph replied to Pharaoh, "but God will give Pharaoh the answer he desires."

ᵃ 16 Or *three wicker baskets*   ᵇ 19 Or *and impale you on a pole*   ᶜ 22 Or *impaled*   ᵈ 13 Or *impaled*

¹⁷Then Pharaoh said to Joseph, "In my dream I was standing on the bank of the Nile, ¹⁸when out of the river there came up seven cows, fat and sleek, and they grazed among the reeds. ¹⁹After them, seven other cows came up—scrawny and very ugly and lean. I had never seen such ugly cows in all the land of Egypt. ²⁰The lean, ugly cows ate up the seven fat cows that came up first. ²¹But even after they ate them, no one could tell that they had done so; they looked just as ugly as before. Then I woke up.

²²"In my dreams I also saw seven heads of grain, full and good, growing on a single stalk. ²³After them, seven other heads sprouted—withered and thin and scorched by the east wind. ²⁴The thin heads of grain swallowed up the seven good heads. I told this to the magicians, but none could explain it to me."

²⁵Then Joseph said to Pharaoh, "The dreams of Pharaoh are one and the same. God has revealed to Pharaoh what he is about to do. ²⁶The seven good cows are seven years, and the seven good heads of grain are seven years; it is one and the same dream. ²⁷The seven lean, ugly cows that came up afterward are seven years, and so are the seven worthless heads of grain scorched by the east wind: They are seven years of famine.

²⁸"It is just as I said to Pharaoh: God has shown Pharaoh what he is about to do. ²⁹Seven years of great abundance are coming throughout the land of Egypt, ³⁰but seven years of famine will follow them. Then all the abundance in Egypt will be forgotten, and the famine will ravage the land. ³¹The abundance in the land will not be remembered, because the famine that follows it will be so severe. ³²The reason the dream was given to Pharaoh in two forms is that the matter has been firmly decided by God, and God will do it soon.

³³"And now let Pharaoh look for a discerning and wise man and put him in charge of the land of Egypt. ³⁴Let Pharaoh appoint commissioners over the land to take a fifth of the harvest of Egypt during the seven years of abundance. ³⁵They should collect all the food of these good years that are coming and store up the grain under the authority of Pharaoh, to be kept in the cities for food. ³⁶This food should be held in reserve for the country, to be used during the seven years of famine that will come upon Egypt, so that the country may not be ruined by the famine."

³⁷The plan seemed good to Pharaoh and to all his officials. ³⁸So Pharaoh asked them, "Can we find anyone like this man, one in whom is the spirit of God ᵃ?"

³⁹Then Pharaoh said to Joseph, "Since God has made all this known to you, there is no one so discerning and wise as you. ⁴⁰You shall be in charge of my palace, and all my people are to submit to your orders. Only with respect to the throne will I be greater than you."

Joseph in Charge of Egypt

⁴¹So Pharaoh said to Joseph, "I hereby put you in charge of the whole land of Egypt." ⁴²Then Pharaoh took his signet ring

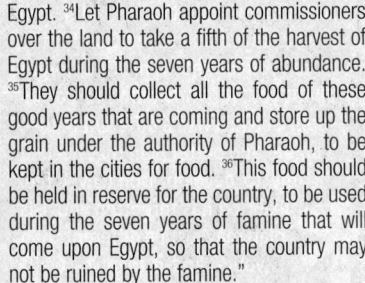

truth or dare

What special talents has God given you to use in his service? Naturally, people will be amazed by these gifts, but remember—all praise goes to God.

41:15–16

genuine confidence » 41:16

Most people see being "self-confident" as a good thing. But that's really not how God wants you to see yourself. Now, don't misunderstand. God doesn't want you to be insecure and unsure. But he does want you to find your confidence in *him* and in what *he* can do in and through you. There's a big difference between having confidence in yourself and having confidence in God. Joseph recognized this. He knew that his ability to interpret dreams came from God. When you rely on yourself, you'll only go so far. But when you rely on God, there's no limit to how far you can go!

ᵃ 38 Or *of the gods*

from his finger and put it on Joseph's finger. He dressed him in robes of fine linen and put a gold chain around his neck. [43]He had him ride in a chariot as his second-in-command, [a] and men shouted before him, "Make way[b]!" Thus he put him in charge of the whole land of Egypt.

[44]Then Pharaoh said to Joseph, "I am Pharaoh, but without your word no one will lift hand or foot in all Egypt." [45]Pharaoh gave Joseph the name Zaphenath-Paneah and gave him Asenath daughter of Potiphera, priest of On,[c] to be his wife. And Joseph went throughout the land of Egypt.

[46]Joseph was thirty years old when he entered the service of Pharaoh king of Egypt. And Joseph went out from Pharaoh's presence and traveled throughout Egypt. [47]During the seven years of abundance the land produced plentifully. [48]Joseph collected all the food produced in those seven years of abundance in Egypt and stored it in the cities. In each city he put the food grown in the fields surrounding it. [49]Joseph stored up huge quantities of grain, like the sand of the sea; it was so much that he stopped keeping records because it was beyond measure.

[50]Before the years of famine came, two sons were born to Joseph by Asenath daughter of Potiphera, priest of On. [51]Joseph named his firstborn Manasseh[d] and said, "It is because God has made me forget all my trouble and all my father's household." [52]The second son he named Ephraim[e] and said, "It is because God has made me fruitful in the land of my suffering."

[53]The seven years of abundance in Egypt came to an end, [54]and the seven years of famine began, just as Joseph had said. There was famine in all the other lands, but in the whole land of Egypt there was food. [55]When all Egypt began to feel the famine, the people cried to Pharaoh for food. Then Pharaoh told all the Egyptians, "Go to Joseph and do what he tells you."

[56]When the famine had spread over the whole country, Joseph opened the storehouses and sold grain to the Egyptians, for the famine was severe throughout Egypt. [57]And all the countries came to Egypt to buy grain from Joseph, because the famine was severe in all the world.

Joseph's Brothers Go to Egypt

42 When Jacob learned that there was grain in Egypt, he said to his sons, "Why do you just keep looking at each other?" [2]He continued, "I have heard that there is grain in Egypt. Go down there and buy some for us, so that we may live and not die."

[3]Then ten of Joseph's brothers went down to buy grain from Egypt. [4]But Jacob did not send Benjamin, Joseph's brother, with the others, because he was afraid that harm might come to him. [5]So Israel's sons were among those who went to buy grain, for the famine was in the land of Canaan also.

[6]Now Joseph was the governor of the land, the one who sold grain to all its people. So when Joseph's brothers arrived, they bowed down to him with their faces to the ground. [7]As soon as Joseph saw his brothers, he recognized them, but he pretended to be a stranger and spoke harshly to them. "Where do you come from?" he asked.

"From the land of Canaan," they replied, "to buy food."

[8]Although Joseph recognized his brothers, they did not recognize him. [9]Then he remembered his dreams about them and said to them, "You are spies! You have come to see where our land is unprotected."

[10]"No, my lord," they answered. "Your servants have come to buy food. [11]We are all the sons of one man. Your servants are honest men, not spies."

[12]"No!" he said to them. "You have come to see where our land is unprotected."

[13]But they replied, "Your servants were twelve brothers, the sons of one man, who lives in the land of Canaan. The youngest is now with our father, and one is no more."

[14]Joseph said to them, "It is just as I told you: You are spies! [15]And this is how you will be tested: As surely as Pharaoh lives, you will not leave this place unless your youngest brother comes here. [16]Send one of your number to get your brother; the rest of you will be kept in prison, so that your words may be tested to see if you are telling the truth. If you are not, then as surely as Pharaoh lives, you are spies!" [17]And he put them all in custody for three days.

[18]On the third day, Joseph said to them, "Do this and you will live, for I fear God: [19]If you are honest men, let one of your brothers stay here in prison, while the rest of you go and take grain

---

[a] 43 Or in the chariot of his second-in-command; or in his second chariot   [b] 43 Or Bow down   [c] 45 That is, Heliopolis; also in verse 50   [d] 51 Manasseh sounds like and may be derived from the Hebrew for forget.
[e] 52 Ephraim sounds like the Hebrew for twice fruitful.

back for your starving households. ²⁰But you must bring your youngest brother to me, so that your words may be verified and that you may not die." This they proceeded to do.

²¹They said to one another, "Surely we are being punished because of our brother. We saw how distressed he was when he pleaded with us for his life, but we would not listen; that's why this distress has come upon us."

²²Reuben replied, "Didn't I tell you not to sin against the boy? But you wouldn't listen! Now we must give an accounting for his blood." ²³They did not realize that Joseph could understand them, since he was using an interpreter.

²⁴He turned away from them and began to weep, but then turned back and spoke to them again. He had Simeon taken from them and bound before their eyes.

²⁵Joseph gave orders to fill their bags with grain, to put each man's silver back in his sack, and to give them provisions for their journey. After this was done for them, ²⁶they loaded their grain on their donkeys and left.

²⁷At the place where they stopped for the night one of them opened his sack to get feed for his donkey, and he saw his silver in the mouth of his sack. ²⁸"My silver has been returned," he said to his brothers. "Here it is in my sack."

Their hearts sank and they turned to each other trembling and said, "What is this that God has done to us?"

²⁹When they came to their father Jacob in the land of Canaan, they told him all that had happened to them. They said, ³⁰"The man who is lord over the land spoke harshly to us and treated us as though we were spying on the land. ³¹But we said to him, 'We are honest men; we are not spies. ³²We were twelve brothers, sons of one father. One is no more, and the youngest is now with our father in Canaan.'

³³"Then the man who is lord over the land said to us, 'This is how I will know whether you are honest men: Leave one of your brothers here with me, and take food for your starving households and go. ³⁴But bring your youngest brother to me so I will know that you are not spies but honest men. Then I will give your brother back to you, and you can trade*ᵃ* in the land.' "

³⁵As they were emptying their sacks, there in each man's sack was his pouch of silver! When they and their father saw the money pouches, they were frightened. ³⁶Their father Jacob said to them, "You have deprived me of my children. Joseph is no more and Simeon is no more, and now you want to take Benjamin. Everything is against me!"

³⁷Then Reuben said to his father, "You may put both of my sons to death if I do not bring him back to you. Entrust him to my care, and I will bring him back."

³⁸But Jacob said, "My son will not go down there with you; his brother is dead and he is the only one left. If harm comes to him on the journey you are taking, you will bring my gray head down to the grave*ᵇ* in sorrow."

The Second Journey to Egypt

43 Now the famine was still severe in the land. ²So when they had eaten all the grain they had brought from Egypt, their father said to them, "Go back and buy us a little more food."

³But Judah said to him, "The man warned us solemnly, 'You will not see my face again unless your brother is with you.' ⁴If you will send our brother along with us, we will go down and buy food for you. ⁵But if you will not send him, we will not go down, because the man said to us, 'You will not see my face again unless your brother is with you.' "

⁶Israel asked, "Why did you bring this trouble on me by telling the man you had another brother?"

⁷They replied, "The man questioned us closely about ourselves and our family. 'Is your father still living?' he asked us. 'Do you have another brother?' We simply answered his questions. How were we to know he would say, 'Bring your brother down here'?"

⁸Then Judah said to Israel his father, "Send the boy along with me and we will go at once, so that we and you and our children may live and not die. ⁹I myself will guarantee his safety; you can hold me personally responsible for him. If I do not bring him back to you and set him here before you, I will bear the blame before you all my life. ¹⁰As it is, if we had not delayed, we could have gone and returned twice."

ᵃ 34 Or *move about freely*   *ᵇ 38* Hebrew *Sheol*

Bonding Moments

focus | Profile: **Andria**

"*It's a bug! It's a bug!*" This was my last conscious thought before I nearly died of embarrassment. Kim, our intern in high school ministry, wanted to introduce me to Craig Henderson after church. There I was, standing next to the girl I admire most in the world, and she was introducing me to this gorgeous guy. I smiled my biggest smile, and a giant mosquito darted in and got caught in my lip gloss. I'm not kidding. Kim started jumping up and down trying to swat it away. Meanwhile, I was dying, and Craig was just staring at me like, "You are a strange girl."

Kim and I still laugh about it. It was kind of a bonding moment for her and me. I'm in her small group at church, and recently she's been taking me out once a week to get a soda or whatever. We talk about my life, my friends and my problems. She really seems interested—even though she's five years older and in college.

She always asks how she can pray for me. I feel like I can tell her anything, and she gives me good advice. She's been there, done that when it comes to the typical high school stuff. She's no expert, so she says. But just knowing she understands what I'm going through makes a difference.

Recently we've been discussing having a consistent quiet time every day. I guess you could say she's my mentor. I just think of her as a good friend.

Find out more about mentoring at www.TrueImageBible.com

mentors in focus

Interested in finding a mentor? Talk to your youth pastor or Sunday school teacher about who might be available to mentor you. Here's what you'll want to keep in mind:

» Mentors show you how to "do" life by sharing their experience when it comes to things like dating, spirituality and friendships.

» You can hang out with your mentor, eat lunch together, work out together, etc. The important thing is talking and spending consistent time together.

» A mentor should be of the same gender and at least a few years older than you.

Having a mentor can really help you grow as a person (especially spiritually). The Apostle Paul mentored Timothy and loved him like his own son. Check out 2 Timothy 1:13–14; 2:1 (page 1576) for a glimpse into their close relationship.

For more on this topic, see the index on page 1656.

¹¹Then their father Israel said to them, "If it must be, then do this: Put some of the best products of the land in your bags and take them down to the man as a gift—a little balm and a little honey, some spices and myrrh, some pistachio nuts and almonds. ¹²Take double the amount of silver with you, for you must return the silver that was put back into the mouths of your sacks. Perhaps it was a mistake. ¹³Take your brother also and go back to the man at once. ¹⁴And may God Almighty*ᵃ* grant you mercy before the man so that he will let your other brother and Benjamin come back with you. As for me, if I am bereaved, I am bereaved."

ᵃ 14 Hebrew El-Shaddai

¹⁵So the men took the gifts and double the amount of silver, and Benjamin also. They hurried down to Egypt and presented themselves to Joseph. ¹⁶When Joseph saw Benjamin with them, he said to the steward of his house, "Take these men to my house, slaughter an animal and prepare dinner; they are to eat with me at noon."

¹⁷The man did as Joseph told him and took the men to Joseph's house. ¹⁸Now the men were frightened when they were taken to his house. They thought, "We were brought here because of the silver that was put back into our sacks the first time. He wants to attack us and overpower us and seize us as slaves and take our donkeys."

¹⁹So they went up to Joseph's steward and spoke to him at the entrance to the house. ²⁰"Please, sir," they said, "we came down here the first time to buy food. ²¹But at the place where we stopped for the night we opened our sacks and each of us found his silver—the exact weight— in the mouth of his sack. So we have brought it back with us. ²²We have also brought additional silver with us to buy food. We don't know who put our silver in our sacks."

²³"It's all right," he said. "Don't be afraid. Your God, the God of your father, has given you treasure in your sacks; I received your silver." Then he brought Simeon out to them.

²⁴The steward took the men into Joseph's house, gave them water to wash their feet and provided fodder for their donkeys. ²⁵They prepared their gifts for Joseph's arrival at noon, because they had heard that they were to eat there.

²⁶When Joseph came home, they presented to him the gifts they had brought into the house, and they bowed down before him to the ground. ²⁷He asked them how they were, and then he said, "How is your aged father you told me about? Is he still living?"

²⁸They replied, "Your servant our father is still alive and well." And they bowed low to pay him honor.

²⁹As he looked about and saw his brother Benjamin, his own mother's son, he asked, "Is this your youngest brother, the one you told me about?" And he said, "God be gracious to you, my son." ³⁰Deeply moved at the sight of his brother, Joseph hurried out and looked for a place to weep. He went into his private room and wept there.

³¹After he had washed his face, he came out and, controlling himself, said, "Serve the food."

³²They served him by himself, the brothers by themselves, and the Egyptians who ate with him by themselves, because Egyptians could not eat with Hebrews, for that is detestable to Egyptians. ³³The men had been seated before him in the order of their ages, from the firstborn to the youngest; and they looked at each other in astonishment. ³⁴When portions were served to them from Joseph's table, Benjamin's portion was five times as much as anyone else's. So they feasted and drank freely with him.

A Silver Cup in a Sack

44 Now Joseph gave these instructions to the steward of his house: "Fill the men's sacks with as much food as they can carry, and put each man's silver in the mouth of his sack. ²Then put my cup, the silver one, in the mouth of the youngest one's sack, along with the silver for his grain." And he did as Joseph said.

³As morning dawned, the men were sent on their way with their donkeys. ⁴They had not gone far from the city when Joseph said to his steward, "Go after those men at once, and when you catch up with them, say to them, 'Why have you repaid good with evil? ⁵Isn't this the cup my master drinks from and also uses for divination? This is a wicked thing you have done.' "

⁶When he caught up with them, he repeated these words to them. ⁷But they said to him, "Why does my lord say such things? Far be it from your servants to do anything like that! ⁸We even brought back to you from the land of Canaan the silver we found inside the mouths of our sacks. So why would we steal silver or gold from your master's house? ⁹If any of your servants is found to have it, he will die; and the rest of us will become my lord's slaves."

¹⁰"Very well, then," he said, "let it be as you say. Whoever is found to have it will become my slave; the rest of you will be free from blame."

¹¹Each of them quickly lowered his sack to the ground and opened it. ¹²Then the steward proceeded to search, beginning with the oldest and ending with the youngest. And the cup was found in Benjamin's sack. ¹³At this, they tore their clothes. Then they all loaded their donkeys and returned to the city.

¹⁴Joseph was still in the house when Judah and his brothers came in, and they threw them-

selves to the ground before him. [15]Joseph said to them, "What is this you have done? Don't you know that a man like me can find things out by divination?"

[16]"What can we say to my lord?" Judah replied. "What can we say? How can we prove our innocence? God has uncovered your servants' guilt. We are now my lord's slaves—we ourselves and the one who was found to have the cup."

[17]But Joseph said, "Far be it from me to do such a thing! Only the man who was found to have the cup will become my slave. The rest of you, go back to your father in peace."

genuine

courage

44:18-34

Judah could have kept his mouth shut. It took a lot of guts to speak up and offer himself in place of Benjamin. You have opportunities every day that take courage to say something—courage to defend what you believe about God to people who couldn't care less. Or courage to stand up for the shy person who is constantly made fun of. Next time one of those opportunities comes your way, what are you going to do? Will you speak up like Judah did—even when you put yourself at risk by doing so—or will you keep your mouth shut?

[18]Then Judah went up to him and said: "Please, my lord, let your servant speak a word to my lord. Do not be angry with your servant, though you are equal to Pharaoh himself. [19]My lord asked his servants, 'Do you have a father or a brother?' [20]And we answered, 'We have an aged father, and there is a young son born to him in his old age. His brother is dead, and he is the only one of his mother's sons left, and his father loves him.'

[21]"Then you said to your servants, 'Bring him down to me so I can see him for myself.' [22]And we said to my lord, 'The boy cannot leave his father; if he leaves him, his father will die.' [23]But you told your servants, 'Unless your youngest brother comes down with you, you will not see my face again.' [24]When we went back to your servant my father, we told him what my lord had said.

[25]"Then our father said, 'Go back and buy a little more food.' [26]But we said, 'We cannot go down. Only if our youngest brother is with us will we go. We cannot see the man's face unless our youngest brother is with us.'

[27]"Your servant my father said to us, 'You know that my wife bore me two sons. [28]One of them went away from me, and I said, "He has surely been torn to pieces." And I have not seen him since. [29]If you take this one from me too and harm comes to him, you will bring my gray head down to the grave[a] in misery.'

[30]"So now, if the boy is not with us when I go back to your servant my father and if my father, whose life is closely bound up with the boy's life, [31]sees that the boy isn't there, he will die. Your servants will bring the gray head of our father down to the grave in sorrow. [32]Your servant guaranteed the boy's safety to my father. I said, 'If I do not bring him back to you, I will bear the blame before you, my father, all my life!'

[33]"Now then, please let your servant remain here as my lord's slave in place of the boy, and let the boy return with his brothers. [34]How can I go back to my father if the boy is not with me? No! Do not let me see the misery that would come upon my father."

Joseph Makes Himself Known

45 Then Joseph could no longer control himself before all his attendants, and he cried out, "Have everyone leave my presence!" So there was no one with Joseph when he made himself known to his brothers. [2]And he wept so loudly that the Egyptians heard him, and Pharaoh's household heard about it.

[3]Joseph said to his brothers, "I am Joseph! Is my father still living?" But his brothers were not able to answer him, because they were terrified at his presence.

[a] 29 Hebrew *Sheol*; also in verse 31

⁴Then Joseph said to his brothers, "Come close to me." When they had done so, he said, "I am your brother Joseph, the one you sold into Egypt! ⁵And now, do not be distressed and do not be angry with yourselves for selling me here, because it was to save lives that God sent me ahead of you. ⁶For two years now there has been famine in the land, and for the next five years there will not be plowing and reaping. ⁷But God sent me ahead of you to preserve for you a remnant on earth and to save your lives by a great deliverance.ᵃ

⁸"So then, it was not you who sent me here, but God. He made me father to Pharaoh, lord of his entire household and ruler of all Egypt. ⁹Now hurry back to my father and say to him, 'This is what your son Joseph says: God has made me lord of all Egypt. Come down to me; don't delay. ¹⁰You shall live in the region of Goshen and be near me—you, your children and grandchildren, your flocks and herds, and all you have. ¹¹I will provide for you there, because five years of famine are still to come. Otherwise you and your household and all who belong to you will become destitute.'

¹²"You can see for yourselves, and so can my brother Benjamin, that it is really I who am speaking to you. ¹³Tell my father about all the honor accorded me in Egypt and about everything you have seen. And bring my father down here quickly."

¹⁴Then he threw his arms around his brother Benjamin and wept, and Benjamin embraced him, weeping. ¹⁵And he kissed all his brothers and wept over them. Afterward his brothers talked with him.

¹⁶When the news reached Pharaoh's palace that Joseph's brothers had come, Pharaoh and all his officials were pleased. ¹⁷Pharaoh said to Joseph, "Tell your brothers, 'Do this: Load your animals and return to the land of Canaan, ¹⁸and bring your father and your families back to me. I will give you the best of the land of Egypt and you can enjoy the fat of the land.'

¹⁹"You are also directed to tell them, 'Do this: Take some carts from Egypt for your children and your wives, and get your father and come. ²⁰Never mind about your belongings, because the best of all Egypt will be yours.' "

²¹So the sons of Israel did this. Joseph gave them carts, as Pharaoh had commanded, and he also gave them provisions for their journey. ²²To each of them he gave new clothing, but to Benjamin he gave three hundred shekelsᵇ of silver and five sets of clothes. ²³And this is what he sent to his father: ten donkeys loaded with the best things of Egypt, and ten female donkeys loaded with grain and bread and other provisions for his journey. ²⁴Then he sent his brothers away, and as they were leaving he said to them, "Don't quarrel on the way!"

²⁵So they went up out of Egypt and came to their father Jacob in the land of Canaan. ²⁶They told him, "Joseph is still alive! In fact, he is ruler of all Egypt." Jacob was stunned; he did not believe them. ²⁷But when they told him everything Joseph had said to them, and when he saw the carts Joseph had sent to carry him back, the spirit of their father Jacob revived. ²⁸And Israel said, "I'm convinced! My son Joseph is still alive. I will go and see him before I die."

Jacob Goes to Egypt

46 So Israel set out with all that was his, and when he reached Beersheba, he offered sacrifices to the God of his father Isaac.

²And God spoke to Israel in a vision at night and said, "Jacob! Jacob!"

"Here I am," he replied.

³"I am God, the God of your father," he said. "Do not be afraid to go down to Egypt, for I will make you into a great nation there. ⁴I will go down to Egypt with you, and I will surely bring you back again. And Joseph's own hand will close your eyes."

⁵Then Jacob left Beersheba, and Israel's sons took their father Jacob and their children and their wives in the carts that Pharaoh had sent to transport him. ⁶They also took with them their livestock and the possessions they had acquired in Canaan, and Jacob and all his offspring went to Egypt. ⁷He took with him to Egypt his sons and grandsons and his daughters and granddaughters—all his offspring.

⁸These are the names of the sons of Israel (Jacob and his descendants) who went to Egypt:

Reuben the firstborn of Jacob.

⁹The sons of Reuben:

Hanoch, Pallu, Hezron and Carmi.

ᵃ 7 Or *save you as a great band of survivors*   ᵇ 22 That is, about 7 1/2 pounds (about 3.5 kilograms)

¹⁰ The sons of Simeon:

Jemuel, Jamin, Ohad, Jakin, Zohar and Shaul the son of a Canaanite woman.

¹¹ The sons of Levi:

Gershon, Kohath and Merari.

¹² The sons of Judah:

Er, Onan, Shelah, Perez and Zerah (but Er and Onan had died in the land of Canaan). The sons of Perez:

Hezron and Hamul.

¹³ The sons of Issachar:

Tola, Puah,^a Jashub^b and Shimron.

¹⁴ The sons of Zebulun:

Sered, Elon and Jahleel.

¹⁵These were the sons Leah bore to Jacob in Paddan Aram,^c besides his daughter Dinah. These sons and daughters of his were thirty-three in all.

¹⁶ The sons of Gad:

Zephon,^d Haggi, Shuni, Ezbon, Eri, Arodi and Areli.

¹⁷ The sons of Asher:

Imnah, Ishvah, Ishvi and Beriah.

Their sister was Serah.

The sons of Beriah:

Heber and Malkiel.

¹⁸These were the children born to Jacob by Zilpah, whom Laban had given to his daughter Leah—sixteen in all.

¹⁹ The sons of Jacob's wife Rachel:

Joseph and Benjamin. ²⁰In Egypt, Manasseh and Ephraim were born to Joseph by Asenath daughter of Potiphera, priest of On.^e

²¹ The sons of Benjamin:

Bela, Beker, Ashbel, Gera, Naaman, Ehi, Rosh, Muppim, Huppim and Ard.

²²These were the sons of Rachel who were born to Jacob—fourteen in all.

²³ The son of Dan:

Hushim.

²⁴ The sons of Naphtali:

Jahziel, Guni, Jezer and Shillem.

²⁵These were the sons born to Jacob by Bilhah, whom Laban had given to his daughter Rachel—seven in all.

²⁶All those who went to Egypt with Jacob—those who were his direct descendants, not counting his sons' wives—numbered sixty-six persons. ²⁷With the two sons^f who had been born to Joseph in Egypt, the members of Jacob's family, which went to Egypt, were seventy^g in all.

²⁸Now Jacob sent Judah ahead of him to Joseph to get directions to Goshen. When they arrived in the region of Goshen, ²⁹Joseph had his chariot made ready and went to Goshen to meet his father Israel. As soon as Joseph appeared before him, he threw his arms around his father^h and wept for a long time.

³⁰Israel said to Joseph, "Now I am ready to die, since I have seen for myself that you are still alive."

³¹Then Joseph said to his brothers and to his father's household, "I will go up and speak to Pharaoh and will say to him, 'My brothers and my father's household, who were living in the land of Canaan, have come to me. ³²The men are shepherds; they tend livestock, and they have brought along their flocks and herds and everything they own.' ³³When Pharaoh calls you in and asks, 'What

a 13 Samaritan Pentateuch and Syriac (see also 1 Chron. 7:1); Masoretic Text Puvah   b 13 Samaritan Pentateuch and some Septuagint manuscripts (see also Num. 26:24 and 1 Chron. 7:1); Masoretic Text Iob   c 15 That is, Northwest Mesopotamia   d 16 Samaritan Pentateuch and Septuagint (see also Num. 26:15); Masoretic Text Ziphion   e 20 That is, Heliopolis   f 27 Hebrew; Septuagint the nine children   g 27 Hebrew (see also Exodus 1:5 and footnote); Septuagint (see also Acts 7:14) seventy-five   h 29 Hebrew around him

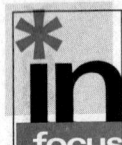

Too Much to Lose

Everyone thinks I have a problem just because I watch what I eat. Sure, I've lost some weight, but trust me, I had some baby fat to spare! When I was in junior high, I hated feeling fat. I hated being me.

When I was 16, I decided to get thin—no matter what. I began to diet. I learned to eat less and less. After a while, I could hardly make myself eat anymore.

When I first started losing weight, I felt like I was finally going to be happy. But no matter how much weight I lost, I never stopped thinking of myself as fat. I just kept thinking that I could lose another five pounds.

My mom was like, "You're losing too much weight, Lyn. Did you eat today?" I started lying to her. But I could tell she didn't believe me. Especially when she started finding clumps of hair in the shower drain. (Now I make sure to clean it before she comes in.)

I kept losing energy. Then came the day when I passed out at school. I'd only eaten a slice of apple that day. When Mom came to pick me up, she started crying and saying I needed help. I didn't answer her.

But as I lay in bed that night, I thought about what she'd said—about her love and God's love and how unbearable it felt to watch me starve myself. Maybe I do have a problem.

anorexia in focus

Like Lynnette, many people with an eating disorder are convinced for a while that everything is okay. But it isn't.

According to the National Association of Anorexia Nervosa and Associated Disorders (ANAD), eight million people suffer from anorexia. Ninety percent of those cases are women, and most begin having problems as teens. What triggers anorexia? Sometimes it starts as just as "easy" way to diet. Other times its a poor self-image. Pressure to succeed. Feeling unloved. Or sexual abuse.

Dealing with an eating disorder requires time and the help of others to overcome. The first step toward healing is when a person admits she needs help. Keep in mind:
» Be quick to listen and slow to offer answers. When she's ready, point her to the truth of God's love and her worth in his sight (Isaiah 43:1–4, page 949).
» Encourage your friend to get help from a trained professional.
» Pray for her.

For more on this topic, see the index on page 1656.

If you have a friend with anorexia, or if you have an eating disorder, check out the Anorexia Link on www.TrueImagesBible.com

is your occupation?' ³⁴you should answer, 'Your servants have tended livestock from our boyhood on, just as our fathers did.' Then you will be allowed to settle in the region of Goshen, for all shepherds are detestable to the Egyptians."

47 Joseph went and told Pharaoh, "My father and brothers, with their flocks and herds and everything they own, have come from the land of Canaan and are now in Goshen." ²He chose five of his brothers and presented them before Pharaoh.

³Pharaoh asked the brothers, "What is your occupation?"

"Your servants are shepherds," they replied to Pharaoh, "just as our fathers were." ⁴They also said to him, "We have come to live here awhile, because the famine is severe in Canaan and your servants' flocks have no pasture. So now, please let your servants settle in Goshen."

[5]Pharaoh said to Joseph, "Your father and your brothers have come to you, [6]and the land of Egypt is before you; settle your father and your brothers in the best part of the land. Let them live in Goshen. And if you know of any among them with special ability, put them in charge of my own livestock."

[7]Then Joseph brought his father Jacob in and presented him before Pharaoh. After Jacob blessed[a] Pharaoh, [8]Pharaoh asked him, "How old are you?"

[9]And Jacob said to Pharaoh, "The years of my pilgrimage are a hundred and thirty. My years have been few and difficult, and they do not equal the years of the pilgrimage of my fathers." [10]Then Jacob blessed[b] Pharaoh and went out from his presence.

[11]So Joseph settled his father and his brothers in Egypt and gave them property in the best part of the land, the district of Rameses, as Pharaoh directed. [12]Joseph also provided his father and his brothers and all his father's household with food, according to the number of their children.

Joseph and the Famine

[13]There was no food, however, in the whole region because the famine was severe; both Egypt and Canaan wasted away because of the famine. [14]Joseph collected all the money that was to be found in Egypt and Canaan in payment for the grain they were buying, and he brought it to Pharaoh's palace. [15]When the money of the people of Egypt and Canaan was gone, all Egypt came to Joseph and said, "Give us food. Why should we die before your eyes? Our money is used up."

[16]"Then bring your livestock," said Joseph. "I will sell you food in exchange for your livestock, since your money is gone." [17]So they brought their livestock to Joseph, and he gave them food in exchange for their horses, their sheep and goats, their cattle and donkeys. And he brought them through that year with food in exchange for all their livestock.

[18]When that year was over, they came to him the following year and said, "We cannot hide from our lord the fact that since our money is gone and our livestock belongs to you, there is nothing left for our lord except our bodies and our land. [19]Why should we perish before your eyes—we and our land as well? Buy us and our land in exchange for food, and we with our land will be in bondage to Pharaoh. Give us seed so that we may live and not die, and that the land may not become desolate."

[20]So Joseph bought all the land in Egypt for Pharaoh. The Egyptians, one and all, sold their fields, because the famine was too severe for them. The land became Pharaoh's, [21]and Joseph reduced the people to servitude,[c] from one end of Egypt to the other. [22]However, he did not buy the land of the priests, because they received a regular allotment from Pharaoh and had food enough from the allotment Pharaoh gave them. That is why they did not sell their land.

[23]Joseph said to the people, "Now that I have bought you and your land today for Pharaoh, here is seed for you so you can plant the ground. [24]But when the crop comes in, give a fifth of it to Pharaoh. The other four-fifths you may keep as seed for the fields and as food for yourselves and your households and your children."

[25]"You have saved our lives," they said. "May we find favor in the eyes of our lord; we will be in bondage to Pharaoh."

[26]So Joseph established it as a law concerning land in Egypt—still in force today—that a fifth of the produce belongs to Pharaoh. It was only the land of the priests that did not become Pharaoh's.

[27]Now the Israelites settled in Egypt in the region of Goshen. They acquired property there and were fruitful and increased greatly in number.

[28]Jacob lived in Egypt seventeen years, and the years of his life were a hundred and forty-seven. [29]When the time drew near for Israel to die, he called for his son Joseph and said to him, "If I have found favor in your eyes, put your hand under my thigh and promise that you will show me kindness and faithfulness. Do not bury me in Egypt, [30]but when I rest with my fathers, carry me out of Egypt and bury me where they are buried."

"I will do as you say," he said.

[31]"Swear to me," he said. Then Joseph swore to him, and Israel worshiped as he leaned on the top of his staff.[d]

---

[a] 7 Or greeted   [b] 10 Or said farewell to   [c] 21 Samaritan Pentateuch and Septuagint (see also Vulgate); Masoretic Text and he moved the people into the cities   [d] 31 Or Israel bowed down at the head of his bed

Manasseh and Ephraim

48 Some time later Joseph was told, "Your father is ill." So he took his two sons Manasseh and Ephraim along with him. ²When Jacob was told, "Your son Joseph has come to you," Israel rallied his strength and sat up on the bed.

³Jacob said to Joseph, "God Almighty° appeared to me at Luz in the land of Canaan, and there he blessed me ⁴and said to me, 'I am going to make you fruitful and will increase your numbers. I will make you a community of peoples, and I will give this land as an everlasting possession to your descendants after you.'

⁵"Now then, your two sons born to you in Egypt before I came to you here will be reckoned as mine; Ephraim and Manasseh will be mine, just as Reuben and Simeon are mine. ⁶Any children born to you after them will be yours; in the territory they inherit they will be reckoned under the names of their brothers. ⁷As I was returning from Paddan,ᵇ to my sorrow Rachel died in the land of Canaan while we were still on the way, a little distance from Ephrath. So I buried her there beside the road to Ephrath" (that is, Bethlehem).

⁸When Israel saw the sons of Joseph, he asked, "Who are these?"

⁹"They are the sons God has given me here," Joseph said to his father.

Then Israel said, "Bring them to me so I may bless them."

¹⁰Now Israel's eyes were failing because of old age, and he could hardly see. So Joseph brought his sons close to him, and his father kissed them and embraced them.

¹¹Israel said to Joseph, "I never expected to see your face again, and now God has allowed me to see your children too."

¹²Then Joseph removed them from Israel's knees and bowed down with his face to the ground. ¹³And Joseph took both of them, Ephraim on his right toward Israel's left hand and Manasseh on his left toward Israel's right hand, and brought them close to him. ¹⁴But Israel reached out his right hand and put it on Ephraim's head, though he was the younger, and crossing his arms, he put his left hand on Manasseh's head, even though Manasseh was the firstborn.

¹⁵Then he blessed Joseph and said,

> "May the God before whom my fathers
>   Abraham and Isaac walked,
> the God who has been my shepherd
>   all my life to this day,
> ¹⁶the Angel who has delivered me from all harm
>   —may he bless these boys.
> May they be called by my name
>   and the names of my fathers Abraham and Isaac,
> and may they increase greatly
>   upon the earth."

truth or dare

A shepherd's job is to protect and care for the sheep. No matter where the shepherd leads, the sheep trust and follow. In what ways is God your Shepherd?

48:15

¹⁷When Joseph saw his father placing his right hand on Ephraim's head he was displeased; so he took hold of his father's hand to move it from Ephraim's head to Manasseh's head. ¹⁸Joseph said to him, "No, my father, this one is the firstborn; put your right hand on his head."

¹⁹But his father refused and said, "I know, my son, I know. He too will become a people, and he too will become great. Nevertheless, his younger brother will be greater than he, and his descendants will become a group of nations." ²⁰He blessed them that day and said,

> "In yourᶜ name will Israel pronounce this blessing:
>   'May God make you like Ephraim and Manasseh.' "

So he put Ephraim ahead of Manasseh.

²¹Then Israel said to Joseph, "I am about to die, but God will be with youᵈ and take youᵈ back

---

ᵃ 3 Hebrew *El-Shaddai*   ᵇ 7 That is, Northwest Mesopotamia   ᶜ 20 The Hebrew is singular.   ᵈ 21 The Hebrew is plural.

to the land of your[a] fathers. [22]And to you, as one who is over your brothers, I give the ridge of land[b] I took from the Amorites with my sword and my bow."

Jacob Blesses His Sons

49 Then Jacob called for his sons and said: "Gather around so I can tell you what will happen to you in days to come.

[2]"Assemble and listen, sons of Jacob;
    listen to your father Israel.

[3]"Reuben, you are my firstborn,
    my might, the first sign of my strength,
    excelling in honor, excelling in power.
[4]Turbulent as the waters, you will no longer excel,
    for you went up onto your father's bed,
    onto my couch and defiled it.

[5]"Simeon and Levi are brothers—
    their swords[c] are weapons of violence.
[6]Let me not enter their council,
    let me not join their assembly,
for they have killed men in their anger
    and hamstrung oxen as they pleased.
[7]Cursed be their anger, so fierce,
    and their fury, so cruel!
I will scatter them in Jacob
    and disperse them in Israel.

[8]"Judah,[d] your brothers will praise you;
    your hand will be on the neck of your enemies;
    your father's sons will bow down to you.
[9]You are a lion's cub, O Judah;
    you return from the prey, my
      son.
Like a lion he crouches and lies
      down,
    like a lioness—who dares to
      rouse him?
[10]The scepter will not depart from
      Judah,
    nor the ruler's staff from
      between his feet,
until he comes to whom it belongs[e]
    and the obedience of the nations is his.
[11]He will tether his donkey to a vine,
    his colt to the choicest branch;
he will wash his garments in wine,
    his robes in the blood of grapes.
[12]His eyes will be darker than wine,
    his teeth whiter than milk.[f]

[13]"Zebulun will live by the seashore
    and become a haven for ships;
    his border will extend toward Sidon.

truth or dare

Far from being a lion of faith, Judah's spiritual report card was covered with bad marks (see Genesis 38). But God blesses anyone who, after messing up, returns to him for strength and forgiveness.

49:9–10

---

[a] 21 The Hebrew is plural.   [b] 22 Or *And to you I give one portion more than to your brothers—the portion*
[c] 5 The meaning of the Hebrew for this word is uncertain.   [d] 8 *Judah* sounds like and may be derived from the Hebrew for *praise*.   [e] 10 Or *until Shiloh comes*; or *until he comes to whom tribute belongs*   [f] 12 Or *will be dull from wine, / his teeth white from milk*

field. [31]There Abraham and his wife Sarah were buried, there Isaac and his wife Rebekah were buried, and there I buried Leah. [32]The field and the cave in it were bought from the Hittites.[a]"

[33]When Jacob had finished giving instructions to his sons, he drew his feet up into the bed, breathed his last and was gathered to his people.

50

Joseph threw himself upon his father and wept over him and kissed him. [2]Then Joseph directed the physicians in his service to embalm his father Israel. So the physicians embalmed him, [3]taking a full forty days, for that was the time required for embalming. And the Egyptians mourned for him seventy days.

[4]When the days of mourning had passed, Joseph said to Pharaoh's court, "If I have found favor in your eyes, speak to Pharaoh for me. Tell him, [5]'My father made me swear an oath and said, "I am about to die; bury me in the tomb I dug for myself in the land of Canaan." Now let me go up and bury my father; then I will return.' "

[6]Pharaoh said, "Go up and bury your father, as he made you swear to do."

[7]So Joseph went up to bury his father. All Pharaoh's officials accompanied him— the dignitaries of his court and all the dignitaries of Egypt— [8]besides all the members of Joseph's household and his brothers and those belonging to his father's household. Only their children and their flocks and herds were left in Goshen. [9]Chariots and horsemen[b] also went up with him. It was a very large company.

[10]When they reached the threshing floor of Atad, near the Jordan, they lamented loudly and bitterly; and there Joseph observed a seven-day period of mourning for his father. [11]When the Canaanites who lived there saw the mourning at the threshing floor of Atad, they said, "The Egyptians are holding a solemn ceremony of mourning." That is why that place near the Jordan is called Abel Mizraim.[c]

[12]So Jacob's sons did as he had commanded them: [13]They carried him to the land of Canaan and buried him in the cave in the field of Machpelah, near Mamre, which Abraham had bought as a burial place from Ephron the Hittite, along with the field. [14]After burying his father, Joseph returned to Egypt, together with his brothers and all the others who had gone with him to bury his father.

Joseph Reassures His Brothers

[15]When Joseph's brothers saw that their father was dead, they said, "What if Joseph holds a grudge against us and pays us back for all the wrongs we did to him?" [16]So they sent word to Joseph, saying, "Your father left these instructions before he died: [17]'This is what you are to say to Joseph: I ask you to forgive your brothers the sins

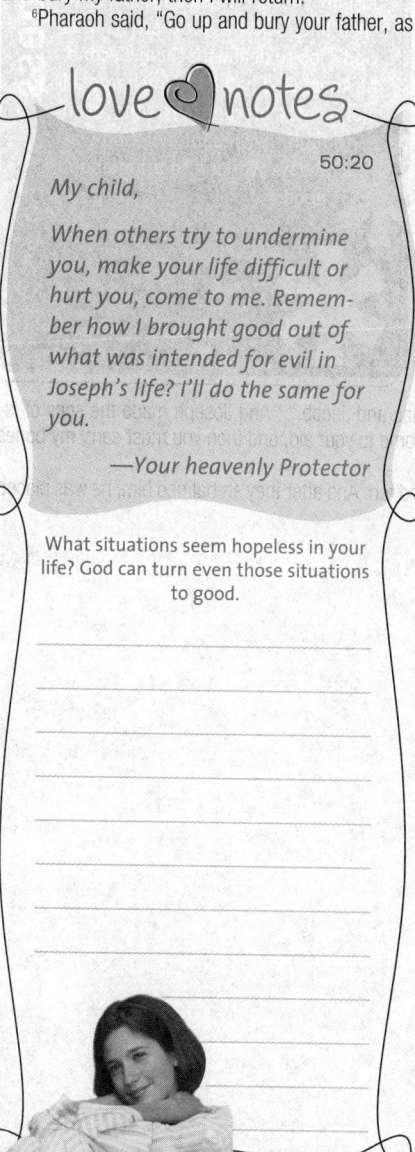

love ❤ notes

50:20

My child,

When others try to undermine you, make your life difficult or hurt you, come to me. Remember how I brought good out of what was intended for evil in Joseph's life? I'll do the same for you.

—Your heavenly Protector

What situations seem hopeless in your life? God can turn even those situations to good.

[a] 32 Or the sons of Heth   [b] 9 Or charioteers
[c] 11 Abel Mizraim means mourning of the Egyptians.

and the wrongs they committed in treating you so badly.' Now please forgive the sins of the servants of the God of your father." When their message came to him, Joseph wept.

[18]His brothers then came and threw themselves down before him. "We are your slaves," they said.

[19]But Joseph said to them, "Don't be afraid. Am I in the place of God? [20]You intended to harm me, but God intended it for good to accomplish what is now being done, the saving of many lives. [21]So then, don't be afraid. I will provide for you and your children." And he reassured them and spoke kindly to them.

The Death of Joseph

[22]Joseph stayed in Egypt, along with all his father's family. He lived a hundred and ten years [23]and saw the third generation of Ephraim's children. Also the children of Makir son of Manasseh were placed at birth on Joseph's knees.[a]

[24]Then Joseph said to his brothers, "I am about to die. But God will surely come to your aid and take you up out of this land to the land he promised on oath to Abraham, Isaac and Jacob." [25]And Joseph made the sons of Israel swear an oath and said, "God will surely come to your aid, and then you must carry my bones up from this place."

[26]So Joseph died at the age of a hundred and ten. And after they embalmed him, he was placed in a coffin in Egypt.

genuine forgiveness
» 50:15-21

When someone stabs you in the back, it's natural to want to take revenge. Joseph had every reason to hold a grudge, but instead he offered his brothers forgiveness. Why?! First, Joseph knew it wasn't his place to "get back" at his brothers. It was God's job to deal with them. Second, he knew God had been in charge all along—not his brothers. And even though *they* meant evil, God was always working to bring about good.

a 23 That is, were counted as his

author:	Moses.
date:	During the 1400s B.C., while the Israelites were traveling in the desert.
setting:	God miraculously liberates the Israelites from slavery in Egypt and then establishes his covenant with them in the desert.
verse to remember:	God heard their groaning and he remembered his covenant with Abraham, with Isaac and with Jacob. So God looked on the Israelites and was concerned about them (2:24–25).
theme to consider:	Exodus is a wonderful example of the extraordinary lengths God will take to reach out and rescue those he loves, including you.

exodus

unchanging truth

Your Life: <u>Scene 1</u>: Was it the leftover Chinese food, the bad haircut or the fight with your friend that started all this? Your life is a hopeless mess. No matter what you do, things keep getting worse. Why would anyone ever want or need you? All you want to do is crawl into bed, pull the covers over your head and sleep for a hundred years or so.

<u>Scene 2</u>: Just when you reach your breaking point, a friend comes alongside you and asks what's wrong. Just the fact that someone actually cares about you is a huge relief.

Most people experience times when life seems pretty bleak. That's when it's wonderful to have someone in your life who loves and cares for you. When you know you're not facing tough times alone, the problems don't seem as frightening.

The Israelites knew all about impossible situations. They were slaves in Egypt with no hope of being free. But God hadn't forgotten about them. He sent a rescuer, Moses. And then he sent ten plagues to convince Pharaoh to let his people go. And although the Israelites would face all kinds of trouble and problems as they trekked across the wilderness, God continued to show them *his* love and concern.

When problems start to overwhelm you, stick your head out from under the covers and look to God. He's into big rescues.

life lessons

1. When God planned his rescue mission, he chose an unlikely leader in a very unusual way (3:1–10). Watch for the different ways God communicates with you.

2. The Israelites had *huge* problems, but repeatedly God came to their rescue (14:9,21–31). He's faithful. Always.

3. There's no guesswork in how God wants us to live—with respect and love for him and for each other (20:1–17).

The Israelites Oppressed

1 These are the names of the sons of Israel who went to Egypt with Jacob, each with his family: ²Reuben, Simeon, Levi and Judah; ³Issachar, Zebulun and Benjamin; ⁴Dan and Naphtali; Gad and Asher. ⁵The descendants of Jacob numbered seventy*ᵃ* in all; Joseph was already in Egypt.

⁶Now Joseph and all his brothers and all that generation died, ⁷but the Israelites were fruitful and multiplied greatly and became exceedingly numerous, so that the land was filled with them.

⁸Then a new king, who did not know about Joseph, came to power in Egypt. ⁹"Look," he said to his people, "the Israelites have become much too numerous for us. ¹⁰Come, we must deal shrewdly with them or they will become even more numerous and, if war breaks out, will join our enemies, fight against us and leave the country."

¹¹So they put slave masters over them to oppress them with forced labor, and they built Pithom and Rameses as store cities for Pharaoh. ¹²But the more they were oppressed, the more they multiplied and spread; so the Egyptians came to dread the Israelites ¹³and worked them ruthlessly.

¹⁴They made their lives bitter with hard labor in brick and mortar and with all kinds of work in the fields; in all their hard labor the Egyptians used them ruthlessly.

¹⁵The king of Egypt said to the Hebrew midwives, whose names were Shiphrah and Puah, ¹⁶"When you help the Hebrew women in childbirth and observe them on the delivery stool, if it is a boy, kill him; but if it is a girl, let her live." ¹⁷The midwives, however, feared God and did not do what the king of Egypt had told them to do; they let the boys live. ¹⁸Then the king of Egypt summoned the midwives and asked them, "Why have you done this? Why have you let the boys live?"

¹⁹The midwives answered Pharaoh, "Hebrew women are not like Egyptian women; they are vigorous and give birth before the midwives arrive."

²⁰So God was kind to the midwives and the people increased and became even more numerous. ²¹And because the midwives feared God, he gave them families of their own.

²²Then Pharaoh gave this order to all his people: "Every boy that is born*ᵇ* you must throw into the Nile, but let every girl live."

genuine courage 1:15-17

If the king noticed any Hebrew little boys running around, he'd know who to blame. He gave direct orders to Shiphrah and Puah to kill the boys. But these gutsy midwives chose to disobey the king in order to do what was right. That's serious courage! When have you had to take a stand for what's right, regardless of the consequences? Maybe you refused to cheat on a test or to smoke a joint—even though everyone else was doing it. God makes no guarantees that doing what's right will be easy. But it will have results way beyond what you can imagine.

The Birth of Moses

2 Now a man of the house of Levi married a Levite woman, ²and she became pregnant and gave birth to a son. When she saw that he was a fine child, she hid him for three months. ³But when she could hide him no longer, she got a papyrus basket for him and coated it with tar and pitch. Then she placed the child in it and put it among the reeds along the bank of the Nile. ⁴His sister stood at a distance to see what would happen to him.

⁵Then Pharaoh's daughter went down to the Nile to bathe, and her attendants were walking along the river bank. She saw the basket among the reeds and sent her slave girl to get it. ⁶She opened it and saw the baby. He was crying, and she felt sorry for him. "This is one of the Hebrew babies," she said.

⁷Then his sister asked Pharaoh's daughter, "Shall I go and get one of the Hebrew women to nurse the baby for you?"

a 5 Masoretic Text (see also Gen. 46:27); Dead Sea Scrolls and Septuagint (see also Acts 7:14 and note at Gen. 46:27) seventy-five   b 22 Masoretic Text; Samaritan Pentateuch, Septuagint and Targums born to the Hebrews

⁸"Yes, go," she answered. And the girl went and got the baby's mother. ⁹Pharaoh's daughter said to her, "Take this baby and nurse him for me, and I will pay you." So the woman took the baby and nursed him. ¹⁰When the child grew older, she took him to Pharaoh's daughter and he became her son. She named him Moses,^a saying, "I drew him out of the water."

Moses Flees to Midian

¹¹One day, after Moses had grown up, he went out to where his own people were and watched them at their hard labor. He saw an Egyptian beating a Hebrew, one of his own people. ¹²Glancing this way and that and seeing no one, he killed the Egyptian and hid him in the sand. ¹³The next day he went out and saw two Hebrews fighting. He asked the one in the wrong, "Why are you hitting your fellow Hebrew?"

¹⁴The man said, "Who made you ruler and judge over us? Are you thinking of killing me as you killed the Egyptian?" Then Moses was afraid and thought, "What I did must have become known."

genuine

courage » 2:7-8

Moses' big sister had some spunk! She was only a slave girl, but she saw an opportunity and made a decision to act—it didn't matter that the woman she approached was the royal princess! Was Moses' sister afraid? Maybe a little. Intimidated? Wouldn't you be? But she took the initiative. God will give you opportunities in life—a chance to share your faith, a moment to be kind to someone—but if you blink, you may miss them. Ask God to help you recognize a good opportunity. Then act on it!

¹⁵When Pharaoh heard of this, he tried to kill Moses, but Moses fled from Pharaoh and went to live in Midian, where he sat down by a well. ¹⁶Now a priest of Midian had seven daughters, and they came to draw water and fill the troughs to water their father's flock. ¹⁷Some shepherds came along and drove them away, but Moses got up and came to their rescue and watered their flock.

¹⁸When the girls returned to Reuel their father, he asked them, "Why have you returned so early today?"

¹⁹They answered, "An Egyptian rescued us from the shepherds. He even drew water for us and watered the flock."

²⁰"And where is he?" he asked his daughters. "Why did you leave him? Invite him to have something to eat."

²¹Moses agreed to stay with the man, who gave his daughter Zipporah to Moses in marriage. ²²Zipporah gave birth to a son, and Moses named him Gershom,^b saying, "I have become an alien in a foreign land."

²³During that long period, the king of Egypt died. The Israelites groaned in their slavery and cried out, and their cry for help because of their slavery went up to God. ²⁴God heard their groaning and he remembered his covenant with Abraham, with Isaac and with Jacob. ²⁵So God looked on the Israelites and was concerned about them.

Moses and the Burning Bush

3 Now Moses was tending the flock of Jethro his father-in-law, the priest of Midian, and he led the flock to the far side of the desert and came to Horeb, the mountain of God. ²There the angel of the LORD appeared to him in flames of fire from within a bush. Moses saw that though the bush was on fire it did not burn up. ³So Moses thought, "I will go over and see this strange sight—why the bush does not burn up."

⁴When the LORD saw that he had gone over to look, God called to him from within the bush, "Moses! Moses!"

And Moses said, "Here I am."

^a 10 *Moses* sounds like the Hebrew for *draw out.*   ^b 22 *Gershom* sounds like the Hebrew for *an alien there.*

truth or dare

A barefoot conversation with God? Going shoeless probably doesn't mean much to you, but Moses' actions reveal an important *attitude* when entering God's presence. How do you approach God?

3:5

⁵"Do not come any closer," God said. "Take off your sandals, for the place where you are standing is holy ground." ⁶Then he said, "I am the God of your father, the God of Abraham, the God of Isaac and the God of Jacob." At this, Moses hid his face, because he was afraid to look at God.

⁷The LORD said, "I have indeed seen the misery of my people in Egypt. I have heard them crying out because of their slave drivers, and I am concerned about their suffering. ⁸So I have come down to rescue them from the hand of the Egyptians and to bring them up out of that land into a good and spacious land, a land flowing with milk and honey—the home of the Canaanites,

love notes

2:23–25

Dear child,

Are you struggling today? Are you facing a problem that seems insurmountable? Cry out to me. I hear you. I will remember my promises to you. I will rescue you in good time.

—Your loving Father

What is the cry of your heart to God today?

Hittites, Amorites, Perizzites, Hivites and Jebusites. ⁹And now the cry of the Israelites has reached me, and I have seen the way the Egyptians are oppressing them. ¹⁰So now, go. I am sending you to Pharaoh to bring my people the Israelites out of Egypt."

¹¹But Moses said to God, "Who am I, that I should go to Pharaoh and bring the Israelites out of Egypt?"

¹²And God said, "I will be with you. And this will be the sign to you that it is I who have sent you: When you have brought the people out of Egypt, you*ᵃ* will worship God on this mountain."

¹³Moses said to God, "Suppose I go to the Israelites and say to them, 'The God of your fathers has sent me to you,' and they ask me, 'What is his name?' Then what shall I tell them?"

¹⁴God said to Moses, "I AM WHO I AM.*ᵇ* This is what you are to say to the Israelites: 'I AM has sent me to you.' "

¹⁵God also said to Moses, "Say to the Israelites, 'The LORD,*ᶜ* the God of your fathers—the God of Abraham, the God of Isaac and the God of Jacob—has sent me to you.' This is my name forever, the name by which I am to be remembered from generation to generation.

¹⁶"Go, assemble the elders of Israel and say to them, 'The LORD, the God of your fathers—the God of Abraham, Isaac and Jacob—appeared to me and said: I have

ᵃ 12 The Hebrew is plural. *ᵇ 14* Or *I WILL BE WHAT I WILL BE* *ᶜ 15* The Hebrew for LORD sounds like and may be derived from the Hebrew for *I AM* in verse 14.

watched over you and have seen what has been done to you in Egypt. ¹⁷And I have promised to bring you up out of your misery in Egypt into the land of the Canaanites, Hittites, Amorites, Perizzites, Hivites and Jebusites—a land flowing with milk and honey.'

¹⁸"The elders of Israel will listen to you. Then you and the elders are to go to the king of Egypt and say to him, 'The Lord, the God of the Hebrews, has met with us. Let us take a three-day journey into the desert to offer sacrifices to the Lord our God.' ¹⁹But I know that the king of Egypt will not let you go unless a mighty hand compels him. ²⁰So I will stretch out my hand and strike the Egyptians with all the wonders that I will perform among them. After that, he will let you go.

²¹"And I will make the Egyptians favorably disposed toward this people, so that when you leave you will not go empty-handed. ²²Every woman is to ask her neighbor and any woman living in her house for articles of silver and gold and for clothing, which you will put on your sons and daughters. And so you will plunder the Egyptians."

Signs for Moses

4 Moses answered, "What if they do not believe me or listen to me and say, 'The Lord did not appear to you'?"

²Then the Lord said to him, "What is that in your hand?"

"A staff," he replied.

³The Lord said, "Throw it on the ground."

Moses threw it on the ground and it became a snake, and he ran from it. ⁴Then the Lord said to him, "Reach out your hand and take it by the tail." So Moses reached out and took hold of the snake and it turned back into a staff in his hand. ⁵"This," said the Lord, "is so that they may believe that the Lord, the God of their fathers—the God of Abraham, the God of Isaac and the God of Jacob—has appeared to you."

⁶Then the Lord said, "Put your hand inside your cloak." So Moses put his hand into his cloak, and when he took it out, it was leprous, ᵃ like snow.

⁷"Now put it back into your cloak," he said. So Moses put his hand back into his cloak, and when he took it out, it was restored, like the rest of his flesh.

⁸Then the Lord said, "If they do not believe you or pay attention to the first miraculous sign, they may believe the second. ⁹But if they do not believe these two signs or listen to you, take some water from the Nile and pour it on the dry ground. The water you take from the river will become blood on the ground."

¹⁰Moses said to the Lord, "O Lord, I have never been eloquent, neither in the past nor since you have spoken to your servant. I am slow of speech and tongue."

¹¹The Lord said to him, "Who gave man his mouth? Who makes him deaf or mute? Who gives him sight or makes him blind? Is it not I, the Lord? ¹²Now go; I will help you speak and will teach you what to say."

¹³But Moses said, "O Lord, please send someone else to do it."

¹⁴Then the Lord's anger burned against Moses and he said, "What about your brother, Aaron the Levite? I know he can speak well. He is already on his way to meet you, and his heart will be glad when he sees you. ¹⁵You shall speak to him and put words in his

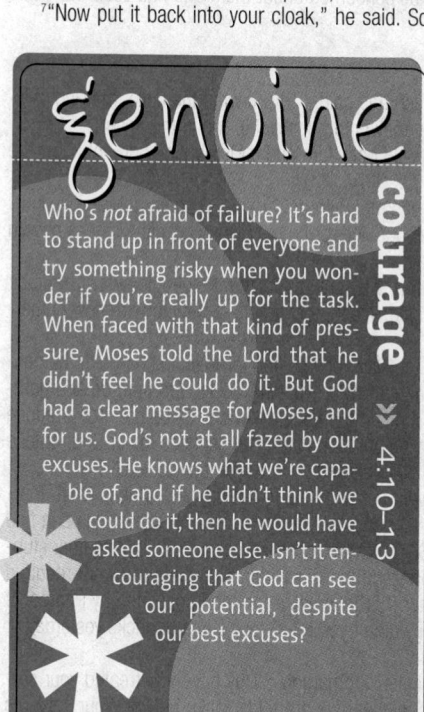

genuine

courage

4:10-13

Who's *not* afraid of failure? It's hard to stand up in front of everyone and try something risky when you wonder if you're really up for the task. When faced with that kind of pressure, Moses told the Lord that he didn't feel he could do it. But God had a clear message for Moses, and for us. God's not at all fazed by our excuses. He knows what we're capable of, and if he didn't think we could do it, then he would have asked someone else. Isn't it encouraging that God can see our potential, despite our best excuses?

ᵃ 6 The Hebrew word was used for various diseases affecting the skin—not necessarily leprosy.

mouth; I will help both of you speak and will teach you what to do. [16]He will speak to the people for you, and it will be as if he were your mouth and as if you were God to him. [17]But take this staff in your hand so you can perform miraculous signs with it."

Moses Returns to Egypt

[18]Then Moses went back to Jethro his father-in-law and said to him, "Let me go back to my own people in Egypt to see if any of them are still alive."

Jethro said, "Go, and I wish you well."

[19]Now the LORD had said to Moses in Midian, "Go back to Egypt, for all the men who wanted to kill you are dead." [20]So Moses took his wife and sons, put them on a donkey and started back to Egypt. And he took the staff of God in his hand.

[21]The LORD said to Moses, "When you return to Egypt, see that you perform before Pharaoh all the wonders I have given you the power to do. But I will harden his heart so that he will not let the people go. [22]Then say to Pharaoh, 'This is what the LORD says: Israel is my firstborn son, [23]and I told you, "Let my son go, so he may worship me." But you refused to let him go; so I will kill your firstborn son.' "

[24]At a lodging place on the way, the LORD met ⌊Moses⌋[a] and was about to kill him. [25]But Zipporah took a flint knife, cut off her son's foreskin and touched ⌊Moses'⌋ feet with it.[b] "Surely you are a bridegroom of blood to me," she said. [26]So the LORD let him alone. (At that time she said "bridegroom of blood," referring to circumcision.)

[27]The LORD said to Aaron, "Go into the desert to meet Moses." So he met Moses at the mountain of God and kissed him. [28]Then Moses told Aaron everything the LORD had sent him to say, and also about all the miraculous signs he had commanded him to perform.

[29]Moses and Aaron brought together all the elders of the Israelites, [30]and Aaron told them everything the LORD had said to Moses. He also performed the signs before the people, [31]and they believed. And when they heard that the LORD was concerned about them and had seen their misery, they bowed down and worshiped.

Bricks Without Straw

5 Afterward Moses and Aaron went to Pharaoh and said, "This is what the LORD, the God of Israel, says: 'Let my people go, so that they may hold a festival to me in the desert.' " [2]Pharaoh said, "Who is the LORD, that I should obey him and let Israel go? I do not know the LORD and I will not let Israel go."

[3]Then they said, "The God of the Hebrews has met with us. Now let us take a three-day journey into the desert to offer sacrifices to the LORD our God, or he may strike us with plagues or with the sword."

[4]But the king of Egypt said, "Moses and Aaron, why are you taking the people away from their labor? Get back to your work!" [5]Then Pharaoh said, "Look, the people of the land are now numerous, and you are stopping them from working."

[6]That same day Pharaoh gave this order to the slave drivers and foremen in charge of the people: [7]"You are no longer to supply the people with straw for making bricks; let them go and gather their own straw. [8]But require them to make the same number of bricks as before; don't reduce the quota. They are lazy; that is why they are crying out, 'Let us go and sacrifice to our God.' [9]Make the work harder for the men so that they keep working and pay no attention to lies."

[10]Then the slave drivers and the foremen went out and said to the people, "This is what Pharaoh says: 'I will not give you any more straw. [11]Go and get your own straw wherever you can find it, but your work will not be reduced at all.' " [12]So the people scattered all over Egypt to gather stubble to use for straw. [13]The slave drivers kept pressing them, saying, "Complete the work required of you for each day, just as when you had straw." [14]The Israelite foremen appointed by Pharaoh's slave drivers were beaten and were asked, "Why didn't you meet your quota of bricks yesterday or today, as before?"

[15]Then the Israelite foremen went and appealed to Pharaoh: "Why have you treated your servants this way? [16]Your servants are given no straw, yet we are told, 'Make bricks!' Your servants are being beaten, but the fault is with your own people."

a 24 Or ⌊Moses' son⌋; Hebrew him   b 25 Or and drew near ⌊Moses'⌋ feet

¹⁷Pharaoh said, "Lazy, that's what you are—lazy! That is why you keep saying, 'Let us go and sacrifice to the LORD.' ¹⁸Now get to work. You will not be given any straw, yet you must produce your full quota of bricks."

¹⁹The Israelite foremen realized they were in trouble when they were told, "You are not to reduce the number of bricks required of you for each day." ²⁰When they left Pharaoh, they found Moses and Aaron waiting to meet them, ²¹and they said, "May the LORD look upon you and judge you! You have made us a stench to Pharaoh and his officials and have put a sword in their hand to kill us."

truth or dare

Have you ever prayed for help, only to have your situation get worse? God may be using that situation to teach you to trust him—through the good times *and* the bad.

5:22–23

love notes

6:6-8

Daughter,

There is no problem beyond my power—whether it's compelling a stubborn king to set my people free or delivering you from bondage in your life. I am the Lord of all.

—Your mighty Father

What overwhelming problem do you need to hand off to God? Release it into his mighty hands.

God Promises Deliverance

²²Moses returned to the LORD and said, "O Lord, why have you brought trouble upon this people? Is this why you sent me? ²³Ever since I went to Pharaoh to speak in your name, he has brought trouble upon this people, and you have not rescued your people at all."

6 Then the LORD said to Moses, "Now you will see what I will do to Pharaoh: Because of my mighty hand he will let them go; because of my mighty hand he will drive them out of his country."

²God also said to Moses, "I am the LORD. ³I appeared to Abraham, to Isaac and to Jacob as God Almighty,ᵃ but by my name the LORDᵇ I did not make myself known to them.ᶜ ⁴I also established my covenant with them to give them the land of Canaan, where they lived as aliens. ⁵Moreover, I have heard the groaning of the Israelites, whom the Egyptians are enslaving, and I have remembered my covenant.

⁶"Therefore, say to the Israelites: 'I am the LORD, and I will bring you out from under the yoke of the Egyptians. I will free you from being slaves to them, and I will redeem you with an outstretched arm and with mighty acts of judgment. ⁷I will take you as my own people, and I will be your God. Then you will know that I am the LORD your God, who brought you out from under the yoke of the Egyptians. ⁸And I will bring

---

ᵃ 3 Hebrew *El-Shaddai*   ᵇ 3 See note at Exodus 3:15.   ᶜ 3 Or *Almighty, and by my name the LORD did not let myself be known to them?*

you to the land I swore with uplifted hand to give to Abraham, to Isaac and to Jacob. I will give it to you as a possession. I am the LORD.' "

⁹Moses reported this to the Israelites, but they did not listen to him because of their discouragement and cruel bondage.

¹⁰Then the LORD said to Moses, ¹¹"Go, tell Pharaoh king of Egypt to let the Israelites go out of his country."

¹²But Moses said to the LORD, "If the Israelites will not listen to me, why would Pharaoh listen to me, since I speak with faltering lips ᵃ?"

Family Record of Moses and Aaron

¹³Now the LORD spoke to Moses and Aaron about the Israelites and Pharaoh king of Egypt, and he commanded them to bring the Israelites out of Egypt.

¹⁴These were the heads of their families ᵇ:

The sons of Reuben the firstborn son of Israel were Hanoch and Pallu, Hezron and Carmi. These were the clans of Reuben.

¹⁵The sons of Simeon were Jemuel, Jamin, Ohad, Jakin, Zohar and Shaul the son of a Canaanite woman. These were the clans of Simeon.

¹⁶These were the names of the sons of Levi according to their records: Gershon, Kohath and Merari. Levi lived 137 years.

¹⁷The sons of Gershon, by clans, were Libni and Shimei.

¹⁸The sons of Kohath were Amram, Izhar, Hebron and Uzziel. Kohath lived 133 years.

¹⁹The sons of Merari were Mahli and Mushi.

These were the clans of Levi according to their records.

²⁰Amram married his father's sister Jochebed, who bore him Aaron and Moses. Amram lived 137 years.

²¹The sons of Izhar were Korah, Nepheg and Zicri.

²²The sons of Uzziel were Mishael, Elzaphan and Sithri.

²³Aaron married Elisheba, daughter of Amminadab and sister of Nahshon, and she bore him Nadab and Abihu, Eleazar and Ithamar.

²⁴The sons of Korah were Assir, Elkanah and Abiasaph. These were the Korahite clans.

²⁵Eleazar son of Aaron married one of the daughters of Putiel, and she bore him Phinehas.

These were the heads of the Levite families, clan by clan.

²⁶It was this same Aaron and Moses to whom the LORD said, "Bring the Israelites out of Egypt by their divisions." ²⁷They were the ones who spoke to Pharaoh king of Egypt about bringing the Israelites out of Egypt. It was the same Moses and Aaron.

Aaron to Speak for Moses

²⁸Now when the LORD spoke to Moses in Egypt, ²⁹he said to him, "I am the LORD. Tell Pharaoh king of Egypt everything I tell you."

³⁰But Moses said to the LORD, "Since I speak with faltering lips, why would Pharaoh listen to me?"

7 Then the LORD said to Moses, "See, I have made you like God to Pharaoh, and your brother Aaron will be your prophet. ²You are to say everything I command you, and your brother Aaron is to tell Pharaoh to let the Israelites go out of his country. ³But I will harden Pharaoh's heart, and though I multiply my miraculous signs and wonders in Egypt, ⁴he will not listen to you. Then I will lay my hand on Egypt and with mighty acts of judgment I will bring out my divisions, my people the Israelites. ⁵And the Egyptians will know that I am the LORD when I stretch out my hand against Egypt and bring the Israelites out of it."

⁶Moses and Aaron did just as the LORD commanded them. ⁷Moses was eighty years old and Aaron eighty-three when they spoke to Pharaoh.

ᵃ 12 Hebrew *I am uncircumcised of lips*; also in verse 30   ᵇ 14 The Hebrew for *families* here and in verse 25 refers to units larger than clans.

mirror images

The angel of the LORD found Hagar near a spring in the desert. . . . And he said, "Hagar, servant of Sarai, where have you come from, and where are you going?" Genesis 16:7–8

Hagar—Headed Nowhere Fast

Poor Hagar was Abraham's servant-slash-mistress. And get this—she lived with Mr. and Mrs. Abraham. So, after God promised Abraham (first known as Abram) that he would have a child in his old age (see Genesis 15:4), he and Sarah (first known as Sarai) decided—without input from God—that Hagar would be the mother.

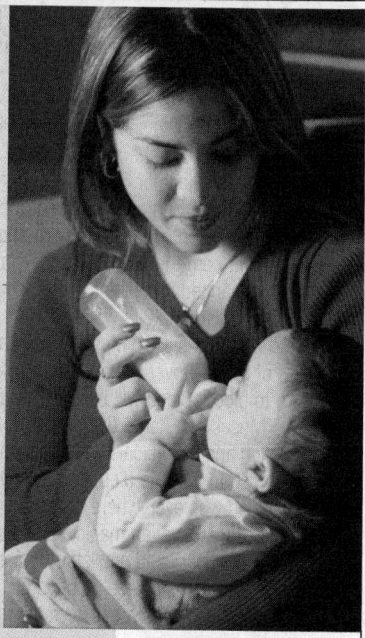

Hagar became pregnant with a son they called Ishmael. However, it became pretty clear this was not the son God promised Abraham. So Hagar got stuck in the middle of a really bad situation that only seemed to be getting worse. Her solution to her difficulties? Running away.

The angel who met her on the run prompted Hagar to think about two very important questions. What was she running away from? Being mistreated. An uncomfortable living situation. An inferiority complex—knowing she would always be second-best to the "real" wife. However, besides all the awful things she was running from, God called her to also examine where she was going.

See, like Hagar, we're never really standing still in life. We may run away from our many problems—but where are we going? To better choices? To a promising future? Or are we like Hagar, sitting in the desert—going nowhere fast? Hagar began to realize maybe she didn't know how to take care of business on her own.

When we hit a crisis on our road, what's our first instinct? Run away? Hide out if we can? Sometimes it seems like we're certain we know just what we're doing until God comes along and asks us to consider our ways.

To read the next Mirror Images profile, go to page 88.

Dear God, sometimes all I can think about is leaving my problems in the dust. Help me to remember Hagar when I feel that way. And help me to turn to you for help instead of going my own way. Amen.

Read more about Hagar in Genesis 16 (pages 18–19), 21:8–21 (page 25).

77

Aaron's Staff Becomes a Snake

[8]The LORD said to Moses and Aaron, [9]"When Pharaoh says to you, 'Perform a miracle,' then say to Aaron, 'Take your staff and throw it down before Pharaoh,' and it will become a snake."

[10]So Moses and Aaron went to Pharaoh and did just as the LORD commanded. Aaron threw his staff down in front of Pharaoh and his officials, and it became a snake. [11]Pharaoh then summoned wise men and sorcerers, and the Egyptian magicians also did the same things by their secret arts: [12]Each one threw down his staff and it became a snake. But Aaron's staff swallowed up their staffs. [13]Yet Pharaoh's heart became hard and he would not listen to them, just as the LORD had said.

The Plague of Blood

[14]Then the LORD said to Moses, "Pharaoh's heart is unyielding; he refuses to let the people go. [15]Go to Pharaoh in the morning as he goes out to the water. Wait on the bank of the Nile to meet him, and take in your hand the staff that was changed into a snake. [16]Then say to him, 'The LORD, the God of the Hebrews, has sent me to say to you: Let my people go, so that they may worship me in the desert. But until now you have not listened. [17]This is what the LORD says: By this you will know that I am the LORD: With the staff that is in my hand I will strike the water of the Nile, and it will be changed into blood. [18]The fish in the Nile will die, and the river will stink; the Egyptians will not be able to drink its water.' "

[19]The LORD said to Moses, "Tell Aaron, 'Take your staff and stretch out your hand over the waters of Egypt—over the streams and canals, over the ponds and all the reservoirs'—and they will turn to blood. Blood will be everywhere in Egypt, even in the wooden buckets and stone jars."

[20]Moses and Aaron did just as the LORD had commanded. He raised his staff in the presence of Pharaoh and his officials and struck the water of the Nile, and all the water was changed into blood. [21]The fish in the Nile died, and the river smelled so bad that the Egyptians could not drink its water. Blood was everywhere in Egypt.

[22]But the Egyptian magicians did the same things by their secret arts, and Pharaoh's heart became hard; he would not listen to Moses and Aaron, just as the LORD had said. [23]Instead, he turned and went into his palace, and did not take even this to heart. [24]And all the Egyptians dug along the Nile to get drinking water, because they could not drink the water of the river.

The Plague of Frogs

8 [25]Seven days passed after the LORD struck the Nile. [1]Then the LORD said to Moses, "Go to Pharaoh and say to him, 'This is what the LORD says: Let my people go, so that they may worship me. [2]If you refuse to let them go, I will plague your whole country with frogs. [3]The Nile will teem with frogs. They will come up into your palace and your bedroom and onto your bed, into the houses of your officials and on your people, and into your ovens and kneading troughs. [4]The frogs will go up on you and your people and all your officials.' "

[5]Then the LORD said to Moses, "Tell Aaron, 'Stretch out your hand with your staff over the streams and canals and ponds, and make frogs come up on the land of Egypt.' "

[6]So Aaron stretched out his hand over the waters of Egypt, and the frogs came up and covered the land. [7]But the magicians did the same things by their secret arts; they also made frogs come up on the land of Egypt.

[8]Pharaoh summoned Moses and Aaron and said, "Pray to the LORD to take the frogs away from me and my people, and I will let your people go to offer sacrifices to the LORD."

[9]Moses said to Pharaoh, "I leave to you the honor of setting the time for me to pray for you and your officials and your people that you and your houses may be rid of the frogs, except for those that remain in the Nile."

[10]"Tomorrow," Pharaoh said.

Moses replied, "It will be as you say, so that you may know there is no one like the LORD our God. [11]The frogs will leave you and your houses, your officials and your people; they will remain only in the Nile."

[12]After Moses and Aaron left Pharaoh, Moses cried out to the LORD about the frogs he had brought on Pharaoh. [13]And the LORD did what Moses asked. The frogs died in the houses, in the courtyards and in the fields. [14]They were piled into heaps, and the land reeked of them. [15]But when Pharaoh saw

that there was relief, he hardened his heart and would not listen to Moses and Aaron, just as the LORD had said.

The Plague of Gnats

[16]Then the LORD said to Moses, "Tell Aaron, 'Stretch out your staff and strike the dust of the ground,' and throughout the land of Egypt the dust will become gnats." [17]They did this, and when Aaron stretched out his hand with the staff and struck the dust of the ground, gnats came upon men and animals. All the dust throughout the land of Egypt became gnats. [18]But when the magicians tried to produce gnats by their secret arts, they could not. And the gnats were on men and animals.

[19]The magicians said to Pharaoh, "This is the finger of God." But Pharaoh's heart was hard and he would not listen, just as the LORD had said.

truth or dare

Just as clay is easier to shape when it's soft, so God can make great things out of your life when your heart is softened to his leading.

8:15

The Plague of Flies

[20]Then the LORD said to Moses, "Get up early in the morning and confront Pharaoh as he goes to the water and say to him, 'This is what the LORD says: Let my people go, so that they may worship me. [21]If you do not let my people go, I will send swarms of flies on you and your officials, on your people and into your houses. The houses of the Egyptians will be full of flies, and even the ground where they are.

[22]"'But on that day I will deal differently with the land of Goshen, where my people live; no swarms of flies will be there, so that you will know that I, the LORD, am in this land. [23]I will make a distinction[a] between my people and your people. This miraculous sign will occur tomorrow.' "

[24]And the LORD did this. Dense swarms of flies poured into Pharaoh's palace and into the houses of his officials, and throughout Egypt the land was ruined by the flies.

[25]Then Pharaoh summoned Moses and Aaron and said, "Go, sacrifice to your God here in the land."

[26]But Moses said, "That would not be right. The sacrifices we offer the LORD our God would be detestable to the Egyptians. And if we offer sacrifices that are detestable in their eyes, will they not stone us? [27]We must take a three-day journey into the desert to offer sacrifices to the LORD our God, as he commands us."

[28]Pharaoh said, "I will let you go to offer sacrifices to the LORD your God in the desert, but you must not go very far. Now pray for me."

[29]Moses answered, "As soon as I leave you, I will pray to the LORD, and tomorrow the flies will leave Pharaoh and his officials and his people. Only be sure that Pharaoh does not act deceitfully again by not letting the people go to offer sacrifices to the LORD."

[30]Then Moses left Pharaoh and prayed to the LORD, [31]and the LORD did what Moses asked: The flies left Pharaoh and his officials and his people; not a fly remained. [32]But this time also Pharaoh hardened his heart and would not let the people go.

The Plague on Livestock

9 Then the LORD said to Moses, "Go to Pharaoh and say to him, 'This is what the LORD, the God of the Hebrews, says: "Let my people go, so that they may worship me." [2]If you refuse to let them go and continue to hold them back, [3]the hand of the LORD will bring a terrible plague on your livestock in the field—on your horses and donkeys and camels and on your cattle and sheep and goats. [4]But the LORD will make a distinction between the livestock of Israel and that of Egypt, so that no animal belonging to the Israelites will die.' "

[5]The LORD set a time and said, "Tomorrow the LORD will do this in the land." [6]And the next day the LORD did it: All the livestock of the Egyptians died, but not one animal belonging to the Israelites died. [7]Pharaoh sent men to investigate and found that not even one of the animals of the Israelites had died. Yet his heart was unyielding and he would not let the people go.

[a] 23 Septuagint and Vulgate; Hebrew *will put a deliverance*

The Plague of Boils

[8]Then the LORD said to Moses and Aaron, "Take handfuls of soot from a furnace and have Moses toss it into the air in the presence of Pharaoh. [9]It will become fine dust over the whole land of Egypt, and festering boils will break out on men and animals throughout the land."

[10]So they took soot from a furnace and stood before Pharaoh. Moses tossed it into the air, and festering boils broke out on men and animals. [11]The magicians could not stand before Moses because of the boils that were on them and on all the Egyptians. [12]But the LORD hardened Pharaoh's heart and he would not listen to Moses and Aaron, just as the LORD had said to Moses.

The Plague of Hail

[13]Then the LORD said to Moses, "Get up early in the morning, confront Pharaoh and say to him, 'This is what the LORD, the God of the Hebrews, says: Let my people go, so that they may worship me, [14]or this time I will send the full force of my plagues against you and against your officials and your people, so you may know that there is no one like me in all the earth. [15]For by now I could have stretched out my hand and struck you and your people with a plague that would have wiped you off the earth. [16]But I have raised you up [a] for this very purpose, that I might show you my power and that my name might be proclaimed in all the earth. [17]You still set yourself against my people and will not let them go. [18]Therefore, at this time tomorrow I will send the worst hailstorm that has ever fallen on Egypt, from the day it was founded till now. [19]Give an order now to bring your livestock and everything you have in the field to a place of shelter, because the hail will fall on every man and animal that has not been brought in and is still out in the field, and they will die.' "

[20]Those officials of Pharaoh who feared the word of the LORD hurried to bring their slaves and their livestock inside. [21]But those who ignored the word of the LORD left their slaves and livestock in the field.

[22]Then the LORD said to Moses, "Stretch out your hand toward the sky so that hail will fall all over Egypt—on men and animals and on everything growing in the fields of Egypt." [23]When Moses stretched out his staff toward the sky, the LORD sent thunder and hail, and lightning flashed down to the ground. So the LORD rained hail on the land of Egypt; [24]hail fell and lightning flashed back and forth. It was the worst storm in all the land of Egypt since it had become a nation. [25]Throughout Egypt hail struck everything in the fields—both men and animals; it beat down everything growing in the fields and stripped every tree. [26]The only place it did not hail was the land of Goshen, where the Israelites were.

[27]Then Pharaoh summoned Moses and Aaron. "This time I have sinned," he said to them. "The LORD is in the right, and I and my people are in the wrong. [28]Pray to the LORD, for we have had enough thunder and hail. I will let you go; you don't have to stay any longer."

[29]Moses replied, "When I have gone out of the city, I will spread out my hands in prayer to the LORD. The thunder will stop and there will be no more hail, so you may know that the earth is the LORD's. [30]But I know that you and your officials still do not fear the LORD God."

[31](The flax and barley were destroyed, since the barley had headed and the flax was in bloom. [32]The wheat and spelt, however, were not destroyed, because they ripen later.)

---

genuine persistence » 9:1

Okay, how many times have Moses and Pharaoh had this conversation? Moses: "Let my people go." Pharaoh: "No." Again. And again. And again. Moses didn't take the hint. He refused to back down. He knew that if he continued to listen to God, the situation would work out for the best. You may be in the middle of a difficult situation—maybe things are getting worse instead of better, and you wonder how much more you can take. Hang on to God—in the end, persistence always wins.

---

[a] 16 Or *have spared you*

[33]Then Moses left Pharaoh and went out of the city. He spread out his hands toward the LORD; the thunder and hail stopped, and the rain no longer poured down on the land. [34]When Pharaoh saw that the rain and hail and thunder had stopped, he sinned again: He and his officials hardened their hearts. [35]So Pharaoh's heart was hard and he would not let the Israelites go, just as the LORD had said through Moses.

The Plague of Locusts

10 Then the LORD said to Moses, "Go to Pharaoh, for I have hardened his heart and the hearts of his officials so that I may perform these miraculous signs of mine among them [2]that you may tell your children and grandchildren how I dealt harshly with the Egyptians and how I performed my signs among them, and that you may know that I am the LORD."

[3]So Moses and Aaron went to Pharaoh and said to him, "This is what the LORD, the God of the Hebrews, says: 'How long will you refuse to humble yourself before me? Let my people go, so that they may worship me. [4]If you refuse to let them go, I will bring locusts into your country tomorrow. [5]They will cover the face of the ground so that it cannot be seen. They will devour what little you have left after the hail, including every tree that is growing in your fields. [6]They will fill your houses and those of all your officials and all the Egyptians—something neither your fathers nor your forefathers have ever seen from the day they settled in this land till now.' " Then Moses turned and left Pharaoh.

[7]Pharaoh's officials said to him, "How long will this man be a snare to us? Let the people go, so that they may worship the LORD their God. Do you not yet realize that Egypt is ruined?"

[8]Then Moses and Aaron were brought back to Pharaoh. "Go, worship the LORD your God," he said. "But just who will be going?"

[9]Moses answered, "We will go with our young and old, with our sons and daughters, and with our flocks and herds, because we are to celebrate a festival to the LORD."

[10]Pharaoh said, "The LORD be with you—if I let you go, along with your women and children! Clearly you are bent on evil. [a] [11]No! Have only the men go; and worship the LORD, since that's what you have been asking for." Then Moses and Aaron were driven out of Pharaoh's presence.

[12]And the LORD said to Moses, "Stretch out your hand over Egypt so that locusts will swarm over the land and devour everything growing in the fields, everything left by the hail."

[13]So Moses stretched out his staff over Egypt, and the LORD made an east wind blow across the land all that day and all that night. By morning the wind had brought the locusts; [14]they invaded all Egypt and settled down in every area of the country in great numbers. Never before had there been such a plague of locusts, nor will there ever be again. [15]They covered all the ground until it was black. They devoured all that was left after the hail—everything growing in the fields and the fruit on the trees. Nothing green remained on tree or plant in all the land of Egypt.

[16]Pharaoh quickly summoned Moses and Aaron and said, "I have sinned against the LORD your God and against you. [17]Now forgive my sin once more and pray to the LORD your God to take this deadly plague away from me."

[18]Moses then left Pharaoh and prayed to the LORD. [19]And the LORD changed the wind to a very strong west wind, which caught up the locusts and carried them into the Red Sea. [b] Not a locust was left anywhere in Egypt. [20]But the LORD hardened Pharaoh's heart, and he would not let the Israelites go.

The Plague of Darkness

[21]Then the LORD said to Moses, "Stretch out your hand toward the sky so that darkness will spread over Egypt—darkness that can be felt." [22]So Moses stretched out his hand toward the sky,

---

truth or dare

Do you keep a journal? Start recording your prayer requests *and* God's answers! Seeing God's answers throughout the pages will remind you (and maybe someday your grandkids!) that he is faithful.

10:2

---

a 10 Or *Be careful, trouble is in store for you!*   *b* 19 Hebrew *Yam Suph*; that is, Sea of Reeds and total darkness covered all Egypt for three days. [23]No one could see anyone else or leave his place for three days. Yet all the Israelites had light in the places where they lived.

[24]Then Pharaoh summoned Moses and said, "Go, worship the LORD. Even your women and children may go with you; only leave your flocks and herds behind."

[25]But Moses said, "You must allow us to have sacrifices and burnt offerings to present to the LORD our God. [26]Our livestock too must go with us; not a hoof is to be left behind. We have to use some of them in worshiping the LORD our God, and until we get there we will not know what we are to use to worship the LORD."

[27]But the LORD hardened Pharaoh's heart, and he was not willing to let them go. [28]Pharaoh said to Moses, "Get out of my sight! Make sure you do not appear before me again! The day you see my face you will die."

[29]"Just as you say," Moses replied, "I will never appear before you again."

The Plague on the Firstborn

11 Now the LORD had said to Moses, "I will bring one more plague on Pharaoh and on Egypt. After that, he will let you go from here, and when he does, he will drive you out completely. [2]Tell the people that men and women alike are to ask their neighbors for articles of silver and gold." [3](The LORD made the Egyptians favorably disposed toward the people, and Moses himself was highly regarded in Egypt by Pharaoh's officials and by the people.)

[4]So Moses said, "This is what the LORD says: 'About midnight I will go throughout Egypt. [5]Every firstborn son in Egypt will die, from the firstborn son of Pharaoh, who sits on the throne, to the firstborn son of the slave girl, who is at her hand mill, and all the firstborn of the cattle as well. [6]There will be loud wailing throughout Egypt—worse than there has ever been or ever will be again. [7]But among the Israelites not a dog will bark at any man or animal.' Then you will know that the LORD makes a distinction between Egypt and Israel. [8]All these officials of yours will come to me, bowing down before me and saying, 'Go, you and all the people who follow you!' After that I will leave." Then Moses, hot with anger, left Pharaoh.

[9]The LORD had said to Moses, "Pharaoh will refuse to listen to you—so that my wonders may be multiplied in Egypt." [10]Moses and Aaron performed all these wonders before Pharaoh, but the LORD hardened Pharaoh's heart, and he would not let the Israelites go out of his country.

The Passover

12 The LORD said to Moses and Aaron in Egypt, [2]"This month is to be for you the first month, the first month of your year. [3]Tell the whole community of Israel that on the tenth day of this month each man is to take a lamb[a] for his family, one for each household. [4]If any household is too small for a whole lamb, they must share one with their nearest neighbor, having taken into account the number of people there are. You are to determine the amount of lamb needed in accordance with what each person will eat. [5]The animals you choose must be year-old males without defect, and you may take them from the sheep or the goats. [6]Take care of them until the fourteenth day of the month, when all the people of the community of Israel must slaughter them at twilight. [7]Then they are to take some of the blood and put it on the sides and tops of the doorframes of the houses where they eat the lambs. [8]That same night they are to eat the meat roasted over the fire, along with bitter herbs, and bread made without yeast. [9]Do not eat the meat raw or cooked in water, but roast it over the fire—head, legs and inner parts. [10]Do not leave any of it till morning; if some is left till morning, you must burn it. [11]This is how you are to eat it: with your cloak tucked into your belt, your sandals on your feet and your staff in your hand. Eat it in haste; it is the LORD's Passover.

[12]"On that same night I will pass through Egypt and strike down every firstborn—both men and animals—and I will bring judgment on all the gods of Egypt. I am the LORD. [13]The blood will be a sign for you on the houses where you are; and when I see the blood, I will pass over you. No destructive plague will touch you when I strike Egypt.

[14]"This is a day you are to commemorate; for the generations to come you shall celebrate it as a festival to the LORD—a lasting ordinance. [15]For seven days you are to eat bread made without yeast. On the first day remove the yeast from your houses, for whoever eats anything with yeast in it from the first day through the seventh must be cut off from Israel. [16]On the first day hold a sa-

a 3 The Hebrew word can mean *lamb* or *kid*; also in verse 4.

A Lasting Mistake

focus — Profile: **Sierra**

I must have sat there for 20 minutes, just staring into my fish tank, hoping I could forget about it all. Fish have no worries, you know? They just swim and feed on disgusting fish food flakes. What a life. I wish mine were that simple. I have this queasy, uneasy feeling in my gut that isn't just stress over my finals. It's morning sickness. And as bad as it feels, it's nothing compared to what's ahead.

Maybe someday I'll be excited to be a mom, but not now. Not when I'm 15. Not when I know my boyfriend Jason will probably leave me as soon as he finds out. My parents are going to freak out. And my friends from church—well, I can hear it now. "Guys, did you hear Sierra's pregnant?! What was she thinking? I always thought she and Jason were messing around. Wait till Pastor Steve hears . . ."

I guess God's probably pretty disgusted with me, too. Can't blame him. I thought sleeping with Jason would be the ultimate test of our love—I figured I could prove to him we were made for each other. Now he always wants to have sex, and he never talks to me anymore—not really.

I feel so empty and scared. Scared God will never love me again, scared about what people will do when they find out, scared that I don't have a clue about having a kid.

Jesus, it's me, Sierra. If there's any chance you still care, if you're even listening, help me, please . . .

For more ideas on how to handle pregnancy, check out the link on www.TrueImagesBible.com

pregnancy in focus

Sierra's in a tight spot, but she's not alone. Each year, over 800,000 teens in the U.S. get pregnant. Thankfully, God loves Sierra and all the girls like her—and he cares about her unborn baby, too (see Psalm 139:13–16, pages 791-792; Romans 8:37–39, page 1494).

If you or someone you know is pregnant, here's how to find help:

» Talk to a trusted Christian adult. He or she can help you sort things out and break the news to others.
» Decide to do what's right. Having an abortion would make another wrong, not a right. Check out all your options, including adoption.
» Commit to "secondary virginity" with God's help. Yes, you messed up. But God wants to forgive you, and he can help you forgive yourself. Make a decision now to stay sexually pure until marriage.

For more on this topic, see the index on page 1656.

cred assembly, and another one on the seventh day. Do no work at all on these days, except to prepare food for everyone to eat—that is all you may do.

[17]"Celebrate the Feast of Unleavened Bread, because it was on this very day that I brought your divisions out of Egypt. Celebrate this day as a lasting ordinance for the generations to come. [18]In the first month you are to eat bread made without yeast, from the evening of the fourteenth day until the evening of the twenty-first day. [19]For seven days no yeast is to be found in your houses. And whoever eats anything with yeast in it must be cut off from the community of Israel, whether he is an alien or native-born. [20]Eat nothing made with yeast. Wherever you live, you must eat unleavened bread."

21Then Moses summoned all the elders of Israel and said to them, "Go at once and select the animals for your families and slaughter the Passover lamb. 22Take a bunch of hyssop, dip it into the blood in the basin and put some of the blood on the top and on both sides of the doorframe. Not one of you shall go out the door of his house until morning. 23When the LORD goes through the land to strike down the Egyptians, he will see the blood on the top and sides of the doorframe and will pass over that doorway, and he will not permit the destroyer to enter your houses and strike you down.

24"Obey these instructions as a lasting ordinance for you and your descendants. 25When you enter the land that the LORD will give you as he promised, observe this ceremony. 26And when your children ask you, 'What does this ceremony mean to you?' 27then tell them, 'It is the Passover sacrifice to the LORD, who passed over the houses of the Israelites in Egypt and spared our homes when he struck down the Egyptians.' " Then the people bowed down and worshiped. 28The Israelites did just what the LORD commanded Moses and Aaron.

29At midnight the LORD struck down all the firstborn in Egypt, from the firstborn of Pharaoh, who sat on the throne, to the firstborn of the prisoner, who was in the dungeon, and the firstborn of all the livestock as well. 30Pharaoh and all his officials and all the Egyptians got up during the night, and there was loud wailing in Egypt, for there was not a house without someone dead.

The Exodus

31During the night Pharaoh summoned Moses and Aaron and said, "Up! Leave my people, you and the Israelites! Go, worship the LORD as you have requested. 32Take your flocks and herds, as you have said, and go. And also bless me."

33The Egyptians urged the people to hurry and leave the country. "For otherwise," they said, "we will all die!" 34So the people took their dough before the yeast was added, and carried it on their shoulders in kneading troughs wrapped in clothing. 35The Israelites did as Moses instructed and asked the Egyptians for articles of silver and gold and for clothing. 36The LORD had made the Egyptians favorably disposed toward the people, and they gave them what they asked for; so they plundered the Egyptians.

37The Israelites journeyed from Rameses to Succoth. There were about six hundred thousand men on foot, besides women and children. 38Many other people went up with them, as well as large droves of livestock, both flocks and herds. 39With the dough they had brought from Egypt, they baked cakes of unleavened bread. The dough was without yeast because they had been driven out of Egypt and did not have time to prepare food for themselves.

40Now the length of time the Israelite people lived in Egypt*a* was 430 years. 41At the end of the 430 years, to the very day, all the LORD's divisions left Egypt. 42Because the LORD kept vigil that night to bring them out of Egypt, on this night all the Israelites are to keep vigil to honor the LORD for the generations to come.

Passover Restrictions

43The LORD said to Moses and Aaron, "These are the regulations for the Passover:

"No foreigner is to eat of it. 44Any slave you have bought may eat of it after you have circumcised him, 45but a temporary resident and a hired worker may not eat of it.

46"It must be eaten inside one house; take none of the meat outside the house. Do not break any of the bones. 47The whole community of Israel must celebrate it.

48"An alien living among you who wants to celebrate the LORD's Passover must have all the males in his household circumcised; then he may take part like one born in the land. No uncircumcised male may eat of it. 49The same law applies to the native-born and to the alien living among you."

50All the Israelites did just what the LORD had commanded Moses and Aaron. 51And on that very day the LORD brought the Israelites out of Egypt by their divisions.

Consecration of the Firstborn

13 The LORD said to Moses, 2"Consecrate to me every firstborn male. The first offspring of every womb among the Israelites belongs to me, whether man or animal."

3Then Moses said to the people, "Commemorate this day, the day you came out of Egypt, out of the land of slavery, because the LORD brought you out of it with a mighty hand. Eat

---

a 40 Masoretic Text; Samaritan Pentateuch and Septuagint *Egypt and Canaan*

truth or dare

Sometimes we're quick to forget what God's done for us. That's why he gave the Israelites certain holidays to remind them of their connection with him. What reminds *you* of God?

13:6–10

nothing containing yeast. ⁴Today, in the month of Abib, you are leaving. ⁵When the LORD brings you into the land of the Canaanites, Hittites, Amorites, Hivites and Jebusites—the land he swore to your forefathers to give you, a land flowing with milk and honey—you are to observe this ceremony in this month: ⁶For seven days eat bread made without yeast and on the seventh day hold a festival to the LORD. ⁷Eat unleavened bread during those seven days; nothing with yeast in it is to be seen among you, nor shall any yeast be seen anywhere within your borders. ⁸On that day tell your son, 'I do this because of what the LORD did for me when I came out of Egypt.' ⁹This observance will be for you like a sign on your hand and a reminder on your forehead that the law of the LORD is to be on your lips. For the LORD brought you out of Egypt with his mighty hand. ¹⁰You must keep this ordinance at the appointed time year after year.

¹¹"After the LORD brings you into the land of the Canaanites and gives it to you, as he promised on oath to you and your forefathers, ¹²you are to give over to the LORD the first offspring of every womb. All the firstborn males of your livestock belong to the LORD. ¹³Redeem with a lamb every firstborn donkey, but if you do not redeem it, break its neck. Redeem every firstborn among your sons.

¹⁴"In days to come, when your son asks you, 'What does this mean?' say to him, 'With a mighty hand the LORD brought us out of Egypt, out of the land of slavery. ¹⁵When Pharaoh stubbornly refused to let us go, the LORD killed every firstborn in Egypt, both man and animal. This is why I sacrifice to the LORD the first male offspring of every womb and redeem each of my firstborn sons.' ¹⁶And it will be like a sign on your hand and a symbol on your forehead that the LORD brought us out of Egypt with his mighty hand."

Crossing the Sea

¹⁷When Pharaoh let the people go, God did not lead them on the road through the Philistine country, though that was shorter. For God said, "If they face war, they might change their minds and return to Egypt." ¹⁸So God led the people around by the desert road toward the Red Sea.ᵃ The Israelites went up out of Egypt armed for battle.

¹⁹Moses took the bones of Joseph with him because Joseph had made the sons of Israel swear an oath. He had said, "God will surely come to your aid, and then you must carry my bones up with you from this place."ᵇ

²⁰After leaving Succoth they camped at Etham on the edge of the desert. ²¹By day the LORD went ahead of them in a pillar of cloud to guide them on their way and by night in a pillar of fire to give them light, so that they could travel by day or night. ²²Neither the pillar of cloud by day nor the pillar of fire by night left its place in front of the people.

truth or dare

The shortest route isn't always the best. If God seems to be taking you the long way around, follow him. He wants you to learn something from the journey.

13:17–18

14 Then the LORD said to Moses, ²"Tell the Israelites to turn back and encamp near Pi Hahiroth, between Migdol and the sea. They are to encamp by the sea, directly opposite Baal Zephon. ³Pharaoh will think, 'The Israelites are wandering around the land in confusion, hemmed in by the desert.' ⁴And I will harden Pharaoh's heart, and he will pursue them. But I will gain glory for myself through Pharaoh and all his army, and the Egyptians will know that I am the LORD." So the Israelites did this.

⁵When the king of Egypt was told that the people had fled, Pharaoh and his officials changed their minds about them and said, "What have we done? We have let the Israelites go and have lost their

ᵃ 18 Hebrew *Yam Suph*; that is, Sea of Reeds   ᵇ 19 See Gen. 50:25.

services!" ⁶So he had his chariot made ready and took his army with him. ⁷He took six hundred of the best chariots, along with all the other chariots of Egypt, with officers over all of them. ⁸The Lord hardened the heart of Pharaoh king of Egypt, so that he pursued the Israelites, who were marching out boldly. ⁹The Egyptians—all Pharaoh's horses and chariots, horsemen*ᵃ* and troops—pursued the Israelites and overtook them as they camped by the sea near Pi Hahiroth, opposite Baal Zephon.

¹⁰As Pharaoh approached, the Israelites looked up, and there were the Egyptians, marching after them. They were terrified and cried out to the Lord. ¹¹They said to Moses, "Was it because there were no graves in Egypt that you brought us to the desert to die? What have you done to us by bringing us out of Egypt? ¹²Didn't we say to you in Egypt, 'Leave us alone; let us serve the Egyptians'? It would have been better for us to serve the Egyptians than to die in the desert!"

¹³Moses answered the people, "Do not be afraid. Stand firm and you will see the deliverance the Lord will bring you today. The Egyptians you see today you will never see again. ¹⁴The Lord will fight for you; you need only to be still."

¹⁵Then the Lord said to Moses, "Why are you crying out to me? Tell the Israelites to move on. ¹⁶Raise your staff and stretch out your hand over the sea to divide the water so that the Israelites can go through the sea on dry ground. ¹⁷I will harden the hearts of the Egyptians so that they will go in after them. And I will gain glory through Pharaoh and all his army, through his chariots and his horsemen. ¹⁸The Egyptians will know that I am the Lord when I gain glory through Pharaoh, his chariots and his horsemen."

¹⁹Then the angel of God, who had been traveling in front of Israel's army, withdrew and went behind them. The pillar of cloud also moved from in front and stood behind them, ²⁰coming between the armies of Egypt and Israel. Throughout the night the cloud brought darkness to the one side and light to the other side; so neither went near the other all night long.

²¹Then Moses stretched out his hand over the sea, and all that night the Lord drove the sea back with a strong east wind and turned it into dry land. The waters were divided, ²²and the Israelites went through the sea on dry ground, with a wall of water on their right and on their left.

²³The Egyptians pursued them, and all Pharaoh's horses and chariots and horsemen followed them into the sea. ²⁴During the last watch of the night the Lord looked down from the pillar of fire and cloud at the Egyptian army and threw it into confusion. ²⁵He made the wheels of their chariots come off*ᵇ* so that they had difficulty driving. And the Egyptians said, "Let's get away from the Israelites! The Lord is fighting for them against Egypt."

²⁶Then the Lord said to Moses, "Stretch out your hand over the sea so that the waters may flow back over the Egyptians and their chariots and horsemen." ²⁷Moses stretched out his hand over the sea, and at daybreak the sea went back to its place. The Egyptians were fleeing toward*ᶜ* it, and the Lord swept them into the sea. ²⁸The water flowed back and covered the chariots and horsemen—the entire army of Pharaoh that had followed the Israelites into the sea. Not one of them survived.

²⁹But the Israelites went through the sea on dry ground, with a wall of water on their right and on their left. ³⁰That day the Lord saved Israel from the hands of the Egyptians, and Israel saw the Egyptians lying dead on the shore. ³¹And when the Israelites saw the great power the Lord displayed against the Egyptians, the people feared the Lord and put their trust in him and in Moses his servant.

The Song of Moses and Miriam

15 Then Moses and the Israelites sang this song to the Lord:

"I will sing to the Lord,
for he is highly exalted.

truth or dare

Feeling trapped can bring out the worst in us—fear, panic, whining. When you're facing a difficult situation, recharge your faith by remembering God's past rescues.

14:10–11

ᵃ 9 Or charioteers; also in verses 17, 18, 23, 26 and 28 ᵇ 25 Or He jammed the wheels of their chariots (see Samaritan Pentateuch, Septuagint and Syriac) ᶜ 27 Or from

The horse and its rider
  he has hurled into the sea.
2 The LORD is my strength and my song;
  he has become my salvation.
He is my God, and I will praise him,
  my father's God, and I will exalt him.
3 The LORD is a warrior;
  the LORD is his name.
4 Pharaoh's chariots and his army
  he has hurled into the sea.
The best of Pharaoh's officers
  are drowned in the Red Sea.*a*
5 The deep waters have covered them;
  they sank to the depths like a stone.

6 "Your right hand, O LORD,
  was majestic in power.
Your right hand, O LORD,
  shattered the enemy.
7 In the greatness of your majesty
  you threw down those who opposed you.
You unleashed your burning anger;
  it consumed them like stubble.
8 By the blast of your nostrils
  the waters piled up.
The surging waters stood firm like a wall;
  the deep waters congealed in the heart of the sea.

9 "The enemy boasted,
  'I will pursue, I will overtake them.
I will divide the spoils;
  I will gorge myself on them.
I will draw my sword
  and my hand will destroy them.'
10 But you blew with your breath,
  and the sea covered them.
They sank like lead
  in the mighty waters.

11 "Who among the gods is like you, O LORD?
  Who is like you—
    majestic in holiness,
    awesome in glory,
    working wonders?
12 You stretched out your right hand
  and the earth swallowed them.

13 "In your unfailing love you will lead
  the people you have redeemed.
In your strength you will guide them
  to your holy dwelling.
14 The nations will hear and tremble;
  anguish will grip the people of Philistia.
15 The chiefs of Edom will be terrified,
  the leaders of Moab will be seized with trembling,
the people*b* of Canaan will melt away;

a 4 Hebrew Yam Suph; that is, Sea of Reeds; also in verse 22   b 15 Or rulers

mirror images

Without saying a word, the man watched her closely to learn whether or not the Lord had made his journey successful. Genesis 24:21

Rebekah—Who Are You When No One's Looking?

He prayed for a sign—just a hint that this was "the one." The servant was on a mission from his master to find the perfect wife for Isaac, Abraham's promised son. Rebekah caught the man's eye by going the extra mile in common courtesy and offering him *and* his camels a drink by the well. Just what he was hoping to see—a selfless, caring woman.

Rebekah had the kind of inner beauty that radiated from her selfless nature and her purity as a virgin. She was a true beauty inside and out. The servant introduced Isaac to this genuine girl, and they immediately married. Rebekah's admirable, kind nature took her from watering camels at the well to becoming a part of a family chosen by God to bless the world (see Genesis 17:16).

But the story doesn't end here. Later in life, Rebekah's inner beauty was again put to the test, and this time she didn't fare so well. She and her younger son, Jacob, double-teamed Isaac in his old age and conned him into giving her favorite boy Isaac's blessing instead of the older son Esau.

Our reputation lies in who people *think* we are when they watch us from afar. However, character is who we *really* are—especially when no one is looking. Rebekah knew what it was like to win and lose in both arenas. She lived up to her selfless reputation one moment, unaware anyone was looking. However, at another time, she showed her entire family a different side of her character altogether.

Like Rebekah, we live in a watching world. Seeing if we're for real. Looking for signs of our true nature. Are you one way at church and another at school? Are you sweet to your friends' parents while mistreating your own? If others catch you in the right moment, at the right time, what are they most likely to see?

Dear God, I want to be like Rebekah when she met the servant at the well, not like her when she tricked her husband. Help my reputation to match my true character. Amen.

dear God

To read the next Mirror Images profile, go to page 129.

▶▶ Read more about Rebekah in Genesis 24–27 (pages 27–36).

> 16 terror and dread will fall upon them.
> By the power of your arm
>   they will be as still as a stone—
> until your people pass by, O Lord,
>   until the people you bought[a] pass by.
> 17 You will bring them in and plant them
>   on the mountain of your inheritance—
> the place, O Lord, you made for your dwelling,
>   the sanctuary, O Lord, your hands established.
> 18 The Lord will reign
>   for ever and ever."

19 When Pharaoh's horses, chariots and horsemen[b] went into the sea, the Lord brought the waters of the sea back over them, but the Israelites walked through the sea on dry ground. 20 Then Miriam the prophetess, Aaron's sister, took a tambourine in her hand, and all the women followed her, with tambourines and dancing. 21 Miriam sang to them:

> "Sing to the Lord,
>   for he is highly exalted.
> The horse and its rider
>   he has hurled into the sea."

The Waters of Marah and Elim

22 Then Moses led Israel from the Red Sea and they went into the Desert of Shur. For three days they traveled in the desert without finding water. 23 When they came to Marah, they could not drink its water because it was bitter. (That is why the place is called Marah.[c]) 24 So the people grumbled against Moses, saying, "What are we to drink?"

25 Then Moses cried out to the Lord, and the Lord showed him a piece of wood. He threw it into the water, and the water became sweet.

There the Lord made a decree and a law for them, and there he tested them. 26 He said, "If you listen carefully to the voice of the Lord your God and do what is right in his eyes, if you pay attention to his commands and keep all his decrees, I will not bring on you any of the diseases I brought on the Egyptians, for I am the Lord, who heals you."

27 Then they came to Elim, where there were twelve springs and seventy palm trees, and they camped there near the water.

Manna and Quail

16 The whole Israelite community set out from Elim and came to the Desert of Sin, which is between Elim and Sinai, on the fifteenth day of the second month after they had come out of Egypt. 2 In the desert the whole community grumbled against Moses and Aaron. 3 The Israelites said to them, "If only we had died by the Lord's hand in Egypt! There we sat around pots of meat and ate all the food we wanted, but you have brought us out into this desert to starve this entire assembly to death."

4 Then the Lord said to Moses, "I will rain down bread from heaven for you. The people are to go out each day and gather enough for that day. In this way I will test them and see whether they will follow my instructions. 5 On the sixth day they are to prepare what they bring in, and that is to be twice as much as they gather on the other days."

6 So Moses and Aaron said to all the Israelites, "In the evening you will know that it was the Lord who brought you out of Egypt, 7 and in the morning you will see the glory of the Lord, because he has heard your grumbling against him. Who are we, that you should grumble against us?" 8 Moses also said, "You will know that it was the Lord when he gives you meat to eat in the evening and all the bread you want in the morning, because he has heard your grumbling against him. Who are we? You are not grumbling against us, but against the Lord."

9 Then Moses told Aaron, "Say to the entire Israelite community, 'Come before the Lord, for he has heard your grumbling.' "

---

a 16 Or *created*   *b 19* Or *charioteers*   *c 23 Marah* means *bitter.*

[10]While Aaron was speaking to the whole Israelite community, they looked toward the desert, and there was the glory of the LORD appearing in the cloud.

[11]The LORD said to Moses, [12]"I have heard the grumbling of the Israelites. Tell them, 'At twilight you will eat meat, and in the morning you will be filled with bread. Then you will know that I am the LORD your God.' "

[13]That evening quail came and covered the camp, and in the morning there was a layer of dew around the camp. [14]When the dew was gone, thin flakes like frost on the ground appeared on the desert floor. [15]When the Israelites saw it, they said to each other, "What is it?" For they did not know what it was.

Moses said to them, "It is the bread the LORD has given you to eat. [16]This is what the LORD has commanded: 'Each one is to gather as much as he needs. Take an omer[a] for each person you have in your tent.' "

[17]The Israelites did as they were told; some gathered much, some little. [18]And when they measured it by the omer, he who gathered much did not have too much, and he who gathered little did not have too little. Each one gathered as much as he needed.

truth or dare

Chances are, you won't get everything you want in life. But you can count on God to provide everything you *need*.

16:14–16

[19]Then Moses said to them, "No one is to keep any of it until morning."

[20]However, some of them paid no attention to Moses; they kept part of it until morning, but it was full of maggots and began to smell. So Moses was angry with them.

[21]Each morning everyone gathered as much as he needed, and when the sun grew hot, it melted away. [22]On the sixth day, they gathered twice as much—two omers[b] for each person—and the leaders of the community came and reported this to Moses. [23]He said to them, "This is what the LORD commanded: 'Tomorrow is to be a day of rest, a holy Sabbath to the LORD. So bake what you want to bake and boil what you want to boil. Save whatever is left and keep it until morning.' "

[24]So they saved it until morning, as Moses commanded, and it did not stink or get maggots in it. [25]"Eat it today," Moses said, "because today is a Sabbath to the LORD. You will not find any of it on the ground today. [26]Six days you are to gather it, but on the seventh day, the Sabbath, there will not be any."

[27]Nevertheless, some of the people went out on the seventh day to gather it, but they found none. [28]Then the LORD said to Moses, "How long will you[c] refuse to keep my commands and my instructions? [29]Bear in mind that the LORD has given you the Sabbath; that is why on the sixth day he gives you bread for two days. Everyone is to stay where he is on the seventh day; no one is to go out." [30]So the people rested on the seventh day.

[31]The people of Israel called the bread manna.[d] It was white like coriander seed and tasted like wafers made with honey. [32]Moses said, "This is what the LORD has commanded: 'Take an omer of manna and keep it for the generations to come, so they can see the bread I gave you to eat in the desert when I brought you out of Egypt.' "

[33]So Moses said to Aaron, "Take a jar and put an omer of manna in it. Then place it before the LORD to be kept for the generations to come."

[34]As the LORD commanded Moses, Aaron put the manna in front of the Testimony, that it might be kept. [35]The Israelites ate manna forty years, until they came to a land that was settled; they ate manna until they reached the border of Canaan.

[36](An omer is one tenth of an ephah.)

Water From the Rock

17 The whole Israelite community set out from the Desert of Sin, traveling from place to place as the LORD commanded. They camped at Rephidim, but there was no water for the people to drink. [2]So they quarreled with Moses and said, "Give us water to drink." Moses replied, "Why do you quarrel with me? Why do you put the LORD to the test?"

a 16 That is, probably about 2 quarts (about 2 liters); also in verses 18, 32, 33 and 36   b 22 That is, probably about 4 quarts (about 4.5 liters)   c 28 The Hebrew is plural.   d 31 Manna means What is it? (see verse 15).

³But the people were thirsty for water there, and they grumbled against Moses. They said, "Why did you bring us up out of Egypt to make us and our children and livestock die of thirst?"

⁴Then Moses cried out to the LORD, "What am I to do with these people? They are almost ready to stone me."

⁵The LORD answered Moses, "Walk on ahead of the people. Take with you some of the elders of Israel and take in your hand the staff with which you struck the Nile, and go. ⁶I will stand there before you by the rock at Horeb. Strike the rock, and water will come out of it for the people to drink." So Moses did this in the sight of the elders of Israel. ⁷And he called the place Massah ª and Meribah ᵇ because the Israelites quarreled and because they tested the LORD saying, "Is the LORD among us or not?"

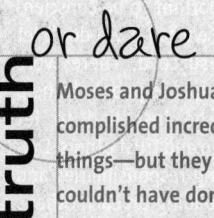

truth or dare

Moses and Joshua accomplished incredible things—but they couldn't have done it without the help of some dedicated supporters. How can you lend a helping hand to your spiritual leaders?

17:10–13

The Amalekites Defeated

⁸The Amalekites came and attacked the Israelites at Rephidim. ⁹Moses said to Joshua, "Choose some of our men and go out to fight the Amalekites. Tomorrow I will stand on top of the hill with the staff of God in my hands."

¹⁰So Joshua fought the Amalekites as Moses had ordered, and Moses, Aaron and Hur went to the top of the hill. ¹¹As long as Moses held up his hands, the Israelites were winning, but whenever he lowered his hands, the Amalekites were winning. ¹²When Moses' hands grew tired, they took a stone and put it under him and he sat on it. Aaron and Hur held his hands up—one on one side, one on the other—so that his hands remained steady till sunset. ¹³So Joshua overcame the Amalekite army with the sword.

¹⁴Then the LORD said to Moses, "Write this on a scroll as something to be remembered and make sure that Joshua hears it, because I will completely blot out the memory of Amalek from under heaven."

¹⁵Moses built an altar and called it The LORD is my Banner. ¹⁶He said, "For hands were lifted up to the throne of the LORD. The ᶜ LORD will be at war against the Amalekites from generation to generation."

Jethro Visits Moses

18 Now Jethro, the priest of Midian and father-in-law of Moses, heard of everything God had done for Moses and for his people Israel, and how the LORD had brought Israel out of Egypt.

²After Moses had sent away his wife Zipporah, his father-in-law Jethro received her ³and her two sons. One son was named Gershom, ᵈ for Moses said, "I have become an alien in a foreign land"; ⁴and the other was named Eliezer, ᵉ for he said, "My father's God was my helper; he saved me from the sword of Pharaoh."

⁵Jethro, Moses' father-in-law, together with Moses' sons and wife, came to him in the desert, where he was camped near the mountain of God. ⁶Jethro had sent word to him, "I, your father-in-law Jethro, am coming to you with your wife and her two sons."

⁷So Moses went out to meet his father-in-law and bowed down and kissed him. They greeted each other and then went into the tent. ⁸Moses told his father-in-law about everything the LORD had done to Pharaoh and the Egyptians for Israel's sake and about all the hardships they had met along the way and how the LORD had saved them.

⁹Jethro was delighted to hear about all the good things the LORD had done for Israel in rescuing them from the hand of the Egyptians. ¹⁰He said, "Praise be to the LORD, who rescued you from the hand of the Egyptians and of Pharaoh, and who rescued the people from the hand of the Egyp-

---

ª 7 Massah means testing.   ᵇ 7 Meribah means quarreling.   ᶜ 16 Or "Because a hand was against the throne of the LORD, the   ᵈ 3 Gershom sounds like the Hebrew for an alien there.   ᵉ 4 Eliezer means my God is helper.

tians. ¹¹Now I know that the Lord is greater than all other gods, for he did this to those who had treated Israel arrogantly." ¹²Then Jethro, Moses' father-in-law, brought a burnt offering and other sacrifices to God, and Aaron came with all the elders of Israel to eat bread with Moses' father-in-law in the presence of God.

¹³The next day Moses took his seat to serve as judge for the people, and they stood around him from morning till evening. ¹⁴When his father-in-law saw all that Moses was doing for the people, he said, "What is this you are doing for the people? Why do you alone sit as judge, while all these people stand around you from morning till evening?"

¹⁵Moses answered him, "Because the people come to me to seek God's will. ¹⁶Whenever they have a dispute, it is brought to me, and I decide between the parties and inform them of God's decrees and laws."

¹⁷Moses' father-in-law replied, "What you are doing is not good. ¹⁸You and these people who come to you will only wear yourselves out. The work is too heavy for you; you cannot handle it alone. ¹⁹Listen now to me and I will give you some advice, and may God be with you. You must be the people's representative before God and bring their disputes to him. ²⁰Teach them the decrees and laws, and show them the way to live and the duties they are to perform. ²¹But select capable men from all the people—men who fear God, trustworthy men who hate dishonest gain—and appoint them as officials over thousands, hundreds, fifties and tens. ²²Have them serve as judges for the people at all times, but have them bring every difficult case to you; the simple cases they can decide themselves. That will make your load lighter, because they will share it with you. ²³If you do this and God so commands, you will be able to stand the strain, and all these people will go home satisfied."

²⁴Moses listened to his father-in-law and did everything he said. ²⁵He chose capable men from all Israel and made them leaders of the people, officials over thousands, hundreds, fifties and tens. ²⁶They served as judges for the people at all times. The difficult cases they brought to Moses, but the simple ones they decided themselves.

²⁷Then Moses sent his father-in-law on his way, and Jethro returned to his own country.

At Mount Sinai

19 In the third month after the Israelites left Egypt—on the very day—they came to the Desert of Sinai. ²After they set out from Rephidim, they entered the Desert of Sinai, and Israel camped there in the desert in front of the mountain.

³Then Moses went up to God, and the Lord called to him from the mountain and said, "This is what you are to say to the house of Jacob and what you are to tell the people of Israel: ⁴'You yourselves have seen what I did to Egypt, and how I carried you on eagles' wings and brought you to myself. ⁵Now if you obey me fully and keep my covenant, then out of all nations you will be my treasured possession. Although the whole earth is mine, ⁶you ᵃ will be for me a kingdom of priests and a holy nation.' These are the words you are to speak to the Israelites."

⁷So Moses went back and summoned the elders of the people and set before them all the words the Lord had commanded him to speak. ⁸The people all responded together, "We will do everything the Lord has said." So Moses brought their answer back to the Lord.

genuine teamwork ≫ 18:13-26

Are you ever guilty of thinking that *only you* can do a particular job? When you're working on a group project for school, do you work with your team or try to do it all alone? When you're playing sports, do you pass or try to score on your own? While it's important to be conscientious leaders, we fail if we don't let anyone else succeed. There were plenty of capable people to help Moses—he just had to let things go and trust others. Delegating responsibilities and building on each other's strengths are important elements of teamwork.

ᵃ 5,6 Or *possession, for the whole earth is mine.* ⁶*You*

9The LORD said to Moses, "I am going to come to you in a dense cloud, so that the people will hear me speaking with you and will always put their trust in you." Then Moses told the LORD what the people had said.

10And the LORD said to Moses, "Go to the people and consecrate them today and tomorrow. Have them wash their clothes 11and be ready by the third day, because on that day the LORD will come down on Mount Sinai in the sight of all the people. 12Put limits for the people around the mountain and tell them, 'Be careful that you do not go up the mountain or touch the foot of it. Whoever touches the mountain shall surely be put to death. 13He shall surely be stoned or shot with arrows; not a hand is to be laid on him. Whether man or animal, he shall not be permitted to live.' Only when the ram's horn sounds a long blast may they go up to the mountain."

14After Moses had gone down the mountain to the people, he consecrated them, and they washed their clothes. 15Then he said to the people, "Prepare yourselves for the third day. Abstain from sexual relations."

16On the morning of the third day there was thunder and lightning, with a thick cloud over the mountain, and a very loud trumpet blast. Everyone in the camp trembled. 17Then Moses led the people out of the camp to meet with God, and they stood at the foot of the mountain. 18Mount Sinai was covered with smoke, because the LORD descended on it in fire. The smoke billowed up from it like smoke from a furnace, the whole mountain[a] trembled violently, 19and the sound of the trumpet grew louder and louder. Then Moses spoke and the voice of God answered him.[b]

20The LORD descended to the top of Mount Sinai and called Moses to the top of the mountain. So Moses went up 21and the LORD said to him, "Go down and warn the people so they do not force their way through to see the LORD and many of them perish. 22Even the priests, who approach the LORD, must consecrate themselves, or the LORD will break out against them."

23Moses said to the LORD, "The people cannot come up Mount Sinai, because you yourself warned us, 'Put limits around the mountain and set it apart as holy.' "

24The LORD replied, "Go down and bring Aaron up with you. But the priests and the people must not force their way through to come up to the LORD, or he will break out against them."

25So Moses went down to the people and told them.

The Ten Commandments

20 And God spoke all these words:

2"I am the LORD your God, who brought you out of Egypt, out of the land of slavery.

---

a 18 Most Hebrew manuscripts; a few Hebrew manuscripts and Septuagint all the people
b 19 Or and God answered him with thunder

---

love notes

19:5–6

Loved one,

You are my treasured possession. Out of the whole earth, which is mine, I chose you—not because of anything you've done, but out of my mercy and love.

—Father

Is your identity based on who you are as God's child, or on what you have and do?

³ "You shall have no other gods before ᵃ me.

⁴ "You shall not make for yourself an idol in the form of anything in heaven above or on the earth beneath or in the waters below. ⁵You shall not bow down to them or worship them; for I, the LORD your God, am a jealous God, punishing the children for the sin of the fathers to the third and fourth generation of those who hate me, ⁶but showing love to a thousand ⌞generations⌟ of those who love me and keep my commandments.

⁷ "You shall not misuse the name of the LORD your God, for the LORD will not hold anyone guiltless who misuses his name.

⁸ "Remember the Sabbath day by keeping it holy. ⁹Six days you shall labor and do all your work, ¹⁰but the seventh day is a Sabbath to the LORD your God. On it you shall not do any work, neither you, nor your son or daughter, nor your manservant or maidservant, nor your animals, nor the alien within your gates. ¹¹For in six days the LORD made the heavens and the earth, the sea, and all that is in them, but he rested on the seventh day. Therefore the LORD blessed the Sabbath day and made it holy.

¹² "Honor your father and your mother, so that you may live long in the land the LORD your God is giving you.

¹³ "You shall not murder.

¹⁴ "You shall not commit adultery.

¹⁵ "You shall not steal.

¹⁶ "You shall not give false testimony against your neighbor.

¹⁷ "You shall not covet your neighbor's house. You shall not covet your neighbor's wife, or his manservant or maidservant, his ox or donkey, or anything that belongs to your neighbor."

¹⁸When the people saw the thunder and lightning and heard the trumpet and saw the mountain in smoke, they trembled with fear. They stayed at a distance ¹⁹and said to Moses, "Speak to us yourself and we will listen. But do not have God speak to us or we will die."

²⁰Moses said to the people, "Do not be afraid. God has come to test you, so that the fear of God will be with you to keep you from sinning."

²¹The people remained at a distance, while Moses approached the thick darkness where God was.

Idols and Altars

²²Then the LORD said to Moses, "Tell the Israelites this: 'You have seen for yourselves that I have spoken to you from heaven: ²³Do not make any gods to be alongside me; do not make for yourselves gods of silver or gods of gold.

²⁴" 'Make an altar of earth for me and sacrifice on it your burnt offerings and fellowship offer-

truth or dare

The law isn't just a long list of do's and don'ts. God gave *useful* instructions that protected the Israelites and made their lives better. Want to improve your life? Follow God's laws.

20:1–17

genuine

honor » 20:12

News Flash: In case you don't already know this, your parents aren't perfect. And they'd probably be the first to admit it. Yet the Bible tells you to honor them. If you think about it honestly, are you obeying this command (one of the Big Ten, by the way)? Do you treat your parents with respect—regardless of how you feel? Do you obey their rules—even when you disagree with them? Your parents may not be perfect, but God already knows that. And just as he promises, you'll find that obedience brings great rewards.

ᵃ 3 Or *besides*

ings,ᵃ your sheep and goats and your cattle. Wherever I cause my name to be honored, I will come to you and bless you. ²⁵If you make an altar of stones for me, do not build it with dressed stones, for you will defile it if you use a tool on it. ²⁶And do not go up to my altar on steps, lest your nakedness be exposed on it.'

21

"These are the laws you are to set before them:

Hebrew Servants

²"If you buy a Hebrew servant, he is to serve you for six years. But in the seventh year, he shall go free, without paying anything. ³If he comes alone, he is to go free alone; but if he has a wife when he comes, she is to go with him. ⁴If his master gives him a wife and she bears him sons or daughters, the woman and her children shall belong to her master, and only the man shall go free.

⁵"But if the servant declares, 'I love my master and my wife and children and do not want to go free,' ⁶then his master must take him before the judges.ᵇ He shall take him to the door or the doorpost and pierce his ear with an awl. Then he will be his servant for life.

⁷"If a man sells his daughter as a servant, she is not to go free as menservants do. ⁸If she does not please the master who has selected her for himself,ᶜ he must let her be redeemed. He has no right to sell her to foreigners, because he has broken faith with her. ⁹If he selects her for his son, he must grant her the rights of a daughter. ¹⁰If he marries another woman, he must not deprive the first one of her food, clothing and marital rights. ¹¹If he does not provide her with these three things, she is to go free, without any payment of money.

Personal Injuries

¹²"Anyone who strikes a man and kills him shall surely be put to death. ¹³However, if he does not do it intentionally, but God lets it happen, he is to flee to a place I will designate. ¹⁴But if a man schemes and kills another man deliberately, take him away from my altar and put him to death.

¹⁵"Anyone who attacksᵈ his father or his mother must be put to death.

¹⁶"Anyone who kidnaps another and either sells him or still has him when he is caught must be put to death.

¹⁷"Anyone who curses his father or mother must be put to death.

¹⁸"If men quarrel and one hits the other with a stone or with his fistᵉ and he does not die but is confined to bed, ¹⁹the one who struck the blow will not be held responsible if the other gets up and walks around outside with his staff; however, he must pay the injured man for the loss of his time and see that he is completely healed.

²⁰"If a man beats his male or female slave with a rod and the slave dies as a direct result, he must be punished, ²¹but he is not to be punished if the slave gets up after a day or two, since the slave is his property.

²²"If men who are fighting hit a pregnant woman and she gives birth prematurelyᶠ but there is no serious injury, the offender must be fined whatever the woman's husband demands and the court allows. ²³But if there is serious injury, you are to take life for life, ²⁴eye for eye, tooth for tooth, hand for hand, foot for foot, ²⁵burn for burn, wound for wound, bruise for bruise.

²⁶"If a man hits a manservant or maidservant in the eye and destroys it, he must let the servant go free to compensate for the eye. ²⁷And if he knocks out the tooth of a manservant or maidservant, he must let the servant go free to compensate for the tooth.

²⁸"If a bull gores a man or a woman to death, the bull must be stoned to death, and its meat must not be eaten. But the owner of the bull will not be held responsible. ²⁹If, however, the bull has had

truth or dare

What if you got a year in prison for littering, but just a scolding for murder? Hello?! The punishment should fit the crime. When you're in a position to judge, strive to be fair.

21:23–25

ᵃ 24 Traditionally *peace offerings*   ᵇ 6 Or *before God*   ᶜ 8 Or *master so that he does not choose her*   ᵈ 15 Or *kills*
ᵉ 18 Or *with a tool*   ᶠ 22 Or *she has a miscarriage*

the habit of goring and the owner has been warned but has not kept it penned up and it kills a man or woman, the bull must be stoned and the owner also must be put to death. ³⁰However, if payment is demanded of him, he may redeem his life by paying whatever is demanded. ³¹This law also applies if the bull gores a son or daughter. ³²If the bull gores a male or female slave, the owner must pay thirty shekels*ᵃ* of silver to the master of the slave, and the bull must be stoned.

³³"If a man uncovers a pit or digs one and fails to cover it and an ox or a donkey falls into it, ³⁴the owner of the pit must pay for the loss; he must pay its owner, and the dead animal will be his.

³⁵"If a man's bull injures the bull of another and it dies, they are to sell the live one and divide both the money and the dead animal equally. ³⁶However, if it was known that the bull had the habit of goring, yet the owner did not keep it penned up, the owner must pay, animal for animal, and the dead animal will be his.

Protection of Property

22 "If a man steals an ox or a sheep and slaughters it or sells it, he must pay back five head of cattle for the ox and four sheep for the sheep.

²"If a thief is caught breaking in and is struck so that he dies, the defender is not guilty of bloodshed; ³but if it happens*ᵇ* after sunrise, he is guilty of bloodshed.

"A thief must certainly make restitution, but if he has nothing, he must be sold to pay for his theft.

⁴"If the stolen animal is found alive in his possession—whether ox or donkey or sheep—he must pay back double.

⁵"If a man grazes his livestock in a field or vineyard and lets them stray and they graze in another man's field, he must make restitution from the best of his own field or vineyard.

⁶"If a fire breaks out and spreads into thornbushes so that it burns shocks of grain or standing grain or the whole field, the one who started the fire must make restitution.

⁷"If a man gives his neighbor silver or goods for safekeeping and they are stolen from the neighbor's house, the thief, if he is caught, must pay back double. ⁸But if the thief is not found, the owner of the house must appear before the judges*ᶜ* to determine whether he has laid his hands on the other man's property. ⁹In all cases of illegal possession of an ox, a donkey, a sheep, a garment, or any other lost property about which somebody says, 'This is mine,' both parties are to bring their cases before the judges. The one whom the judges declare*ᵈ* guilty must pay back double to his neighbor.

¹⁰"If a man gives a donkey, an ox, a sheep or any other animal to his neighbor for safekeeping and it dies or is injured or is taken away while no one is looking, ¹¹the issue between them will be settled by the taking of an oath before the Lᴏʀᴅ that the neighbor did not lay hands on the other person's property. The owner is to accept this, and no restitution is required. ¹²But if the animal was stolen from the neighbor, he must make restitution to the owner. ¹³If it was torn to pieces by a wild animal, he shall bring in the remains as evidence and he will not be required to pay for the torn animal.

¹⁴"If a man borrows an animal from his neighbor and it is injured or dies while the owner is not present, he must make restitution. ¹⁵But if the owner is with the animal, the borrower will not have to pay. If the animal was hired, the money paid for the hire covers the loss.

Social Responsibility

¹⁶"If a man seduces a virgin who is not pledged to be married and sleeps with her, he must pay the bride-price, and she shall be his wife. ¹⁷If her father absolutely refuses to give her to him, he must still pay the bride-price for virgins.

¹⁸"Do not allow a sorceress to live.

¹⁹"Anyone who has sexual relations with an animal must be put to death.

²⁰"Whoever sacrifices to any god other than the Lᴏʀᴅ must be destroyed.*ᵉ*

²¹"Do not mistreat an alien or oppress him, for you were aliens in Egypt.

ᵃ 32 That is, about 12 ounces (about 0.3 kilogram)   *ᵇ 3* Or *if he strikes him*   *ᶜ 8* Or *before God*; also in verse 9   *ᵈ 9* Or *whom God declares*   *ᵉ 20* The Hebrew term refers to the irrevocable giving over of things or persons to the Lᴏʀᴅ, often by totally destroying them.

²²"Do not take advantage of a widow or an orphan. ²³If you do and they cry out to me, I will certainly hear their cry. ²⁴My anger will be aroused, and I will kill you with the sword; your wives will become widows and your children fatherless.

²⁵"If you lend money to one of my people among you who is needy, do not be like a moneylender; charge him no interest. ^a ²⁶If you take your neighbor's cloak as a pledge, return it to him by sunset, ²⁷because his cloak is the only covering he has for his body. What else will he sleep in? When he cries out to me, I will hear, for I am compassionate.

²⁸"Do not blaspheme God ^b or curse the ruler of your people.

²⁹"Do not hold back offerings from your granaries or your vats. ^c

"You must give me the firstborn of your sons. ³⁰Do the same with your cattle and your sheep. Let them stay with their mothers for seven days, but give them to me on the eighth day.

³¹"You are to be my holy people. So do not eat the meat of an animal torn by wild beasts; throw it to the dogs.

Laws of Justice and Mercy

23 "Do not spread false reports. Do not help a wicked man by being a malicious witness. ²"Do not follow the crowd in doing wrong. When you give testimony in a lawsuit, do not pervert justice by siding with the crowd, ³and do not show favoritism to a poor man in his lawsuit.

⁴"If you come across your enemy's ox or donkey wandering off, be sure to take it back to him. ⁵If you see the donkey of someone who hates you fallen down under its load, do not leave it there; be sure you help him with it.

⁶"Do not deny justice to your poor people in their lawsuits. ⁷Have nothing to do with a false charge and do not put an innocent or honest person to death, for I will not acquit the guilty.

⁸"Do not accept a bribe, for a bribe blinds those who see and twists the words of the righteous.

⁹"Do not oppress an alien; you yourselves know how it feels to be aliens, because you were aliens in Egypt.

Sabbath Laws

¹⁰"For six years you are to sow your fields and harvest the crops, ¹¹but during the seventh year let the land lie unplowed and unused. Then the poor among your people may get food from it, and the wild animals may eat what they leave. Do the same with your vineyard and your olive grove.

¹²"Six days do your work, but on the seventh day do not work, so that your ox and your donkey may rest and the slave born in your household, and the alien as well, may be refreshed.

^a 25 Or *excessive interest*   ^b 28 Or *Do not revile the judges*   ^c 29 The meaning of the Hebrew for this phrase is uncertain.

[13]"Be careful to do everything I have said to you. Do not invoke the names of other gods; do not let them be heard on your lips.

The Three Annual Festivals

[14]"Three times a year you are to celebrate a festival to me.

[15]"Celebrate the Feast of Unleavened Bread; for seven days eat bread made without yeast, as I commanded you. Do this at the appointed time in the month of Abib, for in that month you came out of Egypt.

"No one is to appear before me empty-handed.

[16]"Celebrate the Feast of Harvest with the firstfruits of the crops you sow in your field.

"Celebrate the Feast of Ingathering at the end of the year, when you gather in your crops from the field.

[17]"Three times a year all the men are to appear before the Sovereign LORD.

[18]"Do not offer the blood of a sacrifice to me along with anything containing yeast.

"The fat of my festival offerings must not be kept until morning.

[19]"Bring the best of the firstfruits of your soil to the house of the LORD your God.

"Do not cook a young goat in its mother's milk.

God's Angel to Prepare the Way

[20]"See, I am sending an angel ahead of you to guard you along the way and to bring you to the place I have prepared. [21]Pay attention to him and listen to what he says. Do not rebel against him; he will not forgive your rebellion, since my Name is in him. [22]If you listen carefully to what he says and do all that I say, I will be an enemy to your enemies and will oppose those who oppose you. [23]My angel will go ahead of you and bring you into the land of the Amorites, Hittites, Perizzites, Canaanites, Hivites and Jebusites, and I will wipe them out. [24]Do not bow down before their gods or worship them or follow their practices. You must demolish them and break their sacred stones to pieces. [25]Worship the LORD your God, and his blessing will be on your food and water. I will take away sickness from among you, [26]and none will miscarry or be barren in your land. I will give you a full life span.

[27]"I will send my terror ahead of you and throw into confusion every nation you encounter. I will make all your enemies turn their backs and run. [28]I will send the hornet ahead of you to drive the Hivites, Canaanites and Hittites out of your way. [29]But I will not drive them out in a single year, because the land would become desolate and the wild animals too numerous for you. [30]Little by little I will drive them out before you, until you have increased enough to take possession of the land.

[31]"I will establish your borders from the Red Sea[a] to the Sea of the Philistines,[b] and from the desert to the River.[c] I will hand over to you the people who live in the land and you will drive them out before you. [32]Do not make a covenant with them or with their gods. [33]Do not let them live in your land, or they will cause you to sin against me, because the worship of their gods will certainly be a snare to you."

genuine

integrity » 23:24-25

These words may seem a bit strange to you. You may think, *Bow down to sacred stones? There's one thing I don't have to worry about!* But God gave this warning because he knows how easily we're enticed by something new, something a bit more exciting, even something forbidden. So he warned us not to compromise but to stand true to our faith and worship him alone. You may not be enticed by sacred stones, but you may be tempted by something else—materialism, popularity, pride. While others around us bow to those gods, we're called to worship God alone.

a 31 Hebrew *Yam Suph*; that is, Sea of Reeds   *b 31* That is, the Mediterranean   *c 31* That is, the Euphrates

The Covenant Confirmed

24 Then he said to Moses, "Come up to the Lord, you and Aaron, Nadab and Abihu, and seventy of the elders of Israel. You are to worship at a distance, [2]but Moses alone is to approach the Lord; the others must not come near. And the people may not come up with him."

[3]When Moses went and told the people all the Lord's words and laws, they responded with one voice, "Everything the Lord has said we will do." [4]Moses then wrote down everything the Lord had said.

He got up early the next morning and built an altar at the foot of the mountain and set up twelve stone pillars representing the twelve tribes of Israel. [5]Then he sent young Israelite men, and they offered burnt offerings and sacrificed young bulls as fellowship offerings[a] to the Lord. [6]Moses took half of the blood and put it in bowls, and the other half he sprinkled on the altar. [7]Then he took the Book of the Covenant and read it to the people. They responded, "We will do everything the Lord has said; we will obey."

[8]Moses then took the blood, sprinkled it on the people and said, "This is the blood of the covenant that the Lord has made with you in accordance with all these words."

[9]Moses and Aaron, Nadab and Abihu, and the seventy elders of Israel went up [10]and saw the God of Israel. Under his feet was something like a pavement made of sapphire,[b] clear as the sky itself. [11]But God did not raise his hand against these leaders of the Israelites; they saw God, and they ate and drank.

[12]The Lord said to Moses, "Come up to me on the mountain and stay here, and I will give you the tablets of stone, with the law and commands I have written for their instruction."

[13]Then Moses set out with Joshua his aide, and Moses went up on the mountain of God. [14]He said to the elders, "Wait here for us until we come back to you. Aaron and Hur are with you, and anyone involved in a dispute can go to them."

[15]When Moses went up on the mountain, the cloud covered it, [16]and the glory of the Lord settled on Mount Sinai. For six days the cloud covered the mountain, and on the seventh day the Lord called to Moses from within the cloud. [17]To the Israelites the glory of the Lord looked like a consuming fire on top of the mountain. [18]Then Moses entered the cloud as he went on up the mountain. And he stayed on the mountain forty days and forty nights.

Offerings for the Tabernacle

25 The Lord said to Moses, [2]"Tell the Israelites to bring me an offering. You are to receive the offering for me from each man whose heart prompts him to give. [3]These are the offerings you are to receive from them: gold, silver and bronze; [4]blue, purple and scarlet yarn and fine linen; goat hair; [5]ram skins dyed red and hides of sea cows[c]; acacia wood; [6]olive oil for the light; spices for the anointing oil and for the fragrant incense; [7]and onyx stones and other gems to be mounted on the ephod and breastpiece.

[8]"Then have them make a sanctuary for me, and I will dwell among them. [9]Make this tabernacle and all its furnishings exactly like the pattern I will show you.

The Ark

[10]"Have them make a chest of acacia wood—two and a half cubits long, a cubit and a half wide, and a cubit and a half high.[d] [11]Overlay it with pure gold, both inside and out, and make a gold molding around it. [12]Cast four gold rings for it and fasten them to its four feet, with two rings on one side and two rings on the other. [13]Then make poles of acacia wood and overlay them with gold. [14]Insert the poles into the rings on the sides of the chest to carry it. [15]The poles are to remain in the rings of this ark; they are not to be removed. [16]Then put in the ark the Testimony, which I will give you.

[17]"Make an atonement cover[e] of pure gold—two and a half cubits long and a cubit and a half wide.[f] [18]And make two cherubim out of hammered gold at the ends of the cover. [19]Make one cherub on one end and the second cherub on the other; make the cherubim of one piece with the cover, at the two ends. [20]The cherubim are to have their wings spread upward, overshadowing the

---

[a] 5 Traditionally *peace offerings*   [b] 10 Or *lapis lazuli*   [c] 5 That is, dugongs   [d] 10 That is, about 3 3/4 feet (about 1.1 meters) long and 2 1/4 feet (about 0.7 meter) wide and high   [e] 17 Traditionally *a mercy seat*   [f] 17 That is, about 3 3/4 feet (about 1.1 meters) long and 2 1/4 feet (about 0.7 meter) wide

Is Silence a Sin?

Profile: **Jess**

I saw everything because my locker was near his.

It started with typical teenage taunts sometime last year. I don't know when exactly. At first it was the usual bumping in the halls with a heavy backpack, then they slammed him into the lockers. He never showed any emotion or responded in any way. It was weird.

After a few months, it became more vicious. They would get in his face and say, "Big ears, wazzup?" or, "Hey, Mr. Spock!" When they did that, I felt like someone had just punched me in the stomach, but I didn't say anything. Every time I saw them coming, I dreaded what was next.

The guys that were after him were some of the hottest baseball players—very popular in school. I mean, I've talked to these guys at lunch, and they've always been nice to me. In fact, a while ago, before they started to bother him, I had a crush on one of them.

The boy's ears *were* big. They stuck way out. Sometimes I used to try to smile at him, but it was hard because he always kept his head down, and he never talked. He was a transfer student. As far as I know, he never had any friends.

The last time I saw him, they had him pinned to his locker, and they were twisting his ears as hard as they could. He just stared at them. When they were done, they dropped him in a heap on the ground.

Last week, I heard he was admitted to The Oaks because he tried to kill himself.

I've been praying every day about not speaking up. Could it have made a difference if I had tried harder to speak to him or if I had told someone about it?

Read more about bullying online at www.TrueImagesBible.com

bullying in focus

Sometimes it's hard to know when to get involved in a situation when someone else is being bullied or harassed. The natural inclination is to stay out of others' conflicts. Yet, when a situation is so hurtful to watch that it gives you a knot in your stomach, you may need to act.

» Pray for courage and wisdom regarding whether to speak up and get involved. Consider enlisting the help of an adult if you're afraid for your own safety.

» Try to reach out to the person being bullied, even with a smile or a few kind words.

» Read Psalm 9:9 (page 662) and Isaiah 58:6–10 (page 977) for insight into what God thinks of bullying and how bystanders should respond.

For more on this topic, see the index on page 1656.

cover with them. The cherubim are to face each other, looking toward the cover. ²¹Place the cover on top of the ark and put in the ark the Testimony, which I will give you. ²²There, above the cover between the two cherubim that are over the ark of the Testimony, I will meet with you and give you all my commands for the Israelites.

The Table

²³"Make a table of acacia wood—two cubits long, a cubit wide and a cubit and a half high.^a ²⁴Overlay it with pure gold and make a gold molding around it. ²⁵Also make around it a rim a handbreadth^b wide and put a gold molding on the rim. ²⁶Make four gold rings for the table and fasten them to the four corners, where the four legs are. ²⁷The rings are to be close to the rim to hold the poles used in carrying the table. ²⁸Make the poles of acacia wood, overlay them with gold and carry the table with them. ²⁹And make its plates and dishes of pure gold, as well as its pitchers and bowls for the pouring out of offerings. ³⁰Put the bread of the Presence on this table to be before me at all times.

The Lampstand

³¹"Make a lampstand of pure gold and hammer it out, base and shaft; its flowerlike cups, buds and blossoms shall be of one piece with it. ³²Six branches are to extend from the sides of the lampstand—three on one side and three on the other. ³³Three cups shaped like almond flowers with buds and blossoms are to be on one branch, three on the next branch, and the same for all six branches extending from the lampstand. ³⁴And on the lampstand there are to be four cups shaped like almond flowers with buds and blossoms. ³⁵One bud shall be under the first pair of branches extending from the lampstand, a second bud under the second pair, and a third bud under the third pair—six branches in all. ³⁶The buds and branches shall all be of one piece with the lampstand, hammered out of pure gold.

³⁷"Then make its seven lamps and set them up on it so that they light the space in front of it. ³⁸Its wick trimmers and trays are to be of pure gold. ³⁹A talent^c of pure gold is to be used for the lampstand and all these accessories. ⁴⁰See that you make them according to the pattern shown you on the mountain.

The Tabernacle

26 "Make the tabernacle with ten curtains of finely twisted linen and blue, purple and scarlet yarn, with cherubim worked into them by a skilled craftsman. ²All the curtains are to be the same size—twenty-eight cubits long and four cubits wide. ^d ³Join five of the curtains together, and do the same with the other five. ⁴Make loops of blue material along the edge of the end curtain in one set, and do the same with the end curtain in the other set. ⁵Make fifty loops on one curtain and fifty loops on the end curtain of the other set, with the loops opposite each other. ⁶Then make fifty gold clasps and use them to fasten the curtains together so that the tabernacle is a unit.

⁷"Make curtains of goat hair for the tent over the tabernacle—eleven altogether. ⁸All eleven curtains are to be the same size—thirty cubits long and four cubits wide. ^e ⁹Join five of the curtains together into one set and the other six into another set. Fold the sixth curtain double at the front of the tent. ¹⁰Make fifty loops along the edge of the end curtain in one set and also along the edge of the end curtain in the other set. ¹¹Then make fifty bronze clasps and put them in the loops to fasten the tent together as a unit. ¹²As for the additional length of the tent curtains, the half curtain that is left over is to hang down at the rear of the tabernacle. ¹³The tent curtains will be a cubit^f longer on both sides; what is left will hang over the sides of the tabernacle so as to cover it. ¹⁴Make for the tent a covering of ram skins dyed red, and over that a covering of hides of sea cows. ^g

¹⁵"Make upright frames of acacia wood for the tabernacle. ¹⁶Each frame is to be ten cubits long and a cubit and a half wide, ^h ¹⁷with two projections set parallel to each other. Make all the frames of the tabernacle in this way. ¹⁸Make twenty frames for the south side of the tabernacle ¹⁹and make forty silver bases to go under them—two bases for each frame, one under each projection. ²⁰For the other side, the north side of the tabernacle, make twenty frames ²¹and forty silver bases—two under each frame. ²²Make six frames for the far end, that is, the west end of the tabernacle, ²³and make two frames for the corners at the far end. ²⁴At these two corners they must be double from

---

^a 23 That is, about 3 feet (about 0.9 meter) long and 1 1/2 feet (about 0.5 meter) wide and 2 1/4 feet (about 0.7 meter) high   ^b 25 That is, about 3 inches (about 8 centimeters)   ^c 39 That is, about 75 pounds (about 34 kilograms)   ^d 2 That is, about 42 feet (about 12.5 meters) long and 6 feet (about 1.8 meters) wide   ^e 8 That is, about 45 feet (about 13.5 meters) long and 6 feet (about 1.8 meters) wide   ^f 13 That is, about 1 1/2 feet (about 0.5 meter)   ^g 14 That is, dugongs   ^h 16 That is, about 15 feet (about 4.5 meters) long and 2 1/4 feet (about 0.7 meter) wide

the bottom all the way to the top, and fitted into a single ring; both shall be like that. ²⁵So there will be eight frames and sixteen silver bases—two under each frame.

²⁶"Also make crossbars of acacia wood: five for the frames on one side of the tabernacle, ²⁷five for those on the other side, and five for the frames on the west, at the far end of the tabernacle. ²⁸The center crossbar is to extend from end to end at the middle of the frames. ²⁹Overlay the frames with gold and make gold rings to hold the crossbars. Also overlay the crossbars with gold.

³⁰"Set up the tabernacle according to the plan shown you on the mountain.

³¹"Make a curtain of blue, purple and scarlet yarn and finely twisted linen, with cherubim worked into it by a skilled craftsman. ³²Hang it with gold hooks on four posts of acacia wood overlaid with gold and standing on four silver bases. ³³Hang the curtain from the clasps and place the ark of the Testimony behind the curtain. The curtain will separate the Holy Place from the Most Holy Place. ³⁴Put the atonement cover on the ark of the Testimony in the Most Holy Place. ³⁵Place the table outside the curtain on the north side of the tabernacle and put the lampstand opposite it on the south side.

³⁶"For the entrance to the tent make a curtain of blue, purple and scarlet yarn and finely twisted linen—the work of an embroiderer. ³⁷Make gold hooks for this curtain and five posts of acacia wood overlaid with gold. And cast five bronze bases for them.

The Altar of Burnt Offering

27 "Build an altar of acacia wood, three cubits*ᵃ* high; it is to be square, five cubits long and five cubits wide.*ᵇ* ²Make a horn at each of the four corners, so that the horns and the altar are of one piece, and overlay the altar with bronze. ³Make all its utensils of bronze—its pots to remove the ashes, and its shovels, sprinkling bowls, meat forks and firepans. ⁴Make a grating for it, a bronze network, and make a bronze ring at each of the four corners of the network. ⁵Put it under the ledge of the altar so that it is halfway up the altar. ⁶Make poles of acacia wood for the altar and overlay them with bronze. ⁷The poles are to be inserted into the rings so they will be on two sides of the altar when it is carried. ⁸Make the altar hollow, out of boards. It is to be made just as you were shown on the mountain.

The Courtyard

⁹"Make a courtyard for the tabernacle. The south side shall be a hundred cubits*ᶜ* long and is to have curtains of finely twisted linen, ¹⁰with twenty posts and twenty bronze bases and with silver hooks and bands on the posts. ¹¹The north side shall also be a hundred cubits long and is to have curtains, with twenty posts and twenty bronze bases and with silver hooks and bands on the posts.

¹²"The west end of the courtyard shall be fifty cubits*ᵈ* wide and have curtains, with ten posts and ten bases. ¹³On the east end, toward the sunrise, the courtyard shall also be fifty cubits wide. ¹⁴Curtains fifteen cubits*ᵉ* long are to be on one side of the entrance, with three posts and three bases, ¹⁵and curtains fifteen cubits long are to be on the other side, with three posts and three bases.

¹⁶"For the entrance to the courtyard, provide a curtain twenty cubits*ᶠ* long, of blue, purple and scarlet yarn and finely twisted linen—the work of an embroiderer—with four posts and four bases. ¹⁷All the posts around the courtyard are to have silver bands and hooks, and bronze bases. ¹⁸The courtyard shall be a hundred cubits long and fifty cubits wide,*ᵍ* with curtains of finely twisted linen five cubits*ʰ* high, and with bronze bases. ¹⁹All the other articles used in the service of the tabernacle, whatever their function, including all the tent pegs for it and those for the courtyard, are to be of bronze.

Oil for the Lampstand

²⁰"Command the Israelites to bring you clear oil of pressed olives for the light so that the lamps may be kept burning. ²¹In the Tent of Meeting, outside the curtain that is in front of the Testimony, Aaron and his sons are to keep the lamps burning before the Lᴏʀᴅ from evening till morning. This is to be a lasting ordinance among the Israelites for the generations to come.

ᵃ 1 That is, about 4 1/2 feet (about 1.3 meters)   *ᵇ 1* That is, about 7 1/2 feet (about 2.3 meters) long and wide
ᶜ 9 That is, about 150 feet (about 46 meters); also in verse 11   *ᵈ 12* That is, about 75 feet (about 23 meters); also in verse 13   *ᵉ 14* That is, about 22 1/2 feet (about 6.9 meters); also in verse 15   *ᶠ 16* That is, about 30 feet (about 9 meters)   *ᵍ 18* That is, about 150 feet (about 46 meters) long and 75 feet (about 23 meters) wide   *ʰ 18* That is, about 7 1/2 feet (about 2.3 meters)

Pressure or Practicality?

focus Profile: **Soolin**

Last night my friend Lee asked me to help him on today's chemistry test. It was kind of an awkward question. I've never given or received answers on a test before, and I don't think he has either. I guess he's under a lot of pressure right now. His grandmother is in the intensive care unit, and they think she's dying. Lee has no time to study. He's at the top of our class, and he's worried about wrecking his GPA.

Lots of kids share information about quizzes and tests. It's such a pain to be in the earlier section of a hard class. You would think the teachers would figure out why the sixth period classes always do better than the second period classes.

I don't know what to do. If I don't help him, he'll totally resent it. I know it's not right to cheat, but this is an extreme situation. Lee's smart—there's no doubt he could ace the test if he didn't have this family situation.

I feel like I'm being so inflexible if I refuse to bend the rules this once. I don't know what to do, and I only have one more period to figure it out!

For more on cheating, check out www.TrueImagesBible.com

cheating in focus

Cheating may be at an all-time high in American high schools and colleges. Unfortunately, many students consider it "no big deal," just another survival skill to keep up in school. In addition to cheating, many students also lie to cover up their actions if they get caught. Many more get away with it and never get caught.

In a world where cheating is becoming the norm, what's a Christian girl to do?

» Take a firm stand. If you choose not to cheat and not to help others cheat, you're making a bold statement about your faith. Actions speak louder than words (see Matthew 5:16, page 1295; 1 Peter 2:12, page 1609).

» Read more in Proverbs 11:18 (page 818); Proverbs 20:17 (page 833) and Acts 5:1–10 (page 1450), and form your own opinion on cheating.

For more on this topic, see the index on page 1656.

The Priestly Garments

28 "Have Aaron your brother brought to you from among the Israelites, along with his sons Nadab and Abihu, Eleazar and Ithamar, so they may serve me as priests. [2]Make sacred garments for your brother Aaron, to give him dignity and honor. [3]Tell all the skilled men to whom I have given wisdom in such matters that they are to make garments for Aaron, for his consecration, so he may serve me as priest. [4]These are the garments they are to make: a breastpiece, an ephod, a robe, a woven tunic, a turban and a sash. They are to make these sacred garments for your brother Aaron and his sons, so they may serve me as priests. [5]Have them use gold, and blue, purple and scarlet yarn, and fine linen.

The Ephod

[6]"Make the ephod of gold, and of blue, purple and scarlet yarn, and of finely twisted linen—

the work of a skilled craftsman. ⁷It is to have two shoulder pieces attached to two of its corners, so it can be fastened. ⁸Its skillfully woven waistband is to be like it—of one piece with the ephod and made with gold, and with blue, purple and scarlet yarn, and with finely twisted linen.

⁹"Take two onyx stones and engrave on them the names of the sons of Israel ¹⁰in the order of their birth—six names on one stone and the remaining six on the other. ¹¹Engrave the names of the sons of Israel on the two stones the way a gem cutter engraves a seal. Then mount the stones in gold filigree settings ¹²and fasten them on the shoulder pieces of the ephod as memorial stones for the sons of Israel. Aaron is to bear the names on his shoulders as a memorial before the Lord. ¹³Make gold filigree settings ¹⁴and two braided chains of pure gold, like a rope, and attach the chains to the settings.

The Breastpiece

¹⁵"Fashion a breastpiece for making decisions—the work of a skilled craftsman. Make it like the ephod: of gold, and of blue, purple and scarlet yarn, and of finely twisted linen. ¹⁶It is to be square—a span*ᵃ* long and a span wide—and folded double. ¹⁷Then mount four rows of precious stones on it. In the first row there shall be a ruby, a topaz and a beryl; ¹⁸in the second row a turquoise, a sapphire*ᵇ* and an emerald; ¹⁹in the third row a jacinth, an agate and an amethyst; ²⁰in the fourth row a chrysolite, an onyx and a jasper.*ᶜ* Mount them in gold filigree settings. ²¹There are to be twelve stones, one for each of the names of the sons of Israel, each engraved like a seal with the name of one of the twelve tribes.

²²"For the breastpiece make braided chains of pure gold, like a rope. ²³Make two gold rings for it and fasten them to two corners of the breastpiece. ²⁴Fasten the two gold chains to the rings at the corners of the breastpiece, ²⁵and the other ends of the chains to the two settings, attaching them to the shoulder pieces of the ephod at the front. ²⁶Make two gold rings and attach them to the other two corners of the breastpiece on the inside edge next to the ephod. ²⁷Make two more gold rings and attach them to the bottom of the shoulder pieces on the front of the ephod, close to the seam just above the waistband of the ephod. ²⁸The rings of the breastpiece are to be tied to the rings of the ephod with blue cord, connecting it to the waistband, so that the breastpiece will not swing out from the ephod.

²⁹"Whenever Aaron enters the Holy Place, he will bear the names of the sons of Israel over his heart on the breastpiece of decision as a continuing memorial before the Lord. ³⁰Also put the Urim and the Thummim in the breastpiece, so they may be over Aaron's heart whenever he enters the presence of the Lord. Thus Aaron will always bear the means of making decisions for the Israelites over his heart before the Lord.

Other Priestly Garments

³¹"Make the robe of the ephod entirely of blue cloth, ³²with an opening for the head in its center. There shall be a woven edge like a collar*ᵈ* around this opening, so that it will not tear. ³³Make pomegranates of blue, purple and scarlet yarn around the hem of the robe, with gold bells between them. ³⁴The gold bells and the pomegranates are to alternate around the hem of the robe. ³⁵Aaron must wear it when he ministers. The sound of the bells will be heard when he enters the Holy Place before the Lord and when he comes out, so that he will not die.

³⁶"Make a plate of pure gold and engrave on it as on a seal: holy to the Lord. ³⁷Fasten a blue cord to it to attach it to the turban; it is to be on the front of the turban. ³⁸It will be on Aaron's forehead, and he will bear the guilt involved in the sacred gifts the Israelites consecrate, whatever their gifts may be. It will be on Aaron's forehead continually so that they will be acceptable to the Lord.

³⁹"Weave the tunic of fine linen and make the turban of fine linen. The sash is to be the work of an embroiderer. ⁴⁰Make tunics, sashes and headbands for Aaron's sons, to give them dignity and honor. ⁴¹After you put these clothes on your brother Aaron and his sons, anoint and ordain them. Consecrate them so they may serve me as priests.

⁴²"Make linen undergarments as a covering for the body, reaching from the waist to the thigh. ⁴³Aaron and his sons must wear them whenever they enter the Tent of Meeting or approach the altar to minister in the Holy Place, so that they will not incur guilt and die.

"This is to be a lasting ordinance for Aaron and his descendants.

a 16 That is, about 9 inches (about 22 centimeters)   *b 18* Or *lapis lazuli*   *c 20* The precise identification of some of these precious stones is uncertain.   *d 32* The meaning of the Hebrew for this word is uncertain.

Consecration of the Priests

29 "This is what you are to do to consecrate them, so they may serve me as priests: Take a young bull and two rams without defect. ²And from fine wheat flour, without yeast, make bread, and cakes mixed with oil, and wafers spread with oil. ³Put them in a basket and present them in it—along with the bull and the two rams. ⁴Then bring Aaron and his sons to the entrance to the Tent of Meeting and wash them with water. ⁵Take the garments and dress Aaron with the tunic, the robe of the ephod, the ephod itself and the breastpiece. Fasten the ephod on him by its skillfully woven waistband. ⁶Put the turban on his head and attach the sacred diadem to the turban. ⁷Take the anointing oil and anoint him by pouring it on his head. ⁸Bring his sons and dress them in tunics ⁹and put headbands on them. Then tie sashes on Aaron and his sons. *a* The priesthood is theirs by a lasting ordinance. In this way you shall ordain Aaron and his sons.

¹⁰"Bring the bull to the front of the Tent of Meeting, and Aaron and his sons shall lay their hands on its head. ¹¹Slaughter it in the Lord's presence at the entrance to the Tent of Meeting. ¹²Take some of the bull's blood and put it on the horns of the altar with your finger, and pour out the rest of it at the base of the altar. ¹³Then take all the fat around the inner parts, the covering of the liver, and both kidneys with the fat on them, and burn them on the altar. ¹⁴But burn the bull's flesh and its hide and its offal outside the camp. It is a sin offering.

¹⁵"Take one of the rams, and Aaron and his sons shall lay their hands on its head. ¹⁶Slaughter it and take the blood and sprinkle it against the altar on all sides. ¹⁷Cut the ram into pieces and wash the inner parts and the legs, putting them with the head and the other pieces. ¹⁸Then burn the entire ram on the altar. It is a burnt offering to the Lord, a pleasing aroma, an offering made to the Lord by fire.

¹⁹"Take the other ram, and Aaron and his sons shall lay their hands on its head. ²⁰Slaughter it, take some of its blood and put it on the lobes of the right ears of Aaron and his sons, on the thumbs of their right hands, and on the big toes of their right feet. Then sprinkle blood against the altar on all sides. ²¹And take some of the blood on the altar and some of the anointing oil and sprinkle it on Aaron and his garments and on his sons and their garments. Then he and his sons and their garments will be consecrated.

²²"Take from this ram the fat, the fat tail, the fat around the inner parts, the covering of the liver, both kidneys with the fat on them, and the right thigh. (This is the ram for the ordination.) ²³From the basket of bread made without yeast, which is before the Lord, take a loaf, and a cake made with oil, and a wafer. ²⁴Put all these in the hands of Aaron and his sons and wave them before the Lord as a wave offering. ²⁵Then take them from their hands and burn them on the altar along with the burnt offering for a pleasing aroma to the Lord, an offering made to the Lord by fire. ²⁶After you take the breast of the ram for Aaron's ordination, wave it before the Lord as a wave offering, and it will be your share.

²⁷"Consecrate those parts of the ordination ram that belong to Aaron and his sons: the breast that was waved and the thigh that was presented. ²⁸This is always to be the regular share from the Israelites for Aaron and his sons. It is the contribution the Israelites are to make to the Lord from their fellowship offerings. *b*

²⁹"Aaron's sacred garments will belong to his descendants so that they can be anointed and ordained in them. ³⁰The son who succeeds him as priest and comes to the Tent of Meeting to minister in the Holy Place is to wear them seven days.

³¹"Take the ram for the ordination and cook the meat in a sacred place. ³²At the entrance to the Tent of Meeting, Aaron and his sons are to eat the meat of the ram and the bread that is in the basket. ³³They are to eat these offerings by which atonement was made for their ordination and consecration. But no one else may eat them, because they are sacred. ³⁴And if any of the meat of the ordination ram or any bread is left over till morning, burn it up. It must not be eaten, because it is sacred.

³⁵"Do for Aaron and his sons everything I have commanded you, taking seven days to ordain them. ³⁶Sacrifice a bull each day as a sin offering to make atonement. Purify the altar by making atonement for it, and anoint it to consecrate it. ³⁷For seven days make atonement for the altar and consecrate it. Then the altar will be most holy, and whatever touches it will be holy.

³⁸"This is what you are to offer on the altar regularly each day: two lambs a year old. ³⁹Offer

---

a 9 Hebrew; Septuagint *on them*   *b* 28 Traditionally *peace offerings* one in the morning and the other at twilight. ⁴⁰With the first lamb offer a tenth of an ephah^a of fine flour mixed with a quarter of a hin^b of oil from pressed olives, and a quarter of a hin of wine as a drink offering. ⁴¹Sacrifice the other lamb at twilight with the same grain offering and its drink offering as in the morning—a pleasing aroma, an offering made to the LORD by fire.

⁴²"For the generations to come this burnt offering is to be made regularly at the entrance to the Tent of Meeting before the LORD. There I will meet you and speak to you; ⁴³there also I will meet with the Israelites, and the place will be consecrated by my glory.

⁴⁴"So I will consecrate the Tent of Meeting and the altar and will consecrate Aaron and his sons to serve me as priests. ⁴⁵Then I will dwell among the Israelites and be their God. ⁴⁶They will know that I am the LORD their God, who brought them out of Egypt so that I might dwell among them. I am the LORD their God.

truth or dare

What an amazing thing! You don't have to escape your surroundings to find God. Right here, right now, God wants to have a real part in your everyday life.

29:45–46

The Altar of Incense

30 "Make an altar of acacia wood for burning incense. ²It is to be square, a cubit long and a cubit wide, and two cubits high^c—its horns of one piece with it. ³Overlay the top and all the sides and the horns with pure gold, and make a gold molding around it. ⁴Make two gold rings for the altar below the molding—two on opposite sides—to hold the poles used to carry it. ⁵Make the poles of acacia wood and overlay them with gold. ⁶Put the altar in front of the curtain that is before the ark of the Testimony—before the atonement cover that is over the Testimony—where I will meet with you.

⁷"Aaron must burn fragrant incense on the altar every morning when he tends the lamps. ⁸He must burn incense again when he lights the lamps at twilight so incense will burn regularly before the LORD for the generations to come. ⁹Do not offer on this altar any other incense or any burnt offering or grain offering, and do not pour a drink offering on it. ¹⁰Once a year Aaron shall make atonement on its horns. This annual atonement must be made with the blood of the atoning sin offering for the generations to come. It is most holy to the LORD."

Atonement Money

¹¹Then the LORD said to Moses, ¹²"When you take a census of the Israelites to count them, each one must pay the LORD a ransom for his life at the time he is counted. Then no plague will come on them when you number them. ¹³Each one who crosses over to those already counted is to give a half shekel,^d according to the sanctuary shekel, which weighs twenty gerahs. This half shekel is an offering to the LORD. ¹⁴All who cross over, those twenty years old or more, are to give an offering to the LORD. ¹⁵The rich are not to give more than a half shekel and the poor are not to give less when you make the offering to the LORD to atone for your lives. ¹⁶Receive the atonement money from the Israelites and use it for the service of the Tent of Meeting. It will be a memorial for the Israelites before the LORD, making atonement for your lives."

Basin for Washing

¹⁷Then the LORD said to Moses, ¹⁸"Make a bronze basin, with its bronze stand, for washing. Place it between the Tent of Meeting and the altar, and put water in it. ¹⁹Aaron and his sons are to wash their hands and feet with water from it. ²⁰Whenever they enter the Tent of Meeting, they shall wash with water so that they will not die. Also, when they approach the altar to minister by presenting an offering made to the LORD by fire, ²¹they shall wash their hands and feet so that they will not die. This is to be a lasting ordinance for Aaron and his descendants for the generations to come."

---

^a 40 That is, probably about 2 quarts (about 2 liters)   ^b 40 That is, probably about 1 quart (about 1 liter)   ^c 2 That is, about 1 1/2 feet (about 0.5 meter) long and wide and about 3 feet (about 0.9 meter) high   ^d 13 That is, about 1/5 ounce (about 6 grams); also in verse 15

Anointing Oil

²²Then the LORD said to Moses, ²³"Take the following fine spices: 500 shekels ͣ of liquid myrrh, half as much (that is, 250 shekels) of fragrant cinnamon, 250 shekels of fragrant cane, ²⁴500 shekels of cassia—all according to the sanctuary shekel—and a hin ᵇ of olive oil. ²⁵Make these into a sacred anointing oil, a fragrant blend, the work of a perfumer. It will be the sacred anointing oil. ²⁶Then use it to anoint the Tent of Meeting, the ark of the Testimony, ²⁷the table and all its articles, the lampstand and its accessories, the altar of incense, ²⁸the altar of burnt offering and all its utensils, and the basin with its stand. ²⁹You shall consecrate them so they will be most holy, and whatever touches them will be holy.

³⁰"Anoint Aaron and his sons and consecrate them so they may serve me as priests. ³¹Say to the Israelites, 'This is to be my sacred anointing oil for the generations to come. ³²Do not pour it on men's bodies and do not make any oil with the same formula. It is sacred, and you are to consider it sacred. ³³Whoever makes perfume like it and whoever puts it on anyone other than a priest must be cut off from his people.' "

Incense

³⁴Then the LORD said to Moses, "Take fragrant spices—gum resin, onycha and galbanum—and pure frankincense, all in equal amounts, ³⁵and make a fragrant blend of incense, the work of a perfumer. It is to be salted and pure and sacred. ³⁶Grind some of it to powder and place it in front of the Testimony in the Tent of Meeting, where I will meet with you. It shall be most holy to you. ³⁷Do not make any incense with this formula for yourselves; consider it holy to the LORD. ³⁸Whoever makes any like it to enjoy its fragrance must be cut off from his people."

Bezalel and Oholiab

31 Then the LORD said to Moses, ²"See, I have chosen Bezalel son of Uri, the son of Hur, of the tribe of Judah, ³and I have filled him with the Spirit of God, with skill, ability and knowledge in all kinds of crafts— ⁴to make artistic designs for work in gold, silver and bronze, ⁵to cut and set stones, to work in wood, and to engage in all kinds of craftsmanship. ⁶Moreover, I have appointed Oholiab son of Ahisamach, of the tribe of Dan, to help him. Also I have given skill to all the craftsmen to make everything I have commanded you: ⁷the Tent of Meeting, the ark of the Testimony with the atonement cover on it, and all the other furnishings of the tent— ⁸the table and its articles, the pure gold lampstand and all its accessories, the altar of incense, ⁹the altar of burnt offering and all its utensils, the basin with its stand— ¹⁰and also the woven garments, both the sacred garments for Aaron the priest and the garments for his sons when they serve as priests, ¹¹and the anointing oil and fragrant incense for the Holy Place. They are to make them just as I commanded you."

truth or dare

Why do great artists always have such tough names? Michelangelo, da Vinci, Bezalel, Oholiab? Seriously, God gives each of us special talents. He's honored when we use them for him.

31:1–11

The Sabbath

¹²Then the LORD said to Moses, ¹³"Say to the Israelites, 'You must observe my Sabbaths. This will be a sign between me and you for the generations to come, so you may know that I am the LORD, who makes you holy. ͨ

¹⁴" 'Observe the Sabbath, because it is holy to you. Anyone who desecrates it must be put to death; whoever does any work on that day must be cut off from his people. ¹⁵For six days, work is to be done, but the seventh day is a Sabbath of rest, holy to the LORD. Whoever does any work on the Sabbath day must be put to death. ¹⁶The Israelites are to observe the Sabbath, celebrating it for the generations to come as a lasting covenant. ¹⁷It will be a sign between me and the Israelites

---

ͣ 23 That is, about 12 1/2 pounds (about 6 kilograms)   ᵇ 24 That is, probably about 4 quarts (about 4 liters)
ͨ 13 Or who sanctifies you; or who sets you apart as holy

forever, for in six days the LCRD made the heavens and the earth, and on the seventh day he abstained from work and rested.' "

[18]When the LORD finished speaking to Moses on Mount Sinai, he gave him the two tablets of the Testimony, the tablets of stone inscribed by the finger of God.

The Golden Calf

32 When the people saw that Moses was so long in coming down from the mountain, they gathered around Aaron and said, "Come, make us gods[a] who will go before us. As for this fellow Moses who brought us up out of Egypt, we don't know what has happened to him."

[2]Aaron answered them, "Take off the gold earrings that your wives, your sons and your daughters are wearing, and bring them to me." [3]So all the people took off their earrings and brought them to Aaron. [4]He took what they handed him and made it into an idol cast in the shape of a calf, fashioning it with a tool. Then they said, "These are your gods,[b] O Israel, who brought you up out of Egypt."

[5]When Aaron saw this, he built an altar in front of the calf and announced, "Tomorrow there will be a festival to the LORD." [6]So the next day the people rose early and sacrificed burnt offerings and presented fellowship offerings.[c] Afterward they sat down to eat and drink and got up to indulge in revelry.

[7]Then the LORD said to Moses, "Go down, because your people, whom you brought up out of Egypt, have become corrupt. [8]They have been quick to turn away from what I commanded them and have made themselves an idol cast in the shape of a calf. They have bowed down to it and sacrificed to it and have said, 'These are your gods, O Israel, who brought you up out of Egypt.'

[9]"I have seen these people," the LORD said to Moses, "and they are a stiff-necked people. [10]Now leave me alone so that my anger may burn against them and that I may destroy them. Then I will make you into a great nation."

[11]But Moses sought the favor of the LORD his God. "O LORD," he said, "why should your anger burn against your people, whom you brought out of Egypt with great power and a mighty hand? [12]Why should the Egyptians say, 'It was with evil intent that he brought them out, to kill them in the mountains and to wipe them off the face of the earth'? Turn from your fierce anger; relent and do not bring disaster on your people. [13]Remember your servants Abraham, Isaac and Israel, to whom you swore by your own self: 'I will make your descendants as numerous as the stars in the sky and I will give your descendants all this land I promised them, and it will be their inheritance forever.' " [14]Then the

love ♥ notes

31:12-13

Beloved,

Do you have a day set aside to rest? I gave you one day a week as a time to rest and a time to be with me. Are you doing that? This week, make the Sabbath a time to relax, remember and reconnect with me. It's our special day.

—Love, Dad (Abba)

How can you make the Sabbath a special day of rest and time with God?

_____

_____

_____

_____

_____

_____

_____

_____

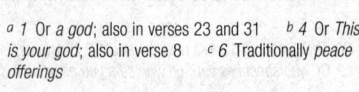

a 1 Or a god; also in verses 23 and 31   *b 4 Or This is your god*; also in verse 8   *c 6 Traditionally peace offerings*

LORD relented and did not bring on his people the disaster he had threatened.

[15]Moses turned and went down the mountain with the two tablets of the Testimony in his hands. They were inscribed on both sides, front and back. [16]The tablets were the work of God; the writing was the writing of God, engraved on the tablets.

[17]When Joshua heard the noise of the people shouting, he said to Moses, "There is the sound of war in the camp."

[18]Moses replied:

> "It is not the sound of victory,
> it is not the sound of defeat;
> it is the sound of singing that I hear."

[19]When Moses approached the camp and saw the calf and the dancing, his anger burned and he threw the tablets out of his hands, breaking them to pieces at the foot of the mountain. [20]And he took the calf they had made and burned it in the fire; then he ground it to powder, scattered it on the water and made the Israelites drink it.

truth or dare

Whenever people think they can confine God to a physical form, they end up creating idols instead. Rather than trying to mold God to fit *your* ideas, allow God to transform you to be more like him.

32:1–10

[21]He said to Aaron, "What did these people do to you, that you led them into such great sin?"

[22]"Do not be angry, my lord," Aaron answered. "You know how prone these people are to evil. [23]They said to me, 'Make us gods who will go before us. As for this fellow Moses who brought us up out of Egypt, we don't know what has happened to him.' [24]So I told them, 'Whoever has any gold jewelry, take it off.' Then they gave me the gold, and I threw it into the fire, and out came this calf!"

[25]Moses saw that the people were running wild and that Aaron had let them get out of control and so become a laughingstock to their enemies. [26]So he stood at the entrance to the camp and said, "Whoever is for the LORD, come to me." And all the Levites rallied to him.

[27]Then he said to them, "This is what the LORD, the God of Israel, says: 'Each man strap a sword to his side. Go back and forth through the camp from one end to the other, each killing his brother and friend and neighbor.' " [28]The Levites did as Moses commanded, and that day about three thousand of the people died. [29]Then Moses said, "You have been set apart to the LORD today, for you were against your own sons and brothers, and he has blessed you this day."

[30]The next day Moses said to the people, "You have committed a great sin. But now I will go up to the LORD; perhaps I can make atonement for your sin."

[31]So Moses went back to the LORD and said, "Oh, what a great sin these people have committed! They have made themselves gods of gold. [32]But now, please forgive their sin—but if not, then blot me out of the book you have written."

[33]The LORD replied to Moses, "Whoever has sinned against me I will blot out of my book. [34]Now go, lead the people to the place I spoke of, and my angel will go before you. However, when the time comes for me to punish, I will punish them for their sin."

[35]And the LORD struck the people with a plague because of what they did with the calf Aaron had made.

33 Then the LORD said to Moses, "Leave this place, you and the people you brought up out of Egypt, and go up to the land I promised on oath to Abraham, Isaac and Jacob, saying, 'I will give it to your descendants.' [2]I will send an angel before you and drive out the Canaanites, Amorites, Hittites, Perizzites, Hivites and Jebusites. [3]Go up to the land flowing with milk and honey. But I will not go with you, because you are a stiff-necked people and I might destroy you on the way."

[4]When the people heard these distressing words, they began to mourn and no one put on any ornaments. [5]For the LORD had said to Moses, "Tell the Israelites, 'You are a stiff-necked people. If I were to go with you even for a moment, I might destroy you. Now take off your ornaments and I will decide what to do with you.' " [6]So the Israelites stripped off their ornaments at Mount Horeb.

The Tent of Meeting

[7]Now Moses used to take a tent and pitch it outside the camp some distance away, calling it

the "tent of meeting." Anyone inquiring of the LORD would go to the tent of meeting outside the camp. ⁸And whenever Moses went out to the tent, all the people rose and stood at the entrances to their tents, watching Moses until he entered the tent. ⁹As Moses went into the tent, the pillar of cloud would come down and stay at the entrance, while the LORD spoke with Moses. ¹⁰Whenever the people saw the pillar of cloud standing at the entrance to the tent, they all stood and worshiped, each at the entrance to his tent. ¹¹The LORD would speak to Moses face to face, as a man speaks with his friend. Then Moses would return to the camp, but his young aide Joshua son of Nun did not leave the tent.

Moses and the Glory of the LORD

¹²Moses said to the LORD, "You have been telling me, 'Lead these people,' but you have not let me know whom you will send with me. You have said, 'I know you by name and you have found favor with me.' ¹³If you are pleased with me, teach me your ways so I may know you and continue to find favor with you. Remember that this nation is your people."

¹⁴The LORD replied, "My Presence will go with you, and I will give you rest."

¹⁵Then Moses said to him, "If your Presence does not go with us, do not send us up from here. ¹⁶How will anyone know that you are pleased with me and with your people unless you go with us? What else will distinguish me and your people from all the other people on the face of the earth?"

¹⁷And the LORD said to Moses, "I will do the very thing you have asked, because I am pleased with you and I know you by name."

¹⁸Then Moses said, "Now show me your glory."

¹⁹And the LORD said, "I will cause all my goodness to pass in front of you, and I will proclaim my name, the LORD, in your presence. I will have mercy on whom I will have mercy, and I will have compassion on whom I will have compassion. ²⁰But," he said, "you cannot see my face, for no one may see me and live."

²¹Then the LORD said, "There is a place near me where you may stand on a rock. ²²When my glory passes by, I will put you in a cleft in the rock and cover you with my hand until I have passed by. ²³Then I will remove my hand and you will see my back; but my face must not be seen."

truth or dare

Speaking face to face with a friend demonstrates openness, intimacy and trust. If you're willing to speak openly with God, he's willing to speak openly with you.

33:11

truth or dare

How do you get to know God? Save the guesswork. God wants to be known, so he gave us his Word—and he introduces himself personally to those who search for him.

34:6–7

The New Stone Tablets

34 The LORD said to Moses, "Chisel out two stone tablets like the first ones, and I will write on them the words that were on the first tablets, which you broke. ²Be ready in the morning, and then come up on Mount Sinai. Present yourself to me there on top of the mountain. ³No one is to come with you or be seen anywhere on the mountain; not even the flocks and herds may graze in front of the mountain."

⁴So Moses chiseled out two stone tablets like the first ones and went up Mount Sinai early in the morning, as the LORD had commanded him; and he carried the two stone tablets in his hands. ⁵Then the LORD came down in the cloud and stood there with him and proclaimed his name, the LORD. ⁶And he passed in front of Moses, proclaiming, "The LORD, the LORD, the compassionate and gracious God, slow to anger, abounding in love and faithfulness, ⁷maintaining love to thousands, and forgiving wickedness, rebellion and sin. Yet he does not leave the guilty unpunished; he punishes the children and their children for the sin of the fathers to the third and fourth generation."

[8]Moses bowed to the ground at once and worshiped. [9]"O Lord, if I have found favor in your eyes," he said, "then let the Lord go with us. Although this is a stiff-necked people, forgive our wickedness and our sin, and take us as your inheritance."

[10]Then the LORD said: "I am making a covenant with you. Before all your people I will do wonders never before done in any nation in all the world. The people you live among will see how awesome is the work that I, the LORD, will do for you. [11]Obey what I command you today. I will drive out before you the Amorites, Canaanites, Hittites, Perizzites, Hivites and Jebusites. [12]Be careful not to make a treaty with those who live in the land where you are going, or they will be a snare among you. [13]Break down their altars, smash their sacred stones and cut down their Asherah poles.[a] [14]Do not worship any other god, for the LORD, whose name is Jealous, is a jealous God.

[15]"Be careful not to make a treaty with those who live in the land; for when they prostitute themselves to their gods and sacrifice to them, they will invite you and you will eat their sacrifices. [16]And when you choose some of their daughters as wives for your sons and those daughters prostitute themselves to their gods, they will lead your sons to do the same.

[17]"Do not make cast idols.

[18]"Celebrate the Feast of Unleavened Bread. For seven days eat bread made without yeast, as I commanded you. Do this at the appointed time in the month of Abib, for in that month you came out of Egypt.

[19]"The first offspring of every womb belongs to me, including all the firstborn males of your livestock, whether from herd or flock. [20]Redeem the firstborn donkey with a lamb, but if you do not redeem it, break its neck. Redeem all your firstborn sons.

"No one is to appear before me empty-handed.

[21]"Six days you shall labor, but on the seventh day you shall rest; even during the plowing season and harvest you must rest.

[22]"Celebrate the Feast of Weeks with the firstfruits of the wheat harvest, and the Feast of Ingathering at the turn of the year.[b] [23]Three times a year all your men are to appear before the Sovereign LORD, the God of Israel. [24]I will drive out nations before you and enlarge your territory, and no one will covet your land when you go up three times each year to appear before the LORD your God.

[25]"Do not offer the blood of a sacrifice to me along with anything containing yeast, and do not let any of the sacrifice from the Passover Feast remain until morning.

[26]"Bring the best of the firstfruits of your soil to the house of the LORD your God.

"Do not cook a young goat in its mother's milk."

[27]Then the LORD said to Moses, "Write down these words, for in accordance with these words I have made a covenant with you and with Israel." [28]Moses was there with the LORD forty days and forty nights without eating bread or drinking water. And he wrote on the tablets the words of the covenant—the Ten Commandments.

The Radiant Face of Moses

[29]When Moses came down from Mount Sinai with the two tablets of the Testimony in his hands, he was not aware that his face was radiant because he had spoken with the LORD. [30]When Aaron and all the Israelites saw Moses, his face was radiant, and they were afraid to come near him. [31]But Moses called to them; so Aaron and all the leaders of the community came back to him, and he spoke to them. [32]Afterward all the Israelites came near him, and he gave them all the commands the LORD had given him on Mount Sinai.

[33]When Moses finished speaking to them, he put a veil over his face. [34]But whenever he entered the LORD's presence to speak with him, he removed the veil until he came out. And when he came out and told the Israelites what he had been commanded, [35]they saw that his face was radiant. Then Moses would put the veil back over his face until he went in to speak with the LORD.

Sabbath Regulations

35 Moses assembled the whole Israelite community and said to them, "These are the things the LORD has commanded you to do: [2]For six days, work is to be done, but the seventh day shall be your holy day, a Sabbath of rest to the LORD. Whoever does any work on it must be put to death. [3]Do not light a fire in any of your dwellings on the Sabbath day."

a 13 That is, symbols of the goddess Asherah   *b 22* That is, in the fall

Materials for the Tabernacle

⁴Moses said to the whole Israelite community, "This is what the Lᴏʀᴅ has commanded: ⁵From what you have, take an offering for the Lᴏʀᴅ. Everyone who is willing is to bring to the Lᴏʀᴅ an offering of gold, silver and bronze; ⁶blue, purple and scarlet yarn and fine linen; goat hair; ⁷ram skins dyed red and hides of sea cows ᵃ; acacia wood; ⁸olive oil for the light; spices for the anointing oil and for the fragrant incense; ⁹and onyx stones and other gems to be mounted on the ephod and breastpiece.

¹⁰"All who are skilled among you are to come and make everything the Lᴏʀᴅ has commanded: ¹¹the tabernacle with its tent and its covering, clasps, frames, crossbars, posts and bases; ¹²the ark with its poles and the atonement cover and the curtain that shields it; ¹³the table with its poles and all its articles and the bread of the Presence; ¹⁴the lampstand that is for light with its accessories, lamps and oil for the light; ¹⁵the altar of incense with its poles, the anointing oil and the fragrant incense; the curtain for the doorway at the entrance to the tabernacle; ¹⁶the altar of burnt offering with its bronze grating, its poles and all its utensils; the bronze basin with its stand; ¹⁷the curtains of the courtyard with its posts and bases, and the curtain for the entrance to the courtyard; ¹⁸the tent pegs for the tabernacle and for the courtyard, and their ropes; ¹⁹the woven garments worn for ministering in the sanctuary—both the sacred garments for Aaron the priest and the garments for his sons when they serve as priests."

²⁰Then the whole Israelite community withdrew from Moses' presence, ²¹and everyone who was willing and whose heart moved him came and brought an offering to the Lᴏʀᴅ for the work on the Tent of Meeting, for all its service, and for the sacred garments. ²²All who were willing, men and women alike, came and brought gold jewelry of all kinds: brooches, earrings, rings and ornaments. They all presented their gold as a wave offering to the Lᴏʀᴅ. ²³Everyone who had blue, purple or scarlet yarn or fine linen, or goat hair, ram skins dyed red or hides of sea cows brought them. ²⁴Those presenting an offering of silver or bronze brought it as an offering to the Lᴏʀᴅ, and everyone who had acacia wood for any part of the work brought it. ²⁵Every skilled woman spun with her hands and brought what she had spun—blue, purple or scarlet yarn or fine linen. ²⁶And all the women who were willing and had the skill spun the goat hair. ²⁷The leaders brought onyx stones and other gems to be mounted on the ephod and breastpiece. ²⁸They also brought spices and olive oil for the light and for the anointing oil and for the fragrant incense. ²⁹All the Israelite men and women who were willing brought to the Lᴏʀᴅ freewill offerings for all the work the Lᴏʀᴅ through Moses had commanded them to do.

genuine generosity » 35:20-22

Imagine this: As the offering plate passes, one girl rolls her eyes and begrudgingly throws in some spare change. A few rows behind her, a second girl silently thanks God for all he's given her and then gives back to him generously. Which gift pleases God more? The Israelites loved the Lord so much that they gave generously toward the building fund. And not just their extra money or some loose coins they dug out of the couch. No, they gave their *best* and were glad to do it. Which kind of heart do you have—stingy or generous?

Bezalel and Oholiab

³⁰Then Moses said to the Israelites, "See, the Lᴏʀᴅ has chosen Bezalel son of Uri, the son of Hur, of the tribe of Judah, ³¹and he has filled him with the Spirit of God, with skill, ability and knowledge in all kinds of crafts— ³²to make artistic designs for work in gold, silver and bronze, ³³to cut and set stones, to work in wood and to engage in all kinds of artistic craftsmanship. ³⁴And he has

ᵃ 7 That is, dugongs; also in verse 23

given both him and Oholiab son of Ahisamach, of the tribe of Dan, the ability to teach others. [35]He has filled them with skill to do all kinds of work as craftsmen, designers, embroiderers in blue, purple and scarlet yarn and fine linen, and weavers—all of them master craftsmen and designers.

36

[1]So Bezalel, Oholiab and every skilled person to whom the LORD has given skill and ability to know how to carry out all the work of constructing the sanctuary are to do the work just as the LORD has commanded."

[2]Then Moses summoned Bezalel and Oholiab and every skilled person to whom the LORD had given ability and who was willing to come and do the work. [3]They received from Moses all the offerings the Israelites had brought to carry out the work of constructing the sanctuary. And the people continued to bring freewill offerings morning after morning. [4]So all the skilled craftsmen who were doing all the work on the sanctuary left their work [5]and said to Moses, "The people are bringing more than enough for doing the work the LORD commanded to be done."

[6]Then Moses gave an order and they sent this word throughout the camp: "No man or woman is to make anything else as an offering for the sanctuary." And so the people were restrained from bringing more, [7]because what they already had was more than enough to do all the work.

The Tabernacle

[8]All the skilled men among the workmen made the tabernacle with ten curtains of finely twisted linen and blue, purple and scarlet yarn, with cherubim worked into them by a skilled craftsman. [9]All the curtains were the same size—twenty-eight cubits long and four cubits wide. [a] [10]They joined five of the curtains together and did the same with the other five. [11]Then they made loops of blue material along the edge of the end curtain in one set, and the same was done with the end curtain in the other set. [12]They also made fifty loops on one curtain and fifty loops on the end curtain of the other set, with the loops opposite each other. [13]Then they made fifty gold clasps and used them to fasten the two sets of curtains together so that the tabernacle was a unit.

[14]They made curtains of goat hair for the tent over the tabernacle—eleven altogether. [15]All eleven curtains were the same size—thirty cubits long and four cubits wide. [b] [16]They joined five of the curtains into one set and the other six into another set. [17]Then they made fifty loops along the edge of the end curtain in one set and also along the edge of the end curtain in the other set. [18]They made fifty bronze clasps to fasten the tent together as a unit. [19]Then they made for the tent a covering of ram skins dyed red, and over that a covering of hides of sea cows. [c]

[20]They made upright frames of acacia wood for the tabernacle. [21]Each frame was ten cubits long and a cubit and a half wide, [d] [22]with two projections set parallel to each other. They made all the frames of the tabernacle in this way. [23]They made twenty frames for the south side of the tabernacle [24]and made forty silver bases to go under them—two bases for each frame, one under each projection. [25]For the other side, the north side of the tabernacle, they made twenty frames [26]and forty silver bases—two under each frame. [27]They made six frames for the far end, that is, the west end of the tabernacle, [28]and two frames were made for the corners of the tabernacle at the far end. [29]At these two corners the frames were double from the bottom all the way to the top and fitted into a single ring; both were made alike. [30]So there were eight frames and sixteen silver bases—two under each frame.

[31]They also made crossbars of acacia wood: five for the frames on one side of the tabernacle, [32]five for those on the other side, and five for the frames on the west, at the far end of the tabernacle. [33]They made the center crossbar so that it extended from end to end at the middle of the frames. [34]They overlaid the frames with gold and made gold rings to hold the crossbars. They also overlaid the crossbars with gold.

[35]They made the curtain of blue, purple and scarlet yarn and finely twisted linen, with cherubim worked into it by a skilled craftsman. [36]They made four posts of acacia wood for it and overlaid them with gold. They made gold hooks for them and cast their four silver bases. [37]For the entrance to the tent they made a curtain of blue, purple and scarlet yarn and finely twisted linen—the work of an embroiderer; [38]and they made five posts with hooks for them. They overlaid the tops of the posts and their bands with gold and made their five bases of bronze.

---

[a] 9 That is, about 42 feet (about 12.5 meters) long and 6 feet (about 1.8 meters) wide (about 13.5 meters) long and 6 feet (about 1.8 meters) wide [c] 19 That is, dugongs [b] 15 That is, about 45 feet [d] 21 That is, about 15 feet (about 4.5 meters) long and 2 1/4 feet (about 0.7 meter) wide

The Ark

37 Bezalel made the ark of acacia wood—two and a half cubits long, a cubit and a half wide, and a cubit and a half high.ª ²He overlaid it with pure gold, both inside and out, and made a gold molding around it. ³He cast four gold rings for it and fastened them to its four feet, with two rings on one side and two rings on the other. ⁴Then he made poles of acacia wood and overlaid them with gold. ⁵And he inserted the poles into the rings on the sides of the ark to carry it.

⁶He made the atonement cover of pure gold—two and a half cubits long and a cubit and a half wide.ᵇ ⁷Then he made two cherubim out of hammered gold at the ends of the cover. ⁸He made one cherub on one end and the second cherub on the other; at the two ends he made them of one piece with the cover. ⁹The cherubim had their wings spread upward, overshadowing the cover with them. The cherubim faced each other, looking toward the cover.

The Table

¹⁰Theyᶜ made the table of acacia wood—two cubits long, a cubit wide, and a cubit and a half high.ᵈ ¹¹Then they overlaid it with pure gold and made a gold molding around it. ¹²They also made around it a rim a handbreadthᵉ wide and put a gold molding on the rim. ¹³They cast four gold rings for the table and fastened them to the four corners, where the four legs were. ¹⁴The rings were put close to the rim to hold the poles used in carrying the table. ¹⁵The poles for carrying the table were made of acacia wood and were overlaid with gold. ¹⁶And they made from pure gold the articles for the table—its plates and dishes and bowls and its pitchers for the pouring out of drink offerings.

The Lampstand

¹⁷They made the lampstand of pure gold and hammered it out, base and shaft; its flowerlike cups, buds and blossoms were of one piece with it. ¹⁸Six branches extended from the sides of the lampstand—three on one side and three on the other. ¹⁹Three cups shaped like almond flowers with buds and blossoms were on one branch, three on the next branch and the same for all six branches extending from the lampstand. ²⁰And on the lampstand were four cups shaped like almond flowers with buds and blossoms. ²¹One bud was under the first pair of branches extending from the lampstand, a second bud under the second pair, and a third bud under the third pair—six branches in all. ²²The buds and the branches were all of one piece with the lampstand, hammered out of pure gold.

²³They made its seven lamps, as well as its wick trimmers and trays, of pure gold. ²⁴They made the lampstand and all its accessories from one talentᶠ of pure gold.

The Altar of Incense

²⁵They made the altar of incense out of acacia wood. It was square, a cubit long and a cubit wide, and two cubits highᵍ—its horns of one piece with it. ²⁶They overlaid the top and all the sides and the horns with pure gold, and made a gold molding around it. ²⁷They made two gold rings below the molding—two on opposite sides—to hold the poles used to carry it. ²⁸They made the poles of acacia wood and overlaid them with gold.

²⁹They also made the sacred anointing oil and the pure, fragrant incense—the work of a perfumer.

The Altar of Burnt Offering

38 Theyʰ built the altar of burnt offering of acacia wood, three cubitsⁱ high; it was square, five cubits long and five cubits wide.ʲ ²They made a horn at each of the four corners, so that the horns and the altar were of one piece, and they overlaid the altar with bronze. ³They made all its utensils of bronze—its pots, shovels, sprinkling bowls, meat forks and firepans. ⁴They made a grating for the altar, a bronze network, to be under its ledge, halfway up the altar. ⁵They cast bronze rings to hold the poles for the four corners of the bronze grating. ⁶They made the poles of acacia wood and overlaid them with bronze. ⁷They inserted the poles into the rings so they would be on the sides of the altar for carrying it. They made it hollow, out of boards.

ª 1 That is, about 3 3/4 feet (about 1.1 meters) long and 2 1/4 feet (about 0.7 meter) wide and high   ᵇ 6 That is, about 3 3/4 feet (about 1.1 meters) long and 2 1/4 feet (about 0.7 meter) wide   ᶜ 10 Or He; also in verses 11-29   ᵈ 10 That is, about 3 feet (about 0.9 meter) long, 1 1/2 feet (about 0.5 meter) wide, and 2 1/4 feet (about 0.7 meter) high
ᵉ 12 That is, about 3 inches (about 8 centimeters)   ᶠ 24 That is, about 75 pounds (about 34 kilograms)   ᵍ 25 That is, about 1 1/2 feet (about 0.5 meter) long and wide, and about 3 feet (about 0.9 meter) high   ʰ 1 Or He; also in verses 2-9
ⁱ 1 That is, about 4 1/2 feet (about 1.3 meters)   ʲ 1 That is, about 7 1/2 feet (about 2.3 meters) long and wide

Divorce: The Aftershocks

focus   Profile: **Tanesha**

It was bad enough when my parents got divorced. After Dad moved out, Mama told me all about their marriage problems, and I was totally crushed. I had just turned 13, and as if life weren't stressful enough, I had to go through that divorce and custody nightmare. It was all too much.

Over the last three years, Mama and I got into a routine. Recently we've been getting along better than we had for a long time . . . until she met "the dude," that is.

He is way younger than Mama. He works at the health club, and he's really fine. Normally, I would think he's cool, but not when I think of him going out with my mama. If this had happened to someone else, I probably would've laughed out loud, but it's happening to me, and it is not funny.

This guy has a wife and two kids. How could my ma ever get mixed up in that? She says they're just friends—it's nothing heavy. Yeah, right!

To make matters worse, my dad said there's someone he wants me to meet this weekend when I visit.

I just want my life to be normal. Instead, it's like a bad movie, and I can't walk out of the theater.

Read more about parents online at www.TrueImagesBible.com

divorce in focus

Almost half the kids in our country come from divorced backgrounds. Many of those kids feel powerless over their family situation, especially when their divorced parents begin to date, which throws off their sense of normalcy again.

If you're struggling with the idea that your parents are beginning to date:
- » Pray for tolerance and respect for your parents.
- » Check out Psalm 27:10 (page 679); Psalm 55:22 (page 707); and Ephesians 6:1–3 (page 1548).
- » Talk with your school counselor, youth group leader or other trusted adult to help you work through your feelings.

For more on this topic, see the index on page 1656.

Basin for Washing

[8]They made the bronze basin and its bronze stand from the mirrors of the women who served at the entrance to the Tent of Meeting.

The Courtyard

[9]Next they made the courtyard. The south side was a hundred cubits [a] long and had curtains of finely twisted linen, [10]with twenty posts and twenty bronze bases, and with silver hooks and bands

[a] 9 That is, about 150 feet (about 46 meters)

on the posts. ¹¹The north side was also a hundred cubits long and had twenty posts and twenty bronze bases, with silver hooks and bands on the posts.

¹²The west end was fifty cubits*ª* wide and had curtains, with ten posts and ten bases, with silver hooks and bands on the posts. ¹³The east end, toward the sunrise, was also fifty cubits wide. ¹⁴Curtains fifteen cubits*ᵇ* long were on one side of the entrance, with three posts and three bases, ¹⁵and curtains fifteen cubits long were on the other side of the entrance to the courtyard, with three posts and three bases. ¹⁶All the curtains around the courtyard were of finely twisted linen. ¹⁷The bases for the posts were bronze. The hooks and bands on the posts were silver, and their tops were overlaid with silver; so all the posts of the courtyard had silver bands.

¹⁸The curtain for the entrance to the courtyard was of blue, purple and scarlet yarn and finely twisted linen—the work of an embroiderer. It was twenty cubits*ᶜ* long and, like the curtains of the courtyard, five cubits*ᵈ* high, ¹⁹with four posts and four bronze bases. Their hooks and bands were silver, and their tops were overlaid with silver. ²⁰All the tent pegs of the tabernacle and of the surrounding courtyard were bronze.

The Materials Used

²¹These are the amounts of the materials used for the tabernacle, the tabernacle of the Testimony, which were recorded at Moses' command by the Levites under the direction of Ithamar son of Aaron, the priest. ²²(Bezalel son of Uri, the son of Hur, of the tribe of Judah, made everything the LORD commanded Moses; ²³with him was Oholiab son of Ahisamach, of the tribe of Dan—a craftsman and designer, and an embroiderer in blue, purple and scarlet yarn and fine linen.) ²⁴The total amount of the gold from the wave offering used for all the work on the sanctuary was 29 talents and 730 shekels,*ᵉ* according to the sanctuary shekel.

²⁵The silver obtained from those of the community who were counted in the census was 100 talents and 1,775 shekels,*ᶠ* according to the sanctuary shekel— ²⁶one beka per person, that is, half a shekel,*ᵍ* according to the sanctuary shekel, from everyone who had crossed over to those counted, twenty years old or more, a total of 603,550 men. ²⁷The 100 talents*ʰ* of silver were used to cast the bases for the sanctuary and for the curtain—100 bases from the 100 talents, one talent for each base. ²⁸They used the 1,775 shekels*ⁱ* to make the hooks for the posts, to overlay the tops of the posts, and to make their bands.

²⁹The bronze from the wave offering was 70 talents and 2,400 shekels.*ʲ* ³⁰They used it to make the bases for the entrance to the Tent of Meeting, the bronze altar with its bronze grating and all its utensils, ³¹the bases for the surrounding courtyard and those for its entrance and all the tent pegs for the tabernacle and those for the surrounding courtyard.

The Priestly Garments

39 From the blue, purple and scarlet yarn they made woven garments for ministering in the sanctuary. They also made sacred garments for Aaron, as the LORD commanded Moses.

The Ephod

²They*ᵏ* made the ephod of gold, and of blue, purple and scarlet yarn, and of finely twisted linen. ³They hammered out thin sheets of gold and cut strands to be worked into the blue, purple and scarlet yarn and fine linen—the work of a skilled craftsman. ⁴They made shoulder pieces for the ephod, which were attached to two of its corners, so it could be fastened. ⁵Its skillfully woven waistband was like it—of one piece with the ephod and made with gold, and with blue, purple and scarlet yarn, and with finely twisted linen, as the LORD commanded Moses.

⁶They mounted the onyx stones in gold filigree settings and engraved them like a seal with the names of the sons of Israel. ⁷Then they fastened them on the shoulder pieces of the ephod as memorial stones for the sons of Israel, as the LORD commanded Moses.

---

a 12 That is, about 75 feet (about 23 meters)   *b 14* That is, about 22 1/2 feet (about 6.9 meters)   *c 18* That is, about 30 feet (about 9 meters)   *d 18* That is, about 7 1/2 feet (about 2.3 meters)   *e 24* The weight of the gold was a little over one ton (about 1 metric ton).   *f 25* The weight of the silver was a little over 3 3/4 tons (about 3.4 metric tons).   *g 26* That is, about 1/5 ounce (about 5.5 grams)   *h 27* That is, about 3 3/4 tons (about 3.4 metric tons)   *i 28* That is, about 45 pounds (about 20 kilograms)   *j 29* The weight of the bronze was about 2 1/2 tons (about 2.4 metric tons).   *k 2* Or *He*; also in verses 7, 8 and 22

The Breastpiece

[8]They fashioned the breastpiece—the work of a skilled craftsman. They made it like the ephod: of gold, and of blue, purple and scarlet yarn, and of finely twisted linen. [9]It was square—a span[a] long and a span wide—and folded double. [10]Then they mounted four rows of precious stones on it. In the first row there was a ruby, a topaz and a beryl; [11]in the second row a turquoise, a sapphire[b] and an emerald; [12]in the third row a jacinth, an agate and an amethyst; [13]in the fourth row a chrysolite, an onyx and a jasper.[c] They were mounted in gold filigree settings. [14]There were twelve stones, one for each of the names of the sons of Israel, each engraved like a seal with the name of one of the twelve tribes.

[15]For the breastpiece they made braided chains of pure gold, like a rope. [16]They made two gold filigree settings and two gold rings, and fastened the rings to two of the corners of the breastpiece. [17]They fastened the two gold chains to the rings at the corners of the breastpiece, [18]and the other ends of the chains to the two settings, attaching them to the shoulder pieces of the ephod at the front. [19]They made two gold rings and attached them to the other two corners of the breastpiece on the inside edge next to the ephod. [20]Then they made two more gold rings and attached them to the bottom of the shoulder pieces on the front of the ephod, close to the seam just above the waistband of the ephod. [21]They tied the rings of the breastpiece to the rings of the ephod with blue cord, connecting it to the waistband so that the breastpiece would not swing out from the ephod—as the LORD commanded Moses.

Other Priestly Garments

[22]They made the robe of the ephod entirely of blue cloth—the work of a weaver— [23]with an opening in the center of the robe like the opening of a collar,[d] and a band around this opening, so that it would not tear. [24]They made pomegranates of blue, purple and scarlet yarn and finely twisted linen around the hem of the robe. [25]And they made bells of pure gold and attached them around the hem between the pomegranates. [26]The bells and pomegranates alternated around the hem of the robe to be worn for ministering, as the LORD commanded Moses.

[27]For Aaron and his sons, they made tunics of fine linen—the work of a weaver— [28]and the turban of fine linen, the linen headbands and the undergarments of finely twisted linen. [29]The sash was of finely twisted linen and blue, purple and scarlet yarn—the work of an embroiderer—as the LORD commanded Moses.

[30]They made the plate, the sacred diadem, out of pure gold and engraved on it, like an inscription on a seal: HOLY TO THE LORD. [31]Then they fastened a blue cord to it to attach it to the turban, as the LORD commanded Moses.

Moses Inspects the Tabernacle

[32]So all the work on the tabernacle, the Tent of Meeting, was completed. The Israelites did everything just as the LORD commanded Moses. [33]Then they brought the tabernacle to Moses: the tent and all its furnishings, its clasps, frames, crossbars, posts and bases; [34]the covering of ram skins dyed red, the covering of hides of sea cows[e] and the shielding curtain; [35]the ark of the Testimony with its poles and the atonement cover; [36]the table with all its articles and the bread of the Presence; [37]the pure gold lampstand with its row of lamps and all its accessories, and the oil for the light; [38]the gold altar, the anointing oil, the fragrant incense, and the curtain for the entrance to the tent; [39]the bronze altar with its bronze grating, its poles and all its utensils; the basin with its stand; [40]the curtains of the courtyard with its posts and bases, and the curtain for the entrance to the courtyard; the ropes and tent pegs for the courtyard; all the furnishings for the tabernacle, the Tent of Meeting; [41]and the

truth or dare

Details, details, details! If you're tempted to skip the small stuff to get the job done, remember that God cares about the details. Following God's way *exactly* is the best way for you.

39:32

---

[a] 9 That is, about 9 inches (about 22 centimeters)   [b] 11 Or *lapis lazuli*   [c] 13 The precise identification of some of these precious stones is uncertain.   [d] 23 The meaning of the Hebrew for this word is uncertain.   [e] 34 That is, dugongs

woven garments worn for ministering in the sanctuary, both the sacred garments for Aaron the priest and the garments for his sons when serving as priests.

⁴²The Israelites had done all the work just as the LORD had commanded Moses. ⁴³Moses inspected the work and saw that they had done it just as the LORD had commanded. So Moses blessed them.

Setting Up the Tabernacle

40 Then the LORD said to Moses: ²"Set up the tabernacle, the Tent of Meeting, on the first day of the first month. ³Place the ark of the Testimony in it and shield the ark with the curtain. ⁴Bring in the table and set out what belongs on it. Then bring in the lampstand and set up its lamps. ⁵Place the gold altar of incense in front of the ark of the Testimony and put the curtain at the entrance to the tabernacle.

⁶"Place the altar of burnt offering in front of the entrance to the tabernacle, the Tent of Meeting; ⁷place the basin between the Tent of Meeting and the altar and put water in it. ⁸Set up the courtyard around it and put the curtain at the entrance to the courtyard.

⁹"Take the anointing oil and anoint the tabernacle and everything in it; consecrate it and all its furnishings, and it will be holy. ¹⁰Then anoint the altar of burnt offering and all its utensils; consecrate the altar, and it will be most holy. ¹¹Anoint the basin and its stand and consecrate them.

¹²"Bring Aaron and his sons to the entrance to the Tent of Meeting and wash them with water. ¹³Then dress Aaron in the sacred garments, anoint him and consecrate him so he may serve me as priest. ¹⁴Bring his sons and dress them in tunics. ¹⁵Anoint them just as you anointed their father, so they may serve me as priests. Their anointing will be to a priesthood that will continue for all generations to come." ¹⁶Moses did everything just as the LORD commanded him.

¹⁷So the tabernacle was set up on the first day of the first month in the second year. ¹⁸When Moses set up the tabernacle, he put the bases in place, erected the frames, inserted the crossbars and set up the posts. ¹⁹Then he spread the tent over the tabernacle and put the covering over the tent, as the LORD commanded him.

²⁰He took the Testimony and placed it in the ark, attached the poles to the ark and put the atonement cover over it. ²¹Then he brought the ark into the tabernacle and hung the shielding curtain and shielded the ark of the Testimony, as the LORD commanded him.

²²Moses placed the table in the Tent of Meeting on the north side of the tabernacle outside the curtain ²³and set out the bread on it before the LORD, as the LORD commanded him.

²⁴He placed the lampstand in the Tent of Meeting opposite the table on the south side of the tabernacle ²⁵and set up the lamps before the LORD, as the LORD commanded him.

²⁶Moses placed the gold altar in the Tent of Meeting in front of the curtain ²⁷and burned fragrant incense on it, as the LORD commanded him. ²⁸Then he put up the curtain at the entrance to the tabernacle.

genuine faith » 40:16

If you started reading at Exodus 25 and got through all of the instructions about the tabernacle and the priests, you might be overwhelmed (and exhausted!). That's a lot to remember! Yet this verse tells us that Moses got everything right. That's a tribute to Moses—not because he had a photographic memory but because he trusted God to help him accomplish this huge task. Maybe you're a bit overwhelmed by a task God has given you. Keep your eyes focused on him, and let him work through you. You'll be surprised at what you can accomplish!

²⁹He set the altar of burnt offering near the entrance to the tabernacle, the Tent of Meeting, and offered on it burnt offerings and grain offerings, as the LORD commanded him.

³⁰He placed the basin between the Tent of Meeting and the altar and put water in it for washing, ³¹and Moses and Aaron and his sons used it to wash their hands and feet. ³²They washed

whenever they entered the Tent of Meeting or approached the altar, as the LORD commanded Moses.

[33]Then Moses set up the courtyard around the tabernacle and altar and put up the curtain at the entrance to the courtyard. And so Moses finished the work.

The Glory of the LORD

[34]Then the cloud covered the Tent of Meeting, and the glory of the LORD filled the tabernacle. [35]Moses could not enter the Tent of Meeting because the cloud had settled upon it, and the glory of the LORD filled the tabernacle.

[36]In all the travels of the Israelites, whenever the cloud lifted from above the tabernacle, they would set out; [37]but if the cloud did not lift, they did not set out—until the day it lifted. [38]So the cloud of the LORD was over the tabernacle by day, and fire was in the cloud by night, in the sight of all the house of Israel during all their travels.

author:	Moses.
date:	During the 1400s B.C., while the Israelites were traveling in the desert.
setting:	The Israelites hear instructions from God at the base of Mount Sinai.
verse to remember:	I am the LORD who brought you up out of Egypt to be your God; therefore be holy, because I am holy (11:45).
theme to consider:	Holiness, holiness, holiness! The book of Leviticus establishes the ground rules for how God's people should live. God desires that his people become "set apart" for him.

leviticus

unchanging truth

Laws, rules, regulations, directions, guidelines. They're everywhere! Laws tell you when you can drive and how fast you can go. Parents dictate rules about homework, dating and curfew. School regulations tell you when to go to class and what's appropriate to wear. It seems no matter what you want to do, there is *always* someone or something telling you how to do it. Just once, wouldn't it be great to do whatever you felt like doing with no restrictions?

Actually, an unrestricted life probably wouldn't be that great. In fact, it could be downright scary! Imagine people driving on the road going their own speed and driving on whichever side of the road they wanted. You think traffic is bad now! Rules and regulations are made to protect people and to give some structure to life at home, school and work. Rules enable us to live together with lots of different people.

God also has rules for his people—rules that might seem impossible to follow. But the point of all the laws and rules in the book of Leviticus is that God wanted his people to be "holy" or "set apart" for him. Today, God has rules for you, too. But now, as in the time of the ancient Israelites, God's one desire is not to ruin your fun. Instead, he wants the very best for you in every aspect of your life.

life lessons

1 God wants us to be like him and "set apart" as his people (11:44–45; 20:26).

2 Holiness may seem impossible for you, but God has a plan for making it possible (20:8).

3 The Lord truly wants only the best for you and all believers (26:3–9,12).

The Burnt Offering

1 The Lord called to Moses and spoke to him from the Tent of Meeting. He said, ²"Speak to the Israelites and say to them: 'When any of you brings an offering to the Lord, bring as your offering an animal from either the herd or the flock.

³" 'If the offering is a burnt offering from the herd, he is to offer a male without defect. He must present it at the entrance to the Tent of Meeting so that it* will be acceptable to the Lord. ⁴He is to lay his hand on the head of the burnt offering, and it will be accepted on his behalf to make atonement for him. ⁵He is to slaughter the young bull before the Lord, and then Aaron's sons the priests shall bring the blood and sprinkle it against the altar on all sides at the entrance to the Tent of Meeting. ⁶He is to skin the burnt offering and cut it into pieces. ⁷The sons of Aaron the priest are to put fire on the altar and arrange wood on the fire. ⁸Then Aaron's sons the priests shall arrange the pieces, including the head and the fat, on the burning wood that is on the altar. ⁹He is to wash the inner parts and the legs with water, and the priest is to burn all of it on the altar. It is a burnt offering, an offering made by fire, an aroma pleasing to the Lord.

¹⁰" 'If the offering is a burnt offering from the flock, from either the sheep or the goats, he is to offer a male without defect. ¹¹He is to slaughter it at the north side of the altar before the Lord, and Aaron's sons the priests shall sprinkle its blood against the altar on all sides. ¹²He is to cut it into pieces, and the priest shall arrange them, including the head and the fat, on the burning wood that is on the altar. ¹³He is to wash the inner parts and the legs with water, and the priest is to bring all of it and burn it on the altar. It is a burnt offering, an offering made by fire, an aroma pleasing to the Lord.

¹⁴" 'If the offering to the Lord is a burnt offering of birds, he is to offer a dove or a young pigeon. ¹⁵The priest shall bring it to the altar, wring off the head and burn it on the altar; its blood shall be drained out on the side of the altar. ¹⁶He is to remove the crop with its contents* and throw it to the east side of the altar, where the ashes are. ¹⁷He shall tear it open by the wings, not severing it completely, and then the priest shall burn it on the wood that is on the fire on the altar. It is a burnt offering, an offering made by fire, an aroma pleasing to the Lord.

truth or dare

Blood, slaughter, sacrifice . . . sounds more like a horror film than the Bible. But this detailed plan for forgiveness teaches us that our holy God is serious about sin.

1:1–17

The Grain Offering

2 " 'When someone brings a grain offering to the Lord, his offering is to be of fine flour. He is to pour oil on it, put incense on it ²and take it to Aaron's sons the priests. The priest shall take a handful of the fine flour and oil, together with all the incense, and burn this as a memorial portion on the altar, an offering made by fire, an aroma pleasing to the Lord. ³The rest of the grain offering belongs to Aaron and his sons; it is a most holy part of the offerings made to the Lord by fire.

⁴" 'If you bring a grain offering baked in an oven, it is to consist of fine flour: cakes made without yeast and mixed with oil, or* wafers made without yeast and spread with oil. ⁵If your grain offering is prepared on a griddle, it is to be made of fine flour mixed with oil, and without yeast. ⁶Crumble it and pour oil on it; it is a grain offering. ⁷If your grain offering is cooked in a pan, it is to be made of fine flour and oil. ⁸Bring the grain offering made of these things to the Lord; present it to the priest, who shall take it to the altar. ⁹He shall take out the memorial portion from the grain offering and burn it on the altar as an offering made by fire, an aroma pleasing to the Lord. ¹⁰The rest of the grain offering belongs to Aaron and his sons; it is a most holy part of the offerings made to the Lord by fire.

¹¹" 'Every grain offering you bring to the Lord must be made without yeast, for you are not to burn any yeast or honey in an offering made to the Lord by fire. ¹²You may bring them to the Lord as an offering of the firstfruits, but they are not to be offered on the altar as a pleasing aroma.

a 3 Or he   *b 16* Or *crop and the feathers*; the meaning of the Hebrew for this word is uncertain.   *c 4* Or *and*

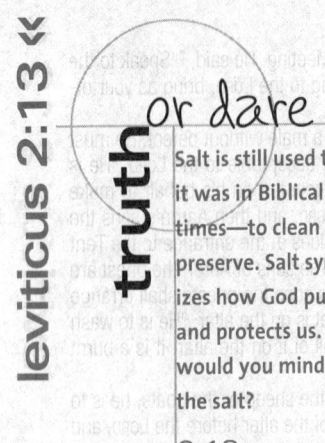

truth or dare

Salt is still used today as it was in Biblical times—to clean and preserve. Salt symbolizes how God purifies and protects us. So would you mind passing the salt?

2:13

¹³Season all your grain offerings with salt. Do not leave the salt of the covenant of your God out of your grain offerings; add salt to all your offerings.

¹⁴" 'If you bring a grain offering of firstfruits to the LORD, offer crushed heads of new grain roasted in the fire. ¹⁵Put oil and incense on it; it is a grain offering. ¹⁶The priest shall burn the memorial portion of the crushed grain and the oil, together with all the incense, as an offering made to the LORD by fire.

The Fellowship Offering

3 " 'If someone's offering is a fellowship offering,ᵃ and he offers an animal from the herd, whether male or female, he is to present before the LORD an animal without defect. ²He is to lay his hand on the head of his offering and slaughter it at the entrance to the Tent of Meeting. Then Aaron's sons the priests shall sprinkle the blood against the altar on all sides. ³From the fellowship offering he is to bring a sacrifice made to the LORD by fire: all the fat that covers the inner parts or is connected to them, ⁴both kidneys with the fat on them near the loins, and the covering of the liver, which he will remove with the kidneys. ⁵Then Aaron's sons are to burn it on the altar on top of the burnt offering that is on the burning wood, an offering made by fire, an aroma pleasing to the LORD.

⁶" 'If he offers an animal from the flock as a fellowship offering to the LORD, he is to offer a male or female without defect. ⁷If he offers a lamb, he is to present it before the LORD. ⁸He is to lay his hand on the head of his offering and slaughter it in front of the Tent of Meeting. Then Aaron's sons shall sprinkle its blood against the altar on all sides. ⁹From the fellowship offering he is to bring a sacrifice made to the LORD by fire: its fat, the entire fat tail cut off close to the backbone, all the fat that covers the inner parts or is connected to them, ¹⁰both kidneys with the fat on them near the loins, and the covering of the liver, which he will remove with the kidneys. ¹¹The priest shall burn them on the altar as food, an offering made to the LORD by fire.

¹²" 'If his offering is a goat, he is to present it before the LORD. ¹³He is to lay his hand on its head and slaughter it in front of the Tent of Meeting. Then Aaron's sons shall sprinkle its blood against the altar on all sides. ¹⁴From what he offers he is to make this offering to the LORD by fire: all the fat that covers the inner parts or is connected to them, ¹⁵both kidneys with the fat on them near the loins, and the covering of the liver, which he will remove with the kidneys. ¹⁶The priest shall burn them on the altar as food, an offering made by fire, a pleasing aroma. All the fat is the LORD's.

¹⁷" 'This is a lasting ordinance for the generations to come, wherever you live: You must not eat any fat or any blood.' "

The Sin Offering

4 The LORD said to Moses, ²"Say to the Israelites: 'When anyone sins unintentionally and does what is forbidden in any of the LORD's commands—

³" 'If the anointed priest sins, bringing guilt on the people, he must bring to the LORD a young bull without defect as a sin offering for the sin he has committed. ⁴He is to present the bull at the entrance to the Tent of Meeting before the LORD. He is to lay his hand on its head and slaughter it before the LORD. ⁵Then the anointed priest shall take some of the bull's blood and carry it into the Tent of Meeting. ⁶He is to dip his finger into the blood and sprinkle some of it seven times before the LORD, in front of the curtain of the sanctuary. ⁷The priest shall then put some of the blood on the horns of the altar of fragrant incense that is before the LORD in the Tent of Meeting. The rest of the bull's blood he shall pour out at the base of the altar of burnt offering at the entrance to the Tent of Meeting. ⁸He shall remove all the fat from the bull of the sin offering—the fat that covers the inner parts or is connected to them, ⁹both kidneys with the fat on them near the loins, and the covering of the liver, which he will remove with the kidneys— ¹⁰just as the fat is removed from the oxᵇ sac-

ᵃ 1 Traditionally *peace offering*; also in verses 3, 6 and 9   ᵇ 10 The Hebrew word can include both male and female.

in

focus

Casual or Not?

Profile: **Ashley**

I'm not sure how the word got out. I know Emma didn't want *me* to know, although she didn't try hard to keep it a secret at school. I guess it was inevitable that I'd find out at some point. But the story is that she had oral sex with a guy friend of ours last week. Just for fun. They're not dating, although they've always flirted with each other a lot. Emma took one look at my face this morning, and she knew I knew.

I skipped the small talk and asked her straight up. She tried to tell me it wasn't a big deal and not to give her grief, "It's not even sex, ask anyone." I just stared at her. How could I respond to *that*? This girl I've known since kindergarten, who's been one of my best friends for years, was avoiding my eyes and trying to convince me that the rules have changed.

Not even sex? I don't buy that.

I've been thinking about it all day now, trying to sort through what I think. *Purity* and *virginity* are words I don't hear often at school. But God's definition of sexual purity covers much more than intercourse. I know that my body belongs to him first and then to the man I will marry. If I share a few body parts with friends for recreation along the way, I'll be giving away my purity, little by little. Then what would I have left to give?

sex in focus

Daily messages from television, movies and public figures present us with a seemingly "new" definition of sex. Though oral sex poses nearly all the physical risks of sexual intercourse, some people believe that only intercourse is sex. Some students view oral sex as a casual alternative to intercourse. However, the physcial and emotional effects of oral sex are similar to intercourse.

If you have a friend who is engaging in risky sexual behavior, here's how you can help:
» Support your friend and pray for her, even though you disagree with her behavior.
» Form your own view of sexual purity, based on God's Word. Read 1 Thessalonians 4:3–8 (page 1562), 1 Corinthians 6:15–20 (page 1511) and 2 Corinthians 6:14 (page 1527) to find out what God has to say.

For more on this topic, see the index on page 1656.

rificed as a fellowship offering.[a] Then the priest shall burn them on the altar of burnt offering. ¹¹But the hide of the bull and all its flesh, as well as the head and legs, the inner parts and offal— ¹²that is, all the rest of the bull—he must take outside the camp to a place ceremonially clean, where the ashes are thrown, and burn it in a wood fire on the ash heap.

¹³" 'If the whole Israelite community sins unintentionally and does what is forbidden in any of the LORD's commands, even though the community is unaware of the matter, they are guilty. ¹⁴When they become aware of the sin they committed, the assembly must bring a young bull as a

a 10 Traditionally *peace offering*; also in verses 26, 31 and 35 sin offering and present it before the Tent of Meeting. ¹⁵The elders of the community are to lay their hands on the bull's head before the LORD, and the bull shall be slaughtered before the LORD. ¹⁶Then the anointed priest is to take some of the bull's blood into the Tent of Meeting. ¹⁷He shall dip his finger into the blood and sprinkle it before the LORD seven times in front of the curtain. ¹⁸He is to put some of the blood on the horns of the altar that is before the LORD in the Tent of Meeting. The rest of the blood he shall pour out at the base of the altar of burnt offering at the entrance to the Tent of Meeting. ¹⁹He shall remove all the fat from it and burn it on the altar, ²⁰and do with this bull just as he did with the bull for the sin offering. In this way the priest will make atonement for them, and they will be forgiven. ²¹Then he shall take the bull outside the camp and burn it as he burned the first bull. This is the sin offering for the community.

²²" 'When a leader sins unintentionally and does what is forbidden in any of the commands of the LORD his God, he is guilty. ²³When he is made aware of the sin he committed, he must bring as his offering a male goat without defect. ²⁴He is to lay his hand on the goat's head and slaughter it at the place where the burnt offering is slaughtered before the LORD. It is a sin offering. ²⁵Then the priest shall take some of the blood of the sin offering with his finger and put it on the horns of the altar of burnt offering and pour out the rest of the blood at the base of the altar. ²⁶He shall burn all the fat on the altar as he burned the fat of the fellowship offering. In this way the priest will make atonement for the man's sin, and he will be forgiven.

²⁷" 'If a member of the community sins unintentionally and does what is forbidden in any of the LORD's commands, he is guilty. ²⁸When he is made aware of the sin he committed, he must bring as his offering for the sin he committed a female goat without defect. ²⁹He is to lay his hand on the head of the sin offering and slaughter it at the place of the burnt offering. ³⁰Then the priest is to take some of the blood with his finger and put it on the horns of the altar of burnt offering and pour out the rest of the blood at the base of the altar. ³¹He shall remove all the fat, just as the fat is removed from the fellowship offering, and the priest shall burn it on the altar as an aroma pleasing to the LORD. In this way the priest will make atonement for him, and he will be forgiven.

³²" 'If he brings a lamb as his sin offering, he is to bring a female without defect. ³³He is to lay his hand on its head and slaughter it for a sin offering at the place where the burnt offering is slaughtered. ³⁴Then the priest shall take some of the blood of the sin offering with his finger and put it on the horns of the altar of burnt offering and pour out the rest of the blood at the base of the altar. ³⁵He shall remove all the fat, just as the fat is removed from the lamb of the fellowship offering, and the priest shall burn it on the altar on top of the offerings made to the LORD by fire. In this way the priest will make atonement for him for the sin he has committed, and he will be forgiven.

5" 'If a person sins because he does not speak up when he hears a public charge to testify regarding something he has seen or learned about, he will be held responsible.
²" 'Or if a person touches anything ceremonially unclean—whether the carcasses of unclean wild animals or of unclean livestock or of unclean creatures that move along the ground—even though he is unaware of it, he has become unclean and is guilty.

³" 'Or if he touches human uncleanness—anything that would make him unclean—even though he is unaware of it, when he learns of it he will be guilty.

⁴" 'Or if a person thoughtlessly takes an oath to do anything, whether good or evil—in any matter one might carelessly swear about—even though he is unaware of it, in any case when he learns of it he will be guilty.

⁵" 'When anyone is guilty in any of these ways, he must confess in what way he has sinned ⁶and, as a penalty for the sin he has committed, he must bring to the LORD a female lamb or goat from the flock as a sin offering; and the priest shall make atonement for him for his sin.

⁷" 'If he cannot afford a lamb, he is to bring two doves or two

truth or dare
A friend just pointed out a personal sin that you were clueless about . . . what's your next move? Make excuses? Deny everything? God is pleased if, after seeing your faults, you humbly acknowledge them.
5:5

young pigeons to the Lord as a penalty for his sin—one for a sin offering and the other for a burnt offering. [8]He is to bring them to the priest, who shall first offer the one for the sin offering. He is to wring its head from its neck, not severing it completely, [9]and is to sprinkle some of the blood of the sin offering against the side of the altar; rest of the blood must be drained out at the base of the altar. It is a sin offering. [10]The priest shall then offer the other as a burnt offering in the prescribed way and make atonement for him for the sin he has committed, and he will be forgiven.

[11]" 'If, however, he cannot afford two doves or two young pigeons, he is to bring as an offering for his sin a tenth of an ephah[a] of fine flour for a sin offering. He must not put oil or incense on it, because it is a sin offering. [12]He is to bring it to the priest, who shall take a handful of it as a memorial portion and burn it on the altar on top of the offerings made to the Lord by fire. It is a sin offering. [13]In this way the priest will make atonement for him for any of these sins he has committed, and he will be forgiven. The rest of the offering will belong to the priest, as in the case of the grain offering.' "

The Guilt Offering

[14]The Lord said to Moses: [15]"When a person commits a violation and sins unintentionally in regard to any of the Lord's holy things, he is to bring to the Lord as a penalty a ram from the flock, one without defect and of the proper value in silver, according to the sanctuary shekel.[b] It is a guilt offering. [16]He must make restitution for what he has failed to do in regard to the holy things, add a fifth of the value to that and give it all to the priest, who will make atonement for him with the ram as a guilt offering, and he will be forgiven.

[17]"If a person sins and does what is forbidden in any of the Lord's commands, even though he does not know it, he is guilty and will be held responsible. [18]He is to bring to the priest as a guilt offering a ram from the flock, one without defect and of the proper value. In this way the priest will make atonement for him for the wrong he has committed unintentionally, and he will be forgiven. [19]It is a guilt offering; he has been guilty of[c] wrongdoing against the Lord."

6 The Lord said to Moses: [2]"If anyone sins and is unfaithful to the Lord by deceiving his neighbor about something entrusted to him or left in his care or stolen, or if he cheats him, [3]or if he finds lost property and lies about it, or if he swears falsely, or if he commits any such sin that people may do— [4]when he thus sins and becomes guilty, he must return what he has stolen or taken by extortion, or what was entrusted to him, or the lost property he found, [5]or whatever it was he swore falsely about. He must make restitution in full, add a fifth of the value to it and give it all to the owner on the day he presents his guilt offering. [6]And as a penalty he must bring to the priest, that is, to the Lord, his guilt offering, a ram from the flock, one without defect and of the proper value. [7]In this way the priest will make atonement for him before the Lord, and he will be forgiven for any of these things he did that made him guilty."

The Burnt Offering

[8]The Lord said to Moses: [9]"Give Aaron and his sons this command: 'These are the regulations for the burnt offering: The burnt offering is to remain on the altar hearth throughout the night, till morning, and the fire must be kept burning on the altar. [10]The priest shall then put on his linen clothes, with linen undergarments next to his body, and shall remove the ashes of the burnt offering that the fire has consumed on the altar and place them beside the altar. [11]Then he is to take off these clothes and put on others, and carry the ashes outside the camp to a place that is ceremonially clean. [12]The fire on the altar must be kept burning; it must not go out. Every morning the priest is to add firewood and arrange the burnt offering on the fire and burn the fat of the fellowship offerings[d] on it. [13]The fire must be kept burning on the altar continuously; it must not go out.

The Grain Offering

[14]" 'These are the regulations for the grain offering: Aaron's sons are to bring it before the Lord, in front of the altar. [15]The priest is to take a handful of fine flour and oil, together with all the incense on the grain offering, and burn the memorial portion on the altar as an aroma pleasing to the Lord. [16]Aaron and his sons shall eat the rest of it, but it is to be eaten without yeast in a holy place; they

---

a 11 That is, probably about 2 quarts (about 2 liters)   *b 15 That is, about 2/5 ounce (about 11.5 grams)*   *c 19 Or has made full expiation for his*   *d 12 Traditionally peace offerings* are to eat it in the courtyard of the Tent of Meeting. ¹⁷It must not be baked with yeast; I have given it as their share of the offerings made to me by fire. Like the sin offering and the guilt offering, it is most holy. ¹⁸Any male descendant of Aaron may eat it. It is his regular share of the offerings made to the LORD by fire for the generations to come. Whatever touches them will become holy.ᵃ' "

¹⁹The LORD also said to Moses, ²⁰"This is the offering Aaron and his sons are to bring to the LORD on the day heᵇ is anointed: a tenth of an ephahᶜ of fine flour as a regular grain offering, half of it in the morning and half in the evening. ²¹Prepare it with oil on a griddle; bring it well-mixed and present the grain offering brokenᵈ in pieces as an aroma pleasing to the LORD. ²²The son who is to succeed him as anointed priest shall prepare it. It is the LORD's regular share and is to be burned completely. ²³Every grain offering of a priest shall be burned completely; it must not be eaten."

The Sin Offering

²⁴The LORD said to Moses, ²⁵"Say to Aaron and his sons: 'These are the regulations for the sin offering: The sin offering is to be slaughtered before the LORD in the place the burnt offering is slaughtered; it is most holy. ²⁶The priest who offers it shall eat it; it is to be eaten in a holy place, in the courtyard of the Tent of Meeting. ²⁷Whatever touches any of the flesh will become holy, and if any of the blood is spattered on a garment, you must wash it in a holy place. ²⁸The clay pot the meat is cooked in must be broken; but if it is cooked in a bronze pot, the pot is to be scoured and rinsed with water. ²⁹Any male in a priest's family may eat it; it is most holy. ³⁰But any sin offering whose blood is brought into the Tent of Meeting to make atonement in the Holy Place must not be eaten; it must be burned.

The Guilt Offering

7 " 'These are the regulations for the guilt offering, which is most holy: ²The guilt offering is to be slaughtered in the place where the burnt offering is slaughtered, and its blood is to be sprinkled against the altar on all sides. ³All its fat shall be offered: the fat tail and the fat that covers the inner parts, ⁴both kidneys with the fat on them near the loins, and the covering of the liver, which is to be removed with the kidneys. ⁵The priest shall burn them on the altar as an offering made to the LORD by fire. It is a guilt offering. ⁶Any male in a priest's family may eat it, but it must be eaten in a holy place; it is most holy.

⁷" 'The same law applies to both the sin offering and the guilt offering: They belong to the priest who makes atonement with them. ⁸The priest who offers a burnt offering for anyone may keep its hide for himself. ⁹Every grain offering baked in an oven or cooked in a pan or on a griddle belongs to the priest who offers it, ¹⁰and every grain offering, whether mixed with oil or dry, belongs equally to all the sons of Aaron.

The Fellowship Offering

¹¹" 'These are the regulations for the fellowship offeringᵉ a person may present to the LORD:

¹²" 'If he offers it as an expression of thankfulness, then along with this thank offering he is to offer cakes of bread made without yeast and mixed with oil, wafers made without yeast and spread with oil, and cakes of fine flour well-kneaded and mixed with oil. ¹³Along with his fellowship offering of thanksgiving he is to present an offering with cakes of bread made with yeast. ¹⁴He is to bring one of each kind as an offering, a contribution to the LORD; it belongs to the priest who sprinkles the blood of the fellowship offerings. ¹⁵The meat of his fellowship offering of thanksgiving must be eaten on the day it is offered; he must leave none of it till morning.

¹⁶" 'If, however, his offering is the result of a vow or is a freewill offering, the sacrifice shall be eaten on the day he offers it, but anything left over may be eaten on the next day. ¹⁷Any meat of the sacrifice left over till the third day must be burned up. ¹⁸If any meat of the fellowship offering is eaten on the third day, it will not be accepted. It will not be credited to the one who offered it, for it is impure; the person who eats any of it will be held responsible.

¹⁹" 'Meat that touches anything ceremonially unclean must not be eaten; it must be burned up. As for other meat, anyone ceremonially clean may eat it. ²⁰But if anyone who is unclean eats any

---

ᵃ 18 Or *Whoever touches them must be holy*; similarly in verse 27   ᵇ 20 Or *each*   ᶜ 20 That is, probably about 2 quarts (about 2 liters)   ᵈ 21 The meaning of the Hebrew for this word is uncertain.   ᵉ 11 Traditionally *peace offering*; also in verses 13-37 meat of the fellowship offering belonging to the LORD, that person must be cut off from his people. [21]If anyone touches something unclean—whether human uncleanness or an unclean animal or any unclean, detestable thing—and then eats any of the meat of the fellowship offering belonging to the LORD, that person must be cut off from his people.' "

Eating Fat and Blood Forbidden

[22]The LORD said to Moses, [23]"Say to the Israelites: 'Do not eat any of the fat of cattle, sheep or goats. [24]The fat of an animal found dead or torn by wild animals may be used for any other purpose, but you must not eat it. [25]Anyone who eats the fat of an animal from which an offering by fire may be[a] made to the LORD must be cut off from his people. [26]And wherever you live, you must not eat the blood of any bird or animal. [27]If anyone eats blood, that person must be cut off from his people.' "

The Priests' Share

[28]The LORD said to Moses, [29]"Say to the Israelites: 'Anyone who brings a fellowship offering to the LORD is to bring part of it as his sacrifice to the LORD. [30]With his own hands he is to bring the offering made to the LORD by fire; he is to bring the fat, together with the breast, and wave the breast before the LORD as a wave offering. [31]The priest shall burn the fat on the altar, but the breast belongs to Aaron and his sons. [32]You are to give the right thigh of your fellowship offerings to the priest as a contribution. [33]The son of Aaron who offers the blood and the fat of the fellowship offering shall have the right thigh as his share. [34]From the fellowship offerings of the Israelites, I have taken the breast that is waved and the thigh that is presented and have given them to Aaron the priest and his sons as their regular share from the Israelites.' "

[35]This is the portion of the offerings made to the LORD by fire that were allotted to Aaron and his sons on the day they were presented to serve the LORD as priests. [36]On the day they were anointed, the LORD commanded that the Israelites give this to them as their regular share for the generations to come.

[37]These, then, are the regulations for the burnt offering, the grain offering, the sin offering, the guilt offering, the ordination offering and the fellowship offering, [38]which the LORD gave Moses on Mount Sinai on the day he commanded the Israelites to bring their offerings to the LORD, in the Desert of Sinai.

The Ordination of Aaron and His Sons

8 The LORD said to Moses, [2]"Bring Aaron and his sons, their garments, the anointing oil, the bull for the sin offering, the two rams and the basket containing bread made without yeast, [3]and gather the entire assembly at the entrance to the Tent of Meeting." [4]Moses did as the LORD commanded him, and the assembly gathered at the entrance to the Tent of Meeting.

[5]Moses said to the assembly, "This is what the LORD has commanded to be done." [6]Then Moses brought Aaron and his sons forward and washed them with water. [7]He put the tunic on Aaron, tied the sash around him, clothed him with the robe and put the ephod on him. He also tied the ephod to him by its skillfully woven waistband; so it was fastened on him. [8]He placed the breastpiece on him and put the Urim and Thummim in the breastpiece. [9]Then he placed the turban on Aaron's head and set the gold plate, the sacred diadem, on the front of it, as the LORD commanded Moses.

[10]Then Moses took the anointing oil and anointed the tabernacle and everything in it, and so consecrated them. [11]He sprinkled some of the oil on the altar seven times, anointing the altar and all its utensils and the basin with its stand, to consecrate them. [12]He poured some of the anointing oil on Aaron's head and anointed him to consecrate him. [13]Then he brought Aaron's sons forward, put tunics on them, tied sashes around them and put headbands on them, as the LORD commanded Moses.

a 25 Or fire is

¹⁴He then presented the bull for the sin offering, and Aaron and his sons laid their hands on its head. ¹⁵Moses slaughtered the bull and took some of the blood, and with his finger he put it on all the horns of the altar to purify the altar. He poured out the rest of the blood at the base of the altar. So he consecrated it to make atonement for it. ¹⁶Moses also took all the fat around the inner parts, the covering of the liver, and both kidneys and their fat, and burned it on the altar. ¹⁷But the bull with its hide and its flesh and its offal he burned up outside the camp, as the LORD commanded Moses.

¹⁸He then presented the ram for the burnt offering, and Aaron and his sons laid their hands on its head. ¹⁹Then Moses slaughtered the ram and sprinkled the blood against the altar on all sides. ²⁰He cut the ram into pieces and burned the head, the pieces and the fat. ²¹He washed the inner parts and the legs with water and burned the whole ram on the altar as a burnt offering, a pleasing aroma, an offering made to the LORD by fire, as the LORD commanded Moses.

²²He then presented the other ram, the ram for the ordination, and Aaron and his sons laid their hands on its head. ²³Moses slaughtered the ram and took some of its blood and put it on the lobe of Aaron's right ear, on the thumb of his right hand and on the big toe of his right foot. ²⁴Moses also brought Aaron's sons forward and put some of the blood on the lobes of their right ears, on the thumbs of their right hands and on the big toes of their right feet. Then he sprinkled blood against the altar on all sides. ²⁵He took the fat, the fat tail, all the fat around the inner parts, the covering of the liver, both kidneys and their fat and the right thigh. ²⁶Then from the basket of bread made without yeast, which was before the LORD, he took a cake of bread, and one made with oil, and a wafer; he put these on the fat portions and on the right thigh. ²⁷He put all these in the hands of Aaron and his sons and waved them before the LORD as a wave offering. ²⁸Then Moses took them from their hands and burned them on the altar on top of the burnt offering as an ordination offering, a pleasing aroma, an offering made to the LORD by fire. ²⁹He also took the breast—Moses' share of the ordination ram—and waved it before the LORD as a wave offering, as the LORD commanded Moses.

³⁰Then Moses took some of the anointing oil and some of the blood from the altar and sprinkled them on Aaron and his garments and on his sons and their garments. So he consecrated Aaron and his garments and his sons and their garments.

³¹Moses then said to Aaron and his sons, "Cook the meat at the entrance to the Tent of Meeting and eat it there with the bread from the basket of ordination offerings, as I commanded, saying,ᵃ 'Aaron and his sons are to eat it.' ³²Then burn up the rest of the meat and the bread. ³³Do not leave the entrance to the Tent of Meeting for seven days, until the days of your ordination are completed, for your ordination will last seven days. ³⁴What has been done today was commanded by the LORD to make atonement for you. ³⁵You must stay at the entrance to the Tent of Meeting day and night for seven days and do what the LORD requires, so you will not die; for that is what I have been commanded." ³⁶So Aaron and his sons did everything the LORD commanded through Moses.

The Priests Begin Their Ministry

9 On the eighth day Moses summoned Aaron and his sons and the elders of Israel. ²He said to Aaron, "Take a bull calf for your sin offering and a ram for your burnt offering, both without defect, and present them before the LORD. ³Then say to the Israelites: 'Take a male goat for a sin offering, a calf and a lamb—both a year old and without defect—for a burnt offering, ⁴and an oxᵇ and a ram for a fellowship offeringᶜ to sacrifice before the LORD, together with a grain offering mixed with oil. For today the LORD will appear to you.' "

⁵They took the things Moses commanded to the front of the Tent of Meeting, and the entire assembly came near and stood before the LORD. ⁶Then Moses said, "This is what the LORD has commanded you to do, so that the glory of the LORD may appear to you."

⁷Moses said to Aaron, "Come to the altar and sacrifice your sin offering and your burnt offering and make atonement for yourself and the people; sacrifice the offering that is for the people and make atonement for them, as the LORD has commanded."

⁸So Aaron came to the altar and slaughtered the calf as a sin offering for himself. ⁹His sons brought the blood to him, and he dipped his finger into the blood and put it on the horns of the

ᵃ 31 Or I was commanded: ᵇ 4 The Hebrew word can include both male and female; also in verses 18 and 19.
ᶜ 4 Traditionally peace offering; also in verses 18 and 22

mirror images

When Shechem . . . saw her, he took her and violated her. His heart was drawn to Dinah . . . and he loved the girl and spoke tenderly to her. Genesis 34:2–3

Dinah—Love's Not Like That

How was the girl supposed to respond? Here was this guy sweet-talking her—the same guy who had moments before taken advantage of her. Double-talk. Two-faced. Whatever you want to call it, Dinah knew the pain of someone talking one way and acting another. It's confusing. It's painful and manipulative. It's just not right.

Yet it happens all the time in relationships. Many guys are willing to give love in order to experience sex. And they usually want the sex first. Girls are just the opposite. They are often more willing to give sex in order to experience love. In Dinah's case, she wasn't a willing participant in either. But she had to wonder after it was over, *Is this all there is to love? He gets what he wants and then he trifles with my emotions?* While, thankfully, not everyone can relate to Dinah's physical rape, many girls often experience emotional rape when it comes to relationships. A guy who manipulates a situation by telling a girl what she wants to hear is dangerous. Don't blow it off as merely smooth talking or just messing with girls' minds. It can be a subtle form of abuse.

Abusive relationships are frightening because of the power one person has over another person—emotionally and often physically. Sometimes we don't even recognize a relationship as being abusive until it becomes painfully obvious.

Fortunately, like Dinah, who was quickly avenged by her overly-zealous brothers, we too have an avenger. His name is Jesus Christ. If you need deliverance from an abusive relationship, he'll give you the strength to take the right steps. If you need healing, he is by your side.

To read the next Mirror Images profile, go to page 170.

Dear Jesus, help me not to confuse lust and love when it comes to relationships. Show me what true love is through an intimate relationship with you. Amen.

dear Jesus

» 129

»» Read more about Dinah in Genesis 34 (pages 44–45).

altar; the rest of the blood he poured out at the base of the altar. ¹⁰On the altar he burned the fat, the kidneys and the covering of the liver from the sin offering, as the Lord commanded Moses; ¹¹the flesh and the hide he burned up outside the camp.

¹²Then he slaughtered the burnt offering. His sons handed him the blood, and he sprinkled it against the altar on all sides. ¹³They handed him the burnt offering piece by piece, including the head, and he burned them on the altar. ¹⁴He washed the inner parts and the legs and burned them on top of the burnt offering on the altar.

¹⁵Aaron then brought the offering that was for the people. He took the goat for the people's sin offering and slaughtered it and offered it for a sin offering as he did with the first one.

¹⁶He brought the burnt offering and offered it in the prescribed way. ¹⁷He also brought the grain offering, took a handful of it and burned it on the altar in addition to the morning's burnt offering.

¹⁸He slaughtered the ox and the ram as the fellowship offering for the people. His sons handed him the blood, and he sprinkled it against the altar on all sides. ¹⁹But the fat portions of the ox and the ram—the fat tail, the layer of fat, the kidneys and the covering of the liver— ²⁰these they laid on the breasts, and then Aaron burned the fat on the altar. ²¹Aaron waved the breasts and the right thigh before the Lord as a wave offering, as Moses commanded.

²²Then Aaron lifted his hands toward the people and blessed them. And having sacrificed the sin offering, the burnt offering and the fellowship offering, he stepped down.

²³Moses and Aaron then went into the Tent of Meeting. When they came out, they blessed the people; and the glory of the Lord appeared to all the people. ²⁴Fire came out from the presence of the Lord and consumed the burnt offering and the fat portions on the altar. And when all the people saw it, they shouted for joy and fell facedown.

The Death of Nadab and Abihu

10 Aaron's sons Nadab and Abihu took their censers, put fire in them and added incense; and they offered unauthorized fire before the Lord, contrary to his command. ²So fire came out from the presence of the Lord and consumed them, and they died before the Lord. ³Moses then said to Aaron, "This is what the Lord spoke of when he said:

" 'Among those who approach me
I will show myself holy;
in the sight of all the people
I will be honored.' "

Aaron remained silent.

⁴Moses summoned Mishael and Elzaphan, sons of Aaron's uncle Uzziel, and said to them, "Come here; carry your cousins outside the camp, away from the front of the sanctuary." ⁵So they came and carried them, still in their tunics, outside the camp, as Moses ordered.

⁶Then Moses said to Aaron and his sons Eleazar and Ithamar, "Do not let your hair become unkempt,ᵃ and do not tear your clothes, or you will die and the Lord will be angry with the whole community. But your relatives, all the house of Israel, may mourn for those the Lord has destroyed by fire. ⁷Do not leave the entrance to the Tent of Meeting or you will die, because the Lord's anointing oil is on you." So they did as Moses said.

⁸Then the Lord said to Aaron, ⁹"You and your sons are not to drink wine or other fermented drink whenever you go into the Tent of Meeting, or you will die. This is a lasting ordinance for the generations to come. ¹⁰You must distinguish between the holy and the common, between the unclean and the clean, ¹¹and you must teach the Israelites all the decrees the Lord has given them through Moses."

¹²Moses said to Aaron and his remaining sons, Eleazar and Ith-

truth or dare

"At times every girl faces a problem where the answer is unclear. The more you read God's Word, the more you can sort out right and wrong in these "gray areas.""

10:10–11

ᵃ 6 Or Do not uncover your heads

genuine

reverence » 10:12

Moses gives these instructions to Aaron's "remaining sons." The other two had just been burned up because they had treated the people's offerings carelessly. How could a loving God do that? While we know that God is loving, merciful and compassionate, we must also remember that he is holy—set apart, spotless and perfect. Think about it. How do you approach God at church or in your quiet time? Are you flippant and careless, or do you show the Lord heartfelt respect?

amar, "Take the grain offering left over from the offerings made to the LORD by fire and eat it prepared without yeast beside the altar, for it is most holy. [13]Eat it in a holy place, because it is your share and your sons' share of the offerings made to the LORD by fire; for so I have been commanded. [14]But you and your sons and your daughters may eat the breast that was waved and the thigh that was presented. Eat them in a ceremonially clean place; they have been given to you and your children as your share of the Israelites' fellowship offerings.[a] [15]The thigh that was presented and the breast that was waved must be brought with the fat portions of the offerings made by fire, to be waved before the LORD as a wave offering. This will be the regular share for you and your children, as the LORD has commanded."

[16]When Moses inquired about the goat of the sin offering and found that it had been burned up, he was angry with Eleazar and Ithamar, Aaron's remaining sons, and asked, [17]"Why didn't you eat the sin offering in the sanctuary area? It is most holy; it was given to you to take away the guilt of the community by making atonement for them before the LORD. [18]Since its blood was not taken into the Holy Place, you should have eaten the goat in the sanctuary area, as I commanded."

[19]Aaron replied to Moses, "Today they sacrificed their sin offering and their burnt offering before the LORD, but such things as this have happened to me. Would the LORD have been pleased if I had eaten the sin offering today?" [20]When Moses heard this, he was satisfied.

Clean and Unclean Food

11 The LORD said to Moses and Aaron, [2]"Say to the Israelites: 'Of all the animals that live on land, these are the ones you may eat: [3]You may eat any animal that has a split hoof completely divided and that chews the cud.

[4]'There are some that only chew the cud or only have a split hoof, but you must not eat them. The camel, though it chews the cud, does not have a split hoof; it is ceremonially unclean for you. [5]The coney,[b] though it chews the cud, does not have a split hoof; it is unclean for you. [6]The rabbit, though it chews the cud, does not have a split hoof; it is unclean for you. [7]And the pig, though it has a split hoof completely divided, does not chew the cud; it is unclean for you. [8]You must not eat their meat or touch their carcasses; they are unclean for you.

[9]'Of all the creatures living in the water of the seas and the streams, you may eat any that have fins and scales. [10]But all creatures in the seas or streams that do not have fins and scales—whether among all the swarming things or among all the other living creatures in the water—you are to detest. [11]And since you are to detest them, you must not eat their meat and you must detest their carcasses. [12]Anything living in the water that does not have fins and scales is to be detestable to you.

[13]'These are the birds you are to detest and not eat because they are detestable: the eagle, the vulture, the black vulture, [14]the red kite, any kind of black kite, [15]any kind of raven, [16]the horned owl, the screech owl, the gull, any kind of hawk, [17]the little owl, the cormorant, the great owl, [18]the white owl, the desert owl, the osprey, [19]the stork, any kind of heron, the hoopoe and the bat.[c]

a 14 Traditionally *peace offerings*   *b 5* That is, the hyrax or rock badger   *c 19* The precise identification of some of the birds, insects and animals in this chapter is uncertain.

²⁰" 'All flying insects that walk on all fours are to be detestable to you. ²¹There are, however, some winged creatures that walk on all fours that you may eat: those that have jointed legs for hopping on the ground. ²²Of these you may eat any kind of locust, katydid, cricket or grasshopper. ²³But all other winged creatures that have four legs you are to detest.

²⁴" 'You will make yourselves unclean by these; whoever touches their carcasses will be unclean till evening. ²⁵Whoever picks up one of their carcasses must wash his clothes, and he will be unclean till evening.

²⁶" 'Every animal that has a split hoof not completely divided or that does not chew the cud is unclean for you; whoever touches ˌthe carcass ofˌ any of them will be unclean. ²⁷Of all the animals that walk on all fours, those that walk on their paws are unclean for you; whoever touches their carcasses will be unclean till evening. ²⁸Anyone who picks up their carcasses must wash his clothes, and he will be unclean till evening. They are unclean for you.

²⁹" 'Of the animals that move about on the ground, these are unclean for you: the weasel, the rat, any kind of great lizard, ³⁰the gecko, the monitor lizard, the wall lizard, the skink and the chameleon. ³¹Of all those that move along the ground, these are unclean for you. Whoever touches them when they are dead will be unclean till evening. ³²When one of them dies and falls on something, that article, whatever its use, will be unclean, whether it is made of wood, cloth, hide or sackcloth. Put it in water; it will be unclean till evening, and then it will be clean. ³³If one of them falls into a clay pot, everything in it will be unclean, and you must break the pot. ³⁴Any food that could be eaten but has water on it from such a pot is unclean, and any liquid that could be drunk from it is unclean. ³⁵Anything that one of their carcasses falls on becomes unclean; an oven or cooking pot must be broken up. They are unclean, and you are to regard them as unclean. ³⁶A spring, however, or a cistern for collecting water remains clean, but anyone who touches one of these carcasses is unclean. ³⁷If a carcass falls on any seeds that are to be planted, they remain clean. ³⁸But if water has been put on the seed and a carcass falls on it, it is unclean for you.

³⁹" 'If an animal that you are allowed to eat dies, anyone who touches the carcass will be unclean till evening. ⁴⁰Anyone who eats some of the carcass must wash his clothes, and he will be unclean till evening. Anyone who picks up the carcass must wash his clothes, and he will be unclean till evening.

⁴¹" 'Every creature that moves about on the ground is detestable; it is not to be eaten. ⁴²You are not to eat any creature that moves about on the ground, whether it moves on its belly or walks on all fours or on many feet; it is detestable. ⁴³Do not defile yourselves by any of these creatures. Do not make yourselves unclean by means of them or be made unclean by them. ⁴⁴I am the LORD your God; consecrate yourselves and be holy, because I am holy. Do not make yourselves unclean by any creature that moves about on the ground. ⁴⁵I am the LORD who brought you up out of Egypt to be your God; therefore be holy, because I am holy.

⁴⁶" 'These are the regulations concerning animals, birds, every living thing that moves in the water and every creature that moves about on the ground. ⁴⁷You must distinguish between the unclean and the clean, between living creatures that may be eaten and those that may not be eaten.' "

Purification After Childbirth

12 The LORD said to Moses, ²"Say to the Israelites: 'A woman who becomes pregnant and gives birth to a son will be ceremonially unclean for seven days, just as she is unclean during her monthly period. ³On the eighth day the boy is to be circumcised. ⁴Then the woman must wait thirty-three days to be purified from her bleeding. She must not touch anything sacred or go to the sanctuary until the days of her purification are over. ⁵If she gives birth to a daughter, for two weeks the woman will be unclean, as during her period. Then she must wait sixty-six days to be purified from her bleeding.

⁶" 'When the days of her purification for a son or daughter are over, she is to bring to the priest at the entrance to the Tent of Meeting a year-old lamb for a burnt offering and a young pigeon or a dove for a sin offering. ⁷He shall offer them before the LORD to make atonement for her, and then she will be ceremonially clean from her flow of blood.

" 'These are the regulations for the woman who gives birth to a boy or a girl. ⁸If she cannot afford a lamb, she is to bring two doves or two young pigeons, one for a burnt offering and the other for a sin offering. In this way the priest will make atonement for her, and she will be clean.' "

Regulations About Infectious Skin Diseases

13 The LORD said to Moses and Aaron, [2]"When anyone has a swelling or a rash or a bright spot on his skin that may become an infectious skin disease, [a] he must be brought to Aaron the priest or to one of his sons [b] who is a priest. [3]The priest is to examine the sore on his skin, and if the hair in the sore has turned white and the sore appears to be more than skin deep, [c] it is an infectious skin disease. When the priest examines him, he shall pronounce him ceremonially unclean. [4]If the spot on his skin is white but does not appear to be more than skin deep and the hair in it has not turned white, the priest is to put the infected person in isolation for seven days. [5]On the seventh day the priest is to examine him, and if he sees that the sore is unchanged and has not spread in the skin, he is to keep him in isolation another seven days. [6]On the seventh day the priest is to examine him again, and if the sore has faded and has not spread in the skin, the priest shall pronounce him clean; it is only a rash. The man must wash his clothes, and he will be clean. [7]But if the rash does spread in his skin after he has shown himself to the priest to be pronounced clean, he must appear before the priest again. [8]The priest is to examine him, and if the rash has spread in the skin, he shall pronounce him unclean; it is an infectious disease.

[9]"When anyone has an infectious skin disease, he must be brought to the priest. [10]The priest is to examine him, and if there is a white swelling in the skin that has turned the hair white and if there is raw flesh in the swelling, [11]it is a chronic skin disease and the priest shall pronounce him unclean. He is not to put him in isolation, because he is already unclean.

[12]"If the disease breaks out all over his skin and, so far as the priest can see, it covers all the skin of the infected person from head to foot, [13]the priest is to examine him, and if the disease has covered his whole body, he shall pronounce that person clean. Since it has all turned white, he is clean. [14]But whenever raw flesh appears on him, he will be unclean. [15]When the priest sees the raw flesh, he shall pronounce him unclean. The raw flesh is unclean; he has an infectious disease. [16]Should the raw flesh change and turn white, he must go to the priest. [17]The priest is to examine him, and if the sores have turned white, the priest shall pronounce the infected person clean; then he will be clean.

[18]"When someone has a boil on his skin and it heals, [19]and in the place where the boil was, a white swelling or reddish-white spot appears, he must present himself to the priest. [20]The priest is to examine it, and if it appears to be more than skin deep and

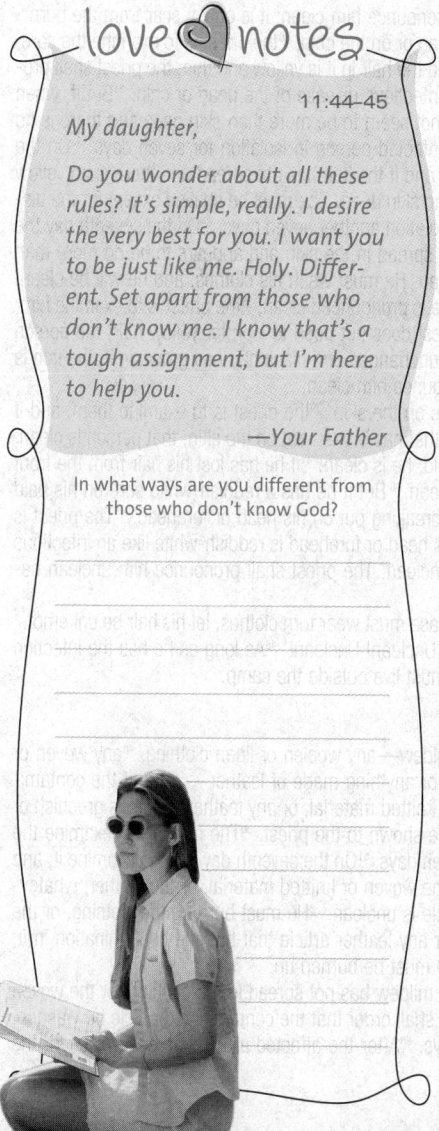

love notes

11:44–45

My daughter,

Do you wonder about all these rules? It's simple, really. I desire the very best for you. I want you to be just like me. Holy. Different. Set apart from those who don't know me. I know that's a tough assignment, but I'm here to help you.

—Your Father

In what ways are you different from those who don't know God?

---

[a] 2 Traditionally *leprosy*; the Hebrew word was used for various diseases affecting the skin—not necessarily leprosy; also elsewhere in this chapter.
[b] 2 Or *descendants*   [c] 3 Or *be lower than the rest of the skin*; also elsewhere in this chapter

the hair in it has turned white, the priest shall pronounce him unclean. It is an infectious skin disease that has broken out where the boil was. ²¹But if, when the priest examines it, there is no white hair in it and it is not more than skin deep and has faded, then the priest is to put him in isolation for seven days. ²²If it is spreading in the skin, the priest shall pronounce him unclean; it is infectious. ²³But if the spot is unchanged and has not spread, it is only a scar from the boil, and the priest shall pronounce him clean.

²⁴"When someone has a burn on his skin and a reddish-white or white spot appears in the raw flesh of the burn, ²⁵the priest is to examine the spot, and if the hair in it has turned white, and it appears to be more than skin deep, it is an infectious disease that has broken out in the burn. The priest shall pronounce him unclean; it is an infectious skin disease. ²⁶But if the priest examines it and there is no white hair in the spot and if it is not more than skin deep and has faded, then the priest is to put him in isolation for seven days. ²⁷On the seventh day the priest is to examine him, and if it is spreading in the skin, the priest shall pronounce him unclean; it is an infectious skin disease. ²⁸If, however, the spot is unchanged and has not spread in the skin but has faded, it is a swelling from the burn, and the priest shall pronounce him clean; it is only a scar from the burn.

²⁹"If a man or woman has a sore on the head or on the chin, ³⁰the priest is to examine the sore, and if it appears to be more than skin deep and the hair in it is yellow and thin, the priest shall pronounce that person unclean; it is an itch, an infectious disease of the head or chin. ³¹But if, when the priest examines this kind of sore, it does not seem to be more than skin deep and there is no black hair in it, then the priest is to put the infected person in isolation for seven days. ³²On the seventh day the priest is to examine the sore, and if the itch has not spread and there is no yellow hair in it and it does not appear to be more than skin deep, ³³he must be shaved except for the diseased area, and the priest is to keep him in isolation another seven days. ³⁴On the seventh day the priest is to examine the itch, and if it has not spread in the skin and appears to be no more than skin deep, the priest shall pronounce him clean. He must wash his clothes, and he will be clean. ³⁵But if the itch does spread in the skin after he is pronounced clean, ³⁶the priest is to examine him, and if the itch has spread in the skin, the priest does not need to look for yellow hair; the person is unclean. ³⁷If, however, in his judgment it is unchanged and black hair has grown in it, the itch is healed. He is clean, and the priest shall pronounce him clean.

³⁸"When a man or woman has white spots on the skin, ³⁹the priest is to examine them, and if the spots are dull white, it is a harmless rash that has broken out on the skin; that person is clean.

⁴⁰"When a man has lost his hair and is bald, he is clean. ⁴¹If he has lost his hair from the front of his scalp and has a bald forehead, he is clean. ⁴²But if he has a reddish-white sore on his bald head or forehead, it is an infectious disease breaking out on his head or forehead. ⁴³The priest is to examine him, and if the swollen sore on his head or forehead is reddish-white like an infectious skin disease, ⁴⁴the man is diseased and is unclean. The priest shall pronounce him unclean because of the sore on his head.

⁴⁵"The person with such an infectious disease must wear torn clothes, let his hair be unkempt,ᵃ cover the lower part of his face and cry out, 'Unclean! Unclean!' ⁴⁶As long as he has the infection he remains unclean. He must live alone; he must live outside the camp.

Regulations About Mildew

⁴⁷"If any clothing is contaminated with mildew—any woolen or linen clothing, ⁴⁸any woven or knitted material of linen or wool, any leather or anything made of leather— ⁴⁹and if the contamination in the clothing, or leather, or woven or knitted material, or any leather article, is greenish or reddish, it is a spreading mildew and must be shown to the priest. ⁵⁰The priest is to examine the mildew and isolate the affected article for seven days. ⁵¹On the seventh day he is to examine it, and if the mildew has spread in the clothing, or the woven or knitted material, or the leather, whatever its use, it is a destructive mildew; the article is unclean. ⁵²He must burn up the clothing, or the woven or knitted material of wool or linen, or any leather article that has the contamination in it, because the mildew is destructive; the article must be burned up.

⁵³"But if, when the priest examines it, the mildew has not spread in the clothing, or the woven or knitted material, or the leather article, ⁵⁴he shall order that the contaminated article be washed. Then he is to isolate it for another seven days. ⁵⁵After the affected article has been washed, the

ᵃ 45 Or *clothes, uncover his head*

priest is to examine it, and if the mildew has not changed its appearance, even though it has not spread, it is unclean. Burn it with fire, whether the mildew has affected one side or the other. ⁵⁶If, when the priest examines it, the mildew has faded after the article has been washed, he is to tear the contaminated part out of the clothing, or the leather, or the woven or knitted material. ⁵⁷But if it reappears in the clothing, or in the woven or knitted material, or in the leather article, it is spreading, and whatever has the mildew must be burned with fire. ⁵⁸The clothing, or the woven or knitted material, or any leather article that has been washed and is rid of the mildew, must be washed again, and it will be clean."

⁵⁹These are the regulations concerning contamination by mildew in woolen or linen clothing, woven or knitted material, or any leather article, for pronouncing them clean or unclean.

Cleansing From Infectious Skin Diseases

14 The LORD said to Moses, ²"These are the regulations for the diseased person at the time of his ceremonial cleansing, when he is brought to the priest: ³The priest is to go outside the camp and examine him. If the person has been healed of his infectious skin disease, ᵃ ⁴the priest shall order that two live clean birds and some cedar wood, scarlet yarn and hyssop be brought for the one to be cleansed. ⁵Then the priest shall order that one of the birds be killed over fresh water in a clay pot. ⁶He is then to take the live bird and dip it, together with the cedar wood, the scarlet yarn and the hyssop, into the blood of the bird that was killed over the fresh water. ⁷Seven times he shall sprinkle the one to be cleansed of the infectious disease and pronounce him clean. Then he is to release the live bird in the open fields.

⁸"The person to be cleansed must wash his clothes, shave off all his hair and bathe with water; then he will be ceremonially clean. After this he may come into the camp, but he must stay outside his tent for seven days. ⁹On the seventh day he must shave off all his hair; he must shave his head, his beard, his eyebrows and the rest of his hair. He must wash his clothes and bathe himself with water, and he will be clean.

¹⁰"On the eighth day he must bring two male lambs and one ewe lamb a year old, each without defect, along with three-tenths of an ephah ᵇ of fine flour mixed with oil for a grain offering, and one log ᶜ of oil. ¹¹The priest who pronounces him clean shall present both the one to be cleansed and his offerings before the LORD at the entrance to the Tent of Meeting.

¹²"Then the priest is to take one of the male lambs and offer it as a guilt offering, along with the log of oil; he shall wave them before the LORD as a wave offering. ¹³He is to slaughter the lamb in the holy place where the sin offering and the burnt offering are slaughtered. Like the sin offering, the guilt offering belongs to the priest; it is most holy. ¹⁴The priest is to take some of the blood of the guilt offering and put it on the lobe of the right ear of the one to be cleansed, on the thumb of his right hand and on the big toe of his right foot. ¹⁵The priest shall then take some of the log of oil, pour it in the palm of his own left hand, ¹⁶dip his right forefinger into the oil in his palm, and with his finger sprinkle some of it before the LORD seven times. ¹⁷The priest is to put some of the oil remaining in his palm on the lobe of the right ear of the one to be cleansed, on the thumb of his right hand and on the big toe of his right foot, on top of the blood of the guilt offering. ¹⁸The rest of the oil in his palm the priest shall put on the head of the one to be cleansed and make atonement for him before the LORD.

¹⁹"Then the priest is to sacrifice the sin offering and make atonement for the one to be cleansed from his uncleanness. After that, the priest shall slaughter the burnt offering ²⁰and offer it on the altar, together with the grain offering, and make atonement for him, and he will be clean.

²¹"If, however, he is poor and cannot afford these, he must take one male lamb as a guilt offering to be waved to make atonement for him, together with a tenth of an ephah ᵈ of fine flour mixed with oil for a grain offering, a log of oil, ²²and two doves or two young pigeons, which he can afford, one for a sin offering and the other for a burnt offering.

²³"On the eighth day he must bring them for his cleansing to the priest at the entrance to the Tent of Meeting, before the LORD. ²⁴The priest is to take the lamb for the guilt offering, together with the log of oil, and wave them before the LORD as a wave offering. ²⁵He shall slaughter the lamb for

ᵃ 3 Traditionally *leprosy*; the Hebrew word was used for various diseases affecting the skin—not necessarily leprosy; also elsewhere in this chapter.   ᵇ 10 That is, probably about 6 quarts (about 6.5 liters)   ᶜ 10 That is, probably about 2/3 pint (about 0.3 liter); also in verses 12, 15, 21 and 24   ᵈ 21 That is, probably about 2 quarts (about 2 liters) the guilt offering and take some of its blood and put it on the lobe of the right ear of the one to be cleansed, on the thumb of his right hand and on the big toe of his right foot. ²⁶The priest is to pour some of the oil into the palm of his own left hand, ²⁷and with his right forefinger sprinkle some of the oil from his palm seven times before the Lord. ²⁸Some of the oil in his palm he is to put on the same places he put the blood of the guilt offering—on the lobe of the right ear of the one to be cleansed, on the thumb of his right hand and on the big toe of his right foot. ²⁹The rest of the oil in his palm the priest shall put on the head of the one to be cleansed, to make atonement for him before the Lord. ³⁰Then he shall sacrifice the doves or the young pigeons, which the person can afford, ³¹one^a as a sin offering and the other as a burnt offering, together with the grain offering. In this way the priest will make atonement before the Lord on behalf of the one to be cleansed."

³²These are the regulations for anyone who has an infectious skin disease and who cannot afford the regular offerings for his cleansing.

Cleansing From Mildew

³³The Lord said to Moses and Aaron, ³⁴"When you enter the land of Canaan, which I am giving you as your possession, and I put a spreading mildew in a house in that land, ³⁵the owner of the house must go and tell the priest, 'I have seen something that looks like mildew in my house.' ³⁶The priest is to order the house to be emptied before he goes in to examine the mildew, so that nothing in the house will be pronounced unclean. After this the priest is to go in and inspect the house. ³⁷He is to examine the mildew on the walls, and if it has greenish or reddish depressions that appear to be deeper than the surface of the wall, ³⁸the priest shall go out the doorway of the house and close it up for seven days. ³⁹On the seventh day the priest shall return to inspect the house. If the mildew has spread on the walls, ⁴⁰he is to order that the contaminated stones be torn out and thrown into an unclean place outside the town. ⁴¹He must have all the inside walls of the house scraped and the material that is scraped off dumped into an unclean place outside the town. ⁴²Then they are to take other stones to replace these and take new clay and plaster the house.

⁴³"If the mildew reappears in the house after the stones have been torn out and the house scraped and plastered, ⁴⁴the priest is to go and examine it and, if the mildew has spread in the house, it is a destructive mildew; the house is unclean. ⁴⁵It must be torn down—its stones, timbers and all the plaster—and taken out of the town to an unclean place.

⁴⁶"Anyone who goes into the house while it is closed up will be unclean till evening. ⁴⁷Anyone who sleeps or eats in the house must wash his clothes.

⁴⁸"But if the priest comes to examine it and the mildew has not spread after the house has been plastered, he shall pronounce the house clean, because the mildew is gone. ⁴⁹To purify the house he is to take two birds and some cedar wood, scarlet yarn and hyssop. ⁵⁰He shall kill one of the birds over fresh water in a clay pot. ⁵¹Then he is to take the cedar wood, the hyssop, the scarlet yarn and the live bird, dip them into the blood of the dead bird and the fresh water, and sprinkle the house seven times. ⁵²He shall purify the house with the bird's blood, the fresh water, the live bird, the cedar wood, the hyssop and the scarlet yarn. ⁵³Then he is to release the live bird in the open fields outside the town. In this way he will make atonement for the house, and it will be clean."

⁵⁴These are the regulations for any infectious skin disease, for an itch, ⁵⁵for mildew in clothing or in a house, ⁵⁶and for a swelling, a rash or a bright spot, ⁵⁷to determine when something is clean or unclean.

These are the regulations for infectious skin diseases and mildew.

Discharges Causing Uncleanness

15 The Lord said to Moses and Aaron, ²"Speak to the Israelites and say to them: 'When any man has a bodily discharge, the discharge is unclean. ³Whether it continues flowing from his body or is blocked, it will make him unclean. This is how his discharge will bring about uncleanness:

⁴"'Any bed the man with a discharge lies on will be unclean, and anything he sits on will be unclean. ⁵Anyone who touches his bed must wash his clothes and bathe with water, and he will be

^a 31 Septuagint and Syriac; Hebrew ³¹such as the person can afford, one

unclean till evening. ⁶Whoever sits on anything that the man with a discharge sat on must wash his clothes and bathe with water, and he will be unclean till evening.

⁷" 'Whoever touches the man who has a discharge must wash his clothes and bathe with water, and he will be unclean till evening.

⁸" 'If the man with the discharge spits on someone who is clean, that person must wash his clothes and bathe with water, and he will be unclean till evening.

⁹" 'Everything the man sits on when riding will be unclean, ¹⁰and whoever touches any of the things that were under him will be unclean till evening; whoever picks up those things must wash his clothes and bathe with water, and he will be unclean till evening.

¹¹" 'Anyone the man with a discharge touches without rinsing his hands with water must wash his clothes and bathe with water, and he will be unclean till evening.

¹²" 'A clay pot that the man touches must be broken, and any wooden article is to be rinsed with water.

¹³" 'When a man is cleansed from his discharge, he is to count off seven days for his ceremonial cleansing; he must wash his clothes and bathe himself with fresh water, and he will be clean. ¹⁴On the eighth day he must take two doves or two young pigeons and come before the LORD to the entrance to the Tent of Meeting and give them to the priest. ¹⁵The priest is to sacrifice them, the one for a sin offering and the other for a burnt offering. In this way he will make atonement before the LORD for the man because of his discharge.

¹⁶" 'When a man has an emission of semen, he must bathe his whole body with water, and he will be unclean till evening. ¹⁷Any clothing or leather that has semen on it must be washed with water, and it will be unclean till evening. ¹⁸When a man lies with a woman and there is an emission of semen, both must bathe with water, and they will be unclean till evening.

¹⁹" 'When a woman has her regular flow of blood, the impurity of her monthly period will last seven days, and anyone who touches her will be unclean till evening.

²⁰" 'Anything she lies on during her period will be unclean, and anything she sits on will be unclean. ²¹Whoever touches her bed must wash his clothes and bathe with water, and he will be unclean till evening. ²²Whoever touches anything she sits on must wash his clothes and bathe with water, and he will be unclean till evening. ²³Whether it is the bed or anything she was sitting on, when anyone touches it, he will be unclean till evening.

²⁴" 'If a man lies with her and her monthly flow touches him, he will be unclean for seven days; any bed he lies on will be unclean.

²⁵" 'When a woman has a discharge of blood for many days at a time other than her monthly period or has a discharge that continues beyond her period, she will be unclean as long as she has the discharge, just as in the days of her period. ²⁶Any bed she lies on while her discharge continues will be unclean, as is her bed during her monthly period, and anything she sits on will be unclean, as during her period. ²⁷Whoever touches them will be unclean; he must wash his clothes and bathe with water, and he will be unclean till evening.

²⁸" 'When she is cleansed from her discharge, she must count off seven days, and after that she will be ceremonially clean. ²⁹On the eighth day she must take two doves or two young pigeons and bring them to the priest at the entrance to the Tent of Meeting. ³⁰The priest is to sacrifice one

§enuine

wisdom » 14:54-57

The laws in Leviticus may seem very strange to you, but remember that these ancient people were living in close quarters and before modern medicine. They needed some guidance from God in order to stay healthy and not catch a quick-spreading plague or disease. When the people followed his commands, they stayed healthy. Even today, there's a reason why we're supposed to eat our vegetables, wash our hands, and not sleep around—it's for our own well-being.

Longtime Friend

I've known her as long as I can remember. We first met when I was bald. She knows I've always hated dresses and hair bows. She used to join me when I made mud pies and dug for earthworms. She has seen me at my best and my worst. Still, she loves me.

She's been to a bazillion of my sports events. I go to her house for dinner. We have sleepovers and tell late-night stories and eat ice cream for breakfast.

We've cruised together, cried together and had a car breakdown together.

We meet at church and then sometimes go out for breakfast, just the two of us.

My friend's name is Grandma—but don't misunderstand. She's definitely not your average grandma. We both swim at least a half a mile every day. Together, we go for bike rides, play tennis and ride the waves at the beach.

She has an incredible sense of style, an artist's eye for color. She is the perfect blend of fun, fitness and fashion. She doesn't try to be younger than she is, but she looks great because she exercises every day.

I have a picture of her when she was 20 at her lake cottage. What a babe! I can see why Grandpa fell for her. And now, 40 years later, they're still in love. Isn't that cool?

Someday, I want to be just like her.

Lord, do you think you could arrange that?

For more ideas on how to relate to your grandparents, check out www.TrueImagesBible.com

grandparents in focus

Not all girls are this lucky. It's a real treasure to have a genuine friendship with a grandparent, someone who knows you and loves you and also knows a thing or two about life. A grandparent can be a friend, confidante and mentor.

If you haven't connected with your grandparents lately, try this:
- » Write a letter (or e-mail, if your grandparents are on-line).
- » Ask your grandparents to tell you a favorite memory from high school. Then ask them about a not-so-favorite time.
- » When you have a chance, take your grandparents out to lunch and catch up on life.
- » Check out Timothy's legacy of faith in 2 Timothy 1:5 (page 1576).

For more on this topic, see the index on page 1656.

for a sin offering and the other for a burnt offering. In this way he will make atonement for her before the Lord for the uncleanness of her discharge.

[31] " 'You must keep the Israelites separate from things that make them unclean, so they will not die in their uncleanness for defiling my dwelling place,[a] which is among them.' "

[32] These are the regulations for a man with a discharge, for anyone made unclean by an emission of semen, [33] for a woman in her monthly period, for a man or a woman with a discharge, and for a man who lies with a woman who is ceremonially unclean.

a 31 Or my tabernacle

The Day of Atonement

16 The LORD spoke to Moses after the death of the two sons of Aaron who died when they approached the LORD. [2]The LORD said to Moses: "Tell your brother Aaron not to come whenever he chooses into the Most Holy Place behind the curtain in front of the atonement cover on the ark, or else he will die, because I appear in the cloud over the atonement cover.

[3]"This is how Aaron is to enter the sanctuary area: with a young bull for a sin offering and a ram for a burnt offering. [4]He is to put on the sacred linen tunic, with linen undergarments next to his body; he is to tie the linen sash around him and put on the linen turban. These are sacred garments; so he must bathe himself with water before he puts them on. [5]From the Israelite community he is to take two male goats for a sin offering and a ram for a burnt offering.

[6]"Aaron is to offer the bull for his own sin offering to make atonement for himself and his household. [7]Then he is to take the two goats and present before the LORD at the entrance to the Tent of Meeting. [8]He is to cast lots for the two goats—one lot for the LORD and the other for the scapegoat.[a] [9]Aaron shall bring the goat whose lot falls to the LORD and sacrifice it for a sin offering. [10]But the goat chosen by lot as the scapegoat shall be presented alive before the LORD to be used for making atonement by sending it into the desert as a scapegoat.

[11]"Aaron shall bring the bull for his own sin offering to make atonement for himself and his household, and he is to slaughter the bull for his own sin offering. [12]He is to take a censer full of burning coals from the altar before the LORD and two handfuls of finely ground fragrant incense and take them behind the curtain. [13]He is to put the incense on the fire before the LORD, and the smoke of the incense will conceal the atonement cover above the Testimony, so that he will not die. [14]He is to take some of the bull's blood and with his finger sprinkle it on the front of the atonement cover; then he shall sprinkle some of it with his finger seven times before the atonement cover.

[15]"He shall then slaughter the goat for the sin offering for the people and take its blood behind the curtain and do with it as he did with the bull's blood: He shall sprinkle it on the atonement cover and in front of it. [16]In this way he will make atonement for the Most Holy Place because of the uncleanness and rebellion of the Israelites, whatever their sins have been. He is to do the same for the Tent of Meeting, which is among them in the midst of their uncleanness. [17]No one is to be in the Tent of Meeting from the time Aaron goes in to make atonement in the Most Holy Place until he comes out, having made atonement for himself, his household and the whole community of Israel.

[18]"Then he shall come out to the altar that is before the LORD and make atonement for it. He shall take some of the bull's blood and some of the goat's blood and put it on all the horns of the altar. [19]He shall sprinkle some of the blood on it with his finger seven times to cleanse it and to consecrate it from the uncleanness of the Israelites.

[20]"When Aaron has finished making atonement for the Most Holy Place, the Tent of Meeting and the altar, he shall bring forward the live goat. [21]He is to lay both hands on the head of the live goat and confess over it all the wickedness and rebellion of the Israelites—all their sins—and put them on the goat's head. He shall send the goat away into the desert in the care of a man appointed for the task. [22]The goat will carry on itself all their sins to a solitary place; and the man shall release it in the desert.

[23]"Then Aaron is to go into the Tent of Meeting and take off the linen garments he put on before he entered the Most Holy Place, and he is to leave them there. [24]He shall bathe himself with water in a holy place and put on his regular garments. Then he shall come out and sacrifice the burnt offering for himself and the burnt offering for the people, to make atonement for himself and for the people. [25]He shall also burn the fat of the sin offering on the altar.

truth or dare

What steps do you take to get ready for a special occasion? Meeting with God involves a similar *internal* preparation. Before you pray, take time to humble your mind, body and spirit.

16:3–5

---

[a] 8 That is, the goat of removal; Hebrew *azazel*; also in verses 10 and 26

²⁶"The man who releases the goat as a scapegoat must wash his clothes and bathe himself with water; afterward he may come into the camp. ²⁷The bull and the goat for the sin offerings, whose blood was brought into the Most Holy Place to make atonement, must be taken outside the camp; their hides, flesh and offal are to be burned up. ²⁸The man who burns them must wash his clothes and bathe himself with water; afterward he may come into the camp.

²⁹"This is to be a lasting ordinance for you: On the tenth day of the seventh month you must deny yourselves^a and not do any work—whether native-born or an alien living among you— ³⁰because on this day atonement will be made for you, to cleanse you. Then, before the LORD, you will be clean from all your sins. ³¹It is a sabbath of rest, and you must deny yourselves; it is a lasting ordinance. ³²The priest who is anointed and ordained to succeed his father as high priest is to make atonement. He is to put on the sacred linen garments ³³and make atonement for the Most Holy Place, for the Tent of Meeting and the altar, and for the priests and all the people of the community.

³⁴"This is to be a lasting ordinance for you: Atonement is to be made once a year for all the sins of the Israelites."

And it was done, as the LORD commanded Moses.

Eating Blood Forbidden

17 The LORD said to Moses, ²"Speak to Aaron and his sons and to all the Israelites and say to them: 'This is what the LORD has commanded: ³Any Israelite who sacrifices an ox,^b a lamb or a goat in the camp or outside of it ⁴instead of bringing it to the entrance to the Tent of Meeting to present it as an offering to the LORD in front of the tabernacle of the LORD—that man shall be considered guilty of bloodshed; he has shed blood and must be cut off from his people. ⁵This is so the Israelites will bring to the LORD the sacrifices they are now making in the open fields. They must bring them to the priest, that is, to the LORD, at the entrance to the Tent of Meeting and sacrifice them as fellowship offerings.^c ⁶The priest is to sprinkle the blood against the altar of the LORD at the entrance to the Tent of Meeting and burn the fat as an aroma pleasing to the LORD. ⁷They must no longer offer any of their sacrifices to the goat idols^d to whom they prostitute themselves. This is to be a lasting ordinance for them and for the generations to come.'

⁸"Say to them: 'Any Israelite or any alien living among them who offers a burnt offering or sacrifice ⁹and does not bring it to the entrance to the Tent of Meeting to sacrifice it to the LORD—that man must be cut off from his people.

¹⁰"'Any Israelite or any alien living among them who eats any blood—I will set my face against that person who eats blood and will cut him off from his people. ¹¹For the life of a creature is in the blood, and I have given it to you to make atonement for yourselves on the altar; it is the blood that makes atonement for one's life. ¹²Therefore I say to the Israelites, "None of you may eat blood, nor may an alien living among you eat blood."

¹³"'Any Israelite or any alien living among you who hunts any animal or bird that may be eaten must drain out the blood and cover it with earth, ¹⁴because the life of every creature is its blood. That is why I have said to the Israelites, "You must not eat the blood of any creature, because the life of every creature is its blood; anyone who eats it must be cut off."

¹⁵"'Anyone, whether native-born or alien, who eats anything found dead or torn by wild animals must wash his clothes and bathe with water, and he will be ceremonially unclean till evening; then he will be clean. ¹⁶But if he does not wash his clothes and bathe himself, he will be held responsible.' "

truth or dare

Reconciliation with God requires blood. A sacrifice pays the penalty for sin because it sheds a creature's blood—its life. The price for your sin was also a life . . . Jesus Christ's.

17:11

^a 29 Or *must fast*; also in verse 31   ^b 3 The Hebrew word can include both male and female.   ^c 5 Traditionally *peace offerings*   ^d 7 Or *demons*

Unlawful Sexual Relations

18 The LORD said to Moses, ²"Speak to the Israelites and say to them: 'I am the LORD your God. ³You must not do as they do in Egypt, where you used to live, and you must not do as they do in the land of Canaan, where I am bringing you. Do not follow their practices. ⁴You must obey my laws and be careful to follow my decrees. I am the LORD your God. ⁵Keep my decrees and laws, for the man who obeys them will live by them. I am the LORD.

⁶" 'No one is to approach any close relative to have sexual relations. I am the LORD.

⁷" 'Do not dishonor your father by having sexual relations with your mother. She is your mother; do not have relations with her.

⁸" 'Do not have sexual relations with your father's wife; that would dishonor your father.

⁹" 'Do not have sexual relations with your sister, either your father's daughter or your mother's daughter, whether she was born in the same home or elsewhere.

¹⁰" 'Do not have sexual relations with your son's daughter or your daughter's daughter; that would dishonor you.

¹¹" 'Do not have sexual relations with the daughter of your father's wife, born to your father; she is your sister.

¹²" 'Do not have sexual relations with your father's sister; she is your father's close relative.

¹³" 'Do not have sexual relations with your mother's sister, because she is your mother's close relative.

¹⁴" 'Do not dishonor your father's brother by approaching his wife to have sexual relations; she is your aunt.

¹⁵" 'Do not have sexual relations with your daughter-in-law. She is your son's wife; do not have relations with her.

¹⁶" 'Do not have sexual relations with your brother's wife; that would dishonor your brother.

¹⁷" 'Do not have sexual relations with both a woman and her daughter. Do not have sexual relations with either her son's daughter or her daughter's daughter; they are her close relatives. That is wickedness.

¹⁸" 'Do not take your wife's sister as a rival wife and have sexual relations with her while your wife is living.

¹⁹" 'Do not approach a woman to have sexual relations during the uncleanness of her monthly period.

²⁰" 'Do not have sexual relations with your neighbor's wife and defile yourself with her.

²¹" 'Do not give any of your children to be sacrificed*ᵃ* to Molech, for you must not profane the name of your God. I am the LORD.

²²" 'Do not lie with a man as one lies with a woman; that is detestable.

²³" 'Do not have sexual relations with an animal and defile yourself with it. A woman must not present herself to an animal to have sexual relations with it; that is a perversion.

²⁴" 'Do not defile yourselves in any of these ways, because this is how the nations that I am going to drive out before you became defiled. ²⁵Even the land was defiled; so I punished it for its sin, and the land vomited out its inhabitants. ²⁶But you must keep my decrees and my laws. The native-born and the aliens living among you must not do any of these detestable things, ²⁷for all these

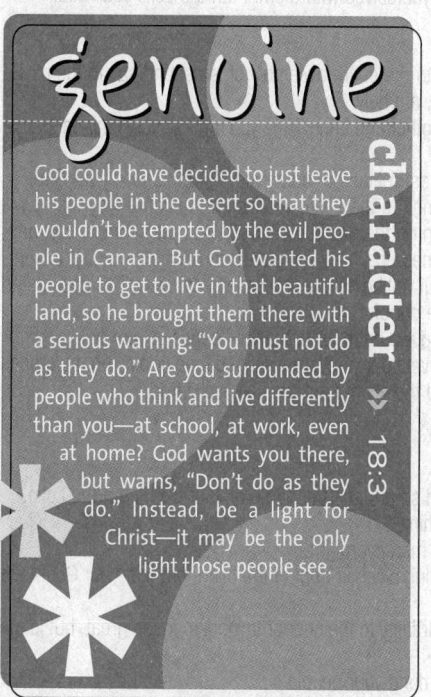

genuine *character »* 18:3

God could have decided to just leave his people in the desert so that they wouldn't be tempted by the evil people in Canaan. But God wanted his people to get to live in that beautiful land, so he brought them there with a serious warning: "You must not do as they do." Are you surrounded by people who think and live differently than you—at school, at work, even at home? God wants you there, but warns, "Don't do as they do." Instead, be a light for Christ—it may be the only light those people see.

---

a 21 Or to be passed through ⸤the fire⸥

things were done by the people who lived in the land before you, and the land became defiled. [28]And if you defile the land, it will vomit you out as it vomited out the nations that were before you.

[29] 'Everyone who does any of these detestable things—such persons must be cut off from their people. [30]Keep my requirements and do not follow any of the detestable customs that were practiced before you came and do not defile yourselves with them. I am the LORD your God.' "

Various Laws

19 The LORD said to Moses, [2]"Speak to the entire assembly of Israel and say to them: 'Be holy because I, the LORD your God, am holy.

[3] 'Each of you must respect his mother and father, and you must observe my Sabbaths. I am the LORD your God.

[4] 'Do not turn to idols or make gods of cast metal for yourselves. I am the LORD your God.

[5] 'When you sacrifice a fellowship offering*a* to the LORD, sacrifice it in such a way that it will be accepted on your behalf. [6]It shall be eaten on the day you sacrifice it or on the next day; anything left over until the third day must be burned up. [7]If any of it is eaten on the third day, it is impure and will not be accepted. [8]Whoever eats it will be held responsible because he has desecrated what is holy to the LORD; that person must be cut off from his people.

[9] 'When you reap the harvest of your land, do not reap to the very edges of your field or gather the gleanings of your harvest. [10]Do not go over your vineyard a second time or pick up the grapes that have fallen. Leave them for the poor and the alien. I am the LORD your God.

[11] 'Do not steal.

" 'Do not lie.

" 'Do not deceive one another.

[12] 'Do not swear falsely by my name and so profane the name of your God. I am the LORD.

[13] 'Do not defraud your neighbor or rob him.

" 'Do not hold back the wages of a hired man overnight.

[14] 'Do not curse the deaf or put a stumbling block in front of the blind, but fear your God. I am the LORD.

[15] 'Do not pervert justice; do not show partiality to the poor or favoritism to the great, but judge your neighbor fairly.

[16] 'Do not go about spreading slander among your people.

" 'Do not do anything that endangers your neighbor's life. I am the LORD.

[17] 'Do not hate your brother in your heart. Rebuke your neighbor frankly so you will not share in his guilt.

[18] 'Do not seek revenge or bear a grudge against one of your people, but love your neighbor as yourself. I am the LORD.

[19] 'Keep my decrees.

" 'Do not mate different kinds of animals.

" 'Do not plant your field with two kinds of seed.

" 'Do not wear clothing woven of two kinds of material.

[20] 'If a man sleeps with a woman who is a slave girl promised to another man but who has not been ransomed or given her freedom, there must be due punishment. Yet they are not to be put to death, because she had not been freed. [21]The man, however, must bring a ram to the entrance to the Tent of Meeting for a guilt offering to the LORD. [22]With the ram of the guilt offering the priest is to make atonement for him before the LORD for the sin he has committed, and his sin will be forgiven.

[23] 'When you enter the land and plant any kind of fruit tree, regard its fruit as forbidden.*b* For three years you are to consider it forbidden*b*; it must not be eaten. [24]In the fourth year all its fruit will be holy, an offering of praise to the LORD. [25]But in the fifth year you may eat its fruit. In this way your harvest will be increased. I am the LORD your God.

[26] 'Do not eat any meat with the blood still in it.

" 'Do not practice divination or sorcery.

[27] 'Do not cut the hair at the sides of your head or clip off the edges of your beard.

[28] 'Do not cut your bodies for the dead or put tattoo marks on yourselves. I am the LORD.

---

a 5 Traditionally *peace offering*   *b 23* Hebrew *uncircumcised*

genuine

respect » 19:32

How do you treat your grandparents? Have you ever wondered what they were like when they were your age or what exciting things they've done? Have you ever asked to hear their stories? True, sometimes older people can be frustrating, but ask God for patience and then settle in to listen. You may hear the story of a heroic soldier, or a romantic tale of falling in love, or some good dirt on their kids (your parents!). You can learn from their life experience. Call, write, e-mail, or chat over coffee. You won't be disappointed.

29" 'Do not degrade your daughter by making her a prostitute, or the land will turn to prostitution and be filled with wickedness.

30" 'Observe my Sabbaths and have reverence for my sanctuary. I am the LORD.

31" 'Do not turn to mediums or seek out spiritists, for you will be defiled by them. I am the LORD your God.

32" 'Rise in the presence of the aged, show respect for the elderly and revere your God. I am the LORD.

33" 'When an alien lives with you in your land, do not mistreat him. 34The alien living with you must be treated as one of your native-born. Love him as yourself, for you were aliens in Egypt. I am the LORD your God.

35" 'Do not use dishonest standards when measuring length, weight or quantity. 36Use honest scales and honest weights, an honest ephah *a* and an honest hin. *b* I am the LORD your God, who brought you out of Egypt.

37" 'Keep all my decrees and all my laws and follow them. I am the LORD.' "

Punishments for Sin

20 The LORD said to Moses, 2"Say to the Israelites: 'Any Israelite or any alien living in Israel who gives *c* any of his children to Molech must be put to death. The people of the community are to stone him. 3I will set my face against that man and I will cut him off from his people; for by giving his children to Molech, he has defiled my sanctuary and profaned my holy name. 4If the people of the community close their eyes when that man gives one of his children to Molech and they fail to put him to death, 5I will set my face against that man and his family and will cut off from their people both him and all who follow him in prostituting themselves to Molech.

6" 'I will set my face against the person who turns to mediums and spiritists to prostitute himself by following them, and I will cut him off from his people.

7" 'Consecrate yourselves and be holy, because I am the LORD your God. 8Keep my decrees and follow them. I am the LORD, who makes you holy. *d*

9" 'If anyone curses his father or mother, he must be put to death. He has cursed his father or his mother, and his blood will be on his own head.

10" 'If a man commits adultery with another man's wife—with the wife of his neighbor—both the adulterer and the adulteress must be put to death.

11" 'If a man sleeps with his father's wife, he has dishonored his father. Both the man and the woman must be put to death; their blood will be on their own heads.

12" 'If a man sleeps with his daughter-in-law, both of them must be put to death. What they have done is a perversion; their blood will be on their own heads.

truth or dare

Do you know what it feels like to be excluded? To be the outsider, the one girl sitting alone, hoping to be invited in? God tells us to treat girls on the fringe with extra compassion.

19:33–34

a 36 An ephah was a dry measure. *b 36* A hin was a liquid measure. *c 2* Or *sacrifices*; also in verses 3 and 4
d 8 Or *who sanctifies you*; or *who sets you apart as holy*

¹³" 'If a man lies with a man as one lies with a woman, both of them have done what is detestable. They must be put to death; their blood will be on their own heads.

¹⁴" 'If a man marries both a woman and her mother, it is wicked. Both he and they must be burned in the fire, so that no wickedness will be among you.

¹⁵" 'If a man has sexual relations with an animal, he must be put to death, and you must kill the animal.

¹⁶" 'If a woman approaches an animal to have sexual relations with it, kill both the woman and the animal. They must be put to death; their blood will be on their own heads.

¹⁷" 'If a man marries his sister, the daughter of either his father or his mother, and they have sexual relations, it is a disgrace. They must be cut off before the eyes of their people. He has dishonored his sister and will be held responsible.

¹⁸" 'If a man lies with a woman during her monthly period and has sexual relations with her, he has exposed the source of her flow, and she has also uncovered it. Both of them must be cut off from their people.

¹⁹" 'Do not have sexual relations with the sister of either your mother or your father, for that would dishonor a close relative; both of you would be held responsible.

²⁰" 'If a man sleeps with his aunt, he has dishonored his uncle. They will be held responsible; they will die childless.

²¹" 'If a man marries his brother's wife, it is an act of impurity; he has dishonored his brother. They will be childless.

²²" 'Keep all my decrees and laws and follow them, so that the land where I am bringing you to live may not vomit you out. ²³You must not live according to the customs of the nations I am going to drive out before you. Because they did all these things, I abhorred them. ²⁴But I said to you, "You will possess their land; I will give it to you as an inheritance, a land flowing with milk and honey." I am the LORD your God, who has set you apart from the nations.

²⁵" 'You must therefore make a distinction between clean and unclean animals and between unclean and clean birds. Do not defile yourselves by any animal or bird or anything that moves along the ground—those which I have set apart as unclean for you. ²⁶You are to be holy to me^a because I, the LORD, am holy, and I have set you apart from the nations to be my own.

²⁷" 'A man or woman who is a medium or spiritist among you must be put to death. You are to stone them; their blood will be on their own heads.' "

Rules for Priests

21 The LORD said to Moses, "Speak to the priests, the sons of Aaron, and say to them: 'A priest must not make himself ceremonially unclean for any of his people who die, ²except for a close relative, such as his mother or father, his son or daughter, his brother, ³or an unmarried sister who is dependent on him since she has no husband—for her he may make himself unclean. ⁴He must not make himself unclean for people related to him by marriage,^b and so defile himself.

⁵" 'Priests must not shave their heads or shave off the edges of their beards or cut their bodies. ⁶They must be holy to their God and must not profane the name of their God. Because they present the offerings made to the LORD by fire, the food of their God, they are to be holy.

⁷" 'They must not marry women defiled by prostitution or divorced from their husbands, because priests are holy to their God. ⁸Regard them as holy, because they offer up the food of your God. Consider them holy, because I the LORD am holy—I who make you holy.^c

⁹" 'If a priest's daughter defiles herself by becoming a prostitute, she disgraces her father; she must be burned in the fire.

truth or dare

God's punishments for sexual sins seem harsh by today's standards. However, these laws show God's deep concern for preserving our most intimate relationship.

20:10–21

^a 26 Or be my holy ones   ^b 4 Or unclean as a leader among his people   ^c 8 Or who sanctify you; or who set you apart as holy

¹⁰" 'The high priest, the one among his brothers who has had the anointing oil poured on his head and who has been ordained to wear the priestly garments, must not let his hair become unkempt*ᵃ* or tear his clothes. ¹¹He must not enter a place where there is a dead body. He must not make himself unclean, even for his father or mother, ¹²nor leave the sanctuary of his God or desecrate it, because he has been dedicated by the anointing oil of his God. I am the LORD.

¹³" 'The woman he marries must be a virgin. ¹⁴He must not marry a widow, a divorced woman, or a woman defiled by prostitution, but only a virgin from his own people, ¹⁵so he will not defile his offspring among his people. I am the LORD, who makes him holy.*ᵇ*' "

¹⁶The LORD said to Moses, ¹⁷"Say to Aaron: 'For the generations to come none of your descendants who has a defect may come near to offer the food of his God. ¹⁸No man who has any defect may come near: no man who is blind or lame, disfigured or deformed; ¹⁹no man with a crippled foot or hand, ²⁰or who is hunchbacked or dwarfed, or who has any eye defect, or who has festering or running sores or damaged testicles. ²¹No descendant of Aaron the priest who has any defect is to come near to present the offerings made to the LORD by fire. He has a defect; he must not come near to offer the food of his God. ²²He may eat the most holy food of his God, as well as the holy food; ²³yet because of his defect, he must not go near the curtain or approach the altar, and so desecrate my sanctuary. I am the LORD, who makes them holy.*ᶜ*' "

²⁴So Moses told this to Aaron and his sons and to all the Israelites.

22 The LORD said to Moses, ²"Tell Aaron and his sons to treat with respect the sacred offerings the Israelites consecrate to me, so they will not profane my holy name. I am the LORD.

³"Say to them: 'For the generations to come, if any of your descendants is ceremonially unclean and yet comes near the sacred offerings that the Israelites consecrate to the LORD, that person must be cut off from my presence. I am the LORD.

⁴" 'If a descendant of Aaron has an infectious skin disease*ᵈ* or a bodily discharge, he may not eat the sacred offerings until he is cleansed. He will also be unclean if he touches something defiled by a corpse or by anyone who has an emission of semen, ⁵or if he touches any crawling thing that makes him unclean, or any person who makes him unclean, whatever the uncleanness may be. ⁶The one who touches any such thing will be unclean till evening. He must not eat any of the sacred offerings unless he has bathed himself with water. ⁷When the sun goes down, he will be clean, and after that he may eat the sacred offerings, for they are his food. ⁸He must not eat anything found dead or torn by wild animals, and so become unclean through it. I am the LORD.

⁹" 'The priests are to keep my requirements so that they do not become guilty and die for treating them with contempt. I am the LORD, who makes them holy.*ᶜ*

¹⁰" 'No one outside a priest's family may eat the sacred offering, nor may the guest of a priest or his hired worker eat it. ¹¹But if a priest buys a slave with money, or if a slave is born in his household, that slave may eat his food. ¹²If a priest's daughter marries anyone other than a priest, she may not eat any of the sacred contributions. ¹³But if a priest's daughter becomes a widow or is divorced, yet has no children, and she returns to live in her father's house as in her youth, she may eat of her father's food. No unauthorized person, however, may eat any of it.

¹⁴" 'If anyone eats a sacred offering by mistake, he must make restitution to the priest for the offering and add a fifth of the value to it. ¹⁵The priests must not desecrate the sacred offerings the Israelites present to the LORD ¹⁶by allowing them to eat the sacred offerings and so bring upon them guilt requiring payment. I am the LORD, who makes them holy.' "

Unacceptable Sacrifices

¹⁷The LORD said to Moses, ¹⁸"Speak to Aaron and his sons and to all the Israelites and say to them: 'If any of you—either an Israelite or an alien living in Israel—presents a gift for a burnt offering to the LORD, either to fulfill a vow or as a freewill offering, ¹⁹you must present a male without defect from the cattle, sheep or goats in order that it may be accepted on your behalf. ²⁰Do not bring anything with a defect, because it will not be accepted on your behalf. ²¹When anyone brings from the herd or flock a fellowship offering*ᵉ* to the LORD to fulfill a special vow or as a freewill offering, it

---

ᵃ 10 Or *not uncover his head*   *ᵇ* 15 Or *who sanctifies him*; or *who sets him apart as holy*   *ᶜ* 23,9 Or *who sanctifies them*; or *who sets them apart as holy*; also in verse 16   *ᵈ* 4 Traditionally *leprosy*; the Hebrew word was used for various diseases affecting the skin—not necessarily leprosy.   *ᵉ* 21 Traditionally *peace offering* must be without defect or blemish to be acceptable. ²²Do not offer to the LORD the blind, the injured or the maimed, or anything with warts or festering or running sores. Do not place any of these on the altar as an offering made to the LORD by fire. ²³You may, however, present as a freewill offering an ox*ᵃ* or a sheep that is deformed or stunted, but it will not be accepted in fulfillment of a vow. ²⁴You must not offer to the LORD an animal whose testicles are bruised, crushed, torn or cut. You must not do this in your own land, ²⁵and you must not accept such animals from the hand of a foreigner and offer them as the food of your God. They will not be accepted on your behalf, because they are deformed and have defects.' "

²⁶The LORD said to Moses, ²⁷"When a calf, a lamb or a goat is born, it is to remain with its mother for seven days. From the eighth day on, it will be acceptable as an offering made to the LORD by fire. ²⁸Do not slaughter a cow or a sheep and its young on the same day.

²⁹"When you sacrifice a thank offering to the LORD, sacrifice it in such a way that it will be accepted on your behalf. ³⁰It must be eaten that same day; leave none of it till morning. I am the LORD.

³¹"Keep my commands and follow them. I am the LORD. ³²Do not profane my holy name. I must be acknowledged as holy by the Israelites. I am the LORD, who makes*ᵇ* you holy*ᶜ* ³³and who brought you out of Egypt to be your God. I am the LORD."

genuine giving »» 22:17-22

Animals with defects, warts and festering sores? What?! The point is that God deserves our very best. God commanded the Israelites to bring him their prize animals—not the sick and lame ones they didn't want anyway. What about you? Do you give God your best—the best of your time, your talent, your heart? For example, do you do your devotions when you're wide awake or when you're half-asleep? Do you give God the first cut of your paycheck or whatever you have leftover after a shopping spree? Don't give God your scraps; he deserves your very best.

23

The LORD said to Moses, ²"Speak to the Israelites and say to them: 'These are my appointed feasts, the appointed feasts of the LORD, which you are to proclaim as sacred assemblies.

The Sabbath

³ " 'There are six days when you may work, but the seventh day is a Sabbath of rest, a day of sacred assembly. You are not to do any work; wherever you live, it is a Sabbath to the LORD.

The Passover and Unleavened Bread

⁴ " 'These are the LORD's appointed feasts, the sacred assemblies you are to proclaim at their appointed times: ⁵The LORD's Passover begins at twilight on the fourteenth day of the first month. ⁶On the fifteenth day of that month the LORD's Feast of Unleavened Bread begins; for seven days you must eat bread made without yeast. ⁷On the first day hold a sacred assembly and do no regular work. ⁸For seven days present an offering made to the LORD by fire. And on the seventh day hold a sacred assembly and do no regular work.' "

truth or dare

Who says following Christ is all work and no play? God wants us to relax and enjoy life so much that he scheduled weekly breaks and yearly celebrations! 23:1-4

ᵃ 23 The Hebrew word can include both male and female. ᵇ 32 Or made ᶜ 32 Or who sanctifies you; or who sets you apart as holy

Firstfruits

[9]The LORD said to Moses, [10]"Speak to the Israelites and say to them: 'When you enter the land I am going to give you and you reap its harvest, bring to the priest a sheaf of the first grain you harvest. [11]He is to wave the sheaf before the LORD so it will be accepted on your behalf; the priest is to wave it on the day after the Sabbath. [12]On the day you wave the sheaf, you must sacrifice as a burnt offering to the LORD a lamb a year old without defect, [13]together with its grain offering of two-tenths of an ephah*a* of fine flour mixed with oil—an offering made to the LORD by fire, a pleasing aroma—and its drink offering of a quarter of a hin*b* of wine. [14]You must not eat any bread, or roasted or new grain, until the very day you bring this offering to your God. This is to be a lasting ordinance for the generations to come, wherever you live.

Feast of Weeks

[15]" 'From the day after the Sabbath, the day you brought the sheaf of the wave offering, count off seven full weeks. [16]Count off fifty days up to the day after the seventh Sabbath, and then present an offering of new grain to the LORD. [17]From wherever you live, bring two loaves made of two-tenths of an ephah of fine flour, baked with yeast, as a wave offering of firstfruits to the LORD. [18]Present with this bread seven male lambs, each a year old and without defect, one young bull and two rams. They will be a burnt offering to the LORD, together with their grain offerings and drink offerings—an offering made by fire, an aroma pleasing to the LORD. [19]Then sacrifice one male goat for a sin offering and two lambs, each a year old, for a fellowship offering.*c* [20]The priest is to wave the two lambs before the LORD as a wave offering, together with the bread of the firstfruits. They are a sacred offering to the LORD for the priest. [21]On that same day you are to proclaim a sacred assembly and do no regular work. This is to be a lasting ordinance for the generations to come, wherever you live.

[22]" 'When you reap the harvest of your land, do not reap to the very edges of your field or gather the gleanings of your harvest. Leave them for the poor and the alien. I am the LORD your God.' "

Feast of Trumpets

[23]The LORD said to Moses, [24]"Say to the Israelites: 'On the first day of the seventh month you are to have a day of rest, a sacred assembly commemorated with trumpet blasts. [25]Do no regular work, but present an offering made to the LORD by fire.' "

Day of Atonement

[26]The LORD said to Moses, [27]"The tenth day of this seventh month is the Day of Atonement. Hold a sacred assembly and deny yourselves,*d* and present an offering made to the LORD by fire. [28]Do no work on that day, because it is the Day of Atonement, when atonement is made for you before the LORD your God. [29]Anyone who does not deny himself on that day must be cut off from his people. [30]I will destroy from among his people anyone who does any work on that day. [31]You shall do no work at all. This is to be a lasting ordinance for the generations to come, wherever you live. [32]It is a sabbath of rest for you, and you must deny yourselves. From the evening of the ninth day of the month until the following evening you are to observe your sabbath."

Feast of Tabernacles

[33]The LORD said to Moses, [34]"Say to the Israelites: 'On the fifteenth day of the seventh month the LORD's Feast of Tabernacles begins, and it lasts for seven days. [35]The first day is a sacred assembly; do no regular work. [36]For seven days present offerings made to the LORD by fire, and on the eighth day hold a sacred assembly and present an offering made to the LORD by fire. It is the closing assembly; do no regular work.

[37](" 'These are the LORD's appointed feasts, which you are to proclaim as sacred assemblies for bringing offerings made to the LORD by fire—the burnt offerings and grain offerings, sacrifices and drink offerings required for each day. [38]These offerings are in addition to those for the LORD's Sabbaths and*e* in addition to your gifts and whatever you have vowed and all the freewill offerings you give to the LORD.)

a 13 That is, probably about 4 quarts (about 4.5 liters); also in verse 17   *b 13* That is, probably about 1 quart (about 1 liter)   *c 19* Traditionally *peace offering*   *d 27* Or *and fast*; also in verses 29 and 32   *e 38* Or *These feasts are in addition to the LORD's Sabbaths, and these offerings are*

39 " 'So beginning with the fifteenth day of the seventh month, after you have gathered the crops of the land, celebrate the festival to the LORD for seven days; the first day is a day of rest, and the eighth day also is a day of rest. 40On the first day you are to take choice fruit from the trees, and palm fronds, leafy branches and poplars, and rejoice before the LORD your God for seven days. 41Celebrate this as a festival to the LORD for seven days each year. This is to be a lasting ordinance for the generations to come; celebrate it in the seventh month. 42Live in booths for seven days: All native-born Israelites are to live in booths 43so your descendants will know that I had the Israelites live in booths when I brought them out of Egypt. I am the LORD your God.' "

44So Moses announced to the Israelites the appointed feasts of the LORD.

Oil and Bread Set Before the LORD

24 The LORD said to Moses, 2"Command the Israelites to bring you clear oil of pressed olives for the light so that the lamps may be kept burning continually. 3Outside the curtain of the Testimony in the Tent of Meeting, Aaron is to tend the lamps before the LORD from evening till morning, continually. This is to be a lasting ordinance for the generations to come. 4The lamps on the pure gold lampstand before the LORD must be tended continually.

5"Take fine flour and bake twelve loaves of bread, using two-tenths of an ephah *a* for each loaf. 6Set them in two rows, six in each row, on the table of pure gold before the LORD. 7Along each row put some pure incense as a memorial portion to represent the bread and to be an offering made to the LORD by fire. 8This bread is to be set out before the LORD regularly, Sabbath after Sabbath, on behalf of the Israelites, as a lasting covenant. 9It belongs to Aaron and his sons, who are to eat it in a holy place, because it is a most holy part of their regular share of the offerings made to the LORD by fire."

A Blasphemer Stoned

10Now the son of an Israelite mother and an Egyptian father went out among the Israelites, and a fight broke out in the camp between him and an Israelite. 11The son of the Israelite woman blasphemed the Name with a curse; so they brought him to Moses. (His mother's name was Shelomith, the daughter of Dibri the Danite.) 12They put him in custody until the will of the LORD should be made clear to them.

13Then the LORD said to Moses: 14"Take the blasphemer outside the camp. All those who heard him are to lay their hands on his head, and the entire assembly is to stone him. 15Say to the Israelites: 'If anyone curses his God, he will be held responsible; 16anyone who blasphemes the name of the LORD must be put to death. The entire assembly must stone him. Whether an alien or native-born, when he blasphemes the Name, he must be put to death.

17" 'If anyone takes the life of a human being, he must be put to death. 18Anyone who takes the life of someone's animal must make restitution—life for life. 19If anyone injures his neighbor, whatever he has done must be done to him: 20fracture for fracture, eye for eye, tooth for tooth. As he has injured the other, so he is to be injured. 21Whoever kills an animal must make restitution, but whoever kills a man must be put to death. 22You are to have the same law for the alien and the native-born. I am the LORD your God.' "

23Then Moses spoke to the Israelites, and they took the blasphemer outside the camp and stoned him. The Israelites did as the LORD commanded Moses.

The Sabbath Year

25 The LORD said to Moses on Mount Sinai, 2"Speak to the Israelites and say to them: 'When you enter the land I am going to give you, the land itself must observe a sabbath to the LORD. 3For six years sow your fields, and for six years prune your vineyards and gather their crops. 4But in the seventh year the land is to have a sabbath of rest, a sabbath to the LORD. Do not sow your fields or prune your vineyards. 5Do not reap what grows of itself or harvest the grapes of your untended vines. The land is to have a year of rest. 6Whatever the land yields during the sabbath year will be food for you—for yourself, your manservant and maidservant, and the hired worker and temporary resident who live among you, 7as well as for your livestock and the wild animals in your land. Whatever the land produces may be eaten.

a 5 That is, probably about 4 quarts (about 4.5 liters)

Moment of Truth

focus Profile: **Caitlin**

Argh. The moment I always hate. I felt like *everyone* was staring at me. "What'll it be, ladies?" J.P., the host of the party, asked us what we wanted to drink.

Senina and Lindsay pointed to the cooler full of beers. "We'll take two of those." They twisted the caps off the beer bottles, looking so confident. So adult. Like they knew what they were doing.

"Um, I'll just have a Coke," I stammered. I sounded *so* lame.

"Aw, come on, Caitlin. It's the first party of our senior year. You're with great friends. You don't need to drive home. And yet you're *still* telling me you just want a Coke?"

Great. Now everyone *was* looking at me. And smirking. "Coca Cola Caitlin," some were saying. "Always Coca Cola," the others chimed in.

Is this really worth it? I wondered.

Sure, I knew underage drinking was wrong. And I did want to set a good example for others. But right then, I just felt like such a *loser*. I was so tired of being the only one holding a Coke.

For more information on peer pressure, check out www.TrueImagesBible.com

peer pressure in focus

Have you ever found yourself in a situation like Caitlin's? Where your heart and conviction told you to do one thing, but you felt pressured by others to do something different?

Peer pressure is rough for everyone. But, as Christians, it's important that we stick to our convictions. Keep these ideas in mind when facing peer pressure:

» Decide what to say before you're in a tough situation. If you've already made the decision in your mind, you'll feel prepared when all eyes turn to you. Check out Proverbs 1:10,15 (page 803) for more on resisting temptation.

» Spend time with Christian friends who will encourage you. There's incredible strength in knowing that you really aren't the only one.

» Be a leader. Don't assume that everyone else wants to conform. If you take a stand, then you may give others the courage to make the right decision, too.

For more on this topic, see the index on page 1656.

The Year of Jubilee

8" 'Count off seven sabbaths of years—seven times seven years—so that the seven sabbaths of years amount to a period of forty-nine years. 9Then have the trumpet sounded everywhere on the tenth day of the seventh month; on the Day of Atonement sound the trumpet throughout your land. 10Consecrate the fiftieth year and proclaim liberty throughout the land to all its inhabitants. It shall be a jubilee for you; each one of you is to return to his family property and each to his own clan. 11The fiftieth year shall be a jubilee for you; do not sow and do not reap what grows of itself or harvest the untended vines. 12For it is a jubilee and is to be holy for you; eat only what is taken directly from the fields.

¹³" 'In this Year of Jubilee everyone is to return to his own property.

¹⁴" 'If you sell land to one of your countrymen or buy any from him, do not take advantage of each other. ¹⁵You are to buy from your countryman on the basis of the number of years since the Jubilee. And he is to sell to you on the basis of the number of years left for harvesting crops. ¹⁶When the years are many, you are to increase the price, and when the years are few, you are to decrease the price, because what he is really selling you is the number of crops. ¹⁷Do not take advantage of each other, but fear your God. I am the LORD your God.

¹⁸" 'Follow my decrees and be careful to obey my laws, and you will live safely in the land. ¹⁹Then the land will yield its fruit, and you will eat your fill and live there in safety. ²⁰You may ask, "What will we eat in the seventh year if we do not plant or harvest our crops?" ²¹I will send you such a blessing in the sixth year that the land will yield enough for three years. ²²While you plant during the eighth year, you will eat from the old crop and will continue to eat from it until the harvest of the ninth year comes in.

²³" 'The land must not be sold permanently, because the land is mine and you are but aliens and my tenants. ²⁴Throughout the country that you hold as a possession, you must provide for the redemption of the land.

²⁵" 'If one of your countrymen becomes poor and sells some of his property, his nearest relative is to come and redeem what his countryman has sold. ²⁶If, however, a man has no one to redeem it for him but he himself prospers and acquires sufficient means to redeem it, ²⁷he is to determine the value for the years since he sold it and refund the balance to the man to whom he sold it; he can then go back to his own property. ²⁸But if he does not acquire the means to repay him, what he sold will remain in the possession of the buyer until the Year of Jubilee. It will be returned in the Jubilee, and he can then go back to his property.

²⁹" 'If a man sells a house in a walled city, he retains the right of redemption a full year after its sale. During that time he may redeem it. ³⁰If it is not redeemed before a full year has passed, the house in the walled city shall belong permanently to the buyer and his descendants. It is not to be returned in the Jubilee. ³¹But houses in villages without walls around them are to be considered as open country. They can be redeemed, and they are to be returned in the Jubilee.

³²" 'The Levites always have the right to redeem their houses in the Levitical towns, which they possess. ³³So the property of the Levites is redeemable—that is, a house sold in any town they hold—and is to be returned in the Jubilee, because the houses in the towns of the Levites are their property among the Israelites. ³⁴But the pastureland belonging to their towns must not be sold; it is their permanent possession.

³⁵" 'If one of your countrymen becomes poor and is unable to support himself among you, help him as you would an alien or a temporary resident, so he can continue to live among you. ³⁶Do not take interest of any kind^a from him, but fear your God, so that your countryman may continue to live among you. ³⁷You must not lend him money at interest or sell him food at a profit. ³⁸I am the LORD your God, who brought you out of Egypt to give you the land of Canaan and to be your God.

³⁹" 'If one of your countrymen becomes poor among you and sells himself to you, do not make him work as a slave. ⁴⁰He is to be treated as a hired worker or a temporary resident among you; he is to work for you until the Year of Jubilee. ⁴¹Then he and his children are to be released, and he will go back to his own clan and to the property of his forefathers. ⁴²Because the Israelites are my servants, whom I brought out of Egypt, they must not be sold as slaves. ⁴³Do not rule over them ruthlessly, but fear your God.

⁴⁴" 'Your male and female slaves are to come from the nations around you; from them you may buy slaves. ⁴⁵You may also buy some of the temporary residents living among you and members of their clans born in your country, and they will become your property. ⁴⁶You can will them to your

truth or dare

How would you feel if God suddenly came to "repossess" all his belongings? You'd be left with nothing. Remember, you're just a steward of God's stuff. Don't get too attached.

25:23

^a 36 Or take excessive interest; similarly in verse 37

children as inherited property and can make them slaves for life, but you must not rule over your fellow Israelites ruthlessly.

47" 'If an alien or a temporary resident among you becomes rich and one of your countrymen becomes poor and sells himself to the alien living among you or to a member of the alien's clan, 48he retains the right of redemption after he has sold himself. One of his relatives may redeem him: 49An uncle or a cousin or any blood relative in his clan may redeem him. Or if he prospers, he may redeem himself. 50He and his buyer are to count the time from the year he sold himself up to the Year of Jubilee. The price for his release is to be based on the rate paid to a hired man for that number of years. 51If many years remain, he must pay for his redemption a larger share of the price paid for him. 52If only a few years remain until the Year of Jubilee, he is to compute that and pay for his redemption accordingly. 53He is to be treated as a man hired from year to year; you must see to it that his owner does not rule over him ruthlessly.

54" 'Even if he is not redeemed in any of these ways, he and his children are to be released in the Year of Jubilee, 55for the Israelites belong to me as servants. They are my servants, whom I brought out of Egypt. I am the LORD your God.

Reward for Obedience

26 " 'Do not make idols or set up an image or a sacred stone for yourselves, and do not place a carved stone in your land to bow down before it. I am the LORD your God.

2" 'Observe my Sabbaths and have reverence for my sanctuary. I am the LORD.

3" 'If you follow my decrees and are careful to obey my commands, 4I will send you rain in its season, and the ground will yield its crops and the trees of the field their fruit. 5Your threshing will continue until grape harvest and the grape harvest will continue until planting, and you will eat all the food you want and live in safety in your land.

6" 'I will grant peace in the land, and you will lie down and no one will make you afraid. I will remove savage beasts from the land, and the sword will not pass through your country. 7You will pursue your enemies, and they will fall by the sword before you. 8Five of you will chase a hundred, and a hundred of you will chase ten thousand, and your enemies will fall by the sword before you.

9" 'I will look on you with favor and make you fruitful and increase your numbers, and I will keep my covenant with you. 10You will still be eating last year's harvest when you will have to move it out to make room for the new. 11I will put my dwelling place*a* among you, and I will not abhor you. 12I will walk among you and be your God, and you will be my people. 13I am the LORD your God, who brought you out of Egypt so that you would no longer be slaves to the Egyptians; I broke the bars of your yoke and enabled you to walk with heads held high.

Punishment for Disobedience

14" 'But if you will not listen to me and carry out all these commands, 15and if you reject my decrees and abhor my laws and fail to carry out all my commands and so violate my covenant, 16then I will do this to you: I will bring upon you sudden terror, wasting diseases and fever that will destroy your sight and drain away your life. You will plant seed in vain, because your enemies will eat it. 17I will set my face against you so that you will be defeated by your enemies; those who hate you will rule over you, and you will flee even when no one is pursuing you.

18" 'If after all this you will not listen to me, I will punish you for your sins seven times over. 19I will break down your stubborn pride and make the sky above you like iron and the ground beneath you like bronze. 20Your strength will be spent in vain, because your soil will not yield its crops, nor will the trees of the land yield their fruit.

21" 'If you remain hostile toward me and refuse to listen to me, I will multiply your afflictions sev-

truth or dare

Idols don't have to be made of stone. A new boyfriend, clothes, your appearance . . . anything that focuses your attention away from God has "idol" potential.

26:1

a 11 Or my tabernacle

en times over, as your sins deserve. ²²I will send wild animals against you, and they will rob you of your children, destroy your cattle and make you so few in number that your roads will be deserted.

²³" 'If in spite of these things you do not accept my correction but continue to be hostile toward me, ²⁴I myself will be hostile toward you and will afflict you for your sins seven times over. ²⁵And I will bring the sword upon you to avenge the breaking of the covenant. When you withdraw into your cities, I will send a plague among you, and you will be given into enemy hands. ²⁶When I cut off your supply of bread, ten women will be able to bake your bread in one oven, and they will dole out the bread by weight. You will eat, but you will not be satisfied.

²⁷" 'If in spite of this you still do not listen to me but continue to be hostile toward me, ²⁸then in my anger I will be hostile toward you, and I myself will punish you for your sins seven times over. ²⁹You will eat the flesh of your sons and the flesh of your daughters. ³⁰I will destroy your high places, cut down your incense altars and pile your dead bodies on the lifeless forms of your idols, and I will abhor you. ³¹I will turn your cities into ruins and lay waste your sanctuaries, and I will take no delight in the pleasing aroma of your offerings. ³²I will lay waste the land, so that your enemies who live there will be appalled. ³³I will scatter you among the nations and will draw out my sword and pursue you. Your land will be laid waste, and your cities will lie in ruins. ³⁴Then the land will enjoy its sabbath years all the time that it lies desolate and you are in the country of your enemies; then the land will rest and enjoy its sabbaths. ³⁵All the time that it lies desolate, the land will have the rest it did not have during the sabbaths you lived in it.

³⁶" 'As for those of you who are left, I will make their hearts so fearful in the lands of their enemies that the sound of a wind-blown leaf will put them to flight. They will run as though fleeing from the sword, and they will fall, even though no one is pursuing them. ³⁷They will stumble over one another as though fleeing from the sword, even though no one is pursuing them. So you will not be able to stand before your enemies. ³⁸You will perish among the nations; the land of your enemies will devour you. ³⁹Those of you who are left will waste away in the lands of their enemies because of their sins; also because of their fathers' sins they will waste away.

⁴⁰" 'But if they will confess their sins and the sins of their fathers—their treachery against me and their hostility toward me, ⁴¹which made me hostile toward them so that I sent them into the land of their enemies—then when their uncircumcised hearts are humbled and they pay for their sin, ⁴²I will remember my covenant with Jacob and my covenant with Isaac and my covenant with Abraham, and I will remember the land. ⁴³For the land will be deserted by them and will enjoy its sabbaths while it lies desolate without them. They will pay for their sins because they rejected my laws and abhorred my de-

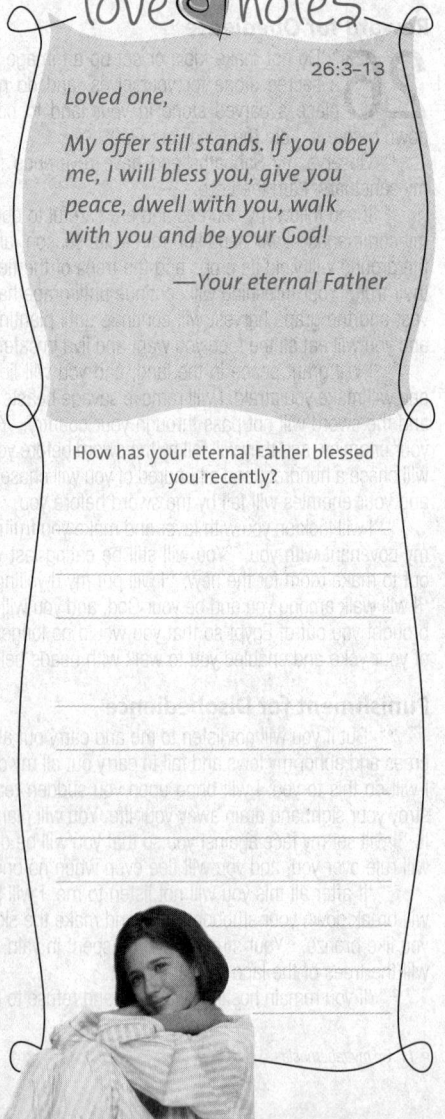

love notes

26:3-13

Loved one,

My offer still stands. If you obey me, I will bless you, give you peace, dwell with you, walk with you and be your God!

—Your eternal Father

How has your eternal Father blessed you recently?

crees. ⁴⁴Yet in spite of this, when they are in the land of their enemies, I will not reject them or abhor them so as to destroy them completely, breaking my covenant with them. I am the Lᴏʀᴅ their God. ⁴⁵But for their sake I will remember the covenant with their ancestors whom I brought out of Egypt in the sight of the nations to be their God. I am the Lᴏʀᴅ.' "

⁴⁶These are the decrees, the laws and the regulations that the Lᴏʀᴅ established on Mount Sinai between himself and the Israelites through Moses.

Redeeming What Is the Lᴏʀᴅ's

27 The Lᴏʀᴅ said to Moses, ²"Speak to the Israelites and say to them: 'If anyone makes a special vow to dedicate persons to the Lᴏʀᴅ by giving equivalent values, ³set the value of a male between the ages of twenty and sixty at fifty shekels ᵃ of silver, according to the sanctuary shekel ᵇ; ⁴and if it is a female, set her value at thirty shekels. ᶜ ⁵If it is a person between the ages of five and twenty, set the value of a male at twenty shekels ᵈ and of a female at ten shekels. ᵉ ⁶If it is a person between one month and five years, set the value of a male at five shekels ᶠ of silver and that of a female at three shekels ᵍ of silver. ⁷If it is a person sixty years old or more, set the value of a male at fifteen shekels ʰ and of a female at ten shekels. ⁸If anyone making the vow is too poor to pay the specified amount, he is to present the person to the priest, who will set the value for him according to what the man making the vow can afford.

⁹" 'If what he vowed is an animal that is acceptable as an offering to the Lᴏʀᴅ, such an animal given to the Lᴏʀᴅ becomes holy. ¹⁰He must not exchange it or substitute a good one for a bad one, or a bad one for a good one; if he should substitute one animal for another, both it and the substitute become holy. ¹¹If what he vowed is a ceremonially unclean animal—one that is not acceptable as an offering to the Lᴏʀᴅ—the animal must be presented to the priest, ¹²who will judge its quality as good or bad. Whatever value the priest then sets, that is what it will be. ¹³If the owner wishes to redeem the animal, he must add a fifth to its value.

¹⁴" 'If a man dedicates his house as something holy to the Lᴏʀᴅ, the priest will judge its quality as good or bad. Whatever value the priest then sets, so it will remain. ¹⁵If the man who dedicates his house redeems it, he must add a fifth to its value, and the house will again become his.

¹⁶" 'If a man dedicates to the Lᴏʀᴅ part of his family land, its value is to be set according to the amount of seed required for it—fifty shekels of silver to a homer ⁱ of barley seed. ¹⁷If he dedicates his field during the Year of Jubilee, the value that has been set remains. ¹⁸But if he dedicates his field after the Jubilee, the priest will determine the value according to the number of years that remain until the next Year of Jubilee, and its set value will be reduced. ¹⁹If the man who dedicates the field wishes to redeem it, he must add a fifth to its value, and the field will again become his. ²⁰If, however, he does not redeem the field, or if he has sold it to someone else, it can never be redeemed. ²¹When the field is released in the Jubilee, it will become holy, like a field devoted to the Lᴏʀᴅ; it will become the property of the priests. ʲ

²²" 'If a man dedicates to the Lᴏʀᴅ a field he has bought, which is not part of his family land, ²³the priest will determine its value up to the Year of Jubilee, and the man must pay its value on that day as something holy to the Lᴏʀᴅ. ²⁴In the Year of Jubilee the field will revert to the person from whom he bought it, the one whose land it was. ²⁵Every value is to be set according to the sanctuary shekel, twenty gerahs to the shekel.

²⁶" 'No one, however, may dedicate the firstborn of an animal, since the firstborn already be-

---

truth or dare

"Strike three! You're out!" Thankfully, you won't hear these words from God, even when you repeatedly fail. Sin always has consequences, but God promises to *never* give up on you.

26:40–45

ᵃ 3 That is, about 1 1/4 pounds (about 0.6 kilogram); also in verse 16   ᵇ 3 That is, about 2/5 ounce (about 11.5 grams); also in verse 25   ᶜ 4 That is, about 12 ounces (about 0.3 kilogram)   ᵈ 5 That is, about 8 ounces (about 0.2 kilogram)
ᵉ 5 That is, about 4 ounces (about 110 grams); also in verse 7   ᶠ 6 That is, about 2 ounces (about 55 grams)
ᵍ 6 That is, about 1 1/4 ounces (about 35 grams)   ʰ 7 That is, about 6 ounces (about 170 grams)   ⁱ 16 That is, probably about 6 bushels (about 220 liters)   ʲ 21 Or *priest*

longs to the LORD; whether an ox[a] or a sheep, it is the LORD's. ²⁷If it is one of the unclean animals, he may buy it back at its set value, adding a fifth of the value to it. If he does not redeem it, it is to be sold at its set value.

²⁸ 'But nothing that a man owns and devotes[b] to the LORD—whether man or animal or family land—may be sold or redeemed; everything so devoted is most holy to the LORD.

²⁹ 'No person devoted to destruction[c] may be ransomed; he must be put to death.

³⁰ 'A tithe of everything from the land, whether grain from the soil or fruit from the trees, belongs to the LORD; it is holy to the LORD. ³¹If a man redeems any of his tithe, he must add a fifth of the value to it. ³²The entire tithe of the herd and flock—every tenth animal that passes under the shepherd's rod—will be holy to the LORD. ³³He must not pick out the good from the bad or make any substitution. If he does make a substitution, both the animal and its substitute become holy and cannot be redeemed.' "

³⁴These are the commands the LORD gave Moses on Mount Sinai for the Israelites.

---

a 26 The Hebrew word can include both male and female.   b 28 The Hebrew term refers to the irrevocable giving over of things or persons to the LORD.   c 29 The Hebrew term refers to the irrevocable giving over of things or persons to the LORD, often by totally destroying them.

at a glance ⌄

author:	Moses.
date:	During the 1400s B.C., while the Israelites were traveling in the desert.
setting:	For 38 years the people of Israel wander in the desert between Mount Sinai and the borders of the land of Canaan.
verse to remember:	The LORD . . . does not leaveve the guilty unpunished (14:18).
theme to consider:	There are often severe consequences for our rebellion against God. But even though God disciplines us, he remains faithful to his promises, showing great patience and mercy.

numbers

unchanging truth

You went to a movie with your friends, and your brother saw you. The problem is that it was a movie your parents said was definitely off limits!

You're late for class—for the third time this month!

The consequences of these actions have the potential to be *quite* unpleasant. Parents and other adults set guidelines that they expect you to follow. They want you to develop a sense of responsibility and self-discipline. You may not always see the point of guidelines; at times, you just want to blow them off entirely. That's when things get ugly! Disobedience brings discipline. But discipline is love in action—it helps you re-evaluate your behavior and learn from it.

God led the Israelites from Egypt to the borders of the promised land. Then the Israelites rebelled. They were afraid and didn't trust God to help them conquer the Canaanites. So God disciplined his children severely. He prohibited that generation from entering the promised land. Thankfully, the story doesn't end there for the Israelites—or for us. Along with his discipline, God showed his mercy, patience and love to the Israelites by bringing the next generation into the promised land 38 years later. In the same way, even when we rebel, God still shows mercy, patience and love to us. Real maturity and growth come from learning from your mistakes . . . and accepting discipline when it comes.

3 life lessons

1 Twelve spies went to explore Canaan before the Israelites entered the land. Their conflicting reports reflected their trust (or *lack of* trust) in God (13:26–33).

2 Even Moses and Aaron rebelled against God's command and were disciplined (20:2,6–12).

3 God showed mercy to the Israelites by using an unusual symbol—a bronze snake on a pole (21:6–9). This event is referred to in John 3:14–15 and symbolizes Jesus' dying for the sins of all people.

⌃

The Census

1 The LORD spoke to Moses in the Tent of Meeting in the Desert of Sinai on the first day of the second month of the second year after the Israelites came out of Egypt. He said: ²"Take a census of the whole Israelite community by their clans and families, listing every man by name, one by one. ³You and Aaron are to number by their divisions all the men in Israel twenty years old or more who are able to serve in the army. ⁴One man from each tribe, each the head of his family, is to help you. ⁵These are the names of the men who are to assist you:

from Reuben, Elizur son of Shedeur;
⁶from Simeon, Shelumiel son of Zurishaddai;
⁷from Judah, Nahshon son of Amminadab;
⁸from Issachar, Nethanel son of Zuar;
⁹from Zebulun, Eliab son of Helon;
¹⁰from the sons of Joseph:
    from Ephraim, Elishama son of Ammihud;
    from Manasseh, Gamaliel son of Pedahzur;
¹¹from Benjamin, Abidan son of Gideoni;
¹²from Dan, Ahiezer son of Ammishaddai;
¹³from Asher, Pagiel son of Ocran;
¹⁴from Gad, Eliasaph son of Deuel;
¹⁵from Naphtali, Ahira son of Enan."

¹⁶These were the men appointed from the community, the leaders of their ancestral tribes. They were the heads of the clans of Israel.

¹⁷Moses and Aaron took these men whose names had been given, ¹⁸and they called the whole community together on the first day of the second month. The people indicated their ancestry by their clans and families, and the men twenty years old or more were listed by name, one by one, ¹⁹as the LORD commanded Moses. And so he counted them in the Desert of Sinai:

truth *or dare*

Leading more than a million Israelites was a tough job—but God didn't expect Moses to do it all on his own. Do you have enough support? Take an inventory of your spiritual helpers.

1:2–15

²⁰From the descendants of Reuben the firstborn son of Israel:
    All the men twenty years old or more who were able to serve in the army were listed by name, one by one, according to the records of their clans and families. ²¹The number from the tribe of Reuben was 46,500.

²²From the descendants of Simeon:
    All the men twenty years old or more who were able to serve in the army were counted and listed by name, one by one, according to the records of their clans and families. ²³The number from the tribe of Simeon was 59,300.

²⁴From the descendants of Gad:
    All the men twenty years old or more who were able to serve in the army were listed by name, according to the records of their clans and families. ²⁵The number from the tribe of Gad was 45,650.

²⁶From the descendants of Judah:
    All the men twenty years old or more who were able to serve in the army were listed by name, according to the records of their clans and families. ²⁷The number from the tribe of Judah was 74,600.

²⁸From the descendants of Issachar:
    All the men twenty years old or more who were able to serve in the army were listed by name, according to the records of their clans and families. ²⁹The number from the tribe of Issachar was 54,400.

³⁰From the descendants of Zebulun:
    All the men twenty years old or more who were able to serve in the army were listed by

name, according to the records of their clans and families. ³¹The number from the tribe of Zebulun was 57,400.

³²From the sons of Joseph:
From the descendants of Ephraim:
All the men twenty years old or more who were able to serve in the army were listed by name, according to the records of their clans and families. ³³The number from the tribe of Ephraim was 40,500.

³⁴From the descendants of Manasseh:
All the men twenty years old or more who were able to serve in the army were listed by name, according to the records of their clans and families. ³⁵The number from the tribe of Manasseh was 32,200.

³⁶From the descendants of Benjamin:
All the men twenty years old or more who were able to serve in the army were listed by name, according to the records of their clans and families. ³⁷The number from the tribe of Benjamin was 35,400.

³⁸From the descendants of Dan:
All the men twenty years old or more who were able to serve in the army were listed by name, according to the records of their clans and families. ³⁹The number from the tribe of Dan was 62,700.

⁴⁰From the descendants of Asher:
All the men twenty years old or more who were able to serve in the army were listed by name, according to the records of their clans and families. ⁴¹The number from the tribe of Asher was 41,500.

⁴²From the descendants of Naphtali:
All the men twenty years old or more who were able to serve in the army were listed by name, according to the records of their clans and families. ⁴³The number from the tribe of Naphtali was 53,400.

⁴⁴These were the men counted by Moses and Aaron and the twelve leaders of Israel, each one representing his family. ⁴⁵All the Israelites twenty years old or more who were able to serve in Israel's army were counted according to their families. ⁴⁶The total number was 603,550.

⁴⁷The families of the tribe of Levi, however, were not counted along with the others. ⁴⁸The LORD had said to Moses: ⁴⁹"You must not count the tribe of Levi or include them in the census of the other Israelites. ⁵⁰Instead, appoint the Levites to be in charge of the tabernacle of the Testimony—over all its furnishings and everything belonging to it. They are to carry the tabernacle and all its furnishings; they are to take care of it and encamp around it. ⁵¹Whenever the tabernacle is to move, the Levites are to take it down, and whenever the tabernacle is to be set up, the Levites shall do it. Anyone else who goes near it shall be put to death. ⁵²The Israelites are to set up their tents by divisions, each man in his own camp under his own standard. ⁵³The Levites, however, are to set up their tents around the tabernacle of the Testimony so that wrath will not fall on the Israelite community. The Levites are to be responsible for the care of the tabernacle of the Testimony."

⁵⁴The Israelites did all this just as the LORD commanded Moses.

The Arrangement of the Tribal Camps

2 The LORD said to Moses and Aaron: ²"The Israelites are to camp around the Tent of Meeting some distance from it, each man under his standard with the banners of his family."

³On the east, toward the sunrise, the divisions of the camp of Judah are to encamp under their standard. The leader of the people of Judah is Nahshon son of Amminadab. ⁴His division numbers 74,600.

⁵The tribe of Issachar will camp next to them. The leader of the people of Issachar is Nethanel son of Zuar. ⁶His division numbers 54,400.

⁷The tribe of Zebulun will be next. The leader of the people of Zebulun is Eliab son of Helon. ⁸His division numbers 57,400.

⁹All the men assigned to the camp of Judah, according to their divisions, number 186,400. They will set out first.

¹⁰On the south will be the divisions of the camp of Reuben under their standard. The leader of the people of Reuben is Elizur son of Shedeur. ¹¹His division numbers 46,500. ¹²The tribe of Simeon will camp next to them. The leader of the people of Simeon is Shelumiel son of Zurishaddai. ¹³His division numbers 59,300. ¹⁴The tribe of Gad will be next. The leader of the people of Gad is Eliasaph son of Deuel.ᵃ ¹⁵His division numbers 45,650. ¹⁶All the men assigned to the camp of Reuben, according to their divisions, number 151,450. They will set out second.

¹⁷Then the Tent of Meeting and the camp of the Levites will set out in the middle of the camps. They will set out in the same order as they encamp, each in his own place under his standard.

¹⁸On the west will be the divisions of the camp of Ephraim under their standard. The leader of the people of Ephraim is Elishama son of Ammihud. ¹⁹His division numbers 40,500. ²⁰The tribe of Manasseh will be next to them. The leader of the people of Manasseh is Gamaliel son of Pedahzur. ²¹His division numbers 32,200. ²²The tribe of Benjamin will be next. The leader of the people of Benjamin is Abidan son of Gideoni. ²³His division numbers 35,400. ²⁴All the men assigned to the camp of Ephraim, according to their divisions, number 108,100. They will set out third.

²⁵On the north will be the divisions of the camp of Dan, under their standard. The leader of the people of Dan is Ahiezer son of Ammishaddai. ²⁶His division numbers 62,700. ²⁷The tribe of Asher will camp next to them. The leader of the people of Asher is Pagiel son of Ocran. ²⁸His division numbers 41,500. ²⁹The tribe of Naphtali will be next. The leader of the people of Naphtali is Ahira son of Enan. ³⁰His division numbers 53,400. ³¹All the men assigned to the camp of Dan number 157,600. They will set out last, under their standards.

³²These are the Israelites, counted according to their families. All those in the camps, by their divisions, number 603,550. ³³The Levites, however, were not counted along with the other Israelites, as the Lord commanded Moses.

³⁴So the Israelites did everything the Lord commanded Moses; that is the way they encamped under their standards, and that is the way they set out, each with his clan and family.

The Levites

3 This is the account of the family of Aaron and Moses at the time the Lord talked with Moses on Mount Sinai.
²The names of the sons of Aaron were Nadab the firstborn and Abihu, Eleazar and Ithamar. ³Those were the names of Aaron's sons, the anointed priests, who were ordained to serve as priests. ⁴Nadab and Abihu, however, fell dead before the Lord when they made an offering with unauthorized fire before him in the Desert of Sinai. They had no sons; so only Eleazar and Ithamar served as priests during the lifetime of their father Aaron.

⁵The Lord said to Moses, ⁶"Bring the tribe of Levi and present them to Aaron the priest to assist him. ⁷They are to perform duties for him and for the whole community at the Tent of Meeting by doing the work of the tabernacle. ⁸They are to take care of all the furnishings of the Tent of Meeting, fulfilling the obligations of the Israelites by doing the work of the tabernacle. ⁹Give the Levites to Aaron and his sons; they are the Israelites who are to be given wholly to him.ᵇ ¹⁰Appoint Aaron and his sons to serve as priests; anyone else who approaches the sanctuary must be put to death."

ᵃ 14 Many manuscripts of the Masoretic Text, Samaritan Pentateuch and Vulgate (see also Num. 1:14); most manuscripts of the Masoretic Text Reuel   ᵇ 9 Most manuscripts of the Masoretic Text; some manuscripts of the Masoretic Text, Samaritan Pentateuch and Septuagint (see also Num. 8:16) to me

Caught in the Middle

focus — Profile: **Brianna**

"Maybe it's just a misunderstanding," I suggested to Julie, as she slammed another book down on the table. "Oh no. She knew exactly what she was doing," Julie snapped as she emptied her backpack on the library table with dramatic flair.

The school librarian glared at us to be quiet. "Hey, don't get mad at me just because you're ticked at Erin. I'm still your friend, remember?" I whispered loudly.

Oh no. Here we go again, I thought. *How do I get myself in the middle of these things?* Erin and Julie were having another one of their typical fights. However, this one was turning into a two-week, all-out war between my best friends. Julie was mad at Erin because Erin had supposedly flirted with Brian (the guy Julie just started dating) in front of her face at a party.

"Erin doesn't even like Brian. Why would she flirt with him?" I tried explaining. I knew I wasn't getting anywhere. Julie was so insecure about her new love interest that she accused everyone of trying to steal him away from her. And Erin *is* a flirt—but she wouldn't do that to Julie! Erin had tried to apologize. Brian even told Julie to get over it. Julie wouldn't budge. As far as she was concerned, the friendship was over.

So what am I supposed to do now? I'm afraid I'm losing both of them. All Julie talks about is Erin. And I feel like a spy whenever Erin tries to get information from me about how Julie feels.

For more on dealing with conflict in relationships, go to www.TrueImagesBible.com

conflict in focus

If you often find yourself in the middle of a fight between friends, keep these tips in mind:

» There's a difference between being a peacemaker and a go-between. Don't play the role of a spy or allow one to pump you for information on the other.

» There's only so much one person can do to keep the peace. It's not your problem to solve. However, you have to be willing to do all you can to pray for and work toward a peaceful solution (see Matthew 5:9, page 1295).

» Sometimes friendships grow apart permanently. People change and move on to different places in life. But that doesn't have to affect your individual friendships with those girls.

For more on this topic, see the index on page 1656.

conflict

[11] The LORD also said to Moses, [12] "I have taken the Levites from among the Israelites in place of the first male offspring of every Israelite woman. The Levites are mine, [13] for all the firstborn are mine. When I struck down all the firstborn in Egypt, I set apart for myself every firstborn in Israel, whether man or animal. They are to be mine. I am the LORD."

[14] The LORD said to Moses in the Desert of Sinai, [15] "Count the Levites by their families and clans. Count every male a month old or more." [16] So Moses counted them, as he was commanded by the word of the LORD.

¹⁷These were the names of the sons of Levi:
    Gershon, Kohath and Merari.
¹⁸These were the names of the Gershonite clans:
    Libni and Shimei.
¹⁹The Kohathite clans:
    Amram, Izhar, Hebron and Uzziel.
²⁰The Merarite clans:
    Mahli and Mushi.
These were the Levite clans, according to their families.

²¹To Gershon belonged the clans of the Libnites and Shimeites; these were the Gershonite clans. ²²The number of all the males a month old or more who were counted was 7,500. ²³The Gershonite clans were to camp on the west, behind the tabernacle. ²⁴The leader of the families of the Gershonites was Eliasaph son of Lael. ²⁵At the Tent of Meeting the Gershonites were responsible for the care of the tabernacle and tent, its coverings, the curtain at the entrance to the Tent of Meeting, ²⁶the curtains of the courtyard, the curtain at the entrance to the courtyard surrounding the tabernacle and altar, and the ropes—and everything related to their use.

²⁷To Kohath belonged the clans of the Amramites, Izharites, Hebronites and Uzzielites; these were the Kohathite clans. ²⁸The number of all the males a month old or more was 8,600.ᵃ The Kohathites were responsible for the care of the sanctuary. ²⁹The Kohathite clans were to camp on the south side of the tabernacle. ³⁰The leader of the families of the Kohathite clans was Elizaphan son of Uzziel. ³¹They were responsible for the care of the ark, the table, the lampstand, the altars, the articles of the sanctuary used in ministering, the curtain, and everything related to their use. ³²The chief leader of the Levites was Eleazar son of Aaron, the priest. He was appointed over those who were responsible for the care of the sanctuary.

³³To Merari belonged the clans of the Mahlites and the Mushites; these were the Merarite clans. ³⁴The number of all the males a month old or more who were counted was 6,200. ³⁵The leader of the families of the Merarite clans was Zuriel son of Abihail; they were to camp on the north side of the tabernacle. ³⁶The Merarites were appointed to take care of the frames of the tabernacle, its crossbars, posts, bases, all its equipment, and everything related to their use, ³⁷as well as the posts of the surrounding courtyard with their bases, tent pegs and ropes.

³⁸Moses and Aaron and his sons were to camp to the east of the tabernacle, toward the sunrise, in front of the Tent of Meeting. They were responsible for the care of the sanctuary on behalf of the Israelites. Anyone else who approached the sanctuary was to be put to death.

³⁹The total number of Levites counted at the LORD's command by Moses and Aaron according to their clans, including every male a month old or more, was 22,000.

⁴⁰The LORD said to Moses, "Count all the firstborn Israelite males who are a month old or more and make a list of their names. ⁴¹Take the Levites for me in place of all the firstborn of the Israelites, and the livestock of the Levites in place of all the firstborn of the livestock of the Israelites. I am the LORD."

⁴²So Moses counted all the firstborn of the Israelites, as the LORD commanded him. ⁴³The total number of firstborn males a month old or more, listed by name, was 22,273.

⁴⁴The LORD also said to Moses, ⁴⁵"Take the Levites in place of all the firstborn of Israel, and the livestock of the Levites in place of their livestock. The Levites are to be mine. I am the LORD. ⁴⁶To redeem the 273 firstborn Israelites who exceed the number of the Levites, ⁴⁷collect five shekelsᵇ for each one, according to the sanctuary shekel, which weighs twenty gerahs. ⁴⁸Give the money for the redemption of the additional Israelites to Aaron and his sons."

⁴⁹So Moses collected the redemption money from those who exceeded the number redeemed by the Levites. ⁵⁰From the firstborn of the Israelites he collected silver weighing 1,365

ᵃ 28 Hebrew; some Septuagint manuscripts 8,300   ᵇ 47 That is, about 2 ounces (about 55 grams) shekels,[a] according to the sanctuary shekel. [51]Moses gave the redemption money to Aaron and his sons, as he was commanded by the word of the LORD.

The Kohathites

4 The LORD said to Moses and Aaron: [2]"Take a census of the Kohathite branch of the Levites by their clans and families. [3]Count all the men from thirty to fifty years of age who come to serve in the work in the Tent of Meeting.

[4]"This is the work of the Kohathites in the Tent of Meeting: the care of the most holy things. [5]When the camp is to move, Aaron and his sons are to go in and take down the shielding curtain and cover the ark of the Testimony with it. [6]Then they are to cover this with hides of sea cows,[b] spread a cloth of solid blue over that and put the poles in place.

[7]"Over the table of the Presence they are to spread a blue cloth and put on it the plates, dishes and bowls, and the jars for drink offerings; the bread that is continually there is to remain on it. [8]Over these they are to spread a scarlet cloth, cover that with hides of sea cows and put its poles in place.

[9]"They are to take a blue cloth and cover the lampstand that is for light, together with its lamps, its wick trimmers and trays, and all its jars for the oil used to supply it. [10]Then they are to wrap it and all its accessories in a covering of hides of sea cows and put it on a carrying frame.

[11]"Over the gold altar they are to spread a blue cloth and cover that with hides of sea cows and put its poles in place.

[12]"They are to take all the articles used for ministering in the sanctuary, wrap them in a blue cloth, cover that with hides of sea cows and put them on a carrying frame.

[13]"They are to remove the ashes from the bronze altar and spread a purple cloth over it. [14]Then they are to place on it all the utensils used for ministering at the altar, including the firepans, meat forks, shovels and sprinkling bowls. Over it they are to spread a covering of hides of sea cows and put its poles in place.

[15]"After Aaron and his sons have finished covering the holy furnishings and all the holy articles, and when the camp is ready to move, the Kohathites are to come to do the carrying. But they must not touch the holy things or they will die. The Kohathites are to carry those things that are in the Tent of Meeting.

[16]"Eleazar son of Aaron, the priest, is to have charge of the oil for the light, the fragrant incense, the regular grain offering and the anointing oil. He is to be in charge of the entire tabernacle and everything in it, including its holy furnishings and articles."

[17]The LORD said to Moses and Aaron, [18]"See that the Kohathite tribal clans are not cut off from the Levites. [19]So that they may live and not die when they come near the most holy things, do this for them: Aaron and his sons are to go into the sanctuary and assign to each man his work and what he is to carry. [20]But the Kohathites must not go in to look at the holy things, even for a moment, or they will die."

The Gershonites

[21]The LORD said to Moses, [22]"Take a census also of the Gershonites by their families and clans. [23]Count all the men from thirty to fifty years of age who come to serve in the work at the Tent of Meeting.

[24]"This is the service of the Gershonite clans as they work and carry burdens: [25]They are to carry the curtains of the tabernacle, the Tent of Meeting, its covering and the outer covering of hides of sea cows, the curtains for the entrance to the Tent of Meeting, [26]the curtains of the courtyard surrounding the tabernacle and altar, the curtain for the entrance, the ropes and all the equipment used in its service. The Gershonites are to do all that needs to be done with these things. [27]All their service, whether carrying or doing other work, is to be done under the direction of Aaron and his sons. You shall assign to them as their responsibility all they are to carry. [28]This is the service of the Gershonite clans at the Tent of Meeting. Their duties are to be under the direction of Ithamar son of Aaron, the priest.

The Merarites

[29]"Count the Merarites by their clans and families. [30]Count all the men from thirty to fifty years of age who come to serve in the work at the Tent of Meeting. [31]This is their duty as they perform

a 50 That is, about 35 pounds (about 15.5 kilograms)   b 6 That is, dugongs; also in verses 8, 10, 11, 12, 14 and 25 service at the Tent of Meeting: to carry the frames of the tabernacle, its crossbars, posts and bases, [32]as well as the posts of the surrounding courtyard with their bases, tent pegs, ropes, all their equipment and everything related to their use. Assign to each man the specific things he is to carry. [33]This is the service of the Merarite clans as they work at the Tent of Meeting under the direction of Ithamar son of Aaron, the priest."

The Numbering of the Levite Clans

[34]Moses, Aaron and the leaders of the community counted the Kohathites by their clans and families. [35]All the men from thirty to fifty years of age who came to serve in the work in the Tent of Meeting, [36]counted by clans, were 2,750. [37]This was the total of all those in the Kohathite clans who served in the Tent of Meeting. Moses and Aaron counted them according to the LORD's command through Moses.

[38]The Gershonites were counted by their clans and families. [39]All the men from thirty to fifty years of age who came to serve in the work at the Tent of Meeting, [40]counted by their clans and families, were 2,630. [41]This was the total of those in the Gershonite clans who served at the Tent of Meeting. Moses and Aaron counted them according to the LORD's command.

[42]The Merarites were counted by their clans and families. [43]All the men from thirty to fifty years of age who came to serve in the work at the Tent of Meeting, [44]counted by their clans, were 3,200. [45]This was the total of those in the Merarite clans. Moses and Aaron counted them according to the LORD's command through Moses.

[46]So Moses, Aaron and the leaders of Israel counted all the Levites by their clans and families. [47]All the men from thirty to fifty years of age who came to do the work of serving and carrying the Tent of Meeting [48]numbered 8,580. [49]At the LORD's command through Moses, each was assigned his work and told what to carry.

Thus they were counted, as the LORD commanded Moses.

The Purity of the Camp

5 The LORD said to Moses, [2]"Command the Israelites to send away from the camp anyone who has an infectious skin disease[a] or a discharge of any kind, or who is ceremonially unclean because of a dead body. [3]Send away male and female alike; send them outside the camp so they will not defile their camp, where I dwell among them." [4]The Israelites did this; they sent them outside the camp. They did just as the LORD had instructed Moses.

truth or dare

Crisis: You're in dire need to make up with a friend after a huge blowout. What to do?! Show her you're sorry by going beyond words—do something thoughtful for her.

5:5–7

Restitution for Wrongs

[5]The LORD said to Moses, [6]"Say to the Israelites: 'When a man or woman wrongs another in any way[b] and so is unfaithful to the LORD, that person is guilty [7]and must confess the sin he has committed. He must make full restitution for his wrong, add one fifth to it and give it all to the person he has wronged. [8]But if that person has no close relative to whom restitution can be made for the wrong, the restitution belongs to the LORD and must be given to the priest, along with the ram with which atonement is made for him. [9]All the sacred contributions the Israelites bring to a priest will belong to him. [10]Each man's sacred gifts are his own, but what he gives to the priest will belong to the priest.' "

The Test for an Unfaithful Wife

[11]Then the LORD said to Moses, [12]"Speak to the Israelites and say to them: 'If a man's wife goes astray and is unfaithful to him [13]by sleeping with another man, and this is hidden from her husband and her impurity is undetected (since there is no witness against her and she has not been caught in the act), [14]and if feelings of jealousy come over

a 2 Traditionally *leprosy*; the Hebrew word was used for various diseases affecting the skin—not necessarily leprosy.
b 6 Or *woman commits any wrong common to mankind*

her husband and he suspects his wife and she is impure—or if he is jealous and suspects her even though she is not impure— ¹⁵then he is to take his wife to the priest. He must also take an offering of a tenth of an ephah*ᵃ* of barley flour on her behalf. He must not pour oil on it or put incense on it, because it is a grain offering for jealousy, a reminder offering to draw attention to guilt.

¹⁶" 'The priest shall bring her and have her stand before the LORD. ¹⁷Then he shall take some holy water in a clay jar and put some dust from the tabernacle floor into the water. ¹⁸After the priest has had the woman stand before the LORD, he shall loosen her hair and place in her hands the reminder offering, the grain offering for jealousy, while he himself holds the bitter water that brings a curse. ¹⁹Then the priest shall put the woman under oath and say to her, "If no other man has slept with you and you have not gone astray and become impure while married to your husband, may this bitter water that brings a curse not harm you. ²⁰But if you have gone astray while married to your husband and you have defiled yourself by sleeping with a man other than your husband"— ²¹here the priest is to put the woman under this curse of the oath—"may the LORD cause your people to curse and denounce you when he causes your thigh to waste away and your abdomen to swell.*ᵇ* ²²May this water that brings a curse enter your body so that your abdomen swells and your thigh wastes away.*ᶜ*"

" 'Then the woman is to say, "Amen. So be it."

²³" 'The priest is to write these curses on a scroll and then wash them off into the bitter water. ²⁴He shall have the woman drink the bitter water that brings a curse, and this water will enter her and cause bitter suffering. ²⁵The priest is to take from her hands the grain offering for jealousy, wave it before the LORD and bring it to the altar. ²⁶The priest is then to take a handful of the grain offering as a memorial offering and burn it on the altar; after that, he is to have the woman drink the water. ²⁷If she has defiled herself and been unfaithful to her husband, then when she is made to drink the water that brings a curse, it will go into her and cause bitter suffering; her abdomen will swell and her thigh waste away,*ᵈ* and she will become accursed among her people. ²⁸If, however, the woman has not defiled herself and is free from impurity, she will be cleared of guilt and will be able to have children.

²⁹" 'This, then, is the law of jealousy when a woman goes astray and defiles herself while married to her husband, ³⁰or when feelings of jealousy come over a man because he suspects his wife. The priest is to have her stand before the LORD and is to apply this entire law to her. ³¹The husband will be innocent of any wrongdoing, but the woman will bear the consequences of her sin.' "

The Nazirite

6 The LORD said to Moses, ²"Speak to the Israelites and say to them: 'If a man or woman wants to make a special vow, a vow of separation to the LORD as a Nazirite, ³he must abstain from wine and other fermented drink and must not drink vinegar made from wine or from other fermented drink. He must not drink grape juice or eat grapes or raisins. ⁴As long as he is a Nazirite, he must not eat anything that comes from the grapevine, not even the seeds or skins.

⁵" 'During the entire period of his vow of separation no razor may be used on his head. He must be holy until the period of his separation to the LORD is over; he must let the hair of his head grow long. ⁶Throughout the period of his separation to the LORD he must not go near a dead body. ⁷Even if his own father or mother or brother or sister dies, he must not make himself ceremonially unclean on account of them, because the symbol of his separation to God is on his head. ⁸Throughout the period of his separation he is consecrated to the LORD.

⁹" 'If someone dies suddenly in his presence, thus defiling the hair he has dedicated, he must shave his head on the day of his cleansing—the seventh day. ¹⁰Then on the eighth day he must bring two doves or two young pigeons to the priest at the entrance to the Tent of Meeting. ¹¹The priest is to offer one as a sin offering and the other as a burnt offering to make atonement for him because he sinned by being in the presence of the dead body. That same day he is to consecrate his head. ¹²He must dedicate himself to the LORD for the period of his separation and must bring a year-old male lamb as a guilt offering. The previous days do not count, because he became defiled during his separation.

ᵃ 15 That is, probably about 2 quarts (about 2 liters)   ᵇ 21 Or causes you to have a miscarrying womb and barrenness   ᶜ 22 Or body and cause you to be barren and have a miscarrying womb   ᵈ 27 Or suffering; she will have barrenness and a miscarrying womb

¹³" 'Now this is the law for the Nazirite when the period of his separation is over. He is to be brought to the entrance to the Tent of Meeting. ¹⁴There he is to present his offerings to the LORD: a year-old male lamb without defect for a burnt offering, a year-old ewe lamb without defect for a sin offering, a ram without defect for a fellowship offering,ᵃ ¹⁵together with their grain offerings and drink offerings, and a basket of bread made without yeast—cakes made of fine flour mixed with oil, and wafers spread with oil.

¹⁶" 'The priest is to present them before the LORD and make the sin offering and the burnt offering. ¹⁷He is to present the basket of unleavened bread and is to sacrifice the ram as a fellowship offering to the LORD, together with its grain offering and drink offering.

¹⁸" 'Then at the entrance to the Tent of Meeting, the Nazirite must shave off the hair that he dedicated. He is to take the hair and put it in the fire that is under the sacrifice of the fellowship offering.

¹⁹" 'After the Nazirite has shaved off the hair of his dedication, the priest is to place in his hands a boiled shoulder of the ram, and a cake and a wafer from the basket, both made without yeast. ²⁰The priest shall then wave them before the LORD as a wave offering; they are holy and belong to the priest, together with the breast that was waved and the thigh that was presented. After that, the Nazirite may drink wine.

²¹" 'This is the law of the Nazirite who vows his offering to the LORD in accordance with his separation, in addition to whatever else he can afford. He must fulfill the vow he has made, according to the law of the Nazirite.' "

love ♡ notes

6:24-26

Daughter,

This is my heart's desire for you: to bless you, to protect you, to be pleased with you, to be gracious to you and to give you my peace.

—Your Father

Take time to thank God for his love.

The Priestly Blessing

²²The LORD said to Moses, ²³"Tell Aaron and his sons, 'This is how you are to bless the Israelites. Say to them:

²⁴" ' "The LORD bless you
and keep you;
²⁵the LORD make his face shine
upon you
and be gracious to you;
²⁶the LORD turn his face toward you
and give you peace." '

²⁷"So they will put my name on the Israelites, and I will bless them."

Offerings at the Dedication of the Tabernacle

7 When Moses finished setting up the tabernacle, he anointed it and consecrated it and all its furnishings. He also anointed and consecrated the altar and all its utensils. ²Then the leaders of Israel, the heads of families who were the tribal leaders in charge of those who were counted, made offerings. ³They brought as their gifts

ᵃ 14 Traditionally peace offering; also in verses 17 and 18

before the Lord six covered carts and twelve oxen—an ox from each leader and a cart from every two. These they presented before the tabernacle.

[4]The Lord said to Moses, [5]"Accept these from them, that they may be used in the work at the Tent of Meeting. Give them to the Levites as each man's work requires."

[6]So Moses took the carts and oxen and gave them to the Levites. [7]He gave two carts and four oxen to the Gershonites, as their work required, [8]and he gave four carts and eight oxen to the Merarites, as their work required. They were all under the direction of Ithamar son of Aaron, the priest. [9]But Moses did not give any to the Kohathites, because they were to carry on their shoulders the holy things, for which they were responsible.

[10]When the altar was anointed, the leaders brought their offerings for its dedication and presented them before the altar. [11]For the Lord had said to Moses, "Each day one leader is to bring his offering for the dedication of the altar."

[12]The one who brought his offering on the first day was Nahshon son of Amminadab of the tribe of Judah.

[13]His offering was one silver plate weighing a hundred and thirty shekels,[a] and one silver sprinkling bowl weighing seventy shekels,[b] both according to the sanctuary shekel, each filled with fine flour mixed with oil as a grain offering; [14]one gold dish weighing ten shekels,[c] filled with incense; [15]one young bull, one ram and one male lamb a year old, for a burnt offering; [16]one male goat for a sin offering; [17]and two oxen, five rams, five male goats and five male lambs a year old, to be sacrificed as a fellowship offering.[d] This was the offering of Nahshon son of Amminadab.

[18]On the second day Nethanel son of Zuar, the leader of Issachar, brought his offering. [19]The offering he brought was one silver plate weighing a hundred and thirty shekels, and one silver sprinkling bowl weighing seventy shekels, both according to the sanctuary shekel, each filled with fine flour mixed with oil as a grain offering; [20]one gold dish weighing ten shekels, filled with incense; [21]one young bull, one ram and one male lamb a year old, for a burnt offering; [22]one male goat for a sin offering; [23]and two oxen, five rams, five male goats and five male lambs a year old, to be sacrificed as a fellowship offering. This was the offering of Nethanel son of Zuar.

[24]On the third day, Eliab son of Helon, the leader of the people of Zebulun, brought his offering. [25]His offering was one silver plate weighing a hundred and thirty shekels, and one silver sprinkling bowl weighing seventy shekels, both according to the sanctuary shekel, each filled with fine flour mixed with oil as a grain offering; [26]one gold dish weighing ten shekels, filled with incense; [27]one young bull, one ram and one male lamb a year old, for a burnt offering; [28]one male goat for a sin offering; [29]and two oxen, five rams, five male goats and five male lambs a year old, to be sacrificed as a fellowship offering. This was the offering of Eliab son of Helon.

[30]On the fourth day Elizur son of Shedeur, the leader of the people of Reuben, brought his offering. [31]His offering was one silver plate weighing a hundred and thirty shekels, and one silver sprinkling bowl weighing seventy shekels, both according to the sanctuary shekel, each filled with fine flour mixed with oil as a grain offering; [32]one gold dish weighing ten shekels, filled with incense; [33]one young bull, one ram and one male lamb a year old, for a burnt offering; [34]one male goat for a sin offering; [35]and two oxen, five rams, five male goats and five male lambs a year old, to be sacrificed as a fellowship offering. This was the offering of Elizur son of Shedeur.

[36]On the fifth day Shelumiel son of Zurishaddai, the leader of the people of Simeon, brought his offering. [37]His offering was one silver plate weighing a hundred and thirty shekels, and one silver sprinkling bowl weighing seventy shekels, both according to the sanctuary shekel, each filled with fine flour mixed with oil as a grain offering; [38]one gold dish weighing ten shekels,

a 13 That is, about 3 1/4 pounds (about 1.5 kilograms); also elsewhere in this chapter   b 13 That is, about 1 3/4 pounds (about 0.8 kilogram); also elsewhere in this chapter   c 14 That is, about 4 ounces (about 110 grams); also elsewhere in this chapter   d 17 Traditionally peace offering; also elsewhere in this chapter filled with incense; ³⁹one young bull, one ram and one male lamb a year old, for a burnt offering; ⁴⁰one male goat for a sin offering; ⁴¹and two oxen, five rams, five male goats and five male lambs a year old, to be sacrificed as a fellowship offering. This was the offering of Shelumiel son of Zurishaddai.

⁴²On the sixth day Eliasaph son of Deuel, the leader of the people of Gad, brought his offering. ⁴³His offering was one silver plate weighing a hundred and thirty shekels, and one silver sprinkling bowl weighing seventy shekels, both according to the sanctuary shekel, each filled with fine flour mixed with oil as a grain offering; ⁴⁴one gold dish weighing ten shekels, filled with incense; ⁴⁵one young bull, one ram and one male lamb a year old, for a burnt offering; ⁴⁶one male goat for a sin offering; ⁴⁷and two oxen, five rams, five male goats and five male lambs a year old, to be sacrificed as a fellowship offering. This was the offering of Eliasaph son of Deuel.

⁴⁸On the seventh day Elishama son of Ammihud, the leader of the people of Ephraim, brought his offering. ⁴⁹His offering was one silver plate weighing a hundred and thirty shekels, and one silver sprinkling bowl weighing seventy shekels, both according to the sanctuary shekel, each filled with fine flour mixed with oil as a grain offering; ⁵⁰one gold dish weighing ten shekels, filled with incense; ⁵¹one young bull, one ram and one male lamb a year old, for a burnt offering; ⁵²one male goat for a sin offering; ⁵³and two oxen, five rams, five male goats and five male lambs a year old, to be sacrificed as a fellowship offering. This was the offering of Elishama son of Ammihud.

⁵⁴On the eighth day Gamaliel son of Pedahzur, the leader of the people of Manasseh, brought his offering. ⁵⁵His offering was one silver plate weighing a hundred and thirty shekels, and one silver sprinkling bowl weighing seventy shekels, both according to the sanctuary shekel, each filled with fine flour mixed with oil as a grain offering; ⁵⁶one gold dish weighing ten shekels, filled with incense; ⁵⁷one young bull, one ram and one male lamb a year old, for a burnt offering; ⁵⁸one male goat for a sin offering; ⁵⁹and two oxen, five rams, five male goats and five male lambs a year old, to be sacrificed as a fellowship offering. This was the offering of Gamaliel son of Pedahzur.

⁶⁰On the ninth day Abidan son of Gideoni, the leader of the people of Benjamin, brought his offering. ⁶¹His offering was one silver plate weighing a hundred and thirty shekels, and one silver sprinkling bowl weighing seventy shekels, both according to the sanctuary shekel, each filled with fine flour mixed with oil as a grain offering; ⁶²one gold dish weighing ten shekels, filled with incense; ⁶³one young bull, one ram and one male lamb a year old, for a burnt offering; ⁶⁴one male goat for a sin offering; ⁶⁵and two oxen, five rams, five male goats and five male lambs a year old, to be sacrificed as a fellowship offering. This was the offering of Abidan son of Gideoni.

⁶⁶On the tenth day Ahiezer son of Ammishaddai, the leader of the people of Dan, brought his offering. ⁶⁷His offering was one silver plate weighing a hundred and thirty shekels, and one silver sprinkling bowl weighing seventy shekels, both according to the sanctuary shekel, each filled with fine flour mixed with oil as a grain offering; ⁶⁸one gold dish weighing ten shekels, filled with incense; ⁶⁹one young bull, one ram and one male lamb a year old, for a burnt offering; ⁷⁰one male goat for a sin offering; ⁷¹and two oxen, five rams, five male goats and five male lambs a year old, to be sacrificed as a fellowship offering. This was the offering of Ahiezer son of Ammishaddai.

⁷²On the eleventh day Pagiel son of Ocran, the leader of the people of Asher, brought his offering. ⁷³His offering was one silver plate weighing a hundred and thirty shekels, and one silver sprinkling bowl weighing seventy shekels, both according to the sanctuary shekel, each filled with fine flour mixed with oil as a grain offering; ⁷⁴one gold dish weighing ten shekels, filled with incense; ⁷⁵one young bull, one ram and one male lamb a year old, for a burnt of-

fering; ⁷⁶one male goat for a sin offering; ⁷⁷and two oxen, five rams, five male goats and five male lambs a year old, to be sacrificed as a fellowship offering. This was the offering of Pagiel son of Ocran.

⁷⁸On the twelfth day Ahira son of Enan, the leader of the people of Naphtali, brought his offering. ⁷⁹His offering was one silver plate weighing a hundred and thirty shekels, and one silver sprinkling bowl weighing seventy shekels, both according to the sanctuary shekel, each filled with fine flour mixed with oil as a grain offering; ⁸⁰one gold dish weighing ten shekels, filled with incense; ⁸¹one young bull, one ram and one male lamb a year old, for a burnt offering; ⁸²one male goat for a sin offering; ⁸³and two oxen, five rams, five male goats and five male lambs a year old, to be sacrificed as a fellowship offering. This was the offering of Ahira son of Enan.

⁸⁴These were the offerings of the Israelite leaders for the dedication of the altar when it was anointed: twelve silver plates, twelve silver sprinkling bowls and twelve gold dishes. ⁸⁵Each silver plate weighed a hundred and thirty shekels, and each sprinkling bowl seventy shekels. Altogether, the silver dishes weighed two thousand four hundred shekels,^a according to the sanctuary shekel. ⁸⁶The twelve gold dishes filled with incense weighed ten shekels each, according to the sanctuary shekel. Altogether, the gold dishes weighed a hundred and twenty shekels.^b ⁸⁷The total number of animals for the burnt offering came to twelve young bulls, twelve rams and twelve male lambs a year old, together with their grain offering. Twelve male goats were used for the sin offering. ⁸⁸The total number of animals for the sacrifice of the fellowship offering came to twenty-four oxen, sixty rams, sixty male goats and sixty male lambs a year old. These were the offerings for the dedication of the altar after it was anointed.

⁸⁹When Moses entered the Tent of Meeting to speak with the Lord, he heard the voice speaking to him from between the two cherubim above the atonement cover on the ark of the Testimony. And he spoke with him.

truth or dare

Why don't we hear God's voice like this today? The truth is, God *does* speak in many ways. Feel like you're getting the silent treatment? Do a sound check: try *listening*.

7:89

Setting Up the Lamps

8 The Lord said to Moses, ²"Speak to Aaron and say to him, 'When you set up the seven lamps, they are to light the area in front of the lampstand.' "
³Aaron did so; he set up the lamps so that they faced forward on the lampstand, just as the Lord commanded Moses. ⁴This is how the lampstand was made: It was made of hammered gold— from its base to its blossoms. The lampstand was made exactly like the pattern the Lord had shown Moses.

The Setting Apart of the Levites

⁵The Lord said to Moses: ⁶"Take the Levites from among the other Israelites and make them ceremonially clean. ⁷To purify them, do this: Sprinkle the water of cleansing on them; then have them shave their whole bodies and wash their clothes, and so purify themselves. ⁸Have them take a young bull with its grain offering of fine flour mixed with oil; then you are to take a second young bull for a sin offering. ⁹Bring the Levites to the front of the Tent of Meeting and assemble the whole Israelite community. ¹⁰You are to bring the Levites before the Lord, and the Israelites are to lay their hands on them. ¹¹Aaron is to present the Levites before the Lord as a wave offering from the Israelites, so that they may be ready to do the work of the Lord.

¹²"After the Levites lay their hands on the heads of the bulls, use the one for a sin offering to the Lord and the other for a burnt offering, to make atonement for the Levites. ¹³Have the Levites stand in front of Aaron and his sons and then present them as a wave offering to the Lord. ¹⁴In this way you are to set the Levites apart from the other Israelites, and the Levites will be mine.

a 85 That is, about 60 pounds (about 28 kilograms)   *b 86* That is, about 3 pounds (about 1.4 kilograms)

¹⁵"After you have purified the Levites and presented them as a wave offering, they are to come to do their work at the Tent of Meeting. ¹⁶They are the Israelites who are to be given wholly to me. I have taken them as my own in place of the firstborn, the first male offspring from every Israelite woman. ¹⁷Every firstborn male in Israel, whether man or animal, is mine. When I struck down all the firstborn in Egypt, I set them apart for myself. ¹⁸And I have taken the Levites in place of all the firstborn sons in Israel. ¹⁹Of all the Israelites, I have given the Levites as gifts to Aaron and his sons to do the work at the Tent of Meeting on behalf of the Israelites and to make atonement for them so that no plague will strike the Israelites when they go near the sanctuary."

²⁰Moses, Aaron and the whole Israelite community did with the Levites just as the LORD commanded Moses. ²¹The Levites purified themselves and washed their clothes. Then Aaron presented them as a wave offering before the LORD and made atonement for them to purify them. ²²After that, the Levites came to do their work at the Tent of Meeting under the supervision of Aaron and his sons. They did with the Levites just as the LORD commanded Moses.

²³The LORD said to Moses, ²⁴"This applies to the Levites: Men twenty-five years old or more shall come to take part in the work at the Tent of Meeting, ²⁵but at the age of fifty, they must retire from their regular service and work no longer. ²⁶They may assist their brothers in performing their duties at the Tent of Meeting, but they themselves must not do the work. This, then, is how you are to assign the responsibilities of the Levites."

The Passover

9 The LORD spoke to Moses in the Desert of Sinai in the first month of the second year after they came out of Egypt. He said, ²"Have the Israelites celebrate the Passover at the appointed time. ³Celebrate it at the appointed time, at twilight on the fourteenth day of this month, in accordance with all its rules and regulations."

⁴So Moses told the Israelites to celebrate the Passover, ⁵and they did so in the Desert of Sinai at twilight on the fourteenth day of the first month. The Israelites did everything just as the LORD commanded Moses.

⁶But some of them could not celebrate the Passover on that day because they were ceremonially unclean on account of a dead body. So they came to Moses and Aaron that same day ⁷and said to Moses, "We have become unclean because of a dead body, but why should we be kept from presenting the LORD's offering with the other Israelites at the appointed time?"

⁸Moses answered them, "Wait until I find out what the LORD commands concerning you."

⁹Then the LORD said to Moses, ¹⁰"Tell the Israelites: 'When any of you or your descendants are unclean because of a dead body or are away on a journey, they may still celebrate the LORD's Passover. ¹¹They are to celebrate it on the fourteenth day of the second month at twilight. They are to eat the lamb, together with unleavened bread and bitter herbs. ¹²They must not leave any of it till morning or break any of its bones. When they celebrate the Passover, they must follow all the regulations. ¹³But if a man who is ceremonially clean and not on a journey fails to celebrate the Passover, that person must be cut off from his people because he did not present the LORD's offering at the appointed time. That man will bear the consequences of his sin.

¹⁴" 'An alien living among you who wants to celebrate the LORD's Passover must do so in accordance with its rules and regulations. You must have the same regulations for the alien and the native-born.' "

The Cloud Above the Tabernacle

¹⁵On the day the tabernacle, the Tent of the Testimony, was set up, the cloud covered it. From evening till morning the cloud above the tabernacle looked like fire. ¹⁶That is how it continued to be; the cloud covered it, and at night it looked like fire. ¹⁷Whenever the cloud lifted from above the Tent, the Israelites set out; wherever the cloud settled, the Israelites encamped. ¹⁸At the LORD's command the Israelites set out, and at his command they encamped. As long as the cloud stayed over the tabernacle, they remained in camp. ¹⁹When the cloud remained over the tabernacle a long time, the Israelites obeyed the LORD's order and did not set out. ²⁰Sometimes the cloud was over the tabernacle only a few days; at the LORD's command they would encamp, and then at his command they would set out. ²¹Sometimes the cloud stayed only from evening till morning, and when it lifted in the morning, they set out. Whether by day or by night, whenever the cloud lifted, they set out. ²²Whether the cloud stayed over the tabernacle for two days or a month or a year, the Is-

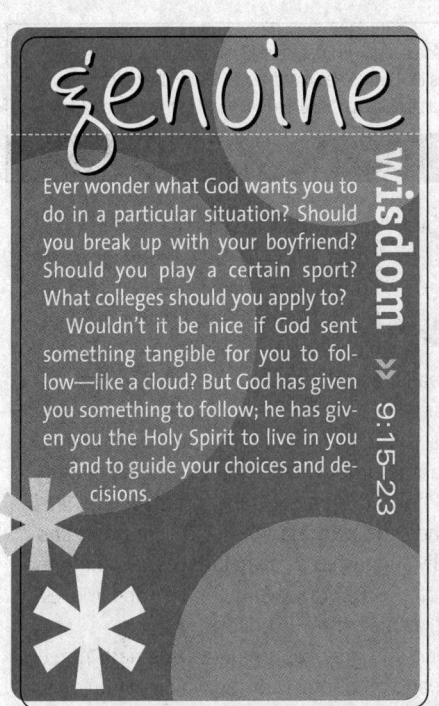

raelites would remain in camp and not set out; but when it lifted, they would set out. [23]At the LORD's command they encamped, and at the LORD's command they set out. They obeyed the LORD's order, in accordance with his command through Moses.

The Silver Trumpets

10 The LORD said to Moses: [2]"Make two trumpets of hammered silver, and use them for calling the community together and for having the camps set out. [3]When both are sounded, the whole community is to assemble before you at the entrance to the Tent of Meeting. [4]If only one is sounded, the leaders—the heads of the clans of Israel—are to assemble before you. [5]When a trumpet blast is sounded, the tribes camping on the east are to set out. [6]At the sounding of a second blast, the camps on the south are to set out. The blast will be the signal for setting out. [7]To gather the assembly, blow the trumpets, but not with the same signal.

[8]"The sons of Aaron, the priests, are to blow the trumpets. This is to be a lasting ordinance for you and the generations to come. [9]When you go into battle in your own land against an enemy who is oppressing you, sound a blast on the trumpets. Then you will be remembered by the LORD your God and rescued from your enemies. [10]Also at your times of rejoicing—your appointed feasts and New Moon festivals—you are to sound the trumpets over your burnt offerings and fellowship offerings,[a] and they will be a memorial for you before your God. I am the LORD your God."

The Israelites Leave Sinai

[11]On the twentieth day of the second month of the second year, the cloud lifted from above the tabernacle of the Testimony. [12]Then the Israelites set out from the Desert of Sinai and traveled from place to place until the cloud came to rest in the Desert of Paran. [13]They set out, this first time, at the LORD's command through Moses.

[14]The divisions of the camp of Judah went first, under their standard. Nahshon son of Amminadab was in command. [15]Nethanel son of Zuar was over the division of the tribe of Issachar, [16]and Eliab son of Helon was over the division of the tribe of Zebulun. [17]Then the tabernacle was taken down, and the Gershonites and Merarites, who carried it, set out.

[18]The divisions of the camp of Reuben went next, under their standard. Elizur son of Shedeur was in command. [19]Shelumiel son of Zurishaddai was over the division of the tribe of Simeon, [20]and Eliasaph son of Deuel was over the division of the tribe of Gad. [21]Then the Kohathites set out, carrying the holy things. The tabernacle was to be set up before they arrived.

[22]The divisions of the camp of Ephraim went next, under their standard. Elishama son of Ammihud was in command. [23]Gamaliel son of Pedahzur was over the division of the tribe of Manasseh, [24]and Abidan son of Gideoni was over the division of the tribe of Benjamin.

[25]Finally, as the rear guard for all the units, the divisions of the camp of Dan set out, under their standard. Ahiezer son of Ammishaddai was in command. [26]Pagiel son of Ocran was over the division of the tribe of Asher, [27]and Ahira son of Enan was over the division of the tribe of Naphtali. [28]This was the order of march for the Israelite divisions as they set out.

[29]Now Moses said to Hobab son of Reuel the Midianite, Moses' father-in-law, "We are setting

mirror images

Miriam and Aaron began to talk against Moses because of his Cushite wife . . . "Has the LORD spoken only through Moses?" they asked. "Hasn't he also spoken through us?" And the LORD heard this. Numbers 12:1–2

Miriam—Leadership Potential

Ever heard the old saying that your greatest strength is also your greatest weakness? Well, that was true for Miriam, Moses' and Aaron's sister, who was gifted with an outgoing personality and the ability to speak her mind.

As a young girl, Miriam watched from afar as her baby brother floated among the reeds outside Pharaoh's palace. She unabashedly approached the princess who discovered him and casually suggested that the princess should hire "one of the Hebrew women" (her and Moses' mom!) as his nanny (Exodus 2:7–8).

When she grew up, Miriam became a noted leader and prophetess for the whole nation of Israel as they migrated from their homeland in Egypt. In fact, one of her finer moments came after the miraculous crossing of the Red Sea when she led the women in song and praise (see Exodus 15:20–21). However, there was a downside to always being the center of attention.

She enjoyed it a little too much.

Numbers 12:1 tells us that Miriam and Aaron cut down Moses' wife; however, later in the verses, it seems that the two were mainly annoyed that God had chosen Moses as his spokesperson. Apparently, Miriam and Aaron were jealous.

Miriam was quick to criticize all that competed for her place as the center of attention, but God was all the quicker to punish her. Miriam turned white with leprosy and lost her leadership role for the next seven days.

We don't have to talk our way into being the center of attention. In fact, when we let our mouths lead the way, we often misuse our potential for leadership. When we insist on being in the limelight—"everyone listen to me"—then we run the risk of making a Miriam-sized mistake.

To read the next Mirror Images profile, go to page 198.

Dear God, teach me to hold my tongue when I am tempted to talk first and think later. Show me how to watch what I say and keep a humble attitude so that I can be the best leader for you. Amen.

>> Read more about Miriam in Exodus 2:1–10 (pages 70–71); 15:20–21 (page 89); Numbers 12 (pages 172–173).

out for the place about which the LORD said, 'I will give it to you.' Come with us and we will treat you well, for the LORD has promised good things to Israel."

³⁰He answered, "No, I will not go; I am going back to my own land and my own people."

³¹But Moses said, "Please do not leave us. You know where we should camp in the desert, and you can be our eyes. ³²If you come with us, we will share with you whatever good things the LORD gives us.

³³So they set out from the mountain of the LORD and traveled for three days. The ark of the covenant of the LORD went before them during those three days to find them a place to rest. ³⁴The cloud of the LORD was over them by day when they set out from the camp.

³⁵Whenever the ark set out, Moses said,

> "Rise up, O LORD!
> May your enemies be scattered;
> may your foes flee before you."

³⁶Whenever it came to rest, he said,

> "Return, O LORD,
> to the countless thousands of Israel."

Fire From the LORD

11 Now the people complained about their hardships in the hearing of the LORD, and when he heard them his anger was aroused. Then fire from the LORD burned among them and consumed some of the outskirts of the camp. ²When the people cried out to Moses, he prayed to the LORD and the fire died down. ³So that place was called Taberah,ᵃ because fire from the LORD had burned among them.

Quail From the LORD

⁴The rabble with them began to crave other food, and again the Israelites started wailing and said, "If only we had meat to eat! ⁵We remember the fish we ate in Egypt at no cost—also the cucumbers, melons, leeks, onions and garlic. ⁶But now we have lost our appetite; we never see anything but this manna!"

⁷The manna was like coriander seed and looked like resin. ⁸The people went around gathering it, and then ground it in a handmill or crushed it in a mortar. They cooked it in a pot or made it into cakes. And it tasted like something made with olive oil. ⁹When the dew settled on the camp at night, the manna also came down.

¹⁰Moses heard the people of every family wailing, each at the entrance to his tent. The LORD became exceedingly angry, and Moses was troubled. ¹¹He asked the LORD, "Why have you brought this trouble on your servant? What have I done to displease you that you put the burden of all these people on me? ¹²Did I conceive all these people? Did I give them birth? Why do you tell me to carry them in my arms, as a nurse carries an infant, to the land you promised on oath to their forefathers? ¹³Where can I get meat for all these people? They keep wailing to me, 'Give us meat to eat!' ¹⁴I cannot carry all these people by myself; the burden is too heavy for me. ¹⁵If this is how you are going to treat me, put me to death right now—if I have found favor in your eyes—and do not let me face my own ruin."

¹⁶The LORD said to Moses: "Bring me seventy of Israel's elders who are known to you as leaders and officials among the people. Have them come to the Tent of Meeting, that they may stand there with you. ¹⁷I will come down and speak with you there, and I will take of the Spirit that is on

truth or dare

Let's face it: Girls love to shop! The downer? Seeing new stuff often makes us crave what we don't have (and don't really need). So enjoy your shopping, but learn to be content with what you have.

11:4–6

ᵃ 3 Taberah means burning.

you and put the Spirit on them. They will help you carry the burden of the people so that you will not have to carry it alone.

18"Tell the people: 'Consecrate yourselves in preparation for tomorrow, when you will eat meat. The LORD heard you when you wailed, "If only we had meat to eat! We were better off in Egypt!" Now the LORD will give you meat, and you will eat it. 19You will not eat it for just one day, or two days, or five, ten or twenty days, 20but for a whole month—until it comes out of your nostrils and you loathe it—because you have rejected the LORD, who is among you, and have wailed before him, saying, "Why did we ever leave Egypt?" ' "

21But Moses said, "Here I am among six hundred thousand men on foot, and you say, 'I will give them meat to eat for a whole month!' 22Would they have enough if flocks and herds were slaughtered for them? Would they have enough if all the fish in the sea were caught for them?"

23The LORD answered Moses, "Is the LORD's arm too short? You will now see whether or not what I say will come true for you."

genuine strength » 11:10-17

Sometimes it feels like God gives you more than you can handle: your parents divorcing, a sibling getting into serious trouble, a friend finding out she's pregnant . . . Can you relate to the discouragement Moses felt when he said, "The burden is too heavy for me"? God doesn't intend for you to carry it alone. Lean on your Christian friends for support. Set that burden down, and allow God to carry it for you. It may be more than *you* can handle, but it's not too much for *him*.

24So Moses went out and told the people what the LORD had said. He brought together seventy of their elders and had them stand around the Tent. 25Then the LORD came down in the cloud and spoke with him, and he took of the Spirit that was on him and put the Spirit on the seventy elders. When the Spirit rested on them, they prophesied, but they did not do so again. [a]

26However, two men, whose names were Eldad and Medad, had remained in the camp. They were listed among the elders, but did not go out to the Tent. Yet the Spirit also rested on them, and they prophesied in the camp. 27A young man ran and told Moses, "Eldad and Medad are prophesying in the camp."

28Joshua son of Nun, who had been Moses' aide since youth, spoke up and said, "Moses, my lord, stop them!"

29But Moses replied, "Are you jealous for my sake? I wish that all the LORD's people were prophets and that the LORD would put his Spirit on them!" 30Then Moses and the elders of Israel returned to the camp.

31Now a wind went out from the LORD and drove quail in from the sea. It brought them [b] down all around the camp to about three feet [c] above the ground, as far as a day's walk in any direction. 32All that day and night and all the next day the people went out and gathered quail. No one gathered less than ten homers. [d] Then they spread them out all around the camp. 33But while the meat was still between their teeth and before it could be consumed, the anger of the LORD burned against the people, and he struck them with a severe plague. 34Therefore the place was named Kibroth Hattaavah, [e] because there they buried the people who had craved other food.

35From Kibroth Hattaavah the people traveled to Hazeroth and stayed there.

Miriam and Aaron Oppose Moses

12 Miriam and Aaron began to talk against Moses because of his Cushite wife, for he had married a Cushite. 2"Has the LORD spoken only through Moses?" they asked. "Hasn't he also spoken through us?" And the LORD heard this.

---

[a] 25 Or *prophesied and continued to do so*   [b] 31 Or *They flew*   [c] 31 Hebrew *two cubits* (about 1 meter)   [d] 32 That is, probably about 60 bushels (about 2.2 kiloliters)   [e] 34 *Kibroth Hattaavah* means *graves of craving*.

genuine

humility »» 12:1-3

Maybe you have a sister or friend who always looks amazing, dates the best guys, says the funniest things and wins every award. You feel like you're forever in her shadow—and frankly it would be nice to feel the sun on *your* face for a change! How do you handle it? Do you take Miriam's approach and tear her down so you can feel better about yourself? Clearly, this doesn't go over so well with God. He wants you to be humble like Moses. God will give you a time to shine; just keep trusting him.

³(Now Moses was a very humble man, more humble than anyone else on the face of the earth.)

⁴At once the LORD said to Moses, Aaron and Miriam, "Come out to the Tent of Meeting, all three of you." So the three of them came out. ⁵Then the LORD came down in a pillar of cloud; he stood at the entrance to the Tent and summoned Aaron and Miriam. When both of them stepped forward, ⁶he said, "Listen to my words:

"When a prophet of the LORD is
        among you,
    I reveal myself to him in visions,
    I speak to him in dreams.
⁷But this is not true of my servant
        Moses;
    he is faithful in all my house.
⁸With him I speak face to face,
    clearly and not in riddles;
    he sees the form of the LORD.
Why then were you not afraid
    to speak against my servant
        Moses?"

⁹The anger of the LORD burned against them, and he left them.

¹⁰When the cloud lifted from above the Tent, there stood Miriam—leprous,ᵃ like snow. Aaron turned toward her and saw that she had leprosy; ¹¹and he said to Moses, "Please, my lord, do not hold against us the sin we have so foolishly committed. ¹²Do not let her be like a stillborn infant coming from its mother's womb with its flesh half eaten away."

¹³So Moses cried out to the LORD, "O God, please heal her!"

¹⁴The LORD replied to Moses, "If her father had spit in her face, would she not have been in disgrace for seven days? Confine her outside the camp for seven days; after that she can be brought back." ¹⁵So Miriam was confined outside the camp for seven days, and the people did not move on till she was brought back.

¹⁶After that, the people left Hazeroth and encamped in the Desert of Paran.

Exploring Canaan

13 The LORD said to Moses, ²"Send some men to explore the land of Canaan, which I am giving to the Israelites. From each ancestral tribe send one of its leaders."

³So at the LORD's command Moses sent them out from the Desert of Paran. All of them were leaders of the Israelites. ⁴These are their names:

    from the tribe of Reuben, Shammua son of Zaccur;
⁵from the tribe of Simeon, Shaphat son of Hori;
⁶from the tribe of Judah, Caleb son of Jephunneh;
⁷from the tribe of Issachar, Igal son of Joseph;
⁸from the tribe of Ephraim, Hoshea son of Nun;
⁹from the tribe of Benjamin, Palti son of Raphu;
¹⁰from the tribe of Zebulun, Gaddiel son of Sodi;
¹¹from the tribe of Manasseh (a tribe of Joseph), Gaddi son of Susi;
¹²from the tribe of Dan, Ammiel son of Gemalli;
¹³from the tribe of Asher, Sethur son of Michael;

---

a 10 The Hebrew word was used for various diseases affecting the skin—not necessarily leprosy.

[14] from the tribe of Naphtali, Nahbi son of Vophsi;
[15] from the tribe of Gad, Geuel son of Maki.

[16] These are the names of the men Moses sent to explore the land. (Moses gave Hoshea son of Nun the name Joshua.)

[17] When Moses sent them to explore Canaan, he said, "Go up through the Negev and on into the hill country. [18] See what the land is like and whether the people who live there are strong or weak, few or many. [19] What kind of land do they live in? Is it good or bad? What kind of towns do they live in? Are they unwalled or fortified? [20] How is the soil? Is it fertile or poor? Are there trees on it or not? Do your best to bring back some of the fruit of the land." (It was the season for the first ripe grapes.)

[21] So they went up and explored the land from the Desert of Zin as far as Rehob, toward Lebo[a] Hamath. [22] They went up through the Negev and came to Hebron, where Ahiman, Sheshai and Talmai, the descendants of Anak, lived. (Hebron had been built seven years before Zoan in Egypt.) [23] When they reached the Valley of Eshcol,[b] they cut off a branch bearing a single cluster of grapes. Two of them carried it on a pole between them, along with some pomegranates and figs. [24] That place was called the Valley of Eshcol because of the cluster of grapes the Israelites cut off there. [25] At the end of forty days they returned from exploring the land.

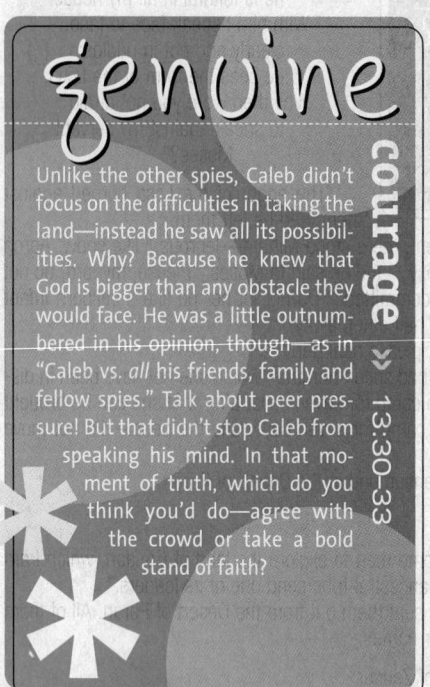

genuine

courage » 13:30-33

Unlike the other spies, Caleb didn't focus on the difficulties in taking the land—instead he saw all its possibilities. Why? Because he knew that God is bigger than any obstacle they would face. He was a little outnumbered in his opinion, though—as in "Caleb vs. *all* his friends, family and fellow spies." Talk about peer pressure! But that didn't stop Caleb from speaking his mind. In that moment of truth, which do you think you'd do—agree with the crowd or take a bold stand of faith?

Report on the Exploration

[26] They came back to Moses and Aaron and the whole Israelite community at Kadesh in the Desert of Paran. There they reported to them and to the whole assembly and showed them the fruit of the land. [27] They gave Moses this account: "We went into the land to which you sent us, and it does flow with milk and honey! Here is its fruit. [28] But the people who live there are powerful, and the cities are fortified and very large. We even saw descendants of Anak there. [29] The Amalekites live in the Negev; the Hittites, Jebusites and Amorites live in the hill country; and the Canaanites live near the sea and along the Jordan."

[30] Then Caleb silenced the people before Moses and said, "We should go up and take possession of the land, for we can certainly do it."

[31] But the men who had gone up with him said, "We can't attack those people; they are stronger than we are." [32] And they spread among the Israelites a bad report about the land they had explored. They said, "The land we explored devours those living in it. All the people we saw there are of great size. [33] We saw the Nephilim there (the descendants of Anak come from the Nephilim). We seemed like grasshoppers in our own eyes, and we looked the same to them."

The People Rebel

14 That night all the people of the community raised their voices and wept aloud. [2] All the Israelites grumbled against Moses and Aaron, and the whole assembly said to them, "If only we had died in Egypt! Or in this desert! [3] Why is the LORD bringing us to this land only to let us fall by the sword? Our wives and children will be taken as plunder. Wouldn't it be better for us to go back to Egypt?" [4] And they said to each other, "We should choose a leader and go back to Egypt."

a 21 Or *toward the entrance to*   *b 23 Eshcol* means *cluster;* also in verse 24.

⁵Then Moses and Aaron fell facedown in front of the whole Israelite assembly gathered there. ⁶Joshua son of Nun and Caleb son of Jephunneh, who were among those who had explored the land, tore their clothes ⁷and said to the entire Israelite assembly, "The land we passed through and explored is exceedingly good. ⁸If the LORD is pleased with us, he will lead us into that land, a land flowing with milk and honey, and will give it to us. ⁹Only do not rebel against the LORD. And do not be afraid of the people of the land, because we will swallow them up. Their protection is gone, but the LORD is with us. Do not be afraid of them."

¹⁰But the whole assembly talked about stoning them. Then the glory of the LORD appeared at the Tent of Meeting to all the Israelites. ¹¹The LORD said to Moses, "How long will these people treat me with contempt? How long will they refuse to believe in me, in spite of all the miraculous signs I have performed among them? ¹²I will strike them down with a plague and destroy them, but I will make you into a nation greater and stronger than they."

¹³Moses said to the LORD, "Then the Egyptians will hear about it! By your power you brought these people up from among them. ¹⁴And they will tell the inhabitants of this land about it. They have already heard that you, O LORD, are with these people and that you, O LORD, have been seen face to face, that your cloud stays over them, and that you go before them in a pillar of cloud by day and a pillar of fire by night. ¹⁵If you put these people to death all at one time, the nations who have heard this report about you will say, ¹⁶'The LORD was not able to bring these people into the land he promised them on oath; so he slaughtered them in the desert.'

¹⁷"Now may the Lord's strength be displayed, just as you have declared: ¹⁸'The LORD is slow to anger, abounding in love and forgiving sin and rebellion. Yet he does not leave the guilty unpunished; he punishes the children for the sin of the fathers to the third and fourth generation.' ¹⁹In accordance with your great love, forgive the sin of these people, just as you have pardoned them from the time they left Egypt until now."

love ♥ notes

14:17-20

Loved one,

Check out this description of me: One who is incredibly patient; 100 percent reliable; forgiving (no matter how many times it takes!) and forever attentive to my children's pleas. Guess what? I haven't changed.

—The God of Moses

Which of God's characteristics—his love, mercy, forgiveness or patience—means the most to you at this point in your life?

truth or dare

"The grass is always greener . . . " When you come up against problems, any place but *facing* them appears heavenly! Stick through it, girl—God is still good through the tough times.

14:5-9

20The LORD replied, "I have forgiven them, as you asked. 21Nevertheless, as surely as I live and as surely as the glory of the LORD fills the whole earth, 22not one of the men who saw my glory and the miraculous signs I performed in Egypt and in the desert but who disobeyed me and tested me ten times— 23not one of them will ever see the land I promised on oath to their forefathers. No one who has treated me with contempt will ever see it. 24But because my servant Caleb has a different spirit and follows me wholeheartedly, I will bring him into the land he went to, and his descendants will inherit it. 25Since the Amalekites and Canaanites are living in the valleys, turn back tomorrow and set out toward the desert along the route to the Red Sea.*"

26The LORD said to Moses and Aaron: 27"How long will this wicked community grumble against me? I have heard the complaints of these grumbling Israelites. 28So tell them, 'As surely as I live, declares the LORD, I will do to you the very things I heard you say: 29In this desert your bodies will fall—every one of you twenty years old or more who was counted in the census and who has grumbled against me. 30Not one of you will enter the land I swore with uplifted hand to make your home, except Caleb son of Jephunneh and Joshua son of Nun. 31As for your children that you said would be taken as plunder, I will bring them in to enjoy the land you have rejected. 32But you—your bodies will fall in this desert. 33Your children will be shepherds here for forty years, suffering for your unfaithfulness, until the last of your bodies lies in the desert. 34For forty years—one year for each of the forty days you explored the land—you will suffer for your sins and know what it is like to have me against you.' 35I, the LORD, have spoken, and I will surely do these things to this whole wicked community, which has banded together against me. They will meet their end in this desert; here they will die."

36So the men Moses had sent to explore the land, who returned and made the whole community grumble against him by spreading a bad report about it— 37these men responsible for spreading the bad report about the land were struck down and died of a plague before the LORD. 38Of the men who went to explore the land, only Joshua son of Nun and Caleb son of Jephunneh survived.

39When Moses reported this to all the Israelites, they mourned bitterly. 40Early the next morning they went up toward the high hill country. "We have sinned," they said. "We will go up to the place the LORD promised."

41But Moses said, "Why are you disobeying the LORD's command? This will not succeed! 42Do not go up, because the LORD is not with you. You will be defeated by your enemies, 43for the Amalekites and Canaanites will face you there. Because you have turned away from the LORD, he will not be with you and you will fall by the sword."

44Nevertheless, in their presumption they went up toward the high hill country, though neither Moses nor the ark of the LORD's covenant moved from the camp. 45Then the Amalekites and Canaanites who lived in that hill country came down and attacked them and beat them down all the way to Hormah.

genuine character » 14:24

Caleb had a *different spirit.* Instead of complaining and arguing with God like everyone else, Caleb followed God wholeheartedly. Could God say the same about you? How easily are you swept up into the crowd? When your friends mock someone, do you join in? When they try to talk you into ignoring your parents' rules, do you listen? Do you make certain choices about music, clothes and movies just because your friends do? Take a good look at yourself and decide which you'd rather be—a people-pleaser or a girl with a different spirit.

a 25 Hebrew *Yam Suph;* that is, Sea of Reeds

Do You Like Yourself?

1. When you look at yourself in the mirror every morning, what do you think?
   - ○ A. If only I were . . .
   - ○ B. Gross.
   - ○ C. Good.

2. You're sitting next to the prom queen in English class. What are your thoughts?
   - ○ A. I'd do anything to be her.
   - ○ B. I wish I knew where she picked up that awesome skirt.
   - ○ C. I wonder if she even read this book . . .

3. As soon as you walk in the doors at school, you . . .
   - ○ A. Quickly scan the crowd, checking out what everyone else is wearing.
   - ○ B. Wish you were invisible.
   - ○ C. Go find your friends.

4. At the top of this year's New Year's resolutions list is . . .
   - ○ A. Start lifting weights—you heard it's good for your bones.
   - ○ B. Work on that muscle tone—no more dreading swimsuit season.
   - ○ C. Lose 15 pounds and buy a push-up bra—the new me!

5. You find out that your teacher's mom died unexpectedly. You . . .
   - ○ A. Stay after class and tell her how sorry you are to hear about it.
   - ○ B. Don't say anything—she probably doesn't know who you are anyway.
   - ○ C. Wish you could say something but aren't sure what, so you just say a little prayer for the family.

6. Quick! Think of three things you like about yourself. (We mean it! Are you doing it? No cheating or reading ahead!) Now . . . how hard was it to come up with those things?
   - ○ A. Impossible—I got stuck on the first one for five minutes.
   - ○ B. No sweat—I could probably come up with a couple more.
   - ○ C. Well, I came up with three, but I'm not sure if they're all that true.

7. If you could trade five years of your life to wake up smarter, prettier and more talented, would you do it?
   - ○ A. Yes
   - ○ B. No

8. You can honestly say you're happy to be exactly the way God made you.
   - ○ A. True
   - ○ B. False

9. Take 30 seconds and think of all the things you'd like to change about yourself. How many things did you come up with?
   - ○ A. Well, how long do you have? I have them subdivided by category. . . .
   - ○ B. Oh, six or so.
   - ○ C. One or two—there's always something.

10. Does anyone have a perfect life?
    - ○ A. Yes! Some girls have everything going for them—the looks, grades, boys, family, friends, opportunities, money . . .
    - ○ B. No way. You never know what's really going on behind that perfect façade.

11. You totally embarrass yourself in front of everyone. Your reaction:
    - ○ A. It was embarrassing at the time, but life goes on.
    - ○ B. You stay home "sick" the next two days.
    - ○ C. You're sure that's all anyone can talk about—even three week[s]

(A) (B) (C) (?)

(0–6) Self-hatred

When you look in the mirror, all you see is flaws. You imagine that other girls have perfect lives, and you'd love to be them. You're sure that everyone else talks about your faults all the time. Because you dislike yourself, you assume everyone else does, too. You struggle to think of something you like about yourself, and don't get you started on all that you'd love to change! Maybe you even wonder if God made a mistake with you. Every blunder you make seems huge in your eyes, and you can't get it out of your mind.

(7–14) Self-doubting

Your thoughts are dominated by the "if onlys"—"If only I were thinner, smarter, more talented, etc." You find yourself trying to imitate other girls. You compare yourself to others all the time. Sometimes you want to do something, but you hold back—you're just not quite sure of yourself. You like some things about yourself, but you tend to focus on the negatives at times. You have a handful of things you'd like to change about yourself. You wonder what other people say about you, which makes you a little self-conscious around other people.

(15–22) Self-accepting

You're comfortable with the way you are. No, you're not perfect, but you can live with yourself. You spend a reasonable amount of time in front of the mirror but don't catch yourself obsessing. When you look at the girl everyone envies, you see the person inside, not her perfect exterior. You're confident enough of yourself that you're not crippled by others' opinions. You want to improve as a person but won't compromise who you are. In general, you feel comfortable around others. You accept the way God made you. You're able to laugh at yourself and brush off your mistakes.

scoring

1. A=1; B=0; C=2
2. A=0; B=1; C=2
3. A=1; B=0; C=2
4. A=2; B=1; C=0
5. A=2; B=0; C=1
6. A=0; B=2; C=1
7. A=0; B=2
8. A=2; B=0
9. A=0; B=1; C=2
10. A=0; B=2
11. A=2; B=1; C=0

6 steps to Accepting Yourself

- Make a list of things you naturally like to do. Chances are, you're gonna pick some things you're good at—and enjoy!

- Find ways to use those gifts and talents—they're God-given and definitely reasons to like yourself.

- Don't compare yourself to others—that never makes a girl feel good!

- Volunteer your time for a ministry and help others. (Get those eyes off yourself!)

- Pray through it. Tell the Lord exactly how you feel.

- Spend time with someone who loves you for you—and then take those warm, sweet feelings that you get from being loved and pour them into someone else's life!

A Note to You from God

There are days when you may not feel crazy about yourself, but God always feels crazy about you. Read the Love Notes from God in Genesis 1:27, 1 Samuel 16:7, Psalm 8:3–6 and Song of Songs 4:1a,7 for a reminder of how valuable you are in God's eyes.

Your Prince Charming

Check which description fits the man of your dreams. (Pssssst! It's okay if you don't have a strong opinion on some of 'em.)

1 The average guy uses several thousand words per day. Your P.C. (Prince Charming) . . .
- Blows past that average by 3rd period!
- Barely uses half that many words—he's the silent, mysterious type.

2 His 7th period elective is . . .
- A.P. gym class.
- Advanced Ceramics VI.
- Philosophy at the local university.

3 Your best friend asks you, "Do you think you already know the guy you're gonna marry?" You say . . .
- That's possible—I'd rather date someone I've known for a while.
- No way—I'm a love-at-first-sight kinda girl.

4 When you close your eyes and picture your P.C., he's . . .
- The basketball build: tall, thin and toned.
- The soccer size: lean, sporty and in great shape.
- The football physique: broad shoulders, big arms and a strong body.

5 Talking generally here, girls, do you like . . .
- The sandy blonde-haired type?
- The dark and handsome variety?

6 What's your pleasure: gentleman or rebel?
- Gentleman—Your clean-cut guy has a noble hero side to him. He's the kind of guy every girl would love to bring home.
- Rebel—Even though he's a good guy, he has that wild, daring streak that you love.

7 On an imaginary night out on the town (someday!), your P.C. would . . .
- Have everything planned perfectly, from your favorite flowers to reservations at a restaurant you've just been dying to try.
- Fly by the seat of his pants, but in a good way—the evening is completely fun and unexpected . . . and perfect.

8 The guy who catches your eye across the room is . . .
- Sporting the latest North Face vest.
- Wearing a vintage sweater (thrift store, for sure).
- Dressed like he just walked out of a J. Crew catalog.
- Decked out in very cool skater-wear.
- Sporty (those running shoes have seen a mile or two).

(A) (B) (C) (?)

Okay, ready to piece together a portrait of your dream man?
Fill in the blanks below based on what you answered above.

① *Extrovert or Introvert?*
It's usually good to complement each other's styles. If you max out
those words per day on your own, then you may be more attracted to
the quiet, mysterious type. If you're the quieter type, you may like the
kind of guy who's got something to say.

② *Athletic, Artistic or Academic?*
It's important to have some of the same interests while not being carbon
copies of each other. You should be able to relate yet also expand each
other's horizons.

③ *Good Friend or Love at First Sight?*
Do you have to get to know a guy before he really starts growing on
you? Or are you the fall-head-over-heels type of gal?

④ *Basketball, Soccer or Football Build?*
Are you always attracted to the same build of guys? Notice any patterns
in your string of crushes?

⑤ *Blonde or Dark?*
Some girls only go for one type—the guy they've always pictured in
their minds. Are you picky about his coloring? Or open to the selection?

⑥ *Rebel or Gentleman?*
Are you charmed by the wild guys? Or do you prefer the dignified type?
Just make sure his heart is good, regardless of his personality.

⑦ *Planner or Spontaneous?*
Some girls get bored by the planners, while others think the spontaneous
guys aren't thoughtful. Your favorite flavor?

⑧ *Outdoorsy, Grunge, Preppy, Skater or
Sporty?* Definitely no right answer here . . . it's just a question of style.
So which one turns your head, sista?

reflections from the other side

question:
**Describe your
dream girl.**

answer:
My dream girl?
Good question.
Realistically, looks
come into play, but
more importantly,
she needs to have a
complete mind of
her own. I don't like
people—girls or guys
—who just do things
because they think they
are supposed to. Of
course she'd have to be
a Christian girl, and the
whole confidence thing
is important. I would
also appreciate a good
sense of humor.

answer:
She has to be smart (but
humble enough not to
flaunt it), relatively
modest, fun, not afraid
of the great outdoors, a
reader (like me).

answer:
I look for independence,
a healthy self-esteem,
a sense of adventure,
a girl who's cultured,
curious, intelligent,
adaptable, easygoing,
outgoing, a Christian.
I guess that's my short
list. Oh yeah, I wouldn't
mind if she's a hottie.

**The
Love
of Your
Life**

Use your profile to help you identify
what qualities you often look for in
guys. Remember to . . .

● Be open to who *God* has in mind for you! He
may bring you someone totally unexpected—
and more amazing than you could have ever
imagined.

● Focus on the internal. Though the exterior
packaging is fun, it's what's inside that really
matters.

● ck out the portrait of a true P.C. in
 ...thy 3:1–10.

Supplementary Offerings

15 The LORD said to Moses, [2]"Speak to the Israelites and say to them: 'After you enter the land I am giving you as a home [3]and you present to the LORD offerings made by fire, from the herd or the flock, as an aroma pleasing to the LORD—whether burnt offerings or sacrifices, for special vows or freewill offerings or festival offerings— [4]then the one who brings his offering shall present to the LORD a grain offering of a tenth of an ephah[a] of fine flour mixed with a quarter of a hin[b] of oil. [5]With each lamb for the burnt offering or the sacrifice, prepare a quarter of a hin of wine as a drink offering.

[6]" 'With a ram prepare a grain offering of two-tenths of an ephah[c] of fine flour mixed with a third of a hin[d] of oil, [7]and a third of a hin of wine as a drink offering. Offer it as an aroma pleasing to the LORD.

[8]" 'When you prepare a young bull as a burnt offering or sacrifice, for a special vow or a fellowship offering[e] to the LORD, [9]bring with the bull a grain offering of three-tenths of an ephah[f] of fine flour mixed with half a hin[g] of oil. [10]Also bring half a hin of wine as a drink offering. It will be an offering made by fire, an aroma pleasing to the LORD. [11]Each bull or ram, each lamb or young goat, is to be prepared in this manner. [12]Do this for each one, for as many as you prepare.

[13]" 'Everyone who is native-born must do these things in this way when he brings an offering made by fire as an aroma pleasing to the LORD. [14]For the generations to come, whenever an alien or anyone else living among you presents an offering made by fire as an aroma pleasing to the LORD, he must do exactly as you do. [15]The community is to have the same rules for you and for the alien living among you; this is a lasting ordinance for the generations to come. You and the alien shall be the same before the LORD: [16]The same laws and regulations will apply both to you and to the alien living among you.' "

[17]The LORD said to Moses, [18]"Speak to the Israelites and say to them: 'When you enter the land to which I am taking you [19]and you eat the food of the land, present a portion as an offering to the LORD. [20]Present a cake from the first of your ground meal and present it as an offering from the threshing floor. [21]Throughout the generations to come you are to give this offering to the LORD from the first of your ground meal.

Offerings for Unintentional Sins

[22]" 'Now if you unintentionally fail to keep any of these commands the LORD gave Moses— [23]any of the LORD's commands to you through him, from the day the LORD gave them and continuing through the generations to come— [24]and if this is done unintentionally without the community being aware of it, then the whole community is to offer a young bull for a burnt offering as an aroma pleasing to the LORD, along with its prescribed grain offering and drink offering, and a male goat for a sin offering. [25]The priest is to make atonement for the whole Israelite community, and they will be forgiven, for it was not intentional and they have brought to the LORD for their wrong an offering made by fire and a sin offering. [26]The whole Israelite community and the aliens living among them will be forgiven, because all the people were involved in the unintentional wrong.

[27]" 'But if just one person sins unintentionally, he must bring a year-old female goat for a sin offering. [28]The priest is to make atonement before the LORD for the one who erred by sinning unintentionally, and when atonement has been made for him, he will be forgiven. [29]One and the same law applies to everyone who sins unintentionally, whether he is a native-born Israelite or an alien.

[30]" 'But anyone who sins defiantly, whether native-born or alien, blasphemes the LORD, and that person must be cut off from his people. [31]Because he has despised the LORD's word and broken his commands, that person must surely be cut off; his guilt remains on him.' "

The Sabbath-Breaker Put to Death

[32]While the Israelites were in the desert, a man was found gathering wood on the Sabbath day. [33]Those who found him gathering wood brought him to Moses and Aaron and the whole assembly, [34]and they kept him in custody, because it was not clear what should be done to him. [35]Then the

---

[a] 4 That is, probably about 2 quarts (about 2 liters)   [b] 4 That is, probably about 1 quart (about 1 liter); also in verse 5   [c] 6 That is, probably about 4 quarts (about 4.5 liters)   [d] 6 That is, probably about 1 1/4 quarts (about 1.2 liters); also in verse 7   [e] 8 Traditionally *peace offering*   [f] 9 That is, probably about 6 quarts (about 6.5 liters)   [g] 9 That is, probably about 2 quarts (about 2 liters); also in verse 10

LORD said to Moses, "The man must die. The whole assembly must stone him outside the camp." [36]So the assembly took him outside the camp and stoned him to death, as the LORD commanded Moses.

Tassels on Garments

[37]The LORD said to Moses, [38]"Speak to the Israelites and say to them: 'Throughout the generations to come you are to make tassels on the corners of your garments, with a blue cord on each tassel. [39]You will have these tassels to look at and so you will remember all the commands of the LORD, that you may obey them and not prostitute yourselves by going after the lusts of your own hearts and eyes. [40]Then you will remember to obey all my commands and will be consecrated to your God. [41]I am the LORD your God, who brought you out of Egypt to be your God. I am the LORD your God.' "

Korah, Dathan and Abiram

16 Korah son of Izhar, the son of Kohath, the son of Levi, and certain Reubenites—Dathan and Abiram, sons of Eliab, and On son of Peleth—became insolent[a] [2]and rose up against Moses. With them were 250 Israelite men, well-known community leaders who had been appointed members of the council. [3]They came as a group to oppose Moses and Aaron and said to them, "You have gone too far! The whole community is holy, every one of them, and the LORD is with them. Why then do you set yourselves above the LORD's assembly?"

[4]When Moses heard this, he fell facedown. [5]Then he said to Korah and all his followers: "In the morning the LORD will show who belongs to him and who is holy, and he will have that person come near him. The man he chooses he will cause to come near him. [6]You, Korah, and all your followers are to do this: Take censers [7]and tomorrow put fire and incense in them before the LORD. The man the LORD chooses will be the one who is holy. You Levites have gone too far!"

[8]Moses also said to Korah, "Now listen, you Levites! [9]Isn't it enough for you that the God of Israel has separated you from the rest of the Israelite community and brought you near himself to do the work at the LORD's tabernacle and to stand before the community and minister to them? [10]He has brought you and all your fellow Levites near himself, but now you are trying to get the priesthood too. [11]It is against the LORD that you and all your followers have banded together. Who is Aaron that you should grumble against him?"

[12]Then Moses summoned Dathan and Abiram, the sons of Eliab. But they said, "We will not come! [13]Isn't it enough that you have brought us up out of a land flowing with milk and honey to kill us in the desert? And now you also want to lord it over us? [14]Moreover, you haven't brought us into a land flowing with milk and hon-

a 1 Or Peleth—took men,

---

truth or dare

Are you forever forgetting things? Don't lose God in the shuffle! Give yourself reminders (notes, Bible verses) throughout your day to keep a constant connection with him.

15:37–41

---

genuine

integrity

Have you noticed how easy it is to camouflage your sin—and even make it sound spiritual? How about that old gossip-turned-prayer request tactic: "We should really pray for Kristin to stop sleeping with her boyfriend."

Korah and his followers tried this kind of spiritual camouflage. But God saw right through that to their hearts. And God sees yours. Don't think you can fool God, even if you can fool everyone else.

16:1-3

ey or given us an inheritance of fields and vineyards. Will you gouge out the eyes of[a] these men? No, we will not come!"

[15]Then Moses became very angry and said to the LORD, "Do not accept their offering. I have not taken so much as a donkey from them, nor have I wronged any of them."

[16]Moses said to Korah, "You and all your followers are to appear before the LORD tomorrow—you and they and Aaron. [17]Each man is to take his censer and put incense in it—250 censers in all—and present it before the LORD. You and Aaron are to present your censers also." [18]So each man took his censer, put fire and incense in it, and stood with Moses and Aaron at the entrance to the Tent of Meeting. [19]When Korah had gathered all his followers in opposition to them at the entrance to the Tent of Meeting, the glory of the LORD appeared to the entire assembly. [20]The LORD said to Moses and Aaron, [21]"Separate yourselves from this assembly so I can put an end to them at once."

[22]But Moses and Aaron fell facedown and cried out, "O God, God of the spirits of all mankind, will you be angry with the entire assembly when only one man sins?"

[23]Then the LORD said to Moses, [24]"Say to the assembly, 'Move away from the tents of Korah, Dathan and Abiram.'"

[25]Moses got up and went to Dathan and Abiram, and the elders of Israel followed him. [26]He warned the assembly, "Move back from the tents of these wicked men! Do not touch anything belonging to them, or you will be swept away because of all their sins." [27]So they moved away from the tents of Korah, Dathan and Abiram. Dathan and Abiram had come out and were standing with their wives, children and little ones at the entrances to their tents.

[28]Then Moses said, "This is how you will know that the LORD has sent me to do all these things and that it was not my idea: [29]If these men die a natural death and experience only what usually happens to men, then the LORD has not sent me. [30]But if the LORD brings about something totally new, and the earth opens its mouth and swallows them, with everything that belongs to them, and they go down alive into the grave,[b] then you will know that these men have treated the LORD with contempt."

[31]As soon as he finished saying all this, the ground under them split apart [32]and the earth opened its mouth and swallowed them, with their households and all Korah's men and all their possessions. [33]They went down alive into the grave, with everything they owned; the earth closed over them, and they perished and were gone from the community. [34]At their cries, all the Israelites around them fled, shouting, "The earth is going to swallow us too!"

[35]And fire came out from the LORD and consumed the 250 men who were offering the incense.

[36]The LORD said to Moses, [37]"Tell Eleazar son of Aaron, the priest, to take the censers out of the smoldering remains and scatter the coals some distance away, for the censers are holy— [38]the censers of the men who sinned at the cost of their lives. Hammer the censers into sheets to overlay the altar, for they were presented before the LORD and have become holy. Let them be a sign to the Israelites."

[39]So Eleazar the priest collected the bronze censers brought by those who had been burned up, and he had them hammered out to overlay the altar, [40]as the LORD directed him through Moses. This was to remind the Israelites that no one except a descendant of Aaron should come to burn incense before the LORD, or he would become like Korah and his followers.

[41]The next day the whole Israelite community grumbled against Moses and Aaron. "You have killed the LORD's people," they said.

[42]But when the assembly gathered in opposition to Moses and Aaron and turned toward the Tent of Meeting, suddenly the cloud covered it and the glory of the LORD appeared. [43]Then Moses and Aaron went to the front of the Tent of Meeting, [44]and the LORD said to Moses, [45]"Get away from this assembly so I can put an end to them at once." And they fell facedown.

[46]Then Moses said to Aaron, "Take your censer and put incense

truth or dare

When you're upset with your leaders, do you talk openly with them about it or complain behind their backs? Hold off on the rebellion until you get an explanation.

16:41

[a] 14 Or *you make slaves of*; or *you deceive*   [b] 30 Hebrew *Sheol*; also in verse 33

in it, along with fire from the altar, and hurry to the assembly to make atonement for them. Wrath has come out from the LORD; the plague has started." ⁴⁷So Aaron did as Moses said, and ran into the midst of the assembly. The plague had already started among the people, but Aaron offered the incense and made atonement for them. ⁴⁸He stood between the living and the dead, and the plague stopped. ⁴⁹But 14,700 people died from the plague, in addition to those who had died because of Korah. ⁵⁰Then Aaron returned to Moses at the entrance to the Tent of Meeting, for the plague had stopped.

The Budding of Aaron's Staff

17 The LORD said to Moses, ²"Speak to the Israelites and get twelve staffs from them, one from the leader of each of their ancestral tribes. Write the name of each man on his staff. ³On the staff of Levi write Aaron's name, for there must be one staff for the head of each ancestral tribe. ⁴Place them in the Tent of Meeting in front of the Testimony, where I meet with you. ⁵The staff belonging to the man I choose will sprout, and I will rid myself of this constant grumbling against you by the Israelites."

⁶So Moses spoke to the Israelites, and their leaders gave him twelve staffs, one for the leader of each of their ancestral tribes, and Aaron's staff was among them. ⁷Moses placed the staffs before the LORD in the Tent of the Testimony.

⁸The next day Moses entered the Tent of the Testimony and saw that Aaron's staff, which represented the house of Levi, had not only sprouted but had budded, blossomed and produced almonds. ⁹Then Moses brought out all the staffs from the LORD's presence to all the Israelites. They looked at them, and each man took his own staff.

¹⁰The LORD said to Moses, "Put back Aaron's staff in front of the Testimony, to be kept as a sign to the rebellious. This will put an end to their grumbling against me, so that they will not die." ¹¹Moses did just as the LORD commanded him.

¹²The Israelites said to Moses, "We will die! We are lost, we are all lost! ¹³Anyone who even comes near the tabernacle of the LORD will die. Are we all going to die?"

truth or dare

Zap! Lightning flashes and another sinner bites the dust. That's how some people perceive God. Fear of the Lord means giving God the respect he deserves, not panicking in his presence.

17:12–13

Duties of Priests and Levites

18 The LORD said to Aaron, "You, your sons and your father's family are to bear the responsibility for offenses against the sanctuary, and you and your sons alone are to bear the responsibility for offenses against the priesthood. ²Bring your fellow Levites from your ancestral tribe to join you and assist you when you and your sons minister before the Tent of the Testimony. ³They are to be responsible to you and are to perform all the duties of the Tent, but they must not go near the furnishings of the sanctuary or the altar, or both they and you will die. ⁴They are to join you and be responsible for the care of the Tent of Meeting—all the work at the Tent—and no one else may come near where you are.

⁵"You are to be responsible for the care of the sanctuary and the altar, so that wrath will not fall on the Israelites again. ⁶I myself have selected your fellow Levites from among the Israelites as a gift to you, dedicated to the LORD to do the work at the Tent of Meeting. ⁷But only you and your sons may serve as priests in connection with everything at the altar and inside the curtain. I am giving you the service of the priesthood as a gift. Anyone else who comes near the sanctuary must be put to death."

Offerings for Priests and Levites

⁸Then the LORD said to Aaron, "I myself have put you in charge of the offerings presented to me; all the holy offerings the Israelites give me I give to you and your sons as your portion and regular share. ⁹You are to have the part of the most holy offerings that is kept from the fire. From all the gifts they bring me as most holy offerings, whether grain or sin or guilt offerings, that part belongs to you and your sons. ¹⁰Eat it as something most holy; every male shall eat it. You must regard it as holy.

¹¹"This also is yours: whatever is set aside from the gifts of all the wave offerings of the Israelites. I give this to you and your sons and daughters as your regular share. Everyone in your household who is ceremonially clean may eat it.

¹²"I give you all the finest olive oil and all the finest new wine and grain they give the LORD as the firstfruits of their harvest. ¹³All the land's firstfruits that they bring to the LORD will be yours. Everyone in your household who is ceremonially clean may eat it.

¹⁴"Everything in Israel that is devoted*ᵃ* to the LORD is yours. ¹⁵The first offspring of every womb, both man and animal, that is offered to the LORD is yours. But you must redeem every firstborn son and every firstborn male of unclean animals. ¹⁶When they are a month old, you must redeem them at the redemption price set at five shekels*ᵇ* of silver, according to the sanctuary shekel, which weighs twenty gerahs.

¹⁷"But you must not redeem the firstborn of an ox, a sheep or a goat; they are holy. Sprinkle their blood on the altar and burn their fat as an offering made by fire, an aroma pleasing to the LORD. ¹⁸Their meat is to be yours, just as the breast of the wave offering and the right thigh are yours. ¹⁹Whatever is set aside from the holy offerings the Israelites present to the LORD I give to you and your sons and daughters as your regular share. It is an everlasting covenant of salt before the LORD for both you and your offspring."

²⁰The LORD said to Aaron, "You will have no inheritance in their land, nor will you have any share among them; I am your share and your inheritance among the Israelites.

²¹"I give to the Levites all the tithes in Israel as their inheritance in return for the work they do while serving at the Tent of Meeting. ²²From now on the Israelites must not go near the Tent of Meeting, or they will bear the consequences of their sin and will die. ²³It is the Levites who are to do the work at the Tent of Meeting and bear the responsibility for offenses against it. This is a lasting ordinance for the generations to come. They will receive no inheritance among the Israelites. ²⁴Instead, I give to the Levites as their inheritance the tithes that the Israelites present as an offering to the LORD. That is why I said concerning them: 'They will have no inheritance among the Israelites.' "

²⁵The LORD said to Moses, ²⁶"Speak to the Levites and say to them: 'When you receive from the Israelites the tithe I give you as your inheritance, you must present a tenth of that tithe as the LORD's offering. ²⁷Your offering will be reckoned to you as grain from the threshing floor or juice from the winepress. ²⁸In this way you also will present an offering to the LORD from all the tithes you receive from the Israelites. From these tithes you must give the LORD's portion to Aaron the priest. ²⁹You must present as the LORD's portion the best and holiest part of everything given to you.'

³⁰"Say to the Levites: 'When you present the best part, it will be reckoned to you as the product of the threshing floor or the winepress. ³¹You and your households may eat the rest of it anywhere, for it is your wages for your work at the Tent of Meeting. ³²By presenting the best part of it you will not be guilty in this matter; then you will not defile the holy offerings of the Israelites, and you will not die.' "

The Water of Cleansing

19 The LORD said to Moses and Aaron: ²"This is a requirement of the law that the LORD has commanded: Tell the Israelites to bring you a red heifer without defect or blemish and that has never been under a yoke. ³Give it to Eleazar the priest; it is to be taken outside the camp and slaughtered in his presence. ⁴Then Eleazar the priest is to take some of its blood on his finger and sprinkle it seven times toward the front of the Tent of Meeting. ⁵While he watches, the heifer is to be burned—its hide, flesh, blood and offal. ⁶The priest is to take some cedar wood, hyssop and scarlet wool and throw them onto the burning heifer. ⁷After that, the priest must wash his clothes and bathe himself with water. He may then come into the camp, but he will be ceremonially unclean till evening. ⁸The man who burns it must also wash his clothes and bathe with water, and he too will be unclean till evening.

⁹"A man who is clean shall gather up the ashes of the heifer and put them in a ceremonially clean place outside the camp. They shall be kept by the Israelite community for use in the water of cleansing; it is for purification from sin. ¹⁰The man who gathers up the ashes of the heifer must also wash his clothes, and he too will be unclean till evening. This will be a lasting ordinance both for the Israelites and for the aliens living among them.

ᵃ 14 The Hebrew term refers to the irrevocable giving over of things or persons to the LORD.   *ᵇ 16* That is, about 2 ounces (about 55 grams)

Failure Isn't Final

Profile: **Hannah**

"Well, that's everyone for this month's cast," I heard my drama teacher say from the corner of the stage. "If you didn't hear your name called, please see Kim if you want to help with the set or costumes. Thanks for coming." As people got up from their seats and began to leave the theater, I realized I was squeezing the arm of my chair so tightly my knuckles had turned white. I didn't make the cast. Again. And I was just trying out for one of the extras. Thank goodness the lights were dimmed so no one could see the tears in my eyes.

As I sat in my room that night, I cried out to God. Literally. I sobbed—I felt like such a failure. What a loser—I couldn't even make it as a nameless extra in a play!

I don't know what it was, but in the middle of my prayer I felt like God put his arms around me. Weird, huh? Yet I knew everything would be okay somehow. No, I don't think he'll miraculously give me the starring lead next year or anything. In fact, I'm beginning to realize that drama may not really be my thing, and I'm okay with that.

When you feel like a failure in life, go to www.TrueImagesBible.com for some added encouragement.

failure in focus

Our response to failure is one of life's biggest tests. Talking to God about our disappointment helps us keep it all in perspective. Keep in mind:

» Failure in one area of life doesn't mean you can't succeed in something else. So if drama's not for you, try running or yearbook or student government. You'll find your niche—and when you do, go after it with all your heart (see Colossians 3:23, page 1559).

» Talk to adult friends about their failures growing up. It happens to everyone. See what they learned from those experiences.

For more on this topic, see the index on page 1656.

failure

11"Whoever touches the dead body of anyone will be unclean for seven days. 12He must purify himself with the water on the third day and on the seventh day; then he will be clean. But if he does not purify himself on the third and seventh days, he will not be clean. 13Whoever touches the dead body of anyone and fails to purify himself defiles the LORD's tabernacle. That person must be cut off from Israel. Because the water of cleansing has not been sprinkled on him, he is unclean; his uncleanness remains on him.

14"This is the law that applies when a person dies in a tent: Anyone who enters the tent and anyone who is in it will be unclean for seven days, 15and every open container without a lid fastened on it will be unclean.

16"Anyone out in the open who touches someone who has been killed with a sword or someone who has died a natural death, or anyone who touches a human bone or a grave, will be unclean for seven days.

¹⁷"For the unclean person, put some ashes from the burned purification offering into a jar and pour fresh water over them. ¹⁸Then a man who is ceremonially clean is to take some hyssop, dip it in the water and sprinkle the tent and all the furnishings and the people who were there. He must also sprinkle anyone who has touched a human bone or a grave or someone who has been killed or someone who has died a natural death. ¹⁹The man who is clean is to sprinkle the unclean person on the third and seventh days, and on the seventh day he is to purify him. The person being cleansed must wash his clothes and bathe with water, and that evening he will be clean. ²⁰But if a person who is unclean does not purify himself, he must be cut off from the community, because he has defiled the sanctuary of the LORD. The water of cleansing has not been sprinkled on him, and he is unclean. ²¹This is a lasting ordinance for them.

"The man who sprinkles the water of cleansing must also wash his clothes, and anyone who touches the water of cleansing will be unclean till evening. ²²Anything that an unclean person touches becomes unclean, and anyone who touches it becomes unclean till evening."

Water From the Rock

20 In the first month the whole Israelite community arrived at the Desert of Zin, and they stayed at Kadesh. There Miriam died and was buried.

²Now there was no water for the community, and the people gathered in opposition to Moses and Aaron. ³They quarreled with Moses and said, "If only we had died when our brothers fell dead before the LORD! ⁴Why did you bring the LORD's community into this desert, that we and our livestock should die here? ⁵Why did you bring us up out of Egypt to this terrible place? It has no grain or figs, grapevines or pomegranates. And there is no water to drink!"

⁶Moses and Aaron went from the assembly to the entrance to the Tent of Meeting and fell face-down, and the glory of the LORD appeared to them. ⁷The LORD said to Moses, ⁸"Take the staff, and you and your brother Aaron gather the assembly together. Speak to that rock before their eyes and it will pour out its water. You will bring water out of the rock for the community so they and their livestock can drink."

⁹So Moses took the staff from the LORD's presence, just as he commanded him. ¹⁰He and Aaron gathered the assembly together in front of the rock and Moses said to them, "Listen, you rebels, must we bring you water out of this rock?" ¹¹Then Moses raised his arm and struck the rock twice with his staff. Water gushed out, and the community and their livestock drank.

¹²But the LORD said to Moses and Aaron, "Because you did not trust in me enough to honor me as holy in the sight of the Israelites, you will not bring this community into the land I give them."

¹³These were the waters of Meribah,ᵃ where the Israelites quarreled with the LORD and where he showed himself holy among them.

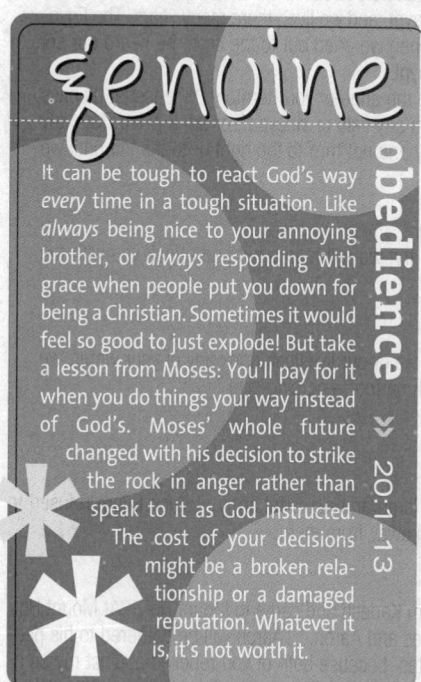

genuine obedience » 20:1–13

It can be tough to react God's way *every* time in a tough situation. Like *always* being nice to your annoying brother, or *always* responding with grace when people put you down for being a Christian. Sometimes it would feel so good to just explode! But take a lesson from Moses: You'll pay for it when you do things your way instead of God's. Moses' whole future changed with his decision to strike the rock in anger rather than speak to it as God instructed. The cost of your decisions might be a broken relationship or a damaged reputation. Whatever it is, it's not worth it.

truth or dare

Uh-oh. Talk about consequences. Moses lost sight of God for a minute, and it changed the rest of his life. Taking honor away from God is never cool.

20:12

ᵃ 13 Meribah means *quarreling*.

Edom Denies Israel Passage

¹⁴Moses sent messengers from Kadesh to the king of Edom, saying:

"This is what your brother Israel says: You know about all the hardships that have come upon us. ¹⁵Our forefathers went down into Egypt, and we lived there many years. The Egyptians mistreated us and our fathers, ¹⁶but when we cried out to the Lord, he heard our cry and sent an angel and brought us out of Egypt.

"Now we are here at Kadesh, a town on the edge of your territory. ¹⁷Please let us pass through your country. We will not go through any field or vineyard, or drink water from any well. We will travel along the king's highway and not turn to the right or to the left until we have passed through your territory."

¹⁸But Edom answered:

"You may not pass through here; if you try, we will march out and attack you with the sword."

¹⁹The Israelites replied:

"We will go along the main road, and if we or our livestock drink any of your water, we will pay for it. We only want to pass through on foot—nothing else."

²⁰Again they answered:

"You may not pass through."

Then Edom came out against them with a large and powerful army. ²¹Since Edom refused to let them go through their territory, Israel turned away from them.

The Death of Aaron

²²The whole Israelite community set out from Kadesh and came to Mount Hor. ²³At Mount Hor, near the border of Edom, the Lord said to Moses and Aaron, ²⁴"Aaron will be gathered to his people. He will not enter the land I give the Israelites, because both of you rebelled against my command at the waters of Meribah. ²⁵Get Aaron and his son Eleazar and take them up Mount Hor. ²⁶Remove Aaron's garments and put them on his son Eleazar, for Aaron will be gathered to his people; he will die there."

²⁷Moses did as the Lord commanded: They went up Mount Hor in the sight of the whole community. ²⁸Moses removed Aaron's garments and put them on his son Eleazar. And Aaron died there on top of the mountain. Then Moses and Eleazar came down from the mountain, ²⁹and when the whole community learned that Aaron had died, the entire house of Israel mourned for him thirty days.

Arad Destroyed

21 When the Canaanite king of Arad, who lived in the Negev, heard that Israel was coming along the road to Atharim, he attacked the Israelites and captured some of them. ²Then Israel made this vow to the Lord: "If you will deliver these people into our hands, we will totally destroy*ᵃ* their cities." ³The Lord listened to Israel's plea and gave the Canaanites over to them. They completely destroyed them and their towns; so the place was named Hormah.*ᵇ*

The Bronze Snake

⁴They traveled from Mount Hor along the route to the Red Sea,*ᶜ* to go around Edom. But the people grew impatient on the way; ⁵they spoke against God and against Moses, and said, "Why have you brought us up out of Egypt to die in the desert? There is no bread! There is no water! And we detest this miserable food!"

⁶Then the Lord sent venomous snakes among them; they bit the people and many Israelites died. ⁷The people came to Moses and said, "We sinned when we spoke against the Lord and against you. Pray that the Lord will take the snakes away from us." So Moses prayed for the people.

a 2 The Hebrew term refers to the irrevocable giving over of things or persons to the Lord, often by totally destroying them; also in verse 3.   b 3 Hormah means destruction.   c 4 Hebrew Yam Suph; that is, Sea of Reeds

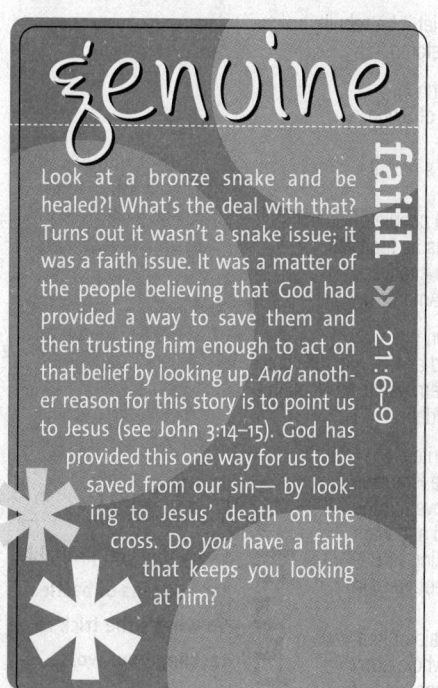

genuine faith » 21:6-9

Look at a bronze snake and be healed?! What's the deal with that? Turns out it wasn't a snake issue; it was a faith issue. It was a matter of the people believing that God had provided a way to save them and then trusting him enough to act on that belief by looking up. *And* another reason for this story is to point us to Jesus (see John 3:14–15). God has provided this one way for us to be saved from our sin— by looking to Jesus' death on the cross. Do *you* have a faith that keeps you looking at him?

[8]The LORD said to Moses, "Make a snake and put it up on a pole; anyone who is bitten can look at it and live." [9]So Moses made a bronze snake and put it up on a pole. Then when anyone was bitten by a snake and looked at the bronze snake, he lived.

The Journey to Moab

[10]The Israelites moved on and camped at Oboth. [11]Then they set out from Oboth and camped in Iye Abarim, in the desert that faces Moab toward the sunrise. [12]From there they moved on and camped in the Zered Valley. [13]They set out from there and camped alongside the Arnon, which is in the desert extending into Amorite territory. The Arnon is the border of Moab, between Moab and the Amorites. [14]That is why the Book of the Wars of the LORD says:

> ". . . Waheb in Suphah[a] and the ravines,
>   the Arnon [15]and[b] the slopes of the ravines
> that lead to the site of Ar
>   and lie along the border of Moab."

[16]From there they continued on to Beer, the well where the LORD said to Moses, "Gather the people together and I will give them water."

[17]Then Israel sang this song:

> "Spring up, O well!
>   Sing about it,
> [18]about the well that the princes dug,
>   that the nobles of the people sank—
>   the nobles with scepters and staffs."

Then they went from the desert to Mattanah, [19]from Mattanah to Nahaliel, from Nahaliel to Bamoth, [20]and from Bamoth to the valley in Moab where the top of Pisgah overlooks the wasteland.

Defeat of Sihon and Og

[21]Israel sent messengers to say to Sihon king of the Amorites:

[22]"Let us pass through your country. We will not turn aside into any field or vineyard, or drink water from any well. We will travel along the king's highway until we have passed through your territory."

[23]But Sihon would not let Israel pass through his territory. He mustered his entire army and marched out into the desert against Israel. When he reached Jahaz, he fought with Israel. [24]Israel, however, put him to the sword and took over his land from the Arnon to the Jabbok, but only as far as the Ammonites, because their border was fortified. [25]Israel captured all the cities of the Amorites and occupied them, including Heshbon and all its surrounding settlements. [26]Heshbon was the city of Sihon king of the Amorites, who had fought against the former king of Moab and had taken from him all his land as far as the Arnon.

[27]That is why the poets say:

a 14 The meaning of the Hebrew for this phrase is uncertain.   *b 14,15* Or *"I have been given from Suphah and the ravines / of the Arnon* [15]*to*

"Come to Heshbon and let it be rebuilt;
    let Sihon's city be restored.

[28] "Fire went out from Heshbon,
    a blaze from the city of Sihon.
It consumed Ar of Moab,
    the citizens of Arnon's heights.
[29] Woe to you, O Moab!
    You are destroyed, O people of Chemosh!
He has given up his sons as fugitives
    and his daughters as captives
    to Sihon king of the Amorites.

[30] "But we have overthrown them;
    Heshbon is destroyed all the way to Dibon.
We have demolished them as far as Nophah,
    which extends to Medeba."

[31] So Israel settled in the land of the Amorites.

[32] After Moses had sent spies to Jazer, the Israelites captured its surrounding settlements and drove out the Amorites who were there. [33] Then they turned and went up along the road toward Bashan, and Og king of Bashan and his whole army marched out to meet them in battle at Edrei.

[34] The LORD said to Moses, "Do not be afraid of him, for I have handed him over to you, with his whole army and his land. Do to him what you did to Sihon king of the Amorites, who reigned in Heshbon."

[35] So they struck him down, together with his sons and his whole army, leaving them no survivors. And they took possession of his land.

Balak Summons Balaam

22 Then the Israelites traveled to the plains of Moab and camped along the Jordan across from Jericho. [a]

[2] Now Balak son of Zippor saw all that Israel had done to the Amorites, [3] and Moab was terrified because there were so many people. Indeed, Moab was filled with dread because of the Israelites.

[4] The Moabites said to the elders of Midian, "This horde is going to lick up everything around us, as an ox licks up the grass of the field."

So Balak son of Zippor, who was king of Moab at that time, [5] sent messengers to summon Balaam son of Beor, who was at Pethor, near the River, [b] in his native land. Balak said:

"A people has come out of Egypt; they cover the face of the land and have settled next to me. [6] Now come and put a curse on these people, because they are too powerful for me. Perhaps then I will be able to defeat them and drive them out of the country. For I know that those you bless are blessed, and those you curse are cursed."

[7] The elders of Moab and Midian left, taking with them the fee for divination. When they came to Balaam, they told him what Balak had said.

[8] "Spend the night here," Balaam said to them, "and I will bring you back the answer the LORD gives me." So the Moabite princes stayed with him.

[9] God came to Balaam and asked, "Who are these men with you?"

[10] Balaam said to God, "Balak son of Zippor, king of Moab, sent me this message: [11] 'A people that has come out of Egypt covers the face of the land. Now come and put a curse on them for me. Perhaps then I will be able to fight them and drive them away.' "

truth **or dare**

Every day you probably face dozens of battles. So what's the trick to tackling your worst fears? Trust in the one who's already won the battle for you.

21:31–35

a 1 Hebrew *Jordan of Jericho*; possibly an ancient name for the Jordan River   b 5 That is, the Euphrates

[12]But God said to Balaam, "Do not go with them. You must not put a curse on those people, because they are blessed."

[13]The next morning Balaam got up and said to Balak's princes, "Go back to your own country, for the LORD has refused to let me go with you."

[14]So the Moabite princes returned to Balak and said, "Balaam refused to come with us." [15]Then Balak sent other princes, more numerous and more distinguished than the first. [16]They came to Balaam and said:

"This is what Balak son of Zippor says: Do not let anything keep you from coming to me, [17]because I will reward you handsomely and do whatever you say. Come and put a curse on these people for me."

[18]But Balaam answered them, "Even if Balak gave me his palace filled with silver and gold, I could not do anything great or small to go beyond the command of the LORD my God. [19]Now stay here tonight as the others did, and I will find out what else the LORD will tell me."

[20]That night God came to Balaam and said, "Since these men have come to summon you, go with them, but do only what I tell you."

Balaam's Donkey

[21]Balaam got up in the morning, saddled his donkey and went with the princes of Moab. [22]But God was very angry when he went, and the angel of the LORD stood in the road to oppose him. Balaam was riding on his donkey, and his two servants were with him. [23]When the donkey saw the angel of the LORD standing in the road with a drawn sword in his hand, she turned off the road into a field. Balaam beat her to get her back on the road.

[24]Then the angel of the LORD stood in a narrow path between two vineyards, with walls on both sides. [25]When the donkey saw the angel of the LORD, she pressed close to the wall, crushing Balaam's foot against it. So he beat her again.

[26]Then the angel of the LORD moved on ahead and stood in a narrow place where there was no room to turn, either to the right or to the left. [27]When the donkey saw the angel of the LORD, she lay down under Balaam, and he was angry and beat her with his staff. [28]Then the LORD opened the donkey's mouth, and she said to Balaam, "What have I done to you to make you beat me these three times?"

[29]Balaam answered the donkey, "You have made a fool of me! If I had a sword in my hand, I would kill you right now."

[30]The donkey said to Balaam, "Am I not your own donkey, which you have always ridden, to this day? Have I been in the habit of doing this to you?"

"No," he said.

[31]Then the LORD opened Balaam's eyes, and he saw the angel of the LORD standing in the road with his sword drawn. So he bowed low and fell facedown.

[32]The angel of the LORD asked him, "Why have you beaten your donkey these three times? I have come here to oppose you because your path is a reckless one before me.[a] [33]The donkey saw me and turned away from me these three times. If she had not turned away, I would certainly have killed you by now, but I would have spared her."

[34]Balaam said to the angel of the LORD, "I have sinned. I did not realize you were standing in the road to oppose me. Now if you are displeased, I will go back."

[35]The angel of the LORD said to Balaam, "Go with the men, but speak only what I tell you." So Balaam went with the princes of Balak.

[36]When Balak heard that Balaam was coming, he went out to meet him at the Moabite town on the Arnon border, at the edge of his territory. [37]Balak said to Balaam, "Did I not send you an urgent summons? Why didn't you come to me? Am I really not able to reward you?"

truth or dare

You just lashed out at a friend. Then you snapped at your little sister. If you've been constantly irritated with *others* lately, you might be overdue for your *own* heart check.

22:26–31

[a] 32 The meaning of the Hebrew for this clause is uncertain.

[38]"Well, I have come to you now," Balaam replied. "But can I say just anything? I must speak only what God puts in my mouth."

[39]Then Balaam went with Balak to Kiriath Huzoth. [40]Balak sacrificed cattle and sheep, and gave some to Balaam and the princes who were with him. [41]The next morning Balak took Balaam up to Bamoth Baal, and from there he saw part of the people.

Balaam's First Oracle

23 Balaam said, "Build me seven altars here, and prepare seven bulls and seven rams for me." [2]Balak did as Balaam said, and the two of them offered a bull and a ram on each altar.

[3]Then Balaam said to Balak, "Stay here beside your offering while I go aside. Perhaps the LORD will come to meet with me. Whatever he reveals to me I will tell you." Then he went off to a barren height.

[4]God met with him, and Balaam said, "I have prepared seven altars, and on each altar I have offered a bull and a ram."

[5]The LORD put a message in Balaam's mouth and said, "Go back to Balak and give him this message."

[6]So he went back to him and found him standing beside his offering, with all the princes of Moab. [7]Then Balaam uttered his oracle:

> "Balak brought me from Aram,
>   the king of Moab from the eastern mountains.
> 'Come,' he said, 'curse Jacob for me;
>   come, denounce Israel.'
> [8]How can I curse
>   those whom God has not cursed?
> How can I denounce
>   those whom the LORD has not denounced?
> [9]From the rocky peaks I see them,
>   from the heights I view them.
> I see a people who live apart
>   and do not consider themselves one of the nations.
> [10]Who can count the dust of Jacob
>   or number the fourth part of Israel?
> Let me die the death of the righteous,
>   and may my end be like theirs!"

[11]Balak said to Balaam, "What have you done to me? I brought you to curse my enemies, but you have done nothing but bless them!"

[12]He answered, "Must I not speak what the LORD puts in my mouth?"

Balaam's Second Oracle

[13]Then Balak said to him, "Come with me to another place where you can see them; you will see only a part but not all of them. And from there, curse them for me." [14]So he took him to the field of Zophim on the top of Pisgah, and there he built seven altars and offered a bull and a ram on each altar.

[15]Balaam said to Balak, "Stay here beside your offering while I meet with him over there."

[16]The LORD met with Balaam and put a message in his mouth and said, "Go back to Balak and give him this message."

[17]So he went to him and found him standing beside his offering, with the princes of Moab. Balak asked him, "What did the LORD say?"

[18]Then he uttered his oracle:

> "Arise, Balak, and listen;
>   hear me, son of Zippor.
> [19]God is not a man, that he should lie,
>   nor a son of man, that he should change his mind.

Does he speak and then not act?
Does he promise and not fulfill?
20 I have received a command to bless;
he has blessed, and I cannot change it.

21 "No misfortune is seen in Jacob,
no misery observed in Israel. *a*
The LORD their God is with them;
the shout of the King is among them.
22 God brought them out of Egypt;
they have the strength of a wild ox.
23 There is no sorcery against Jacob,
no divination against Israel.

It will now be said of Jacob
and of Israel, 'See what God
has done!'
24 The people rise like a lioness;
they rouse themselves like a
lion
that does not rest till he devours
his prey
and drinks the blood of his
victims."

25 Then Balak said to Balaam, "Neither curse them at all nor bless them at all!"
26 Balaam answered, "Did I not tell you I must do whatever the LORD says?"

Balaam's Third Oracle

27 Then Balak said to Balaam, "Come, let me take you to another place. Perhaps it will please God to let you curse them for me from there." 28 And Balak took Balaam to the top of Peor, overlooking the wasteland.

29 Balaam said, "Build me seven altars here, and prepare seven bulls and seven rams for me." 30 Balak did as Balaam had said, and offered a bull and a ram on each altar.

24 Now when Balaam saw that it pleased the LORD to bless Israel, he did not resort to sorcery as at other times, but turned his face toward the desert. 2 When Balaam looked out and saw Israel encamped tribe by tribe, the Spirit of God came upon him 3 and he uttered his oracle:

"The oracle of Balaam son of
Beor,
the oracle of one whose eye
sees clearly,
4 the oracle of one who hears the
words of God,

love notes

23:19

My child,

You live in a world where everything's always changing. But there are two constants: my Word and me. If I said it, I'll do it. My Word never fails. I'll never say one thing and do another.

—The everlasting One

In what ways have others disappointed you? Remember that God is completely reliable.

a 21 Or *He has not looked on Jacob's offenses / or on the wrongs found in Israel.*

who sees a vision from the Almighty,[a]
who falls prostrate, and whose eyes are opened:

5 "How beautiful are your tents, O Jacob,
your dwelling places, O Israel!

6 "Like valleys they spread out,
like gardens beside a river,
like aloes planted by the LORD,
like cedars beside the waters.
7 Water will flow from their buckets;
their seed will have abundant water.

"Their king will be greater than Agag;
their kingdom will be exalted.

8 "God brought them out of Egypt;
they have the strength of a wild ox.
They devour hostile nations
and break their bones in pieces;
with their arrows they pierce them.
9 Like a lion they crouch and lie down,
like a lioness—who dares to rouse them?

"May those who bless you be blessed
and those who curse you be cursed!"

10 Then Balak's anger burned against Balaam. He struck his hands together and said to him, "I summoned you to curse my enemies, but you have blessed them these three times. 11 Now leave at once and go home! I said I would reward you handsomely, but the LORD has kept you from being rewarded."

12 Balaam answered Balak, "Did I not tell the messengers you sent me, 13 'Even if Balak gave me his palace filled with silver and gold, I could not do anything of my own accord, good or bad, to go beyond the command of the LORD—and I must say only what the LORD says'? 14 Now I am going back to my people, but come, let me warn you of what this people will do to your people in days to come."

Balaam's Fourth Oracle

15 Then he uttered his oracle:

"The oracle of Balaam son of Beor,
the oracle of one whose eye sees clearly,
16 the oracle of one who hears the words of God,
who has knowledge from the Most High,
who sees a vision from the Almighty,
who falls prostrate, and whose eyes are opened:

17 "I see him, but not now;
I behold him, but not near.
A star will come out of Jacob;
a scepter will rise out of Israel.
He will crush the foreheads of Moab,
the skulls[b] of[c] all the sons of Sheth.[d]
18 Edom will be conquered;
Seir, his enemy, will be conquered,
but Israel will grow strong.
19 A ruler will come out of Jacob
and destroy the survivors of the city."

---

[a] 4 Hebrew *Shaddai*; also in verse 16   [b] 17 Samaritan Pentateuch (see also Jer. 48:45); the meaning of the word in the Masoretic Text is uncertain.   [c] 17 Or possibly *Moab, / batter*   [d] 17 Or *all the noisy boasters*

Balaam's Final Oracles

[20]Then Balaam saw Amalek and uttered his oracle:

> "Amalek was first among the nations,
>   but he will come to ruin at last."

[21]Then he saw the Kenites and uttered his oracle:

> "Your dwelling place is secure,
>   your nest is set in a rock;
> [22]yet you Kenites will be destroyed
>   when Asshur takes you captive."

[23]Then he uttered his oracle:

> "Ah, who can live when God does this?[a]
> [24]   Ships will come from the shores of Kittim;
>   they will subdue Asshur and Eber,
>   but they too will come to ruin."

[25]Then Balaam got up and returned home and Balak went his own way.

Moab Seduces Israel

25 While Israel was staying in Shittim, the men began to indulge in sexual immorality with Moabite women, [2]who invited them to the sacrifices to their gods. The people ate and bowed down before these gods. [3]So Israel joined in worshiping the Baal of Peor. And the LORD's anger burned against them.

[4]The LORD said to Moses, "Take all the leaders of these people, kill them and expose them in broad daylight before the LORD, so that the LORD's fierce anger may turn away from Israel."

[5]So Moses said to Israel's judges, "Each of you must put to death those of your men who have joined in worshiping the Baal of Peor."

[6]Then an Israelite man brought to his family a Midianite woman right before the eyes of Moses and the whole assembly of Israel while they were weeping at the entrance to the Tent of Meeting. [7]When Phinehas son of Eleazar, the son of Aaron, the priest, saw this, he left the assembly, took a spear in his hand [8]and followed the Israelite into the tent. He drove the spear through both of them—through the Israelite and into the woman's body. Then the plague against the Israelites was stopped; [9]but those who died in the plague numbered 24,000.

[10]The LORD said to Moses, [11]"Phinehas son of Eleazar, the son of Aaron, the priest, has turned my anger away from the Israelites; for he was as zealous as I am for my honor among them, so that in my zeal I did not put an end to them. [12]Therefore tell him I am making my covenant of peace with him. [13]He and his descendants will have a covenant of a lasting priesthood, because he was zealous for the honor of his God and made atonement for the Israelites."

[14]The name of the Israelite who was killed with the Midianite woman was Zimri son of Salu, the leader of a Simeonite family. [15]And the name of the Midianite woman who was put to death was Cozbi daughter of Zur, a tribal chief of a Midianite family.

[16]The LORD said to Moses, [17]"Treat the Midianites as enemies and kill them, [18]because they treated you as enemies when they deceived you in the affair of Peor and their sister Cozbi, the daughter of a Midianite leader, the woman who was killed when the plague came as a result of Peor."

The Second Census

26 After the plague the LORD said to Moses and Eleazar son of Aaron, the priest, [2]"Take a census of the whole Israelite community by families—all those twenty years old or more who are able to serve in the army of Israel." [3]So on the plains of Moab by the Jordan across from Jericho,[b] Moses and Eleazar the priest spoke with them and said, [4]"Take a census of the men twenty years old or more, as the LORD commanded Moses."

---

[a] *23* Masoretic Text; with a different word division of the Hebrew *A people will gather from the north.*   [b] *3* Hebrew *Jordan of Jericho*; possibly an ancient name for the Jordan River; also in verse 63

Only Child for a Day

focus Profile: **Brandy**

I wish I were . . . I wish I might . . . be the only child in this family tonight. I thought silently to myself as I was getting ready for Dominic, my date, to pick me up. I could hardly think straight—what with the war cries of my little brothers playing up and down the halls and my six-year-old sister whining outside my locked door like a hyena.

"Just a minute, Justine!" I yelled as I put the finishing touches on my make-up. "What does it take to get a little privacy around here?" I muttered as I stormed across the room and whipped open the door to let her inside.

"What?!" I growled. Wouldn't you know, at that moment my mom happened to walk by, just in time to see Justine strategically burst into tears. Give me a break.

"Why do you talk to your sister that way?" my mom scolded me, as Justine smirked at me through her fake tears. Just then the doorbell rang—Dominic!

As I raced downstairs, Justine whined all the louder for effect. My brothers were already roaring toward the front door whooping and hollering. "Shut up!" I yelled. "Do you want him thinking we live in a zoo?" I straightened my shirt and tried to gain some composure as I opened the door.

"Sounds like fun in there. Are you ready?" he smiled and asked.

"Just get me out of here," I said and slammed the door behind me.

siblings in focus

Ever wonder if God was having a bad day when he created brothers and sisters? Whenever you feel like you can't take it anymore, try these ideas:

» Pray for patience. God will help you keep your cool when you feel you're about to lose it. Hold that temper, girl!

» Do your part to live in peace with your siblings (see Romans 12:18, page 1500).

» Talk to your parents. Sometimes parents tend to see only one side of the story. Pick a calm time when you can talk to them alone and tell them your concerns.

For more on this topic, see the index on page 1656.

For more on dealing with the ups and downs of sibling relationships, go online www.TrueImagesBible.com

siblings

These were the Israelites who came out of Egypt:

⁵The descendants of Reuben, the firstborn son of Israel, were:
> through Hanoch, the Hanochite clan;
> through Pallu, the Palluite clan;
> ⁶through Hezron, the Hezronite clan;
> through Carmi, the Carmite clan.
⁷These were the clans of Reuben; those numbered were 43,730.

[8]The son of Pallu was Eliab, [9]and the sons of Eliab were Nemuel, Dathan and Abiram. The same Dathan and Abiram were the community officials who rebelled against Moses and Aaron and were among Korah's followers when they rebelled against the LORD. [10]The earth opened its mouth and swallowed them along with Korah, whose followers died when the fire devoured the 250 men. And they served as a warning sign. [11]The line of Korah, however, did not die out.

[12]The descendants of Simeon by their clans were:

    through Nemuel, the Nemuelite clan;
    through Jamin, the Jaminite clan;
    through Jakin, the Jakinite clan;
    [13]through Zerah, the Zerahite clan;
    through Shaul, the Shaulite clan.

[14]These were the clans of Simeon; there were 22,200 men.

[15]The descendants of Gad by their clans were:

    through Zephon, the Zephonite clan;
    through Haggi, the Haggite clan;
    through Shuni, the Shunite clan;
    [16]through Ozni, the Oznite clan;
    through Eri, the Erite clan;
    [17]through Arodi,[a] the Arodite clan;
    through Areli, the Arelite clan.

[18]These were the clans of Gad; those numbered were 40,500.

[19]Er and Onan were sons of Judah, but they died in Canaan.
[20]The descendants of Judah by their clans were:

    through Shelah, the Shelanite clan;
    through Perez, the Perezite clan;
    through Zerah, the Zerahite clan.
    [21]The descendants of Perez were:
        through Hezron, the Hezronite clan;
        through Hamul, the Hamulite clan.

[22]These were the clans of Judah; those numbered were 76,500.

[23]The descendants of Issachar by their clans were:

    through Tola, the Tolaite clan;
    through Puah, the Puite[b] clan;
    [24]through Jashub, the Jashubite clan;
    through Shimron, the Shimronite clan.

[25]These were the clans of Issachar; those numbered were 64,300.

[26]The descendants of Zebulun by their clans were:

    through Sered, the Seredite clan;
    through Elon, the Elonite clan;
    through Jahleel, the Jahleelite clan.

[27]These were the clans of Zebulun; those numbered were 60,500.

[28]The descendants of Joseph by their clans through Manasseh and Ephraim were:

[29]The descendants of Manasseh:

    through Makir, the Makirite clan (Makir was the father of Gilead);
    through Gilead, the Gileadite clan.
    [30]These were the descendants of Gilead:
        through Iezer, the Iezerite clan;
        through Helek, the Helekite clan;
        [31]through Asriel, the Asrielite clan;
        through Shechem, the Shechemite clan;

[a] 17 Samaritan Pentateuch and Syriac (see also Gen. 46:16); Masoretic Text *Arod*   [b] 23 Samaritan Pentateuch, Septuagint, Vulgate and Syriac (see also 1 Chron. 7:1); Masoretic Text *through Puvah, the Punite*

[32] through Shemida, the Shemidaite clan;
through Hepher, the Hepherite clan.

[33] (Zelophehad son of Hepher had no sons; he had only daughters, whose names were Mahlah, Noah, Hoglah, Milcah and Tirzah.)

[34] These were the clans of Manasseh; those numbered were 52,700.

[35] These were the descendants of Ephraim by their clans:
through Shuthelah, the Shuthelahite clan;
through Beker, the Bekerite clan;
through Tahan, the Tahanite clan.
[36] These were the descendants of Shuthelah:
through Eran, the Eranite clan.

[37] These were the clans of Ephraim; those numbered were 32,500.

These were the descendants of Joseph by their clans.

[38] The descendants of Benjamin by their clans were:
through Bela, the Belaite clan;
through Ashbel, the Ashbelite clan;
through Ahiram, the Ahiramite clan;
[39] through Shupham,[a] the Shuphamite clan;
through Hupham, the Huphamite clan.
[40] The descendants of Bela through Ard and Naaman were:
through Ard,[b] the Ardite clan;
through Naaman, the Naamite clan.

[41] These were the clans of Benjamin; those numbered were 45,600.

[42] These were the descendants of Dan by their clans:
through Shuham, the Shuhamite clan.
These were the clans of Dan: [43] All of them were Shuhamite clans; and those numbered were 64,400.

[44] The descendants of Asher by their clans were:
through Imnah, the Imnite clan;
through Ishvi, the Ishvite clan;
through Beriah, the Beriite clan;
[45] and through the descendants of Beriah:
through Heber, the Heberite clan;
through Malkiel, the Malkielite clan.
[46] (Asher had a daughter named Serah.)
[47] These were the clans of Asher; those numbered were 53,400.

[48] The descendants of Naphtali by their clans were:
through Jahzeel, the Jahzeelite clan;
through Guni, the Gunite clan;
[49] through Jezer, the Jezerite clan;
through Shillem, the Shillemite clan.
[50] These were the clans of Naphtali; those numbered were 45,400.

[51] The total number of the men of Israel was 601,730.

[52] The LORD said to Moses, [53] "The land is to be allotted to them as an inheritance based on the number of names. [54] To a larger group give a larger inheritance, and to a smaller group a smaller one; each is to receive its inheritance according to the number of those listed. [55] Be sure that the land is distributed by lot. What each group inherits will be according to the names for its ancestral tribe. [56] Each inheritance is to be distributed by lot among the larger and smaller groups."

a 39 A few manuscripts of the Masoretic Text, Samaritan Pentateuch, Vulgate and Syriac (see also Septuagint); most manuscripts of the Masoretic Text *Shephupham*   *b 40* Samaritan Pentateuch and Vulgate (see also Septuagint); Masoretic Text does not have *through Ard.*

[57]These were the Levites who were counted by their clans:

through Gershon, the Gershonite clan;
through Kohath, the Kohathite clan;
through Merari, the Merarite clan.

[58]These also were Levite clans:

the Libnite clan,
the Hebronite clan,
the Mahlite clan,
the Mushite clan,
the Korahite clan.

(Kohath was the forefather of Amram; [59]the name of Amram's wife was Jochebed, a descendant of Levi, who was born to the Levites[a] in Egypt. To Amram she bore Aaron, Moses and their sister Miriam. [60]Aaron was the father of Nadab and Abihu, Eleazar and Ithamar. [61]But Nadab and Abihu died when they made an offering before the LORD with unauthorized fire.)

[62]All the male Levites a month old or more numbered 23,000. They were not counted along with the other Israelites because they received no inheritance among them.

[63]These are the ones counted by Moses and Eleazar the priest when they counted the Israelites on the plains of Moab by the Jordan across from Jericho. [64]Not one of them was among those counted by Moses and Aaron the priest when they counted the Israelites in the Desert of Sinai. [65]For the LORD had told those Israelites they would surely die in the desert, and not one of them was left except Caleb son of Jephunneh and Joshua son of Nun.

Zelophehad's Daughters

27 The daughters of Zelophehad son of Hepher, the son of Gilead, the son of Makir, the son of Manasseh, belonged to the clans of Manasseh son of Joseph. The names of the daughters were Mahlah, Noah, Hoglah, Milcah and Tirzah. They approached [2]the entrance to the Tent of Meeting and stood before Moses, Eleazar the priest, the leaders and the whole assembly, and said, [3]"Our father died in the desert. He was not among Korah's followers, who banded together against the LORD, but he died for his own sin and left no sons. [4]Why should our father's name disappear from his clan because he had no son? Give us property among our father's relatives."

[5]So Moses brought their case before the LORD [6]and the LORD said to him, [7]"What Zelophehad's daughters are saying is right. You must certainly give them property as an inheritance among their father's relatives and turn their father's inheritance over to them.

[8]"Say to the Israelites, 'If a man dies and leaves no son, turn his inheritance over to his daughter. [9]If he has no daughter, give his inheritance to his brothers. [10]If he has no brothers, give his inheritance to his father's brothers. [11]If his father had no brothers, give his inheritance to the nearest relative in his clan, that he may possess it. This is to be a legal requirement for the Israelites, as the LORD commanded Moses.' "

Joshua to Succeed Moses

[12]Then the LORD said to Moses, "Go up this mountain in the Abarim range and see the land I have given the Israelites. [13]After you have seen it, you too will be gathered to your people, as your brother Aaron was, [14]for when the community rebelled at the waters in the Desert of Zin, both of you disobeyed my command to honor me as holy before their eyes." (These were the waters of Meribah Kadesh, in the Desert of Zin.)

[15]Moses said to the LORD, [16]"May the LORD, the God of the spirits of all mankind, appoint a man over this community [17]to go out and come in before them, one who will lead them out and bring them in, so the LORD's people will not be like sheep without a shepherd."

[18]So the LORD said to Moses, "Take Joshua son of Nun, a man in whom is the spirit,[b] and lay your hand on him. [19]Have him stand before Eleazar the priest and the entire assembly and commission him in their presence. [20]Give him some of your authority so the whole Israelite community

a 59 Or Jochebed, a daughter of Levi, who was born to Levi   b 18 Or Spirit will obey him. ²¹He is to stand before Eleazar the priest, who will obtain decisions for him by inquiring of the Urim before the Lord. At his command he and the entire community of the Israelites will go out, and at his command they will come in."

²²Moses did as the Lord commanded him. He took Joshua and had him stand before Eleazar the priest and the whole assembly. ²³Then he laid his hands on him and commissioned him, as the Lord instructed through Moses.

Daily Offerings

28 The Lord said to Moses, ²"Give this command to the Israelites and say to them: 'See that you present to me at the appointed time the food for my offerings made by fire, as an aroma pleasing to me.' ³Say to them: 'This is the offering made by fire that you are to present to the Lord: two lambs a year old without defect, as a regular burnt offering each day. ⁴Prepare one lamb in the morning and the other at twilight, ⁵together with a grain offering of a tenth of an ephah ª of fine flour mixed with a quarter of a hin ᵇ of oil from pressed olives. ⁶This is the regular burnt offering instituted at Mount Sinai as a pleasing aroma, an offering made to the Lord by fire. ⁷The accompanying drink offering is to be a quarter of a hin of fermented drink with each lamb. Pour out the drink offering to the Lord at the sanctuary. ⁸Prepare the second lamb at twilight, along with the same kind of grain offering and drink offering that you prepare in the morning. This is an offering made by fire, an aroma pleasing to the Lord.

Sabbath Offerings

⁹" 'On the Sabbath day, make an offering of two lambs a year old without defect, together with its drink offering and a grain offering of two-tenths of an ephah ᶜ of fine flour mixed with oil. ¹⁰This is the burnt offering for every Sabbath, in addition to the regular burnt offering and its drink offering.

Monthly Offerings

¹¹" 'On the first of every month, present to the Lord a burnt offering of two young bulls, one ram and seven male lambs a year old, all without defect. ¹²With each bull there is to be a grain offering of three-tenths of an ephah ᵈ of fine flour mixed with oil; with the ram, a grain offering of two-tenths of an ephah of fine flour mixed with oil; ¹³and with each lamb, a grain offering of a tenth of an ephah of fine flour mixed with oil. This is for a burnt offering, a pleasing aroma, an offering made to the Lord by fire. ¹⁴With each bull there is to be a drink offering of half a hin ᵉ of wine; with the ram, a third of a hin ᶠ; and with each lamb, a quarter of a hin. This is the monthly burnt offering to be made at each new moon during the year. ¹⁵Besides the regular burnt offering with its drink offering, one male goat is to be presented to the Lord as a sin offering.

The Passover

¹⁶" 'On the fourteenth day of the first month the Lord's Passover is to be held. ¹⁷On the fifteenth day of this month there is to be a festival; for seven days eat bread made without yeast. ¹⁸On the first day hold a sacred assembly and do no regular work. ¹⁹Present to the Lord an offering made by fire, a burnt offering of two young bulls, one ram and seven male lambs a year old, all without defect. ²⁰With each bull prepare a grain offering of three-tenths of an ephah of fine flour mixed with oil; with the ram, two-tenths; ²¹and with each of the seven lambs, one-tenth. ²²Include one male goat as a sin offering to make atonement for you. ²³Prepare these in addition to the regular morning burnt offering. ²⁴In this way prepare the food for the offering made by fire every day for seven days as an aroma pleasing to the Lord; it is to be prepared in addition to the regular burnt offering and its drink offering. ²⁵On the seventh day hold a sacred assembly and do no regular work.

Feast of Weeks

²⁶" 'On the day of firstfruits, when you present to the Lord an offering of new grain during the Feast of Weeks, hold a sacred assembly and do no regular work. ²⁷Present a burnt offering of two young bulls, one ram and seven male lambs a year old as an aroma pleasing to the Lord. ²⁸With

ª 5 That is, probably about 2 quarts (about 2 liters); also in verses 13, 21 and 29   ᵇ 5 That is, probably about 1 quart (about 1 liter); also in verses 7 and 14   ᶜ 9 That is, probably about 4 quarts (about 4.5 liters); also in verses 12, 20 and 28   ᵈ 12 That is, probably about 6 quarts (about 6.5 liters); also in verses 20 and 28   ᵉ 14 That is, probably about 2 quarts (about 2 liters)   ᶠ 14 That is, probably about 1 1/4 quarts (about 1.2 liters) each bull there is to be a grain offering of three-tenths of an ephah of fine flour mixed with oil; with the ram, two-tenths; [29]and with each of the seven lambs, one-tenth. [30]Include one male goat to make atonement for you. [31]Prepare these together with their drink offerings, in addition to the regular burnt offering and its grain offering. Be sure the animals are without defect.

Feast of Trumpets

29 [1]" 'On the first day of the seventh month hold a sacred assembly and do no regular work. It is a day for you to sound the trumpets. [2]As an aroma pleasing to the LORD, prepare a burnt offering of one young bull, one ram and seven male lambs a year old, all without defect. [3]With the bull prepare a grain offering of three-tenths of an ephah[a] of fine flour mixed with oil; with the ram, two-tenths[b]; [4]and with each of the seven lambs, one-tenth.[c] [5]Include one male goat as a sin offering to make atonement for you. [6]These are in addition to the monthly and daily burnt offerings with their grain offerings and drink offerings as specified. They are offerings made to the LORD by fire—a pleasing aroma.

Day of Atonement

[7]" 'On the tenth day of this seventh month hold a sacred assembly. You must deny yourselves[d] and do no work. [8]Present as an aroma pleasing to the LORD a burnt offering of one young bull, one ram and seven male lambs a year old, all without defect. [9]With the bull prepare a grain offering of three-tenths of an ephah of fine flour mixed with oil; with the ram, two-tenths; [10]and with each of the seven lambs, one-tenth. [11]Include one male goat as a sin offering, in addition to the sin offering for atonement and the regular burnt offering with its grain offering, and their drink offerings.

Feast of Tabernacles

[12]" 'On the fifteenth day of the seventh month, hold a sacred assembly and do no regular work. Celebrate a festival to the LORD for seven days. [13]Present an offering made by fire as an aroma pleasing to the LORD, a burnt offering of thirteen young bulls, two rams and fourteen male lambs a year old, all without defect. [14]With each of the thirteen bulls prepare a grain offering of three-tenths of an ephah of fine flour mixed with oil; with each of the two rams, two-tenths; [15]and with each of the fourteen lambs, one-tenth. [16]Include one male goat as a sin offering, in addition to the regular burnt offering with its grain offering and drink offering.

[17]" 'On the second day prepare twelve young bulls, two rams and fourteen male lambs a year old, all without defect. [18]With the bulls, rams and lambs, prepare their grain offerings and drink offerings according to the number specified. [19]Include one male goat as a sin offering, in addition to the regular burnt offering with its grain offering, and their drink offerings.

[20]" 'On the third day prepare eleven bulls, two rams and fourteen male lambs a year old, all without defect. [21]With the bulls, rams and lambs, prepare their grain offerings and drink offerings according to the number specified. [22]Include one male goat as a sin offering, in addition to the regular burnt offering with its grain offering and drink offering.

[23]" 'On the fourth day prepare ten bulls, two rams and fourteen male lambs a year old, all without defect. [24]With the bulls, rams and lambs, prepare their grain offerings and drink offerings according to the number specified. [25]Include one male goat as a sin offering, in addition to the regular burnt offering with its grain offering and drink offering.

[26]" 'On the fifth day prepare nine bulls, two rams and fourteen male lambs a year old, all without defect. [27]With the bulls, rams and lambs, prepare their grain offerings and drink offerings according to the number specified. [28]Include one male goat as a sin offering, in addition to the regular burnt offering with its grain offering and drink offering.

[29]" 'On the sixth day prepare eight bulls, two rams and fourteen male lambs a year old, all without defect. [30]With the bulls, rams and lambs, prepare their grain offerings and drink offerings according to the number specified. [31]Include one male goat as a sin offering, in addition to the regular burnt offering with its grain offering and drink offering.

[32]" 'On the seventh day prepare seven bulls, two rams and fourteen male lambs a year old, all

---

[a] 3 That is, probably about 6 quarts (about 6.5 liters); also in verses 9 and 14   [b] 3 That is, probably about 4 quarts (about 4.5 liters); also in verses 9 and 14   [c] 4 That is, probably about 2 quarts (about 2 liters); also in verses 10 and 15
[d] 7 Or *must fast*

mirror images

Rachel—Winning Isn't Everything

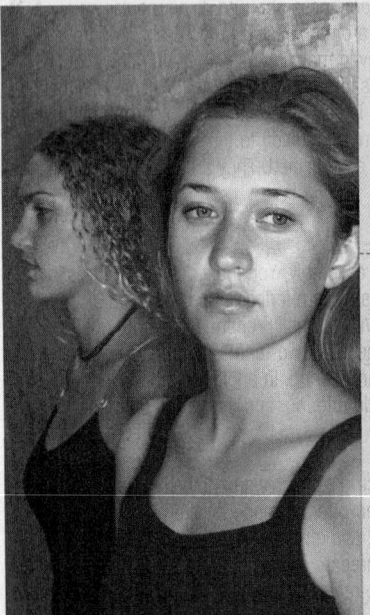

Ever had a friend who could turn a Friday night game of spades into a fierce competition? Ever seen a girl go after someone in debate class like a ravenous lion after a gladiator? That was Rachel—to her, everything was a competition—especially when it came to her sister, Leah.

The two girls, both married to Jacob (according to the customs of the day), began competing over who could win her husband's heart. Their shared strategy? Give the guy sons for his inheritance. Unfortunately for Rachel, for all her sister lacked in beauty, Leah was a baby-making machine. Mostly barren and totally desperate, Rachel forced her servant-girl to have more babies in her stead just to keep pace with "Fertile Myrtle" Leah. At the end of the day, sports fans, it was Leah 8, Rachel 4.

Their combined total played a significant role in God's plan as the heads of each of the 12 tribes of Israel. For all their mothers did to manipulate the family tree, at least the boys came out the winners. However, Rachel lost more than the battle of the babies. She lost her sister's faith and trust. Girls are often competitive with other girls, and in the process, lose out on real friendship.

An overly competitive spirit means we can never be close to others because they might pose a potential threat. So, like Rachel, we keep our distance just in case. And like Rachel, it's often too late before we realize how much we stand to lose when we go all out to win.

To read the next Mirror Images profile, go to page 220.

Dear God, I confess the jealousy I sometimes feel toward other girls. When I feel the need to win at all costs, remind me of all I stand to lose with that attitude. Amen.

»» Read more about Rachel in Genesis 29—35:20 (pages 36–46).

without defect. ³³With the bulls, rams and lambs, prepare their grain offerings and drink offerings according to the number specified. ³⁴Include one male goat as a sin offering, in addition to the regular burnt offering with its grain offering and drink offering.

³⁵" 'On the eighth day hold an assembly and do no regular work. ³⁶Present an offering made by fire as an aroma pleasing to the LORD, a burnt offering of one bull, one ram and seven male lambs a year old, all without defect. ³⁷With the bull, the ram and the lambs, prepare their grain offerings and drink offerings according to the number specified. ³⁸Include one male goat as a sin offering, in addition to the regular burnt offering with its grain offering and drink offering.

³⁹" 'In addition to what you vow and your freewill offerings, prepare these for the LORD at your appointed feasts: your burnt offerings, grain offerings, drink offerings and fellowship offerings.ᵃ' "

⁴⁰Moses told the Israelites all that the LORD commanded him.

Vows

30

Moses said to the heads of the tribes of Israel: "This is what the LORD commands: ²When a man makes a vow to the LORD or takes an oath to obligate himself by a pledge, he must not break his word but must do everything he said.

³"When a young woman still living in her father's house makes a vow to the LORD or obligates herself by a pledge ⁴and her father hears about her vow or pledge but says nothing to her, then all her vows and every pledge by which she obligated herself will stand. ⁵But if her father forbids her when he hears about it, none of her vows or the pledges by which she obligated herself will stand; the LORD will release her because her father has forbidden her.

⁶"If she marries after she makes a vow or after her lips utter a rash promise by which she obligates herself ⁷and her husband hears about it but says nothing to her, then her vows or the pledges by which she obligated herself will stand. ⁸But if her husband forbids her when he hears about it, he nullifies the vow that obligates her or the rash promise by which she obligates herself, and the LORD will release her.

⁹"Any vow or obligation taken by a widow or divorced woman will be binding on her.

¹⁰"If a woman living with her husband makes a vow or obligates herself by a pledge under oath ¹¹and her husband hears about it but says nothing to her and does not forbid her, then all her vows or the pledges by which she obligated herself will stand. ¹²But if her husband nullifies them when he hears about them, then none of the vows or pledges that came from her lips will stand. Her husband has nullified them, and the LORD will release her. ¹³Her husband may confirm or nullify any vow she makes or any sworn pledge to deny herself. ¹⁴But if her husband says nothing to her about it from day to day, then he confirms all her vows or the pledges binding on her. He confirms them by saying nothing to her when he hears about them. ¹⁵If, however, he nullifies them some time after he hears about them, then he is responsible for her guilt."

¹⁶These are the regulations the LORD gave Moses concerning relationships between a man and his wife, and between a father and his young daughter still living in his house.

Vengeance on the Midianites

31

The LORD said to Moses, ²"Take vengeance on the Midianites for the Israelites. After that, you will be gathered to your people."

³So Moses said to the people, "Arm some of your men to go to war against the Midianites and to carry out the LORD's vengeance on them. ⁴Send into battle a thousand men from each of the tribes of Israel." ⁵So twelve thousand men armed for battle, a thousand from each tribe, were supplied from the clans of Israel. ⁶Moses sent them into battle, a thousand from each tribe, along with Phinehas son of Eleazar, the priest, who took with him articles from the sanctuary and the trumpets for signaling.

⁷They fought against Midian, as the LORD commanded Moses, and killed every man. ⁸Among their victims were Evi, Rekem, Zur, Hur and Reba—the five kings of Midian. They also killed Balaam son of Beor with the sword. ⁹The Israelites captured the Midianite women and children and took all the Midianite herds, flocks and goods as plunder. ¹⁰They burned all the towns where the Midianites had settled, as well as all their camps. ¹¹They took all the plunder and spoils, including the people and animals, ¹²and brought the captives, spoils and plunder to Moses and Eleazar the

ᵃ 39 Traditionally *peace offerings*

priest and the Israelite assembly at their camp on the plains of Moab, by the Jordan across from Jericho.[a]

[13]Moses, Eleazar the priest and all the leaders of the community went to meet them outside the camp. [14]Moses was angry with the officers of the army—the commanders of thousands and commanders of hundreds—who returned from the battle.

[15]"Have you allowed all the women to live?" he asked them. [16]"They were the ones who followed Balaam's advice and were the means of turning the Israelites away from the LORD in what happened at Peor, so that a plague struck the LORD's people. [17]Now kill all the boys. And kill every woman who has slept with a man, [18]but save for yourselves every girl who has never slept with a man.

[19]"All of you who have killed anyone or touched anyone who was killed must stay outside the camp seven days. On the third and seventh days you must purify yourselves and your captives. [20]Purify every garment as well as everything made of leather, goat hair or wood."

[21]Then Eleazar the priest said to the soldiers who had gone into battle, "This is the requirement of the law that the LORD gave Moses: [22]Gold, silver, bronze, iron, tin, lead [23]and anything else that can withstand fire must be put through the fire, and then it will be clean. But it must also be purified with the water of cleansing. And whatever cannot withstand fire must be put through that water. [24]On the seventh day wash your clothes and you will be clean. Then you may come into the camp."

Dividing the Spoils

[25]The LORD said to Moses, [26]"You and Eleazar the priest and the family heads of the community are to count all the people and animals that were captured. [27]Divide the spoils between the soldiers who took part in the battle and the rest of the community. [28]From the soldiers who fought in the battle, set apart as tribute for the LORD one out of every five hundred, whether persons, cattle, donkeys, sheep or goats. [29]Take this tribute from their half share and give it to Eleazar the priest as the LORD's part. [30]From the Israelites' half, select one out of every fifty, whether persons, cattle, donkeys, sheep, goats or other animals. Give them to the Levites, who are responsible for the care of the LORD's tabernacle." [31]So Moses and Eleazar the priest did as the LORD commanded Moses.

[32]The plunder remaining from the spoils that the soldiers took was 675,000 sheep, [33]72,000 cattle, [34]61,000 donkeys [35]and 32,000 women who had never slept with a man.

[36]The half share of those who fought in the battle was:

337,500 sheep, [37]of which the tribute for the LORD was 675;
[38] 36,000 cattle, of which the tribute for the LORD was 72;
[39] 30,500 donkeys, of which the tribute for the LORD was 61;
[40] 16,000 people, of which the tribute for the LORD was 32.

[41]Moses gave the tribute to Eleazar the priest as the LORD's part, as the LORD commanded Moses.

[42]The half belonging to the Israelites, which Moses set apart from that of the fighting men— [43]the community's half—was 337,500 sheep, [44]36,000 cattle, [45]30,500 donkeys [46]and 16,000 people. [47]From the Israelites' half, Moses selected one out of every fifty persons and animals, as the LORD commanded him, and gave them to the Levites, who were responsible for the care of the LORD's tabernacle.

[48]Then the officers who were over the units of the army—the commanders of thousands and commanders of hundreds—went to Moses [49]and said to him, "Your servants have counted the soldiers under our command, and not one is missing. [50]So we have brought as an offering to the LORD the gold articles each of us acquired—armlets, bracelets, signet rings, earrings and necklaces—to make atonement for ourselves before the LORD."

[51]Moses and Eleazar the priest accepted from them the gold—all the crafted articles. [52]All the gold from the commanders of thousands and commanders of hun-

truth or dare

The perfect battle? A victory with *no* casualties. No wonder they took up a spontaneous offering of thanks to God! When was the last time you gave God some major accolades?

31:48-50

a 12 Hebrew *Jordan of Jericho*; possibly an ancient name for the Jordan River dreds that Moses and Eleazar presented as a gift to the LORD weighed 16,750 shekels. [a] [53]Each soldier had taken plunder for himself. [54]Moses and Eleazar the priest accepted the gold from the commanders of thousands and commanders of hundreds and brought it into the Tent of Meeting as a memorial for the Israelites before the LORD.

The Transjordan Tribes

32 The Reubenites and Gadites, who had very large herds and flocks, saw that the lands of Jazer and Gilead were suitable for livestock. [2]So they came to Moses and Eleazar the priest and to the leaders of the community, and said, [3]"Ataroth, Dibon, Jazer, Nimrah, Heshbon, Elealeh, Sebam, Nebo and Beon— [4]the land the LORD subdued before the people of Israel—are suitable for livestock, and your servants have livestock. [5]If we have found favor in your eyes," they said, "let this land be given to your servants as our possession. Do not make us cross the Jordan."

[6]Moses said to the Gadites and Reubenites, "Shall your countrymen go to war while you sit here? [7]Why do you discourage the Israelites from going over into the land the LORD has given them? [8]This is what your fathers did when I sent them from Kadesh Barnea to look over the land. [9]After they went up to the Valley of Eshcol and viewed the land, they discouraged the Israelites from entering the land the LORD had given them. [10]The LORD's anger was aroused that day and he swore this oath: [11]'Because they have not followed me wholeheartedly, not one of the men twenty years old or more who came up out of Egypt will see the land I promised on oath to Abraham, Isaac and Jacob— [12]not one except Caleb son of Jephunneh the Kenizzite and Joshua son of Nun, for they followed the LORD wholeheartedly.' [13]The LORD's anger burned against Israel and he made them wander in the desert forty years, until the whole generation of those who had done evil in his sight was gone.

[14]"And here you are, a brood of sinners, standing in the place of your fathers and making the LORD even more angry with Israel. [15]If you turn away from following him, he will again leave all this people in the desert, and you will be the cause of their destruction."

[16]Then they came up to him and said, "We would like to build pens here for our livestock and cities for our women and children. [17]But we are ready to arm ourselves and go ahead of the Israelites until we have brought them to their place. Meanwhile our women and children will live in fortified cities, for protection from the inhabitants of the land. [18]We will not return to our homes until every Israelite has received his inheritance. [19]We will not receive any inheritance with them on the other side of the Jordan, because our inheritance has come to us on the east side of the Jordan."

[20]Then Moses said to them, "If you will do this—if you will arm yourselves before the LORD for battle, [21]and if all of you will go armed over the Jordan before the LORD until he has driven his enemies out before him— [22]then when the land is subdued before the LORD, you may return and be free from your obligation to the LORD and to Israel. And this land will be your possession before the LORD.

[23]"But if you fail to do this, you will be sinning against the LORD; and you may be sure that your sin will find you out. [24]Build cities for your women and children, and pens for your flocks, but do what you have promised."

[25]The Gadites and Reubenites said to Moses, "We your servants will do as our lord commands. [26]Our children and wives, our flocks and herds will remain here in the cities of Gilead. [27]But your servants, every man armed for battle, will cross over to fight before the LORD, just as our lord says."

[28]Then Moses gave orders about them to Eleazar the priest and Joshua son of Nun and to the family heads of the Israelite tribes. [29]He said to them, "If the Gadites and Reubenites, every man armed for battle, cross over the Jordan with you before the LORD, then when the land is subdued before you, give them the land of Gilead as their possession. [30]But if they do not cross over with you armed, they must accept their possession with you in Canaan."

truth or dare

Moses gave some of the people a severe tongue-lashing based on some faulty assumptions. Don't jump to conclusions about another person's motives. First find out the facts.

32:1–18

[a] 52 That is, about 420 pounds (about 190 kilograms)

³¹The Gadites and Reubenites answered, "Your servants will do what the LORD has said. ³²We will cross over before the LORD into Canaan armed, but the property we inherit will be on this side of the Jordan."

³³Then Moses gave to the Gadites, the Reubenites and the half-tribe of Manasseh son of Joseph the kingdom of Sihon king of the Amorites and the kingdom of Og king of Bashan—the whole land with its cities and the territory around them.

³⁴The Gadites built up Dibon, Ataroth, Aroer, ³⁵Atroth Shophan, Jazer, Jogbehah, ³⁶Beth Nimrah and Beth Haran as fortified cities, and built pens for their flocks. ³⁷And the Reubenites rebuilt Heshbon, Elealeh and Kiriathaim, ³⁸as well as Nebo and Baal Meon (these names were changed) and Sibmah. They gave names to the cities they rebuilt.

³⁹The descendants of Makir son of Manasseh went to Gilead, captured it and drove out the Amorites who were there. ⁴⁰So Moses gave Gilead to the Makirites, the descendants of Manasseh, and they settled there. ⁴¹Jair, a descendant of Manasseh, captured their settlements and called them Havvoth Jair.ᵃ ⁴²And Nobah captured Kenath and its surrounding settlements and called it Nobah after himself.

Stages in Israel's Journey

33 Here are the stages in the journey of the Israelites when they came out of Egypt by divisions under the leadership of Moses and Aaron. ²At the LORD's command Moses recorded the stages in their journey. This is their journey by stages:

³The Israelites set out from Rameses on the fifteenth day of the first month, the day after the Passover. They marched out boldly in full view of all the Egyptians, ⁴who were burying all their firstborn, whom the LORD had struck down among them; for the LORD had brought judgment on their gods.

⁵The Israelites left Rameses and camped at Succoth.

⁶They left Succoth and camped at Etham, on the edge of the desert.

⁷They left Etham, turned back to Pi Hahiroth, to the east of Baal Zephon, and camped near Migdol.

⁸They left Pi Hahirothᵇ and passed through the sea into the desert, and when they had traveled for three days in the Desert of Etham, they camped at Marah.

⁹They left Marah and went to Elim, where there were twelve springs and seventy palm trees, and they camped there.

¹⁰They left Elim and camped by the Red Sea.ᶜ

¹¹They left the Red Sea and camped in the Desert of Sin.

¹²They left the Desert of Sin and camped at Dophkah.

¹³They left Dophkah and camped at Alush.

¹⁴They left Alush and camped at Rephidim, where there was no water for the people to drink.

¹⁵They left Rephidim and camped in the Desert of Sinai.

¹⁶They left the Desert of Sinai and camped at Kibroth Hattaavah.

¹⁷They left Kibroth Hattaavah and camped at Hazeroth.

¹⁸They left Hazeroth and camped at Rithmah.

¹⁹They left Rithmah and camped at Rimmon Perez.

²⁰They left Rimmon Perez and camped at Libnah.

²¹They left Libnah and camped at Rissah.

²²They left Rissah and camped at Kehelathah.

²³They left Kehelathah and camped at Mount Shepher.

²⁴They left Mount Shepher and camped at Haradah.

²⁵They left Haradah and camped at Makheloth.

²⁶They left Makheloth and camped at Tahath.

²⁷They left Tahath and camped at Terah.

²⁸They left Terah and camped at Mithcah.

ᵃ 41 Or them the settlements of Jair   ᵇ 8 Many manuscripts of the Masoretic Text, Samaritan Pentateuch and Vulgate; most manuscripts of the Masoretic Text left from before Hahiroth   ᶜ 10 Hebrew Yam Suph; that is, Sea of Reeds; also in verse 11

²⁹They left Mithcah and camped at Hashmonah.
³⁰They left Hashmonah and camped at Moseroth.
³¹They left Moseroth and camped at Bene Jaakan.
³²They left Bene Jaakan and camped at Hor Haggidgad.
³³They left Hor Haggidgad and camped at Jotbathah.
³⁴They left Jotbathah and camped at Abronah.
³⁵They left Abronah and camped at Ezion Geber.
³⁶They left Ezion Geber and camped at Kadesh, in the Desert of Zin.
³⁷They left Kadesh and camped at Mount Hor, on the border of Edom. ³⁸At the LORD's command Aaron the priest went up Mount Hor, where he died on the first day of the fifth month of the fortieth year after the Israelites came out of Egypt. ³⁹Aaron was a hundred and twenty-three years old when he died on Mount Hor.

⁴⁰The Canaanite king of Arad, who lived in the Negev of Canaan, heard that the Israelites were coming.

⁴¹They left Mount Hor and camped at Zalmonah.
⁴²They left Zalmonah and camped at Punon.
⁴³They left Punon and camped at Oboth.
⁴⁴They left Oboth and camped at Iye Abarim, on the border of Moab.
⁴⁵They left Iyim^a and camped at Dibon Gad.
⁴⁶They left Dibon Gad and camped at Almon Diblathaim.
⁴⁷They left Almon Diblathaim and camped in the mountains of Abarim, near Nebo.
⁴⁸They left the mountains of Abarim and camped on the plains of Moab by the Jordan across from Jericho.^b ⁴⁹There on the plains of Moab they camped along the Jordan from Beth Jeshimoth to Abel Shittim.

truth or dare

Even though splinters are tiny, they can be super-painful and annoying. Sin affects you in the same way—if it's not removed right away, it gets worse and worse.

33:55

⁵⁰On the plains of Moab by the Jordan across from Jericho the LORD said to Moses, ⁵¹"Speak to the Israelites and say to them: 'When you cross the Jordan into Canaan, ⁵²drive out all the inhabitants of the land before you. Destroy all their carved images and their cast idols, and demolish all their high places. ⁵³Take possession of the land and settle in it, for I have given you the land to possess. ⁵⁴Distribute the land by lot, according to your clans. To a larger group give a larger inheritance, and to a smaller group a smaller one. Whatever falls to them by lot will be theirs. Distribute it according to your ancestral tribes.

⁵⁵" 'But if you do not drive out the inhabitants of the land, those you allow to remain will become barbs in your eyes and thorns in your sides. They will give you trouble in the land where you will live. ⁵⁶And then I will do to you what I plan to do to them.' "

Boundaries of Canaan

34 The LORD said to Moses, ²"Command the Israelites and say to them: 'When you enter Canaan, the land that will be allotted to you as an inheritance will have these boundaries:

³" 'Your southern side will include some of the Desert of Zin along the border of Edom. On the east, your southern boundary will start from the end of the Salt Sea,^c ⁴cross south of Scorpion^d Pass, continue on to Zin and go south of Kadesh Barnea. Then it will go to Hazar Addar and over to Azmon, ⁵where it will turn, join the Wadi of Egypt and end at the Sea.^e

⁶" 'Your western boundary will be the coast of the Great Sea. This will be your boundary on the west.

^a 45 That is, Iye Abarim   ^b 48 Hebrew *Jordan of Jericho*; possibly an ancient name for the Jordan River; also in verse 50
^c 3 That is, the Dead Sea; also in verse 12   ^d 4 Hebrew *Akrabbim*   ^e 5 That is, the Mediterranean; also in verses 6 and 7

7" 'For your northern boundary, run a line from the Great Sea to Mount Hor ⁸and from Mount Hor to Lebo^a Hamath. Then the boundary will go to Zedad, ⁹continue to Ziphron and end at Hazar Enan. This will be your boundary on the north.

¹⁰" 'For your eastern boundary, run a line from Hazar Enan to Shepham. ¹¹The boundary will go down from Shepham to Riblah on the east side of Ain and continue along the slopes east of the Sea of Kinnereth.^{b} ¹²Then the boundary will go down along the Jordan and end at the Salt Sea.

" 'This will be your land, with its boundaries on every side.' "

¹³Moses commanded the Israelites: "Assign this land by lot as an inheritance. The Lord has ordered that it be given to the nine and a half tribes, ¹⁴because the families of the tribe of Reuben, the tribe of Gad and the half-tribe of Manasseh have received their inheritance. ¹⁵These two and a half tribes have received their inheritance on the east side of the Jordan of Jericho,^{c} toward the sunrise."

¹⁶The Lord said to Moses, ¹⁷"These are the names of the men who are to assign the land for you as an inheritance: Eleazar the priest and Joshua son of Nun. ¹⁸And appoint one leader from each tribe to help assign the land. ¹⁹These are their names:

Caleb son of Jephunneh,
  from the tribe of Judah;
²⁰Shemuel son of Ammihud,
  from the tribe of Simeon;
²¹Elidad son of Kislon,
  from the tribe of Benjamin;
²²Bukki son of Jogli,
  the leader from the tribe of Dan;
²³Hanniel son of Ephod,
  the leader from the tribe of Manasseh son of Joseph;
²⁴Kemuel son of Shiphtan,
  the leader from the tribe of Ephraim son of Joseph;
²⁵Elizaphan son of Parnach,
  the leader from the tribe of Zebulun;
²⁶Paltiel son of Azzan,
  the leader from the tribe of Issachar;
²⁷Ahihud son of Shelomi,
  the leader from the tribe of Asher;
²⁸Pedahel son of Ammihud,
  the leader from the tribe of Naphtali."

²⁹These are the men the Lord commanded to assign the inheritance to the Israelites in the land of Canaan.

Towns for the Levites

35 On the plains of Moab by the Jordan across from Jericho,^{d} the Lord said to Moses, ²"Command the Israelites to give the Levites towns to live in from the inheritance the Israelites will possess. And give them pasturelands around the towns. ³Then they will have towns to live in and pasturelands for their cattle, flocks and all their other livestock.

⁴"The pasturelands around the towns that you give the Levites will extend out fifteen hundred feet^e from the town wall. ⁵Outside the town, measure three thousand feet^f on the east side, three thousand on the south side, three thousand on the west and three thousand on the north, with the town in the center. They will have this area as pastureland for the towns.

Cities of Refuge

⁶"Six of the towns you give the Levites will be cities of refuge, to which a person who has killed someone may flee. In addition, give them forty-two other towns. ⁷In all you must give the Levites forty-eight towns, together with their pasturelands. ⁸The towns you give the Levites from the land

---

^{a} 8 Or to the entrance to ^{b} 11 That is, Galilee ^{c} 15 Jordan of Jericho was possibly an ancient name for the Jordan River. ^{d} 1 Hebrew Jordan of Jericho; possibly an ancient name for the Jordan River ^{e} 4 Hebrew a thousand cubits (about 450 meters) ^{f} 5 Hebrew two thousand cubits (about 900 meters)

Family Secret

"Hello, my name is Gina. My dad is an alcoholic."

That's my recurring nightmare—but I'm not at an AA meeting where that kind of thing is expected. No, in my whacked-out dream, I'm at school, in front of the class, giving a speech about the Bermuda triangle or something, and I end up confessing the family's deep dark secret.

To make matters worse, I'm afraid this nightmare might actually happen. "Hey world! My dad is a drunk!" I worry about him every day—sometimes minute to minute. What if he has a wreck on his way home from the "business meeting" that kept him five hours late after work? What if he kills somebody instead of just getting a DUI this time?

My dad's a wonderful man—when he's sober. It's just that he can't stop drinking. Maybe it's genetic. My granddad was the same way—and my mom says my uncle has issues with alcohol, too. I've never even had so much as a sip of beer. I'm scared to death I might have the same weak genes. What if I can't control myself and end up in the exact same place? I am praying that Jesus will help my dad stop drinking. If he doesn't help him, I don't know what will happen.

Find out more about alcoholism and its effects online at www.TrueImagesBible.com

alcoholism in focus

Alcohol and tobacco kill more than fifty times the number of people killed by cocaine, heroin and every other illegal drug combined. Ten million Americans are addicted to alcohol. With these kinds of statistics, there's a strong likelihood that someone in your family or a friend's family is an alcoholic.

» Remember, having the disease of alcoholism does not make a person bad or evil.
» It's hard to see those you love hurting themselves, but they have to make the choice to pursue recovery. You can't do it for them.
» Don't let embarrassment keep you from sharing your fears if you suspect someone you love is an alcoholic. Seek a trusted adult to talk through this issue, and consider professional help. Psalm 73:24 says God's counsel will guide you (page 725).

For more on this topic, see the index on page 1656.

the Israelites possess are to be given in proportion to the inheritance of each tribe: Take many towns from a tribe that has many, but few from one that has few."

⁹Then the LORD said to Moses: ¹⁰"Speak to the Israelites and say to them: 'When you cross the Jordan into Canaan, ¹¹select some towns to be your cities of refuge, to which a person who has killed someone accidentally may flee. ¹²They will be places of refuge from the avenger, so that a person accused of murder may not die before he stands trial before the assembly. ¹³These six towns you give will be your cities of refuge. ¹⁴Give three on this side of the Jordan and three in Canaan as cities of refuge. ¹⁵These six towns will be a place of refuge for Israelites, aliens and any other people living among them, so that anyone who has killed another accidentally can flee there.

¹⁶' 'If a man strikes someone with an iron object so that he dies, he is a murderer; the murder-

er shall be put to death. ¹⁷Or if anyone has a stone in his hand that could kill, and he strikes someone so that he dies, he is a murderer; the murderer shall be put to death. ¹⁸Or if anyone has a wooden object in his hand that could kill, and he hits someone so that he dies, he is a murderer; the murderer shall be put to death. ¹⁹The avenger of blood shall put the murderer to death; when he meets him, he shall put him to death. ²⁰If anyone with malice aforethought shoves another or throws something at him intentionally so that he dies ²¹or if in hostility he hits him with his fist so that he dies, that person shall be put to death; he is a murderer. The avenger of blood shall put the murderer to death when he meets him.

²²" 'But if without hostility someone suddenly shoves another or throws something at him unintentionally ²³or, without seeing him, drops a stone on him that could kill him, and he dies, then since he was not his enemy and he did not intend to harm him, ²⁴the assembly must judge between him and the avenger of blood according to these regulations. ²⁵The assembly must protect the one accused of murder from the avenger of blood and send him back to the city of refuge to which he fled. He must stay there until the death of the high priest, who was anointed with the holy oil.

²⁶" 'But if the accused ever goes outside the limits of the city of refuge to which he has fled ²⁷and the avenger of blood finds him outside the city, the avenger of blood may kill the accused without being guilty of murder. ²⁸The accused must stay in his city of refuge until the death of the high priest; only after the death of the high priest may he return to his own property.

²⁹" 'These are to be legal requirements for you throughout the generations to come, wherever you live.

³⁰" 'Anyone who kills a person is to be put to death as a murderer only on the testimony of witnesses. But no one is to be put to death on the testimony of only one witness.

³¹" 'Do not accept a ransom for the life of a murderer, who deserves to die. He must surely be put to death.

³²" 'Do not accept a ransom for anyone who has fled to a city of refuge and so allow him to go back and live on his own land before the death of the high priest.

³³" 'Do not pollute the land where you are. Bloodshed pollutes the land, and atonement cannot be made for the land on which blood has been shed, except by the blood of the one who shed it. ³⁴Do not defile the land where you live and where I dwell, for I, the LORD, dwell among the Israelites.' "

Inheritance of Zelophehad's Daughters

36 The family heads of the clan of Gilead son of Makir, the son of Manasseh, who were from the clans of the descendants of Joseph, came and spoke before Moses and the leaders, the heads of the Israelite families. ²They said, "When the LORD commanded my lord to give the land as an inheritance to the Israelites by lot, he ordered you to give the inheritance of our brother Zelophehad to his daughters. ³Now suppose they marry men from other Israelite tribes; then their inheritance will be taken from our ancestral inheritance and added to that of the tribe they marry into. And so part of the inheritance allotted to us will be taken away. ⁴When the Year of Jubilee for the Israelites comes, their inheritance will be added to that of the tribe into which they marry, and their property will be taken from the tribal inheritance of our forefathers."

⁵Then at the LORD's command Moses gave this order to the Israelites: "What the tribe of the descendants of Joseph is saying is right. ⁶This is what the LORD commands for Zelophehad's daughters: They may marry anyone they please as long as they marry within the tribal clan of their father. ⁷No inheritance in Israel is to pass from tribe to tribe, for every Israelite shall keep the tribal land inherited from his forefathers. ⁸Every daughter who inherits land in any Israelite tribe must marry someone in her father's tribal clan, so that every Israelite will possess the inheritance of his fathers. ⁹No inheritance may pass from tribe to tribe, for each Israelite tribe is to keep the land it inherits."

¹⁰So Zelophehad's daughters did as the LORD commanded Moses. ¹¹Zelophehad's daughters—Mahlah, Tirzah, Hoglah, Milcah and Noah—married their cousins on their father's side. ¹²They married within the clans of the descendants of Manasseh son of Joseph, and their inheritance remained in their father's clan and tribe.

¹³These are the commands and regulations the LORD gave through Moses to the Israelites on the plains of Moab by the Jordan across from Jericho.ᵃ

ᵃ 13 Hebrew *Jordan of Jericho*; possibly an ancient name for the Jordan River

author:	Moses.
date:	About 1406 B.C.
setting:	Moses delivers his farewell speeches to the Israelites on the plains of Moab, east of the Jordan River.
verse to remember:	And now, O Israel, what does the LORD your God ask of you but to fear the LORD your God, to walk in all his ways, to love him, to serve the LORD your God with all your heart and with all your soul? (10:12).
theme to consider:	The book of Deuteronomy is a call to *remember* what God has done for you and then to *respond* with a renewed commitment.

deuteronomy

unchanging truth

How do you feel about thank-yous? When someone takes the time to say "thank-you," you know she appreciated what you did. Those two little words can make all your efforts seem worthwhile.

Receiving thanks is great, but how about giving it? When your pastor gives a sermon that really touches your heart, how do you respond? Or when a friend spends time to listen to your problem? Or how about when a guy pays you a genuine compliment—without an ulterior motive?

Sometimes it's harder to give thanks than to receive thanks. Maybe you're in a hurry, or it seems like a total mom-thing to do. But being genuinely thankful is never out of style. You can show thanks with a note or an e-mail or just by saying the words.

The book of Deuteronomy is all about remembering what God has done for his people and responding. The love relationship between God and his people is a recurring theme throughout the book. It's a call to total commitment to God in worship, obedience and yes, even saying thank-you, in response to his love and care.

This reminder of God's care and the call to commitment is not just for the Israelites, but it's also for all believers—including you! Think of all God's gifts to you. When was the last time you really thanked him for all he has done?

life lessons

1 No matter how rough the journey of life gets, God will be with you, and you won't lack anything (2:7).

2 We're constantly tempted to make other things or people more important than God. Will you pass the test (13:1–4)?

3 The same encouraging message Moses gave to Joshua applies to us as well—God will *always* be with us (31:8).

⌃

The Command to Leave Horeb

1 These are the words Moses spoke to all Israel in the desert east of the Jordan—that is, in the Arabah—opposite Suph, between Paran and Tophel, Laban, Hazeroth and Dizahab. ²(It takes eleven days to go from Horeb to Kadesh Barnea by the Mount Seir road.)

³In the fortieth year, on the first day of the eleventh month, Moses proclaimed to the Israelites all that the Lord had commanded him concerning them. ⁴This was after he had defeated Sihon king of the Amorites, who reigned in Heshbon, and at Edrei had defeated Og king of Bashan, who reigned in Ashtaroth.

⁵East of the Jordan in the territory of Moab, Moses began to expound this law, saying:

⁶The Lord our God said to us at Horeb, "You have stayed long enough at this mountain. ⁷Break camp and advance into the hill country of the Amorites; go to all the neighboring peoples in the Arabah, in the mountains, in the western foothills, in the Negev and along the coast, to the land of the Canaanites and to Lebanon, as far as the great river, the Euphrates. ⁸See, I have given you this land. Go in and take possession of the land that the Lord swore he would give to your fathers—to Abraham, Isaac and Jacob—and to their descendants after them."

The Appointment of Leaders

⁹At that time I said to you, "You are too heavy a burden for me to carry alone. ¹⁰The Lord your God has increased your numbers so that today you are as many as the stars in the sky. ¹¹May the Lord, the God of your fathers, increase you a thousand times and bless you as he has promised! ¹²But how can I bear your problems and your burdens and your disputes all by myself? ¹³Choose some wise, understanding and respected men from each of your tribes, and I will set them over you."

¹⁴You answered me, "What you propose to do is good."

¹⁵So I took the leading men of your tribes, wise and respected men, and appointed them to have authority over you— as commanders of thousands, of hundreds, of fifties and of tens and as tribal officials. ¹⁶And I charged your judges at that time: Hear the disputes between your brothers and judge fairly, whether the case is between brother Israelites or between one of them and an alien. ¹⁷Do not show partiality in judging; hear both small and great alike. Do not be afraid of any man, for judgment belongs to God. Bring me any case too hard for you, and I will hear it. ¹⁸And at that time I told you everything you were to do.

Spies Sent Out

¹⁹Then, as the Lord our God commanded us, we set out from Horeb and went toward the hill country of the Amorites through all that vast and dreadful desert that you have seen, and so we reached Kadesh Barnea. ²⁰Then I said to you, "You have reached the hill country of the Amorites, which the Lord our God is giving us. ²¹See, the Lord your God has given you the land. Go up and take possession of it as the Lord, the God of your fathers, told you. Do not be afraid; do not be discouraged."

²²Then all of you came to me and said, "Let us send men ahead to spy out the land for us and bring back a report about the route we are to take and the towns we will come to."

²³The idea seemed good to me; so I selected twelve of you, one man from each tribe. ²⁴They

genuine judgment » 1:16–17

Time to 'fess up. If you got elected to settle an argument between a hot guy you'd love to go out with and an obnoxious guy you always avoid at school, you'd side with contestant #1. Without a doubt, right? But God values all people equally, and he wants you to do the same—popular or not, in the same crowd as you or not, likeable or not. You might not often be in a situation to act as "judge," but deep down you pass judgment all the time. Don't look down on anyone—judge everyone fairly in your heart.

left and went up into the hill country, and came to the Valley of Eshcol and explored it. ²⁵Taking with them some of the fruit of the land, they brought it down to us and reported, "It is a good land that the LORD our God is giving us."

Rebellion Against the LORD

²⁶But you were unwilling to go up; you rebelled against the command of the LORD your God. ²⁷You grumbled in your tents and said, "The LORD hates us; so he brought us out of Egypt to deliver us into the hands of the Amorites to destroy us. ²⁸Where can we go? Our brothers have made us lose heart. They say, 'The people are stronger and taller than we are; the cities are large, with walls up to the sky. We even saw the Anakites there.' "

²⁹Then I said to you, "Do not be terrified; do not be afraid of them. ³⁰The LORD your God, who is going before you, will fight for you, as he did for you in Egypt, before your very eyes, ³¹and in the desert. There you saw how the LORD your God carried you, as a father carries his son, all the way you went until you reached this place."

³²In spite of this, you did not trust in the LORD your God, ³³who went ahead of you on your journey, in fire by night and in a cloud by day, to search out places for you to camp and to show you the way you should go.

³⁴When the LORD heard what you said, he was angry and solemnly swore: ³⁵"Not a man of this evil generation shall see the good land I swore to give your forefathers, ³⁶except Caleb son of Jephunneh. He will see it, and I will give him and his descendants the land he set his feet on, because he followed the LORD wholeheartedly."

³⁷Because of you the LORD became angry with me also and said, "You shall not enter it, either. ³⁸But your assistant, Joshua son of Nun, will enter it. Encourage him, because he will lead Israel to inherit it. ³⁹And the little ones that you said would be taken captive, your children who do not yet know good from bad—they will enter the land. I will give it to them and they will take possession of it. ⁴⁰But as for you, turn around and set out toward the desert along the route to the Red Sea.ᵃ"

⁴¹Then you replied, "We have sinned against the LORD. We will go up and fight, as the LORD our God commanded us." So every one of you put on his weapons, thinking it easy to go up into the hill country.

⁴²But the LORD said to me, "Tell them, 'Do not go up and fight, because I will not be with you. You will be defeated by your enemies.' "

⁴³So I told you, but you would not listen. You rebelled against the LORD's command and in your arrogance you marched up into the hill country. ⁴⁴The Amorites who lived in those hills came out against you; they chased you like a swarm of bees and beat you down from Seir all the way to Hormah. ⁴⁵You came back and wept before the LORD, but he paid no attention to your weeping and turned a deaf ear to you. ⁴⁶And so you stayed in Kadesh many days—all the time you spent there.

Wanderings in the Desert

2 Then we turned back and set out toward the desert along the route to the Red Sea,ᵃ as the LORD had directed me. For a long time we made our way around the hill country of Seir.

²Then the LORD said to me, ³"You have made your way around this hill country long enough; now turn north. ⁴Give the people these orders: 'You are about to pass through the territory of your brothers the descendants of Esau, who live in Seir. They will be afraid of you, but be very careful. ⁵Do not provoke them to war, for I will not give you any of their land, not even enough to put your foot on. I have given Esau the hill country of Seir as his own. ⁶You are to pay them in silver for the food you eat and the water you drink.' "

⁷The LORD your God has blessed you in all the work of your hands. He has watched over your journey through this vast desert. These forty years the LORD your God has been with you, and you have not lacked anything.

⁸So we went on past our brothers the descendants of Esau, who live in Seir. We turned from the Arabah road, which comes up from Elath and Ezion Geber, and traveled along the desert road of Moab.

ᵃ 40,1 Hebrew *Yam Suph*; that is, Sea of Reeds

⁹Then the LORD said to me, "Do not harass the Moabites or provoke them to war, for I will not give you any part of their land. I have given Ar to the descendants of Lot as a possession."

¹⁰(The Emites used to live there—a people strong and numerous, and as tall as the Anakites. ¹¹Like the Anakites, they too were considered Rephaites, but the Moabites called them Emites. ¹²Horites used to live in Seir, but the descendants of Esau drove them out. They destroyed the Horites from before them and settled in their place, just as Israel did in the land the LORD gave them as their possession.)

¹³And the LORD said, "Now get up and cross the Zered Valley." So we crossed the valley.

¹⁴Thirty-eight years passed from the time we left Kadesh Barnea until we crossed the Zered Valley. By then, that entire generation of fighting men had perished from the camp, as the LORD had sworn to them. ¹⁵The LORD's hand was against them until he had completely eliminated them from the camp.

¹⁶Now when the last of these fighting men among the people had died, ¹⁷the LORD said to me, ¹⁸"Today you are to pass by the region of Moab at Ar. ¹⁹When you come to the Ammonites, do not harass them or provoke them to war, for I will not give you possession of any land belonging to the Ammonites. I have given it as a possession to the descendants of Lot."

²⁰(That too was considered a land of the Rephaites, who used to live there; but the Ammonites called them Zamzummites. ²¹They were a people strong and numerous, and as tall as the Anakites. The LORD destroyed them from before the Ammonites, who drove them out and settled in their place. ²²The LORD had done the same for the descendants of Esau, who lived in Seir, when he destroyed the Horites from before them. They drove them out and have lived in their place to this day. ²³And as for the Avites who lived in villages as far as Gaza, the Caphtorites coming out from Caphtor*a* destroyed them and settled in their place.)

Defeat of Sihon King of Heshbon

²⁴"Set out now and cross the Arnon Gorge. See, I have given into your hand Sihon the Amorite, king of Heshbon, and his country. Begin to take possession of it and engage him in battle. ²⁵This very day I will begin to put the terror and fear of you on all the nations under heaven. They will hear reports of you and will tremble and be in anguish because of you."

²⁶From the desert of Kedemoth I sent messengers to Sihon king of Heshbon offering peace and saying, ²⁷"Let us pass through your country. We will stay on the main road; we will not turn aside to the right or to the left. ²⁸Sell us food to eat and water to drink for their price in silver. Only let us pass

love notes

2:7

Beloved,

Are you going through a desert right now? Feel like you're lost and alone? Remember that for 40 long years I watched over and cared for the Israelites. I will do the same and take care of you.

—Your Father in heaven

When have you gone through a "desert experience" (a hard time) in your life?

a 23 That is, Crete

through on foot— ²⁹as the descendants of Esau, who live in Seir, and the Moabites, who live in Ar, did for us—until we cross the Jordan into the land the LORD our God is giving us." ³⁰But Sihon king of Heshbon refused to let us pass through. For the LORD your God had made his spirit stubborn and his heart obstinate in order to give him into your hands, as he has now done.

³¹The LORD said to me, "See, I have begun to deliver Sihon and his country over to you. Now begin to conquer and possess his land."

³²When Sihon and all his army came out to meet us in battle at Jahaz, ³³the LORD our God delivered him over to us and we struck him down, together with his sons and his whole army. ³⁴At that time we took all his towns and completely destroyed *a* them—men, women and children. We left no survivors. ³⁵But the livestock and the plunder from the towns we had captured we carried off for ourselves. ³⁶From Aroer on the rim of the Arnon Gorge, and from the town in the gorge, even as far as Gilead, not one town was too strong for us. The LORD our God gave us all of them. ³⁷But in accordance with the command of the LORD our God, you did not encroach on any of the land of the Ammonites, neither the land along the course of the Jabbok nor that around the towns in the hills.

Defeat of Og King of Bashan

3 Next we turned and went up along the road toward Bashan, and Og king of Bashan with his whole army marched out to meet us in battle at Edrei. ²The LORD said to me, "Do not be afraid of him, for I have handed him over to you with his whole army and his land. Do to him what you did to Sihon king of the Amorites, who reigned in Heshbon."

³So the LORD our God also gave into our hands Og king of Bashan and all his army. We struck them down, leaving no survivors. ⁴At that time we took all his cities. There was not one of the sixty cities that we did not take from them—the whole region of Argob, Og's kingdom in Bashan. ⁵All these cities were fortified with high walls and with gates and bars, and there were also a great many unwalled villages. ⁶We completely destroyed *a* them, as we had done with Sihon king of Heshbon, destroying *a* every city—men, women and children. ⁷But all the livestock and the plunder from their cities we carried off for ourselves.

⁸So at that time we took from these two kings of the Amorites the territory east of the Jordan, from the Arnon Gorge as far as Mount Hermon. ⁹(Hermon is called Sirion by the Sidonians; the Amorites call it Senir.) ¹⁰We took all the towns on the plateau, and all Gilead, and all Bashan as far as Salecah and Edrei, towns of Og's kingdom in Bashan. ¹¹(Only Og king of Bashan was left of the remnant of the Rephaites. His bed *b* was made of iron and was more than thirteen feet long and six feet wide. *c* It is still in Rabbah of the Ammonites.)

Division of the Land

¹²Of the land that we took over at that time, I gave the Reubenites and the Gadites the territory north of Aroer by the Arnon Gorge, including half the hill country of Gilead, together with its towns. ¹³The rest of Gilead and also all of Bashan, the kingdom of Og, I gave to the half-tribe of Manasseh. (The whole region of Argob in Bashan used to be known as a land of the Rephaites. ¹⁴Jair, a descendant of Manasseh, took the whole region of Argob as far as the border of the Geshurites and the Maacathites; it was named after him, so that to this day Bashan is called Havvoth Jair. *d*) ¹⁵And I gave Gilead to Makir. ¹⁶But to the Reubenites and the Gadites I gave the territory extending from Gilead down to the Arnon Gorge (the middle of the gorge being the border) and out to the Jabbok River, which is the border of the Ammonites. ¹⁷Its western border was the Jordan in the Arabah, from Kinnereth to the Sea of the Arabah (the Salt Sea *e*), below the slopes of Pisgah.

¹⁸I commanded you at that time: "The LORD your God has given you this land to take possession of it. But all your able-bodied men, armed for battle, must cross over ahead of your brother Israelites. ¹⁹However, your wives, your children and your livestock (I know you have much livestock) may stay in the towns I have given you, ²⁰until the LORD gives rest to your brothers as he has to you, and they too have taken over the land that the LORD your God is giving them, across the Jordan. After that, each of you may go back to the possession I have given you."

---

a 34,6 The Hebrew term refers to the irrevocable giving over of things or persons to the LORD, often by totally destroying them. *b 11* Or *sarcophagus* *c 11* Hebrew *nine cubits long and four cubits wide* (about 4 meters long and 1.8 meters wide) *d 14* Or *called the settlements of Jair* *e 17* That is, the Dead Sea

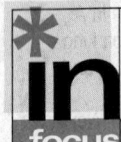

Hello, Anyone Up There?

"**S**ay your prayers," mom would say each night before I went to sleep as a child. It seemed so easy then—talking to God like he was really in the room with me. Now that I'm older, I feel like such an idiot. "Hello?! Anyone up there?" It's not like I think God isn't real, or he doesn't care about me—it's just I'm not convinced he *hears* me!

To make matters worse, I have friends who say they "feel" like God is right there with them when they pray. Good grief. Here God is having an all-out conversation with them, and meanwhile my experience is just the opposite—I don't feel or hear *anything*. So what am I doing wrong? It's like God has some cosmic caller ID, and he never takes my calls. Needless to say, lately I've stopped dialing.

My mom says I analyze too much and make things more complicated than they really are. She says I should just talk to God "like I'm talking to a friend." Easier said than done, Mom. At least I can *see* my friends! I know when they're listening, and I can actually hear them talk. I want to believe God hears me, but how do I know for sure? With everyone in the world talking to him at once, how can he possibly hear me anyway?

The Bible teaches us to pray and believe God hears us. Read more online at www.TrueImagesBible.com

prayer in focus

Prayer doesn't come easily to everyone. In fact, even the disciples asked Jesus for tips on how to pray better (see Luke 11:1, page 1383). And the psalms are full of David's cries for God to hear him (see Psalm 143, page 794). Also, keep in mind . . .

» Prayer is something you *learn* to do—like most everything else in life. Try some creativity while you practice—journaling your prayers, talking aloud, or even singing a praise song to God.

» Prayer is all about faith—believing God hears you even when it doesn't seem like it. He promises to hear you, so you have to trust in that.

For more on this topic, see the index on page 1656.

prayer

Moses Forbidden to Cross the Jordan

²¹At that time I commanded Joshua: "You have seen with your own eyes all that the Lord your God has done to these two kings. The Lord will do the same to all the kingdoms over there where you are going. ²²Do not be afraid of them; the Lord your God himself will fight for you."

²³At that time I pleaded with the Lord: ²⁴"O Sovereign Lord, you have begun to show to your servant your greatness and your strong hand. For what god is there in heaven or on earth who can do the deeds and mighty works you do? ²⁵Let me go over and see the good land beyond the Jordan—that fine hill country and Lebanon."

²⁶But because of you the Lord was angry with me and would not listen to me. "That is enough," the Lord said. "Do not speak to me anymore about this matter. ²⁷Go up to the top of Pisgah and look west and north and south and east. Look at the land with your own eyes, since you are not

going to cross this Jordan. ²⁸But commission Joshua, and encourage and strengthen him, for he will lead this people across and will cause them to inherit the land that you will see." ²⁹So we stayed in the valley near Beth Peor.

Obedience Commanded

4 Hear now, O Israel, the decrees and laws I am about to teach you. Follow them so that you may live and may go in and take possession of the land that the LORD, the God of your fathers, is giving you. ²Do not add to what I command you and do not subtract from it, but keep the commands of the LORD your God that I give you.

³You saw with your own eyes what the LORD did at Baal Peor. The LORD your God destroyed from among you everyone who followed the Baal of Peor, ⁴but all of you who held fast to the LORD your God are still alive today.

⁵See, I have taught you decrees and laws as the LORD my God commanded me, so that you may follow them in the land you are entering to take possession of it. ⁶Observe them carefully, for this will show your wisdom and understanding to the nations, who will hear about all these decrees and say, "Surely this great nation is a wise and understanding people." ⁷What other nation is so great as to have their gods near them the way the LORD our God is near us whenever we pray to him? ⁸And what other nation is so great as to have such righteous decrees and laws as this body of laws I am setting before you today?

⁹Only be careful, and watch yourselves closely so that you do not forget the things your eyes have seen or let them slip from your heart as long as you live. Teach them to your children and to their children after them. ¹⁰Remember the day you stood before the LORD your God at Horeb, when he said to me, "Assemble the people before me to hear my words so that they may learn to revere me as long as they live in the land and may teach them to their children." ¹¹You came near and stood at the foot of the mountain while it blazed with fire to the very heavens, with black clouds and deep darkness. ¹²Then the LORD spoke to you out of the fire. You heard the sound of words but saw no form; there was only a voice. ¹³He declared to you his covenant, the Ten Commandments, which he commanded you to follow and then wrote them on two stone tablets. ¹⁴And the LORD directed me at that time to teach you the decrees and laws you are to follow in the land that you are crossing the Jordan to possess.

Idolatry Forbidden

¹⁵You saw no form of any kind the day the LORD spoke to you at Horeb out of the fire. Therefore watch yourselves very carefully, ¹⁶so that you do not become corrupt and make for yourselves an idol, an image of any shape, whether formed like a man or a woman, ¹⁷or like any animal on earth or any bird that flies in the air, ¹⁸or like any creature that moves along the ground or any fish in the waters below. ¹⁹And when you look up to the sky and see the sun, the moon and the stars—all the heavenly array—do not be enticed into bowing down to them and worshiping things the LORD your God has apportioned to all the nations under heaven. ²⁰But as for you, the LORD took you and brought you out of the iron-smelting furnace, out of Egypt, to be the people of his inheritance, as you now are.

²¹The LORD was angry with me because of you, and he solemnly swore that I would not cross the Jordan and enter the good land the LORD your God is giving you as your inheritance. ²²I will die in this land; I will not cross the Jordan; but you are about to cross over and take possession of that

genuine prayer » 4:7

Our God is near us whenever we pray to him. How great is that?! He doesn't just *hear* us. He's right there *with* us! When you're eating lunch, or shopping, or working hard on the job—God is near you when you pray. When you find yourself faced with a hard choice and don't know what to do—God is near you when you pray. When you feel hurt and alone—God is near you when you pray. All the time, no matter what—don't forget that God is near you when you pray.

good land. ²³Be careful not to forget the covenant of the LORD your God that he made with you; do not make for yourselves an idol in the form of anything the LORD your God has forbidden. ²⁴For the LORD your God is a consuming fire, a jealous God.

²⁵After you have had children and grandchildren and have lived in the land a long time—if you then become corrupt and make any kind of idol, doing evil in the eyes of the LORD your God and provoking him to anger, ²⁶I call heaven and earth as witnesses against you this day that you will quickly perish from the land that you are crossing the Jordan to possess. You will not live there long but will certainly be destroyed. ²⁷The LORD will scatter you among the peoples, and only a few of you will survive among the nations to which the LORD will drive you. ²⁸There you will worship man-made gods of wood and stone, which cannot see or hear or eat or smell. ²⁹But if from there you seek the LORD your God, you will find him if you look for him with all your heart and with all your soul. ³⁰When you are in distress and all these things have happened to you, then in later days you will return to the LORD your God and obey him. ³¹For the LORD your God is a merciful God; he will not abandon or destroy you or forget the covenant with your forefathers, which he confirmed to them by oath.

The LORD Is God

³²Ask now about the former days, long before your time, from the day God created man on the earth; ask from one end of the heavens to the other. Has anything so great as this ever happened, or has anything like it ever been heard of? ³³Has any other people heard the voice of God*ᵃ* speaking out of fire, as you have, and lived? ³⁴Has any god ever tried to take for himself one nation out of another nation, by testings, by miraculous signs and wonders, by war, by a mighty hand and an outstretched arm, or by great and awesome deeds, like all the things the LORD your God did for you in Egypt before your very eyes?

³⁵You were shown these things so that you might know that the LORD is God; besides him there is no other. ³⁶From heaven he made you hear his voice to discipline you. On earth he showed you his great fire,

love notes

4:29

Dear daughter,

There's no mystery here, no un-solvable puzzle, no secret. Do you want to know me? I am knowable, and I want to be known. All you have to do is have the desire to search for me. I will be found.

—Father

What does it mean to seek the Lord with all your heart and soul?

truth or dare

Truth or dare? Yes. God *dares* you to discover the *truth* about who he is. There's no other god, and God is ready for your toughest scrutiny. Bring it on.

4:32–35

ᵃ 33 Or of a god

and you heard his words from out of the fire. [37]Because he loved your forefathers and chose their descendants after them, he brought you out of Egypt by his Presence and his great strength, [38]to drive out before you nations greater and stronger than you and to bring you into their land to give it to you for your inheritance, as it is today.

[39]Acknowledge and take to heart this day that the Lord is God in heaven above and on the earth below. There is no other. [40]Keep his decrees and commands, which I am giving you today, so that it may go well with you and your children after you and that you may live long in the land the Lord your God gives you for all time.

Cities of Refuge

[41]Then Moses set aside three cities east of the Jordan, [42]to which anyone who had killed a person could flee if he had unintentionally killed his neighbor without malice aforethought. He could flee into one of these cities and save his life. [43]The cities were these: Bezer in the desert plateau, for the Reubenites; Ramoth in Gilead, for the Gadites; and Golan in Bashan, for the Manassites.

Introduction to the Law

[44]This is the law Moses set before the Israelites. [45]These are the stipulations, decrees and laws Moses gave them when they came out of Egypt [46]and were in the valley near Beth Peor east of the Jordan, in the land of Sihon king of the Amorites, who reigned in Heshbon and was defeated by Moses and the Israelites as they came out of Egypt. [47]They took possession of his land and the land of Og king of Bashan, the two Amorite kings east of the Jordan. [48]This land extended from Aroer on the rim of the Arnon Gorge to Mount Siyon[a] (that is, Hermon), [49]and included all the Arabah east of the Jordan, as far as the Sea of the Arabah,[b] below the slopes of Pisgah.

The Ten Commandments

5 Moses summoned all Israel and said:
Hear, O Israel, the decrees and laws I declare in your hearing today. Learn them and be sure to follow them. [2]The Lord our God made a covenant with us at Horeb. [3]It was not with our fathers that the Lord made this covenant, but with us, with all of us who are alive here today. [4]The Lord spoke to you face to face out of the fire on the mountain. [5](At that time I stood between the Lord and you to declare to you the word of the Lord, because you were afraid of the fire and did not go up the mountain.) And he said:

[6]"I am the Lord your God, who brought you out of Egypt, out of the land of slavery.

[7]"You shall have no other gods before[c] me.

[8]"You shall not make for yourself an idol in the form of anything in heaven above or on the earth beneath or in the waters below. [9]You shall not bow down to them or worship them; for I, the Lord your God, am a jealous God, punishing the children for the sin of the fathers to the third and fourth generation of those who hate me, [10]but showing love to a thousand ⌊generations⌋ of those who love me and keep my commandments.

[11]"You shall not misuse the name of the Lord your God, for the Lord will not hold anyone guiltless who misuses his name.

[12]"Observe the Sabbath day by keeping it holy, as the Lord your God has commanded you. [13]Six days you shall labor and do all your work, [14]but the seventh day is a Sabbath to the Lord your God. On it you shall not do any work, neither you, nor your son or daughter, nor your manservant or maidservant, nor your ox, your donkey or any of your animals, nor the alien within your gates, so that your manservant and maidservant may rest, as you do. [15]Remember that you were slaves in Egypt and that the

truth or dare

Catch that? *Hear. Learn. Follow.* It's not enough to just do steps 1 and 2. Obedience—acting on what you hear and learn—that's the test of faith.

5:1

a 48 Hebrew; Syriac (see also Deut. 3:9) Sirion   b 49 That is, the Dead Sea   c 7 Or besides

LORD your God brought you out of there with a mighty hand and an outstretched arm. Therefore the LORD your God has commanded you to observe the Sabbath day.

¹⁶ "Honor your father and your mother, as the LORD your God has commanded you, so that you may live long and that it may go well with you in the land the LORD your God is giving you.

¹⁷ "You shall not murder.

¹⁸ "You shall not commit adultery.

¹⁹ "You shall not steal.

²⁰ "You shall not give false testimony against your neighbor.

²¹ "You shall not covet your neighbor's wife. You shall not set your desire on your neighbor's house or land, his manservant or maidservant, his ox or donkey, or anything that belongs to your neighbor."

²²These are the commandments the LORD proclaimed in a loud voice to your whole assembly there on the mountain from out of the fire, the cloud and the deep darkness; and he added nothing more. Then he wrote them on two stone tablets and gave them to me.

²³When you heard the voice out of the darkness, while the mountain was ablaze with fire, all the leading men of your tribes and your elders came to me. ²⁴And you said, "The LORD our God has shown us his glory and his majesty, and we have heard his voice from the fire. Today we have seen that a man can live even if God speaks with him. ²⁵But now, why should we die? This great fire will consume us, and we will die if we hear the voice of the LORD our God any longer. ²⁶For what mortal man has ever heard the voice of the living God speaking out of fire, as we have, and survived? ²⁷Go near and listen to all that the LORD our God says. Then tell us whatever the LORD our God tells you. We will listen and obey."

²⁸The LORD heard you when you spoke to me and the LORD said to me, "I have heard what this people said to you. Everything they said was good. ²⁹Oh, that their hearts would be inclined to fear me and keep all my commands always, so that it might go well with them and their children forever!

³⁰ "Go, tell them to return to their tents. ³¹But you stay here with me so that I may give you all the commands, decrees and laws you are to teach them to follow in the land I am giving them to possess."

³²So be careful to do what the LORD your God has commanded you; do not turn aside to the right or to the left. ³³Walk in all the way that the LORD your God has commanded you, so that you may live and prosper and prolong your days in the land that you will possess.

genuine obedience

Some people think being a Christian is all about following a heavy-duty list of rules. "Do this." "Don't do this." "Look like this." But God makes it clear that it's really about recognizing him for who he is and what he's done, and it means loving him with all that you are—heart, soul and strength. And yeah, God does have things he wants you to do or not do—but he wants you to obey him out of love and gratitude from your heart. That goes a lot deeper than a list of rules, don't you think?

6:4-6

Love the LORD Your God

6 These are the commands, decrees and laws the LORD your God directed me to teach you to observe in the land that you are crossing the Jordan to possess, ²so that you, your children and their children after them may fear the LORD your God as long as you live by keeping all his decrees and commands that I give you, and so that you may enjoy long life. ³Hear, O Israel, and be careful to obey so that it may go well with you and that you may increase greatly in a land flowing with milk and honey, just as the LORD, the God of your fathers, promised you.

⁴Hear, O Israel: The LORD our God, the LORD is one. ª ⁵Love the LORD your God with all your heart

---

ª 4 Or *The LORD our God is one LORD*; or *The LORD is our God, the LORD is one*; or *The LORD is our God, the LORD alone* and with all your soul and with all your strength. ⁶These commandments that I give you today are to be upon your hearts. ⁷Impress them on your children. Talk about them when you sit at home and when you walk along the road, when you lie down and when you get up. ⁸Tie them as symbols on your hands and bind them on your foreheads. ⁹Write them on the doorframes of your houses and on your gates.

¹⁰When the Lord your God brings you into the land he swore to your fathers, to Abraham, Isaac and Jacob, to give you—a land with large, flourishing cities you did not build, ¹¹houses filled with all kinds of good things you did not provide, wells you did not dig, and vineyards and olive groves you did not plant—then when you eat and are satisfied, ¹²be careful that you do not forget the Lord, who brought you out of Egypt, out of the land of slavery.

¹³Fear the Lord your God, serve him only and take your oaths in his name. ¹⁴Do not follow other gods, the gods of the peoples around you; ¹⁵for the Lord your God, who is among you, is a jealous God and his anger will burn against you, and he will destroy you from the face of the land. ¹⁶Do not test the Lord your God as you did at Massah. ¹⁷Be sure to keep the commands of the Lord your God and the stipulations and decrees he has given you. ¹⁸Do what is right and good in the Lord's sight, so that it may go well with you and you may go in and take over the good land that the Lord promised on oath to your forefathers, ¹⁹thrusting out all your enemies before you, as the Lord said.

²⁰In the future, when your son asks you, "What is the meaning of the stipulations, decrees and laws the Lord our God has commanded you?" ²¹tell him: "We were slaves of Pharaoh in Egypt, but the Lord brought us out of Egypt with a mighty hand. ²²Before our eyes the Lord sent miraculous signs and wonders—great and terrible—upon Egypt and Pharaoh and his whole household. ²³But he brought us out from there to bring us in and give us the land that he promised on oath to our forefathers. ²⁴The Lord commanded us to obey all these decrees and to fear the Lord our God, so that we might always prosper and be kept alive, as is the case today. ²⁵And if we are careful to obey all this law before the Lord our God, as he has commanded us, that will be our righteousness."

Driving Out the Nations

7 When the Lord your God brings you into the land you are entering to possess and drives out before you many nations—the Hittites, Girgashites, Amorites, Canaanites, Perizzites, Hivites and Jebusites, seven nations larger and stronger than you— ²and when the Lord your God has delivered them over to you and you have defeated them, then you must destroy them totally.ᵃ Make no treaty with them, and show them no mercy. ³Do not intermarry with them. Do not give your daughters to their sons or take their daughters for your sons, ⁴for they will turn your sons away from following me to serve other gods, and the Lord's anger will burn against you and will quickly destroy you. ⁵This is what you are to do to them: Break down their altars, smash their sacred stones, cut down their Asherah polesᵇ and burn their idols in the fire. ⁶For you are a people holy to the Lord your God. The Lord your God has chosen you out of all the peoples on the face of the earth to be his people, his treasured possession.

⁷The Lord did not set his affection on you and choose you because you were more numerous than other peoples, for you were the

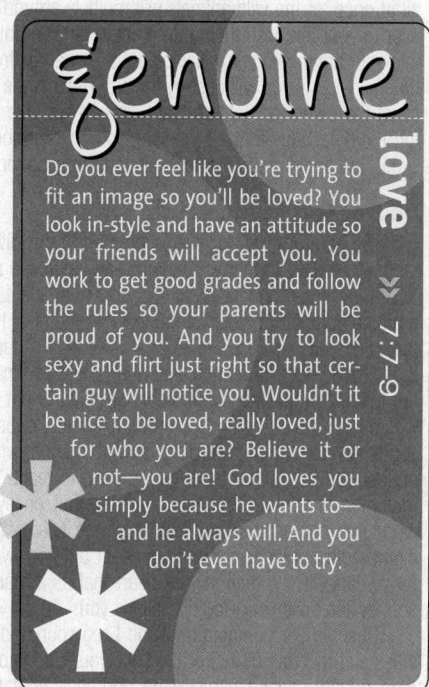

genuine love

7:7-9

Do you ever feel like you're trying to fit an image so you'll be loved? You look in-style and have an attitude so your friends will accept you. You work to get good grades and follow the rules so your parents will be proud of you. And you try to look sexy and flirt just right so that certain guy will notice you. Wouldn't it be nice to be loved, really loved, just for who you are? Believe it or not—you are! God loves you simply because he wants to—and he always will. And you don't even have to try.

ᵃ 2 The Hebrew term refers to the irrevocable giving over of things or persons to the Lord, often by totally destroying them; also in verse 26. ᵇ 5 That is, symbols of the goddess Asherah; here and elsewhere in Deuteronomy fewest of all peoples. [8]But it was because the LORD loved you and kept the oath he swore to your forefathers that he brought you out with a mighty hand and redeemed you from the land of slavery, from the power of Pharaoh king of Egypt. [9]Know therefore that the LORD your God is God; he is the faithful God, keeping his covenant of love to a thousand generations of those who love him and keep his commands. [10]But

> those who hate him he will repay to their face by destruction;
> he will not be slow to repay to their face those who hate him.

[11]Therefore, take care to follow the commands, decrees and laws I give you today.

[12]If you pay attention to these laws and are careful to follow them, then the LORD your God will keep his covenant of love with you, as he swore to your forefathers. [13]He will love you and bless you and increase your numbers. He will bless the fruit of your womb, the crops of your land—your grain, new wine and oil—the calves of your herds and the lambs of your flocks in the land that he swore to your forefathers to give you. [14]You will be blessed more than any other people; none of your men or women will be childless, nor any of your livestock without young. [15]The LORD will keep you free from every disease. He will not inflict on you the horrible diseases you knew in Egypt, but he will inflict them on all who hate you. [16]You must destroy all the peoples the LORD your God gives over to you. Do not look on them with pity and do not serve their gods, for that will be a snare to you.

[17]You may say to yourselves, "These nations are stronger than we are. How can we drive them out?" [18]But do not be afraid of them; remember well what the LORD your God did to Pharaoh and to all Egypt. [19]You saw with your own eyes the great trials, the miraculous signs and wonders, the mighty hand and outstretched arm, with which the LORD your God brought you out. The LORD your God will do the same to all the peoples you now fear. [20]Moreover, the LORD your God will send the hornet among them until even the survivors who hide from you have perished. [21]Do not be terrified by them, for the LORD your God, who is among you, is a great and awesome God. [22]The LORD your God will drive out those nations before you, little by little. You will not be allowed to eliminate them all at once, or the wild animals will multiply around you. [23]But the LORD your God will deliver them over to you, throwing them into great confusion until they are destroyed. [24]He will give their kings into your hand, and you will wipe out their names from under heaven. No one will be able to stand up against you; you will destroy them. [25]The images of their gods you are to burn in the fire. Do not covet the silver and gold on them, and do not take it for yourselves, or you will be ensnared by it, for it is detestable to the LORD your God. [26]Do not bring a detestable thing into your house or you, like it, will be set apart for destruction. Utterly abhor and detest it, for it is set apart for destruction.

Do Not Forget the LORD

8 Be careful to follow every command I am giving you today, so that you may live and increase and may enter and possess the land that the LORD promised on oath to your forefathers. [2]Remember how the LORD your God led you all the way in the desert these forty years, to humble you and to test you in order to know what was in your heart, whether or not you would keep his commands. [3]He humbled you, causing you to hunger and then feeding you with manna, which neither you nor your fathers had known, to teach you that man does not live on bread alone but on every word that comes from the mouth of the LORD. [4]Your clothes did not wear out and your feet did not swell during these forty years. [5]Know then in your heart that as a man disciplines his son, so the LORD your God disciplines you.

[6]Observe the commands of the LORD your God, walking in his ways and revering him. [7]For the LORD your God is bringing you into a good land—a land with streams and pools of water, with springs flowing in the valleys and hills; [8]a land with wheat and barley, vines and fig trees, pomegranates, olive oil and honey; [9]a land where bread will not be scarce and you will lack nothing; a land where the rocks are iron and you can dig copper out of the hills.

truth or dare

Eating a book for lunch? Sounds *so* appetizing! But seriously, God's Word *feeds* your spirit. It has the perfect ingredients for a healthy relationship with God. Stop running on empty!

8:3

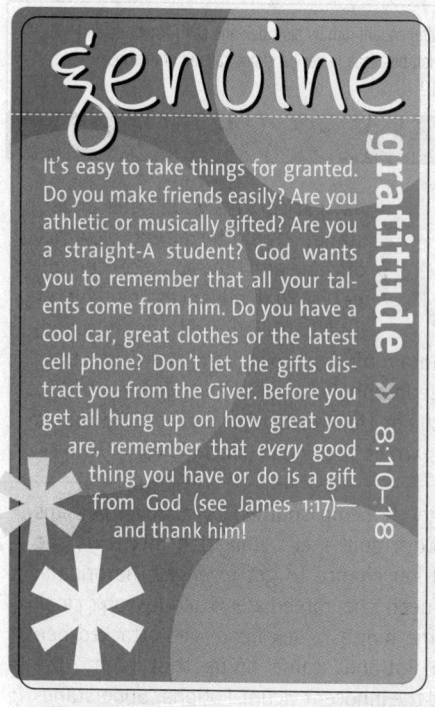

genuine

gratitude » 8:10-18

It's easy to take things for granted. Do you make friends easily? Are you athletic or musically gifted? Are you a straight-A student? God wants you to remember that all your talents come from him. Do you have a cool car, great clothes or the latest cell phone? Don't let the gifts distract you from the Giver. Before you get all hung up on how great you are, remember that *every* good thing you have or do is a gift from God (see James 1:17)—and thank him!

¹⁰When you have eaten and are satisfied, praise the Lord your God for the good land he has given you. ¹¹Be careful that you do not forget the Lord your God, failing to observe his commands, his laws and his decrees that I am giving you this day. ¹²Otherwise, when you eat and are satisfied, when you build fine houses and settle down, ¹³and when your herds and flocks grow large and your silver and gold increase and all you have is multiplied, ¹⁴then your heart will become proud and you will forget the Lord your God, who brought you out of Egypt, out of the land of slavery. ¹⁵He led you through the vast and dreadful desert, that thirsty and waterless land, with its venomous snakes and scorpions. He brought you water out of hard rock. ¹⁶He gave you manna to eat in the desert, something your fathers had never known, to humble and to test you so that in the end it might go well with you. ¹⁷You may say to yourself, "My power and the strength of my hands have produced this wealth for me." ¹⁸But remember the Lord your God, for it is he who gives you the ability to produce wealth, and so confirms his covenant, which he swore to your forefathers, as it is today.

¹⁹If you ever forget the Lord your God and follow other gods and worship and bow down to them, I testify against you today that you will surely be destroyed. ²⁰Like the nations the Lord destroyed before you, so you will be destroyed for not obeying the Lord your God.

Not Because of Israel's Righteousness

9 Hear, O Israel. You are now about to cross the Jordan to go in and dispossess nations greater and stronger than you, with large cities that have walls up to the sky. ²The people are strong and tall—Anakites! You know about them and have heard it said: "Who can stand up against the Anakites?" ³But be assured today that the Lord your God is the one who goes across ahead of you like a devouring fire. He will destroy them; he will subdue them before you. And you will drive them out and annihilate them quickly, as the Lord has promised you.

⁴After the Lord your God has driven them out before you, do not say to yourself, "The Lord has brought me here to take possession of this land because of my righteousness." No, it is on account of the wickedness of these nations that the Lord is going to drive them out before you. ⁵It is not because of your righteousness or your integrity that you are going in to take possession of their land; but on account of the wickedness of these nations, the Lord your God will drive them out before you, to accomplish what he swore to your fathers, to Abraham, Isaac and Jacob. ⁶Understand, then, that it is not·because of your righteousness that the Lord your God is giving you this good land to possess, for you are a stiff-necked people.

The Golden Calf

⁷Remember this and never forget how you provoked the Lord your God to anger in the desert. From the day you left Egypt until you arrived here, you have been rebellious against the Lord. ⁸At Horeb you aroused the Lord's wrath so that he was angry enough to destroy you. ⁹When I went up on the mountain to receive the tablets of stone, the tablets of the covenant that the Lord had made with you, I stayed on the mountain forty days and forty nights; I ate no bread and drank no water. ¹⁰The Lord gave me two stone tablets inscribed by the finger of God. On them were all the commandments the Lord proclaimed to you on the mountain out of the fire, on the day of the assembly.

mirror images

[Potiphar's wife] caught him by his cloak and said, "Come to bed with me!" But he left his cloak in her hand and ran out of the house. Genesis 39:12

Potiphar's Wife—Spin Queen

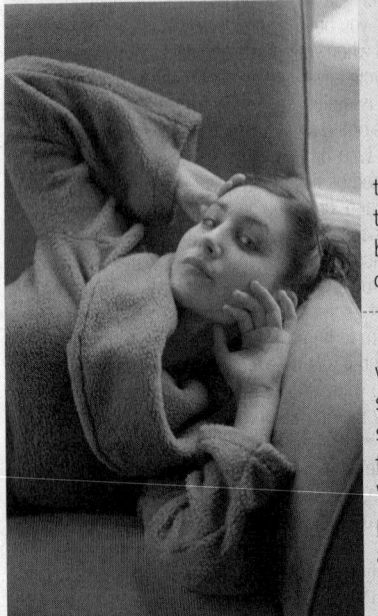

What part of "no" didn't she understand? Even after Joseph blew her off time and time again concerning her sexual advances, she didn't quit. Likely ignored by her husband, the captain of Pharaoh's guard, she finally tried to force Joseph (Potiphar's handsome servant) to be with her. He wrestled free and actually left his outer garment behind in her clutches.

Angry at being spurned by a slave, perhaps with both guilt and humiliation mixed in, she seized her chance to get revenge. The original spin queen, she immediately used Joseph's cloak to frame him as a sex fiend who attacked her. When Potiphar came home that night, she played the innocent victim. Potiphar understandably freaked out and sent Joseph to prison.

Okay, this woman had some serious issues. Yet can we catch a glimpse of ourselves in her actions? Trying to cover up our misdeeds? Back-pedaling when we do wrong? Shifting the blame? We have to admit that Potiphar's wife's strategies are alive and well today. "I didn't know there would be drinking at that party." "I didn't want to sneak out of the house—it was *her* idea." Stretching the truth to cover for ourselves is dangerously habit-forming. Ever had a "white" lie slip out—even when it would have been just as easy to tell the truth? That's scary enough. Then there's the fear of not remembering what lies we told to whom so we can keep our stories straight. The story of Potiphar's wife reminds us it's better to tell the truth than to spin it.

To read the next Mirror Images profile, go to page 244.

Dear God, I admit I often turn to my own devices when I do something wrong. I often want to spin the truth, not tell it. Forgive me and teach me the value of always telling the truth. Amen.

dear God

Read more about Potiphar's wife in Genesis 39 (pages 51–52).

[11]At the end of the forty days and forty nights, the LORD gave me the two stone tablets, the tablets of the covenant. [12]Then the LORD told me, "Go down from here at once, because your people whom you brought out of Egypt have become corrupt. They have turned away quickly from what I commanded them and have made a cast idol for themselves."

[13]And the LORD said to me, "I have seen this people, and they are a stiff-necked people indeed! [14]Let me alone, so that I may destroy them and blot out their name from under heaven. And I will make you into a nation stronger and more numerous than they."

[15]So I turned and went down from the mountain while it was ablaze with fire. And the two tablets of the covenant were in my hands.[a] [16]When I looked, I saw that you had sinned against the LORD your God; you had made for yourselves an idol cast in the shape of a calf. You had turned aside quickly from the way that the LORD had commanded you. [17]So I took the two tablets and threw them out of my hands, breaking them to pieces before your eyes.

[18]Then once again I fell prostrate before the LORD for forty days and forty nights; I ate no bread and drank no water, because of all the sin you had committed, doing what was evil in the LORD's sight and so provoking him to anger. [19]I feared the anger and wrath of the LORD, for he was angry enough with you to destroy you. But again the LORD listened to me. [20]And the LORD was angry enough with Aaron to destroy him, but at that time I prayed for Aaron too. [21]Also I took that sinful thing of yours, the calf you had made, and burned it in the fire. Then I crushed it and ground it to powder as fine as dust and threw the dust into a stream that flowed down the mountain.

[22]You also made the LORD angry at Taberah, at Massah and at Kibroth Hattaavah.

[23]And when the LORD sent you out from Kadesh Barnea, he said, "Go up and take possession of the land I have given you." But you rebelled against the command of the LORD your God. You did not trust him or obey him. [24]You have been rebellious against the LORD ever since I have known you.

[25]I lay prostrate before the LORD those forty days and forty nights because the LORD had said he would destroy you. [26]I prayed to the LORD and said, "O Sovereign LORD, do not destroy your people, your own inheritance that you redeemed by your great power and brought out of Egypt with a mighty hand. [27]Remember your servants Abraham, Isaac and Jacob. Overlook the stubbornness of this people, their wickedness and their sin. [28]Otherwise, the country from which you brought us will say, 'Because the LORD was not able to take them into the land he had promised them, and because he hated them, he brought them out to put them to death in the desert.' [29]But they are your people, your inheritance that you brought out by your great power and your outstretched arm."

Tablets Like the First Ones

10 At that time the LORD said to me, "Chisel out two stone tablets like the first ones and come up to me on the mountain. Also make a wooden chest.[b] [2]I will write on the tablets the words that were on the first tablets, which you broke. Then you are to put them in the chest."

[3]So I made the ark out of acacia wood and chiseled out two stone tablets like the first ones, and I went up on the mountain with the two tablets in my hands. [4]The LORD wrote on these tablets what he had written before, the Ten Commandments he had proclaimed to you on the mountain, out of the fire, on the day of the assembly. And the LORD gave them to me. [5]Then I came back down the mountain and put the tablets in the ark I had made, as the LORD commanded me, and they are there now.

[6](The Israelites traveled from the wells of the Jaakanites to Moserah. There Aaron died and was buried, and Eleazar his son succeeded him as priest. [7]From there they traveled to Gudgodah and on to Jotbathah, a land with streams of water. [8]At that time the LORD set apart the tribe of Levi to carry the ark of the covenant of the LORD, to stand before the LORD to minister and to pronounce blessings in his name, as they still do today. [9]That is why the Levites have no share or inheritance among their brothers; the LORD is their inheritance, as the LORD your God told them.)

[10]Now I had stayed on the mountain forty days and nights, as I did the first time, and the LORD listened to me at this time also. It was not his will to destroy you. [11]"Go," the LORD said to me, "and lead the people on their way, so that they may enter and possess the land that I swore to their fathers to give them."

---

[a] 15 Or And I had the two tablets of the covenant with me, one in each hand   [b] 1 That is, an ark

Fear the LORD

[12]And now, O Israel, what does the LORD your God ask of you but to fear the LORD your God, to walk in all his ways, to love him, to serve the LORD your God with all your heart and with all your soul, [13]and to observe the LORD's commands and decrees that I am giving you today for your own good?

[14]To the LORD your God belong the heavens, even the highest heavens, the earth and everything in it. [15]Yet the LORD set his affection on your forefathers and loved them, and he chose you, their descendants, above all the nations, as it is today. [16]Circumcise your hearts, therefore, and do not be stiff-necked any longer. [17]For the LORD your God is God of gods and Lord of lords, the great God, mighty and awesome, who shows no partiality and accepts no bribes. [18]He defends the cause of the fatherless and the widow, and loves the alien, giving him food and clothing. [19]And you are to love those who are aliens, for you yourselves were aliens in Egypt. [20]Fear the LORD your God and serve him. Hold fast to him and take your oaths in his name. [21]He is your praise; he is your God, who performed for you those great and awesome wonders you saw with your own eyes. [22]Your forefathers who went down into Egypt were seventy in all, and now the LORD your God has made you as numerous as the stars in the sky.

Love and Obey the LORD

11 Love the LORD your God and keep his requirements, his decrees, his laws and his commands always. [2]Remember today that your children were not the ones who saw and experienced the discipline of the LORD your God: his majesty, his mighty hand, his outstretched arm; [3]the signs he performed and the things he did in the heart of Egypt, both to Pharaoh king of Egypt and to his whole country; [4]what he did to the Egyptian army, to its horses and chariots, how he overwhelmed them with the waters of the Red Sea[a] as they were pursuing you, and how the LORD brought lasting ruin on them. [5]It was not your children who saw what he did for you in the desert until you ar-

love notes

10:17–22

My child,

Know this: My love and mercy are infinite. My love extends to all who come to me—the disabled, the weak, the fatherless, the unlovely, the strangers, the sinners. (You fall into at least that last category, dear.) Always know that I love you.

—Your loving Father

Write a prayer of thanks to God for his incredible love.

truth or dare

Oh, that's all the Lord requires of me? Hello! Can you say *impossible?!* God's "short" list of requirements looks intimidating. That's where God's grace and his strength come in. Phew!

10:12–13

a 4 Hebrew *Yam Suph*; that is, Sea of Reeds

rived at this place, [6]and what he did to Dathan and Abiram, sons of Eliab the Reubenite, when the earth opened its mouth right in the middle of all Israel and swallowed them up with their households, their tents and every living thing that belonged to them. [7]But it was your own eyes that saw all these great things the LORD has done.

[8]Observe therefore all the commands I am giving you today, so that you may have the strength to go in and take over the land that you are crossing the Jordan to possess, [9]and so that you may live long in the land that the LORD swore to your forefathers to give to them and their descendants, a land flowing with milk and honey. [10]The land you are entering to take over is not like the land of Egypt, from which you have come, where you planted your seed and irrigated it by foot as in a vegetable garden. [11]But the land you are crossing the Jordan to take possession of is a land of mountains and valleys that drinks rain from heaven. [12]It is a land the LORD your God cares for; the eyes of the LORD your God are continually on it from the beginning of the year to its end.

[13]So if you faithfully obey the commands I am giving you today—to love the LORD your God and to serve him with all your heart and with all your soul— [14]then I will send rain on your land in its season, both autumn and spring rains, so that you may gather in your grain, new wine and oil. [15]I will provide grass in the fields for your cattle, and you will eat and be satisfied.

[16]Be careful, or you will be enticed to turn away and worship other gods and bow down to them. [17]Then the LORD's anger will burn against you, and he will shut the heavens so that it will not rain and the ground will yield no produce, and you will soon perish from the good land the LORD is giving you. [18]Fix these words of mine in your hearts and minds; tie them as symbols on your hands and bind them on your foreheads.

[19]Teach them to your children, talking about them when you sit at home and when you walk along the road, when you lie down and when you get up. [20]Write them on the doorframes of your houses and on your gates, [21]so that your days and the days of your children may be many in the land that the LORD swore to give your forefathers, as many as the days that the heavens are above the earth.

[22]If you carefully observe all these commands I am giving you to follow—to love the LORD your God, to walk in all his ways and to hold fast to him— [23]then the LORD will drive out all these nations before you, and you will dispossess nations larger and stronger than you. [24]Every place where you set your foot will be yours: Your territory will extend from the desert to Lebanon, and from the Euphrates River to the western sea.[a] [25]No man will be able to stand against you. The LORD your God, as he promised you, will put the terror and fear of you on the whole land, wherever you go.

[26]See, I am setting before you today a blessing and a curse— [27]the blessing if you obey the commands of the LORD your God that I am giving you today; [28]the curse if you disobey the commands of the LORD your God

---

truth or dare

Having trouble cramming a Bible in your backpack? Simple solution: Start memorizing verses! When tough situations crop up, you'll be ready to stamp them down with God's words of truth.

11:18

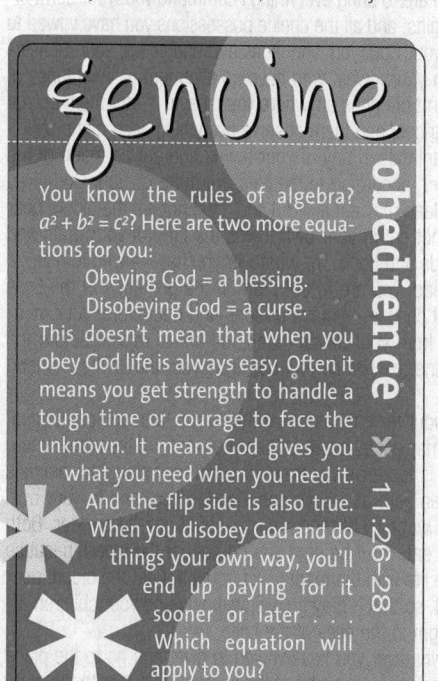

genuine

obedience »» 11:26-28

You know the rules of algebra? $a^2 + b^2 = c^2$? Here are two more equations for you:

Obeying God = a blessing.
Disobeying God = a curse.

This doesn't mean that when you obey God life is always easy. Often it means you get strength to handle a tough time or courage to face the unknown. It means God gives you what you need when you need it. And the flip side is also true. When you disobey God and do things your own way, you'll end up paying for it sooner or later . . . Which equation will apply to you?

---

a 24 That is, the Mediterranean

and turn from the way that I command you today by following other gods, which you have not known. ²⁹When the LORD your God has brought you into the land you are entering to possess, you are to proclaim on Mount Gerizim the blessings, and on Mount Ebal the curses. ³⁰As you know, these mountains are across the Jordan, west of the road,ᵃ toward the setting sun, near the great trees of Moreh, in the territory of those Canaanites living in the Arabah in the vicinity of Gilgal. ³¹You are about to cross the Jordan to enter and take possession of the land the LORD your God is giving you. When you have taken it over and are living there, ³²be sure that you obey all the decrees and laws I am setting before you today.

The One Place of Worship

12 These are the decrees and laws you must be careful to follow in the land that the LORD, the God of your fathers, has given you to possess—as long as you live in the land. ²Destroy completely all the places on the high mountains and on the hills and under every spreading tree where the nations you are dispossessing worship their gods. ³Break down their altars, smash their sacred stones and burn their Asherah poles in the fire; cut down the idols of their gods and wipe out their names from those places.

⁴You must not worship the LORD your God in their way. ⁵But you are to seek the place the LORD your God will choose from among all your tribes to put his Name there for his dwelling. To that place you must go; ⁶there bring your burnt offerings and sacrifices, your tithes and special gifts, what you have vowed to give and your freewill offerings, and the firstborn of your herds and flocks. ⁷There, in the presence of the LORD your God, you and your families shall eat and shall rejoice in everything you have put your hand to, because the LORD your God has blessed you.

⁸You are not to do as we do here today, everyone as he sees fit, ⁹since you have not yet reached the resting place and the inheritance the LORD your God is giving you. ¹⁰But you will cross the Jordan and settle in the land the LORD your God is giving you as an inheritance, and he will give you rest from all your enemies around you so that you will live in safety. ¹¹Then to the place the LORD your God will choose as a dwelling for his Name—there you are to bring everything I command you: your burnt offerings and sacrifices, your tithes and special gifts, and all the choice possessions you have vowed to the LORD. ¹²And there rejoice before the LORD your God, you, your sons and daughters, your menservants and maidservants, and the Levites from your towns, who have no allotment or inheritance of their own. ¹³Be careful not to sacrifice your burnt offerings anywhere you please. ¹⁴Offer them only at the place the LORD will choose in one of your tribes, and there observe everything I command you.

¹⁵Nevertheless, you may slaughter your animals in any of your towns and eat as much of the meat as you want, as if it were gazelle or deer, according to the blessing the LORD your God gives you. Both the ceremonially unclean and the clean may eat it. ¹⁶But you must not eat the blood; pour it out on the ground like water. ¹⁷You must not eat in your own towns the tithe of your grain and new wine and oil, or the firstborn of your herds and flocks, or whatever you have vowed to give, or your freewill offerings or special gifts. ¹⁸Instead, you are to eat them in the presence of the LORD your God at the place the LORD your God will choose—you, your sons and daughters, your menservants and maidservants, and the Levites from your towns—and you are to rejoice before the LORD your God in everything you put your hand to. ¹⁹Be careful not to neglect the Levites as long as you live in your land.

²⁰When the LORD your God has enlarged your territory as he promised you, and you crave meat and say, "I would like some meat," then you may eat as much of it as you want. ²¹If the place where the LORD your God chooses to put his Name is too far away from you, you may slaughter animals from the herds and flocks the LORD has given you, as I have commanded you, and in your own towns you may eat as much of them as you want. ²²Eat them as you would gazelle or deer. Both the ceremonially unclean and the clean may eat. ²³But be sure you do not eat the blood, because the blood is the life, and you must not eat the life with the meat. ²⁴You must not eat the blood; pour it out on the ground like water. ²⁵Do not eat it, so that it may go well with you and your children after you, because you will be doing what is right in the eyes of the LORD.

²⁶But take your consecrated things and whatever you have vowed to give, and go to the place the LORD will choose. ²⁷Present your burnt offerings on the altar of the LORD your God, both the meat and the blood. The blood of your sacrifices must be poured beside the altar of the LORD your God,

ᵃ 30 Or Jordan, westward

truth or dare

Math 101: adding to or subtracting from God's laws = wrong answers! God has already calculated the best method for you to live. Follow his equation for life.

12:32

but you may eat the meat. [28]Be careful to obey all these regulations I am giving you, so that it may always go well with you and your children after you, because you will be doing what is good and right in the eyes of the LORD your God.

[29]The LORD your God will cut off before you the nations you are about to invade and dispossess. But when you have driven them out and settled in their land, [30]and after they have been destroyed before you, be careful not to be ensnared by inquiring about their gods, saying, "How do these nations serve their gods? We will do the same." [31]You must not worship the LORD your God in their way, because in worshiping their gods, they do all kinds of detestable things the LORD hates. They even burn their sons and daughters in the fire as sacrifices to their gods.

[32]See that you do all I command you; do not add to it or take away from it.

Worshiping Other Gods

13 If a prophet, or one who foretells by dreams, appears among you and announces to you a miraculous sign or wonder, [2]and if the sign or wonder of which he has spoken takes place, and he says, "Let us follow other gods" (gods you have not known) "and let us worship them," [3]you must not listen to the words of that prophet or dreamer. The LORD your God is testing you to find out whether you love him with all your heart and with all your soul. [4]It is the LORD your God you must follow, and him you must revere. Keep his commands and obey him; serve him and hold fast to him. [5]That prophet or dreamer must be put to death, because he preached rebellion against the LORD your God, who brought you out of Egypt and redeemed you from the land of slavery; he has tried to turn you from the way the LORD your God commanded you to follow. You must purge the evil from among you.

[6]If your very own brother, or your son or daughter, or the wife you love, or your closest friend secretly entices you, saying, "Let us go and worship other gods" (gods that neither you nor your fathers have known, [7]gods of the peoples around you, whether near or far, from one end of the land to the other), [8]do not yield to him or listen to him. Show him no pity. Do not spare him or shield him. [9]You must certainly put him to death. Your hand must be the first in putting him to death, and then the hands of all the people. [10]Stone him to death, because he tried to turn you away from the LORD your God, who brought you out of Egypt, out of the land of slavery. [11]Then all Israel will hear and be afraid, and no one among you will do such an evil thing again.

[12]If you hear it said about one of the towns the LORD your God is giving you to live in [13]that wicked men have arisen among you and have led the people of their town astray, saying, "Let us go and worship other gods" (gods you have not known), [14]then you must inquire, probe and investigate it thoroughly. And if it is true and it has been proved that this detestable thing has been done among you, [15]you must certainly put to the sword all who live in that town. Destroy it completely,[a] both its people and its livestock. [16]Gather all the plunder of the town into the middle of the public square and completely burn the town and all its plunder as a whole burnt offering to the LORD your God. It is to remain a ruin forever, never to be rebuilt. [17]None of those condemned things[a] shall be found in your hands, so that the LORD will turn from his fierce anger; he will show you mercy, have compas-

truth or dare

There's nothing wrong with having friends or family who aren't believers. Your life can lead them to God. However, if someone steps *between* you and God, sound the retreat.

13:6–8

---

[a] 15,17 The Hebrew term refers to the irrevocable giving over of things or persons to the LORD, often by totally destroying them.

sion on you, and increase your numbers, as he promised on oath to your forefathers, [18]because you obey the LORD your God, keeping all his commands that I am giving you today and doing what is right in his eyes.

Clean and Unclean Food

14 You are the children of the LORD your God. Do not cut yourselves or shave the front of your heads for the dead, [2]for you are a people holy to the LORD your God. Out of all the peoples on the face of the earth, the LORD has chosen you to be his treasured possession.

[3]Do not eat any detestable thing. [4]These are the animals you may eat: the ox, the sheep, the goat, [5]the deer, the gazelle, the roe deer, the wild goat, the ibex, the antelope and the mountain sheep.[a] [6]You may eat any animal that has a split hoof divided in two and that chews the cud. [7]However, of those that chew the cud or that have a split hoof completely divided you may not eat the camel, the rabbit or the coney.[b] Although they chew the cud, they do not have a split hoof; they are ceremonially unclean for you. [8]The pig is also unclean; although it has a split hoof, it does not chew the cud. You are not to eat their meat or touch their carcasses.

[9]Of all the creatures living in the water, you may eat any that has fins and scales. [10]But anything that does not have fins and scales you may not eat; for you it is unclean.

[11]You may eat any clean bird. [12]But these you may not eat: the eagle, the vulture, the black vulture, [13]the red kite, the black kite, any kind of falcon, [14]any kind of raven, [15]the horned owl, the screech owl, the gull, any kind of hawk, [16]the little owl, the great owl, the white owl, [17]the desert owl, the osprey, the cormorant, [18]the stork, any kind of heron, the hoopoe and the bat.

[19]All flying insects that swarm are unclean to you; do not eat them. [20]But any winged creature that is clean you may eat.

[21]Do not eat anything you find already dead. You may give it to an alien living in any of your towns, and he may eat it, or you may sell it to a foreigner. But you are a people holy to the LORD your God.

Do not cook a young goat in its mother's milk.

Tithes

[22]Be sure to set aside a tenth of all that your fields produce each year. [23]Eat the tithe of your grain, new wine and oil, and the firstborn of your herds and flocks in the presence of the LORD your God at the place he will choose as a dwelling for his Name, so that you may learn to revere the LORD your God always. [24]But if that place is too distant and you have been blessed by the LORD your God and cannot carry your tithe (because the place where the LORD will choose to put his Name is so far away), [25]then exchange your tithe for silver, and take the silver with you and go to the place the LORD your God will choose. [26]Use the silver to buy whatever you like: cattle, sheep, wine or other fermented drink, or anything you wish. Then you and your household shall eat there in the presence of the LORD your God and rejoice. [27]And do not neglect the Levites living in your towns, for they have no allotment or inheritance of their own.

[28]At the end of every three years, bring all the tithes of that year's produce and store it in your towns, [29]so that the Levites (who have no allotment or inheritance of their own) and the aliens, the fatherless and the widows who live in your towns may come and eat and be satisfied, and so that the LORD your God may bless you in all the work of your hands.

The Year for Canceling Debts

15 At the end of every seven years you must cancel debts. [2]This is how it is to be done: Every creditor shall cancel the loan he has made to his fellow Israelite. He shall not require payment from his fellow Israelite or brother, because the LORD's time for cancel-

truth or dare

Paycheck time! How often is *tithing* the first thing on your mind? Bypass the urge to splurge by setting aside your offering *first*. This keeps God #1 in your heart.

14:22

[a] 5 The precise identification of some of the birds and animals in this chapter is uncertain.   [b] 7 That is, the hyrax or rock badger

ing debts has been proclaimed. ³You may require payment from a foreigner, but you must cancel any debt your brother owes you. ⁴However, there should be no poor among you, for in the land the Lord your God is giving you to possess as your inheritance, he will richly bless you, ⁵if only you fully obey the Lord your God and are careful to follow all these commands I am giving you today. ⁶For the Lord your God will bless you as he has promised, and you will lend to many nations but will borrow from none. You will rule over many nations but none will rule over you.

⁷If there is a poor man among your brothers in any of the towns of the land that the Lord your God is giving you, do not be hardhearted or tightfisted toward your poor brother. ⁸Rather be openhanded and freely lend him whatever he needs. ⁹Be careful not to harbor this wicked thought: "The seventh year, the year for canceling debts, is near," so that you do not show ill will toward your needy brother and give him nothing. He may then appeal to the Lord against you, and you will be found guilty of sin. ¹⁰Give generously to him and do so without a grudging heart; then because of this the Lord your God will bless you in all your work and in everything you put your hand to. ¹¹There will always be poor people in the land. Therefore I command you to be openhanded toward your brothers and toward the poor and needy in your land.

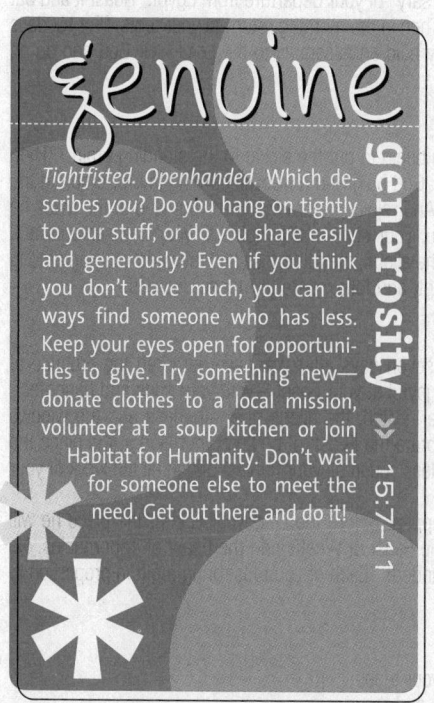

genuine

generosity » 15:7–11

Tightfisted. Openhanded. Which describes *you?* Do you hang on tightly to your stuff, or do you share easily and generously? Even if you think you don't have much, you can always find someone who has less. Keep your eyes open for opportunities to give. Try something new— donate clothes to a local mission, volunteer at a soup kitchen or join Habitat for Humanity. Don't wait for someone else to meet the need. Get out there and do it!

Freeing Servants

¹²If a fellow Hebrew, a man or a woman, sells himself to you and serves you six years, in the seventh year you must let him go free. ¹³And when you release him, do not send him away empty-handed. ¹⁴Supply him liberally from your flock, your threshing floor and your winepress. Give to him as the Lord your God has blessed you. ¹⁵Remember that you were slaves in Egypt and the Lord your God redeemed you. That is why I give you this command today.

¹⁶But if your servant says to you, "I do not want to leave you," because he loves you and your family and is well off with you, ¹⁷then take an awl and push it through his ear lobe into the door, and he will become your servant for life. Do the same for your maidservant.

¹⁸Do not consider it a hardship to set your servant free, because his service to you these six years has been worth twice as much as that of a hired hand. And the Lord your God will bless you in everything you do.

The Firstborn Animals

¹⁹Set apart for the Lord your God every firstborn male of your herds and flocks. Do not put the firstborn of your oxen to work, and do not shear the firstborn of your sheep. ²⁰Each year you and your family are to eat them in the presence of the Lord your God at the place he will choose. ²¹If an animal has a defect, is lame or blind, or has any serious flaw, you must not sacrifice it to the Lord your God. ²²You are to eat it in your own towns. Both the ceremonially unclean and the clean may eat it, as if it were gazelle or deer. ²³But you must not eat the blood; pour it out on the ground like water.

Passover

16 Observe the month of Abib and celebrate the Passover of the Lord your God, because in the month of Abib he brought you out of Egypt by night. ²Sacrifice as the Passover to the Lord your God an animal from your flock or herd at the place the Lord will choose as a dwelling for his Name. ³Do not eat it with bread made with yeast, but for seven days eat unleavened bread, the bread of affliction, because you left Egypt in haste—so that all the days of your life you may remember the time of your departure from Egypt. ⁴Let no yeast be found in your possession in all your land for seven days. Do not let any of the meat you sacrifice on the evening of the first day remain until morning.

⁵You must not sacrifice the Passover in any town the LORD your God gives you ⁶except in the place he will choose as a dwelling for his Name. There you must sacrifice the Passover in the evening, when the sun goes down, on the anniversary*ᵃ* of your departure from Egypt. ⁷Roast it and eat it at the place the LORD your God will choose. Then in the morning return to your tents. ⁸For six days eat unleavened bread and on the seventh day hold an assembly to the LORD your God and do no work.

Feast of Weeks

⁹Count off seven weeks from the time you begin to put the sickle to the standing grain. ¹⁰Then celebrate the Feast of Weeks to the LORD your God by giving a freewill offering in proportion to the blessings the LORD your God has given you. ¹¹And rejoice before the LORD your God at the place he will choose as a dwelling for his Name—you, your sons and daughters, your menservants and maidservants, the Levites in your towns, and the aliens, the fatherless and the widows living among you. ¹²Remember that you were slaves in Egypt, and follow carefully these decrees.

Feast of Tabernacles

¹³Celebrate the Feast of Tabernacles for seven days after you have gathered the produce of your threshing floor and your winepress. ¹⁴Be joyful at your Feast—you, your sons and daughters, your menservants and maidservants, and the Levites, the aliens, the fatherless and the widows who live in your towns. ¹⁵For seven days celebrate the Feast to the LORD your God at the place the LORD will choose. For the LORD your God will bless you in all your harvest and in all the work of your hands, and your joy will be complete.

¹⁶Three times a year all your men must appear before the LORD your God at the place he will choose: at the Feast of Unleavened Bread, the Feast of Weeks and the Feast of Tabernacles. No man should appear before the LORD empty-handed: ¹⁷Each of you must bring a gift in proportion to the way the LORD your God has blessed you.

Judges

¹⁸Appoint judges and officials for each of your tribes in every town the LORD your God is giving you, and they shall judge the people fairly. ¹⁹Do not pervert justice or show partiality. Do not accept a bribe, for a bribe blinds the eyes of the wise and twists the words of the righteous. ²⁰Follow justice and justice alone, so that you may live and possess the land the LORD your God is giving you.

Worshiping Other Gods

²¹Do not set up any wooden Asherah pole*ᵇ* beside the altar you build to the LORD your God, ²²and do not erect a sacred stone, for these the LORD your God hates.

17 Do not sacrifice to the LORD your God an ox or a sheep that has any defect or flaw in it, for that would be detestable to him.

²If a man or woman living among you in one of the towns the LORD gives you is found doing evil in the eyes of the LORD your God in violation of his covenant, ³and contrary to my command has worshiped other gods, bowing down to them or to the sun or the moon or the stars of the sky, ⁴and this has been brought to your attention, then you must investigate it thoroughly. If it is true and it has been proved that this detestable thing has been done in Israel, ⁵take the man or woman who has done this evil deed to your city gate and stone that person to death.

truth or dare

Ugh ... leftovers *again!* Don't you hate getting the scraps, wearing hand-me-down clothes, being treated as second best? So does God. Imagine how he feels when he gets your *left-over* time and attention.

17:1

ᵃ 6 Or down, at the time of day · ᵇ 21 Or Do not plant any tree dedicated to Asherah

⁶On the testimony of two or three witnesses a man shall be put to death, but no one shall be put to death on the testimony of only one witness. ⁷The hands of the witnesses must be the first in putting him to death, and then the hands of all the people. You must purge the evil from among you.

Law Courts

⁸If cases come before your courts that are too difficult for you to judge—whether bloodshed, lawsuits or assaults—take them to the place the LORD your God will choose. ⁹Go to the priests, who are Levites, and to the judge who is in office at that time. Inquire of them and they will give you the verdict. ¹⁰You must act according to the decisions they give you at the place the LORD will choose. Be careful to do everything they direct you to do. ¹¹Act according to the law they teach you and the decisions they give you. Do not turn aside from what they tell you, to the right or to the left. ¹²The man who shows contempt for the judge or for the priest who stands ministering there to the LORD your God must be put to death. You must purge the evil from Israel. ¹³All the people will hear and be afraid, and will not be contemptuous again.

The King

¹⁴When you enter the land the LORD your God is giving you and have taken possession of it and settled in it, and you say, "Let us set a king over us like all the nations around us," ¹⁵be sure to appoint over you the king the LORD your God chooses. He must be from among your own brothers. Do not place a foreigner over you, one who is not a brother Israelite. ¹⁶The king, moreover, must not acquire great numbers of horses for himself or make the people return to Egypt to get more of them, for the LORD has told you, "You are not to go back that way again." ¹⁷He must not take many wives, or his heart will be led astray. He must not accumulate large amounts of silver and gold.

¹⁸When he takes the throne of his kingdom, he is to write for himself on a scroll a copy of this law, taken from that of the priests, who are Levites. ¹⁹It is to be with him, and he is to read it all the days of his life so that he may learn to revere the LORD his God and follow carefully all the words of this law and these decrees ²⁰and not consider himself better than his brothers and turn from the law to the right or to the left. Then he and his descendants will reign a long time over his kingdom in Israel.

Offerings for Priests and Levites

18 The priests, who are Levites—indeed the whole tribe of Levi—are to have no allotment or inheritance with Israel. They shall live on the offerings made to the LORD by fire, for that is their inheritance. ²They shall have no inheritance among their brothers; the LORD is their inheritance, as he promised them.

³This is the share due the priests from the people who sacrifice a bull or a sheep: the shoulder, the jowls and the inner parts. ⁴You are to give them the firstfruits of your grain, new wine and oil, and the first wool from the shearing of your sheep, ⁵for the LORD your God has chosen them and their descendants out of all your tribes to stand and minister in the LORD's name always.

⁶If a Levite moves from one of your towns anywhere in Israel where he is living, and comes in all earnestness to the place the LORD will choose, ⁷he may minister in the name of the LORD his God like all his fellow Levites who serve there in the presence of the LORD. ⁸He is to share equally in their benefits, even though he has received money from the sale of family possessions.

Detestable Practices

⁹When you enter the land the LORD your God is giving you, do not learn to imitate the detestable ways of the nations there. ¹⁰Let no one be found among you who sacrifices his son or daughter in[a] the fire, who

truth or dare

The new trends in witchcraft involve more nature-loving pixies than pointy, black hats. However, the *message*—trying to gain power over God and his creation—hasn't changed.

18:9–13

---

a 10 Or *who makes his son or daughter pass through*

practices divination or sorcery, interprets omens, engages in witchcraft, ¹¹or casts spells, or who is a medium or spiritist or who consults the dead. ¹²Anyone who does these things is detestable to the LORD, and because of these detestable practices the LORD your God will drive out those nations before you. ¹³You must be blameless before the LORD your God.

The Prophet

¹⁴The nations you will dispossess listen to those who practice sorcery or divination. But as for you, the LORD your God has not permitted you to do so. ¹⁵The LORD your God will raise up for you a prophet like me from among your own brothers. You must listen to him. ¹⁶For this is what you asked of the LORD your God at Horeb on the day of the assembly when you said, "Let us not hear the voice of the LORD our God nor see this great fire anymore, or we will die."

¹⁷The LORD said to me: "What they say is good. ¹⁸I will raise up for them a prophet like you from among their brothers; I will put my words in his mouth, and he will tell them everything I command him. ¹⁹If anyone does not listen to my words that the prophet speaks in my name, I myself will call him to account. ²⁰But a prophet who presumes to speak in my name anything I have not command-ed him to say, or a prophet who speaks in the name of other gods, must be put to death."

²¹You may say to yourselves, "How can we know when a message has not been spoken by the LORD?" ²²If what a prophet proclaims in the name of the LORD does not take place or come true, that is a message the LORD has not spoken. That prophet has spoken presumptuously. Do not be afraid of him.

Cities of Refuge

19 When the LORD your God has destroyed the nations whose land he is giving you, and when you have driven them out and settled in their towns and houses, ²then set aside for yourselves three cities centrally located in the land the LORD your God is giving you to possess. ³Build roads to them and divide into three parts the land the LORD your God is giving you as an inheritance, so that anyone who kills a man may flee there.

⁴This is the rule concerning the man who kills another and flees there to save his life—one who kills his neighbor unintentionally, without malice aforethought. ⁵For instance, a man may go into the forest with his neighbor to cut wood, and as he swings his ax to fell a tree, the head may fly off and hit his neighbor and kill him. That man may flee to one of these cities and save his life. ⁶Otherwise, the avenger of blood might pursue him in a rage, overtake him if the distance is too great, and kill him even though he is not deserving of death, since he did it to his neighbor with-out malice aforethought. ⁷This is why I command you to set aside for yourselves three cities.

⁸If the LORD your God enlarges your territory, as he promised on oath to your forefathers, and gives you the whole land he promised them, ⁹because you carefully follow all these laws I com-mand you today—to love the LORD your God and to walk always in his ways—then you are to set aside three more cities. ¹⁰Do this so that innocent blood will not be shed in your land, which the LORD your God is giving you as your inheritance, and so that you will not be guilty of bloodshed.

¹¹But if a man hates his neighbor and lies in wait for him, assaults and kills him, and then flees to one of these cities, ¹²the elders of his town shall send for him, bring him back from the city, and hand him over to the avenger of blood to die. ¹³Show him no pity. You must purge from Israel the guilt of shedding innocent blood, so that it may go well with you.

¹⁴Do not move your neighbor's boundary stone set up by your predecessors in the inheritance you receive in the land the LORD your God is giving you to possess.

Witnesses

¹⁵One witness is not enough to convict a man accused of any crime or offense he may have committed. A matter must be established by the testimony of two or three witnesses.

¹⁶If a malicious witness takes the stand to accuse a man of a crime, ¹⁷the two men involved in the dispute must stand in the presence of the LORD before the priests and the judges who are in office at the time. ¹⁸The judges must make a thorough investigation, and if the witness proves to be a liar, giving false testimony against his brother, ¹⁹then do to him as he intended to do to his brother. You must purge the evil from among you. ²⁰The rest of the people will hear of this and be afraid, and never again will such an evil thing be done among you. ²¹Show no pity: life for life, eye for eye, tooth for tooth, hand for hand, foot for foot.

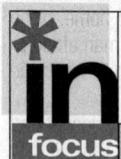

*in focus

Give Me One Good Reason

Profile: **Gabi**

I promised my parents I wouldn't have sex till I got married. We did the whole "waiting on true love" thing, and they even gave me a special ring to wear as a sign of my commitment. I remember feeling so certain at the time—there was no way I was going to mess around. Now I just don't feel as strongly about it. When I look at the ring, I feel less certain about what it really means to me.

My friends say sex is a rite of passage into adulthood. If that's true, then I ought to be ready for it. It's not that I want to do it because *everyone else* is doing it. I want to do it for me, that's all. It's something I feel like I need to experience now.

Sometimes I imagine that somewhere the guy I'm supposed to be with someday is feeling the same pressure and temptations. I even say a prayer for him to stay strong. Maybe he's praying the same for me. Of course, sometimes I even doubt that this guy exists. He doesn't go to my school, that's for sure.

My guy friends tell me I'll never meet a guy who lives up to my standards. They say almost every guy has already done it anyway. So why fight so hard to be a virgin?

When you are feeling pressured to compromise your purity, go to www.TrueImagesBible.com

purity in focus

God calls us to purity to protect us from the dangers of misusing our sexuality. Having second thoughts about pursuing purity? Remember this:

> » God calls us to purity—not because it's the easy thing, but because it is the best thing for us. See 2 Corinthians 7:1 (page 1529) to see why purity is best.
> » Temptation is not sin. Giving in to temptation is the problem. If you're feeling doubtful and having questions about your views on sex, seek counsel and talk it over with someone you trust.

For more on this topic, see the index on page 1656.

purity

Going to War

20 When you go to war against your enemies and see horses and chariots and an army greater than yours, do not be afraid of them, because the LORD your God, who brought you up out of Egypt, will be with you. ²When you are about to go into battle, the priest shall come forward and address the army. ³He shall say: "Hear, O Israel, today you are going into battle against your enemies. Do not be fainthearted or afraid; do not be terrified or give way to panic before them. ⁴For the LORD your God is the one who goes with you to fight for you against your enemies to give you victory."

⁵The officers shall say to the army: "Has anyone built a new house and not dedicated it? Let him go home, or he may die in battle and someone else may dedicate it. ⁶Has anyone planted a vineyard and not begun to enjoy it? Let him go home, or he may die in battle and someone else

enjoy it. [7]Has anyone become pledged to a woman and not married her? Let him go home, or he may die in battle and someone else marry her." [8]Then the officers shall add, "Is any man afraid or fainthearted? Let him go home so that his brothers will not become disheartened too." [9]When the officers have finished speaking to the army, they shall appoint commanders over it.

[10]When you march up to attack a city, make its people an offer of peace. [11]If they accept and open their gates, all the people in it shall be subject to forced labor and shall work for you. [12]If they refuse to make peace and they engage you in battle, lay siege to that city. [13]When the LORD your God delivers it into your hand, put to the sword all the men in it. [14]As for the women, the children, the livestock and everything else in the city, you may take these as plunder for yourselves. And you may use the plunder the LORD your God gives you from your enemies. [15]This is how you are to treat all the cities that are at a distance from you and do not belong to the nations nearby.

[16]However, in the cities of the nations the LORD your God is giving you as an inheritance, do not leave alive anything that breathes. [17]Completely destroy[a] them—the Hittites, Amorites, Canaanites, Perizzites, Hivites and Jebusites—as the LORD your God has commanded you. [18]Otherwise, they will teach you to follow all the detestable things they do in worshiping their gods, and you will sin against the LORD your God.

[19]When you lay siege to a city for a long time, fighting against it to capture it, do not destroy its trees by putting an ax to them, because you can eat their fruit. Do not cut them down. Are the trees of the field people, that you should besiege them?[b] [20]However, you may cut down trees that you know are not fruit trees and use them to build siege works until the city at war with you falls.

Atonement for an Unsolved Murder

21 If a man is found slain, lying in a field in the land the LORD your God is giving you to possess, and it is not known who killed him, [2]your elders and judges shall go out and measure the distance from the body to the neighboring towns. [3]Then the elders of the town nearest the body shall take a heifer that has never been worked and has never worn a yoke [4]and lead her down to a valley that has not been plowed or planted and where there is a flowing stream. There in the valley they are to break the heifer's neck. [5]The priests, the sons of Levi, shall step forward, for the LORD your God has chosen them to minister and to pronounce blessings in the name of the LORD and to decide all cases of dispute and assault. [6]Then all the elders of the town nearest the body shall wash their hands over the heifer whose neck was broken in the valley, [7]and they shall declare: "Our hands did not shed this blood, nor did our eyes see it done. [8]Accept this atonement for your people Israel, whom you have redeemed, O LORD, and do not hold your people guilty of the blood of an innocent man." And the bloodshed will be atoned for. [9]So you will purge from yourselves the guilt of shedding innocent blood, since you have done what is right in the eyes of the LORD.

Marrying a Captive Woman

[10]When you go to war against your enemies and the LORD your God delivers them into your hands and you take captives, [11]if you notice among the captives a beautiful woman and are attracted to her, you may take her as your wife. [12]Bring her into your home and have her shave her head, trim her nails [13]and put aside the clothes she was wearing when captured. After she has lived in your house and mourned her father and mother for a full month, then you may go to her and be her husband and she shall be your wife. [14]If you are not pleased with her, let her go wherever she wishes. You must not sell her or treat her as a slave, since you have dishonored her.

The Right of the Firstborn

[15]If a man has two wives, and he loves one but not the other, and both bear him sons but the firstborn is the son of the wife he does not love, [16]when he wills his property to his sons, he must not give the rights of the firstborn to the son of the wife he loves in preference to his actual firstborn, the son of the wife he does not love. [17]He must acknowledge the son of his unloved wife as the firstborn by giving him a double share of all he has. That son is the first sign of his father's strength. The right of the firstborn belongs to him.

a 17 The Hebrew term refers to the irrevocable giving over of things or persons to the LORD, often by totally destroying them.
b 19 Or down to use in the siege, for the fruit trees are for the benefit of man.

A Rebellious Son

[18]If a man has a stubborn and rebellious son who does not obey his father and mother and will not listen to them when they discipline him, [19]his father and mother shall take hold of him and bring him to the elders at the gate of his town. [20]They shall say to the elders, "This son of ours is stubborn and rebellious. He will not obey us. He is a profligate and a drunkard." [21]Then all the men of his town shall stone him to death. You must purge the evil from among you. All Israel will hear of it and be afraid.

Various Laws

[22]If a man guilty of a capital offense is put to death and his body is hung on a tree, [23]you must not leave his body on the tree overnight. Be sure to bury him that same day, because anyone who is hung on a tree is under God's curse. You must not desecrate the land the LORD your God is giving you as an inheritance.

22 If you see your brother's ox or sheep straying, do not ignore it but be sure to take it back to him. [2]If the brother does not live near you or if you do not know who he is, take it home with you and keep it until he comes looking for it. Then give it back to him. [3]Do the same if you find your brother's donkey or his cloak or anything he loses. Do not ignore it.

[4]If you see your brother's donkey or his ox fallen on the road, do not ignore it. Help him get it to its feet.

[5]A woman must not wear men's clothing, nor a man wear women's clothing, for the LORD your God detests anyone who does this.

[6]If you come across a bird's nest beside the road, either in a tree or on the ground, and the mother is sitting on the young or on the eggs, do not take the mother with the young. [7]You may take the young, but be sure to let the mother go, so that it may go well with you and you may have a long life.

[8]When you build a new house, make a parapet around your roof so that you may not bring the guilt of bloodshed on your house if someone falls from the roof.

[9]Do not plant two kinds of seed in your vineyard; if you do, not only the crops you plant but also the fruit of the vineyard will be defiled. [a]

truth or dare

"It's not my problem." Yeah, but it's *somebody's* problem. And when you see an opportunity to help, take it! God applauds those random acts of kindness.

22:1–4

[10]Do not plow with an ox and a donkey yoked together.
[11]Do not wear clothes of wool and linen woven together.
[12]Make tassels on the four corners of the cloak you wear.

Marriage Violations

[13]If a man takes a wife and, after lying with her, dislikes her [14]and slanders her and gives her a bad name, saying, "I married this woman, but when I approached her, I did not find proof of her virginity," [15]then the girl's father and mother shall bring proof that she was a virgin to the town elders at the gate. [16]The girl's father will say to the elders, "I gave my daughter in marriage to this man, but he dislikes her. [17]Now he has slandered her and said, 'I did not find your daughter to be a virgin.' But here is the proof of my daughter's virginity." Then her parents shall display the cloth before the elders of the town, [18]and the elders shall take the man and punish him. [19]They shall fine him a hundred shekels of silver[b] and give them to the girl's father, because this man has given an Israelite virgin a bad name. She shall continue to be his wife; he must not divorce her as long as he lives.

[20]If, however, the charge is true and no proof of the girl's virginity can be found, [21]she shall be brought to the door of her father's house and there the men of her town shall stone her to death. She has done a disgraceful thing in Israel by being promiscuous while still in her father's house. You must purge the evil from among you.

[a] 9 Or *be forfeited to the sanctuary*   [b] 19 That is, about 2 1/2 pounds (about 1 kilogram)

²²If a man is found sleeping with another man's wife, both the man who slept with her and the woman must die. You must purge the evil from Israel.

²³If a man happens to meet in a town a virgin pledged to be married and he sleeps with her, ²⁴you shall take both of them to the gate of that town and stone them to death—the girl because she was in a town and did not scream for help, and the man because he violated another man's wife. You must purge the evil from among you.

²⁵But if out in the country a man happens to meet a girl pledged to be married and rapes her, only the man who has done this shall die. ²⁶Do nothing to the girl; she has committed no sin deserving death. This case is like that of someone who attacks and murders his neighbor, ²⁷for the man found the girl out in the country, and though the betrothed girl screamed, there was no one to rescue her.

²⁸If a man happens to meet a virgin who is not pledged to be married and rapes her and they are discovered, ²⁹he shall pay the girl's father fifty shekels of silver.ᵃ He must marry the girl, for he has violated her. He can never divorce her as long as he lives.

³⁰A man is not to marry his father's wife; he must not dishonor his father's bed.

Exclusion From the Assembly

23 No one who has been emasculated by crushing or cutting may enter the assembly of the LORD. ²No one born of a forbidden marriageᵇ nor any of his descendants may enter the assembly of the LORD, even down to the tenth generation.

³No Ammonite or Moabite or any of his descendants may enter the assembly of the LORD, even down to the tenth generation. ⁴For they did not come to meet you with bread and water on your way when you came out of Egypt, and they hired Balaam son of Beor from Pethor in Aram Naharaimᶜ to pronounce a curse on you. ⁵However, the LORD your God would not listen to Balaam but turned the curse into a blessing for you, because the LORD your God loves you. ⁶Do not seek a treaty of friendship with them as long as you live.

⁷Do not abhor an Edomite, for he is your brother. Do not abhor an Egyptian, because you lived as an alien in his country. ⁸The third generation of children born to them may enter the assembly of the LORD.

Uncleanness in the Camp

⁹When you are encamped against your enemies, keep away from everything impure. ¹⁰If one of your men is unclean because of a nocturnal emission, he is to go outside the camp and stay there. ¹¹But as evening approaches he is to wash himself, and at sunset he may return to the camp.

¹²Designate a place outside the camp where you can go to relieve yourself. ¹³As part of your equipment have something to dig with, and when you relieve yourself, dig a hole and cover up your excrement. ¹⁴For the LORD your God moves about in your camp to protect you and to deliver your enemies to you. Your camp must be holy, so that he will not see among you anything indecent and turn away from you.

Miscellaneous Laws

¹⁵If a slave has taken refuge with you, do not hand him over to his master. ¹⁶Let him live among you wherever he likes and in whatever town he chooses. Do not oppress him.

¹⁷No Israelite man or woman is to become a shrine prostitute. ¹⁸You must not bring the earnings of a female prostitute or of a male prostituteᵈ into the house of the LORD your God to pay any vow, because the LORD your God detests them both.

¹⁹Do not charge your brother interest, whether on money or food or anything else that may earn interest. ²⁰You may charge a foreigner interest, but not a brother Israelite, so that the LORD your God may bless you in everything you put your hand to in the land you are entering to possess.

²¹If you make a vow to the LORD your God, do not be slow to pay it, for the LORD your God will certainly demand it of you and you will be guilty of sin. ²²But if you refrain from making a vow, you will not be guilty. ²³Whatever your lips utter you must be sure to do, because you made your vow freely to the LORD your God with your own mouth.

ᵃ 29 That is, about 1 1/4 pounds (about 0.6 kilogram)　　ᵇ 2 Or *one of illegitimate birth*　　ᶜ 4 That is, Northwest Mesopotamia　　ᵈ 18 Hebrew *of a dog*

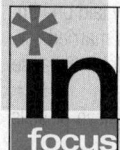

WANTED: Child Prodigy

Profile: Sandy

I'm the child my parents always secretly wanted. My brother Dan is their jock—a natural at any sport. And my sister, Rebecca, is our resident cheerleader—popular and beautiful. Somewhere along the way I fell into the role of the "smart one."

When I was a child, "gifted and talented" meant I got to do fun stuff—like field trips and special activities. Well, those days are over. Now that I'm in high school, I feel like this "giftedness" or whatever it is they say I have is more of a burden than anything else. Advanced English. AP Biology. College prep courses. I'm sick of it. Unfortunately, my mom doesn't understand why my grades are slipping in certain classes. I get the "you've got so much potential" speech about once a week, it seems. You'd think I was in danger of flunking out of school the way she gets so uptight.

It's not that I *can't* do the work—I just have no desire to. It's all busywork, the same mundane assignments just to help the teachers keep their jobs. I can do most of what I learn in school in my sleep. So what's the point? Basically, I'm just biding my time till I graduate and move on to real life. In the meantime, I'll do what it takes to get by—but nothing more.

For more information on being a good steward of the gifts God's given you, go to www.TrueImagesBible.com

laziness in focus

Sometimes we can take advantage of God's blessings and become poor stewards of what he gives us. Like Sandy, we can do just enough to get by and nothing more. However, take this to heart:

» God's Word says we are to be good managers of his blessings. Read the parable in Matthew 25:14–30 (page 1326) to see what happened to a guy who blew off what had been entrusted to him.

» God warns us of the dangers of becoming lazy. It can affect the whole course of our lives. See Proverbs 10:4; 12:24 (page 816,820).

» Believe it or not, some of the most gifted kids often experience problems in traditional school systems. If you find that you're easily bored and distracted, talk to your school counselor to see if there are alternative classes for gifted students in your school system.

For more on this topic, see the index on page 1656.

²⁴If you enter your neighbor's vineyard, you may eat all the grapes you want, but do not put any in your basket. ²⁵If you enter your neighbor's grainfield, you may pick kernels with your hands, but you must not put a sickle to his standing grain.

24

If a man marries a woman who becomes displeasing to him because he finds something indecent about her, and he writes her a certificate of divorce, gives it to her and sends her from his house, ²and if after she leaves his house she becomes the wife of another man, ³and her second husband dislikes her and writes her a certificate of divorce, gives it to her and sends her from his house, or if he dies, ⁴then her first husband, who divorced her, is not allowed to marry her again after she has been defiled. That would be detestable in the eyes of the LORD. Do not bring sin upon the land the LORD your God is giving you as an inheritance.

⁵If a man has recently married, he must not be sent to war or have any other duty laid on him. For one year he is to be free to stay at home and bring happiness to the wife he has married.

⁶Do not take a pair of millstones—not even the upper one—as security for a debt, because that would be taking a man's livelihood as security.

⁷If a man is caught kidnapping one of his brother Israelites and treats him as a slave or sells him, the kidnapper must die. You must purge the evil from among you.

⁸In cases of leprous ᵃ diseases be very careful to do exactly as the priests, who are Levites, instruct you. You must follow carefully what I have commanded them. ⁹Remember what the LORD your God did to Miriam along the way after you came out of Egypt.

¹⁰When you make a loan of any kind to your neighbor, do not go into his house to get what he is offering as a pledge. ¹¹Stay outside and let the man to whom you are making the loan bring the pledge out to you. ¹²If the man is poor, do not go to sleep with his pledge in your possession. ¹³Return his cloak to him by sunset so that he may sleep in it. Then he will thank you, and it will be regarded as a righteous act in the sight of the LORD your God.

¹⁴Do not take advantage of a hired man who is poor and needy, whether he is a brother Israelite or an alien living in one of your towns. ¹⁵Pay him his wages each day before sunset, because he is poor and is counting on it. Otherwise he may cry to the LORD against you, and you will be guilty of sin.

¹⁶Fathers shall not be put to death for their children, nor children put to death for their fathers; each is to die for his own sin.

¹⁷Do not deprive the alien or the fatherless of justice, or take the cloak of the widow as a pledge. ¹⁸Remember that you were slaves in Egypt and the LORD your God redeemed you from there. That is why I command you to do this.

¹⁹When you are harvesting in your field and you overlook a sheaf, do not go back to get it. Leave it for the alien, the fatherless and the widow, so that the LORD your God may bless you in all the work of your hands. ²⁰When you beat the olives from your trees, do not go over the branches a second time. Leave what remains for the alien, the fatherless and the widow. ²¹When you harvest the grapes in your vineyard, do not go over the vines again. Leave what remains for the alien, the fatherless and the widow. ²²Remember that you were slaves in Egypt. That is why I command you to do this.

25 When men have a dispute, they are to take it to court and the judges will decide the case, acquitting the innocent and condemning the guilty. ²If the guilty man deserves to be beaten, the judge shall make him lie down and have him flogged in his presence with the number of lashes his crime deserves, ³but he must not give him more than forty lashes. If he is flogged more than that, your brother will be degraded in your eyes.

⁴Do not muzzle an ox while it is treading out the grain.

⁵If brothers are living together and one of them dies without a son, his widow must not marry outside the family. Her husband's brother shall take her and marry her and fulfill the duty of a brother-in-law to her. ⁶The first son she bears shall carry on the name of the dead brother so that his name will not be blotted out from Israel.

⁷However, if a man does not want to marry his brother's wife, she shall go to the elders at the town gate and say, "My husband's brother refuses to carry on his brother's name in Israel. He will not fulfill the duty of a brother-in-law to me." ⁸Then the elders of his town shall summon him and talk to him. If he persists in saying, "I do not want to marry her," ⁹his brother's widow shall go up to him in the presence of the elders, take off one of his sandals, spit in his face and say, "This is what is done to the man who will not build up his brother's family line." ¹⁰That man's line shall be known in Israel as The Family of the Unsandaled.

¹¹If two men are fighting and the wife of one of them comes to rescue her husband from his assailant, and she reaches out and seizes him by his private parts, ¹²you shall cut off her hand. Show her no pity.

¹³Do not have two differing weights in your bag—one heavy, one light. ¹⁴Do not have two differing measures in your house—one large, one small. ¹⁵You must have accurate and honest weights and measures, so that you may live long in the land the LORD your God is giving you. ¹⁶For the LORD your God detests anyone who does these things, anyone who deals dishonestly.

ᵃ 8 The Hebrew word was used for various diseases affecting the skin—not necessarily leprosy.

[17]Remember what the Amalekites did to you along the way when you came out of Egypt. [18]When you were weary and worn out, they met you on your journey and cut off all who were lagging behind; they had no fear of God. [19]When the LORD your God gives you rest from all the enemies around you in the land he is giving you to possess as an inheritance, you shall blot out the memory of Amalek from under heaven. Do not forget!

Firstfruits and Tithes

26 When you have entered the land the LORD your God is giving you as an inheritance and have taken possession of it and settled in it, [2]take some of the firstfruits of all that you produce from the soil of the land the LORD your God is giving you and put them in a basket. Then go to the place the LORD your God will choose as a dwelling for his Name [3]and say to the priest in office at the time, "I declare today to the LORD your God that I have come to the land the LORD swore to our forefathers to give us." [4]The priest shall take the basket from your hands and set it down in front of the altar of the LORD your God. [5]Then you shall declare before the LORD your God: "My father was a wandering Aramean, and he went down into Egypt with a few people and lived there and became a great nation, powerful and numerous. [6]But the Egyptians mistreated us and made us suffer, putting us to hard labor. [7]Then we cried out to the LORD, the God of our fathers, and the LORD heard our voice and saw our misery, toil and oppression. [8]So the LORD brought us out of Egypt with a mighty hand and an outstretched arm, with great terror and with miraculous signs and wonders. [9]He brought us to this place and gave us this land, a land flowing with milk and honey; [10]and now I bring the firstfruits of the soil that you, O LORD, have given me." Place the basket before the LORD your God and bow down before him. [11]And you and the Levites and the aliens among you shall rejoice in all the good things the LORD your God has given to you and your household.

[12]When you have finished setting aside a tenth of all your produce in the third year, the year of the tithe, you shall give it to the Levite, the alien, the fatherless and the widow, so that they may eat in your towns and be satisfied. [13]Then say to the LORD your God: "I have removed from my house the sacred portion and have given it to the Levite, the alien, the fatherless and the widow, according to all you commanded. I have not turned aside from your commands nor have I forgotten any of them. [14]I have not eaten any of the sacred portion while I was in mourning, nor have I removed any of it while I was unclean, nor have I offered any of it to the dead. I have obeyed the LORD my God; I have done everything you commanded me. [15]Look down from heaven, your holy dwelling place, and bless your people Israel and the land you have given us as you promised on oath to our forefathers, a land flowing with milk and honey."

Follow the LORD's Commands

[16]The LORD your God commands you this day to follow these decrees and laws; carefully observe them with all your heart and with all your soul. [17]You have declared this day that the LORD is your God and that you will walk in his ways, that you will keep his decrees, commands and laws, and that you will obey him. [18]And the LORD has declared this day that you are his people, his treasured possession as he promised, and that you are to keep all his commands. [19]He has declared that he will set you in praise, fame and honor high above all the nations he has made and that you will be a people holy to the LORD your God, as he promised.

The Altar on Mount Ebal

27 Moses and the elders of Israel commanded the people: "Keep all these commands that I give you today. ²When you have crossed the Jordan into the land the Lᴏʀᴅ your God is giving you, set up some large stones and coat them with plaster. ³Write on them all the words of this law when you have crossed over to enter the land the Lᴏʀᴅ your God is giving you, a land flowing with milk and honey, just as the Lᴏʀᴅ, the God of your fathers, promised you. ⁴And when you have crossed the Jordan, set up these stones on Mount Ebal, as I command you today, and coat them with plaster. ⁵Build there an altar to the Lᴏʀᴅ your God, an altar of stones. Do not use any iron tool upon them. ⁶Build the altar of the Lᴏʀᴅ your God with fieldstones and offer burnt offerings on it to the Lᴏʀᴅ your God. ⁷Sacrifice fellowship offerings[a] there, eating them and rejoicing in the presence of the Lᴏʀᴅ your God. ⁸And you shall write very clearly all the words of this law on these stones you have set up."

Curses From Mount Ebal

⁹Then Moses and the priests, who are Levites, said to all Israel, "Be silent, O Israel, and listen! You have now become the people of the Lᴏʀᴅ your God. ¹⁰Obey the Lᴏʀᴅ your God and follow his commands and decrees that I give you today."

¹¹On the same day Moses commanded the people:

¹²When you have crossed the Jordan, these tribes shall stand on Mount Gerizim to bless the people: Simeon, Levi, Judah, Issachar, Joseph and Benjamin. ¹³And these tribes shall stand on Mount Ebal to pronounce curses: Reuben, Gad, Asher, Zebulun, Dan and Naphtali.

¹⁴The Levites shall recite to all the people of Israel in a loud voice:

¹⁵"Cursed is the man who carves an image or casts an idol—a thing detestable to the Lᴏʀᴅ, the work of the craftsman's hands—and sets it up in secret."

Then all the people shall say, "Amen!"

¹⁶"Cursed is the man who dishonors his father or his mother."

Then all the people shall say, "Amen!"

¹⁷"Cursed is the man who moves his neighbor's boundary stone."

Then all the people shall say, "Amen!"

¹⁸"Cursed is the man who leads the blind astray on the road."

Then all the people shall say, "Amen!"

¹⁹"Cursed is the man who withholds justice from the alien, the fatherless or the widow."

Then all the people shall say, "Amen!"

²⁰"Cursed is the man who sleeps with his father's wife, for he dishonors his father's bed."

Then all the people shall say, "Amen!"

²¹"Cursed is the man who has sexual relations with any animal."

Then all the people shall say, "Amen!"

²²"Cursed is the man who sleeps with his sister, the daughter of his father or the daughter of his mother."

Then all the people shall say, "Amen!"

²³"Cursed is the man who sleeps with his mother-in-law."

Then all the people shall say, "Amen!"

²⁴"Cursed is the man who kills his neighbor secretly."

Then all the people shall say, "Amen!"

²⁵"Cursed is the man who accepts a bribe to kill an innocent person."

Then all the people shall say, "Amen!"

²⁶"Cursed is the man who does not uphold the words of this law by carrying them out."

Then all the people shall say, "Amen!"

a 7 Traditionally *peace offerings*

Blessings for Obedience

28 If you fully obey the LORD your God and carefully follow all his commands I give you today, the LORD your God will set you high above all the nations on earth. [2]All these blessings will come upon you and accompany you if you obey the LORD your God:

[3]You will be blessed in the city and blessed in the country.

[4]The fruit of your womb will be blessed, and the crops of your land and the young of your livestock—the calves of your herds and the lambs of your flocks.

[5]Your basket and your kneading trough will be blessed.

[6]You will be blessed when you come in and blessed when you go out.

[7]The LORD will grant that the enemies who rise up against you will be defeated before you. They will come at you from one direction but flee from you in seven.

[8]The LORD will send a blessing on your barns and on everything you put your hand to. The LORD your God will bless you in the land he is giving you.

[9]The LORD will establish you as his holy people, as he promised you on oath, if you keep the commands of the LORD your God and walk in his ways. [10]Then all the peoples on earth will see that you are called by the name of the LORD, and they will fear you. [11]The LORD will grant you abundant prosperity—in the fruit of your womb, the young of your livestock and the crops of your ground—in the land he swore to your forefathers to give you.

[12]The LORD will open the heavens, the storehouse of his bounty, to send rain on your land in season and to bless all the work of your hands. You will lend to many nations but will borrow from none. [13]The LORD will make you the head, not the tail. If you pay attention to the commands of the LORD your God that I give you this day and carefully follow them, you will always be at the top, never at the bottom. [14]Do not turn aside from any of the commands I give you today, to the right or to the left, following other gods and serving them.

Curses for Disobedience

[15]However, if you do not obey the LORD your God and do not carefully follow all his commands and decrees I am giving you today, all these curses will come upon you and overtake you:

[16]You will be cursed in the city and cursed in the country.

[17]Your basket and your kneading trough will be cursed.

[18]The fruit of your womb will be cursed, and the crops of your land, and the calves of your herds and the lambs of your flocks.

[19]You will be cursed when you come in and cursed when you go out.

[20]The LORD will send on you curses, confusion and rebuke in everything you put your hand to, until you are destroyed and come to sudden ruin because of the evil you have done in forsaking him. [a] [21]The LORD will plague you with diseases until he has destroyed you from the land you are entering to possess. [22]The LORD will strike you with wasting disease, with fever and inflammation, with scorching heat and drought, with blight and mildew, which will plague you until you perish. [23]The sky over your head will be bronze, the ground beneath you iron. [24]The LORD will turn the rain of your country into dust and powder; it will come down from the skies until you are destroyed.

[25]The LORD will cause you to be defeated before your enemies. You will come at them from one direction but flee from them in seven, and you will become a thing of horror to all the kingdoms on earth. [26]Your carcasses will be food for all the birds of the air and the beasts of the earth, and there will be no one to frighten them away. [27]The LORD will afflict you with the boils of Egypt and with tumors, festering sores and the itch, from which you cannot be cured. [28]The LORD will afflict you with madness, blindness and confusion of mind. [29]At midday you will grope about like a blind man in the dark. You will be unsuccessful in everything you do; day after day you will be oppressed and robbed, with no one to rescue you.

[30]You will be pledged to be married to a woman, but another will take her and ravish her. You will build a house, but you will not live in it. You will plant a vineyard, but you will not even begin to enjoy its fruit. [31]Your ox will be slaughtered before your eyes, but you will eat none of it. Your donkey will be forcibly taken from you and will not be returned. Your sheep will be given to your

a 20 Hebrew me

enemies, and no one will rescue them. [32]Your sons and daughters will be given to another nation, and you will wear out your eyes watching for them day after day, powerless to lift a hand. [33]A people that you do not know will eat what your land and labor produce, and you will have nothing but cruel oppression all your days. [34]The sights you see will drive you mad. [35]The LORD will afflict your knees and legs with painful boils that cannot be cured, spreading from the soles of your feet to the top of your head.

[36]The LORD will drive you and the king you set over you to a nation unknown to you or your fathers. There you will worship other gods, gods of wood and stone. [37]You will become a thing of horror and an object of scorn and ridicule to all the nations where the LORD will drive you.

[38]You will sow much seed in the field but you will harvest little, because locusts will devour it. [39]You will plant vineyards and cultivate them but you will not drink the wine or gather the grapes, because worms will eat them. [40]You will have olive trees throughout your country but you will not use the oil, because the olives will drop off. [41]You will have sons and daughters but you will not keep them, because they will go into captivity. [42]Swarms of locusts will take over all your trees and the crops of your land.

[43]The alien who lives among you will rise above you higher and higher, but you will sink lower and lower. [44]He will lend to you, but you will not lend to him. He will be the head, but you will be the tail.

[45]All these curses will come upon you. They will pursue you and overtake you until you are destroyed, because you did not obey the LORD your God and observe the commands and decrees he gave you. [46]They will be a sign and a wonder to you and your descendants forever. [47]Because you did not serve the LORD your God joyfully and gladly in the time of prosperity, [48]therefore in hunger and thirst, in nakedness and dire poverty, you will serve the enemies the LORD sends against you. He will put an iron yoke on your neck until he has destroyed you.

[49]The LORD will bring a nation against you from far away, from the ends of the earth, like an eagle swooping down, a nation whose language you will not understand, [50]a fierce-looking nation without respect for the old or pity for the young. [51]They will devour the young of your livestock and the crops of your land until you are destroyed. They will leave you no grain, new wine or oil, nor any calves of your herds or lambs of your flocks until you are ruined. [52]They will lay siege to all the cities throughout your land until the high fortified walls in which you trust fall down. They will besiege all the cities throughout the land the LORD your God is giving you.

[53]Because of the suffering that your enemy will inflict on you during the siege, you will eat the fruit of the womb, the flesh of the sons and daughters the LORD your God has given you. [54]Even the most gentle and sensitive man among you will have no compassion on his own brother or the wife he loves or his surviving children, [55]and he will not give to one of them any of the flesh of his children that he is eating. It will be all he has left because of the suffering your enemy will inflict on you during the siege of all your cities. [56]The most gentle and sensitive woman among you—so sensitive and gentle that she would not venture to touch the ground with the sole of her foot—will begrudge the husband she loves and her own son or daughter [57]the afterbirth from her womb and the children she bears. For she intends to eat them secretly during the siege and in the distress that your enemy will inflict on you in your cities.

[58]If you do not carefully follow all the words of this law, which are written in this book, and do not revere this glorious and awesome name—the LORD your God— [59]the LORD will send fearful plagues on you and your descendants, harsh and prolonged disasters, and severe and lingering illnesses. [60]He will bring upon you all the diseases of Egypt that you dreaded, and they will cling to you. [61]The LORD will also bring on you every kind of sickness and disaster not recorded in this Book of the Law, until you are destroyed. [62]You who were as numerous as the stars in the sky will be left but few in number, because you did not obey the LORD your God. [63]Just as it pleased the LORD to

truth or dare

Some people equate holiness with living a boring, miserable life in sackcloth and ashes. Nope! God's expectations are quite different. Bag the moaning. Serve God joyfully and gladly!

28:47-48

make you prosper and increase in number, so it will please him to ruin and destroy you. You will be uprooted from the land you are entering to possess. [64]Then the LORD will scatter you among all nations, from one end of the earth to the other. There you will worship other gods—gods of wood and stone, which neither you nor your fathers have known. [65]Among those nations you will find no repose, no resting place for the sole of your foot. There the LORD will give you an anxious mind, eyes weary with longing, and a despairing heart. [66]You will live in constant suspense, filled with dread both night and day, never sure of your life. [67]In the morning you will say, "If only it were evening!" and in the evening, "If only it were morning!"—because of the terror that will fill your hearts and the sights that your eyes will see. [68]The LORD will send you back in ships to Egypt on a journey I said you should never make again. There you will offer yourselves for sale to your enemies as male and female slaves, but no one will buy you.

Renewal of the Covenant

29 These are the terms of the covenant the LORD commanded Moses to make with the Israelites in Moab, in addition to the covenant he had made with them at Horeb. [2]Moses summoned all the Israelites and said to them:

Your eyes have seen all that the LORD did in Egypt to Pharaoh, to all his officials and to all his land. [3]With your own eyes you saw those great trials, those miraculous signs and great wonders. [4]But to this day the LORD has not given you a mind that understands or eyes that see or ears that hear. [5]During the forty years that I led you through the desert, your clothes did not wear out, nor did the sandals on your feet. [6]You ate no bread and drank no wine or other fermented drink. I did this so that you might know that I am the LORD your God.

[7]When you reached this place, Sihon king of Heshbon and Og king of Bashan came out to fight against us, but we defeated them. [8]We took their land and gave it as an inheritance to the Reubenites, the Gadites and the half-tribe of Manasseh.

[9]Carefully follow the terms of this covenant, so that you may prosper in everything you do. [10]All of you are standing today in the presence of the LORD your God—your leaders and chief men, your elders and officials, and all the other men of Israel, [11]together with your children and your wives, and the aliens living in your camps who chop your wood and carry your water. [12]You are standing here in order to enter into a covenant with the LORD your God, a covenant the LORD is making with you this day and sealing with an oath, [13]to confirm you this day as his people, that he may be your God as he promised you and as he swore to your fathers, Abraham, Isaac and Jacob. [14]I am making this covenant, with its oath, not only with you [15]who are standing here with us today in the presence of the LORD our God but also with those who are not here today.

truth **or dare**

Do you demand the best from God while only giving him 50 percent? Keep your end of the bargain—obey God—and he'll do his part!

29:9

[16]You yourselves know how we lived in Egypt and how we passed through the countries on the way here. [17]You saw among them their detestable images and idols of wood and stone, of silver and gold. [18]Make sure there is no man or woman, clan or tribe among you today whose heart turns away from the LORD our God to go and worship the gods of those nations; make sure there is no root among you that produces such bitter poison.

[19]When such a person hears the words of this oath, he invokes a blessing on himself and therefore thinks, "I will be safe, even though I persist in going my own way." This will bring disaster on the watered land as well as the dry.[a] [20]The LORD will never be willing to forgive him; his wrath and zeal will burn against that man. All the curses written in this book will fall upon him, and the LORD will blot out his name from under heaven. [21]The LORD will single him out from all the tribes of Israel for disaster, according to all the curses of the covenant written in this Book of the Law.

[22]Your children who follow you in later generations and foreigners who come from distant lands will see the calamities that have fallen on the land and the diseases with which the LORD has af-

a 19 Or way, in order to add drunkenness to thirst."

flicted it. [23]The whole land will be a burning waste of salt and sulfur—nothing planted, nothing sprouting, no vegetation growing on it. It will be like the destruction of Sodom and Gomorrah, Admah and Zeboiim, which the LORD overthrew in fierce anger. [24]All the nations will ask: "Why has the LORD done this to this land? Why this fierce, burning anger?"

[25]And the answer will be: "It is because this people abandoned the covenant of the LORD, the God of their fathers, the covenant he made with them when he brought them out of Egypt. [26]They went off and worshiped other gods and bowed down to them, gods they did not know, gods he had not given them. [27]Therefore the LORD's anger burned against this land, so that he brought on it all the curses written in this book. [28]In furious anger and in great wrath the LORD uprooted them from their land and thrust them into another land, as it is now."

[29]The secret things belong to the LORD our God, but the things revealed belong to us and to our children forever, that we may follow all the words of this law.

truth or dare

God is working with us on a need-to-know basis. He tells us more than enough through his Word, but he doesn't overwhelm us with every last piece of info on earth.

29:29

Prosperity After Turning to the LORD

30 When all these blessings and curses I have set before you come upon you and you take them to heart wherever the LORD your God disperses you among the nations, [2]and when you and your children return to the LORD your God and obey him with all your heart and with all your soul according to everything I command you today, [3]then the LORD your God will restore your fortunes[a] and have compassion on you and gather you again from all the nations where he scattered you. [4]Even if you have been banished to the most distant land under the heavens, from there the LORD your God will gather you and bring you back. [5]He will bring you to the land that belonged to your fathers, and you will take possession of it. He will make you more prosperous and numerous than your fathers. [6]The LORD your God will circumcise your hearts and the hearts of your descendants, so that you may love him with all your heart and with all your soul, and live. [7]The LORD your God will put all these curses on your enemies who hate and persecute you. [8]You will again obey the LORD and follow all his commands I am giving you today. [9]Then the LORD your God will make you most prosperous in all the work of your hands and in the fruit of your womb, the young of your livestock and the crops of your land. The LORD will again delight in you and make you prosperous, just as he delighted in your fathers, [10]if you obey the LORD your God and keep his commands and decrees that are written in this Book of the Law and turn to the LORD your God with all your heart and with all your soul.

truth or dare

When God set the rules for life, he didn't create an impossible dream. You don't even have to be a Bible scholar. The Christian life is well within your reach.

30:11-14

The Offer of Life or Death

[11]Now what I am commanding you today is not too difficult for you or beyond your reach. [12]It is not up in heaven, so that you have to ask, "Who will ascend into heaven to get it and proclaim it to us so we may obey it?" [13]Nor is it beyond the sea, so that you have to ask, "Who will cross the sea to get it and proclaim it to us so we may obey it?" [14]No, the word is very near you; it is in your mouth and in your heart so you may obey it.

[15]See, I set before you today life and prosperity, death and destruction. [16]For I command you today to love the LORD your God, to walk in his ways, and to keep his commands, decrees and laws; then you will live and increase, and the LORD your God will bless you in the land you are entering to possess.

[a] 3 Or will bring you back from captivity

[17]But if your heart turns away and you are not obedient, and if you are drawn away to bow down to other gods and worship them, [18]I declare to you this day that you will certainly be destroyed. You will not live long in the land you are crossing the Jordan to enter and possess.

[19]This day I call heaven and earth as witnesses against you that I have set before you life and death, blessings and curses. Now choose life, so that you and your children may live [20]and that you may love the LORD your God, listen to his voice, and hold fast to him. For the LORD is your life, and he will give you many years in the land he swore to give to your fathers, Abraham, Isaac and Jacob.

Joshua to Succeed Moses

31 Then Moses went out and spoke these words to all Israel: [2]"I am now a hundred and twenty years old and I am no longer able to lead you. The LORD has said to me, 'You shall not cross the Jordan.' [3]The LORD your God himself will cross over ahead of you. He will destroy these nations before you, and you will take possession of their land. Joshua also will cross over ahead of you, as the LORD said. [4]And the LORD will do to them what he did to Sihon and Og, the kings of the Amorites, whom he destroyed along with their land. [5]The LORD will deliver them to you, and you must do to them all that I have commanded you. [6]Be strong and courageous. Do not be afraid or terrified because of them, for the LORD your God goes with you; he will never leave you nor forsake you."

[7]Then Moses summoned Joshua and said to him in the presence of all Israel, "Be strong and courageous, for you must go with this people into the land that the LORD swore to their forefathers to give them, and you must divide it among them as their inheritance. [8]The LORD himself goes before you and will be with you; he will never leave you nor forsake you. Do not be afraid; do not be discouraged."

The Reading of the Law

[9]So Moses wrote down this law and gave it to the priests, the sons of Levi, who carried the ark of the covenant of the LORD, and to all the elders of Israel. [10]Then Moses commanded them: "At the end of every seven years, in the year for canceling debts, during the Feast of Tabernacles, [11]when all Israel comes to appear before the LORD your God at the place he will choose, you shall read this law before them in their hearing. [12]Assemble the people—men, women and children, and the aliens living in your towns—so they can listen and learn to fear the LORD your God and follow carefully all the words of this law. [13]Their children, who do not know this law, must hear it and learn to fear the LORD your God as long as you live in the land you are crossing the Jordan to possess."

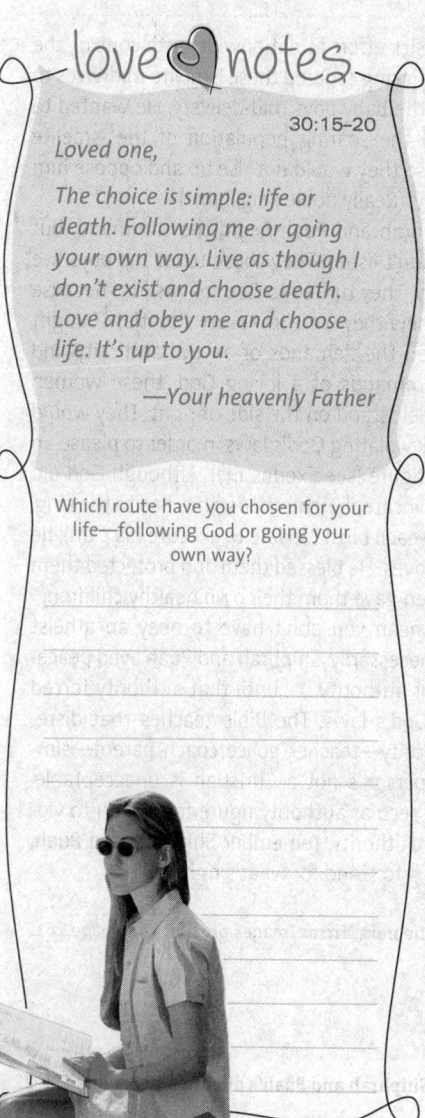

love notes

30:15–20

Loved one,

The choice is simple: life or death. Following me or going your own way. Live as though I don't exist and choose death. Love and obey me and choose life. It's up to you.

—Your heavenly Father

Which route have you chosen for your life—following God or going your own way?

mirror images

Shiphrah and Puah—Authority Issues

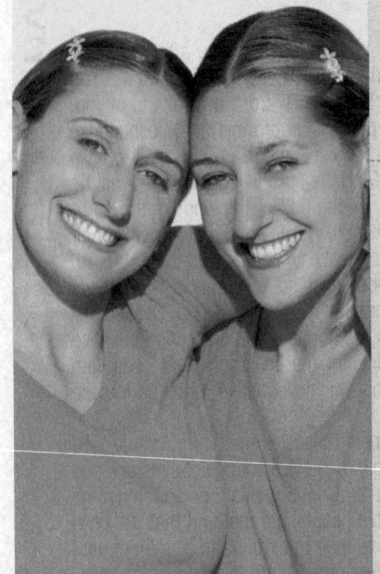

Shiphrah and Puah—not necessarily names you'd want to pass down to your own daughters. However, their heroism in the face of great danger is worth repeating.

In a sick effort at nationwide birth control, the Egyptian king ordered these Israelite midwives to kill all the baby boys mid-delivery. He wanted to control the soaring population of the Israelite slaves so they would not rise up and oppose him one day. (Really noble king, huh?)

Shiphrah and Puah heard the command, but they didn't listen. They chose to let the boys live anyway. They turned to God for wisdom because they knew they were in a scary situation. Caught between the demands of an evil authority and the commands of a loving God, these women took their stand on the side of right. They would not risk violating God's laws in order to please an earthly authority figure (see Exodus 1:17). Although God did not necessarily advocate their methods (they lied to the king, saying they got to each birth too late to execute his plan), he honored their motives. He blessed them and protected them from harm. He even gave them their own healthy children.

So, does that mean you don't have to obey an atheist teacher? No, not necessarily. Shiphrah and Puah lived peacefully under secular authority . . . until that authority forced them to violate God's laws. The Bible teaches that disrespecting any authority—teacher, police, coach, parent—simply because the person's not a Christian is unacceptable. However, when a secular authority figure forces you to violate God's higher authority, remember Shiphrah and Puah, two women willing to stand for what's right.

Dear God, thank you for the brave example of Shiphrah and Puah. Give me the same wisdom to know how to deal with ungodly authority figures without dishonoring you. Amen.

To read the next Mirror Images profile, go to page 261.

Read more about Shiphrah and Puah's dilemma in Exodus 1:8–22 (page 70).

Israel's Rebellion Predicted

¹⁴The LORD said to Moses, "Now the day of your death is near. Call Joshua and present yourselves at the Tent of Meeting, where I will commission him." So Moses and Joshua came and presented themselves at the Tent of Meeting.

¹⁵Then the LORD appeared at the Tent in a pillar of cloud, and the cloud stood over the entrance to the Tent. ¹⁶And the LORD said to Moses: "You are going to rest with your fathers, and these people will soon prostitute themselves to the foreign gods of the land they are entering. They will forsake me and break the covenant I made with them. ¹⁷On that day I will become angry with them and forsake them; I will hide my face from them, and they will be destroyed. Many disasters and difficulties will come upon them, and on that day they will ask, 'Have not these disasters come upon us because our God is not with us?' ¹⁸And I will certainly hide my face on that day because of all their wickedness in turning to other gods.

¹⁹"Now write down for yourselves this song and teach it to the Israelites and have them sing it, so that it may be a witness for me against them. ²⁰When I have brought them into the land flowing with milk and honey, the land I promised on oath to their forefathers, and when they eat their fill and thrive, they will turn to other gods and worship them, rejecting me and breaking my covenant. ²¹And when many disasters and difficulties come upon them, this song will testify against them, because it will not be forgotten by their descendants. I know what they are disposed to do, even before I bring them into the land I promised them on oath." ²²So Moses wrote down this song that day and taught it to the Israelites.

²³The LORD gave this command to Joshua son of Nun: "Be strong and courageous, for you will bring the Israelites into the land I promised them on oath, and I myself will be with you."

²⁴After Moses finished writing in a book the words of this law from beginning to end, ²⁵he gave this command to the Levites who carried the ark of the covenant of the LORD: ²⁶"Take this Book of the Law and place it beside the ark of the covenant of the LORD your God. There it will remain as a witness against you. ²⁷For I know how rebellious and stiff-necked you are. If you have been rebellious against the LORD while I am still alive and with you, how much more will you rebel after I die! ²⁸Assemble before me all the elders of your tribes and all your officials, so that I can speak these words in their hearing and call heaven and earth to testify against them. ²⁹For I know that after my death you are sure to become utterly corrupt and to turn from the way I have commanded you. In days to come, disaster will fall upon you because you will do evil in the sight of the LORD and provoke him to anger by what your hands have made."

truth or dare

Feel like the world is ending? In those insecure moments every girl faces, picture God as your rock. He's unshakeable. He's strong. He's a safe shelter.

32:4

The Song of Moses

³⁰And Moses recited the words of this song from beginning to end in the hearing of the whole assembly of Israel:

32

> Listen, O heavens, and I will speak;
>   hear, O earth, the words of my mouth.
> ²Let my teaching fall like rain
>   and my words descend like dew,
> like showers on new grass,
>   like abundant rain on tender plants.
>
> ³I will proclaim the name of the LORD.
>   Oh, praise the greatness of our God!
> ⁴He is the Rock, his works are perfect,
>   and all his ways are just.
> A faithful God who does no wrong,
>   upright and just is he.

⁵They have acted corruptly toward him;
　　to their shame they are no longer his children,
　　but a warped and crooked generation.^a
⁶Is this the way you repay the LORD,
　　O foolish and unwise people?
Is he not your Father, your Creator,^b
　　who made you and formed you?

⁷Remember the days of old;
　　consider the generations long past.
Ask your father and he will tell you,
　　your elders, and they will explain to you.
⁸When the Most High gave the nations their inheritance,
　　when he divided all mankind,
he set up boundaries for the peoples
　　according to the number of the sons of Israel.^c
⁹For the LORD's portion is his people,
　　Jacob his allotted inheritance.

¹⁰In a desert land he found him,
　　in a barren and howling waste.
He shielded him and cared for him;
　　he guarded him as the apple of his eye,
¹¹like an eagle that stirs up its nest
　　and hovers over its young,
that spreads its wings to catch them
　　and carries them on its pinions.
¹²The LORD alone led him;
　　no foreign god was with him.

¹³He made him ride on the heights of the land
　　and fed him with the fruit of the fields.
He nourished him with honey from the rock,
　　and with oil from the flinty crag,
¹⁴with curds and milk from herd and flock
　　and with fattened lambs and goats,
with choice rams of Bashan
　　and the finest kernels of wheat.
You drank the foaming blood of the grape.

¹⁵Jeshurun^d grew fat and kicked;
　　filled with food, he became heavy and sleek.
He abandoned the God who made him
　　and rejected the Rock his Savior.
¹⁶They made him jealous with their foreign gods
　　and angered him with their detestable idols.
¹⁷They sacrificed to demons, which are not God—
　　gods they had not known,
　　gods that recently appeared,
　　gods your fathers did not fear.
¹⁸You deserted the Rock, who fathered you;
　　you forgot the God who gave you birth.

¹⁹The LORD saw this and rejected them
　　because he was angered by his sons and daughters.

^a 5 Or *Corrupt are they and not his children, / a generation warped and twisted to their shame*　^b 6 Or *Father, who bought you*　^c 8 Masoretic Text; Dead Sea Scrolls (see also Septuagint) *sons of God*　^d 15 *Jeshurun* means *the upright one*, that is, Israel.

²⁰ "I will hide my face from them," he said,
  "and see what their end will be;
for they are a perverse generation,
  children who are unfaithful.
²¹ They made me jealous by what is no god
  and angered me with their worthless idols.
I will make them envious by those who are not a people;
  I will make them angry by a nation that has no understanding.
²² For a fire has been kindled by my wrath,
  one that burns to the realm of death*ᵃ* below.
It will devour the earth and its harvests
  and set afire the foundations of the mountains.

²³ "I will heap calamities upon them
  and spend my arrows against them.
²⁴ I will send wasting famine against them,
  consuming pestilence and deadly plague;
I will send against them the fangs of wild beasts,
  the venom of vipers that glide in the dust.
²⁵ In the street the sword will make them childless;
  in their homes terror will reign.
Young men and young women will perish,
  infants and gray-haired men.
²⁶ I said I would scatter them
  and blot out their memory from mankind,
²⁷ but I dreaded the taunt of the enemy,
  lest the adversary misunderstand
and say, 'Our hand has triumphed;
  the LORD has not done all this.' "

²⁸ They are a nation without sense,
  there is no discernment in them.
²⁹ If only they were wise and would understand this
  and discern what their end will be!
³⁰ How could one man chase a thousand,
  or two put ten thousand to flight,
unless their Rock had sold them,
  unless the LORD had given them up?
³¹ For their rock is not like our Rock,
  as even our enemies concede.
³² Their vine comes from the vine of Sodom
  and from the fields of Gomorrah.
Their grapes are filled with poison,
  and their clusters with bitterness.
³³ Their wine is the venom of serpents,
  the deadly poison of cobras.

³⁴ "Have I not kept this in reserve
  and sealed it in my vaults?
³⁵ It is mine to avenge; I will repay.
  In due time their foot will slip;
their day of disaster is near
  and their doom rushes upon them."

³⁶ The LORD will judge his people
  and have compassion on his servants

---

a 22 Hebrew *to Sheol*

when he sees their strength is gone
and no one is left, slave or free.
[37] He will say: "Now where are their gods,
the rock they took refuge in,
[38] the gods who ate the fat of their sacrifices
and drank the wine of their drink offerings?
Let them rise up to help you!
Let them give you shelter!

[39] "See now that I myself am He!
There is no god besides me.
I put to death and I bring to life,
I have wounded and I will heal,
and no one can deliver out of my hand.
[40] I lift my hand to heaven and declare:
As surely as I live forever,
[41] when I sharpen my flashing sword
and my hand grasps it in judgment,
I will take vengeance on my adversaries
and repay those who hate me.
[42] I will make my arrows drunk with blood,
while my sword devours flesh:
the blood of the slain and the captives,
the heads of the enemy leaders."

[43] Rejoice, O nations, with his people,[a, b]
for he will avenge the blood of his servants;
he will take vengeance on his enemies
and make atonement for his land and people.

[44] Moses came with Joshua[c] son of Nun and spoke all the words of this song in the hearing of the people. [45] When Moses finished reciting all these words to all Israel, [46] he said to them, "Take to heart all the words I have solemnly declared to you this day, so that you may command your children to obey carefully all the words of this law. [47] They are not just idle words for you—they are your life. By them you will live long in the land you are crossing the Jordan to possess."

Moses to Die on Mount Nebo

[48] On that same day the LORD told Moses, [49] "Go up into the Abarim Range to Mount Nebo in Moab, across from Jericho, and view Canaan, the land I am giving the Israelites as their own possession. [50] There on the mountain that you have climbed you will die and be gathered to your people, just as your brother Aaron died on Mount Hor and was gathered to his people. [51] This is because both of you broke faith with me in the presence of the Israelites at the waters of Meribah Kadesh in the Desert of Zin and because you did not uphold my holiness among the Israelites. [52] Therefore, you will see the land only from a distance; you will not enter the land I am giving to the people of Israel."

truth or dare

The Bible isn't like other books. It's not a feel-good storybook or a dry operations manual. It's in a class all its own—powerful, dynamic, life-changing. It is your life.

32:45–47

Moses Blesses the Tribes

33 This is the blessing that Moses the man of God pronounced on the Israelites before his death. [2] He said:

[a] 43 Or *Make his people rejoice, O nations*   [b] 43 Masoretic Text; Dead Sea Scrolls (see also Septuagint) *people, / and let all the angels worship him /*   [c] 44 Hebrew *Hoshea*, a variant of *Joshua*

"The LORD came from Sinai
 and dawned over them from Seir;
 he shone forth from Mount Paran.
He came with[a] myriads of holy ones
 from the south, from his mountain slopes.[b]
[3] Surely it is you who love the people;
 all the holy ones are in your hand.
At your feet they all bow down,
 and from you receive instruction,
[4] the law that Moses gave us,
 the possession of the assembly of Jacob.
[5] He was king over Jeshurun[c]
 when the leaders of the people assembled,
 along with the tribes of Israel.

[6] "Let Reuben live and not die,
 nor[d] his men be few."

[7] And this he said about Judah:

"Hear, O LORD, the cry of Judah;
 bring him to his people.
With his own hands he defends his cause.
 Oh, be his help against his foes!"

[8] About Levi he said:

"Your Thummim and Urim belong
 to the man you favored.
You tested him at Massah;
 you contended with him at the waters of Meribah.
[9] He said of his father and mother,
 'I have no regard for them.'
He did not recognize his brothers
 or acknowledge his own children,
but he watched over your word
 and guarded your covenant.
[10] He teaches your precepts to Jacob
 and your law to Israel.
He offers incense before you
 and whole burnt offerings on your altar.
[11] Bless all his skills, O LORD,
 and be pleased with the work of his hands.
Smite the loins of those who rise up against him;
 strike his foes till they rise no more."

[12] About Benjamin he said:

"Let the beloved of the LORD rest secure in him,
 for he shields him all day long,
 and the one the LORD loves rests between his shoulders."

[13] About Joseph he said:

"May the LORD bless his land
 with the precious dew from heaven above
 and with the deep waters that lie below;
[14] with the best the sun brings forth

---

a 2 Or *from*   *b 2* The meaning of the Hebrew for this phrase is uncertain.   *c 5 Jeshurun* means *the upright one,* that is, Israel; also in verse 26.   *d 6* Or *but let*

and the finest the moon can yield;
¹⁵ with the choicest gifts of the ancient mountains
and the fruitfulness of the everlasting hills;
¹⁶ with the best gifts of the earth and its fullness
and the favor of him who dwelt in the burning bush.
Let all these rest on the head of Joseph,
on the brow of the prince among* his brothers.
¹⁷ In majesty he is like a firstborn bull;
his horns are the horns of a wild ox.
With them he will gore the nations,
even those at the ends of the earth.
Such are the ten thousands of Ephraim;
such are the thousands of Manasseh."

love notes

33:12

Daughter,

What burdens are you carrying today? Pressure from friends? Deadlines? Demands? Disappointments? Rest secure in me.

—Father God

Write a prayer to God asking him to be your shield during the storms of life.

_____
_____
_____
_____
_____
_____
_____
_____
_____
_____
_____

¹⁸ About Zebulun he said:

"Rejoice, Zebulun, in your going out,
and you, Issachar, in your tents.
¹⁹ They will summon peoples to the mountain
and there offer sacrifices of righteousness;
they will feast on the abundance of the seas,
on the treasures hidden in the sand."

²⁰ About Gad he said:

"Blessed is he who enlarges Gad's domain!
Gad lives there like a lion,
tearing at arm or head.
²¹ He chose the best land for himself;
the leader's portion was kept for him.
When the heads of the people assembled,
he carried out the LORD's righteous will,
and his judgments concerning Israel."

²² About Dan he said:

"Dan is a lion's cub,
springing out of Bashan."

²³ About Naphtali he said:

"Naphtali is abounding with the favor of the LORD
and is full of his blessing;
he will inherit southward to the lake."

a 16 Or of the one separated from

24 About Asher he said:

"Most blessed of sons is Asher;
let him be favored by his brothers,
and let him bathe his feet in oil.
25 The bolts of your gates will be iron and bronze,
and your strength will equal your days.

26 "There is no one like the God of Jeshurun,
who rides on the heavens to help you
and on the clouds in his majesty.
27 The eternal God is your refuge,
and underneath are the everlasting arms.
He will drive out your enemy before you,
saying, 'Destroy him!'
28 So Israel will live in safety alone;
Jacob's spring is secure
in a land of grain and new wine,
where the heavens drop dew.
29 Blessed are you, O Israel!
Who is like you,
a people saved by the LORD?
He is your shield and helper
and your glorious sword.
Your enemies will cower before you,
and you will trample down
their high places. a"

love notes

33:27

Dear child,

I am your refuge. When you feel like you're falling, don't be afraid. You may not be able to see my arms or feel my touch, but I am right there beneath you. I'll never let you fall.

—Your Father in heaven

Where do you find your security—in God or somewhere else?

The Death of Moses

34 Then Moses climbed Mount Nebo from the plains of Moab to the top of Pisgah, across from Jericho. There the LORD showed him the whole land—from Gilead to Dan, 2 all of Naphtali, the territory of Ephraim and Manasseh, all the land of Judah as far as the western sea, b 3 the Negev and the whole region from the Valley of Jericho, the City of Palms, as far as Zoar. 4 Then the LORD said to him, "This is the land I promised on oath to Abraham, Isaac and Jacob when I said, 'I will give it to your descendants.' I have let you see it with your eyes, but you will not cross over into it."

5 And Moses the servant of the LORD died there in Moab, as the LORD had said. 6 He buried him c in Moab, in the valley opposite Beth Peor, but to this day no one knows where his grave is. 7 Moses was a hundred and twenty years old when he died, yet his eyes were not weak nor his strength gone. 8 The Israelites grieved for Moses in the plains of Moab thirty days, until the time of weeping and mourning was over.

a 29 Or will tread upon their bodies   b 2 That is, the Mediterranean   c 6 Or He was buried

When Life Hurts

focus **Profile: Samantha**

June 26, 2:56 A.M. That's when Kavon was born and our lives changed forever. Instead of celebrating the birth of my older sister's first child, we found ourselves huddled in the waiting room outside of the intensive care unit. Kavon was born with severe handicaps—he would never walk or even be able to feed himself. The doctors had warned that there would be complications—they just hadn't explained how serious they might be.

I've always believed God has a reason for everything that happens. That was before I saw the pain in my sister's eyes when she held Kavon for the first time. She was smiling and talking softly to him, with tears streaming quietly down her face. I couldn't take my eyes off her while the doctors explained everything to our family. "It's going to be okay. Just pray," I whispered to her.

Yet inside I was screaming. *Why did you let this happen in the first place, God? Why my sister and her husband? They are such good people. If you had the power to heal my nephew, then why didn't you? What did they do to deserve this?* I left the room so my sister wouldn't see me crying, too. My heart felt like it was breaking.

If God is good, then why does he let things like this happen? I want to believe he knows what he's doing … but right now it sure doesn't seem like it.

suffering in focus

Why do bad things happen to good people? You might be able to come up with the right "Sunday school" answer—but when you're the one who's hurting, then that answer feels pretty empty. The Bible reveals that suffering is a mystery this side of heaven. If you or someone you know is going through suffering right now, keep this in mind:

» The Bible offers peace "which transcends all understanding"—meaning that even though you may not have the answers *why*, you can still experience God's peace (see Philippians 4:7, page 1553).

» Sometimes we need to talk through our pain—a friend, parent or counselor can help you sort out all the emotions you're feeling.

» Jesus himself knows the depth of human suffering—he alone truly knows how you feel. See Hebrews 4:15 (page 1588) and Isaiah 53:3 (page 969).

For more on this topic, see the index on page 1656.

[9]Now Joshua son of Nun was filled with the spirit[a] of wisdom because Moses had laid his hands on him. So the Israelites listened to him and did what the LORD had commanded Moses.

[10]Since then, no prophet has risen in Israel like Moses, whom the LORD knew face to face, [11]who did all those miraculous signs and wonders the LORD sent him to do in Egypt—to Pharaoh and to all his officials and to his whole land. [12]For no one has ever shown the mighty power or performed the awesome deeds that Moses did in the sight of all Israel.

a 9 Or *Spirit*

author:	Joshua, except for the ending, which may have been written by the high priest, Phinehas.
date:	Probably about 1390 B.C.
setting:	Canaan (the promised land), which today is Israel.
verse to remember:	So the LORD gave Israel all the land he had sworn to give their forefathers, and they took possession of it and settled there (21:43).
theme to consider:	God gives us second chances! Though the people failed to enter the promised land the first time, God fulfilled his promise to Abraham by giving his people another chance.

joshua

unchanging truth

Three strikes and you're out. You drop the fly ball, and the other team scores the winning run. You miss your final free throw or penalty kick, and the other team advances in the play-offs. In sports there are no second chances. No fourth strike to see if you can connect with the ball. No replays on a fly ball or a free throw or a penalty kick to give you another chance to succeed.

Thankfully, not all of life is like a sporting event. Think of how many times you really blow it in life! You do it with your family, friends and schoolwork all the time. But thankfully, you *do* get a fourth, and maybe even a fifth or sixth or twentieth "strike." There's another chance to try again and improve things. Second chances help us to learn from our mistakes and grow. They also help us to become more tolerant of others' failures.

The Israelites really blew their chance of entering the promised land the first time. Because of their disobedience, God punished them, but he didn't give up on them (see Numbers 14:29–31). God gave them a second chance. They had learned from their mistake and were now ready to move ahead. God gives us second chances, too. When we disobey him or don't trust him, God doesn't give up on us. Thank goodness he's a God of second chances!

life lessons

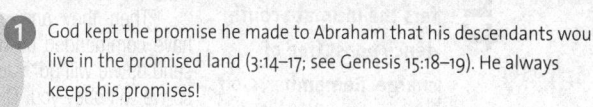

1. God kept the promise he made to Abraham that his descendants would live in the promised land (3:14–17; see Genesis 15:18–19). He always keeps his promises!

2. Rahab lived a life that wasn't pleasing to God, but she was given a second chance (6:23–25).

3. In his farewell speech, Joshua *reminded* the Israelites of the promises of God and asked the people to *remember* those promises (23:14).

The LORD Commands Joshua

1 After the death of Moses the servant of the LORD, the LORD said to Joshua son of Nun, Moses' aide: ²"Moses my servant is dead. Now then, you and all these people, get ready to cross the Jordan River into the land I am about to give to them—to the Israelites. ³I will give you every place where you set your foot, as I promised Moses. ⁴Your territory will extend from the desert to Lebanon, and from the great river, the Euphrates—all the Hittite country—to the Great Sea ᵃ on the west. ⁵No one will be able to stand up against you all the days of your life. As I was with Moses, so I will be with you; I will never leave you nor forsake you.

⁶"Be strong and courageous, because you will lead these people to inherit the land I swore to their forefathers to give them. ⁷Be strong and very courageous. Be careful to obey all the law my servant Moses gave you; do not turn from it to the right or to the left, that you may be successful wherever you go. ⁸Do not let this Book of the Law depart from your mouth; meditate on it day and night, so that you may be careful to do everything written in it. Then you will be prosperous and successful. ⁹Have I not commanded you? Be strong and courageous. Do not be terrified; do not be discouraged, for the LORD your God will be with you wherever you go."

¹⁰So Joshua ordered the officers of the people: ¹¹"Go through the camp and tell the people, 'Get your supplies ready. Three days from now you will cross the Jordan here to go in and take possession of the land the LORD your God is giving you for your own.'"

¹²But to the Reubenites, the Gadites and the half-tribe of Manasseh, Joshua said, ¹³"Remember the command that Moses the servant of the LORD gave you: 'The LORD your God is giving you rest and has granted you this land.' ¹⁴Your wives, your children and your livestock may stay in the land that Moses gave you east of the Jordan, but all your fighting men, fully armed, must cross over ahead of your brothers. You are to help your brothers ¹⁵until the LORD gives them rest, as he has done for you, and until they too have taken possession of the land that the LORD your God is giving them. After that, you may go back and occupy your own land, which Moses the servant of the LORD gave you east of the Jordan toward the sunrise."

¹⁶Then they answered Joshua, "Whatever you have commanded us we will do, and wherever you send us we will go. ¹⁷Just as we fully obeyed Moses, so we will obey you. Only may the LORD your God be with you as he was with Moses. ¹⁸Whoever rebels against your word and does not obey your words, whatever you may command them, will be put to death. Only be strong and courageous!"

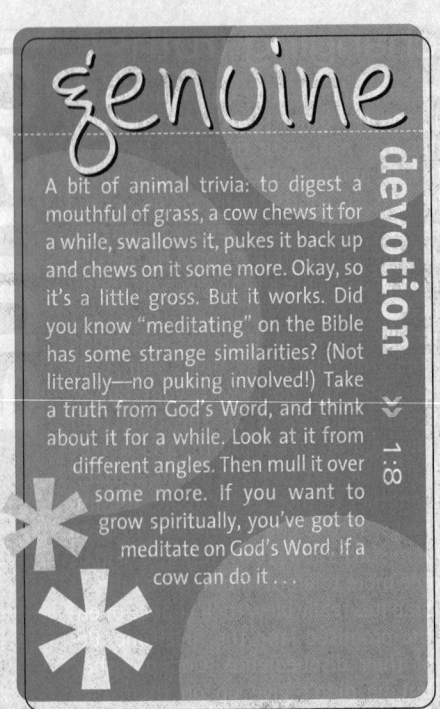

genuine devotion ≫ 1:8

A bit of animal trivia: to digest a mouthful of grass, a cow chews it for a while, swallows it, pukes it back up and chews on it some more. Okay, so it's a little gross. But it works. Did you know "meditating" on the Bible has some strange similarities? (Not literally—no puking involved!) Take a truth from God's Word, and think about it for a while. Look at it from different angles. Then mull it over some more. If you want to grow spiritually, you've got to meditate on God's Word. If a cow can do it . . .

truth or dare

Which boost would you like—protein, vitamin or confidence? God offers the ultimate confidence boost free of charge. Remember, God is supporting you—he'll never leave you.

1:9

ᵃ 4 That is, the Mediterranean

Rahab and the Spies

2 Then Joshua son of Nun secretly sent tw[o]
from Shittim. "Go, look over the land," h[e]
"especially Jericho." So they went and entered the
house of a prostitute *a* named Rahab and stayed there.

²The king of Jericho was told, "Look! Some of the Israelites have come here tonight to spy out the land." ³So
the king of Jericho sent this message to Rahab: "Bring
out the men who came to you and entered your house,
because they have come to spy out the whole land."

⁴But the woman had taken the two men and hidden
them. She said, "Yes, the men came to me, but I did
not know where they had come from. ⁵At dusk, when it
was time to close the city gate, the men left. I don't
know which way they went. Go after them quickly. You
may catch up with them." ⁶(But she had taken them up
to the roof and hidden them under the stalks of flax she
had laid out on the roof.) ⁷So the men set out in pursuit of the spies on the road that leads to the
fords of the Jordan, and as soon as the pursuers had gone out, the gate was shut.

⁸Before the spies lay down for the night, she went
up on the roof ⁹and said to them, "I know that the LORD
has given this land to you and that a great fear of you
has fallen on us, so that all who live in this country are
melting in fear because of you. ¹⁰We have heard how
the LORD dried up the water of the Red Sea *b* for you
when you came out of Egypt, and what you did to Sihon
and Og, the two kings of the Amorites east of the Jordan, whom you completely destroyed. *c* ¹¹When we
heard of it, our hearts melted and everyone's courage
failed because of you, for the LORD your God is God in
heaven above and on the earth below. ¹²Now then, please swear to
me by the LORD that you will show kindness to my family, because
I have shown kindness to you. Give me a sure sign ¹³that you will
spare the lives of my father and mother, my brothers and sisters,
and all who belong to them, and that you will save us from death."

¹⁴"Our lives for your lives!" the men assured her. "If you don't
tell what we are doing, we will treat you kindly and faithfully when the LORD gives us the land."

¹⁵So she let them down by a rope through the window, for the house she lived in was part of
the city wall. ¹⁶Now she had said to them, "Go to the hills so the pursuers will not find you. Hide
yourselves there three days until they return, and then go on your way."

¹⁷The men said to her, "This oath you made us swear will not be binding on us ¹⁸unless, when
we enter the land, you have tied this scarlet cord in the window through which you let us down,
and unless you have brought your father and mother, your brothers and all your family into your
house. ¹⁹If anyone goes outside your house into the street, his blood will be on his own head; we
will not be responsible. As for anyone who is in the house with you, his blood will be on our head
if a hand is laid on him. ²⁰But if you tell what we are doing, we will be released from the oath you
made us swear."

²¹"Agreed," she replied. "Let it be as you say." So she sent them away and they departed. And
she tied the scarlet cord in the window.

²²When they left, they went into the hills and stayed there three days, until the pursuers had
searched all along the road and returned without finding them. ²³Then the two men started back.
They went down out of the hills, forded the river and came to Joshua son of Nun and told him ev-

---

truth or dare

Does the word *authority*
make you cringe? Fol-
lowing a leader doesn't
squash your individuali-
ty! Leaders are great
sources for wisdom and
a fresh perspective.

1:16

---

truth or dare

Rahab lived in a pagan
land with unbelieving
people (hmmm, sounds
like *our* culture!), yet
she still respected God's
power. Don't let the
world distract you from
serving God.

2:11

---

a 1 Or possibly *an innkeeper*   *b 10* Hebrew *Yam Suph*; that is, Sea of Reeds   *c 10* The Hebrew term refers to the
irrevocable giving over of things or persons to the LORD, often by totally destroying them.

erything that had happened to them. ²⁴They said to Joshua, "The LORD has surely given the whole land into our hands; all the people are melting in fear because of us."

Crossing the Jordan

3 Early in the morning Joshua and all the Israelites set out from Shittim and went to the Jordan, where they camped before crossing over. ²After three days the officers went throughout the camp, ³giving orders to the people: "When you see the ark of the covenant of the LORD your God, and the priests, who are Levites, carrying it, you are to move out from your positions and follow it. ⁴Then you will know which way to go, since you have never been this way before. But keep a distance of about a thousand yards*ᵃ* between you and the ark; do not go near it."

⁵Joshua told the people, "Consecrate yourselves, for tomorrow the LORD will do amazing things among you."

⁶Joshua said to the priests, "Take up the ark of the covenant and pass on ahead of the people." So they took it up and went ahead of them.

⁷And the LORD said to Joshua, "Today I will begin to exalt you in the eyes of all Israel, so they may know that I am with you as I was with Moses. ⁸Tell the priests who carry the ark of the covenant: 'When you reach the edge of the Jordan's waters, go and stand in the river.' "

⁹Joshua said to the Israelites, "Come here and listen to the words of the LORD your God. ¹⁰This is how you will know that the living God is among you and that he will certainly drive out before you the Canaanites, Hittites, Hivites, Perizzites, Girgashites, Amorites and Jebusites. ¹¹See, the ark of the covenant of the Lord of all the earth will go into the Jordan ahead of you. ¹²Now then, choose twelve men from the tribes of Israel, one from each tribe. ¹³And as soon as the priests who carry the ark of the LORD—the Lord of all the earth—set foot in the Jordan, its waters flowing downstream will be cut off and stand up in a heap."

¹⁴So when the people broke camp to cross the Jordan, the priests carrying the ark of the covenant went ahead of them. ¹⁵Now the Jordan is at flood stage all during harvest. Yet as soon as the priests who carried the ark reached the Jordan and their feet touched the water's edge, ¹⁶the water from upstream stopped flowing. It piled up in a heap a great distance away, at a town called Adam in the vicinity of Zarethan, while the water flowing down to the Sea of the Arabah (the Salt Sea*ᵇ*) was completely cut off. So the people crossed over opposite Jericho. ¹⁷The priests who carried the ark of the covenant of the LORD stood firm on dry ground in the middle of the Jordan, while all Israel passed by until the whole nation had completed the crossing on dry ground.

4 When the whole nation had finished crossing the Jordan, the LORD said to Joshua, ²"Choose twelve men from among the people, one from each tribe, ³and tell them to take up twelve stones from the middle of the Jordan from right where the priests stood and to carry them over with you and put them down at the place where you stay tonight."

⁴So Joshua called together the twelve men he had appointed from the Israelites, one from each tribe, ⁵and said to them, "Go over before the ark of the LORD your God into the middle of the Jordan. Each of you is to take up a stone on his shoulder, according to the number of the tribes of the Israelites, ⁶to serve as a sign among you. In the future, when your children ask you, 'What do these stones mean?' ⁷tell them that the flow of the Jordan was cut off before the ark of the covenant

truth or dare

Talk about a *literal* step of faith! The priests risked everything because they knew God would protect them. What faith steps does God want *you* to take?

3:8–13

truth or dare

Next time you experience an awesome victory, you might be tempted to charge on ahead. Instead, take some time to listen to God.

4:1–7

ᵃ 4 Hebrew about two thousand cubits (about 900 meters)   *ᵇ 16 That is, the Dead Sea* of the LORD. When it crossed the Jordan, the waters of the Jordan were cut off. These stor[es] to be a memorial to the people of Israel forever."

⁸So the Israelites did as Joshua commanded them. They took twelve stones from the m[iddle of] the Jordan, according to the number of the tribes of the Israelites, as the LORD had told Joshua, and they carried them over with them to their camp, where they put them down. ⁹Joshua set up the twelve stones that had been *a* in the middle of the Jordan at the spot where the priests who carried the ark of the covenant had stood. And they are there to this day.

¹⁰Now the priests who carried the ark remained standing in the middle of the Jordan until everything the LORD had commanded Joshua was done by the people, just as Moses had directed Joshua. The people hurried over, ¹¹and as soon as all of them had crossed, the ark of the LORD and the priests came to the other side while the people watched. ¹²The men of Reuben, Gad and the half-tribe of Manasseh crossed over, armed, in front of the Israelites, as Moses had directed them. ¹³About forty thousand armed for battle crossed over before the LORD to the plains of Jericho for war.

¹⁴That day the LORD exalted Joshua in the sight of all Israel; and they revered him all the days of his life, just as they had revered Moses.

¹⁵Then the LORD said to Joshua, ¹⁶"Command the priests carrying the ark of the Testimony to come up out of the Jordan."

¹⁷So Joshua commanded the priests, "Come up out of the Jordan."

¹⁸And the priests came up out of the river carrying the ark of the covenant of the LORD. No sooner had they set their feet on the dry ground than the waters of the Jordan returned to their place and ran at flood stage as before.

¹⁹On the tenth day of the first month the people went up from the Jordan and camped at Gilgal on the eastern border of Jericho. ²⁰And Joshua set up at Gilgal the twelve stones they had taken out of the Jordan. ²¹He said to the Israelites, "In the future when your descendants ask their fathers, 'What do these stones mean?' ²²tell them, 'Israel crossed the Jordan on dry ground.' ²³For the LORD your God dried up the Jordan before you until you had crossed over. The LORD your God did to the Jordan just what he had done to the Red Sea *b* when he dried it up before us until we had crossed over. ²⁴He did this so that all the peoples of the earth might know that the hand of the LORD is powerful and so that you might always fear the LORD your God."

genuine

gratitude »» 4:19-24

"Oops, I forgot." You've probably said that dozens of times. To your mom, when she asked why you were on the computer instead of cleaning your room. To your friend, when she wanted to know why you didn't bring back the sweater you borrowed. To your teacher, when he collected a homework assignment. It's easy to forget stuff. But God wants us to remember the things he's done. It's common courtesy to remember the great things others have done for you. How has God provided for you? How has he answered your prayers? Satan wants you to forget; God wants you to remember.

Circumcision at Gilgal

5 Now when all the Amorite kings west of the Jordan and all the Canaanite kings along the coast heard how the LORD had dried up the Jordan before the Israelites until we had crossed over, their hearts melted and they no longer had the courage to face the Israelites.

²At that time the LORD said to Joshua, "Make flint knives and circumcise the Israelites again." ³So Joshua made flint knives and circumcised the Israelites at Gibeath Haaraloth. *c*

⁴Now this is why he did so: All those who came out of Egypt—all the men of military age—died in the desert on the way after leaving Egypt. ⁵All the people that came out had been circumcised, but all the people born in the desert during the journey from Egypt had not. ⁶The Israelites had moved

a 9 Or *Joshua also set up twelve stones*   *b 23* Hebrew *Yam Suph*; that is, Sea of Reeds   *c 3 Gibeath Haaraloth* means *hill of foreskins.*

about in the desert forty years until all the men who were of military age when they left Egypt had died, since they had not obeyed the LORD. For the LORD had sworn to them that they would not see the land that he had solemnly promised their fathers to give us, a land flowing with milk and honey. ⁷So he raised up their sons in their place, and these were the ones Joshua circumcised. They were still uncircumcised because they had not been circumcised on the way. ⁸And after the whole nation had been circumcised, they remained where they were in camp until they were healed.

⁹Then the LORD said to Joshua, "Today I have rolled away the reproach of Egypt from you." So the place has been called Gilgal *a* to this day.

¹⁰On the evening of the fourteenth day of the month, while camped at Gilgal on the plains of Jericho, the Israelites celebrated the Passover. ¹¹The day after the Passover, that very day, they ate some of the produce of the land: unleavened bread and roasted grain. ¹²The manna stopped the day after *b* they ate this food from the land; there was no longer any manna for the Israelites, but that year they ate of the produce of Canaan.

The Fall of Jericho

¹³Now when Joshua was near Jericho, he looked up and saw a man standing in front of him with a drawn sword in his hand. Joshua went up to him and asked, "Are you for us or for our enemies?"

¹⁴"Neither," he replied, "but as commander of the army of the LORD I have now come." Then Joshua fell facedown to the ground in reverence, and asked him, "What message does my Lord *c* have for his servant?"

¹⁵The commander of the LORD's army replied, "Take off your sandals, for the place where you are standing is holy." And Joshua did so.

6 Now Jericho was tightly shut up because of the Israelites. No one went out and no one came in.

²Then the LORD said to Joshua, "See, I have delivered Jericho into your hands, along with its king and its fighting men. ³March around the city once with all the armed men. Do this for six days. ⁴Have seven priests carry trumpets of rams' horns in front of the ark. On the seventh day, march around the city seven times, with the priests blowing the trumpets. ⁵When you hear them sound a long blast on the trumpets, have all the people give a loud shout; then the wall of the city will collapse and the people will go up, every man straight in."

⁶So Joshua son of Nun called the priests and said to them, "Take up the ark of the covenant of the LORD and have seven priests carry trumpets in front of it." ⁷And he ordered the people, "Advance! March around the city, with the armed guard going ahead of the ark of the LORD."

⁸When Joshua had spoken to the people, the seven priests carrying the seven trumpets before the LORD went forward, blowing their trumpets, and the ark of the LORD's covenant followed them. ⁹The armed guard marched ahead of the priests who blew the trumpets, and the rear guard followed the ark. All this time the trumpets were sounding. ¹⁰But Joshua had commanded the people, "Do not give a war cry, do not raise your voices, do not say a word until the day I tell you to shout. Then shout!" ¹¹So he had the ark of the LORD carried around the city, circling it once. Then the people returned to camp and spent the night there.

¹²Joshua got up early the next morning and the priests took up the ark of the LORD. ¹³The seven priests carrying the seven trumpets went forward, marching before the ark of the LORD and blowing the trumpets. The armed men went ahead of them and the rear guard followed the ark of the LORD, while the trumpets kept sounding. ¹⁴So on the second day they marched around the city once and returned to the camp. They did this for six days.

¹⁵On the seventh day, they got up at daybreak and marched around the city seven times in the

truth or dare

Going into battle armed with . . . trumpets? This strategy seems crazy—if you're looking at it in *human* terms. When you face challenges, do you rely on your own strength or God's?

6:2–5

---

a 9 Gilgal sounds like the Hebrew for *roll.*   *b 12* Or *the day*   *c 14* Or *lord* same manner, except that on that day they circled the city seven times. ¹⁶The seventh time around, when the priests sounded the trumpet blast, Joshua commanded the people, "Shout! For the LORD has given you the city! ¹⁷The city and all that is in it are to be devoted*ᵃ* to the LORD. Only Rahab the prostitute*ᵇ* and all who are with her in her house shall be spared, because she hid the spies we sent. ¹⁸But keep away from the devoted things, so that you will not bring about your own destruction by taking any of them. Otherwise you will make the camp of Israel liable to destruction and bring trouble on it. ¹⁹All the silver and gold and the articles of bronze and iron are sacred to the LORD and must go into his treasury."

²⁰When the trumpets sounded, the people shouted, and at the sound of the trumpet, when the people gave a loud shout, the wall collapsed; so every man charged straight in, and they took the city. ²¹They devoted the city to the LORD and destroyed with the sword every living thing in it—men and women, young and old, cattle, sheep and donkeys.

²²Joshua said to the two men who had spied out the land, "Go into the prostitute's house and bring her out and all who belong to her, in accordance with your oath to her." ²³So the young men who had done the spying went in and brought out Rahab, her father and mother and brothers and all who belonged to her. They brought out her entire family and put them in a place outside the camp of Israel.

²⁴Then they burned the whole city and everything in it, but they put the silver and gold and the articles of bronze and iron into the treasury of the LORD's house. ²⁵But Joshua spared Rahab the prostitute, with her family and all who belonged to her, because she hid the men Joshua had sent as spies to Jericho—and she lives among the Israelites to this day.

²⁶At that time Joshua pronounced this solemn oath: "Cursed before the LORD is the man who undertakes to rebuild this city, Jericho:

> "At the cost of his firstborn son
> will he lay its foundations;
> at the cost of his youngest
> will he set up its gates."

²⁷So the LORD was with Joshua, and his fame spread throughout the land.

Achan's Sin

7 But the Israelites acted unfaithfully in regard to the devoted things*ᶜ*; Achan son of Carmi, the son of Zimri,*ᵈ* the son of Zerah, of the tribe of Judah, took some of them. So the LORD's anger burned against Israel.

²Now Joshua sent men from Jericho to Ai, which is near Beth Aven to the east of Bethel, and told them, "Go up and spy out the region." So the men went up and spied out Ai.

³When they returned to Joshua, they said, "Not all the people will have to go up against Ai. Send two or three thousand men to take it and do not weary all the people, for only a few men are there." ⁴So about three thousand men went up; but they were routed by the men of Ai, ⁵who killed about thirty-six of them. They chased the Israelites from the city gate as far as the stone quarries*ᵉ* and struck them down on the slopes. At this the hearts of the people melted and became like water.

⁶Then Joshua tore his clothes and fell facedown to the ground before the ark of the LORD, remaining there till evening. The elders of Israel did the same, and sprinkled dust on their heads. ⁷And Joshua said, "Ah, Sovereign LORD, why did you ever bring this people across the Jordan to deliver us into the hands of the Amorites to destroy us? If only we had been content to stay on the other side of the Jordan! ⁸O Lord, what can I say, now that Israel has been routed by its enemies? ⁹The Canaanites and the other people of the country will hear about this and they will surround us and wipe out our name from the earth. What then will you do for your own great name?"

¹⁰The LORD said to Joshua, "Stand up! What are you doing down on your face? ¹¹Israel has sinned; they have violated my covenant, which I commanded them to keep. They have taken some of the devoted things; they have stolen, they have lied, they have put them with their own possessions. ¹²That is why the Israelites cannot stand against their enemies; they turn their backs and run

---

ᵃ 17 The Hebrew term refers to the irrevocable giving over of things or persons to the LORD, often by totally destroying them; also in verses 18 and 21.   *ᵇ 17* Or possibly *innkeeper*; also in verses 22 and 25   *ᶜ 1* The Hebrew term refers to the irrevocable giving over of things or persons to the LORD, often by totally destroying them; also in verses 11, 12, 13 and 15.   *ᵈ 1* See Septuagint and 1 Chron. 2:6; Hebrew *Zabdi*; also in verses 17 and 18.   *ᵉ 5* Or *as far as Shebarim* because they have been made liable to destruction. I will not be with you anymore unless you destroy whatever among you is devoted to destruction.

¹³"Go, consecrate the people. Tell them, 'Consecrate yourselves in preparation for tomorrow; for this is what the LORD, the God of Israel, says: That which is devoted is among you, O Israel. You cannot stand against your enemies until you remove it.

¹⁴" 'In the morning, present yourselves tribe by tribe. The tribe that the LORD takes shall come forward clan by clan; the clan that the LORD takes shall come forward family by family; and the family that the LORD takes shall come forward man by man. ¹⁵He who is caught with the devoted things shall be destroyed by fire, along with all that belongs to him. He has violated the covenant of the LORD and has done a disgraceful thing in Israel!' "

¹⁶Early the next morning Joshua had Israel come forward by tribes, and Judah was taken. ¹⁷The clans of Judah came forward, and he took the Zerahites. He had the clan of the Zerahites come forward by families, and Zimri was taken. ¹⁸Joshua had his family come forward man by man, and Achan son of Carmi, the son of Zimri, the son of Zerah, of the tribe of Judah, was taken.

¹⁹Then Joshua said to Achan, "My son, give glory to the LORD,ᵃ the God of Israel, and give him the praise.ᵇ Tell me what you have done; do not hide it from me."

²⁰Achan replied, "It is true! I have sinned against the LORD, the God of Israel. This is what I have done: ²¹When I saw in the plunder a beautiful robe from Babylonia,ᶜ two hundred shekelsᵈ of silver and a wedge of gold weighing fifty shekels,ᵉ I coveted them and took them. They are hidden in the ground inside my tent, with the silver underneath."

²²So Joshua sent messengers, and they ran to the tent, and there it was, hidden in his tent, with the silver underneath. ²³They took the things from the tent, brought them to Joshua and all the Israelites and spread them out before the LORD.

²⁴Then Joshua, together with all Israel, took Achan son of Zerah, the silver, the robe, the gold wedge, his sons and daughters, his cattle, donkeys and sheep, his tent and all that he had, to the Valley of Achor. ²⁵Joshua said, "Why have you brought this trouble on us? The LORD will bring trouble on you today."

Then all Israel stoned him, and after they had stoned the rest, they burned them. ²⁶Over Achan they heaped up a large pile of rocks, which remains to this day. Then the LORD turned from his fierce anger. Therefore that place has been called the Valley of Achorᶠ ever since.

Ai Destroyed

8 Then the LORD said to Joshua, "Do not be afraid; do not be discouraged. Take the whole army with you, and go up and attack Ai. For I have delivered into your hands the king of Ai, his people, his city and his land. ²You shall do to Ai and its king as you did to Jericho and its king, except that you may carry off their plunder and livestock for yourselves. Set an ambush behind the city."

³So Joshua and the whole army moved out to attack Ai. He chose thirty thousand of his best fighting men and sent them out at night ⁴with these orders: "Listen carefully. You are to set an ambush behind the city. Don't go very far from it. All of you be on the alert. ⁵I and all those with me will advance on the city, and when the men come out against us, as they did before, we will flee from them. ⁶They will pursue us until we have lured them away from the city, for they will say, 'They are running away from us as they did before.' So when we flee from them, ⁷you are to rise up from ambush and take the city. The LORD your God will give it into your hand. ⁸When you have taken the city, set it on fire. Do what the LORD has commanded. See to it; you have my orders."

⁹Then Joshua sent them off, and they went to the place of ambush and lay in wait between Bethel and Ai, to the west of Ai—but Joshua spent that night with the people.

¹⁰Early the next morning Joshua mustered his men, and he and the leaders of Israel marched before them to Ai. ¹¹The entire force that was with him marched up and approached the city and arrived in front of it. They set up camp north of Ai, with the valley between them and the city. ¹²Joshua had taken about five thousand men and set them in ambush between Bethel and Ai, to the west of the city. ¹³They had the soldiers take up their positions—all those in the camp to the north of the city and the ambush to the west of it. That night Joshua went into the valley. ¹⁴When the king of Ai saw this, he and all the men of the city hurried out early in the morning

ᵃ 19 A solemn charge to tell the truth   ᵇ 19 Or and confess to him   ᶜ 21 Hebrew Shinar   ᵈ 21 That is, about 5 pounds (about 2.3 kilograms)   ᵉ 21 That is, about 1 1/4 pounds (about 0.6 kilogram)   ᶠ 26 Achor means trouble.

mirror images

But Joshua spared Rahab the prostitute, with her family and all who belonged to her, because she hid the men Joshua had sent as spies to Jericho—and she lives among the Israelites to this day. Joshua 6:25

Rahab—A Second Chance

"Do you know Jessica? She failed algebra twice." "There goes Dana—that girl who slept with all those guys last summer." "Oh, don't sit with Maggie. She got busted for drugs." Those who become known by less-than-flattering credentials know the pain of being reduced to something less than a person. Jessica, the flunky. Dana, the slut. Maggie, the druggie. Rahab, the prostitute. This was Rahab's whole identity in the town of Jericho. She wasn't known as a person at all. She was a thing—a prostitute. Until the day God gave her a new start.

That day started when Joshua sent two spies to scope out her hometown of Jericho and plan a strategy of attack. However, the king of Jericho was soon on to them and shortly he had tracked them to Rahab's house. Yet she had already safely hidden the spies on her rooftop. The spies rewarded her act of faith. When the Israelites captured the city, they followed through on their promise to rescue her and her family.

Rahab's new life then began among the God-followers. She was now Rahab, the great woman of faith (see Hebrews 11:31; James 2:25). She worshiped God and served him faithfully. She became not only the great-grandmother of King David but also one of *Jesus'* direct ancestors (see Ruth 4:18–21; Matthew 1:5).

Rahab reminds us that behind every questionable reputation is someone who needs a second chance. We just can't write someone off as less than human—incapable of feeling the weight of every slur and insult. You may know a Rahab. Who knows? You may even *be* one. Rahab had a total change of heart the day she encountered someone who knew God. As Rahab illustrates, if you take one step of faith toward him, Jesus welcomes you into his family and gives you a new start.

Dear Jesus, forgive me for when I have kept girls like Rahab at arm's length—unwilling to show them your love. Thank you for responding to our cries for a new start whenever we need it most. Amen.

dear Jesus

To read the next Mirror Images profile, go to page 297.

» Read more about Rahab's change of heart in Joshua 2 (page 255) and 6 (pages 258–259).

to meet Israel in battle at a certain place overlooking the Arabah. But he did not know that an ambush had been set against him behind the city. [15]Joshua and all Israel let themselves be driven back before them, and they fled toward the desert. [16]All the men of Ai were called to pursue them, and they pursued Joshua and were lured away from the city. [17]Not a man remained in Ai or Bethel who did not go after Israel. They left the city open and went in pursuit of Israel.

[18]Then the LORD said to Joshua, "Hold out toward Ai the javelin that is in your hand, for into your hand I will deliver the city." So Joshua held out his javelin toward Ai. [19]As soon as he did this, the men in the ambush rose quickly from their position and rushed forward. They entered the city and captured it and quickly set it on fire.

[20]The men of Ai looked back and saw the smoke of the city rising against the sky, but they had no chance to escape in any direction, for the Israelites who had been fleeing toward the desert had turned back against their pursuers. [21]For when Joshua and all Israel saw that the ambush had taken the city and that smoke was going up from the city, they turned around and attacked the men of Ai. [22]The men of the ambush also came out of the city against them, so that they were caught in the middle, with Israelites on both sides. Israel cut them down, leaving them neither survivors nor fugitives. [23]But they took the king of Ai alive and brought him to Joshua.

[24]When Israel had finished killing all the men of Ai in the fields and in the desert where they had chased them, and when every one of them had been put to the sword, all the Israelites returned to Ai and killed those who were in it. [25]Twelve thousand men and women fell that day—all the people of Ai. [26]For Joshua did not draw back the hand that held out his javelin until he had destroyed[a] all who lived in Ai. [27]But Israel did carry off for themselves the livestock and plunder of this city, as the LORD had instructed Joshua.

[28]So Joshua burned Ai and made it a permanent heap of ruins, a desolate place to this day. [29]He hung the king of Ai on a tree and left him there until evening. At sunset, Joshua ordered them to take his body from the tree and throw it down at the entrance of the city gate. And they raised a large pile of rocks over it, which remains to this day.

The Covenant Renewed at Mount Ebal

[30]Then Joshua built on Mount Ebal an altar to the LORD, the God of Israel, [31]as Moses the servant of the LORD had commanded the Israelites. He built it according to what is written in the Book of the Law of Moses—an altar of uncut stones, on which no iron tool had been used. On it they offered to the LORD burnt offerings and sacrificed fellowship offerings.[b] [32]There, in the presence of the Israelites, Joshua copied on stones the law of Moses, which he had written. [33]All Israel, aliens and citizens alike, with their elders, officials and judges, were standing on both sides of the ark of the covenant of the LORD, facing those who carried it—the priests, who were Levites. Half of the people stood in front of Mount Gerizim and half of them in front of Mount Ebal, as Moses the servant of the LORD had formerly commanded when he gave instructions to bless the people of Israel.

[34]Afterward, Joshua read all the words of the law—the blessings and the curses—just as it is written in the Book of the Law. [35]There was not a word of all that Moses had commanded that Joshua did not read to the whole assembly of Israel, including the women and children, and the aliens who lived among them.

The Gibeonite Deception

9 Now when all the kings west of the Jordan heard about these things—those in the hill country, in the western foothills, and along the entire coast of the Great Sea[c] as far as Lebanon (the kings of the Hittites, Amorites, Canaanites, Perizzites, Hivites and Jebusites)— [2]they came together to make war against Joshua and Israel.

[3]However, when the people of Gibeon heard what Joshua had done to Jericho and Ai, [4]they resorted to a ruse: They went as a delegation whose donkeys were loaded[d] with worn-out sacks and old wineskins, cracked and mended. [5]The men put worn and patched sandals on their feet and wore old clothes. All the bread of their food supply was dry and moldy. [6]Then they went to Joshua

---

a 26 The Hebrew term refers to the irrevocable giving over of things or persons to the LORD, often by totally destroying them.   b 31 Traditionally peace offerings   c 1 That is, the Mediterranean   d 4 Most Hebrew manuscripts; some Hebrew manuscripts, Vulgate and Syriac (see also Septuagint) They prepared provisions and loaded their donkeys in the camp at Gilgal and said to him and the men of Israel, "We have come from a distant country; make a treaty with us."

[7]The men of Israel said to the Hivites, "But perhaps you live near us. How then can we make a treaty with you?"

[8]"We are your servants," they said to Joshua.

But Joshua asked, "Who are you and where do you come from?"

[9]They answered: "Your servants have come from a very distant country because of the fame of the LORD your God. For we have heard reports of him: all that he did in Egypt, [10]and all that he did to the two kings of the Amorites east of the Jordan—Sihon king of Heshbon, and Og king of Bashan, who reigned in Ashtaroth. [11]And our elders and all those living in our country said to us, 'Take provisions for your journey; go and meet them and say to them, "We are your servants; make a treaty with us." ' [12]This bread of ours was warm when we packed it at home on the day we left to come to you. But now see how dry and moldy it is. [13]And these wineskins that we filled were new, but see how cracked they are. And our clothes and sandals are worn out by the very long journey."

[14]The men of Israel sampled their provisions but did not inquire of the LORD. [15]Then Joshua made a treaty of peace with them to let them live, and the leaders of the assembly ratified it by oath.

[16]Three days after they made the treaty with the Gibeonites, the Israelites heard that they were neighbors, living near them. [17]So the Israelites set out and on the third day came to their cities: Gibeon, Kephirah, Beeroth and Kiriath Jearim. [18]But the Israelites did not attack them, because the leaders of the assembly had sworn an oath to them by the LORD, the God of Israel.

The whole assembly grumbled against the leaders, [19]but all the leaders answered, "We have given them our oath by the LORD, the God of Israel, and we cannot touch them now. [20]This is what we will do to them: We will let them live, so that wrath will not fall on us for breaking the oath we swore to them." [21]They continued, "Let them live, but let them be woodcutters and water carriers for the entire community." So the leaders' promise to them was kept.

[22]Then Joshua summoned the Gibeonites and said, "Why did you deceive us by saying, 'We live a long way from you,' while actually you live near us? [23]You are now under a curse: You will never cease to serve as woodcutters and water carriers for the house of my God."

[24]They answered Joshua, "Your servants were clearly told how the LORD your God had commanded his servant Moses to give you the whole land and to wipe out all its inhabitants from before you. So we feared for our lives because of you, and that is why we did this. [25]We are now in your hands. Do to us whatever seems good and right to you."

[26]So Joshua saved them from the Israelites, and they did not kill them. [27]That day he made the Gibeonites woodcutters and water carriers for the community and for the altar of the LORD at the place the LORD would choose. And that is what they are to this day.

The Sun Stands Still

10 Now Adoni-Zedek king of Jerusalem heard that Joshua had taken Ai and totally destroyed[a] it, doing to Ai and its king as he had done to Jericho and its king, and that the people of Gibeon had made a treaty of peace with Israel and were living near them. [2]He and his people were very much alarmed at this, because Gibeon was an important city, like one of the royal cities; it was larger than Ai, and all its men were good fighters. [3]So Adoni-Zedek king of Jerusalem appealed to Hoham king of Hebron, Piram king of Jarmuth, Japhia king of Lachish and Debir king of Eglon. [4]"Come up and help me attack Gibeon," he said, "because it has made peace with Joshua and the Israelites."

[5]Then the five kings of the Amorites—the kings of Jerusalem, Hebron, Jarmuth, Lachish and Eglon—joined forces. They moved up with all their troops and took up positions against Gibeon and attacked it.

[6]The Gibeonites then sent word to Joshua in the camp at Gilgal: "Do not abandon your servants. Come up to us quickly and save us! Help us, because all the Amorite kings from the hill country have joined forces against us."

[7]So Joshua marched up from Gilgal with his entire army, including all the best fighting men.

---

[a] 1 The Hebrew term refers to the irrevocable giving over of things or persons to the LORD, often by totally destroying them; also in verses 28, 35, 37, 39 and 40.

truth or dare

If God could make the sun stand still for Joshua, imagine what he can do if you trust him with your life. Never underestimate his awesome power!

10:12-14

[8]The LORD said to Joshua, "Do not be afraid of them; I have given them into your hand. Not one of them will be able to withstand you."

[9]After an all-night march from Gilgal, Joshua took them by surprise. [10]The LORD threw them into confusion before Israel, who defeated them in a great victory at Gibeon. Israel pursued them along the road going up to Beth Horon and cut them down all the way to Azekah and Makkedah. [11]As they fled before Israel on the road down from Beth Horon to Azekah, the LORD hurled large hailstones down on them from the sky, and more of them died from the hailstones than were killed by the swords of the Israelites.

[12]On the day the LORD gave the Amorites over to Israel, Joshua said to the LORD in the presence of Israel:

"O sun, stand still over Gibeon,
O moon, over the Valley of Aijalon."
[13]So the sun stood still,
and the moon stopped,
till the nation avenged itself on[a] its enemies,

as it is written in the Book of Jashar.

The sun stopped in the middle of the sky and delayed going down about a full day. [14]There has never been a day like it before or since, a day when the LORD listened to a man. Surely the LORD was fighting for Israel!

[15]Then Joshua returned with all Israel to the camp at Gilgal.

Five Amorite Kings Killed

[16]Now the five kings had fled and hidden in the cave at Makkedah. [17]When Joshua was told that the five kings had been found hiding in the cave at Makkedah, [18]he said, "Roll large rocks up to the mouth of the cave, and post some men there to guard it. [19]But don't stop! Pursue your enemies, attack them from the rear and don't let them reach their cities, for the LORD your God has given them into your hand."

[20]So Joshua and the Israelites destroyed them completely—almost to a man—but the few who were left reached their fortified cities. [21]The whole army then returned safely to Joshua in the camp at Makkedah, and no one uttered a word against the Israelites.

[22]Joshua said, "Open the mouth of the cave and bring those five kings out to me." [23]So they brought the five kings out of the cave—the kings of Jerusalem, Hebron, Jarmuth, Lachish and Eglon. [24]When they had brought these kings to Joshua, he summoned all the men of Israel and said to the army commanders who had come with him, "Come here and put your feet on the necks of these kings." So they came forward and placed their feet on their necks.

[25]Joshua said to them, "Do not be afraid; do not be discouraged. Be strong and courageous. This is what the LORD will do to all the enemies you are going to fight." [26]Then Joshua struck and killed the kings and hung them on five trees, and they were left hanging on the trees until evening.

[27]At sunset Joshua gave the order and they took them down from the trees and threw them into the cave where they had been hiding. At the mouth of the cave they placed large rocks, which are there to this day.

[28]That day Joshua took Makkedah. He put the city and its king to the sword and totally destroyed everyone in it. He left no survivors. And he did to the king of Makkedah as he had done to the king of Jericho.

a 13 Or nation triumphed over

Southern Cities Conquered

²⁹Then Joshua and all Israel with him moved on from Makkedah to Libnah and attacked it. ³⁰The LORD also gave that city and its king into Israel's hand. The city and everyone in it Joshua put to the sword. He left no survivors there. And he did to its king as he had done to the king of Jericho.

³¹Then Joshua and all Israel with him moved on from Libnah to Lachish; he took up positions against it and attacked it. ³²The LORD handed Lachish over to Israel, and Joshua took it on the second day. The city and everyone in it he put to the sword, just as he had done to Libnah. ³³Meanwhile, Horam king of Gezer had come up to help Lachish, but Joshua defeated him and his army—until no survivors were left.

³⁴Then Joshua and all Israel with him moved on from Lachish to Eglon; they took up positions against it and attacked it. ³⁵They captured it that same day and put it to the sword and totally destroyed everyone in it, just as they had done to Lachish.

³⁶Then Joshua and all Israel with him went up from Eglon to Hebron and attacked it. ³⁷They took the city and put it to the sword, together with its king, its villages and everyone in it. They left no survivors. Just as at Eglon, they totally destroyed it and everyone in it.

³⁸Then Joshua and all Israel with him turned around and attacked Debir. ³⁹They took the city, its king and its villages, and put them to the sword. Everyone in it they totally destroyed. They left no survivors. They did to Debir and its king as they had done to Libnah and its king and to Hebron.

⁴⁰So Joshua subdued the whole region, including the hill country, the Negev, the western foothills and the mountain slopes, together with all their kings. He left no survivors. He totally destroyed all who breathed, just as the LORD, the God of Israel, had commanded. ⁴¹Joshua subdued them from Kadesh Barnea to Gaza and from the whole region of Goshen to Gibeon. ⁴²All these kings and their lands Joshua conquered in one campaign, because the LORD, the God of Israel, fought for Israel.

⁴³Then Joshua returned with all Israel to the camp at Gilgal.

Northern Kings Defeated

11 When Jabin king of Hazor heard of this, he sent word to Jobab king of Madon, to the kings of Shimron and Acshaph, ²and to the northern kings who were in the mountains, in the Arabah south of Kinnereth, in the western foothills and in Naphoth Dor^a on the west; ³to the Canaanites in the east and west; to the Amorites, Hittites, Perizzites and Jebusites in the hill country; and to the Hivites below Hermon in the region of Mizpah. ⁴They came out with all their troops and a large number of horses and chariots—a huge army, as numerous as the sand on the seashore. ⁵All these kings joined forces and made camp together at the Waters of Merom, to fight against Israel.

⁶The LORD said to Joshua, "Do not be afraid of them, because by this time tomorrow I will hand all of them over to Israel, slain. You are to hamstring their horses and burn their chariots."

⁷So Joshua and his whole army came against them suddenly at the Waters of Merom and attacked them, ⁸and the LORD gave them into the hand of Israel. They defeated them and pursued them all the way to Greater Sidon, to Misrephoth Maim, and to the Valley of Mizpah on the east, until no survivors were left. ⁹Joshua did to them as the LORD had directed: He hamstrung their horses and burned their chariots.

¹⁰At that time Joshua turned back and captured Hazor and put its king to the sword. (Hazor had been the head of all these kingdoms.) ¹¹Everyone in it they put to the sword. They totally destroyed^b them, not sparing anything that breathed, and he burned up Hazor itself.

¹²Joshua took all these royal cities and their kings and put them to the sword. He totally destroyed them, as Moses the servant of the LORD had commanded. ¹³Yet Israel did not burn any of the cities built on their mounds—except Hazor, which Joshua burned. ¹⁴The Israelites carried off for themselves all the plunder and livestock of these cities, but all the people they put to the sword until they completely destroyed them, not sparing anyone that breathed. ¹⁵As the LORD command-

---

^a 2 Or *in the heights of Dor*   ^b 11 The Hebrew term refers to the irrevocable giving over of things or persons to the LORD, often by totally destroying them; also in verses 12, 20 and 21.

ed his servant Moses, so Moses commanded Joshua, and Joshua did it; he left nothing undone of all that the Lord commanded Moses.

16So Joshua took this entire land: the hill country, all the Negev, the whole region of Goshen, the western foothills, the Arabah and the mountains of Israel with their foothills, 17from Mount Halak, which rises toward Seir, to Baal Gad in the Valley of Lebanon below Mount Hermon. He captured all their kings and struck them down, putting them to death. 18Joshua waged war against all these kings for a long time. 19Except for the Hivites living in Gibeon, not one city made a treaty of peace with the Israelites, who took them all in battle. 20For it was the Lord himself who hardened their hearts to wage war against Israel, so that he might destroy them totally, exterminating them without mercy, as the Lord had commanded Moses.

21At that time Joshua went and destroyed the Anakites from the hill country: from Hebron, Debir and Anab, from all the hill country of Judah, and from all the hill country of Israel. Joshua totally destroyed them and their towns. 22No Anakites were left in Israelite territory; only in Gaza, Gath and Ashdod did any survive. 23So Joshua took the entire land, just as the Lord had directed Moses, and he gave it as an inheritance to Israel according to their tribal divisions.

Then the land had rest from war.

List of Defeated Kings

12 These are the kings of the land whom the Israelites had defeated and whose territory they took over east of the Jordan, from the Arnon Gorge to Mount Hermon, including all the eastern side of the Arabah:

2Sihon king of the Amorites,

who reigned in Heshbon. He ruled from Aroer on the rim of the Arnon Gorge—from the middle of the gorge—to the Jabbok River, which is the border of the Ammonites. This included half of Gilead. 3He also ruled over the eastern Arabah from the Sea of Kinnereth*a* to the Sea of the Arabah (the Salt Sea*b*), to Beth Jeshimoth, and then southward below the slopes of Pisgah.

4And the territory of Og king of Bashan,

one of the last of the Rephaites, who reigned in Ashtaroth and Edrei. 5He ruled over Mount Hermon, Salecah, all of Bashan to the border of the people of Geshur and Maacah, and half of Gilead to the border of Sihon king of Heshbon.

6Moses, the servant of the Lord, and the Israelites conquered them. And Moses the servant of the Lord gave their land to the Reubenites, the Gadites and the half-tribe of Manasseh to be their possession.

7These are the kings of the land that Joshua and the Israelites conquered on the west side of the Jordan, from Baal Gad in the Valley of Lebanon to Mount Halak, which rises toward Seir (their lands Joshua gave as an inheritance to the tribes of Israel according to their tribal divisions—8the hill country, the western foothills, the Arabah, the mountain slopes, the desert and the Negev—the lands of the Hittites, Amorites, Canaanites, Perizzites, Hivites and Jebusites):

9the king of Jericho	one
the king of Ai (near Bethel)	one
10the king of Jerusalem	one
the king of Hebron	one
11the king of Jarmuth	one
the king of Lachish	one

truth or dare

Discipleship is all about allowing God to lead us *through* another person. If you want to grow closer to God, try linking up with an older, godly woman.

11:15

a 3 That is, Galilee   b 3 That is, the Dead Sea

Atheism 101

Profile: Susanne

My history teacher is an atheist, and I'm her favorite student. Favorite student to *pick on,* that is. She spends more time lecturing us on her beliefs than she does teaching history. It's like being enrolled in Atheism 101 every morning—only I didn't sign up for this course!

Yesterday she saw my Bible in my backpack. "What is *that?*" She disdainfully pointed at the leather-bound book as if she'd seen a roach. "Do you have a hymnal in there, too?" she sarcastically inquired. "Perhaps Susanne's planning on having church at lunchtime," she announced amid the class's giggles. I wanted to die. For the rest of the class, she called attention to me any way she could. And then when she gave back our papers on the American Revolution, I saw that she'd asked me to rewrite an entire section. And why? Silly me, I referred to our forefathers' belief in God. What a heretic!

"I suppose you believe the myth about little George Washington chopping down the cherry tree, too?" she asked as the class looked at me, nervously waiting for my response. I felt so stupid, but I couldn't think of anything to say in my defense. I totally froze.

I'm afraid she's getting the best of me. I hate it that I don't know how to stand up for what I believe.

Want more info about defending your faith? Check out www.TrueImagesBible.com

atheism in focus

You're not likely to win a debate over religious beliefs—especially with someone in authority over you. The best defense against atheism is a good offense:

» Pray for that person—don't argue the facts.
» Share your testimony if you don't know what else to say. You alone are the expert on that topic—and no one can argue with what's happened to you.
» An atheistic teacher, for all the trouble he or she might cause you, might also motivate you to figure out what you really believe and why (see 2 Timothy 2:15, page 1577).

For more on this topic, see the index on page 1656.

atheism

12 the king of Eglon	one
the king of Gezer	one
13 the king of Debir	one
the king of Geder	one
14 the king of Hormah	one
the king of Arad	one
15 the king of Libnah	one
the king of Adullam	one
16 the king of Makkedah	one
the king of Bethel	one

[17] the king of Tappuah	one
the king of Hepher	one
[18] the king of Aphek	one
the king of Lasharon	one
[19] the king of Madon	one
the king of Hazor	one
[20] the king of Shimron Meron	one
the king of Acshaph	one
[21] the king of Taanach	one
the king of Megiddo	one
[22] the king of Kedesh	one
the king of Jokneam in Carmel	one
[23] the king of Dor (in Naphoth Dor[a])	one
the king of Goyim in Gilgal	one
[24] the king of Tirzah	one

thirty-one kings in all.

Land Still to Be Taken

13 When Joshua was old and well advanced in years, the LORD said to him, "You are very old, and there are still very large areas of land to be taken over.

[2]"This is the land that remains: all the regions of the Philistines and Geshurites: [3]from the Shihor River on the east of Egypt to the territory of Ekron on the north, all of it counted as Canaanite (the territory of the five Philistine rulers in Gaza, Ashdod, Ashkelon, Gath and Ekron—that of the Avvites); [4]from the south, all the land of the Canaanites, from Arah of the Sidonians as far as Aphek, the region of the Amorites, [5]the area of the Gebalites[b]; and all Lebanon to the east, from Baal Gad below Mount Hermon to Lebo[c] Hamath.

[6]"As for all the inhabitants of the mountain regions from Lebanon to Misrephoth Maim, that is, all the Sidonians, I myself will drive them out before the Israelites. Be sure to allocate this land to Israel for an inheritance, as I have instructed you, [7]and divide it as an inheritance among the nine tribes and half of the tribe of Manasseh."

Division of the Land East of the Jordan

[8]The other half of Manasseh,[d] the Reubenites and the Gadites had received the inheritance that Moses had given them east of the Jordan, as he, the servant of the LORD, had assigned it to them.

[9]It extended from Aroer on the rim of the Arnon Gorge, and from the town in the middle of the gorge, and included the whole plateau of Medeba as far as Dibon, [10]and all the towns of Sihon king of the Amorites, who ruled in Heshbon, out to the border of the Ammonites. [11]It also included Gilead, the territory of the people of Geshur and Maacah, all of Mount Hermon and all Bashan as far as Salecah— [12]that is, the whole kingdom of Og in Bashan, who had reigned in Ashtaroth and Edrei and had survived as one of the last of the Rephaites. Moses had defeated them and taken over their land. [13]But the Israelites did not drive out the people of Geshur and Maacah, so they continue to live among the Israelites to this day.

[14]But to the tribe of Levi he gave no inheritance, since the offerings made by fire to the LORD, the God of Israel, are their inheritance, as he promised them.

[15]This is what Moses had given to the tribe of Reuben, clan by clan:

[16]The territory from Aroer on the rim of the Arnon Gorge, and from the town in the middle of the gorge, and the whole plateau past Medeba [17]to Heshbon and all its towns on the plateau, including Dibon, Bamoth Baal, Beth Baal Meon, [18]Jahaz, Kedemoth, Mephaath, [19]Kiriathaim, Sibmah, Zereth Shahar on the hill in the valley, [20]Beth Peor, the slopes of Pisgah, and Beth Jeshimoth [21]—all the towns on the plateau and the entire realm of Sihon king of the

[a] 23 Or *in the heights of Dor*   [b] 5 That is, the area of Byblos   [c] 5 Or *to the entrance to*   [d] 8 Hebrew *With it* (that is, with the other half of Manasseh)

genuine

obedience » 13:13

Is there an attitude or action you know is wrong, but you keep doing it anyway? You've talked yourself into believing it doesn't really hurt anyone, so what's the problem? The problem is that those things have a way of coming back to haunt you. Just ask the Israelites. God told them to drive out everyone in Canaan. But they didn't. And they paid for it afterward. Even if your sin doesn't seem like a big deal now—it is. If God says to get rid of it—do it.

Amorites, who ruled at Heshbon. Moses had defeated him and the Midianite chiefs, Evi, Rekem, Zur, Hur and Reba—princes allied with Sihon—who lived in that country. ²²In addition to those slain in battle, the Israelites had put to the sword Balaam son of Beor, who practiced divination. ²³The boundary of the Reubenites was the bank of the Jordan. These towns and their villages were the inheritance of the Reubenites, clan by clan.

²⁴This is what Moses had given to the tribe of Gad, clan by clan:

²⁵The territory of Jazer, all the towns of Gilead and half the Ammonite country as far as Aroer, near Rabbah; ²⁶and from Heshbon to Ramath Mizpah and Betonim, and from Mahanaim to the territory of Debir; ²⁷and in the valley, Beth Haram, Beth Nimrah, Succoth and Zaphon with the rest of the realm of Sihon king of Heshbon (the east side of the Jordan, the territory up to the end of the Sea of Kinnereth*). ²⁸These towns and their villages were the inheritance of the Gadites, clan by clan.

²⁹This is what Moses had given to the half-tribe of Manasseh, that is, to half the family of the descendants of Manasseh, clan by clan:

³⁰The territory extending from Mahanaim and including all of Bashan, the entire realm of Og king of Bashan—all the settlements of Jair in Bashan, sixty towns, ³¹half of Gilead, and Ashtaroth and Edrei (the royal cities of Og in Bashan). This was for the descendants of Makir son of Manasseh—for half of the sons of Makir, clan by clan.

³²This is the inheritance Moses had given when he was in the plains of Moab across the Jordan east of Jericho. ³³But to the tribe of Levi, Moses had given no inheritance; the LORD, the God of Israel, is their inheritance, as he promised them.

Division of the Land West of the Jordan

14 Now these are the areas the Israelites received as an inheritance in the land of Canaan, which Eleazar the priest, Joshua son of Nun and the heads of the tribal clans of Israel allotted to them. ²Their inheritances were assigned by lot to the nine-and-a-half tribes, as the LORD had commanded through Moses. ³Moses had granted the two-and-a-half tribes their inheritance east of the Jordan but had not granted the Levites an inheritance among the rest, ⁴for the sons of Joseph had become two tribes—Manasseh and Ephraim. The Levites received no share of the land but only towns to live in, with pasturelands for their flocks and herds. ⁵So the Israelites divided the land, just as the LORD had commanded Moses.

Hebron Given to Caleb

⁶Now the men of Judah approached Joshua at Gilgal, and Caleb son of Jephunneh the Kenizzite said to him, "You know what the LORD said to Moses the man of God at Kadesh Barnea about you and me. ⁷I was forty years old when Moses the servant of the LORD sent me from Kadesh Barnea to explore the land. And I brought him back a report according to my convictions, ⁸but my broth-

a 27 That is, Galilee

ers who went up with me made the hearts of the people melt with fear. I, however, followed the LORD my God wholeheartedly. ⁹So on that day Moses swore to me, 'The land on which your feet have walked will be your inheritance and that of your children forever, because you have followed the LORD my God wholeheartedly.'ᵃ

¹⁰"Now then, just as the LORD promised, he has kept me alive for forty-five years since the time he said this to Moses, while Israel moved about in the desert. So here I am today, eighty-five years old! ¹¹I am still as strong today as the day Moses sent me out; I'm just as vigorous to go out to battle now as I was then. ¹²Now give me this hill country that the LORD promised me that day. You yourself heard then that the Anakites were there and their cities were large and fortified, but, the LORD helping me, I will drive them out just as he said."

¹³Then Joshua blessed Caleb son of Jephunneh and gave him Hebron as his inheritance. ¹⁴So Hebron has belonged to Caleb son of Jephunneh the Kenizzite ever since, because he followed the LORD, the God of Israel, wholeheartedly. ¹⁵(Hebron used to be called Kiriath Arba after Arba, who was the greatest man among the Anakites.)

Then the land had rest from war.

Allotment for Judah

15 The allotment for the tribe of Judah, clan by clan, extended down to the territory of Edom, to the Desert of Zin in the extreme south. ²Their southern boundary started from the bay at the southern end of the Salt Sea,ᵇ ³crossed south of Scorpionᶜ Pass, continued on to Zin and went over to the south of Kadesh Barnea. Then it ran past Hezron up to Addar and curved around to Karka. ⁴It then passed along to Azmon and joined the Wadi of Egypt, ending at the sea. This is theirᵈ southern boundary.

⁵The eastern boundary is the Salt Sea as far as the mouth of the Jordan.

The northern boundary started from the bay of the sea at the mouth of the Jordan, ⁶went up to Beth Hoglah and continued north of Beth Arabah to the Stone of Bohan son of Reuben. ⁷The boundary then went up to Debir from the Valley of Achor and turned north to Gilgal, which faces the Pass of Adummim south of the gorge. It continued along to the waters of En Shemesh and came out at En Rogel. ⁸Then it ran up the Valley of Ben Hinnom along the southern slope of the Jebusite city (that is, Jerusalem). From there it climbed to the top of the hill west of the Hinnom Valley at the northern end of the Valley of Rephaim. ⁹From the hilltop the boundary headed toward the spring of the waters of Nephtoah, came out at the towns of Mount Ephron and went down toward Baalah (that is, Kiriath Jearim). ¹⁰Then it curved westward from Baalah to Mount Seir, ran along the northern slope of Mount Jearim (that is, Kesalon), continued down to Beth Shemesh and crossed to Timnah. ¹¹It went to the northern slope of Ekron, turned toward Shikkeron, passed along to Mount Baalah and reached Jabneel. The boundary ended at the sea.

¹²The western boundary is the coastline of the Great Sea.ᵉ
These are the boundaries around the people of Judah by their clans.

¹³In accordance with the LORD's command to him, Joshua gave to Caleb son of Jephunneh a portion in Judah—Kiriath Arba, that is, Hebron. (Arba was the forefather of Anak.) ¹⁴From Hebron Caleb drove out the three Anakites—Sheshai, Ahiman and Talmai—descendants of Anak. ¹⁵From there he marched against the people living in Debir (formerly called Kiriath Sepher). ¹⁶And Caleb said, "I will give my daughter Acsah in marriage to the man who attacks and captures Kiriath Sepher." ¹⁷Othniel son of Kenaz, Caleb's brother, took it; so Caleb gave his daughter Acsah to him in marriage.

truth or dare

If God makes a promise, he might not choose to fulfill it tomorrow. The important thing is that he'll always keep his promises—so wait for his timing.

14:10–12

ᵃ 9 Deut. 1:36   ᵇ 2 That is, the Dead Sea; also in verse 5   ᶜ 3 Hebrew *Akrabbim*   ᵈ 4 Hebrew *your*   ᵉ 12 That is, the Mediterranean; also in verse 47

C Is for Clueless

focus Profile: **Danielle**

"What do you want to be when you grow up, Danielle?" Oh, the dreaded question. Most little kids love the chance to spout off some dream they have for their lives—a lawyer, a doctor or a teacher. For me, it was just the opposite experience. Awkward pause. Stress. Look at Mom. "I don't know," I would say in my isn't-she-cute little kid voice. Now that I'm older—well, let's just say I still don't have a clue. And it isn't that cute anymore.

My parents "try to help" by suggesting all these hard-line careers where you have the "joy" of working eighty-hour weeks and earning six figures. I'm just trying to find something I like enough to consider doing it for the rest of my life. Once I mentioned I might want to become an artist—but they blew that off and said I'd never make enough money.

While my friends are already talking about what college majors they're choosing, here I am with that same old blank look on my face. I feel the pressure to succeed—but succeed at what? What if my life doesn't turn out right, and I disappoint everyone? How am I supposed to know what I want to do with the next 50 years of my life?

When you need a good reminder about God's plans for your future, check out www.TrueImagesBible.com

future in focus

Even when we feel totally clueless about what choices to make in life, God has it all under control. We can remind ourselves . . .

> » He alone knows the future. See Proverbs 23:18 (page 837).
> » Talk to some people you know who are in college, and ask them how they made their tough life decisions.
> » When you feel like you're starting to panic, ask God to help you replace worry with prayer (see Philippians 4:6–7, page 1553).

For more on this topic, see the index on page 1656.

future

[18]One day when she came to Othniel, she urged him[a] to ask her father for a field. When she got off her donkey, Caleb asked her, "What can I do for you?"

[19]She replied, "Do me a special favor. Since you have given me land in the Negev, give me also springs of water." So Caleb gave her the upper and lower springs.

[20]This is the inheritance of the tribe of Judah, clan by clan:

[21]The southernmost towns of the tribe of Judah in the Negev toward the boundary of Edom were: Kabzeel, Eder, Jagur, [22]Kinah, Dimonah, Adadah, [23]Kedesh, Hazor, Ithnan, [24]Ziph, Telem,

[a] 18 Hebrew and some Septuagint manuscripts; other Septuagint manuscripts (see also note at Judges 1:14) *Othniel, he urged her*

Bealoth, [25]Hazor Hadattah, Kerioth Hezron (that is, Hazor), [26]Amam, Shema, Moladah, [27]Hazar Gaddah, Heshmon, Beth Pelet, [28]Hazar Shual, Beersheba, Biziothiah, [29]Baalah, Iim, Ezem, [30]Eltolad, Kesil, Hormah, [31]Ziklag, Madmannah, Sansannah, [32]Lebaoth, Shilhim, Ain and Rimmon—a total of twenty-nine towns and their villages.

[33]In the western foothills:

Eshtaol, Zorah, Ashnah, [34]Zanoah, En Gannim, Tappuah, Enam, [35]Jarmuth, Adullam, Socoh, Azekah, [36]Shaaraim, Adithaim and Gederah (or Gederothaim)[a]—fourteen towns and their villages.

[37]Zenan, Hadashah, Migdal Gad, [38]Dilean, Mizpah, Joktheel, [39]Lachish, Bozkath, Eglon, [40]Cabbon, Lahmas, Kitlish, [41]Gederoth, Beth Dagon, Naamah and Makkedah—sixteen towns and their villages.

[42]Libnah, Ether, Ashan, [43]Iphtah, Ashnah, Nezib, [44]Keilah, Aczib and Mareshah—nine towns and their villages.

[45]Ekron, with its surrounding settlements and villages; [46]west of Ekron, all that were in the vicinity of Ashdod, together with their villages; [47]Ashdod, its surrounding settlements and villages; and Gaza, its settlements and villages, as far as the Wadi of Egypt and the coastline of the Great Sea.

[48]In the hill country:

Shamir, Jattir, Socoh, [49]Dannah, Kiriath Sannah (that is, Debir), [50]Anab, Eshtemoh, Anim, [51]Goshen, Holon and Giloh—eleven towns and their villages.

[52]Arab, Dumah, Eshan, [53]Janim, Beth Tappuah, Aphekah, [54]Humtah, Kiriath Arba (that is, Hebron) and Zior—nine towns and their villages.

[55]Maon, Carmel, Ziph, Juttah, [56]Jezreel, Jokdeam, Zanoah, [57]Kain, Gibeah and Timnah—ten towns and their villages.

[58]Halhul, Beth Zur, Gedor, [59]Maarath, Beth Anoth and Eltekon—six towns and their villages.

[60]Kiriath Baal (that is, Kiriath Jearim) and Rabbah—two towns and their villages.

[61]In the desert:

Beth Arabah, Middin, Secacah, [62]Nibshan, the City of Salt and En Gedi—six towns and their villages.

[63]Judah could not dislodge the Jebusites, who were living in Jerusalem; to this day the Jebusites live there with the people of Judah.

Allotment for Ephraim and Manasseh

16 The allotment for Joseph began at the Jordan of Jericho,[b] east of the waters of Jericho, and went up from there through the desert into the hill country of Bethel. [2]It went on from Bethel (that is, Luz),[c] crossed over to the territory of the Arkites in Ataroth, [3]descended westward to the territory of the Japhletites as far as the region of Lower Beth Horon and on to Gezer, ending at the sea.

[4]So Manasseh and Ephraim, the descendants of Joseph, received their inheritance.

[5]This was the territory of Ephraim, clan by clan:

The boundary of their inheritance went from Ataroth Addar in the east to Upper Beth Horon [6]and continued to the sea. From Micmethath on the north it curved eastward to Taanath Shiloh, passing by it to Janoah on the east. [7]Then it went down from Janoah to Ataroth and Naarah, touched Jericho and came out at the Jordan. [8]From Tappuah the border went west to the Kanah Ravine and ended at the sea. This was the inheritance of the tribe of the Ephraimites, clan by clan. [9]It also included all the towns and their villages that were set aside for the Ephraimites within the inheritance of the Manassites.

[10]They did not dislodge the Canaanites living in Gezer; to this day the Canaanites live among the people of Ephraim but are required to do forced labor.

a 36 Or Gederah and Gederothaim   b 1 Jordan of Jericho was possibly an ancient name for the Jordan River.
c 2 Septuagint; Hebrew Bethel to Luz

17 This was the allotment for the tribe of Manasseh as Joseph's firstborn, that is, for Makir, Manasseh's firstborn. Makir was the ancestor of the Gileadites, who had received Gilead and Bashan because the Makirites were great soldiers. ²So this allotment was for the rest of the people of Manasseh—the clans of Abiezer, Helek, Asriel, Shechem, Hepher and Shemida. These are the other male descendants of Manasseh son of Joseph by their clans.

³Now Zelophehad son of Hepher, the son of Gilead, the son of Makir, the son of Manasseh, had no sons but only daughters, whose names were Mahlah, Noah, Hoglah, Milcah and Tirzah. ⁴They went to Eleazar the priest, Joshua son of Nun, and the leaders and said, "The LORD commanded Moses to give us an inheritance among our brothers." So Joshua gave them an inheritance along with the brothers of their father, according to the LORD's command. ⁵Manasseh's share consisted of ten tracts of land besides Gilead and Bashan east of the Jordan, ⁶because the daughters of the tribe of Manasseh received an inheritance among the sons. The land of Gilead belonged to the rest of the descendants of Manasseh.

⁷The territory of Manasseh extended from Asher to Micmethath east of Shechem. The boundary ran southward from there to include the people living at En Tappuah. ⁸(Manasseh had the land of Tappuah, but Tappuah itself, on the boundary of Manasseh, belonged to the Ephraimites.) ⁹Then the boundary continued south to the Kanah Ravine. There were towns belonging to Ephraim lying among the towns of Manasseh, but the boundary of Manasseh was the northern side of the ravine and ended at the sea. ¹⁰On the south the land belonged to Ephraim, on the north to Manasseh. The territory of Manasseh reached the sea and bordered Asher on the north and Issachar on the east.

¹¹Within Issachar and Asher, Manasseh also had Beth Shan, Ibleam and the people of Dor, Endor, Taanach and Megiddo, together with their surrounding settlements (the third in the list is Naphoth*).

¹²Yet the Manassites were not able to occupy these towns, for the Canaanites were determined to live in that region. ¹³However, when the Israelites grew stronger, they subjected the Canaanites to forced labor but did not drive them out completely.

¹⁴The people of Joseph said to Joshua, "Why have you given us only one allotment and one portion for an inheritance? We are a numerous people and the LORD has blessed us abundantly."

¹⁵"If you are so numerous," Joshua answered, "and if the hill country of Ephraim is too small for you, go up into the forest and clear land for yourselves there in the land of the Perizzites and Rephaites."

¹⁶The people of Joseph replied, "The hill country is not enough for us, and all the Canaanites who live in the plain have iron chariots, both those in Beth Shan and its settlements and those in the Valley of Jezreel."

¹⁷But Joshua said to the house of Joseph—to Ephraim and Manasseh—"You are numerous and very powerful. You will have not only one allotment ¹⁸but the forested hill country as well. Clear it, and its farthest limits will be yours; though the Canaanites have iron chariots and though they are strong, you can drive them out."

Division of the Rest of the Land

18 The whole assembly of the Israelites gathered at Shiloh and set up the Tent of Meeting there. The country was brought under their control, ²but there were still seven Israelite tribes who had not yet received their inheritance.

³So Joshua said to the Israelites: "How long will you wait before you begin to take possession of the land that the LORD, the God of your fathers, has given you? ⁴Appoint three men from each tribe. I will send them out to make a survey of the land and to write a description of it, according to the inheritance of each. Then they will return to me. ⁵You are to divide the land into seven parts. Judah is to remain in its territory on the south and the house of Joseph in its territory on the north. ⁶After you have written descriptions of the seven parts of the land, bring them here to me and I will cast lots for you in the presence of the LORD our God. ⁷The Levites, however, do not get a portion among you, because the priestly service of the LORD is their inheritance. And Gad, Reuben and the half-tribe of Manasseh have already received their inheritance on the east side of the Jordan. Moses the servant of the LORD gave it to them."

---

a 11 That is, Naphoth Dor

[8]As the men started on their way to map out the land, Joshua instructed them, "Go and make a survey of the land and write a description of it. Then return to me, and I will cast lots for you here at Shiloh in the presence of the LORD." [9]So the men left and went through the land. They wrote its description on a scroll, town by town, in seven parts, and returned to Joshua in the camp at Shiloh. [10]Joshua then cast lots for them in Shiloh in the presence of the LORD, and there he distributed the land to the Israelites according to their tribal divisions.

Allotment for Benjamin

[11]The lot came up for the tribe of Benjamin, clan by clan. Their allotted territory lay between the tribes of Judah and Joseph:

[12]On the north side their boundary began at the Jordan, passed the northern slope of Jericho and headed west into the hill country, coming out at the desert of Beth Aven. [13]From there it crossed to the south slope of Luz (that is, Bethel) and went down to Ataroth Addar on the hill south of Lower Beth Horon.

[14]From the hill facing Beth Horon on the south the boundary turned south along the western side and came out at Kiriath Baal (that is, Kiriath Jearim), a town of the people of Judah. This was the western side.

[15]The southern side began at the outskirts of Kiriath Jearim on the west, and the boundary came out at the spring of the waters of Nephtoah. [16]The boundary went down to the foot of the hill facing the Valley of Ben Hinnom, north of the Valley of Rephaim. It continued down the Hinnom Valley along the southern slope of the Jebusite city and so to En Rogel. [17]It then curved north, went to En Shemesh, continued to Geliloth, which faces the Pass of Adummim, and ran down to the Stone of Bohan son of Reuben. [18]It continued to the northern slope of Beth Arabah[a] and on down into the Arabah. [19]It then went to the northern slope of Beth Hoglah and came out at the northern bay of the Salt Sea,[b] at the mouth of the Jordan in the south. This was the southern boundary.

[20]The Jordan formed the boundary on the eastern side.

These were the boundaries that marked out the inheritance of the clans of Benjamin on all sides.

[21]The tribe of Benjamin, clan by clan, had the following cities:

Jericho, Beth Hoglah, Emek Keziz, [22]Beth Arabah, Zemaraim, Bethel, [23]Avvim, Parah, Ophrah, [24]Kephar Ammoni, Ophni and Geba—twelve towns and their villages.

[25]Gibeon, Ramah, Beeroth, [26]Mizpah, Kephirah, Mozah, [27]Rekem, Irpeel, Taralah, [28]Zelah, Haeleph, the Jebusite city (that is, Jerusalem), Gibeah and Kiriath—fourteen towns and their villages.

This was the inheritance of Benjamin for its clans.

Allotment for Simeon

19 The second lot came out for the tribe of Simeon, clan by clan. Their inheritance lay within the territory of Judah. [2]It included:

Beersheba (or Sheba),[c] Moladah, [3]Hazar Shual, Balah, Ezem, [4]Eltolad, Bethul, Hormah, [5]Ziklag, Beth Marcaboth, Hazar Susah, [6]Beth Lebaoth and Sharuhen—thirteen towns and their villages;

[7]Ain, Rimmon, Ether and Ashan—four towns and their villages— [8]and all the villages around these towns as far as Baalath Beer (Ramah in the Negev).

This was the inheritance of the tribe of the Simeonites, clan by clan. [9]The inheritance of the Simeonites was taken from the share of Judah, because Judah's portion was more than they needed. So the Simeonites received their inheritance within the territory of Judah.

Allotment for Zebulun

[10]The third lot came up for Zebulun, clan by clan:

The boundary of their inheritance went as far as Sarid. [11]Going west it ran to Maralah, touched Dabbesheth, and extended to the ravine near Jokneam. [12]It turned east from Sarid toward the sunrise to the territory of Kisloth Tabor and went on to Daberath and up to

---

a 18 Septuagint; Hebrew *slope facing the Arabah*   *b 19* That is, the Dead Sea   *c 2* Or *Beersheba, Sheba*; 1 Chron. 4:28 does not have *Sheba*.

Too Much of a Good Thing

focus Profile: **Kyla**

I'm health-conscious, you might say. I eat right. Count those calories. And I work out. I mean, I really work out. Pear-shapes like me have to keep it up. It's all about being self-motivated. If I don't work out first thing in the morning, then I'll stay up to any hour to get my workout in—even if it's 2:00 A.M.

I'm working on tone now. There's a problem area on my thighs that I just can't seem to get rid of. Flab terrifies me. I run, I do aerobics, I do kick-boxing, I swim—anything to get a well-rounded workout and better tone. The other day I downloaded some stuff about targeting problem areas, so I've been doing those exercises, too.

My sister says I'm obsessed with exercise. Whatever. She's just jealous because she can't get her rear end off the couch. It takes discipline to keep my body looking the way I want. My coach says I'm the best athlete in track. Seriously! I ran all winter—even during the cold and snow—to get there. Now, if I can tone my thighs a little more, I'll finally be near-perfect.

exercise addiction in focus

A preoccupation with exercise, weight and/or food is a problem for many girls. Eating disorders. Exercise addictions. Many girls struggle with them, and they can be all-consuming. Keep this advice in mind:

» These outward obsessions are signs of an inner pain—abuse, neglect, self-esteem issues, etc. It's not just about changing eating or exercise habits. True recovery comes when we deal with the root problems in our lives (see Psalm 139:23–24, page 792).

» When we can't control our problems, we often turn to things we *can* control to feel better about ourselves—like food, weight or exercise.

» Exercise addiction and eating disorders can be life-threatening. If you suspect you or someone you know has a disorder, a qualified and compassionate professional can help.

For more on this topic, see the index on page 1656.

Japhia. ¹³Then it continued eastward to Gath Hepher and Eth Kazin; it came out at Rimmon and turned toward Neah. ¹⁴There the boundary went around on the north to Hannathon and ended at the Valley of Iphtah El. ¹⁵Included were Kattath, Nahalal, Shimron, Idalah and Bethlehem. There were twelve towns and their villages.

¹⁶These towns and their villages were the inheritance of Zebulun, clan by clan.

Allotment for Issachar

¹⁷The fourth lot came out for Issachar, clan by clan. ¹⁸Their territory included:

Jezreel, Kesulloth, Shunem, ¹⁹Hapharaim, Shion, Anaharath, ²⁰Rabbith, Kishion, Ebez, ²¹Remeth, En Gannim, En Haddah and Beth Pazzez. ²²The boundary touched Tabor, Shahazumah and Beth Shemesh, and ended at the Jordan. There were sixteen towns and their villages.

²³These towns and their villages were the inheritance of the tribe of Issachar, clan by clan.

Allotment for Asher

²⁴The fifth lot came out for the tribe of Asher, clan by clan. ²⁵Their territory included:

Helkath, Hali, Beten, Acshaph, ²⁶Allammelech, Amad and Mishal. On the west the boundary touched Carmel and Shihor Libnath. ²⁷It then turned east toward Beth Dagon, touched Zebulun and the Valley of Iphtah El, and went north to Beth Emek and Neiel, passing Cabul on the left. ²⁸It went to Abdon,ᵃ Rehob, Hammon and Kanah, as far as Greater Sidon. ²⁹The boundary then turned back toward Ramah and went to the fortified city of Tyre, turned toward Hosah and came out at the sea in the region of Aczib, ³⁰Ummah, Aphek and Rehob. There were twenty-two towns and their villages.

³¹These towns and their villages were the inheritance of the tribe of Asher, clan by clan.

Allotment for Naphtali

³²The sixth lot came out for Naphtali, clan by clan:

³³Their boundary went from Heleph and the large tree in Zaanannim, passing Adami Nekeb and Jabneel to Lakkum and ending at the Jordan. ³⁴The boundary ran west through Aznoth Tabor and came out at Hukkok. It touched Zebulun on the south, Asher on the west and the Jordanᵇ on the east. ³⁵The fortified cities were Ziddim, Zer, Hammath, Rakkath, Kinnereth, ³⁶Adamah, Ramah, Hazor, ³⁷Kedesh, Edrei, En Hazor, ³⁸Iron, Migdal El, Horem, Beth Anath and Beth Shemesh. There were nineteen towns and their villages.

³⁹These towns and their villages were the inheritance of the tribe of Naphtali, clan by clan.

Allotment for Dan

⁴⁰The seventh lot came out for the tribe of Dan, clan by clan. ⁴¹The territory of their inheritance included:

Zorah, Eshtaol, Ir Shemesh, ⁴²Shaalabbin, Aijalon, Ithlah, ⁴³Elon, Timnah, Ekron, ⁴⁴Eltekeh, Gibbethon, Baalath, ⁴⁵Jehud, Bene Berak, Gath Rimmon, ⁴⁶Me Jarkon and Rakkon, with the area facing Joppa.

⁴⁷(But the Danites had difficulty taking possession of their territory, so they went up and attacked Leshem, took it, put it to the sword and occupied it. They settled in Leshem and named it Dan after their forefather.)

⁴⁸These towns and their villages were the inheritance of the tribe of Dan, clan by clan.

Allotment for Joshua

⁴⁹When they had finished dividing the land into its allotted portions, the Israelites gave Joshua son of Nun an inheritance among them, ⁵⁰as the Lord had commanded. They gave him the town he asked for—Timnath Serahᶜ in the hill country of Ephraim. And he built up the town and settled there.

⁵¹These are the territories that Eleazar the priest, Joshua son of Nun and the heads of the tribal clans of Israel assigned by lot at Shiloh in the presence of the Lord at the entrance to the Tent of Meeting. And so they finished dividing the land.

Cities of Refuge

20 Then the Lord said to Joshua: ²"Tell the Israelites to designate the cities of refuge, as I instructed you through Moses, ³so that anyone who kills a person accidentally and unintentionally may flee there and find protection from the avenger of blood.

⁴"When he flees to one of these cities, he is to stand in the entrance of the city gate and state his case before the elders of that city. Then they are to admit him into their city and give him a place to live with them. ⁵If the avenger of blood pursues him, they must not surrender the one accused, because he killed his neighbor unintentionally and without malice aforethought. ⁶He is to stay in that city until he has stood trial before the assembly and until the death of the high priest who is serving at that time. Then he may go back to his own home in the town from which he fled."

⁷So they set apart Kedesh in Galilee in the hill country of Naphtali, Shechem in the hill country of Ephraim, and Kiriath Arba (that is, Hebron) in the hill country of Judah. ⁸On the east side

---

ᵃ 28 Some Hebrew manuscripts (see also Joshua 21:30); most Hebrew manuscripts *Ebron*   ᵇ 34 Septuagint; Hebrew *west, and Judah, the Jordan,*   ᶜ 50 Also known as *Timnath Heres* (see Judges 2:9) of the Jordan of Jericho[a] they designated Bezer in the desert on the plateau in the tribe of Reuben, Ramoth in Gilead in the tribe of Gad, and Golan in Bashan in the tribe of Manasseh. [9]Any of the Israelites or any alien living among them who killed someone accidentally could flee to these designated cities and not be killed by the avenger of blood prior to standing trial before the assembly.

Towns for the Levites

21 Now the family heads of the Levites approached Eleazar the priest, Joshua son of Nun, and the heads of the other tribal families of Israel [2]at Shiloh in Canaan and said to them, "The LORD commanded through Moses that you give us towns to live in, with pasturelands for our livestock." [3]So, as the LORD had commanded, the Israelites gave the Levites the following towns and pasturelands out of their own inheritance.

[4]The first lot came out for the Kohathites, clan by clan. The Levites who were descendants of Aaron the priest were allotted thirteen towns from the tribes of Judah, Simeon and Benjamin. [5]The rest of Kohath's descendants were allotted ten towns from the clans of the tribes of Ephraim, Dan and half of Manasseh.

[6]The descendants of Gershon were allotted thirteen towns from the clans of the tribes of Issachar, Asher, Naphtali and the half-tribe of Manasseh in Bashan.

[7]The descendants of Merari, clan by clan, received twelve towns from the tribes of Reuben, Gad and Zebulun.

[8]So the Israelites allotted to the Levites these towns and their pasturelands, as the LORD had commanded through Moses.

[9]From the tribes of Judah and Simeon they allotted the following towns by name [10](these towns were assigned to the descendants of Aaron who were from the Kohathite clans of the Levites, because the first lot fell to them):

[11]They gave them Kiriath Arba (that is, Hebron), with its surrounding pastureland, in the hill country of Judah. (Arba was the forefather of Anak.) [12]But the fields and villages around the city they had given to Caleb son of Jephunneh as his possession.

[13]So to the descendants of Aaron the priest they gave Hebron (a city of refuge for one accused of murder), Libnah, [14]Jattir, Eshtemoa, [15]Holon, Debir, [16]Ain, Juttah and Beth Shemesh, together with their pasturelands—nine towns from these two tribes.

[17]And from the tribe of Benjamin they gave them Gibeon, Geba, [18]Anathoth and Almon, together with their pasturelands—four towns.

[19]All the towns for the priests, the descendants of Aaron, were thirteen, together with their pasturelands.

[20]The rest of the Kohathite clans of the Levites were allotted towns from the tribe of Ephraim:

[21]In the hill country of Ephraim they were given Shechem (a city of refuge for one accused of murder) and Gezer, [22]Kibzaim and Beth Horon, together with their pasturelands—four towns.

[23]Also from the tribe of Dan they received Eltekeh, Gibbethon, [24]Aijalon and Gath Rimmon, together with their pasturelands—four towns.

[25]From half the tribe of Manasseh they received Taanach and Gath Rimmon, together with their pasturelands—two towns.

[26]All these ten towns and their pasturelands were given to the rest of the Kohathite clans.

[27]The Levite clans of the Gershonites were given:

from the half-tribe of Manasseh,

Golan in Bashan (a city of refuge for one accused of murder) and Be Eshtarah, together with their pasturelands—two towns;

[28]from the tribe of Issachar,

Kishion, Daberath, [29]Jarmuth and En Gannim, together with their pasturelands—four towns;

[30]from the tribe of Asher,

Mishal, Abdon, [31]Helkath and Rehob, together with their pasturelands—four towns;

[a] 8 *Jordan of Jericho* was possibly an ancient name for the Jordan River.

³²from the tribe of Naphtali,
Kedesh in Galilee (a city of refuge for one accused of murder), Hammoth Dor and Kartan,
together with their pasturelands—three towns.
³³All the towns of the Gershonite clans were thirteen, together with their pasturelands.

³⁴The Merarite clans (the rest of the Levites) were given:
from the tribe of Zebulun,
Jokneam, Kartah, ³⁵Dimnah and Nahalal, together with their pasturelands—four towns;
³⁶from the tribe of Reuben,
Bezer, Jahaz, ³⁷Kedemoth and Mephaath, together with their pasturelands—four towns;
³⁸from the tribe of Gad,
Ramoth in Gilead (a city of refuge for one accused of murder), Mahanaim, ³⁹Heshbon and
Jazer, together with their pasturelands—four towns in all.

⁴⁰All the towns allotted to the Merarite clans, who were the rest of the Levites, were twelve.
⁴¹The towns of the Levites in the territory held by the Israelites were forty-eight in all, together with their pasturelands. ⁴²Each of these towns had pasturelands surrounding it; this was true for all these towns.

⁴³So the LORD gave Israel all the land he had sworn to give their forefathers, and they took possession of it and settled there. ⁴⁴The LORD gave them rest on every side, just as he had sworn to their forefathers. Not one of their enemies withstood them; the LORD handed all their enemies over to them. ⁴⁵Not one of all the LORD's good promises to the house of Israel failed; every one was fulfilled.

love notes

21:43–45

Loved one,

I know it is hard to wait when you want an answer now. It's easy to become impatient, or worse, to think I've forgotten you. Remember the Israelites. Not one of my promises to them failed. Every one was fulfilled. At the right time.

—Your Father

What are waiting for right now? Ask God to help you wait on his timing.

_____

_____

_____

_____

_____

_____

_____

Eastern Tribes Return Home

22 Then Joshua summoned the Reubenites, the Gadites and the half-tribe of Manasseh ²and said to them, "You have done all that Moses the servant of the LORD commanded, and you have obeyed me in everything I commanded. ³For a long time now—to this very day—you have not deserted your brothers but have carried out the mission the LORD your God gave you. ⁴Now that the LORD your God has given your brothers rest as he promised, return to your homes in the land that Moses the servant of the LORD gave you on the other side of the Jordan. ⁵But be very careful to keep the commandment and the law that Moses the servant of the LORD gave you: to love the LORD your God, to walk in all his ways, to obey his commands, to hold fast to him and to serve him with all your heart and all your soul."

⁶Then Joshua blessed them and sent them away, and they went to their homes. ⁷(To the half-tribe of Manasseh Moses had given land in Bashan, and to the other half of the tribe Joshua gave land on the west

truth or dare

Trying to obey God can make you miserable if your heart's not in it. Relax and get to know and love him. Obedience starts with the heart!

22:5

side of the Jordan with their brothers.) When Joshua sent them home, he blessed them, [8]saying, "Return to your homes with your great wealth—with large herds of livestock, with silver, gold, bronze and iron, and a great quantity of clothing—and divide with your brothers the plunder from your enemies."

[9]So the Reubenites, the Gadites and the half-tribe of Manasseh left the Israelites at Shiloh in Canaan to return to Gilead, their own land, which they had acquired in accordance with the command of the Lord through Moses.

[10]When they came to Geliloth near the Jordan in the land of Canaan, the Reubenites, the Gadites and the half-tribe of Manasseh built an imposing altar there by the Jordan. [11]And when the Israelites heard that they had built the altar on the border of Canaan at Geliloth near the Jordan on the Israelite side, [12]the whole assembly of Israel gathered at Shiloh to go to war against them.

[13]So the Israelites sent Phinehas son of Eleazar, the priest, to the land of Gilead—to Reuben, Gad and the half-tribe of Manasseh. [14]With him they sent ten of the chief men, one for each of the tribes of Israel, each the head of a family division among the Israelite clans.

[15]When they went to Gilead—to Reuben, Gad and the half-tribe of Manasseh—they said to them: [16]"The whole assembly of the Lord says: 'How could you break faith with the God of Israel like this? How could you turn away from the Lord and build yourselves an altar in rebellion against him now? [17]Was not the sin of Peor enough for us? Up to this very day we have not cleansed ourselves from that sin, even though a plague fell on the community of the Lord! [18]And are you now turning away from the Lord?

" 'If you rebel against the Lord today, tomorrow he will be angry with the whole community of Israel. [19]If the land you possess is defiled, come over to the Lord's land, where the Lord's tabernacle stands, and share the land with us. But do not rebel against the Lord or against us by building an altar for yourselves, other than the altar of the Lord our God. [20]When Achan son of Zerah acted unfaithfully regarding the devoted things,[a] did not wrath come upon the whole community of Israel? He was not the only one who died for his sin.' "

[21]Then Reuben, Gad and the half-tribe of Manasseh replied to the heads of the clans of Israel: [22]"The Mighty One, God, the Lord! The Mighty One, God, the Lord! He knows! And let Israel know! If this has been in rebellion or disobedience to the Lord, do not spare us this day. [23]If we have built our own altar to turn away from the Lord and to offer burnt offerings and grain offerings, or to sacrifice fellowship offerings[b] on it, may the Lord himself call us to account.

[24]"No! We did it for fear that some day your descendants might say to ours, 'What do you have to do with the Lord, the God of Israel? [25]The Lord has made the Jordan a boundary between us and you—you Reubenites and Gadites! You have no share in the Lord.' So your descendants might cause ours to stop fearing the Lord.

[26]"That is why we said, 'Let us get ready and build an altar—but not for burnt offerings or sacrifices.' [27]On the contrary, it is to be a witness between us and you and the generations that follow, that we will worship the Lord at his sanctuary with our burnt offerings, sacrifices and fellowship offerings. Then in the future your descendants will not be able to say to ours, 'You have no share in the Lord.'

[28]"And we said, 'If they ever say this to us, or to our descendants, we will answer: Look at the replica of the Lord's altar, which our fathers built, not for burnt offerings and sacrifices, but as a witness between us and you.'

[29]"Far be it from us to rebel against the Lord and turn away from him today by building an altar for burnt offerings, grain offerings and sacrifices, other than the altar of the Lord our God that stands before his tabernacle."

[a] 20 The Hebrew term refers to the irrevocable giving over of things or persons to the Lord, often by totally destroying them.
[b] 23 Traditionally *peace offerings*; also in verse 27

³⁰When Phinehas the priest and the leaders of the community—the heads of the clans of the Israelites—heard what Reuben, Gad and Manasseh had to say, they were pleased. ³¹And Phinehas son of Eleazar, the priest, said to Reuben, Gad and Manasseh, "Today we know that the LORD is with us, because you have not acted unfaithfully toward the LORD in this matter. Now you have rescued the Israelites from the LORD's hand."

³²Then Phinehas son of Eleazar, the priest, and the leaders returned to Canaan from their meeting with the Reubenites and Gadites in Gilead and reported to the Israelites. ³³They were glad to hear the report and praised God. And they talked no more about going to war against them to devastate the country where the Reubenites and the Gadites lived.

³⁴And the Reubenites and the Gadites gave the altar this name: A Witness Between Us that the LORD is God.

Joshua's Farewell to the Leaders

23 After a long time had passed and the LORD had given Israel rest from all their enemies around them, Joshua, by then old and well advanced in years, ²summoned all Israel—their elders, leaders, judges and officials—and said to them: "I am old and well advanced in years. ³You yourselves have seen everything the LORD your God has done to all these nations for your sake; it was the LORD your God who fought for you. ⁴Remember how I have allotted as an inheritance for your tribes all the land of the nations that remain—the nations I conquered—between the Jordan and the Great Sea*ᵃ* in the west. ⁵The LORD your God himself will drive them out of your way. He will push them out before you, and you will take possession of their land, as the LORD your God promised you.

⁶"Be very strong; be careful to obey all that is written in the Book of the Law of Moses, without turning aside to the right or to the left. ⁷Do not associate with these nations that remain among you; do not invoke the names of their gods or swear by them. You must not serve them or bow down to them. ⁸But you are to hold fast to the LORD your God, as you have until now.

⁹"The LORD has driven out before you great and powerful nations; to this day no one has been able to withstand you. ¹⁰One of you routs a thousand, because the LORD your God fights for you, just as he promised. ¹¹So be very careful to love the LORD your God.

¹²"But if you turn away and ally yourselves with the survivors of these nations that remain among you and if you intermarry with them and associate with them, ¹³then you may be sure that the LORD your God will no longer drive out these nations before you. Instead, they will become snares and traps for you, whips on your backs and thorns in your eyes, until you perish from this good land, which the LORD your God has given you.

¹⁴"Now I am about to go the way of all the earth. You know with all your heart and

genuine comfort ›› 23:14

People break promises all the time. You know what it's like. Friends tell you they'll be there and then bail on you. Parents change their minds about letting you do something. The world promises that if you look sexy, you'll get the guy of your dreams. (But of course your crush asks out your arch-rival instead.) Life is full of broken promises, and it hurts. Isn't it great to know that God always keeps his promises—and not a single one will fail? Lean on that when you're suffering the sting of another broken promise.

soul that not one of all the good promises the LORD your God gave you has failed. Every promise has been fulfilled; not one has failed. ¹⁵But just as every good promise of the LORD your God has come true, so the LORD will bring on you all the evil he has threatened, until he has destroyed you from this good land he has given you. ¹⁶If you violate the covenant of the LORD your God, which he

ᵃ 4 That is, the Mediterranean

commanded you, and go and serve other gods and bow down to them, the LORD's anger will burn against you, and you will quickly perish from the good land he has given you."

The Covenant Renewed at Shechem

24 Then Joshua assembled all the tribes of Israel at Shechem. He summoned the elders, leaders, judges and officials of Israel, and they presented themselves before God. [2]Joshua said to all the people, "This is what the LORD, the God of Israel, says: 'Long ago your forefathers, including Terah the father of Abraham and Nahor, lived beyond the River *a* and worshiped other gods. [3]But I took your father Abraham from the land beyond the River and led him throughout Canaan and gave him many descendants. I gave him Isaac, [4]and to Isaac I gave Jacob and Esau. I assigned the hill country of Seir to Esau, but Jacob and his sons went down to Egypt.

[5]" 'Then I sent Moses and Aaron, and I afflicted the Egyptians by what I did there, and I brought you out. [6]When I brought your fathers out of Egypt, you came to the sea, and the Egyptians pursued them with chariots and horsemen *b* as far as the Red Sea. *c* [7]But they cried to the LORD for help, and he put darkness between you and the Egyptians; he brought the sea over them and covered them. You saw with your own eyes what I did to the Egyptians. Then you lived in the desert for a long time.

[8]" 'I brought you to the land of the Amorites who lived east of the Jordan. They fought against you, but I gave them into your hands. I destroyed them from before you, and you took possession of their land. [9]When Balak son of Zippor, the king of Moab, prepared to fight against Israel, he sent for Balaam son of Beor to put a curse on you. [10]But I would not listen to Balaam, so he blessed you again and again, and I delivered you out of his hand.

[11]" 'Then you crossed the Jordan and came to Jericho. The citizens of Jericho fought against you, as did also the Amorites, Perizzites, Canaanites, Hittites, Girgashites, Hivites and Jebusites, but I gave them into your hands. [12]I sent the hornet ahead of you, which drove them out before you—also the two Amorite kings. You did not do it with your own sword and bow. [13]So I gave you a land on which you did not toil and cities you did not build; and you live in them and eat from vineyards and olive groves that you did not plant.'

[14]"Now fear the LORD and serve him with all faithfulness. Throw away the gods your forefathers worshiped beyond the River and in Egypt, and serve the LORD. [15]But if serving the LORD seems undesirable to you, then choose for yourselves this day whom you will serve, whether the gods your forefathers served beyond the River, or the gods of the Amorites, in whose land you are living. But as for me and my household, we will serve the LORD."

[16]Then the people answered, "Far be it from us to forsake the LORD to serve other gods! [17]It was the LORD our God himself who brought us and our fathers up out of Egypt, from that land of slavery, and performed those great signs before our eyes. He protected us on our entire journey and among all the nations through which we traveled. [18]And the LORD drove out before us all the nations, including the Amorites, who lived in the land. We too will serve the LORD, because he is our God."

genuine commitment » 24:14-15

If you've grown up around Christianity, you most likely know all the "right" things to say and do. "Read your Bible, go to church, say your prayers, be a good girl . . ." Maybe it's easy for you to go with the flow and make it look like you're serving God. But are you really? You see, growing up around Christians doesn't automatically make you part of the group. God wants you to choose to serve him for yourself—not because of your parents, or your sister, or your friends. He wants you to do it because *you* want to! Will you?

a 2 That is, the Euphrates; also in verses 3, 14 and 15   *b 6* Or *charioteers*   *c 6* Hebrew *Yam Suph*; that is, Sea of Reeds

¹⁹Joshua said to the people, "You are not able to serve the LORD. He is a holy God; he is a jealous God. He will not forgive your rebellion and your sins. ²⁰If you forsake the LORD and serve foreign gods, he will turn and bring disaster on you and make an end of you, after he has been good to you."

²¹But the people said to Joshua, "No! We will serve the LORD."

²²Then Joshua said, "You are witnesses against yourselves that you have chosen to serve the LORD."

"Yes, we are witnesses," they replied.

²³"Now then," said Joshua, "throw away the foreign gods that are among you and yield your hearts to the LORD, the God of Israel."

²⁴And the people said to Joshua, "We will serve the LORD our God and obey him."

²⁵On that day Joshua made a covenant for the people, and there at Shechem he drew up for them decrees and laws. ²⁶And Joshua recorded these things in the Book of the Law of God. Then he took a large stone and set it up there under the oak near the holy place of the LORD.

²⁷"See!" he said to all the people. "This stone will be a witness against us. It has heard all the words the LORD has said to us. It will be a witness against you if you are untrue to your God."

Buried in the Promised Land

²⁸Then Joshua sent the people away, each to his own inheritance.

²⁹After these things, Joshua son of Nun, the servant of the LORD, died at the age of a hundred and ten. ³⁰And they buried him in the land of his inheritance, at Timnath Serah ᵃ in the hill country of Ephraim, north of Mount Gaash.

³¹Israel served the LORD throughout the lifetime of Joshua and of the elders who outlived him and who had experienced everything the LORD had done for Israel.

³²And Joseph's bones, which the Israelites had brought up from Egypt, were buried at Shechem in the tract of land that Jacob bought for a hundred pieces of silver ᵇ from the sons of Hamor, the father of Shechem. This became the inheritance of Joseph's descendants.

³³And Eleazar son of Aaron died and was buried at Gibeah, which had been allotted to his son Phinehas in the hill country of Ephraim.

ᵃ 30 Also known as *Timnath Heres* (see Judges 2:9)   ᵇ 32 Hebrew *hundred kesitahs*; a kesitah was a unit of money of unknown weight and value.

author:	Unknown (possibly Samuel).
date:	Around 1000 B.C.
setting:	The events take place in the land of Canaan, which today is Israel. In danger of losing the promised land, the Israelites were rescued by many leaders, known as "judges," during this period.
verse to remember:	In those days Israel had no king; everyone did as he saw fit (17:6).
theme to consider:	Judges is a book of bad news/good news. The bad news is that, left to ourselves, we tend to forget God and turn to sin. The good news is that even though God knows what we're like, he still loves us.

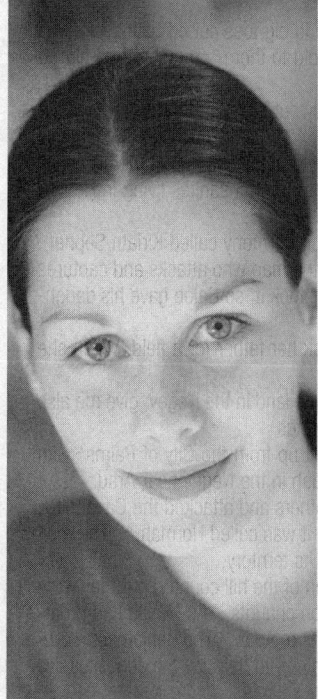

unchanging truth

Good news/bad news . . . which would you rather hear first? It's probably a toss-up. If you get the bad news first, the worst is over and it has to get better, right? But if you get the good news first, you'll end on a sour note.

Some good news/bad news situations aren't all that traumatic—your favorite shirt is clean *but* a button is missing. Other good news/bad news can cause genuine concern—you've been asked to be in a wedding *but* the dress costs $300. Each time one of these situations comes up, you have to figure out how to make the most of the bad news so that it becomes good—or at least something you can live with.

The Israelites, with God's help, had defeated the people of Canaan, and the land was theirs for the taking. Good news! But the Israelites soon disobeyed God and worshiped false gods. Bad news. God punished them, the people pleaded for mercy and God forgave them. Back and forth, endless cycle—you'd think they'd get a clue! But sometimes, we too forget about God and sin. But God, in his love and mercy, forgives us when we come back to him. Now *that* is incredibly good news!

judges

life lessons

1 The Israelites had a memory problem and a sin problem. They forgot all that God had done for them and turned away from him (2:17–19).

2 God knows what we're like—that we sin often—yet he still hears our prayers, forgives us and helps us when we turn back to him (16:23–30).

3 Don't fall for Satan's same old lies. True happiness comes from obeying God, not doing whatever you feel like doing (21:25).

Israel Fights the Remaining Canaanites

1 After the death of Joshua, the Israelites asked the LORD, "Who will be the first to go up and fight for us against the Canaanites?"

[2]The LORD answered, "Judah is to go; I have given the land into their hands."

[3]Then the men of Judah said to the Simeonites their brothers, "Come up with us into the territory allotted to us, to fight against the Canaanites. We in turn will go with you into yours." So the Simeonites went with them.

[4]When Judah attacked, the LORD gave the Canaanites and Perizzites into their hands and they struck down ten thousand men at Bezek. [5]It was there that they found Adoni-Bezek and fought against him, putting to rout the Canaanites and Perizzites. [6]Adoni-Bezek fled, but they chased him and caught him, and cut off his thumbs and big toes.

[7]Then Adoni-Bezek said, "Seventy kings with their thumbs and big toes cut off have picked up scraps under my table. Now God has paid me back for what I did to them." They brought him to Jerusalem, and he died there.

[8]The men of Judah attacked Jerusalem also and took it. They put the city to the sword and set it on fire.

[9]After that, the men of Judah went down to fight against the Canaanites living in the hill country, the Negev and the western foothills. [10]They advanced against the Canaanites living in Hebron (formerly called Kiriath Arba) and defeated Sheshai, Ahiman and Talmai.

[11]From there they advanced against the people living in Debir (formerly called Kiriath Sepher). [12]And Caleb said, "I will give my daughter Acsah in marriage to the man who attacks and captures Kiriath Sepher." [13]Othniel son of Kenaz, Caleb's younger brother, took it; so Caleb gave his daughter Acsah to him in marriage.

[14]One day when she came to Othniel, she urged him[a] to ask her father for a field. When she got off her donkey, Caleb asked her, "What can I do for you?"

[15]She replied, "Do me a special favor. Since you have given me land in the Negev, give me also springs of water." Then Caleb gave her the upper and lower springs.

[16]The descendants of Moses' father-in-law, the Kenite, went up from the City of Palms[b] with the men of Judah to live among the people of the Desert of Judah in the Negev near Arad.

[17]Then the men of Judah went with the Simeonites their brothers and attacked the Canaanites living in Zephath, and they totally destroyed[c] the city. Therefore it was called Hormah.[d] [18]The men of Judah also took[e] Gaza, Ashkelon and Ekron—each city with its territory.

[19]The LORD was with the men of Judah. They took possession of the hill country, but they were unable to drive the people from the plains, because they had iron chariots. [20]As Moses had promised, Hebron was given to Caleb, who drove from it the three sons of Anak. [21]The Benjamites, however, failed to dislodge the Jebusites, who were living in Jerusalem; to this day the Jebusites live there with the Benjamites.

[22]Now the house of Joseph attacked Bethel, and the LORD was with them. [23]When they sent men to spy out Bethel (formerly called Luz), [24]the spies saw a man coming out of the city and they said to him, "Show us how to get into the city and we will see that you are treated well." [25]So he showed them, and they put the city to the sword but spared the man and his whole family. [26]He then went to the land of the Hittites, where he built a city and called it Luz, which is its name to this day.

[27]But Manasseh did not drive out the people of Beth Shan or Taanach or Dor or Ibleam or Megiddo and their surrounding settlements, for the Canaanites were determined to live in that land. [28]When Israel became strong, they pressed the Canaanites into forced labor but never drove them out completely. [29]Nor did Ephraim drive out the Canaanites living in Gezer, but the Canaanites continued to live there among them. [30]Neither did Zebulun drive out the Canaanites living in Kitron or Nahalol, who remained among them; but they did subject them to forced labor. [31]Nor did Asher drive out those living in Acco or Sidon or Ahlab or Aczib or Helbah or Aphek or Rehob, [32]and because of this the people of Asher lived among the Canaanite inhabitants of the land. [33]Neither did Naphtali drive out those living in Beth Shemesh or Beth Anath; but the Naphtalites too lived among the Canaanite inhabitants of the land, and those living in Beth Shemesh and Beth Anath became

---

a 14 Hebrew; Septuagint and Vulgate *Othniel, he urged her*   b 16 That is, Jericho   c 17 The Hebrew term refers to the irrevocable giving over of things or persons to the LORD, often by totally destroying them.   d 17 *Hormah* means *destruction.*   e 18 Hebrew; Septuagint *Judah did not take*

in focus

Dreaming of Zzzzz's

Profile: Maura

My alarm clock says 1:37 A.M. And I'm still lying here, wide awake as usual. Every night it's the same old thing: Maura goes to bed at 11:00. Maura tosses and turns for hours until her sheets and blankets end up in a pile on the floor. Maura thinks about all the junk that might happen at school tomorrow and what might happen if her grade in French slips or her best friend finally moves to Montana or she can't find an excuse to miss the wild party happening this weekend.

Pathetic, isn't it? All day I walk around like a zombie, daydreaming about a nice long nap. My chemistry teacher caught me dozing off in class yesterday, and even my best friends tell me I'm always "zoning out."

But what can I do? It's like I'm obsessed with everything that could go wrong and anything I can't fix. Today I read an advertisement for sleeping pills and wondered if I should check it out. But with my luck I'd probably have to take one every night, and I'd get addicted or something.

All I know is that without sleep I'm as snippy as "Oscar the Grouch," and my test scores are Cs instead of B-pluses. Last night I got desperate and prayed that God would help me fall asleep by midnight. When 12:30 came, I was so mad I stayed awake till 4:00. Today I'm so tired I can't stop crying. I'm such a mess.

stress in focus

Doctors say most teens are sleep-deprived because of stress and anxiety. So how can girls like Maura find the sleep they need?

» Give it up. You weren't meant to carry your stress alone—in fact, you weren't meant to carry it at all! Read 1 Peter 5:7 (page 1612) and Psalm 62 (page 713). Then pray a prayer like this when you're stressed: "God, I'm worried about _____, but I want to give that worry to you. Help me let it go."

» Get help. Talking to your school nurse or guidance counselor can help you find ways to work through stress and reestablish a regular sleep pattern.

For more on this topic, see the index on page 1656

stress

forced laborers for them. [34]The Amorites confined the Danites to the hill country, not allowing them to come down into the plain. [35]And the Amorites were determined also to hold out in Mount Heres, Aijalon and Shaalbim, but when the power of the house of Joseph increased, they too were pressed into forced labor. [36]The boundary of the Amorites was from Scorpion[a] Pass to Sela and beyond.

a 36 Hebrew *Akrabbim*

The Angel of the Lord at Bokim

2 The angel of the Lord went up from Gilgal to Bokim and said, "I brought you up out of Egypt and led you into the land that I swore to give to your forefathers. I said, 'I will never break my covenant with you, ²and you shall not make a covenant with the people of this land, but you shall break down their altars.' Yet you have disobeyed me. Why have you done this? ³Now therefore I tell you that I will not drive them out before you; they will be ⌐thorns¬ in your sides and their gods will be a snare to you."

⁴When the angel of the Lord had spoken these things to all the Israelites, the people wept aloud, ⁵and they called that place Bokim.ª There they offered sacrifices to the Lord.

Disobedience and Defeat

⁶After Joshua had dismissed the Israelites, they went to take possession of the land, each to his own inheritance. ⁷The people served the Lord throughout the lifetime of Joshua and of the elders who outlived him and who had seen all the great things the Lord had done for Israel.

⁸Joshua son of Nun, the servant of the Lord, died at the age of a hundred and ten. ⁹And they buried him in the land of his inheritance, at Timnath Heresᵇ in the hill country of Ephraim, north of Mount Gaash.

¹⁰After that whole generation had been gathered to their fathers, another generation grew up, who knew neither the Lord nor what he had done for Israel. ¹¹Then the Israelites did evil in the eyes of the Lord and served the Baals. ¹²They forsook the Lord, the God of their fathers, who had brought them out of Egypt. They followed and worshiped various gods of the peoples around them. They provoked the Lord to anger ¹³because they forsook him and served Baal and the Ashtoreths. ¹⁴In his anger against Israel the Lord handed them over to raiders who plundered them. He sold them to their enemies all around, whom they were no longer able to resist. ¹⁵Whenever Israel went out to fight, the hand of the Lord was against them to defeat them, just as he had sworn to them. They were in great distress.

¹⁶Then the Lord raised up judges,ᶜ who saved them out of the hands of these raiders. ¹⁷Yet they would not listen to their judges but prostituted themselves to other gods and worshiped them. Unlike their fathers, they quickly turned from the way in which their fathers had walked, the way of obedience to the Lord's commands. ¹⁸Whenever the Lord raised up a judge for them, he was with the judge and saved them out of the hands of their enemies as long as the judge lived; for the Lord had compassion on them as they groaned under those who oppressed and afflicted them. ¹⁹But when the judge died, the people returned to ways even more corrupt than those of their fathers, following other gods and serving and worshiping them. They refused to give up their evil practices and stubborn ways.

²⁰Therefore the Lord was very angry with Israel and said, "Because this nation has violated the covenant that I laid down for their forefathers and has not listened to me, ²¹I will no longer drive out before them any of the nations Joshua left when he died. ²²I will use them to test Israel and see whether they will keep the way of the Lord and walk in it as their forefathers did." ²³The Lord had allowed those nations to remain; he did not drive them out at once by giving them into the hands of Joshua.

3 These are the nations the Lord left to test all those Israelites who had not experienced any of the wars in Canaan ²(he did this only to teach warfare to the descendants of the Israelites who had not had previous battle experience): ³the five rulers of the Philistines, all the Canaanites, the Sidonians, and the Hivites living in the Lebanon mountains from Mount Baal Hermon to Leboᵈ Hamath. ⁴They were left to test the Israelites to see whether they would obey the Lord's commands, which he had given their forefathers through Moses.

truth or dare

Ever feel like you're on a spiritual roller coaster—first on a spiritual high, then plunging to an all-time low? Welcome to the life of the Israelites! Was God inconsistent? Or were they?

2:16–19

ª 5 *Bokim* means *weepers.*   ᵇ 9 Also known as *Timnath Serah* (see Joshua 19:50 and 24:30)   ᶜ 16 Or *leaders;* similarly in verses 17-19   ᵈ 3 Or *to the entrance to*

⁵The Israelites lived among the Canaanites, Hittites, Amorites, Perizzites, Hivites and Jebusites. ⁶They took their daughters in marriage and gave their own daughters to their sons, and served their gods.

Othniel

⁷The Israelites did evil in the eyes of the LORD; they forgot the LORD their God and served the Baals and the Asherahs. ⁸The anger of the LORD burned against Israel so that he sold them into the hands of Cushan-Rishathaim king of Aram Naharaim,ᵃ to whom the Israelites were subject for eight years. ⁹But when they cried out to the LORD, he raised up for them a deliverer, Othniel son of Kenaz, Caleb's younger brother, who saved them. ¹⁰The Spirit of the LORD came upon him, so that he became Israel's judgeᵇ and went to war. The LORD gave Cushan-Rishathaim king of Aram into the hands of Othniel, who overpowered him. ¹¹So the land had peace for forty years, until Othniel son of Kenaz died.

Ehud

¹²Once again the Israelites did evil in the eyes of the LORD, and because they did this evil the LORD gave Eglon king of Moab power over Israel. ¹³Getting the Ammonites and Amalekites to join him, Eglon came and attacked Israel, and they took possession of the City of Palms.ᶜ ¹⁴The Israelites were subject to Eglon king of Moab for eighteen years.

¹⁵Again the Israelites cried out to the LORD, and he gave them a deliverer—Ehud, a left-handed man, the son of Gera the Benjamite. The Israelites sent him with tribute to Eglon king of Moab. ¹⁶Now Ehud had made a double-edged sword about a foot and a halfᵈ long, which he strapped to his right thigh under his clothing. ¹⁷He presented the tribute to Eglon king of Moab, who was a very fat man. ¹⁸After Ehud had presented the tribute, he sent on their way the men who had carried it. ¹⁹At the idolsᵉ near Gilgal he himself turned back and said, "I have a secret message for you, O king."

The king said, "Quiet!" And all his attendants left him.

²⁰Ehud then approached him while he was sitting alone in the upper room of his summer palaceᶠ and said, "I have a message from God for you." As the king rose from his seat, ²¹Ehud reached with his left hand, drew the sword from his right thigh and plunged it into the king's belly. ²²Even the handle sank in after the blade, which came out his back. Ehud did not pull the sword out, and the fat closed in over it. ²³Then Ehud went out to the porchᵍ; he shut the doors of the upper room behind him and locked them.

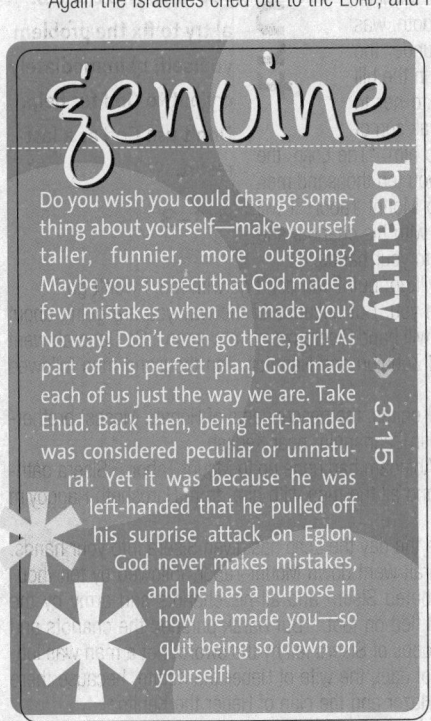

ᵃ *8* That is, Northwest Mesopotamia   ᵇ *10* Or *leader*   ᶜ *13* That is, Jericho   ᵈ *16* Hebrew *a cubit* (about 0.5 meter)   ᵉ *19* Or *the stone quarries*; also in verse 26   ᶠ *20* The meaning of the Hebrew for this phrase is uncertain.   ᵍ *23* The meaning of the Hebrew for this word is uncertain.

²⁴After he had gone, the servants came and found the doors of the upper room locked. They said, "He must be relieving himself in the inner room of the house." ²⁵They waited to the point of embarrassment, but when he did not open the doors of the room, they took a key and unlocked them. There they saw their lord fallen to the floor, dead.

²⁶While they waited, Ehud got away. He passed by the idols and escaped to Seirah. ²⁷When he arrived there, he blew a trumpet in the hill country of Ephraim, and the Israelites went down with him from the hills, with him leading them.

²⁸"Follow me," he ordered, "for the LORD has given Moab, your enemy, into your hands." So they followed him down and, taking possession of the fords of the Jordan that led to Moab, they allowed no one to cross over. ²⁹At that time they struck down about ten thousand Moabites, all vigorous and strong; not a man escaped. ³⁰That day Moab was made subject to Israel, and the land had peace for eighty years.

Shamgar

³¹After Ehud came Shamgar son of Anath, who struck down six hundred Philistines with an oxgoad. He too saved Israel.

Deborah

4 After Ehud died, the Israelites once again did evil in the eyes of the LORD. ²So the LORD sold them into the hands of Jabin, a king of Canaan, who reigned in Hazor. The commander of his army was Sisera, who lived in Harosheth Haggoyim. ³Because he had nine hundred iron chariots and had cruelly oppressed the Israelites for twenty years, they cried to the LORD for help.

⁴Deborah, a prophetess, the wife of Lappidoth, was leading ª Israel at that time. ⁵She held court under the Palm of Deborah between Ramah and Bethel in the hill country of Ephraim, and the Israelites came to her to have their disputes decided. ⁶She sent for Barak son of Abinoam from Kedesh in Naphtali and said to him, "The LORD, the God of Israel, commands you: 'Go, take with you ten thousand men of Naphtali and Zebulun and lead the way to Mount Tabor. ⁷I will lure Sisera, the commander of Jabin's army, with his chariots and his troops to the Kishon River and give him into your hands.' "

truth or dare

When you're in trouble, you have two choices: a) try to fix the problem yourself; b) immediately cry out to God for help. Don't use God as a last-resort.

4:1–3

⁸Barak said to her, "If you go with me, I will go; but if you don't go with me, I won't go."

⁹"Very well," Deborah said, "I will go with you. But because of the way you are going about this, ᵇ the honor will not be yours, for the LORD will hand Sisera over to a woman." So Deborah went with Barak to Kedesh, ¹⁰where he summoned Zebulun and Naphtali. Ten thousand men followed him, and Deborah also went with him.

¹¹Now Heber the Kenite had left the other Kenites, the descendants of Hobab, Moses' brother-in-law, ᶜ and pitched his tent by the great tree in Zaanannim near Kedesh.

¹²When they told Sisera that Barak son of Abinoam had gone up to Mount Tabor, ¹³Sisera gathered together his nine hundred iron chariots and all the men with him, from Harosheth Haggoyim to the Kishon River.

¹⁴Then Deborah said to Barak, "Go! This is the day the LORD has given Sisera into your hands. Has not the LORD gone ahead of you?" So Barak went down Mount Tabor, followed by ten thousand men. ¹⁵At Barak's advance, the LORD routed Sisera and all his chariots and army by the sword, and Sisera abandoned his chariot and fled on foot. ¹⁶But Barak pursued the chariots and army as far as Harosheth Haggoyim. All the troops of Sisera fell by the sword; not a man was left.

¹⁷Sisera, however, fled on foot to the tent of Jael, the wife of Heber the Kenite, because there were friendly relations between Jabin king of Hazor and the clan of Heber the Kenite.

¹⁸Jael went out to meet Sisera and said to him, "Come, my lord, come right in. Don't be afraid." So he entered her tent, and she put a covering over him.

ª 4 Traditionally *judging*   ᵇ 9 Or *But on the expedition you are undertaking*   ᶜ 11 Or *father-in-law*

¹⁹"I'm thirsty," he said. "Please give me some water." She opened a skin of milk, gave him a drink, and covered him up.

²⁰"Stand in the doorway of the tent," he told her. "If someone comes by and asks you, 'Is anyone here?' say 'No.'"

²¹But Jael, Heber's wife, picked up a tent peg and a hammer and went quietly to him while he lay fast asleep, exhausted. She drove the peg through his temple into the ground, and he died.

²²Barak came by in pursuit of Sisera, and Jael went out to meet him. "Come," she said, "I will show you the man you're looking for." So he went in with her, and there lay Sisera with the tent peg through his temple—dead.

²³On that day God subdued Jabin, the Canaanite king, before the Israelites. ²⁴And the hand of the Israelites grew stronger and stronger against Jabin, the Canaanite king, until they destroyed him.

The Song of Deborah

5 On that day Deborah and Barak son of Abinoam sang this song:

²"When the princes in Israel take the lead,
>> when the people willingly offer themselves—
>> praise the LORD!

³"Hear this, you kings! Listen, you
>> rulers!
>> I will sing to^a the LORD, I will
>> sing;
>> I will make music to^b the LORD,
>> the God of Israel.

⁴"O LORD, when you went out from
>> Seir,
>> when you marched from the
>> land of Edom,
>> the earth shook, the heavens
>> poured,
>> the clouds poured down water.
⁵The mountains quaked before the LORD, the
>> One of Sinai,
>> before the LORD, the God of Israel.

⁶"In the days of Shamgar son of Anath,
>> in the days of Jael, the roads were abandoned;
>> travelers took to winding paths.
⁷Village life^c in Israel ceased,
>> ceased until I,^d Deborah, arose,
>> arose a mother in Israel.

ǥenuine purpose >> 4:17-22

Most people would consider Jael a nobody. She wasn't famous or powerful or prestigious like Deborah and Barak. Yet *she* was the one who brought down mighty Sisera, playing a key role in Israel's liberation from its enemy. God has a habit of using the "nobodies" of this world to do incredible things. Do you feel like you're nothing special? Too ordinary to do anything extraordinary for God? Don't count yourself out yet! Remember that God has a history of using the average Joe (or Jael, in this case!) to do above-average things.

truth or dare

Right after battle, Deborah decided to . . . sing? Yep! This woman had her priorities straight. She immediately began to praise God.

5:1–3

^a 3 Or *of*   ^b 3 Or / *with song I will praise*   ^c 7 Or *Warriors*   ^d 7 Or *you*

⁸When they chose new gods,
  war came to the city gates,
and not a shield or spear was seen
  among forty thousand in Israel.
⁹My heart is with Israel's princes,
  with the willing volunteers among the people.
  Praise the LORD!

¹⁰"You who ride on white donkeys,
  sitting on your saddle blankets,
  and you who walk along the road,
consider ¹¹the voice of the singers*a* at the watering places.
  They recite the righteous acts of the LORD,
  the righteous acts of his warriors*b* in Israel.

"Then the people of the LORD
  went down to the city gates.
¹²'Wake up, wake up, Deborah!
  Wake up, wake up, break out in song!
Arise, O Barak!
  Take captive your captives, O son of Abinoam.'

¹³"Then the men who were left
  came down to the nobles;
the people of the LORD
  came to me with the mighty.
¹⁴Some came from Ephraim, whose roots were in Amalek;
  Benjamin was with the people who followed you.
From Makir captains came down,
  from Zebulun those who bear a commander's staff.
¹⁵The princes of Issachar were with Deborah;
  yes, Issachar was with Barak,
  rushing after him into the valley.
In the districts of Reuben
  there was much searching of heart.
¹⁶Why did you stay among the campfires*c*
  to hear the whistling for the flocks?
In the districts of Reuben
  there was much searching of heart.
¹⁷Gilead stayed beyond the Jordan.
  And Dan, why did he linger by the ships?
Asher remained on the coast
  and stayed in his coves.
¹⁸The people of Zebulun risked their very lives;
  so did Naphtali on the heights of the field.

¹⁹"Kings came, they fought;
  the kings of Canaan fought
at Taanach by the waters of Megiddo,
  but they carried off no silver, no plunder.
²⁰From the heavens the stars fought,
  from their courses they fought against Sisera.
²¹The river Kishon swept them away,
  the age-old river, the river Kishon.
  March on, my soul; be strong!

a 11 Or *archers*; the meaning of the Hebrew for this word is uncertain.   *b 11* Or *villagers*   *c 16* Or *saddlebags*

²² Then thundered the horses' hoofs—
  galloping, galloping go his mighty steeds.
²³ 'Curse Meroz,' said the angel of the LORD.
  'Curse its people bitterly,
because they did not come to help the LORD,
  to help the LORD against the mighty.'

²⁴ "Most blessed of women be Jael,
  the wife of Heber the Kenite,
  most blessed of tent-dwelling women.
²⁵ He asked for water, and she gave him milk;
  in a bowl fit for nobles she brought him curdled milk.
²⁶ Her hand reached for the tent peg,
  her right hand for the
    workman's hammer.
  She struck Sisera, she crushed
    his head,
  she shattered and pierced his
    temple.
²⁷ At her feet he sank,
  he fell; there he lay.
  At her feet he sank, he fell;
  where he sank, there he
    fell—dead.

²⁸ "Through the window peered
    Sisera's mother;
  behind the lattice she cried
    out,
  'Why is his chariot so long in
    coming?
  Why is the clatter of his
    chariots delayed?'
²⁹ The wisest of her ladies answer
    her;
  indeed, she keeps saying to
    herself,
³⁰ 'Are they not finding and dividing
    the spoils:
  a girl or two for each man,
  colorful garments as plunder
    for Sisera,
  colorful garments
    embroidered,
  highly embroidered garments
    for my neck—
  all this as plunder?'

³¹ "So may all your enemies perish,
    O LORD!
  But may they who love you be
    like the sun
  when it rises in its strength."

Then the land had peace forty years.

love notes

5:31

Child,

*The next time you witness the
beauty of a sunrise, remember
Deborah's words. My loved ones
will be like the sun rising in all
its power, beauty and strength.
Shine for me today.*

—*The Creator*

In what ways do you reflect God's
power, beauty and strength to others?

_____

_____

_____

_____

_____

_____

_____

_____

_____

6 Again the Israelites did evil in the eyes of the Lord, and for seven years he gave them into the hands of the Midianites. ²Because the power of Midian was so oppressive, the Israelites prepared shelters for themselves in mountain clefts, caves and strongholds. ³Whenever the Israelites planted their crops, the Midianites, Amalekites and other eastern peoples invaded the country. ⁴They camped on the land and ruined the crops all the way to Gaza and did not spare a living thing for Israel, neither sheep nor cattle nor donkeys. ⁵They came up with their livestock and their tents like swarms of locusts. It was impossible to count the men and their camels; they invaded the land to ravage it. ⁶Midian so impoverished the Israelites that they cried out to the Lord for help.

⁷When the Israelites cried to the Lord because of Midian, ⁸he sent them a prophet, who said, "This is what the Lord, the God of Israel, says: I brought you up out of Egypt, out of the land of slavery. ⁹I snatched you from the power of Egypt and from the hand of all your oppressors. I drove them from before you and gave you their land. ¹⁰I said to you, 'I am the Lord your God; do not worship the gods of the Amorites, in whose land you live.' But you have not listened to me."

¹¹The angel of the Lord came and sat down under the oak in Ophrah that belonged to Joash the Abiezrite, where his son Gideon was threshing wheat in a winepress to keep it from the Midianites. ¹²When the angel of the Lord appeared to Gideon, he said, "The Lord is with you, mighty warrior."

¹³"But sir," Gideon replied, "if the Lord is with us, why has all this happened to us? Where are all his wonders that our fathers told us about when they said, 'Did not the Lord bring us up out of Egypt?' But now the Lord has abandoned us and put us into the hand of Midian."

¹⁴The Lord turned to him and said, "Go in the strength you have and save Israel out of Midian's hand. Am I not sending you?"

¹⁵"But Lord,ᵃ" Gideon asked, "how can I save Israel? My clan is the weakest in Manasseh, and I am the least in my family."

¹⁶The Lord answered, "I will be with you, and you will strike down all the Midianites together."

¹⁷Gideon replied, "If now I have found favor in your eyes, give me a sign that it is really you talking to me. ¹⁸Please do not go away until I come back and bring my offering and set it before you."

And the Lord said, "I will wait until you return."

¹⁹Gideon went in, prepared a young goat, and from an ephahᵇ of flour he made bread without yeast. Putting the meat in a basket and its broth in a pot, he brought them out and offered them to him under the oak.

²⁰The angel of God said to him, "Take the meat and the unleavened bread, place them on this rock, and pour out the broth." And Gideon did so. ²¹With the tip of the staff that was in his hand, the angel of the Lord touched the meat and the unleavened bread. Fire flared from the rock, consuming the meat and the bread. And the angel of the Lord disappeared. ²²When Gideon realized that it was the angel of the Lord, he exclaimed, "Ah, Sovereign Lord! I have seen the angel of the Lord face to face!"

²³But the Lord said to him, "Peace! Do not be afraid. You are not going to die."

²⁴So Gideon built an altar to the Lord there and called it The Lord is Peace. To this day it stands in Ophrah of the Abiezrites.

genuine strength » 6:14-16

When God nudges you to do something, do you answer like Gideon? "*But Lord . . . I don't know enough Bible verses to tell my friends about Jesus . . . But Lord . . . I'm not smart enough to talk about creationism in my science class . . . But Lord . . . I'm not enough of a leader to start a Bible study at school.*" Like Gideon, do you focus more on yourself and your weakness than on God and his strength? You know, it doesn't really matter what you can or can't do—all that matters is that God will be with you, and he can do all things. So go for it!

ᵃ 15 Or *sir* ᵇ 19 That is, probably about 3/5 bushel (about 22 liters)

²⁵That same night the LORD said to him, "Take the second bull from your father's herd, the one seven years old.ᵃ Tear down your father's altar to Baal and cut down the Asherah poleᵇ beside it. ²⁶Then build a proper kind ofᶜ altar to the LORD your God on the top of this height. Using the wood of the Asherah pole that you cut down, offer the secondᵈ bull as a burnt offering."

²⁷So Gideon took ten of his servants and did as the LORD told him. But because he was afraid of his family and the men of the town, he did it at night rather than in the daytime.

²⁸In the morning when the men of the town got up, there was Baal's altar, demolished, with the Asherah pole beside it cut down and the second bull sacrificed on the newly built altar!

²⁹They asked each other, "Who did this?"

When they carefully investigated, they were told, "Gideon son of Joash did it."

³⁰The men of the town demanded of Joash, "Bring out your son. He must die, because he has broken down Baal's altar and cut down the Asherah pole beside it."

³¹But Joash replied to the hostile crowd around him, "Are you going to plead Baal's cause? Are you trying to save him? Whoever fights for him shall be put to death by morning! If Baal really is a god, he can defend himself when someone breaks down his altar." ³²So that day they called Gideon "Jerub-Baal,ᵉ" saying, "Let Baal contend with him," because he broke down Baal's altar.

³³Now all the Midianites, Amalekites and other eastern peoples joined forces and crossed over the Jordan and camped in the Valley of Jezreel. ³⁴Then the Spirit of the LORD came upon Gideon, and he blew a trumpet, summoning the Abiezrites to follow him. ³⁵He sent messengers throughout Manasseh, calling them to arms, and also into Asher, Zebulun and Naphtali, so that they too went up to meet them.

³⁶Gideon said to God, "If you will save Israel by my hand as you have promised— ³⁷look, I will place a wool fleece on the threshing floor. If there is dew only on the fleece and all the ground is dry, then I will know that you will save Israel by my hand, as you said." ³⁸And that is what happened. Gideon rose early the next day; he squeezed the fleece and wrung out the dew—a bowlful of water.

³⁹Then Gideon said to God, "Do not be angry with me. Let me make just one more request. Allow me one more test with the fleece. This time make the fleece dry and the ground covered with dew." ⁴⁰That night God did so. Only the fleece was dry; all the ground was covered with dew.

truth or dare

"Just give me a sign!" Gideon pleaded. Ever feel that need for confirmation? God's Word is full of signs—flashing lights, warnings, helpful hints, practical guidelines, ads for holy living.

6:39–40

Gideon Defeats the Midianites

7 Early in the morning, Jerub-Baal (that is, Gideon) and all his men camped at the spring of Harod. The camp of Midian was north of them in the valley near the hill of Moreh. ²The LORD said to Gideon, "You have too many men for me to deliver Midian into their hands. In order that Israel may not boast against me that her own strength has saved her, ³announce now to the people, 'Anyone who trembles with fear may turn back and leave Mount Gilead.' " So twenty-two thousand men left, while ten thousand remained.

⁴But the LORD said to Gideon, "There are still too many men. Take them down to the water, and I will sift them for you there. If I say, 'This one shall go with you,' he shall go; but if I say, 'This one shall not go with you,' he shall not go."

truth or dare

Your weaknesses don't faze God. In fact, having too much strength or confidence can actually make you trust in yourself. Put your trust totally in God—he can use you!

7:2–3

ᵃ 25 Or Take a full-grown, mature bull from your father's herd elsewhere in Judges   ᶜ 26 Or build with layers of stone an   ᵈ 26 Or full-grown; also in verse 28   ᵉ 32 Jerub-Baal means let Baal contend.   ᵇ 25 That is, a symbol of the goddess Asherah; here and

⁵So Gideon took the men down to the water. There the LORD told him, "Separate those who lap the water with their tongues like a dog from those who kneel down to drink." ⁶Three hundred men lapped with their hands to their mouths. All the rest got down on their knees to drink.

⁷The LORD said to Gideon, "With the three hundred men that lapped I will save you and give the Midianites into your hands. Let all the other men go, each to his own place." ⁸So Gideon sent the rest of the Israelites to their tents but kept the three hundred, who took over the provisions and trumpets of the others.

Now the camp of Midian lay below him in the valley. ⁹During that night the LORD said to Gideon, "Get up, go down against the camp, because I am going to give it into your hands. ¹⁰If you are afraid to attack, go down to the camp with your servant Purah ¹¹and listen to what they are saying. Afterward, you will be encouraged to attack the camp." So he and Purah his servant went down to the outposts of the camp. ¹²The Midianites, the Amalekites and all the other eastern peoples had settled in the valley, thick as locusts. Their camels could no more be counted than the sand on the seashore.

¹³Gideon arrived just as a man was telling a friend his dream. "I had a dream," he was saying. "A round loaf of barley bread came tumbling into the Midianite camp. It struck the tent with such force that the tent overturned and collapsed."

¹⁴His friend responded, "This can be nothing other than the sword of Gideon son of Joash, the Israelite. God has given the Midianites and the whole camp into his hands."

¹⁵When Gideon heard the dream and its interpretation, he worshiped God. He returned to the camp of Israel and called out, "Get up! The LORD has given the Midianite camp into your hands." ¹⁶Dividing the three hundred men into three companies, he placed trumpets and empty jars in the hands of all of them, with torches inside.

¹⁷"Watch me," he told them. "Follow my lead. When I get to the edge of the camp, do exactly as I do. ¹⁸When I and all who are with me blow our trumpets, then from all around the camp blow yours and shout, 'For the LORD and for Gideon.' "

¹⁹Gideon and the hundred men with him reached the edge of the camp at the beginning of the middle watch, just after they had changed the guard. They blew their trumpets and broke the jars that were in their hands. ²⁰The three companies blew the trumpets and smashed the jars. Grasping the torches in their left hands and holding in their right hands the trumpets they were to blow, they shouted, "A sword for the LORD and for Gideon!" ²¹While each man held his position around the camp, all the Midianites ran, crying out as they fled.

²²When the three hundred trumpets sounded, the LORD caused the men throughout the camp to turn on each other with their swords. The army fled to Beth Shittah toward Zererah as far as the border of Abel Meholah near Tabbath. ²³Israelites from Naphtali, Asher and all Manasseh were called out, and they pursued the Midianites. ²⁴Gideon sent messengers throughout the hill country of Ephraim, saying, "Come down against the Midianites and seize the waters of the Jordan ahead of them as far as Beth Barah."

So all the men of Ephraim were called out and they took the waters of the Jordan as far as Beth Barah. ²⁵They also captured two of the Midianite leaders, Oreb and Zeeb. They killed Oreb at the rock of Oreb, and Zeeb at the winepress of Zeeb. They pursued the Midianites and brought the heads of Oreb and Zeeb to Gideon, who was by the Jordan.

Zebah and Zalmunna

8 Now the Ephraimites asked Gideon, "Why have you treated us like this? Why didn't you call us when you went to fight Midian?" And they criticized him sharply.

²But he answered them, "What have I accomplished compared to you? Aren't the gleanings of Ephraim's grapes better than the full grape harvest of Abiezer? ³God gave Oreb and Zeeb, the Midianite leaders, into your hands. What was I able to do compared to you?" At this, their resentment against him subsided.

⁴Gideon and his three hundred men, exhausted yet keeping up the pursuit, came to the Jordan and crossed it. ⁵He said to the men of Succoth, "Give my troops some bread; they are worn out, and I am still pursuing Zebah and Zalmunna, the kings of Midian."

⁶But the officials of Succoth said, "Do you already have the hands of Zebah and Zalmunna in your possession? Why should we give bread to your troops?"

⁷Then Gideon replied, "Just for that, when the LORD has given Zebah and Zalmunna into my hand, I will tear your flesh with desert thorns and briers."

⁸From there he went up to Peniel ᵃ and made the same request of them, but they answered as the men of Succoth had. ⁹So he said to the men of Peniel, "When I return in triumph, I will tear down this tower."

¹⁰Now Zebah and Zalmunna were in Karkor with a force of about fifteen thousand men, all that were left of the armies of the eastern peoples; a hundred and twenty thousand swordsmen had fallen. ¹¹Gideon went up by the route of the nomads east of Nobah and Jogbehah and fell upon the unsuspecting army. ¹²Zebah and Zalmunna, the two kings of Midian, fled, but he pursued them and captured them, routing their entire army.

¹³Gideon son of Joash then returned from the battle by the Pass of Heres. ¹⁴He caught a young man of Succoth and questioned him, and the young man wrote down for him the names of the seventy-seven officials of Succoth, the elders of the town. ¹⁵Then Gideon came and said to the men of Succoth, "Here are Zebah and Zalmunna, about whom you taunted me by saying, 'Do you already have the hands of Zebah and Zalmunna in your possession? Why should we give bread to your exhausted men?' " ¹⁶He took the elders of the town and taught the men of Succoth a lesson by punishing them with desert thorns and briers. ¹⁷He also pulled down the tower of Peniel and killed the men of the town.

¹⁸Then he asked Zebah and Zalmunna, "What kind of men did you kill at Tabor?"

"Men like you," they answered, "each one with the bearing of a prince."

¹⁹Gideon replied, "Those were my brothers, the sons of my own mother. As surely as the Lᴏʀᴅ lives, if you had spared their lives, I would not kill you." ²⁰Turning to Jether, his oldest son, he said, "Kill them!" But Jether did not draw his sword, because he was only a boy and was afraid.

²¹Zebah and Zalmunna said, "Come, do it yourself. 'As is the man, so is his strength.' " So Gideon stepped forward and killed them, and took the ornaments off their camels' necks.

Gideon's Ephod

²²The Israelites said to Gideon, "Rule over us—you, your son and your grandson—because you have saved us out of the hand of Midian."

²³But Gideon told them, "I will not rule over you, nor will my son rule over you. The Lᴏʀᴅ will rule over you." ²⁴And he said, "I do have one request, that each of you give me an earring from your share of the plunder." (It was the custom of the Ishmaelites to wear gold earrings.)

²⁵They answered, "We'll be glad to give them." So they spread out a garment, and each man threw a ring from his plunder onto it. ²⁶The weight of the gold rings he asked for came to seventeen hundred shekels,ᵇ not counting the ornaments, the pendants and the purple garments worn by the kings of Midian or the chains that were on their camels' necks. ²⁷Gideon made the gold into an ephod, which he placed in Ophrah, his town. All Israel prostituted themselves by worshiping it there, and it became a snare to Gideon and his family.

Gideon's Death

²⁸Thus Midian was subdued before the Israelites and did not raise its head again. During Gideon's lifetime, the land enjoyed peace forty years.

²⁹Jerub-Baal son of Joash went back home to live. ³⁰He had seventy sons of his own, for he had many wives. ³¹His concubine, who lived in Shechem, also bore him a son, whom he named Abimelech. ³²Gideon son of Joash died at a good old age and was buried in the tomb of his father Joash in Ophrah of the Abiezrites.

³³No sooner had Gideon died than the Israelites again prostituted themselves to the Baals. They set up Baal-Berith as their god and ³⁴did not remember the Lᴏʀᴅ their God, who had rescued them from the hands of all their enemies on every side. ³⁵They also failed to show kindness to the family of Jerub-Baal (that is, Gideon) for all the good things he had done for them.

truth or dare

Gideon had the chance of a lifetime—to rule an empire! Instead, despite all his successes, he stayed humble. Do you have a big head or a humble heart?

8:22–23

ᵃ 8 Hebrew Penuel, a variant of Peniel; also in verses 9 and 17   ᵇ 26 That is, about 43 pounds (about 19.5 kilograms)

Abimelech

9 Abimelech son of Jerub-Baal went to his mother's brothers in Shechem and said to them and to all his mother's clan, ²"Ask all the citizens of Shechem, 'Which is better for you: to have all seventy of Jerub-Baal's sons rule over you, or just one man?' Remember, I am your flesh and blood."

³When the brothers repeated all this to the citizens of Shechem, they were inclined to follow Abimelech, for they said, "He is our brother." ⁴They gave him seventy shekels*ᵃ* of silver from the temple of Baal-Berith, and Abimelech used it to hire reckless adventurers, who became his followers. ⁵He went to his father's home in Ophrah and on one stone murdered his seventy brothers, the sons of Jerub-Baal. But Jotham, the youngest son of Jerub-Baal, escaped by hiding. ⁶Then all the citizens of Shechem and Beth Millo gathered beside the great tree at the pillar in Shechem to crown Abimelech king.

⁷When Jotham was told about this, he climbed up on the top of Mount Gerizim and shouted to them, "Listen to me, citizens of Shechem, so that God may listen to you. ⁸One day the trees went out to anoint a king for themselves. They said to the olive tree, 'Be our king.'

⁹"But the olive tree answered, 'Should I give up my oil, by which both gods and men are honored, to hold sway over the trees?'

¹⁰"Next, the trees said to the fig tree, 'Come and be our king.'

¹¹"But the fig tree replied, 'Should I give up my fruit, so good and sweet, to hold sway over the trees?'

¹²"Then the trees said to the vine, 'Come and be our king.'

¹³"But the vine answered, 'Should I give up my wine, which cheers both gods and men, to hold sway over the trees?'

¹⁴"Finally all the trees said to the thornbush, 'Come and be our king.'

¹⁵"The thornbush said to the trees, 'If you really want to anoint me king over you, come and take refuge in my shade; but if not, then let fire come out of the thornbush and consume the cedars of Lebanon!'

¹⁶"Now if you have acted honorably and in good faith when you made Abimelech king, and if you have been fair to Jerub-Baal and his family, and if you have treated him as he deserves— ¹⁷and to think that my father fought for you, risked his life to rescue you from the hand of Midian ¹⁸(but today you have revolted against my father's family, murdered his seventy sons on a single stone, and made Abimelech, the son of his slave girl, king over the citizens of Shechem because he is your brother)— ¹⁹if then you have acted honorably and in good faith toward Jerub-Baal and his family today, may Abimelech be your joy, and may you be his, too! ²⁰But if you have not, let fire come out from Abimelech and consume you, citizens of Shechem and Beth Millo, and let fire come out from you, citizens of Shechem and Beth Millo, and consume Abimelech!"

²¹Then Jotham fled, escaping to Beer, and he lived there because he was afraid of his brother Abimelech.

²²After Abimelech had governed Israel three years, ²³God sent an evil spirit between Abimelech and the citizens of Shechem, who acted treacherously against Abimelech. ²⁴God did this in order that the crime against Jerub-Baal's seventy sons, the shedding of their blood, might be avenged on their brother Abimelech and on the citizens of Shechem, who had helped him murder his brothers. ²⁵In opposition to him these citizens of Shechem set men on the hilltops to ambush and rob everyone who passed by, and this was reported to Abimelech.

²⁶Now Gaal son of Ebed moved with his brothers into Shechem, and its citizens put their confidence in him. ²⁷After they had gone out into the fields and gathered the grapes and trodden them, they held a festival in the temple of their god. While they were eating and drinking, they cursed Abimelech. ²⁸Then Gaal son of Ebed said, "Who is Abimelech, and who is Shechem, that we should be subject to him? Isn't he Jerub-Baal's son, and isn't Zebul his deputy? Serve the men of Hamor, Shechem's father! Why should we serve Abimelech? ²⁹If only this people were under my command! Then I would get rid of him. I would say to Abimelech, 'Call out your whole army!' "ᵇ

³⁰When Zebul the governor of the city heard what Gaal son of Ebed said, he was very angry. ³¹Under cover he sent messengers to Abimelech, saying, "Gaal son of Ebed and his brothers have

---

ᵃ 4 That is, about 1 3/4 pounds (about 0.8 kilogram)   *ᵇ 29* Septuagint; Hebrew *him." Then he said to Abimelech, "Call out your whole army!"*

mirror images

Deborah—Girl Power

Deborah had the unique position of being a female leader in a guy's world. She led the nation of Israel during a time when women did not normally have leadership roles. Deborah was an example of true girl power. Throughout her time as judge, she relied on God for her wisdom and prominence, not on her own strength.

While Deborah was a judge, Israel had to go to battle against the cruel commander Sisera. (Israel's "judges" not only ruled in court cases but also led Israel militarily.) Deborah summoned Barak to lead Israel's army, but he refused to go to war without her. She agreed, but not before pointing out that his lack of courage would translate into greater fame for women (see Judges 4:9). Barak didn't care. He had observed Deborah's character and God's obvious favor upon her and wanted her with him at all costs.

When it came to being a leader, Deborah had all the right moves. Deborah served like a girl. She ruled like a girl. She strategized like a girl—Humbly. Authoritatively. Decisively.

She didn't try to make a name for herself—she let God do that for her. When we're tempted to run for class office to promote our own popularity, we would do well to remember Deborah's humility.

She also used her girl power as a witness to others—leading the people in praise and worship after their victory. How many times do we think of giving God the credit for our authority as student body president or team captain?

Finally, her decisive strategy shines as an example of godly leadership. She used teamwork and shared the glory with her comrades. Don't try the do-it-yourself thing when it comes to being a student leader. Others in your circle of influence might be the very people you need to help turn a good idea into something great.

To read the next Mirror Images profile, go to page 317.

> Dear God, thank you that I come from a long line of godly, wise women like Deborah. Help me use my influence in my own circles to bring you praise and glory. Amen.

dear God

▶▶ Read more about Deborah in Judges 4 and 5 (pages 288–291).

come to Shechem and are stirring up the city against you. ³²Now then, during the night you and your men should come and lie in wait in the fields. ³³In the morning at sunrise, advance against the city. When Gaal and his men come out against you, do whatever your hand finds to do."

³⁴So Abimelech and all his troops set out by night and took up concealed positions near Shechem in four companies. ³⁵Now Gaal son of Ebed had gone out and was standing at the entrance to the city gate just as Abimelech and his soldiers came out from their hiding place.

³⁶When Gaal saw them, he said to Zebul, "Look, people are coming down from the tops of the mountains!"

Zebul replied, "You mistake the shadows of the mountains for men."

³⁷But Gaal spoke up again: "Look, people are coming down from the center of the land, and a company is coming from the direction of the soothsayers' tree."

³⁸Then Zebul said to him, "Where is your big talk now, you who said, 'Who is Abimelech that we should be subject to him?' Aren't these the men you ridiculed? Go out and fight them!"

³⁹So Gaal led outᵃ the citizens of Shechem and fought Abimelech. ⁴⁰Abimelech chased him, and many fell wounded in the flight—all the way to the entrance to the gate. ⁴¹Abimelech stayed in Arumah, and Zebul drove Gaal and his brothers out of Shechem.

⁴²The next day the people of Shechem went out to the fields, and this was reported to Abimelech. ⁴³So he took his men, divided them into three companies and set an ambush in the fields. When he saw the people coming out of the city, he rose to attack them. ⁴⁴Abimelech and the companies with him rushed forward to a position at the entrance to the city gate. Then two companies rushed upon those in the fields and struck them down. ⁴⁵All that day Abimelech pressed his attack against the city until he had captured it and killed its people. Then he destroyed the city and scattered salt over it.

⁴⁶On hearing this, the citizens in the tower of Shechem went into the stronghold of the temple of El-Berith. ⁴⁷When Abimelech heard that they had assembled there, ⁴⁸he and all his men went up Mount Zalmon. He took an ax and cut off some branches, which he lifted to his shoulders. He ordered the men with him, "Quick! Do what you have seen me do!" ⁴⁹So all the men cut branches and followed Abimelech. They piled them against the stronghold and set it on fire over the people inside. So all the people in the tower of Shechem, about a thousand men and women, also died.

⁵⁰Next Abimelech went to Thebez and besieged it and captured it. ⁵¹Inside the city, however, was a strong tower, to which all the men and women—all the people of the city—fled. They locked themselves in and climbed up on the tower roof. ⁵²Abimelech went to the tower and stormed it. But as he approached the entrance to the tower to set it on fire, ⁵³a woman dropped an upper millstone on his head and cracked his skull.

⁵⁴Hurriedly he called to his armor-bearer, "Draw your sword and kill me, so that they can't say, 'A woman killed him.' " So his servant ran him through, and he died. ⁵⁵When the Israelites saw that Abimelech was dead, they went home.

⁵⁶Thus God repaid the wickedness that Abimelech had done to his father by murdering his seventy brothers. ⁵⁷God also made the men of Shechem pay for all their wickedness. The curse of Jotham son of Jerub-Baal came on them.

Tola

10 After the time of Abimelech a man of Issachar, Tola son of Puah, the son of Dodo, rose to save Israel. He lived in Shamir, in the hill country of Ephraim. ²He ledᵇ Israel twenty-three years; then he died, and was buried in Shamir.

Jair

³He was followed by Jair of Gilead, who led Israel twenty-two years. ⁴He had thirty sons, who rode thirty donkeys. They controlled thirty towns in Gilead, which to this day are called Havvoth Jair.ᶜ ⁵When Jair died, he was buried in Kamon.

Jephthah

⁶Again the Israelites did evil in the eyes of the LORD. They served the Baals and the Ashtoreths, and the gods of Aram, the gods of Sidon, the gods of Moab, the gods of the Ammonites and the

ᵃ 39 Or *Gaal went out in the sight of*   ᵇ 2 Traditionally *judged*; also in verse 3   ᶜ 4 Or *called the settlements of Jair* gods of the Philistines. And because the Israelites forsook the LORD and no longer served him, [7]he became angry with them. He sold them into the hands of the Philistines and the Ammonites, [8]who that year shattered and crushed them. For eighteen years they oppressed all the Israelites on the east side of the Jordan in Gilead, the land of the Amorites. [9]The Ammonites also crossed the Jordan to fight against Judah, Benjamin and the house of Ephraim; and Israel was in great distress. [10]Then the Israelites cried out to the LORD, "We have sinned against you, forsaking our God and serving the Baals."

[11]The LORD replied, "When the Egyptians, the Amorites, the Ammonites, the Philistines, [12]the Sidonians, the Amalekites and the Maonites[a] oppressed you and you cried to me for help, did I not save you from their hands? [13]But you have forsaken me and served other gods, so I will no longer save you. [14]Go and cry out to the gods you have chosen. Let them save you when you are in trouble!"

[15]But the Israelites said to the LORD, "We have sinned. Do with us whatever you think best, but please rescue us now." [16]Then they got rid of the foreign gods among them and served the LORD. And he could bear Israel's misery no longer.

[17]When the Ammonites were called to arms and camped in Gilead, the Israelites assembled and camped at Mizpah. [18]The leaders of the people of Gilead said to each other, "Whoever will launch the attack against the Ammonites will be the head of all those living in Gilead."

11 Jephthah the Gileadite was a mighty warrior. His father was Gilead; his mother was a prostitute. [2]Gilead's wife also bore him sons, and when they were grown up, they drove Jephthah away. "You are not going to get any inheritance in our family," they said, "because you are the son of another woman." [3]So Jephthah fled from his brothers and settled in the land of Tob, where a group of adventurers gathered around him and followed him.

[4]Some time later, when the Ammonites made war on Israel, [5]the elders of Gilead went to get Jephthah from the land of Tob. [6]"Come," they said, "be our commander, so we can fight the Ammonites."

[7]Jephthah said to them, "Didn't you hate me and drive me from my father's house? Why do you come to me now, when you're in trouble?"

[8]The elders of Gilead said to him, "Nevertheless, we are turning to you now; come with us to fight the Ammonites, and you will be our head over all who live in Gilead."

[9]Jephthah answered, "Suppose you take me back to fight the Ammonites and the LORD gives them to me—will I really be your head?"

[10]The elders of Gilead replied, "The LORD is our witness; we will certainly do as you say." [11]So Jephthah went with the elders of Gilead, and the people made him head and commander over them. And he repeated all his words before the LORD in Mizpah.

[12]Then Jephthah sent messengers to the Ammonite king with the question: "What do you have against us that you have attacked our country?"

[13]The king of the Ammonites answered Jephthah's messengers, "When Israel came up out of Egypt, they took away my land from the Arnon to the Jabbok, all the way to the Jordan. Now give it back peaceably."

[14]Jephthah sent back messengers to the Ammonite king, [15]saying:

"This is what Jephthah says: Israel did not take the land of Moab or the land of the Ammonites. [16]But when they came up out of Egypt, Israel went through the desert to the Red Sea[b] and on to Kadesh. [17]Then Israel sent messengers to the king of Edom, saying, 'Give us permission to go through your country,' but the king of Edom would not listen. They sent also to the king of Moab, and he refused. So Israel stayed at Kadesh.

[18]"Next they traveled through the desert, skirted the lands of Edom and Moab, passed along the eastern side of the country of Moab, and camped on the other side of the Arnon. They did not enter the territory of Moab, for the Arnon was its border.

[19]"Then Israel sent messengers to Sihon king of the Amorites, who ruled in Heshbon, and said to him, 'Let us pass through your country to our own place.' [20]Sihon, however, did not trust Israel[c] to pass through his territory. He mustered all his men and encamped at Jahaz and fought with Israel.

---

[a] 12 Hebrew; some Septuagint manuscripts Midianites   [b] 16 Hebrew Yam Suph; that is, Sea of Reeds
[c] 20 Or however, would not make an agreement for Israel

²¹"Then the Lord, the God of Israel, gave Sihon and all his men into Israel's hands, and they defeated them. Israel took over all the land of the Amorites who lived in that country, ²²capturing all of it from the Arnon to the Jabbok and from the desert to the Jordan.

²³"Now since the Lord, the God of Israel, has driven the Amorites out before his people Israel, what right have you to take it over? ²⁴Will you not take what your god Chemosh gives you? Likewise, whatever the Lord our God has given us, we will possess. ²⁵Are you better than Balak son of Zippor, king of Moab? Did he ever quarrel with Israel or fight with them? ²⁶For three hundred years Israel occupied Heshbon, Aroer, the surrounding settlements and all the towns along the Arnon. Why didn't you retake them during that time? ²⁷I have not wronged you, but you are doing me wrong by waging war against me. Let the Lord, the Judge,ᵃ decide the dispute this day between the Israelites and the Ammonites."

²⁸The king of Ammon, however, paid no attention to the message Jephthah sent him.

²⁹Then the Spirit of the Lord came upon Jephthah. He crossed Gilead and Manasseh, passed through Mizpah of Gilead, and from there he advanced against the Ammonites. ³⁰And Jephthah made a vow to the Lord: "If you give the Ammonites into my hands, ³¹whatever comes out of the door of my house to meet me when I return in triumph from the Ammonites will be the Lord's, and I will sacrifice it as a burnt offering."

³²Then Jephthah went over to fight the Ammonites, and the Lord gave them into his hands. ³³He devastated twenty towns from Aroer to the vicinity of Minnith, as far as Abel Keramim. Thus Israel subdued Ammon.

³⁴When Jephthah returned to his home in Mizpah, who should come out to meet him but his daughter, dancing to the sound of tambourines! She was an only child. Except for her he had neither son nor daughter. ³⁵When he saw her, he tore his clothes and cried, "Oh! My daughter! You have made me miserable and wretched, because I have made a vow to the Lord that I cannot break."

³⁶"My father," she replied, "you have given your word to the Lord. Do to me just as you promised, now that the Lord has avenged you of your enemies, the Ammonites. ³⁷But grant me this one request," she said. "Give me two months to roam the hills and weep with my friends, because I will never marry."

³⁸"You may go," he said. And he let her go for two months. She and the girls went into the hills and wept because she would never marry. ³⁹After the two months, she returned to her father and he did to her as he had vowed. And she was a virgin.

From this comes the Israelite custom ⁴⁰that each year the young women of Israel go out for four days to commemorate the daughter of Jephthah the Gileadite.

Jephthah and Ephraim

12 The men of Ephraim called out their forces, crossed over to Zaphon and said to Jephthah, "Why did you go to fight the Ammonites without calling us to go with you? We're going to burn down your house over your head."

²Jephthah answered, "I and my people were engaged in a great struggle with the Ammonites, and although I called, you didn't save me out of their hands. ³When I saw that you wouldn't help, I took my life in my hands and crossed over to fight the Ammonites, and the Lord gave me the victory over them. Now why have you come up today to fight me?"

truth or dare
Every argument has two sides. If you're involved in a disagreement between two friends, sometimes it's hard to tell who's right. Pray for God's perfect judgment.
11:27

truth or dare
"Lord, if you'll only do this, I promise I'll . . ." In desperate times, spouting pledges to God is all too easy. However, God takes your words seriously. So should you.
11:34–35

ᵃ 27 Or Ruler

⁴Jephthah then called together the men of Gilead and fought against Ephraim. The Gileadites struck them down because the Ephraimites had said, "You Gileadites are renegades from Ephraim and Manasseh." ⁵The Gileadites captured the fords of the Jordan leading to Ephraim, and whenever a survivor of Ephraim said, "Let me cross over," the men of Gilead asked him, "Are you an Ephraimite?" If he replied, "No," ⁶they said, "All right, say 'Shibboleth.' " If he said, "Sibboleth," because he could not pronounce the word correctly, they seized him and killed him at the fords of the Jordan. Forty-two thousand Ephraimites were killed at that time.

⁷Jephthah led*ᵃ* Israel six years. Then Jephthah the Gileadite died, and was buried in a town in Gilead.

Ibzan, Elon and Abdon

⁸After him, Ibzan of Bethlehem led Israel. ⁹He had thirty sons and thirty daughters. He gave his daughters away in marriage to those outside his clan, and for his sons he brought in thirty young women as wives from outside his clan. Ibzan led Israel seven years. ¹⁰Then Ibzan died, and was buried in Bethlehem.

¹¹After him, Elon the Zebulunite led Israel ten years. ¹²Then Elon died, and was buried in Aijalon in the land of Zebulun.

¹³After him, Abdon son of Hillel, from Pirathon, led Israel. ¹⁴He had forty sons and thirty grandsons, who rode on seventy donkeys. He led Israel eight years. ¹⁵Then Abdon son of Hillel died, and was buried at Pirathon in Ephraim, in the hill country of the Amalekites.

The Birth of Samson

13 Again the Israelites did evil in the eyes of the Lᴏʀᴅ, so the Lᴏʀᴅ delivered them into the hands of the Philistines for forty years.
²A certain man of Zorah, named Manoah, from the clan of the Danites, had a wife who was sterile and remained childless. ³The angel of the Lᴏʀᴅ appeared to her and said, "You are sterile and childless, but you are going to conceive and have a son. ⁴Now see to it that you drink no wine or other fermented drink and that you do not eat anything unclean, ⁵because you will conceive and give birth to a son. No razor may be used on his head, because the boy is to be a Nazirite, set apart to God from birth, and he will begin the deliverance of Israel from the hands of the Philistines."

⁶Then the woman went to her husband and told him, "A man of God came to me. He looked like an angel of God, very awesome. I didn't ask him where he came from, and he didn't tell me his name. ⁷But he said to me, 'You will conceive and give birth to a son. Now then, drink no wine or other fermented drink and do not eat anything unclean, because the boy will be a Nazirite of God from birth until the day of his death.' "

⁸Then Manoah prayed to the Lᴏʀᴅ: "O Lord, I beg you, let the man of God you sent to us come again to teach us how to bring up the boy who is to be born."

⁹God heard Manoah, and the angel of God came again to the woman while she was out in the field; but her husband Manoah was not with her. ¹⁰The woman hurried to tell her husband, "He's here! The man who appeared to me the other day!"

¹¹Manoah got up and followed his wife. When he came to the man, he said, "Are you the one who talked to my wife?"

"I am," he said.

¹²So Manoah asked him, "When your words are fulfilled, what is to be the rule for the boy's life and work?"

¹³The angel of the Lᴏʀᴅ answered, "Your wife must do all that I have told her. ¹⁴She must not eat anything that comes from the grapevine, nor drink any wine or other fermented drink nor eat anything unclean. She must do everything I have commanded her."

¹⁵Manoah said to the angel of the Lᴏʀᴅ, "We would like you to stay until we prepare a young goat for you."

¹⁶The angel of the Lᴏʀᴅ replied, "Even though you detain me, I will not eat any of your food. But if you prepare a burnt offering, offer it to the Lᴏʀᴅ." (Manoah did not realize that it was the angel of the Lᴏʀᴅ.)

ᵃ 7 Traditionally *judged*; also in verses 8-14

in

Parental Control

Profile: Emily

"Your mom is so cool! I wish my mom was like that." That's what my friends say all the time. If only they knew. They don't live with her. She has her good moments, I guess, but she treats me like I can't think for myself. It's like she tries to control every aspect of my life—what I wear, who I see, where I go. I can't wait to move out.

Here's the killer. Lately she's been coming up with these goofy mother/daughter things for us to do together. She's getting all sentimental that I'm leaving for college in a year. Thanks but no thanks. I know she means well, but I just need my space. I wish she'd give it a rest. Honestly, shopping with my friends or shopping with my mom? Dinner with the girls or a movie with my mom? Hmmm, tough choices.

I'm not sure why I feel so angry at her. Like when she tells me to pick my clothes up off the floor, I feel this rage deep inside come to the surface. We get into this huge fight, and then she wants to make up and pretend everything is okay. Well, it's not okay.

parents in focus

When you start to feel like your parents are ruining your life, keep this in mind:

» Remember this is their first time parenting you—they've never done this before either. So, cut 'em some slack.

» Like it or not, God says honoring your parents is a necessary prerequisite for living a long and happy life—Ephesians 6:1–3 (page 1548).

» Find something to help you relieve your stress—take a walk, take up kickboxing, or call a friend—so you don't explode at your parents.

For more on this topic, see the index on page 1656

For more on dealing with the inevitable woes of parental conflict, go online to www.TrueImagesBible.com

parents

[17] Then Manoah inquired of the angel of the Lord, "What is your name, so that we may honor you when your word comes true?"

[18] He replied, "Why do you ask my name? It is beyond understanding.[a]" [19] Then Manoah took a young goat, together with the grain offering, and sacrificed it on a rock to the Lord. And the Lord did an amazing thing while Manoah and his wife watched: [20] As the flame blazed up from the altar toward heaven, the angel of the Lord ascended in the flame. Seeing this, Manoah and his wife fell with their faces to the ground. [21] When the angel of the Lord did not show himself again to Manoah and his wife, Manoah realized that it was the angel of the Lord.

[22] "We are doomed to die!" he said to his wife. "We have seen God!"

[23] But his wife answered, "If the Lord had meant to kill us, he would not have accepted a burnt offering and grain offering from our hands, nor shown us all these things or now told us this."

a 18 Or is wonderful

[24]The woman gave birth to a boy and named him Samson. He grew and the LORD blessed him, [25]and the Spirit of the LORD began to stir him while he was in Mahaneh Dan, between Zorah and Eshtaol.

Samson's Marriage

14 Samson went down to Timnah and saw there a young Philistine woman. [2]When he returned, he said to his father and mother, "I have seen a Philistine woman in Timnah; now get her for me as my wife."

[3]His father and mother replied, "Isn't there an acceptable woman among your relatives or among all our people? Must you go to the uncircumcised Philistines to get a wife?"

But Samson said to his father, "Get her for me. She's the right one for me." [4](His parents did not know that this was from the LORD, who was seeking an occasion to confront the Philistines; for at that time they were ruling over Israel.) [5]Samson went down to Timnah together with his father and mother. As they approached the vineyards of Timnah, suddenly a young lion came roaring toward him. [6]The Spirit of the LORD came upon him in power so that he tore the lion apart with his bare hands as he might have torn a young goat. But he told neither his father nor his mother what he had done. [7]Then he went down and talked with the woman, and he liked her.

[8]Some time later, when he went back to marry her, he turned aside to look at the lion's carcass. In it was a swarm of bees and some honey, [9]which he scooped out with his hands and ate as he went along. When he rejoined his parents, he gave them some, and they too ate it. But he did not tell them that he had taken the honey from the lion's carcass.

[10]Now his father went down to see the woman. And Samson made a feast there, as was customary for bridegrooms. [11]When he appeared, he was given thirty companions.

[12]"Let me tell you a riddle," Samson said to them. "If you can give me the answer within the seven days of the feast, I will give you thirty linen garments and thirty sets of clothes. [13]If you can't tell me the answer, you must give me thirty linen garments and thirty sets of clothes."

"Tell us your riddle," they said. "Let's hear it."

[14]He replied,

> "Out of the eater, something to eat;
> out of the strong, something sweet."

For three days they could not give the answer.

[15]On the fourth[a] day, they said to Samson's wife, "Coax your husband into explaining the riddle for us, or we will burn you and your father's household to death. Did you invite us here to rob us?"

[16]Then Samson's wife threw herself on him, sobbing, "You hate me! You don't really love me. You've given my people a riddle, but you haven't told me the answer."

"I haven't even explained it to my father or mother," he replied, "so why should I explain it to you?" [17]She cried the whole seven days of the feast. So on the seventh day he finally told her, because she continued to press him. She in turn explained the riddle to her people.

[18]Before sunset on the seventh day the men of the town said to him,

> "What is sweeter than honey?
> What is stronger than a lion?"

Samson said to them,

> "If you had not plowed with my heifer,
> you would not have solved my riddle."

[19]Then the Spirit of the LORD came upon him in power. He went down to Ashkelon, struck down thirty of their men, stripped them of their belongings and gave their clothes to those who had explained the riddle. Burning with anger, he went up to his father's house. [20]And Samson's wife was given to the friend who had attended him at his wedding.

a 15 Some Septuagint manuscripts and Syriac; Hebrew *seventh*

Samson's Vengeance on the Philistines

15 Later on, at the time of wheat harvest, Samson took a young goat and went to visit his wife. He said, "I'm going to my wife's room." But her father would not let him go in.

[2]"I was so sure you thoroughly hated her," he said, "that I gave her to your friend. Isn't her younger sister more attractive? Take her instead."

[3]Samson said to them, "This time I have a right to get even with the Philistines; I will really harm them." [4]So he went out and caught three hundred foxes and tied them tail to tail in pairs. He then fastened a torch to every pair of tails, [5]lit the torches and let the foxes loose in the standing grain of the Philistines. He burned up the shocks and standing grain, together with the vineyards and olive groves.

truth or dare

When someone hurts you, you have a choice to make: You can either get back at her or forgive her. Revenge can turn into a vicious cycle.

15:1–11

[6]When the Philistines asked, "Who did this?" they were told, "Samson, the Timnite's son-in-law, because his wife was given to his friend."

So the Philistines went up and burned her and her father to death. [7]Samson said to them, "Since you've acted like this, I won't stop until I get my revenge on you." [8]He attacked them viciously and slaughtered many of them. Then he went down and stayed in a cave in the rock of Etam.

[9]The Philistines went up and camped in Judah, spreading out near Lehi. [10]The men of Judah asked, "Why have you come to fight us?"

"We have come to take Samson prisoner," they answered, "to do to him as he did to us."

[11]Then three thousand men from Judah went down to the cave in the rock of Etam and said to Samson, "Don't you realize that the Philistines are rulers over us? What have you done to us?"

He answered, "I merely did to them what they did to me."

[12]They said to him, "We've come to tie you up and hand you over to the Philistines."

Samson said, "Swear to me that you won't kill me yourselves."

[13]"Agreed," they answered. "We will only tie you up and hand you over to them. We will not kill you." So they bound him with two new ropes and led him up from the rock. [14]As he approached Lehi, the Philistines came toward him shouting. The Spirit of the LORD came upon him in power. The ropes on his arms became like charred flax, and the bindings dropped from his hands. [15]Finding a fresh jawbone of a donkey, he grabbed it and struck down a thousand men.

[16]Then Samson said,

> "With a donkey's jawbone
> I have made donkeys of them. [a]
> With a donkey's jawbone
> I have killed a thousand men."

[17]When he finished speaking, he threw away the jawbone; and the place was called Ramath Lehi. [b]

[18]Because he was very thirsty, he cried out to the LORD, "You have given your servant this great victory. Must I now die of thirst and fall into the hands of the uncircumcised?" [19]Then God opened up the hollow place in Lehi, and water came out of it. When Samson drank, his strength returned and he revived. So the spring was called En Hakkore, [c] and it is still there in Lehi.

[20]Samson led [d] Israel for twenty years in the days of the Philistines.

Samson and Delilah

16 One day Samson went to Gaza, where he saw a prostitute. He went in to spend the night with her. [2]The people of Gaza were told, "Samson is here!" So they surrounded the place and lay in wait for him all night at the city gate. They made no move during the night, saying, "At dawn we'll kill him."

[3]But Samson lay there only until the middle of the night. Then he got up and took hold of the

a 16 Or made a heap or two; the Hebrew for donkey sounds like the Hebrew for heap.   *b 17 Ramath Lehi means jawbone hill.*   *c 19 En Hakkore means caller's spring.*   *d 20 Traditionally judged* doors of the city gate, together with the two posts, and tore them loose, bar and all. He lifted them to his shoulders and carried them to the top of the hill that faces Hebron.

⁴Some time later, he fell in love with a woman in the Valley of Sorek whose name was Delilah. ⁵The rulers of the Philistines went to her and said, "See if you can lure him into showing you the secret of his great strength and how we can overpower him so we may tie him up and subdue him. Each one of us will give you eleven hundred shekels ᵃ of silver."

⁶So Delilah said to Samson, "Tell me the secret of your great strength and how you can be tied up and subdued."

⁷Samson answered her, "If anyone ties me with seven fresh thongs ᵇ that have not been dried, I'll become as weak as any other man."

⁸Then the rulers of the Philistines brought her seven fresh thongs that had not been dried, and she tied him with them. ⁹With men hidden in the room, she called to him, "Samson, the Philistines are upon you!" But he snapped the thongs as easily as a piece of string snaps when it comes close to a flame. So the secret of his strength was not discovered.

¹⁰Then Delilah said to Samson, "You have made a fool of me; you lied to me. Come now, tell me how you can be tied."

¹¹He said, "If anyone ties me securely with new ropes that have never been used, I'll become as weak as any other man."

¹²So Delilah took new ropes and tied him with them. Then, with men hidden in the room, she called to him, "Samson, the Philistines are upon you!" But he snapped the ropes off his arms as if they were threads.

¹³Delilah then said to Samson, "Until now, you have been making a fool of me and lying to me. Tell me how you can be tied."

He replied, "If you weave the seven braids of my head into the fabric ⌊on the loom⌋ and tighten it with the pin, I'll become as weak as any other man." So while he was sleeping, Delilah took the seven braids of his head, wove them into the fabric ¹⁴and ᶜ tightened it with the pin.

genuine love

>> 16:15-21

Obviously, Samson wasn't using his head. He thought he was in love with Delilah, so nothing else mattered to him. He wasn't the first one to fall into this trap—and he certainly wasn't the last. It's a common story for us girls: A girl thinks she's in love with a guy and does a lot of things she never thought she'd do—like changing her personality to fit his, dropping her friends to be with him, or going further sexually because he pushed her. Don't let that be you! In your relationships, make sure your head has control over your heart.

truth or dare

Some guys will pressure you and pressure you till finally they wear down your defenses. It's better to show guys like that the door than to compromise who you are.

16:16–17

Again she called to him, "Samson, the Philistines are upon you!" He awoke from his sleep and pulled up the pin and the loom, with the fabric.

¹⁵Then she said to him, "How can you say, 'I love you,' when you won't confide in me? This is the third time you have made a fool of me and haven't told me the secret of your great strength." ¹⁶With such nagging she prodded him day after day until he was tired to death.

¹⁷So he told her everything. "No razor has ever been used on my head," he said, "because I have been a

---

ᵃ 5 That is, about 28 pounds (about 13 kilograms)   ᵇ 7 Or bowstrings; also in verses 8 and 9   ᶜ 13,14 Some Septuagint manuscripts; Hebrew "⌊I can,⌋ if you weave the seven braids of my head into the fabric ⌊on the loom⌋." ¹⁴So she

Nazirite set apart to God since birth. If my head were shaved, my strength would leave me, and I would become as weak as any other man."

¹⁸When Delilah saw that he had told her everything, she sent word to the rulers of the Philistines, "Come back once more; he has told me everything." So the rulers of the Philistines returned with the silver in their hands. ¹⁹Having put him to sleep on her lap, she called a man to shave off the seven braids of his hair, and so began to subdue him.ᵃ And his strength left him.

²⁰Then she called, "Samson, the Philistines are upon you!"

He awoke from his sleep and thought, "I'll go out as before and shake myself free." But he did not know that the Lord had left him.

²¹Then the Philistines seized him, gouged out his eyes and took him down to Gaza. Binding him with bronze shackles, they set him to grinding in the prison. ²²But the hair on his head began to grow again after it had been shaved.

The Death of Samson

²³Now the rulers of the Philistines assembled to offer a great sacrifice to Dagon their god and to celebrate, saying, "Our god has delivered Samson, our enemy, into our hands."

²⁴When the people saw him, they praised their god, saying,

> "Our god has delivered our enemy
>   into our hands,
>   the one who laid waste our land
>   and multiplied our slain."

²⁵While they were in high spirits, they shouted, "Bring out Samson to entertain us." So they called Samson out of the prison, and he performed for them.

When they stood him among the pillars, ²⁶Samson said to the servant who held his hand, "Put me where I can feel the pillars that support the temple, so that I may lean against them." ²⁷Now the temple was crowded with men and women; all the rulers of the Philistines were there, and on the roof were about three thousand men and women watching Samson perform. ²⁸Then Samson prayed to the Lord, "O Sovereign Lord, remember me. O God, please strengthen me just once more, and let me with one blow get revenge on the Philistines for my two eyes." ²⁹Then Samson reached toward the two central pillars on which the temple stood. Bracing himself against them, his right hand on the one and his left hand on the other, ³⁰Samson said, "Let me die with the Philistines!" Then he pushed with all his might, and down came the temple on the rulers and all the people in it. Thus he killed many more when he died than while he lived.

³¹Then his brothers and his father's whole family went down to get him. They brought him back and buried him between Zorah and Eshtaol in the tomb of Manoah his father. He had ledᵇ Israel twenty years.

Micah's Idols

17Now a man named Micah from the hill country of Ephraim ²said to his mother, "The eleven hundred shekelsᶜ of silver that were taken from you and about which I heard you utter a curse—I have that silver with me; I took it."

Then his mother said, "The Lord bless you, my son!"

³When he returned the eleven hundred shekels of silver to his mother, she said, "I solemnly consecrate my silver to the Lord for my son to make a carved image and a cast idol. I will give it back to you."

⁴So he returned the silver to his mother, and she took two hundred shekelsᵈ of silver and gave them to a silversmith, who made them into the image and the idol. And they were put in Micah's house.

⁵Now this man Micah had a shrine, and he made an ephod and some idols and installed one of his sons as his priest. ⁶In those days Israel had no king; everyone did as he saw fit.

⁷A young Levite from Bethlehem in Judah, who had been living within the clan of Judah, ⁸left that town in search of some other place to stay. On his wayᵉ he came to Micah's house in the hill country of Ephraim.

ᵃ 19 Hebrew; some Septuagint manuscripts *and he began to weaken*   ᵇ 31 Traditionally *judged*   ᶜ 2 That is, about 28 pounds (about 13 kilograms)   ᵈ 4 That is, about 5 pounds (about 2.3 kilograms)   ᵉ 8 Or *To carry on his profession*

⁹Micah asked him, "Where are you from?"

"I'm a Levite from Bethlehem in Judah," he said, "and I'm looking for a place to stay."

¹⁰Then Micah said to him, "Live with me and be my father and priest, and I'll give you ten shekelsᵃ of silver a year, your clothes and your food." ¹¹So the Levite agreed to live with him, and the young man was to him like one of his sons. ¹²Then Micah installed the Levite, and the young man became his priest and lived in his house. ¹³And Micah said, "Now I know that the LORD will be good to me, since this Levite has become my priest."

Danites Settle in Laish

18 In those days Israel had no king.

And in those days the tribe of the Danites was seeking a place of their own where they might settle, because they had not yet come into an inheritance among the tribes of Israel. ²So the Danites sent five warriors from Zorah and Eshtaol to spy out the land and explore it. These men represented all their clans. They told them, "Go, explore the land."

The men entered the hill country of Ephraim and came to the house of Micah, where they spent the night. ³When they were near Micah's house, they recognized the voice of the young Levite; so they turned in there and asked him, "Who brought you here? What are you doing in this place? Why are you here?"

⁴He told them what Micah had done for him, and said, "He has hired me and I am his priest."

⁵Then they said to him, "Please inquire of God to learn whether our journey will be successful."

⁶The priest answered them, "Go in peace. Your journey has the LORD's approval."

⁷So the five men left and came to Laish, where they saw that the people were living in safety, like the Sidonians, unsuspecting and secure. And since their land lacked nothing, they were prosperous.ᵇ Also, they lived a long way from the Sidonians and had no relationship with anyone else.ᶜ

⁸When they returned to Zorah and Eshtaol, their brothers asked them, "How did you find things?"

⁹They answered, "Come on, let's attack them! We have seen that the land is very good. Aren't you going to do something? Don't hesitate to go there and take it over. ¹⁰When you get there, you will find an unsuspecting people and a spacious land that God has put into your hands, a land that lacks nothing whatever."

¹¹Then six hundred men from the clan of the Danites, armed for battle, set out from Zorah and Eshtaol. ¹²On their way they set up camp near Kiriath Jearim in Judah. This is why the place west of Kiriath Jearim is called Mahaneh Danᵈ to this day. ¹³From there they went on to the hill country of Ephraim and came to Micah's house.

¹⁴Then the five men who had spied out the land of Laish said to their brothers, "Do you know that one of these houses has an ephod, other household gods, a carved image and a cast idol? Now you know what to do." ¹⁵So they turned in there and went to the house of the young Levite at Micah's place and greeted him. ¹⁶The six hundred Danites, armed for battle, stood at the entrance to the gate. ¹⁷The five men who had spied out the land went inside and took the carved image, the ephod, the other household gods and the cast idol while the priest and the six hundred armed men stood at the entrance to the gate.

¹⁸When these men went into Micah's house and took the carved image, the ephod, the other household gods and the cast idol, the priest said to them, "What are you doing?"

¹⁹They answered him, "Be quiet! Don't say a word. Come with us, and be our father and priest. Isn't it better that you serve a tribe and clan in Israel as priest rather than just one man's household?" ²⁰Then the priest was glad. He took the ephod, the other household gods and the carved image and went along with the people. ²¹Putting their little children, their livestock and their possessions in front of them, they turned away and left.

²²When they had gone some distance from Micah's house, the men who lived near Micah were called together and overtook the Danites. ²³As they shouted after them, the Danites turned and said to Micah, "What's the matter with you that you called out your men to fight?"

²⁴He replied, "You took the gods I made, and my priest, and went away. What else do I have? How can you ask, 'What's the matter with you?' "

ᵃ 10 That is, about 4 ounces (about 110 grams)   ᵇ 7 The meaning of the Hebrew for this clause is uncertain.
ᶜ 7 Hebrew; some Septuagint manuscripts *with the Arameans*   ᵈ 12 *Mahaneh Dan* means *Dan's camp*.

²⁵The Danites answered, "Don't argue with us, or some hot-tempered men will attack you, and you and your family will lose your lives." ²⁶So the Danites went their way, and Micah, seeing that they were too strong for him, turned around and went back home.

²⁷Then they took what Micah had made, and his priest, and went on to Laish, against a peaceful and unsuspecting people. They attacked them with the sword and burned down their city. ²⁸There was no one to rescue them because they lived a long way from Sidon and had no relationship with anyone else. The city was in a valley near Beth Rehob.

The Danites rebuilt the city and settled there. ²⁹They named it Dan after their forefather Dan, who was born to Israel—though the city used to be called Laish. ³⁰There the Danites set up for themselves the idols, and Jonathan son of Gershom, the son of Moses,ᵃ and his sons were priests for the tribe of Dan until the time of the captivity of the land. ³¹They continued to use the idols Micah had made, all the time the house of God was in Shiloh.

truth or dare

When this guy lost his homemade idol and his personal priest, his whole "faith" fell apart. Is your faith built on a solid relationship with God or on empty religious traditions?

18:24

A Levite and His Concubine

19 In those days Israel had no king.
Now a Levite who lived in a remote area in the hill country of Ephraim took a concubine from Bethlehem in Judah. ²But she was unfaithful to him. She left him and went back to her father's house in Bethlehem, Judah. After she had been there four months, ³her husband went to her to persuade her to return. He had with him his servant and two donkeys. She took him into her father's house, and when her father saw him, he gladly welcomed him. ⁴His father-in-law, the girl's father, prevailed upon him to stay; so he remained with him three days, eating and drinking, and sleeping there.

⁵On the fourth day they got up early and he prepared to leave, but the girl's father said to his son-in-law, "Refresh yourself with something to eat; then you can go." ⁶So the two of them sat down to eat and drink together. Afterward the girl's father said, "Please stay tonight and enjoy yourself." ⁷And when the man got up to go, his father-in-law persuaded him, so he stayed there that night. ⁸On the morning of the fifth day, when he rose to go, the girl's father said, "Refresh yourself. Wait till afternoon!" So the two of them ate together.

⁹Then when the man, with his concubine and his servant, got up to leave, his father-in-law, the girl's father, said, "Now look, it's almost evening. Spend the night here; the day is nearly over. Stay and enjoy yourself. Early tomorrow morning you can get up and be on your way home." ¹⁰But, unwilling to stay another night, the man left and went toward Jebus (that is, Jerusalem), with his two saddled donkeys and his concubine.

¹¹When they were near Jebus and the day was almost gone, the servant said to his master, "Come, let's stop at this city of the Jebusites and spend the night."

¹²His master replied, "No. We won't go into an alien city, whose people are not Israelites. We will go on to Gibeah." ¹³He added, "Come, let's try to reach Gibeah or Ramah and spend the night in one of those places." ¹⁴So they went on, and the sun set as they neared Gibeah in Benjamin. ¹⁵There they stopped to spend the night. They went and sat in the city square, but no one took them into his home for the night.

¹⁶That evening an old man from the hill country of Ephraim, who was living in Gibeah (the men of the place were Benjamites), came in from his work in the fields. ¹⁷When he looked and saw the traveler in the city square, the old man asked, "Where are you going? Where did you come from?"

¹⁸He answered, "We are on our way from Bethlehem in Judah to a remote area in the hill country of Ephraim where I live. I have been to Bethlehem in Judah and now I am going to the house of the LORD. No one has taken me into his house. ¹⁹We have both straw and fodder for our donkeys and bread and wine for ourselves your servants—me, your maidservant, and the young man with us. We don't need anything."

ᵃ 30 An ancient Hebrew scribal tradition, some Septuagint manuscripts and Vulgate; Masoretic Text *Manasseh*

²⁰"You are welcome at my house," the old man said. "Let me supply whatever you need. Only don't spend the night in the square." ²¹So he took him into his house and fed his donkeys. After they had washed their feet, they had something to eat and drink.

²²While they were enjoying themselves, some of the wicked men of the city surrounded the house. Pounding on the door, they shouted to the old man who owned the house, "Bring out the man who came to your house so we can have sex with him."

²³The owner of the house went outside and said to them, "No, my friends, don't be so vile. Since this man is my guest, don't do this disgraceful thing. ²⁴Look, here is my virgin daughter, and his concubine. I will bring them out to you now, and you can use them and do to them whatever you wish. But to this man, don't do such a disgraceful thing."

²⁵But the men would not listen to him. So the man took his concubine and sent her outside to them, and they raped her and abused her throughout the night, and at dawn they let her go. ²⁶At daybreak the woman went back to the house where her master was staying, fell down at the door and lay there until daylight.

²⁷When her master got up in the morning and opened the door of the house and stepped out to continue on his way, there lay his concubine, fallen in the doorway of the house, with her hands on the threshold. ²⁸He said to her, "Get up; let's go." But there was no answer. Then the man put her on his donkey and set out for home.

²⁹When he reached home, he took a knife and cut up his concubine, limb by limb, into twelve parts and sent them into all the areas of Israel. ³⁰Everyone who saw it said, "Such a thing has never been seen or done, not since the day the Israelites came up out of Egypt. Think about it! Consider it! Tell us what to do!"

Israelites Fight the Benjamites

20 Then all the Israelites from Dan to Beersheba and from the land of Gilead came out as one man and assembled before the LORD in Mizpah. ²The leaders of all the people of the tribes of Israel took their places in the assembly of the people of God, four hundred thousand soldiers armed with swords. ³(The Benjamites heard that the Israelites had gone up to Mizpah.) Then the Israelites said, "Tell us how this awful thing happened."

⁴So the Levite, the husband of the murdered woman, said, "I and my concubine came to Gibeah in Benjamin to spend the night. ⁵During the night the men of Gibeah came after me and surrounded the house, intending to kill me. They raped my concubine, and she died. ⁶I took my concubine, cut her into pieces and sent one piece to each region of Israel's inheritance, because they committed this lewd and disgraceful act in Israel. ⁷Now, all you Israelites, speak up and give your verdict."

⁸All the people rose as one man, saying, "None of us will go home. No, not one of us will return to his house. ⁹But now this is what we'll do to Gibeah: We'll go up against it as the lot directs. ¹⁰We'll take ten men out of every hundred from all the tribes of Israel, and a hundred from a thousand, and a thousand from ten thousand, to get provisions for the army. Then, when the army arrives at Gibeah ᵃ in Benjamin, it can give them what they deserve for all this vileness done in Israel." ¹¹So all the men of Israel got together and united as one man against the city.

¹²The tribes of Israel sent men throughout the tribe of Benjamin, saying, "What about this awful crime that was committed among you? ¹³Now surrender those wicked men of Gibeah so that we may put them to death and purge the evil from Israel."

But the Benjamites would not listen to their fellow Israelites. ¹⁴From their towns they came together at Gibeah to fight against the Israelites. ¹⁵At once the Benjamites mobilized twenty-six thousand swordsmen from their towns, in addition to seven hundred chosen men from those living in Gibeah. ¹⁶Among all these soldiers there were seven hundred chosen men who were left-handed, each of whom could sling a stone at a hair and not miss.

¹⁷Israel, apart from Benjamin, mustered four hundred thousand swordsmen, all of them fighting men.

¹⁸The Israelites went up to Bethel ᵇ and inquired of God. They said, "Who of us shall go first to fight against the Benjamites?"

The LORD replied, "Judah shall go first."

ᵃ 10 One Hebrew manuscript; most Hebrew manuscripts Geba, a variant of Gibeah   ᵇ 18 Or to the house of God; also in verse 26

The Shallow End of the Dating Pool

focus Profile: **Kate**

"Oh, you're such a pretty girl. I can't believe you don't have a boyfriend!" Yeah, just what you want to hear from your parents' 50-year-old, overweight, well-meaning friends. I just clench my teeth and smile. But if I have to hear that one more time, I think I'll scream. I really don't know why I don't have a guy, okay? It's not like I'm opposed to the idea. Who doesn't want someone to cuddle with on the couch? Someone to go to dances with? Someone to love me for *me*? It's just that I've never really been good at the dating thing—we're talking *never*. In fact, when a boy asked me to "go with him" in third grade, I naively asked, "Go with you where?" Unless that short-lived playground romance counts, then I'm 0 for 0.

Is there something wrong with me? I sometimes wonder. *Why does no one consider me dating material?* Sure, I have a few guy friends, but that's as far as it goes. "The girl with the nice personality. Everyone's pal." That's me. It seems like I'm destined to wade in the shallow end of the dating pool for the rest of my life. Meanwhile all my other more experienced friends are swimming laps around me. My dreams of the perfect boyfriend are just that—dreams.

dating in focus

It's frustrating when God doesn't seem to cooperate with our plans for our lives. It's hard to trust that he knows what he's doing. But remember . . .

» Good things *do* come to those who wait. The Bible teaches the benefits of waiting on God (see Psalm 40:1, page 693).

» God has not forgotten his plan for you. See Jeremiah 29:11 (page 1041) for a good reminder!

» Sure, you could compromise your standards and settle for less. But is that the kind of guy you really want? If you settle for second-best, then God can't bring the best into your life.

For more on this topic, see the index on page 1656

When you need more encouragement in your love life, go to www.TrueImagesBible.com

dating

[19] The next morning the Israelites got up and pitched camp near Gibeah. [20] The men of Israel went out to fight the Benjamites and took up battle positions against them at Gibeah. [21] The Benjamites came out of Gibeah and cut down twenty-two thousand Israelites on the battlefield that day. [22] But the men of Israel encouraged one another and again took up their positions where they had stationed themselves the first day. [23] The Israelites went up and wept before the LORD until evening, and they inquired of the LORD. They said, "Shall we go up again to battle against the Benjamites, our brothers?"

The LORD answered, "Go up against them."

[24] Then the Israelites drew near to Benjamin the second day. [25] This time, when the Benjamites came out from Gibeah to oppose them, they cut down another eighteen thousand Israelites, all of them armed with swords.

²⁶Then the Israelites, all the people, went up to Bethel, and there they sat weeping before the Lord. They fasted that day until evening and presented burnt offerings and fellowship offerings ᵃ to the Lord. ²⁷And the Israelites inquired of the Lord. (In those days the ark of the covenant of God was there, ²⁸with Phinehas son of Eleazar, the son of Aaron, ministering before it.) They asked, "Shall we go up again to battle with Benjamin our brother, or not?"

The Lord responded, "Go, for tomorrow I will give them into your hands."

²⁹Then Israel set an ambush around Gibeah. ³⁰They went up against the Benjamites on the third day and took up positions against Gibeah as they had done before. ³¹The Benjamites came out to meet them and were drawn away from the city. They began to inflict casualties on the Israelites as before, so that about thirty men fell in the open field and on the roads—the one leading to Bethel and the other to Gibeah.

³²While the Benjamites were saying, "We are defeating them as before," the Israelites were saying, "Let's retreat and draw them away from the city to the roads."

³³All the men of Israel moved from their places and took up positions at Baal Tamar, and the Israelite ambush charged out of its place on the west ᵇ of Gibeah. ᶜ ³⁴Then ten thousand of Israel's finest men made a frontal attack on Gibeah. The fighting was so heavy that the Benjamites did not realize how near disaster was. ³⁵The Lord defeated Benjamin before Israel, and on that day the Israelites struck down 25,100 Benjamites, all armed with swords. ³⁶Then the Benjamites saw that they were beaten.

Now the men of Israel had given way before Benjamin, because they relied on the ambush they had set near Gibeah. ³⁷The men who had been in ambush made a sudden dash into Gibeah, spread out and put the whole city to the sword. ³⁸The men of Israel had arranged with the ambush that they should send up a great cloud of smoke from the city, ³⁹and then the men of Israel would turn in the battle.

The Benjamites had begun to inflict casualties on the men of Israel (about thirty), and they said, "We are defeating them as in the first battle." ⁴⁰But when the column of smoke began to rise from the city, the Benjamites turned and saw the smoke of the whole city going up into the sky. ⁴¹Then the men of Israel turned on them, and the men of Benjamin were terrified, because they realized that disaster had come upon them. ⁴²So they fled before the Israelites in the direction of the desert, but they could not escape the battle. And the men of Israel who came out of the towns cut them down there. ⁴³They surrounded the Benjamites, chased them and easily ᵇ overran them in the vicinity of Gibeah on the east. ⁴⁴Eighteen thousand Benjamites fell, all of them valiant fighters. ⁴⁵As they turned and fled toward the desert to the rock of Rimmon, the Israelites cut down five thousand men along the roads. They kept pressing after the Benjamites as far as Gidom and struck down two thousand more.

⁴⁶On that day twenty-five thousand Benjamite swordsmen fell, all of them valiant fighters. ⁴⁷But six hundred men turned and fled into the desert to the rock of Rimmon, where they stayed four months. ⁴⁸The men of Israel went back to Benjamin and put all the towns to the sword, including the animals and everything else they found. All the towns they came across they set on fire.

Wives for the Benjamites

21 The men of Israel had taken an oath at Mizpah: "Not one of us will give his daughter in marriage to a Benjamite."

²The people went to Bethel, ᵈ where they sat before God until evening, raising their voices and weeping bitterly. ³"O Lord, the God of Israel," they cried, "why has this happened to Israel? Why should one tribe be missing from Israel today?"

⁴Early the next day the people built an altar and presented burnt offerings and fellowship offerings. ᵃ

⁵Then the Israelites asked, "Who from all the tribes of Israel has failed to assemble before the Lord?" For they had taken a solemn oath that anyone who failed to assemble before the Lord at Mizpah should certainly be put to death.

⁶Now the Israelites grieved for their brothers, the Benjamites. "Today one tribe is cut off from Israel," they said. ⁷"How can we provide wives for those who are left, since we have taken an oath

ᵃ 26,4 Traditionally *peace offerings*   ᵇ 33,43 Some Septuagint manuscripts and Vulgate; the meaning of the Hebrew for this word is uncertain.   ᶜ 33 Hebrew *Geba,* a variant of *Gibeah*   ᵈ 2 Or *to the house of God* by the Lord not to give them any of our daughters in marriage?" ⁸Then they asked, "Which one of the tribes of Israel failed to assemble before the Lord at Mizpah?" They discovered that no one from Jabesh Gilead had come to the camp for the assembly. ⁹For when they counted the people, they found that none of the people of Jabesh Gilead were there.

¹⁰So the assembly sent twelve thousand fighting men with instructions to go to Jabesh Gilead and put to the sword those living there, including the women and children. ¹¹"This is what you are to do," they said. "Kill every male and every woman who is not a virgin." ¹²They found among the people living in Jabesh Gilead four hundred young women who had never slept with a man, and they took them to the camp at Shiloh in Canaan.

¹³Then the whole assembly sent an offer of peace to the Benjamites at the rock of Rimmon. ¹⁴So the Benjamites returned at that time and were given the women of Jabesh Gilead who had been spared. But there were not enough for all of them.

¹⁵The people grieved for Benjamin, because the Lord had made a gap in the tribes of Israel. ¹⁶And the elders of the assembly said, "With the women of Benjamin destroyed, how shall we provide wives for the men who are left? ¹⁷The Benjamite survivors must have heirs," they said, "so that a tribe of Israel will not be wiped out. ¹⁸We can't give them our daughters as wives, since we Israelites have taken this oath: 'Cursed be anyone who gives a wife to a Benjamite.' ¹⁹But look, there is the annual festival of the Lord in Shiloh, to the north of Bethel, and east of the road that goes from Bethel to Shechem, and to the south of Lebonah."

²⁰So they instructed the Benjamites, saying, "Go and hide in the vineyards ²¹and watch. When the girls of Shiloh come out to join in the dancing, then rush from the vineyards and each of you seize a wife from the girls of Shiloh and go to the land of Benjamin. ²²When their fathers or brothers complain to us, we will say to them, 'Do us a kindness by helping them, because we did not get wives for them during the war, and you are innocent, since you did not give your daughters to them.' "

²³So that is what the Benjamites did. While the girls were dancing, each man caught one and carried her off to be his wife. Then they returned to their inheritance and rebuilt the towns and settled in them.

²⁴At that time the Israelites left that place and went home to their tribes and clans, each to his own inheritance.

²⁵In those days Israel had no king; everyone did as he saw fit.

genuine obedience » 21:25

Everyone in Israel "did as he saw fit." If it felt good, they did it. Right and wrong kept changing. And they didn't let anybody else tell them what to do. Sound familiar? Bet you could find those same attitudes all around you—maybe even in yourself. It wasn't supposed to be that way in Israel. God was supposed to be their king, and they were supposed to do things *his* way. But they didn't, and they suffered for it. Learn from Israel's mistakes. Doing whatever you want doesn't lead to happiness; it leads to suffering.

author:	Unknown.
date:	Around 1000 B.C.
setting:	The story is set during the time of the judges, during a temporary time of peace between the nations of Moab and Israel.
verse to remember:	But Ruth replied, "Don't urge me to leave you or to turn back from you. Where you go I will go, and where you stay I will stay. Your people will be my people and your God my God" (1:16).
theme to consider:	Ruth and Naomi are wonderful role models of friendship, loyalty and commitment—to God and to each other. Take notes!

unchanging truth

ruth

Every year a popular magazine lists twenty women who are well known for some accomplishment. The group typically includes doctors, writers, politicians, actors, singers, scientists, sports figures, religious workers, etc. The one thing all these women have in common is that they are all "trying to make the world a better place to live." Readers are asked to rank the women, and when all the votes are tallied, one woman is declared "Woman of the Year."

If you were choosing a Woman of the Year among your friends and acquaintances, what qualities would you look for? Leadership? Positive influence on others? The ability to accomplish a task? This girl would probably be someone you respected, someone you trusted to do the right thing. You'd probably think about how friendly, caring, loyal and genuine she is.

What if the people of Bethlehem had chosen a Woman of the Year three thousand years ago? It probably would have ended in a dead tie between Ruth and her mother-in-law, Naomi. These women were totally committed to God and to each other. This commitment showed in the way they lived their lives. Ruth and Naomi had a great bond of friendship, loyalty and genuine love for each other. What an example they set for the people around them—and for us!

life lessons

1 Commitment and loyalty to God and to one another are true marks of godly character (1:14–18).

2 The Christian life always involves others. The Lord wants us to help others in any way we can (2:2,17–18).

3 God gives us incredible blessings when we're totally committed to him in all we think, say and do (4:13–16).

» Naomi and Ruth «

1 In the days when the judges ruled,ᵃ there was a famine in the land, and a man from Bethlehem in Judah, together with his wife and two sons, went to live for a while in the country of Moab. ²The man's name was Elimelech, his wife's name Naomi, and the names of his two sons were Mahlon and Kilion. They were Ephrathites from Bethlehem, Judah. And they went to Moab and lived there.

³Now Elimelech, Naomi's husband, died, and she was left with her two sons. ⁴They married Moabite women, one named Orpah and the other Ruth. After they had lived there about ten years, ⁵both Mahlon and Kilion also died, and Naomi was left without her two sons and her husband.

⁶When she heard in Moab that the Lord had come to the aid of his people by providing food for them, Naomi and her daughters-in-law prepared to return home from there. ⁷With her two daughters-in-law she left the place where she had been living and set out on the road that would take them back to the land of Judah.

⁸Then Naomi said to her two daughters-in-law, "Go back, each of you, to your mother's home. May the Lord show kindness to you, as you have shown to your dead and to me. ⁹May the Lord grant that each of you will find rest in the home of another husband."

Then she kissed them and they wept aloud ¹⁰and said to her, "We will go back with you to your people."

¹¹But Naomi said, "Return home, my daughters. Why would you come with me? Am I going to have any more sons, who could become your husbands? ¹²Return home, my daughters; I am too old to have another husband. Even if I thought there was still hope for me—even if I had a husband tonight and then gave birth to sons— ¹³would you wait until they grew up? Would you remain unmarried for them? No, my daughters. It is more bitter for me than for you, because the Lord's hand has gone out against me!"

¹⁴At this they wept again. Then Orpah kissed her mother-in-law good-by, but Ruth clung to her.

¹⁵"Look," said Naomi, "your sister-in-law is going back to her people and her gods. Go back with her."

¹⁶But Ruth replied, "Don't urge me to leave you or to turn back from you. Where you go I will go, and where you stay I will stay. Your people will be my people and your God my God. ¹⁷Where you die I will die, and there I will be buried. May the Lord deal with me, be it ever so severely, if anything but death separates you and me." ¹⁸When Naomi realized that Ruth was determined to go with her, she stopped urging her.

genuine loyalty » 1:15-18

Ever had a friend who dumps you at the first sign of trouble? That's not loyalty. It's those tough times when you need a friend the most! When you're having a bad day. When your boyfriend breaks up with you. When you just aren't feeling lively or fun. A friend who bails on you in times like that is no true friend. In contrast, meet the poster girl for loyalty— Ruth. She gave up everything to support her grieving mother-in-law, Naomi, knowing that Naomi couldn't give her anything in return. If Naomi were your friend, would you have done the same?

¹⁹So the two women went on until they came to Bethlehem. When they arrived in Bethlehem, the whole town was stirred because of them, and the women exclaimed, "Can this be Naomi?"

²⁰"Don't call me Naomi,ᵇ" she told them. "Call me Mara,ᶜ because the Almightyᵈ has made my life very bitter. ²¹I went away full, but the Lord has brought me back empty. Why call me Naomi? The Lord has afflictedᵉ me; the Almighty has brought misfortune upon me."

²²So Naomi returned from Moab accompanied by Ruth the Moabitess, her daughter-in-law, arriving in Bethlehem as the barley harvest was beginning.

ᵃ 1 Traditionally judged   ᵇ 20 Naomi means pleasant; also in verse 21.   ᶜ 20 Mara means bitter.   ᵈ 20 Hebrew Shaddai; also in verse 21   ᵉ 21 Or has testified against

Ruth Meets Boaz

2 Now Naomi had a relative on her husband's side, from the clan of Elimelech, a man of standing, whose name was Boaz.

²And Ruth the Moabitess said to Naomi, "Let me go to the fields and pick up the leftover grain behind anyone in whose eyes I find favor."

Naomi said to her, "Go ahead, my daughter." ³So she went out and began to glean in the fields behind the harvesters. As it turned out, she found herself working in a field belonging to Boaz, who was from the clan of Elimelech.

⁴Just then Boaz arrived from Bethlehem and greeted the harvesters, "The LORD be with you!"

"The LORD bless you!" they called back.

⁵Boaz asked the foreman of his harvesters, "Whose young woman is that?"

⁶The foreman replied, "She is the Moabitess who came back from Moab with Naomi. ⁷She said, 'Please let me glean and gather among the sheaves behind the harvesters.' She went into the field and has worked steadily from morning till now, except for a short rest in the shelter."

⁸So Boaz said to Ruth, "My daughter, listen to me. Don't go and glean in another field and don't go away from here. Stay here with my servant girls. ⁹Watch the field where the men are harvesting, and follow along after the girls. I have told the men not to touch you. And whenever you are thirsty, go and get a drink from the water jars the men have filled."

¹⁰At this, she bowed down with her face to the ground. She exclaimed, "Why have I found such favor in your eyes that you notice me—a foreigner?"

¹¹Boaz replied, "I've been told all about what you have done for your mother-in-law since the death of your husband—how you left your father and mother and your homeland and came to live with a people you did not know before. ¹²May the LORD repay you for what you have done. May you be richly rewarded by the LORD, the God of Israel, under whose wings you have come to take refuge."

¹³"May I continue to find favor in your eyes, my lord," she said. "You have given me comfort and have spoken kindly to your servant—though I do not have the standing of one of your servant girls."

¹⁴At mealtime Boaz said to her, "Come over here. Have some bread and dip it in the wine vinegar." When she sat down with the harvesters, he offered her some roasted grain. She ate all she wanted and had some left over. ¹⁵As she got up to glean, Boaz gave orders to his men, "Even if she gathers among the sheaves, don't embarrass her. ¹⁶Rather, pull out some stalks for her from the bundles and leave them for her to pick up, and don't rebuke her."

¹⁷So Ruth gleaned in the field until evening. Then she threshed the barley she had gathered, and it amounted to about an ephah. ᵃ ¹⁸She carried it back to town, and her mother-in-law saw how much she had gathered. Ruth also brought out and gave her what she had left over after she had eaten enough.

¹⁹Her mother-in-law asked her, "Where did you glean today? Where did you work? Blessed be the man who took notice of you!"

Then Ruth told her mother-in-law about the one at whose place she had been working. "The name of the man I worked with today is Boaz," she said.

²⁰"The LORD bless him!" Naomi said to her daugh-

truth or dare

God loves it when we take some initiative! Ruth could have wasted a lot of time sitting around waiting for God. Instead, she actively worked *with* God. Get going, girl!

2:2–3

truth or dare

Coincidence or not? God's at work in your life even when you can't see him. Everything he sends your way is for a *purpose*. There are no coincidences for God's children.

2:19–23

ᵃ 17 That is, probably about 3/5 bushel (about 22 liters)

ter-in-law. "He has not stopped showing his kindness to the living and the dead." She added, "That man is our close relative; he is one of our kinsman-redeemers."

²¹Then Ruth the Moabitess said, "He even said to me, 'Stay with my workers until they finish harvesting all my grain.' "

²²Naomi said to Ruth her daughter-in-law, "It will be good for you, my daughter, to go with his girls, because in someone else's field you might be harmed."

²³So Ruth stayed close to the servant girls of Boaz to glean until the barley and wheat harvests were finished. And she lived with her mother-in-law.

Ruth and Boaz at the Threshing Floor

3 One day Naomi her mother-in-law said to her, "My daughter, should I not try to find a home*ᵃ* for you, where you will be well provided for? ²Is not Boaz, with whose servant girls you have been, a kinsman of ours? Tonight he will be winnowing barley on the threshing floor. ³Wash and perfume yourself, and put on your best clothes. Then go down to the threshing floor, but don't let him know you are there until he has finished eating and drinking. ⁴When he lies down, note the place where he is lying. Then go and uncover his feet and lie down. He will tell you what to do."

⁵"I will do whatever you say," Ruth answered. ⁶So she went down to the threshing floor and did everything her mother-in-law told her to do.

⁷When Boaz had finished eating and drinking and was in good spirits, he went over to lie down at the far end of the grain pile. Ruth approached quietly, uncovered his feet and lay down. ⁸In the middle of the night something startled the man, and he turned and discovered a woman lying at his feet.

⁹"Who are you?" he asked.

"I am your servant Ruth," she said. "Spread the corner of your garment over me, since you are a kinsman-redeemer."

¹⁰"The LORD bless you, my daughter," he replied. "This kindness is greater than that which you showed earlier: You have not run after the younger men, whether rich or poor. ¹¹And now, my daughter, don't be afraid. I will do for you all you ask. All my fellow townsmen know that you are a woman of noble character. ¹²Although it is true that I am near of kin, there is a kinsman-redeemer nearer than I. ¹³Stay here for the night, and in the morning if he wants to redeem, good; let him redeem. But if he is not willing, as surely as the LORD lives I will do it. Lie here until morning."

¹⁴So she lay at his feet until morning, but got up before anyone could be recognized; and he said, "Don't let it be known that a woman came to the threshing floor."

¹⁵He also said, "Bring me the shawl you are wearing and hold it out." When she did so, he poured into it six measures of barley and put it on her. Then he*ᵇ* went back to town.

¹⁶When Ruth came to her mother-in-law, Naomi asked, "How did it go, my daughter?"

Then she told her everything Boaz had done for her ¹⁷and added, "He gave me these six measures of barley, saying, 'Don't go back to your mother-in-law empty-handed.' "

¹⁸Then Naomi said, "Wait, my daughter, until you find out what happens. For the man will not rest until the matter is settled today."

Boaz Marries Ruth

4 Meanwhile Boaz went up to the town gate and sat there. When the kinsman-redeemer he had mentioned came along, Boaz said, "Come over here, my friend, and sit down." So he went over and sat down.

²Boaz took ten of the elders of the town and said, "Sit here," and they did so. ³Then he said to the kinsman-redeemer, "Naomi, who has come back from Moab, is selling the piece of land that

truth or dare

Kinsman-redeemer? How 'bout a modern translation? Kinsman = family. Redeemer = guardian/defender/protector. Ruth's kinsman-redeemer was Boaz. Yours is Jesus.

3:9

ᵃ 1 Hebrew *find rest* (see Ruth 1:9)   *ᵇ 15* Most Hebrew manuscripts; many Hebrew manuscripts, Vulgate and Syriac *she*

mirror images

Ruth—What Godly Guys Like in a Girl

Going stag. Flying solo. Table for one. Ruth thought she'd be single forever. Sitting at home alone on Friday nights, she figured love had already passed her by at a young age. Although she had been married at one time, her young husband had tragically died, and now she lived in a foreign land with her mother-in-law, Naomi. For Ruth, her decision to leave Moab in order to remain with Naomi meant that the prospect of a future wedding in Israel would surely be bleak.

What Ruth didn't know was that God was preparing her to one day meet the man of her dreams. But while God was preparing her, Ruth wasn't idle. She was learning about God through Naomi, and she was growing in her faith through obedience to God and her mother-in-law. During this time, Ruth didn't realize that God was arranging a meeting between her and the man she would one day marry.

The man's name was Boaz, and he noticed some things about Ruth. He noticed how she cared for her family. He watched her willingness to work hard. He took note of her devotion to God. He might have asked God if Ruth was the one, and what he saw in her character gave him his answer. Even the circumstances worked out just right as they slowly fell in love in the golden fields of Bethlehem.

So, what does Ruth's example teach us girls? Take off as hard and fast as you can toward Jesus. You'll be leaving a lot of ordinary guys in the dust at that point. You may even spend some Friday nights at home playing Scrabble with the fam. But stay focused on your relationship with Jesus with all your might. Then, at the right time, God will say, "Hey! Look who's beside you." A guy who is equally passionate about his relationship with Christ will catch your eye. And your godly character will catch his. And the rest? Well, the rest is history.

Dear God, show me how to fall in love with you first, so I'll know how to care for the guy of my dreams. I know I can trust you like Ruth did to send the right guy my way at the right time. Amen.

dear God

To read the next Mirror Images profile, go to page 327.

≫ Ruth's love story is told in the book of Ruth (pages 314–319).

belonged to our brother Elimelech. ⁴I thought I should bring the matter to your attention and suggest that you buy it in the presence of these seated here and in the presence of the elders of my people. If you will redeem it, do so. But if you ᵃ will not, tell me, so I will know. For no one has the right to do it except you, and I am next in line."

"I will redeem it," he said.

⁵Then Boaz said, "On the day you buy the land from Naomi and from Ruth the Moabitess, you acquire ᵇ the dead man's widow, in order to maintain the name of the dead with his property."

⁶At this, the kinsman-redeemer said, "Then I cannot redeem it because I might endanger my own estate. You redeem it yourself. I cannot do it."

⁷(Now in earlier times in Israel, for the redemption and transfer of property to become final, one party took off his sandal and gave it to the other. This was the method of legalizing transactions in Israel.)

⁸So the kinsman-redeemer said to Boaz, "Buy it yourself." And he removed his sandal.

⁹Then Boaz announced to the elders and all the people, "Today you are witnesses that I have bought from Naomi all the property of Elimelech, Kilion and Mahlon. ¹⁰I have also acquired Ruth the Moabitess, Mahlon's widow, as my wife, in order to maintain the name of the dead with his property, so that his name will not disappear from among his family or from the town records. Today you are witnesses!"

¹¹Then the elders and all those at the gate said, "We are witnesses. May the LORD make the woman who is coming into your home like Rachel and Leah, who together built up the house of Israel. May you have standing in Ephrathah and be famous in Bethlehem. ¹²Through the offspring the LORD gives you by this young woman, may your family be like that of Perez, whom Tamar bore to Judah."

The Genealogy of David

¹³So Boaz took Ruth and she became his wife. Then he went to her, and the LORD enabled her to conceive, and she gave birth to a son. ¹⁴The women said to Naomi: "Praise be to the LORD, who this day has not left you without a kinsman-redeemer! May he become famous throughout Israel! ¹⁵He will renew your life and sustain you in your old age. For your daughter-in-law, who loves you and who is better to you than seven sons, has given him birth."

¹⁶Then Naomi took the child, laid him in her lap and cared for him. ¹⁷The women living there said, "Naomi has a son." And they named him Obed. He was the father of Jesse, the father of David.

love notes

4:15

Loved one,

Trust me in the hard times, in the lonely moments, in the disappointments, in your grief. Just as I did for Naomi, so I will also take care of you. Your tragedies won't be the end of the story. Trust me.

—Lord God

What difficult situation in your life would you like to see God change?

_____

_____

_____

_____

_____

_____

_____

_____

_____

_____

_____

ᵃ 4 Many Hebrew manuscripts, Septuagint, Vulgate and Syriac; most Hebrew manuscripts *he*
ᵇ 5 Hebrew; Vulgate and Syriac *Naomi, you acquire Ruth the Moabitess,*

¹⁸This, then, is the family line of Perez:

Perez was the father of Hezron,
¹⁹Hezron the father of Ram,
Ram the father of Amminadab,
²⁰Amminadab the father of Nahshon,
Nahshon the father of Salmon,^a
²¹Salmon the father of Boaz,
Boaz the father of Obed,
²²Obed the father of Jesse,
and Jesse the father of David.

^a 20 A few Hebrew manuscripts, some Septuagint manuscripts and Vulgate (see also verse 21 and Septuagint of 1 Chron. 2:11); most Hebrew manuscripts *Salma*

at a glance

author:	Unknown.
date:	Sometime after the division of Israel into the northern and southern kingdoms, around 930 B.C.
setting:	The nation of Israel went from being led by God to being led by a human king.
verse to remember:	"To obey is better than sacrifice, and to heed is better than the fat of rams" (15:22).
theme to consider:	God desires that we worship, obey, serve and follow him with all our heart and not just with superficial words.

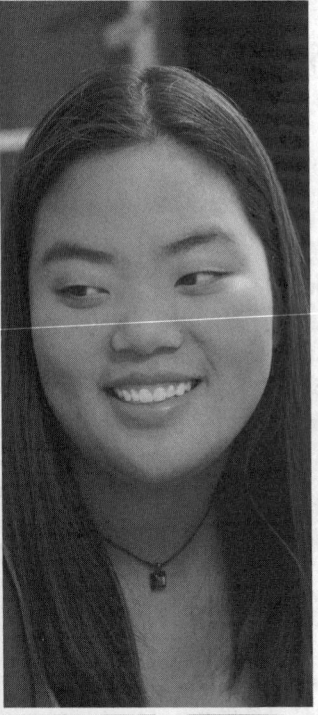

1 samuel

unchanging truth

"Use our special lotion made from exotic herbs! You'll have a blemish-free complexion in ten days!"

"Drink our power drink and run a marathon in record time—with energy to spare!"

Hundreds of TV commercials and magazine ads make fantastic claims of how their products can improve your life, make you more beautiful or transform you into the most popular girl in school. Eagerly you lay down your hard-earned money. Unfortunately, the products rarely deliver the far-fetched results they promise. They don't *do* what they *say*—their actions don't match their words. You may even feel a little foolish for believing them in the first place.

The Israelites' behavior as recorded in 1 Samuel was much like modern-day commercials. They said all the right things, but they didn't follow through with God-pleasing actions. But the results of the Israelites' lack of commitment were much more tragic than losing some money or feeling foolish. They were dissatisfied with God's leadership. They wanted to be like all the other nations and have a king (see 1 Samuel 8). The Israelites promised to still worship, serve and obey God, but they didn't really mean it. Their actions proved otherwise.

What about you? Are you living it or just saying it? Make sure your actions are consistent with your words.

life lessons

1. God expects us to follow through on what we say. Only full commitment is good enough for him (1:10–11,24–28).

2. God sees past your good words and image and sees you exactly as you are. Saying the right things can't compensate for not doing the right things (15:20–22).

3. The truest, closest friendships possible are rooted in a love for God and for each other (20:42).

The Birth of Samuel

1 There was a certain man from Ramathaim, a Zuphite[a] from the hill country of Ephraim, whose name was Elkanah son of Jeroham, the son of Elihu, the son of Tohu, the son of Zuph, an Ephraimite. [2]He had two wives; one was called Hannah and the other Peninnah. Peninnah had children, but Hannah had none.

[3]Year after year this man went up from his town to worship and sacrifice to the LORD Almighty at Shiloh, where Hophni and Phinehas, the two sons of Eli, were priests of the LORD. [4]Whenever the day came for Elkanah to sacrifice, he would give portions of the meat to his wife Peninnah and to all her sons and daughters. [5]But to Hannah he gave a double portion because he loved her, and the LORD had closed her womb. [6]And because the LORD had closed her womb, her rival kept provoking her in order to irritate her. [7]This went on year after year. Whenever Hannah went up to the house of the LORD, her rival provoked her till she wept and would not eat. [8]Elkanah her husband would say to her, "Hannah, why are you weeping? Why don't you eat? Why are you downhearted? Don't I mean more to you than ten sons?"

[9]Once when they had finished eating and drinking in Shiloh, Hannah stood up. Now Eli the priest was sitting on a chair by the doorpost of the LORD's temple.[b] [10]In bitterness of soul Hannah wept much and prayed to the LORD. [11]And she made a vow, saying, "O LORD Almighty, if you will only look upon your servant's misery and remember me, and not forget your servant but give her a son, then I will give him to the LORD for all the days of his life, and no razor will ever be used on his head."

[12]As she kept on praying to the LORD, Eli observed her mouth. [13]Hannah was praying in her heart, and her lips were moving but her voice was not heard. Eli thought she was drunk [14]and said to her, "How long will you keep on getting drunk? Get rid of your wine."

[15]"Not so, my lord," Hannah replied, "I am a woman who is deeply troubled. I have not been drinking wine or beer; I was pouring out my soul to the LORD. [16]Do not take your servant for a wicked woman; I have been praying here out of my great anguish and grief."

[17]Eli answered, "Go in peace, and may the God of Israel grant you what you have asked of him."

genuine prayer » 1:10-16

How do you handle a crisis? Do you get on the phone and talk it over (and over and over) with a friend? Or do you internalize it and try to solve it on your own? Guess it depends on what the problem *is*, right? Hannah had a major problem: She wanted a child but couldn't have one. She could've talked it over with a friend on the tabernacle pay phone. But she knew that wouldn't solve anything. But talking it over with the *right* friend would, if that friend was God. Got a problem? Talk it over with a friend—God.

[18]She said, "May your servant find favor in your eyes." Then she went her way and ate something, and her face was no longer downcast.

[19]Early the next morning they arose and worshiped before the LORD and then went back to their home at Ramah. Elkanah lay with Hannah his wife, and the LORD remembered her. [20]So in the course of time Hannah conceived and gave birth to a son. She named him Samuel,[c] saying, "Because I asked the LORD for him."

Hannah Dedicates Samuel

[21]When the man Elkanah went up with all his family to offer the annual sacrifice to the LORD and to fulfill his vow, [22]Hannah did not go. She said to her husband, "After the boy is weaned, I will take him and present him before the LORD, and he will live there always."

[23]"Do what seems best to you," Elkanah her husband told her. "Stay here until you have

---

[a] 1 Or *from Ramathaim Zuphim*   [b] 9 That is, tabernacle   [c] 20 *Samuel* sounds like the Hebrew for *heard of God.*

weaned him; only may the LORD make good his[a] word." So the woman stayed at home and nursed her son until she had weaned him.

²⁴After he was weaned, she took the boy with her, young as he was, along with a three-year-old bull,[b] an ephah[c] of flour and a skin of wine, and brought him to the house of the LORD at Shiloh. ²⁵When they had slaughtered the bull, they brought the boy to Eli, ²⁶and she said to him, "As surely as you live, my lord, I am the woman who stood here beside you praying to the LORD. ²⁷I prayed for this child, and the LORD has granted me what I asked of him. ²⁸So now I give him to the LORD. For his whole life he will be given over to the LORD." And he worshiped the LORD there.

Hannah's Prayer

2 Then Hannah prayed and said:

"My heart rejoices in the LORD;
    in the LORD my horn[d] is lifted high.
My mouth boasts over my enemies,
    for I delight in your deliverance.

² "There is no one holy[e] like the LORD;
    there is no one besides you;
    there is no Rock like our God.

³ "Do not keep talking so proudly
    or let your mouth speak such arrogance,
for the LORD is a God who knows,
    and by him deeds are weighed.

⁴ "The bows of the warriors are broken,
    but those who stumbled are armed with strength.
⁵ Those who were full hire themselves out for food,
    but those who were hungry hunger no more.
She who was barren has borne seven children,
    but she who has had many sons pines away.

⁶ "The LORD brings death and makes alive;
    he brings down to the grave[f] and raises up.
⁷ The LORD sends poverty and wealth;
    he humbles and he exalts.
⁸ He raises the poor from the dust
    and lifts the needy from the ash heap;
he seats them with princes
    and has them inherit a throne of honor.

"For the foundations of the earth are the LORD's;
    upon them he has set the world.
⁹ He will guard the feet of his saints,
    but the wicked will be silenced in darkness.

"It is not by strength that one prevails;
¹⁰   those who oppose the LORD will be shattered.
He will thunder against them from heaven;
    the LORD will judge the ends of the earth.

truth or dare

It's pointless to keep secrets from God. He already knows all the nitty-gritty details of your life . . . and he *still* loves you! Go ahead—show him the real you.

2:3

---

a 23 Masoretic Text; Dead Sea Scrolls, Septuagint and Syriac *your*   *b 24* Dead Sea Scrolls, Septuagint and Syriac; Masoretic Text *with three bulls*   *c 24* That is, probably about 3/5 bushel (about 22 liters)   *d 1 Horn* here symbolizes strength; also in verse 10.   *e 2* Or *no Holy One*   *f 6* Hebrew *Sheol*

> "He will give strength to his king
> and exalt the horn of his anointed."

[11] Then Elkanah went home to Ramah, but the boy ministered before the LORD under Eli the priest.

Eli's Wicked Sons

[12] Eli's sons were wicked men; they had no regard for the LORD. [13] Now it was the practice of the priests with the people that whenever anyone offered a sacrifice and while the meat was being boiled, the servant of the priest would come with a three-pronged fork in his hand. [14] He would plunge it into the pan or kettle or caldron or pot, and the priest would take for himself whatever the fork brought up. This is how they treated all the Israelites who came to Shiloh. [15] But even before the fat was burned, the servant of the priest would come and say to the man who was sacrificing, "Give the priest some meat to roast; he won't accept boiled meat from you, but only raw."

[16] If the man said to him, "Let the fat be burned up first, and then take whatever you want," the servant would then answer, "No, hand it over now; if you don't, I'll take it by force."

[17] This sin of the young men was very great in the LORD's sight, for they[a] were treating the LORD's offering with contempt.

[18] But Samuel was ministering before the LORD—a boy wearing a linen ephod. [19] Each year his mother made him a little robe and took it to him when she went up with her husband to offer the annual sacrifice. [20] Eli would bless Elkanah and his wife, saying, "May the LORD give you children by this woman to take the place of the one she prayed for and gave to the LORD." Then they would go home. [21] And the LORD was gracious to Hannah; she conceived and gave birth to three sons and two daughters. Meanwhile, the boy Samuel grew up in the presence of the LORD.

[22] Now Eli, who was very old, heard about

love ♡ notes

2:2

Treasured one,

I alone am God, your Rock—immoveable, strong and unchanging. Friends may come and go. Your circumstances may change. But I will always remain rock solid.

—Your Rock

How does knowing God help when your circumstances seem unsteady?

truth or dare

Don't be surprised when God blesses your prayer of faith with *more* than you asked for. The problem for most of us is that we lose hope before even *asking.*

2:20–21

[a] 17 Or men

everything his sons were doing to all Israel and how they slept with the women who served at the entrance to the Tent of Meeting. [23]So he said to them, "Why do you do such things? I hear from all the people about these wicked deeds of yours. [24]No, my sons; it is not a good report that I hear spreading among the LORD's people. [25]If a man sins against another man, God[a] may mediate for him; but if a man sins against the LORD, who will intercede for him?" His sons, however, did not listen to their father's rebuke, for it was the LORD's will to put them to death.

[26]And the boy Samuel continued to grow in stature and in favor with the LORD and with men.

Prophecy Against the House of Eli

[27]Now a man of God came to Eli and said to him, "This is what the LORD says: 'Did I not clearly reveal myself to your father's house when they were in Egypt under Pharaoh? [28]I chose your father out of all the tribes of Israel to be my priest, to go up to my altar, to burn incense, and to wear an ephod in my presence. I also gave your father's house all the offerings made with fire by the Israelites. [29]Why do you[b] scorn my sacrifice and offering that I prescribed for my dwelling? Why do you honor your sons more than me by fattening yourselves on the choice parts of every offering made by my people Israel?'

[30]"Therefore the LORD, the God of Israel, declares: 'I promised that your house and your father's house would minister before me forever.' But now the LORD declares: 'Far be it from me! Those who honor me I will honor, but those who despise me will be disdained. [31]The time is coming when I will cut short your strength and the strength of your father's house, so that there will not be an old man in your family line [32]and you will see distress in my dwelling. Although good will be done to Israel, in your family line there will never be an old man. [33]Every one of you that I do not cut off from my altar will be spared only to blind your eyes with tears and to grieve your heart, and all your descendants will die in the prime of life.

[34]" 'And what happens to your two sons, Hophni and Phinehas, will be a sign to you—they will both die on the same day. [35]I will raise up for myself a faithful priest, who will do according to what is in my heart and mind. I will firmly establish his house, and he will minister before my anointed one always. [36]Then everyone left in your family line will come and bow down before him for a piece of silver and a crust of bread and plead, "Appoint me to some priestly office so I can have food to eat." ' "

The LORD Calls Samuel

3 The boy Samuel ministered before the LORD under Eli. In those days the word of the LORD was rare; there were not many visions.
[2]One night Eli, whose eyes were becoming so weak that he could barely see, was lying down in his usual place. [3]The lamp of God had not yet gone out, and Samuel was lying down in the temple[c] of the LORD, where the ark of God was. [4]Then the LORD called Samuel.

Samuel answered, "Here I am." [5]And he ran to Eli and said, "Here I am; you called me."

But Eli said, "I did not call; go back and lie down." So he went and lay down.

[6]Again the LORD called, "Samuel!" And Samuel got up and went to Eli and said, "Here I am; you called me."

"My son," Eli said, "I did not call; go back and lie down."

[7]Now Samuel did not yet know the LORD: The word of the LORD had not yet been revealed to him.

[8]The LORD called Samuel a third time, and Samuel got up and went to Eli and said, "Here I am; you called me."

Then Eli realized that the LORD was calling the boy. [9]So Eli told Samuel, "Go and lie down, and if he calls you, say, 'Speak, LORD, for your servant is listening.' " So Samuel went and lay down in his place.

truth or dare

"Say what, Lord?" Hearing God's voice doesn't depend on age or experience. For instance, when you approach God's Word, are you ready to listen?

3:8–9

[a] 25 Or *the judges*   [b] 29 The Hebrew is plural.   [c] 3 That is, tabernacle

¹⁰The LORD came and stood there, calling as at the other times, "Samuel! Samuel!"

Then Samuel said, "Speak, for your servant is listening."

¹¹And the LORD said to Samuel: "See, I am about to do something in Israel that will make the ears of everyone who hears of it tingle. ¹²At that time I will carry out against Eli everything I spoke against his family—from beginning to end. ¹³For I told him that I would judge his family forever because of the sin he knew about; his sons made themselves contemptible, *a* and he failed to restrain them. ¹⁴Therefore, I swore to the house of Eli, 'The guilt of Eli's house will never be atoned for by sacrifice or offering.' "

¹⁵Samuel lay down until morning and then opened the doors of the house of the LORD. He was afraid to tell Eli the vision, ¹⁶but Eli called him and said, "Samuel, my son."

Samuel answered, "Here I am."

¹⁷"What was it he said to you?" Eli asked. "Do not hide it from me. May God deal with you, be it ever so severely, if you hide from me anything he told you." ¹⁸So Samuel told him everything, hiding nothing from him. Then Eli said, "He is the LORD; let him do what is good in his eyes."

¹⁹The LORD was with Samuel as he grew up, and he let none of his words fall to the ground. ²⁰And all Israel from Dan to Beersheba recognized that Samuel was attested as a prophet of the LORD. ²¹The LORD continued to appear at Shiloh, and there he revealed himself to Samuel through his word.

4 And Samuel's word came to all Israel.

The Philistines Capture the Ark

Now the Israelites went out to fight against the Philistines. The Israelites camped at Ebenezer, and the Philistines at Aphek. ²The Philistines deployed their forces to meet Israel, and as the battle spread, Israel was defeated by the Philistines, who killed about four thousand of them on the battlefield. ³When the soldiers returned to camp, the elders of Israel asked, "Why did the LORD bring defeat upon us today before the Philistines? Let us bring the ark of the LORD's covenant from Shiloh, so that it *b* may go with us and save us from the hand of our enemies."

⁴So the people sent men to Shiloh, and they brought back the ark of the covenant of the LORD Almighty, who is enthroned between the cherubim. And Eli's two sons, Hophni and Phinehas, were there with the ark of the covenant of God.

truth or dare

"So that *it* may save us?" *It* can never save you—only *he* can. Are you clinging to a symbol of God? Or trusting in the real thing?

4:3

⁵When the ark of the LORD's covenant came into the camp, all Israel raised such a great shout that the ground shook. ⁶Hearing the uproar, the Philistines asked, "What's all this shouting in the Hebrew camp?"

When they learned that the ark of the LORD had come into the camp, ⁷the Philistines were afraid. "A god has come into the camp," they said. "We're in trouble! Nothing like this has happened before. ⁸Woe to us! Who will deliver us from the hand of these mighty gods? They are the gods who struck the Egyptians with all kinds of plagues in the desert. ⁹Be strong, Philistines! Be men, or you will be subject to the Hebrews, as they have been to you. Be men, and fight!"

¹⁰So the Philistines fought, and the Israelites were defeated and every man fled to his tent. The slaughter was very great; Israel lost thirty thousand foot soldiers. ¹¹The ark of God was captured, and Eli's two sons, Hophni and Phinehas, died.

Death of Eli

¹²That same day a Benjamite ran from the battle line and went to Shiloh, his clothes torn and dust on his head. ¹³When he arrived, there was Eli sitting on his chair by the side of the road, watching, because his heart feared for the ark of God. When the man entered the town and told what had happened, the whole town sent up a cry.

a 13 Masoretic Text; an ancient Hebrew scribal tradition and Septuagint *sons blasphemed God*   *b 3* Or *he*

¹⁴Eli heard the outcry and asked, "What is the meaning of this uproar?"

The man hurried over to Eli, ¹⁵who was ninety-eight years old and whose eyes were set so that he could not see. ¹⁶He told Eli, "I have just come from the battle line; I fled from it this very day."

Eli asked, "What happened, my son?"

¹⁷The man who brought the news replied, "Israel fled before the Philistines, and the army has suffered heavy losses. Also your two sons, Hophni and Phinehas, are dead, and the ark of God has been captured."

¹⁸When he mentioned the ark of God, Eli fell backward off his chair by the side of the gate. His neck was broken and he died, for he was an old man and heavy. He had led ᵃ Israel forty years.

¹⁹His daughter-in-law, the wife of Phinehas, was pregnant and near the time of delivery. When she heard the news that the ark of God had been captured and that her father-in-law and her husband were dead, she went into labor and gave birth, but was overcome by her labor pains. ²⁰As she was dying, the women attending her said, "Don't despair; you have given birth to a son." But she did not respond or pay any attention.

²¹She named the boy Ichabod, ᵇ saying, "The glory has departed from Israel"—because of the capture of the ark of God and the deaths of her father-in-law and her husband. ²²She said, "The glory has departed from Israel, for the ark of God has been captured."

The Ark in Ashdod and Ekron

5 After the Philistines had captured the ark of God, they took it from Ebenezer to Ashdod. ²Then they carried the ark into Dagon's temple and set it beside Dagon. ³When the people of Ashdod rose early the next day, there was Dagon, fallen on his face on the ground before the ark of the LORD! They took Dagon and put him back in his place. ⁴But the following morning when they rose, there was Dagon, fallen on his face on the ground before the ark of the LORD! His head and hands had been broken off and were lying on the threshold; only his body remained. ⁵That is why to this day neither the priests of Dagon nor any others who enter Dagon's temple at Ashdod step on the threshold.

⁶The LORD's hand was heavy upon the people of Ashdod and its vicinity; he brought devastation upon them and afflicted them with tumors. ᶜ ⁷When the men of Ashdod saw what was happening, they said, "The ark of the god of Israel must not stay here with us, because his hand is heavy upon us and upon Dagon our god." ⁸So they called together all the rulers of the Philistines and asked them, "What shall we do with the ark of the god of Israel?"

They answered, "Have the ark of the god of Israel moved to Gath." So they moved the ark of the God of Israel.

⁹But after they had moved it, the LORD's hand was against that city, throwing it into a great panic. He afflicted the people of the city, both young and old, with an outbreak of tumors. ᵈ ¹⁰So they sent the ark of God to Ekron.

As the ark of God was entering Ekron, the people of Ekron cried out, "They have brought the ark of the god of Israel around to us to kill us and our people." ¹¹So they called together all the rulers of the Philistines and said, "Send the ark of the god of Israel away; let it go back to its own place, or it ᵉ will kill us and our people." For death had filled the city with panic; God's hand was very heavy upon it. ¹²Those who did not die were afflicted with tumors, and the outcry of the city went up to heaven.

The Ark Returned to Israel

6 When the ark of the LORD had been in Philistine territory seven months, ²the Philistines called for the priests and the diviners and said, "What shall we do with the ark of the LORD? Tell us how we should send it back to its place."

³They answered, "If you return the ark of the god of Israel, do not send it away empty, but by all means send a guilt offering to him. Then you will be healed, and you will know why his hand has not been lifted from you."

⁴The Philistines asked, "What guilt offering should we send to him?"

ᵃ 18 Traditionally judged   ᵇ 21 Ichabod means no glory.   ᶜ 6 Hebrew; Septuagint and Vulgate tumors. And rats appeared in their land, and death and destruction were throughout the city   ᵈ 9 Or with tumors in the groin (see Septuagint)   ᵉ 11 Or he

mirror images

"I prayed for this child, and the LORD has granted me what I asked of him. So now I give him to the LORD." 1 Samuel 1:27–28

Hannah—Please and Thank You

"*ord, I* need *a new leather jacket.*"
"*God,* please *let him call me tonight.*"

Sometimes we treat God like a big cosmic Santa Claus, asking him for things we *want* but don't necessarily *need*. We even try to bribe God by promising we'll do something nice for him in return. "If you'll just give me this, then I'll do my devotions faithfully. I promise!" "I won't argue with my mom anymore if you'd just do this one thing for me." As if God needs *us* to do *him* little favors!

Hannah asked for something she really wanted. She asked God for a baby because she hadn't been able to have one. Then in her desperation and sadness, she did what we all tend to do. She made a deal with God. Hannah told God that if he gave her a son, she would give him back to God as a way to thank him. That was a pretty big promise—to give back the very gift she had wanted for so long.

God knew Hannah's heart. He knew she longed for a child. God doesn't always give us what we think we want, but in this case, God gave Hannah a son. And in return, Hannah thanked God by keeping her word. When her son Samuel was old enough, she took him back to the tabernacle, where he served God for the rest of his life. (By the way, because she was faithful with what she had been given, God also blessed Hannah with five more children.)

Hannah reminds us that God loves to bless us with good things. And when God does give us what we want, like Hannah, we need to remember that everything we have is his. Sometimes we are so busy asking God for more and more things that we don't take time to thank him for what he's already given us. And sometimes we tend to blow off our promises, distracted by the next all-important request. Are you like Hannah when it comes to showing God thanks for his good gifts?

> *Dear God, thank you for hearing and answering my prayers. Teach me to pray from a pure heart like Hannah and to be truly thankful. Amen.*

dear God

To read the next Mirror Images profile, go to page 368.

» Read more about Hannah in 1 Samuel 1–2 (page 321–324).

They replied, "Five gold tumors and five gold rats, according to the number of the Philistine rulers, because the same plague has struck both you and your rulers. ⁵Make models of the tumors and of the rats that are destroying the country, and pay honor to Israel's god. Perhaps he will lift his hand from you and your gods and your land. ⁶Why do you harden your hearts as the Egyptians and Pharaoh did? When he *ᵃ* treated them harshly, did they not send the Israelites out so they could go on their way?

⁷"Now then, get a new cart ready, with two cows that have calved and have never been yoked. Hitch the cows to the cart, but take their calves away and pen them up. ⁸Take the ark of the Lord and put it on the cart, and in a chest beside it put the gold objects you are sending back to him as a guilt offering. Send it on its way, ⁹but keep watching it. If it goes up to its own territory, toward Beth Shemesh, then the Lord has brought this great disaster on us. But if it does not, then we will know that it was not his hand that struck us and that it happened to us by chance."

¹⁰So they did this. They took two such cows and hitched them to the cart and penned up their calves. ¹¹They placed the ark of the Lord on the cart and along with it the chest containing the gold rats and the models of the tumors. ¹²Then the cows went straight up toward Beth Shemesh, keeping on the road and lowing all the way; they did not turn to the right or to the left. The rulers of the Philistines followed them as far as the border of Beth Shemesh.

¹³Now the people of Beth Shemesh were harvesting their wheat in the valley, and when they looked up and saw the ark, they rejoiced at the sight. ¹⁴The cart came to the field of Joshua of Beth Shemesh, and there it stopped beside a large rock. The people chopped up the wood of the cart and sacrificed the cows as a burnt offering to the Lord. ¹⁵The Levites took down the ark of the Lord, together with the chest containing the gold objects, and placed them on the large rock. On that day the people of Beth Shemesh offered burnt offerings and made sacrifices to the Lord. ¹⁶The five rulers of the Philistines saw all this and then returned that same day to Ekron.

¹⁷These are the gold tumors the Philistines sent as a guilt offering to the Lord—one each for Ashdod, Gaza, Ashkelon, Gath and Ekron. ¹⁸And the number of the gold rats was according to the number of Philistine towns belonging to the five rulers—the fortified towns with their country villages. The large rock, on which *ᵇ* they set the ark of the Lord, is a witness to this day in the field of Joshua of Beth Shemesh.

¹⁹But God struck down some of the men of Beth Shemesh, putting seventy *ᶜ* of them to death because they had looked into the ark of the Lord. The people mourned because of the heavy blow the Lord had dealt them, ²⁰and the men of Beth Shemesh asked, "Who can stand in the presence of the Lord, this holy God? To whom will the ark go up from here?"

²¹Then they sent messengers to the people of Kiriath Jearim, saying, "The Philistines have returned the ark of the Lord. Come down and take it up to your place." ¹So the men of Kiriath Jearim came and took up the ark of the Lord. They took it to Abinadab's house on the hill and consecrated Eleazar his son to guard the ark of the Lord.

Samuel Subdues the Philistines at Mizpah

²It was a long time, twenty years in all, that the ark remained at Kiriath Jearim, and all the people of Israel mourned and sought after the Lord. ³And Samuel said to the whole house of Israel, "If you are returning to the Lord with all your hearts, then rid yourselves of the foreign gods and the Ashtoreths and commit yourselves to the Lord and serve him only, and he will deliver you out of the hand of the Philistines." ⁴So the Israelites put away their Baals and Ashtoreths, and served the Lord only.

⁵Then Samuel said, "Assemble all Israel at Mizpah and I will intercede with the Lord for you." ⁶When they had assembled at Mizpah, they drew water and poured

truth *or dare*

Time to clean house! If you've veered from God but now want to get back on track, take Samuel's advice—chuck anything that steers you the wrong way.

7:3

ᵃ 6 That is, God   ᵇ 18 A few Hebrew manuscripts (see also Septuagint); most Hebrew manuscripts villages as far as Greater Abel, where   ᶜ 19 A few Hebrew manuscripts; most Hebrew manuscripts and Septuagint 50,070 it out before the Lord. On that day they fasted and there they confessed, "We have sinned against the Lord." And Samuel was leader* of Israel at Mizpah.

⁷When the Philistines heard that Israel had assembled at Mizpah, the rulers of the Philistines came up to attack them. And when the Israelites heard of it, they were afraid because of the Philistines. ⁸They said to Samuel, "Do not stop crying out to the Lord our God for us, that he may rescue us from the hand of the Philistines." ⁹Then Samuel took a suckling lamb and offered it up as a whole burnt offering to the Lord. He cried out to the Lord on Israel's behalf, and the Lord answered him.

¹⁰While Samuel was sacrificing the burnt offering, the Philistines drew near to engage Israel in battle. But that day the Lord thundered with loud thunder against the Philistines and threw them into such a panic that they were routed before the Israelites. ¹¹The men of Israel rushed out of Mizpah and pursued the Philistines, slaughtering them along the way to a point below Beth Car.

¹²Then Samuel took a stone and set it up between Mizpah and Shen. He named it Ebenezer,ᵇ saying, "Thus far has the Lord helped us." ¹³So the Philistines were subdued and did not invade Israelite territory again.

Throughout Samuel's lifetime, the hand of the Lord was against the Philistines. ¹⁴The towns from Ekron to Gath that the Philistines had captured from Israel were restored to her, and Israel delivered the neighboring territory from the power of the Philistines. And there was peace between Israel and the Amorites.

¹⁵Samuel continued as judge over Israel all the days of his life. ¹⁶From year to year he went on a circuit from Bethel to Gilgal to Mizpah, judging Israel in all those places. ¹⁷But he always went back to Ramah, where his home was, and there he also judged Israel. And he built an altar there to the Lord.

Israel Asks for a King

8 When Samuel grew old, he appointed his sons as judges for Israel. ²The name of his firstborn was Joel and the name of his second was Abijah, and they served at Beersheba. ³But his sons did not walk in his ways. They turned aside after dishonest gain and accepted bribes and perverted justice.

⁴So all the elders of Israel gathered together and came to Samuel at Ramah. ⁵They said to him, "You are old, and your sons do not walk in your ways; now appoint a king to leadᶜ us, such as all the other nations have."

⁶But when they said, "Give us a king to lead us," this displeased Samuel; so he prayed to the Lord. ⁷And the Lord told him: "Listen to all that the people are saying to you; it is not you they have rejected, but they have rejected me as their king. ⁸As they have done from the day I brought them up out of Egypt until this day, forsaking me and serving other gods, so they are doing to you. ⁹Now listen to them; but warn them solemnly and let them know what the king who will reign over them will do."

¹⁰Samuel told all the words of the Lord to the people who were asking him for a king. ¹¹He said, "This is what the king who will reign over you will do: He will take your sons and make them serve with his chariots and horses, and they will run in front of his chariots. ¹²Some he will assign to be commanders of thousands and commanders of fifties, and others to plow his ground and reap his harvest, and still others to make weapons of war and equipment for his chariots. ¹³He will take your daughters to be perfumers and cooks and bakers. ¹⁴He will take the best of your fields and vineyards and olive groves and give them to his attendants. ¹⁵He will take a tenth of your grain and of your vintage and give it to his officials and attendants. ¹⁶Your menservants and maidservants and the best of your cattleᵈ and donkeys he will take for his own use. ¹⁷He will take a tenth of your flocks, and you yourselves will become his slaves. ¹⁸When that day comes, you will cry out for relief from the king you have chosen, and the Lord will not answer you in that day."

¹⁹But the people refused to listen to Samuel. "No!" they said. "We want a king over us. ²⁰Then we will be like all the other nations, with a king to lead us and to go out before us and fight our battles."

---

a 6 Traditionally *judge*   *b 12 Ebenezer* means *stone of help.*   *c 5* Traditionally *judge*; also in verses 6 and 20
d 16 Septuagint; Hebrew *young men*

²¹When Samuel heard all that the people said, he repeated it before the Lord. ²²The Lord answered, "Listen to them and give them a king."

Then Samuel said to the men of Israel, "Everyone go back to his town."

Samuel Anoints Saul

9 There was a Benjamite, a man of standing, whose name was Kish son of Abiel, the son of Zeror, the son of Becorath, the son of Aphiah of Benjamin. ²He had a son named Saul, an impressive young man without equal among the Israelites—a head taller than any of the others.

³Now the donkeys belonging to Saul's father Kish were lost, and Kish said to his son Saul, "Take one of the servants with you and go and look for the donkeys." ⁴So he passed through the hill country of Ephraim and through the area around Shalisha, but they did not find them. They went on into the district of Shaalim, but the donkeys were not there. Then he passed through the territory of Benjamin, but they did not find them.

⁵When they reached the district of Zuph, Saul said to the servant who was with him, "Come, let's go back, or my father will stop thinking about the donkeys and start worrying about us."

⁶But the servant replied, "Look, in this town there is a man of God; he is highly respected, and everything he says comes true. Let's go there now. Perhaps he will tell us what way to take."

⁷Saul said to his servant, "If we go, what can we give the man? The food in our sacks is gone. We have no gift to take to the man of God. What do we have?"

⁸The servant answered him again. "Look," he said, "I have a quarter of a shekel⁰ of silver. I will give it to the man of God so that he will tell us what way to take." ⁹(Formerly in Israel, if a man went to inquire of God, he would say, "Come, let us go to the seer," because the prophet of today used to be called a seer.)

¹⁰"Good," Saul said to his servant. "Come, let's go." So they set out for the town where the man of God was.

¹¹As they were going up the hill to the town, they met some girls coming out to draw water, and they asked them, "Is the seer here?"

¹²"He is," they answered. "He's ahead of you. Hurry now; he has just come to our town today, for the people have a sacrifice at the high place. ¹³As soon as you enter the town, you will find him before he goes up to the high place to eat. The people will not begin eating until he comes, because he must bless the sacrifice; afterward, those who are invited will eat. Go up now; you should find him about this time."

¹⁴They went up to the town, and as they were entering it, there was Samuel, coming toward them on his way up to the high place.

¹⁵Now the day before Saul came, the Lord had revealed this to Samuel: ¹⁶"About this time tomorrow I will send you a man from the land of Benjamin. Anoint him leader over my people Israel; he will deliver my people from the hand of the Philistines. I have looked upon my people, for their cry has reached me."

¹⁷When Samuel caught sight of Saul, the Lord said to him, "This is the man I spoke to you about; he will govern my people."

¹⁸Saul approached Samuel in the gateway and asked, "Would you please tell me where the seer's house is?"

¹⁹"I am the seer," Samuel replied. "Go up ahead of me to the high place, for today you

genuine confidence » 9:17-21

What is your confidence in? Your family's status? How you look? Your talent? When Saul was chosen to be Israel's first king, he wasn't confident that he was up to the task. After all, he was from a no-name clan in the smallest tribe. He was nobody special—or so he thought. Ever feel like that? If God calls you to do something for him, then he must think you're right for the job—even if you doubt yourself. He doesn't want your confidence to be based solely on your abilities or looks or status. He wants you to be confident in him.

⁰ 8 That is, about 1/10 ounce (about 3 grams)

are to eat with me, and in the morning I will let you go and will tell you all that is in your heart. [20]As for the donkeys you lost three days ago, do not worry about them; they have been found. And to whom is all the desire of Israel turned, if not to you and all your father's family?"

[21]Saul answered, "But am I not a Benjamite, from the smallest tribe of Israel, and is not my clan the least of all the clans of the tribe of Benjamin? Why do you say such a thing to me?"

[22]Then Samuel brought Saul and his servant into the hall and seated them at the head of those who were invited—about thirty in number. [23]Samuel said to the cook, "Bring the piece of meat I gave you, the one I told you to lay aside."

[24]So the cook took up the leg with what was on it and set it in front of Saul. Samuel said, "Here is what has been kept for you. Eat, because it was set aside for you for this occasion, from the time I said, 'I have invited guests.' " And Saul dined with Samuel that day.

[25]After they came down from the high place to the town, Samuel talked with Saul on the roof of his house. [26]They rose about daybreak and Samuel called to Saul on the roof, "Get ready, and I will send you on your way." When Saul got ready, he and Samuel went outside together. [27]As they were going down to the edge of the town, Samuel said to Saul, "Tell the servant to go on ahead of us"—and the servant did so—"but you stay here awhile, so that I may give you a message from God."

10 Then Samuel took a flask of oil and poured it on Saul's head and kissed him, saying, "Has not the LORD anointed you leader over his inheritance?[a] [2]When you leave me today, you will meet two men near Rachel's tomb, at Zelzah on the border of Benjamin. They will say to you, 'The donkeys you set out to look for have been found. And now your father has stopped thinking about them and is worried about you. He is asking, "What shall I do about my son?" '

[3]"Then you will go on from there until you reach the great tree of Tabor. Three men going up to God at Bethel will meet you there. One will be carrying three young goats, another three loaves of bread, and another a skin of wine. [4]They will greet you and offer you two loaves of bread, which you will accept from them.

[5]"After that you will go to Gibeah of God, where there is a Philistine outpost. As you approach the town, you will meet a procession of prophets coming down from the high place with lyres, tambourines, flutes and harps being played before them, and they will be prophesying. [6]The Spirit of the LORD will come upon you in power, and you will prophesy with them; and you will be changed into a different person. [7]Once these signs are fulfilled, do whatever your hand finds to do, for God is with you.

[8]"Go down ahead of me to Gilgal. I will surely come down to you to sacrifice burnt offerings and fellowship offerings,[b] but you must wait seven days until I come to you and tell you what you are to do."

Saul Made King

[9]As Saul turned to leave Samuel, God changed Saul's heart, and all these signs were fulfilled that day. [10]When they arrived at Gibeah, a procession of prophets met him; the Spirit of God came upon him in power, and he joined in their prophesying. [11]When all those who had formerly known him saw him prophesying with the prophets, they asked each other, "What is this that has happened to the son of Kish? Is Saul also among the prophets?"

[12]A man who lived there answered, "And who is their father?" So it became a saying: "Is Saul also among the prophets?" [13]After Saul stopped prophesying, he went to the high place.

[14]Now Saul's uncle asked him and his servant, "Where have you been?"

"Looking for the donkeys," he said. "But when we saw they were not to be found, we went to Samuel."

[15]Saul's uncle said, "Tell me what Samuel said to you."

[16]Saul replied, "He assured us that the donkeys had been found." But he did not tell his uncle what Samuel had said about the kingship.

[17]Samuel summoned the people of Israel to the LORD at Mizpah [18]and said to them, "This is what the LORD, the God of Israel, says: 'I brought Israel up out of Egypt, and I delivered you from the power of Egypt and all the kingdoms that oppressed you.' [19]But you have now rejected your God, who saves you out of all your calamities and distresses. And you have said, 'No, set a king over us.' So now present yourselves before the LORD by your tribes and clans."

---

[a] 1 Hebrew; Septuagint and Vulgate *over his people Israel? You will reign over the LORD's people and save them from the power of their enemies round about. And this will be a sign to you that the LORD has anointed you leader over his inheritance:*   [b] 8 Traditionally *peace offerings*

20When Samuel brought all the tribes of Israel near, the tribe of Benjamin was chosen. 21Then he brought forward the tribe of Benjamin, clan by clan, and Matri's clan was chosen. Finally Saul son of Kish was chosen. But when they looked for him, he was not to be found. 22So they inquired further of the LORD, "Has the man come here yet?"

And the LORD said, "Yes, he has hidden himself among the baggage."

23They ran and brought him out, and as he stood among the people he was a head taller than any of the others. 24Samuel said to all the people, "Do you see the man the LORD has chosen? There is no one like him among all the people."

Then the people shouted, "Long live the king!"

25Samuel explained to the people the regulations of the kingship. He wrote them down on a scroll and deposited it before the LORD. Then Samuel dismissed the people, each to his own home.

26Saul also went to his home in Gibeah, accompanied by valiant men whose hearts God had touched. 27But some troublemakers said, "How can this fellow save us?" They despised him and brought him no gifts. But Saul kept silent.

truth or dare

Feeling overwhelmed by responsibilities? Don't sweat it! Sometimes God intentionally throws us in the deep end so that we learn to rely on him.

10:20–22

Saul Rescues the City of Jabesh

11 Nahash the Ammonite went up and besieged Jabesh Gilead. And all the men of Jabesh said to him, "Make a treaty with us, and we will be subject to you."

2But Nahash the Ammonite replied, "I will make a treaty with you only on the condition that I gouge out the right eye of every one of you and so bring disgrace on all Israel."

3The elders of Jabesh said to him, "Give us seven days so we can send messengers throughout Israel; if no one comes to rescue us, we will surrender to you."

4When the messengers came to Gibeah of Saul and reported these terms to the people, they all wept aloud. 5Just then Saul was returning from the fields, behind his oxen, and he asked, "What is wrong with the people? Why are they weeping?" Then they repeated to him what the men of Jabesh had said.

6When Saul heard their words, the Spirit of God came upon him in power, and he burned with anger. 7He took a pair of oxen, cut them into pieces, and sent the pieces by messengers throughout Israel, proclaiming, "This is what will be done to the oxen of anyone who does not follow Saul and Samuel." Then the terror of the LORD fell on the people, and they turned out as one man. 8When Saul mustered them at Bezek, the men of Israel numbered three hundred thousand and the men of Judah thirty thousand.

9They told the messengers who had come, "Say to the men of Jabesh Gilead, 'By the time the sun is hot tomorrow, you will be delivered.' " When the messengers went and reported this to the men of Jabesh, they were elated. 10They said to the Ammonites, "Tomorrow we will surrender to you, and you can do to us whatever seems good to you."

11The next day Saul separated his men into three divisions; during the last watch of the night they broke into the camp of the Ammonites and slaughtered them until the heat of the day. Those who survived were scattered, so that no two of them were left together.

Saul Confirmed as King

12The people then said to Samuel, "Who was it that asked, 'Shall Saul reign over us?' Bring these men to us and we will put them to death."

13But Saul said, "No one shall be put to death today, for this day the LORD has rescued Israel."

14Then Samuel said to the people, "Come, let us go to Gilgal and there reaffirm the kingship." 15So all the people went to Gilgal and confirmed Saul as king in the presence of the LORD. There they sacrificed fellowship offerings^a before the LORD, and Saul and all the Israelites held a great celebration.

a 15 Traditionally *peace offerings*

Step Aside

focus Profile: **Melissa**

Why did she ever have to meet him? Our lives were fine till *he* came along. He might as well have taken my mom away from me. That's what I feel like he did anyway.

It was two years ago when my mom married him. *He* is my stepfather, and he's a beast. I wouldn't say that in front of them, of course. It's just that he's like this huge creature that constantly demands food and attention, and he's never satisfied. In my vocab, there's a word that totally fits him—*insatiable*.

Mom and I never go shopping together anymore. And she never has time for things like girls' night out or highlighting our hair or going to movies just the two of us. He tells me, "Find one of your friends to do that. You're old enough to entertain yourself. Your mom is tired." And then he kisses her right in front of me! Ugh!

Who is he to boss me around? My mom and I were fine for ten years without him. Then here comes Mr. Macho, the builder, bulldozing his way in here and ordering me around like he's my *father* or something. Do I really need two dads? Especially since this one's stricter than a Nazi. He gives me curfew and rules and chores, and he nags my mom about my attitude and my grades and everything else in life I do wrong.

I know it upsets my mom that I don't like him. She can tell I'm unhappy. But it's not like she's going to ask *him* to change—so where does that leave me?

For more information and advice about living in a stepfamily, go to www.TrueImagesBible.com

stepparents in focus

Chances are good that you either live with a stepparent or you have close friends who do. It's a growing trend in America. Many therapists have noted that teenaged girls have more problems as stepchildren than boys do. If you are a stepchild . . .

» Pray about the hurt and loneliness you feel around your "new" parent. Pour out your feelings to God; he's listening.

» Give your situation another chance. Kids who try not to write off a stepparent completely may do better after they give things some time to settle down.

» Even when your own family seems crazy, remember that you are God's child and a part of his perfect family (see 1 John 3:1–2, page 1619).

For more on this topic, see the index on page 1656.

Samuel's Farewell Speech

12 Samuel said to all Israel, "I have listened to everything you said to me and have set a king over you. ²Now you have a king as your leader. As for me, I am old and gray, and my sons are here with you. I have been your leader from my youth until this day. ³Here I stand. Testify against me in the presence of the Lord and his anointed. Whose ox have I taken?

Whose donkey have I taken? Whom have I cheated? Whom have I oppressed? From whose hand have I accepted a bribe to make me shut my eyes? If I have done any of these, I will make it right."

⁴"You have not cheated or oppressed us," they replied. "You have not taken anything from anyone's hand."

⁵Samuel said to them, "The LORD is witness against you, and also his anointed is witness this day, that you have not found anything in my hand."

"He is witness," they said.

⁶Then Samuel said to the people, "It is the LORD who appointed Moses and Aaron and brought your forefathers up out of Egypt. ⁷Now then, stand here, because I am going to confront you with evidence before the LORD as to all the righteous acts performed by the LORD for you and your fathers.

⁸"After Jacob entered Egypt, they cried to the LORD for help, and the LORD sent Moses and Aaron, who brought your forefathers out of Egypt and settled them in this place.

⁹"But they forgot the LORD their God; so he sold them into the hand of Sisera, the commander of the army of Hazor, and into the hands of the Philistines and the king of Moab, who fought against them. ¹⁰They cried out to the LORD and said, 'We have sinned; we have forsaken the LORD and served the Baals and the Ashtoreths. But now deliver us from the hands of our enemies, and we will serve you.' ¹¹Then the LORD sent Jerub-Baal,ᵃ Barak,ᵇ Jephthah and Samuel,ᶜ and he delivered you from the hands of your enemies on every side, so that you lived securely.

¹²"But when you saw that Nahash king of the Ammonites was moving against you, you said to me, 'No, we want a king to rule over us'—even though the LORD your God was your king. ¹³Now here is the king you have chosen, the one you asked for; see, the LORD has set a king over you. ¹⁴If you fear the LORD and serve and obey him and do not rebel against his commands, and if both you and the king who reigns over you follow the LORD your God—good! ¹⁵But if you do not obey the LORD, and if you rebel against his commands, his hand will be against you, as it was against your fathers.

¹⁶"Now then, stand still and see this great thing the LORD is about to do before your eyes! ¹⁷Is it not wheat harvest now? I will call upon the LORD to send thunder and rain. And you will realize what an evil thing you did in the eyes of the LORD when you asked for a king."

¹⁸Then Samuel called upon the LORD, and that same day the LORD sent thunder and rain. So all the people stood in awe of the LORD and of Samuel.

¹⁹The people all said to Samuel, "Pray to the LORD your God for your servants so that we will not die, for we have added to all our other sins the evil of asking for a king."

²⁰"Do not be afraid," Samuel replied. "You have done all this evil; yet do not turn away from the LORD, but serve the LORD with all your heart. ²¹Do not turn away after useless idols. They can do you no good, nor can they rescue you, because they are useless. ²²For the sake of his great name the LORD will not reject his people, because the LORD was pleased to make you his own. ²³As for me, far be it from me that I should sin against the LORD by failing to pray for you. And I will teach you the way that is good and right. ²⁴But be sure to fear the LORD and serve him faithfully with all your heart; consider what great things he has done for you. ²⁵Yet if you persist in doing evil, both you and your king will be swept away."

---

truth or dare

Be careful what you wish for . . . the Israelites' mistakes can teach you a ton. God doesn't take your requests lightly. Neither should you.

12:16–17

---

truth or dare

Can *not* praying be a sin? According to Samuel it can! Know someone you should be praying for? Stick it out— even if it takes years till you get an answer.

12:23

ᵃ 11 Also called *Gideon*   ᵇ 11 Some Septuagint manuscripts and Syriac; Hebrew *Bedan*   ᶜ 11 Hebrew; some Septuagint manuscripts and Syriac *Samson*

Samuel Rebukes Saul

13 Saul was ⌊thirty⌋[a] years old when he became king, and he reigned over Israel ⌊forty-⌋[b] two years. [2]Saul[c] chose three thousand men from Israel; two thousand were with him at Micmash and in the hill country of Bethel, and a thousand were with Jonathan at Gibeah in Benjamin. The rest of the men he sent back to their homes.

[3]Jonathan attacked the Philistine outpost at Geba, and the Philistines heard about it. Then Saul had the trumpet blown throughout the land and said, "Let the Hebrews hear!" [4]So all Israel heard the news: "Saul has attacked the Philistine outpost, and now Israel has become a stench to the Philistines." And the people were summoned to join Saul at Gilgal.

[5]The Philistines assembled to fight Israel, with three thousand[d] chariots, six thousand charioteers, and soldiers as numerous as the sand on the seashore. They went up and camped at Micmash, east of Beth Aven. [6]When the men of Israel saw that their situation was critical and that their army was hard pressed, they hid in caves and thickets, among the rocks, and in pits and cisterns. [7]Some Hebrews even crossed the Jordan to the land of Gad and Gilead.

Saul remained at Gilgal, and all the troops with him were quaking with fear. [8]He waited seven days, the time set by Samuel; but Samuel did not come to Gilgal, and Saul's men began to scatter.

[9]So he said, "Bring me the burnt offering and the fellowship offerings.[e]" And Saul offered up the burnt offering. [10]Just as he finished making the offering, Samuel arrived, and Saul went out to greet him.

[11]"What have you done?" asked Samuel.

Saul replied, "When I saw that the men were scattering, and that you did not come at the set time, and that the Philistines were assembling at Micmash, [12]I thought, 'Now the Philistines will come down against me at Gilgal, and I have not sought the Lord's favor.' So I felt compelled to offer the burnt offering."

[13]"You acted foolishly," Samuel said. "You have not kept the command the Lord your God gave you; if you had, he would have established your kingdom over Israel for all time. [14]But now your kingdom will not endure; the Lord has sought out a man after his own heart and appointed him leader of his people, because you have not kept the Lord's command."

[15]Then Samuel left Gilgal[f] and went up to Gibeah in Benjamin, and Saul counted the men who were with him. They numbered about six hundred.

truth or dare

Saul thought he had a legit reason for breaking God's rules. But sin is still sin. Your excuses or clever explanations for disobeying will *never* fly with God.

13:11–13

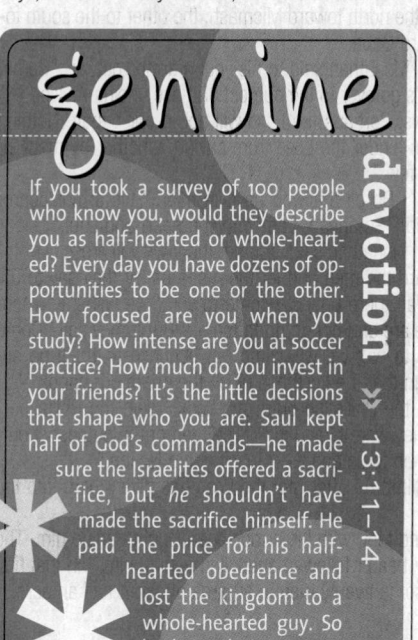

genuine devotion » 13:11–14

If you took a survey of 100 people who know you, would they describe you as half-hearted or whole-hearted? Every day you have dozens of opportunities to be one or the other. How focused are you when you study? How intense are you at soccer practice? How much do you invest in your friends? It's the little decisions that shape who you are. Saul kept half of God's commands—he made sure the Israelites offered a sacrifice, but *he* shouldn't have made the sacrifice himself. He paid the price for his half-hearted obedience and lost the kingdom to a whole-hearted guy. So back to that survey—which one are you?

---

[a] 1 A few late manuscripts of the Septuagint; Hebrew does not have *thirty*.   [b] 1 See the round number in Acts 13:21; Hebrew does not have *forty-*.   [c] 1,2 Or *and when he had reigned over Israel two years,* [2]*he*   [d] 5 Some Septuagint manuscripts and Syriac; Hebrew *thirty thousand*   [e] 9 Traditionally *peace offerings*   [f] 15 Hebrew; Septuagint *Gilgal and went his way; the rest of the people went after Saul to meet the army, and they went out of Gilgal*

Israel Without Weapons

[16]Saul and his son Jonathan and the men with them were staying in Gibeah[a] in Benjamin, while the Philistines camped at Micmash. [17]Raiding parties went out from the Philistine camp in three detachments. One turned toward Ophrah in the vicinity of Shual, [18]another toward Beth Horon, and the third toward the borderland overlooking the Valley of Zeboim facing the desert.

[19]Not a blacksmith could be found in the whole land of Israel, because the Philistines had said, "Otherwise the Hebrews will make swords or spears!" [20]So all Israel went down to the Philistines to have their plowshares, mattocks, axes and sickles[b] sharpened. [21]The price was two thirds of a shekel[c] for sharpening plowshares and mattocks, and a third of a shekel[d] for sharpening forks and axes and for repointing goads.

[22]So on the day of the battle not a soldier with Saul and Jonathan had a sword or spear in his hand; only Saul and his son Jonathan had them.

Jonathan Attacks the Philistines

14

[23]Now a detachment of Philistines had gone out to the pass at Micmash. [1]One day Jonathan son of Saul said to the young man bearing his armor, "Come, let's go over to the Philistine outpost on the other side." But he did not tell his father.

[2]Saul was staying on the outskirts of Gibeah under a pomegranate tree in Migron. With him were about six hundred men, [3]among whom was Ahijah, who was wearing an ephod. He was a son of Ichabod's brother Ahitub son of Phinehas, the son of Eli, the LORD's priest in Shiloh. No one was aware that Jonathan had left.

[4]On each side of the pass that Jonathan intended to cross to reach the Philistine outpost was a cliff; one was called Bozez, and the other Seneh. [5]One cliff stood to the north toward Micmash, the other to the south toward Geba.

[6]Jonathan said to his young armor-bearer, "Come, let's go over to the outpost of those uncircumcised fellows. Perhaps the LORD will act in our behalf. Nothing can hinder the LORD from saving, whether by many or by few."

[7]"Do all that you have in mind," his armor-bearer said. "Go ahead; I am with you heart and soul."

[8]Jonathan said, "Come, then; we will cross over toward the men and let them see us. [9]If they say to us, 'Wait there until we come to you,' we will stay where we are and not go up to them. [10]But if they say, 'Come up to us,' we will climb up, because that will be our sign that the LORD has given them into our hands."

truth or dare

The odds of two guys single-handedly thrashing an army outpost? Pretty slim. The odds that two faithful people fighting with God's strength can tackle any obstacle? Fantastic!

14:6

[11]So both of them showed themselves to the Philistine outpost. "Look!" said the Philistines. "The Hebrews are crawling out of the holes they were hiding in." [12]The men of the outpost shouted to Jonathan and his armor-bearer, "Come up to us and we'll teach you a lesson."

So Jonathan said to his armor-bearer, "Climb up after me; the LORD has given them into the hand of Israel."

[13]Jonathan climbed up, using his hands and feet, with his armor-bearer right behind him. The Philistines fell before Jonathan, and his armor-bearer followed and killed behind him. [14]In that first attack Jonathan and his armor-bearer killed some twenty men in an area of about half an acre.[e]

Israel Routs the Philistines

[15]Then panic struck the whole army—those in the camp and field, and those in the outposts and raiding parties—and the ground shook. It was a panic sent by God.[f]

[16]Saul's lookouts at Gibeah in Benjamin saw the army melting away in all directions. [17]Then Saul

a 16 Two Hebrew manuscripts; most Hebrew manuscripts *Geba,* a variant of *Gibeah* *b 20* Septuagint; Hebrew *plowshares* *c 21* Hebrew *pim;* that is, about 1/4 ounce (about 8 grams) *d 21* That is, about 1/8 ounce (about 4 grams) *e 14* Hebrew *half a yoke;* a "yoke" was the land plowed by a yoke of oxen in one day. *f 15* Or *a terrible panic* said to the men who were with him, "Muster the forces and see who has left us." When they did, it was Jonathan and his armor-bearer who were not there.

[18]Saul said to Ahijah, "Bring the ark of God." (At that time it was with the Israelites.)[a] [19]While Saul was talking to the priest, the tumult in the Philistine camp increased more and more. So Saul said to the priest, "Withdraw your hand."

[20]Then Saul and all his men assembled and went to the battle. They found the Philistines in total confusion, striking each other with their swords. [21]Those Hebrews who had previously been with the Philistines and had gone up with them to their camp went over to the Israelites who were with Saul and Jonathan. [22]When all the Israelites who had hidden in the hill country of Ephraim heard that the Philistines were on the run, they joined the battle in hot pursuit. [23]So the LORD rescued Israel that day, and the battle moved on beyond Beth Aven.

Jonathan Eats Honey

[24]Now the men of Israel were in distress that day, because Saul had bound the people under an oath, saying, "Cursed be any man who eats food before evening comes, before I have avenged myself on my enemies!" So none of the troops tasted food.

[25]The entire army[b] entered the woods, and there was honey on the ground. [26]When they went into the woods, they saw the honey oozing out, yet no one put his hand to his mouth, because they feared the oath. [27]But Jonathan had not heard that his father had bound the people with the oath, so he reached out the end of the staff that was in his hand and dipped it into the honeycomb. He raised his hand to his mouth, and his eyes brightened.[c] [28]Then one of the soldiers told him, "Your father bound the army under a strict oath, saying, 'Cursed be any man who eats food today!' That is why the men are faint."

[29]Jonathan said, "My father has made trouble for the country. See how my eyes brightened[d] when I tasted a little of this honey. [30]How much better it would have been if the men had eaten today some of the plunder they took from their enemies. Would not the slaughter of the Philistines have been even greater?"

[31]That day, after the Israelites had struck down the Philistines from Micmash to Aijalon, they were exhausted. [32]They pounced on the plunder and, taking sheep, cattle and calves, they butchered them on the ground and ate them, together with the blood. [33]Then someone said to Saul, "Look, the men are sinning against the LORD by eating meat that has blood in it."

"You have broken faith," he said. "Roll a large stone over here at once." [34]Then he said, "Go out among the men and tell them, 'Each of you bring me your cattle and sheep, and slaughter them here and eat them. Do not sin against the LORD by eating meat with blood still in it.' "

So everyone brought his ox that night and slaughtered it there. [35]Then Saul built an altar to the LORD; it was the first time he had done this.

[36]Saul said, "Let us go down after the Philistines by night and plunder them till dawn, and let us not leave one of them alive."

"Do whatever seems best to you," they replied.

But the priest said, "Let us inquire of God here."

[37]So Saul asked God, "Shall I go down after the Philistines? Will you give them into Israel's hand?" But God did not answer him that day.

[38]Saul therefore said, "Come here, all you who are leaders of the army, and let us find out what sin has been committed today. [39]As surely as the LORD who rescues Israel lives, even if it lies with my son Jonathan, he must die." But not one of the men said a word.

[40]Saul then said to all the Israelites, "You stand over there; I and Jonathan my son will stand over here."

"Do what seems best to you," the men replied.

truth or dare

Red alert! Mayday, Mayday! Bad move, Saul. Ask God's opinion first—not as a last resort.

14:36

[a] 18 Hebrew; Septuagint "Bring the ephod." (At that time he wore the ephod before the Israelites.)   [b] 25 Or Now all the people of the land   [c] 27 Or his strength was renewed   [d] 29 Or my strength was renewed

⁴¹Then Saul prayed to the Lord, the God of Israel, "Give me the right answer." ᵃ And Jonathan and Saul were taken by lot, and the men were cleared. ⁴²Saul said, "Cast the lot between me and Jonathan my son." And Jonathan was taken.

⁴³Then Saul said to Jonathan, "Tell me what you have done."

So Jonathan told him, "I merely tasted a little honey with the end of my staff. And now must I die?"

⁴⁴Saul said, "May God deal with me, be it ever so severely, if you do not die, Jonathan."

⁴⁵But the men said to Saul, "Should Jonathan die—he who has brought about this great deliverance in Israel? Never! As surely as the Lord lives, not a hair of his head will fall to the ground, for he did this today with God's help." So the men rescued Jonathan, and he was not put to death.

⁴⁶Then Saul stopped pursuing the Philistines, and they withdrew to their own land.

⁴⁷After Saul had assumed rule over Israel, he fought against their enemies on every side: Moab, the Ammonites, Edom, the kingsᵇ of Zobah, and the Philistines. Wherever he turned, he inflicted punishment on them. ᶜ ⁴⁸He fought valiantly and defeated the Amalekites, delivering Israel from the hands of those who had plundered them.

Saul's Family

⁴⁹Saul's sons were Jonathan, Ishvi and Malki-Shua. The name of his older daughter was Merab, and that of the younger was Michal. ⁵⁰His wife's name was Ahinoam daughter of Ahimaaz. The name of the commander of Saul's army was Abner son of Ner, and Ner was Saul's uncle. ⁵¹Saul's father Kish and Abner's father Ner were sons of Abiel.

⁵²All the days of Saul there was bitter war with the Philistines, and whenever Saul saw a mighty or brave man, he took him into his service.

The Lord Rejects Saul as King

15 Samuel said to Saul, "I am the one the Lord sent to anoint you king over his people Israel; so listen now to the message from the Lord. ²This is what the Lord Almighty says: 'I will punish the Amalekites for what they did to Israel when they waylaid them as they came up from Egypt. ³Now go, attack the Amalekites and totally destroyᵈ everything that belongs to them. Do not spare them; put to death men and women, children and infants, cattle and sheep, camels and donkeys.' "

⁴So Saul summoned the men and mustered them at Telaim—two hundred thousand foot soldiers and ten thousand men from Judah. ⁵Saul went to the city of Amalek and set an ambush in the ravine. ⁶Then he said to the Kenites, "Go away, leave the Amalekites so that I do not destroy you along with them; for you showed kindness to all the Israelites when they came up out of Egypt." So the Kenites moved away from the Amalekites.

⁷Then Saul attacked the Amalekites all the way from Havilah to Shur, to the east of Egypt. ⁸He took Agag king of the Amalekites alive, and all his people he totally destroyed with the sword. ⁹But Saul and the army spared Agag and the best of the sheep and cattle, the fat calvesᵉ and lambs—everything that was good. These they were unwilling to destroy completely, but everything that was despised and weak they totally destroyed.

¹⁰Then the word of the Lord came to Samuel: ¹¹"I am grieved that I have made Saul king, because he has turned away from me and has not carried out my instructions." Samuel was troubled, and he cried out to the Lord all that night.

¹²Early in the morning Samuel got up and went to meet Saul, but he was told, "Saul has gone to Carmel. There he has set up a monument in his own honor and has turned and gone on down to Gilgal."

¹³When Samuel reached him, Saul said, "The Lord bless you! I have carried out the Lord's instructions."

¹⁴But Samuel said, "What then is this bleating of sheep in my ears? What is this lowing of cattle that I hear?"

ᵃ 41 Hebrew; Septuagint "Why have you not answered your servant today? If the fault is in me or my son Jonathan, respond with Urim, but if the men of Israel are at fault, respond with Thummim."   ᵇ 47 Masoretic Text; Dead Sea Scrolls and Septuagint king   ᶜ 47 Hebrew; Septuagint he was victorious   ᵈ 3 The Hebrew term refers to the irrevocable giving over of things or persons to the Lord, often by totally destroying them; also in verses 8, 9, 15, 18, 20 and 21.   ᵉ 9 Or the grown bulls; the meaning of the Hebrew for this phrase is uncertain.

genuine

obedience » 15:17-23

Welcome to Celebrity Challenge! Today's contestant is King Saul. Okay, Saul (can we call you Saul?), you have two options: You can either disobey God a teeny little bit but give him enormous offerings OR you can be plain old obedient and destroy everything like God told you. Which one makes God happy? Hmmm . . . need another example? Okay, you can either make money dishonestly yet give God a fat tithe OR you can live a life of integrity and give him what little you have. Which one will you choose?

[15]Saul answered, "The soldiers brought them from the Amalekites; they spared the best of the sheep and cattle to sacrifice to the LORD your God, but we totally destroyed the rest."

[16]"Stop!" Samuel said to Saul. "Let me tell you what the LORD said to me last night."

"Tell me," Saul replied.

[17]Samuel said, "Although you were once small in your own eyes, did you not become the head of the tribes of Israel? The LORD anointed you king over Israel. [18]And he sent you on a mission, saying, 'Go and completely destroy those wicked people, the Amalekites; make war on them until you have wiped them out.' [19]Why did you not obey the LORD? Why did you pounce on the plunder and do evil in the eyes of the LORD?"

[20]"But I did obey the LORD," Saul said. "I went on the mission the LORD assigned me. I completely destroyed the Amalekites and brought back Agag their king. [21]The soldiers took sheep and cattle from the plunder, the best of what was devoted to God, in order to sacrifice them to the LORD your God at Gilgal."

[22]But Samuel replied:

"Does the LORD delight in burnt offerings and sacrifices
as much as in obeying the voice of the LORD?
To obey is better than sacrifice,
and to heed is better than the fat of rams.
[23]For rebellion is like the sin of divination,
and arrogance like the evil of idolatry.
Because you have rejected the word of the LORD,
he has rejected you as king."

[24]Then Saul said to Samuel, "I have sinned. I violated the LORD's command and your instructions. I was afraid of the people and so I gave in to them. [25]Now I beg you, forgive my sin and come back with me, so that I may worship the LORD."

[26]But Samuel said to him, "I will not go back with you. You have rejected the word of the LORD, and the LORD has rejected you as king over Israel!"

[27]As Samuel turned to leave, Saul caught hold of the hem of his robe, and it tore. [28]Samuel said to him, "The LORD has torn the kingdom of Israel from you today and has given it to one of your neighbors—to one better than you. [29]He who is the Glory of Israel does not lie or change his mind; for he is not a man, that he should change his mind."

[30]Saul replied, "I have sinned. But please honor me before the elders of my people and before Israel; come back with me, so that I may worship the LORD your God." [31]So Samuel went back with Saul, and Saul worshiped the LORD.

[32]Then Samuel said, "Bring me Agag king of the Amalekites."

Agag came to him confidently,[a] thinking, "Surely the bitterness of death is past."

[33]But Samuel said,

"As your sword has made women childless,
so will your mother be childless among women."

a 32 Or him trembling, yet

And Samuel put Agag to death before the Lord at Gilgal.

[34]Then Samuel left for Ramah, but Saul went up to his home in Gibeah of Saul. [35]Until the day Samuel died, he did not go to see Saul again, though Samuel mourned for him. And the Lord was grieved that he had made Saul king over Israel.

Samuel Anoints David

16 The Lord said to Samuel, "How long will you mourn for Saul, since I have rejected him as king over Israel? Fill your horn with oil and be on your way; I am sending you to Jesse of Bethlehem. I have chosen one of his sons to be king."

[2]But Samuel said, "How can I go? Saul will hear about it and kill me."

genuine *worth » 16:1-13*

How do you measure your worth? Popularity? Academic success? Looks? Sometimes we feel worthless because we don't have what others seem to value most. God searched for a king to take Saul's place. He sent the prophet Samuel to anoint a king from among the eight sons of Jesse. But he wasn't looking for the handsomest, the tallest, the strongest, the smartest or the oldest. He chose David based on the beauty of his heart. A heart that totally seeks God has true worth in his eyes.

The Lord said, "Take a heifer with you and say, 'I have come to sacrifice to the Lord.' [3]Invite Jesse to the sacrifice, and I will show you what to do. You are to anoint for me the one I indicate."

[4]Samuel did what the Lord said. When he arrived at Bethlehem, the elders of the town trembled when they met him. They asked, "Do you come in peace?"

[5]Samuel replied, "Yes, in peace; I have come to sacrifice to the Lord. Consecrate yourselves and come to the sacrifice with me." Then he consecrated Jesse and his sons and invited them to the sacrifice.

[6]When they arrived, Samuel saw Eliab and thought, "Surely the Lord's anointed stands here before the Lord."

[7]But the Lord said to Samuel, "Do not consider his appearance or his height, for I have rejected him. The Lord does not look at the things man looks at. Man looks at the outward appearance, but the Lord looks at the heart."

[8]Then Jesse called Abinadab and had him pass in front of Samuel. But Samuel said, "The Lord has not chosen this one either." [9]Jesse then had Shammah pass by, but Samuel said, "Nor has the Lord chosen this one." [10]Jesse had seven of his sons pass before Samuel, but Samuel said to him, "The Lord has not chosen these." [11]So he asked Jesse, "Are these all the sons you have?"

"There is still the youngest," Jesse answered, "but he is tending the sheep."

Samuel said, "Send for him; we will not sit down[a] until he arrives."

[12]So he sent and had him brought in. He was ruddy, with a fine appearance and handsome features.

Then the Lord said, "Rise and anoint him; he is the one."

[13]So Samuel took the horn of oil and anointed him in the presence of his brothers, and from that day on the Spirit of the Lord came upon David in power. Samuel then went to Ramah.

David in Saul's Service

[14]Now the Spirit of the Lord had departed from Saul, and an evil[b] spirit from the Lord tormented him.

[15]Saul's attendants said to him, "See, an evil spirit from God is tormenting you. [16]Let our lord command his servants here to search for someone who can play the harp. He will play when the evil spirit from God comes upon you, and you will feel better."

[a] 11 Some Septuagint manuscripts; Hebrew *not gather around*   [b] 14 Or *injurious*; also in verses 15, 16 and 23

¹⁷So Saul said to his attendants, "Find someone who plays well and bring him to me."

¹⁸One of the servants answered, "I have seen a son of Jesse of Bethlehem who knows how to play the harp. He is a brave man and a warrior. He speaks well and is a fine-looking man. And the LORD is with him."

¹⁹Then Saul sent messengers to Jesse and said, "Send me your son David, who is with the sheep." ²⁰So Jesse took a donkey loaded with bread, a skin of wine and a young goat and sent them with his son David to Saul.

²¹David came to Saul and entered his service. Saul liked him very much, and David became one of his armor-bearers. ²²Then Saul sent word to Jesse, saying, "Allow David to remain in my service, for I am pleased with him."

²³Whenever the spirit from God came upon Saul, David would take his harp and play. Then relief would come to Saul; he would feel better, and the evil spirit would leave him.

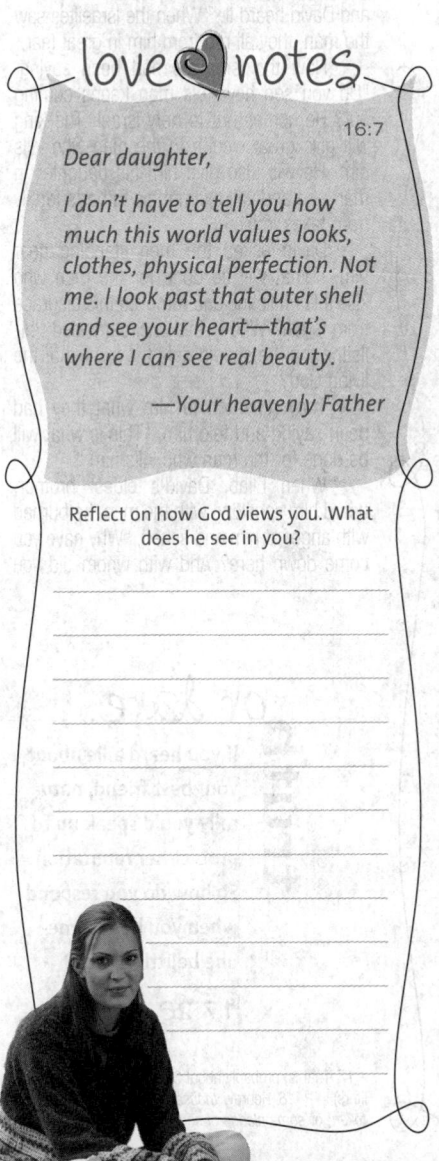

love notes

16:7

Dear daughter,

I don't have to tell you how much this world values looks, clothes, physical perfection. Not me. I look past that outer shell and see your heart—that's where I can see real beauty.

—Your heavenly Father

Reflect on how God views you. What does he see in you?

David and Goliath

17 Now the Philistines gathered their forces for war and assembled at Socoh in Judah. They pitched camp at Ephes Dammim, between Socoh and Azekah. ²Saul and the Israelites assembled and camped in the Valley of Elah and drew up their battle line to meet the Philistines. ³The Philistines occupied one hill and the Israelites another, with the valley between them.

⁴A champion named Goliath, who was from Gath, came out of the Philistine camp. He was over nine feet*ᵃ* tall. ⁵He had a bronze helmet on his head and wore a coat of scale armor of bronze weighing five thousand shekels*ᵇ*; ⁶on his legs he wore bronze greaves, and a bronze javelin was slung on his back. ⁷His spear shaft was like a weaver's rod, and its iron point weighed six hundred shekels.*ᶜ* His shield bearer went ahead of him.

⁸Goliath stood and shouted to the ranks of Israel, "Why do you come out and line up for battle? Am I not a Philistine, and are you not the servants of Saul? Choose a man and have him come down to me. ⁹If he is able to fight and kill me, we will become your subjects; but if I overcome him and kill him, you will become our subjects and serve us." ¹⁰Then the Philistine said, "This day I defy the ranks of Israel! Give me a man and let us fight each other." ¹¹On hearing the Philistine's words, Saul and all the Israelites were dismayed and terrified.

¹²Now David was the son of an Ephrathite named Jesse, who was from Bethlehem in Judah. Jesse had eight sons, and in Saul's time he was old and well advanced in

ᵃ 4 Hebrew was six cubits and a span (about 3 meters) ᵇ 5 That is, about 125 pounds (about 57 kilograms) ᶜ 7 That is, about 15 pounds (about 7 kilograms) years. ¹³Jesse's three oldest sons had followed Saul to the war: The firstborn was Eliab; the second, Abinadab; and the third, Shammah. ¹⁴David was the youngest. The three oldest followed Saul, ¹⁵but David went back and forth from Saul to tend his father's sheep at Bethlehem.

¹⁶For forty days the Philistine came forward every morning and evening and took his stand.

¹⁷Now Jesse said to his son David, "Take this ephah *ᵃ* of roasted grain and these ten loaves of bread for your brothers and hurry to their camp. ¹⁸Take along these ten cheeses to the commander of their unit. *ᵇ* See how your brothers are and bring back some assurance *ᶜ* from them. ¹⁹They are with Saul and all the men of Israel in the Valley of Elah, fighting against the Philistines."

²⁰Early in the morning David left the flock with a shepherd, loaded up and set out, as Jesse had directed. He reached the camp as the army was going out to its battle positions, shouting the war cry. ²¹Israel and the Philistines were drawing up their lines facing each other. ²²David left his things with the keeper of supplies, ran to the battle lines and greeted his brothers. ²³As he was talking with them, Goliath, the Philistine champion from Gath, stepped out from his lines and shouted his usual defiance, and David heard it. ²⁴When the Israelites saw the man, they all ran from him in great fear.

²⁵Now the Israelites had been saying, "Do you see how this man keeps coming out? He comes out to defy Israel. The king will give great wealth to the man who kills him. He will also give him his daughter in marriage and will exempt his father's family from taxes in Israel."

²⁶David asked the men standing near him, "What will be done for the man who kills this Philistine and removes this disgrace from Israel? Who is this uncircumcised Philistine that he should defy the armies of the living God?"

²⁷They repeated to him what they had been saying and told him, "This is what will be done for the man who kills him."

²⁸When Eliab, David's oldest brother, heard him speaking with the men, he burned with anger at him and asked, "Why have you come down here? And with whom did you

love ♥ notes

17:28–32

My child,

When you are stopped by criticism or discouraged by negative comments, remember David. He ignored his detractors and focused on doing what was right in my sight. I love it when you choose my opinion over the opinion of others!

The One whose opinion counts

When have you chosen pleasing God over pleasing someone else? What happened?

_____

_____

_____

_____

_____

_____

_____

_____

truth or dare

If you heard a lie about your best friend, naturally you'd speak up to protect her reputation. So how do you respond when you hear someone belittling God?

17:26

ᵃ 17 That is, probably about 3/5 bushel (about 22 liters)   *ᵇ 18* Hebrew *thousand*   *ᶜ 18* Or *some token*; or *some pledge of spoils*

leave those few sheep in the desert? I know how conceited you are and how wicked your heart is; you came down only to watch the battle."

²⁹"Now what have I done?" said David. "Can't I even speak?" ³⁰He then turned away to someone else and brought up the same matter, and the men answered him as before. ³¹What David said was overheard and reported to Saul, and Saul sent for him.

³²David said to Saul, "Let no one lose heart on account of this Philistine; your servant will go and fight him."

³³Saul replied, "You are not able to go out against this Philistine and fight him; you are only a boy, and he has been a fighting man from his youth."

³⁴But David said to Saul, "Your servant has been keeping his father's sheep. When a lion or a bear came and carried off a sheep from the flock, ³⁵I went after it, struck it and rescued the sheep from its mouth. When it turned on me, I seized it by its hair, struck it and killed it. ³⁶Your servant has killed both the lion and the bear; this uncircumcised Philistine will be like one of them, because he has defied the armies of the living God. ³⁷The LORD who delivered me from the paw of the lion and the paw of the bear will deliver me from the hand of this Philistine."

Saul said to David, "Go, and the LORD be with you."

³⁸Then Saul dressed David in his own tunic. He put a coat of armor on him and a bronze helmet on his head. ³⁹David fastened on his sword over the tunic and tried walking around, because he was not used to them.

"I cannot go in these," he said to Saul, "because I am not used to them." So he took them off. ⁴⁰Then he took his staff in his hand, chose five smooth stones from the stream, put them in the pouch of his shepherd's bag and, with his sling in his hand, approached the Philistine.

⁴¹Meanwhile, the Philistine, with his shield bearer in front of him, kept coming closer to David. ⁴²He looked David over and saw that he was only a boy, ruddy and handsome, and he despised him. ⁴³He said to David, "Am I a dog, that you come at me with sticks?" And the Philistine cursed David by his gods. ⁴⁴"Come here," he said, "and I'll give your flesh to the birds of the air and the beasts of the field!"

⁴⁵David said to the Philistine, "You come against me with sword and spear and javelin, but I come against you in the name of the LORD Almighty, the God of the armies of Israel, whom you have defied. ⁴⁶This day the LORD will hand you over to me, and I'll strike you down and cut off your head. Today I will give the carcasses of the Philistine army to the birds of the air and the beasts of the earth, and the whole world will know that there is a God in Israel. ⁴⁷All those gathered here will know that it is not by sword or spear that the LORD saves; for the battle is the LORD's, and he will give all of you into our hands."

⁴⁸As the Philistine moved closer to attack him, David ran quickly toward the battle line to meet him. ⁴⁹Reaching into his bag and taking out a stone, he slung it and struck the Philistine on the forehead. The stone sank into his forehead, and he fell facedown on the ground.

⁵⁰So David triumphed over the Philistine with a sling and a stone; without a sword in his hand he struck down the Philistine and killed him.

⁵¹David ran and stood over him. He took hold of the Philistine's sword and drew it from the scabbard. After he killed him, he cut off his head with the sword.

When the Philistines saw that their hero was dead, they turned and ran. ⁵²Then the men of Israel and Judah surged forward with a shout and pursued the Philistines to the entrance of Gath ᵃ and to the gates of Ekron. Their dead were strewn along the Shaaraim road to Gath and Ekron. ⁵³When the Israelites returned from chasing the Philistines, they plundered their camp. ⁵⁴David took the Philistine's head and brought it to Jerusalem, and he put the Philistine's weapons in his own tent.

⁵⁵As Saul watched David going out to meet the Philistine, he said to Abner, commander of the army, "Abner, whose son is that young man?"

Abner replied, "As surely as you live, O king, I don't know."

⁵⁶The king said, "Find out whose son this young man is."

⁵⁷As soon as David returned from killing the Philistine, Abner took him and brought him before Saul, with David still holding the Philistine's head.

⁵⁸"Whose son are you, young man?" Saul asked him.

David said, "I am the son of your servant Jesse of Bethlehem."

ᵃ 52 Some Septuagint manuscripts; Hebrew a valley

Saul's Jealousy of David

18 After David had finished talking with Saul, Jonathan became one in spirit with David, and he loved him as himself. ²From that day Saul kept David with him and did not let him return to his father's house. ³And Jonathan made a covenant with David because he loved him as himself. ⁴Jonathan took off the robe he was wearing and gave it to David, along with his tunic, and even his sword, his bow and his belt.

⁵Whatever Saul sent him to do, David did it so successfully *a* that Saul gave him a high rank in the army. This pleased all the people, and Saul's officers as well.

genuine
friendship »

Who are your true-blue, stick-to-ya-like-glue friends? Is your friendship like Jonathan and David's? These two had the kind of friendship that everyone seeks. Both were willing to do anything for the other. They had a "what's mine is yours" attitude. They even promised to look out for each other's families. A genuine friend is loyal and seeks to serve; she doesn't just seek to *be* served. Would your friends say that you're that kind of friend?

18:1–3

⁶When the men were returning home after David had killed the Philistine, the women came out from all the towns of Israel to meet King Saul with singing and dancing, with joyful songs and with tambourines and lutes. ⁷As they danced, they sang:

"Saul has slain his thousands,
and David his tens of
thousands."

⁸Saul was very angry; this refrain galled him. "They have credited David with tens of thousands," he thought, "but me with only thousands. What more can he get but the kingdom?" ⁹And from that time on Saul kept a jealous eye on David.

¹⁰The next day an evil *b* spirit from God came forcefully upon Saul. He was prophesying in his house, while David was playing the harp, as he usually did. Saul had a spear in his hand ¹¹and he hurled it, saying to himself, "I'll pin David to the wall." But David eluded him twice.

¹²Saul was afraid of David, because the LORD was with David but had left Saul. ¹³So he sent David away from him and gave him command over a thousand men, and David led the troops in their campaigns. ¹⁴In everything he did he had great success, *c* because the LORD was with him. ¹⁵When Saul saw how successful *d* he was, he was afraid of him. ¹⁶But all Israel and Judah loved David, because he led them in their campaigns.

¹⁷Saul said to David, "Here is my older daughter Merab. I will give her to you in marriage; only serve me bravely and fight the battles of the LORD." For Saul said to himself, "I will not raise a hand against him. Let the Philistines do that!"

¹⁸But David said to Saul, "Who am I, and what is my family or my father's clan in Israel, that I should become the king's son-in-law?" ¹⁹So *e* when the time came for Merab, Saul's daughter, to be given to David, she was given in marriage to Adriel of Meholah.

²⁰Now Saul's daughter Michal was in love with David, and when they told Saul about it, he was pleased. ²¹"I will give her to him," he thought, "so that she may be a snare to him and so that the hand of the Philistines may be against him." So Saul said

truth or dare

Do you compare your "good deeds" to other people's? Like Saul, don't rob yourself of joy by falling in the jealousy trap.

18:6–9

a 5 Or *wisely*   *b 10* Or *injurious*   *c 14* Or *he was very wise*   *d 15* Or *wise*   *e 19* Or *However,*

truth or dare

Girls sometimes think that "making it" in life means achieving everything *by themselves.* Want to know the real secret of success? David was devoted to God; and God was *with him.*

18:14

to David, "Now you have a second opportunity to become my son-in-law."

²²Then Saul ordered his attendants: "Speak to David privately and say, 'Look, the king is pleased with you, and his attendants all like you; now become his son-in-law.' "

²³They repeated these words to David. But David said, "Do you think it is a small matter to become the king's son-in-law? I'm only a poor man and little known."

²⁴When Saul's servants told him what David had said, ²⁵Saul replied, "Say to David, 'The king wants no other price for the bride than a hundred Philistine foreskins, to take revenge on his enemies.' " Saul's plan was to have David fall by the hands of the Philistines.

²⁶When the attendants told David these things, he was pleased to become the king's son-in-law. So before the allotted time elapsed, ²⁷David and his men went out and killed two hundred Philistines. He brought their foreskins and presented the full number to the king so that he might become the king's son-in-law. Then Saul gave him his daughter Michal in marriage.

²⁸When Saul realized that the LORD was with David and that his daughter Michal loved David, ²⁹Saul became still more afraid of him, and he remained his enemy the rest of his days.

³⁰The Philistine commanders continued to go out to battle, and as often as they did, David met with more success *a* than the rest of Saul's officers, and his name became well known.

Saul Tries to Kill David

19 Saul told his son Jonathan and all the attendants to kill David. But Jonathan was very fond of David ²and warned him, "My father Saul is looking for a chance to kill you. Be on your guard tomorrow morning; go into hiding and stay there. ³I will go out and stand with my father in the field where you are. I'll speak to him about you and will tell you what I find out."

⁴Jonathan spoke well of David to Saul his father and said to him, "Let not the king do wrong to his servant David; he has not wronged you, and what he has done has benefited you greatly. ⁵He took his life in his hands when he killed the Philistine. The LORD won a great victory for all Israel, and you saw it and were glad. Why then would you do wrong to an innocent man like David by killing him for no reason?"

⁶Saul listened to Jonathan and took this oath: "As surely as the LORD lives, David will not be put to death."

⁷So Jonathan called David and told him the whole conversation. He brought him to Saul, and David was with Saul as before.

⁸Once more war broke out, and David went out and fought the Philistines. He struck them with such force that they fled before him.

⁹But an evil *b* spirit from the LORD came upon Saul as he was sitting in his house with his spear in his hand. While David was playing the harp, ¹⁰Saul tried to pin him to the wall with his spear, but David eluded him as Saul drove the spear into the wall. That night David made good his escape.

¹¹Saul sent men to David's house to watch it and to kill him in the morning. But Michal, David's wife, warned him, "If you don't run for your life tonight, tomorrow you'll be killed." ¹²So Michal let David down through a window, and he fled and escaped. ¹³Then Michal took an idol *c* and laid it on the bed, covering it with a garment and putting some goats' hair at the head.

¹⁴When Saul sent the men to capture David, Michal said, "He is ill."

¹⁵Then Saul sent the men back to see David and told them, "Bring him up to me in his bed so that I may kill him." ¹⁶But when the men entered, there was the idol in the bed, and at the head was some goats' hair.

---

a 30 Or *David acted more wisely* *b 9* Or *injurious* *c 13* Hebrew *teraphim*; also in verse 16

¹⁷Saul said to Michal, "Why did you deceive me like this and send my enemy away so that he escaped?"

Michal told him, "He said to me, 'Let me get away. Why should I kill you?' "

¹⁸When David had fled and made his escape, he went to Samuel at Ramah and told him all that Saul had done to him. Then he and Samuel went to Naioth and stayed there. ¹⁹Word came to Saul: "David is in Naioth at Ramah"; ²⁰so he sent men to capture him. But when they saw a group of prophets prophesying, with Samuel standing there as their leader, the Spirit of God came upon Saul's men and they also prophesied. ²¹Saul was told about it, and he sent more men, and they prophesied too. Saul sent men a third time, and they also prophesied. ²²Finally, he himself left for Ramah and went to the great cistern at Secu. And he asked, "Where are Samuel and David?"

"Over in Naioth at Ramah," they said.

²³So Saul went to Naioth at Ramah. But the Spirit of God came even upon him, and he walked along prophesying until he came to Naioth. ²⁴He stripped off his robes and also prophesied in Samuel's presence. He lay that way all that day and night. This is why people say, "Is Saul also among the prophets?"

David and Jonathan

20 Then David fled from Naioth at Ramah and went to Jonathan and asked, "What have I done? What is my crime? How have I wronged your father, that he is trying to take my life?"

²"Never!" Jonathan replied. "You are not going to die! Look, my father doesn't do anything, great or small, without confiding in me. Why would he hide this from me? It's not so!"

³But David took an oath and said, "Your father knows very well that I have found favor in your eyes, and he has said to himself, 'Jonathan must not know this or he will be grieved.' Yet as surely as the Lord lives and as you live, there is only a step between me and death."

⁴Jonathan said to David, "Whatever you want me to do, I'll do for you."

⁵So David said, "Look, tomorrow is the New Moon festival, and I am supposed to dine with the king; but let me go and hide in the field until the evening of the day after tomorrow. ⁶If your father misses me at all, tell him, 'David earnestly asked my permission to hurry to Bethlehem, his hometown, because an annual sacrifice is being made there for his whole clan.' ⁷If he says, 'Very well,' then your servant is safe. But if he loses his temper, you can be sure that he is determined to harm me. ⁸As for you, show kindness to your servant, for you have brought him into a covenant with you before the Lord. If I am guilty, then kill me yourself! Why hand me over to your father?"

⁹"Never!" Jonathan said. "If I had the least inkling that my father was determined to harm you, wouldn't I tell you?"

¹⁰David asked, "Who will tell me if your father answers you harshly?"

¹¹"Come," Jonathan said, "let's go out into the field." So they went there together.

¹²Then Jonathan said to David: "By the Lord, the God of Israel, I will surely sound out my father by this time the day after tomorrow! If he is favorably disposed toward you, will I not send you word and let you know? ¹³But if my father is inclined to harm you, may the Lord deal with me, be it ever so severely, if I do not let you know and send you away safely. May the Lord be with you as he has been with my father. ¹⁴But show me unfailing kindness like that of the Lord as long as I live, so that I may not be killed, ¹⁵and do not ever cut off your kindness from my family—not even when the Lord has cut off every one of David's enemies from the face of the earth."

¹⁶So Jonathan made a covenant with the house of David, saying, "May the Lord call David's enemies to account." ¹⁷And Jonathan had David reaffirm his oath out of love for him, because he loved him as he loved himself.

¹⁸Then Jonathan said to David: "Tomorrow is the New Moon festival. You will be missed, because your seat will be empty. ¹⁹The day after tomorrow, toward evening, go to the place where

truth or dare

Hmmm . . . can we learn the secret to lasting friendship by watching two of the closest friends of all time? Hint: Do you love your friends as much as you love yourself?

20:17

you hid when this trouble began, and wait by the stone Ezel. ²⁰I will shoot three arrows to the side of it, as though I were shooting at a target. ²¹Then I will send a boy and say, 'Go, find the arrows.' If I say to him, 'Look, the arrows are on this side of you; bring them here,' then come, because, as surely as the LORD lives, you are safe; there is no danger. ²²But if I say to the boy, 'Look, the arrows are beyond you,' then you must go, because the LORD has sent you away. ²³And about the matter you and I discussed—remember, the LORD is witness between you and me forever."

²⁴So David hid in the field, and when the New Moon festival came, the king sat down to eat. ²⁵He sat in his customary place by the wall, opposite Jonathan,^a and Abner sat next to Saul, but David's place was empty. ²⁶Saul said nothing that day, for he thought, "Something must have happened to David to make him ceremonially unclean—surely he is unclean." ²⁷But the next day, the second day of the month, David's place was empty again. Then Saul said to his son Jonathan, "Why hasn't the son of Jesse come to the meal, either yesterday or today?"

²⁸Jonathan answered, "David earnestly asked me for permission to go to Bethlehem. ²⁹He said, 'Let me go, because our family is observing a sacrifice in the town and my brother has ordered me to be there. If I have found favor in your eyes, let me get away to see my brothers.' That is why he has not come to the king's table."

³⁰Saul's anger flared up at Jonathan and he said to him, "You son of a perverse and rebellious woman! Don't I know that you have sided with the son of Jesse to your own shame and to the shame of the mother who bore you? ³¹As long as the son of Jesse lives on this earth, neither you nor your kingdom will be established. Now send and bring him to me, for he must die!"

³²"Why should he be put to death? What has he done?" Jonathan asked his father. ³³But Saul hurled his spear at him to kill him. Then Jonathan knew that his father intended to kill David.

³⁴Jonathan got up from the table in fierce anger; on that second day of the month he did not eat, because he was grieved at his father's shameful treatment of David.

³⁵In the morning Jonathan went out to the field for his meeting with David. He had a small boy with him, ³⁶and he said to the boy, "Run and find the arrows I shoot." As the boy ran, he shot an arrow beyond him. ³⁷When the boy came to the place where Jonathan's arrow had fallen, Jonathan called out after him, "Isn't the arrow beyond you?" ³⁸Then he shouted, "Hurry! Go quickly! Don't stop!" The boy picked up the arrow and returned to his master. ³⁹(The boy knew nothing of all this; only Jonathan and David knew.) ⁴⁰Then Jonathan gave his weapons to the boy and said, "Go, carry them back to town."

⁴¹After the boy had gone, David got up from the south side ∟of the stone⌐ and bowed down before Jonathan three times, with his face to the ground. Then they kissed each other and wept together—but David wept the most.

⁴²Jonathan said to David, "Go in peace, for we have sworn friendship with each other in the name of the LORD, saying, 'The LORD is witness between you and me, and between your descendants and my descendants forever.' " Then David left, and Jonathan went back to the town.

David at Nob

21 David went to Nob, to Ahimelech the priest. Ahimelech trembled when he met him, and asked, "Why are you alone? Why is no one with you?"

²David answered Ahimelech the priest, "The king charged me with a certain matter and said to me, 'No one is to know anything about your mission and your instructions.' As for my men, I have told them to meet me at a certain place. ³Now then, what do you have on hand? Give me five loaves of bread, or whatever you can find."

⁴But the priest answered David, "I don't have any ordinary bread on hand; however, there is some consecrated bread here—provided the men have kept themselves from women."

⁵David replied, "Indeed women have been kept from us, as usual whenever^b I set out. The men's things^c are holy even on missions that are not holy. How much more so today!" ⁶So the priest gave him the consecrated bread, since there was no bread there except the bread of the Presence that had been removed from before the LORD and replaced by hot bread on the day it was taken away.

⁷Now one of Saul's servants was there that day, detained before the LORD; he was Doeg the Edomite, Saul's head shepherd.

Not Good Enough

One more college rejection letter. One more, *Dear Nikki: We are sorry to inform you that you have not been accepted . . .* and I'll scream. I'm beginning to think I might be flipping burgers for the rest of my life. Hey, at least I'd always get free food . . .

But seriously, what if I never make it to college? I'm at a grand total of four rejection letters, with only one more college to hear back from. It's embarrassing. And it's not like I applied to all Ivy League schools or anything. Plus, since my older brother and sister went to college, I just might become the black sheep of the family. I think I better give up on my idea of being a veterinarian. Sure, I love animals, but no one wants a vet without a decent GPA or good test scores. I don't have what it takes.

Today in orchestra, this girl Kia announced that she got accepted to Stanford. Then our teacher asked who knows where they're headed for college next year. I lowered my head and acted suddenly very interested in my cello strings. I just sat there quietly, staring down at Kia's chunky-heeled boots, hoping no one would ask me directly.

I've always been told that God has a plan for our lives—where we'll live, who we'll marry and stuff like that. But I have to wonder if God has a plan for me—and if so, why he insists on keeping it such a secret from me.

For more encouragement, check out the link on www.TrueImagesBible.com

future in focus

Tough times for Nikki—and all the girls out there who feel like they don't measure up. If you find yourself doubting your abilities, remember a scrawny shepherd boy named David. If you'd asked David about his career plans, he'd have probably thought he'd be tending sheep for a few decades. But not so. God had other plans for him. That's because God looks at the heart—not the way things appear (see 1 Samuel 16:7, page 340). The truth is that God wants more for us than we even want for ourselves. Hard to believe—we want a lot, don't we? But God has our best interests at heart.

For more on this topic, see the index on page 1656.

[8]David asked Ahimelech, "Don't you have a spear or a sword here? I haven't brought my sword or any other weapon, because the king's business was urgent."

[9]The priest replied, "The sword of Goliath the Philistine, whom you killed in the Valley of Elah, is here; it is wrapped in a cloth behind the ephod. If you want it, take it; there is no sword here but that one."

David said, "There is none like it; give it to me."

David at Gath

[10]That day David fled from Saul and went to Achish king of Gath. [11]But the servants of Achish said to him, "Isn't this David, the king of the land? Isn't he the one they sing about in their dances:

> " 'Saul has slain his thousands,
> and David his tens of thousands'?"

¹²David took these words to heart and was very much afraid of Achish king of Gath. ¹³So he pretended to be insane in their presence; and while he was in their hands he acted like a madman, making marks on the doors of the gate and letting saliva run down his beard.

¹⁴Achish said to his servants, "Look at the man! He is insane! Why bring him to me? ¹⁵Am I so short of madmen that you have to bring this fellow here to carry on like this in front of me? Must this man come into my house?"

David at Adullam and Mizpah

22 David left Gath and escaped to the cave of Adullam. When his brothers and his father's household heard about it, they went down to him there. ²All those who were in distress or in debt or discontented gathered around him, and he became their leader. About four hundred men were with him.

³From there David went to Mizpah in Moab and said to the king of Moab, "Would you let my father and mother come and stay with you until I learn what God will do for me?" ⁴So he left them with the king of Moab, and they stayed with him as long as David was in the stronghold.

⁵But the prophet Gad said to David, "Do not stay in the stronghold. Go into the land of Judah." So David left and went to the forest of Hereth.

Saul Kills the Priests of Nob

⁶Now Saul heard that David and his men had been discovered. And Saul, spear in hand, was seated under the tamarisk tree on the hill at Gibeah, with all his officials standing around him. ⁷Saul said to them, "Listen, men of Benjamin! Will the son of Jesse give all of you fields and vineyards? Will he make all of you commanders of thousands and commanders of hundreds? ⁸Is that why you have all conspired against me? No one tells me when my son makes a covenant with the son of Jesse. None of you is concerned about me or tells me that my son has incited my servant to lie in wait for me, as he does today."

⁹But Doeg the Edomite, who was standing with Saul's officials, said, "I saw the son of Jesse come to Ahimelech son of Ahitub at Nob. ¹⁰Ahimelech inquired of the LORD for him; he also gave him provisions and the sword of Goliath the Philistine."

¹¹Then the king sent for the priest Ahimelech son of Ahitub and his father's whole family, who were the priests at Nob, and they all came to the king. ¹²Saul said, "Listen now, son of Ahitub."

"Yes, my lord," he answered.

¹³Saul said to him, "Why have you conspired against me, you and the son of Jesse, giving him bread and a sword and inquiring of God for him, so that he has rebelled against me and lies in wait for me, as he does today?"

¹⁴Ahimelech answered the king, "Who of all your servants is as loyal as David, the king's son-in-law, captain of your bodyguard and highly respected in your household? ¹⁵Was that day the first time I inquired of God for him? Of course not! Let not the king accuse your servant or any of his father's family, for your servant knows nothing at all about this whole affair."

¹⁶But the king said, "You will surely die, Ahimelech, you and your father's whole family."

¹⁷Then the king ordered the guards at his side: "Turn and kill the priests of the LORD, because they too have sided with David. They knew he was fleeing, yet they did not tell me."

But the king's officials were not willing to raise a hand to strike the priests of the LORD.

¹⁸The king then ordered Doeg, "You turn and strike down the priests." So Doeg the Edomite turned and struck them down. That day he killed eighty-five men who wore the linen ephod. ¹⁹He also put to the sword Nob, the town of the priests, with its men and women, its children and infants, and its cattle, donkeys and sheep.

²⁰But Abiathar, a son of Ahimelech son of Ahitub, escaped and fled to join David. ²¹He told David that Saul had killed the priests of the LORD. ²²Then David said to Abiathar: "That day, when Doeg the Edomite was there, I knew he would be sure to tell Saul. I am responsible for the death of your father's whole family. ²³Stay with me; don't be afraid; the man who is seeking your life is seeking mine also. You will be safe with me."

David Saves Keilah

23 When David was told, "Look, the Philistines are fighting against Keilah and are looting the threshing floors," [2]he inquired of the LORD, saying, "Shall I go and attack these Philistines?"

The LORD answered him, "Go, attack the Philistines and save Keilah."

[3]But David's men said to him, "Here in Judah we are afraid. How much more, then, if we go to Keilah against the Philistine forces!"

[4]Once again David inquired of the LORD, and the LORD answered him, "Go down to Keilah, for I am going to give the Philistines into your hand." [5]So David and his men went to Keilah, fought the Philistines and carried off their livestock. He inflicted heavy losses on the Philistines and saved the people of Keilah. [6](Now Abiathar son of Ahimelech had brought the ephod down with him when he fled to David at Keilah.)

Saul Pursues David

[7]Saul was told that David had gone to Keilah, and he said, "God has handed him over to me, for David has imprisoned himself by entering a town with gates and bars." [8]And Saul called up all his forces for battle, to go down to Keilah to besiege David and his men.

[9]When David learned that Saul was plotting against him, he said to Abiathar the priest, "Bring the ephod." [10]David said, "O LORD, God of Israel, your servant has heard definitely that Saul plans to come to Keilah and destroy the town on account of me. [11]Will the citizens of Keilah surrender me to him? Will Saul come down, as your servant has heard? O LORD, God of Israel, tell your servant."

And the LORD said, "He will."

[12]Again David asked, "Will the citizens of Keilah surrender me and my men to Saul?"

And the LORD said, "They will."

[13]So David and his men, about six hundred in number, left Keilah and kept moving from place to place. When Saul was told that David had escaped from Keilah, he did not go there.

[14]David stayed in the desert strongholds and in the hills of the Desert of Ziph. Day after day Saul searched for him, but God did not give David into his hands.

[15]While David was at Horesh in the Desert of Ziph, he learned that Saul had come out to take his life. [16]And Saul's son Jonathan went to David at Horesh and helped him find strength in God. [17]"Don't be afraid," he said. "My father Saul will not lay a hand on you. You will be king over Israel, and I will be second to you. Even my father Saul knows this." [18]The two of them made a covenant before the LORD. Then Jonathan went home, but David remained at Horesh.

[19]The Ziphites went up to Saul at Gibeah and said, "Is not David hiding among us in the strongholds at Horesh, on the hill of Hakilah, south of Jeshimon? [20]Now, O king, come down whenever it pleases you to do so, and we will be responsible for handing him over to the king."

[21]Saul replied, "The LORD bless you for your concern for me. [22]Go and make further preparation. Find out where David usually goes and who has seen him there. They tell me he is very crafty. [23]Find out about all the hiding places he uses and come back to me with definite information.[a] Then I will go with you; if he is in the area, I will track him down among all the clans of Judah."

[24]So they set out and went to Ziph ahead of Saul. Now David and his men were in the Desert of Maon, in the Arabah south of Jeshimon. [25]Saul and his men began the search, and when David was told about it, he went down to the rock and stayed in the Desert of Maon. When Saul heard this, he went into the Desert of Maon in pursuit of David.

[26]Saul was going along one side of the mountain, and David and his men were on the other side, hurrying to get away from Saul. As Saul and his forces were closing in on David and his men to cap-

truth or dare

Every girl has days when she feels totally bummed. That's what makes girlfriends the best! Make a point to say something encouraging to a friend today.

23:15–16

[a] 23 Or me at Nacon

ture them, [27]a messenger came to Saul, saying, "Come quickly! The Philistines are raiding the land." [28]Then Saul broke off his pursuit of David and went to meet the Philistines. That is why they call this place Sela Hammahlekoth.[a] [29]And David went up from there and lived in the strongholds of En Gedi.

David Spares Saul's Life

24 After Saul returned from pursuing the Philistines, he was told, "David is in the Desert of En Gedi." [2]So Saul took three thousand chosen men from all Israel and set out to look for David and his men near the Crags of the Wild Goats.

[3]He came to the sheep pens along the way; a cave was there, and Saul went in to relieve himself. David and his men were far back in the cave. [4]The men said, "This is the day the LORD spoke of when he said[b] to you, 'I will give your enemy into your hands for you to deal with as you wish.' " Then David crept up unnoticed and cut off a corner of Saul's robe.

[5]Afterward, David was conscience-stricken for having cut off a corner of his robe. [6]He said to his men, "The LORD forbid that I should do such a thing to my master, the LORD's anointed, or lift my hand against him; for he is the anointed of the LORD." [7]With these words David rebuked his men and did not allow them to attack Saul. And Saul left the cave and went his way.

[8]Then David went out of the cave and called out to Saul, "My lord the king!" When Saul looked behind him, David bowed down and prostrated himself with his face to the ground. [9]He said to Saul, "Why do you listen when men say, 'David is bent on harming you'? [10]This day you have seen with your own eyes how the LORD delivered you into my hands in the cave. Some urged me to kill you, but I spared you; I said, 'I will not lift my hand against my master, because he is the LORD's anointed.' [11]See, my father, look at this piece of your robe in my hand! I cut off the corner of your robe but did not kill you. Now understand and recognize that I am not guilty of wrongdoing or rebellion. I have not wronged you, but you are hunting me down to take my life. [12]May the LORD judge between you and me. And may the LORD avenge the wrongs you have done to me, but my hand will not touch you. [13]As the old saying goes, 'From evildoers come evil deeds,' so my hand will not touch you.

[14]"Against whom has the king of Israel come out? Whom are you pursuing? A dead dog? A flea? [15]May the LORD be our judge and decide between us. May he consider my cause and uphold it; may he vindicate me by delivering me from your hand."

[16]When David finished saying this, Saul asked, "Is that your voice, David my son?" And he wept aloud. [17]"You are more righteous than I," he said. "You have treated me well, but I have treated you badly. [18]You have just now told me of the good you did to me; the LORD delivered me into your hands, but you did not kill me. [19]When a man finds his enemy, does he let him get away unharmed? May the LORD reward you well for the way you treated me today. [20]I know that you will surely be king and that the kingdom of Israel will be established in your hands. [21]Now swear to me by the LORD that you will not cut off my descendants or wipe out my name from my father's family."

[22]So David gave his oath to Saul. Then Saul returned home, but David and his men went up to the stronghold.

---

genuine — **respect »** 24:1-13

Ever had a teacher who totally seemed to have it out for you? Respecting him or her was probably a challenge equal to climbing a mountain backwards.

King Saul wanted to kill David. He didn't just *want* to—he *tried* to several times. When David had the opportunity to do some serious damage to Saul, he refused to do it. He showed respect for the man God had made king. What would you have done if you'd been in David's place? Like David, could you have shown respect to those in authority over you—even if they don't "deserve" it?

---

a 28 Sela Hammahlekoth means rock of parting.   *b 4 Or "Today the LORD is saying*

David, Nabal and Abigail

25 Now Samuel died, and all Israel assembled and mourned for him; and they buried him at his home in Ramah.

Then David moved down into the Desert of Maon. [a] [2] A certain man in Maon, who had property there at Carmel, was very wealthy. He had a thousand goats and three thousand sheep, which he was shearing in Carmel. [3] His name was Nabal and his wife's name was Abigail. She was an intelligent and beautiful woman, but her husband, a Calebite, was surly and mean in his dealings.

[4] While David was in the desert, he heard that Nabal was shearing sheep. [5] So he sent ten young men and said to them, "Go up to Nabal at Carmel and greet him in my name. [6] Say to him: 'Long life to you! Good health to you and your household! And good health to all that is yours!

[7] " 'Now I hear that it is sheep-shearing time. When your shepherds were with us, we did not mistreat them, and the whole time they were at Carmel nothing of theirs was missing. [8] Ask your own servants and they will tell you. Therefore be favorable toward my young men, since we come at a festive time. Please give your servants and your son David whatever you can find for them.' "

[9] When David's men arrived, they gave Nabal this message in David's name. Then they waited.

[10] Nabal answered David's servants, "Who is this David? Who is this son of Jesse? Many servants are breaking away from their masters these days. [11] Why should I take my bread and water, and the meat I have slaughtered for my shearers, and give it to men coming from who knows where?"

[12] David's men turned around and went back. When they arrived, they reported every word. [13] David said to his men, "Put on your swords!" So they put on their swords, and David put on his. About four hundred men went up with David, while two hundred stayed with the supplies.

[14] One of the servants told Nabal's wife Abigail: "David sent messengers from the desert to give our master his greetings, but he hurled insults at them. [15] Yet these men were very good to us. They did not mistreat us, and the whole time we were out in the fields near them nothing was missing. [16] Night and day they were a wall around us all the time we were herding our sheep near them. [17] Now think it over and see what you can do, because disaster is hanging over our master and his whole household. He is such a wicked man that no one can talk to him."

[18] Abigail lost no time. She took two hundred loaves of bread, two skins of wine, five dressed sheep, five seahs [b] of roasted grain, a hundred cakes of raisins and two hundred cakes of pressed figs, and loaded them on donkeys. [19] Then she told her servants, "Go on ahead; I'll follow you." But she did not tell her husband Nabal.

[20] As she came riding her donkey into a mountain ravine, there were David and his men descending toward her, and she met them. [21] David had just said, "It's been useless—all my watching over this fellow's property in the desert so that nothing of his was missing. He has paid me back evil for good. [22] May God deal with David, [c] be it ever so severely, if by morning I leave alive one male of all who belong to him!"

[23] When Abigail saw David, she quickly got off her donkey and bowed down before David with her face to the ground. [24] She fell at his feet and said: "My lord, let the blame be on me alone. Please let your servant speak to you; hear what your servant has to say. [25] May my lord pay no attention to that

genuine wisdom » 25:14-33

Know anyone who lacks common sense? Nabal falls in that category. In fact, his name even means "fool," and he sure lived up to it. After refusing to give supplies to David and David's men—men who protected his property—Nabal earned himself a death sentence by mouthing off to David's messengers. Not smart. Lucky for Nabal, his wife Abigail smoothed things over. Smart. When you're under pressure, do you stay calm and act wisely like Abigail or lash out and make new enemies like Nabal?

[a] 1 Some Septuagint manuscripts; Hebrew *Paran*   [b] 18 That is, probably about a bushel (about 37 liters)   [c] 22 Some Septuagint manuscripts; Hebrew *with David's enemies*

wicked man Nabal. He is just like his name—his name is Fool, and folly goes with him. But as for me, your servant, I did not see the men my master sent.

[26]"Now since the LORD has kept you, my master, from bloodshed and from avenging yourself with your own hands, as surely as the LORD lives and as you live, may your enemies and all who intend to harm my master be like Nabal. [27]And let this gift, which your servant has brought to my master, be given to the men who follow you. [28]Please forgive your servant's offense, for the LORD will certainly make a lasting dynasty for my master, because he fights the LORD's battles. Let no wrongdoing be found in you as long as you live. [29]Even though someone is pursuing you to take your life, the life of my master will be bound securely in the bundle of the living by the LORD your God. But the lives of your enemies he will hurl away as from the pocket of a sling. [30]When the LORD has done for my master every good thing he promised concerning him and has appointed him leader over Israel, [31]my master will not have on his conscience the staggering burden of needless bloodshed or of having avenged himself. And when the LORD has brought my master success, remember your servant."

[32]David said to Abigail, "Praise be to the LORD, the God of Israel, who has sent you today to meet me. [33]May you be blessed for your good judgment and for keeping me from bloodshed this day and from avenging myself with my own hands. [34]Otherwise, as surely as the LORD, the God of Israel, lives, who has kept me from harming you, if you had not come quickly to meet me, not one male belonging to Nabal would have been left alive by daybreak."

[35]Then David accepted from her hand what she had brought him and said, "Go home in peace. I have heard your words and granted your request."

[36]When Abigail went to Nabal, he was in the house holding a banquet like that of a king. He was in high spirits and very drunk. So she told him nothing until daybreak. [37]Then in the morning, when Nabal was sober, his wife told him all these things, and his heart failed him and he became like a stone. [38]About ten days later, the LORD struck Nabal and he died.

[39]When David heard that Nabal was dead, he said, "Praise be to the LORD, who has upheld my cause against Nabal for treating me with contempt. He has kept his servant from doing wrong and has brought Nabal's wrongdoing down on his own head."

Then David sent word to Abigail, asking her to become his wife. [40]His servants went to Carmel and said to Abigail, "David has sent us to you to take you to become his wife."

[41]She bowed down with her face to the ground and said, "Here is your maidservant, ready to serve you and wash the feet of my master's servants." [42]Abigail quickly got on a donkey and, attended by her five maids, went with David's messengers and became his wife. [43]David had also married Ahinoam of Jezreel, and they both were his wives. [44]But Saul had given his daughter Michal, David's wife, to Paltiel[a] son of Laish, who was from Gallim.

David Again Spares Saul's Life

26 The Ziphites went to Saul at Gibeah and said, "Is not David hiding on the hill of Hakilah, which faces Jeshimon?"

[2]So Saul went down to the Desert of Ziph, with his three thousand chosen men of Israel, to search there for David. [3]Saul made his camp beside the road on the hill of Hakilah facing Jeshimon, but David stayed in the desert. When he saw that Saul had followed him there, [4]he sent out scouts and learned that Saul had definitely arrived.[b]

[5]Then David set out and went to the place where Saul had camped. He saw where Saul and Abner son of Ner, the commander of the army, had lain down. Saul was lying inside the camp, with the army encamped around him.

[6]David then asked Ahimelech the Hittite and Abishai son of Zeruiah, Joab's brother, "Who will go down into the camp with me to Saul?"

"I'll go with you," said Abishai.

[7]So David and Abishai went to the army by night, and there was Saul, lying asleep inside the camp with his spear stuck in the ground near his head. Abner and the soldiers were lying around him.

[8]Abishai said to David, "Today God has delivered your enemy into your hands. Now let me pin him to the ground with one thrust of my spear; I won't strike him twice."

[9]But David said to Abishai, "Don't destroy him! Who can lay a hand on the LORD's anointed and be guiltless? [10]As surely as the LORD lives," he said, "the LORD himself will strike him; either his time

a 44 Hebrew Palti, a variant of Paltiel   b 4 Or had come to Nacon will come and he will die, or he will go into battle and perish. ¹¹But the LORD forbid that I should lay a hand on the LORD's anointed. Now get the spear and water jug that are near his head, and let's go."

¹²So David took the spear and water jug near Saul's head, and they left. No one saw or knew about it, nor did anyone wake up. They were all sleeping, because the LORD had put them into a deep sleep.

¹³Then David crossed over to the other side and stood on top of the hill some distance away; there was a wide space between them. ¹⁴He called out to the army and to Abner son of Ner, "Aren't you going to answer me, Abner?"

Abner replied, "Who are you who calls to the king?"

¹⁵David said, "You're a man, aren't you? And who is like you in Israel? Why didn't you guard your lord the king? Someone came to destroy your lord the king. ¹⁶What you have done is not good. As surely as the LORD lives, you and your men deserve to die, because you did not guard your master, the LORD's anointed. Look around you. Where are the king's spear and water jug that were near his head?"

¹⁷Saul recognized David's voice and said, "Is that your voice, David my son?"

David replied, "Yes it is, my lord the king." ¹⁸And he added, "Why is my lord pursuing his servant? What have I done, and what wrong am I guilty of? ¹⁹Now let my lord the king listen to his servant's words. If the LORD has incited you against me, then may he accept an offering. If, however, men have done it, may they be cursed before the LORD! They have now driven me from my share in the LORD's inheritance and have said, 'Go, serve other gods.' ²⁰Now do not let my blood fall to the ground far from the presence of the LORD. The king of Israel has come out to look for a flea—as one hunts a partridge in the mountains."

²¹Then Saul said, "I have sinned. Come back, David my son. Because you considered my life precious today, I will not try to harm you again. Surely I have acted like a fool and have erred greatly."

²²"Here is the king's spear," David answered. "Let one of your young men come over and get it. ²³The LORD rewards every man for his righteousness and faithfulness. The LORD delivered you into my hands today, but I would not lay a hand on the LORD's anointed. ²⁴As surely as I valued your life today, so may the LORD value my life and deliver me from all trouble."

²⁵Then Saul said to David, "May you be blessed, my son David; you will do great things and surely triumph."

So David went on his way, and Saul returned home.

David Among the Philistines

27 But David thought to himself, "One of these days I will be destroyed by the hand of Saul. The best thing I can do is to escape to the land of the Philistines. Then Saul will give up searching for me anywhere in Israel, and I will slip out of his hand."

²So David and the six hundred men with him left and went over to Achish son of Maoch king of Gath. ³David and his men settled in Gath with Achish. Each man had his family with him, and David had his two wives: Ahinoam of Jezreel and Abigail of Carmel, the widow of Nabal. ⁴When Saul was told that David had fled to Gath, he no longer searched for him.

⁵Then David said to Achish, "If I have found favor in your eyes, let a place be assigned to me in one of the country towns, that I may live there. Why should your servant live in the royal city with you?"

⁶So on that day Achish gave him Ziklag, and it has belonged to the kings of Judah ever since. ⁷David lived in Philistine territory a year and four months.

⁸Now David and his men went up and raided the Geshurites, the Girzites and the Amalekites. (From ancient times these peoples had lived in the land extending to Shur and Egypt.) ⁹Whenever David attacked an area, he did not leave a man or woman alive, but took sheep and cattle, donkeys and camels, and clothes. Then he returned to Achish.

¹⁰When Achish asked, "Where did you go raiding today?" David would say, "Against the Negev of Judah" or "Against the Negev of Jerahmeel" or "Against the Negev of the Kenites." ¹¹He did not leave a man or woman alive to be brought to Gath, for he thought, "They might inform on us and say, 'This is what David did.' " And such was his practice as long as he lived in Philistine territory. ¹²Achish trusted David and said to himself, "He has become so odious to his people, the Israelites, that he will be my servant forever."

in focus

The Five-Finger Discount

Profile: **Shea**

My friends have been into shoplifting for a while now. It seems like every time we go to the mall, someone takes *something*.

Mostly they stick to easy grabs like makeup or CDs. But sometimes one of the girls will get really bold. Like the one time my friend Missy scored a $60 pair of jeans from Abercrombie. Somehow she managed to avoid the cameras and got the sensors and tags off without hurting the fabric. I didn't even know until after we'd left the store.

We've all heard stories about people getting caught. It seems risky to me. The sad thing is that I'm starting to get used to it. The girls say that it's actually really easy. They've been daring me to try it for a while. I always say no, but I never say *why*. And that bothers me.

You know what else bothers me? The fact that because I don't shoplift, I have less stuff than they do. I'll never be able to afford such nice clothes, music, makeup, you name it. It's like they're being rewarded for doing wrong. After all, it *is* stealing, so it must be wrong. But that doesn't seem to stop anybody else from doing it.

For more on shoplifting, go to
www.TrueImagesBible.com

shoplifting in focus

Some girls shoplift so they can have nice things they can't really afford. Other girls do it for the thrill. Still others rationalize shoplifting by saying it's "no big deal" because the stores are so big that they won't miss the stuff anyway. But let's get a few things straight:

- » Shoplifting is stealing. Period. And God forbids stealing (see Exodus 20:15, page 94). It's one of his Top Ten rules.
- » Even if you're not the one shoplifting, you have a responsibility to hold your friends accountable—not in an "I'm better than you" tone but because you genuinely care about them.
- » If your friends shoplift or pressure you to join them, then you may want to shop for some new friends. No matter how strong you are personally, bad friends *will* bring you down (see 1 Corinthians 15:33, page 1521).

For more on this topic, see the index on page 1656.

Saul and the Witch of Endor

28 In those days the Philistines gathered their forces to fight against Israel. Achish said to David, "You must understand that you and your men will accompany me in the army." ²David said, "Then you will see for yourself what your servant can do."

Achish replied, "Very well, I will make you my bodyguard for life."

³Now Samuel was dead, and all Israel had mourned for him and buried him in his own town of Ramah. Saul had expelled the mediums and spiritists from the land.

⁴The Philistines assembled and came and set up camp at Shunem, while Saul gathered all the Israelites and set up camp at Gilboa. ⁵When Saul saw the Philistine army, he was afraid; terror filled his heart. ⁶He inquired of the LORD, but the LORD did not answer him by dreams or Urim or prophets. ⁷Saul then said to his attendants, "Find me a woman who is a medium, so I may go and inquire of her."

"There is one in Endor," they said.

[8]So Saul disguised himself, putting on other clothes, and at night he and two men went to the woman. "Consult a spirit for me," he said, "and bring up for me the one I name."

[9]But the woman said to him, "Surely you know what Saul has done. He has cut off the mediums and spiritists from the land. Why have you set a trap for my life to bring about my death?"

[10]Saul swore to her by the LORD, "As surely as the LORD lives, you will not be punished for this."

[11]Then the woman asked, "Whom shall I bring up for you?"

"Bring up Samuel," he said.

[12]When the woman saw Samuel, she cried out at the top of her voice and said to Saul, "Why have you deceived me? You are Saul!"

[13]The king said to her, "Don't be afraid. What do you see?"

The woman said, "I see a spirit[a] coming up out of the ground."

[14]"What does he look like?" he asked.

"An old man wearing a robe is coming up," she said.

Then Saul knew it was Samuel, and he bowed down and prostrated himself with his face to the ground.

[15]Samuel said to Saul, "Why have you disturbed me by bringing me up?"

"I am in great distress," Saul said. "The Philistines are fighting against me, and God has turned away from me. He no longer answers me, either by prophets or by dreams. So I have called on you to tell me what to do."

[16]Samuel said, "Why do you consult me, now that the LORD has turned away from you and become your enemy? [17]The LORD has done what he predicted through me. The LORD has torn the kingdom out of your hands and given it to one of your neighbors—to David. [18]Because you did not obey the LORD or carry out his fierce wrath against the Amalekites, the LORD has done this to you today. [19]The LORD will hand over both Israel and you to the Philistines, and tomorrow you and your sons will be with me. The LORD will also hand over the army of Israel to the Philistines."

[20]Immediately Saul fell full length on the ground, filled with fear because of Samuel's words. His strength was gone, for he had eaten nothing all that day and night.

[21]When the woman came to Saul and saw that he was greatly shaken, she said, "Look, your maidservant has obeyed you. I took my life in my hands and did what you told me to do. [22]Now please listen to your servant and let me give you some food so you may eat and have the strength to go on your way."

[23]He refused and said, "I will not eat."

But his men joined the woman in urging him, and he listened to them. He got up from the ground and sat on the couch.

[24]The woman had a fattened calf at the house, which she butchered at once. She took some flour, kneaded it and baked bread without yeast. [25]Then she set it before Saul and his men, and they ate. That same night they got up and left.

Achish Sends David Back to Ziklag

29 The Philistines gathered all their forces at Aphek, and Israel camped by the spring in Jezreel. [2]As the Philistine rulers marched with their units of hundreds and thousands, David and his men were marching at the rear with Achish. [3]The commanders of the Philistines asked, "What about these Hebrews?"

Achish replied, "Is this not David, who was an officer of Saul king of Israel? He has already been with me for over a year, and from the day he left Saul until now, I have found no fault in him."

[4]But the Philistine commanders were angry with him and said, "Send the man back, that he may return to the place you assigned him. He must not go with us into battle, or he will turn against us during the fighting. How better could he regain his master's favor than by taking the heads of our own men? [5]Isn't this the David they sang about in their dances:

" 'Saul has slain his thousands,
    and David his tens of thousands'?"

[6]So Achish called David and said to him, "As surely as the LORD lives, you have been reliable,

a 13 Or *see spirits*; or *see gods*

and I would be pleased to have you serve with me in the army. From the day you came to me until now, I have found no fault in you, but the rulers don't approve of you. [7]Turn back and go in peace; do nothing to displease the Philistine rulers."

[8]"But what have I done?" asked David. "What have you found against your servant from the day I came to you until now? Why can't I go and fight against the enemies of my lord the king?"

[9]Achish answered, "I know that you have been as pleasing in my eyes as an angel of God; nevertheless, the Philistine commanders have said, 'He must not go up with us into battle.' [10]Now get up early, along with your master's servants who have come with you, and leave in the morning as soon as it is light."

[11]So David and his men got up early in the morning to go back to the land of the Philistines, and the Philistines went up to Jezreel.

David Destroys the Amalekites

30 David and his men reached Ziklag on the third day. Now the Amalekites had raided the Negev and Ziklag. They had attacked Ziklag and burned it, [2]and had taken captive the women and all who were in it, both young and old. They killed none of them, but carried them off as they went on their way.

[3]When David and his men came to Ziklag, they found it destroyed by fire and their wives and sons and daughters taken captive. [4]So David and his men wept aloud until they had no strength left to weep. [5]David's two wives had been captured—Ahinoam of Jezreel and Abigail, the widow of Nabal of Carmel. [6]David was greatly distressed because the men were talking of stoning him; each one was bitter in spirit because of his sons and daughters. But David found strength in the LORD his God.

[7]Then David said to Abiathar the priest, the son of Ahimelech, "Bring me the ephod." Abiathar brought it to him, [8]and David inquired of the LORD, "Shall I pursue this raiding party? Will I overtake them?"

"Pursue them," he answered. "You will certainly overtake them and succeed in the rescue."

[9]David and the six hundred men with him came to the Besor Ravine, where some stayed behind, [10]for two hundred men were too exhausted to cross the ravine. But David and four hundred men continued the pursuit.

[11]They found an Egyptian in a field and brought him to David. They gave him water to drink and food to eat— [12]part of a cake of pressed figs and two cakes of raisins. He ate and was revived, for he had not eaten any food or drunk any water for three days and three nights.

[13]David asked him, "To whom do you belong, and where do you come from?"

He said, "I am an Egyptian, the slave of an Amalekite. My master abandoned me when I became ill three days ago. [14]We raided the Negev of the Kerethites and the territory belonging to Judah and the Negev of Caleb. And we burned Ziklag."

[15]David asked him, "Can you lead me down to this raiding party?"

He answered, "Swear to me before God that you will not kill me or hand me over to my master, and I will take you down to them."

[16]He led David down, and there they were, scattered over the countryside, eating, drinking and reveling because of the great amount of plunder they had taken from the land of the Philistines and from Judah. [17]David fought them from dusk until the evening of the next day, and none of them got away, except four hundred young men who rode off on camels and fled. [18]David recovered everything the Amalekites had taken, including his two wives. [19]Nothing was missing: young or old, boy or girl, plunder or anything else they had taken. David brought everything back. [20]He took all the flocks and herds, and his men drove them ahead of the other livestock, saying, "This is David's plunder."

[21]Then David came to the two hundred men who had been too exhausted to follow him and who were left behind at the Besor Ravine. They came out to meet David and the people with him. As

Caught off Guard

Profile: **Rena**

"I hope I have a lot of classes with senior guys," Myra said excitedly. We were at Myra's house, enjoying the last weekend of summer. Classes were going to start Wednesday. Day 1 of freshman year. Finally we were out of the "pit" of middle school, as we affectionately called it. I felt so excited for the year ahead.

"If I get my permit later on in the year, I can drive us all to school," said Leah with a grin.

"Like we'd want to be seen in your parents' beater!" I teased and reached for another piece of pizza.

I was in mid-bite when Chelsea said, "Yeah, well we'll look hot in those little red skirts for cheer squad, so we can drive whatever we want."

"Yeah right, can't you just see us as cheerleaders?" I joked and struck a mock cheerleading pose. "Whatever. Let those ditzy girls go for it." Suddenly I realized no one was laughing with me.

"You mean you're not even willing to try out with all of us?" Leah asked suspiciously.

"What? When did 'all of us' decide this?" I asked in disbelief. I still hoped they were joking. We'd always been together in volleyball and track. Always. We'd been on the same teams together for years. Why would we want to give that up for something like *cheerleading*?

"You're not seriously going to play volleyball again this year, are you? The team's horrible. I heard the coach is way too extreme," Myra retorted. "You'll miss out on all the fun if you're stuck in volleyball practice all the time."

Jess nodded. "Plus I heard none of the girls on the team even shave."

"Gross!" Chelsea yelled and accidentally snorted. All the girls collapsed in laughter.

Only I wasn't laughing.

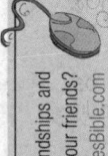

friendship in focus

Have you felt like Rena . . . knowing what you really want to do, yet feeling the pain of being out of step with the group?

» Longstanding friendships often change in high school. People have different interests and start to make other friends. You're not alone if this is happening to you. It's a natural phase in life.

» Don't compromise who you are just to make someone else happy. Easier said than done, of course, but it's worth it to be true to yourself.

» Proverbs 29:25 (page 846) says that when you're afraid of what others will think of your decisions, it's like being caught in a trap. Don't let the real you get trapped in someone else's expectations for your life.

For more on this topic, see the index on page 1656.

friendship

David and his men approached, he greeted them. ²²But all the evil men and troublemakers among David's followers said, "Because they did not go out with us, we will not share with them the plunder we recovered. However, each man may take his wife and children and go."

²³David replied, "No, my brothers, you must not do that with what the LORD has given us. He has protected us and handed over to us the forces that came against us. ²⁴Who will listen to what you say? The share of the man who stayed with the supplies is to be the same as that of him who went down to the battle. All will share alike." ²⁵David made this a statute and ordinance for Israel from that day to this.

²⁶When David arrived in Ziklag, he sent some of the plunder to the elders of Judah, who were his friends, saying, "Here is a present for you from the plunder of the LORD's enemies."

²⁷He sent it to those who were in Bethel, Ramoth Negev and Jattir; ²⁸to those in Aroer, Siphmoth, Eshtemoa ²⁹and Racal; to those in the towns of the Jerahmeelites and the Kenites; ³⁰to those in Hormah, Bor Ashan, Athach ³¹and Hebron; and to those in all the other places where David and his men had roamed.

or dare

truth

In a group, what role do you usually fall into? Leader? Supporter? Keep your group tight by valuing everyone's role equally.

30:24–25

Saul Takes His Life

31 Now the Philistines fought against Israel; the Israelites fled before them, and many fell slain on Mount Gilboa. ²The Philistines pressed hard after Saul and his sons, and they killed his sons Jonathan, Abinadab and Malki-Shua. ³The fighting grew fierce around Saul, and when the archers overtook him, they wounded him critically.

⁴Saul said to his armor-bearer, "Draw your sword and run me through, or these uncircumcised fellows will come and run me through and abuse me."

But his armor-bearer was terrified and would not do it; so Saul took his own sword and fell on it. ⁵When the armor-bearer saw that Saul was dead, he too fell on his sword and died with him. ⁶So Saul and his three sons and his armor-bearer and all his men died together that same day.

⁷When the Israelites along the valley and those across the Jordan saw that the Israelite army had fled and that Saul and his sons had died, they abandoned their towns and fled. And the Philistines came and occupied them.

⁸The next day, when the Philistines came to strip the dead, they found Saul and his three sons fallen on Mount Gilboa. ⁹They cut off his head and stripped off his armor, and they sent messengers throughout the land of the Philistines to proclaim the news in the temple of their idols and among their people. ¹⁰They put his armor in the temple of the Ashtoreths and fastened his body to the wall of Beth Shan.

¹¹When the people of Jabesh Gilead heard of what the Philistines had done to Saul, ¹²all their valiant men journeyed through the night to Beth Shan. They took down the bodies of Saul and his sons from the wall of Beth Shan and went to Jabesh, where they burned them. ¹³Then they took their bones and buried them under a tamarisk tree at Jabesh, and they fasted seven days.

author:	Unknown.
date:	Sometime after the division of Israel into the northern and southern kingdoms, around 930 B.C.
setting:	The land of Israel when David ruled as their king.
verse to remember:	Then David said to Nathan, "I have sinned against the LORD." Nathan replied, "The LORD has taken away your sin." (12:13).
theme to consider:	What great news! No matter how terribly we mess up or how bad the consequences are, we can share our pain and sadness with God and ask for forgiveness as David did.

2 samuel

unchanging truth

How do you react when you mess up? Do you cover up or 'fess up? Well, there are mess-ups and then there are MESS-UPS. Let's say you get up late and throw on the first thing in your closet. You don't notice the chocolate stain on your shirt until you get to school. This calls for a cover-up—if you're lucky, you have a sweater in your locker. Otherwise a well-placed book will have to do.

But how about more serious stuff like not studying for a test and then cheating to get a good grade? Or perhaps you heard a nasty rumor about a friend and passed on the gossip, even though you didn't believe it. These are the times when you need to confess your mess-ups to those you've hurt, including God. He hears you and is *always* willing to forgive—no matter what you've done.

David was famous for killing the giant Goliath and for winning many battles against the enemies of Israel. He was a feared and respected king. But David also messed up big time. David slept with another man's wife. Then he arranged for her husband to be killed in battle so that he could marry her. When the prophet Nathan confronted David, David repented and sincerely asked God for forgiveness. God forgave David just as he forgives us when we are truly sorry.

Made a few mistakes? Chosen the wrong way? Tell God about it—he's waiting to hear from you.

life lessons

1 The Lord is great! There's no one like him, and he deserves our praise (7:22).

2 Sin and deception have a snowball effect—one sin leads to the next, to the next. There's no escaping the consequences of our sin (11:1–27).

3 When you sin, you may face severe consequences, as David did. But no matter how severe your sin, God will forgive you if you confess your sin and ask for his forgiveness (12:13–23).

David Hears of Saul's Death

1 After the death of Saul, David returned from defeating the Amalekites and stayed in Ziklag two days. ²On the third day a man arrived from Saul's camp, with his clothes torn and with dust on his head. When he came to David, he fell to the ground to pay him honor.

³"Where have you come from?" David asked him.

He answered, "I have escaped from the Israelite camp."

⁴"What happened?" David asked. "Tell me."

He said, "The men fled from the battle. Many of them fell and died. And Saul and his son Jonathan are dead."

⁵Then David said to the young man who brought him the report, "How do you know that Saul and his son Jonathan are dead?"

⁶"I happened to be on Mount Gilboa," the young man said, "and there was Saul, leaning on his spear, with the chariots and riders almost upon him. ⁷When he turned around and saw me, he called out to me, and I said, 'What can I do?'

⁸"He asked me, 'Who are you?'

" 'An Amalekite,' I answered.

⁹"Then he said to me, 'Stand over me and kill me! I am in the throes of death, but I'm still alive.'

¹⁰"So I stood over him and killed him, because I knew that after he had fallen he could not survive. And I took the crown that was on his head and the band on his arm and have brought them here to my lord."

¹¹Then David and all the men with him took hold of their clothes and tore them. ¹²They mourned and wept and fasted till evening for Saul and his son Jonathan, and for the army of the LORD and the house of Israel, because they had fallen by the sword.

¹³David said to the young man who brought him the report, "Where are you from?"

"I am the son of an alien, an Amalekite," he answered.

¹⁴David asked him, "Why were you not afraid to lift your hand to destroy the LORD's anointed?"

¹⁵Then David called one of his men and said, "Go, strike him down!" So he struck him down, and he died. ¹⁶For David had said to him, "Your blood be on your own head. Your own mouth testified against you when you said, 'I killed the LORD's anointed.' "

David's Lament for Saul and Jonathan

¹⁷David took up this lament concerning Saul and his son Jonathan, ¹⁸and ordered that the men of Judah be taught this lament of the bow (it is written in the Book of Jashar):

¹⁹ "Your glory, O Israel, lies slain on your heights.
How the mighty have fallen!

²⁰ "Tell it not in Gath,
proclaim it not in the streets of Ashkelon,
lest the daughters of the Philistines be glad,
lest the daughters of the uncircumcised rejoice.

²¹ "O mountains of Gilboa,
may you have neither dew nor rain,
nor fields that yield offerings ⌊of grain⌋.
For there the shield of the mighty was defiled,
the shield of Saul—no longer rubbed with oil.
²² From the blood of the slain,
from the flesh of the mighty,
the bow of Jonathan did not turn back,
the sword of Saul did not return unsatisfied.

²³ "Saul and Jonathan—
in life they were loved and gracious,
and in death they were not parted.
They were swifter than eagles,
they were stronger than lions.

²⁴ "O daughters of Israel,
>   weep for Saul,
> who clothed you in scarlet and finery,
>   who adorned your garments with ornaments of gold.

²⁵ "How the mighty have fallen in battle!
>   Jonathan lies slain on your heights.
²⁶ I grieve for you, Jonathan my brother;
>   you were very dear to me.
> Your love for me was wonderful,
>   more wonderful than that of women.

²⁷ "How the mighty have fallen!
>   The weapons of war have perished!"

David Anointed King Over Judah

2 In the course of time, David inquired of the LORD. "Shall I go up to one of the towns of Judah?" he asked.

The LORD said, "Go up."

David asked, "Where shall I go?"

"To Hebron," the LORD answered.

²So David went up there with his two wives, Ahinoam of Jezreel and Abigail, the widow of Nabal of Carmel. ³David also took the men who were with him, each with his family, and they settled in Hebron and its towns. ⁴Then the men of Judah came to Hebron and there they anointed David king over the house of Judah.

When David was told that it was the men of Jabesh Gilead who had buried Saul, ⁵he sent messengers to the men of Jabesh Gilead to say to them, "The LORD bless you for showing this kindness to Saul your master by burying him. ⁶May the LORD now show you kindness and faithfulness, and I too will show you the same favor because you have done this. ⁷Now then, be strong and brave, for Saul your master is dead, and the house of Judah has anointed me king over them."

War Between the Houses of David and Saul

⁸Meanwhile, Abner son of Ner, the commander of Saul's army, had taken Ish-Bosheth son of Saul and brought him over to Mahanaim. ⁹He made him king over Gilead, Ashuri[a] and Jezreel, and also over Ephraim, Benjamin and all Israel.

¹⁰Ish-Bosheth son of Saul was forty years old when he became king over Israel, and he reigned two years. The house of Judah, however, followed David. ¹¹The length of time David was king in Hebron over the house of Judah was seven years and six months.

¹²Abner son of Ner, together with the men of Ish-Bosheth son of Saul, left Mahanaim and went to Gibeon. ¹³Joab son of Zeruiah and David's men went out and met them at the pool of Gibeon. One group sat down on one side of the pool and one group on the other side.

¹⁴Then Abner said to Joab, "Let's have some of the young men get up and fight hand to hand in front of us."

"All right, let them do it," Joab said.

¹⁵So they stood up and were counted off—twelve men for Benjamin and Ish-Bosheth son of Saul, and twelve for David. ¹⁶Then each man grabbed his opponent by the head and thrust his dagger into his opponent's side, and they fell down together. So that place in Gibeon was called Helkath Hazzurim.[b]

¹⁷The battle that day was very fierce, and Abner and the men of Israel were defeated by David's men.

¹⁸The three sons of Zeruiah were there: Joab, Abishai and Asahel. Now Asahel was as fleet-footed as a wild gazelle. ¹⁹He chased Abner, turning neither to the right nor to the left as he pursued him. ²⁰Abner looked behind him and asked, "Is that you, Asahel?"

"It is," he answered.

---

a 9 Or *Asher*   *b 16 Helkath Hazzurim* means *field of daggers* or *field of hostilities.*

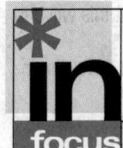

Always the Reject

focus Profile: **Marianne**

What do you get when you take one foster kid who's been moved thirteen times and can't even remember what her real mom looks like? (Trust me, this isn't a joke.) You get someone exactly like me—a reject.

Once I almost had a real family. I lived with the Martins for a year and a half, and they treated me like their own child. But then they had a new baby and decided it was just too much to have me around. They said, "Marianne, I hope you understand that we still love you." Hard to believe.

I'm sixteen. I've attended seven different schools, and I don't have a real family. There's this stigma that goes with being a foster kid. Girls make fun of me or avoid me. Guys don't dare ask me out—unless they're desperate or think I'm easy.

I've never been able to stay put long enough to play sports, but I think I'd be good at it. If I can't be like other girls, you'd think God would at least have the decency to give me one good friend. I've given up on ever having a real family. And by the way, if there is a God, then my life is one cruel joke. What kind of a God would create a person only to mess her life up like this? If I'm going to make it, I'll just have to make it on my own.

For more ideas on how to cope in foster care, check out the link on www.TrueImagesBible.com

foster care in focus

Around 200,000 teens live in foster care each year in the U.S.—and many of them feel alone. Still, there's always hope:

» Psalm 27:10 says, "Though my father and mother forsake me, the LORD will receive me." God didn't cause the pain you're in, but *he hurts with you* and wants to heal your broken heart (see Psalm 34:18–20, page 679).

» Plenty of foster teens like you have used their experiences to make a difference—including Domino's Pizza owner Tom Monaghan, baseball legend Babe Ruth and former first lady Eleanor Roosevelt.

For more on this topic, see the index on page 1656.

foster care

[21]Then Abner said to him, "Turn aside to the right or to the left; take on one of the young men and strip him of his weapons." But Asahel would not stop chasing him.

[22]Again Abner warned Asahel, "Stop chasing me! Why should I strike you down? How could I look your brother Joab in the face?"

[23]But Asahel refused to give up the pursuit; so Abner thrust the butt of his spear into Asahel's stomach, and the spear came out through his back. He fell there and died on the spot. And every man stopped when he came to the place where Asahel had fallen and died.

[24]But Joab and Abishai pursued Abner, and as the sun was setting, they came to the hill of Ammah, near Giah on the way to the wasteland of Gibeon. [25]Then the men of Benjamin rallied behind Abner. They formed themselves into a group and took their stand on top of a hill.

²⁶Abner called out to Joab, "Must the sword devour forever? Don't you realize that this will end in bitterness? How long before you order your men to stop pursuing their brothers?"

²⁷Joab answered, "As surely as God lives, if you had not spoken, the men would have continued the pursuit of their brothers until morning.ᵃ"

²⁸So Joab blew the trumpet, and all the men came to a halt; they no longer pursued Israel, nor did they fight anymore.

²⁹All that night Abner and his men marched through the Arabah. They crossed the Jordan, continued through the whole Bithronᵇ and came to Mahanaim.

³⁰Then Joab returned from pursuing Abner and assembled all his men. Besides Asahel, nineteen of David's men were found missing. ³¹But David's men had killed three hundred and sixty Benjamites who were with Abner. ³²They took Asahel and buried him in his father's tomb at Bethlehem. Then Joab and his men marched all night and arrived at Hebron by daybreak.

3 The war between the house of Saul and the house of David lasted a long time. David grew stronger and stronger, while the house of Saul grew weaker and weaker.

²Sons were born to David in Hebron:

His firstborn was Amnon the son of Ahinoam of Jezreel;

³his second, Kileab the son of Abigail the widow of Nabal of Carmel;

the third, Absalom the son of Maacah daughter of Talmai king of Geshur;

⁴the fourth, Adonijah the son of Haggith;

the fifth, Shephatiah the son of Abital;

⁵and the sixth, Ithream the son of David's wife Eglah.

These were born to David in Hebron.

Abner Goes Over to David

⁶During the war between the house of Saul and the house of David, Abner had been strengthening his own position in the house of Saul. ⁷Now Saul had had a concubine named Rizpah daughter of Aiah. And Ish-Bosheth said to Abner, "Why did you sleep with my father's concubine?"

⁸Abner was very angry because of what Ish-Bosheth said and he answered, "Am I a dog's head—on Judah's side? This very day I am loyal to the house of your father Saul and to his family and friends. I haven't handed you over to David. Yet now you accuse me of an offense involving this woman! ⁹May God deal with Abner, be it ever so severely, if I do not do for David what the LORD promised him on oath ¹⁰and transfer the kingdom from the house of Saul and establish David's throne over Israel and Judah from Dan to Beersheba." ¹¹Ish-Bosheth did not dare to say another word to Abner, because he was afraid of him.

¹²Then Abner sent messengers on his behalf to say to David, "Whose land is it? Make an agreement with me, and I will help you bring all Israel over to you."

¹³"Good," said David. "I will make an agreement with you. But I demand one thing of you: Do not come into my presence unless you bring Michal daughter of Saul when you come to see me." ¹⁴Then David sent messengers to Ish-Bosheth son of Saul, demanding, "Give me my wife Michal, whom I betrothed to myself for the price of a hundred Philistine foreskins."

¹⁵So Ish-Bosheth gave orders and had her taken away from her husband Paltiel son of Laish. ¹⁶Her husband, however, went with her, weeping behind her all the way to Bahurim. Then Abner said to him, "Go back home!" So he went back.

¹⁷Abner conferred with the elders of Israel and said, "For some time you have wanted to make David your king. ¹⁸Now do it! For the LORD promised David, 'By my servant David I will rescue my people Israel from the hand of the Philistines and from the hand of all their enemies.'"

¹⁹Abner also spoke to the Benjamites in person. Then he went to Hebron to tell David everything that Israel and the whole house of Benjamin wanted to do. ²⁰When Abner, who had twenty men with him, came to David at Hebron, David prepared a feast for him and his men. ²¹Then Abner said to David, "Let me go at once and assemble all Israel for my lord the king, so that they may make a compact with you, and that you may rule over all that your heart desires." So David sent Abner away, and he went in peace.

ᵃ 27 Or *spoken this morning, the men would not have taken up the pursuit of their brothers*; or *spoken, the men would have given up the pursuit of their brothers by morning*   ᵇ 29 Or *morning*; or *ravine*; the meaning of the Hebrew for this word is uncertain.

Joab Murders Abner

²²Just then David's men and Joab returned from a raid and brought with them a great deal of plunder. But Abner was no longer with David in Hebron, because David had sent him away, and he had gone in peace. ²³When Joab and all the soldiers with him arrived, he was told that Abner son of Ner had come to the king and that the king had sent him away and that he had gone in peace.

²⁴So Joab went to the king and said, "What have you done? Look, Abner came to you. Why did you let him go? Now he is gone! ²⁵You know Abner son of Ner; he came to deceive you and observe your movements and find out everything you are doing."

²⁶Joab then left David and sent messengers after Abner, and they brought him back from the well of Sirah. But David did not know it. ²⁷Now when Abner returned to Hebron, Joab took him aside into the gateway, as though to speak with him privately. And there, to avenge the blood of his brother Asahel, Joab stabbed him in the stomach, and he died.

²⁸Later, when David heard about this, he said, "I and my kingdom are forever innocent before the LORD concerning the blood of Abner son of Ner. ²⁹May his blood fall upon the head of Joab and upon all his father's house! May Joab's house never be without someone who has a running sore or leprosy*ᵃ* or who leans on a crutch or who falls by the sword or who lacks food."

³⁰(Joab and his brother Abishai murdered Abner because he had killed their brother Asahel in the battle at Gibeon.)

³¹Then David said to Joab and all the people with him, "Tear your clothes and put on sackcloth and walk in mourning in front of Abner." King David himself walked behind the bier. ³²They buried Abner in Hebron, and the king wept aloud at Abner's tomb. All the people wept also.

³³The king sang this lament for Abner:

> "Should Abner have died as the lawless die?
> ³⁴ Your hands were not bound,
>   your feet were not fettered.
>   You fell as one falls before wicked men."

And all the people wept over him again.

³⁵Then they all came and urged David to eat something while it was still day; but David took an oath, saying, "May God deal with me, be it ever so severely, if I taste bread or anything else before the sun sets!"

³⁶All the people took note and were pleased; indeed, everything the king did pleased them. ³⁷So on that day all the people and all Israel knew that the king had no part in the murder of Abner son of Ner.

³⁸Then the king said to his men, "Do you not realize that a prince and a great man has fallen in Israel this day? ³⁹And today, though I am the anointed king, I am weak, and these sons of Zeruiah are too strong for me. May the LORD repay the evildoer according to his evil deeds!"

Ish-Bosheth Murdered

4 When Ish-Bosheth son of Saul heard that Abner had died in Hebron, he lost courage, and all Israel became alarmed. ²Now Saul's son had two men who were leaders of raiding bands. One was named Baanah and the other Recab; they were sons of Rimmon the Beerothite from the tribe of Benjamin—Beeroth is considered part of Benjamin, ³because the people of Beeroth fled to Gittaim and have lived there as aliens to this day.

⁴(Jonathan son of Saul had a son who was lame in both feet. He was five years old when the news about Saul and Jonathan came from Jezreel. His nurse picked him up and fled, but as she hurried to leave, he fell and became crippled. His name was Mephibosheth.)

⁵Now Recab and Baanah, the sons of Rimmon the Beerothite, set out for the house of Ish-Bosheth, and they arrived there in the heat of the day while he was taking his noonday rest. ⁶They went into the inner part of the house as if to get some wheat, and they stabbed him in the stomach. Then Recab and his brother Baanah slipped away.

⁷They had gone into the house while he was lying on the bed in his bedroom. After they stabbed and killed him, they cut off his head. Taking it with them, they traveled all night by way of the Arabah. ⁸They brought the head of Ish-Bosheth to David at Hebron and said to the king, "Here is the

ᵃ 29 The Hebrew word was used for various diseases affecting the skin—not necessarily leprosy.

head of Ish-Bosheth son of Saul, your enemy, who tried to take your life. This day the LORD has avenged my lord the king against Saul and his offspring."

⁹David answered Recab and his brother Baanah, the sons of Rimmon the Beerothite, "As surely as the LORD lives, who has delivered me out of all trouble, ¹⁰when a man told me, 'Saul is dead,' and thought he was bringing good news, I seized him and put him to death in Ziklag. That was the reward I gave him for his news! ¹¹How much more—when wicked men have killed an innocent man in his own house and on his own bed—should I not now demand his blood from your hand and rid the earth of you!"

¹²So David gave an order to his men, and they killed them. They cut off their hands and feet and hung the bodies by the pool in Hebron. But they took the head of Ish-Bosheth and buried it in Abner's tomb at Hebron.

David Becomes King Over Israel

5 All the tribes of Israel came to David at Hebron and said, "We are your own flesh and blood. ²In the past, while Saul was king over us, you were the one who led Israel on their military campaigns. And the LORD said to you, 'You will shepherd my people Israel, and you will become their ruler.' "

³When all the elders of Israel had come to King David at Hebron, the king made a compact with them at Hebron before the LORD, and they anointed David king over Israel.

⁴David was thirty years old when he became king, and he reigned forty years. ⁵In Hebron he reigned over Judah seven years and six months, and in Jerusalem he reigned over all Israel and Judah thirty-three years.

David Conquers Jerusalem

⁶The king and his men marched to Jerusalem to attack the Jebusites, who lived there. The Jebusites said to David, "You will not get in here; even the blind and the lame can ward you off." They thought, "David cannot get in here." ⁷Nevertheless, David captured the fortress of Zion, the City of David.

⁸On that day, David said, "Anyone who conquers the Jebusites will have to use the water shaft*ª* to reach those 'lame and blind' who are David's enemies.*ᵇ*" That is why they say, "The 'blind and lame' will not enter the palace."

⁹David then took up residence in the fortress and called it the City of David. He built up the area around it, from the supporting terracesᶜ inward. ¹⁰And he became more and more powerful, because the LORD God Almighty was with him.

¹¹Now Hiram king of Tyre sent messengers to David, along with cedar logs and carpenters and stonemasons, and they built a palace for David. ¹²And David knew that the LORD had established him as king over Israel and had exalted his kingdom for the sake of his people Israel.

¹³After he left Hebron, David took more concubines and wives in Jerusalem, and more sons and daughters were born to him. ¹⁴These are the names of the children born to him there: Shammua, Shobab, Nathan, Solomon, ¹⁵Ibhar, Elishua, Nepheg, Japhia, ¹⁶Elishama, Eliada and Eliphelet.

David Defeats the Philistines

¹⁷When the Philistines heard that David had been anointed king over Israel, they went up in full force to search for him, but David heard about it and went down to the stronghold. ¹⁸Now the Philistines had come and spread out in the Valley of Rephaim; ¹⁹so David inquired of the LORD, "Shall I go and attack the Philistines? Will you hand them over to me?"

The LORD answered him, "Go, for I will surely hand the Philistines over to you."

truth or dare

Just when the newly appointed king could have reveled in his fame, David kept raving about God! He knew that God gave him the position he had. When successes come your way, who gets the credit?

5:12

ª 8 Or use scaling hooks   ᵇ 8 Or are hated by David   ᶜ 9 Or the Millo

²⁰So David went to Baal Perazim, and there he defeated them. He said, "As waters break out, the LORD has broken out against my enemies before me." So that place was called Baal Perazim.ᵃ ²¹The Philistines abandoned their idols there, and David and his men carried them off.

²²Once more the Philistines came up and spread out in the Valley of Rephaim; ²³so David inquired of the LORD, and he answered, "Do not go straight up, but circle around behind them and attack them in front of the balsam trees. ²⁴As soon as you hear the sound of marching in the tops of the balsam trees, move quickly, because that will mean the LORD has gone out in front of you to strike the Philistine army." ²⁵So David did as the LORD commanded him, and he struck down the Philistines all the way from Gibeonᵇ to Gezer.

The Ark Brought to Jerusalem

6 David again brought together out of Israel chosen men, thirty thousand in all. ²He and all his men set out from Baalah of Judahᶜ to bring up from there the ark of God, which is called by the Name,ᵈ the name of the LORD Almighty, who is enthroned between the cherubim that are on the ark. ³They set the ark of God on a new cart and brought it from the house of Abinadab, which was on the hill. Uzzah and Ahio, sons of Abinadab, were guiding the new cart ⁴with the ark of God on it,ᵉ and Ahio was walking in front of it. ⁵David and the whole house of Israel were celebrating with all their might before the LORD, with songsᶠ and with harps, lyres, tambourines, sistrums and cymbals.

⁶When they came to the threshing floor of Nacon, Uzzah reached out and took hold of the ark of God, because the oxen stumbled. ⁷The LORD's anger burned against Uzzah because of his irreverent act; therefore God struck him down and he died there beside the ark of God.

⁸Then David was angry because the LORD's wrath had broken out against Uzzah, and to this day that place is called Perez Uzzah.ᵍ

⁹David was afraid of the LORD that day and said, "How can the ark of the LORD ever come to me?" ¹⁰He was not willing to take the ark of the LORD to be with him in the City of David. Instead, he took it aside to the house of Obed-Edom the Gittite. ¹¹The ark of the LORD remained in the house of Obed-Edom the Gittite for three months, and the LORD blessed him and his entire household.

¹²Now King David was told, "The LORD has blessed the household of Obed-Edom and everything he has, because of the ark of God." So David went down and brought up the ark of God from the house of Obed-Edom to the City of David with rejoicing. ¹³When those who were carrying the ark of the LORD had taken six steps, he sacrificed a bull and a fattened calf. ¹⁴David, wearing a linen ephod, danced before the LORD with all his might, ¹⁵while he and the entire house of Israel brought up the ark of the LORD with shouts and the sound of trumpets.

¹⁶As the ark of the LORD was entering the City of David, Michal daughter of Saul watched from a window. And when she saw King David leaping and dancing before the LORD, she despised him in her heart.

truth or dare

Ever feel self-conscious about your relationship with God? God digs a girl who'll openly reveal she's crazy about him.

6:12–15

¹⁷They brought the ark of the LORD and set it in its place inside the tent that David had pitched for it, and David sacrificed burnt offerings and fellowship offeringsʰ before the LORD. ¹⁸After he had finished sacrificing the burnt offerings and fellowship offerings, he blessed the people in the name of the LORD Almighty. ¹⁹Then he gave a loaf of bread, a cake of dates and a cake of raisins to each person in the whole crowd of Israelites, both men and women. And all the people went to their homes.

²⁰When David returned home to bless his household, Michal daughter of Saul came out to meet

---

ᵃ 20 Baal Perazim means the lord who breaks out. ᵇ 25 Septuagint (see also 1 Chron. 14:16); Hebrew Geba ᶜ 2 That is, Kiriath Jearim; Hebrew Baale Judah, a variant of Baalah of Judah ᵈ 2 Hebrew; Septuagint and Vulgate do not have the Name. ᵉ 3,4 Dead Sea Scrolls and some Septuagint manuscripts; Masoretic Text cart ⁴and they brought it with the ark of God from the house of Abinadab, which was on the hill ᶠ 5 See Dead Sea Scrolls, Septuagint and 1 Chronicles 13:8; Masoretic Text celebrating before the LORD with all kinds of instruments made of pine. ᵍ 8 Perez Uzzah means outbreak against Uzzah. ʰ 17 Traditionally peace offerings; also in verse 18

mirror images

As the ark of the LORD was entering the City of David, Michal daughter of Saul watched from a window. And when she saw King David leaping and dancing before the LORD, she despised him in her heart. 2 Samuel 6:16

Michal—What Will People Think?

Michal was royalty in more ways than one. She was the daughter of the former King Saul, and she was married to King David. She probably learned at an early age that she was special, different from the "common" people. Some girls might have grown up seeing their position as an honor and used it to help others or do great things. But Michal was caught up in appearances and what was proper for royalty, and she missed out on an opportunity to do real good.

As the ark of the Lord's covenant entered the city, the people of Israel celebrated with singing and dancing and shouting. And leading the whole party was David, who had shed his stuffy royal clothes, and was rejoicing and praising God with all of his might.

And Michal's reaction?

I am so embarrassed. He's humiliating me! What will everyone think of my immature husband?

Michal had a chance to join in leading the people of the city in worshiping God. She could have been a part of a royal worship service! But Michal just didn't get it. What David did in pure worship of the Lord, Michal saw as undignified. God was pleased with David, and the people of Israel witnessed David's passionate, sincere display of thanks to the Lord. Michal was the only one rolling her eyes.

Like Michal, sometimes we spend way too much time thinking about how we appear to others. If we worship God in the way he deserves, we might look ridiculous to some people. Passionate people often come across as fools, while princesses play it safe. They're so busy keeping up appearances that they miss truly worshiping God from the heart and maybe influencing others to do the same. Do you approach worship with the passion of David—or do you worry about how you look to others, like Michal? Are you more concerned with being regal than you are with being real before God?

Dear God, I will celebrate before you with all my heart. And I will not be ashamed to praise your name. Amen.

dear God

To read the next Mirror Images profile, go to page 412.

>> Read more about Michal in 1 Samuel 18–19 (page 344–346) and 2 Samuel 6 (page 367–369).

him and said, "How the king of Israel has distinguished himself today, disrobing in the sight of the slave girls of his servants as any vulgar fellow would!"

²¹David said to Michal, "It was before the Lord, who chose me rather than your father or anyone from his house when he appointed me ruler over the Lord's people Israel—I will celebrate before the Lord. ²²I will become even more undignified than this, and I will be humiliated in my own eyes. But by these slave girls you spoke of, I will be held in honor."

²³And Michal daughter of Saul had no children to the day of her death.

God's Promise to David

7 After the king was settled in his palace and the Lord had given him rest from all his enemies around him, ²he said to Nathan the prophet, "Here I am, living in a palace of cedar, while the ark of God remains in a tent."

³Nathan replied to the king, "Whatever you have in mind, go ahead and do it, for the Lord is with you."

⁴That night the word of the Lord came to Nathan, saying:

⁵"Go and tell my servant David, 'This is what the Lord says: Are you the one to build me a house to dwell in? ⁶I have not dwelt in a house from the day I brought the Israelites up out of Egypt to this day. I have been moving from place to place with a tent as my dwelling. ⁷Wherever I have moved with all the Israelites, did I ever say to any of their rulers whom I commanded to shepherd my people Israel, "Why have you not built me a house of cedar?" '

⁸"Now then, tell my servant David, 'This is what the Lord Almighty says: I took you from the pasture and from following the flock to be ruler over my people Israel. ⁹I have been with you wherever you have gone, and I have cut off all your enemies from before you. Now I will make your name great, like the names of the greatest men of the earth. ¹⁰And I will provide a place for my people Israel and will plant them so that they can have a home of their own and no longer be disturbed. Wicked people will not oppress them anymore, as they did at the beginning ¹¹and have done ever since the time I appointed leaders[a] over my people Israel. I will also give you rest from all your enemies.

" 'The Lord declares to you that the Lord himself will establish a house for you: ¹²When your days are over and you rest with your fathers, I will raise up your offspring to succeed you, who will come from your own body, and I will establish his kingdom. ¹³He is the one who will build a house

love notes

7:10–11

My loved one,

At times, the world doesn't seem like a safe place to live. At times, it feels like more people are against you than for you. Don't despair. I'll plant you in a safe place.

—Your heavenly Protector

Imagine that safe place of refuge. What does it look like? What does it feel like to be there?

_____

_____

_____

_____

_____

_____

_____

_____

_____

_____

a 11 Traditionally judges

for my Name, and I will establish the throne of his kingdom forever. [14]I will be his father, and he will be my son. When he does wrong, I will punish him with the rod of men, with floggings inflicted by men. [15]But my love will never be taken away from him, as I took it away from Saul, whom I removed from before you. [16]Your house and your kingdom will endure forever before me *a*; your throne will be established forever.' "

[17]Nathan reported to David all the words of this entire revelation.

David's Prayer

[18]Then King David went in and sat before the LORD, and he said:

"Who am I, O Sovereign LORD, and what is my family, that you have brought me this far? [19]And as if this were not enough in your sight, O Sovereign LORD, you have also spoken about the future of the house of your servant. Is this your usual way of dealing with man, O Sovereign LORD?

[20]"What more can David say to you? For you know your servant, O Sovereign LORD. [21]For the sake of your word and according to your will, you have done this great thing and made it known to your servant.

[22]"How great you are, O Sovereign LORD! There is no one like you, and there is no God but you, as we have heard with our own ears. [23]And who is like your people Israel—the one nation on earth that God went out to redeem as a people for himself, and to make a name for himself, and to perform great and awesome wonders by driving out nations and their gods from before your people, whom you redeemed from Egypt? *b* [24]You have established your people Israel as your very own forever, and you, O LORD, have become their God.

[25]"And now, LORD God, keep forever the promise you have made concerning your servant and his house. Do as you promised, [26]so that your name will be great forever. Then men will say, 'The LORD Almighty is God over Israel!' And the house of your servant David will be established before you.

[27]"O LORD Almighty, God of Israel, you have revealed this to your servant, saying, 'I will build a house for you.' So your servant has found courage to offer you this prayer. [28]O Sovereign LORD, you are God! Your words are trustworthy, and you have promised these good things to your servant. [29]Now be pleased to bless the house of your servant, that it may continue forever in your sight; for you, O Sovereign LORD, have spoken, and with your blessing the house of your servant will be blessed forever."

truth or **dare**

Even if you've got a killer plan, God might say "no" because he has something much bigger in mind.

7:1–16

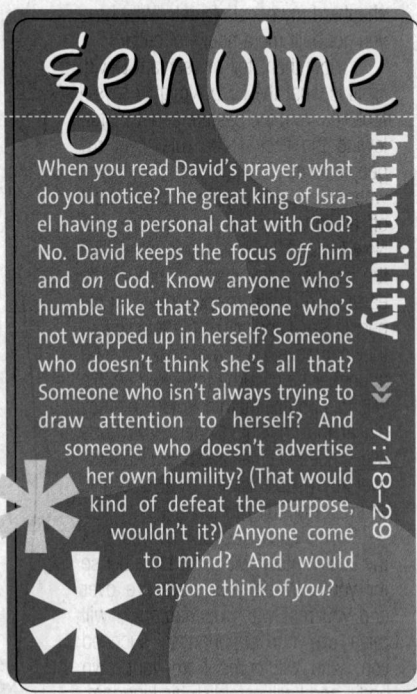

genuine humility »

When you read David's prayer, what do you notice? The great king of Israel having a personal chat with God? No. David keeps the focus *off* him and *on* God. Know anyone who's humble like that? Someone who's not wrapped up in herself? Someone who doesn't think she's all that? Someone who isn't always trying to draw attention to herself? And someone who doesn't advertise her own humility? (That would kind of defeat the purpose, wouldn't it?) Anyone come to mind? And would anyone think of *you*?

7:18–29

a 16 Some Hebrew manuscripts and Septuagint; most Hebrew manuscripts *you*   *b 23* See Septuagint and 1 Chron. 17:21; Hebrew *wonders for your land and before your people, whom you redeemed from Egypt, from the nations and their gods.*

David's Victories

8 In the course of time, David defeated the Philistines and subdued them, and he took Metheg Ammah from the control of the Philistines.

²David also defeated the Moabites. He made them lie down on the ground and measured them off with a length of cord. Every two lengths of them were put to death, and the third length was allowed to live. So the Moabites became subject to David and brought tribute.

³Moreover, David fought Hadadezer son of Rehob, king of Zobah, when he went to restore his control along the Euphrates River. ⁴David captured a thousand of his chariots, seven thousand charioteers*a* and twenty thousand foot soldiers. He hamstrung all but a hundred of the chariot horses.

⁵When the Arameans of Damascus came to help Hadadezer king of Zobah, David struck down twenty-two thousand of them. ⁶He put garrisons in the Aramean kingdom of Damascus, and the Arameans became subject to him and brought tribute. The LORD gave David victory wherever he went.

⁷David took the gold shields that belonged to the officers of Hadadezer and brought them to Jerusalem. ⁸From Tebah*b* and Berothai, towns that belonged to Hadadezer, King David took a great quantity of bronze.

⁹When Tou*c* king of Hamath heard that David had defeated the entire army of Hadadezer, ¹⁰he sent his son Joram*d* to King David to greet him and congratulate him on his victory in battle over Hadadezer, who had been at war with Tou. Joram brought with him articles of silver and gold and bronze.

¹¹King David dedicated these articles to the LORD, as he had done with the silver and gold from all the nations he had subdued: ¹²Edom*e* and Moab, the Ammonites and the Philistines, and Amalek. He also dedicated the plunder taken from Hadadezer son of Rehob, king of Zobah.

¹³And David became famous after he returned from striking down eighteen thousand Edomites*f* in the Valley of Salt.

¹⁴He put garrisons throughout Edom, and all the Edomites became subject to David. The LORD gave David victory wherever he went.

David's Officials

¹⁵David reigned over all Israel, doing what was just and right for all his people. ¹⁶Joab son of Zeruiah was over the army; Jehoshaphat son of Ahilud was recorder; ¹⁷Zadok son of Ahitub and Ahimelech son of Abiathar were priests; Seraiah was secretary; ¹⁸Benaiah son of Jehoiada was over the Kerethites and Pelethites; and David's sons were royal advisers.*g*

truth or dare

David had the power. He could've supported or slammed anyone he chose. But David won major respect for being a fair leader. Says something about him, doesn't it?

8:15

David and Mephibosheth

9 David asked, "Is there anyone still left of the house of Saul to whom I can show kindness for Jonathan's sake?"

²Now there was a servant of Saul's household named Ziba. They called him to appear before David, and the king said to him, "Are you Ziba?"

"Your servant," he replied.

³The king asked, "Is there no one still left of the house of Saul to whom I can show God's kindness?"

Ziba answered the king, "There is still a son of Jonathan; he is crippled in both feet."

⁴"Where is he?" the king asked.

Ziba answered, "He is at the house of Makir son of Ammiel in Lo Debar."

a 4 Septuagint (see also Dead Sea Scrolls and 1 Chron. 18:4); Masoretic Text *captured seventeen hundred of his charioteers*   b 8 See some Septuagint manuscripts (see also 1 Chron. 18:8); Hebrew *Betah.*   c 9 Hebrew *Toi,* a variant of *Tou*; also in verse 10   d 10 A variant of *Hadoram*   e 12 Some Hebrew manuscripts, Septuagint and Syriac (see also 1 Chron. 18:11); most Hebrew manuscripts *Aram*   f 13 A few Hebrew manuscripts, Septuagint and Syriac (see also 1 Chron. 18:12); most Hebrew manuscripts *Aram* (that is, Arameans)   g 18 Or *were priests*

[5]So King David had him brought from Lo Debar, from the house of Makir son of Ammiel.

[6]When Mephibosheth son of Jonathan, the son of Saul, came to David, he bowed down to pay him honor.

David said, "Mephibosheth!"

"Your servant," he replied.

[7]"Don't be afraid," David said to him, "for I will surely show you kindness for the sake of your father Jonathan. I will restore to you all the land that belonged to your grandfather Saul, and you will always eat at my table."

[8]Mephibosheth bowed down and said, "What is your servant, that you should notice a dead dog like me?"

[9]Then the king summoned Ziba, Saul's servant, and said to him, "I have given your master's grandson everything that belonged to Saul and his family. [10]You and your sons and your servants are to farm the land for him and bring in the crops, so that your master's grandson may be provided for. And Mephibosheth, grandson of your master, will always eat at my table." (Now Ziba had fifteen sons and twenty servants.)

genuine kindness » 9:1-8

It's easier to be kind to someone who can do something for you in return, isn't it? The socially connected girl. The teacher who gives you good grades. The grandparent who gives you generous gifts. But what about those who can never repay you? David showed extra kindness to Mephibosheth, the physically challenged son of his best friend, Jonathan. Mephibosheth could never repay him—all he had came from David. And Jonathan could never repay him—he'd died years before. David's motive was pure kindness. When was the last time you were kind to someone, knowing you'd get nothing in return?

genuine friendship » 10:1-5

When a friend is totally humiliated, you feel embarrassed too, right? That's what empathy is. You feel what she feels. But empathy isn't just a "wow, that's too bad." Empathy can also involve doing something practical to help a friend, just as David did. When his men were completely humiliated by the Ammonites, David was sensitive to their feelings and made sure they weren't embarrassed any further. How can you show empathy for a friend in need?

[11]Then Ziba said to the king, "Your servant will do whatever my lord the king commands his servant to do." So Mephibosheth ate at David's[a] table like one of the king's sons.

[12]Mephibosheth had a young son named Mica, and all the members of Ziba's household were servants of Mephibosheth. [13]And Mephibosheth lived in Jerusalem, because he always ate at the king's table, and he was crippled in both feet.

David Defeats the Ammonites

10 In the course of time, the king of the Ammonites died, and his son Hanun succeeded him as king. [2]David thought, "I will show kindness to Hanun son of Nahash, just as his father showed kindness to me." So David sent a delegation to express his sympathy to Hanun concerning his father.

When David's men came to the land of the Ammonites, [3]the Ammonite nobles said to Hanun their lord, "Do you think David is honoring your father by sending men to you to express sympathy? Hasn't David sent them to you to explore the city and spy it out

a 11 Septuagint; Hebrew *my*

and overthrow it?" ⁴So Hanun seized David's men, shaved off half of each man's beard, cut off their garments in the middle at the buttocks, and sent them away.

⁵When David was told about this, he sent messengers to meet the men, for they were greatly humiliated. The king said, "Stay at Jericho till your beards have grown, and then come back."

⁶When the Ammonites realized that they had become a stench in David's nostrils, they hired twenty thousand Aramean foot soldiers from Beth Rehob and Zobah, as well as the king of Maacah with a thousand men, and also twelve thousand men from Tob.

⁷On hearing this, David sent Joab out with the entire army of fighting men. ⁸The Ammonites came out and drew up in battle formation at the entrance to their city gate, while the Arameans of Zobah and Rehob and the men of Tob and Maacah were by themselves in the open country.

⁹Joab saw that there were battle lines in front of him and behind him; so he selected some of the best troops in Israel and deployed them against the Arameans. ¹⁰He put the rest of the men under the command of Abishai his brother and deployed them against the Ammonites. ¹¹Joab said, "If the Arameans are too strong for me, then you are to come to my rescue; but if the Ammonites are too strong for you, then I will come to rescue you. ¹²Be strong and let us fight bravely for our people and the cities of our God. The LORD will do what is good in his sight."

¹³Then Joab and the troops with him advanced to fight the Arameans, and they fled before him. ¹⁴When the Ammonites saw that the Arameans were fleeing, they fled before Abishai and went inside the city. So Joab returned from fighting the Ammonites and came to Jerusalem.

¹⁵After the Arameans saw that they had been routed by Israel, they regrouped. ¹⁶Hadadezer had Arameans brought from beyond the River ᵃ; they went to Helam, with Shobach the commander of Hadadezer's army leading them.

¹⁷When David was told of this, he gathered all Israel, crossed the Jordan and went to Helam. The Arameans formed their battle lines to meet David and fought against him. ¹⁸But they fled before Israel, and David killed seven hundred of their charioteers and forty thousand of their foot soldiers. ᵇ He also struck down Shobach the commander of their army, and he died there. ¹⁹When all the kings who were vassals of Hadadezer saw that they had been defeated by Israel, they made peace with the Israelites and became subject to them.

So the Arameans were afraid to help the Ammonites anymore.

David and Bathsheba

11 In the spring, at the time when kings go off to war, David sent Joab out with the king's men and the whole Israelite army. They destroyed the Ammonites and besieged Rabbah. But David remained in Jerusalem.

²One evening David got up from his bed and walked around on the roof of the palace. From the roof he saw a woman bathing. The woman was very beautiful, ³and David sent someone to find out about her. The man said, "Isn't this Bathsheba, the daughter of Eliam and the wife of Uriah the Hittite?" ⁴Then David sent messengers to get her. She came to him, and he slept with her. (She had purified herself from her uncleanness.) Then ᶜ she went back home. ⁵The woman conceived and sent word to David, saying, "I am pregnant."

⁶So David sent this word to Joab: "Send me Uriah the Hittite." And Joab sent him to David. ⁷When Uriah came to him, David asked him how Joab was, how the soldiers were and how the war was going. ⁸Then David said to Uriah, "Go down to your house and wash your feet." So Uriah left the palace, and a gift from the king was sent after him. ⁹But Uriah slept at the entrance to the palace with all his master's servants and did not go down to his house.

¹⁰When David was told, "Uriah did not go home," he asked him, "Haven't you just come from a distance? Why didn't you go home?"

¹¹Uriah said to David, "The ark and Israel and Judah are staying in tents, and my master Joab and my lord's men are camped in the open fields. How could I go to my house to eat and drink and lie with my wife? As surely as you live, I will not do such a thing!"

¹²Then David said to him, "Stay here one more day, and tomorrow I will send you back." So Uriah remained in Jerusalem that day and the next. ¹³At David's invitation, he ate and drank with him,

---

ᵃ *16* That is, the Euphrates   ᵇ *18* Some Septuagint manuscripts (see also 1 Chron. 19:18); Hebrew *horsemen*
ᶜ *4* Or *with her. When she purified herself from her uncleanness,*

in

Going Too Far

M y boyfriend Jeremy's on his way over, and I can't wait! A picnic on the beach, a romantic walk along the shore, maybe we'll even walk out on the jetty to watch the sunset. It's almost *too* perfect. It's hard to believe we've been dating for nine months!

Jeremy's the first guy I've ever been serious about. And when we graduate in May, I wouldn't be surprised if we start talking marriage—not right away, but someday. We've already talked about our careers and places we'd like to live and stuff like that. I can't imagine myself with anyone else, because no one's ever understood me like Jeremy does.

Lately we've been spending more time alone—just talking, watching movies . . . and kissing, of course. Sometimes I think I enjoy that part a little too much, but I'm not too worried. After all, we're still virgins. What's wrong with a little kissing (or a *lot* of kissing) if you really care about someone?

What I'm really wondering is, how far should we go? We'll probably get married anyway, so if we don't have sex, it seems like it would be okay to do just about anything else. It seems like the Bible's really unclear on how far is too far.

I guess I'll just leave it up to Jeremy. I trust him, and I think he'll make the right decision.

---

purity in focus

When it comes to sexual purity . . .

» Don't rely on the guy. When the hormones start flowing, *you* have to be prepared to draw the line. So think through in advance how you'll handle it.

» Practice God's plan. "Put to death . . . sexual immorality, impurity, lust" (Colossians 3:5, page 1558). Any activity that arouses sexual feelings should be off limits.

» Remember the benefits of purity. We tend to practice purity for negative reasons—fear of God, fear of our parents, fear of pregnancy, fear of STDs. But the purpose of purity isn't just to avoid bad consequences; it brings us God's blessing. God's not asking you to stay pure as a mean trick to cheat you out of fun. It's for your benefit. You won't believe how incredibly fun, exciting, romantic and perfect sex can be in the safety and commitment of marriage.

For more on this topic, see the index on page 1656.

For more ideas on purity and sexual boundaries, check out the link on www.TrueImagesBible.com

---

and David made him drunk. But in the evening Uriah went out to sleep on his mat among his master's servants; he did not go home.

[14]In the morning David wrote a letter to Joab and sent it with Uriah. [15]In it he wrote, "Put Uriah in the front line where the fighting is fiercest. Then withdraw from him so he will be struck down and die."

[16]So while Joab had the city under siege, he put Uriah at a place where he knew the strongest defenders were. [17]When the men of the city came out and fought against Joab, some of the men in David's army fell; moreover, Uriah the Hittite died.

[18]Joab sent David a full account of the battle. [19]He instructed the messenger: "When you have finished giving the king this account of the battle, [20]the king's anger may flare up, and he may ask you, 'Why did you get so close to the city to fight? Didn't you know they would shoot arrows from

the wall? [21]Who killed Abimelech son of Jerub-Besheth[a]? Didn't a woman throw an upper millstone on him from the wall, so that he died in Thebez? Why did you get so close to the wall?' If he asks you this, then say to him, 'Also, your servant Uriah the Hittite is dead.' "

[22]The messenger set out, and when he arrived he told David everything Joab had sent him to say. [23]The messenger said to David, "The men overpowered us and came out against us in the open, but we drove them back to the entrance to the city gate. [24]Then the archers shot arrows at your servants from the wall, and some of the king's men died. Moreover, your servant Uriah the Hittite is dead."

[25]David told the messenger, "Say this to Joab: 'Don't let this upset you; the sword devours one as well as another. Press the attack against the city and destroy it.' Say this to encourage Joab."

[26]When Uriah's wife heard that her husband was dead, she mourned for him. [27]After the time of mourning was over, David had her brought to his house, and she became his wife and bore him a son. But the thing David had done displeased the LORD.

Nathan Rebukes David

12 The LORD sent Nathan to David. When he came to him, he said, "There were two men in a certain town, one rich and the other poor. [2]The rich man had a very large number of sheep and cattle, [3]but the poor man had nothing except one little ewe lamb he had bought. He raised it, and it grew up with him and his children. It shared his food, drank from his cup and even slept in his arms. It was like a daughter to him.

[4]"Now a traveler came to the rich man, but the rich man refrained from taking one of his own sheep or cattle to prepare a meal for the traveler who had come to him. Instead, he took the ewe lamb that belonged to the poor man and prepared it for the one who had come to him."

[5]David burned with anger against the man and said to Nathan, "As surely as the LORD lives, the man who did this deserves to die! [6]He must pay for that lamb four times over, because he did such a thing and had no pity."

[7]Then Nathan said to David, "You are the man! This is what the LORD, the God of Israel, says: 'I anointed you king over Israel, and I delivered you from the hand of Saul. [8]I gave your master's house to you, and your master's wives into your arms. I gave you the house of Israel and Judah. And if all this had been too little, I would have given you even more. [9]Why did you despise the word of the LORD by doing what is evil in his eyes? You struck down Uriah the Hittite with the sword and took his wife to be your own. You killed him with the sword of the Ammonites. [10]Now, therefore, the sword will never depart from your house, because you despised me and took the wife of Uriah the Hittite to be your own.'

[11]"This is what the LORD says: 'Out of your own household I am going to bring calamity upon you. Before your very eyes I will take your wives and give them to one who is close to you, and he will lie with your wives in broad daylight. [12]You did it in secret, but I will do this thing in broad daylight before all Israel.' "

[13]Then David said to Nathan, "I have sinned against the LORD."

Nathan replied, "The LORD has taken away your sin. You are not going to die. [14]But because by doing this you have made the enemies of the LORD show utter contempt,[b] the son born to you will die."

[15]After Nathan had gone home, the LORD struck the child that Uriah's wife had borne to David, and he became ill. [16]David pleaded with God for the child. He fasted and went into his house and spent the nights lying on the ground. [17]The elders of his household stood beside him to get him up from the ground, but he refused, and he would not eat any food with them.

[18]On the seventh day the child died. David's servants were afraid to tell him that the child was dead, for they thought, "While the child was still living, we spoke to David but he would not listen to us. How can we tell him the child is dead? He may do something desperate."

[19]David noticed that his servants were whispering among themselves and he realized the child was dead. "Is the child dead?" he asked.

"Yes," they replied, "he is dead."

[20]Then David got up from the ground. After he had washed, put on lotions and changed his

a 21 Also known as Jerub-Baal (that is, Gideon)   b 14 Masoretic Text; an ancient Hebrew scribal tradition this you have shown utter contempt for the LORD clothes, he went into the house of the Lord and worshiped. Then he went to his own house, and at his request they served him food, and he ate.

²¹His servants asked him, "Why are you acting this way? While the child was alive, you fasted and wept, but now that the child is dead, you get up and eat!"

²²He answered, "While the child was still alive, I fasted and wept. I thought, 'Who knows? The Lord may be gracious to me and let the child live.' ²³But now that he is dead, why should I fast? Can I bring him back again? I will go to him, but he will not return to me."

²⁴Then David comforted his wife Bathsheba, and he went to her and lay with her. She gave birth to a son, and they named him Solomon. The Lord loved him; ²⁵and because the Lord loved him, he sent word through Nathan the prophet to name him Jedidiah. ᵃ

²⁶Meanwhile Joab fought against Rabbah of the Ammonites and captured the royal citadel. ²⁷Joab then sent messengers to David, saying, "I have fought against Rabbah and taken its water supply. ²⁸Now muster the rest of the troops and besiege the city and capture it. Otherwise I will take the city, and it will be named after me."

²⁹So David mustered the entire army and went to Rabbah, and attacked and captured it. ³⁰He took the crown from the head of their king ᵇ—its weight was a talent ᶜ of gold, and it was set with precious stones—and it was placed on David's head. He took a great quantity of plunder from the city ³¹and brought out the people who were there, consigning them to labor with saws and with iron picks and axes, and he made them work at brickmaking. ᵈ He did this to all the Ammonite towns. Then David and his entire army returned to Jerusalem.

genuine

persistence » 12:22

Let's say you really, really need God to do something for you. Would you pray about the matter once and then give up? If you're like David (and most of us probably are), then you wouldn't. He kept on praying for God to heal his sick child (see 12:16) until he received an answer. And when the answer was no, he didn't pout, nor did he try to manipulate a "yes" out of God by his persistence. Instead he accepted God's answer. Persistence helps you keep on praying . . . and keep on believing that God knows best, even if he says no.

Amnon and Tamar

13 In the course of time, Amnon son of David fell in love with Tamar, the beautiful sister of Absalom son of David. ²Amnon became frustrated to the point of illness on account of his sister Tamar, for she was a virgin, and it seemed impossible for him to do anything to her.

³Now Amnon had a friend named Jonadab son of Shimeah, David's brother. Jonadab was a very shrewd man. ⁴He asked Amnon, "Why do you, the king's son, look so haggard morning after morning? Won't you tell me?"

Amnon said to him, "I'm in love with Tamar, my brother Absalom's sister."

⁵"Go to bed and pretend to be ill," Jonadab said. "When your father comes to see you, say to him, 'I would like my sister Tamar to come and give me something to eat. Let her prepare the food in my sight so I may watch her and then eat it from her hand.' "

⁶So Amnon lay down and pretended to be ill. When the king came to see him, Amnon said to him, "I would like my sister Tamar to come and make some special bread in my sight, so I may eat from her hand."

⁷David sent word to Tamar at the palace: "Go to the house of your brother Amnon and prepare

ᵃ 25 *Jedidiah* means *loved by the Lord.*   ᵇ 30 Or *of Milcom* (that is, Molech)   ᶜ 30 That is, about 75 pounds (about 34 kilograms)   ᵈ 31 The meaning of the Hebrew for this clause is uncertain.

some food for him." [8]So Tamar went to the house of her brother Amnon, who was lying down. She took some dough, kneaded it, made the bread in his sight and baked it. [9]Then she took the pan and served him the bread, but he refused to eat.

"Send everyone out of here," Amnon said. So everyone left him. [10]Then Amnon said to Tamar, "Bring the food here into my bedroom so I may eat from your hand." And Tamar took the bread she had prepared and brought it to her brother Amnon in his bedroom. [11]But when she took it to him to eat, he grabbed her and said, "Come to bed with me, my sister."

[12]"Don't, my brother!" she said to him. "Don't force me. Such a thing should not be done in Israel! Don't do this wicked thing. [13]What about me? Where could I get rid of my disgrace? And what about you? You would be like one of the wicked fools in Israel. Please speak to the king; he will not keep me from being married to you." [14]But he refused to listen to her, and since he was stronger than she, he raped her.

truth or dare

Think the Bible's full of cuddly stories and perfect endings? It's actually full of true stories and real life experiences, like Tamar's rape. She felt the same shame and pain that many girls face today.

13:12–14

[15]Then Amnon hated her with intense hatred. In fact, he hated her more than he had loved her. Amnon said to her, "Get up and get out!"

[16]"No!" she said to him. "Sending me away would be a greater wrong than what you have already done to me."

But he refused to listen to her. [17]He called his personal servant and said, "Get this woman out of here and bolt the door after her." [18]So his servant put her out and bolted the door after her. She was wearing a richly ornamented[a] robe, for this was the kind of garment the virgin daughters of the king wore. [19]Tamar put ashes on her head and tore the ornamented[b] robe she was wearing. She put her hand on her head and went away, weeping aloud as she went.

[20]Her brother Absalom said to her, "Has that Amnon, your brother, been with you? Be quiet now, my sister; he is your brother. Don't take this thing to heart." And Tamar lived in her brother Absalom's house, a desolate woman.

[21]When King David heard all this, he was furious. [22]Absalom never said a word to Amnon, either good or bad; he hated Amnon because he had disgraced his sister Tamar.

truth or dare

Make up your mind, buddy! Do you love her or hate her? If Amnon's "love" turned to hate so quickly, we can safely conclude it was lust and definitely not love.

13:15

Absalom Kills Amnon

[23]Two years later, when Absalom's sheepshearers were at Baal Hazor near the border of Ephraim, he invited all the king's sons to come there. [24]Absalom went to the king and said, "Your servant has had shearers come. Will the king and his officials please join me?"

[25]"No, my son," the king replied. "All of us should not go; we would only be a burden to you." Although Absalom urged him, he still refused to go, but gave him his blessing.

[26]Then Absalom said, "If not, please let my brother Amnon come with us."

The king asked him, "Why should he go with you?" [27]But Absalom urged him, so he sent with him Amnon and the rest of the king's sons.

[28]Absalom ordered his men, "Listen! When Amnon is in high spirits from drinking wine and I say to you, 'Strike Amnon down,' then kill him. Don't be afraid. Have not I given you this order? Be

---

a 18 The meaning of the Hebrew for this phrase is uncertain.   b 19 The meaning of the Hebrew for this word is uncertain.

strong and brave." ²⁹So Absalom's men did to Amnon what Absalom had ordered. Then all the king's sons got up, mounted their mules and fled.

³⁰While they were on their way, the report came to David: "Absalom has struck down all the king's sons; not one of them is left." ³¹The king stood up, tore his clothes and lay down on the ground; and all his servants stood by with their clothes torn.

³²But Jonadab son of Shimeah, David's brother, said, "My lord should not think that they killed all the princes; only Amnon is dead. This has been Absalom's expressed intention ever since the day Amnon raped his sister Tamar. ³³My lord the king should not be concerned about the report that all the king's sons are dead. Only Amnon is dead."

³⁴Meanwhile, Absalom had fled.

Now the man standing watch looked up and saw many people on the road west of him, coming down the side of the hill. The watchman went and told the king, "I see men in the direction of Horonaim, on the side of the hill."ᵃ

³⁵Jonadab said to the king, "See, the king's sons are here; it has happened just as your servant said."

³⁶As he finished speaking, the king's sons came in, wailing loudly. The king, too, and all his servants wept very bitterly.

³⁷Absalom fled and went to Talmai son of Ammihud, the king of Geshur. But King David mourned for his son every day.

³⁸After Absalom fled and went to Geshur, he stayed there three years. ³⁹And the spirit of the kingᵇ longed to go to Absalom, for he was consoled concerning Amnon's death.

Absalom Returns to Jerusalem

14 Joab son of Zeruiah knew that the king's heart longed for Absalom. ²So Joab sent someone to Tekoa and had a wise woman brought from there. He said to her, "Pretend you are in mourning. Dress in mourning clothes, and don't use any cosmetic lotions. Act like a woman who has spent many days grieving for the dead. ³Then go to the king and speak these words to him." And Joab put the words in her mouth.

⁴When the woman from Tekoa wentᶜ to the king, she fell with her face to the ground to pay him honor, and she said, "Help me, O king!"

⁵The king asked her, "What is troubling you?"

She said, "I am indeed a widow; my husband is dead. ⁶I your servant had two sons. They got into a fight with each other in the field, and no one was there to separate them. One struck the other and killed him. ⁷Now the whole clan has risen up against your servant; they say, 'Hand over the one who struck his brother down, so that we may put him to death for the life of his brother whom he killed; then we will get rid of the heir as well.' They would put out the only burning coal I have left, leaving my husband neither name nor descendant on the face of the earth."

⁸The king said to the woman, "Go home, and I will issue an order in your behalf."

⁹But the woman from Tekoa said to him, "My lord the king, let the blame rest on me and on my father's family, and let the king and his throne be without guilt."

¹⁰The king replied, "If anyone says anything to you, bring him to me, and he will not bother you again."

¹¹She said, "Then let the king invoke the LORD his God to prevent the avenger of blood from adding to the destruction, so that my son will not be destroyed."

"As surely as the LORD lives," he said, "not one hair of your son's head will fall to the ground."

¹²Then the woman said, "Let your servant speak a word to my lord the king."

"Speak," he replied.

¹³The woman said, "Why then have you devised a thing like this against the people of God? When the king says this, does he not convict himself, for the king has not brought back his banished son? ¹⁴Like water spilled on the ground, which cannot be recovered, so we must die. But God does not take away life; instead, he devises ways so that a banished person may not remain estranged from him.

ᵃ 34 Septuagint; Hebrew does not have this sentence.   ᵇ 39 Dead Sea Scrolls and some Septuagint manuscripts; Masoretic Text But the spirit of, David the king   ᶜ 4 Many Hebrew manuscripts, Septuagint, Vulgate and Syriac; most Hebrew manuscripts spoke

¹⁵"And now I have come to say this to my lord the king because the people have made me afraid. Your servant thought, 'I will speak to the king; perhaps he will do what his servant asks. ¹⁶Perhaps the king will agree to deliver his servant from the hand of the man who is trying to cut off both me and my son from the inheritance God gave us.'

¹⁷"And now your servant says, 'May the word of my lord the king bring me rest, for my lord the king is like an angel of God in discerning good and evil. May the Lᴏʀᴅ your God be with you.' "

¹⁸Then the king said to the woman, "Do not keep from me the answer to what I am going to ask you."

"Let my lord the king speak," the woman said.

¹⁹The king asked, "Isn't the hand of Joab with you in all this?"

The woman answered, "As surely as you live, my lord the king, no one can turn to the right or to the left from anything my lord the king says. Yes, it was your servant Joab who instructed me to do this and who put all these words into the mouth of your servant. ²⁰Your servant Joab did this to change the present situation. My lord has wisdom like that of an angel of God—he knows everything that happens in the land."

²¹The king said to Joab, "Very well, I will do it. Go, bring back the young man Absalom."

²²Joab fell with his face to the ground to pay him honor, and he blessed the king. Joab said, "Today your servant knows that he has found favor in your eyes, my lord the king, because the king has granted his servant's request."

²³Then Joab went to Geshur and brought Absalom back to Jerusalem. ²⁴But the king said, "He must go to his own house; he must not see my face." So Absalom went to his own house and did not see the face of the king.

²⁵In all Israel there was not a man so highly praised for his handsome appearance as Absalom. From the top of his head to the sole of his foot there was no blemish in him. ²⁶Whenever he cut the hair of his head—he used to cut his hair from time to time when it became too heavy for him— he would weigh it, and its weight was two hundred shekels*a* by the royal standard.

²⁷Three sons and a daughter were born to Absalom. The daughter's name was Tamar, and she became a beautiful woman.

²⁸Absalom lived two years in Jerusalem without seeing the king's face. ²⁹Then Absalom sent for Joab in order to send him to the king, but Joab refused to come to him. So he sent a second time, but he refused to come. ³⁰Then he said to his servants, "Look, Joab's field is next to mine, and he has barley there. Go and set it on fire." So Absalom's servants set the field on fire.

³¹Then Joab did go to Absalom's house and he said to him, "Why have your servants set my field on fire?"

³²Absalom said to Joab, "Look, I sent word to you and said, 'Come here so I can send you to the king to ask, "Why have I come from Geshur? It would be better for me if I were still there!" ' Now then, I want to see the king's face, and if I am guilty of anything, let him put me to death."

³³So Joab went to the king and told him this. Then the king summoned Absalom, and he came in and bowed down with his face to the ground before the king. And the king kissed Absalom.

Absalom's Conspiracy

15 In the course of time, Absalom provided himself with a chariot and horses and with fifty men to run ahead of him. ²He would get up early and stand by the side of the road leading to the city gate. Whenever anyone came with a complaint to be placed before the king for a decision, Absalom would call out to him, "What town are you from?" He would answer, "Your servant is from one of the tribes of Israel." ³Then Absalom would say to him, "Look, your claims are valid and proper, but there is no representative of the king to hear you." ⁴And Absalom would add, "If only I were appointed judge in the land! Then everyone who has a complaint or case could come to me and I would see that he gets justice."

⁵Also, whenever anyone approached him to bow down before him, Absalom would reach out his hand, take hold of him and kiss him. ⁶Absalom behaved in this way toward all the Israelites who came to the king asking for justice, and so he stole the hearts of the men of Israel.

⁷At the end of four*b* years, Absalom said to the king, "Let me go to Hebron and fulfill a vow I

---

a 26 That is, about 5 pounds (about 2.3 kilograms)   *b 7* Some Septuagint manuscripts, Syriac and Josephus; Hebrew *forty* made to the Lord. [8]While your servant was living at Geshur in Aram, I made this vow: 'If the Lord takes me back to Jerusalem, I will worship the Lord in Hebron.[a]' "

[9]The king said to him, "Go in peace." So he went to Hebron.

[10]Then Absalom sent secret messengers throughout the tribes of Israel to say, "As soon as you hear the sound of the trumpets, then say, 'Absalom is king in Hebron.' " [11]Two hundred men from Jerusalem had accompanied Absalom. They had been invited as guests and went quite innocently, knowing nothing about the matter. [12]While Absalom was offering sacrifices, he also sent for Ahithophel the Gilonite, David's counselor, to come from Giloh, his hometown. And so the conspiracy gained strength, and Absalom's following kept on increasing.

David Flees

[13]A messenger came and told David, "The hearts of the men of Israel are with Absalom."

[14]Then David said to all his officials who were with him in Jerusalem, "Come! We must flee, or none of us will escape from Absalom. We must leave immediately, or he will move quickly to overtake us and bring ruin upon us and put the city to the sword."

[15]The king's officials answered him, "Your servants are ready to do whatever our lord the king chooses."

[16]The king set out, with his entire household following him; but he left ten concubines to take care of the palace. [17]So the king set out, with all the people following him, and they halted at a place some distance away. [18]All his men marched past him, along with all the Kerethites and Pelethites; and all the six hundred Gittites who had accompanied him from Gath marched before the king.

[19]The king said to Ittai the Gittite, "Why should you come along with us? Go back and stay with King Absalom. You are a foreigner, an exile from your homeland. [20]You came only yesterday. And today shall I make you wander about with us, when I do not know where I am going? Go back, and take your countrymen. May kindness and faithfulness be with you."

[21]But Ittai replied to the king, "As surely as the Lord lives, and as my lord the king lives, wherever my lord the king may be, whether it means life or death, there will your servant be."

[22]David said to Ittai, "Go ahead, march on." So Ittai the Gittite marched on with all his men and the families that were with him.

[23]The whole countryside wept aloud as all the people passed by. The king also crossed the Kidron Valley, and all the people moved on toward the desert.

[24]Zadok was there, too, and all the Levites who were with him were carrying the ark of the covenant of God. They set down the ark of God, and Abiathar offered sacrifices[b] until all the people had finished leaving the city.

[25]Then the king said to Zadok, "Take the ark of God back into the city. If I find favor in the Lord's eyes, he will bring me back and let me see it and his dwelling place again. [26]But if he says, 'I am not pleased with you,' then I am ready; let him do to me whatever seems good to him."

[27]The king also said to Zadok the priest, "Aren't you a seer? Go back to the city in peace, with your son Ahimaaz and Jonathan son of Abiathar. You and Abiathar take your two sons with you. [28]I will wait at the fords in the desert until word comes from you to inform me." [29]So Zadok and Abiathar took the ark of God back to Jerusalem and stayed there.

[30]But David continued up the Mount of Olives, weeping as he went; his head was covered and he was barefoot. All the people with him covered their heads too and were weeping as they went up. [31]Now David had been told, "Ahithophel is among the conspirators with Absalom." So David prayed, "O Lord, turn Ahithophel's counsel into foolishness."

[32]When David arrived at the summit, where people used to worship God, Hushai the Arkite was there to meet him, his robe torn and dust on his head. [33]David said to him, "If you go with me, you will be a burden to me. [34]But if you return to the city and say to Absalom, 'I will be your servant, O king; I was your father's servant in the past, but now I will be your servant,' then you can help me by frustrating Ahithophel's advice. [35]Won't the priests Zadok and Abiathar be there with you? Tell them anything you hear in the king's palace. [36]Their two sons, Ahimaaz son of Zadok and Jonathan son of Abiathar, are there with them. Send them to me with anything you hear."

[37]So David's friend Hushai arrived at Jerusalem as Absalom was entering the city.

a 8 Some Septuagint manuscripts; Hebrew does not have *in Hebron.*   *b 24* Or *Abiathar went up*

David and Ziba

16 When David had gone a short distance beyond the summit, there was Ziba, the steward of Mephibosheth, waiting to meet him. He had a string of donkeys saddled and loaded with two hundred loaves of bread, a hundred cakes of raisins, a hundred cakes of figs and a skin of wine.

²The king asked Ziba, "Why have you brought these?"

Ziba answered, "The donkeys are for the king's household to ride on, the bread and fruit are for the men to eat, and the wine is to refresh those who become exhausted in the desert."

³The king then asked, "Where is your master's grandson?"

Ziba said to him, "He is staying in Jerusalem, because he thinks, 'Today the house of Israel will give me back my grandfather's kingdom.' "

⁴Then the king said to Ziba, "All that belonged to Mephibosheth is now yours."

"I humbly bow," Ziba said. "May I find favor in your eyes, my lord the king."

Shimei Curses David

⁵As King David approached Bahurim, a man from the same clan as Saul's family came out from there. His name was Shimei son of Gera, and he cursed as he came out. ⁶He pelted David and all the king's officials with stones, though all the troops and the special guard were on David's right and left. ⁷As he cursed, Shimei said, "Get out, get out, you man of blood, you scoundrel! ⁸The LORD has repaid you for all the blood you shed in the household of Saul, in whose place you have reigned. The LORD has handed the kingdom over to your son Absalom. You have come to ruin because you are a man of blood!"

⁹Then Abishai son of Zeruiah said to the king, "Why should this dead dog curse my lord the king? Let me go over and cut off his head."

¹⁰But the king said, "What do you and I have in common, you sons of Zeruiah? If he is cursing because the LORD said to him, 'Curse David,' who can ask, 'Why do you do this?' "

¹¹David then said to Abishai and all his officials, "My son, who is of my own flesh, is trying to take my life. How much more, then, this Benjamite! Leave him alone; let him curse, for the LORD has told him to. ¹²It may be that the LORD will see my distress and repay me with good for the cursing I am receiving today."

¹³So David and his men continued along the road while Shimei was going along the hillside opposite him, cursing as he went and throwing stones at him and showering him with dirt. ¹⁴The king and all the people with him arrived at their destination exhausted. And there he refreshed himself.

The Advice of Ahithophel and Hushai

¹⁵Meanwhile, Absalom and all the men of Israel came to Jerusalem, and Ahithophel was with him. ¹⁶Then Hushai the Arkite, David's friend, went to Absalom and said to him, "Long live the king! Long live the king!"

¹⁷Absalom asked Hushai, "Is this the love you show your friend? Why didn't you go with your friend?"

¹⁸Hushai said to Absalom, "No, the one chosen by the LORD, by these people, and by all the men of Israel—his I will be, and I will remain with him. ¹⁹Furthermore, whom should I serve? Should I not serve the son? Just as I served your father, so I will serve you."

²⁰Absalom said to Ahithophel, "Give us your advice. What should we do?"

²¹Ahithophel answered, "Lie with your father's concubines whom he left to take care of the palace. Then all Israel will hear that you have made yourself a stench in your father's nostrils, and the hands of everyone with you will be strengthened." ²²So they pitched a tent for Absalom on the roof, and he lay with his father's concubines in the sight of all Israel.

²³Now in those days the advice Ahithophel gave was like that of one who inquires of God. That was how both David and Absalom regarded all of Ahithophel's advice.

17 Ahithophel said to Absalom, "I would ᵃ choose twelve thousand men and set out tonight in pursuit of David. ²I would ᵇ attack him while he is weary and weak. I would ᵇ strike him with terror, and then all the people with him will flee. I would ᵇ strike down only the king ³and bring all the people back to you. The death of the man you seek will mean the return of all;

ᵃ 1 Or *Let me*   ᵇ 2 Or *will*

all the people will be unharmed." [4]This plan seemed good to Absalom and to all the elders of Israel.

[5]But Absalom said, "Summon also Hushai the Arkite, so we can hear what he has to say." [6]When Hushai came to him, Absalom said, "Ahithophel has given this advice. Should we do what he says? If not, give us your opinion."

[7]Hushai replied to Absalom, "The advice Ahithophel has given is not good this time. [8]You know your father and his men; they are fighters, and as fierce as a wild bear robbed of her cubs. Besides, your father is an experienced fighter; he will not spend the night with the troops. [9]Even now, he is hidden in a cave or some other place. If he should attack your troops first,[a] whoever hears about it will say, 'There has been a slaughter among the troops who follow Absalom.' [10]Then even the bravest soldier, whose heart is like the heart of a lion, will melt with fear, for all Israel knows that your father is a fighter and that those with him are brave.

[11]"So I advise you: Let all Israel, from Dan to Beersheba—as numerous as the sand on the seashore—be gathered to you, with you yourself leading them into battle. [12]Then we will attack him wherever he may be found, and we will fall on him as dew settles on the ground. Neither he nor any of his men will be left alive. [13]If he withdraws into a city, then all Israel will bring ropes to that city, and we will drag it down to the valley until not even a piece of it can be found."

[14]Absalom and all the men of Israel said, "The advice of Hushai the Arkite is better than that of Ahithophel." For the LORD had determined to frustrate the good advice of Ahithophel in order to bring disaster on Absalom.

[15]Hushai told Zadok and Abiathar, the priests, "Ahithophel has advised Absalom and the elders of Israel to do such and such, but I have advised them to do so and so. [16]Now send a message immediately and tell David, 'Do not spend the night at the fords in the desert; cross over without fail, or the king and all the people with him will be swallowed up.' "

[17]Jonathan and Ahimaaz were staying at En Rogel. A servant girl was to go and inform them, and they were to go and tell King David, for they could not risk being seen entering the city. [18]But a young man saw them and told Absalom. So the two of them left quickly and went to the house of a man in Bahurim. He had a well in his courtyard, and they climbed down into it. [19]His wife took a covering and spread it out over the opening of the well and scattered grain over it. No one knew anything about it.

[20]When Absalom's men came to the woman at the house, they asked, "Where are Ahimaaz and Jonathan?"

The woman answered them, "They crossed over the brook."[b] The men searched but found no one, so they returned to Jerusalem.

[21]After the men had gone, the two climbed out of the well and went to inform King David. They said to him, "Set out and cross the river at once; Ahithophel has advised such and such against you." [22]So David and all the people with him set out and crossed the Jordan. By daybreak, no one was left who had not crossed the Jordan.

[23]When Ahithophel saw that his advice had not been followed, he saddled his donkey and set out for his house in his hometown. He put his house in order and then hanged himself. So he died and was buried in his father's tomb.

[24]David went to Mahanaim, and Absalom crossed the Jordan with all the men of Israel. [25]Absalom had appointed Amasa over the army in place of Joab. Amasa was the son of a man named Jether,[c] an Israelite[d] who had married Abigail,[e] the daughter of Nahash and sister of Zeruiah the mother of Joab. [26]The Israelites and Absalom camped in the land of Gilead.

[27]When David came to Mahanaim, Shobi son of Nahash from Rabbah of the Ammonites, and Makir son of Ammiel from Lo Debar, and Barzillai the Gileadite from Rogelim [28]brought bedding and bowls and articles of pottery. They also brought wheat and barley, flour and roasted grain, beans and lentils,[f] [29]honey and curds, sheep, and cheese from cows' milk for David and his people to eat. For they said, "The people have become hungry and tired and thirsty in the desert."

---

[a] 9 Or *When some of the men fall at the first attack*   [b] 20 Or *"They passed by the sheep pen toward the water."*
[c] 25 Hebrew *Ithra*, a variant of *Jether*   [d] 25 Hebrew and some Septuagint manuscripts; other Septuagint manuscripts
(see also 1 Chron. 2:17) *Ishmaelite* or *Jezreelite*   [e] 25 Hebrew *Abigal*, a variant of *Abigail*   [f] 28 Most Septuagint
manuscripts and Syriac; Hebrew *lentils, and roasted grain*

Absalom's Death

18 David mustered the men who were with him and appointed over them commanders of thousands and commanders of hundreds. ²David sent the troops out—a third under the command of Joab, a third under Joab's brother Abishai son of Zeruiah, and a third under Ittai the Gittite. The king told the troops, "I myself will surely march out with you."

³But the men said, "You must not go out; if we are forced to flee, they won't care about us. Even if half of us die, they won't care; but you are worth ten thousand of us.ᵃ It would be better now for you to give us support from the city."

⁴The king answered, "I will do whatever seems best to you."

So the king stood beside the gate while all the men marched out in units of hundreds and of thousands. ⁵The king commanded Joab, Abishai and Ittai, "Be gentle with the young man Absalom for my sake." And all the troops heard the king giving orders concerning Absalom to each of the commanders.

⁶The army marched into the field to fight Israel, and the battle took place in the forest of Ephraim. ⁷There the army of Israel was defeated by David's men, and the casualties that day were great—twenty thousand men. ⁸The battle spread out over the whole countryside, and the forest claimed more lives that day than the sword.

⁹Now Absalom happened to meet David's men. He was riding his mule, and as the mule went under the thick branches of a large oak, Absalom's head got caught in the tree. He was left hanging in midair, while the mule he was riding kept on going.

¹⁰When one of the men saw this, he told Joab, "I just saw Absalom hanging in an oak tree."

¹¹Joab said to the man who had told him this, "What! You saw him? Why didn't you strike him to the ground right there? Then I would have had to give you ten shekelsᵇ of silver and a warrior's belt."

¹²But the man replied, "Even if a thousand shekelsᶜ were weighed out into my hands, I would not lift my hand against the king's son. In our hearing the king commanded you and Abishai and Ittai, 'Protect the young man Absalom for my sake.ᵈ' ¹³And if I had put my life in jeopardyᵉ—and nothing is hidden from the king—you would have kept your distance from me."

¹⁴Joab said, "I'm not going to wait like this for you." So he took three javelins in his hand and plunged them into Absalom's heart while Absalom was still alive in the oak tree. ¹⁵And ten of Joab's armor-bearers surrounded Absalom, struck him and killed him.

¹⁶Then Joab sounded the trumpet, and the troops stopped pursuing Israel, for Joab halted them. ¹⁷They took Absalom, threw him into a big pit in the forest and piled up a large heap of rocks over him. Meanwhile, all the Israelites fled to their homes.

¹⁸During his lifetime Absalom had taken a pillar and erected it in the King's Valley as a monument to himself, for he thought, "I have no son to carry on the memory of my name." He named the pillar after himself, and it is called Absalom's Monument to this day.

genuine

hospitality ›› 17:27-29

How welcoming are you toward others? When David was forced to flee from his home, Shobi was one of those who rolled out the welcome wagon by providing food, bedding and a kind welcome for David and his people. What's even more interesting is the fact that Shobi's people were enemies of Israel at one point. A hospitable person not only welcomes others; she also provides for their needs in practical ways. She also doesn't limit her warm welcomes to just friends and family. After all, even a former enemy might need hospitality. Is that the kind of welcome you offer others?

ᵃ 3 Two Hebrew manuscripts, some Septuagint manuscripts and Vulgate; most Hebrew manuscripts *care; for now there are ten thousand like us* ᵇ 11 That is, about 4 ounces (about 115 grams) ᶜ 12 That is, about 25 pounds (about 11 kilograms) ᵈ 12 A few Hebrew manuscripts, Septuagint, Vulgate and Syriac; most Hebrew manuscripts may be translated *Absalom, whoever you may be.* ᵉ 13 Or *Otherwise, if I had acted treacherously toward him*

[19]Now Ahimaaz son of Zadok said, "Let me run and take the news to the king that the Lord has delivered him from the hand of his enemies."

[20]"You are not the one to take the news today," Joab told him. "You may take the news another time, but you must not do so today, because the king's son is dead."

[21]Then Joab said to a Cushite, "Go, tell the king what you have seen." The Cushite bowed down before Joab and ran off.

[22]Ahimaaz son of Zadok again said to Joab, "Come what may, please let me run behind the Cushite."

But Joab replied, "My son, why do you want to go? You don't have any news that will bring you a reward."

[23]He said, "Come what may, I want to run."

So Joab said, "Run!" Then Ahimaaz ran by way of the plain*a* and outran the Cushite.

[24]While David was sitting between the inner and outer gates, the watchman went up to the roof of the gateway by the wall. As he looked out, he saw a man running alone. [25]The watchman called out to the king and reported it.

The king said, "If he is alone, he must have good news." And the man came closer and closer.

[26]Then the watchman saw another man running, and he called down to the gatekeeper, "Look, another man running alone!"

The king said, "He must be bringing good news, too."

[27]The watchman said, "It seems to me that the first one runs like Ahimaaz son of Zadok."

"He's a good man," the king said. "He comes with good news."

[28]Then Ahimaaz called out to the king, "All is well!" He bowed down before the king with his face to the ground and said, "Praise be to the Lord your God! He has delivered up the men who lifted their hands against my lord the king."

[29]The king asked, "Is the young man Absalom safe?"

Ahimaaz answered, "I saw great confusion just as Joab was about to send the king's servant and me, your servant, but I don't know what it was."

[30]The king said, "Stand aside and wait here." So he stepped aside and stood there.

[31]Then the Cushite arrived and said, "My lord the king, hear the good news! The Lord has delivered you today from all who rose up against you."

[32]The king asked the Cushite, "Is the young man Absalom safe?"

The Cushite replied, "May the enemies of my lord the king and all who rise up to harm you be like that young man."

[33]The king was shaken. He went up to the room over the gateway and wept. As he went, he said: "O my son Absalom! My son, my son Absalom! If only I had died instead of you—O Absalom, my son, my son!"

19 Joab was told, "The king is weeping and mourning for Absalom." [2]And for the whole army the victory that day was turned into mourning, because on that day the troops heard it said, "The king is grieving for his son." [3]The men stole into the city that day as men steal in who are ashamed when they flee from battle. [4]The king covered his face and cried aloud, "O my son Absalom! O Absalom, my son, my son!"

[5]Then Joab went into the house to the king and said, "Today you have humiliated all your men, who have just saved your life and the lives of your sons and daughters and the lives of your wives and concubines. [6]You love those who hate you and hate those who love you. You have made it clear today that the commanders and their men mean nothing to you. I see that you would be pleased if Absalom were alive today and all of us were dead. [7]Now go out and encourage your men. I swear by the Lord that if you don't go out, not a man will be left with you by nightfall. This will be worse for you than all the calamities that have come upon you from your youth till now."

[8]So the king got up and took his seat in the gateway. When the men were told, "The king is sitting in the gateway," they all came before him.

a 23 That is, the plain of the Jordan

David Returns to Jerusalem

Meanwhile, the Israelites had fled to their homes. [9]Throughout the tribes of Israel, the people were all arguing with each other, saying, "The king delivered us from the hand of our enemies; he is the one who rescued us from the hand of the Philistines. But now he has fled the country because of Absalom; [10]and Absalom, whom we anointed to rule over us, has died in battle. So why do you say nothing about bringing the king back?"

[11]King David sent this message to Zadok and Abiathar, the priests: "Ask the elders of Judah, 'Why should you be the last to bring the king back to his palace, since what is being said throughout Israel has reached the king at his quarters? [12]You are my brothers, my own flesh and blood. So why should you be the last to bring back the king?' [13]And say to Amasa, 'Are you not my own flesh and blood? May God deal with me, be it ever so severely, if from now on you are not the commander of my army in place of Joab.' "

[14]He won over the hearts of all the men of Judah as though they were one man. They sent word to the king, "Return, you and all your men." [15]Then the king returned and went as far as the Jordan.

Now the men of Judah had come to Gilgal to go out and meet the king and bring him across the Jordan. [16]Shimei son of Gera, the Benjamite from Bahurim, hurried down with the men of Judah to meet King David. [17]With him were a thousand Benjamites, along with Ziba, the steward of Saul's household, and his fifteen sons and twenty servants. They rushed to the Jordan, where the king was. [18]They crossed at the ford to take the king's household over and to do whatever he wished.

When Shimei son of Gera crossed the Jordan, he fell prostrate before the king [19]and said to him, "May my lord not hold me guilty. Do not remember how your servant did wrong on the day my lord the king left Jerusalem. May the king put it out of his mind. [20]For I your servant know that I have sinned, but today I have come here as the first of the whole house of Joseph to come down and meet my lord the king."

[21]Then Abishai son of Zeruiah said, "Shouldn't Shimei be put to death for this? He cursed the LORD's anointed."

[22]David replied, "What do you and I have in common, you sons of Zeruiah? This day you have become my adversaries! Should anyone be put to death in Israel today? Do I not know that today I am king over Israel?" [23]So the king said to Shimei, "You shall not die." And the king promised him on oath.

[24]Mephibosheth, Saul's grandson, also went down to meet the king. He had not taken care of his feet or trimmed his mustache or washed his clothes from the day the king left until the day he returned safely. [25]When he came from Jerusalem to meet the king, the king asked him, "Why didn't you go with me, Mephibosheth?"

[26]He said, "My lord the king, since I your servant am lame, I said, 'I will have my donkey saddled and will ride on it, so I can go with the king.' But Ziba my servant betrayed me. [27]And he has slandered your servant to my lord the king. My lord the king is like an angel of God; so do whatever pleases you. [28]All my grandfather's descendants deserved nothing but death from my lord the king, but you gave your servant a place among those who eat at your table. So what right do I have to make any more appeals to the king?"

[29]The king said to him, "Why say more? I order you and Ziba to divide the fields."

[30]Mephibosheth said to the king, "Let him take everything, now that my lord the king has arrived home safely."

[31]Barzillai the Gileadite also came down from Rogelim to cross the Jordan with the king and to send him on his way from there. [32]Now Barzillai was a very old man, eighty years of age. He had provided for the king during his stay in Mahanaim, for he was a very wealthy man. [33]The king said to Barzillai, "Cross over with me and stay with me in Jerusalem, and I will provide for you."

[34]But Barzillai answered the king, "How many more years will I live, that I should go up to Jerusalem with the king? [35]I am now eighty years old. Can I tell the difference between what is good and what is not? Can your servant taste what he eats and drinks? Can I still hear the voices of men and women singers? Why should your servant be an added burden to my lord the king? [36]Your servant will cross over the Jordan with the king for a short distance, but why should the king reward me in this way? [37]Let your servant return, that I may die in my own town near the tomb of my father and mother. But here is your servant Kimham. Let him cross over with my lord the king. Do for him whatever pleases you."

³⁸The king said, "Kimham shall cross over with me, and I will do for him whatever pleases you. And anything you desire from me I will do for you."

³⁹So all the people crossed the Jordan, and then the king crossed over. The king kissed Barzillai and gave him his blessing, and Barzillai returned to his home.

⁴⁰When the king crossed over to Gilgal, Kimham crossed with him. All the troops of Judah and half the troops of Israel had taken the king over.

⁴¹Soon all the men of Israel were coming to the king and saying to him, "Why did our brothers, the men of Judah, steal the king away and bring him and his household across the Jordan, together with all his men?"

⁴²All the men of Judah answered the men of Israel, "We did this because the king is closely related to us. Why are you angry about it? Have we eaten any of the king's provisions? Have we taken anything for ourselves?"

⁴³Then the men of Israel answered the men of Judah, "We have ten shares in the king; and besides, we have a greater claim on David than you have. So why do you treat us with contempt? Were we not the first to speak of bringing back our king?"

But the men of Judah responded even more harshly than the men of Israel.

truth or dare

Just as the different tribes claimed they had a bigger stake in David, so we sometimes think that being a Christian for years gives us the corner on God. God's love is for everyone. Don't hoard it.

19:41–43

Sheba Rebels Against David

20 Now a troublemaker named Sheba son of Bicri, a Benjamite, happened to be there. He sounded the trumpet and shouted,

"We have no share in David,
    no part in Jesse's son!
Every man to his tent, O Israel!"

²So all the men of Israel deserted David to follow Sheba son of Bicri. But the men of Judah stayed by their king all the way from the Jordan to Jerusalem.

³When David returned to his palace in Jerusalem, he took the ten concubines he had left to take care of the palace and put them in a house under guard. He provided for them, but did not lie with them. They were kept in confinement till the day of their death, living as widows.

⁴Then the king said to Amasa, "Summon the men of Judah to come to me within three days, and be here yourself." ⁵But when Amasa went to summon Judah, he took longer than the time the king had set for him.

⁶David said to Abishai, "Now Sheba son of Bicri will do us more harm than Absalom did. Take your master's men and pursue him, or he will find fortified cities and escape from us." ⁷So Joab's men and the Kerethites and Pelethites and all the mighty warriors went out under the command of Abishai. They marched out from Jerusalem to pursue Sheba son of Bicri.

⁸While they were at the great rock in Gibeon, Amasa came to meet them. Joab was wearing his military tunic, and strapped over it at his waist was a belt with a dagger in its sheath. As he stepped forward, it dropped out of its sheath.

⁹Joab said to Amasa, "How are you, my brother?" Then Joab took Amasa by the beard with his right hand to kiss him. ¹⁰Amasa was not on his guard against the dagger in Joab's hand, and Joab plunged it into his belly, and his intestines spilled out on the ground. Without being stabbed again, Amasa died. Then Joab and his brother Abishai pursued Sheba son of Bicri.

¹¹One of Joab's men stood beside Amasa and said, "Whoever favors Joab, and whoever is for David, let him follow Joab!" ¹²Amasa lay wallowing in his blood in the middle of the road, and the man saw that all the troops came to a halt there. When he realized that everyone who came up to Amasa stopped, he dragged him from the road into a field and threw a garment over him. ¹³After Amasa had been removed from the road, all the men went on with Joab to pursue Sheba son of Bicri.

¹⁴Sheba passed through all the tribes of Israel to Abel Beth Maacah*ᵃ and through the entire region of the Berites, who gathered together and followed him. ¹⁵All the troops with Joab came and besieged Sheba in Abel Beth Maacah. They built a siege ramp up to the city, and it stood against the outer fortifications. While they were battering the wall to bring it down, ¹⁶a wise woman called from the city, "Listen! Listen! Tell Joab to come here so I can speak to him." ¹⁷He went toward her, and she asked, "Are you Joab?"

"I am," he answered.

She said, "Listen to what your servant has to say."

"I'm listening," he said.

¹⁸She continued, "Long ago they used to say, 'Get your answer at Abel,' and that settled it. ¹⁹We are the peaceful and faithful in Israel. You are trying to destroy a city that is a mother in Israel. Why do you want to swallow up the Lord's inheritance?"

²⁰"Far be it from me!" Joab replied, "Far be it from me to swallow up or destroy! ²¹That is not the case. A man named Sheba son of Bicri, from the hill country of Ephraim, has lifted up his hand against the king, against David. Hand over this one man, and I'll withdraw from the city."

The woman said to Joab, "His head will be thrown to you from the wall."

²²Then the woman went to all the people with her wise advice, and they cut off the head of Sheba son of Bicri and threw it to Joab. So he sounded the trumpet, and his men dispersed from the city, each returning to his home. And Joab went back to the king in Jerusalem.

²³Joab was over Israel's entire army; Benaiah son of Jehoiada was over the Kerethites and Pelethites; ²⁴Adoniram*ᵇ was in charge of forced labor; Jehoshaphat son of Ahilud was recorder; ²⁵Sheva was secretary; Zadok and Abiathar were priests; ²⁶and Ira the Jairite was David's priest.

The Gibeonites Avenged

21 During the reign of David, there was a famine for three successive years; so David sought the face of the Lord. The Lord said, "It is on account of Saul and his bloodstained house; it is because he put the Gibeonites to death."

²The king summoned the Gibeonites and spoke to them. (Now the Gibeonites were not a part of Israel but were survivors of the Amorites; the Israelites had sworn to spare them, but Saul in his zeal for Israel and Judah had tried to annihilate them.) ³David asked the Gibeonites, "What shall I do for you? How shall I make amends so that you will bless the Lord's inheritance?"

⁴The Gibeonites answered him, "We have no right to demand silver or gold from Saul or his family, nor do we have the right to put anyone in Israel to death."

"What do you want me to do for you?" David asked.

⁵They answered the king, "As for the man who destroyed us and plotted against us so that we have been decimated and have no place anywhere in Israel, ⁶let seven of his male descendants be given to us to be killed and exposed before the Lord at Gibeah of Saul— the Lord's chosen one."

So the king said, "I will give them to you."

⁷The king spared Mephibosheth son of Jonathan, the son of Saul, because of the oath before the Lord between David and Jonathan son of Saul. ⁸But the king took Armoni and Mephibosheth, the two sons of Aiah's daughter Rizpah, whom she had borne to Saul, together with the five sons of Saul's daughter Merab,ᶜ whom she had borne to Adriel son of Barzillai the Meholathite. ⁹He handed them over to the Gibeonites, who killed and exposed them on a hill before the Lord. All seven of them fell together; they were put to death during the first days of the harvest, just as the barley harvest was beginning.

¹⁰Rizpah daughter of Aiah took sackcloth and spread it out for herself on a rock. From the be-

truth or dare

Occasionally grudges get passed down from generation to generation. If your family has unresolved bitterness, pray for ways to start reconciliation.

21:1-3

ᵃ 14 Or *Abel, even Beth Maacah*; also in verse 15   ᵇ 24 Some Septuagint manuscripts (see also 1 Kings 4:6 and 5:14); Hebrew *Adoram*   ᶜ 8 Two Hebrew manuscripts, some Septuagint manuscripts and Syriac (see also 1 Samuel 18:19); most Hebrew and Septuagint manuscripts *Michal* ginning of the harvest till the rain poured down from the heavens on the bodies, she did not let the birds of the air touch them by day or the wild animals by night. [11]When David was told what Aiah's daughter Rizpah, Saul's concubine, had done, [12]he went and took the bones of Saul and his son Jonathan from the citizens of Jabesh Gilead. (They had taken them secretly from the public square at Beth Shan, where the Philistines had hung them after they struck Saul down on Gilboa.) [13]David brought the bones of Saul and his son Jonathan from there, and the bones of those who had been killed and exposed were gathered up.

[14]They buried the bones of Saul and his son Jonathan in the tomb of Saul's father Kish, at Zela in Benjamin, and did everything the king commanded. After that, God answered prayer in behalf of the land.

Wars Against the Philistines

[15]Once again there was a battle between the Philistines and Israel. David went down with his men to fight against the Philistines, and he became exhausted. [16]And Ishbi-Benob, one of the descendants of Rapha, whose bronze spearhead weighed three hundred shekels[a] and who was armed with a new ˌswordˌ, said he would kill David. [17]But Abishai son of Zeruiah came to David's rescue; he struck the Philistine down and killed him. Then David's men swore to him, saying, "Never again will you go out with us to battle, so that the lamp of Israel will not be extinguished."

[18]In the course of time, there was another battle with the Philistines, at Gob. At that time Sibbecai the Hushathite killed Saph, one of the descendants of Rapha.

[19]In another battle with the Philistines at Gob, Elhanan son of Jaare-Oregim[b] the Bethlehemite killed Goliath[c] the Gittite, who had a spear with a shaft like a weaver's rod.

[20]In still another battle, which took place at Gath, there was a huge man with six fingers on each hand and six toes on each foot—twenty-four in all. He also was descended from Rapha. [21]When he taunted Israel, Jonathan son of Shimeah, David's brother, killed him.

[22]These four were descendants of Rapha in Gath, and they fell at the hands of David and his men.

David's Song of Praise

22 David sang to the LORD the words of this song when the LORD delivered him from the hand of all his enemies and from the hand of Saul. [2]He said:

> "The LORD is my rock, my fortress and my deliverer;
> [3]   my God is my rock, in whom I take refuge,
>   my shield and the horn[d] of my salvation.
> He is my stronghold, my refuge and my savior—
>   from violent men you save me.
> [4]I call to the LORD, who is worthy
>   of praise,
>   and I am saved from my
>   enemies.
> [5]"The waves of death swirled
>   about me;
>   the torrents of destruction
>   overwhelmed me.
> [6]The cords of the grave[e] coiled
>   around me;
>   the snares of death confronted
>   me.
> [7]In my distress I called to the LORD;
>   I called out to my God.
> From his temple he heard my voice;
>   my cry came to his ears.

truth or dare

Don't hold back! There's nothing too big (or too small) for God to handle. So don't be afraid to cry out to him. He hears you.

22:5–7

a 16 That is, about 7 1/2 pounds (about 3.5 kilograms)   *b 19* Or *son of Jair the weaver*   *c 19* Hebrew and Septuagint; 1 Chron. 20:5 *son of Jair killed Lahmi the brother of Goliath*   *d 3* Horn here symbolizes strength.   *e 6* Hebrew Sheol

8 "The earth trembled and quaked,
  the foundations of the heavens[a] shook;
  they trembled because he was angry.
9 Smoke rose from his nostrils;
  consuming fire came from his mouth,
  burning coals blazed out of it.
10 He parted the heavens and came down;
  dark clouds were under his feet.
11 He mounted the cherubim and flew;
  he soared[b] on the wings of the wind.
12 He made darkness his canopy around him—
  the dark[c] rain clouds of the sky.

13 Out of the brightness of his presence
  bolts of lightning blazed forth.
14 The Lord thundered from heaven;
  the voice of the Most High resounded.
15 He shot arrows and scattered ⌊the enemies⌋,
  bolts of lightning and routed them.
16 The valleys of the sea were exposed
  and the foundations of the earth laid bare
at the rebuke of the Lord,
  at the blast of breath from his nostrils.

17 "He reached down from on high and took hold of me;
  he drew me out of deep waters.
18 He rescued me from my powerful enemy,
  from my foes, who were too strong for me.
19 They confronted me in the day of my disaster,
  but the Lord was my support.
20 He brought me out into a spacious place;
  he rescued me because he delighted in me.

21 "The Lord has dealt with me according to my righteousness;
  according to the cleanness of my hands he has rewarded me.

love♥notes

22:2–51

Dear daughter,

Want to know more about me? David called me the Saving, Worthy, Hearing, Rescuing, Rewarding, Seeing, Faithful, Shielding and Living God. I want you to discover that for yourself, too.

—Your God

Think of one of the above attributes of God that you have experienced personally. What was the circumstance?

_____

_____

_____

_____

_____

_____

_____

_____

_____

_____

a 8 Hebrew; Vulgate and Syriac (see also Psalm 18:7)
mountains   b 11 Many Hebrew manuscripts (see also
Psalm 18:10); most Hebrew manuscripts *appeared*
c 12 Septuagint and Vulgate (see also Psalm 18:11);
Hebrew *massed*

²² For I have kept the ways of the
LORD;
I have not done evil by turning
from my God.
²³ All his laws are before me;
I have not turned away from
his decrees.
²⁴ I have been blameless before him
and have kept myself from sin.
²⁵ The LORD has rewarded me
according to my
righteousness,
according to my cleanness^a in
his sight.

²⁶ "To the faithful you show yourself faithful,
to the blameless you show yourself
blameless,
²⁷ to the pure you show yourself pure,
but to the crooked you show yourself shrewd.
²⁸ You save the humble,
but your eyes are on the haughty to bring them low.
²⁹ You are my lamp, O LORD;
the LORD turns my darkness into light.
³⁰ With your help I can advance against a troop^b;
with my God I can scale a wall.

³¹ "As for God, his way is perfect;
the word of the LORD is flawless.
He is a shield
for all who take refuge in him.
³² For who is God besides the LORD?
And who is the Rock except our God?
³³ It is God who arms me with strength^c
and makes my way perfect.
³⁴ He makes my feet like the feet of a deer;
he enables me to stand on the heights.
³⁵ He trains my hands for battle;
my arms can bend a bow of bronze.
³⁶ You give me your shield of victory;
you stoop down to make me great.
³⁷ You broaden the path beneath me,
so that my ankles do not turn.

³⁸ "I pursued my enemies and crushed them;
I did not turn back till they were destroyed.
³⁹ I crushed them completely, and they could not rise;
they fell beneath my feet.
⁴⁰ You armed me with strength for battle;
you made my adversaries bow at my feet.
⁴¹ You made my enemies turn their backs in flight,
and I destroyed my foes.
⁴² They cried for help, but there was no one to save them—
to the LORD, but he did not answer.

truth or dare

Sinning becomes easier the more time you spend away from God's Word. Keep your conscience razor-sharp by staying in the Word.

22:22–24

---

^a 25 Hebrew; Septuagint and Vulgate (see also Psalm 18:24) *to the cleanness of my hands*   ^b 30 Or *can run through a barricade*   ^c 33 Dead Sea Scrolls, some Septuagint manuscripts, Vulgate and Syriac (see also Psalm 18:32); Masoretic Text *who is my strong refuge*

⁴³ I beat them as fine as the dust of the earth;
    I pounded and trampled them like mud in the streets.

⁴⁴ "You have delivered me from the attacks of my people;
    you have preserved me as the head of nations.
 People I did not know are subject to me,
⁴⁵   and foreigners come cringing to me;
    as soon as they hear me, they obey me.
⁴⁶ They all lose heart;
    they come trembling^a from their strongholds.

⁴⁷ "The LORD lives! Praise be to my Rock!
    Exalted be God, the Rock, my Savior!
⁴⁸ He is the God who avenges me,
    who puts the nations under me,
⁴⁹   who sets me free from my enemies.
 You exalted me above my foes;
    from violent men you rescued me.
⁵⁰ Therefore I will praise you, O LORD, among the nations;
    I will sing praises to your name.
⁵¹ He gives his king great victories;
    he shows unfailing kindness to his anointed,
    to David and his descendants forever."

The Last Words of David

23 These are the last words of David:

"The oracle of David son of Jesse,
    the oracle of the man exalted by the Most High,
    the man anointed by the God of Jacob,
    Israel's singer of songs^b:

² "The Spirit of the LORD spoke through me;
    his word was on my tongue.
³ The God of Israel spoke,
    the Rock of Israel said to me:
 'When one rules over men in righteousness,
    when he rules in the fear of God,
⁴ he is like the light of morning at sunrise
    on a cloudless morning,
 like the brightness after rain
    that brings the grass from the earth.'
⁵ "Is not my house right with God?
    Has he not made with me an everlasting covenant,
    arranged and secured in every part?
 Will he not bring to fruition my salvation
    and grant me my every desire?
⁶ But evil men are all to be cast aside like thorns,
    which are not gathered with the hand.
⁷ Whoever touches thorns
    uses a tool of iron or the shaft of a spear;
    they are burned up where they lie."

^a 46 Some Septuagint manuscripts and Vulgate (see also Psalm 18:45); Masoretic Text *they arm themselves.*
^b 1 Or *Israel's beloved singer*

► David's Mighty Men ◄

[8]These are the names of David's mighty men:

Josheb-Basshebeth,[a] a Tahkemonite,[b] was chief of the Three; he raised his spear against eight hundred men, whom he killed[c] in one encounter.

[9]Next to him was Eleazar son of Dodai the Ahohite. As one of the three mighty men, he was with David when they taunted the Philistines gathered ⌊at Pas Dammim⌋[d] for battle. Then the men of Israel retreated, [10]but he stood his ground and struck down the Philistines till his hand grew tired and froze to the sword. The LORD brought about a great victory that day. The troops returned to Eleazar, but only to strip the dead.

[11]Next to him was Shammah son of Agee the Hararite. When the Philistines banded together at a place where there was a field full of lentils, Israel's troops fled from them. [12]But Shammah took his stand in the middle of the field. He defended it and struck the Philistines down, and the LORD brought about a great victory.

[13]During harvest time, three of the thirty chief men came down to David at the cave of Adullam, while a band of Philistines was encamped in the Valley of Rephaim. [14]At that time David was in the stronghold, and the Philistine garrison was at Bethlehem. [15]David longed for water and said, "Oh, that someone would get me a drink of water from the well near the gate of Bethlehem!" [16]So the three mighty men broke through the Philistine lines, drew water from the well near the gate of Bethlehem and carried it back to David. But he refused to drink it; instead, he poured it out before the LORD. [17]"Far be it from me, O LORD, to do this!" he said. "Is it not the blood of men who went at the risk of their lives?" And David would not drink it.

Such were the exploits of the three mighty men.

[18]Abishai the brother of Joab son of Zeruiah was chief of the Three.[e] He raised his spear against three hundred men, whom he killed, and so he became as famous as the Three. [19]Was he not held in greater honor than the Three? He became their commander, even though he was not included among them.

[20]Benaiah son of Jehoiada was a valiant fighter from Kabzeel, who performed great exploits. He struck down two of Moab's best men. He also went down into a pit on a snowy day and killed a lion. [21]And he struck down a huge Egyptian. Although the Egyptian had a spear in his hand, Benaiah went against him with a club. He snatched the spear from the Egyptian's hand and killed him with his own spear. [22]Such were the exploits of Benaiah son of Jehoiada; he too was as famous as the three mighty men. [23]He was held in greater honor than any of the Thirty, but he was not included among the Three. And David put him in charge of his bodyguard.

[24]Among the Thirty were:

Asahel the brother of Joab,
Elhanan son of Dodo from Bethlehem,
[25]Shammah the Harodite,
Elika the Harodite,
[26]Helez the Paltite,
Ira son of Ikkesh from Tekoa,
[27]Abiezer from Anathoth,
Mebunnai[f] the Hushathite,
[28]Zalmon the Ahohite,
Maharai the Netophathite,
[29]Heled[g] son of Baanah the Netophathite,
Ithai son of Ribai from Gibeah in Benjamin,
[30]Benaiah the Pirathonite,
Hiddai[h] from the ravines of Gaash,

---

a 8 Hebrew; some Septuagint manuscripts suggest *Ish-Bosheth,* that is, *Esh-Baal* (see also 1 Chron. 11:11 *Jashobeam*). *b 8* Probably a variant of *Hacmonite* (see 1 Chron. 11:11) *c 8* Some Septuagint manuscripts (see also 1 Chron. 11:11); Hebrew and other Septuagint manuscripts *Three; it was Adino the Eznite who killed eight hundred men* *d 9* See 1 Chron. 11:13; Hebrew *gathered there.* *e 18* Most Hebrew manuscripts (see also 1 Chron. 11:20); two Hebrew manuscripts and Syriac *Thirty* *f 27* Hebrew; some Septuagint manuscripts (see also 1 Chron. 11:29) *Sibbecai* *g 29* Some Hebrew manuscripts and Vulgate (see also 1 Chron. 11:30); most Hebrew manuscripts *Heleb* *h 30* Hebrew; some Septuagint manuscripts (see also 1 Chron. 11:32) *Hurai*

Unforgettable

Profile: Nora

I met Nidia on the first day of our missions trip to Nicaragua. I couldn't speak Spanish, so I didn't think I'd get to really know any of the kids we were working with. But she caught my eye right away—she was so cute and extra-small for her age. She stared up at me with her big brown eyes and just kept smiling. Eventually she introduced herself.

It was pretty funny trying to communicate with each other. We used sign language and drew pictures. I used my Spanish-English dictionary. We ended up laughing a lot, because half the time we had no idea what the other was saying.

On the third day, Nidia took me to her house. I have to admit, I was completely shocked. Her house was about the size of my parents' kitchen! Her grandparents lived there, too. Talk about crowded.

Nidia slept on a small mattress in the corner of the main room—the same room her mom cooked in. And she didn't have a closet or dresser or anything. I guess she didn't need them—the only clothes she had were the ones she wore every day. Everything she had—a few books, pencils and some magazines—fit in a small box at the end of her bed.

The last night of the camp, when we had to say good-bye, Nidia gave me her hairclip as a going away gift. It was the hairclip she'd worn all week—her only hairclip. I didn't want to accept it. I already felt guilty for all that I had . . . how could she expect me to take something of *hers*? But she kept insisting. She wanted me to have it to remember her by.

Every time I look at the hairclip now, I think of Nidia. She had so little . . . yet she gave me so much. I just wish I could have given her more in return.

For more info on ways to combat poverty, go online to www.TrueImagesBible.com

poverty in focus

Have you ever seen poverty firsthand? Most of us are like Nora—we live pretty sheltered lives. And even if we are aware of how much poverty there is in the world, it's easy for us to just feel overwhelmed, to feel guilty for what we have and to wonder what we can possibly do to help those who don't have as much.

But the Bible tells us two specific things that we, as Christians, are to do for the poor:

» Tell them about the Gospel (see Luke 4:18, page 1369).

» Take care of their physical needs (see Galatians 2:10, page 1536). This could mean going on a missions trip, volunteering in a soup kitchen or local mission or sponsoring a child through a Christian sponsorship program.

For more on this topic, see the index on page 1656.

---

³¹ Abi-Albon the Arbathite,
Azmaveth the Barhumite,
³² Eliahba the Shaalbonite,
the sons of Jashen,

Jonathan [33]son of[a] Shammah the Hararite,
Ahiam son of Sharar[b] the Hararite,
[34]Eliphelet son of Ahasbai the Maacathite,
Eliam son of Ahithophel the Gilonite,
[35]Hezro the Carmelite,
Paarai the Arbite,
[36]Igal son of Nathan from Zobah,
the son of Hagri,[c]
[37]Zelek the Ammonite,
Naharai the Beerothite, the armor-bearer of Joab son of Zeruiah,
[38]Ira the Ithrite,
Gareb the Ithrite
[39]and Uriah the Hittite.
There were thirty-seven in all.

David Counts the Fighting Men

24 Again the anger of the LORD burned against Israel, and he incited David against them, saying, "Go and take a census of Israel and Judah."

[2]So the king said to Joab and the army commanders[d] with him, "Go throughout the tribes of Israel from Dan to Beersheba and enroll the fighting men, so that I may know how many there are."

[3]But Joab replied to the king, "May the LORD your God multiply the troops a hundred times over, and may the eyes of my lord the king see it. But why does my lord the king want to do such a thing?"

[4]The king's word, however, overruled Joab and the army commanders; so they left the presence of the king to enroll the fighting men of Israel.

[5]After crossing the Jordan, they camped near Aroer, south of the town in the gorge, and then went through Gad and on to Jazer. [6]They went to Gilead and the region of Tahtim Hodshi, and on to Dan Jaan and around toward Sidon. [7]Then they went toward the fortress of Tyre and all the towns of the Hivites and Canaanites. Finally, they went on to Beersheba in the Negev of Judah.

[8]After they had gone through the entire land, they came back to Jerusalem at the end of nine months and twenty days.

[9]Joab reported the number of the fighting men to the king: In Israel there were eight hundred thousand able-bodied men who could handle a sword, and in Judah five hundred thousand.

[10]David was conscience-stricken after he had counted the fighting men, and he said to the LORD, "I have sinned greatly in what I have done. Now, O LORD, I beg you, take away the guilt of your servant. I have done a very foolish thing."

[11]Before David got up the next morning, the word of the LORD had come to Gad the prophet, David's seer: [12]"Go and tell David, 'This is what the LORD says: I am giving you three options. Choose one of them for me to carry out against you.' "

[13]So Gad went to David and said to him, "Shall there come upon you three[e] years of famine in your land? Or three months of fleeing from your enemies while they pursue you? Or three days of plague in your land? Now then, think it over and decide how I should answer the one who sent me."

[14]David said to Gad, "I am in deep distress. Let us fall into the hands of the LORD, for his mercy is great; but do not let me fall into the hands of men."

[15]So the LORD sent a plague on Israel from that morning until the end of the time designated, and seventy thousand of the people from Dan to Beersheba died. [16]When the angel stretched out his hand to destroy Jerusalem, the LORD was grieved because of the calamity and said to the angel who was afflicting the people, "Enough! Withdraw your hand." The angel of the LORD was then at the threshing floor of Araunah the Jebusite.

[17]When David saw the angel who was striking down the people, he said to the LORD, "I am the

---

[a] 33 Some Septuagint manuscripts (see also 1 Chron. 11:34); Hebrew does not have *son of*.   [b] 33 Hebrew; some Septuagint manuscripts (see also 1 Chron. 11:35) *Sacar*   [c] 36 Some Septuagint manuscripts (see also 1 Chron. 11:38); Hebrew *Haggadi*   [d] 2 Septuagint (see also verse 4 and 1 Chron. 21:2); Hebrew *Joab the army commander*   [e] 13 Septuagint (see also 1 Chron. 21:12); Hebrew *seven*

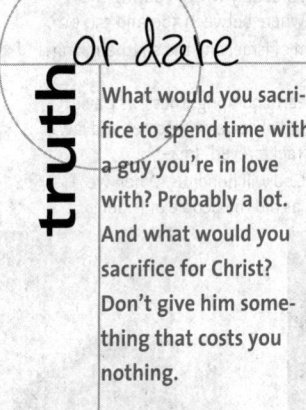

truth or dare

What would you sacrifice to spend time with a guy you're in love with? Probably a lot. And what would you sacrifice for Christ? Don't give him something that costs you nothing.

24:22–24

one who has sinned and done wrong. These are but sheep. What have they done? Let your hand fall upon me and my family."

David Builds an Altar

[18]On that day Gad went to David and said to him, "Go up and build an altar to the LORD on the threshing floor of Araunah the Jebusite." [19]So David went up, as the LORD had commanded through Gad. [20]When Araunah looked and saw the king and his men coming toward him, he went out and bowed down before the king with his face to the ground.

[21]Araunah said, "Why has my lord the king come to his servant?"

"To buy your threshing floor," David answered, "so I can build an altar to the LORD, that the plague on the people may be stopped."

[22]Araunah said to David, "Let my lord the king take whatever pleases him and offer it up. Here are oxen for the burnt offering, and here are threshing sledges and ox yokes for the wood. [23]O king, Araunah gives all this to the king." Araunah also said to him, "May the LORD your God accept you."

[24]But the king replied to Araunah, "No, I insist on paying you for it. I will not sacrifice to the LORD my God burnt offerings that cost me nothing."

So David bought the threshing floor and the oxen and paid fifty shekels[a] of silver for them. [25]David built an altar to the LORD there and sacrificed burnt offerings and fellowship offerings.[b] Then the LORD answered prayer in behalf of the land, and the plague on Israel was stopped.

---

[a] 24 That is, about 1 1/4 pounds (about 0.6 kilogram)   [b] 25 Traditionally peace offerings

at a glance

author:	Unknown.
date:	Originally, 1 and 2 Kings were one book, probably written during the Babylonian exile of the Israelites, somewhere between 560 and 550 B.C.
setting:	Israel divides into the northern kingdom of Israel and the southern kingdom of Judah.
verse to remember:	"If you walk before me in integrity of heart and uprightness, as David your father did, and do all I command and observe my decrees and laws, I will establish your royal throne over Israel forever'" (9:4–5).
theme to consider:	When we obey him and keep his laws, God will honor us. When we don't, we *will* suffer the consequences, as did the people of Israel.

1 kings

unchanging truth

Has anyone ever told you to "remember who you are"? Even if those weren't the exact words, the implication was the same. *Be sure to say and do what you were taught. Be true to yourself.*

Your actions not only affect you; they also have an impact on your whole family. When you act in an honorable way, it brings honor to your family. Unfortunately, the flip side is also true. Your whole family may feel the consequences of your bad choices. But that's nothing compared to the consequences that occur when you disobey and dishonor your heavenly Father. God expects us to honor and obey only him, and when that doesn't happen, we *will* suffer the consequences.

King Solomon was the wisest person who had ever lived. God was with him in everything he did. Under Solomon's rule, Israel grew into a mighty nation. But then the Israelites and Solomon forgot who they were and whose they were. They worshiped idols. God's anger was fierce, and the consequences were terrible. The kingdom of Israel was divided into two kingdoms that constantly fought. When they repented, God forgave them and they prospered. Unfortunately, they soon slipped back into their old ways again. It was a vicious cycle of honor and dishonor.

Ask God to help you to always remember who you are—God's child—and to live up to that.

life lessons

1. Wisdom is a gift from God, free for the taking. All we have to do is ask (3:4–14).

2. We need to speak up when those around us dishonor God—even if it puts us at odds with others (16:30–33; 17:1).

3. The Lord doesn't usually speak to us with lightning bolts and storms; we have to get quiet and listen for his gentle whisper (19:11–13).

Adonijah Sets Himself Up as King

1 When King David was old and well advanced in years, he could not keep warm even when they put covers over him. [2]So his servants said to him, "Let us look for a young virgin to attend the king and take care of him. She can lie beside him so that our lord the king may keep warm."

[3]Then they searched throughout Israel for a beautiful girl and found Abishag, a Shunammite, and brought her to the king. [4]The girl was very beautiful; she took care of the king and waited on him, but the king had no intimate relations with her.

[5]Now Adonijah, whose mother was Haggith, put himself forward and said, "I will be king." So he got chariots and horses[a] ready, with fifty men to run ahead of him. [6](His father had never interfered with him by asking, "Why do you behave as you do?" He was also very handsome and was born next after Absalom.)

[7]Adonijah conferred with Joab son of Zeruiah and with Abiathar the priest, and they gave him their support. [8]But Zadok the priest, Benaiah son of Jehoiada, Nathan the prophet, Shimei and Rei[b] and David's special guard did not join Adonijah.

[9]Adonijah then sacrificed sheep, cattle and fattened calves at the Stone of Zoheleth near En Rogel. He invited all his brothers, the king's sons, and all the men of Judah who were royal officials, [10]but he did not invite Nathan the prophet or Benaiah or the special guard or his brother Solomon.

[11]Then Nathan asked Bathsheba, Solomon's mother, "Have you not heard that Adonijah, the son of Haggith, has become king without our lord David's knowing it? [12]Now then, let me advise you how you can save your own life and the life of your son Solomon. [13]Go in to King David and say to him, 'My lord the king, did you not swear to me your servant: "Surely Solomon your son shall be king after me, and he will sit on my throne"? Why then has Adonijah become king?' [14]While you are still there talking to the king, I will come in and confirm what you have said."

[15]So Bathsheba went to see the aged king in his room, where Abishag the Shunammite was attending him. [16]Bathsheba bowed low and knelt before the king.

"What is it you want?" the king asked.

[17]She said to him, "My lord, you yourself swore to me your servant by the LORD your God: 'Solomon your son shall be king after me, and he will sit on my throne.' [18]But now Adonijah has become king, and you, my lord the king, do not know about it. [19]He has sacrificed great numbers of cattle, fattened calves, and sheep, and has invited all the king's sons, Abiathar the priest and Joab the commander of the army, but he has not invited Solomon your servant. [20]My lord the king, the eyes of all Israel are on you, to learn from you who will sit on the throne of my lord the king after him. [21]Otherwise, as soon as my lord the king is laid to rest with his fathers, I and my son Solomon will be treated as criminals."

[22]While she was still speaking with the king, Nathan the prophet arrived. [23]And they told the king, "Nathan the prophet is here." So he went before the king and bowed with his face to the ground.

[24]Nathan said, "Have you, my lord the king, declared that Adonijah shall be king after you, and that he will sit on your throne? [25]Today he has gone down and sacrificed great numbers of cattle, fattened calves, and sheep. He has invited all the king's sons, the commanders of the army and Abiathar the priest. Right now they are eating and drinking with him and saying, 'Long live King Adonijah!' [26]But me your servant, and Zadok the priest, and Benaiah son of Jehoiada, and your servant Solomon he did not invite. [27]Is this something my lord the king has done without letting his servants know who should sit on the throne of my lord the king after him?"

David Makes Solomon King

[28]Then King David said, "Call in Bathsheba." So she came into the king's presence and stood before him.

[29]The king then took an oath: "As surely as the LORD lives, who has delivered me out of every trouble, [30]I will surely carry out today what I swore to you by the LORD, the God of Israel: Solomon your son shall be king after me, and he will sit on my throne in my place."

[31]Then Bathsheba bowed low with her face to the ground and, kneeling before the king, said, "May my lord King David live forever!"

[32]King David said, "Call in Zadok the priest, Nathan the prophet and Benaiah son of Jehoiada."

a 5 Or *charioteers*   b 8 Or *and his friends*

When they came before the king, ³³he said to them: "Take your lord's servants with you and set Solomon my son on my own mule and take him down to Gihon. ³⁴There have Zadok the priest and Nathan the prophet anoint him king over Israel. Blow the trumpet and shout, 'Long live King Solomon!' ³⁵Then you are to go up with him, and he is to come and sit on my throne and reign in my place. I have appointed him ruler over Israel and Judah."

³⁶Benaiah son of Jehoiada answered the king, "Amen! May the LORD, the God of my lord the king, so declare it. ³⁷As the LORD was with my lord the king, so may he be with Solomon to make his throne even greater than the throne of my lord King David!"

³⁸So Zadok the priest, Nathan the prophet, Benaiah son of Jehoiada, the Kerethites and the Pelethites went down and put Solomon on King David's mule and escorted him to Gihon. ³⁹Zadok the priest took the horn of oil from the sacred tent and anointed Solomon. Then they sounded the trumpet and all the people shouted, "Long live King Solomon!" ⁴⁰And all the people went up after him, playing flutes and rejoicing greatly, so that the ground shook with the sound.

truth or dare

Make a joyful noise, sister! No more hymn singing under your breath. Get some volume with that worship!

1:40

⁴¹Adonijah and all the guests who were with him heard it as they were finishing their feast. On hearing the sound of the trumpet, Joab asked, "What's the meaning of all the noise in the city?"

⁴²Even as he was speaking, Jonathan son of Abiathar the priest arrived. Adonijah said, "Come in. A worthy man like you must be bringing good news."

⁴³"Not at all!" Jonathan answered. "Our lord King David has made Solomon king. ⁴⁴The king has sent with him Zadok the priest, Nathan the prophet, Benaiah son of Jehoiada, the Kerethites and the Pelethites, and they have put him on the king's mule, ⁴⁵and Zadok the priest and Nathan the prophet have anointed him king at Gihon. From there they have gone up cheering, and the city resounds with it. That's the noise you hear. ⁴⁶Moreover, Solomon has taken his seat on the royal throne. ⁴⁷Also, the royal officials have come to congratulate our lord King David, saying, 'May your God make Solomon's name more famous than yours and his throne greater than yours!' And the king bowed in worship on his bed ⁴⁸and said, 'Praise be to the LORD, the God of Israel, who has allowed my eyes to see a successor on my throne today.' "

⁴⁹At this, all Adonijah's guests rose in alarm and dispersed. ⁵⁰But Adonijah, in fear of Solomon, went and took hold of the horns of the altar. ⁵¹Then Solomon was told, "Adonijah is afraid of King Solomon and is clinging to the horns of the altar. He says, 'Let King Solomon swear to me today that he will not put his servant to death with the sword.' "

⁵²Solomon replied, "If he shows himself to be a worthy man, not a hair of his head will fall to the ground; but if evil is found in him, he will die." ⁵³Then King Solomon sent men, and they brought him down from the altar. And Adonijah came and bowed down to King Solomon, and Solomon said, "Go to your home."

David's Charge to Solomon

2 When the time drew near for David to die, he gave a charge to Solomon his son.

²"I am about to go the way of all the earth," he said. "So be strong, show yourself a man, ³and observe what the LORD your God requires: Walk in his ways, and keep his decrees and commands, his laws and requirements, as written in the Law of Moses, so that you may prosper in all you do and wherever you go, ⁴and that the LORD may keep his promise to me: 'If your descendants watch how they live, and if they walk faithfully before me with all their heart and soul, you will never fail to have a man on the throne of Israel.'

⁵"Now you yourself know what Joab son of Zeruiah did to me—what he did to the two commanders of Israel's armies, Abner son of Ner and Amasa son of Jether. He killed them, shedding their blood in peacetime as if in battle, and with that blood stained the belt around his waist and the sandals on his feet. ⁶Deal with him according to your wisdom, but do not let his gray head go down to the graveᵃ in peace.

ᵃ 6 Hebrew Sheol; also in verse 9

7"But show kindness to the sons of Barzillai of Gilead and let them be among those who eat at your table. They stood by me when I fled from your brother Absalom.

8"And remember, you have with you Shimei son of Gera, the Benjamite from Bahurim, who called down bitter curses on me the day I went to Mahanaim. When he came down to meet me at the Jordan, I swore to him by the Lord: 'I will not put you to death by the sword.' 9But now, do not consider him innocent. You are a man of wisdom; you will know what to do to him. Bring his gray head down to the grave in blood."

10Then David rested with his fathers and was buried in the City of David. 11He had reigned forty years over Israel—seven years in Hebron and thirty-three in Jerusalem. 12So Solomon sat on the throne of his father David, and his rule was firmly established.

truth or dare

Take David's advice and show some kindness at the table. The cafeteria can become Clique City. Open up your heart and your table, and invite a new girl to join you.

2:7

Solomon's Throne Established

13Now Adonijah, the son of Haggith, went to Bathsheba, Solomon's mother. Bathsheba asked him, "Do you come peacefully?"

He answered, "Yes, peacefully." 14Then he added, "I have something to say to you."

"You may say it," she replied.

15"As you know," he said, "the kingdom was mine. All Israel looked to me as their king. But things changed, and the kingdom has gone to my brother; for it has come to him from the Lord. 16Now I have one request to make of you. Do not refuse me."

"You may make it," she said.

17So he continued, "Please ask King Solomon—he will not refuse you—to give me Abishag the Shunammite as my wife."

18"Very well," Bathsheba replied, "I will speak to the king for you."

19When Bathsheba went to King Solomon to speak to him for Adonijah, the king stood up to meet her, bowed down to her and sat down on his throne. He had a throne brought for the king's mother, and she sat down at his right hand.

20"I have one small request to make of you," she said. "Do not refuse me."

The king replied, "Make it, my mother; I will not refuse you."

21So she said, "Let Abishag the Shunammite be given in marriage to your brother Adonijah."

22King Solomon answered his mother, "Why do you request Abishag the Shunammite for Adonijah? You might as well request the kingdom for him—after all, he is my older brother—yes, for him and for Abiathar the priest and Joab son of Zeruiah!"

23Then King Solomon swore by the Lord: "May God deal with me, be it ever so severely, if Adonijah does not pay with his life for this request! 24And now, as surely as the Lord lives—he who has established me securely on the throne of my father David and has founded a dynasty for me as he promised—Adonijah shall be put to death today!" 25So King Solomon gave orders to Benaiah son of Jehoiada, and he struck down Adonijah and he died.

26To Abiathar the priest the king said, "Go back to your fields in Anathoth. You deserve to die, but I will not put you to death now, because you carried the ark of the Sovereign Lord before my father David and shared all my father's hardships." 27So Solomon removed Abiathar from the priesthood of the Lord, fulfilling the word the Lord had spoken at Shiloh about the house of Eli.

28When the news reached Joab, who had conspired with Adonijah though not with Absalom, he fled to the tent of the Lord and took hold of the horns of the altar. 29King Solomon was told that Joab had fled to the tent of the Lord and was beside the altar. Then Solomon ordered Benaiah son of Jehoiada, "Go, strike him down!"

30So Benaiah entered the tent of the Lord and said to Joab, "The king says, 'Come out!'"

But he answered, "No, I will die here."

Benaiah reported to the king, "This is how Joab answered me."

31Then the king commanded Benaiah, "Do as he says. Strike him down and bury him, and so clear me and my father's house of the guilt of the innocent blood that Joab shed. 32The Lord will repay him for the blood he shed, because without the knowledge of my father David he attacked two men and killed them with the sword. Both of them—Abner son of Ner, commander of Israel's army, and Amasa son of Jether, commander of Judah's army—were better men and more upright than he. [33]May the guilt of their blood rest on the head of Joab and his descendants forever. But on David and his descendants, his house and his throne, may there be the LORD's peace forever."

[34]So Benaiah son of Jehoiada went up and struck down Joab and killed him, and he was buried on his own land [a] in the desert. [35]The king put Benaiah son of Jehoiada over the army in Joab's position and replaced Abiathar with Zadok the priest.

[36]Then the king sent for Shimei and said to him, "Build yourself a house in Jerusalem and live there, but do not go anywhere else. [37]The day you leave and cross the Kidron Valley, you can be sure you will die; your blood will be on your own head."

[38]Shimei answered the king, "What you say is good. Your servant will do as my lord the king has said." And Shimei stayed in Jerusalem for a long time.

[39]But three years later, two of Shimei's slaves ran off to Achish son of Maacah, king of Gath, and Shimei was told, "Your slaves are in Gath." [40]At this, he saddled his donkey and went to Achish at Gath in search of his slaves. So Shimei went away and brought the slaves back from Gath.

[41]When Solomon was told that Shimei had gone from Jerusalem to Gath and had returned, [42]the king summoned Shimei and said to him, "Did I not make you swear by the LORD and warn you, 'On the day you leave to go anywhere else, you can be sure you will die'? At that time you said to me, 'What you say is good. I will obey.' [43]Why then did you not keep your oath to the LORD and obey the command I gave you?"

[44]The king also said to Shimei, "You know in your heart all the wrong you did to my father David. Now the LORD will repay you for your wrongdoing. [45]But King Solomon will be blessed, and David's throne will remain secure before the LORD forever."

[46]Then the king gave the order to Benaiah son of Jehoiada, and he went out and struck Shimei down and killed him.

The kingdom was now firmly established in Solomon's hands.

Solomon Asks for Wisdom

3 Solomon made an alliance with Pharaoh king of Egypt and married his daughter. He brought her to the City of David until he finished building his palace and the temple of the LORD, and the wall around Jerusalem. [2]The people, however, were still sacrificing at the high places, because a temple had not yet been built for the Name of the LORD. [3]Solomon showed his love for the LORD by walking according to the statutes of his father David, except that he offered sacrifices and burned incense on the high places.

[4]The king went to Gibeon to offer sacrifices, for that was the most important high place, and Solomon offered a thousand burnt offerings on that altar. [5]At Gibeon the LORD appeared to Solomon during the night in a dream, and God said, "Ask for whatever you want me to give you."

[6]Solomon answered, "You have shown great kindness to your servant, my father David, because he was faithful to you and righteous and upright in heart. You have continued this great kindness to him and have given him a son to sit on his throne this very day.

[7]"Now, O LORD my God, you have made your servant king in place of my father David. But I am only a little child and do not know how to carry out my duties. [8]Your servant is here among the people you have chosen, a great people, too numerous to count or number. [9]So give your servant a discerning heart to govern your people and to distinguish between right and wrong. For who is able to govern this great people of yours?"

truth or dare

God gave Solomon the ultimate open door. And his selfless answer freed God to pour on the blessing. So . . . what would you have asked for?

3:5-14

a 34 Or buried in his tomb

¹⁰The Lord was pleased that Solomon had asked for this. ¹¹So God said to him, "Since you have asked for this and not for long life or wealth for yourself, nor have asked for the death of your enemies but for discernment in administering justice, ¹²I will do what you have asked. I will give you a wise and discerning heart, so that there will never have been anyone like you, nor will there ever be. ¹³Moreover, I will give you what you have not asked for—both riches and honor—so that in your lifetime you will have no equal among kings. ¹⁴And if you walk in my ways and obey my statutes and commands as David your father did, I will give you a long life." ¹⁵Then Solomon awoke—and he realized it had been a dream.

He returned to Jerusalem, stood before the ark of the Lord's covenant and sacrificed burnt offerings and fellowship offerings.ᵃ Then he gave a feast for all his court.

A Wise Ruling

¹⁶Now two prostitutes came to the king and stood before him. ¹⁷One of them said, "My lord, this woman and I live in the same house. I had a baby while she was there with me. ¹⁸The third day after my child was born, this woman also had a baby. We were alone; there was no one in the house but the two of us.

¹⁹"During the night this woman's son died because she lay on him. ²⁰So she got up in the middle of the night and took my son from my side while I your servant was asleep. She put him by her breast and put her dead son by my breast. ²¹The next morning, I got up to nurse my son—and he was dead! But when I looked at him closely in the morning light, I saw that it wasn't the son I had borne."

²²The other woman said, "No! The living one is my son; the dead one is yours."

But the first one insisted, "No! The dead one is yours; the living one is mine." And so they argued before the king.

²³The king said, "This one says, 'My son is alive and your son is dead,' while that one says, 'No! Your son is dead and mine is alive.' "

²⁴Then the king said, "Bring me a sword." So they brought a sword for the king. ²⁵He then gave an order: "Cut the living child in two and give half to one and half to the other."

²⁶The woman whose son was alive was filled with compassion for her son and said to the king, "Please, my lord, give her the living baby! Don't kill him!"

But the other said, "Neither I nor you shall have him. Cut him in two!"

²⁷Then the king gave his ruling: "Give the living baby to the first woman. Do not kill him; she is his mother."

²⁸When all Israel heard the verdict the king had given, they held the king in awe, because they saw that he had wisdom from God to administer justice.

Solomon's Officials and Governors

4 So King Solomon ruled over all Israel. ²And these were his chief officials:

Azariah son of Zadok—the priest;
³Elihoreph and Ahijah, sons of Shisha—secretaries;
Jehoshaphat son of Ahilud—recorder;

---

genuine wisdom

We're all about free stuff, aren't we? Those free shampoo samples. Free AOL software. Free t-shirts. Sometimes you really score with something like free perfume or lotion or movie passes. Whether you use it or not is up to you. But there's one thing you can get for free that God is counting on you to use: wisdom. It's free—yours for the taking. All you have to do is ask (see James 1:5). Given just one wish, Solomon asked God for wisdom, and God offers us that same unlimited resource— free for the taking.

ᵃ 15 Traditionally *peace offerings*

⁴Benaiah son of Jehoiada—commander in chief;
    Zadok and Abiathar—priests;
⁵Azariah son of Nathan—in charge of the district officers;
    Zabud son of Nathan—a priest and personal adviser to the king;
⁶Ahishar—in charge of the palace;
    Adoniram son of Abda—in charge of forced labor.

⁷Solomon also had twelve district governors over all Israel, who supplied provisions for the king and the royal household. Each one had to provide supplies for one month in the year. ⁸These are their names:

    Ben-Hur—in the hill country of Ephraim;
⁹Ben-Deker—in Makaz, Shaalbim, Beth Shemesh and Elon Bethhanan;
¹⁰Ben-Hesed—in Arubboth (Socoh and all the land of Hepher were his);
¹¹Ben-Abinadab—in Naphoth Dor* (he was married to Taphath daughter of Solomon);
¹²Baana son of Ahilud—in Taanach and Megiddo, and in all of Beth Shan next to Zarethan below Jezreel, from Beth Shan to Abel Meholah across to Jokmeam;
¹³Ben-Geber—in Ramoth Gilead (the settlements of Jair son of Manasseh in Gilead were his, as well as the district of Argob in Bashan and its sixty large walled cities with bronze gate bars);
¹⁴Ahinadab son of Iddo—in Mahanaim;
¹⁵Ahimaaz—in Naphtali (he had married Basemath daughter of Solomon);
¹⁶Baana son of Hushai—in Asher and in Aloth;
¹⁷Jehoshaphat son of Paruah—in Issachar;
¹⁸Shimei son of Ela—in Benjamin;
¹⁹Geber son of Uri—in Gilead (the country of Sihon king of the Amorites and the country of Og king of Bashan). He was the only governor over the district.

Solomon's Daily Provisions

²⁰The people of Judah and Israel were as numerous as the sand on the seashore; they ate, they drank and they were happy. ²¹And Solomon ruled over all the kingdoms from the River ᵇ to the land of the Philistines, as far as the border of Egypt. These countries brought tribute and were Solomon's subjects all his life.

²²Solomon's daily provisions were thirty cors ᶜ of fine flour and sixty cors ᵈ of meal, ²³ten head of stall-fed cattle, twenty of pasture-fed cattle and a hundred sheep and goats, as well as deer, gazelles, roebucks and choice fowl. ²⁴For he ruled over all the kingdoms west of the River, from Tiphsah to Gaza, and had peace on all sides. ²⁵During Solomon's lifetime Judah and Israel, from Dan to Beersheba, lived in safety, each man under his own vine and fig tree.

²⁶Solomon had four ᵉ thousand stalls for chariot horses, and twelve thousand horses.ᶠ

²⁷The district officers, each in his month, supplied provisions for King Solomon and all who came to the king's table. They saw to it that nothing was lacking. ²⁸They also brought to the proper place their quotas of barley and straw for the chariot horses and the other horses.

Solomon's Wisdom

²⁹God gave Solomon wisdom and very great insight, and a breadth of understanding as measureless as the sand on the seashore. ³⁰Solomon's wisdom was greater than the wisdom of all the men of the East, and greater than all the wisdom of Egypt. ³¹He was wiser than any other man, including Ethan the Ezrahite—wiser than Heman, Calcol and Darda, the sons of Mahol. And his fame spread to all the surrounding nations. ³²He spoke three thousand proverbs and his songs numbered a thousand and five. ³³He described plant life, from the cedar of Lebanon to the hyssop that grows out of walls. He also taught about animals and birds, reptiles and fish. ³⁴Men of all nations came to listen to Solomon's wisdom, sent by all the kings of the world, who had heard of his wisdom.

a 11 Or in the heights of Dor   b 21 That is, the Euphrates; also in verse 24   c 22 That is, probably about 185 bushels (about 6.6 kiloliters)   d 22 That is, probably about 375 bushels (about 13.2 kiloliters)   e 26 Some Septuagint manuscripts (see also 2 Chron. 9:25); Hebrew forty   f 26 Or charioteers

Not Enough Hours in the Day

focus Profile: **Rachael**

What's my problem? No matter what I do, I just can't stay on track with my quiet times. I try to be consistent with them, which lasts like a week or so, and then I go through this long drought. And it seems like every new strategy I try just ends up failing.

For a while I was doing okay. That was last summer, when my friends and I were in a small group together, and we had this Bible reading schedule that we all followed. The five of us met each week to talk about our reading and pray together. The accountability was great. I was so consistent, every day, for a couple of months.

But then the fall came . . . and field hockey season started, and I just kind of stopped going. I went for the first few weeks, but to be honest, once school started, I just couldn't keep up with the reading. I am *not* a morning person (understatement!), and by the time I finished practice and homework each night, I was so tired I'd just collapse into bed.

The worst part is that I *know* that spending time with God is important, which makes me feel so frustrated. I *want* to do better. I mean, God *should* be the most important thing in my life. But for some reason, everything else just seems so much more pressing.

quiet times in focus

Spiritual disciplines like Bible reading and prayer are exactly that—disciplines! They don't come easily to most of us. But over time, if you work to develop consistent habits, you'll get to the place where you can't stand to miss that time with God.

If you want to establish a consistent quiet time . . .

- » Set a time and a place where you'll meet with God each day. (No free time, you say? How about cutting out TV, phone or Internet to *make* some time?)
- » Keep a journal to record your prayers and thoughts on Scripture.
- » Use a good devotional book to guide you on what to read.
- » Find an accountability partner. (Trust us—it helps!)
- » Don't give up (see Galatians 6:9, page 1540)! Even if you fall behind, God always wants you to come back to him . . . even if it's been a while!

For more on this topic, see the index on page 1656.

For more ideas for your quiet time, go to www.TrueImagesBible.com

Preparations for Building the Temple

5 When Hiram king of Tyre heard that Solomon had been anointed king to succeed his father David, he sent his envoys to Solomon, because he had always been on friendly terms with David. ²Solomon sent back this message to Hiram:

³"You know that because of the wars waged against my father David from all sides, he could not build a temple for the Name of the Lord his God until the Lord put his enemies under his feet. ⁴But now the Lord my God has given me rest on every side, and there is no adversary or disaster. ⁵I intend, therefore, to build a temple for the Name of the Lord my God, as the Lord told my father David, when he said, 'Your son whom I will put on the throne in your place will build the temple for my Name.'

⁶"So give orders that cedars of Lebanon be cut for me. My men will work with yours, and I will pay you for your men whatever wages you set. You know that we have no one so skilled in felling timber as the Sidonians."

⁷When Hiram heard Solomon's message, he was greatly pleased and said, "Praise be to the LORD today, for he has given David a wise son to rule over this great nation."

⁸So Hiram sent word to Solomon:

"I have received the message you sent me and will do all you want in providing the cedar and pine logs. ⁹My men will haul them down from Lebanon to the sea, and I will float them in rafts by sea to the place you specify. There I will separate them and you can take them away. And you are to grant my wish by providing food for my royal household."

¹⁰In this way Hiram kept Solomon supplied with all the cedar and pine logs he wanted, ¹¹and Solomon gave Hiram twenty thousand cors*ᵃ* of wheat as food for his household, in addition to twenty thousand baths*ᵇ, ᶜ* of pressed olive oil. Solomon continued to do this for Hiram year after year. ¹²The LORD gave Solomon wisdom, just as he had promised him. There were peaceful relations between Hiram and Solomon, and the two of them made a treaty.

¹³King Solomon conscripted laborers from all Israel—thirty thousand men. ¹⁴He sent them off to Lebanon in shifts of ten thousand a month, so that they spent one month in Lebanon and two months at home. Adoniram was in charge of the forced labor. ¹⁵Solomon had seventy thousand carriers and eighty thousand stonecutters in the hills, ¹⁶as well as thirty-three hundred*ᵈ* foremen who supervised the project and directed the workmen. ¹⁷At the king's command they removed from the quarry large blocks of quality stone to provide a foundation of dressed stone for the temple. ¹⁸The craftsmen of Solomon and Hiram and the men of Gebal*ᵉ* cut and prepared the timber and stone for the building of the temple.

Solomon Builds the Temple

6 In the four hundred and eightieth*ᶠ* year after the Israelites had come out of Egypt, in the fourth year of Solomon's reign over Israel, in the month of Ziv, the second month, he began to build the temple of the LORD.

²The temple that King Solomon built for the LORD was sixty cubits long, twenty wide and thirty high.*ᵍ* ³The portico at the front of the main hall of the temple extended the width of the temple, that is twenty cubits,*ʰ* and projected ten cubits*ⁱ* from the front of the temple. ⁴He made narrow clerestory windows in the temple. ⁵Against the walls of the main hall and inner sanctuary he built a structure around the building, in which there were side rooms. ⁶The lowest floor was five cubits*ʲ* wide, the middle floor six cubits*ᵏ* and the third floor seven.*ˡ* He made offset ledges around the outside of the temple so that nothing would be inserted into the temple walls.

⁷In building the temple, only blocks dressed at the quarry were used, and no hammer, chisel or any other iron tool was heard at the temple site while it was being built.

⁸The entrance to the lowest*ᵐ* floor was on the south side of the temple; a stairway led up to the middle level and from there to the third. ⁹So he built the temple and completed it, roofing it with beams and cedar planks. ¹⁰And he built the side rooms all along the temple. The height of each was five cubits, and they were attached to the temple by beams of cedar.

truth or dare

Solomon built the temple from scratch, yet he poured himself into his project, wanting to give God his best. Time to harness *your* energy! In what ways are you serving God?

6:1–10

ᵃ 11 That is, probably about 125,000 bushels (about 4,400 kiloliters)   *ᵇ 11* Septuagint (see also 2 Chron. 2:10); Hebrew *twenty cors*   *ᶜ 11* That is, about 115,000 gallons (about 440 kiloliters)   *ᵈ 16* Hebrew; some Septuagint manuscripts (see also 2 Chron. 2:2,18) *thirty-six hundred*   *ᵉ 18* That is, Byblos   *ᶠ 1* Hebrew; Septuagint *four hundred and fortieth*   *ᵍ 2* That is, about 90 feet (about 27 meters) long and 30 feet (about 9 meters) wide and 45 feet (about 13.5 meters) high   *ʰ 3* That is, about 30 feet (about 9 meters)   *ⁱ 3* That is, about 15 feet (about 4.5 meters)   *ʲ 6* That is, about 7 1/2 feet (about 2.3 meters); also in verses 10 and 24   *ᵏ 6* That is, about 9 feet (about 2.7 meters)   *ˡ 6* That is, about 10 1/2 feet (about 3.1 meters)   *ᵐ 8* Septuagint; Hebrew *middle*

¹¹The word of the Lord came to Solomon: ¹²"As for this temple you are building, if you follow my decrees, carry out my regulations and keep all my commands and obey them, I will fulfill through you the promise I gave to David your father. ¹³And I will live among the Israelites and will not abandon my people Israel."

¹⁴So Solomon built the temple and completed it. ¹⁵He lined its interior walls with cedar boards, paneling them from the floor of the temple to the ceiling, and covered the floor of the temple with planks of pine. ¹⁶He partitioned off twenty cubits*ᵃ* at the rear of the temple with cedar boards from floor to ceiling to form within the temple an inner sanctuary, the Most Holy Place. ¹⁷The main hall in front of this room was forty cubits*ᵇ* long. ¹⁸The inside of the temple was cedar, carved with gourds and open flowers. Everything was cedar; no stone was to be seen.

¹⁹He prepared the inner sanctuary within the temple to set the ark of the covenant of the Lord there. ²⁰The inner sanctuary was twenty cubits long, twenty wide and twenty high.*ᶜ* He overlaid the inside with pure gold, and he also overlaid the altar of cedar. ²¹Solomon covered the inside of the temple with pure gold, and he extended gold chains across the front of the inner sanctuary, which was overlaid with gold. ²²So he overlaid the whole interior with gold. He also overlaid with gold the altar that belonged to the inner sanctuary.

²³In the inner sanctuary he made a pair of cherubim of olive wood, each ten cubits*ᵈ* high. ²⁴One wing of the first cherub was five cubits long, and the other wing five cubits—ten cubits from wing tip to wing tip. ²⁵The second cherub also measured ten cubits, for the two cherubim were identical in size and shape. ²⁶The height of each cherub was ten cubits. ²⁷He placed the cherubim inside the innermost room of the temple, with their wings spread out. The wing of one cherub touched one wall, while the wing of the other touched the other wall, and their wings touched each other in the middle of the room. ²⁸He overlaid the cherubim with gold.

²⁹On the walls all around the temple, in both the inner and outer rooms, he carved cherubim, palm trees and open flowers. ³⁰He also covered the floors of both the inner and outer rooms of the temple with gold.

³¹For the entrance of the inner sanctuary he made doors of olive wood with five-sided jambs. ³²And on the two olive wood doors he carved cherubim, palm trees and open flowers, and overlaid the cherubim and palm trees with beaten gold. ³³In the same way he made four-sided jambs of olive wood for the entrance to the main hall. ³⁴He also made two pine doors, each having two leaves that turned in sockets. ³⁵He carved cherubim, palm trees and open flowers on them and overlaid them with gold hammered evenly over the carvings.

³⁶And he built the inner courtyard of three courses of dressed stone and one course of trimmed cedar beams.

³⁷The foundation of the temple of the Lord was laid in the fourth year, in the month of Ziv. ³⁸In the eleventh year in the month of Bul, the eighth month, the temple was finished in all its details according to its specifications. He had spent seven years building it.

Solomon Builds His Palace

7 It took Solomon thirteen years, however, to complete the construction of his palace. ²He built the Palace of the Forest of Lebanon a hundred cubits long, fifty wide and thirty high,*ᵉ* with four rows of cedar columns supporting trimmed cedar beams. ³It was roofed with cedar above the beams that rested on the columns—forty-five beams, fifteen to a row. ⁴Its windows were placed high in sets of three, facing each other. ⁵All the doorways had rectangular frames; they were in the front part in sets of three, facing each other.*ᶠ*

⁶He made a colonnade fifty cubits long and thirty wide.*ᵍ* In front of it was a portico, and in front of that were pillars and an overhanging roof.

⁷He built the throne hall, the Hall of Justice, where he was to judge, and he covered it with cedar from floor to ceiling.*ʰ* ⁸And the palace in which he was to live, set farther back, was similar in design. Solomon also made a palace like this hall for Pharaoh's daughter, whom he had married.

⁹All these structures, from the outside to the great courtyard and from foundation to eaves,

ᵃ 16 That is, about 30 feet (about 9 meters)   *ᵇ 17* That is, about 60 feet (about 18 meters)   *ᶜ 20* That is, about 30 feet (about 9 meters) long, wide and high   *ᵈ 23* That is, about 15 feet (about 4.5 meters)   *ᵉ 2* That is, about 150 feet (about 46 meters) long, 75 feet (about 23 meters) wide and 45 feet (about 13.5 meters) high   *ᶠ 5* The meaning of the Hebrew for this verse is uncertain.   *ᵍ 6* That is, about 75 feet (about 23 meters) long and 45 feet (about 13.5 meters) wide   *ʰ 7* Vulgate and Syriac; Hebrew *floor* were made of blocks of high-grade stone cut to size and trimmed with a saw on their inner and outer faces. [10]The foundations were laid with large stones of good quality, some measuring ten cubits[a] and some eight. [b] [11]Above were high-grade stones, cut to size, and cedar beams. [12]The great courtyard was surrounded by a wall of three courses of dressed stone and one course of trimmed cedar beams, as was the inner courtyard of the temple of the LORD with its portico.

The Temple's Furnishings

[13]King Solomon sent to Tyre and brought Huram,[c] [14]whose mother was a widow from the tribe of Naphtali and whose father was a man of Tyre and a craftsman in bronze. Huram was highly skilled and experienced in all kinds of bronze work. He came to King Solomon and did all the work assigned to him.

[15]He cast two bronze pillars, each eighteen cubits high and twelve cubits around,[d] by line. [16]He also made two capitals of cast bronze to set on the tops of the pillars; each capital was five cubits[e] high. [17]A network of interwoven chains festooned the capitals on top of the pillars, seven for each capital. [18]He made pomegranates in two rows[f] encircling each network to decorate the capitals on top of the pillars.[g] He did the same for each capital. [19]The capitals on top of the pillars in the portico were in the shape of lilies, four cubits[h] high. [20]On the capitals of both pillars, above the bowl-shaped part next to the network, were the two hundred pomegranates in rows all around. [21]He erected the pillars at the portico of the temple. The pillar to the south he named Jakin[i] and the one to the north Boaz.[j] [22]The capitals on top were in the shape of lilies. And so the work on the pillars was completed.

genuine talent » 7:13-14

Most of us aren't called to be missionaries or preachers. (Was that a sigh of relief from some of you?) But that doesn't mean that God doesn't have a role for us in his kingdom. Maybe you consider your talent a little too random for God's work. Huram probably thought the same thing. Little did he know that God wanted him to do something that only he could do. The same goes for you. Whatever your talent is—letter writing, organization, cooking, tennis—you name it, God can use it.

[23]He made the Sea of cast metal, circular in shape, measuring ten cubits[a] from rim to rim and five cubits high. It took a line of thirty cubits[k] to measure around it. [24]Below the rim, gourds encircled it—ten to a cubit. The gourds were cast in two rows in one piece with the Sea.

[25]The Sea stood on twelve bulls, three facing north, three facing west, three facing south and three facing east. The Sea rested on top of them, and their hindquarters were toward the center. [26]It was a handbreadth[l] in thickness, and its rim was like the rim of a cup, like a lily blossom. It held two thousand baths.[m]

[27]He also made ten movable stands of bronze; each was four cubits long, four wide and three high.[n] [28]This is how the stands were made: They had side panels attached to uprights. [29]On the panels between the uprights were lions, bulls and cherubim—and on the uprights as well. Above and below the lions and bulls were wreaths of hammered work. [30]Each stand had four bronze wheels with bronze axles, and each had a basin resting on four supports, cast with wreaths on each side. [31]On the inside of the stand there was an opening that had a circular frame one cubit[o]

---

[a] 10,23 That is, about 15 feet (about 4.5 meters)   [b] 10 That is, about 12 feet (about 3.6 meters)   [c] 13 Hebrew Hiram, a variant of Huram; also in verses 40 and 45   [d] 15 That is, about 27 feet (about 8.1 meters) high and 18 feet (about 5.4 meters) around   [e] 16 That is, about 7 1/2 feet (about 2.3 meters); also in verse 23   [f] 18 Two Hebrew manuscripts and Septuagint; most Hebrew manuscripts made the pillars, and there were two rows   [g] 18 Many Hebrew manuscripts and Syriac; most Hebrew manuscripts pomegranates   [h] 19 That is, about 6 feet (about 1.8 meters); also in verse 38   [i] 21 Jakin probably means he establishes.   [j] 21 Boaz probably means in him is strength.   [k] 23 That is, about 45 feet (about 13.5 meters)   [l] 26 That is, about 3 inches (about 8 centimeters)   [m] 26 That is, probably about 11,500 gallons (about 44 kiloliters); the Septuagint does not have this sentence.   [n] 27 That is, about 6 feet (about 1.8 meters) long and wide and about 4 1/2 feet (about 1.3 meters) high   [o] 31 That is, about 1 1/2 feet (about 0.5 meter)

deep. This opening was round, and with its basework it measured a cubit and a half.[a] Around its opening there was engraving. The panels of the stands were square, not round. [32]The four wheels were under the panels, and the axles of the wheels were attached to the stand. The diameter of each wheel was a cubit and a half. [33]The wheels were made like chariot wheels; the axles, rims, spokes and hubs were all of cast metal.

[34]Each stand had four handles, one on each corner, projecting from the stand. [35]At the top of the stand there was a circular band half a cubit[b] deep. The supports and panels were attached to the top of the stand. [36]He engraved cherubim, lions and palm trees on the surfaces of the supports and on the panels, in every available space, with wreaths all around. [37]This is the way he made the ten stands. They were all cast in the same molds and were identical in size and shape.

[38]He then made ten bronze basins, each holding forty baths[c] and measuring four cubits across, one basin to go on each of the ten stands. [39]He placed five of the stands on the south side of the temple and five on the north. He placed the Sea on the south side, at the southeast corner of the temple. [40]He also made the basins and shovels and sprinkling bowls.

So Huram finished all the work he had undertaken for King Solomon in the temple of the LORD:

[41]the two pillars;

the two bowl-shaped capitals on top of the pillars;

the two sets of network decorating the two bowl-shaped capitals on top of the pillars;

[42]the four hundred pomegranates for the two sets of network (two rows of pomegranates for each network, decorating the bowl-shaped capitals on top of the pillars);

[43]the ten stands with their ten basins;

[44]the Sea and the twelve bulls under it;

[45]the pots, shovels and sprinkling bowls.

All these objects that Huram made for King Solomon for the temple of the LORD were of burnished bronze. [46]The king had them cast in clay molds in the plain of the Jordan between Succoth and Zarethan. [47]Solomon left all these things unweighed, because there were so many; the weight of the bronze was not determined.

[48]Solomon also made all the furnishings that were in the LORD's temple:

the golden altar;

the golden table on which was the bread of the Presence;

[49]the lampstands of pure gold (five on the right and five on the left, in front of the inner sanctuary);

the gold floral work and lamps and tongs;

[50]the pure gold basins, wick trimmers, sprinkling bowls, dishes and censers;

and the gold sockets for the doors of the innermost room, the Most Holy Place, and also for the doors of the main hall of the temple.

[51]When all the work King Solomon had done for the temple of the LORD was finished, he brought in the things his father David had dedicated—the silver and gold and the furnishings—and he placed them in the treasuries of the LORD's temple.

The Ark Brought to the Temple

8 Then King Solomon summoned into his presence at Jerusalem the elders of Israel, all the heads of the tribes and the chiefs of the Israelite families, to bring up the ark of the LORD's covenant from Zion, the City of David. [2]All the men of Israel came together to King Solomon at the time of the festival in the month of Ethanim, the seventh month.

[3]When all the elders of Israel had arrived, the priests took up the ark, [4]and they brought up the ark of the LORD and the Tent of Meeting and all the sacred furnishings in it. The priests and Levites carried them up, [5]and King Solomon and the entire assembly of Israel that had gathered about him were before the ark, sacrificing so many sheep and cattle that they could not be recorded or counted.

[6]The priests then brought the ark of the LORD's covenant to its place in the inner sanctuary of the temple, the Most Holy Place, and put it beneath the wings of the cherubim. [7]The cherubim

a 31 That is, about 2 1/4 feet (about 0.7 meter); also in verse 32   b 35 That is, about 3/4 foot (about 0.2 meter)
c 38 That is, about 230 gallons (about 880 liters)

spread their wings over the place of the ark and overshadowed the ark and its carrying poles. [8]These poles were so long that their ends could be seen from the Holy Place in front of the inner sanctuary, but not from outside the Holy Place; and they are still there today. [9]There was nothing in the ark except the two stone tablets that Moses had placed in it at Horeb, where the LORD made a covenant with the Israelites after they came out of Egypt.

[10]When the priests withdrew from the Holy Place, the cloud filled the temple of the LORD. [11]And the priests could not perform their service because of the cloud, for the glory of the LORD filled his temple.

[12]Then Solomon said, "The LORD has said that he would dwell in a dark cloud; [13]I have indeed built a magnificent temple for you, a place for you to dwell forever."

[14]While the whole assembly of Israel was standing there, the king turned around and blessed them. [15]Then he said:

"Praise be to the LORD, the God of Israel, who with his own hand has fulfilled what he promised with his own mouth to my father David. For he said, [16]'Since the day I brought my people Israel out of Egypt, I have not chosen a city in any tribe of Israel to have a temple built for my Name to be there, but I have chosen David to rule my people Israel.'

[17]"My father David had it in his heart to build a temple for the Name of the LORD, the God of Israel. [18]But the LORD said to my father David, 'Because it was in your heart to build a temple for my Name, you did well to have this in your heart. [19]Nevertheless, you are not the one to build the temple, but your son, who is your own flesh and blood—he is the one who will build the temple for my Name.'

[20]"The LORD has kept the promise he made: I have succeeded David my father and now I sit on the throne of Israel, just as the LORD promised, and I have built the temple for the Name of the LORD, the God of Israel. [21]I have provided a place there for the ark, in which is the covenant of the LORD that he made with our fathers when he brought them out of Egypt."

Solomon's Prayer of Dedication

[22]Then Solomon stood before the altar of the LORD in front of the whole assembly of Israel, spread out his hands toward heaven [23]and said:

"O LORD, God of Israel, there is no God like you in heaven above or on earth below—you who keep your covenant of love with your servants who continue wholeheartedly in your way. [24]You have kept your promise to your servant David my father; with your mouth you have promised and with your hand you have fulfilled it—as it is today.

[25]"Now LORD, God of Israel, keep for your servant David my father the promises you made to him when you said, 'You shall never fail to have a man to sit before me on the throne of Israel, if only your sons are careful in all they do to walk before me as you have done.' [26]And now, O God of Israel, let your word that you promised your servant David my father come true.

[27]"But will God really dwell on earth? The heavens, even the highest heaven, cannot contain you. How much less this temple I have built! [28]Yet give attention to your servant's prayer and his plea for mercy, O LORD my God. Hear the cry and the prayer that your servant is praying in your presence this day. [29]May your eyes be open toward this temple night and day, this place of which you said, 'My Name shall be there,' so that you will hear the prayer your servant prays toward this place. [30]Hear the supplication of your servant and of your people Israel when they pray toward this place. Hear from heaven, your dwelling place, and when you hear, forgive.

[31]"When a man wrongs his neighbor and is required to take an oath and he comes and swears the oath before your altar in this temple, [32]then hear from heaven and act. Judge between your servants, condemning the guilty and bringing down on his own head what he has done. Declare the innocent not guilty, and so establish his innocence.

[33]"When your people Israel have been defeated by an enemy because they have sinned against you, and when they turn back to you and confess your name, praying and making supplication to you in this temple, [34]then hear from heaven and forgive the sin of your people Israel and bring them back to the land you gave to their fathers.

[35]"When the heavens are shut up and there is no rain because your people have sinned

against you, and when they pray toward this place and confess your name and turn from their sin because you have afflicted them, ³⁶then hear from heaven and forgive the sin of your servants, your people Israel. Teach them the right way to live, and send rain on the land you gave your people for an inheritance.

³⁷"When famine or plague comes to the land, or blight or mildew, locusts or grasshoppers, or when an enemy besieges them in any of their cities, whatever disaster or disease may come, ³⁸and when a prayer or plea is made by any of your people Israel—each one aware of the afflictions of his own heart, and spreading out his hands toward this temple—³⁹then hear from heaven, your dwelling place. Forgive and act; deal with each man according to all he does, since you know his heart (for you alone know the hearts of all men), ⁴⁰so that they will fear you all the time they live in the land you gave our fathers.

⁴¹"As for the foreigner who does not belong to your people Israel but has come from a distant land because of your name— ⁴²for men will hear of your great name and your mighty hand and your outstretched arm—when he comes and prays toward this temple, ⁴³then hear from heaven, your dwelling place, and do whatever the foreigner asks of you, so that all the peoples of the earth may know your name and fear you, as do your own people Israel, and may know that this house I have built bears your Name.

⁴⁴"When your people go to war against their enemies, wherever you send them, and when they pray to the LORD toward the city you have chosen and the temple I have built for your Name, ⁴⁵then hear from heaven their prayer and their plea, and uphold their cause.

⁴⁶"When they sin against you—for there is no one who does not sin—and you become angry with them and give them over to the enemy, who takes them captive to his own land, far away or near; ⁴⁷and if they have a change of heart in the land where they are held captive, and repent and plead with you in the land of their conquerors and say, 'We have sinned, we have done wrong, we have acted wickedly'; ⁴⁸and if they turn back to you with all their heart and soul in the land of their enemies who took them captive, and pray to you toward the land you gave their fathers, toward the city you have chosen and the temple I have built for your Name; ⁴⁹then from heaven, your dwelling place, hear their prayer and their plea, and uphold their cause. ⁵⁰And forgive your people, who have sinned against you; forgive all the offenses they have committed against you, and cause their conquerors to show them mercy; ⁵¹for they are your people and your inheritance, whom you brought out of Egypt, out of that iron-smelting furnace.

love notes

8:27

Beloved,

Gaze up into the sky. Not even the entire heavens can contain me! Yet I want to make my home with you, in your heart. I won't impose, though. You have to invite me in.

—God of the heavens

What is your response to God, knowing that the Lord of the universe wants to live within you?

⁵²"May your eyes be open to your servant's plea and to the plea of your people Israel, and may you listen to them whenever they cry out to you. ⁵³For you singled them out from all the nations of the world to be your own inheritance, just as you declared through your servant Moses when you, O Sovereign LORD, brought our fathers out of Egypt."

⁵⁴When Solomon had finished all these prayers and supplications to the LORD, he rose from before the altar of the LORD, where he had been kneeling with his hands spread out toward heaven. ⁵⁵He stood and blessed the whole assembly of Israel in a loud voice, saying:

⁵⁶"Praise be to the LORD, who has given rest to his people Israel just as he promised. Not one word has failed of all the good promises he gave through his servant Moses. ⁵⁷May the LORD our God be with us as he was with our fathers; may he never leave us nor forsake us. ⁵⁸May he turn our hearts to him, to walk in all his ways and to keep the commands, decrees and regulations he gave our fathers. ⁵⁹And may these words of mine, which I have prayed before the LORD, be near to the LORD our God day and night, that he may uphold the cause of his servant and the cause of his people Israel according to each day's need, ⁶⁰so that all the peoples of the earth may know that the LORD is God and that there is no other. ⁶¹But your hearts must be fully committed to the LORD our God, to live by his decrees and obey his commands, as at this time."

The Dedication of the Temple

⁶²Then the king and all Israel with him offered sacrifices before the LORD. ⁶³Solomon offered a sacrifice of fellowship offerings *ᵃ* to the LORD: twenty-two thousand cattle and a hundred and twenty thousand sheep and goats. So the king and all the Israelites dedicated the temple of the LORD.

⁶⁴On that same day the king consecrated the middle part of the courtyard in front of the temple of the LORD, and there he offered burnt offerings, grain offerings and the fat of the fellowship offerings, because the bronze altar before the LORD was too small to hold the burnt offerings, the grain offerings and the fat of the fellowship offerings.

⁶⁵So Solomon observed the festival at that time, and all Israel with him—a vast assembly, people from Lebo *ᵇ* Hamath to the Wadi of Egypt. They celebrated it before the LORD our God for seven days and seven days more, fourteen days in all. ⁶⁶On the following day he sent the people away. They blessed the king and then went home, joyful and glad in heart for all the good things the LORD had done for his servant David and his people Israel.

The LORD Appears to Solomon

9 When Solomon had finished building the temple of the LORD and the royal palace, and had achieved all he had desired to do, ²the LORD appeared to him a second time, as he had appeared to him at Gibeon. ³The LORD said to him:

"I have heard the prayer and plea you have made before me; I have consecrated this temple, which you have built, by putting my Name there forever. My eyes and my heart will always be there.

⁴"As for you, if you walk before me in integrity of heart and uprightness, as David your father did, and do all I command and observe my decrees and laws, ⁵I will establish your royal throne over Israel forever, as I promised David your father when I said, 'You shall never fail to have a man on the throne of Israel.'

⁶"But if you *ᶜ* or your sons turn away from me and do not observe the commands and decrees I have given you *ᶜ* and go off to serve other gods and worship them, ⁷then I will cut off Israel from the land I have given them and will reject this temple I have consecrated for my Name. Israel will then become a byword and an object of ridicule among all peoples. ⁸And though this temple is now imposing, all who pass by will be ap-

truth or dare

There's no autopilot for staying connected to God. Malfunctions begin with the first sin. That's why obedience (and continual confession) is the key to closeness.

9:6–8

ᵃ 63 Traditionally *peace offerings*; also in verse 64   *ᵇ 65* Or *from the entrance to*   *ᶜ 6* The Hebrew is plural.

palled and will scoff and say, 'Why has the Lord done such a thing to this land and to this temple?' ⁹People will answer, 'Because they have forsaken the Lord their God, who brought their fathers out of Egypt, and have embraced other gods, worshiping and serving them—that is why the Lord brought all this disaster on them.' "

Solomon's Other Activities

¹⁰At the end of twenty years, during which Solomon built these two buildings—the temple of the Lord and the royal palace— ¹¹King Solomon gave twenty towns in Galilee to Hiram king of Tyre, because Hiram had supplied him with all the cedar and pine and gold he wanted. ¹²But when Hiram went from Tyre to see the towns that Solomon had given him, he was not pleased with them. ¹³"What kind of towns are these you have given me, my brother?" he asked. And he called them the Land of Cabul,ᵃ a name they have to this day. ¹⁴Now Hiram had sent to the king 120 talentsᵇ of gold.

¹⁵Here is the account of the forced labor King Solomon conscripted to build the Lord's temple, his own palace, the supporting terraces,ᶜ the wall of Jerusalem, and Hazor, Megiddo and Gezer. ¹⁶(Pharaoh king of Egypt had attacked and captured Gezer. He had set it on fire. He killed its Canaanite inhabitants and then gave it as a wedding gift to his daughter, Solomon's wife. ¹⁷And Solomon rebuilt Gezer.) He built up Lower Beth Horon, ¹⁸Baalath, and Tadmorᵈ in the desert, within his land, ¹⁹as well as all his store cities and the towns for his chariots and for his horsesᵉ—whatever he desired to build in Jerusalem, in Lebanon and throughout all the territory he ruled.

²⁰All the people left from the Amorites, Hittites, Perizzites, Hivites and Jebusites (these peoples were not Israelites), ²¹that is, their descendants remaining in the land, whom the Israelites could not exterminateᶠ—these Solomon conscripted for his slave labor force, as it is to this day. ²²But Solomon did not make slaves of any of the Israelites; they were his fighting men, his government officials, his officers, his captains, and the commanders of his chariots and charioteers. ²³They were also the chief officials in charge of Solomon's projects—550 officials supervising the men who did the work.

²⁴After Pharaoh's daughter had come up from the City of David to the palace Solomon had built for her, he constructed the supporting terraces.

²⁵Three times a year Solomon sacrificed burnt offerings and fellowship offeringsᵍ on the altar he had built for the Lord, burning incense before the Lord along with them, and so fulfilled the temple obligations.

²⁶King Solomon also built ships at Ezion Geber, which is near Elath in Edom, on the shore of the Red Sea.ʰ ²⁷And Hiram sent his men—sailors who knew the sea—to serve in the fleet with Solomon's men. ²⁸They sailed to Ophir and brought back 420 talentsⁱ of gold, which they delivered to King Solomon.

The Queen of Sheba Visits Solomon

10 When the queen of Sheba heard about the fame of Solomon and his relation to the name of the Lord, she came to test him with hard questions. ²Arriving at Jerusalem with a very great caravan—with camels carrying spices, large quantities of gold, and precious stones—she came to Solomon and talked with him about all that she had on her mind. ³Solomon answered all her questions; nothing was too hard for the king to explain to her. ⁴When the queen of Sheba saw all the wisdom of Solomon and the palace he had built, ⁵the food on his table, the seating of his officials, the attending servants in their robes, his cupbearers, and the burnt offerings he made atʲ the temple of the Lord, she was overwhelmed.

⁶She said to the king, "The report I heard in my own country about your achievements and your wisdom is true. ⁷But I did not believe

truth or dare

The Queen of Sheba possessed wisdom of her own! She easily spotted the link between Solomon's greatness and his God. Are you wise enough to recognize God at work?

10:6–9

ᵃ 13 *Cabul* sounds like the Hebrew for *good-for-nothing.*   ᵇ 14 That is, about 4 1/2 tons (about 4 metric tons)
ᶜ 15 Or *the Millo*; also in verse 24   ᵈ 18 The Hebrew may also be read *Tamar.*   ᵉ 19 Or *charioteers*
ᶠ 21 The Hebrew term refers to the irrevocable giving over of things or persons to the Lord, often by totally destroying them.
ᵍ 25 Traditionally *peace offerings*   ʰ 26 Hebrew *Yam Suph*; that is, Sea of Reeds   ⁱ 28 That is, about 16 tons (about
14.5 metric tons)   ʲ 5 Or *the ascent by which he went up to*

mirror images

When the queen of Sheba heard about the fame of Solomon and his relation to the name of the LORD, she came to test him with hard questions. 1 Kings 10:1

Queen of Sheba—Believing Is Seeing

The Queen of Sheba—an independent woman running a country back in the day when that was a pretty male thing to do. Do you know girls like her? Girls who run for office, lead committees, run the show? That was the Queen. She was someone to be reckoned with.

When she started hearing reports of Solomon, the new king of Israel, and his great wealth, vast wisdom and impressive achievements, the Queen decided to check it out for herself. She traveled a long distance to size him up and see if God's blessings had been exaggerated.

The Queen was overwhelmed by Solomon's beautiful city and the peace and prosperity of the nation. She saw the palace, the food and the temple. It had seemed too good to be true. She'd heard the rumors, but she didn't believe it till she saw it with her own eyes (see 1 Kings 10:7).

Can you blame her? We're told great things about God—outrageous claims from parents and pastors. "You're telling me Jesus lived a sinless life, died on a cross, and came back to life—all because he loves me? You're saying he wants me in heaven with him someday? Yeah right. I'll believe it when I see it." Our little earthly brains don't buy it. The world says, "Seeing is believing." But God says, *"Believing is seeing."* That's what faith is all about (see John 20:29). However, for girls like the Queen—believing on faith alone is a big stretch. That's why it's called *faith*.

Dear God, help me to trust what you say is true. Give me the faith I need so I don't have to see it to believe it. Amen.

To read the next Mirror Images profile, go to page 444.

>> Read more about the Queen of Sheba in 1 Kings 10 (pages 411–413) and 2 Chronicles 9 (pages 524–525).

these things until I came and saw with my own eyes. Indeed, not even half was told me; in wisdom and wealth you have far exceeded the report I heard. ⁸How happy your men must be! How happy your officials, who continually stand before you and hear your wisdom! ⁹Praise be to the Lord your God, who has delighted in you and placed you on the throne of Israel. Because of the Lord's eternal love for Israel, he has made you king, to maintain justice and righteousness."

¹⁰And she gave the king 120 talents⁰ of gold, large quantities of spices, and precious stones. Never again were so many spices brought in as those the queen of Sheba gave to King Solomon.

¹¹(Hiram's ships brought gold from Ophir; and from there they brought great cargoes of almug-wood ᵇ and precious stones. ¹²The king used the almugwood to make supports for the temple of the Lord and for the royal palace, and to make harps and lyres for the musicians. So much almug-wood has never been imported or seen since that day.)

¹³King Solomon gave the queen of Sheba all she desired and asked for, besides what he had given her out of his royal bounty. Then she left and returned with her retinue to her own country.

Solomon's Splendor

¹⁴The weight of the gold that Solomon received yearly was 666 talents, ᶜ ¹⁵not including the revenues from merchants and traders and from all the Arabian kings and the governors of the land.

¹⁶King Solomon made two hundred large shields of hammered gold; six hundred bekas ᵈ of gold went into each shield. ¹⁷He also made three hundred small shields of hammered gold, with three minas ᵉ of gold in each shield. The king put them in the Palace of the Forest of Lebanon.

¹⁸Then the king made a great throne inlaid with ivory and overlaid with fine gold. ¹⁹The throne had six steps, and its back had a rounded top. On both sides of the seat were armrests, with a lion standing beside each of them. ²⁰Twelve lions stood on the six steps, one at either end of each step. Nothing like it had ever been made for any other kingdom. ²¹All King Solomon's goblets were gold, and all the household articles in the Palace of the Forest of Lebanon were pure gold. Nothing was made of silver, because silver was considered of little value in Solomon's days. ²²The king had a fleet of trading ships ᶠ at sea along with the ships of Hiram. Once every three years it returned, carrying gold, silver and ivory, and apes and baboons.

²³King Solomon was greater in riches and wisdom than all the other kings of the earth. ²⁴The whole world sought audience with Solomon to hear the wisdom God had put in his heart. ²⁵Year after year, everyone who came brought a gift—articles of silver and gold, robes, weapons and spices, and horses and mules.

²⁶Solomon accumulated chariots and horses; he had fourteen hundred chariots and twelve thousand horses, ᵍ which he kept in the chariot cities and also with him in Jerusalem. ²⁷The king made silver as common in Jerusalem as stones, and cedar as plentiful as sycamore-fig trees in the foothills. ²⁸Solomon's horses were imported from Egypt ʰ and from Kue ⁱ—the royal merchants purchased them from Kue. ²⁹They imported a chariot from Egypt for six hundred shekels ʲ of silver, and a horse for a hundred and fifty. ᵏ They also exported them to all the kings of the Hittites and of the Arameans.

Solomon's Wives

11 King Solomon, however, loved many foreign women besides Pharaoh's daughter—Moabites, Ammonites, Edomites, Sidonians and Hittites. ²They were from nations about which the Lord had told the Israelites, "You must not intermarry with them, because they will surely turn your hearts after their gods." Nevertheless, Solomon held fast to them in love. ³He had seven hundred

truth or dare

Solomon totally watered down his faith. His mix of worshiping false gods and the true God was all wrong. In what ways have you diluted your faith with sin?

11:1–8

a 10 That is, about 4 1/2 tons (about 4 metric tons)   b 11 Probably a variant of algumwood; also in verse 12   c 14 That is, about 25 tons (about 23 metric tons)   d 16 That is, about 7 1/2 pounds (about 3.5 kilograms)   e 17 That is, about 3 3/4 pounds (about 1.7 kilograms)   f 22 Hebrew of ships of Tarshish   g 26 Or charioteers   h 28 Or possibly Muzur, a region in Cilicia; also in verse 29   i 28 Probably Cilicia   j 29 That is, about 15 pounds (about 7 kilograms)   k 29 That is, about 3 3/4 pounds (about 1.7 kilograms) wives of royal birth and three hundred concubines, and his wives led him astray. [4]As Solomon grew old, his wives turned his heart after other gods, and his heart was not fully devoted to the LORD his God, as the heart of David his father had been. [5]He followed Ashtoreth the goddess of the Sidonians, and Molech[a] the detestable god of the Ammonites. [6]So Solomon did evil in the eyes of the LORD; he did not follow the LORD completely, as David his father had done.

[7]On a hill east of Jerusalem, Solomon built a high place for Chemosh the detestable god of Moab, and for Molech the detestable god of the Ammonites. [8]He did the same for all his foreign wives, who burned incense and offered sacrifices to their gods.

[9]The LORD became angry with Solomon because his heart had turned away from the LORD, the God of Israel, who had appeared to him twice. [10]Although he had forbidden Solomon to follow other gods, Solomon did not keep the LORD's command. [11]So the LORD said to Solomon, "Since this is your attitude and you have not kept my covenant and my decrees, which I commanded you, I will most certainly tear the kingdom away from you and give it to one of your subordinates. [12]Nevertheless, for the sake of David your father, I will not do it during your lifetime. I will tear it out of the hand of your son. [13]Yet I will not tear the whole kingdom from him, but will give him one tribe for the sake of David my servant and for the sake of Jerusalem, which I have chosen."

genuine faith » 11:1-13

Which is harder: (1) to fail or (2) to keep going after you've failed? Number 2, right? Anyone can fail at something. But to keep going—to persevere—is one challenge many of us, well, *fail* to do. Solomon, the wisest king in the world, sinned by marrying foreign women who led him into worshiping idols. Whoops. Whether he returned to God after that is anyone's guess. Faith takes perseverance. Even if you fail—a month without devotions, a season of prayerlessness, giving in to peer pressure—you have to get back on your feet and keep going. Genuine faith never quits.

Solomon's Adversaries

[14]Then the LORD raised up against Solomon an adversary, Hadad the Edomite, from the royal line of Edom. [15]Earlier when David was fighting with Edom, Joab the commander of the army, who had gone up to bury the dead, had struck down all the men in Edom. [16]Joab and all the Israelites stayed there for six months, until they had destroyed all the men in Edom. [17]But Hadad, still only a boy, fled to Egypt with some Edomite officials who had served his father. [18]They set out from Midian and went to Paran. Then taking men from Paran with them, they went to Egypt, to Pharaoh king of Egypt, who gave Hadad a house and land and provided him with food.

[19]Pharaoh was so pleased with Hadad that he gave him a sister of his own wife, Queen Tahpenes, in marriage. [20]The sister of Tahpenes bore him a son named Genubath, whom Tahpenes brought up in the royal palace. There Genubath lived with Pharaoh's own children.

[21]While he was in Egypt, Hadad heard that David rested with his fathers and that Joab the commander of the army was also dead. Then Hadad said to Pharaoh, "Let me go, that I may return to my own country."

[22]"What have you lacked here that you want to go back to your own country?" Pharaoh asked.

"Nothing," Hadad replied, "but do let me go!"

[23]And God raised up against Solomon another adversary, Rezon son of Eliada, who had fled from his master, Hadadezer king of Zobah. [24]He gathered men around him and became the leader of a band of rebels when David destroyed the forces[b] ⌊of Zobah⌋; the rebels went to Damascus, where they settled and took control. [25]Rezon was Israel's adversary as long as Solomon lived, adding to the trouble caused by Hadad. So Rezon ruled in Aram and was hostile toward Israel.

a 5 Hebrew *Milcom*; also in verse 33   *b 24* Hebrew *destroyed them*

Jeroboam Rebels Against Solomon

²⁶Also, Jeroboam son of Nebat rebelled against the king. He was one of Solomon's officials, an Ephraimite from Zeredah, and his mother was a widow named Zeruah.

²⁷Here is the account of how he rebelled against the king: Solomon had built the supporting terraces *a* and had filled in the gap in the wall of the city of David his father. ²⁸Now Jeroboam was a man of standing, and when Solomon saw how well the young man did his work, he put him in charge of the whole labor force of the house of Joseph.

²⁹About that time Jeroboam was going out of Jerusalem, and Ahijah the prophet of Shiloh met him on the way, wearing a new cloak. The two of them were alone out in the country, ³⁰and Ahijah took hold of the new cloak he was wearing and tore it into twelve pieces. ³¹Then he said to Jeroboam, "Take ten pieces for yourself, for this is what the LORD, the God of Israel, says: 'See, I am going to tear the kingdom out of Solomon's hand and give you ten tribes. ³²But for the sake of my servant David and the city of Jerusalem, which I have chosen out of all the tribes of Israel, he will have one tribe. ³³I will do this because they have *b* forsaken me and worshiped Ashtoreth the goddess of the Sidonians, Chemosh the god of the Moabites, and Molech the god of the Ammonites, and have not walked in my ways, nor done what is right in my eyes, nor kept my statutes and laws as David, Solomon's father, did.

³⁴" 'But I will not take the whole kingdom out of Solomon's hand; I have made him ruler all the days of his life for the sake of David my servant, whom I chose and who observed my commands and statutes. ³⁵I will take the kingdom from his son's hands and give you ten tribes. ³⁶I will give one tribe to his son so that David my servant may always have a lamp before me in Jerusalem, the city where I chose to put my Name. ³⁷However, as for you, I will take you, and you will rule over all that your heart desires; you will be king over Israel. ³⁸If you do whatever I command you and walk in my ways and do what is right in my eyes by keeping my statutes and commands, as David my servant did, I will be with you. I will build you a dynasty as enduring as the one I built for David and will give Israel to you. ³⁹I will humble David's descendants because of this, but not forever.' "

⁴⁰Solomon tried to kill Jeroboam, but Jeroboam fled to Egypt, to Shishak the king, and stayed there until Solomon's death.

Solomon's Death

⁴¹As for the other events of Solomon's reign—all he did and the wisdom he displayed—are they not written in the book of the annals of Solomon? ⁴²Solomon reigned in Jerusalem over all Israel forty years. ⁴³Then he rested with his fathers and was buried in the city of David his father. And Rehoboam his son succeeded him as king.

Israel Rebels Against Rehoboam

12 Rehoboam went to Shechem, for all the Israelites had gone there to make him king. ²When Jeroboam son of Nebat heard this (he was still in Egypt, where he had fled from King Solomon), he returned from *c* Egypt. ³So they sent for Jeroboam, and he and the whole assembly of Israel went to Rehoboam and said to him: ⁴"Your father put a heavy yoke on us, but now lighten the harsh labor and the heavy yoke he put on us, and we will serve you."

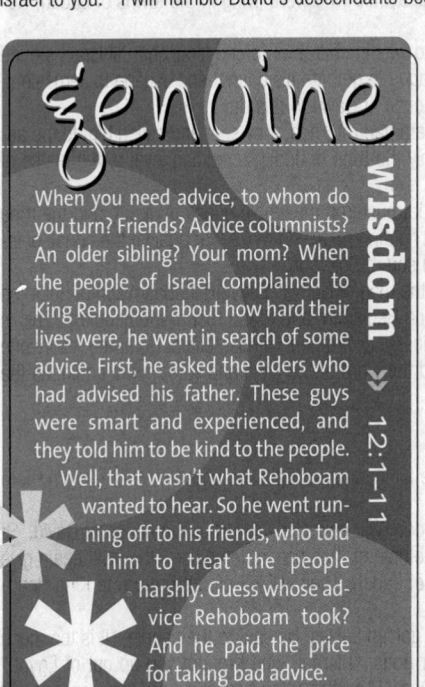

genuine wisdom » 12:1-11

When you need advice, to whom do you turn? Friends? Advice columnists? An older sibling? Your mom? When the people of Israel complained to King Rehoboam about how hard their lives were, he went in search of some advice. First, he asked the elders who had advised his father. These guys were smart and experienced, and they told him to be kind to the people. Well, that wasn't what Rehoboam wanted to hear. So he went running off to his friends, who told him to treat the people harshly. Guess whose advice Rehoboam took? And he paid the price for taking bad advice.

---

a 27 Or *the Millo*   *b 33* Hebrew; Septuagint, Vulgate and Syriac *because he has*   *c 2* Or *he remained in*

⁵Rehoboam answered, "Go away for three days and then come back to me." So the people went away.

⁶Then King Rehoboam consulted the elders who had served his father Solomon during his lifetime. "How would you advise me to answer these people?" he asked.

⁷They replied, "If today you will be a servant to these people and serve them and give them a favorable answer, they will always be your servants."

⁸But Rehoboam rejected the advice the elders gave him and consulted the young men who had grown up with him and were serving him. ⁹He asked them, "What is your advice? How should we answer these people who say to me, 'Lighten the yoke your father put on us'?"

¹⁰The young men who had grown up with him replied, "Tell these people who have said to you, 'Your father put a heavy yoke on us, but make our yoke lighter'—tell them, 'My little finger is thicker than my father's waist. ¹¹My father laid on you a heavy yoke; I will make it even heavier. My father scourged you with whips; I will scourge you with scorpions.' "

¹²Three days later Jeroboam and all the people returned to Rehoboam, as the king had said, "Come back to me in three days." ¹³The king answered the people harshly. Rejecting the advice given him by the elders, ¹⁴he followed the advice of the young men and said, "My father made your yoke heavy; I will make it even heavier. My father scourged you with whips; I will scourge you with scorpions." ¹⁵So the king did not listen to the people, for this turn of events was from the Lord, to fulfill the word the Lord had spoken to Jeroboam son of Nebat through Ahijah the Shilonite.

¹⁶When all Israel saw that the king refused to listen to them, they answered the king:

> "What share do we have in David,
>   what part in Jesse's son?
> To your tents, O Israel!
> Look after your own house, O David!"

So the Israelites went home. ¹⁷But as for the Israelites who were living in the towns of Judah, Rehoboam still ruled over them.

¹⁸King Rehoboam sent out Adoniram,ᵃ who was in charge of forced labor, but all Israel stoned him to death. King Rehoboam, however, managed to get into his chariot and escape to Jerusalem. ¹⁹So Israel has been in rebellion against the house of David to this day.

²⁰When all the Israelites heard that Jeroboam had returned, they sent and called him to the assembly and made him king over all Israel. Only the tribe of Judah remained loyal to the house of David.

²¹When Rehoboam arrived in Jerusalem, he mustered the whole house of Judah and the tribe of Benjamin—a hundred and eighty thousand fighting men—to make war against the house of Israel and to regain the kingdom for Rehoboam son of Solomon.

²²But this word of God came to Shemaiah the man of God: ²³"Say to Rehoboam son of Solomon king of Judah, to the whole house of Judah and Benjamin, and to the rest of the people, ²⁴'This is what the Lord says: Do not go up to fight against your brothers, the Israelites. Go home, every one of you, for this is my doing.' " So they obeyed the word of the Lord and went home again, as the Lord had ordered.

Golden Calves at Bethel and Dan

²⁵Then Jeroboam fortified Shechem in the hill country of Ephraim and lived there. From there he went out and built up Peniel.ᵇ

²⁶Jeroboam thought to himself, "The kingdom will now likely revert to the house of David. ²⁷If these people go up to offer sacrifices at the temple of the Lord in Jerusalem, they will again give their allegiance to their lord, Rehoboam king of Judah. They will kill me and return to King Rehoboam."

²⁸After seeking advice, the king made two golden calves. He said to the people, "It is too much for you to go up to Jerusalem. Here are your gods, O Israel, who brought you up out of Egypt." ²⁹One he set up in Bethel, and the other in Dan. ³⁰And this thing became a sin; the people went even as far as Dan to worship the one there.

ᵃ 18 Some Septuagint manuscripts and Syriac (see also 1 Kings 4:6 and 5:14); Hebrew *Adoram*   ᵇ 25 Hebrew *Penuel*, a variant of *Peniel*

³¹Jeroboam built shrines on high places and appointed priests from all sorts of people, even though they were not Levites. ³²He instituted a festival on the fifteenth day of the eighth month, like the festival held in Judah, and offered sacrifices on the altar. This he did in Bethel, sacrificing to the calves he had made. And at Bethel he also installed priests at the high places he had made. ³³On the fifteenth day of the eighth month, a month of his own choosing, he offered sacrifices on the altar he had built at Bethel. So he instituted the festival for the Israelites and went up to the altar to make offerings.

The Man of God From Judah

13 By the word of the LORD a man of God came from Judah to Bethel, as Jeroboam was standing by the altar to make an offering. ²He cried out against the altar by the word of the LORD: "O altar, altar! This is what the LORD says: 'A son named Josiah will be born to the house of David. On you he will sacrifice the priests of the high places who now make offerings here, and human bones will be burned on you.' " ³That same day the man of God gave a sign: "This is the sign the LORD has declared: The altar will be split apart and the ashes on it will be poured out."

⁴When King Jeroboam heard what the man of God cried out against the altar at Bethel, he stretched out his hand from the altar and said, "Seize him!" But the hand he stretched out toward the man shriveled up, so that he could not pull it back. ⁵Also, the altar was split apart and its ashes poured out according to the sign given by the man of God by the word of the LORD.

⁶Then the king said to the man of God, "Intercede with the LORD your God and pray for me that my hand may be restored." So the man of God interceded with the LORD, and the king's hand was restored and became as it was before.

⁷The king said to the man of God, "Come home with me and have something to eat, and I will give you a gift."

⁸But the man of God answered the king, "Even if you were to give me half your possessions, I would not go with you, nor would I eat bread or drink water here. ⁹For I was commanded by the word of the LORD: 'You must not eat bread or drink water or return by the way you came.' " ¹⁰So he took another road and did not return by the way he had come to Bethel.

¹¹Now there was a certain old prophet living in Bethel, whose sons came and told him all that the man of God had done there that day. They also told their father what he had said to the king. ¹²Their father asked them, "Which way did he go?" And his sons showed him which road the man of God from Judah had taken. ¹³So he said to his sons, "Saddle the donkey for me." And when they had saddled the donkey for him, he mounted it ¹⁴and rode after the man of God. He found him sitting under an oak tree and asked, "Are you the man of God who came from Judah?"

"I am," he replied.

¹⁵So the prophet said to him, "Come home with me and eat."

¹⁶The man of God said, "I cannot turn back and go with you, nor can I eat bread or drink water with you in this place. ¹⁷I have been told by the word of the LORD: 'You must not eat bread or drink water there or return by the way you came.' "

¹⁸The old prophet answered, "I too am a prophet, as you are. And an angel said to me by the word of the LORD: 'Bring him back with you to your house so that he may eat bread and drink water.' " (But he was lying to him.) ¹⁹So the man of God returned with him and ate and drank in his house.

²⁰While they were sitting at the table, the word of the LORD came to the old prophet who had brought him back. ²¹He cried out to the man of God who had come from Judah, "This is what the LORD says: 'You have defied the word of the LORD and have not kept the command the LORD your God gave you. ²²You came back and ate bread and drank water in the place where he told you not to eat or drink. Therefore your body will not be buried in the tomb of your fathers.' "

²³When the man of God had finished eating and drinking, the prophet who had brought him back saddled his donkey for him. ²⁴As he went on his way, a lion met him on the road and killed him, and his body was thrown down on the road, with both the donkey and the lion standing beside it. ²⁵Some people who passed by saw the body thrown down there, with the lion standing beside the body, and they went and reported it in the city where the old prophet lived.

²⁶When the prophet who had brought him back from his journey heard of it, he said, "It is the man of God who defied the word of the LORD. The LORD has given him over to the lion, which has mauled him and killed him, as the word of the LORD had warned him."

²⁷The prophet said to his sons, "Saddle the donkey for me," and they did so. ²⁸Then he went out

Monkeys to Men

Either I'm going to ace this biology final, or I'll die trying. Seriously, I've been studying my tail off. The worst part is that I'm forced to memorize all this stuff that I don't even believe. I'm a Christian, so I've always believed that God created the world. But what about all this scientific "evidence" that proves evolution and ignores God?

If I asked my teacher, I'm sure she'd make me feel like an idiot. Once she made this snide comment about how some people don't understand Darwin's theory of evolution because they're ignorant. Then she rattled off a list of fossils that are "proof positive" of an earth that's been around for millions of years. Her evidence sounds convincing, I guess. But the Big Bang Theory seems like a stretch to me. One big "poof" and the world appeared? I'm skeptical.

The book of Genesis tells a totally different story—Creationism—the heavens and the earth, the day and the night, the land and the water, the plants and the animals and then Adam and Eve. God created it all. I wonder if God knew then that so many people wouldn't believe he created us.

So I guess I'm saying there's no way I'll buy the "I-evolved-from-a-monkey" concept, but I don't know enough to argue for creationism. If God did create the world, then why isn't there more evidence to prove it?

creationism in focus

No matter how many people believe otherwise, you can confirm your belief that the Bible's account of creation is true.

» Intelligent Design. Many scientists now admit there must be intelligence behind everything from the solar system to the tiniest bug. Look for articles and books about intelligent design.

» Faith. By reading the Creation story in Genesis 1 and 2 (pages 2–4), we can begin to trust God with what we don't know.

For more on this topic, see the index on page 1656.

creationism

For more resources on supporting your views on creationism, check out the link on www.TrueImagesBible.com

and found the body thrown down on the road, with the donkey and the lion standing beside it. The lion had neither eaten the body nor mauled the donkey. [29]So the prophet picked up the body of the man of God, laid it on the donkey, and brought it back to his own city to mourn for him and bury him. [30]Then he laid the body in his own tomb, and they mourned over him and said, "Oh, my brother!"

[31]After burying him, he said to his sons, "When I die, bury me in the grave where the man of God is buried; lay my bones beside his bones. [32]For the message he declared by the word of the LORD against the altar in Bethel and against all the shrines on the high places in the towns of Samaria will certainly come true."

[33]Even after this, Jeroboam did not change his evil ways, but once more appointed priests for

the high places from all sorts of people. Anyone who wanted to become a priest he consecrated for the high places. [34]This was the sin of the house of Jeroboam that led to its downfall and to its destruction from the face of the earth.

Ahijah's Prophecy Against Jeroboam

14 At that time Abijah son of Jeroboam became ill, [2]and Jeroboam said to his wife, "Go, disguise yourself, so you won't be recognized as the wife of Jeroboam. Then go to Shiloh. Ahijah the prophet is there—the one who told me I would be king over this people. [3]Take ten loaves of bread with you, some cakes and a jar of honey, and go to him. He will tell you what will happen to the boy." [4]So Jeroboam's wife did what he said and went to Ahijah's house in Shiloh.

Now Ahijah could not see; his sight was gone because of his age. [5]But the Lord had told Ahijah, "Jeroboam's wife is coming to ask you about her son, for he is ill, and you are to give her such and such an answer. When she arrives, she will pretend to be someone else."

[6]So when Ahijah heard the sound of her footsteps at the door, he said, "Come in, wife of Jeroboam. Why this pretense? I have been sent to you with bad news. [7]Go, tell Jeroboam that this is what the Lord, the God of Israel, says: 'I raised you up from among the people and made you a leader over my people Israel. [8]I tore the kingdom away from the house of David and gave it to you, but you have not been like my servant David, who kept my commands and followed me with all his heart, doing only what was right in my eyes. [9]You have done more evil than all who lived before you. You have made for yourself other gods, idols made of metal; you have provoked me to anger and thrust me behind your back.

[10]" 'Because of this, I am going to bring disaster on the house of Jeroboam. I will cut off from Jeroboam every last male in Israel—slave or free. I will burn up the house of Jeroboam as one burns dung, until it is all gone. [11]Dogs will eat those belonging to Jeroboam who die in the city, and the birds of the air will feed on those who die in the country. The Lord has spoken!'

[12]"As for you, go back home. When you set foot in your city, the boy will die. [13]All Israel will mourn for him and bury him. He is the only one belonging to Jeroboam who will be buried, because he is the only one in the house of Jeroboam in whom the Lord, the God of Israel, has found anything good.

[14]"The Lord will raise up for himself a king over Israel who will cut off the family of Jeroboam. This is the day! What? Yes, even now.[a] [15]And the Lord will strike Israel, so that it will be like a reed swaying in the water. He will uproot Israel from this good land that he gave to their forefathers and scatter them beyond the River,[b] because they provoked the Lord to anger by making Asherah poles.[c] [16]And he will give Israel up because of the sins Jeroboam has committed and has caused Israel to commit."

[17]Then Jeroboam's wife got up and left and went to Tirzah. As soon as she stepped over the threshold of the house, the boy died. [18]They buried him, and all Israel mourned for him, as the Lord had said through his servant the prophet Ahijah.

[19]The other events of Jeroboam's reign, his wars and how he ruled, are written in the book of the annals of the kings of Israel. [20]He reigned for twenty-two years and then rested with his fathers. And Nadab his son succeeded him as king.

Rehoboam King of Judah

[21]Rehoboam son of Solomon was king in Judah. He was forty-one years old when he became king, and he reigned seventeen years in Jerusalem, the city the Lord had chosen out of all the tribes of Israel in which to put his Name. His mother's name was Naamah; she was an Ammonite.

truth or dare

Trying to sneak one past God? He's not fooled by your disguises or pretenses. So if you're hiding something from him—'fess up. And if you're holding back from him—give it up.

14:1–6

---

a 14 The meaning of the Hebrew for this sentence is uncertain.   b 15 That is, the Euphrates   c 15 That is, symbols of the goddess Asherah; here and elsewhere in 1 Kings

²²Judah did evil in the eyes of the LORD. By the sins they committed they stirred up his jealous anger more than their fathers had done. ²³They also set up for themselves high places, sacred stones and Asherah poles on every high hill and under every spreading tree. ²⁴There were even male shrine prostitutes in the land; the people engaged in all the detestable practices of the nations the LORD had driven out before the Israelites.

²⁵In the fifth year of King Rehoboam, Shishak king of Egypt attacked Jerusalem. ²⁶He carried off the treasures of the temple of the LORD and the treasures of the royal palace. He took everything, including all the gold shields Solomon had made. ²⁷So King Rehoboam made bronze shields to replace them and assigned these to the commanders of the guard on duty at the entrance to the royal palace. ²⁸Whenever the king went to the LORD's temple, the guards bore the shields, and afterward they returned them to the guardroom.

²⁹As for the other events of Rehoboam's reign, and all he did, are they not written in the book of the annals of the kings of Judah? ³⁰There was continual warfare between Rehoboam and Jeroboam. ³¹And Rehoboam rested with his fathers and was buried with them in the City of David. His mother's name was Naamah; she was an Ammonite. And Abijah*a* his son succeeded him as king.

Abijah King of Judah

15 In the eighteenth year of the reign of Jeroboam son of Nebat, Abijah*b* became king of Judah, ²and he reigned in Jerusalem three years. His mother's name was Maacah daughter of Abishalom.*c*

³He committed all the sins his father had done before him; his heart was not fully devoted to the LORD his God, as the heart of David his forefather had been. ⁴Nevertheless, for David's sake the LORD his God gave him a lamp in Jerusalem by raising up a son to succeed him and by making Jerusalem strong. ⁵For David had done what was right in the eyes of the LORD and had not failed to keep any of the LORD's commands all the days of his life—except in the case of Uriah the Hittite.

⁶There was war between Rehoboam*d* and Jeroboam throughout ⌐Abijah's⌐ lifetime. ⁷As for the other events of Abijah's reign, and all he did, are they not written in the book of the annals of the kings of Judah? There was war between Abijah and Jeroboam. ⁸And Abijah rested with his fathers and was buried in the City of David. And Asa his son succeeded him as king.

Asa King of Judah

⁹In the twentieth year of Jeroboam king of Israel, Asa became king of Judah, ¹⁰and he reigned in Jerusalem forty-one years. His grandmother's name was Maacah daughter of Abishalom.

¹¹Asa did what was right in the eyes of the LORD, as his father David had done. ¹²He expelled the male shrine prostitutes from the land and got rid of all the idols his fathers had made. ¹³He even deposed his grandmother Maacah from her position as queen mother, because she had made a repulsive Asherah pole. Asa cut the pole down and burned it in the Kidron Valley. ¹⁴Although he did not remove the high places, Asa's heart was fully committed to the LORD all his life. ¹⁵He brought into the temple of the LORD the silver and gold and the articles that he and his father had dedicated.

¹⁶There was war between Asa and Baasha king of Israel throughout their reigns. ¹⁷Baasha king of Israel went up against Judah and fortified Ramah to prevent anyone from leaving or entering the territory of Asa king of Judah.

¹⁸Asa then took all the silver and gold that was left in the treasuries of the LORD's temple and of his own palace. He entrusted it to his officials and sent them to Ben-Hadad son of Tabrimmon, the son of Hezion, the king of Aram, who was ruling in Damascus. ¹⁹"Let there be a treaty between me

truth or dare

Your world a mess like Asa's was? Don't get discouraged. You may not be able to correct every problem in your world, but you can sure make a difference.

15:11-14

---

a 31 Some Hebrew manuscripts and Septuagint (see also 2 Chron. 12:16); most Hebrew manuscripts *Abijam* *b 1* Some Hebrew manuscripts and Septuagint (see also 2 Chron. 12:16); most Hebrew manuscripts *Abijam*; also in verses 7 and 8 *c 2* A variant of *Absalom*; also in verse 10 *d 6* Most Hebrew manuscripts; some Hebrew manuscripts and Syriac *Abijam* (that is, Abijah) and you," he said, "as there was between my father and your father. See, I am sending you a gift of silver and gold. Now break your treaty with Baasha king of Israel so he will withdraw from me."

[20]Ben-Hadad agreed with King Asa and sent the commanders of his forces against the towns of Israel. He conquered Ijon, Dan, Abel Beth Maacah and all Kinnereth in addition to Naphtali. [21]When Baasha heard this, he stopped building Ramah and withdrew to Tirzah. [22]Then King Asa issued an order to all Judah—no one was exempt—and they carried away from Ramah the stones and timber Baasha had been using there. With them King Asa built up Geba in Benjamin, and also Mizpah.

[23]As for all the other events of Asa's reign, all his achievements, all he did and the cities he built, are they not written in the book of the annals of the kings of Judah? In his old age, however, his feet became diseased. [24]Then Asa rested with his fathers and was buried with them in the city of his father David. And Jehoshaphat his son succeeded him as king.

Nadab King of Israel

[25]Nadab son of Jeroboam became king of Israel in the second year of Asa king of Judah, and he reigned over Israel two years. [26]He did evil in the eyes of the LORD, walking in the ways of his father and in his sin, which he had caused Israel to commit.

[27]Baasha son of Ahijah of the house of Issachar plotted against him, and he struck him down at Gibbethon, a Philistine town, while Nadab and all Israel were besieging it. [28]Baasha killed Nadab in the third year of Asa king of Judah and succeeded him as king.

[29]As soon as he began to reign, he killed Jeroboam's whole family. He did not leave Jeroboam anyone that breathed, but destroyed them all, according to the word of the LORD given through his servant Ahijah the Shilonite— [30]because of the sins Jeroboam had committed and had caused Israel to commit, and because he provoked the LORD, the God of Israel, to anger.

[31]As for the other events of Nadab's reign, and all he did, are they not written in the book of the annals of the kings of Israel? [32]There was war between Asa and Baasha king of Israel throughout their reigns.

Baasha King of Israel

[33]In the third year of Asa king of Judah, Baasha son of Ahijah became king of all Israel in Tirzah, and he reigned twenty-four years. [34]He did evil in the eyes of the LORD, walking in the ways of Jeroboam and in his sin, which he had caused Israel to commit.

16 Then the word of the LORD came to Jehu son of Hanani against Baasha: [2]"I lifted you up from the dust and made you leader of my people Israel, but you walked in the ways of Jeroboam and caused my people Israel to sin and to provoke me to anger by their sins. [3]So I am about to consume Baasha and his house, and I will make your house like that of Jeroboam son of Nebat. [4]Dogs will eat those belonging to Baasha who die in the city, and the birds of the air will feed on those who die in the country."

[5]As for the other events of Baasha's reign, what he did and his achievements, are they not written in the book of the annals of the kings of Israel? [6]Baasha rested with his fathers and was buried in Tirzah. And Elah his son succeeded him as king.

[7]Moreover, the word of the LORD came through the prophet Jehu son of Hanani to Baasha and his house, because of all the evil he had done in the eyes of the LORD, provoking him to anger by the things he did, and becoming like the house of Jeroboam—and also because he destroyed it.

Elah King of Israel

[8]In the twenty-sixth year of Asa king of Judah, Elah son of Baasha became king of Israel, and he reigned in Tirzah two years.

[9]Zimri, one of his officials, who had command of half his chariots, plotted against him. Elah was in Tirzah at the time, getting drunk in the home of Arza, the man in charge of the palace at Tirzah. [10]Zimri came in, struck him down and killed him in the twenty-seventh year of Asa king of Judah. Then he succeeded him as king.

[11]As soon as he began to reign and was seated on the throne, he killed off Baasha's whole family. He did not spare a single male, whether relative or friend. [12]So Zimri destroyed the whole family of Baasha, in accordance with the word of the LORD spoken against Baasha through the prophet Jehu— [13]because of all the sins Baasha and his son Elah had committed and had caused Israel to commit, so that they provoked the LORD, the God of Israel, to anger by their worthless idols.

¹⁴As for the other events of Elah's reign, and all he did, are they not written in the book of the annals of the kings of Israel?

Zimri King of Israel

¹⁵In the twenty-seventh year of Asa king of Judah, Zimri reigned in Tirzah seven days. The army was encamped near Gibbethon, a Philistine town. ¹⁶When the Israelites in the camp heard that Zimri had plotted against the king and murdered him, they proclaimed Omri, the commander of the army, king over Israel that very day there in the camp. ¹⁷Then Omri and all the Israelites with him withdrew from Gibbethon and laid siege to Tirzah. ¹⁸When Zimri saw that the city was taken, he went into the citadel of the royal palace and set the palace on fire around him. So he died, ¹⁹because of the sins he had committed, doing evil in the eyes of the LORD and walking in the ways of Jeroboam and in the sin he had committed and had caused Israel to commit.

²⁰As for the other events of Zimri's reign, and the rebellion he carried out, are they not written in the book of the annals of the kings of Israel?

Omri King of Israel

²¹Then the people of Israel were split into two factions; half supported Tibni son of Ginath for king, and the other half supported Omri. ²²But Omri's followers proved stronger than those of Tibni son of Ginath. So Tibni died and Omri became king.

²³In the thirty-first year of Asa king of Judah, Omri became king of Israel, and he reigned twelve years, six of them in Tirzah. ²⁴He bought the hill of Samaria from Shemer for two talents*ᵃ* of silver and built a city on the hill, calling it Samaria, after Shemer, the name of the former owner of the hill.

²⁵But Omri did evil in the eyes of the LORD and sinned more than all those before him. ²⁶He walked in all the ways of Jeroboam son of Nebat and in his sin, which he had caused Israel to commit, so that they provoked the LORD, the God of Israel, to anger by their worthless idols.

²⁷As for the other events of Omri's reign, what he did and the things he achieved, are they not written in the book of the annals of the kings of Israel? ²⁸Omri rested with his fathers and was buried in Samaria. And Ahab his son succeeded him as king.

Ahab Becomes King of Israel

²⁹In the thirty-eighth year of Asa king of Judah, Ahab son of Omri became king of Israel, and he reigned in Samaria over Israel twenty-two years. ³⁰Ahab son of Omri did more evil in the eyes of the LORD than any of those before him. ³¹He not only considered it trivial to commit the sins of Jeroboam son of Nebat, but he also married Jezebel daughter of Ethbaal king of the Sidonians, and began to serve Baal and worship him. ³²He set up an altar for Baal in the temple of Baal that he built in Samaria. ³³Ahab also made an Asherah pole and did more to provoke the LORD, the God of Israel, to anger than did all the kings of Israel before him.

³⁴In Ahab's time, Hiel of Bethel rebuilt Jericho. He laid its foundations at the cost of his firstborn son Abiram, and he set up its gates at the cost of his youngest son Segub, in accordance with the word of the LORD spoken by Joshua son of Nun.

Elijah Fed by Ravens

17 Now Elijah the Tishbite, from Tishbe*ᵇ* in Gilead, said to Ahab, "As the LORD, the God of Israel, lives, whom I serve, there will be neither dew nor rain in the next few years except at my word."

²Then the word of the LORD came to Elijah: ³"Leave here, turn eastward and hide in the Kerith Ravine, east of the Jordan. ⁴You will drink from the brook, and I have ordered the ravens to feed you there."

⁵So he did what the LORD had told him. He went to the Kerith Ravine, east of the Jordan, and stayed there. ⁶The ravens brought him bread and meat in the morning and bread and meat in the evening, and he drank from the brook.

ᵃ 24 That is, about 150 pounds (about 70 kilograms)   ᵇ 1 Or Tishbite, of the settlers

The Widow at Zarephath

[7]Some time later the brook dried up because there had been no rain in the land. [8]Then the word of the LORD came to him: [9]"Go at once to Zarephath of Sidon and stay there. I have commanded a widow in that place to supply you with food." [10]So he went to Zarephath. When he came to the town gate, a widow was there gathering sticks. He called to her and asked, "Would you bring me a little water in a jar so I may have a drink?" [11]As she was going to get it, he called, "And bring me, please, a piece of bread."

genuine faith

» 17:8-16

What was the last thing you did that caused your faith in God to grow? For the widow at Zarephath, giving Elijah her last bit of food changed her life. She only had a handful of flour left during a time of drought. Then this prophet came along and told her to make bread for *him* before making anything for herself and her son. What would you have done—enjoyed your last piece of bread or given it away in faith? Trusting God can seem risky. But sometimes, taking a risk is the only way that you can grow in faith.

[12]"As surely as the LORD your God lives," she replied, "I don't have any bread—only a handful of flour in a jar and a little oil in a jug. I am gathering a few sticks to take home and make a meal for myself and my son, that we may eat it—and die."

[13]Elijah said to her, "Don't be afraid. Go home and do as you have said. But first make a small cake of bread for me from what you have and bring it to me, and then make something for yourself and your son. [14]For this is what the LORD, the God of Israel, says: 'The jar of flour will not be used up and the jug of oil will not run dry until the day the LORD gives rain on the land.' "

[15]She went away and did as Elijah had told her. So there was food every day for Elijah and for the woman and her family. [16]For the jar of flour was not used up and the jug of oil did not run dry, in keeping with the word of the LORD spoken by Elijah.

[17]Some time later the son of the woman who owned the house became ill. He grew worse and worse, and finally stopped breathing. [18]She said to Elijah, "What do you have against me, man of God? Did you come to remind me of my sin and kill my son?"

[19]"Give me your son," Elijah replied. He took him from her arms, carried him to the upper room where he was staying, and laid him on his bed. [20]Then he cried out to the LORD, "O LORD my God, have you brought tragedy also upon this widow I am staying with, by causing her son to die?" [21]Then he stretched himself out on the boy three times and cried to the LORD, "O LORD my God, let this boy's life return to him!"

[22]The LORD heard Elijah's cry, and the boy's life returned to him, and he lived. [23]Elijah picked up the child and carried him down from the room into the house. He gave him to his mother and said, "Look, your son is alive!"

[24]Then the woman said to Elijah, "Now I know that you are a man of God and that the word of the LORD from your mouth is the truth."

Elijah and Obadiah

18 After a long time, in the third year, the word of the LORD came to Elijah: "Go and present yourself to Ahab, and I will send rain on the land." [2]So Elijah went to present himself to Ahab.

Now the famine was severe in Samaria, [3]and Ahab had summoned Obadiah, who was in charge of his palace. (Obadiah was a devout believer in the LORD. [4]While Jezebel was killing off the LORD's prophets, Obadiah had taken a hundred prophets and hidden them in two caves, fifty in each, and had supplied them with food and water.) [5]Ahab had said to Obadiah, "Go through the land to all the springs and valleys. Maybe we can find some grass to keep the horses and mules alive so we will not have to kill any of our animals." ⁶So they divided the land they were to cover, Ahab going in one direction and Obadiah in another.

⁷As Obadiah was walking along, Elijah met him. Obadiah recognized him, bowed down to the ground, and said, "Is it really you, my lord Elijah?"

⁸"Yes," he replied. "Go tell your master, 'Elijah is here.' "

⁹"What have I done wrong," asked Obadiah, "that you are handing your servant over to Ahab to be put to death? ¹⁰As surely as the LORD your God lives, there is not a nation or kingdom where my master has not sent someone to look for you. And whenever a nation or kingdom claimed you were not there, he made them swear they could not find you. ¹¹But now you tell me to go to my master and say, 'Elijah is here.' ¹²I don't know where the Spirit of the LORD may carry you when I leave you. If I go and tell Ahab and he doesn't find you, he will kill me. Yet I your servant have worshiped the LORD since my youth. ¹³Haven't you heard, my lord, what I did while Jezebel was killing the prophets of the LORD? I hid a hundred of the LORD's prophets in two caves, fifty in each, and supplied them with food and water. ¹⁴And now you tell me to go to my master and say, 'Elijah is here.' He will kill me!"

¹⁵Elijah said, "As the LORD Almighty lives, whom I serve, I will surely present myself to Ahab today."

Elijah on Mount Carmel

¹⁶So Obadiah went to meet Ahab and told him, and Ahab went to meet Elijah. ¹⁷When he saw Elijah, he said to him, "Is that you, you troubler of Israel?"

¹⁸"I have not made trouble for Israel," Elijah replied. "But you and your father's family have. You have abandoned the LORD's commands and have followed the Baals. ¹⁹Now summon the people from all over Israel to meet me on Mount Carmel. And bring the four hundred and fifty prophets of Baal and the four hundred prophets of Asherah, who eat at Jezebel's table."

²⁰So Ahab sent word throughout all Israel and assembled the prophets on Mount Carmel. ²¹Elijah went before the people and said, "How long will you waver between two opinions? If the LORD is God, follow him; but if Baal is God, follow him."

But the people said nothing.

²²Then Elijah said to them, "I am the only one of the LORD's prophets left, but Baal has four hundred and fifty prophets. ²³Get two bulls for us. Let them choose one for themselves, and let them cut it into pieces and put it on the wood but not set fire to it. I will prepare the other bull and put it on the wood but not set fire to it. ²⁴Then you call on the name of your god, and I will call on the name of the LORD. The god who answers by fire—he is God."

Then all the people said, "What you say is good."

²⁵Elijah said to the prophets of Baal, "Choose one of the bulls and prepare it first, since there are so many of you. Call on the name of your god, but do not light the fire." ²⁶So they took the bull given them and prepared it.

truth or dare

As a girl, you make tons of decisions every day. With so many choices, you've probably perfected your stalling technique. There's one thing, however, that God needs an answer about now.

18:20–21

Then they called on the name of Baal from morning till noon. "O Baal, answer us!" they shouted. But there was no response; no one answered. And they danced around the altar they had made.

²⁷At noon Elijah began to taunt them. "Shout louder!" he said. "Surely he is a god! Perhaps he is deep in thought, or busy, or traveling. Maybe he is sleeping and must be awakened." ²⁸So they shouted louder and slashed themselves with swords and spears, as was their custom, until their blood flowed. ²⁹Midday passed, and they continued their frantic prophesying until the time for the evening sacrifice. But there was no response, no one answered, no one paid attention.

³⁰Then Elijah said to all the people, "Come here to me." They came to him, and he repaired the altar of the LORD, which was in ruins. ³¹Elijah took twelve stones, one for each of the tribes descended from Jacob, to whom the word of the LORD had come, saying, "Your name shall be Israel." ³²With

the stones he built an altar in the name of the LORD, and he dug a trench around it large enough to hold two seahsᵃ of seed. ³³He arranged the wood, cut the bull into pieces and laid it on the wood. Then he said to them, "Fill four large jars with water and pour it on the offering and on the wood."

³⁴"Do it again," he said, and they did it again.

"Do it a third time," he ordered, and they did it the third time. ³⁵The water ran down around the altar and even filled the trench.

³⁶At the time of sacrifice, the prophet Elijah stepped forward and prayed: "O LORD, God of Abraham, Isaac and Israel, let it be known today that you are God in Israel and that I am your servant and have done all these things at your command. ³⁷Answer me, O LORD, answer me, so these people will know that you, O LORD, are God, and that you are turning their hearts back again."

³⁸Then the fire of the LORD fell and burned up the sacrifice, the wood, the stones and the soil, and also licked up the water in the trench.

³⁹When all the people saw this, they fell prostrate and cried, "The LORD—he is God! The LORD—he is God!"

⁴⁰Then Elijah commanded them, "Seize the prophets of Baal. Don't let anyone get away!" They seized them, and Elijah had them brought down to the Kishon Valley and slaughtered there.

⁴¹And Elijah said to Ahab, "Go, eat and drink, for there is the sound of a heavy rain." ⁴²So Ahab went off to eat and drink, but Elijah climbed to the top of Carmel, bent down to the ground and put his face between his knees.

⁴³"Go and look toward the sea," he told his servant. And he went up and looked.

"There is nothing there," he said.

Seven times Elijah said, "Go back."

⁴⁴The seventh time the servant reported, "A cloud as small as a man's hand is rising from the sea."

So Elijah said, "Go and tell Ahab, 'Hitch up your chariot and go down before the rain stops you.' "

⁴⁵Meanwhile, the sky grew black with clouds, the wind rose, a heavy rain came on and Ahab rode off to Jezreel. ⁴⁶The power of the LORD came upon Elijah and, tucking his cloak into his belt, he ran ahead of Ahab all the way to Jezreel.

Elijah Flees to Horeb

19 Now Ahab told Jezebel everything Elijah had done and how he had killed all the prophets with the sword. ²So Jezebel sent a messenger to Elijah to say, "May the gods deal with me, be it ever so severely, if by this time tomorrow I do not make your life like that of one of them."

³Elijah was afraidᵇ and ran for his life. When he came to Beersheba in Judah, he left his servant there, ⁴while he himself went a day's journey into the desert. He came to a broom tree, sat down under it and prayed that he might die. "I have had enough, LORD," he said. "Take my life; I am no better than my ancestors." ⁵Then he lay down under the tree and fell asleep.

All at once an angel touched him and said, "Get up and eat." ⁶He looked around, and there by his head was a cake of bread baked over hot coals, and a jar of water. He ate and drank and then lay down again.

⁷The angel of the LORD came back a second time and touched him and said, "Get up and eat, for the journey is too much for you." ⁸So he got up and ate and drank. Strengthened by that food, he traveled forty days and forty nights until he reached Horeb, the mountain of God. ⁹There he went into a cave and spent the night.

The LORD Appears to Elijah

And the word of the LORD came to him: "What are you doing here, Elijah?"

¹⁰He replied, "I have been very zealous for the LORD God Almighty. The Israelites have rejected your covenant, broken down your altars, and put your prophets to death with the sword. I am the only one left, and now they are trying to kill me too."

¹¹The LORD said, "Go out and stand on the mountain in the presence of the LORD, for the LORD is about to pass by."

ᵃ 32 That is, probably about 13 quarts (about 15 liters)   ᵇ 3 Or *Elijah saw*

Then a great and powerful wind tore the mountains apart and shattered the rocks before the Lord, but the Lord was not in the wind. After the wind there was an earthquake, but the Lord was not in the earthquake. ¹²After the earthquake came a fire, but the Lord was not in the fire. And after the fire came a gentle whisper. ¹³When Elijah heard it, he pulled his cloak over his face and went out and stood at the mouth of the cave.

Then a voice said to him, "What are you doing here, Elijah?"

¹⁴He replied, "I have been very zealous for the Lord God Almighty. The Israelites have rejected your covenant, broken down your altars, and put your prophets to death with the sword. I am the only one left, and now they are trying to kill me too."

¹⁵The Lord said to him, "Go back the way you came, and go to the Desert of Damascus. When you get there, anoint Hazael king over Aram. ¹⁶Also, anoint Jehu son of Nimshi king over Israel, and anoint Elisha son of Shaphat from Abel Meholah to succeed you as prophet. ¹⁷Jehu will put to death any who escape the sword of Hazael, and Elisha will put to death any who escape the sword of Jehu. ¹⁸Yet I reserve seven thousand in Israel—all whose knees have not bowed down to Baal and all whose mouths have not kissed him."

The Call of Elisha

¹⁹So Elijah went from there and found Elisha son of Shaphat. He was plowing with twelve yoke of oxen, and he himself was driving the twelfth pair. Elijah went up to him and threw his cloak around him. ²⁰Elisha then left his oxen and ran after Elijah. "Let me kiss my father and mother good-by," he said, "and then I will come with you."

"Go back," Elijah replied. "What have I done to you?"

²¹So Elisha left him and went back. He took his yoke of oxen and slaughtered them. He burned the plowing equipment to cook the meat and gave it to the people, and they ate. Then he set out to follow Elijah and became his attendant.

love ♥ notes

19:11–12

Daughter,

Are you having trouble hearing my voice above all the noise in your world? Get quiet and listen. I am not in the windstorm, the earthquake or the fire. I am in the gentle whisper. Listen. I'm speaking to you.

—Your Father

How can you listen closely for God's voice?

_____

_____

_____

_____

_____

truth or dare

Ever feel like you're the only Christian on earth? Ironically, most believers experience these feelings! Start taking a stand. Girls *just like you* will come out of the woodwork.

19:14,18

Ben-Hadad Attacks Samaria

20 Now Ben-Hadad king of Aram mustered his entire army. Accompanied by thirty-two kings with their horses and chariots, he went up and besieged Samaria and attacked it. ²He sent messengers into the city to Ahab king of Israel, saying, "This is what Ben-Hadad says: ³'Your silver and gold are mine, and the best of your wives and children are mine.'"

⁴The king of Israel answered, "Just as you say, my lord the king. I and all I have are yours."

⁵The messengers came again and said, "This is what Ben-Hadad says: 'I sent to demand your silver and gold, your wives and your children. ⁶But about this time tomorrow I am going to send my officials to search your palace and the houses of your officials. They will seize everything you value and carry it away.'"

⁷The king of Israel summoned all the elders of the land and said to them, "See how this man is looking for trouble! When he sent for my wives and my children, my silver and my gold, I did not refuse him."

⁸The elders and the people all answered, "Don't listen to him or agree to his demands."

⁹So he replied to Ben-Hadad's messengers, "Tell my lord the king, 'Your servant will do all you demanded the first time, but this demand I cannot meet.'" They left and took the answer back to Ben-Hadad.

¹⁰Then Ben-Hadad sent another message to Ahab: "May the gods deal with me, be it ever so severely, if enough dust remains in Samaria to give each of my men a handful."

¹¹The king of Israel answered, "Tell him: 'One who puts on his armor should not boast like one who takes it off.'"

¹²Ben-Hadad heard this message while he and the kings were drinking in their tents,[a] and he ordered his men: "Prepare to attack." So they prepared to attack the city.

Ahab Defeats Ben-Hadad

¹³Meanwhile a prophet came to Ahab king of Israel and announced, "This is what the LORD says: 'Do you see this vast army? I will give it into your hand today, and then you will know that I am the LORD.'"

¹⁴"But who will do this?" asked Ahab.

The prophet replied, "This is what the LORD says: 'The young officers of the provincial commanders will do it.'"

"And who will start the battle?" he asked.

The prophet answered, "You will."

¹⁵So Ahab summoned the young officers of the provincial commanders, 232 men. Then he assembled the rest of the Israelites, 7,000 in all. ¹⁶They set out at noon while Ben-Hadad and the 32 kings allied with him were in their tents getting drunk. ¹⁷The young officers of the provincial commanders went out first.

Now Ben-Hadad had dispatched scouts, who reported, "Men are advancing from Samaria."

¹⁸He said, "If they have come out for peace, take them alive; if they have come out for war, take them alive."

¹⁹The young officers of the provincial commanders marched out of the city with the army behind them ²⁰and each one struck down his opponent. At that, the Arameans fled, with the Israelites in pursuit. But Ben-Hadad king of Aram escaped on horseback with some of his horsemen. ²¹The king of Israel advanced and overpowered the horses and chariots and inflicted heavy losses on the Arameans.

²²Afterward, the prophet came to the king of Israel and said, "Strengthen your position and see what must be done, because next spring the king of Aram will attack you again."

²³Meanwhile, the officials of the king of Aram advised him, "Their gods are gods of the hills. That is why they were too strong for us. But if we fight them on the plains, surely we will be stronger than they. ²⁴Do this: Remove all the kings from their commands and replace them with other officers. ²⁵You must also raise an army like the one you lost—horse for horse and chariot for chariot—so we can fight Israel on the plains. Then surely we will be stronger than they." He agreed with them and acted accordingly.

²⁶The next spring Ben-Hadad mustered the Arameans and went up to Aphek to fight against Is-

rael. [27]When the Israelites were also mustered and given provisions, they marched out to meet them. The Israelites camped opposite them like two small flocks of goats, while the Arameans covered the countryside.

[28]The man of God came up and told the king of Israel, "This is what the LORD says: 'Because the Arameans think the LORD is a god of the hills and not a god of the valleys, I will deliver this vast army into your hands, and you will know that I am the LORD.' "

[29]For seven days they camped opposite each other, and on the seventh day the battle was joined. The Israelites inflicted a hundred thousand casualties on the Aramean foot soldiers in one day. [30]The rest of them escaped to the city of Aphek, where the wall collapsed on twenty-seven thousand of them. And Ben-Hadad fled to the city and hid in an inner room.

[31]His officials said to him, "Look, we have heard that the kings of the house of Israel are merciful. Let us go to the king of Israel with sackcloth around our waists and ropes around our heads. Perhaps he will spare your life."

[32]Wearing sackcloth around their waists and ropes around their heads, they went to the king of Israel and said, "Your servant Ben-Hadad says: 'Please let me live.' "

The king answered, "Is he still alive? He is my brother."

[33]The men took this as a good sign and were quick to pick up his word. "Yes, your brother Ben-Hadad!" they said.

"Go and get him," the king said. When Ben-Hadad came out, Ahab had him come up into his chariot.

[34]"I will return the cities my father took from your father," Ben-Hadad offered. "You may set up your own market areas in Damascus, as my father did in Samaria."

⌊Ahab said,⌋ "On the basis of a treaty I will set you free." So he made a treaty with him, and let him go.

A Prophet Condemns Ahab

[35]By the word of the LORD one of the sons of the prophets said to his companion, "Strike me with your weapon," but the man refused.

[36]So the prophet said, "Because you have not obeyed the LORD, as soon as you leave me a lion will kill you." And after the man went away, a lion found him and killed him.

[37]The prophet found another man and said, "Strike me, please." So the man struck him and wounded him. [38]Then the prophet went and stood by the road waiting for the king. He disguised himself with his headband down over his eyes. [39]As the king passed by, the prophet called out to him, "Your servant went into the thick of the battle, and someone came to me with a captive and said, 'Guard this man. If he is missing, it will be your life for his life, or you must pay a talent[a] of silver.' [40]While your servant was busy here and there, the man disappeared."

"That is your sentence," the king of Israel said. "You have pronounced it yourself."

[41]Then the prophet quickly removed the headband from his eyes, and the king of Israel recognized him as one of the prophets. [42]He said to the king, "This is what the LORD says: 'You have set free a man I had determined should die.[b] Therefore it is your life for his life, your people for his people.' " [43]Sullen and angry, the king of Israel went to his palace in Samaria.

Naboth's Vineyard

21 Some time later there was an incident involving a vineyard belonging to Naboth the Jezreelite. The vineyard was in Jezreel, close to the palace of Ahab king of Samaria. [2]Ahab said to Naboth, "Let me have your vineyard to use for a vegetable garden, since it is close to my palace. In exchange I will give you a better vineyard or, if you prefer, I will pay you whatever it is worth."

[3]But Naboth replied, "The LORD forbid that I should give you the inheritance of my fathers."

[4]So Ahab went home, sullen and angry because Naboth the Jezreelite had said, "I will not give you the inheritance of my fathers." He lay on his bed sulking and refused to eat.

[5]His wife Jezebel came in and asked him, "Why are you so sullen? Why won't you eat?"

a 39 That is, about 75 pounds (about 34 kilograms)   b 42 The Hebrew term refers to the irrevocable giving over of things or persons to the LORD, often by totally destroying them.

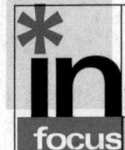

Am I Gay?

focus Profile: **Trish**

Am I gay? I don't know. I just don't know. The thought has crossed my mind. All my friends are wondering if this guy or that guy likes them. I don't like any guys right now. Instead, I wonder if I have a crush on Sierra. She's one of my best friends. I think about her sometimes and wish I could look like her. Everybody thinks she's pretty. I've never felt pretty. A lot of my guy friends really like her. She's also really kind. I feel jealous sometimes when she hangs out with other people besides me. Does that mean I'm gay?

Ever since I turned 12 two years ago, I've been a little confused about all of this. That's when my uncle tried to rape me one night when he was drunk. He told me not to tell anyone. But my mom found out. Even though my uncle got in trouble, Mom seemed mad at me for what happened. Ever since then I haven't wanted *any* guy to touch me—not even my dad.

On one of my favorite TV shows, some of the characters are gay. They say you shouldn't hide how you feel. You should be who you really are. Does that mean that if I'm gay I need to just accept it?

There's a girl on my soccer team who's gay. Most of the other girls avoid her because of it. She seems nice, though. She's been talking to me more. I wonder if she thinks I'm gay. Maybe she knows something about me that I don't know yet.

---

homosexuality in focus

Most teens spend some time thinking deeply about who they are. In the process of establishing their identity, some also consider experimenting sexually. Being abused or feeling that they were somehow "born that way" may contribute to homosexual feelings. If you're in that situation, then what do you do with those feelings? Is it okay to experiment to make sure you know who you are?

» God is very clear about homosexuality. Read Romans 1:24–32 (page 1487) and Leviticus 18:22 (page 14).

» Your identity is much bigger than your feelings of sexuality. You are valuable because God made you and he loves you, just as you are.

» Having a certain *feeling* isn't sinful. Fantasizing something or acting on it is sinful and will damage you physically, emotionally and spiritually.

For more on this topic, see the index on page 1656.

⁶He answered her, "Because I said to Naboth the Jezreelite, 'Sell me your vineyard; or if you prefer, I will give you another vineyard in its place.' But he said, 'I will not give you my vineyard.' "

⁷Jezebel his wife said, "Is this how you act as king over Israel? Get up and eat! Cheer up. I'll get you the vineyard of Naboth the Jezreelite."

⁸So she wrote letters in Ahab's name, placed his seal on them, and sent them to the elders and nobles who lived in Naboth's city with him. ⁹In those letters she wrote:

"Proclaim a day of fasting and seat Naboth in a prominent place among the people. ¹⁰But seat two scoundrels opposite him and have them testify that he has cursed both God and the king. Then take him out and stone him to death."

[11]So the elders and nobles who lived in Naboth's city did as Jezebel directed in the letters she had written to them. [12]They proclaimed a fast and seated Naboth in a prominent place among the people. [13]Then two scoundrels came and sat opposite him and brought charges against Naboth before the people, saying, "Naboth has cursed both God and the king." So they took him outside the city and stoned him to death. [14]Then they sent word to Jezebel: "Naboth has been stoned and is dead."

[15]As soon as Jezebel heard that Naboth had been stoned to death, she said to Ahab, "Get up and take possession of the vineyard of Naboth the Jezreelite that he refused to sell you. He is no longer alive, but dead." [16]When Ahab heard that Naboth was dead, he got up and went down to take possession of Naboth's vineyard.

[17]Then the word of the LORD came to Elijah the Tishbite: [18]"Go down to meet Ahab king of Israel, who rules in Samaria. He is now in Naboth's vineyard, where he has gone to take possession of it. [19]Say to him, 'This is what the LORD says: Have you not murdered a man and seized his property?' Then say to him, 'This is what the LORD says: In the place where dogs licked up Naboth's blood, dogs will lick up your blood—yes, yours!' "

[20]Ahab said to Elijah, "So you have found me, my enemy!"

"I have found you," he answered, "because you have sold yourself to do evil in the eyes of the LORD. [21]I am going to bring disaster on you. I will consume your descendants and cut off from Ahab every last male in Israel—slave or free. [22]I will make your house like that of Jeroboam son of Nebat and that of Baasha son of Ahijah, because you have provoked me to anger and have caused Israel to sin.'

[23]"And also concerning Jezebel the LORD says: 'Dogs will devour Jezebel by the wall of[a] Jezreel.'

[24]"Dogs will eat those belonging to Ahab who die in the city, and the birds of the air will feed on those who die in the country."

[25](There was never a man like Ahab, who sold himself to do evil in the eyes of the LORD, urged on by Jezebel his wife. [26]He behaved in the vilest manner by going after idols, like the Amorites the LORD drove out before Israel.)

[27]When Ahab heard these words, he tore his clothes, put on sackcloth and fasted. He lay in sackcloth and went around meekly.

[28]Then the word of the LORD came to Elijah the Tishbite: [29]"Have you noticed how Ahab has humbled himself before me? Because he has humbled himself, I will not bring this disaster in his day, but I will bring it on his house in the days of his son."

Micaiah Prophesies Against Ahab

22 For three years there was no war between Aram and Israel. [2]But in the third year Jehoshaphat king of Judah went down to see the king of Israel. [3]The king of Israel had said to his officials, "Don't you know that Ramoth Gilead belongs to us and yet we are doing nothing to retake it from the king of Aram?"

[4]So he asked Jehoshaphat, "Will you go with me to fight against Ramoth Gilead?"

Jehoshaphat replied to the king of Israel, "I am as you are, my people as your people, my horses as your horses." [5]But Jehoshaphat also said to the king of Israel, "First seek the counsel of the LORD."

[6]So the king of Israel brought together the prophets—about four hundred men—and asked them, "Shall I go to war against Ramoth Gilead, or shall I refrain?"

"Go," they answered, "for the Lord will give it into the king's hand."

[7]But Jehoshaphat asked, "Is there not a prophet of the LORD here whom we can inquire of?"

[8]The king of Israel answered Jehoshaphat, "There is still one man through whom we can in-

truth or dare

Know any Jezebels? Girls who get whatever they want and step on anyone who's in their way? Take comfort in the fact that God sees, and he'll make everything right in the end.

21:5–10

[a] 23 Most Hebrew manuscripts; a few Hebrew manuscripts, Vulgate and Syriac (see also 2 Kings 9:26) *the plot of ground at*

quire of the LORD, but I hate him because he never prophesies anything good about me, but always bad. He is Micaiah son of Imlah."

"The king should not say that," Jehoshaphat replied.

⁹So the king of Israel called one of his officials and said, "Bring Micaiah son of Imlah at once."

¹⁰Dressed in their royal robes, the king of Israel and Jehoshaphat king of Judah were sitting on their thrones at the threshing floor by the entrance of the gate of Samaria, with all the prophets prophesying before them. ¹¹Now Zedekiah son of Kenaanah had made iron horns and he declared, "This is what the LORD says: 'With these you will gore the Arameans until they are destroyed.' "

¹²All the other prophets were prophesying the same thing. "Attack Ramoth Gilead and be victorious," they said, "for the LORD will give it into the king's hand."

¹³The messenger who had gone to summon Micaiah said to him, "Look, as one man the other prophets are predicting success for the king. Let your word agree with theirs, and speak favorably."

¹⁴But Micaiah said, "As surely as the LORD lives, I can tell him only what the LORD tells me."

genuine courage

Are you willing to stand for what's right—even if no one else will? When King Ahab asked King Jehoshaphat to join him in a war, Jehoshaphat wanted to ask God for advice. So Ahab called for the prophets, all 401 of them. While the 400 false prophets advised the kings to go, only one—Micaiah—said no. Micaiah was brave enough to speak the truth when everyone else was telling Ahab what he wanted to hear. Resisting the urge to follow the crowd takes courage. Have you got it?

¹⁵When he arrived, the king asked him, "Micaiah, shall we go to war against Ramoth Gilead, or shall I refrain?"

"Attack and be victorious," he answered, "for the LORD will give it into the king's hand."

¹⁶The king said to him, "How many times must I make you swear to tell me nothing but the truth in the name of the LORD?"

¹⁷Then Micaiah answered, "I saw all Israel scattered on the hills like sheep without a shepherd, and the LORD said, 'These people have no master. Let each one go home in peace.' "

¹⁸The king of Israel said to Jehoshaphat, "Didn't I tell you that he never prophesies anything good about me, but only bad?"

¹⁹Micaiah continued, "Therefore hear the word of the LORD: I saw the LORD sitting on his throne with all the host of heaven standing around him on his right and on his left. ²⁰And the LORD said, 'Who will entice Ahab into attacking Ramoth Gilead and going to his death there?'

"One suggested this, and another that. ²¹Finally, a spirit came forward, stood before the LORD and said, 'I will entice him.'

²²" 'By what means?' the LORD asked.

" 'I will go out and be a lying spirit in the mouths of all his prophets,' he said.

" 'You will succeed in enticing him,' said the LORD. 'Go and do it.'

²³"So now the LORD has put a lying spirit in the mouths of all these prophets of yours. The LORD has decreed disaster for you."

²⁴Then Zedekiah son of Kenaanah went up and slapped Micaiah in the face. "Which way did the spirit from ᵃ the LORD go when he went from me to speak to you?" he asked.

²⁵Micaiah replied, "You will find out on the day you go to hide in an inner room."

²⁶The king of Israel then ordered, "Take Micaiah and send him back to Amon the ruler of the city and to Joash the king's son ²⁷and say, 'This is what the king says: Put this fellow in prison and give him nothing but bread and water until I return safely.' "

ᵃ 24 Or Spirit of

²⁸Micaiah declared, "If you ever return safely, the LORD has not spoken through me." Then he added, "Mark my words, all you people!"

Ahab Killed at Ramoth Gilead

²⁹So the king of Israel and Jehoshaphat king of Judah went up to Ramoth Gilead. ³⁰The king of Israel said to Jehoshaphat, "I will enter the battle in disguise, but you wear your royal robes." So the king of Israel disguised himself and went into battle.

³¹Now the king of Aram had ordered his thirty-two chariot commanders, "Do not fight with anyone, small or great, except the king of Israel." ³²When the chariot commanders saw Jehoshaphat, they thought, "Surely this is the king of Israel." So they turned to attack him, but when Jehoshaphat cried out, ³³the chariot commanders saw that he was not the king of Israel and stopped pursuing him.

³⁴But someone drew his bow at random and hit the king of Israel between the sections of his armor. The king told his chariot driver, "Wheel around and get me out of the fighting. I've been wounded." ³⁵All day long the battle raged, and the king was propped up in his chariot facing the Arameans. The blood from his wound ran onto the floor of the chariot, and that evening he died. ³⁶As the sun was setting, a cry spread through the army: "Every man to his town; everyone to his land!"

³⁷So the king died and was brought to Samaria, and they buried him there. ³⁸They washed the chariot at a pool in Samaria (where the prostitutes bathed),ᵃ and the dogs licked up his blood, as the word of the LORD had declared.

³⁹As for the other events of Ahab's reign, including all he did, the palace he built and inlaid with ivory, and the cities he fortified, are they not written in the book of the annals of the kings of Israel? ⁴⁰Ahab rested with his fathers. And Ahaziah his son succeeded him as king.

Jehoshaphat King of Judah

⁴¹Jehoshaphat son of Asa became king of Judah in the fourth year of Ahab king of Israel. ⁴²Jehoshaphat was thirty-five years old when he became king, and he reigned in Jerusalem twenty-five years. His mother's name was Azubah daughter of Shilhi. ⁴³In everything he walked in the ways of his father Asa and did not stray from them; he did what was right in the eyes of the LORD. The high places, however, were not removed, and the people continued to offer sacrifices and burn incense there. ⁴⁴Jehoshaphat was also at peace with the king of Israel.

⁴⁵As for the other events of Jehoshaphat's reign, the things he achieved and his military exploits, are they not written in the book of the annals of the kings of Judah? ⁴⁶He rid the land of the rest of the male shrine prostitutes who remained there even after the reign of his father Asa. ⁴⁷There was then no king in Edom; a deputy ruled.

⁴⁸Now Jehoshaphat built a fleet of trading shipsᵇ to go to Ophir for gold, but they never set sail—they were wrecked at Ezion Geber. ⁴⁹At that time Ahaziah son of Ahab said to Jehoshaphat, "Let my men sail with your men," but Jehoshaphat refused.

⁵⁰Then Jehoshaphat rested with his fathers and was buried with them in the city of David his father. And Jehoram his son succeeded him.

Ahaziah King of Israel

⁵¹Ahaziah son of Ahab became king of Israel in Samaria in the seventeenth year of Jehoshaphat king of Judah, and he reigned over Israel two years. ⁵²He did evil in the eyes of the LORD, because he walked in the ways of his father and mother and in the ways of Jeroboam son of Nebat, who caused Israel to sin. ⁵³He served and worshiped Baal and provoked the LORD, the God of Israel, to anger, just as his father had done.

ᵃ 38 Or Samaria and cleaned the weapons   ᵇ 48 Hebrew of ships of Tarshish

Getting along with Mom & Dad

You & your parents have a great relationship, right? Take this quiz and find out!

1 Judging by the way your parents enforce rules, which of the following dinosaurs are your parents most like?
- A. Spinosauruses: They get mad when a rule is broken but cool off quickly.
- B. Velociraptors: They hunt as a team and are a little too strict about rules.
- C. Apatosauruses: They're gentle and laidback.

2 You get along with your parents . . .
- A. Anywhere between 50 to 80 percent of the time.
- B. You're ready to file for emancipation right now.
- C. 100 percent of the time.

3 How good are you at avoiding pushing your parents' hot buttons? (You know what they are, *right?*)
- A. Not good. You push them on a regular basis. (Go to 4.)
- B. You hardly ever make your parents mad. (Go to 5.)
- C. Okay. You annoy them from time to time. But somebody's gotta do it, right? (Go to 6.)

4 The best thing you could do to get along with your parents that you're currently *not* doing is . . .
- A. Respect and obey them. (Go to 5.)
- B. Stop pushing their buttons. (Go to 6.)
- C. Nothing. You're already doing everything you could possibly do to get along. (Go to 6.)

5 If you had to give your parents advice on getting along with you, you would tell them to . . .
- A. Keep up the good work. They're doing great. (Go to 7.)
- B. Learn your likes and dislikes. (Go to 6.)
- C. Please stop giving you so much advice. (Go to 8.)

6 As far as goals for your life are concerned, you and your parents . . .
- A. Are in sync. (Go to 9.)
- B. Disagree somewhat. (Go to 8.)
- C. Don't even talk about them—you totally disagree. (Go to 7.)

7 The coolest thing about your relationship with your folks:
- A. You can talk about anything and everything. (Go to 9.)
- B. You're still not sure what's cool about your relationship. (Go to 8.)
- C. You don't bug each other as much as you used to. (Go to 9.)

8 Lately, you see your parents as . . .
- A. A little overprotective, but still okay. (Go to Normal.)
- B. Just right. (Go to Simpático.)
- C. People you haven't really paid much attention to lately. (Go to 9.)

9 Which of the following statements do you most agree with concerning your parents?
- A. I wish they paid more attention to how I feel. (Go to Normal.)
- B. I don't have a clue what's up with them. (Go to Difícil.)
- C. They're cool. I wouldn't trade 'em for anything in the world! (Go to Simpático.)

A B C ?

Simpático *(Pleasant, Nice)*

You've got a great thing going with your folks. That's awesome! You've clearly taken God's command to honor your parents seriously (see Exodus 20:12; Ephesians 6:2). Muy bien! (Very good!)

Normal *(Average)*

You're normal! That means you get along for the most part but sometimes hit a bump or two in your relationship. What's important is that you continue to communicate despite the occasional bump.

Difícil *(Difficult)*

You probably already realize that your relationship with your parents is difficult. But it doesn't always have to be like this. Good relationships take lots of work and prayer. Are you willing to work at it?

If you are in a difficult family situation and feel that you can't talk with your parent or parents at all, seek the help of a pastor or another trusted individual.

reflections from the parents' side

question:
What's the most challenging aspect about your relationship with your teens?

answer:
The most challenging thing right now is trying not to give advice unless they ask for it. Many times they resent the advice that I give, so I've learned to hold my advice for the really important issues and let them make their own mistakes on minor issues when it's something they can learn the hard way without being hurt.

Another challenging issue is when they seem embarrassed by me. It's a shock when you realize what is happening. I find it's best to keep a low profile at school events and let my kids "find" me when they want to talk to me.

TIPS for the Home Front

tip.1 "A gentle answer turns away wrath, but a harsh word stirs up anger" *(Proverbs 15:1)*.

tip.2 "Be kind and compassionate to one another, forgiving each other" *(Ephesians 4:32)*.

tip.3 "Honor your father and mother" *(Ephesians 6:2)*.

tip.4 "Love one another" *(1 John 4:7)*.

Good Parent-Offspring Relationships

- David and Solomon (1 Kings 2:1–4)
- Mary and Jesus (Luke 2:51–52; John 2:1–11)
- God and you (John 1:12)

What's your Confidence Factor?

1. Gotta love that mandatory Fine Arts credit. When Drama 101 calls, you think...

A. If they don't give me the lead, I don't know what they're thinking!

B. Sweet! Wonder if I could pull off that British accent?

C. Every production needs a props person . . . right?

2. The ref blows the whistle on a dirty defensive play. It's PK (penalty kick) time. You . . .

A. Avoid eye contact with the coach and hide behind your teammates.

B. Yell, "Let me at it! I'll rip a hole through the back of the net!"

C. Think, *I'm ready if he needs me.*

3. Friday's the French final you've been hearing about all year—academic casualties galore! Your pre-test stress level:

A. Out of this world. I'm so nervous, I'm sure I'll never remember what I studied.

B. I've put in my time. Now I've just gotta keep my head clear and do my best.

C. Studying's overrated. I've got this thing covered. Plus, I have Monsieur Stephens wrapped around my finger. . . .

4. Geometry is going from bad to worse. You realize the only thing that's gonna save this ship is some one-on-one help from your teacher. Your response:

A. I've been putting it off for weeks. This is way out of my comfort zone.

B. I deserve an A anyway. It's the least the teacher could do.

C. So Geometry isn't my strong point. A little help never hurt anyone.

5. The weekend's coming up, and you don't have any plans yet. You feel . . .

A. It's no big deal—if something doesn't come up, I'll ask the girls to do something Saturday.

B. Stress! What if my friends leave me out?! I don't want to sit at home all weekend.

C. Duh—I'm the life of the party. There *is* no weekend without me!

6. You find out you and your bud like the same hottie. You think . . .

A. Shoot—I don't stand a chance. If only I could be more outgoing like she is around him.

B. I've got to be straight-up with her about this. I don't want anything to wreck our friendship.

C. Step aside, sista! Let the flirting begin! You don't stand a chance.

7. You know your friend did not get that A on her own . . . plus, you saw her cheat sheet. What to do?

A. Confront it head-on. You call it what it is (cheating!) and make her face up to it.

B. Go on the offensive. Attack her, tell the teacher, the principal and all your friends. She's reaping what she sowed.

C. Pretend it didn't happen. She doesn't know you know . . . so why create a controversy?

8. After the homecoming dance, your date is coming in for the goodnight kiss. However, this was not on your agenda. You . . .

A. Take a step back and clearly cut him off. "See ya!"

B. Insult him and tell him to dream on.

C. Get nailed with the wet one. You're hating every second of it but have no idea how to get yourself out of this mess!

(A) (B) (C) (?)

Add up your points:

1. A=4; B=2; C=0
2. A=0; B=4; C=2
3. A=0; B=2; C=4
4. A=0; B=4; C=2
5. A=2; B=0; C=4
6. A=0; B=2; C=4
7. A=2; B=4; C=0
8. A=2; B=4; C=0

(21–32) *Cocky Cari*

Ever considered that you might be a little *too* confident? Confidence is good . . . to a certain extent. But when it borders on cockiness or arrogance, it's time to pull back. You may be a little too willing to step on others in pursuit of your own self-interests. Read Philippians 2:3–4. Better yet, memorize it and make it your motto!

(11–20) *Secure Shari*

Congrats! You have a healthy self-confidence that helps you stay true to yourself. You're realistic about your abilities but willing to take some risks and try something new. You're not afraid to take matters into your own hands and do the right thing. Keep up that confidence, girl! And make sure you keep that confidence in the right place—God (see Philippians 1:6).

(0–10) *Timid Teri*

Time to come out of that shell! We know you're in there. Yeah, *you,* the one with the great personality who's afraid to show it. During those times when you feel intimidated or overwhelmed, try taking a risk and trying something new. Those baby steps will help you build the confidence you need! Trust us—people aren't watching you nearly as much as you think (see 2 Timothy 1:6–7).

reflections from the other side

question:
Do you like girls who are confident?

answer:
Yes, confidence is a major plus for girls. They shouldn't be so confident that they're cocky, but they need to be sure of themselves and willing to act normal.

Confidence Builder

Try one new thing every month—take a sculpting class or join the debate team or learn how to drive a stick shift. Little risks like that will give you the confidence to keep trying new things!

Befriend someone you have *nothing* in common with! It's amazing how you can stretch yourself by learning about someone else's background and interests.

Base your self-confidence on God, not on yourself. You'll do lots of dumb and embarrassing things in life (and that's okay!), but God never will.

God's thoughts on confidence

- You can do all things through my Son, who gives you strength (Philippians 4:13).
- I've given you a powerful, loving, disciplined spirit (2 Timothy 1:7).
- You can come to me confidently. Just ask (1 John 3:21–22).

at a glance ⌄

author: Unknown.

date: Somewhere between 560 and 550 B.C.

setting: Second Kings covers the period from about 850 to 560 B.C., including the defeat of both kingdoms.

verse to remember: So the LORD said, "I will remove Judah also from my presence as I removed Israel, and I will reject Jerusalem, the city I chose, and this temple, about which I said, 'There shall my Name be' " (23:27).

theme to consider: God punished his chosen people because they rejected him and chose to worship other gods. No one can escape God's judgment.

unchanging truth

Have you ever tried swimming against the ocean current? Or how about pedaling your bike against a strong wind? It's tough, sometimes even impossible, to overcome that force dragging you back. At times, trying to maintain your faith in a culture that is seemingly going against your beliefs can feel the same way.

Throughout much of the book of 2 Kings, most of the people of Israel and Judah and many of their kings were heading in one direction—worshiping idols and rejecting God. Against this current stood God's prophets and a few faithful kings who tried to stem the tide and turn the people back to God.

At times, they succeeded, and the people enjoyed brief periods of peace, revival and God's blessings. Unfortunately, the current was too strong, and by the end of the book, the people of Israel and Judah were swept away by idol worship, their nations punished and destroyed as God had promised if they rejected him. At the book's end, we witness Israel's darkest moment as the people are taken away into captivity.

The message of 2 Kings couldn't be clearer. If we reject God, he will reject us. The choice is *ours*, just as it was for the people of Israel. Even if the tide is against you, hold fast to your faith. Stay connected to God through studying his Word, praying and staying close to other believers.

life lessons

1 We are never too young to tell others of the love and power of God (5:1–5).

2 When God-fearing leaders take charge, they have an incredible opportunity to influence others (11:12,17–18,21).

3 Even in the worst of times, hold onto your faith in God. He is always in control and always faithful (19:14–19).

The LORD's Judgment on Ahaziah

1 After Ahab's death, Moab rebelled against Israel. ²Now Ahaziah had fallen through the lattice of his upper room in Samaria and injured himself. So he sent messengers, saying to them, "Go and consult Baal-Zebub, the god of Ekron, to see if I will recover from this injury."

³But the angel of the LORD said to Elijah the Tishbite, "Go up and meet the messengers of the king of Samaria and ask them, 'Is it because there is no God in Israel that you are going off to consult Baal-Zebub, the god of Ekron?' ⁴Therefore this is what the LORD says: 'You will not leave the bed you are lying on. You will certainly die!' " So Elijah went.

⁵When the messengers returned to the king, he asked them, "Why have you come back?"

⁶"A man came to meet us," they replied. "And he said to us, 'Go back to the king who sent you and tell him, "This is what the LORD says: Is it because there is no God in Israel that you are sending men to consult Baal-Zebub, the god of Ekron? Therefore you will not leave the bed you are lying on. You will certainly die!" ' "

⁷The king asked them, "What kind of man was it who came to meet you and told you this?"

⁸They replied, "He was a man with a garment of hair and with a leather belt around his waist." The king said, "That was Elijah the Tishbite."

⁹Then he sent to Elijah a captain with his company of fifty men. The captain went up to Elijah, who was sitting on the top of a hill, and said to him, "Man of God, the king says, 'Come down!' "

¹⁰Elijah answered the captain, "If I am a man of God, may fire come down from heaven and consume you and your fifty men!" Then fire fell from heaven and consumed the captain and his men.

¹¹At this the king sent to Elijah another captain with his fifty men. The captain said to him, "Man of God, this is what the king says, 'Come down at once!' "

¹²"If I am a man of God," Elijah replied, "may fire come down from heaven and consume you and your fifty men!" Then the fire of God fell from heaven and consumed him and his fifty men.

¹³So the king sent a third captain with his fifty men. This third captain went up and fell on his knees before Elijah. "Man of God," he begged, "please have respect for my life and the lives of these fifty men, your servants! ¹⁴See, fire has fallen from heaven and consumed the first two captains and all their men. But now have respect for my life!"

¹⁵The angel of the LORD said to Elijah, "Go down with him; do not be afraid of him." So Elijah got up and went down with him to the king.

¹⁶He told the king, "This is what the LORD says: Is it because there is no God in Israel for you to consult that you have sent messengers to consult Baal-Zebub, the god of Ekron? Because you have done this, you will never leave the bed you are lying on. You will certainly die!" ¹⁷So he died, according to the word of the LORD that Elijah had spoken.

Because Ahaziah had no son, Joram*ᵃ* succeeded him as king in the second year of Jehoram son of Jehoshaphat king of Judah. ¹⁸As for all the other events of Ahaziah's reign, and what he did, are they not written in the book of the annals of the kings of Israel?

Elijah Taken Up to Heaven

2 When the LORD was about to take Elijah up to heaven in a whirlwind, Elijah and Elisha were on their way from Gilgal. ²Elijah said to Elisha, "Stay here; the LORD has sent me to Bethel." But Elisha said, "As surely as the LORD lives and as you live, I will not leave you." So they went down to Bethel.

³The company of the prophets at Bethel came out to Elisha and asked, "Do you know that the LORD is going to take your master from you today?"

"Yes, I know," Elisha replied, "but do not speak of it."

⁴Then Elijah said to him, "Stay here, Elisha; the LORD has sent me to Jericho."

And he replied, "As surely as the LORD lives and as you live, I will not leave you." So they went to Jericho.

⁵The company of the prophets at Jericho went up to Elisha and asked him, "Do you know that the LORD is going to take your master from you today?"

"Yes, I know," he replied, "but do not speak of it."

⁶Then Elijah said to him, "Stay here; the LORD has sent me to the Jordan."

ᵃ 17 Hebrew *Jehoram,* a variant of *Joram*

And he replied, "As surely as the Lord lives and as you live, I will not leave you." So the two of them walked on.

⁷Fifty men of the company of the prophets went and stood at a distance, facing the place where Elijah and Elisha had stopped at the Jordan. ⁸Elijah took his cloak, rolled it up and struck the water with it. The water divided to the right and to the left, and the two of them crossed over on dry ground.

⁹When they had crossed, Elijah said to Elisha, "Tell me, what can I do for you before I am taken from you?"

"Let me inherit a double portion of your spirit," Elisha replied.

¹⁰"You have asked a difficult thing," Elijah said, "yet if you see me when I am taken from you, it will be yours—otherwise not."

¹¹As they were walking along and talking together, suddenly a chariot of fire and horses of fire appeared and separated the two of them, and Elijah went up to heaven in a whirlwind. ¹²Elisha saw this and cried out, "My father! My father! The chariots and horsemen of Israel!" And Elisha saw him no more. Then he took hold of his own clothes and tore them apart.

¹³He picked up the cloak that had fallen from Elijah and went back and stood on the bank of the Jordan. ¹⁴Then he took the cloak that had fallen from him and struck the water with it. "Where now is the Lord, the God of Elijah?" he asked. When he struck the water, it divided to the right and to the left, and he crossed over.

¹⁵The company of the prophets from Jericho, who were watching, said, "The spirit of Elijah is resting on Elisha." And they went to meet him and bowed to the ground before him. ¹⁶"Look," they said, "we your servants have fifty able men. Let them go and look for your master. Perhaps the Spirit of the Lord has picked him up and set him down on some mountain or in some valley."

"No," Elisha replied, "do not send them."

¹⁷But they persisted until he was too ashamed to refuse. So he said, "Send them." And they sent fifty men, who searched for three days but did not find him. ¹⁸When they returned to Elisha, who was staying in Jericho, he said to them, "Didn't I tell you not to go?"

Healing of the Water

¹⁹The men of the city said to Elisha, "Look, our lord, this town is well situated, as you can see, but the water is bad and the land is unproductive."

²⁰"Bring me a new bowl," he said, "and put salt in it." So they brought it to him.

²¹Then he went out to the spring and threw the salt into it, saying, "This is what the Lord says: 'I have healed this water. Never again will it cause death or make the land unproductive.' " ²²And the water has remained wholesome to this day, according to the word Elisha had spoken.

Elisha Is Jeered

²³From there Elisha went up to Bethel. As he was walking along the road, some youths came out of the town and jeered at him. "Go on up, you baldhead!" they said. "Go on up, you baldhead!" ²⁴He turned around, looked at them and called down a curse on them in the name of the Lord. Then two bears came out of the woods and mauled forty-two of the youths. ²⁵And he went on to Mount Carmel and from there returned to Samaria.

Moab Revolts

3 Joram[a] son of Ahab became king of Israel in Samaria in the eighteenth year of Jehoshaphat king of Judah, and he reigned twelve years. ²He did evil in the eyes of the Lord, but not as his father and mother had done. He got rid of the sacred stone of Baal that his father had made. ³Nevertheless he clung to the sins of Jeroboam son of Nebat, which he had caused Israel to commit; he did not turn away from them.

⁴Now Mesha king of Moab raised sheep, and he had to supply the king of Israel with a hundred thousand lambs and with the wool of a hundred thousand rams. ⁵But after Ahab died, the king of Moab rebelled against the king of Israel. ⁶So at that time King Joram set out from Samaria and mobilized all Israel. ⁷He also sent this message to Jehoshaphat king of Judah: "The king of Moab has rebelled against me. Will you go with me to fight against Moab?"

a 1 Hebrew *Jehoram*, a variant of *Joram*; also in verse 6

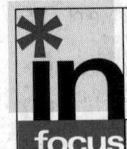

*in focus

Constant Critic

Profile: **Monica**

"Life is hard, but you need to suck it up and move on," I said to my sister Cheryl. She was curled up on her bed, crying about her ex-boyfriend Justin. I mean, give me a break, that jerk broke up with her over a month ago. You'd think she'd be over him by now.

But no, she sits there and cries like some desperate ditz. She says it's awful to see him in geometry every day. My sister just doesn't have her act together. Unlike me, she only goes to youth group when she feels like it. And the way I see it, she only does the church thing on Sundays to please our parents. What a scam.

Last weekend Cheryl introduced me to her new best friend, Rae. *Here we go again*, I thought. Rae was dressed in all black, with this red collar thing strapped around her throat and a thick bar through her tongue (You should hear her try to talk!), and she plays in a punk band at the local coffee shop. You know she's got to be a loser. She'll never get a decent job when she gets out of school.

But whenever I mention any of that to Cheryl, she always brushes me off. "Monica, you don't get me at all," she says. "No one's ever good enough for you. Why do you have to be so harsh?"

She is so wrong about me. I only have her best interests at heart! I wish she'd be more responsible, that she'd get a clue. Is that too much to ask?

For more ideas on how to deal with judgmentalism, check out the link on www.TrueImagesBible.com

judgmentalism in focus

We all can be judgmental at times. We judge people on their appearance, on who their friends are or even on how "spiritual" we think they are.

Jesus gives us a funny but serious way to look at it: "Why do you look at the speck of sawdust in your brother's eye and pay no attention to the plank in your own eye?" (Matthew 7:3, page 1299). In other words, *You judge someone else for her problem, yet you have a much bigger problem!* When we take time to honestly evaluate ourselves, we'll be less likely to be judgmental toward others.

For more on this topic, see the index on page 1656.

judgmentalism

"I will go with you," he replied. "I am as you are, my people as your people, my horses as your horses."

[8]"By what route shall we attack?" he asked.

"Through the Desert of Edom," he answered.

[9]So the king of Israel set out with the king of Judah and the king of Edom. After a roundabout march of seven days, the army had no more water for themselves or for the animals with them.

[10]"What!" exclaimed the king of Israel. "Has the LORD called us three kings together only to hand us over to Moab?"

¹¹But Jehoshaphat asked, "Is there no prophet of the LORD here, that we may inquire of the LORD through him?"

An officer of the king of Israel answered, "Elisha son of Shaphat is here. He used to pour water on the hands of Elijah.ᵃ"

¹²Jehoshaphat said, "The word of the LORD is with him." So the king of Israel and Jehoshaphat and the king of Edom went down to him.

¹³Elisha said to the king of Israel, "What do we have to do with each other? Go to the prophets of your father and the prophets of your mother."

"No," the king of Israel answered, "because it was the LORD who called us three kings together to hand us over to Moab."

¹⁴Elisha said, "As surely as the LORD Almighty lives, whom I serve, if I did not have respect for the presence of Jehoshaphat king of Judah, I would not look at you or even notice you. ¹⁵But now bring me a harpist."

While the harpist was playing, the hand of the LORD came upon Elisha ¹⁶and he said, "This is what the LORD says: Make this valley full of ditches. ¹⁷For this is what the LORD says: You will see neither wind nor rain, yet this valley will be filled with water, and you, your cattle and your other animals will drink. ¹⁸This is an easy thing in the eyes of the LORD; he will also hand Moab over to you. ¹⁹You will overthrow every fortified city and every major town. You will cut down every good tree, stop up all the springs, and ruin every good field with stones."

²⁰The next morning, about the time for offering the sacrifice, there it was—water flowing from the direction of Edom! And the land was filled with water.

²¹Now all the Moabites had heard that the kings had come to fight against them; so every man, young and old, who could bear arms was called up and stationed on the border. ²²When they got up early in the morning, the sun was shining on the water. To the Moabites across the way, the water looked red—like blood. ²³"That's blood!" they said. "Those kings must have fought and slaughtered each other. Now to the plunder, Moab!"

²⁴But when the Moabites came to the camp of Israel, the Israelites rose up and fought them until they fled. And the Israelites invaded the land and slaughtered the Moabites. ²⁵They destroyed the towns, and each man threw a stone on every good field until it was covered. They stopped up all the springs and cut down every good tree. Only Kir Hareseth was left with its stones in place, but men armed with slings surrounded it and attacked it as well.

²⁶When the king of Moab saw that the battle had gone against him, he took with him seven hundred swordsmen to break through to the king of Edom, but they failed. ²⁷Then he took his firstborn son, who was to succeed him as king, and offered him as a sacrifice on the city wall. The fury against Israel was great; they withdrew and returned to their own land.

The Widow's Oil

4 The wife of a man from the company of the prophets cried out to Elisha, "Your servant my husband is dead, and you know that he revered the LORD. But now his creditor is coming to take my two boys as his slaves."

²Elisha replied to her, "How can I help you? Tell me, what do you have in your house?"

"Your servant has nothing there at all," she said, "except a little oil."

³Elisha said, "Go around and ask all your neighbors for empty jars. Don't ask for just a few. ⁴Then go inside and shut the door behind you and your sons. Pour oil into all the jars, and as each is filled, put it to one side."

⁵She left him and afterward shut the door behind her and her sons. They brought the jars to her and she kept pouring. ⁶When all the jars were full, she said to her son, "Bring me another one."

But he replied, "There is not a jar left." Then the oil stopped flowing.

truth or dare

Feel like you have nothing to offer God? Don't despair! Give him everything you've got anyway. God can take your "little" and produce "a lot"!

4:1–7

ᵃ 11 That is, he was Elijah's personal servant.

[7]She went and told the man of God, and he said, "Go, sell the oil and pay your debts. You and your sons can live on what is left."

The Shunammite's Son Restored to Life

[8]One day Elisha went to Shunem. And a well-to-do woman was there, who urged him to stay for a meal. So whenever he came by, he stopped there to eat. [9]She said to her husband, "I know that this man who often comes our way is a holy man of God. [10]Let's make a small room on the roof and put in it a bed and a table, a chair and a lamp for him. Then he can stay there whenever he comes to us."

[11]One day when Elisha came, he went up to his room and lay down there. [12]He said to his servant Gehazi, "Call the Shunammite." So he called her, and she stood before him. [13]Elisha said to him, "Tell her, 'You have gone to all this trouble for us. Now what can be done for you? Can we speak on your behalf to the king or the commander of the army?' "

She replied, "I have a home among my own people."

[14]"What can be done for her?" Elisha asked.

Gehazi said, "Well, she has no son and her husband is old."

[15]Then Elisha said, "Call her." So he called her, and she stood in the doorway. [16]"About this time next year," Elisha said, "you will hold a son in your arms."

"No, my lord," she objected. "Don't mislead your servant, O man of God!"

[17]But the woman became pregnant, and the next year about that same time she gave birth to a son, just as Elisha had told her.

genuine
hospitality » 4:8-17

It all started with a dinner invitation. The well-to-do woman noticed the traveling prophet and figured he must be hungry. That one thoughtful invitation led to some regular family dinners together and then a personal suite for the prophet whenever he came to town. What a comfort that must have been to Elisha, who was on the road all the time. But the benefits weren't just for Elisha, the recipient—the giver's kindness returned to her, and she received a son. A little bit of kindness goes a long way. Have you ever known that to happen in your life?

[18]The child grew, and one day he went out to his father, who was with the reapers. [19]"My head! My head!" he said to his father.

His father told a servant, "Carry him to his mother." [20]After the servant had lifted him up and carried him to his mother, the boy sat on her lap until noon, and then he died. [21]She went up and laid him on the bed of the man of God, then shut the door and went out.

[22]She called her husband and said, "Please send me one of the servants and a donkey so I can go to the man of God quickly and return."

[23]"Why go to him today?" he asked. "It's not the New Moon or the Sabbath."

"It's all right," she said.

[24]She saddled the donkey and said to her servant, "Lead on; don't slow down for me unless I tell you." [25]So she set out and came to the man of God at Mount Carmel.

When he saw her in the distance, the man of God said to his servant Gehazi, "Look! There's the Shunammite! [26]Run to meet her and ask her, 'Are you all right? Is your husband all right? Is your child all right?' "

"Everything is all right," she said.

[27]When she reached the man of God at the mountain, she took hold of his feet. Gehazi came over to push her away, but the man of God said, "Leave her alone! She is in bitter distress, but the LORD has hidden it from me and has not told me why."

[28]"Did I ask you for a son, my lord?" she said. "Didn't I tell you, 'Don't raise my hopes'?"

[29]Elisha said to Gehazi, "Tuck your cloak into your belt, take my staff in your hand and run. If you meet anyone, do not greet him, and if anyone greets you, do not answer. Lay my staff on the boy's face."

³⁰But the child's mother said, "As surely as the Lord lives and as you live, I will not leave you." So he got up and followed her.

³¹Gehazi went on ahead and laid the staff on the boy's face, but there was no sound or response. So Gehazi went back to meet Elisha and told him, "The boy has not awakened."

³²When Elisha reached the house, there was the boy lying dead on his couch. ³³He went in, shut the door on the two of them and prayed to the Lord. ³⁴Then he got on the bed and lay upon the boy, mouth to mouth, eyes to eyes, hands to hands. As he stretched himself out upon him, the boy's body grew warm. ³⁵Elisha turned away and walked back and forth in the room and then got on the bed and stretched out upon him once more. The boy sneezed seven times and opened his eyes.

³⁶Elisha summoned Gehazi and said, "Call the Shunammite." And he did. When she came, he said, "Take your son." ³⁷She came in, fell at his feet and bowed to the ground. Then she took her son and went out.

Death in the Pot

³⁸Elisha returned to Gilgal and there was a famine in that region. While the company of the prophets was meeting with him, he said to his servant, "Put on the large pot and cook some stew for these men."

³⁹One of them went out into the fields to gather herbs and found a wild vine. He gathered some of its gourds and filled the fold of his cloak. When he returned, he cut them up into the pot of stew, though no one knew what they were. ⁴⁰The stew was poured out for the men, but as they began to eat it, they cried out, "O man of God, there is death in the pot!" And they could not eat it.

⁴¹Elisha said, "Get some flour." He put it into the pot and said, "Serve it to the people to eat." And there was nothing harmful in the pot.

Feeding of a Hundred

⁴²A man came from Baal Shalishah, bringing the man of God twenty loaves of barley bread baked from the first ripe grain, along with some heads of new grain. "Give it to the people to eat," Elisha said.

⁴³"How can I set this before a hundred men?" his servant asked.

But Elisha answered, "Give it to the people to eat. For this is what the Lord says: 'They will eat and have some left over.' " ⁴⁴Then he set it before them, and they ate and had some left over, according to the word of the Lord.

Naaman Healed of Leprosy

5 Now Naaman was commander of the army of the king of Aram. He was a great man in the sight of his master and highly regarded, because through him the Lord had given victory to Aram. He was a valiant soldier, but he had leprosy.ᵃ

²Now bands from Aram had gone out and had taken captive a young girl from Israel, and she served Naaman's wife. ³She said to her mistress, "If only my master would see the prophet who is in Samaria! He would cure him of his leprosy."

⁴Naaman went to his master and told him what the girl from Israel had said. ⁵"By all means, go," the king of Aram replied. "I will send a letter to the king of Israel." So Naaman left, taking with him ten talentsᵇ of silver, six thousand shekelsᶜ of gold and ten sets of clothing. ⁶The letter that he took to the king of Israel read: "With this letter I am sending my servant Naaman to you so that you may cure him of his leprosy."

⁷As soon as the king of Israel read the letter, he tore his robes and said, "Am I God? Can I kill and bring back to life? Why does this fellow send someone to me to be cured of his leprosy? See how he is trying to pick a quarrel with me!"

truth or dare

A slave. An outsider. This girl's life was far from cush. But out of this sorry situation, God used her faith in a great way. Keep believing!

5:1–4

ᵃ 1 The Hebrew word was used for various diseases affecting the skin—not necessarily leprosy; also in verses 3, 6, 7, 11 and 27.   ᵇ 5 That is, about 750 pounds (about 340 kilograms)   ᶜ 5 That is, about 150 pounds (about 70 kilograms)

[8]When Elisha the man of God heard that the king of Israel had torn his robes, he sent him this message: "Why have you torn your robes? Have the man come to me and he will know that there is a prophet in Israel." [9]So Naaman went with his horses and chariots and stopped at the door of Elisha's house. [10]Elisha sent a messenger to say to him, "Go, wash yourself seven times in the Jordan, and your flesh will be restored and you will be cleansed."

[11]But Naaman went away angry and said, "I thought that he would surely come out to me and stand and call on the name of the LORD his God, wave his hand over the spot and cure me of my leprosy. [12]Are not Abana and Pharpar, the rivers of Damascus, better than any of the waters of Israel? Couldn't I wash in them and be cleansed?" So he turned and went off in a rage.

[13]Naaman's servants went to him and said, "My father, if the prophet had told you to do some great thing, would you not have done it? How much more, then, when he tells you, 'Wash and be cleansed'!" [14]So he went down and dipped himself in the Jordan seven times, as the man of God had told him, and his flesh was restored and became clean like that of a young boy.

genuine obedience

Naaman had some expectations of how he wanted to be healed. He expected some dramatic words from the prophet Elisha and a quick and easy finish to his disease. But that's not what God had in mind. When Elisha told Naaman how to be healed, Naaman hesitated. The treatment plan wasn't what he had anticipated. But God acts on his terms, not ours. And his way is always best.

» 5:1-14

[15]Then Naaman and all his attendants went back to the man of God. He stood before him and said, "Now I know that there is no God in all the world except in Israel. Please accept now a gift from your servant."

[16]The prophet answered, "As surely as the LORD lives, whom I serve, I will not accept a thing." And even though Naaman urged him, he refused.

[17]"If you will not," said Naaman, "please let me, your servant, be given as much earth as a pair of mules can carry, for your servant will never again make burnt offerings and sacrifices to any other god but the LORD. [18]But may the LORD forgive your servant for this one thing: When my master enters the temple of Rimmon to bow down and he is leaning on my arm and I bow there also— when I bow down in the temple of Rimmon, may the LORD forgive your servant for this."

[19]"Go in peace," Elisha said.

After Naaman had traveled some distance, [20]Gehazi, the servant of Elisha the man of God, said to himself, "My master was too easy on Naaman, this Aramean, by not accepting from him what he brought. As surely as the LORD lives, I will run after him and get something from him."

[21]So Gehazi hurried after Naaman. When Naaman saw him running toward him, he got down from the chariot to meet him. "Is everything all right?" he asked.

[22]"Everything is all right," Gehazi answered. "My master sent me to say, 'Two young men from the company of the prophets have just come to me from the hill country of Ephraim. Please give them a talent[a] of silver and two sets of clothing.'"

[23]"By all means, take two talents," said Naaman. He urged Gehazi to accept them, and then tied up the two talents of silver in two bags, with two sets of clothing. He gave them to two of his servants, and they carried them ahead of Gehazi. [24]When Gehazi came to the hill, he took the things from the servants and put them away in the house. He sent the men away and they left. [25]Then he went in and stood before his master Elisha.

"Where have you been, Gehazi?" Elisha asked.

"Your servant didn't go anywhere," Gehazi answered.

a 22 That is, about 75 pounds (about 34 kilograms)

[26]But Elisha said to him, "Was not my spirit with you when the man got down from his chariot to meet you? Is this the time to take money, or to accept clothes, olive groves, vineyards, flocks, herds, or menservants and maidservants? [27]Naaman's leprosy will cling to you and to your descendants forever." Then Gehazi went from Elisha's presence and he was leprous, as white as snow.

An Axhead Floats

The company of the prophets said to Elisha, "Look, the place where we meet with you is too small for us. [2]Let us go to the Jordan, where each of us can get a pole; and let us build a place there for us to live."

And he said, "Go."

[3]Then one of them said, "Won't you please come with your servants?"

"I will," Elisha replied. [4]And he went with them.

They went to the Jordan and began to cut down trees. [5]As one of them was cutting down a tree, the iron axhead fell into the water. "Oh, my lord," he cried out, "it was borrowed!"

[6]The man of God asked, "Where did it fall?" When he showed him the place, Elisha cut a stick and threw it there, and made the iron float. [7]"Lift it out," he said. Then the man reached out his hand and took it.

Elisha Traps Blinded Arameans

[8]Now the king of Aram was at war with Israel. After conferring with his officers, he said, "I will set up my camp in such and such a place."

[9]The man of God sent word to the king of Israel: "Beware of passing that place, because the Arameans are going down there." [10]So the king of Israel checked on the place indicated by the man of God. Time and again Elisha warned the king, so that he was on his guard in such places.

[11]This enraged the king of Aram. He summoned his officers and demanded of them, "Will you not tell me which of us is on the side of the king of Israel?"

[12]"None of us, my lord the king," said one of his officers, "but Elisha, the prophet who is in Israel, tells the king of Israel the very words you speak in your bedroom."

[13]"Go, find out where he is," the king ordered, "so I can send men and capture him." The report came back: "He is in Dothan." [14]Then he sent horses and chariots and a strong force there. They went by night and surrounded the city.

[15]When the servant of the man of God got up and went out early the next morning, an army with horses and chariots had surrounded the city. "Oh, my lord, what shall we do?" the servant asked.

[16]"Don't be afraid," the prophet answered. "Those who are with us are more than those who are with them."

[17]And Elisha prayed, "O LORD, open his

---

love notes

6:17

My child,

You may not see me at work in your circumstances. You may not be aware that I am there. But I am. Look with eyes of faith, and see the reality of my heavenly resources at work.

—Lord God Almighty

Write a prayer to God describing your faith in him.

eyes so he may see." Then the LORD opened the servant's eyes, and he looked and saw the hills full of horses and chariots of fire all around Elisha.

¹⁸As the enemy came down toward him, Elisha prayed to the LORD, "Strike these people with blindness." So he struck them with blindness, as Elisha had asked.

¹⁹Elisha told them, "This is not the road and this is not the city. Follow me, and I will lead you to the man you are looking for." And he led them to Samaria.

²⁰After they entered the city, Elisha said, "LORD, open the eyes of these men so they can see." Then the LORD opened their eyes and they looked, and there they were, inside Samaria.

²¹When the king of Israel saw them, he asked Elisha, "Shall I kill them, my father? Shall I kill them?"

²²"Do not kill them," he answered. "Would you kill men you have captured with your own sword or bow? Set food and water before them so that they may eat and drink and then go back to their master." ²³So he prepared a great feast for them, and after they had finished eating and drinking, he sent them away, and they returned to their master. So the bands from Aram stopped raiding Israel's territory.

Famine in Besieged Samaria

²⁴Some time later, Ben-Hadad king of Aram mobilized his entire army and marched up and laid siege to Samaria. ²⁵There was a great famine in the city; the siege lasted so long that a donkey's head sold for eighty shekels *a* of silver, and a quarter of a cab *b* of seed pods *c* for five shekels. *d*

²⁶As the king of Israel was passing by on the wall, a woman cried to him, "Help me, my lord the king!"

²⁷The king replied, "If the LORD does not help you, where can I get help for you? From the threshing floor? From the winepress?" ²⁸Then he asked her, "What's the matter?"

She answered, "This woman said to me, 'Give up your son so we may eat him today, and tomorrow we'll eat my son.' ²⁹So we cooked my son and ate him. The next day I said to her, 'Give up your son so we may eat him,' but she had hidden him."

³⁰When the king heard the woman's words, he tore his robes. As he went along the wall, the people looked, and there, underneath, he had sackcloth on his body. ³¹He said, "May God deal with me, be it ever so severely, if the head of Elisha son of Shaphat remains on his shoulders today!"

³²Now Elisha was sitting in his house, and the elders were sitting with him. The king sent a messenger ahead, but before he arrived, Elisha said to the elders, "Don't you see how this murderer is sending someone to cut off my head? Look, when the messenger comes, shut the door and hold it shut against him. Is not the sound of his master's footsteps behind him?"

³³While he was still talking to them, the messenger came down to him. And ⌊the king⌋ said, "This disaster is from the LORD. Why should I wait for the LORD any longer?"

7 Elisha said, "Hear the word of the LORD. This is what the LORD says: About this time tomorrow, a seah *e* of flour will sell for a shekel *f* and two seahs *g* of barley for a shekel at the gate of Samaria."

²The officer on whose arm the king was leaning said to the man of God, "Look, even if the LORD should open the floodgates of the heavens, could this happen?"

"You will see it with your own eyes," answered Elisha, "but you will not eat any of it!"

The Siege Lifted

³Now there were four men with leprosy *h* at the entrance of the city gate. They said to each other, "Why stay here until we die? ⁴If we say, 'We'll go into the city'—the famine is there, and we will die. And if we stay here, we will die. So let's go over to the camp of the Arameans and surrender. If they spare us, we live; if they kill us, then we die."

⁵At dusk they got up and went to the camp of the Arameans. When they reached the edge of the camp, not a man was there, ⁶for the Lord had caused the Arameans to hear the sound of chariots and horses and a great army, so that they said to one another, "Look, the king of Israel has

a 25 That is, about 2 pounds (about 1 kilogram)   *b 25* That is, probably about 1/2 pint (about 0.3 liter)   *c 25* Or *of doves' dung*   *d 25* That is, about 2 ounces (about 55 grams)   *e 1* That is, probably about 7 quarts (about 7.3 liters); also in verses 16 and 18   *f 1* That is, about 2/5 ounce (about 11 grams); also in verses 16 and 18   *g 1* That is, probably about 13 quarts (about 15 liters); also in verses 16 and 18   *h 3* The Hebrew word is used for various diseases affecting the skin—not necessarily leprosy; also in verse 8.

hired the Hittite and Egyptian kings to attack us!" [7]So they got up and fled in the dusk and abandoned their tents and their horses and donkeys. They left the camp as it was and ran for their lives.

[8]The men who had leprosy reached the edge of the camp and entered one of the tents. They ate and drank, and carried away silver, gold and clothes, and went off and hid them. They returned and entered another tent and took some things from it and hid them also.

[9]Then they said to each other, "We're not doing right. This is a day of good news and we are keeping it to ourselves. If we wait until daylight, punishment will overtake us. Let's go at once and report this to the royal palace."

[10]So they went and called out to the city gatekeepers and told them, "We went into the Aramean camp and not a man was there—not a sound of anyone—only tethered horses and donkeys, and the tents left just as they were." [11]The gatekeepers shouted the news, and it was reported within the palace.

[12]The king got up in the night and said to his officers, "I will tell you what the Arameans have done to us. They know we are starving; so they have left the camp to hide in the countryside, thinking, 'They will surely come out, and then we will take them alive and get into the city.' "

[13]One of his officers answered, "Have some men take five of the horses that are left in the city. Their plight will be like that of all the Israelites left here—yes, they will only be like all these Israelites who are doomed. So let us send them to find out what happened."

[14]So they selected two chariots with their horses, and the king sent them after the Aramean army. He commanded the drivers, "Go and find out what has happened." [15]They followed them as far as the Jordan, and they found the whole road strewn with the clothing and equipment the Arameans had thrown away in their headlong flight. So the messengers returned and reported to the king. [16]Then the people went out and plundered the camp of the Arameans. So a seah of flour sold for a shekel, and two seahs of barley sold for a shekel, as the LORD had said.

[17]Now the king had put the officer on whose arm he leaned in charge of the gate, and the people trampled him in the gateway, and he died, just as the man of God had foretold when the king came down to his house. [18]It happened as the man of God had said to the king: "About this time tomorrow, a seah of flour will sell for a shekel and two seahs of barley for a shekel at the gate of Samaria."

[19]The officer had said to the man of God, "Look, even if the LORD should open the floodgates of the heavens, could this happen?" The man of God had replied, "You will see it with your own eyes, but you will not eat any of it!" [20]And that is exactly what happened to him, for the people trampled him in the gateway, and he died.

The Shunammite's Land Restored

8 Now Elisha had said to the woman whose son he had restored to life, "Go away with your family and stay for a while wherever you can, because the LORD has decreed a famine in the land that will last seven years." [2]The woman proceeded to do as the man of God said. She and her family went away and stayed in the land of the Philistines seven years.

[3]At the end of the seven years she came back from the land of the Philistines and went to the king to beg for her house and land. [4]The king was talking to Gehazi, the servant of the man of God, and had said, "Tell me about all the great things Elisha has done." [5]Just as Gehazi was telling the king how Elisha had restored the dead to life, the woman whose son Elisha had brought back to life came to beg the king for her house and land.

Gehazi said, "This is the woman, my lord the king, and this is her son whom Elisha restored to life." [6]The king asked the woman about it, and she told him.

Then he assigned an official to her case and said to him, "Give back everything that belonged to her, including all the income from her land from the day she left the country until now."

Hazael Murders Ben-Hadad

[7]Elisha went to Damascus, and Ben-Hadad king of Aram was ill. When the king was told, "The man of God has come all the way up here," [8]he said to Hazael, "Take a gift with you and go to meet the man of God. Consult the LORD through him; ask him, 'Will I recover from this illness?' "

[9]Hazael went to meet Elisha, taking with him as a gift forty camel-loads of all the finest wares of Damascus. He went in and stood before him, and said, "Your son Ben-Hadad king of Aram has sent me to ask, 'Will I recover from this illness?' "

She said to her mistress, "If only my master would see the prophet who is in Samaria! He would cure him of his leprosy." 2 Kings 5:3

Naaman's Wife's Slave Girl—Unconditional Care

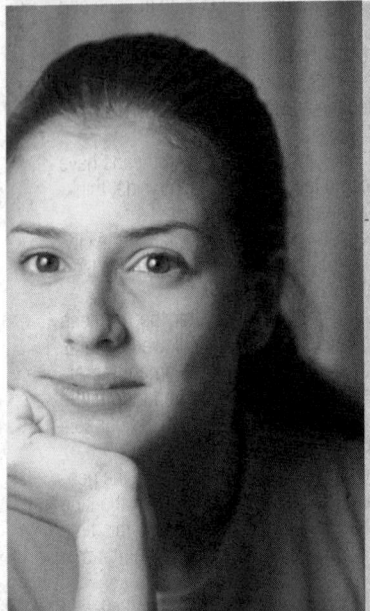

Poor girl. We don't even know her name. Foreigners captured her and took her away from her homeland, Israel. Far away from all her family and friends, she was forced to be a slave for the rich wife of the nation's top soldier, Naaman.

Poor Naaman. Don't you think he'd give anything—fame, fortune, military honors—just to get rid of his leprosy? Absolutely. This disease afflicted the skin, and various symptoms were involved, which could include discoloration, rashes, itching, etc. Sounds horrible.

But why should this slave girl care about her master? Serves him right for attacking her homeland and making her a slave, right? After all, he was the enemy! She could've said, "You can rot away for all I care! Then I wouldn't have to make your food and clean your clothes and keep your wife company while you're out attacking innocent people! I'd take the first camel train home to Israel." But this girl didn't react that way at all. She *did* care—even though she didn't have to.

She took the initiative and told Naaman's wife about the prophet Elisha. The prophet offered something Naaman needed more than anything else—hope.

So why in the world would this little slave girl go out of her way to help her master? Not for money, glory, freedom or even thanks. Her master had a need, and the compassionate girl suggested a solution.

Many times we only want to help someone who seems deserving. But God's door is equally open to everyone. He invites us all in.

This slave girl could have allowed bitterness to stop her from offering help; instead, she chose the high road. You might not do anything bad to the people you consider your opponents; but would you go out of your way to do something good for them?

Dear God, open my heart to the people I know who are in need. Teach me to tear down the walls between us and show them your compassion. Amen.

dear God

To read the next Mirror Images profile, go to page 477.

➤➤ Read more about this Israelite girl in 2 Kings 5:1–6 (page 439).

¹⁰Elisha answered, "Go and say to him, 'You will certainly recover'; but *a* the LORD has revealed to me that he will in fact die." ¹¹He stared at him with a fixed gaze until Hazael felt ashamed. Then the man of God began to weep.

¹²"Why is my lord weeping?" asked Hazael.

"Because I know the harm you will do to the Israelites," he answered. "You will set fire to their fortified places, kill their young men with the sword, dash their little children to the ground, and rip open their pregnant women."

¹³Hazael said, "How could your servant, a mere dog, accomplish such a feat?"

"The LORD has shown me that you will become king of Aram," answered Elisha.

¹⁴Then Hazael left Elisha and returned to his master. When Ben-Hadad asked, "What did Elisha say to you?" Hazael replied, "He told me that you would certainly recover." ¹⁵But the next day he took a thick cloth, soaked it in water and spread it over the king's face, so that he died. Then Hazael succeeded him as king.

Jehoram King of Judah

¹⁶In the fifth year of Joram son of Ahab king of Israel, when Jehoshaphat was king of Judah, Jehoram son of Jehoshaphat began his reign as king of Judah. ¹⁷He was thirty-two years old when he became king, and he reigned in Jerusalem eight years. ¹⁸He walked in the ways of the kings of Israel, as the house of Ahab had done, for he married a daughter of Ahab. He did evil in the eyes of the LORD. ¹⁹Nevertheless, for the sake of his servant David, the LORD was not willing to destroy Judah. He had promised to maintain a lamp for David and his descendants forever.

²⁰In the time of Jehoram, Edom rebelled against Judah and set up its own king. ²¹So Jehoram *b* went to Zair with all his chariots. The Edomites surrounded him and his chariot commanders, but he rose up and broke through by night; his army, however, fled back home. ²²To this day Edom has been in rebellion against Judah. Libnah revolted at the same time.

²³As for the other events of Jehoram's reign, and all he did, are they not written in the book of the annals of the kings of Judah? ²⁴Jehoram rested with his fathers and was buried with them in the City of David. And Ahaziah his son succeeded him as king.

Ahaziah King of Judah

²⁵In the twelfth year of Joram son of Ahab king of Israel, Ahaziah son of Jehoram king of Judah began to reign. ²⁶Ahaziah was twenty-two years old when he became king, and he reigned in Jerusalem one year. His mother's name was Athaliah, a granddaughter of Omri king of Israel. ²⁷He walked in the ways of the house of Ahab and did evil in the eyes of the LORD, as the house of Ahab had done, for he was related by marriage to Ahab's family.

²⁸Ahaziah went with Joram son of Ahab to war against Hazael king of Aram at Ramoth Gilead. The Arameans wounded Joram; ²⁹so King Joram returned to Jezreel to recover from the wounds the Arameans had inflicted on him at Ramoth *c* in his battle with Hazael king of Aram.

Then Ahaziah son of Jehoram king of Judah went down to Jezreel to see Joram son of Ahab, because he had been wounded.

Jehu Anointed King of Israel

9 The prophet Elisha summoned a man from the company of the prophets and said to him, "Tuck your cloak into your belt, take this flask of oil with you and go to Ramoth Gilead. ²When you get there, look for Jehu son of Jehoshaphat, the son of Nimshi. Go to him, get him away from his companions and take him into an inner room. ³Then take the flask and pour the oil on his head and declare, 'This is what the LORD says: I anoint you king over Israel.' Then open the door and run; don't delay!"

⁴So the young man, the prophet, went to Ramoth Gilead. ⁵When he arrived, he found the army officers sitting together. "I have a message for you, commander," he said.

"For which of us?" asked Jehu.

"For you, commander," he replied.

⁶Jehu got up and went into the house. Then the prophet poured the oil on Jehu's head and de-

a 10 The Hebrew may also be read *Go and say, 'You will certainly not recover,' for.*   *b 21* Hebrew *Joram*, a variant of *Jehoram*; also in verses 23 and 24   *c 29* Hebrew *Ramah*, a variant of *Ramoth* clared, "This is what the LORD, the God of Israel, says: 'I anoint you king over the LORD's people Israel. ⁷You are to destroy the house of Ahab your master, and I will avenge the blood of my servants the prophets and the blood of all the LORD's servants shed by Jezebel. ⁸The whole house of Ahab will perish. I will cut off from Ahab every last male in Israel—slave or free. ⁹I will make the house of Ahab like the house of Jeroboam son of Nebat and like the house of Baasha son of Ahijah. ¹⁰As for Jezebel, dogs will devour her on the plot of ground at Jezreel, and no one will bury her.' " Then he opened the door and ran.

¹¹When Jehu went out to his fellow officers, one of them asked him, "Is everything all right? Why did this madman come to you?"

"You know the man and the sort of things he says," Jehu replied.

¹²"That's not true!" they said. "Tell us."

Jehu said, "Here is what he told me: 'This is what the LORD says: I anoint you king over Israel.' "

¹³They hurried and took their cloaks and spread them under him on the bare steps. Then they blew the trumpet and shouted, "Jehu is king!"

Jehu Kills Joram and Ahaziah

¹⁴So Jehu son of Jehoshaphat, the son of Nimshi, conspired against Joram. (Now Joram and all Israel had been defending Ramoth Gilead against Hazael king of Aram, ¹⁵but King Joramᵃ had returned to Jezreel to recover from the wounds the Arameans had inflicted on him in the battle with Hazael king of Aram.) Jehu said, "If this is the way you feel, don't let anyone slip out of the city to go and tell the news in Jezreel." ¹⁶Then he got into his chariot and rode to Jezreel, because Joram was resting there and Ahaziah king of Judah had gone down to see him.

¹⁷When the lookout standing on the tower in Jezreel saw Jehu's troops approaching, he called out, "I see some troops coming."

"Get a horseman," Joram ordered. "Send him to meet them and ask, 'Do you come in peace?' "

¹⁸The horseman rode off to meet Jehu and said, "This is what the king says: 'Do you come in peace?' "

"What do you have to do with peace?" Jehu replied. "Fall in behind me."

The lookout reported, "The messenger has reached them, but he isn't coming back."

¹⁹So the king sent out a second horseman. When he came to them he said, "This is what the king says: 'Do you come in peace?' "

Jehu replied, "What do you have to do with peace? Fall in behind me."

²⁰The lookout reported, "He has reached them, but he isn't coming back either. The driving is like that of Jehu son of Nimshi—he drives like a madman."

²¹"Hitch up my chariot," Joram ordered. And when it was hitched up, Joram king of Israel and Ahaziah king of Judah rode out, each in his own chariot, to meet Jehu. They met him at the plot of ground that had belonged to Naboth the Jezreelite. ²²When Joram saw Jehu he asked, "Have you come in peace, Jehu?"

"How can there be peace," Jehu replied, "as long as all the idolatry and witchcraft of your mother Jezebel abound?"

²³Joram turned about and fled, calling out to Ahaziah, "Treachery, Ahaziah!"

²⁴Then Jehu drew his bow and shot Joram between the shoulders. The arrow pierced his heart and he slumped down in his chariot. ²⁵Jehu said to Bidkar, his chariot officer, "Pick him up and throw him on the field that belonged to Naboth the Jezreelite. Remember how you and I were riding together in chariots behind Ahab his father when the LORD made this prophecy about him: ²⁶'Yesterday I saw the blood of Naboth and the blood of his sons, declares the LORD, and I will surely make you pay for it on this plot of ground, declares the LORD.'ᵇ Now then, pick him up and throw him on that plot, in accordance with the word of the LORD."

²⁷When Ahaziah king of Judah saw what had happened, he fled up the road to Beth Haggan.ᶜ Jehu chased him, shouting, "Kill him too!" They wounded him in his chariot on the way up to Gur near Ibleam, but he escaped to Megiddo and died there. ²⁸His servants took him by chariot to Je-

ᵃ 15 Hebrew Jehoram, a variant of Joram; also in verses 17 and 21-24   ᵇ 26 See 1 Kings 21:19.   ᶜ 27 Or fled by way of the garden house rusalem and buried him with his fathers in his tomb in the City of David. [29](In the eleventh year of Joram son of Ahab, Ahaziah had become king of Judah.)

Jezebel Killed

[30]Then Jehu went to Jezreel. When Jezebel heard about it, she painted her eyes, arranged her hair and looked out of a window. [31]As Jehu entered the gate, she asked, "Have you come in peace, Zimri, you murderer of your master?" [a]

[32]He looked up at the window and called out, "Who is on my side? Who?" Two or three eunuchs looked down at him. [33]"Throw her down!" Jehu said. So they threw her down, and some of her blood spattered the wall and the horses as they trampled her underfoot.

[34]Jehu went in and ate and drank. "Take care of that cursed woman," he said, "and bury her, for she was a king's daughter." [35]But when they went out to bury her, they found nothing except her skull, her feet and her hands. [36]They went back and told Jehu, who said, "This is the word of the Lord that he spoke through his servant Elijah the Tishbite: On the plot of ground at Jezreel dogs will devour Jezebel's flesh. [b] [37]Jezebel's body will be like refuse on the ground in the plot at Jezreel, so that no one will be able to say, 'This is Jezebel.' "

Ahab's Family Killed

10 Now there were in Samaria seventy sons of the house of Ahab. So Jehu wrote letters and sent them to Samaria: to the officials of Jezreel, [c] to the elders and to the guardians of Ahab's children. He said, [2]"As soon as this letter reaches you, since your master's sons are with you and you have chariots and horses, a fortified city and weapons, [3]choose the best and most worthy of your master's sons and set him on his father's throne. Then fight for your master's house."

[4]But they were terrified and said, "If two kings could not resist him, how can we?"

[5]So the palace administrator, the city governor, the elders and the guardians sent this message to Jehu: "We are your servants and we will do anything you say. We will not appoint anyone as king; you do whatever you think best."

[6]Then Jehu wrote them a second letter, saying, "If you are on my side and will obey me, take the heads of your master's sons and come to me in Jezreel by this time tomorrow."

Now the royal princes, seventy of them, were with the leading men of the city, who were rearing them. [7]When the letter arrived, these men took the princes and slaughtered all seventy of them. They put their heads in baskets and sent them to Jehu in Jezreel. [8]When the messenger arrived, he told Jehu, "They have brought the heads of the princes."

Then Jehu ordered, "Put them in two piles at the entrance of the city gate until morning."

[9]The next morning Jehu went out. He stood before all the people and said, "You are innocent. It was I who conspired against my master and killed him, but who killed all these? [10]Know then, that not a word the Lord has spoken against the house of Ahab will fail. The Lord has done what he promised through his servant Elijah." [11]So Jehu killed everyone in Jezreel who remained of the house of Ahab, as well as all his chief men, his close friends and his priests, leaving him no survivor.

[12]Jehu then set out and went toward Samaria. At Beth Eked of the Shepherds, [13]he met some relatives of Ahaziah king of Judah and asked, "Who are you?"

They said, "We are relatives of Ahaziah, and we have come down to greet the families of the king and of the queen mother."

[14]"Take them alive!" he ordered. So they took them alive and slaughtered them by the well of Beth Eked—forty-two men. He left no survivor.

[15]After he left there, he came upon Jehonadab son of Recab, who was on his way to meet him. Jehu greeted him and said, "Are you in accord with me, as I am with you?"

"I am," Jehonadab answered.

"If so," said Jehu, "give me your hand." So he did, and Jehu helped him up into the chariot. [16]Jehu said, "Come with me and see my zeal for the Lord." Then he had him ride along in his chariot.

[17]When Jehu came to Samaria, he killed all who were left there of Ahab's family; he destroyed them, according to the word of the Lord spoken to Elijah.

a 31 Or *"Did Zimri have peace, who murdered his master?"*   *b 36* See 1 Kings 21:23.   *c 1* Hebrew; some Septuagint manuscripts and Vulgate *of the city*

Ministers of Baal Killed

[18]Then Jehu brought all the people together and said to them, "Ahab served Baal a little; Jehu will serve him much. [19]Now summon all the prophets of Baal, all his ministers and all his priests. See that no one is missing, because I am going to hold a great sacrifice for Baal. Anyone who fails to come will no longer live." But Jehu was acting deceptively in order to destroy the ministers of Baal.

[20]Jehu said, "Call an assembly in honor of Baal." So they proclaimed it. [21]Then he sent word throughout Israel, and all the ministers of Baal came; not one stayed away. They crowded into the temple of Baal until it was full from one end to the other. [22]And Jehu said to the keeper of the wardrobe, "Bring robes for all the ministers of Baal." So he brought out robes for them.

[23]Then Jehu and Jehonadab son of Recab went into the temple of Baal. Jehu said to the ministers of Baal, "Look around and see that no servants of the LORD are here with you—only ministers of Baal." [24]So they went in to make sacrifices and burnt offerings. Now Jehu had posted eighty men outside with this warning: "If one of you lets any of the men I am placing in your hands escape, it will be your life for his life."

[25]As soon as Jehu had finished making the burnt offering, he ordered the guards and officers: "Go in and kill them; let no one escape." So they cut them down with the sword. The guards and officers threw the bodies out and then entered the inner shrine of the temple of Baal. [26]They brought the sacred stone out of the temple of Baal and burned it. [27]They demolished the sacred stone of Baal and tore down the temple of Baal, and people have used it for a latrine to this day.

[28]So Jehu destroyed Baal worship in Israel. [29]However, he did not turn away from the sins of Jeroboam son of Nebat, which he had caused Israel to commit—the worship of the golden calves at Bethel and Dan.

[30]The LORD said to Jehu, "Because you have done well in accomplishing what is right in my eyes and have done to the house of Ahab all I had in mind to do, your descendants will sit on the throne of Israel to the fourth generation." [31]Yet Jehu was not careful to keep the law of the LORD, the God of Israel, with all his heart. He did not turn away from the sins of Jeroboam, which he had caused Israel to commit.

[32]In those days the LORD began to reduce the size of Israel. Hazael overpowered the Israelites throughout their territory [33]east of the Jordan in all the land of Gilead (the region of Gad, Reuben and Manasseh), from Aroer by the Arnon Gorge through Gilead to Bashan.

[34]As for the other events of Jehu's reign, all he did, and all his achievements, are they not written in the book of the annals of the kings of Israel?

[35]Jehu rested with his fathers and was buried in Samaria. And Jehoahaz his son succeeded him as king. [36]The time that Jehu reigned over Israel in Samaria was twenty-eight years.

Athaliah and Joash

11 When Athaliah the mother of Ahaziah saw that her son was dead, she proceeded to destroy the whole royal family. [2]But Jehosheba, the daughter of King Jehoram[a] and sister of Ahaziah, took Joash son of Ahaziah and stole him away from among the royal princes, who were about to be murdered. She put him and his nurse in a bedroom to hide him from Athaliah; so he was not killed. [3]He remained hidden with his nurse at the temple of the LORD for six years while Athaliah ruled the land.

[4]In the seventh year Jehoiada sent for the commanders of units of a hundred, the Carites and the guards and had them brought to him at the temple of the LORD. He made a covenant with them and put them under oath at the temple of the LORD. Then he showed them the king's son. [5]He commanded them, saying, "This is what you are to do: You who are in the three companies that are going on duty on the Sabbath—a third of you guarding the royal palace, [6]a third at the Sur Gate, and a third at the gate behind the guard, who take turns guarding the temple— [7]and you

truth or dare

Athaliah did awful things to get power. But her plan backfired (see 11:12–16). If you're willing to do anything to get on top—you won't be there long.

11:1

---

a 2 Hebrew Joram, a variant of Jehoram

who are in the other two companies that normally go off Sabbath duty are all to guard the temple for the king. [8]Station yourselves around the king, each man with his weapon in his hand. Anyone who approaches your ranks[a] must be put to death. Stay close to the king wherever he goes."

[9]The commanders of units of a hundred did just as Jehoiada the priest ordered. Each one took his men—those who were going on duty on the Sabbath and those who were going off duty—and came to Jehoiada the priest. [10]Then he gave the commanders the spears and shields that had belonged to King David and that were in the temple of the LORD. [11]The guards, each with his weapon in his hand, stationed themselves around the king—near the altar and the temple, from the south side to the north side of the temple.

[12]Jehoiada brought out the king's son and put the crown on him; he presented him with a copy of the covenant and proclaimed him king. They anointed him, and the people clapped their hands and shouted, "Long live the king!"

[13]When Athaliah heard the noise made by the guards and the people, she went to the people at the temple of the LORD. [14]She looked and there was the king, standing by the pillar, as the custom was. The officers and the trumpeters were beside the king, and all the people of the land were rejoicing and blowing trumpets. Then Athaliah tore her robes and called out, "Treason! Treason!"

[15]Jehoiada the priest ordered the commanders of units of a hundred, who were in charge of the troops: "Bring her out between the ranks[b] and put to the sword anyone who follows her." For the priest had said, "She must not be put to death in the temple of the LORD." [16]So they seized her as she reached the place where the horses enter the palace grounds, and there she was put to death.

[17]Jehoiada then made a covenant between the LORD and the king and people that they would be the LORD's people. He also made a covenant between the king and the people. [18]All the people of the land went to the temple of Baal and tore it down. They smashed the altars and idols to pieces and killed Mattan the priest of Baal in front of the altars.

Then Jehoiada the priest posted guards at the temple of the LORD. [19]He took with him the commanders of hundreds, the Carites, the guards and all the people of the land, and together they brought the king down from the temple of the LORD and went into the palace, entering by way of the gate of the guards. The king then took his place on the royal throne, [20]and all the people of the land rejoiced. And the city was quiet, because Athaliah had been slain with the sword at the palace.

[21]Joash[c] was seven years old when he began to reign.

Joash Repairs the Temple

12 In the seventh year of Jehu, Joash[d] became king, and he reigned in Jerusalem forty years. His mother's name was Zibiah; she was from Beersheba. [2]Joash did what was right in the eyes of the LORD all the years Jehoiada the priest instructed him. [3]The high places, however, were not removed; the people continued to offer sacrifices and burn incense there.

[4]Joash said to the priests, "Collect all the money that is brought as sacred offerings to the temple of the LORD—the money collected in the census, the money received from personal vows and the money brought voluntarily to the temple. [5]Let every priest receive the money from one of the treasurers, and let it be used to repair whatever damage is found in the temple."

[6]But by the twenty-third year of King Joash the priests still had not repaired the temple. [7]Therefore King Joash summoned Jehoiada the priest and the other priests and asked them, "Why aren't you repairing the damage done to the temple? Take no more money from your treasurers, but hand it over for repairing the temple." [8]The priests agreed that they would not collect any more money from the people and that they would not repair the temple themselves.

[9]Jehoiada the priest took a chest and bored a hole in its lid. He placed it beside the altar, on

truth **or dare**

Tithing not only helps you focus on God (rather than money), but it also keeps your church building up and running. Giving just makes cents! (Okay, okay, it's corny, we know.)

12:4-5

---

a 8 Or *approaches the precincts*   b 15 Or *out from the precincts*   c 21 Hebrew *Jehoash*, a variant of *Joash*
d 1 Hebrew *Jehoash*, a variant of *Joash*; also in verses 2, 4, 6, 7 and 18

the right side as one enters the temple of the LORD. The priests who guarded the entrance put into the chest all the money that was brought to the temple of the LORD. ¹⁰Whenever they saw that there was a large amount of money in the chest, the royal secretary and the high priest came, counted the money that had been brought into the temple of the LORD and put it into bags. ¹¹When the amount had been determined, they gave the money to the men appointed to supervise the work on the temple. With it they paid those who worked on the temple of the LORD—the carpenters and builders, ¹²the masons and stonecutters. They purchased timber and dressed stone for the repair of the temple of the LORD, and met all the other expenses of restoring the temple.

¹³The money brought into the temple was not spent for making silver basins, wick trimmers, sprinkling bowls, trumpets or any other articles of gold or silver for the temple of the LORD; ¹⁴it was paid to the workmen, who used it to repair the temple. ¹⁵They did not require an accounting from those to whom they gave the money to pay the workers, because they acted with complete honesty. ¹⁶The money from the guilt offerings and sin offerings was not brought into the temple of the LORD; it belonged to the priests.

¹⁷About this time Hazael king of Aram went up and attacked Gath and captured it. Then he turned to attack Jerusalem. ¹⁸But Joash king of Judah took all the sacred objects dedicated by his fathers—Jehoshaphat, Jehoram and Ahaziah, the kings of Judah—and the gifts he himself had dedicated and all the gold found in the treasuries of the temple of the LORD and of the royal palace, and he sent them to Hazael king of Aram, who then withdrew from Jerusalem.

¹⁹As for the other events of the reign of Joash, and all he did, are they not written in the book of the annals of the kings of Judah? ²⁰His officials conspired against him and assassinated him at Beth Millo, on the road down to Silla. ²¹The officials who murdered him were Jozabad son of Shimeath and Jehozabad son of Shomer. He died and was buried with his fathers in the City of David. And Amaziah his son succeeded him as king.

Jehoahaz King of Israel

13 In the twenty-third year of Joash son of Ahaziah king of Judah, Jehoahaz son of Jehu became king of Israel in Samaria, and he reigned seventeen years. ²He did evil in the eyes of the LORD by following the sins of Jeroboam son of Nebat, which he had caused Israel to commit, and he did not turn away from them. ³So the LORD's anger burned against Israel, and for a long time he kept them under the power of Hazael king of Aram and Ben-Hadad his son.

⁴Then Jehoahaz sought the LORD's favor, and the LORD listened to him, for he saw how severely the king of Aram was oppressing Israel. ⁵The LORD provided a deliverer for Israel, and they escaped from the power of Aram. So the Israelites lived in their own homes as they had before. ⁶But they did not turn away from the sins of the house of Jeroboam, which he had caused Israel to commit; they continued in them. Also, the Asherah pole ᵃ remained standing in Samaria.

⁷Nothing had been left of the army of Jehoahaz except fifty horsemen, ten chariots and ten thousand foot soldiers, for the king of Aram had destroyed the rest and made them like the dust at threshing time.

genuine — integrity » 12:15

If someone came up with a one-word description of you, what do you think she'd say? What would you *want* her to say? That you're . . . clever? Cool? Kind? Glamorous? Honest? You can build a reputation by consistent behavior. When the people of Israel gave money for the temple to be repaired, the supervisors of the workers weren't even required to show their receipts for all their supplies. Why? Because they were known for their honesty. They showed it in all that they did. Do you?

ᵃ 6 That is, a symbol of the goddess Asherah; here and elsewhere in 2 Kings

[8]As for the other events of the reign of Jehoahaz, all he did and his achievements, are they not written in the book of the annals of the kings of Israel? [9]Jehoahaz rested with his fathers and was buried in Samaria. And Jehoash[a] his son succeeded him as king.

Jehoash King of Israel

[10]In the thirty-seventh year of Joash king of Judah, Jehoash son of Jehoahaz became king of Israel in Samaria, and he reigned sixteen years. [11]He did evil in the eyes of the LORD and did not turn away from any of the sins of Jeroboam son of Nebat, which he had caused Israel to commit; he continued in them.

[12]As for the other events of the reign of Jehoash, all he did and his achievements, including his war against Amaziah king of Judah, are they not written in the book of the annals of the kings of Israel? [13]Jehoash rested with his fathers, and Jeroboam succeeded him on the throne. Jehoash was buried in Samaria with the kings of Israel.

[14]Now Elisha was suffering from the illness from which he died. Jehoash king of Israel went down to see him and wept over him. "My father! My father!" he cried. "The chariots and horsemen of Israel!"

[15]Elisha said, "Get a bow and some arrows," and he did so. [16]"Take the bow in your hands," he said to the king of Israel. When he had taken it, Elisha put his hands on the king's hands.

[17]"Open the east window," he said, and he opened it. "Shoot!" Elisha said, and he shot. "The LORD's arrow of victory, the arrow of victory over Aram!" Elisha declared. "You will completely destroy the Arameans at Aphek."

[18]Then he said, "Take the arrows," and the king took them. Elisha told him, "Strike the ground." He struck it three times and stopped. [19]The man of God was angry with him and said, "You should have struck the ground five or six times; then you would have defeated Aram and completely destroyed it. But now you will defeat it only three times."

[20]Elisha died and was buried.

truth or dare

There are different attitudes toward obedience—from enthusiastic to anemic. Just doing what God asks isn't enough. Get into it!

13:15–19

Now Moabite raiders used to enter the country every spring. [21]Once while some Israelites were burying a man, suddenly they saw a band of raiders; so they threw the man's body into Elisha's tomb. When the body touched Elisha's bones, the man came to life and stood up on his feet.

[22]Hazael king of Aram oppressed Israel throughout the reign of Jehoahaz. [23]But the LORD was gracious to them and had compassion and showed concern for them because of his covenant with Abraham, Isaac and Jacob. To this day he has been unwilling to destroy them or banish them from his presence.

[24]Hazael king of Aram died, and Ben-Hadad his son succeeded him as king. [25]Then Jehoash son of Jehoahaz recaptured from Ben-Hadad son of Hazael the towns he had taken in battle from his father Jehoahaz. Three times Jehoash defeated him, and so he recovered the Israelite towns.

Amaziah King of Judah

14 In the second year of Jehoash[a] son of Jehoahaz king of Israel, Amaziah son of Joash king of Judah began to reign. [2]He was twenty-five years old when he became king, and he reigned in Jerusalem twenty-nine years. His mother's name was Jehoaddin; she was from Jerusalem. [3]He did what was right in the eyes of the LORD, but not as his father David had done. In everything he followed the example of his father Joash. [4]The high places, however, were not removed; the people continued to offer sacrifices and burn incense there.

[5]After the kingdom was firmly in his grasp, he executed the officials who had murdered his father the king. [6]Yet he did not put the sons of the assassins to death, in accordance with what is

a 9 Hebrew Joash, a variant of Jehoash; also in verses 12-14 and 25 written in the Book of the Law of Moses where the LORD commanded: "Fathers shall not be put to death for their children, nor children put to death for their fathers; each is to die for his own sins." [b]

[7]He was the one who defeated ten thousand Edomites in the Valley of Salt and captured Sela in battle, calling it Joktheel, the name it has to this day.

[8]Then Amaziah sent messengers to Jehoash son of Jehoahaz, the son of Jehu, king of Israel, with the challenge: "Come, meet me face to face."

[9]But Jehoash king of Israel replied to Amaziah king of Judah: "A thistle in Lebanon sent a message to a cedar in Lebanon, 'Give your daughter to my son in marriage.' Then a wild beast in Lebanon came along and trampled the thistle underfoot. [10]You have indeed defeated Edom and now you are arrogant. Glory in your victory, but stay at home! Why ask for trouble and cause your own downfall and that of Judah also?"

[11]Amaziah, however, would not listen, so Jehoash king of Israel attacked. He and Amaziah king of Judah faced each other at Beth Shemesh in Judah. [12]Judah was routed by Israel, and every man fled to his home. [13]Jehoash king of Israel captured Amaziah king of Judah, the son of Joash, the son of Ahaziah, at Beth Shemesh. Then Jehoash went to Jerusalem and broke down the wall of Jerusalem from the Ephraim Gate to the Corner Gate—a section about six hundred feet long. [c] [14]He took all the gold and silver and all the articles found in the temple of the LORD and in the treasuries of the royal palace. He also took hostages and returned to Samaria.

[15]As for the other events of the reign of Jehoash, what he did and his achievements, including his war against Amaziah king of Judah, are they not written in the book of the annals of the kings of Israel? [16]Jehoash rested with his fathers and was buried in Samaria with the kings of Israel. And Jeroboam his son succeeded him as king.

[17]Amaziah son of Joash king of Judah lived for fifteen years after the death of Jehoash son of Jehoahaz king of Israel. [18]As for the other events of Amaziah's reign, are they not written in the book of the annals of the kings of Judah?

[19]They conspired against him in Jerusalem, and he fled to Lachish, but they sent men after him to Lachish and killed him there. [20]He was brought back by horse and was buried in Jerusalem with his fathers, in the City of David.

[21]Then all the people of Judah took Azariah, [d] who was sixteen years old, and made him king in place of his father Amaziah. [22]He was the one who rebuilt Elath and restored it to Judah after Amaziah rested with his fathers.

love notes

13:23

Dear loved one,

There may be times when you will fail me. There may be times when I am disappointed with your choices or actions. But I will never turn my back on you or exclude you from my presence.

—Everlasting Father

How does knowing that God will always love you give you a sense of security?

_____
_____
_____
_____
_____
_____
_____
_____
_____
_____
_____
_____
_____
_____

---

a 1 Hebrew Joash, a variant of Jehoash; also in verses 13, 23 and 27   b 6 Deut. 24:16   c 13 Hebrew four hundred cubits (about 180 meters)   d 21 Also called Uzziah

Jeroboam II King of Israel

[23]In the fifteenth year of Amaziah son of Joash king of Judah, Jeroboam son of Jehoash king of Israel became king in Samaria, and he reigned forty-one years. [24]He did evil in the eyes of the LORD and did not turn away from any of the sins of Jeroboam son of Nebat, which he had caused Israel to commit. [25]He was the one who restored the boundaries of Israel from Lebo[a] Hamath to the Sea of the Arabah,[b] in accordance with the word of the LORD, the God of Israel, spoken through his servant Jonah son of Amittai, the prophet from Gath Hepher.

[26]The LORD had seen how bitterly everyone in Israel, whether slave or free, was suffering; there was no one to help them. [27]And since the LORD had not said he would blot out the name of Israel from under heaven, he saved them by the hand of Jeroboam son of Jehoash.

[28]As for the other events of Jeroboam's reign, all he did, and his military achievements, including how he recovered for Israel both Damascus and Hamath, which had belonged to Yaudi,[c] are they not written in the book of the annals of the kings of Israel? [29]Jeroboam rested with his fathers, the kings of Israel. And Zechariah his son succeeded him as king.

Azariah King of Judah

15 In the twenty-seventh year of Jeroboam king of Israel, Azariah son of Amaziah king of Judah began to reign. [2]He was sixteen years old when he became king, and he reigned in Jerusalem fifty-two years. His mother's name was Jecoliah; she was from Jerusalem. [3]He did what was right in the eyes of the LORD, just as his father Amaziah had done. [4]The high places, however, were not removed; the people continued to offer sacrifices and burn incense there.

[5]The LORD afflicted the king with leprosy[d] until the day he died, and he lived in a separate house.[e] Jotham the king's son had charge of the palace and governed the people of the land.

[6]As for the other events of Azariah's reign, and all he did, are they not written in the book of the annals of the kings of Judah? [7]Azariah rested with his fathers and was buried near them in the City of David. And Jotham his son succeeded him as king.

Zechariah King of Israel

[8]In the thirty-eighth year of Azariah king of Judah, Zechariah son of Jeroboam became king of Israel in Samaria, and he reigned six months. [9]He did evil in the eyes of the LORD, as his fathers had done. He did not turn away from the sins of Jeroboam son of Nebat, which he had caused Israel to commit.

[10]Shallum son of Jabesh conspired against Zechariah. He attacked him in front of the people,[f] assassinated him and succeeded him as king. [11]The other events of Zechariah's reign are written in the book of the annals of the kings of Israel. [12]So the word of the LORD spoken to Jehu was fulfilled: "Your descendants will sit on the throne of Israel to the fourth generation."[g]

Shallum King of Israel

[13]Shallum son of Jabesh became king in the thirty-ninth year of Uzziah king of Judah, and he reigned in Samaria one month. [14]Then Menahem son of Gadi went from Tir-

genuine devotion » 15:4

Ever half-do something? (You wouldn't, would you? Wholehearted is your middle name, right?) Sometimes a half-hearted effort isn't so noticeable. It's like dust swept under a rug—you wouldn't know it was there. But sometimes a half-hearted effort is screamingly obvious. Although King Azariah was obedient to the Lord, he didn't remove the "high places" where the Israelites should not have been worshiping. That's one sign of a half-hearted effort. He also let pride get the better of him. Not good. He wound up with leprosy for the rest of his life (see 2 Chronicles 26:16–21). Sometimes a half-hearted effort can lead to a whole disaster.

---

[a] 25 Or *from the entrance to*   [b] 25 That is, the Dead Sea   [c] 28 Or *Judah*   [d] 5 The Hebrew word was used for various diseases affecting the skin—not necessarily leprosy.   [e] 5 Or *in a house where he was relieved of responsibility*   [f] 10 Hebrew; some Septuagint manuscripts *in Ibleam*   [g] 12 2 Kings 10:30

zah up to Samaria. He attacked Shallum son of Jabesh in Samaria, assassinated him and succeeded him as king.

¹⁵The other events of Shallum's reign, and the conspiracy he led, are written in the book of the annals of the kings of Israel.

¹⁶At that time Menahem, starting out from Tirzah, attacked Tiphsah and everyone in the city and its vicinity, because they refused to open their gates. He sacked Tiphsah and ripped open all the pregnant women.

Menahem King of Israel

¹⁷In the thirty-ninth year of Azariah king of Judah, Menahem son of Gadi became king of Israel, and he reigned in Samaria ten years. ¹⁸He did evil in the eyes of the LORD. During his entire reign he did not turn away from the sins of Jeroboam son of Nebat, which he had caused Israel to commit.

¹⁹Then Pul*ᵃ* king of Assyria invaded the land, and Menahem gave him a thousand talents*ᵇ* of silver to gain his support and strengthen his own hold on the kingdom. ²⁰Menahem exacted this money from Israel. Every wealthy man had to contribute fifty shekels*ᶜ* of silver to be given to the king of Assyria. So the king of Assyria withdrew and stayed in the land no longer.

²¹As for the other events of Menahem's reign, and all he did, are they not written in the book of the annals of the kings of Israel? ²²Menahem rested with his fathers. And Pekahiah his son succeeded him as king.

Pekahiah King of Israel

²³In the fiftieth year of Azariah king of Judah, Pekahiah son of Menahem became king of Israel in Samaria, and he reigned two years. ²⁴Pekahiah did evil in the eyes of the LORD. He did not turn away from the sins of Jeroboam son of Nebat, which he had caused Israel to commit. ²⁵One of his chief officers, Pekah son of Remaliah, conspired against him. Taking fifty men of Gilead with him, he assassinated Pekahiah, along with Argob and Arieh, in the citadel of the royal palace at Samaria. So Pekah killed Pekahiah and succeeded him as king.

²⁶The other events of Pekahiah's reign, and all he did, are written in the book of the annals of the kings of Israel.

Pekah King of Israel

²⁷In the fifty-second year of Azariah king of Judah, Pekah son of Remaliah became king of Israel in Samaria, and he reigned twenty years. ²⁸He did evil in the eyes of the LORD. He did not turn away from the sins of Jeroboam son of Nebat, which he had caused Israel to commit.

²⁹In the time of Pekah king of Israel, Tiglath-Pileser king of Assyria came and took Ijon, Abel Beth Maacah, Janoah, Kedesh and Hazor. He took Gilead and Galilee, including all the land of Naphtali, and deported the people to Assyria. ³⁰Then Hoshea son of Elah conspired against Pekah son of Remaliah. He attacked and assassinated him, and then succeeded him as king in the twentieth year of Jotham son of Uzziah.

³¹As for the other events of Pekah's reign, and all he did, are they not written in the book of the annals of the kings of Israel?

Jotham King of Judah

³²In the second year of Pekah son of Remaliah king of Israel, Jotham son of Uzziah king of Judah began to reign. ³³He was twenty-five years old when he became king, and he reigned in Jerusalem sixteen years. His mother's name was Jerusha daughter of Zadok. ³⁴He did what was right in the eyes of the LORD, just as his father Uzziah had done. ³⁵The high places, however, were not removed; the people continued to offer sacrifices and burn incense there. Jotham rebuilt the Upper Gate of the temple of the LORD.

³⁶As for the other events of Jotham's reign, and what he did, are they not written in the book of the annals of the kings of Judah? ³⁷(In those days the LORD began to send Rezin king of Aram and Pekah son of Remaliah against Judah.) ³⁸Jotham rested with his fathers and was buried with them in the City of David, the city of his father. And Ahaz his son succeeded him as king.

ᵃ 19 Also called *Tiglath-Pileser*   *ᵇ 19* That is, about 37 tons (about 34 metric tons)   *ᶜ 20* That is, about 1 1/4 pounds (about 0.6 kilogram)

Ahaz King of Judah

16 In the seventeenth year of Pekah son of Remaliah, Ahaz son of Jotham king of Judah began to reign. ²Ahaz was twenty years old when he became king, and he reigned in Jerusalem sixteen years. Unlike David his father, he did not do what was right in the eyes of the LORD his God. ³He walked in the ways of the kings of Israel and even sacrificed his son in *a* the fire, following the detestable ways of the nations the LORD had driven out before the Israelites. ⁴He offered sacrifices and burned incense at the high places, on the hilltops and under every spreading tree.

⁵Then Rezin king of Aram and Pekah son of Remaliah king of Israel marched up to fight against Jerusalem and besieged Ahaz, but they could not overpower him. ⁶At that time, Rezin king of Aram recovered Elath for Aram by driving out the men of Judah. Edomites then moved into Elath and have lived there to this day.

⁷Ahaz sent messengers to say to Tiglath-Pileser king of Assyria, "I am your servant and vassal. Come up and save me out of the hand of the king of Aram and of the king of Israel, who are attacking me." ⁸And Ahaz took the silver and gold found in the temple of the LORD and in the treasuries of the royal palace and sent it as a gift to the king of Assyria. ⁹The king of Assyria complied by attacking Damascus and capturing it. He deported its inhabitants to Kir and put Rezin to death.

¹⁰Then King Ahaz went to Damascus to meet Tiglath-Pileser king of Assyria. He saw an altar in Damascus and sent to Uriah the priest a sketch of the altar, with detailed plans for its construction. ¹¹So Uriah the priest built an altar in accordance with all the plans that King Ahaz had sent from Damascus and finished it before King Ahaz returned. ¹²When the king came back from Damascus and saw the altar, he approached it and presented offerings *b* on it. ¹³He offered up his burnt offering and grain offering, poured out his drink offering, and sprinkled the blood of his fellowship offerings *c* on the altar. ¹⁴The bronze altar that stood before the LORD he brought from the front of the temple—from between the new altar and the temple of the LORD—and put it on the north side of the new altar.

¹⁵King Ahaz then gave these orders to Uriah the priest: "On the large new altar, offer the morning burnt offering and the evening grain offering, the king's burnt offering and his grain offering, and the burnt offering of all the people of the land, and their grain offering and their drink offering. Sprinkle on the altar all the blood of the burnt offerings and sacrifices. But I will use the bronze altar for seeking guidance." ¹⁶And Uriah the priest did just as King Ahaz had ordered.

¹⁷King Ahaz took away the side panels and removed the basins from the movable stands. He removed the Sea from the bronze bulls that supported it and set it on a stone base. ¹⁸He took away the Sabbath canopy *d* that had been built at the temple and removed the royal entryway outside the temple of the LORD, in deference to the king of Assyria.

¹⁹As for the other events of the reign of Ahaz, and what he did, are they not written in the book of the annals of the kings of Judah? ²⁰Ahaz rested with his fathers and was buried with them in the City of David. And Hezekiah his son succeeded him as king.

Hoshea Last King of Israel

17 In the twelfth year of Ahaz king of Judah, Hoshea son of Elah became king of Israel in Samaria, and he reigned nine years. ²He did evil in the eyes of the LORD, but not like the kings of Israel who preceded him.

³Shalmaneser king of Assyria came up to attack Hoshea, who had been Shalmaneser's vassal and had paid him tribute. ⁴But the king of Assyria discovered that Hoshea was a traitor, for he had sent envoys to So *e* king of Egypt, and he no longer paid tribute to the king of Assyria, as he had done year by year. Therefore Shalmaneser seized him and put him in prison. ⁵The king of Assyria invaded the entire land, marched against Samaria and laid siege to it for three years. ⁶In the ninth year of Hoshea, the king of Assyria captured Samaria and deported the Israelites to Assyria. He settled them in Halah, in Gozan on the Habor River and in the towns of the Medes.

Israel Exiled Because of Sin

⁷All this took place because the Israelites had sinned against the LORD their God, who had brought them up out of Egypt from under the power of Pharaoh king of Egypt. They worshiped oth-

---

a 3 Or *even made his son pass through*　　*b 12* Or *and went up*　　*c 13* Traditionally *peace offerings*　　*d 18* Or *the dais of his throne* (see Septuagint)　　*e 4* Or *to Sais, to the; So* is possibly an abbreviation for *Osorkon.*

Scared to Go Home

focus — Profile: **Denise**

What's a girl to do when she can't go home—and her best friend's not home either? I guess I could go to a movie. But I'd just sit there all alone, and I'm so sick of being alone. So sick of . . . everything.

Last week, my dad yelled at me for burning his grilled cheese sandwich. I can still hear him now. "Denise, I always knew you were good for nothing!" Then he slapped me right across the face. I had an ugly mark I tried to cover up with concealer, but everyone could tell. And the burn I got from bumping into the frying pan made a bright red stripe across my arm.

The weird thing is that later Dad apologized, and it seemed like he was genuinely sorry. He even said he loved me and he'd never do it again. But just yesterday I came home and my mom had a black eye. She said she slipped while she was planting geraniums in the front yard. I knew better, though. We both did.

What really worries me is that my six-year-old brother might tick Dad off someday. If Dad ever laid a finger on Richy, I'd really lose it. But what could I do anyway? Dad's too strong, and besides, no one wants to believe he would hurt us like this. I know he doesn't really want to. It's just like something inside him snaps. It's scary.

physical abuse in focus

For Denise and millions of others who are physically abused, life seems out of control. And Denise may not find the help she needs—because she's frightened, embarrassed or simply doesn't know where to turn.

Here are a few things to keep in mind:
- » Physical abuse is *never* okay with God. Your heavenly Father has wonderful plans for you, and he wants you to be safe from harm (see Jeremiah 29:11, page 1041).
- » The problem won't likely just "go away." Admit that your abuser needs help. It's not *your* fault.
- » Get help now, not later. Talk to your school counselor or another adult immediately; and if you're in real danger, call 911.

For more on this topic, see the index on page 1656.

er gods [8]and followed the practices of the nations the Lord had driven out before them, as well as the practices that the kings of Israel had introduced. [9]The Israelites secretly did things against the Lord their God that were not right. From watchtower to fortified city they built themselves high places in all their towns. [10]They set up sacred stones and Asherah poles on every high hill and under every spreading tree. [11]At every high place they burned incense, as the nations whom the Lord had driven out before them had done. They did wicked things that provoked the Lord to anger. [12]They worshiped idols, though the Lord had said, "You shall not do this." [a] [13]The Lord warned Israel and Judah through all his prophets and seers: "Turn from your evil ways. Observe my commands and

a 12 Exodus 20:4,5

decrees, in accordance with the entire Law that I commanded your fathers to obey and that I delivered to you through my servants the prophets."

¹⁴But they would not listen and were as stiff-necked as their fathers, who did not trust in the LORD their God. ¹⁵They rejected his decrees and the covenant he had made with their fathers and the warnings he had given them. They followed worthless idols and themselves became worthless. They imitated the nations around them although the LORD had ordered them, "Do not do as they do," and they did the things the LORD had forbidden them to do.

¹⁶They forsook all the commands of the LORD their God and made for themselves two idols cast in the shape of calves, and an Asherah pole. They bowed down to all the starry hosts, and they worshiped Baal. ¹⁷They sacrificed their sons and daughters in[a] the fire. They practiced divination and sorcery and sold themselves to do evil in the eyes of the LORD, provoking him to anger.

¹⁸So the LORD was very angry with Israel and removed them from his presence. Only the tribe of Judah was left, ¹⁹and even Judah did not keep the commands of the LORD their God. They followed the practices Israel had introduced. ²⁰Therefore the LORD rejected all the people of Israel; he afflicted them and gave them into the hands of plunderers, until he thrust them from his presence.

²¹When he tore Israel away from the house of David, they made Jeroboam son of Nebat their king. Jeroboam enticed Israel away from following the LORD and caused them to commit a great sin. ²²The Israelites persisted in all the sins of Jeroboam and did not turn away from them ²³until the LORD removed them from his presence, as he had warned through all his servants the prophets. So the people of Israel were taken from their homeland into exile in Assyria, and they are still there.

truth or dare

Stiff-necked? That's just another way of saying *stubborn*. Don't let your strong will keep you from God.

17:12–14

Samaria Resettled

²⁴The king of Assyria brought people from Babylon, Cuthah, Avva, Hamath and Sepharvaim and settled them in the towns of Samaria to replace the Israelites. They took over Samaria and lived in its towns. ²⁵When they first lived there, they did not worship the LORD; so he sent lions among them and they killed some of the people. ²⁶It was reported to the king of Assyria: "The people you deported and resettled in the towns of Samaria do not know what the god of that country requires. He has sent lions among them, which are killing them off, because the people do not know what he requires."

²⁷Then the king of Assyria gave this order: "Have one of the priests you took captive from Samaria go back to live there and teach the people what the god of the land requires." ²⁸So one of the priests who had been exiled from Samaria came to live in Bethel and taught them how to worship the LORD.

²⁹Nevertheless, each national group made its own gods in the several towns where they settled, and set them up in the shrines the people of Samaria had made at the high places. ³⁰The men from Babylon

genuine character

You've heard the phrase, "You are what you eat." (Did that ever make any sense to you?!) What you eat affects how you feel. Well, how about this one: "You are what you *do*"? (Ah, that makes more sense!) What you do reflects who you are. If you love God, that shows in your actions. And if you don't—well, that shows, too. After worshiping worthless idols for years, the people of Israel became—you guessed it—worthless. So if it's true that you are what you do, then what does that make you?

17:14–15

---

a 17 Or *They made their sons and daughters pass through*

made Succoth Benoth, the men from Cuthah made Nergal, and the men from Hamath made Ashima; ³¹the Avvites made Nibhaz and Tartak, and the Sepharvites burned their children in the fire as sacrifices to Adrammelech and Anammelech, the gods of Sepharvaim. ³²They worshiped the LORD, but they also appointed all sorts of their own people to officiate for them as priests in the shrines at the high places. ³³They worshiped the LORD, but they also served their own gods in accordance with the customs of the nations from which they had been brought.

³⁴To this day they persist in their former practices. They neither worship the LORD nor adhere to the decrees and ordinances, the laws and commands the LORD gave the descendants of Jacob, whom he named Israel. ³⁵When the LORD made a covenant with the Israelites, he commanded them: "Do not worship any other gods or bow down to them, serve them or sacrifice to them. ³⁶But the LORD, who brought you up out of Egypt with mighty power and outstretched arm, is the one you must worship. To him you shall bow down and to him offer sacrifices. ³⁷You must always be careful to keep the decrees and ordinances, the laws and commands he wrote for you. Do not worship other gods. ³⁸Do not forget the covenant I have made with you, and do not worship other gods. ³⁹Rather, worship the LORD your God; it is he who will deliver you from the hand of all your enemies."

⁴⁰They would not listen, however, but persisted in their former practices. ⁴¹Even while these people were worshiping the LORD, they were serving their idols. To this day their children and grandchildren continue to do as their fathers did.

Hezekiah King of Judah

18 In the third year of Hoshea son of Elah king of Israel, Hezekiah son of Ahaz king of Judah began to reign. ²He was twenty-five years old when he became king, and he reigned in Jerusalem twenty-nine years. His mother's name was Abijah*ᵃ* daughter of Zechariah. ³He did what was right in the eyes of the LORD, just as his father David had done. ⁴He removed the high places, smashed the sacred stones and cut down the Asherah poles. He broke into pieces the bronze snake Moses had made, for up to that time the Israelites had been burning incense to it. (It was called*ᵇ* Nehushtan.*ᶜ*)

⁵Hezekiah trusted in the LORD, the God of Israel. There was no one like him among all the kings of Judah, either before him or after him. ⁶He held fast to the LORD and did not cease to follow him; he kept the commands the LORD had given Moses. ⁷And the LORD was with him; he was successful in whatever he undertook. He rebelled against the king of Assyria and did not serve him. ⁸From watchtower to fortified city, he defeated the Philistines, as far as Gaza and its territory.

⁹In King Hezekiah's fourth year, which was the seventh year of Hoshea son of Elah king of Israel, Shalmaneser king of Assyria marched against Samaria and laid siege to it. ¹⁰At the end of three years the Assyrians took it. So Samaria was captured in Hezekiah's sixth year, which was the ninth year of Hoshea king of Israel. ¹¹The king of Assyria deported Israel to Assyria and settled them in Halah, in Gozan on the Habor River and in towns of the Medes. ¹²This happened because they had not obeyed the LORD their God, but had violated his covenant—all that Moses the servant of the LORD commanded. They neither listened to the commands nor carried them out.

¹³In the fourteenth year of King Hezekiah's reign, Sennacherib king of Assyria attacked all the fortified cities of Judah and captured them. ¹⁴So Hezekiah king of Judah sent this message to the king of Assyria at Lachish: "I have done wrong. Withdraw from me, and I will pay whatever you demand of me." The king of Assyria exacted from Hezekiah king of Judah three hundred talents*ᵈ* of silver and thirty talents*ᵉ* of gold. ¹⁵So Hezekiah gave him all the silver that was found in the temple of the LORD and in the treasuries of the royal palace.

¹⁶At this time Hezekiah king of Judah stripped off the gold with which he had covered the doors and doorposts of the temple of the LORD, and gave it to the king of Assyria.

Sennacherib Threatens Jerusalem

¹⁷The king of Assyria sent his supreme commander, his chief officer and his field commander with a large army, from Lachish to King Hezekiah at Jerusalem. They came up to Jerusalem and stopped at the aqueduct of the Upper Pool, on the road to the Washerman's Field. ¹⁸They called for the king;

ᵃ 2 Hebrew *Abi,* a variant of *Abijah*   *ᵇ 4* Or *He called it*   *ᶜ 4 Nehushtan* sounds like the Hebrew for *bronze* and *snake* and *unclean thing.*   *ᵈ 14* That is, about 11 tons (about 10 metric tons)   *ᵉ 14* That is, about 1 ton (about 1 metric ton)

genuine

prayer »

18:31-33

Has someone ever tried to intimidate you? Maybe she or he tried to chip away at your confidence in God by criticizing your beliefs or by trying to convince you *not* to believe. The powerful Assyrian army surrounded Jerusalem. Talk about intimidation! This army had already conquered many cities in the region, and Jerusalem was next on the agenda. Their king then sent a messenger to try to intimidate King Hezekiah and the people of Israel by telling them that God couldn't rescue them. Nice try. Instead of listening to the skeptics, Hezekiah prayed. That's one tactic that stops intimidation cold.

and Eliakim son of Hilkiah the palace administrator, Shebna the secretary, and Joah son of Asaph the recorder went out to them.

[19]The field commander said to them, "Tell Hezekiah:

" 'This is what the great king, the king of Assyria, says: On what are you basing this confidence of yours? [20]You say you have strategy and military strength—but you speak only empty words. On whom are you depending, that you rebel against me? [21]Look now, you are depending on Egypt, that splintered reed of a staff, which pierces a man's hand and wounds him if he leans on it! Such is Pharaoh king of Egypt to all who depend on him. [22]And if you say to me, "We are depending on the LORD our God"—isn't he the one whose high places and altars Hezekiah removed, saying to Judah and Jerusalem, "You must worship before this altar in Jerusalem"?

[23]" 'Come now, make a bargain with my master, the king of Assyria: I will give you two thousand horses—if you can put riders on them! [24]How can you repulse one officer of the least of my master's officials, even though you are depending on Egypt for chariots and horsemen[a]? [25]Furthermore, have I come to attack and destroy this place without word from the LORD? The LORD himself told me to march against this country and destroy it.' "

[26]Then Eliakim son of Hilkiah, and Shebna and Joah said to the field commander, "Please speak to your servants in Aramaic, since we understand it. Don't speak to us in Hebrew in the hearing of the people on the wall."

[27]But the commander replied, "Was it only to your master and you that my master sent me to say these things, and not to the men sitting on the wall—who, like you, will have to eat their own filth and drink their own urine?"

[28]Then the commander stood and called out in Hebrew: "Hear the word of the great king, the king of Assyria! [29]This is what the king says: Do not let Hezekiah deceive you. He cannot deliver you from my hand. [30]Do not let Hezekiah persuade you to trust in the LORD when he says, 'The LORD will surely deliver us; this city will not be given into the hand of the king of Assyria.'

[31]"Do not listen to Hezekiah. This is what the king of Assyria says: Make peace with me and come out to me. Then every one of you will eat from his own vine and fig tree and drink water from his own cistern, [32]until I come and take you to a land like your own, a land of grain and new wine, a land of bread and vineyards, a land of olive trees and honey. Choose life and not death!

"Do not listen to Hezekiah, for he is misleading you when he says, 'The LORD will deliver us.' [33]Has the god of any nation ever delivered his land from the hand of the king of Assyria? [34]Where are the gods of Hamath and Arpad? Where are the gods of Sepharvaim, Hena and Ivvah? Have they rescued Samaria from my hand? [35]Who of all the gods of these countries has been able to save his land from me? How then can the LORD deliver Jerusalem from my hand?"

[36]But the people remained silent and said nothing in reply, because the king had commanded, "Do not answer him."

[37]Then Eliakim son of Hilkiah the palace administrator, Shebna the secretary and Joah son of Asaph the recorder went to Hezekiah, with their clothes torn, and told him what the field commander had said.

a 24 Or charioteers

Jerusalem's Deliverance Foretold

19 When King Hezekiah heard this, he tore his clothes and put on sackcloth and went into the temple of the Lord. ²He sent Eliakim the palace administrator, Shebna the secretary and the leading priests, all wearing sackcloth, to the prophet Isaiah son of Amoz. ³They told him, "This is what Hezekiah says: This day is a day of distress and rebuke and disgrace, as when children come to the point of birth and there is no strength to deliver them. ⁴It may be that the Lord your God will hear all the words of the field commander, whom his master, the king of Assyria, has sent to ridicule the living God, and that he will rebuke him for the words the Lord your God has heard. Therefore pray for the remnant that still survives."

⁵When King Hezekiah's officials came to Isaiah, ⁶Isaiah said to them, "Tell your master, 'This is what the Lord says: Do not be afraid of what you have heard—those words with which the underlings of the king of Assyria have blasphemed me. ⁷Listen! I am going to put such a spirit in him that when he hears a certain report, he will return to his own country, and there I will have him cut down with the sword.' "

⁸When the field commander heard that the king of Assyria had left Lachish, he withdrew and found the king fighting against Libnah.

⁹Now Sennacherib received a report that Tirhakah, the Cushite*ᵃ* king ⌊of Egypt⌋, was marching out to fight against him. So he again sent messengers to Hezekiah with this word: ¹⁰"Say to Hezekiah king of Judah: Do not let the god you depend on deceive you when he says, 'Jerusalem will not be handed over to the king of Assyria.' ¹¹Surely you have heard what the kings of Assyria have done to all the countries, destroying them completely. And will you be delivered? ¹²Did the gods of the nations that were destroyed by my forefathers deliver them: the gods of Gozan, Haran, Rezeph and the people of Eden who were in Tel Assar? ¹³Where is the king of Hamath, the king of Arpad, the king of the city of Sepharvaim, or of Hena or Ivvah?"

Hezekiah's Prayer

¹⁴Hezekiah received the letter from the messengers and read it. Then he went up to the temple of the Lord and spread it out before the Lord. ¹⁵And Hezekiah prayed to the Lord: "O Lord, God of Israel, enthroned between the cherubim, you alone are God over all the kingdoms of the earth. You have made heaven and earth. ¹⁶Give ear, O Lord, and hear; open your eyes, O Lord, and see; listen to the words Sennacherib has sent to insult the living God.

¹⁷"It is true, O Lord, that the Assyrian kings have laid waste these nations and their lands. ¹⁸They have thrown their gods into the fire and destroyed them, for they were not gods but only wood and stone, fashioned by men's hands. ¹⁹Now, O Lord our God, deliver us from his hand, so that all kingdoms on earth may know that you alone, O Lord, are God."

Isaiah Prophesies Sennacherib's Fall

²⁰Then Isaiah son of Amoz sent a message to Hezekiah: "This is what the Lord, the God of Israel, says: I have heard your prayer concerning Sennacherib king of Assyria. ²¹This is the word that the Lord has spoken against him:

" 'The Virgin Daughter of Zion
  despises you and mocks you.
The Daughter of Jerusalem
  tosses her head as you flee.
²²Who is it you have insulted and blasphemed?
  Against whom have you raised your voice
and lifted your eyes in pride?
  Against the Holy One of Israel!
²³By your messengers
  you have heaped insults on the Lord.
And you have said,
  "With my many chariots
I have ascended the heights of the mountains,
  the utmost heights of Lebanon.

ᵃ 9 That is, from the upper Nile region

I have cut down its tallest cedars,
    the choicest of its pines.
I have reached its remotest parts,
    the finest of its forests.
24 I have dug wells in foreign lands
    and drunk the water there.
With the soles of my feet
    I have dried up all the streams of Egypt."

25 " 'Have you not heard?
    Long ago I ordained it.
In days of old I planned it;
    now I have brought it to pass,
that you have turned fortified cities
    into piles of stone.
26 Their people, drained of power,
    are dismayed and put to shame.
They are like plants in the field,
    like tender green shoots,
like grass sprouting on the roof,
    scorched before it grows up.

27 " 'But I know where you stay
    and when you come and go
    and how you rage against me.
28 Because you rage against me
    and your insolence has
        reached my ears,
I will put my hook in your nose
    and my bit in your mouth,
and I will make you return
    by the way you came.'

29 "This will be the sign for you, O Hezekiah:

"This year you will eat what grows
    by itself,
    and the second year what
        springs from that.
But in the third year sow and reap,
    plant vineyards and eat their fruit.
30 Once more a remnant of the house of Judah
    will take root below and bear fruit above.
31 For out of Jerusalem will come a remnant,
    and out of Mount Zion a band of survivors.

The zeal of the LORD Almighty will accomplish this.

32 "Therefore this is what the LORD says concerning the king of Assyria:

"He will not enter this city
    or shoot an arrow here.
He will not come before it with shield
    or build a siege ramp against it.
33 By the way that he came he will return;
    he will not enter this city,

                      declares the LORD.

34 I will defend this city and save it,
    for my sake and for the sake of David my servant."

truth or dare

From settling in the promised land to surviving an exile, Israel's condition was always directed by God. Look at the major events you've experienced. Guess who's in control of your life, too?

19:30–31

³⁵That night the angel of the LORD went out and put to death a hundred and eighty-five thousand men in the Assyrian camp. When the people got up the next morning—there were all the dead bodies! ³⁶So Sennacherib king of Assyria broke camp and withdrew. He returned to Nineveh and stayed there.

³⁷One day, while he was worshiping in the temple of his god Nisroch, his sons Adrammelech and Sharezer cut him down with the sword, and they escaped to the land of Ararat. And Esarhaddon his son succeeded him as king.

Hezekiah's Illness

20 In those days Hezekiah became ill and was at the point of death. The prophet Isaiah son of Amoz went to him and said, "This is what the LORD says: Put your house in order, because you are going to die; you will not recover."

²Hezekiah turned his face to the wall and prayed to the LORD, ³"Remember, O LORD, how I have walked before you faithfully and with wholehearted devotion and have done what is good in your eyes." And Hezekiah wept bitterly.

⁴Before Isaiah had left the middle court, the word of the LORD came to him: ⁵"Go back and tell Hezekiah, the leader of my people, 'This is what the LORD, the God of your father David, says: I have heard your prayer and seen your tears; I will heal you. On the third day from now you will go up to the temple of the LORD. ⁶I will add fifteen years to your life. And I will deliver you and this city from the hand of the king of Assyria. I will defend this city for my sake and for the sake of my servant David.' "

⁷Then Isaiah said, "Prepare a poultice of figs." They did so and applied it to the boil, and he recovered.

⁸Hezekiah had asked Isaiah, "What will be the sign that the LORD will heal me and that I will go up to the temple of the LORD on the third day from now?"

⁹Isaiah answered, "This is the LORD's sign to you that the LORD will do what he has promised: Shall the shadow go forward ten steps, or shall it go back ten steps?"

¹⁰"It is a simple matter for the shadow to go forward ten steps," said Hezekiah. "Rather, have it go back ten steps."

¹¹Then the prophet Isaiah called upon the LORD, and the LORD made the shadow go back the ten steps it had gone down on the stairway of Ahaz.

Envoys From Babylon

¹²At that time Merodach-Baladan son of Baladan king of Babylon sent Hezekiah letters and a gift, because he had heard of Hezekiah's illness. ¹³Hezekiah received the messengers and showed them all that was in his storehouses—the silver, the gold, the spices and the fine oil—his armory and ev-

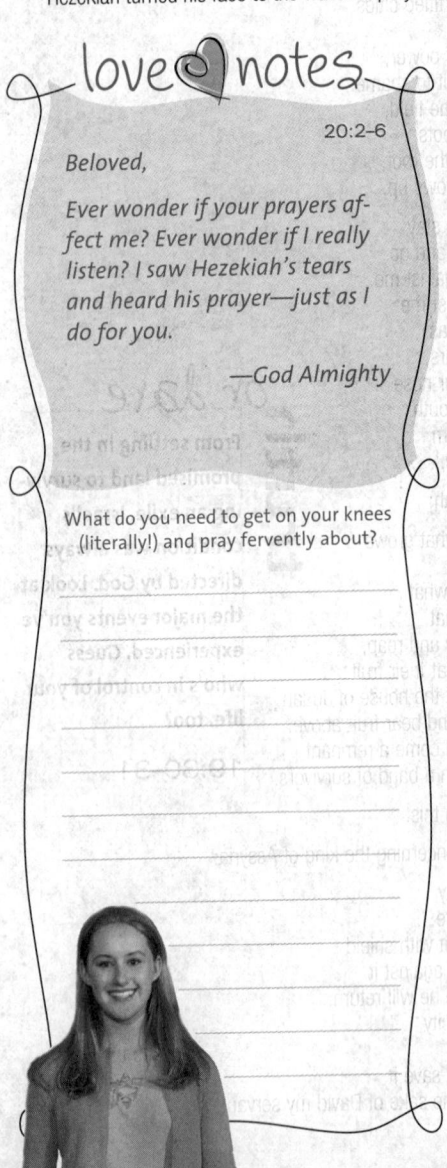

love notes

20:2–6

Beloved,

Ever wonder if your prayers affect me? Ever wonder if I really listen? I saw Hezekiah's tears and heard his prayer—just as I do for you.

—God Almighty

What do you need to get on your knees (literally!) and pray fervently about?

erything found among his treasures. There was nothing in his palace or in all his kingdom that Hezekiah did not show them.

[14]Then Isaiah the prophet went to King Hezekiah and asked, "What did those men say, and where did they come from?"

"From a distant land," Hezekiah replied. "They came from Babylon."

[15]The prophet asked, "What did they see in your palace?"

"They saw everything in my palace," Hezekiah said. "There is nothing among my treasures that I did not show them."

[16]Then Isaiah said to Hezekiah, "Hear the word of the LORD: [17]The time will surely come when everything in your palace, and all that your fathers have stored up until this day, will be carried off to Babylon. Nothing will be left, says the LORD. [18]And some of your descendants, your own flesh and blood, that will be born to you, will be taken away, and they will become eunuchs in the palace of the king of Babylon."

[19]"The word of the LORD you have spoken is good," Hezekiah replied. For he thought, "Will there not be peace and security in my lifetime?"

[20]As for the other events of Hezekiah's reign, all his achievements and how he made the pool and the tunnel by which he brought water into the city, are they not written in the book of the annals of the kings of Judah? [21]Hezekiah rested with his fathers. And Manasseh his son succeeded him as king.

Manasseh King of Judah

21

Manasseh was twelve years old when he became king, and he reigned in Jerusalem fifty-five years. His mother's name was Hephzibah. [2]He did evil in the eyes of the LORD, following the detestable practices of the nations the LORD had driven out before the Israelites. [3]He rebuilt the high places his father Hezekiah had destroyed; he also erected altars to Baal and made an Asherah pole, as Ahab king of Israel had done. He bowed down to all the starry hosts and worshiped them. [4]He built altars in the temple of the LORD, of which the LORD had said, "In Jerusalem I will put my Name." [5]In both courts of the temple of the LORD, he built altars to all the starry hosts. [6]He sacrificed his own son in[a] the fire, practiced sorcery and divination, and consulted mediums and spiritists. He did much evil in the eyes of the LORD, provoking him to anger.

[7]He took the carved Asherah pole he had made and put it in the temple, of which the LORD had said to David and to his son Solomon, "In this temple and in Jerusalem, which I have chosen out of all the tribes of Israel, I will put my Name forever. [8]I will not again make the feet of the Israelites wander from the land I gave their forefathers, if only they will be careful to do everything I commanded them and will keep the whole Law that my servant Moses gave them." [9]But the people did not listen. Manasseh led them astray, so that they did more evil than the nations the LORD had destroyed before the Israelites.

[10]The LORD said through his servants the prophets: [11]"Manasseh king of Judah has committed these detestable sins. He has done more evil than the Amorites who preceded him and has led Judah into sin with his idols. [12]Therefore this is what the LORD, the God of Israel, says: I am going to bring such disaster on Jerusalem and Judah that the ears of everyone who hears of it will tingle. [13]I will stretch out over Jerusalem the measuring line used against Samaria and the plumb line used against the house of Ahab. I will wipe out Jerusalem as one wipes a dish, wiping it and turning it upside down. [14]I will forsake the remnant of my inheritance and hand them over to their enemies. They will be looted and plundered by all their foes, [15]because they have done evil in my eyes and have provoked me to anger from the day their forefathers came out of Egypt until this day."

[16]Moreover, Manasseh also shed so much innocent blood that he filled Jerusalem from end to end—besides the sin that he had caused Judah to commit, so that they did evil in the eyes of the LORD.

[17]As for the other events of Manasseh's reign, and all he did, including the sin he committed, are they not written in the book of the annals of the kings of Judah? [18]Manasseh rested with his fathers and was buried in his palace garden, the garden of Uzza. And Amon his son succeeded him as king.

a 6 Or He made his own son pass through

Amon King of Judah

[19]Amon was twenty-two years old when he became king, and he reigned in Jerusalem two years. His mother's name was Meshullemeth daughter of Haruz; she was from Jotbah. [20]He did evil in the eyes of the LORD, as his father Manasseh had done. [21]He walked in all the ways of his father; he worshiped the idols his father had worshiped, and bowed down to them. [22]He forsook the LORD, the God of his fathers, and did not walk in the way of the LORD.

[23]Amon's officials conspired against him and assassinated the king in his palace. [24]Then the people of the land killed all who had plotted against King Amon, and they made Josiah his son king in his place.

[25]As for the other events of Amon's reign, and what he did, are they not written in the book of the annals of the kings of Judah? [26]He was buried in his grave in the garden of Uzza. And Josiah his son succeeded him as king.

The Book of the Law Found

22 Josiah was eight years old when he became king, and he reigned in Jerusalem thirty-one years. His mother's name was Jedidah daughter of Adaiah; she was from Bozkath. [2]He did what was right in the eyes of the LORD and walked in all the ways of his father David, not turning aside to the right or to the left.

[3]In the eighteenth year of his reign, King Josiah sent the secretary, Shaphan son of Azaliah, the son of Meshullam, to the temple of the LORD. He said: [4]"Go up to Hilkiah the high priest and have him get ready the money that has been brought into the temple of the LORD, which the doorkeepers have collected from the people. [5]Have them entrust it to the men appointed to supervise the work on the temple. And have these men pay the workers who repair the temple of the LORD— [6]the carpenters, the builders and the masons. Also have them purchase timber and dressed stone to repair the temple. [7]But they need not account for the money entrusted to them, because they are acting faithfully."

[8]Hilkiah the high priest said to Shaphan the secretary, "I have found the Book of the Law in the temple of the LORD." He gave it to Shaphan, who read it. [9]Then Shaphan the secretary went to the king and reported to him: "Your officials have paid out the money that was in the temple of the LORD and have entrusted it to the workers and supervisors at the temple." [10]Then Shaphan the secretary informed the king, "Hilkiah the priest has given me a book." And Shaphan read from it in the presence of the king.

[11]When the king heard the words of the Book of the Law, he tore his robes. [12]He gave these orders to Hilkiah the priest, Ahikam son of Shaphan, Acbor son of Micaiah, Shaphan the secretary and Asaiah the king's attendant: [13]"Go and inquire of the LORD for me and for the people and for all Judah about what is written in this book that has been found. Great is the LORD's anger that burns against us because our fathers have not obeyed the words of this book; they have not acted in accordance with all that is written there concerning us."

[14]Hilkiah the priest, Ahikam, Acbor, Shaphan and Asaiah went to speak to the prophetess Huldah, who was the wife of Shallum son of Tikvah, the son of Harhas, keeper of the wardrobe. She lived in Jerusalem, in the Second District.

[15]She said to them, "This is what the LORD, the God of Israel, says: Tell the man who sent you

truth or dare

R-E-S-P-E-C-T. That's what Josiah had for God's Word, and his reaction to hearing the Word showed it. Do you take God's Word casually, or do you show respect?

22:8–13

truth or dare

Equal Opportunity Employer! Clearly, Huldah's position as prophetess displays how a woman can do awesome things for God. God has big plans for his girls.

22:14

to me, [16]'This is what the LORD says: I am going to bring disaster on this place and its people, according to everything written in the book the king of Judah has read. [17]Because they have forsaken me and burned incense to other gods and provoked me to anger by all the idols their hands have made,[a] my anger will burn against this place and will not be quenched.' [18]Tell the king of Judah, who sent you to inquire of the LORD, 'This is what the LORD, the God of Israel, says concerning the words you heard: [19]Because your heart was responsive and you humbled yourself before the LORD when you heard what I have spoken against this place and its people, that they would become accursed and laid waste, and because you tore your robes and wept in my presence, I have heard you, declares the LORD. [20]Therefore I will gather you to your fathers, and you will be buried in peace. Your eyes will not see all the disaster I am going to bring on this place.' "

So they took her answer back to the king.

Josiah Renews the Covenant

23 Then the king called together all the elders of Judah and Jerusalem. [2]He went up to the temple of the LORD with the men of Judah, the people of Jerusalem, the priests and the prophets—all the people from the least to the greatest. He read in their hearing all the words of the Book of the Covenant, which had been found in the temple of the LORD. [3]The king stood by the pillar and renewed the covenant in the presence of the LORD—to follow the LORD and keep his commands, regulations and decrees with all his heart and all his soul, thus confirming the words of the covenant written in this book. Then all the people pledged themselves to the covenant.

[4]The king ordered Hilkiah the high priest, the priests next in rank and the doorkeepers to remove from the temple of the LORD all the articles made for Baal and Asherah and all the starry hosts. He burned them outside Jerusalem in the fields of the Kidron Valley and took the ashes to Bethel. [5]He did away with the pagan priests appointed by the kings of Judah to burn incense on the high places of the towns of Judah and on those around Jerusalem—those who burned incense to Baal, to the sun and moon, to the constellations and to all the starry hosts. [6]He took the Asherah pole from the temple of the LORD to the Kidron Valley outside Jerusalem and burned it there. He ground it to powder and scattered the dust over the graves of the common people. [7]He also tore down the quarters of the male shrine prostitutes, which were in the temple of the LORD and where women did weaving for Asherah.

[8]Josiah brought all the priests from the towns of Judah and desecrated the high places, from Geba to Beersheba, where the priests had burned incense. He broke down the shrines[b] at the gates—at the entrance to the Gate of Joshua, the city governor, which is on the left of the city gate. [9]Although the priests of the high places did not serve at the altar of the LORD in Jerusalem, they ate unleavened bread with their fellow priests.

[10]He desecrated Topheth, which was in the Valley of Ben Hinnom, so no one could use it to sacrifice his son or daughter in[c] the fire to Molech. [11]He removed from the entrance to the temple of the LORD the horses that the kings of Judah had dedicated to the sun. They were in the court near the room of an official named Nathan-Melech. Josiah then burned the chariots dedicated to the sun.

[12]He pulled down the altars the kings of Judah had erected on the roof near the upper room of Ahaz, and the altars Manasseh had built in the two courts of the temple of the LORD. He removed them from there, smashed them to pieces and threw the rubble into the Kidron Valley. [13]The king also desecrated the high places that were east of Jerusalem on the south of the Hill of Corruption—the ones Solomon king of Israel had built for Ashtoreth the vile goddess of the Sidonians, for Chemosh the vile god of Moab, and for Molech[d] the detestable god of the people of Ammon. [14]Josiah smashed the sacred stones and cut down the Asherah poles and covered the sites with human bones.

truth or dare

Notice a cooling off in your relationship with God? Recommit yourself to him. Start today—it's never too late to begin walking with him again.

23:1–3

---

[a] 17 Or by everything they have done   [b] 8 Or high places   [c] 10 Or to make his son or daughter pass through
[d] 13 Hebrew Milcom

¹⁵Even the altar at Bethel, the high place made by Jeroboam son of Nebat, who had caused Israel to sin—even that altar and high place he demolished. He burned the high place and ground it to powder, and burned the Asherah pole also. ¹⁶Then Josiah looked around, and when he saw the tombs that were there on the hillside, he had the bones removed from them and burned on the altar to defile it, in accordance with the word of the LORD proclaimed by the man of God who foretold these things.

¹⁷The king asked, "What is that tombstone I see?"

The men of the city said, "It marks the tomb of the man of God who came from Judah and pronounced against the altar of Bethel the very things you have done to it."

¹⁸"Leave it alone," he said. "Don't let anyone disturb his bones." So they spared his bones and those of the prophet who had come from Samaria.

genuine

joy » 23:21-22

What makes you want to all-out celebrate? Being asked out on a date by someone you've been *dying* to go out with? (Oh yeah!) Winning a tough basketball game? Passing a killer exam? Celebration can be a quiet "wow that's cool" or a time of loud, spontaneous "WOO-HOO!!!" When King Josiah told the people to celebrate, he had that all-out, joyful kind of celebration in mind (check out the long version in 2 Chronicles 35:1–19). He thought that a great God deserved great honor—and what better way to show that than with a little spirit? When was the last time you celebrated God like that?

¹⁹Just as he had done at Bethel, Josiah removed and defiled all the shrines at the high places that the kings of Israel had built in the towns of Samaria that had provoked the LORD to anger. ²⁰Josiah slaughtered all the priests of those high places on the altars and burned human bones on them. Then he went back to Jerusalem.

²¹The king gave this order to all the people: "Celebrate the Passover to the LORD your God, as it is written in this Book of the Covenant." ²²Not since the days of the judges who led Israel, nor throughout the days of the kings of Israel and the kings of Judah, had any such Passover been observed. ²³But in the eighteenth year of King Josiah, this Passover was celebrated to the LORD in Jerusalem.

²⁴Furthermore, Josiah got rid of the mediums and spiritists, the household gods, the idols and all the other detestable things seen in Judah and Jerusalem. This he did to fulfill the requirements of the law written in the book that Hilkiah the priest had discovered in the temple of the LORD. ²⁵Neither before nor after Josiah was there a king like him who turned to the LORD as he did—with all his heart and with all his soul and with all his strength, in accordance with all the Law of Moses.

²⁶Nevertheless, the LORD did not turn away from the heat of his fierce anger, which burned against Judah because of all that Manasseh had done to provoke him to anger. ²⁷So the LORD said, "I will remove Judah also from my presence as I removed Israel, and I will reject Jerusalem, the city I chose, and this temple, about which I said, 'There shall my Name be.'ᵃ"

²⁸As for the other events of Josiah's reign, and all he did, are they not written in the book of the annals of the kings of Judah?

²⁹While Josiah was king, Pharaoh Neco king of Egypt went up to the Euphrates River to help the king of Assyria. King Josiah marched out to meet him in battle, but Neco faced him and killed him at Megiddo. ³⁰Josiah's servants brought his body in a chariot from Megiddo to Jerusalem and buried him in his own tomb. And the people of the land took Jehoahaz son of Josiah and anointed him and made him king in place of his father.

Jehoahaz King of Judah

³¹Jehoahaz was twenty-three years old when he became king, and he reigned in Jerusalem three months. His mother's name was Hamutal daughter of Jeremiah; she was from Libnah. ³²He

a 27 1 Kings 8:29

did evil in the eyes of the Lord, just as his fathers had done. [33]Pharaoh Neco put him in chains at Riblah in the land of Hamath[a] so that he might not reign in Jerusalem, and he imposed on Judah a levy of a hundred talents[b] of silver and a talent[c] of gold. [34]Pharaoh Neco made Eliakim son of Josiah king in place of his father Josiah and changed Eliakim's name to Jehoiakim. But he took Jehoahaz and carried him off to Egypt, and there he died. [35]Jehoiakim paid Pharaoh Neco the silver and gold he demanded. In order to do so, he taxed the land and exacted the silver and gold from the people of the land according to their assessments.

Jehoiakim King of Judah

[36]Jehoiakim was twenty-five years old when he became king, and he reigned in Jerusalem eleven years. His mother's name was Zebidah daughter of Pedaiah; she was from Rumah. [37]And he did evil in the eyes of the Lord, just as his fathers had done.

24 During Jehoiakim's reign, Nebuchadnezzar king of Babylon invaded the land, and Jehoiakim became his vassal for three years. But then he changed his mind and rebelled against Nebuchadnezzar. [2]The Lord sent Babylonian,[d] Aramean, Moabite and Ammonite raiders against him. He sent them to destroy Judah, in accordance with the word of the Lord proclaimed by his servants the prophets. [3]Surely these things happened to Judah according to the Lord's command, in order to remove them from his presence because of the sins of Manasseh and all he had done, [4]including the shedding of innocent blood. For he had filled Jerusalem with innocent blood, and the Lord was not willing to forgive.

[5]As for the other events of Jehoiakim's reign, and all he did, are they not written in the book of the annals of the kings of Judah? [6]Jehoiakim rested with his fathers. And Jehoiachin his son succeeded him as king.

[7]The king of Egypt did not march out from his own country again, because the king of Babylon had taken all his territory, from the Wadi of Egypt to the Euphrates River.

Jehoiachin King of Judah

[8]Jehoiachin was eighteen years old when he became king, and he reigned in Jerusalem three months. His mother's name was Nehushta daughter of Elnathan; she was from Jerusalem. [9]He did evil in the eyes of the Lord, just as his father had done.

[10]At that time the officers of Nebuchadnezzar king of Babylon advanced on Jerusalem and laid siege to it, [11]and Nebuchadnezzar himself came up to the city while his officers were besieging it. [12]Jehoiachin king of Judah, his mother, his attendants, his nobles and his officials all surrendered to him.

In the eighth year of the reign of the king of Babylon, he took Jehoiachin prisoner. [13]As the Lord had declared, Nebuchadnezzar removed all the treasures from the temple of the Lord and from the royal palace, and took away all the gold articles that Solomon king of Israel had made for the temple of the Lord. [14]He carried into exile all Jerusalem: all the officers and fighting men, and all the craftsmen and artisans—a total of ten thousand. Only the poorest people of the land were left.

[15]Nebuchadnezzar took Jehoiachin captive to Babylon. He also took from Jerusalem to Babylon the king's mother, his wives, his officials and the leading men of the land. [16]The king of Babylon also deported to Babylon the entire force of seven thousand fighting men, strong and fit for war, and a thousand craftsmen and artisans. [17]He made Mattaniah, Jehoiachin's uncle, king in his place and changed his name to Zedekiah.

Zedekiah King of Judah

[18]Zedekiah was twenty-one years old when he became king, and he reigned in Jerusalem eleven years. His mother's name was Hamutal daughter of Jeremiah; she was from Libnah. [19]He did evil in the eyes of the Lord, just as Jehoiakim had done. [20]It was because of the Lord's anger that all this happened to Jerusalem and Judah, and in the end he thrust them from his presence.

The Fall of Jerusalem

Now Zedekiah rebelled against the king of Babylon.

---

a 33 Hebrew; Septuagint (see also 2 Chron. 36:3) *Neco at Riblah in Hamath removed him*   *b 33* That is, about 3 3/4 tons (about 3.4 metric tons)   *c 33* That is, about 75 pounds (about 34 kilograms)   *d 2* Or *Chaldean*

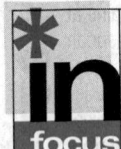

Home Is Where the Hurt Is

focus Profile: **Dominique**

Today my brother slammed the front door so hard that one of my mom's glass vases fell and shattered all over the floor. As I cleaned it up, I couldn't help but think how that glass was just like my family—so broken that we'll never be able to put the pieces back together.

My older brother Cotter used to be the one who told the best stories at dinner every night. He made family vacations a blast. He's the kind of guy who makes friends everywhere because he is so much fun to hang out with. Make that, *was* fun to hang out with.

This summer Cotter changed. He started hanging out with some sketchy people. So my normally cool brother turned into a rebel . . . and a user. Cotter always tells my parents he's not doing drugs, but they're not clueless. One look at him, and you can tell he's not there.

Last night, he got home at 2:30 AM, and I heard my dad yelling at him. "That's it! You miss curfew one more time and you're out on your own, Cotter! Get it together or you can't live here anymore."

Mom was so upset this morning that Dad decided to take her on a weekend getaway. They need a break. I do too. This doesn't feel like a family anymore. And as bad as it sounds, maybe our family would be better off without Cotter.

For more ideas on how to deal with conflict, check out the conflict link on www.TrueImagesBible.com

conflict in focus

Sometimes home isn't comfortable; it's miserable. Like Dominique, you may feel frustrated and desperate about the situation. Even when you can't change your family situation, you can . . .

» Find peace. God promises to bring peace when we think on him and meditate on his Word (see Isaiah 26:3, page 919).

» Practice perfect love. Philippians 1:6 (page 1550) shows us that God never gives up on us. No matter how bleak the situation looks, don't give up on your family. There is no pain beyond God's healing, no problem too great for his power. Keep praying!

For more on this topic, see the index on page 1656.

conflict

25 So in the ninth year of Zedekiah's reign, on the tenth day of the tenth month, Nebuchadnezzar king of Babylon marched against Jerusalem with his whole army. He encamped outside the city and built siege works all around it. [2] The city was kept under siege until the eleventh year of King Zedekiah. [3] By the ninth day of the ⌊fourth⌋ [a] month the famine in the city had become so severe that there was no food for the people to eat. [4] Then the city wall was broken through, and the whole army fled at night through the gate between the two walls near the king's garden, though the Babylonians [b] were surrounding the city. They fled toward the Arabah, [c] [5] but the Babylonian [d] army pursued the king and overtook him in the plains of Jericho. All his sol-

a 3 See Jer. 52:6.   *b 4* Or *Chaldeans*; also in verses 13, 25 and 26   *c 4* Or *the Jordan Valley*   *d 5* Or *Chaldean*; also in verses 10 and 24 diers were separated from him and scattered, [6]and he was captured. He was taken to the king of Babylon at Riblah, where sentence was pronounced on him. [7]They killed the sons of Zedekiah before his eyes. Then they put out his eyes, bound him with bronze shackles and took him to Babylon.

[8]On the seventh day of the fifth month, in the nineteenth year of Nebuchadnezzar king of Babylon, Nebuzaradan commander of the imperial guard, an official of the king of Babylon, came to Jerusalem. [9]He set fire to the temple of the LORD, the royal palace and all the houses of Jerusalem. Every important building he burned down. [10]The whole Babylonian army, under the commander of the imperial guard, broke down the walls around Jerusalem. [11]Nebuzaradan the commander of the guard carried into exile the people who remained in the city, along with the rest of the populace and those who had gone over to the king of Babylon. [12]But the commander left behind some of the poorest people of the land to work the vineyards and fields.

[13]The Babylonians broke up the bronze pillars, the movable stands and the bronze Sea that were at the temple of the LORD and they carried the bronze to Babylon. [14]They also took away the pots, shovels, wick trimmers, dishes and all the bronze articles used in the temple service. [15]The commander of the imperial guard took away the censers and sprinkling bowls—all that were made of pure gold or silver.

[16]The bronze from the two pillars, the Sea and the movable stands, which Solomon had made for the temple of the LORD, was more than could be weighed. [17]Each pillar was twenty-seven feet[a] high. The bronze capital on top of one pillar was four and a half feet[b] high and was decorated with a network and pomegranates of bronze all around. The other pillar, with its network, was similar.

[18]The commander of the guard took as prisoners Seraiah the chief priest, Zephaniah the priest next in rank and the three doorkeepers. [19]Of those still in the city, he took the officer in charge of the fighting men and five royal advisers. He also took the secretary who was chief officer in charge of conscripting the people of the land and sixty of his men who were found in the city. [20]Nebuzaradan the commander took them all and brought them to the king of Babylon at Riblah. [21]There at Riblah, in the land of Hamath, the king had them executed.

So Judah went into captivity, away from her land.

[22]Nebuchadnezzar king of Babylon appointed Gedaliah son of Ahikam, the son of Shaphan, to be over the people he had left behind in Judah. [23]When all the army officers and their men heard that the king of Babylon had appointed Gedaliah as governor, they came to Gedaliah at Mizpah—Ishmael son of Nethaniah, Johanan son of Kareah, Seraiah son of Tanhumeth the Netophathite, Jaazaniah the son of the Maacathite, and their men. [24]Gedaliah took an oath to reassure them and their men. "Do not be afraid of the Babylonian officials," he said. "Settle down in the land and serve the king of Babylon, and it will go well with you."

[25]In the seventh month, however, Ishmael son of Nethaniah, the son of Elishama, who was of royal blood, came with ten men and assassinated Gedaliah and also the men of Judah and the Babylonians who were with him at Mizpah. [26]At this, all the people from the least to the greatest, together with the army officers, fled to Egypt for fear of the Babylonians.

Jehoiachin Released

[27]In the thirty-seventh year of the exile of Jehoiachin king of Judah, in the year Evil-Merodach[c] became king of Babylon, he released Jehoiachin from prison on the twenty-seventh day of the twelfth month. [28]He spoke kindly to him and gave him a seat of honor higher than those of the other kings who were with him in Babylon. [29]So Jehoiachin put aside his prison clothes and for the rest of his life ate regularly at the king's table. [30]Day by day the king gave Jehoiachin a regular allowance as long as he lived.

---

a 17 Hebrew *eighteen cubits* (about 8.1 meters)   b 17 Hebrew *three cubits* (about 1.3 meters)   c 27 Also called Amel-Marduk

at a glance

author: Unknown, but possibly Ezra.

date: About 430 B.C.

setting: Begins with Israel's genealogical records and then focuses on King David's reign, paralleling many of the events of 2 Samuel.

verse to remember: And David knew that the LORD had established him as king over Israel and that his kingdom had been highly exalted (14:2).

theme to consider: The book of 1 Chronicles is a family history—including *your* history and spiritual roots—and an account of God's work throughout history to bring people to himself.

1 chronicles

unchanging truth

The roots reach deep beneath the soil, the trunk is massive and the branches stretch far in every direction. This could describe a majestic oak that's lived for hundreds of years, yet it also describes another type of tree—one that has never grown in a forest, park or yard. A family tree. The larger branches represent ancestors reaching back centuries. Their children branch off them, and then the next generation and so on until we see the smallest, newest branches, which are the youngest family members. The tree has scars from years of storms and wild weather, yet it's strong as ever and contains new life and growth.

The book of 1 Chronicles is a virtual "Who's Who" of Israel's history, with a special emphasis on tracing David's royal family line. While it was written to remind the Israelites in the period following the exile to Babylon who they were historically and spiritually, this book also reminds us of our spiritual heritage.

As you read through the genealogies, think back to the thousands of faithful people who have gone before you in shaping your spiritual family tree. Imagine your place in the line, and be encouraged that just as God worked in the lives of his people centuries ago, so he continues to work in your life today.

life lessons

1 God always keeps his promises—to David, to the Israelites and to us (11:1–3).

2 In the Christian family, it's our job to pass along the info about God and his love to the younger generations (28:8–9).

3 Everything good comes from God. He deserves all our praise (29:10–13)!

Historical Records From Adam to Abraham

To Noah's Sons

1 Adam, Seth, Enosh, [2]Kenan, Mahalalel, Jared, [3]Enoch, Methuselah, Lamech, Noah.

[4]The sons of Noah:[a]
Shem, Ham and Japheth.

The Japhethites

[5]The sons[b] of Japheth:
Gomer, Magog, Madai, Javan, Tubal, Meshech and Tiras.
[6]The sons of Gomer:
Ashkenaz, Riphath[c] and Togarmah.
[7]The sons of Javan:
Elishah, Tarshish, the Kittim and the Rodanim.

The Hamites

[8]The sons of Ham:
Cush, Mizraim,[d] Put and Canaan.
[9]The sons of Cush:
Seba, Havilah, Sabta, Raamah and Sabteca.
The sons of Raamah:
Sheba and Dedan.
[10]Cush was the father[e] of
Nimrod, who grew to be a mighty warrior on earth.
[11]Mizraim was the father of
the Ludites, Anamites, Lehabites, Naphtuhites, [12]Pathrusites, Casluhites (from whom the Philistines came) and Caphtorites.
[13]Canaan was the father of
Sidon his firstborn,[f] and of the Hittites, [14]Jebusites, Amorites, Girgashites, [15]Hivites, Arkites, Sinites, [16]Arvadites, Zemarites and Hamathites.

The Semites

[17]The sons of Shem:
Elam, Asshur, Arphaxad, Lud and Aram.
The sons of Aram:[g]
Uz, Hul, Gether and Meshech.
[18]Arphaxad was the father of Shelah,
and Shelah the father of Eber.
[19]Two sons were born to Eber:
One was named Peleg,[h] because in his time the earth was divided; his brother was named Joktan.
[20]Joktan was the father of
Almodad, Sheleph, Hazarmaveth, Jerah, [21]Hadoram, Uzal, Diklah, [22]Obal,[i] Abimael, Sheba, [23]Ophir, Havilah and Jobab. All these were sons of Joktan.

[24]Shem, Arphaxad,[j] Shelah,
[25]Eber, Peleg, Reu,

truth or dare

What's with the mile-long list of names? Think of it as your spiritual family tree. God preserved his message all these years so that you could hear it, too!

1:1—9:44

---

a 4 Septuagint; Hebrew does not have this line.   *b 5 Sons* may mean *descendants* or *successors* or *nations*; also in verses 6-10, 17 and 20.   *c 6* Many Hebrew manuscripts and Vulgate (see also Septuagint and Gen. 10:3); most Hebrew manuscripts *Diphath*   *d 8* That is, Egypt; also in verse 11   *e 10 Father* may mean *ancestor* or *predecessor* or *founder*; also in verses 11, 13, 18 and 20.   *f 13* Or *of the Sidonians, the foremost*   *g 17* One Hebrew manuscript and some Septuagint manuscripts (see also Gen. 10:23); most Hebrew manuscripts do not have this line.   *h 19 Peleg* means *division.*   *i 22* Some Hebrew manuscripts and Syriac (see also Gen. 10:28); most Hebrew manuscripts *Ebal*.   *j 24* Hebrew; some Septuagint manuscripts *Arphaxad, Cainan* (see also note at Gen. 11:10)

²⁶ Serug, Nahor, Terah
²⁷ and Abram (that is, Abraham).

The Family of Abraham

²⁸ The sons of Abraham:
Isaac and Ishmael.

Descendants of Hagar

²⁹ These were their descendants:
Nebaioth the firstborn of Ishmael, Kedar, Adbeel, Mibsam, ³⁰ Mishma, Dumah, Massa, Hadad, Tema, ³¹ Jetur, Naphish and Kedemah. These were the sons of Ishmael.

Descendants of Keturah

³² The sons born to Keturah, Abraham's concubine:
Zimran, Jokshan, Medan, Midian, Ishbak and Shuah.
The sons of Jokshan:
Sheba and Dedan.
³³ The sons of Midian:
Ephah, Epher, Hanoch, Abida and Eldaah.
All these were descendants of Keturah.

Descendants of Sarah

³⁴ Abraham was the father of Isaac.
The sons of Isaac:
Esau and Israel.

Esau's Sons

³⁵ The sons of Esau:
Eliphaz, Reuel, Jeush, Jalam and Korah.
³⁶ The sons of Eliphaz:
Teman, Omar, Zepho,^a Gatam and Kenaz;
by Timna: Amalek.^b
³⁷ The sons of Reuel:
Nahath, Zerah, Shammah and Mizzah.

The People of Seir in Edom

³⁸ The sons of Seir:
Lotan, Shobal, Zibeon, Anah, Dishon, Ezer and Dishan.
³⁹ The sons of Lotan:
Hori and Homam. Timna was Lotan's sister.
⁴⁰ The sons of Shobal:
Alvan,^c Manahath, Ebal, Shepho and Onam.
The sons of Zibeon:
Aiah and Anah.
⁴¹ The son of Anah:
Dishon.
The sons of Dishon:
Hemdan,^d Eshban, Ithran and Keran.
⁴² The sons of Ezer:
Bilhan, Zaavan and Akan.^e

---

a 36 Many Hebrew manuscripts, some Septuagint manuscripts and Syriac (see also Gen. 36:11); most Hebrew manuscripts *Zephi*   *b 36* Some Septuagint manuscripts (see also Gen. 36:12); Hebrew *Gatam, Kenaz, Timna and Amalek*
c 40 Many Hebrew manuscripts and some Septuagint manuscripts (see also Gen. 36:23); most Hebrew manuscripts *Alian*
d 41 Many Hebrew manuscripts and some Septuagint manuscripts (see also Gen. 36:26); most Hebrew manuscripts *Hamran*   *e 42* Many Hebrew and Septuagint manuscripts (see also Gen. 36:27); most Hebrew manuscripts *Zaavan, Jaakan*

The sons of Dishan[a]:
Uz and Aran.

The Rulers of Edom

[43] These were the kings who reigned in Edom before any Israelite king reigned[b]:
Bela son of Beor, whose city was named Dinhabah.

[44] When Bela died, Jobab son of Zerah from Bozrah succeeded him as king.

[45] When Jobab died, Husham from the land of the Temanites succeeded him as king.

[46] When Husham died, Hadad son of Bedad, who defeated Midian in the country of Moab, succeeded him as king. His city was named Avith.

[47] When Hadad died, Samlah from Masrekah succeeded him as king.

[48] When Samlah died, Shaul from Rehoboth on the river[c] succeeded him as king.

[49] When Shaul died, Baal-Hanan son of Acbor succeeded him as king.

[50] When Baal-Hanan died, Hadad succeeded him as king. His city was named Pau,[d] and his wife's name was Mehetabel daughter of Matred, the daughter of Me-Zahab. [51] Hadad also died.

The chiefs of Edom were:
Timna, Alvah, Jetheth, [52]Oholibamah, Elah, Pinon, [53]Kenaz, Teman, Mibzar, [54]Magdiel and Iram. These were the chiefs of Edom.

Israel's Sons

2 These were the sons of Israel:
Reuben, Simeon, Levi, Judah, Issachar, Zebulun, [2]Dan, Joseph, Benjamin, Naphtali, Gad and Asher.

Judah

To Hezron's Sons

[3] The sons of Judah:
Er, Onan and Shelah. These three were born to him by a Canaanite woman, the daughter of Shua. Er, Judah's firstborn, was wicked in the LORD's sight; so the LORD put him to death. [4]Tamar, Judah's daughter-in-law, bore him Perez and Zerah. Judah had five sons in all.

[5] The sons of Perez:
Hezron and Hamul.

[6] The sons of Zerah:
Zimri, Ethan, Heman, Calcol and Darda[e]—five in all.

[a] 42 Hebrew *Dishon*, a variant of *Dishan*
[b] 43 Or *before an Israelite king reigned over them*
[c] 48 Possibly the Euphrates   [d] 50 Many Hebrew manuscripts, some Septuagint manuscripts, Vulgate and Syriac (see also Gen. 36:39); most Hebrew manuscripts *Pai*   [e] 6 Many Hebrew manuscripts, some Septuagint manuscripts and Syriac (see also 1 Kings 4:31); most Hebrew manuscripts *Dara*

love notes

1:1—9:44

My child,

As you glance over this long list of names, remember that it's not just a crowd to me. I know every one of these people, their names and everything about them—just as I know you.

—Your Creator

What does it mean to you that God knows your name and everything about you?

⁷The son of Carmi:

Achar,ᵃ who brought trouble on Israel by violating the ban on taking devoted things. ᵇ

⁸The son of Ethan:

Azariah.

⁹The sons born to Hezron were:

Jerahmeel, Ram and Caleb. ᶜ

From Ram Son of Hezron

¹⁰Ram was the father of

Amminadab, and Amminadab the father of Nahshon, the leader of the people of Judah. ¹¹Nahshon was the father of Salmon,ᵈ Salmon the father of Boaz, ¹²Boaz the father of Obed and Obed the father of Jesse.

¹³Jesse was the father of

Eliab his firstborn; the second son was Abinadab, the third Shimea, ¹⁴the fourth Nethanel, the fifth Raddai, ¹⁵the sixth Ozem and the seventh David. ¹⁶Their sisters were Zeruiah and Abigail. Zeruiah's three sons were Abishai, Joab and Asahel. ¹⁷Abigail was the mother of Amasa, whose father was Jether the Ishmaelite.

Caleb Son of Hezron

¹⁸Caleb son of Hezron had children by his wife Azubah (and by Jerioth). These were her sons: Jesher, Shobab and Ardon. ¹⁹When Azubah died, Caleb married Ephrath, who bore him Hur. ²⁰Hur was the father of Uri, and Uri the father of Bezalel.

²¹Later, Hezron lay with the daughter of Makir the father of Gilead (he had married her when he was sixty years old), and she bore him Segub. ²²Segub was the father of Jair, who controlled twenty-three towns in Gilead. ²³(But Geshur and Aram captured Havvoth Jair,ᵉ as well as Kenath with its surrounding settlements—sixty towns.) All these were descendants of Makir the father of Gilead.

²⁴After Hezron died in Caleb Ephrathah, Abijah the wife of Hezron bore him Ashhur the fatherᶠ of Tekoa.

Jerahmeel Son of Hezron

²⁵The sons of Jerahmeel the firstborn of Hezron:

Ram his firstborn, Bunah, Oren, Ozem andᵍ Ahijah. ²⁶Jerahmeel had another wife, whose name was Atarah; she was the mother of Onam.

²⁷The sons of Ram the firstborn of Jerahmeel:

Maaz, Jamin and Eker.

²⁸The sons of Onam:

Shammai and Jada.

The sons of Shammai:

Nadab and Abishur.

²⁹Abishur's wife was named Abihail, who bore him Ahban and Molid.

³⁰The sons of Nadab:

Seled and Appaim. Seled died without children.

³¹The son of Appaim:

Ishi, who was the father of Sheshan.

Sheshan was the father of Ahlai.

³²The sons of Jada, Shammai's brother:

Jether and Jonathan. Jether died without children.

³³The sons of Jonathan:

Peleth and Zaza.

These were the descendants of Jerahmeel.

---

a 7 Achar means *trouble*; Achar is called Achan in Joshua.   *b 7* The Hebrew term refers to the irrevocable giving over of things or persons to the Lᴏʀᴅ, often by totally destroying them.   *c 9* Hebrew Kelubai, a variant of *Caleb*
d 11 Septuagint (see also Ruth 4:21); Hebrew Salma   *e 23* Or captured the settlements of Jair   *f 24* Father may mean civic leader or military leader; also in verses 42, 45, 49–52 and possibly elsewhere.   *g 25* Or Oren and Ozem, by

34 Sheshan had no sons—only daughters.
 He had an Egyptian servant named Jarha. 35 Sheshan gave his daughter in marriage to his servant Jarha, and she bore him Attai.
36 Attai was the father of Nathan,
 Nathan the father of Zabad,
 37 Zabad the father of Ephlal,
 Ephlal the father of Obed,
 38 Obed the father of Jehu,
 Jehu the father of Azariah,
 39 Azariah the father of Helez,
 Helez the father of Eleasah,
 40 Eleasah the father of Sismai,
 Sismai the father of Shallum,
 41 Shallum the father of Jekamiah,
 and Jekamiah the father of Elishama.

The Clans of Caleb

42 The sons of Caleb the brother of Jerahmeel:
 Mesha his firstborn, who was the father of Ziph, and his son Mareshah,*a* who was the father of Hebron.
43 The sons of Hebron:
 Korah, Tappuah, Rekem and Shema. 44 Shema was the father of Raham, and Raham the father of Jorkeam. Rekem was the father of Shammai. 45 The son of Shammai was Maon, and Maon was the father of Beth Zur.
46 Caleb's concubine Ephah was the mother of Haran, Moza and Gazez. Haran was the father of Gazez.
47 The sons of Jahdai:
 Regem, Jotham, Geshan, Pelet, Ephah and Shaaph.
48 Caleb's concubine Maacah was the mother of Sheber and Tirhanah. 49 She also gave birth to Shaaph the father of Madmannah and to Sheva the father of Macbenah and Gibea. Caleb's daughter was Acsah. 50 These were the descendants of Caleb.

 The sons of Hur the firstborn of Ephrathah:
 Shobal the father of Kiriath Jearim, 51 Salma the father of Bethlehem, and Hareph the father of Beth Gader.
52 The descendants of Shobal the father of Kiriath Jearim were:
 Haroeh, half the Manahathites, 53 and the clans of Kiriath Jearim: the Ithrites, Puthites, Shumathites and Mishraites. From these descended the Zorathites and Eshtaolites.
54 The descendants of Salma:
 Bethlehem, the Netophathites, Atroth Beth Joab, half the Manahathites, the Zorites, 55 and the clans of scribes*b* who lived at Jabez: the Tirathites, Shimeathites and Sucathites. These are the Kenites who came from Hammath, the father of the house of Recab.*c*

The Sons of David

3 These were the sons of David born to him in Hebron:
 The firstborn was Amnon the son of Ahinoam of Jezreel;
 the second, Daniel the son of Abigail of Carmel;
 2 the third, Absalom the son of Maacah daughter of Talmai king of Geshur;
 the fourth, Adonijah the son of Haggith;
 3 the fifth, Shephatiah the son of Abital;
 and the sixth, Ithream, by his wife Eglah.
 4 These six were born to David in Hebron, where he reigned seven years and six months. David reigned in Jerusalem thirty-three years, 5 and these were the children born to him there:

a 42 The meaning of the Hebrew for this phrase is uncertain.   *b 55* Or *of the Sopherites*   *c 55* Or *father of Beth Recab*

Shammua,^a Shobab, Nathan and Solomon. These four were by Bathsheba^b daughter of Ammiel. ⁶There were also Ibhar, Elishua,^c Eliphelet, ⁷Nogah, Nepheg, Japhia, ⁸Elishama, Eliada and Eliphelet—nine in all. ⁹All these were the sons of David, besides his sons by his concubines. And Tamar was their sister.

The Kings of Judah

¹⁰Solomon's son was Rehoboam,
Abijah his son,
Asa his son,
Jehoshaphat his son,
¹¹Jehoram^d his son,
Ahaziah his son,
Joash his son,
¹²Amaziah his son,
Azariah his son,
Jotham his son,
¹³Ahaz his son,
Hezekiah his son,
Manasseh his son,
¹⁴Amon his son,
Josiah his son.
¹⁵The sons of Josiah:
Johanan the firstborn,
Jehoiakim the second son,
Zedekiah the third,
Shallum the fourth.
¹⁶The successors of Jehoiakim:
Jehoiachin^e his son,
and Zedekiah.

The Royal Line After the Exile

¹⁷The descendants of Jehoiachin the captive:
Shealtiel his son, ¹⁸Malkiram, Pedaiah, Shenazzar, Jekamiah, Hoshama and Nedabiah.
¹⁹The sons of Pedaiah:
Zerubbabel and Shimei.
The sons of Zerubbabel:
Meshullam and Hananiah.
Shelomith was their sister.
²⁰There were also five others:
Hashubah, Ohel, Berekiah, Hasadiah and Jushab-Hesed.
²¹The descendants of Hananiah:
Pelatiah and Jeshaiah, and the sons of Rephaiah, of Arnan, of Obadiah and of Shecaniah.
²²The descendants of Shecaniah:
Shemaiah and his sons:
Hattush, Igal, Bariah, Neariah and Shaphat—six in all.
²³The sons of Neariah:
Elioenai, Hizkiah and Azrikam—three in all.
²⁴The sons of Elioenai:
Hodaviah, Eliashib, Pelaiah, Akkub, Johanan, Delaiah and Anani—seven in all.

^a 5 Hebrew Shimea, a variant of Shammua   ^b 5 One Hebrew manuscript and Vulgate (see also Septuagint and 2 Samuel 11:3); most Hebrew manuscripts Bathshua   ^c 6 Two Hebrew manuscripts (see also 2 Samuel 5:15 and 1 Chron. 14:5); most Hebrew manuscripts Elishama   ^d 11 Hebrew Joram, a variant of Jehoram   ^e 16 Hebrew Jeconiah, a variant of Jehoiachin; also in verse 17

mirror images

Jezebel—An Influence for Evil

What a tragedy! Jezebel had been raised as a princess in a pagan country that worshiped the false god Baal. When she married King Ahab of Israel, she brought Baal worship into God's nation. Then she began to kill all of the faithful prophets of God. Jezebel was smart, clever and scheming, but she used her talents for persuasion and the power of her position to do incredible evil instead of using it for good.

Jezebel is probably most known for the ungodly influence she had on her husband, King Ahab. She introduced Ahab to Baal worship, and as a result, this king went from "bad" to "evil" in the history books. And when spoiled little Ahab didn't get the vineyard he wanted, she concocted a plan that involved everything from political corruption to false accusations, lies and murder.

Without a doubt, our friends and relationships have an enormous influence on our lives. Some bad influences may be very subtle and even seem harmless. Maybe it's a friend who says, "Where I come from, underage drinking is no big deal." "I just smoke marijuana to relax and think more clearly." "I think you're old enough and mature enough to have sex."

But any "friend" who influences another to do something wrong or to turn away from God is no friend at all. Those friends whom we allow into our personal inner circle—our best, closest friends—are the ones with the biggest influence on our lives. Are they leaving good impressions on us? Are they helping us to be better or making it harder to be good? There's no harmless, neutral ground—it's either one or the other. If our close friends are not lifting us up toward God, then they are bringing us down. Jezebel was no exception. Looking at her life reminds us to take a long hard look at who is influencing us; and even more so, to make sure we're not being the evil influence in someone else's life.

To read the next Mirror Images profile, go to page 538.

Dear God, please help me to choose friends who will be good influences on me. And make me aware of and accountable for the influence I have in my friends' lives. Amen.

dear God

Read more about Jezebel in 1 Kings 16–21 (pages 421–430) and 2 Kings 9 (pages 445–447).

4

The descendants of Judah:
Perez, Hezron, Carmi, Hur and Shobal.
²Reaiah son of Shobal was the father of Jahath, and Jahath the father of Ahumai and Lahad. These were the clans of the Zorathites.

³These were the sons*a* of Etam:
Jezreel, Ishma and Idbash. Their sister was named Hazzelelponi. ⁴Penuel was the father of Gedor, and Ezer the father of Hushah.

These were the descendants of Hur, the firstborn of Ephrathah and father*b* of Bethlehem.

⁵Ashhur the father of Tekoa had two wives, Helah and Naarah.

⁶Naarah bore him Ahuzzam, Hepher, Temeni and Haahashtari. These were the descendants of Naarah.

⁷The sons of Helah:
Zereth, Zohar, Ethnan, ⁸and Koz, who was the father of Anub and Hazzobebah and of the clans of Aharhel son of Harum.

⁹Jabez was more honorable than his brothers. His mother had named him Jabez,*c* saying, "I gave birth to him in pain." ¹⁰Jabez cried out to the God of Israel, "Oh, that you would bless me and enlarge my territory! Let your hand be with me, and keep me from harm so that I will be free from pain." And God granted his request.

¹¹Kelub, Shuhah's brother, was the father of Mehir, who was the father of Eshton. ¹²Eshton was the father of Beth Rapha, Paseah and Tehinnah the father of Ir Nahash.*d* These were the men of Recah.

¹³The sons of Kenaz:
Othniel and Seraiah.
The sons of Othniel:
Hathath and Meonothai.*e* ¹⁴Meonothai was the father of Ophrah.
Seraiah was the father of Joab,
the father of Ge Harashim.*f* It was called this because its people were craftsmen.

¹⁵The sons of Caleb son of Jephunneh:
Iru, Elah and Naam.
The son of Elah:
Kenaz.

¹⁶The sons of Jehallelel:
Ziph, Ziphah, Tiria and Asarel.

¹⁷The sons of Ezrah:
Jether, Mered, Epher and Jalon. One of Mered's wives gave birth to Miriam, Shammai and Ishbah the father of Eshtemoa. ¹⁸(His Judean wife gave birth to Jered the father of Gedor, Heber the father of Soco, and Jekuthiel the father of Zanoah.) These were the children of Pharaoh's daughter Bithiah, whom Mered had married.

¹⁹The sons of Hodiah's wife, the sister of Naham:

ξenuine

confidence

» 4:9-10

Can you imagine your mom sticking you with a name like "Ouch" or "Ugh"?! Well, that's basically what happened to poor Jabez, whose name sounded like the Hebrew word for *pain*. Did Jabez give in to the destiny his name implied? No way! He knew that God alone controlled his future, so he asked God to direct it and protect him. Are you stuck with some family baggage of your own—divorce, drug or alcohol addiction, cruddy relationships, abuse? It may seem like there's no escaping it, but by God's grace you don't have to carry that with you into your own future.

a 3 Some Septuagint manuscripts (see also Vulgate); Hebrew father   *b 4 Father may mean civic leader or military leader; also in verses 12, 14, 17, 18 and possibly elsewhere.*   *c 9 Jabez sounds like the Hebrew for pain.*   *d 12 Or of the city of Nahash*   *e 13 Some Septuagint manuscripts and Vulgate; Hebrew does not have and Meonothai.*   *f 14 Ge Harashim means valley of craftsmen.*

the father of Keilah the Garmite, and Eshtemoa the Maacathite.

²⁰ The sons of Shimon:

Amnon, Rinnah, Ben-Hanan and Tilon.

The descendants of Ishi:

Zoheth and Ben-Zoheth.

²¹ The sons of Shelah son of Judah:

Er the father of Lecah, Laadah the father of Mareshah and the clans of the linen workers at Beth Ashbea, ²² Jokim, the men of Cozeba, and Joash and Saraph, who ruled in Moab and Jashubi Lehem. (These records are from ancient times.) ²³ They were the potters who lived at Netaim and Gederah; they stayed there and worked for the king.

Simeon

²⁴ The descendants of Simeon:

Nemuel, Jamin, Jarib, Zerah and Shaul;

²⁵ Shallum was Shaul's son, Mibsam his son and Mishma his son.

²⁶ The descendants of Mishma:

Hammuel his son, Zaccur his son and Shimei his son.

²⁷ Shimei had sixteen sons and six daughters, but his brothers did not have many children; so their entire clan did not become as numerous as the people of Judah. ²⁸ They lived in Beersheba, Moladah, Hazar Shual, ²⁹ Bilhah, Ezem, Tolad, ³⁰ Bethuel, Hormah, Ziklag, ³¹ Beth Marcaboth, Hazar Susim, Beth Biri and Shaaraim. These were their towns until the reign of David. ³² Their surrounding villages were Etam, Ain, Rimmon, Token and Ashan—five towns— ³³ and all the villages around these towns as far as Baalath. ᵃ These were their settlements. And they kept a genealogical record.

³⁴ Meshobab, Jamlech, Joshah son of Amaziah, ³⁵ Joel, Jehu son of Joshibiah, the son of Seraiah, the son of Asiel, ³⁶ also Elioenai, Jaakobah, Jeshohaiah, Asaiah, Adiel, Jesimiel, Benaiah, ³⁷ and Ziza son of Shiphi, the son of Allon, the son of Jedaiah, the son of Shimri, the son of Shemaiah.

³⁸ The men listed above by name were leaders of their clans. Their families increased greatly, ³⁹ and they went to the outskirts of Gedor to the east of the valley in search of pasture for their flocks. ⁴⁰ They found rich, good pasture, and the land was spacious, peaceful and quiet. Some Hamites had lived there formerly.

⁴¹ The men whose names were listed came in the days of Hezekiah king of Judah. They attacked the Hamites in their dwellings and also the Meunites who were there and completely destroyed ᵇ them, as is evident to this day. Then they settled in their place, because there was pasture for their flocks. ⁴² And five hundred of these Simeonites, led by Pelatiah, Neariah, Rephaiah and Uzziel, the sons of Ishi, invaded the hill country of Seir. ⁴³ They killed the remaining Amalekites who had escaped, and they have lived there to this day.

Reuben

5 The sons of Reuben the firstborn of Israel (he was the firstborn, but when he defiled his father's marriage bed, his rights as firstborn were given to the sons of Joseph son of Israel; so he could not be listed in the genealogical record in accordance with his birthright, ²and though Judah was the strongest of his brothers and a ruler came from him, the rights of the firstborn belonged to Joseph)— ³the sons of Reuben the firstborn of Israel:

Hanoch, Pallu, Hezron and Carmi.

⁴ The descendants of Joel:

Shemaiah his son, Gog his son,

Shimei his son, ⁵ Micah his son,

Reaiah his son, Baal his son,

⁶ and Beerah his son, whom Tiglath-Pileser ᶜ king of Assyria took into exile. Beerah was a leader of the Reubenites.

ᵃ 33 Some Septuagint manuscripts (see also Joshua 19:8); Hebrew *Baal*   ᵇ 41 The Hebrew term refers to the irrevocable giving over of things or persons to the LORD, often by totally destroying them.   ᶜ 6 Hebrew *Tilgath-Pilneser,* a variant of *Tiglath-Pileser;* also in verse 26

[7] Their relatives by clans, listed according to their genealogical records:

Jeiel the chief, Zechariah, [8]and Bela son of Azaz, the son of Shema, the son of Joel. They settled in the area from Aroer to Nebo and Baal Meon. [9]To the east they occupied the land up to the edge of the desert that extends to the Euphrates River, because their livestock had increased in Gilead.

[10]During Saul's reign they waged war against the Hagrites, who were defeated at their hands; they occupied the dwellings of the Hagrites throughout the entire region east of Gilead.

Gad

[11] The Gadites lived next to them in Bashan, as far as Salecah:

[12] Joel was the chief, Shapham the second, then Janai and Shaphat, in Bashan.

[13] Their relatives, by families, were:

Michael, Meshullam, Sheba, Jorai, Jacan, Zia and Eber—seven in all.

[14] These were the sons of Abihail son of Huri, the son of Jaroah, the son of Gilead, the son of Michael, the son of Jeshishai, the son of Jahdo, the son of Buz.

[15] Ahi son of Abdiel, the son of Guni, was head of their family.

[16] The Gadites lived in Gilead, in Bashan and its outlying villages, and on all the pasturelands of Sharon as far as they extended.

[17] All these were entered in the genealogical records during the reigns of Jotham king of Judah and Jeroboam king of Israel.

[18]The Reubenites, the Gadites and the half-tribe of Manasseh had 44,760 men ready for military service—able-bodied men who could handle shield and sword, who could use a bow, and who were trained for battle. [19]They waged war against the Hagrites, Jetur, Naphish and Nodab. [20]They were helped in fighting them, and God handed the Hagrites and all their allies over to them, because they cried out to him during the battle. He answered their prayers, because they trusted in him. [21]They seized the livestock of the Hagrites—fifty thousand camels, two hundred fifty thousand sheep and two thousand donkeys. They also took one hundred thousand people captive, [22]and many others fell slain, because the battle was God's. And they occupied the land until the exile.

The Half-Tribe of Manasseh

[23]The people of the half-tribe of Manasseh were numerous; they settled in the land from Bashan to Baal Hermon, that is, to Senir (Mount Hermon).

[24]These were the heads of their families: Epher, Ishi, Eliel, Azriel, Jeremiah, Hodaviah and Jahdiel. They were brave warriors, famous men, and heads of their families. [25]But they were unfaithful to the God of their fathers and prostituted themselves to the gods of the peoples of the land, whom God had destroyed before them. [26]So the God of Israel stirred up the spirit of Pul king of Assyria (that is, Tiglath-Pileser king of Assyria), who took the Reubenites, the Gadites and the half-tribe of Manasseh into exile. He took them to Halah, Habor, Hara and the river of Gozan, where they are to this day.

genuine faith » 5:18–20

Does your life sometimes feel like a battleground? Are you struggling to keep up with the pressures of school, work and home? At odds with your family or friends? Fighting within yourself as you have to choose again and again to obey God or follow the world? Want to know how to win this war? Take a lesson from the Israelites: Don't trust your own talents and strength; those alone won't get you very far. Instead, put your faith in God and trust him to lead you through life.

Levi

6 The sons of Levi:
Gershon, Kohath and Merari.
² The sons of Kohath:
Amram, Izhar, Hebron and Uzziel.
³ The children of Amram:
Aaron, Moses and Miriam.

The sons of Aaron:
Nadab, Abihu, Eleazar and Ithamar.
⁴ Eleazar was the father of Phinehas,
Phinehas the father of Abishua,
⁵ Abishua the father of Bukki,
Bukki the father of Uzzi,
⁶ Uzzi the father of Zerahiah,
Zerahiah the father of Meraioth,
⁷ Meraioth the father of Amariah,
Amariah the father of Ahitub,
⁸ Ahitub the father of Zadok,
Zadok the father of Ahimaaz,
⁹ Ahimaaz the father of Azariah,
Azariah the father of Johanan,
¹⁰ Johanan the father of Azariah (it was he who served as priest in the temple Solomon built in Jerusalem),
¹¹ Azariah the father of Amariah,
Amariah the father of Ahitub,
¹² Ahitub the father of Zadok,
Zadok the father of Shallum,
¹³ Shallum the father of Hilkiah,
Hilkiah the father of Azariah,
¹⁴ Azariah the father of Seraiah,
and Seraiah the father of Jehozadak.

¹⁵ Jehozadak was deported when the Lᴏʀᴅ sent Judah and Jerusalem into exile by the hand of Nebuchadnezzar.

¹⁶ The sons of Levi:
Gershon,ᵃ Kohath and Merari.
¹⁷ These are the names of the sons of Gershon:
Libni and Shimei.
¹⁸ The sons of Kohath:
Amram, Izhar, Hebron and Uzziel.
¹⁹ The sons of Merari:
Mahli and Mushi.

These are the clans of the Levites listed according to their fathers:
²⁰ Of Gershon:
Libni his son, Jehath his son,
Zimmah his son, ²¹ Joah his son,
Iddo his son, Zerah his son
and Jeatherai his son.
²² The descendants of Kohath:
Amminadab his son, Korah his son,
Assir his son, ²³ Elkanah his son,
Ebiasaph his son, Assir his son,
²⁴ Tahath his son, Uriel his son,
Uzziah his son and Shaul his son.

ᵃ 16 Hebrew *Gershom*, a variant of *Gershon*; also in verses 17, 20, 43, 62 and 71

²⁵ The descendants of Elkanah:
   Amasai, Ahimoth,
   ²⁶ Elkanah his son, ^a Zophai his son,
   Nahath his son, ²⁷ Eliab his son,
   Jeroham his son, Elkanah his son
   and Samuel his son. ^b
²⁸ The sons of Samuel:
   Joel ^c the firstborn
   and Abijah the second son.
²⁹ The descendants of Merari:
   Mahli, Libni his son,
   Shimei his son, Uzzah his son,
   ³⁰ Shimea his son, Haggiah his son
   and Asaiah his son.

The Temple Musicians

³¹ These are the men David put in charge of the music in the house of the LORD after the ark came to rest there. ³² They ministered with music before the tabernacle, the Tent of Meeting, until Solomon built the temple of the LORD in Jerusalem. They performed their duties according to the regulations laid down for them.

³³ Here are the men who served, together with their sons:
From the Kohathites:
   Heman, the musician,
   the son of Joel, the son of Samuel,
   ³⁴ the son of Elkanah, the son of Jeroham,
   the son of Eliel, the son of Toah,
   ³⁵ the son of Zuph, the son of Elkanah,
   the son of Mahath, the son of Amasai,
   ³⁶ the son of Elkanah, the son of Joel,
   the son of Azariah, the son of Zephaniah,
   ³⁷ the son of Tahath, the son of Assir,
   the son of Ebiasaph, the son of Korah,
   ³⁸ the son of Izhar, the son of Kohath,
   the son of Levi, the son of Israel;
³⁹ and Heman's associate Asaph, who served at his right hand:
   Asaph son of Berekiah, the son of Shimea,
   ⁴⁰ the son of Michael, the son of Baaseiah, ^d
   the son of Malkijah, ⁴¹ the son of Ethni,
   the son of Zerah, the son of Adaiah,
   ⁴² the son of Ethan, the son of Zimmah,
   the son of Shimei, ⁴³ the son of Jahath,
   the son of Gershon, the son of Levi;
⁴⁴ and from their associates, the Merarites, at his left hand:
   Ethan son of Kishi, the son of Abdi,
   the son of Malluch, ⁴⁵ the son of Hashabiah,
   the son of Amaziah, the son of Hilkiah,
   ⁴⁶ the son of Amzi, the son of Bani,
   the son of Shemer, ⁴⁷ the son of Mahli,
   the son of Mushi, the son of Merari,
   the son of Levi.

truth or dare

It takes all kinds of people to keep a church going strong—not just missionaries and pastors. What's your unique ministry?

6:31–49

^a 26 Some Hebrew manuscripts, Septuagint and Syriac; most Hebrew manuscripts *Ahimoth* ²⁶*and Elkanah. The sons of Elkanah:* ^b 27 Some Septuagint manuscripts (see also 1 Samuel 1:19,20 and 1 Chron. 6:33,34); Hebrew does not have *and Samuel his son.* ^c 28 Some Septuagint manuscripts and Syriac (see also 1 Samuel 8:2 and 1 Chron. 6:33); Hebrew does not have *Joel.* ^d 40 Most Hebrew manuscripts; some Hebrew manuscripts, one Septuagint manuscript and Syriac *Maaseiah*

[48]Their fellow Levites were assigned to all the other duties of the tabernacle, the house of God. [49]But Aaron and his descendants were the ones who presented offerings on the altar of burnt offering and on the altar of incense in connection with all that was done in the Most Holy Place, making atonement for Israel, in accordance with all that Moses the servant of God had commanded.

[50]These were the descendants of Aaron:

Eleazar his son, Phinehas his son,
Abishua his son, [51]Bukki his son,
Uzzi his son, Zerahiah his son,
[52]Meraioth his son, Amariah his son,
Ahitub his son, [53]Zadok his son
and Ahimaaz his son.

[54]These were the locations of their settlements allotted as their territory (they were assigned to the descendants of Aaron who were from the Kohathite clan, because the first lot was for them):
[55]They were given Hebron in Judah with its surrounding pasturelands. [56]But the fields and villages around the city were given to Caleb son of Jephunneh.
[57]So the descendants of Aaron were given Hebron (a city of refuge), and Libnah,[a] Jattir, Eshtemoa, [58]Hilen, Debir, [59]Ashan, Juttah[b] and Beth Shemesh, together with their pasturelands. [60]And from the tribe of Benjamin they were given Gibeon,[c] Geba, Alemeth and Anathoth, together with their pasturelands.

These towns, which were distributed among the Kohathite clans, were thirteen in all.
[61]The rest of Kohath's descendants were allotted ten towns from the clans of half the tribe of Manasseh.
[62]The descendants of Gershon, clan by clan, were allotted thirteen towns from the tribes of Issachar, Asher and Naphtali, and from the part of the tribe of Manasseh that is in Bashan.
[63]The descendants of Merari, clan by clan, were allotted twelve towns from the tribes of Reuben, Gad and Zebulun.
[64]So the Israelites gave the Levites these towns and their pasturelands. [65]From the tribes of Judah, Simeon and Benjamin they allotted the previously named towns.
[66]Some of the Kohathite clans were given as their territory towns from the tribe of Ephraim.
[67]In the hill country of Ephraim they were given Shechem (a city of refuge), and Gezer,[d] [68]Jokmeam, Beth Horon, [69]Aijalon and Gath Rimmon, together with their pasturelands.
[70]And from half the tribe of Manasseh the Israelites gave Aner and Bileam, together with their pasturelands, to the rest of the Kohathite clans.

[71]The Gershonites received the following:

From the clan of the half-tribe of Manasseh
they received Golan in Bashan and also Ashtaroth, together with their pasturelands;
[72]from the tribe of Issachar
they received Kedesh, Daberath, [73]Ramoth and Anem, together with their pasturelands;
[74]from the tribe of Asher
they received Mashal, Abdon, [75]Hukok and Rehob, together with their pasturelands;
[76]and from the tribe of Naphtali
they received Kedesh in Galilee, Hammon and Kiriathaim, together with their pasturelands.

[77]The Merarites (the rest of the Levites) received the following:

From the tribe of Zebulun
they received Jokneam, Kartah,[e] Rimmono and Tabor, together with their pasturelands;
[78]from the tribe of Reuben across the Jordan east of Jericho
they received Bezer in the desert, Jahzah, [79]Kedemoth and Mephaath, together with their pasturelands;
[80]and from the tribe of Gad

---

[a] 57 See Joshua 21:13; Hebrew given the cities of refuge: Hebron, Libnah.   [b] 59 Syriac (see also Septuagint and Joshua 21:16); Hebrew does not have Juttah.   [c] 60 See Joshua 21:17; Hebrew does not have Gibeon.   [d] 67 See Joshua 21:21; Hebrew given the cities of refuge: Shechem, Gezer.   [e] 77 See Septuagint and Joshua 21:34; Hebrew does not have Jokneam, Kartah.

they received Ramoth in Gilead, Mahanaim, [81]Heshbon and Jazer, together with their pasturelands.

Issachar

7 The sons of Issachar:
Tola, Puah, Jashub and Shimron—four in all. [2]The sons of Tola:
Uzzi, Rephaiah, Jeriel, Jahmai, Ibsam and Samuel—heads of their families. During the reign of David, the descendants of Tola listed as fighting men in their genealogy numbered 22,600.
[3]The son of Uzzi:
Izrahiah.
The sons of Izrahiah:
Michael, Obadiah, Joel and Isshiah. All five of them were chiefs. [4]According to their family genealogy, they had 36,000 men ready for battle, for they had many wives and children.
[5]The relatives who were fighting men belonging to all the clans of Issachar, as listed in their genealogy, were 87,000 in all.

Benjamin

[6]Three sons of Benjamin:
Bela, Beker and Jediael.
[7]The sons of Bela:
Ezbon, Uzzi, Uzziel, Jerimoth and Iri, heads of families—five in all. Their genealogical record listed 22,034 fighting men.
[8]The sons of Beker:
Zemirah, Joash, Eliezer, Elioenai, Omri, Jeremoth, Abijah, Anathoth and Alemeth. All these were the sons of Beker. [9]Their genealogical record listed the heads of families and 20,200 fighting men.
[10]The son of Jediael:
Bilhan.
The sons of Bilhan:
Jeush, Benjamin, Ehud, Kenaanah, Zethan, Tarshish and Ahishahar. [11]All these sons of Jediael were heads of families. There were 17,200 fighting men ready to go out to war.
[12]The Shuppites and Huppites were the descendants of Ir, and the Hushites the descendants of Aher.

Naphtali

[13]The sons of Naphtali:
Jahziel, Guni, Jezer and Shillem[a]—the descendants of Bilhah.

Manasseh

[14]The descendants of Manasseh:
Asriel was his descendant through his Aramean concubine. She gave birth to Makir the father of Gilead. [15]Makir took a wife from among the Huppites and Shuppites. His sister's name was Maacah.
Another descendant was named Zelophehad, who had only daughters.
[16]Makir's wife Maacah gave birth to a son and named him Peresh. His brother was named Sheresh, and his sons were Ulam and Rakem.
[17]The son of Ulam:
Bedan.
These were the sons of Gilead son of Makir, the son of Manasseh. [18]His sister Hammoleketh gave birth to Ishhod, Abiezer and Mahlah.
[19]The sons of Shemida were:
Ahian, Shechem, Likhi and Aniam.

a 13 Some Hebrew and Septuagint manuscripts (see also Gen. 46:24 and Num. 26:49); most Hebrew manuscripts Shallum

[7]Naaman, Ahijah, and Gera, who deported them and who was the father of Uzza and Ahihud.

[8]Sons were born to Shaharaim in Moab after he had divorced his wives Hushim and Baara. [9]By his wife Hodesh he had Jobab, Zibia, Mesha, Malcam, [10]Jeuz, Sakia and Mirmah. These were his sons, heads of families. [11]By Hushim he had Abitub and Elpaal.

[12]The sons of Elpaal:

Eber, Misham, Shemed (who built Ono and Lod with its surrounding villages), [13]and Beriah and Shema, who were heads of families of those living in Aijalon and who drove out the inhabitants of Gath.

[14]Ahio, Shashak, Jeremoth, [15]Zebadiah, Arad, Eder, [16]Michael, Ishpah and Joha were the sons of Beriah.

[17]Zebadiah, Meshullam, Hizki, Heber, [18]Ishmerai, Izliah and Jobab were the sons of Elpaal.

[19]Jakim, Zicri, Zabdi, [20]Elienai, Zillethai, Eliel, [21]Adaiah, Beraiah and Shimrath were the sons of Shimei.

[22]Ishpan, Eber, Eliel, [23]Abdon, Zicri, Hanan, [24]Hananiah, Elam, Anthothijah, [25]Iphdeiah and Penuel were the sons of Shashak.

[26]Shamsherai, Shehariah, Athaliah, [27]Jaareshiah, Elijah and Zicri were the sons of Jeroham.

[28]All these were heads of families, chiefs as listed in their genealogy, and they lived in Jerusalem.

[29]Jeiel[a] the father[b] of Gibeon lived in Gibeon.

His wife's name was Maacah, [30]and his firstborn son was Abdon, followed by Zur, Kish, Baal, Ner,[c] Nadab, [31]Gedor, Ahio, Zeker [32]and Mikloth, who was the father of Shimeah. They too lived near their relatives in Jerusalem.

[33]Ner was the father of Kish, Kish the father of Saul, and Saul the father of Jonathan, Malki-Shua, Abinadab and Esh-Baal.[d]

[34]The son of Jonathan:

Merib-Baal,[e] who was the father of Micah.

[35]The sons of Micah:

Pithon, Melech, Tarea and Ahaz.

[36]Ahaz was the father of Jehoaddah, Jehoaddah was the father of Alemeth, Azmaveth and Zimri, and Zimri was the father of Moza. [37]Moza was the father of Binea; Raphah was his son, Eleasah his son and Azel his son.

[38]Azel had six sons, and these were their names:

Azrikam, Bokeru, Ishmael, Sheariah, Obadiah and Hanan. All these were the sons of Azel.

[39]The sons of his brother Eshek:

Ulam his firstborn, Jeush the second son and Eliphelet the third. [40]The sons of Ulam were brave warriors who could handle the bow. They had many sons and grandsons—150 in all.

All these were the descendants of Benjamin.

9

All Israel was listed in the genealogies recorded in the book of the kings of Israel.

The People in Jerusalem

The people of Judah were taken captive to Babylon because of their unfaithfulness. [2]Now the first to resettle on their own property in their own towns were some Israelites, priests, Levites and temple servants.

[3]Those from Judah, from Benjamin, and from Ephraim and Manasseh who lived in Jerusalem were:

[4]Uthai son of Ammihud, the son of Omri, the son of Imri, the son of Bani, a descendant of Perez son of Judah.

---

a 29 Some Septuagint manuscripts (see also 1 Chron. 9:35); Hebrew does not have Jeiel.   *b 29 Father may mean civic leader or military leader.*   *c 30 Some Septuagint manuscripts (see also 1 Chron. 9:36); Hebrew does not have Ner.*   *d 33 Also known as Ish-Bosheth*   *e 34 Also known as Mephibosheth*

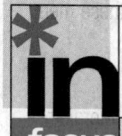

Only a Shadow

Profile: **Carrie**

Who's gorgeous and talented and this year's valedictorian? That would be my sister. They even published an article about Cassie in this month's school newspaper, and it almost made me sick. Her friends gave quotes like, "Cassie's always got time for me," and, "She's just real with everyone she meets," and "I think Cassie Smith could be the next President . . . or at least Miss America."

Everyone at our school is always saying, "Oh, so you're Cassie's sister. Cool." As if that's the only thing worth noticing about me. As if anyone cares what *I* think or do. I study hard, but I'll never get grades like Cassie does. She's the one with the boyfriend; she's the captain of the volleyball team . . . and she's always been the center of attention since we were kids.

You'd think that being the baby of the family would be ideal. I could let my older sister measure up to all of our parents' expectations. But somehow, because Cassie's so great at everything, I'm always in her shadow. Unnoticed. And it's hard to hate her because she's a genuinely nice person—thoughtful, caring and friendly to everyone.

If God wanted to create Supergirl, I'm wondering why he put her in our family. I can't help but feeling jealous of her. For some reason God decided to make Cassie better at *everything*.

jealousy in focus

When you start feeling jealous, try these steps:

» Remind yourself of what God thinks of you. You're chosen by God and precious to him, and you have a place in his family that only you can fill (see 1 Corinthians 12:14–20, page 1517).

» Go beyond your feelings by reading God's Word and drawing closer to him. The more you become like Jesus, the less you'll be tempted by jealousy (see Philippians 2:3–8, page 1551).

For more on this topic, see the index on page 1656.

jealousy

[5] Of the Shilonites:

Asaiah the firstborn and his sons.

[6] Of the Zerahites:

Jeuel.

The people from Judah numbered 690.

[7] Of the Benjamites:

Sallu son of Meshullam, the son of Hodaviah, the son of Hassenuah;

[8] Ibneiah son of Jeroham; Elah son of Uzzi, the son of Micri; and Meshullam son of Shephatiah, the son of Reuel, the son of Ibnijah.

9 The people from Benjamin, as listed in their genealogy, numbered 956. All these men were heads of their families.

10 Of the priests:

Jedaiah; Jehoiarib; Jakin;

11 Azariah son of Hilkiah, the son of Meshullam, the son of Zadok, the son of Meraioth, the son of Ahitub, the official in charge of the house of God;

12 Adaiah son of Jeroham, the son of Pashhur, the son of Malkijah; and Maasai son of Adiel, the son of Jahzerah, the son of Meshullam, the son of Meshillemith, the son of Immer.

13 The priests, who were heads of families, numbered 1,760. They were able men, responsible for ministering in the house of God.

14 Of the Levites:

Shemaiah son of Hasshub, the son of Azrikam, the son of Hashabiah, a Merarite; 15 Bakbakkar, Heresh, Galal and Mattaniah son of Mica, the son of Zicri, the son of Asaph; 16 Obadiah son of Shemaiah, the son of Galal, the son of Jeduthun; and Berekiah son of Asa, the son of Elkanah, who lived in the villages of the Netophathites.

17 The gatekeepers:

Shallum, Akkub, Talmon, Ahiman and their brothers, Shallum their chief 18 being stationed at the King's Gate on the east, up to the present time. These were the gatekeepers belonging to the camp of the Levites. 19 Shallum son of Kore, the son of Ebiasaph, the son of Korah, and his fellow gatekeepers from his family (the Korahites) were responsible for guarding the thresholds of the Tent *a* just as their fathers had been responsible for guarding the entrance to the dwelling of the LORD. 20 In earlier times Phinehas son of Eleazar was in charge of the gatekeepers, and the LORD was with him. 21 Zechariah son of Meshelemiah was the gatekeeper at the entrance to the Tent of Meeting.

22 Altogether, those chosen to be gatekeepers at the thresholds numbered 212. They were registered by genealogy in their villages. The gatekeepers had been assigned to their positions of trust by David and Samuel the seer. 23 They and their descendants were in charge of guarding the gates of the house of the LORD—the house called the Tent. 24 The gatekeepers were on the four sides: east, west, north and south. 25 Their brothers in their villages had to come from time to time and share their duties for seven-day periods. 26 But the four principal gatekeepers, who were Levites, were entrusted with the responsibility for the rooms and treasuries in the house of God. 27 They would spend the night stationed around the house of God, because they had to guard it; and they had charge of the key for opening it each morning.

28 Some of them were in charge of the articles used in the temple service; they counted them when they were brought in and when they were taken out. 29 Others were assigned to take care of the furnishings and all the other articles of the sanctuary, as well as the flour and wine, and the oil, incense and spices. 30 But some of the priests took care of mixing the spices. 31 A Levite named Mattithiah, the firstborn son of Shallum the Korahite, was entrusted with the responsibility for baking the offering bread. 32 Some of their Kohathite brothers were in charge of preparing for every Sabbath the bread set out on the table.

33 Those who were musicians, heads of Levite families, stayed in the rooms of the temple and were exempt from other duties because they were responsible for the work day and night.

34 All these were heads of Levite families, chiefs as listed in their genealogy, and they lived in Jerusalem.

The Genealogy of Saul

35 Jeiel the father *b* of Gibeon lived in Gibeon.

His wife's name was Maacah, 36 and his firstborn son was Abdon, followed by Zur, Kish, Baal, Ner, Nadab, 37 Gedor, Ahio, Zechariah and Mikloth. 38 Mikloth was the father of Shimeam. They too lived near their relatives in Jerusalem.

39 Ner was the father of Kish, Kish the father of Saul, and Saul the father of Jonathan, Malki-Shua, Abinadab and Esh-Baal. *c*

---

a 19 That is, the temple; also in verses 21 and 23   *b 35* Father may mean *civic leader* or *military leader.*   *c 39* Also known as *Ish-Bosheth*

[40] The son of Jonathan:

Merib-Baal, [a] who was the father of Micah.

[41] The sons of Micah:

Pithon, Melech, Tahrea and Ahaz. [b]

[42] Ahaz was the father of Jadah, Jadah [c] was the father of Alemeth, Azmaveth and Zimri, and Zimri was the father of Moza. [43] Moza was the father of Binea; Rephaiah was his son, Eleasah his son and Azel his son.

[44] Azel had six sons, and these were their names:

Azrikam, Bokeru, Ishmael, Sheariah, Obadiah and Hanan. These were the sons of Azel.

Saul Takes His Life

10 Now the Philistines fought against Israel; the Israelites fled before them, and many fell slain on Mount Gilboa. [2] The Philistines pressed hard after Saul and his sons, and they killed his sons Jonathan, Abinadab and Malki-Shua. [3] The fighting grew fierce around Saul, and when the archers overtook him, they wounded him.

[4] Saul said to his armor-bearer, "Draw your sword and run me through, or these uncircumcised fellows will come and abuse me."

But his armor-bearer was terrified and would not do it; so Saul took his own sword and fell on it. [5] When the armor-bearer saw that Saul was dead, he too fell on his sword and died. [6] So Saul and his three sons died, and all his house died together.

[7] When all the Israelites in the valley saw that the army had fled and that Saul and his sons had died, they abandoned their towns and fled. And the Philistines came and occupied them.

[8] The next day, when the Philistines came to strip the dead, they found Saul and his sons fallen on Mount Gilboa. [9] They stripped him and took his head and his armor, and sent messengers throughout the land of the Philistines to proclaim the news among their idols and their people. [10] They put his armor in the temple of their gods and hung up his head in the temple of Dagon.

[11] When all the inhabitants of Jabesh Gilead heard of everything the Philistines had done to Saul, [12] all their valiant men went and took the bodies of Saul and his sons and brought them to Jabesh. Then they buried their bones under the great tree in Jabesh, and they fasted seven days.

[13] Saul died because he was unfaithful to the LORD; he did not keep the word of the LORD and even consulted a medium for guidance, [14] and did not inquire of the LORD. So the LORD put him to death and turned the kingdom over to David son of Jesse.

truth or dare

Saul outright did wrong, and he also failed to do the right thing. If you want to follow God, you can't remain passive.

10:13–14

David Becomes King Over Israel

11 All Israel came together to David at Hebron and said, "We are your own flesh and blood. [2] In the past, even while Saul was king, you were the one who led Israel on their military campaigns. And the LORD your God said to you, 'You will shepherd my people Israel, and you will become their ruler.' "

[3] When all the elders of Israel had come to King David at Hebron, he made a compact with them at Hebron before the LORD, and they anointed David king over Israel, as the LORD had promised through Samuel.

David Conquers Jerusalem

[4] David and all the Israelites marched to Jerusalem (that is, Jebus). The Jebusites who lived there [5] said to David, "You will not get in here." Nevertheless, David captured the fortress of Zion, the City of David.

---

a 40 Also known as *Mephibosheth*   *b 41* Vulgate and Syriac (see also Septuagint and 1 Chron. 8:35); Hebrew does not have *and Ahaz.*   *c 42* Some Hebrew manuscripts and Septuagint (see also 1 Chron. 8:36); most Hebrew manuscripts *Jarah, Jarah*

⁶David had said, "Whoever leads the attack on the Jebusites will become commander-in-chief." Joab son of Zeruiah went up first, and so he received the command.

⁷David then took up residence in the fortress, and so it was called the City of David. ⁸He built up the city around it, from the supporting terraces[a] to the surrounding wall, while Joab restored the rest of the city. ⁹And David became more and more powerful, because the LORD Almighty was with him.

David's Mighty Men

¹⁰These were the chiefs of David's mighty men—they, together with all Israel, gave his kingship strong support to extend it over the whole land, as the LORD had promised— ¹¹this is the list of David's mighty men:

Jashobeam,[b] a Hacmonite, was chief of the officers[c]; he raised his spear against three hundred men, whom he killed in one encounter.

¹²Next to him was Eleazar son of Dodai the Ahohite, one of the three mighty men. ¹³He was with David at Pas Dammim when the Philistines gathered there for battle. At a place where there was a field full of barley, the troops fled from the Philistines. ¹⁴But they took their stand in the middle of the field. They defended it and struck the Philistines down, and the LORD brought about a great victory.

¹⁵Three of the thirty chiefs came down to David to the rock at the cave of Adullam, while a band of Philistines was encamped in the Valley of Rephaim. ¹⁶At that time David was in the stronghold, and the Philistine garrison was at Bethlehem. ¹⁷David longed for water and said, "Oh, that someone would get me a drink of water from the well near the gate of Bethlehem!" ¹⁸So the Three broke through the Philistine lines, drew water from the well near the gate of Bethlehem and carried it back to David. But he refused to drink it; instead, he poured it out before the LORD. ¹⁹"God forbid that I should do this!" he said. "Should I drink the blood of these men who went at the risk of their lives?" Because they risked their lives to bring it back, David would not drink it.

Such were the exploits of the three mighty men.

²⁰Abishai the brother of Joab was chief of the Three. He raised his spear against three hundred men, whom he killed, and so he became as famous as the Three. ²¹He was doubly honored above the Three and became their commander, even though he was not included among them.

²²Benaiah son of Jehoiada was a valiant fighter from Kabzeel, who performed great exploits. He struck down two of Moab's best men. He also went down into a pit on a snowy day and killed a lion. ²³And he struck down an Egyptian who was seven and a half feet[d] tall. Although the Egyptian had a spear like a

---

truth or dare

David became more and more powerful because power wasn't his main goal. Like David, make God your #1 priority. Then watch God take care of everything else in your life.

11:9

---

genuine

courage » 11:12-14

God's perspective frequently clashes with popular opinion. Most people claim there are many ways to heaven; God says there's only one. Society tells you to get back at those who hurt you; God wants you to forgive them. Many think you should only wait to have sex until it feels right; God says to save yourself for your husband. Doing things God's way often means going against the flow. It can be really hard to take a stand when everyone around you is running the other way. Eleazar and David had the courage to stand firm and face the battle—will you?

---

a 8 Or the Millo   b 11 Possibly a variant of Jashob-Baal   c 11 Or Thirty; some Septuagint manuscripts Three (see also 2 Samuel 23:8)   d 23 Hebrew five cubits (about 2.3 meters) weaver's rod in his hand, Benaiah went against him with a club. He snatched the spear from the Egyptian's hand and killed him with his own spear. ²⁴Such were the exploits of Benaiah son of Jehoiada; he too was as famous as the three mighty men. ²⁵He was held in greater honor than any of the Thirty, but he was not included among the Three. And David put him in charge of his bodyguard.

²⁶The mighty men were:

Asahel the brother of Joab,
Elhanan son of Dodo from Bethlehem,
²⁷Shammoth the Harorite,
Helez the Pelonite,
²⁸Ira son of Ikkesh from Tekoa,
Abiezer from Anathoth,
²⁹Sibbecai the Hushathite,
Ilai the Ahohite,
³⁰Maharai the Netophathite,
Heled son of Baanah the Netophathite,
³¹Ithai son of Ribai from Gibeah in Benjamin,
Benaiah the Pirathonite,
³²Hurai from the ravines of Gaash,
Abiel the Arbathite,
³³Azmaveth the Baharumite,
Eliahba the Shaalbonite,
³⁴the sons of Hashem the Gizonite,
Jonathan son of Shagee the Hararite,
³⁵Ahiam son of Sacar the Hararite,
Eliphal son of Ur,
³⁶Hepher the Mekerathite,
Ahijah the Pelonite,
³⁷Hezro the Carmelite,
Naarai son of Ezbai,
³⁸Joel the brother of Nathan,
Mibhar son of Hagri,
³⁹Zelek the Ammonite,
Naharai the Berothite, the armor-bearer of Joab son of Zeruiah,
⁴⁰Ira the Ithrite,
Gareb the Ithrite,
⁴¹Uriah the Hittite,
Zabad son of Ahlai,
⁴²Adina son of Shiza the Reubenite, who was chief of the Reubenites, and the thirty with him,
⁴³Hanan son of Maacah,
Joshaphat the Mithnite,
⁴⁴Uzzia the Ashterathite,
Shama and Jeiel the sons of Hotham the Aroerite,
⁴⁵Jediael son of Shimri,
his brother Joha the Tizite,
⁴⁶Eliel the Mahavite,
Jeribai and Joshaviah the sons of Elnaam,
Ithmah the Moabite,
⁴⁷Eliel, Obed and Jaasiel the Mezobaite.

Warriors Join David

12 These were the men who came to David at Ziklag, while he was banished from the presence of Saul son of Kish (they were among the warriors who helped him in battle; ²they were armed with bows and were able to shoot arrows or to sling stones right-handed or left-handed; they were kinsmen of Saul from the tribe of Benjamin):

³Ahiezer their chief and Joash the sons of Shemaah the Gibeathite; Jeziel and Pelet the sons of Azmaveth; Beracah, Jehu the Anathothite, ⁴and Ishmaiah the Gibeonite, a mighty man among the Thirty, who was a leader of the Thirty; Jeremiah, Jahaziel, Johanan, Jozabad the Gederathite, ⁵Eluzai, Jerimoth, Bealiah, Shemariah and Shephatiah the Haruphite; ⁶Elkanah, Isshiah, Azarel, Joezer and Jashobeam the Korahites; ⁷and Joelah and Zebadiah the sons of Jeroham from Gedor.

⁸Some Gadites defected to David at his stronghold in the desert. They were brave warriors, ready for battle and able to handle the shield and spear. Their faces were the faces of lions, and they were as swift as gazelles in the mountains.

⁹Ezer was the chief,
Obadiah the second in command, Eliab the third,
¹⁰Mishmannah the fourth, Jeremiah the fifth,
¹¹Attai the sixth, Eliel the seventh,
¹²Johanan the eighth, Elzabad the ninth,
¹³Jeremiah the tenth and Macbannai the eleventh.

¹⁴These Gadites were army commanders; the least was a match for a hundred, and the greatest for a thousand. ¹⁵It was they who crossed the Jordan in the first month when it was overflowing all its banks, and they put to flight everyone living in the valleys, to the east and to the west.

¹⁶Other Benjamites and some men from Judah also came to David in his stronghold. ¹⁷David went out to meet them and said to them, "If you have come to me in peace, to help me, I am ready to have you unite with me. But if you have come to betray me to my enemies when my hands are free from violence, may the God of our fathers see it and judge you."

¹⁸Then the Spirit came upon Amasai, chief of the Thirty, and he said:

> "We are yours, O David!
> We are with you, O son of Jesse!
> Success, success to you,
> and success to those who help you,
> for your God will help you."

So David received them and made them leaders of his raiding bands.

¹⁹Some of the men of Manasseh defected to David when he went with the Philistines to fight against Saul. (He and his men did not help the Philistines because, after consultation, their rulers sent him away. They said, "It will cost us our heads if he deserts to his master Saul.") ²⁰When David went to Ziklag, these were the men of Manasseh who defected to him: Adnah, Jozabad, Jediael, Michael, Jozabad, Elihu and Zillethai, leaders of units of a thousand in Manasseh. ²¹They helped David against raiding bands, for all of them were brave warriors, and they were commanders in his army. ²²Day after day men came to help David, until he had a great army, like the army of God. ᵃ

Others Join David at Hebron

²³These are the numbers of the men armed for battle who came to David at Hebron to turn Saul's kingdom over to him, as the LORD had said:

²⁴men of Judah, carrying shield and spear—6,800 armed for battle;
²⁵men of Simeon, warriors ready for battle—7,100;
²⁶men of Levi—4,600, ²⁷including Jehoiada, leader of the family of Aaron, with 3,700 men,
²⁸and Zadok, a brave young warrior, with 22 officers from his family;
²⁹men of Benjamin, Saul's kinsmen—3,000, most of whom had remained loyal to Saul's house until then;
³⁰men of Ephraim, brave warriors, famous in their own clans—20,800;
³¹men of half the tribe of Manasseh, designated by name to come and make David king— 18,000;
³²men of Issachar, who understood the times and knew what Israel should do—200 chiefs, with all their relatives under their command;

ᵃ 22 Or a great and mighty army

³³ men of Zebulun, experienced soldiers prepared for battle with every type of weapon, to help David with undivided loyalty—50,000;

³⁴ men of Naphtali—1,000 officers, together with 37,000 men carrying shields and spears;

³⁵ men of Dan, ready for battle—28,600;

³⁶ men of Asher, experienced soldiers prepared for battle—40,000;

³⁷ and from east of the Jordan, men of Reuben, Gad and the half-tribe of Manasseh, armed with every type of weapon—120,000.

³⁸ All these were fighting men who volunteered to serve in the ranks. They came to Hebron fully determined to make David king over all Israel. All the rest of the Israelites were also of one mind to make David king. ³⁹The men spent three days there with David, eating and drinking, for their families had supplied provisions for them. ⁴⁰Also, their neighbors from as far away as Issachar, Zebulun and Naphtali came bringing food on donkeys, camels, mules and oxen. There were plentiful supplies of flour, fig cakes, raisin cakes, wine, oil, cattle and sheep, for there was joy in Israel.

Bringing Back the Ark

13 David conferred with each of his officers, the commanders of thousands and commanders of hundreds. ²He then said to the whole assembly of Israel, "If it seems good to you and if it is the will of the LORD our God, let us send word far and wide to the rest of our brothers throughout the territories of Israel, and also to the priests and Levites who are with them in their towns and pasturelands, to come and join us. ³Let us bring the ark of our God back to us, for we did not inquire of^a it^b during the reign of Saul." ⁴The whole assembly agreed to do this, because it seemed right to all the people.

⁵So David assembled all the Israelites, from the Shihor River in Egypt to Lebo^c Hamath, to bring the ark of God from Kiriath Jearim. ⁶David and all the Israelites with him went to Baalah of Judah (Kiriath Jearim) to bring up from there the ark of God the LORD, who is enthroned between the cherubim—the ark that is called by the Name.

⁷They moved the ark of God from Abinadab's house on a new cart, with Uzzah and Ahio guiding it. ⁸David and all the Israelites were celebrating with all their might before God, with songs and with harps, lyres, tambourines, cymbals and trumpets.

⁹When they came to the threshing floor of Kidon, Uzzah reached out his hand to steady the ark, because the oxen stumbled. ¹⁰The LORD's anger burned against Uzzah, and he struck him down because he had put his hand on the ark. So he died there before God.

¹¹Then David was angry because the LORD's wrath had broken out against Uzzah, and to this day that place is called Perez Uzzah.^d

¹²David was afraid of God that day and asked, "How can I ever bring the ark of God to me?" ¹³He did not take the ark to be with him in the City of David. Instead, he took it aside to the house of Obed-Edom the Gittite. ¹⁴The ark of God remained with the family of Obed-Edom in his house for three months, and the LORD blessed his household and everything he had.

David's House and Family

14 Now Hiram king of Tyre sent messengers to David, along with cedar logs, stonemasons and carpenters to build a palace for him. ²And David knew that the LORD had established him as king over Israel and that his kingdom had been highly exalted for the sake of his people Israel.

³In Jerusalem David took more wives and became the father of more sons and daughters. ⁴These are the names of the children born to him there: Shammua, Shobab, Nathan, Solomon, ⁵Ibhar, Elishua, Elpelet, ⁶Nogah, Nepheg, Japhia, ⁷Elishama, Beeliada^e and Eliphelet.

truth or dare

When you need advice, you probably head straight to your most trusted buds. That's what friends are for! Just don't forget to include God at the top of your list of confidantes.

13:1

^a 3 Or we neglected   ^b 3 Or him   ^c 5 Or to the entrance to   ^d 11 Perez Uzzah means outbreak against Uzzah.
^e 7 A variant of Eliada

David Defeats the Philistines

[8]When the Philistines heard that David had been anointed king over all Israel, they went up in full force to search for him, but David heard about it and went out to meet them. [9]Now the Philistines had come and raided the Valley of Rephaim; [10]so David inquired of God: "Shall I go and attack the Philistines? Will you hand them over to me?"

The Lord answered him, "Go, I will hand them over to you."

[11]So David and his men went up to Baal Perazim, and there he defeated them. He said, "As waters break out, God has broken out against my enemies by my hand." So that place was called Baal Perazim.[a] [12]The Philistines had abandoned their gods there, and David gave orders to burn them in the fire.

[13]Once more the Philistines raided the valley; [14]so David inquired of God again, and God answered him, "Do not go straight up, but circle around them and attack them in front of the balsam trees. [15]As soon as you hear the sound of marching in the tops of the balsam trees, move out to battle, because that will mean God has gone out in front of you to strike the Philistine army." [16]So David did as God commanded him, and they struck down the Philistine army, all the way from Gibeon to Gezer.

[17]So David's fame spread throughout every land, and the Lord made all the nations fear him.

truth or dare

Facing opposition to your faith is inevitable. If you're quick to react, check your motives. Are you out to show God's strength or your own?

14:8–11

The Ark Brought to Jerusalem

15 After David had constructed buildings for himself in the City of David, he prepared a place for the ark of God and pitched a tent for it. [2]Then David said, "No one but the Levites may carry the ark of God, because the Lord chose them to carry the ark of the Lord and to minister before him forever."

[3]David assembled all Israel in Jerusalem to bring up the ark of the Lord to the place he had prepared for it. [4]He called together the descendants of Aaron and the Levites:

[5]From the descendants of Kohath,
Uriel the leader and 120 relatives;
[6]from the descendants of Merari,
Asaiah the leader and 220 relatives;
[7]from the descendants of Gershon,[b]
Joel the leader and 130 relatives;
[8]from the descendants of Elizaphan,
Shemaiah the leader and 200 relatives;
[9]from the descendants of Hebron,
Eliel the leader and 80 relatives;
[10]from the descendants of Uzziel,
Amminadab the leader and 112 relatives.

genuine obedience

The Israelites found out that when God gives a command, he means it! They did things their own way, and it did *not* go well (see 13:10). Obeying God is not like extra credit on a test—as in nice but not necessary. It's the whole test, and you either pass or you fail. Do you always speak truth—even when a "little white lie" would make life so much easier? Do you steer clear of gossip—even when there's "juicy news" just begging to be shared? God doesn't consider any of his commands to be optional. Neither should you.

15:11-13

[11]Then David summoned Zadok and Abiathar the priests, and Uriel, Asaiah, Joel, Shemaiah, Eliel and Amminadab the Levites. [12]He said to them, "You are the heads of the Levitical families; you and your fellow Levites are to consecrate yourselves and bring up the ark of the Lord, the God of

a 11 *Baal Perazim* means *the lord who breaks out.*   b 7 Hebrew *Gershom*, a variant of *Gershon*

Israel, to the place I have prepared for it. ¹³It was because you, the Levites, did not bring it up the first time that the LORD our God broke out in anger against us. We did not inquire of him about how to do it in the prescribed way." ¹⁴So the priests and Levites consecrated themselves in order to bring up the ark of the LORD, the God of Israel. ¹⁵And the Levites carried the ark of God with the poles on their shoulders, as Moses had commanded in accordance with the word of the LORD.

¹⁶David told the leaders of the Levites to appoint their brothers as singers to sing joyful songs, accompanied by musical instruments: lyres, harps and cymbals.

¹⁷So the Levites appointed Heman son of Joel; from his brothers, Asaph son of Berekiah; and from their brothers the Merarites, Ethan son of Kushaiah; ¹⁸and with them their brothers next in rank: Zechariah,ᵃ Jaaziel, Shemiramoth, Jehiel, Unni, Eliab, Benaiah, Maaseiah, Mattithiah, Eliphelehu, Mikneiah, Obed-Edom and Jeiel,ᵇ the gatekeepers.

¹⁹The musicians Heman, Asaph and Ethan were to sound the bronze cymbals; ²⁰Zechariah, Aziel, Shemiramoth, Jehiel, Unni, Eliab, Maaseiah and Benaiah were to play the lyres according to *alamoth*,ᶜ ²¹and Mattithiah, Eliphelehu, Mikneiah, Obed-Edom, Jeiel and Azaziah were to play the harps, directing according to *sheminith*.ᶜ ²²Kenaniah the head Levite was in charge of the singing; that was his responsibility because he was skillful at it.

²³Berekiah and Elkanah were to be doorkeepers for the ark. ²⁴Shebaniah, Joshaphat, Nethanel, Amasai, Zechariah, Benaiah and Eliezer the priests were to blow trumpets before the ark of God. Obed-Edom and Jehiah were also to be doorkeepers for the ark.

²⁵So David and the elders of Israel and the commanders of units of a thousand went to bring up the ark of the covenant of the LORD from the house of Obed-Edom, with rejoicing. ²⁶Because God had helped the Levites who were carrying the ark of the covenant of the LORD, seven bulls and seven rams were sacrificed. ²⁷Now David was clothed in a robe of fine linen, as were all the Levites who were carrying the ark, and as were the singers, and Kenaniah, who was in charge of the singing of the choirs. David also wore a linen ephod. ²⁸So all Israel brought up the ark of the covenant of the LORD with shouts, with the sounding of rams' horns and trumpets, and of cymbals, and the playing of lyres and harps.

²⁹As the ark of the covenant of the LORD was entering the City of David, Michal daughter of Saul watched from a window. And when she saw King David dancing and celebrating, she despised him in her heart.

16 They brought the ark of God and set it inside the tent that David had pitched for it, and they presented burnt offerings and fellowship offeringsᵈ before God. ²After David had finished sacrificing the burnt offerings and fellowship offerings, he blessed the people in the name of the LORD. ³Then he gave a loaf of bread, a cake of dates and a cake of raisins to each Israelite man and woman.

⁴He appointed some of the Levites to minister before the ark of the LORD, to make petition, to give thanks, and to praise the LORD, the God of Israel: ⁵Asaph was the chief, Zechariah second, then Jeiel, Shemiramoth, Jehiel, Mattithiah, Eliab, Benaiah, Obed-Edom and Jeiel. They were to play the lyres and harps, Asaph was to sound the cymbals, ⁶and Benaiah and Jahaziel the priests were to blow the trumpets regularly before the ark of the covenant of God.

David's Psalm of Thanks

⁷That day David first committed to Asaph and his associates this psalm of thanks to the LORD:

⁸Give thanks to the LORD, call on his name;
  make known among the nations what he has done.
⁹Sing to him, sing praise to him;
  tell of all his wonderful acts.
¹⁰Glory in his holy name;
  let the hearts of those who seek the LORD rejoice.
¹¹Look to the LORD and his strength;
  seek his face always.
¹²Remember the wonders he has done,

ᵃ *18* Three Hebrew manuscripts and most Septuagint manuscripts (see also verse 20 and 1 Chron. 16:5); most Hebrew manuscripts *Zechariah son and* or *Zechariah, Ben and*   ᵇ *18* Hebrew; Septuagint (see also verse 21) *Jeiel and Azaziah*   ᶜ *20,21* Probably a musical term   ᵈ *1* Traditionally *peace offerings*; also in verse 2 his miracles, and the judgments he pronounced,

[13] O descendants of Israel his servant,
O sons of Jacob, his chosen ones.

[14] He is the LORD our God;
his judgments are in all the earth.

[15] He remembers[a] his covenant forever,
the word he commanded, for a thousand generations,

[16] the covenant he made with Abraham,
the oath he swore to Isaac.

[17] He confirmed it to Jacob as a decree,
to Israel as an everlasting covenant:

[18] "To you I will give the land of Canaan
as the portion you will inherit."

[19] When they were but few in number,
few indeed, and strangers in it,

[20] they[b] wandered from nation to nation,
from one kingdom to another.

[21] He allowed no man to oppress them;
for their sake he rebuked kings:

[22] "Do not touch my anointed ones;
do my prophets no harm."

[23] Sing to the LORD, all the earth;
proclaim his salvation day after day.

[24] Declare his glory among the nations,
his marvelous deeds among all peoples.

[25] For great is the LORD and most worthy of praise;
he is to be feared above all gods.

[26] For all the gods of the nations are idols,
but the LORD made the heavens.

[27] Splendor and majesty are before him;
strength and joy in his dwelling place.

[28] Ascribe to the LORD, O families of nations,
ascribe to the LORD glory and strength,

love ♥ notes

16:11-12

Dear daughter,

Where do you turn in tough times? To a friend, a parent, perhaps a teacher? That's fine, but don't forget to look first to me. Rely on my strength. I am always here for you.

—Your heavenly Dad

Do you tend to look first to God, or do you rely too much on others?

_____

_____

_____

_____

_____

_____

_____

_____

_____

a 15 Some Septuagint manuscripts (see also Psalm 105:8); Hebrew *Remember* *b 18-20* One Hebrew manuscript, Septuagint and Vulgate (see also Psalm 105:12); most Hebrew manuscripts *inherit, / [19]though you are but few in number, / few indeed, and strangers in it." / [20]They*

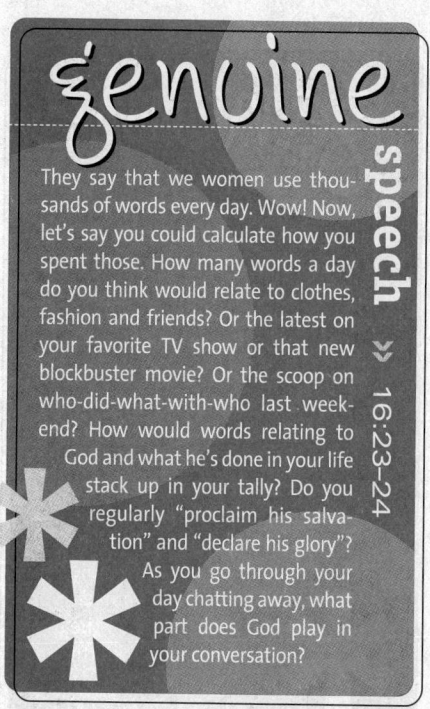

²⁹ ascribe to the LORD the glory due
  his name.
Bring an offering and come
    before him;
  worship the LORD in the
    splendor of his^a
    holiness.
³⁰ Tremble before him, all the earth!
  The world is firmly
    established; it cannot
    be moved.
³¹ Let the heavens rejoice, let the
    earth be glad;
  let them say among the
    nations, "The LORD
    reigns!"
³² Let the sea resound, and all that
    is in it;
  let the fields be jubilant, and
    everything in them!
³³ Then the trees of the forest will
    sing,
  they will sing for joy before
    the LORD,
  for he comes to judge the
    earth.
³⁴ Give thanks to the LORD, for he is
    good;
  his love endures forever.
³⁵ Cry out, "Save us, O God our Savior;
  gather and deliver us from the nations,
  that we may give thanks to your holy name,
    that we may glory in your praise."
³⁶ Praise be to the LORD, the God of Israel,
  from everlasting to everlasting.

Then all the people said "Amen" and "Praise the LORD."

³⁷ David left Asaph and his associates before the ark of the covenant of the LORD to minister there regularly, according to each day's requirements. ³⁸ He also left Obed-Edom and his sixty-eight associates to minister with them. Obed-Edom son of Jeduthun, and also Hosah, were gatekeepers.

³⁹ David left Zadok the priest and his fellow priests before the tabernacle of the LORD at the high place in Gibeon ⁴⁰ to present burnt offerings to the LORD on the altar of burnt offering regularly, morning and evening, in accordance with everything written in the Law of the LORD, which he had given Israel. ⁴¹ With them were Heman and Jeduthun and the rest of those chosen and designated by name to give thanks to the LORD, "for his love endures forever." ⁴² Heman and Jeduthun were responsible for the sounding of the trumpets and cymbals and for the playing of the other instruments for sacred song. The sons of Jeduthun were stationed at the gate.

⁴³ Then all the people left, each for his own home, and David returned home to bless his family.

God's Promise to David

17 After David was settled in his palace, he said to Nathan the prophet, "Here I am, living in a palace of cedar, while the ark of the covenant of the LORD is under a tent." ² Nathan replied to David, "Whatever you have in mind, do it, for God is with you." ³ That night the word of God came to Nathan, saying:

^a 29 Or LORD with the splendor of

⁴"Go and tell my servant David, 'This is what the LORD says: You are not the one to build me a house to dwell in. ⁵I have not dwelt in a house from the day I brought Israel up out of Egypt to this day. I have moved from one tent site to another, from one dwelling place to another. ⁶Wherever I have moved with all the Israelites, did I ever say to any of their leaders*a* whom I commanded to shepherd my people, "Why have you not built me a house of cedar?"'

⁷"Now then, tell my servant David, 'This is what the LORD Almighty says: I took you from the pasture and from following the flock, to be ruler over my people Israel. ⁸I have been with you wherever you have gone, and I have cut off all your enemies from before you. Now I will make your name like the names of the greatest men of the earth. ⁹And I will provide a place for my people Israel and will plant them so that they can have a home of their own and no longer be disturbed. Wicked people will not oppress them anymore, as they did at the beginning ¹⁰and have done ever since the time I appointed leaders over my people Israel. I will also subdue all your enemies.

" 'I declare to you that the LORD will build a house for you: ¹¹When your days are over and you go to be with your fathers, I will raise up your offspring to succeed you, one of your own sons, and I will establish his kingdom. ¹²He is the one who will build a house for me, and I will establish his throne forever. ¹³I will be his father, and he will be my son. I will never take my love away from him, as I took it away from your predecessor. ¹⁴I will set him over my house and my kingdom forever; his throne will be established forever.' "

¹⁵Nathan reported to David all the words of this entire revelation.

David's Prayer

¹⁶Then King David went in and sat before the LORD, and he said:

"Who am I, O LORD God, and what is my family, that you have brought me this far? ¹⁷And as if this were not enough in your sight, O God, you have spoken about the future of the house of your servant. You have looked on me as though I were the most exalted of men, O LORD God.

¹⁸"What more can David say to you for honoring your servant? For you know your servant, ¹⁹O LORD. For the sake of your servant and according to your will, you have done this great thing and made known all these great promises.

²⁰"There is no one like you, O LORD, and there is no God but you, as we have heard with our own ears. ²¹And who is like your

genuine humility 17:16-22

Admit it: You compare yourself to other people—a lot. We all do. And we often do it hoping to boost our ego. David, on the other hand, compared himself to God. He saw how great God is and how small he was in comparison—which boosted his humility. So when God blessed him, he didn't say, "Glad you noticed how great I am, God!" Instead, he said, "Who am I . . . that you have brought me this far?" If you're going to compare yourself, follow David's example and compare yourself to God. That's the only comparison worth making.

truth or dare 17:20

It's study time, girls! The topic: World Religions. The conclusion: There's nothing that comes close to our great and merciful God! See for yourself.

a 6 Traditionally judges; also in verse 10

people Israel—the one nation on earth whose God went out to redeem a people for himself, and to make a name for yourself, and to perform great and awesome wonders by driving out nations from before your people, whom you redeemed from Egypt? [22]You made your people Israel your very own forever, and you, O LORD, have become their God.

[23]"And now, LORD, let the promise you have made concerning your servant and his house be established forever. Do as you promised, [24]so that it will be established and that your name will be great forever. Then men will say, 'The LORD Almighty, the God over Israel, is Israel's God!' And the house of your servant David will be established before you.

[25]"You, my God, have revealed to your servant that you will build a house for him. So your servant has found courage to pray to you. [26]O LORD, you are God! You have promised these good things to your servant. [27]Now you have been pleased to bless the house of your servant, that it may continue forever in your sight; for you, O LORD, have blessed it, and it will be blessed forever."

David's Victories

18 In the course of time, David defeated the Philistines and subdued them, and he took Gath and its surrounding villages from the control of the Philistines.

[2]David also defeated the Moabites, and they became subject to him and brought tribute.

[3]Moreover, David fought Hadadezer king of Zobah, as far as Hamath, when he went to establish his control along the Euphrates River. [4]David captured a thousand of his chariots, seven thousand charioteers and twenty thousand foot soldiers. He hamstrung all but a hundred of the chariot horses.

[5]When the Arameans of Damascus came to help Hadadezer king of Zobah, David struck down twenty-two thousand of them. [6]He put garrisons in the Aramean kingdom of Damascus, and the Arameans became subject to him and brought tribute. The LORD gave David victory everywhere he went.

[7]David took the gold shields carried by the officers of Hadadezer and brought them to Jerusalem. [8]From Tebah[a] and Cun, towns that belonged to Hadadezer, David took a great quantity of bronze, which Solomon used to make the bronze Sea, the pillars and various bronze articles.

[9]When Tou king of Hamath heard that David had defeated the entire army of Hadadezer king of Zobah, [10]he sent his son Hadoram to King David to greet him and congratulate him on his victory in battle over Hadadezer, who had been at war with Tou. Hadoram brought all kinds of articles of gold and silver and bronze.

[11]King David dedicated these articles to the LORD, as he had done with the silver and gold he had taken from all these nations: Edom and Moab, the Ammonites and the Philistines, and Amalek.

[12]Abishai son of Zeruiah struck down eighteen thousand Edomites in the Valley of Salt. [13]He put garrisons in Edom, and all the Edomites became subject to David. The LORD gave David victory everywhere he went.

David's Officials

[14]David reigned over all Israel, doing what was just and right for all his people. [15]Joab son of Zeruiah was over the army; Jehoshaphat son of Ahilud was recorder;

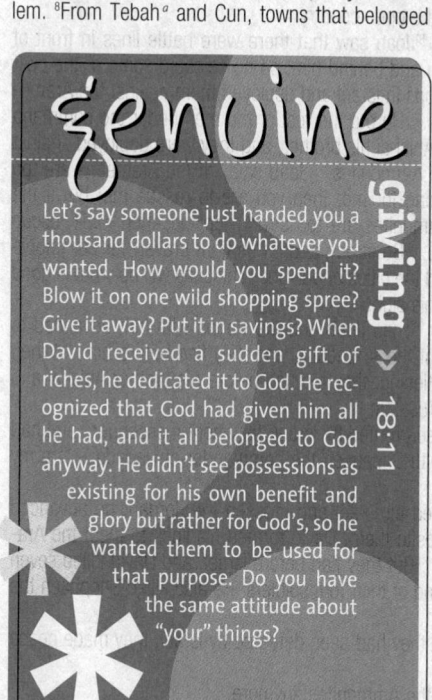

genuine giving « 18:11

Let's say someone just handed you a thousand dollars to do whatever you wanted. How would you spend it? Blow it on one wild shopping spree? Give it away? Put it in savings? When David received a sudden gift of riches, he dedicated it to God. He recognized that God had given him all he had, and it all belonged to God anyway. He didn't see possessions as existing for his own benefit and glory but rather for God's, so he wanted them to be used for that purpose. Do you have the same attitude about "your" things?

[16]Zadok son of Ahitub and Ahimelech[a] son of Abiathar were priests; Shavsha was secretary; [17]Benaiah son of Jehoiada was over the Kerethites and Pelethites; and David's sons were chief officials at the king's side.

The Battle Against the Ammonites

19 In the course of time, Nahash king of the Ammonites died, and his son succeeded him as king. [2]David thought, "I will show kindness to Hanun son of Nahash, because his father showed kindness to me." So David sent a delegation to express his sympathy to Hanun concerning his father.

When David's men came to Hanun in the land of the Ammonites to express sympathy to him, [3]the Ammonite nobles said to Hanun, "Do you think David is honoring your father by sending men to you to express sympathy? Haven't his men come to you to explore and spy out the country and overthrow it?" [4]So Hanun seized David's men, shaved them, cut off their garments in the middle at the buttocks, and sent them away.

[5]When someone came and told David about the men, he sent messengers to meet them, for they were greatly humiliated. The king said, "Stay at Jericho till your beards have grown, and then come back."

[6]When the Ammonites realized that they had become a stench in David's nostrils, Hanun and the Ammonites sent a thousand talents[b] of silver to hire chariots and charioteers from Aram Naharaim,[c] Aram Maacah and Zobah. [7]They hired thirty-two thousand chariots and charioteers, as well as the king of Maacah with his troops, who came and camped near Medeba, while the Ammonites were mustered from their towns and moved out for battle.

[8]On hearing this, David sent Joab out with the entire army of fighting men. [9]The Ammonites came out and drew up in battle formation at the entrance to their city, while the kings who had come were by themselves in the open country.

[10]Joab saw that there were battle lines in front of him and behind him; so he selected some of the best troops in Israel and deployed them against the Arameans. [11]He put the rest of the men under the command of Abishai his brother, and they were deployed against the Ammonites. [12]Joab said, "If the Arameans are too strong for me, then you are to rescue me; but if the Ammonites are too strong for you, then I will rescue you. [13]Be strong and let us fight bravely for our people and the cities of our God. The LORD will do what is good in his sight."

[14]Then Joab and the troops with him advanced to fight the Arameans, and they fled before him. [15]When the Ammonites saw that the Arameans were fleeing, they too fled before his brother Abishai and went inside the city. So Joab went back to Jerusalem.

[16]After the Arameans saw that they had been routed by Israel, they sent messengers and had Arameans brought from beyond the River,[d] with Shophach the commander of Hadadezer's army leading them.

[17]When David was told of this, he gathered all Israel and crossed the Jordan; he advanced against them and formed his battle lines opposite them. David formed his lines to meet the Arameans in battle, and they fought against him. [18]But they fled before Israel, and David killed seven thousand of their charioteers and forty thousand of their foot soldiers. He also killed Shophach the commander of their army.

[19]When the vassals of Hadadezer saw that they had been defeated by Israel, they made peace with David and became subject to him.

So the Arameans were not willing to help the Ammonites anymore.

---

truth or dare

There's no guarantee you'll win all your battles. But God has already won the war for you! So keep your life in perspective—even in losses, God is still good.

19:10–13

---

[a] 16 Some Hebrew manuscripts, Vulgate and Syriac (see also 2 Samuel 8:17); most Hebrew manuscripts *Abimelech*
[b] 6 That is, about 37 tons (about 34 metric tons)   [c] 6 That is, Northwest Mesopotamia   [d] 16 That is, the Euphrates

It's Not Fair

focus Profile: Jayla

I just found out I have cystic fibrosis. My friends thought I was lucky because I could eat anything and not gain an ounce. It turns out the reason for this is not so lucky—I have a progressive disease. Cystic fibrosis mostly affects my lungs. Extra mucous builds up there, and the air can't get through my lungs.

It's scary being in the hospital. Some people have even more trouble breathing than I do. I worry that I'll get like that . . . or worse. I heard that someone on our floor died last night. I know I'll go to heaven when I die, but I want to grow up, get married, have kids, write a book, stuff like that. I want to be the first person with CF to live to old age.

Some of my friends say that because they're praying for me everything will be okay. I know it's not that simple. The guy who just died was a Christian, and his whole church was praying he'd be healed.

I worry that when I go back to school people will treat me like some kind of freak. What if they stop inviting me to stuff? What if they avoid me because they feel awkward? It's terrifying to have this disease. But being all alone would be worse.

crisis in focus

It's hard to watch a friend go through a health crisis, but she needs you more than ever. And if you're the one in crisis, you know just how true that is. To love as Jesus loves . . .

» Do the practical things your friend needs, like take notes for her in class, keep her up-to-date on what's going on at school, etc.

» Listen. Don't interpret or predict; don't finish her sentences for her and don't try to make it all seem okay. Just listen.

» Keep up the friendship. Treat her as you always have—telling secrets, inviting her to do things, crying and laughing together (see Romans 12:15, page 1462).

» If you're the one in crisis, read Psalm 69 to see how David expressed his fear and pain to God.

For more on this topic, see the index on page 1656.

For more ideas on how to help in a crisis, check out the Crisis Link on www.TrueImagesBible.com

The Capture of Rabbah

20 In the spring, at the time when kings go off to war, Joab led out the armed forces. He laid waste the land of the Ammonites and went to Rabbah and besieged it, but David remained in Jerusalem. Joab attacked Rabbah and left it in ruins. ²David took the crown from the head of their king *a*—its weight was found to be a talent *b* of gold, and it was set with precious stones—and it was placed on David's head. He took a great quantity of plunder from the city ³and brought out the people who were there, consigning them to labor with saws and with iron picks and axes. David did this to all the Ammonite towns. Then David and his entire army returned to Jerusalem.

a 2 Or of Milcom, that is, Molech   *b 2 That is, about 75 pounds (about 34 kilograms)*

War With the Philistines

[4]In the course of time, war broke out with the Philistines, at Gezer. At that time Sibbecai the Hushathite killed Sippai, one of the descendants of the Rephaites, and the Philistines were subjugated.

[5]In another battle with the Philistines, Elhanan son of Jair killed Lahmi the brother of Goliath the Gittite, who had a spear with a shaft like a weaver's rod.

[6]In still another battle, which took place at Gath, there was a huge man with six fingers on each hand and six toes on each foot—twenty-four in all. He also was descended from Rapha. [7]When he taunted Israel, Jonathan son of Shimea, David's brother, killed him.

[8]These were descendants of Rapha in Gath, and they fell at the hands of David and his men.

David Numbers the Fighting Men

21 Satan rose up against Israel and incited David to take a census of Israel. [2]So David said to Joab and the commanders of the troops, "Go and count the Israelites from Beersheba to Dan. Then report back to me so that I may know how many there are."

[3]But Joab replied, "May the LORD multiply his troops a hundred times over. My lord the king, are they not all my lord's subjects? Why does my lord want to do this? Why should he bring guilt on Israel?"

[4]The king's word, however, overruled Joab; so Joab left and went throughout Israel and then came back to Jerusalem. [5]Joab reported the number of the fighting men to David: In all Israel there were one million one hundred thousand men who could handle a sword, including four hundred and seventy thousand in Judah.

[6]But Joab did not include Levi and Benjamin in the numbering, because the king's command was repulsive to him. [7]This command was also evil in the sight of God; so he punished Israel.

[8]Then David said to God, "I have sinned greatly by doing this. Now, I beg you, take away the guilt of your servant. I have done a very foolish thing."

[9]The LORD said to Gad, David's seer, [10]"Go and tell David, 'This is what the LORD says: I am giving you three options. Choose one of them for me to carry out against you.' "

[11]So Gad went to David and said to him, "This is what the LORD says: 'Take your choice: [12]three years of famine, three months of being swept away[a] before your enemies, with their swords overtaking you, or three days of the sword of the LORD—days of plague in the land, with the angel of the LORD ravaging every part of Israel.' Now then, decide how I should answer the one who sent me."

[13]David said to Gad, "I am in deep distress. Let me fall into the hands of the LORD, for his mercy is very great; but do not let me fall into the hands of men."

[14]So the LORD sent a plague on Israel, and seventy thousand men of Israel fell dead. [15]And God sent an angel to destroy Jerusalem. But as the angel was doing so, the LORD saw it and was grieved because of the calamity and said to the angel who was destroying the people, "Enough! Withdraw your hand." The angel of the LORD was then standing at the threshing floor of Araunah[b] the Jebusite.

[16]David looked up and saw the angel of the LORD standing between heaven and earth, with a drawn sword in his hand extended over Jerusalem. Then David and the elders, clothed in sackcloth, fell facedown.

[17]David said to God, "Was it not I who ordered the fighting men to be counted? I am the one who has sinned and done wrong. These are but sheep. What have they done? O LORD my God, let your hand fall upon me and my family, but do not let this plague remain on your people."

[18]Then the angel of the LORD ordered Gad to tell David to go up and build an altar to the LORD

truth *or dare*

You're psyched about your look, your friends and your stuff. Finding it hard to hide your pride? Learn from David's mistake—don't put your faith in your own strength.

21:1–5

---

[a] 12 Hebrew; Septuagint and Vulgate (see also 2 Samuel 24:13) *of fleeing*   [b] 15 Hebrew *Ornan*, a variant of *Araunah*; also in verses 18-28

on the threshing floor of Araunah the Jebusite. [19]So David went up in obedience to the word that Gad had spoken in the name of the LORD.

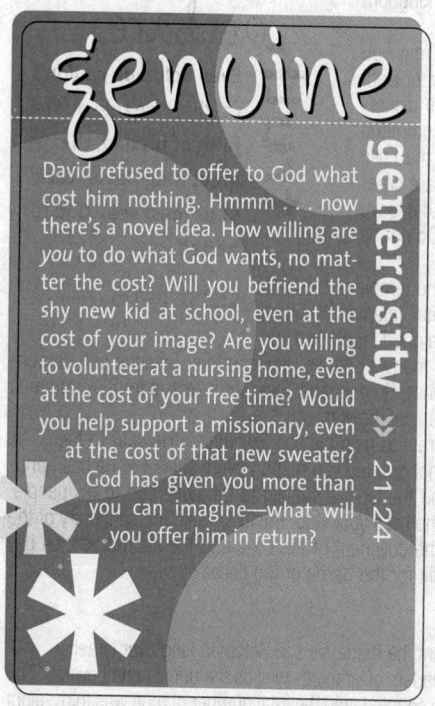

[20]While Araunah was threshing wheat, he turned and saw the angel; his four sons who were with him hid themselves. [21]Then David approached, and when Araunah looked and saw him, he left the threshing floor and bowed down before David with his face to the ground.

[22]David said to him, "Let me have the site of your threshing floor so I can build an altar to the LORD, that the plague on the people may be stopped. Sell it to me at the full price."

[23]Araunah said to David, "Take it! Let my lord the king do whatever pleases him. Look, I will give the oxen for the burnt offerings, the threshing sledges for the wood, and the wheat for the grain offering. I will give all this."

[24]But King David replied to Araunah, "No, I insist on paying the full price. I will not take for the LORD what is yours, or sacrifice a burnt offering that costs me nothing."

[25]So David paid Araunah six hundred shekels[a] of gold for the site. [26]David built an altar to the LORD there and sacrificed burnt offerings and fellowship offerings.[b] He called on the LORD, and the LORD answered him with fire from heaven on the altar of burnt offering.

[27]Then the LORD spoke to the angel, and he put his sword back into its sheath. [28]At that time, when David saw that the LORD had answered him on the threshing floor of Araunah the Jebusite, he offered sacrifices there. [29]The tabernacle of the LORD, which Moses had made in the desert, and the altar of burnt offering were at that time on the high place at Gibeon. [30]But David could not go before it to inquire of God, because he was afraid of the sword of the angel of the LORD.

22 Then David said, "The house of the LORD God is to be here, and also the altar of burnt offering for Israel."

Preparations for the Temple

[2]So David gave orders to assemble the aliens living in Israel, and from among them he appointed stonecutters to prepare dressed stone for building the house of God. [3]He provided a large amount of iron to make nails for the doors of the gateways and for the fittings, and more bronze than could be weighed. [4]He also provided more cedar logs than could be counted, for the Sidonians and Tyrians had brought large numbers of them to David.

[5]David said, "My son Solomon is young and inexperienced, and the house to be built for the LORD should be of great magnificence and fame and splendor in the sight of all the nations. Therefore I will make preparations for it." So David made extensive preparations before his death.

[6]Then he called for his son Solomon and charged him to build a house for the LORD, the God of Israel. [7]David said to Solomon: "My son, I had it in my heart to build a house for the Name of the LORD my God. [8]But this word of the LORD came to me: 'You have shed much blood and have fought many wars. You are not to build a house for my Name, because you have shed much blood on the earth in my sight. [9]But you will have a son who will be a man of peace and rest, and I will give him rest from all his enemies on every side. His name will be Solomon,[c] and I will grant Israel peace

a 25 That is, about 15 pounds (about 7 kilograms)   *b 26* Traditionally *peace offerings*   *c 9 Solomon* sounds like and may be derived from the Hebrew for *peace.*

and quiet during his reign. ¹⁰He is the one who will build a house for my Name. He will be my son, and I will be his father. And I will establish the throne of his kingdom over Israel forever.'

¹¹"Now, my son, the LORD be with you, and may you have success and build the house of the LORD your God, as he said you would. ¹²May the LORD give you discretion and understanding when he puts you in command over Israel, so that you may keep the law of the LORD your God. ¹³Then you will have success if you are careful to observe the decrees and laws that the LORD gave Moses for Israel. Be strong and courageous. Do not be afraid or discouraged.

¹⁴"I have taken great pains to provide for the temple of the LORD a hundred thousand talents*a* of gold, a million talents*b* of silver, quantities of bronze and iron too great to be weighed, and wood and stone. And you may add to them. ¹⁵You have many workmen: stonecutters, masons and carpenters, as well as men skilled in every kind of work ¹⁶in gold and silver, bronze and iron—craftsmen beyond number. Now begin the work, and the LORD be with you."

¹⁷Then David ordered all the leaders of Israel to help his son Solomon. ¹⁸He said to them, "Is not the LORD your God with you? And has he not granted you rest on every side? For he has handed the inhabitants of the land over to me, and the land is subject to the LORD and to his people. ¹⁹Now devote your heart and soul to seeking the LORD your God. Begin to build the sanctuary of the LORD God, so that you may bring the ark of the covenant of the LORD and the sacred articles belonging to God into the temple that will be built for the Name of the LORD."

The Levites

23 When David was old and full of years, he made his son Solomon king over Israel.
²He also gathered together all the leaders of Israel, as well as the priests and Levites. ³The Levites thirty years old or more were counted, and the total number of men was thirty-eight thousand. ⁴David said, "Of these, twenty-four thousand are to supervise the work of the temple of the LORD and six thousand are to be officials and judges. ⁵Four thousand are to be gatekeepers and four thousand are to praise the LORD with the musical instruments I have provided for that purpose."

⁶David divided the Levites into groups corresponding to the sons of Levi: Gershon, Kohath and Merari.

Gershonites

⁷Belonging to the Gershonites:
Ladan and Shimei.
⁸The sons of Ladan:
Jehiel the first, Zetham and Joel—three in all.
⁹The sons of Shimei:
Shelomoth, Haziel and Haran—three in all.
These were the heads of the families of Ladan.
¹⁰And the sons of Shimei:
Jahath, Ziza,*c* Jeush and Beriah.
These were the sons of Shimei—four in all.
¹¹Jahath was the first and Ziza the second, but Jeush and Beriah did not have many sons;
so they were counted as one family with one assignment.

Kohathites

¹²The sons of Kohath:
Amram, Izhar, Hebron and Uzziel—four in all.

truth *or dare*

Even Solomon couldn't catch a free ride on the faith of his dad, the great King David. Each of us must seek God for herself.

22:11–13

---

a 14 That is, about 3,750 tons (about 3,450 metric tons)   *b 14* That is, about 37,500 tons (about 34,500 metric tons)
c 10 One Hebrew manuscript, Septuagint and Vulgate (see also verse 11); most Hebrew manuscripts *Zina*

¹³The sons of Amram:

Aaron and Moses.

Aaron was set apart, he and his descendants forever, to consecrate the most holy things, to offer sacrifices before the LORD, to minister before him and to pronounce blessings in his name forever. ¹⁴The sons of Moses the man of God were counted as part of the tribe of Levi.

¹⁵The sons of Moses:

Gershom and Eliezer.

¹⁶The descendants of Gershom:

Shubael was the first.

¹⁷The descendants of Eliezer:

Rehabiah was the first.

Eliezer had no other sons, but the sons of Rehabiah were very numerous.

¹⁸The sons of Izhar:

Shelomith was the first.

¹⁹The sons of Hebron:

Jeriah the first, Amariah the second, Jahaziel the third and Jekameam the fourth.

²⁰The sons of Uzziel:

Micah the first and Isshiah the second.

Merarites

²¹The sons of Merari:

Mahli and Mushi.

The sons of Mahli:

Eleazar and Kish.

²²Eleazar died without having sons: he had only daughters. Their cousins, the sons of Kish, married them.

²³The sons of Mushi:

Mahli, Eder and Jerimoth—three in all.

²⁴These were the descendants of Levi by their families—the heads of families as they were registered under their names and counted individually, that is, the workers twenty years old or more who served in the temple of the LORD. ²⁵For David had said, "Since the LORD, the God of Israel, has granted rest to his people and has come to dwell in Jerusalem forever, ²⁶the Levites no longer need to carry the tabernacle or any of the articles used in its service." ²⁷According to the last instructions of David, the Levites were counted from those twenty years old or more.

²⁸The duty of the Levites was to help Aaron's descendants in the service of the temple of the LORD: to be in charge of the courtyards, the side rooms, the purification of all sacred things and the performance of other duties at the house of God. ²⁹They were in charge of the bread set out on the table, the flour for the grain offerings, the unleavened wafers, the baking and the mixing, and all measurements of quantity and size. ³⁰They were also to stand every morning to thank and praise the LORD. They were to do the same in the evening ³¹and whenever burnt offerings were presented to the LORD on Sabbaths and at New Moon festivals and at appointed feasts. They were to serve before the LORD regularly in the proper number and in the way prescribed for them.

³²And so the Levites carried out their responsibilities for the Tent of Meeting, for the Holy Place and, under their brothers the descendants of Aaron, for the service of the temple of the LORD.

The Divisions of Priests

24 These were the divisions of the sons of Aaron:

The sons of Aaron were Nadab, Abihu, Eleazar and Ithamar. ²But Nadab and Abihu died before their father did, and they had no sons; so Eleazar and Ithamar served as the priests. ³With the help of Zadok a descendant of Eleazar and Ahimelech a descendant of Ithamar, David separated them into divisions for their appointed order of ministering. ⁴A larger number of leaders were found among Eleazar's descendants than among Ithamar's, and they were divided accordingly: sixteen heads of families from Eleazar's descendants and eight heads of families from Ithamar's descendants. ⁵They divided them impartially by drawing lots, for there were officials of the sanctuary and officials of God among the descendants of both Eleazar and Ithamar.

⁶The scribe Shemaiah son of Nethanel, a Levite, recorded their names in the presence of the king and of the officials: Zadok the priest, Ahimelech son of Abiathar and the heads of families of the priests and of the Levites—one family being taken from Eleazar and then one from Ithamar.

⁷The first lot fell to Jehoiarib,
   the second to Jedaiah,
⁸the third to Harim,
   the fourth to Seorim,
⁹the fifth to Malkijah,
   the sixth to Mijamin,
¹⁰the seventh to Hakkoz,
   the eighth to Abijah,
¹¹the ninth to Jeshua,
   the tenth to Shecaniah,
¹²the eleventh to Eliashib,
   the twelfth to Jakim,
¹³the thirteenth to Huppah,
   the fourteenth to Jeshebeab,
¹⁴the fifteenth to Bilgah,
   the sixteenth to Immer,
¹⁵the seventeenth to Hezir,
   the eighteenth to Happizzez,
¹⁶the nineteenth to Pethahiah,
   the twentieth to Jehezkel,
¹⁷the twenty-first to Jakin,
   the twenty-second to Gamul,
¹⁸the twenty-third to Delaiah
   and the twenty-fourth to Maaziah.

truth or dare

The priests, who were all qualified, could've squabbled over the best jobs. Instead, they took turns in the temple. How much do you value a prime position over serving God?

24:5

¹⁹This was their appointed order of ministering when they entered the temple of the LORD, according to the regulations prescribed for them by their forefather Aaron, as the LORD, the God of Israel, had commanded him.

The Rest of the Levites

²⁰As for the rest of the descendants of Levi:
   from the sons of Amram: Shubael;
      from the sons of Shubael: Jehdeiah.
   ²¹ As for Rehabiah, from his sons:
      Isshiah was the first.
²²From the Izharites: Shelomoth;
   from the sons of Shelomoth: Jahath.
²³The sons of Hebron: Jeriah the first,ᵃ Amariah the second, Jahaziel the third and Jekameam the fourth.
²⁴The son of Uzziel: Micah;
   from the sons of Micah: Shamir.
   ²⁵The brother of Micah: Isshiah;
      from the sons of Isshiah: Zechariah.
²⁶The sons of Merari: Mahli and Mushi.
   The son of Jaaziah: Beno.
²⁷The sons of Merari:
   from Jaaziah: Beno, Shoham, Zaccur and Ibri.
²⁸From Mahli: Eleazar, who had no sons.
²⁹From Kish: the son of Kish:
   Jerahmeel.
³⁰And the sons of Mushi: Mahli, Eder and Jerimoth.

ᵃ 23 Two Hebrew manuscripts and some Septuagint manuscripts (see also 1 Chron. 23:19); most Hebrew manuscripts *The sons of Jeriah:*

These were the Levites, according to their families. [31]They also cast lots, just as their brothers the descendants of Aaron did, in the presence of King David and of Zadok, Ahimelech, and the heads of families of the priests and of the Levites. The families of the oldest brother were treated the same as those of the youngest.

The Singers

25 David, together with the commanders of the army, set apart some of the sons of Asaph, Heman and Jeduthun for the ministry of prophesying, accompanied by harps, lyres and cymbals. Here is the list of the men who performed this service:

[2]From the sons of Asaph:

Zaccur, Joseph, Nethaniah and Asarelah. The sons of Asaph were under the supervision of Asaph, who prophesied under the king's supervision.

[3]As for Jeduthun, from his sons:

Gedaliah, Zeri, Jeshaiah, Shimei, [a] Hashabiah and Mattithiah, six in all, under the supervision of their father Jeduthun, who prophesied, using the harp in thanking and praising the LORD.

[4]As for Heman, from his sons:

Bukkiah, Mattaniah, Uzziel, Shubael and Jerimoth; Hananiah, Hanani, Eliathah, Giddalti and Romamti-Ezer; Joshbekashah, Mallothi, Hothir and Mahazioth. [5]All these were sons of Heman the king's seer. They were given him through the promises of God to exalt him. [b] God gave Heman fourteen sons and three daughters.

[6]All these men were under the supervision of their fathers for the music of the temple of the LORD, with cymbals, lyres and harps, for the ministry at the house of God. Asaph, Jeduthun and Heman were under the supervision of the king. [7]Along with their relatives—all of them trained and skilled in music for the LORD—they numbered 288. [8]Young and old alike, teacher as well as student, cast lots for their duties.

[9]The first lot, which was for Asaph, fell to Joseph,
his sons and relatives, [c] 12[d]
the second to Gedaliah,
he and his relatives and sons, 12
[10]the third to Zaccur,
his sons and relatives, 12
[11]the fourth to Izri, [e]
his sons and relatives, 12
[12]the fifth to Nethaniah,
his sons and relatives, 12
[13]the sixth to Bukkiah,
his sons and relatives, 12
[14]the seventh to Jesarelah, [f]
his sons and relatives, 12
[15]the eighth to Jeshaiah,
his sons and relatives, 12
[16]the ninth to Mattaniah,
his sons and relatives, 12
[17]the tenth to Shimei,
his sons and relatives, 12
[18]the eleventh to Azarel, [g]
his sons and relatives, 12
[19]the twelfth to Hashabiah,
his sons and relatives, 12
[20]the thirteenth to Shubael,
his sons and relatives, 12

a 3 One Hebrew manuscript and some Septuagint manuscripts (see also verse 17); most Hebrew manuscripts do not have Shimei.   b 5 Hebrew exalt the horn   c 9 See Septuagint; Hebrew does not have his sons and relatives.   d 9 See the total in verse 7; Hebrew does not have twelve.   e 11 A variant of Zeri   f 14 A variant of Asarelah   g 18 A variant of Uzziel

²¹ the fourteenth to Mattithiah,
    his sons and relatives,   12
²² the fifteenth to Jerimoth,
    his sons and relatives,   12
²³ the sixteenth to Hananiah,
    his sons and relatives,   12
²⁴ the seventeenth to Joshbekashah,
    his sons and relatives,   12
²⁵ the eighteenth to Hanani,
    his sons and relatives,   12
²⁶ the nineteenth to Mallothi,
    his sons and relatives,   12
²⁷ the twentieth to Eliathah,
    his sons and relatives,   12
²⁸ the twenty-first to Hothir,
    his sons and relatives,   12
²⁹ the twenty-second to Giddalti,
    his sons and relatives,   12
³⁰ the twenty-third to Mahazioth,
    his sons and relatives,   12
³¹ the twenty-fourth to Romamti-Ezer,
    his sons and relatives,   12

The Gatekeepers

26 The divisions of the gatekeepers:

From the Korahites: Meshelemiah son of Kore, one of the sons of Asaph.
² Meshelemiah had sons:
    Zechariah the firstborn,
    Jediael the second,
    Zebadiah the third,
    Jathniel the fourth,
³ Elam the fifth,
    Jehohanan the sixth
    and Eliehoenai the seventh.
⁴ Obed-Edom also had sons:
    Shemaiah the firstborn,
    Jehozabad the second,
    Joah the third,
    Sacar the fourth,
    Nethanel the fifth,
⁵ Ammiel the sixth,
    Issachar the seventh
    and Peullethai the eighth.
    (For God had blessed Obed-Edom.)

⁶ His son Shemaiah also had sons, who were leaders in their father's family because they were very capable men. ⁷ The sons of Shemaiah: Othni, Rephael, Obed and Elzabad; his relatives Elihu and Semakiah were also able men. ⁸ All these were descendants of Obed-Edom; they and their sons and their relatives were capable men with the strength to do the work—descendants of Obed-Edom, 62 in all.

⁹ Meshelemiah had sons and relatives, who were able men—18 in all.

¹⁰ Hosah the Merarite had sons: Shimri the first (although he was not the firstborn, his father had appointed him the first), ¹¹ Hilkiah the second, Tabaliah the third and Zechariah the fourth. The sons and relatives of Hosah were 13 in all.

¹² These divisions of the gatekeepers, through their chief men, had duties for ministering in the

Let Doubts Drive You Deeper

focus Profile: **Katya**

I was raised in the church. Started going before I was even born. I know every Bible story, and I've heard about a million sermons. But lately I'm starting to wonder. My biology teacher says we human beings need a "god" to make us feel secure and cared for. So we make one up.

I'm scared because I have to admit this makes sense. How do I know whether somewhere way back, some well-meaning people didn't make up God just so we'd feel better about ourselves? How do I know that God made us rather than we made him?

I asked my brother, Michael, what he thinks. He's 26 and in grad school and is a deep thinker. I was surprised by his response.

"Don't be afraid to ask questions. A real God will stand up to questions because he is actually there. Look at the evidence, and go where it takes you. Have you ever considered the fact that every human is unique? If an impersonal force created us, we'd be more like clones. And what about the perfect order you see in creation? You think that could happen by chance? And what about the fact that every human has a built-in sense of right and wrong? Where does that come from?"

"Katya, I can't decide for you. You have to decide for yourself. When you look at the evidence, what do you see?"

doubting God in focus

Doubts aren't wrong. Thinking through your faith can actually make it stronger. If you're having doubts about God . . .

- » Do a study of apologetics. *Apologetics* is not apologizing for what you believe but finding concrete evidences for God and what he is like. Look for books on apologetics at your local bookstore.
- » Ask God. He is tough enough to handle your questions.
- » All of creation declares there is a God (see Psalm 19:1–4, page 671). Don't avoid your doubts; think through the questions for yourself.
- » Some great thinkers have gone down the road of doubt before you, such as C. S. Lewis, Josh McDowell and Lee Strobel. What they discovered was facts, not fiction.

For more on this topic, see the index on page 1656.

See the Apologetics Link at
www.TrueImagesBible.com
for more.

---

temple of the LORD, just as their relatives had. [13]Lots were cast for each gate, according to their families, young and old alike.

[14]The lot for the East Gate fell to Shelemiah. [a] Then lots were cast for his son Zechariah, a wise counselor, and the lot for the North Gate fell to him. [15]The lot for the South Gate fell to Obed-Edom, and the lot for the storehouse fell to his sons. [16]The lots for the West Gate and the Shalleketh Gate on the upper road fell to Shuppim and Hosah.

a 14 A variant of Meshelemiah

Guard was alongside of guard: ¹⁷There were six Levites a day on the east, four a day on the north, four a day on the south and two at a time at the storehouse. ¹⁸As for the court to the west, there were four at the road and two at the court itself.

¹⁹These were the divisions of the gatekeepers who were descendants of Korah and Merari.

The Treasurers and Other Officials

²⁰Their fellow Levites were*ᵃ* in charge of the treasuries of the house of God and the treasuries for the dedicated things.

²¹The descendants of Ladan, who were Gershonites through Ladan and who were heads of families belonging to Ladan the Gershonite, were Jehieli, ²²the sons of Jehieli, Zetham and his brother Joel. They were in charge of the treasuries of the temple of the LORD.

²³From the Amramites, the Izharites, the Hebronites and the Uzzielites:

²⁴Shubael, a descendant of Gershom son of Moses, was the officer in charge of the treasuries. ²⁵His relatives through Eliezer: Rehabiah his son, Jeshaiah his son, Joram his son, Zicri his son and Shelomith his son. ²⁶Shelomith and his relatives were in charge of all the treasuries for the things dedicated by King David, by the heads of families who were the commanders of thousands and commanders of hundreds, and by the other army commanders. ²⁷Some of the plunder taken in battle they dedicated for the repair of the temple of the LORD. ²⁸And everything dedicated by Samuel the seer and by Saul son of Kish, Abner son of Ner and Joab son of Zeruiah, and all the other dedicated things were in the care of Shelomith and his relatives.

²⁹From the Izharites: Kenaniah and his sons were assigned duties away from the temple, as officials and judges over Israel.

³⁰From the Hebronites: Hashabiah and his relatives—seventeen hundred able men—were responsible in Israel west of the Jordan for all the work of the LORD and for the king's service. ³¹As for the Hebronites, Jeriah was their chief according to the genealogical records of their families. In the fortieth year of David's reign a search was made in the records, and capable men among the Hebronites were found at Jazer in Gilead. ³²Jeriah had twenty-seven hundred relatives, who were able men and heads of families, and King David put them in charge of the Reubenites, the Gadites and the half-tribe of Manasseh for every matter pertaining to God and for the affairs of the king.

Army Divisions

27 This is the list of the Israelites—heads of families, commanders of thousands and commanders of hundreds, and their officers, who served the king in all that concerned the army divisions that were on duty month by month throughout the year. Each division consisted of 24,000 men.

²In charge of the first division, for the first month, was Jashobeam son of Zabdiel. There were 24,000 men in his division. ³He was a descendant of Perez and chief of all the army officers for the first month.

⁴In charge of the division for the second month was Dodai the Ahohite; Mikloth was the leader of his division. There were 24,000 men in his division.

⁵The third army commander, for the third month, was Benaiah son of Jehoiada the priest. He was chief and there were 24,000 men in his division. ⁶This was the Benaiah who was a mighty man among the Thirty and was over the Thirty. His son Ammizabad was in charge of his division.

⁷The fourth, for the fourth month, was Asahel the brother of Joab; his son Zebadiah was his successor. There were 24,000 men in his division.

⁸The fifth, for the fifth month, was the commander Shamhuth the Izrahite. There were 24,000 men in his division.

⁹The sixth, for the sixth month, was Ira the son of Ikkesh the Tekoite. There were 24,000 men in his division.

¹⁰The seventh, for the seventh month, was Helez the Pelonite, an Ephraimite. There were 24,000 men in his division.

ᵃ 20 Septuagint; Hebrew As for the Levites, Ahijah was

¹¹ The eighth, for the eighth month, was Sibbecai the Hushathite, a Zerahite. There were 24,000 men in his division.

¹² The ninth, for the ninth month, was Abiezer the Anathothite, a Benjamite. There were 24,000 men in his division.

¹³ The tenth, for the tenth month, was Maharai the Netophathite, a Zerahite. There were 24,000 men in his division.

¹⁴ The eleventh, for the eleventh month, was Benaiah the Pirathonite, an Ephraimite. There were 24,000 men in his division.

¹⁵ The twelfth, for the twelfth month, was Heldai the Netophathite, from the family of Othniel. There were 24,000 men in his division.

Officers of the Tribes

¹⁶ The officers over the tribes of Israel:

over the Reubenites: Eliezer son of Zicri;
over the Simeonites: Shephatiah son of Maacah;
¹⁷ over Levi: Hashabiah son of Kemuel;
over Aaron: Zadok;
¹⁸ over Judah: Elihu, a brother of David;
over Issachar: Omri son of Michael;
¹⁹ over Zebulun: Ishmaiah son of Obadiah;
over Naphtali: Jerimoth son of Azriel;
²⁰ over the Ephraimites: Hoshea son of Azaziah;
over half the tribe of Manasseh: Joel son of Pedaiah;
²¹ over the half-tribe of Manasseh in Gilead: Iddo son of Zechariah;
over Benjamin: Jaasiel son of Abner;
²² over Dan: Azarel son of Jeroham.

These were the officers over the tribes of Israel.

²³ David did not take the number of the men twenty years old or less, because the LORD had promised to make Israel as numerous as the stars in the sky. ²⁴ Joab son of Zeruiah began to count the men but did not finish. Wrath came on Israel on account of this numbering, and the number was not entered in the book *a* of the annals of King David.

The King's Overseers

²⁵ Azmaveth son of Adiel was in charge of the royal storehouses.

Jonathan son of Uzziah was in charge of the storehouses in the outlying districts, in the towns, the villages and the watchtowers.

²⁶ Ezri son of Kelub was in charge of the field workers who farmed the land.

²⁷ Shimei the Ramathite was in charge of the vineyards.

Zabdi the Shiphmite was in charge of the produce of the vineyards for the wine vats.

²⁸ Baal-Hanan the Gederite was in charge of the olive and sycamore-fig trees in the western foothills.

Joash was in charge of the supplies of olive oil.

²⁹ Shitrai the Sharonite was in charge of the herds grazing in Sharon.

Shaphat son of Adlai was in charge of the herds in the valleys.

³⁰ Obil the Ishmaelite was in charge of the camels.

Jehdeiah the Meronothite was in charge of the donkeys.

³¹ Jaziz the Hagrite was in charge of the flocks.

All these were the officials in charge of King David's property.

³² Jonathan, David's uncle, was a counselor, a man of insight and a scribe. Jehiel son of Hacmoni took care of the king's sons.

³³ Ahithophel was the king's counselor.

Hushai the Arkite was the king's friend. ³⁴ Ahithophel was succeeded by Jehoiada son of Benaiah and by Abiathar.

Joab was the commander of the royal army.

a 24 Septuagint; Hebrew *number*

David's Plans for the Temple

28 David summoned all the officials of Israel to assemble at Jerusalem: the officers over the tribes, the commanders of the divisions in the service of the king, the commanders of thousands and commanders of hundreds, and the officials in charge of all the property and livestock belonging to the king and his sons, together with the palace officials, the mighty men and all the brave warriors.

²King David rose to his feet and said: "Listen to me, my brothers and my people. I had it in my heart to build a house as a place of rest for the ark of the covenant of the LORD, for the footstool of our God, and I made plans to build it. ³But God said to me, 'You are not to build a house for my Name, because you are a warrior and have shed blood.'

⁴"Yet the LORD, the God of Israel, chose me from my whole family to be king over Israel forever. He chose Judah as leader, and from the house of Judah he chose my family, and from my father's sons he was pleased to make me king over all Israel. ⁵Of all my sons—and the LORD has given me many—he has chosen my son Solomon to sit on the throne of the kingdom of the LORD over Israel. ⁶He said to me: 'Solomon your son is the one who will build my house and my courts, for I have chosen him to be my son, and I will be his father. ⁷I will establish his kingdom forever if he is unswerving in carrying out my commands and laws, as is being done at this time.'

⁸"So now I charge you in the sight of all Israel and of the assembly of the LORD, and in the hearing of our God: Be careful to follow all the commands of the LORD your God, that you may possess this good land and pass it on as an inheritance to your descendants forever.

⁹"And you, my son Solomon, acknowledge the God of your father, and serve him with wholehearted devotion and with a willing mind, for the LORD searches every heart and understands every motive behind the thoughts. If you seek him, he will be found by you; but if you forsake him, he will reject you forever. ¹⁰Consider now, for the LORD has chosen you to build a temple as a sanctuary. Be strong and do the work."

¹¹Then David gave his son Solomon the plans for the portico of the temple, its buildings, its storerooms, its upper parts, its inner rooms and the place of atonement. ¹²He gave him the plans of all that the Spirit had put in his mind for the courts of the temple of the LORD and all the surrounding rooms, for the treasuries of the temple of God and for the treasuries for the dedicated things. ¹³He gave him instructions for the divisions of the priests and Levites, and for all the work of serving in the temple of the LORD, as well as for all the articles to be used in its service. ¹⁴He designated the weight of gold for all the gold articles to be used in various kinds of service, and the weight of silver for all the silver articles to be used in various kinds of service:

---

love ♥ notes

28:9

Beloved,

There are no secrets between us—absolutely none. I know your every thought, your every motive. And guess what? I still love you as thoroughly and completely as I know you.

—Your loving Father

Talk honestly with God about any secret you might have. It's okay—he already knows.

the weight of gold for the gold lampstands and their lamps, with the weight for each lampstand and its lamps; and the weight of silver for each silver lampstand and its lamps, according to the use of each lampstand; ¹⁶the weight of gold for each table for consecrated bread; the weight of silver for the silver tables; ¹⁷the weight of pure gold for the forks, sprinkling bowls and pitchers; the weight of gold for each gold dish; the weight of silver for each silver dish; ¹⁸and the weight of the refined gold for the altar of incense. He also gave him the plan for the chariot, that is, the cherubim of gold that spread their wings and shelter the ark of the covenant of the Lord.

¹⁹"All this," David said, "I have in writing from the hand of the Lord upon me, and he gave me understanding in all the details of the plan."

²⁰David also said to Solomon his son, "Be strong and courageous, and do the work. Do not be afraid or discouraged, for the Lord God, my God, is with you. He will not fail you or forsake you until all the work for the service of the temple of the Lord is finished. ²¹The divisions of the priests and Levites are ready for all the work on the temple of God, and every willing man skilled in any craft will help you in all the work. The officials and all the people will obey your every command."

Gifts for Building the Temple

29 Then King David said to the whole assembly: "My son Solomon, the one whom God has chosen, is young and inexperienced. The task is great, because this palatial structure is not for man but for the Lord God. ²With all my resources I have provided for the temple of my God—gold for the gold work, silver for the silver, bronze for the bronze, iron for the iron and wood for the wood, as well as onyx for the settings, turquoise,ᵃ stones of various colors, and all kinds of fine stone and marble—all of these in large quantities. ³Besides, in my devotion to the temple of my God I now give my personal treasures of gold and silver for the temple of my God, over and above everything I have provided for this holy temple: ⁴three thousand talentsᵇ of gold (gold of Ophir) and seven thousand talentsᶜ of refined silver, for the overlaying of the walls of the buildings, ⁵for the gold work and the silver work, and for all the work to be done by the craftsmen. Now, who is willing to consecrate himself today to the Lord?"

truth or dare

How would you feel if, every year on your birthday, your family complained bitterly that they had to give you a present? The point: God loves a generous and cheerful giver!

29:6–9

⁶Then the leaders of families, the officers of the tribes of Israel, the commanders of thousands and commanders of hundreds, and the officials in charge of the king's work gave willingly. ⁷They gave toward the work on the temple of God five thousand talentsᵈ and ten thousand daricsᵉ of gold, ten thousand talentsᶠ of silver, eighteen thousand talentsᵍ of bronze and a hundred thousand talentsʰ of iron. ⁸Any who had precious stones gave them to the treasury of the temple of the Lord in the custody of Jehiel the Gershonite. ⁹The people rejoiced at the willing response of their leaders, for they had given freely and wholeheartedly to the Lord. David the king also rejoiced greatly.

David's Prayer

¹⁰David praised the Lord in the presence of the whole assembly, saying,

"Praise be to you, O Lord,
    God of our father Israel,
    from everlasting to everlasting.
¹¹Yours, O Lord, is the greatness and the power
    and the glory and the majesty and the splendor,
    for everything in heaven and earth is yours.
Yours, O Lord, is the kingdom;

ᵃ 2 The meaning of the Hebrew for this word is uncertain.   ᵇ 4 That is, about 110 tons (about 100 metric tons)
ᶜ 4 That is, about 260 tons (about 240 metric tons)   ᵈ 7 That is, about 190 tons (about 170 metric tons)   ᵉ 7 That is, about 185 pounds (about 84 kilograms)   ᶠ 7 That is, about 375 tons (about 345 metric tons)   ᵍ 7 That is, about 675 tons (about 610 metric tons)   ʰ 7 That is, about 3,750 tons (about 3,450 metric tons)

you are exalted as head over all.
¹²Wealth and honor come from you;
    you are the ruler of all things.
In your hands are strength and power
    to exalt and give strength to all.
¹³Now, our God, we give you thanks,
    and praise your glorious name.

¹⁴"But who am I, and who are my people, that we should be able to give as generously as this? Everything comes from you, and we have given you only what comes from your hand. ¹⁵We are aliens and strangers in your sight, as were all our forefathers. Our days on earth are like a shadow, without hope. ¹⁶O LORD our God, as for all this abundance that we have provided for building you a temple for your Holy Name, it comes from your hand, and all of it belongs to you. ¹⁷I know, my God, that you test the heart and are pleased with integrity. All these things have I given willingly and with honest intent. And now I have

genuine

integrity » 29:17

Don't you hate it when someone tries to be something she's not? God is an expert at spotting a fake. When he looked at David's heart, he saw genuine and unselfish motives for giving. What does God see when he checks out *your* heart? Do you do the "right things" because you want to look good to God and others? Or are you motivated by love for God and gratitude for all he's done? The actions might look the same, but the motive is vastly different. Do you pass the integrity test?

seen with joy how willingly your people who are here have given to you. ¹⁸O LORD, God of our fathers Abraham, Isaac and Israel, keep this desire in the hearts of your people forever, and keep their hearts loyal to you. ¹⁹And give my son Solomon the wholehearted devotion to keep your commands, requirements and decrees and to do everything to build the palatial structure for which I have provided."

²⁰Then David said to the whole assembly, "Praise the LORD your God." So they all praised the LORD, the God of their fathers; they bowed low and fell prostrate before the LORD and the king.

Solomon Acknowledged as King

²¹The next day they made sacrifices to the LORD and presented burnt offerings to him: a thousand bulls, a thousand rams and a thousand male lambs, together with their drink offerings, and other sacrifices in abundance for all Israel. ²²They ate and drank with great joy in the presence of the LORD that day.

Then they acknowledged Solomon son of David as king a second time, anointing him before the LORD to be ruler and Zadok to be priest. ²³So Solomon sat on the throne of the LORD as king in place of his father David. He prospered and all Israel obeyed him. ²⁴All the officers and mighty men, as well as all of King David's sons, pledged their submission to King Solomon.

²⁵The LORD highly exalted Solomon in the sight of all Israel and bestowed on him royal splendor such as no king over Israel ever had before.

The Death of David

²⁶David son of Jesse was king over all Israel. ²⁷He ruled over Israel forty years—seven in Hebron and thirty-three in Jerusalem. ²⁸He died at a good old age, having enjoyed long life, wealth and honor. His son Solomon succeeded him as king.

²⁹As for the events of King David's reign, from beginning to end, they are written in the records of Samuel the seer, the records of Nathan the prophet and the records of Gad the seer, ³⁰together with the details of his reign and power, and the circumstances that surrounded him and Israel and the kingdoms of all the other lands.

at a glance ⌄

author:	Unknown, but possibly Ezra.
date:	About 430 B.C.
setting:	Covers the period from Solomon's reign (970 B.C.) to the Babylonian exile (586 B.C.), paralleling many of the events of 1 and 2 Kings.
verse to remember:	"If my people, who are called by my name, will humble themselves and pray and seek my face and turn from their wicked ways, then will I hear from heaven and will forgive their sin and will heal their land" (7:14).
theme to consider:	Hear God's call that echoes through the ages—come to him, confess to him and receive his healing and forgiveness.

2 chronicles

unchanging truth

Don't you just love family reunions? (*Yeah right*, some of you are thinking.) How about those corny comments? "Oh, you look just like your mother did when she was your age!" "You have your great-aunt Mildred's nose!" "Well, we all know where you got that athletic ability! Your Grandpa Joe was a real wildcat back in his day." Sometimes it's all you can do to smile politely as you wonder if you really do have a nose as big as Mildred's. Even though we can't always see the resemblance, family characteristics—both good and not so good—are passed down through the generations.

That's the beauty of family stories. Even though you might not remember all that much about your ancestors, when you really listen to stories about them, you can discover some interesting facts about them and about you. Those family legends not only connect you to past events, but they also help you grasp your place in the family line.

The book of 2 Chronicles is very similar to 1 Chronicles (originally they were one book) in the way it relates the family history of God's people and recounts God's grace and love through history. God is still calling his people to come to him. This loving call of God will continue through all the generations that are to come until the end of the world. That's one great family story to be included in!

life lessons

1. Need something to do the job God's given you? Just ask. He gives generously (1:7–10).

2. God wants us to learn from our spiritual ancestors and then pass our wisdom along to the next generation (17:3–6).

3. Following God means dedicating your whole life to him (29:1–5; 30:23–27).

Solomon Asks for Wisdom

1 Solomon son of David established himself firmly over his kingdom, for the LORD his God was with him and made him exceedingly great.

²Then Solomon spoke to all Israel—to the commanders of thousands and commanders of hundreds, to the judges and to all the leaders in Israel, the heads of families— ³and Solomon and the whole assembly went to the high place at Gibeon, for God's Tent of Meeting was there, which Moses the LORD's servant had made in the desert. ⁴Now David had brought up the ark of God from Kiriath Jearim to the place he had prepared for it, because he had pitched a tent for it in Jerusalem. ⁵But the bronze altar that Bezalel son of Uri, the son of Hur, had made was in Gibeon in front of the tabernacle of the LORD; so Solomon and the assembly inquired of him there. ⁶Solomon went up to the bronze altar before the LORD in the Tent of Meeting and offered a thousand burnt offerings on it.

⁷That night God appeared to Solomon and said to him, "Ask for whatever you want me to give you."

⁸Solomon answered God, "You have shown great kindness to David my father and have made me king in his place. ⁹Now, LORD God, let your promise to my father David be confirmed, for you have made me king over a people who are as numerous as the dust of the earth. ¹⁰Give me wisdom and knowledge, that I may lead this people, for who is able to govern this great people of yours?"

¹¹God said to Solomon, "Since this is your heart's desire and you have not asked for wealth, riches or honor, nor for the death of your enemies, and since you have not asked for a long life but for wisdom and knowledge to govern my people over whom I have made you king, ¹²therefore wisdom and knowledge will be given you. And I will also give you wealth, riches and honor, such as no king who was before you ever had and none after you will have."

¹³Then Solomon went to Jerusalem from the high place at Gibeon, from before the Tent of Meeting. And he reigned over Israel.

¹⁴Solomon accumulated chariots and horses; he had fourteen hundred chariots and twelve thousand horses,ᵃ which he kept in the chariot cities and also with him in Jerusalem. ¹⁵The king made silver and gold as common in Jerusalem as stones, and cedar as plentiful as sycamore-fig trees in the foothills. ¹⁶Solomon's horses were imported from Egyptᵇ and from Kueᶜ—the royal merchants purchased them from Kue. ¹⁷They imported a chariot from Egypt for six hundred shekelsᵈ of silver, and a horse for a hundred and fifty.ᵉ They also exported them to all the kings of the Hittites and of the Arameans.

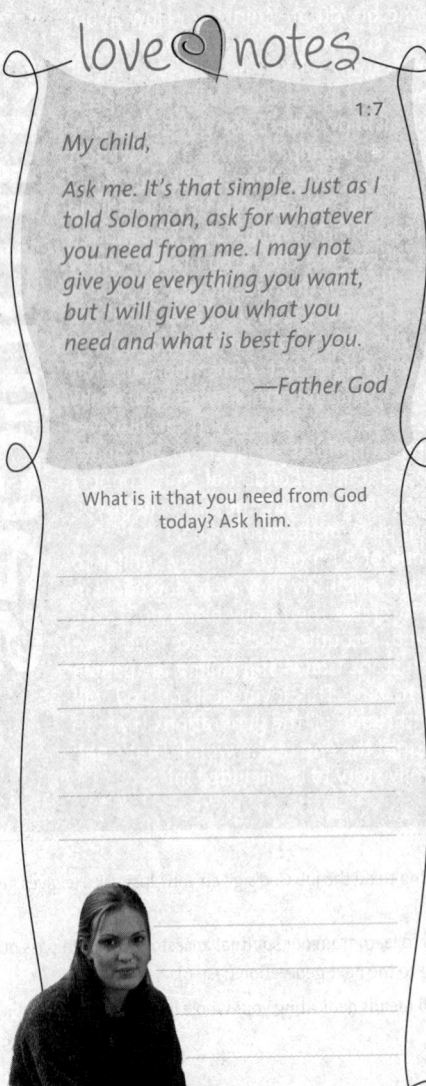

love ❤ notes

1:7

My child,

Ask me. It's that simple. Just as I told Solomon, ask for whatever you need from me. I may not give you everything you want, but I will give you what you need and what is best for you.

—Father God

What is it that you need from God today? Ask him.

_____

_____

_____

_____

_____

_____

_____

_____

_____

_____

_____

_____

ᵃ 14 Or *charioteers*   *ᵇ 16* Or possibly *Muzur,* a region in Cilicia; also in verse 17   *ᶜ 16* Probably Cilicia   *ᵈ 17* That is, about 15 pounds (about 7 kilograms)   *ᵉ 17* That is, about 3 3/4 pounds (about 1.7 kilograms)

Preparations for Building the Temple

2 Solomon gave orders to build a temple for the Name of the Lord and a royal palace for himself. [2]He conscripted seventy thousand men as carriers and eighty thousand as stonecutters in the hills and thirty-six hundred as foremen over them.

[3]Solomon sent this message to Hiram[a] king of Tyre:

"Send me cedar logs as you did for my father David when you sent him cedar to build a palace to live in. [4]Now I am about to build a temple for the Name of the Lord my God and to dedicate it to him for burning fragrant incense before him, for setting out the consecrated bread regularly, and for making burnt offerings every morning and evening and on Sabbaths and New Moons and at the appointed feasts of the Lord our God. This is a lasting ordinance for Israel.

[5]"The temple I am going to build will be great, because our God is greater than all other gods. [6]But who is able to build a temple for him, since the heavens, even the highest heavens, cannot contain him? Who then am I to build a temple for him, except as a place to burn sacrifices before him?

[7]"Send me, therefore, a man skilled to work in gold and silver, bronze and iron, and in purple, crimson and blue yarn, and experienced in the art of engraving, to work in Judah and Jerusalem with my skilled craftsmen, whom my father David provided.

[8]"Send me also cedar, pine and algum[b] logs from Lebanon, for I know that your men are skilled in cutting timber there. My men will work with yours [9]to provide me with plenty of lumber, because the temple I build must be large and magnificent. [10]I will give your servants, the woodsmen who cut the timber, twenty thousand cors[c] of ground wheat, twenty thousand cors of barley, twenty thousand baths[d] of wine and twenty thousand baths of olive oil."

[11]Hiram king of Tyre replied by letter to Solomon:

"Because the Lord loves his people, he has made you their king."

[12]And Hiram added:

"Praise be to the Lord, the God of Israel, who made heaven and earth! He has given King David a wise son, endowed with intelligence and discernment, who will build a temple for the Lord and a palace for himself.

[13]"I am sending you Huram-Abi, a man of great skill, [14]whose mother was from Dan and whose father was from Tyre. He is trained to work in gold and silver, bronze and iron, stone and wood, and with purple and blue and crimson yarn and fine linen. He is experienced in all kinds of engraving and can execute any design given to him. He will work with your craftsmen and with those of my lord, David your father.

[15]"Now let my lord send his servants the wheat and barley and the olive oil and wine he promised, [16]and we will cut all the logs from Lebanon that you need and will float them in rafts by sea down to Joppa. You can then take them up to Jerusalem."

[17]Solomon took a census of all the aliens who were in Israel, after the census his father David had taken; and they were found to be 153,600. [18]He assigned 70,000 of them to be carriers and 80,000 to be stonecutters in the hills, with 3,600 foremen over them to keep the people working.

truth or dare

God loves it when a girl recognizes her smallness next to him and at the same time offers him her *best* in everything she does.

2:5–6

---

[a] *3* Hebrew *Huram,* a variant of *Hiram*; also in verses 11 and 12   [b] *8* Probably a variant of *almug*; possibly juniper
[c] *10* That is, probably about 125,000 bushels (about 4,400 kiloliters)   [d] *10* That is, probably about 115,000 gallons (about 440 kiloliters)

Solomon Builds the Temple

3 Then Solomon began to build the temple of the Lord in Jerusalem on Mount Moriah, where the Lord had appeared to his father David. It was on the threshing floor of Araunah[a] the Jebusite, the place provided by David. [2]He began building on the second day of the second month in the fourth year of his reign.

[3]The foundation Solomon laid for building the temple of God was sixty cubits long and twenty cubits wide[b] (using the cubit of the old standard). [4]The portico at the front of the temple was twenty cubits[c] long across the width of the building and twenty cubits[d] high.

He overlaid the inside with pure gold. [5]He paneled the main hall with pine and covered it with fine gold and decorated it with palm tree and chain designs. [6]He adorned the temple with precious stones. And the gold he used was gold of Parvaim. [7]He overlaid the ceiling beams, doorframes, walls and doors of the temple with gold, and he carved cherubim on the walls.

[8]He built the Most Holy Place, its length corresponding to the width of the temple—twenty cubits long and twenty cubits wide. He overlaid the inside with six hundred talents[e] of fine gold. [9]The gold nails weighed fifty shekels.[f] He also overlaid the upper parts with gold.

[10]In the Most Holy Place he made a pair of sculptured cherubim and overlaid them with gold. [11]The total wingspan of the cherubim was twenty cubits. One wing of the first cherub was five cubits[g] long and touched the temple wall, while its other wing, also five cubits long, touched the wing of the other cherub. [12]Similarly one wing of the second cherub was five cubits long and touched the other temple wall, and its other wing, also five cubits long, touched the wing of the first cherub. [13]The wings of these cherubim extended twenty cubits. They stood on their feet, facing the main hall.[h]

[14]He made the curtain of blue, purple and crimson yarn and fine linen, with cherubim worked into it.

[15]In the front of the temple he made two pillars, which together were thirty-five cubits[i] long, each with a capital on top measuring five cubits. [16]He made interwoven chains[j] and put them on top of the pillars. He also made a hundred pomegranates and attached them to the chains. [17]He erected the pillars in the front of the temple, one to the south and one to the north. The one to the south he named Jakin[k] and the one to the north Boaz.[l]

The Temple's Furnishings

4 He made a bronze altar twenty cubits long, twenty cubits wide and ten cubits high.[m] [2]He made the Sea of cast metal, circular in shape, measuring ten cubits from rim to rim and five cubits[n] high. It took a line of thirty cubits[o] to measure around it. [3]Below the rim, figures of bulls encircled it—ten to a cubit.[p] The bulls were cast in two rows in one piece with the Sea.

[4]The Sea stood on twelve bulls, three facing north, three facing west, three facing south and three facing east. The Sea rested on top of them, and their hindquarters were toward the center. [5]It was a handbreadth[q] in thickness, and its rim was like the rim of a cup, like a lily blossom. It held three thousand baths.[r]

[6]He then made ten basins for washing and placed five on the south side and five on the north. In them the things to be used for the burnt offerings were rinsed, but the Sea was to be used by the priests for washing.

[7]He made ten gold lampstands according to the specifications for them and placed them in the temple, five on the south side and five on the north.

[8]He made ten tables and placed them in the temple, five on the south side and five on the north. He also made a hundred gold sprinkling bowls.

[9]He made the courtyard of the priests, and the large court and the doors for the court, and overlaid the doors with bronze. [10]He placed the Sea on the south side, at the southeast corner.

a 1 Hebrew *Ornan,* a variant of *Araunah*   *b 3* That is, about 90 feet (about 27 meters) long and 30 feet (about 9 meters) wide   *c 4* That is, about 30 feet (about 9 meters); also in verses 8, 11 and 13   *d 4* Some Septuagint and Syriac manuscripts; Hebrew *and a hundred and twenty*   *e 8* That is, about 23 tons (about 21 metric tons)   *f 9* That is, about 1 1/4 pounds (about 0.6 kilogram)   *g 11* That is, about 7 1/2 feet (about 2.3 meters); also in verse 15   *h 13* Or *facing inward*   *i 15* That is, about 52 feet (about 16 meters)   *j 16* Or possibly *made chains in the inner sanctuary*; the meaning of the Hebrew for this phrase is uncertain.   *k 17 Jakin* probably means *he establishes.*   *l 17 Boaz* probably means *in him is strength.*   *m 1* That is, about 30 feet (about 9 meters) long and wide, and about 15 feet (about 4.5 meters) high   *n 2* That is, about 7 1/2 feet (about 2.3 meters)   *o 2* That is, about 45 feet (about 13.5 meters)   *p 3* That is, about 1 1/2 feet (about 0.5 meter)   *q 5* That is, about 3 inches (about 8 centimeters)   *r 5* That is, about 17,500 gallons (about 66 kiloliters)

in
focus
Wanted: A Few Good Friends

Profile: **Bridget**

Maybe you enjoy eating lunch alone every day. Not me. I'm sick of being the only Christian in the entire school. Whenever I bow my head to pray at lunch, everyone steers clear. And the few friends I do have don't respect my relationship with Jesus at all.

Is it too much to ask to find a couple of decent friends—the kind who share my same interests and accept me as I am? Instead, I'm surrounded by filthy language and people constantly bragging about drinking and sex.

As much as I try to be strong, some days I find myself slipping. I'm torn between wanting to keep my relationship with Jesus strong and just giving in. Some days I even wonder how long I'll stick to my faith. By senior year, I may be too tired to keep fighting all the time.

At least I have one close Christian friend from church. Tonya says she struggles with the same stuff at her school and that she could use some accountability to keep herself pure. She invited me to do coffee on Saturday and talk about encouraging each other. I'm not sure what she means, but I do know this—I need all the help I can get.

accountability in focus

If you've trusted in Jesus, the devil wants to destroy you (see 1 Peter 5:8, page 1612). One of his best tactics is to make you feel isolated. Remember, the Christian life isn't meant to be lived alone!

- » There's strength in numbers. Find a Christian girlfriend you can trust and talk with every week.
- » Find ways to encourage each other—notes, phone calls and prayer (see Hebrews 10:23–25, page 1595).
- » Satan wants you to hide your sins. Instead, air them out. Confess them first to God and then be open about them with a friend who can hold you accountable (see James 5:16, page 1606).
- » If you haven't found a strong Christian friend yet, pray that God will send an accountability partner who can encourage you to stay on track.

For more on this topic, see the index on page 1656.

For more on accountability, check out the link on www.TrueImagesBible.com

[11] He also made the pots and shovels and sprinkling bowls.
So Huram finished the work he had undertaken for King Solomon in the temple of God:

[12] the two pillars;
the two bowl-shaped capitals on top of the pillars;
the two sets of network decorating the two bowl-shaped capitals on top of the pillars;
[13] the four hundred pomegranates for the two sets of network (two rows of pomegranates for each network, decorating the bowl-shaped capitals on top of the pillars);
[14] the stands with their basins;
[15] the Sea and the twelve bulls under it;
[16] the pots, shovels, meat forks and all related articles.

All the objects that Huram-Abi made for King Solomon for the temple of the LORD were of polished bronze. [17]The king had them cast in clay molds in the plain of the Jordan between Succoth and Zarethan.[a] [18]All these things that Solomon made amounted to so much that the weight of the bronze was not determined.

[19]Solomon also made all the furnishings that were in God's temple:

the golden altar;
the tables on which was the bread of the Presence;
[20]the lampstands of pure gold with their lamps, to burn in front of the inner sanctuary as prescribed;
[21]the gold floral work and lamps and tongs (they were solid gold);
[22]the pure gold wick trimmers, sprinkling bowls, dishes and censers; and the gold doors of the temple: the inner doors to the Most Holy Place and the doors of the main hall.

5 When all the work Solomon had done for the temple of the LORD was finished, he brought in the things his father David had dedicated—the silver and gold and all the furnishings—and he placed them in the treasuries of God's temple.

The Ark Brought to the Temple

[2]Then Solomon summoned to Jerusalem the elders of Israel, all the heads of the tribes and the chiefs of the Israelite families, to bring up the ark of the LORD's covenant from Zion, the City of David. [3]And all the men of Israel came together to the king at the time of the festival in the seventh month.

[4]When all the elders of Israel had arrived, the Levites took up the ark, [5]and they brought up the ark and the Tent of Meeting and all the sacred furnishings in it. The priests, who were Levites, carried them up; [6]and King Solomon and the entire assembly of Israel that had gathered about him were before the ark, sacrificing so many sheep and cattle that they could not be recorded or counted.

[7]The priests then brought the ark of the LORD's covenant to its place in the inner sanctuary of the temple, the Most Holy Place, and put it beneath the wings of the cherubim. [8]The cherubim spread their wings over the place of the ark and covered the ark and its carrying poles. [9]These poles were so long that their ends, extending from the ark, could be seen from in front of the inner sanctuary, but not from outside the Holy Place; and they are still there today. [10]There was nothing in the ark except the two tablets that Moses had placed in it at Horeb, where the LORD made a covenant with the Israelites after they came out of Egypt.

[11]The priests then withdrew from the Holy Place. All the priests who were there had consecrated themselves, regardless of their divisions. [12]All the Levites who were musicians—Asaph, Heman, Jeduthun and their sons and relatives—stood on the east side of the altar, dressed in fine linen and playing cymbals, harps and lyres. They were accompanied by 120 priests sounding trumpets. [13]The trumpeters and singers joined in unison, as with one voice, to give praise and thanks to the LORD. Accompanied by trumpets, cymbals and other instruments, they raised their voices in praise to the LORD and sang:

"He is good;
his love endures forever."

Then the temple of the LORD was filled with a cloud, [14]and the priests could not perform their service because of the cloud, for the glory of the LORD filled the temple of God.

6 Then Solomon said, "The LORD has said that he would dwell in a dark cloud; [2]I have built a magnificent temple for you, a place for you to dwell forever."
[3]While the whole assembly of Israel was standing there, the king turned around and blessed them. [4]Then he said:

"Praise be to the LORD, the God of Israel, who with his hands has fulfilled what he promised with his mouth to my father David. For he said, [5]'Since the day I brought my people out of Egypt, I have not chosen a city in any tribe of Israel to have a temple built for my Name to be there, nor have I chosen anyone to be the leader over my people Israel. [6]But now I have chosen Jerusalem for my Name to be there, and I have chosen David to rule my people Israel.'

a 17 Hebrew *Zeredatha*, a variant of *Zarethan*

7"My father David had it in his heart to build a temple for the Name of the Lord, the God of Israel. 8But the Lord said to my father David, 'Because it was in your heart to build a temple for my Name, you did well to have this in your heart. 9Nevertheless, you are not the one to build the temple, but your son, who is your own flesh and blood—he is the one who will build the temple for my Name.'

10"The Lord has kept the promise he made. I have succeeded David my father and now I sit on the throne of Israel, just as the Lord promised, and I have built the temple for the Name of the Lord, the God of Israel. 11There I have placed the ark, in which is the covenant of the Lord that he made with the people of Israel."

Solomon's Prayer of Dedication

12Then Solomon stood before the altar of the Lord in front of the whole assembly of Israel and spread out his hands. 13Now he had made a bronze platform, five cubits*ᵃ* long, five cubits wide and three cubits*ᵇ* high, and had placed it in the center of the outer court. He stood on the platform and then knelt down before the whole assembly of Israel and spread out his hands toward heaven. 14He said:

"O Lord, God of Israel, there is no God like you in heaven or on earth—you who keep your covenant of love with your servants who continue wholeheartedly in your way. 15You have kept your promise to your servant David my father; with your mouth you have promised and with your hand you have fulfilled it—as it is today.

16"Now Lord, God of Israel, keep for your servant David my father the promises you made to him when you said, 'You shall never fail to have a man to sit before me on the throne of Israel, if only your sons are careful in all they do to walk before me according to my law, as you have done.' 17And now, O Lord, God of Israel, let your word that you promised your servant David come true.

18"But will God really dwell on earth with men? The heavens, even the highest heavens, cannot contain you. How much less this temple I have built! 19Yet give attention to your servant's prayer and his plea for mercy, O Lord my God. Hear the cry and the prayer that your servant is praying in your presence. 20May your eyes be open toward this temple day and night, this place of which you said you would put your Name there. May you hear the prayer your servant prays toward this place. 21Hear the supplications of your servant and of your people Israel when they pray toward this place. Hear from heaven, your dwelling place; and when you hear, forgive.

22"When a man wrongs his neighbor and is required to take an oath and he comes and swears the oath before your altar in this temple, 23then hear from heaven and act. Judge between your servants, repaying the guilty by bringing down on his own head what he has done. Declare the innocent not guilty and so establish his innocence.

24"When your people Israel have been defeated by an enemy because they have sinned against you and when they turn back and confess your name, praying and making supplication before you in this temple, 25then hear from heaven and forgive the sin of your people Israel and bring them back to the land you gave to them and their fathers.

26"When the heavens are shut up and there is no rain because your people have sinned against you, and when they pray toward this place and confess your name and turn from their sin because you have afflicted them, 27then hear from heaven and forgive the sin of your servants, your people Israel. Teach them the right way to live, and send rain on the land you gave your people for an inheritance.

28"When famine or plague comes to the land, or blight or mildew, locusts or grasshoppers, or when enemies besiege them in any of their cities, whatever disaster or disease may come, 29and when a prayer or plea is made by any of your people Israel—each one aware

truth or dare

A king on his knees? Solomon greatly respected God—even in front of his subjects! How do you clue the crowd that you're a diehard fan of God?

6:12–13

ᵃ 13 That is, about 7 1/2 feet (about 2.3 meters)   *ᵇ 13* That is, about 4 1/2 feet (about 1.3 meters) of his afflictions and pains, and spreading out his hands toward this temple— ³⁰then hear from heaven, your dwelling place. Forgive, and deal with each man according to all he does, since you know his heart (for you alone know the hearts of men), ³¹so that they will fear you and walk in your ways all the time they live in the land you gave our fathers.

³²"As for the foreigner who does not belong to your people Israel but has come from a distant land because of your great name and your mighty hand and your outstretched arm—when he comes and prays toward this temple, ³³then hear from heaven, your dwelling place, and do whatever the foreigner asks of you, so that all the peoples of the earth may know your name and fear you, as do your own people Israel, and may know that this house I have built bears your Name.

³⁴"When your people go to war against their enemies, wherever you send them, and when they pray to you toward this city you have chosen and the temple I have built for your Name, ³⁵then hear from heaven their prayer and their plea, and uphold their cause.

³⁶"When they sin against you—for there is no one who does not sin—and you become angry with them and give them over to the enemy, who takes them captive to a land far away or near; ³⁷and if they have a change of heart in the land where they are held captive, and repent and plead with you in the land of their captivity and say, 'We have sinned, we have done wrong and acted wickedly'; ³⁸and if they turn back to you with all their heart and soul in the land of their captivity where they were taken, and pray toward the land you gave their fathers, toward the city you have chosen and toward the temple I have built for your Name; ³⁹then from heaven, your dwelling place, hear their prayer and their pleas, and uphold their cause. And forgive your people, who have sinned against you.

⁴⁰"Now, my God, may your eyes be open and your ears attentive to the prayers offered in this place.

⁴¹ "Now arise, O LORD God, and come to your resting place,
  you and the ark of your might.
May your priests, O LORD God, be clothed with salvation,
  may your saints rejoice in your goodness.
⁴²O LORD God, do not reject your anointed one.
  Remember the great love promised to David your servant."

The Dedication of the Temple

7 When Solomon finished praying, fire came down from heaven and consumed the burnt offering and the sacrifices, and the glory of the LORD filled the temple. ²The priests could not enter the temple of the LORD because the glory of the LORD filled it. ³When all the Israelites saw the fire coming down and the glory of the LORD above the temple, they knelt on the pavement with their faces to the ground, and they worshiped and gave thanks to the LORD, saying,

"He is good;
  his love endures forever."

⁴Then the king and all the people offered sacrifices before the LORD. ⁵And King Solomon offered a sacrifice of twenty-two thousand head of cattle and a hundred and twenty thousand sheep and goats. So the king and all the people dedicated the temple of God. ⁶The priests took their positions, as did the Levites with the LORD's musical instruments, which King David had made for praising the LORD and which were used when he gave thanks, saying, "His love endures forever." Opposite the Levites, the priests blew their trumpets, and all the Israelites were standing.

⁷Solomon consecrated the middle part of the courtyard in front of the temple of the LORD, and there he offered burnt offerings and the fat of the fellowship offerings,ᵃ because the bronze altar he had made could not hold the burnt offerings, the grain offerings and the fat portions.

⁸So Solomon observed the festival at that time for seven days, and all Israel with him—a vast assembly, people from Leboᵇ Hamath to the Wadi of Egypt. ⁹On the eighth day they held an assembly, for they had celebrated the dedication of the altar for seven days and the festival for seven days more. ¹⁰On the twenty-third day of the seventh month he sent the people to their homes, joyful and glad in heart for the good things the LORD had done for David and Solomon and for his people Israel.

ᵃ 7 Traditionally *peace offerings*   ᵇ 8 Or *from the entrance to*

The Lord Appears to Solomon

[11]When Solomon had finished the temple of the Lord and the royal palace, and had succeeded in carrying out all he had in mind to do in the temple of the Lord and in his own palace, [12]the Lord appeared to him at night and said:

"I have heard your prayer and have chosen this place for myself as a temple for sacrifices.

[13]"When I shut up the heavens so that there is no rain, or command locusts to devour the land or send a plague among my people, [14]if my people, who are called by my name, will humble themselves and pray and seek my face and turn from their wicked ways, then will I hear from heaven and will forgive their sin and will heal their land. [15]Now my eyes will be open and my ears attentive to the prayers offered in this place. [16]I have chosen and consecrated this temple so that my Name may be there forever. My eyes and my heart will always be there.

love notes

7:13–14

Treasured one,

Do you like it when someone hurts you and then flippantly says, "Oh, I'm sorry"? Neither do I. I desire a heart that is truly repentant, moving away from sin. Those ingredients will always lead to forgiveness.

—Your merciful God

What steps do you need to take to seek God's forgiveness? Tell him!

[17]"As for you, if you walk before me as David your father did, and do all I command, and observe my decrees and laws, [18]I will establish your royal throne, as I covenanted with David your father when I said, 'You shall never fail to have a man to rule over Israel.'

[19]"But if you[a] turn away and forsake the decrees and commands I have given you[a] and go off to serve other gods and worship them, [20]then I will uproot Israel from my land, which I have given them, and will reject this temple I have consecrated for my Name. I will make it a byword and an object of ridicule among all peoples. [21]And though this temple is now so imposing, all who pass by will be appalled and say, 'Why has the Lord done such a thing to this land and to this temple?' [22]People will answer, 'Because they have forsaken the Lord, the God of their fathers, who brought them out of Egypt, and have embraced other gods, worshiping and serving them—that is why he brought all this disaster on them.' "

Solomon's Other Activities

8 At the end of twenty years, during which Solomon built the temple of the Lord and his own palace, [2]Solomon rebuilt the villages that Hiram[b] had given him, and settled Israelites in them. [3]Solomon then went to Hamath Zobah and captured it. [4]He also built up Tadmor in the desert and all the store cities he had built in Hamath. [5]He rebuilt Upper Beth Horon and Lower Beth Horon as fortified cities, with walls and

a 19 The Hebrew is plural. b 2 Hebrew Huram, a variant of Hiram; also in verse 18 with gates and bars, ⁶as well as Baalath and all his store cities, and all the cities for his chariots and for his horses*—whatever he desired to build in Jerusalem, in Lebanon and throughout all the territory he ruled.

⁷All the people left from the Hittites, Amorites, Perizzites, Hivites and Jebusites (these peoples were not Israelites), ⁸that is, their descendants remaining in the land, whom the Israelites had not destroyed—these Solomon conscripted for his slave labor force, as it is to this day. ⁹But Solomon did not make slaves of the Israelites for his work; they were his fighting men, commanders of his captains, and commanders of his chariots and charioteers. ¹⁰They were also King Solomon's chief officials—two hundred and fifty officials supervising the men.

¹¹Solomon brought Pharaoh's daughter up from the City of David to the palace he had built for her, for he said, "My wife must not live in the palace of David king of Israel, because the places the ark of the LORD has entered are holy."

¹²On the altar of the LORD that he had built in front of the portico, Solomon sacrificed burnt offerings to the LORD, ¹³according

genuine

persistence » 8:14-15

How would you rate your diligence—that full-steam-ahead quality you put into completing a task? For many of us, diligence depends on how interesting or fun an assignment is. The duller the task, the dimmer the desire we have to be diligent about doing it. The priests and Levites were diligent about their assigned duties—all of them. They didn't have to be coaxed, bribed or put on a guilt trip about them. They just did them. Diligence is a trait that a disciple of God develops to please him in everything she does. Would you say that's your desire?

to the daily requirement for offerings commanded by Moses for Sabbaths, New Moons and the three annual feasts—the Feast of Unleavened Bread, the Feast of Weeks and the Feast of Tabernacles. ¹⁴In keeping with the ordinance of his father David, he appointed the divisions of the priests for their duties, and the Levites to lead the praise and to assist the priests according to each day's requirement. He also appointed the gatekeepers by divisions for the various gates, because this was what David the man of God had ordered. ¹⁵They did not deviate from the king's commands to the priests or to the Levites in any matter, including that of the treasuries.

¹⁶All Solomon's work was carried out, from the day the foundation of the temple of the LORD was laid until its completion. So the temple of the LORD was finished.

¹⁷Then Solomon went to Ezion Geber and Elath on the coast of Edom. ¹⁸And Hiram sent him ships commanded by his own officers, men who knew the sea. These, with Solomon's men, sailed to Ophir and brought back four hundred and fifty talents* of gold, which they delivered to King Solomon.

The Queen of Sheba Visits Solomon

9 When the queen of Sheba heard of Solomon's fame, she came to Jerusalem to test him with hard questions. Arriving with a very great caravan—with camels carrying spices, large quantities of gold, and precious stones—she came to Solomon and talked with him about all she had on her mind. ²Solomon answered all her questions; nothing was too hard for him to explain to her. ³When the queen of Sheba saw the wisdom of Solomon, as well as the palace he had built, ⁴the food on his table, the seating of his officials, the attending servants in their robes, the cupbearers in their robes and the burnt offerings he made at* the temple of the LORD, she was overwhelmed.

⁵She said to the king, "The report I heard in my own country about your achievements and your wisdom is true. ⁶But I did not believe what they said until I came and saw with my own eyes. Indeed, not even half the greatness of your wisdom was told me; you have far exceeded the report I heard. ⁷How happy your men must be! How happy your officials, who continually stand before you and hear your wisdom! ⁸Praise be to the LORD your God, who has delighted in you and placed you on his throne as king to rule for the LORD your God. Because of the love of your God

a 6 Or *charioteers*   *b 18* That is, about 17 tons (about 16 metric tons)   *c 4* Or *the ascent by which he went up to* for Israel and his desire to uphold them forever, he has made you king over them, to maintain justice and righteousness."

⁹Then she gave the king 120 talents*ᵃ* of gold, large quantities of spices, and precious stones. There had never been such spices as those the queen of Sheba gave to King Solomon.

¹⁰(The men of Hiram and the men of Solomon brought gold from Ophir; they also brought algumwood*ᵇ* and precious stones. ¹¹The king used the algumwood to make steps for the temple of the Lord and for the royal palace, and to make harps and lyres for the musicians. Nothing like them had ever been seen in Judah.)

¹²King Solomon gave the queen of Sheba all she desired and asked for; he gave her more than she had brought to him. Then she left and returned with her retinue to her own country.

Solomon's Splendor

¹³The weight of the gold that Solomon received yearly was 666 talents,*ᶜ* ¹⁴not including the revenues brought in by merchants and traders. Also all the kings of Arabia and the governors of the land brought gold and silver to Solomon.

¹⁵King Solomon made two hundred large shields of hammered gold; six hundred bekas*ᵈ* of hammered gold went into each shield. ¹⁶He also made three hundred small shields of hammered gold, with three hundred bekas*ᵉ* of gold in each shield. The king put them in the Palace of the Forest of Lebanon.

¹⁷Then the king made a great throne inlaid with ivory and overlaid with pure gold. ¹⁸The throne had six steps, and a footstool of gold was attached to it. On both sides of the seat were armrests, with a lion standing beside each of them. ¹⁹Twelve lions stood on the six steps, one at either end of each step. Nothing like it had ever been made for any other kingdom. ²⁰All King Solomon's goblets were gold, and all the household articles in the Palace of the Forest of Lebanon were pure gold. Nothing was made of silver, because silver was considered of little value in Solomon's day. ²¹The king had a fleet of trading ships*ᶠ* manned by Hiram's*ᵍ* men. Once every three years it returned, carrying gold, silver and ivory, and apes and baboons.

²²King Solomon was greater in riches and wisdom than all the other kings of the earth. ²³All the kings of the earth sought audience with Solomon to hear the wisdom God had put in his heart. ²⁴Year after year, everyone who came brought a gift—articles of silver and gold, and robes, weapons and spices, and horses and mules.

²⁵Solomon had four thousand stalls for horses and chariots, and twelve thousand horses,*ʰ* which he kept in the chariot cities and also with him in Jerusalem. ²⁶He ruled over all the kings from the River*ⁱ* to the land of the Philistines, as far as the border of Egypt. ²⁷The king made silver as common in Jerusalem as stones, and cedar as plentiful as sycamore-fig trees in the foothills. ²⁸Solomon's horses were imported from Egypt*ʲ* and from all other countries.

Solomon's Death

²⁹As for the other events of Solomon's reign, from beginning to end, are they not written in the records of Nathan the prophet, in the prophecy of Ahijah the Shilonite and in the visions of Iddo the seer concerning Jeroboam son of Nebat? ³⁰Solomon reigned in Jerusalem over all Israel forty years. ³¹Then he rested with his fathers and was buried in the city of David his father. And Rehoboam his son succeeded him as king.

Israel Rebels Against Rehoboam

10 Rehoboam went to Shechem, for all the Israelites had gone there to make him king. ²When Jeroboam son of Nebat heard this (he was in Egypt, where he had fled from King Solomon), he returned from Egypt. ³So they sent for Jeroboam, and he and all Israel went to Rehoboam and said to him: ⁴"Your father put a heavy yoke on us, but now lighten the harsh labor and the heavy yoke he put on us, and we will serve you."

⁵Rehoboam answered, "Come back to me in three days." So the people went away.

⁶Then King Rehoboam consulted the elders who had served his father Solomon during his life-

---

ᵃ 9 That is, about 4 1/2 tons (about 4 metric tons)   *ᵇ 10* Probably a variant of *almugwood*   *ᶜ 13* That is, about 25 tons (about 23 metric tons)   *ᵈ 15* That is, about 7 1/2 pounds (about 3.5 kilograms)   *ᵉ 16* That is, about 3 3/4 pounds (about 1.7 kilograms)   *ᶠ 21* Hebrew *of ships that could go to Tarshish*   *ᵍ 21* Hebrew *Huram*, a variant of *Hiram*   *ʰ 25* Or *charioteers*   *ⁱ 26* That is, the Euphrates   *ʲ 28* Or possibly *Muzur*, a region in Cilicia time. "How would you advise me to answer these people?" he asked.

[7]They replied, "If you will be kind to these people and please them and give them a favorable answer, they will always be your servants."

[8]But Rehoboam rejected the advice the elders gave him and consulted the young men who had grown up with him and were serving him. [9]He asked them, "What is your advice? How should we answer these people who say to me, 'Lighten the yoke your father put on us'?"

[10]The young men who had grown up with him replied, "Tell the people who have said to you, 'Your father put a heavy yoke on us, but make our yoke lighter'—tell them, 'My little finger is thicker than my father's waist. [11]My father laid on you a heavy yoke; I will make it even heavier. My father scourged you with whips; I will scourge you with scorpions.' "

[12]Three days later Jeroboam and all the people returned to Rehoboam, as the king had said, "Come back to me in three days." [13]The king answered them harshly. Rejecting the advice of the elders, [14]he followed the advice of the young men and said, "My father made your yoke heavy; I will make it even heavier. My father scourged you with whips; I will scourge you with scorpions." [15]So the king did not listen to the people, for this turn of events was from God, to fulfill the word the Lord had spoken to Jeroboam son of Nebat through Ahijah the Shilonite.

[16]When all Israel saw that the king refused to listen to them, they answered the king:

> "What share do we have in David,
>   what part in Jesse's son?
> To your tents, O Israel!
>   Look after your own house, O David!"

So all the Israelites went home. [17]But as for the Israelites who were living in the towns of Judah, Rehoboam still ruled over them.

[18]King Rehoboam sent out Adoniram,[a] who was in charge of forced labor, but the Israelites stoned him to death. King Rehoboam, however, managed to get into his chariot and escape to Jerusalem. [19]So Israel has been in rebellion against the house of David to this day.

11 When Rehoboam arrived in Jerusalem, he mustered the house of Judah and Benjamin—a hundred and eighty thousand fighting men—to make war against Israel and to regain the kingdom for Rehoboam.

[2]But this word of the Lord came to Shemaiah the man of God: [3]"Say to Rehoboam son of Solomon king of Judah and to all the Israelites in Judah and Benjamin, [4]'This is what the Lord says: Do not go up to fight against your brothers. Go home, every one of you, for this is my doing.' " So they obeyed the words of the Lord and turned back from marching against Jeroboam.

Rehoboam Fortifies Judah

[5]Rehoboam lived in Jerusalem and built up towns for defense in Judah: [6]Bethlehem, Etam, Tekoa, [7]Beth Zur, Soco, Adullam, [8]Gath, Mareshah, Ziph, [9]Adoraim, Lachish, Azekah, [10]Zorah, Aijalon and Hebron. These were fortified cities in Judah and Benjamin. [11]He strengthened their defenses and put commanders in them, with supplies of food, olive oil and wine. [12]He put shields and spears in all the cities, and made them very strong. So Judah and Benjamin were his.

[13]The priests and Levites from all their districts throughout Israel sided with him. [14]The Levites even abandoned their pasturelands and property, and came to Judah and Jerusalem because Jeroboam and his sons had rejected them as priests of the Lord. [15]And he appointed his own priests for the high places and for the goat and calf idols he had made. [16]Those from every tribe of Israel who set their hearts on seeking the Lord, the God of Israel, followed the Levites to Jerusalem to offer sacrifices to the Lord, the God of their fathers. [17]They strengthened the kingdom of Judah and supported Rehoboam son of Solomon three years, walking in the ways of David and Solomon during this time.

[a] 18 Hebrew *Hadoram*, a variant of *Adoniram*

Rehoboam's Family

[18]Rehoboam married Mahalath, who was the daughter of David's son Jerimoth and of Abihail, the daughter of Jesse's son Eliab. [19]She bore him sons: Jeush, Shemariah and Zaham. [20]Then he married Maacah daughter of Absalom, who bore him Abijah, Attai, Ziza and Shelomith. [21]Rehoboam loved Maacah daughter of Absalom more than any of his other wives and concubines. In all, he had eighteen wives and sixty concubines, twenty-eight sons and sixty daughters.

[22]Rehoboam appointed Abijah son of Maacah to be the chief prince among his brothers, in order to make him king. [23]He acted wisely, dispersing some of his sons throughout the districts of Judah and Benjamin, and to all the fortified cities. He gave them abundant provisions and took many wives for them.

Shishak Attacks Jerusalem

12 After Rehoboam's position as king was established and he had become strong, he and all Israel[a] with him abandoned the law of the Lord. [2]Because they had been unfaithful to the Lord, Shishak king of Egypt attacked Jerusalem in the fifth year of King Rehoboam. [3]With twelve hundred chariots and sixty thousand horsemen and the innumerable troops of Libyans, Sukkites and Cushites[b] that came with him from Egypt, [4]he captured the fortified cities of Judah and came as far as Jerusalem.

[5]Then the prophet Shemaiah came to Rehoboam and to the leaders of Judah who had assembled in Jerusalem for fear of Shishak, and he said to them, "This is what the Lord says, 'You have abandoned me; therefore, I now abandon you to Shishak.' "

[6]The leaders of Israel and the king humbled themselves and said, "The Lord is just."

[7]When the Lord saw that they humbled themselves, this word of the Lord came to Shemaiah: "Since they have humbled themselves, I will not destroy them but will soon give them deliverance. My wrath will not be poured out on Jerusalem through Shishak. [8]They will, however, become subject to him, so that they may learn the difference between serving me and serving the kings of other lands."

[9]When Shishak king of Egypt attacked Jerusalem, he carried off the treasures of the temple of the Lord and the treasures of the royal palace. He took everything, including the gold shields Solomon had made. [10]So King Rehoboam made bronze shields to replace them and assigned these to the commanders of the guard on duty at the entrance to the royal palace. [11]Whenever the king went to the Lord's temple, the guards went with him, bearing the shields, and afterward they returned them to the guardroom.

[12]Because Rehoboam humbled himself, the Lord's anger turned from him, and he was not totally destroyed. Indeed, there was some good in Judah.

[13]King Rehoboam established himself firmly in Jerusalem and continued as king. He was forty-one years old when he became king, and he reigned seventeen years in Jerusalem, the city the Lord had chosen out of all the tribes of Israel in which to put his Name. His mother's name was Naamah; she was an Ammonite. [14]He did evil because he had not set his heart on seeking the Lord.

[15]As for the events of Rehoboam's reign, from beginning to end, are they not written in the records of Shemaiah the prophet and of Iddo the seer that deal with genealogies? There was continual warfare between Rehoboam and Jeroboam. [16]Rehoboam rested with his fathers and was buried in the City of David. And Abijah his son succeeded him as king.

Abijah King of Judah

13 In the eighteenth year of the reign of Jeroboam, Abijah became king of Judah, [2]and he reigned in Jerusalem three years. His mother's name was Maacah,[c] a daughter[d] of Uriel of Gibeah.

There was war between Abijah and Jeroboam. [3]Abijah went into battle with a force of four hundred thousand able fighting men, and Jeroboam drew up a battle line against him with eight hundred thousand able troops.

[4]Abijah stood on Mount Zemaraim, in the hill country of Ephraim, and said, "Jeroboam and all Israel, listen to me! [5]Don't you know that the Lord, the God of Israel, has given the kingship of Is-

---

[a] 1 That is, Judah, as frequently in 2 Chronicles   [b] 3 That is, people from the upper Nile region   [c] 2 Most Septuagint manuscripts and Syriac (see also 2 Chron. 11:20 and 1 Kings 15:2); Hebrew *Micaiah*   [d] 2 Or *granddaughter*

in
focus

Speechless

Profile: **Natalie**

I've had it with my little problem. It's ruining my life, it's ruining my friendships and now it's ruining my grade in speech. This is the first class I'm actually worried about flunking!

Some days I blame it all on my family. They've always been shy. Mom and Dad don't talk very much. My brother never even asked out a girl till he was 19! But now I realize that being shy is *my* problem. And if I don't snap out of it soon, I'll never get anything I want out of life. You might not believe this, but I'd love to be the girl with the lead in the school musical or at least a part in the chorus. Too bad the mere thought of auditioning in front of the music teacher makes me nauseous!

I was actually excited about the speech I was going to give last week about jazz music. I even brought in my favorite CD for a demo. Over and over I told myself I'd be fine, that I could impress everyone in the class, including Ms. Barton. But when I stood up and faced the class, I froze. It took me a full minute to start speaking, and I almost started crying when I heard several kids snickering in the back. When I sat down, I saw a note on the desk across from me—*Who's going to teach this chick how to talk?* I ran out of the room without saying a word.

shyness in focus

Forty percent of Americans struggle with shyness. And so did Moses, the great leader of the Israelites. When God called him to lead the people out of Egypt, he turned God down and told him he was "slow of speech and tongue" (Exodus 4:10). But God used him anyway.

When you struggle with shyness, remember . . .
> » God will help you speak, just as he helped Moses (see Exodus 4:12, page 73). Ask him.
> » God's grace can overcome our weaknesses (see 2 Corinthians 12:9, page 1532).

For more on this topic, see the index on page 1656.

For more on overcoming shyness, check out the link on www.TrueImagesBible.com

shyness

rael to David and his descendants forever by a covenant of salt? [6]Yet Jeroboam son of Nebat, an official of Solomon son of David, rebelled against his master. [7]Some worthless scoundrels gathered around him and opposed Rehoboam son of Solomon when he was young and indecisive and not strong enough to resist them.

[8]"And now you plan to resist the kingdom of the LORD, which is in the hands of David's descendants. You are indeed a vast army and have with you the golden calves that Jeroboam made to be your gods. [9]But didn't you drive out the priests of the LORD, the sons of Aaron, and the Levites, and make priests of your own as the peoples of other lands do? Whoever comes to consecrate himself with a young bull and seven rams may become a priest of what are not gods.

[10]"As for us, the LORD is our God, and we have not forsaken him. The priests who serve the LORD are sons of Aaron, and the Levites assist them. [11]Every morning and evening they present burnt offerings and fragrant incense to the LORD. They set out the bread on the ceremonially clean table and light the lamps on the gold lampstand every evening. We are observing the requirements of the LORD our God. But you have forsaken him. [12]God is with us; he is our leader. His priests with their trumpets will sound the battle cry against you. Men of Israel, do not fight against the LORD, the God of your fathers, for you will not succeed."

[13]Now Jeroboam had sent troops around to the rear, so that while he was in front of Judah the ambush was behind them. [14]Judah turned and saw that they were being attacked at both front and rear. Then they cried out to the LORD. The priests blew their trumpets [15]and the men of Judah raised the battle cry. At the sound of their battle cry, God routed Jeroboam and all Israel before Abijah and Judah. [16]The Israelites fled before Judah, and God delivered them into their hands. [17]Abijah and his men inflicted heavy losses on them, so that there were five hundred thousand casualties among Israel's able men. [18]The men of Israel were subdued on that occasion, and the men of Judah were victorious because they relied on the LORD, the God of their fathers.

[19]Abijah pursued Jeroboam and took from him the towns of Bethel, Jeshanah and Ephron, with their surrounding villages. [20]Jeroboam did not regain power during the time of Abijah. And the LORD struck him down and he died.

[21]But Abijah grew in strength. He married fourteen wives and had twenty-two sons and sixteen daughters.

[22]The other events of Abijah's reign, what he did and what he said, are written in the annotations of the prophet Iddo.

14

And Abijah rested with his fathers and was buried in the City of David. Asa his son succeeded him as king, and in his days the country was at peace for ten years.

Asa King of Judah

[2]Asa did what was good and right in the eyes of the LORD his God. [3]He removed the foreign altars and the high places, smashed the sacred stones and cut down the Asherah poles. [a] [4]He commanded Judah to seek the LORD, the God of their fathers, and to obey his laws and commands. [5]He removed the high places and incense altars in every town in Judah, and the kingdom was at peace under him. [6]He built up the fortified cities of Judah, since the land was at peace. No one was at war with him during those years, for the LORD gave him rest.

[7]"Let us build up these towns," he said to Judah, "and put walls around them, with towers, gates and bars. The land is still ours, because we have sought the LORD our God; we sought him and he has given us rest on every side." So they built and prospered.

[8]Asa had an army of three hundred thousand men from Judah, equipped with large shields and with spears, and two hundred and eighty thousand from Benjamin, armed with small shields and with bows. All these were brave fighting men.

[9]Zerah the Cushite marched out against them with a vast army [b] and three hundred chariots, and came as far as Mareshah. [10]Asa went out to meet him, and they took up battle positions in the Valley of Zephathah near Mareshah.

[11]Then Asa called to the LORD his God and said, "LORD, there is no one like you to help the powerless against the mighty. Help us, O LORD our God, for we rely on you, and in your name we have come against this vast army. O LORD, you are our God; do not let man prevail against you."

[12]The LORD struck down the Cushites before Asa and Judah. The Cushites fled, [13]and Asa and his army pursued them as far as Ge-

truth or dare

Feeling like all your support has dried up? God has made helping the powerless his personal business. He can supply all the backing you'll need.

14:11

---

[a] 3 That is, symbols of the goddess Asherah; here and elsewhere in 2 Chronicles   [b] 9 Hebrew *with an army of a thousand thousands* or *with an army of thousands upon thousands*

rar. Such a great number of Cushites fell that they could not recover; they were crushed before the LORD and his forces. The men of Judah carried off a large amount of plunder. ¹⁴They destroyed all the villages around Gerar, for the terror of the LORD had fallen upon them. They plundered all these villages, since there was much booty there. ¹⁵They also attacked the camps of the herdsmen and carried off droves of sheep and goats and camels. Then they returned to Jerusalem.

Asa's Reform

15 The Spirit of God came upon Azariah son of Oded. ²He went out to meet Asa and said to him, "Listen to me, Asa and all Judah and Benjamin. The LORD is with you when you are with him. If you seek him, he will be found by you, but if you forsake him, he will forsake you. ³For a long time Israel was without the true God, without a priest to teach and without the law. ⁴But in their distress they turned to the LORD, the God of Israel, and sought him, and he was found by them. ⁵In those days it was not safe to travel about, for all the inhabitants of the lands were in great turmoil. ⁶One nation was being crushed by another and one city by another, because God was troubling them with every kind of distress. ⁷But as for you, be strong and do not give up, for your work will be rewarded."

⁸When Asa heard these words and the prophecy of Azariah son of ᵃ Oded the prophet, he took courage. He removed the detestable idols from the whole land of Judah and Benjamin and from the towns he had captured in the hills of Ephraim. He repaired the altar of the LORD that was in front of the portico of the LORD's temple.

⁹Then he assembled all Judah and Benjamin and the people from Ephraim, Manasseh and Simeon who had settled among them, for large numbers had come over to him from Israel when they saw that the LORD his God was with him.

¹⁰They assembled at Jerusalem in the third month of the fifteenth year of Asa's reign. ¹¹At that time they sacrificed to the LORD seven hundred head of cattle and seven thousand sheep and goats from the plunder they had brought back. ¹²They entered into a covenant to seek the LORD, the God of their fathers, with all their heart and soul. ¹³All who would not seek the LORD, the God of Israel, were to be put to death, whether small or great, man or woman. ¹⁴They took an oath to the LORD with loud acclamation, with shouting and with trumpets and horns. ¹⁵All Judah rejoiced about the oath because they had sworn it wholeheartedly. They sought God eagerly, and he was found by them. So the LORD gave them rest on every side.

¹⁶King Asa also deposed his grandmother Maacah from her position as queen mother, because she had made a repulsive Asherah pole. Asa cut the pole down, broke it up and burned it in the Kidron Valley. ¹⁷Although he did not remove the high places from Israel, Asa's heart was fully committed ⌊to the LORD⌋ all his life. ¹⁸He brought into the temple of God the silver and gold and the articles that he and his father had dedicated.

¹⁹There was no more war until the thirty-fifth year of Asa's reign.

Asa's Last Years

16 In the thirty-sixth year of Asa's reign Baasha king of Israel went up against Judah and fortified Ramah to prevent anyone from leaving or entering the territory of Asa king of Judah.

²Asa then took the silver and gold out of the treasuries of the LORD's temple and of his own palace and sent it to Ben-Hadad king of Aram, who was ruling in Damascus. ³"Let there be a treaty between me and you," he said, "as there was between my father and your father. See, I am sending you silver and gold. Now break your treaty with Baasha king of Israel so he will withdraw from me."

⁴Ben-Hadad agreed with King Asa and sent the commanders of his forces against the towns of

truth or dare

Even if you've strayed *way* off the path, or maybe *never* really knew God, he's still there waiting to welcome you back in his arms.

15:3–4

ᵃ 8 Vulgate and Syriac (see also Septuagint and verse 1); Hebrew does not have *Azariah son of*.

Israel. They conquered Ijon, Dan, Abel Maim*ᵃ* and all the store cities of Naphtali. ⁵When Baasha heard this, he stopped building Ramah and abandoned his work. ⁶Then King Asa brought all the men of Judah, and they carried away from Ramah the stones and timber Baasha had been using. With them he built up Geba and Mizpah.

⁷At that time Hanani the seer came to Asa king of Judah and said to him: "Because you relied on the king of Aram and not on the LORD your God, the army of the king of Aram has escaped from your hand. ⁸Were not the Cushites*ᵇ* and Libyans a mighty army with great numbers of chariots and horsemen*ᶜ*? Yet when you relied on the LORD, he delivered them into your hand. ⁹For the eyes of the LORD range throughout the earth to strengthen those whose hearts are fully committed to him. You have done a foolish thing, and from now on you will be at war."

¹⁰Asa was angry with the seer because of this; he was so enraged that he put him in prison. At the same time Asa brutally oppressed some of the people.

¹¹The events of Asa's reign, from beginning to end, are written in the book of the kings of Judah and Israel. ¹²In the thirty-ninth year of his reign Asa was afflicted with a disease in his feet. Though his disease was severe, even in his illness he did not seek help from the LORD, but only from the physicians. ¹³Then in the forty-first year of his reign Asa died and rested with his fathers. ¹⁴They buried him in the tomb that he had cut out for himself in the City of David. They laid him on a bier covered with spices and various blended perfumes, and they made a huge fire in his honor.

Jehoshaphat King of Judah

17 Jehoshaphat his son succeeded him as king and strengthened himself against Israel. ²He stationed troops in all the fortified cities of Judah and put garrisons in Judah and in the towns of Ephraim that his father Asa had captured.

³The LORD was with Jehoshaphat because in his early years he walked in the ways his father David had followed. He did not consult the Baals ⁴but sought the God of his father and followed his commands rather than the practices of Israel. ⁵The LORD established the kingdom under his control; and all Judah brought gifts to Jehoshaphat, so that he had great wealth and honor. ⁶His heart was devoted to the ways of the LORD; furthermore, he removed the high places and the Asherah poles from Judah.

⁷In the third year of his reign he sent his officials Ben-Hail, Obadiah, Zechariah, Nethanel and Micaiah to teach in the towns of Judah. ⁸With them were certain Levites—Shemaiah, Nethaniah, Zebadiah, Asahel, Shemiramoth, Jehonathan, Adonijah, Tobijah and Tob-Adonijah—and the priests Elishama and Jehoram. ⁹They taught throughout Judah, taking with them the Book of the Law of the LORD; they went around to all the towns of Judah and taught the people.

a 4 Also known as *Abel Beth Maacah*   *b 8* That is, people from the upper Nile region   *c 8* Or *charioteers*

¹⁰The fear of the Lord fell on all the kingdoms of the lands surrounding Judah, so that they did not make war with Jehoshaphat. ¹¹Some Philistines brought Jehoshaphat gifts and silver as tribute, and the Arabs brought him flocks: seven thousand seven hundred rams and seven thousand seven hundred goats.

¹²Jehoshaphat became more and more powerful; he built forts and store cities in Judah ¹³and had large supplies in the towns of Judah. He also kept experienced fighting men in Jerusalem. ¹⁴Their enrollment by families was as follows:

From Judah, commanders of units of 1,000:
Adnah the commander, with 300,000 fighting men;
¹⁵next, Jehohanan the commander, with 280,000;
¹⁶next, Amasiah son of Zicri, who volunteered himself for the service of the Lord, with 200,000.
¹⁷From Benjamin:
Eliada, a valiant soldier, with 200,000 men armed with bows and shields;
¹⁸next, Jehozabad, with 180,000 men armed for battle.

¹⁹These were the men who served the king, besides those he stationed in the fortified cities throughout Judah.

Micaiah Prophesies Against Ahab

18 Now Jehoshaphat had great wealth and honor, and he allied himself with Ahab by marriage. ²Some years later he went down to visit Ahab in Samaria. Ahab slaughtered many sheep and cattle for him and the people with him and urged him to attack Ramoth Gilead. ³Ahab king of Israel asked Jehoshaphat king of Judah, "Will you go with me against Ramoth Gilead?"

Jehoshaphat replied, "I am as you are, and my people as your people; we will join you in the war." ⁴But Jehoshaphat also said to the king of Israel, "First seek the counsel of the Lord."

⁵So the king of Israel brought together the prophets—four hundred men—and asked them, "Shall we go to war against Ramoth Gilead, or shall I refrain?"

"Go," they answered, "for God will give it into the king's hand."

⁶But Jehoshaphat asked, "Is there not a prophet of the Lord here whom we can inquire of?"

⁷The king of Israel answered Jehoshaphat, "There is still one man through whom we can inquire of the Lord, but I hate him because he never prophesies anything good about me, but always bad. He is Micaiah son of Imlah."

"The king should not say that," Jehoshaphat replied.

⁸So the king of Israel called one of his officials and said, "Bring Micaiah son of Imlah at once."

⁹Dressed in their royal robes, the king of Israel and Jehoshaphat king of Judah were sitting on their thrones at the threshing floor by the entrance to the gate of Samaria, with all the prophets prophesying before them. ¹⁰Now Zedekiah son of Kenaanah had made iron horns, and he declared, "This is what the Lord says: 'With these you will gore the Arameans until they are destroyed.' "

¹¹All the other prophets were prophesying the same thing. "Attack Ramoth Gilead and be victorious," they said, "for the Lord will give it into the king's hand."

¹²The messenger who had gone to summon Micaiah said to him, "Look, as one man the other prophets are predicting success for the king. Let your word agree with theirs, and speak favorably."

¹³But Micaiah said, "As surely as the Lord lives, I can tell him only what my God says."

¹⁴When he arrived, the king asked him, "Micaiah, shall we go to war against Ramoth Gilead, or shall I refrain?"

"Attack and be victorious," he answered, "for they will be given into your hand."

¹⁵The king said to him, "How many times must I make you swear to tell me nothing but the truth in the name of the Lord?"

truth or dare

If you're trying to save face in a sticky situation, is it cool to lie? No way! An honest (but loving!) answer avoids a future mess.

18:12–13

[16]Then Micaiah answered, "I saw all Israel scattered on the hills like sheep without a shepherd, and the Lord said, 'These people have no master. Let each one go home in peace.' "

[17]The king of Israel said to Jehoshaphat, "Didn't I tell you that he never prophesies anything good about me, but only bad?"

[18]Micaiah continued, "Therefore hear the word of the Lord: I saw the Lord sitting on his throne with all the host of heaven standing on his right and on his left. [19]And the Lord said, 'Who will entice Ahab king of Israel into attacking Ramoth Gilead and going to his death there?'

"One suggested this, and another that. [20]Finally, a spirit came forward, stood before the Lord and said, 'I will entice him.'

" 'By what means?' the Lord asked.

[21]" 'I will go and be a lying spirit in the mouths of all his prophets,' he said.

" 'You will succeed in enticing him,' said the Lord. 'Go and do it.'

[22]"So now the Lord has put a lying spirit in the mouths of these prophets of yours. The Lord has decreed disaster for you."

[23]Then Zedekiah son of Kenaanah went up and slapped Micaiah in the face. "Which way did the spirit from*a* the Lord go when he went from me to speak to you?" he asked.

[24]Micaiah replied, "You will find out on the day you go to hide in an inner room."

[25]The king of Israel then ordered, "Take Micaiah and send him back to Amon the ruler of the city and to Joash the king's son, [26]and say, 'This is what the king says: Put this fellow in prison and give him nothing but bread and water until I return safely.' "

[27]Micaiah declared, "If you ever return safely, the Lord has not spoken through me." Then he added, "Mark my words, all you people!"

Ahab Killed at Ramoth Gilead

[28]So the king of Israel and Jehoshaphat king of Judah went up to Ramoth Gilead. [29]The king of Israel said to Jehoshaphat, "I will enter the battle in disguise, but you wear your royal robes." So the king of Israel disguised himself and went into battle.

[30]Now the king of Aram had ordered his chariot commanders, "Do not fight with anyone, small or great, except the king of Israel." [31]When the chariot commanders saw Jehoshaphat, they thought, "This is the king of Israel." So they turned to attack him, but Jehoshaphat cried out, and the Lord helped him. God drew them away from him, [32]for when the chariot commanders saw that he was not the king of Israel, they stopped pursuing him.

[33]But someone drew his bow at random and hit the king of Israel between the sections of his armor. The king told the chariot driver, "Wheel around and get me out of the fighting. I've been wounded." [34]All day long the battle raged, and the king of Israel propped himself up in his chariot facing the Arameans until evening. Then at sunset he died.

19 When Jehoshaphat king of Judah returned safely to his palace in Jerusalem, [2]Jehu the seer, the son of Hanani, went out to meet him and said to the king, "Should you help the wicked and love*b* those who hate the Lord? Because of this, the wrath of the Lord is upon you. [3]There is, however, some good in you, for you have rid the land of the Asherah poles and have set your heart on seeking God."

Jehoshaphat Appoints Judges

[4]Jehoshaphat lived in Jerusalem, and he went out again among the people from Beersheba to the hill country of Ephraim and turned them back to the Lord, the God of their fathers. [5]He appointed judges in the land, in each of the fortified cities of Judah. [6]He told them, "Consider carefully what you do, because you are not judging for man but for the Lord, who is with you whenever you give a verdict. [7]Now let the fear of the Lord be upon you. Judge carefully, for with the Lord our God there is no injustice or partiality or bribery."

[8]In Jerusalem also, Jehoshaphat appointed some of the Levites, priests and heads of Israelite families to administer the law of the Lord and to settle disputes. And they lived in Jerusalem. [9]He gave them these orders: "You must serve faithfully and wholeheartedly in the fear of the Lord. [10]In every case that comes before you from your fellow countrymen who live in the cities—whether bloodshed or other concerns of the law, commands, decrees or ordinances—you are to warn them

a 23 Or Spirit of   b 2 Or and make alliances with

genuine judgment » 19:4-7

Got a thing for fairness? Ever find yourself saying (or thinking) "but that's not fair"? Let's be honest—we tend to get a little miffed when we think we've been treated unfairly. But what happens when you have to make a judgment call? Every day you make tons of little judgments—opinions about other people and things. What influences your opinions? Your own good sense? What your friends think? What seems fair at the time? Jehoshaphat wanted his judges to be careful in their rulings—no playing favorites, no standards contrary to God's. Want to use good judgment? Stick with a higher standard—God's.

not to sin against the LORD; otherwise his wrath will come on you and your brothers. Do this, and you will not sin.

¹¹"Amariah the chief priest will be over you in any matter concerning the LORD, and Zebadiah son of Ishmael, the leader of the tribe of Judah, will be over you in any matter concerning the king, and the Levites will serve as officials before you. Act with courage, and may the LORD be with those who do well."

Jehoshaphat Defeats Moab and Ammon

20 After this, the Moabites and Ammonites with some of the Meunites ᵃ came to make war on Jehoshaphat.

²Some men came and told Jehoshaphat, "A vast army is coming against you from Edom, ᵇ from the other side of the Sea. ᶜ It is already in Hazazon Tamar" (that is, En Gedi). ³Alarmed, Jehoshaphat resolved to inquire of the LORD, and he proclaimed a fast for all Judah. ⁴The people of Judah came together to seek help from the LORD; indeed, they came from every town in Judah to seek him.

⁵Then Jehoshaphat stood up in the assembly of Judah and Jerusalem at the temple of the LORD in the front of the new courtyard ⁶and said:

"O LORD, God of our fathers, are you not the God who is in heaven? You rule over all the kingdoms of the nations. Power and might are in your hand, and no one can withstand you. ⁷O our God, did you not drive out the inhabitants of this land before your people Israel and give it forever to the descendants of Abraham your friend? ⁸They have lived in it and have built in it a sanctuary for your Name, saying, ⁹'If calamity comes upon us, whether the sword of judgment, or plague or famine, we will stand in your presence before this temple that bears your Name and will cry out to you in our distress, and you will hear us and save us.'

¹⁰"But now here are men from Ammon, Moab and Mount Seir, whose territory you would not allow Israel to invade when they came from Egypt; so they turned away from them and did not destroy them. ¹¹See how they are repaying us by coming to drive us out of the possession you gave us as an inheritance. ¹²O our God, will you not judge them? For we have no power to face this vast army that is attacking us. We do not know what to do, but our eyes are upon you."

¹³All the men of Judah, with their wives and children and little ones, stood there before the LORD.

¹⁴Then the Spirit of the LORD came upon Jahaziel son of Zechariah, the son of Benaiah, the son

truth or dare

Parents, pastors, principals. God isn't trying to suffocate you with supervision! Actually, he's placed a combo of people around you to help you do what's right.

19:11

ᵃ 1 Some Septuagint manuscripts; Hebrew *Ammonites*   ᵇ 2 One Hebrew manuscript; most Hebrew manuscripts, Septuagint and Vulgate *Aram*   ᶜ 2 That is, the Dead Sea of Jeiel, the son of Mattaniah, a Levite and descendant of Asaph, as he stood in the assembly.

[15]He said: "Listen, King Jehoshaphat and all who live in Judah and Jerusalem! This is what the Lord says to you: 'Do not be afraid or discouraged because of this vast army. For the battle is not yours, but God's. [16]Tomorrow march down against them. They will be climbing up by the Pass of Ziz, and you will find them at the end of the gorge in the Desert of Jeruel. [17]You will not have to fight this battle. Take up your positions; stand firm and see the deliverance the Lord will give you, O Judah and Jerusalem. Do not be afraid; do not be discouraged. Go out to face them tomorrow, and the Lord will be with you.' "

[18]Jehoshaphat bowed with his face to the ground, and all the people of Judah and Jerusalem fell down in worship before the Lord. [19]Then some Levites from the Kohathites and Korahites stood up and praised the Lord, the God of Israel, with a very loud voice.

[20]Early in the morning they left for the Desert of Tekoa. As they set out, Jehoshaphat stood and said, "Listen to me, Judah and people of Jerusalem! Have faith in the Lord your God and you will be upheld; have faith in his prophets and you will be successful." [21]After consulting the people, Jehoshaphat appointed men to sing to the Lord and to praise him for the splendor of his[a] holiness as they went out at the head of the army, saying:

> "Give thanks to the Lord,
> for his love endures forever."

truth or dare

How many Christians do you know in your school? The numbers can get discouraging! If you're feeling overwhelmed, remember that the battle is really God's, not yours.

20:15

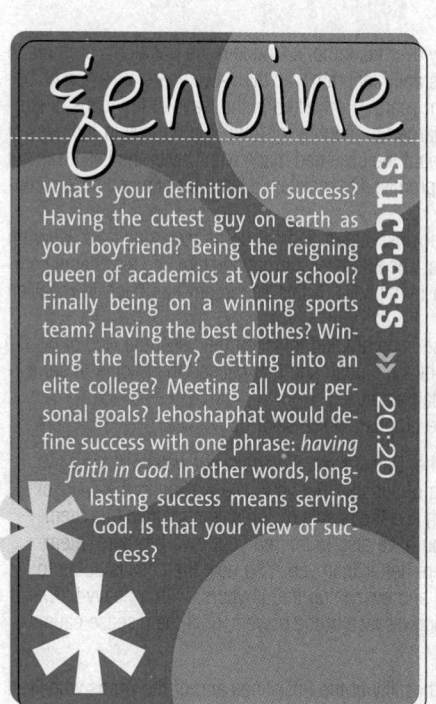

genuine success » 20:20

What's your definition of success? Having the cutest guy on earth as your boyfriend? Being the reigning queen of academics at your school? Finally being on a winning sports team? Having the best clothes? Winning the lottery? Getting into an elite college? Meeting all your personal goals? Jehoshaphat would define success with one phrase: *having faith in God*. In other words, long-lasting success means serving God. Is that your view of success?

[22]As they began to sing and praise, the Lord set ambushes against the men of Ammon and Moab and Mount Seir who were invading Judah, and they were defeated. [23]The men of Ammon and Moab rose up against the men from Mount Seir to destroy and annihilate them. After they finished slaughtering the men from Seir, they helped to destroy one another.

[24]When the men of Judah came to the place that overlooks the desert and looked toward the vast army, they saw only dead bodies lying on the ground; no one had escaped. [25]So Jehoshaphat and his men went to carry off their plunder, and they found among them a great amount of equipment and clothing[b] and also articles of value—more than they could take away. There was so much plunder that it took three days to collect it. [26]On the fourth day they assembled in the Valley of Beracah, where they praised the Lord. This is why it is called the Valley of Beracah[c] to this day.

[27]Then, led by Jehoshaphat, all the men of Judah and Jerusalem returned joyfully to Jerusalem, for the Lord had given them

---

[a] 21 Or *him with the splendor of*   [b] 25 Some Hebrew manuscripts and Vulgate; most Hebrew manuscripts *corpses*
[c] 26 *Beracah* means *praise*.

cause to rejoice over their enemies. [28]They entered Jerusalem and went to the temple of the Lord with harps and lutes and trumpets.

[29]The fear of God came upon all the kingdoms of the countries when they heard how the Lord had fought against the enemies of Israel. [30]And the kingdom of Jehoshaphat was at peace, for his God had given him rest on every side.

The End of Jehoshaphat's Reign

[31]So Jehoshaphat reigned over Judah. He was thirty-five years old when he became king of Judah, and he reigned in Jerusalem twenty-five years. His mother's name was Azubah daughter of Shilhi. [32]He walked in the ways of his father Asa and did not stray from them; he did what was right in the eyes of the Lord. [33]The high places, however, were not removed, and the people still had not set their hearts on the God of their fathers.

[34]The other events of Jehoshaphat's reign, from beginning to end, are written in the annals of Jehu son of Hanani, which are recorded in the book of the kings of Israel.

[35]Later, Jehoshaphat king of Judah made an alliance with Ahaziah king of Israel, who was guilty of wickedness. [36]He agreed with him to construct a fleet of trading ships.[a] After these were built at Ezion Geber, [37]Eliezer son of Dodavahu of Mareshah prophesied against Jehoshaphat, saying, "Because you have made an alliance with Ahaziah, the Lord will destroy what you have made." The ships were wrecked and were not able to set sail to trade.[b]

21 Then Jehoshaphat rested with his fathers and was buried with them in the City of David. And Jehoram his son succeeded him as king. [2]Jehoram's brothers, the sons of Jehoshaphat, were Azariah, Jehiel, Zechariah, Azariahu, Michael and Shephatiah. All these were sons of Jehoshaphat king of Israel.[c] [3]Their father had given them many gifts of silver and gold and articles of value, as well as fortified cities in Judah, but he had given the kingdom to Jehoram because he was his firstborn son.

Jehoram King of Judah

[4]When Jehoram established himself firmly over his father's kingdom, he put all his brothers to the sword along with some of the princes of Israel. [5]Jehoram was thirty-two years old when he became king, and he reigned in Jerusalem eight years. [6]He walked in the ways of the kings of Israel, as the house of Ahab had done, for he married a daughter of Ahab. He did evil in the eyes of the Lord. [7]Nevertheless, because of the covenant the Lord had made with David, the Lord was not willing to destroy the house of David. He had promised to maintain a lamp for him and his descendants forever.

[8]In the time of Jehoram, Edom rebelled against Judah and set up its own king. [9]So Jehoram went there with his officers and all his chariots. The Edomites surrounded him and his chariot commanders, but he rose up and broke through by night. [10]To this day Edom has been in rebellion against Judah.

Libnah revolted at the same time, because Jehoram had forsaken the Lord, the God of his fathers. [11]He had also built high places on the hills of Judah and had caused the people of Jerusalem to prostitute themselves and had led Judah astray.

[12]Jehoram received a letter from Elijah the prophet, which said:

"This is what the Lord, the God of your father David, says: 'You have not walked in the ways of your father Jehoshaphat or of Asa king of Judah. [13]But you have walked in the ways of the kings of Israel, and you have led Judah and the people of Jerusalem to prostitute themselves, just as the house of Ahab did. You have also murdered your own brothers, members of your father's house, men who were better than you. [14]So now the Lord is about to strike your people, your sons, your wives and everything that is yours, with a heavy blow. [15]You yourself will be very ill with a lingering disease of the bowels, until the disease causes your bowels to come out.' "

[16]The Lord aroused against Jehoram the hostility of the Philistines and of the Arabs who lived near the Cushites. [17]They attacked Judah, invaded it and carried off all the goods found in the

a 36 Hebrew of ships that could go to Tarshish   b 37 Hebrew sail for Tarshish   c 2 That is, Judah, as frequently in 2 Chronicles king's palace, together with his sons and wives. Not a son was left to him except Ahaziah,^a the youngest.

¹⁸After all this, the LORD afflicted Jehoram with an incurable disease of the bowels. ¹⁹In the course of time, at the end of the second year, his bowels came out because of the disease, and he died in great pain. His people made no fire in his honor, as they had for his fathers.

²⁰Jehoram was thirty-two years old when he became king, and he reigned in Jerusalem eight years. He passed away, to no one's regret, and was buried in the City of David, but not in the tombs of the kings.

Ahaziah King of Judah

22 The people of Jerusalem made Ahaziah, Jehoram's youngest son, king in his place, since the raiders, who came with the Arabs into the camp, had killed all the older sons. So Ahaziah son of Jehoram king of Judah began to reign.

²Ahaziah was twenty-two^b years old when he became king, and he reigned in Jerusalem one year. His mother's name was Athaliah, a granddaughter of Omri.

³He too walked in the ways of the house of Ahab, for his mother encouraged him in doing wrong. ⁴He did evil in the eyes of the LORD, as the house of Ahab had done, for after his father's death they became his advisers, to his undoing. ⁵He also followed their counsel when he went with Joram^c son of Ahab king of Israel to war against Hazael king of Aram at Ramoth Gilead. The Arameans wounded Joram; ⁶so he returned to Jezreel to recover from the wounds they had inflicted on him at Ramoth^d in his battle with Hazael king of Aram.

Then Ahaziah^e son of Jehoram king of Judah went down to Jezreel to see Joram son of Ahab because he had been wounded.

⁷Through Ahaziah's visit to Joram, God brought about Ahaziah's downfall. When Ahaziah arrived, he went out with Joram to meet Jehu son of Nimshi, whom the LORD had anointed to destroy the house of Ahab. ⁸While Jehu was executing judgment on the house of Ahab, he found the princes of Judah and the sons of Ahaziah's relatives, who had been attending Ahaziah, and he killed them. ⁹He then went in search of Ahaziah, and his men captured him while he was hiding in Samaria. He was brought to Jehu and put to death. They buried him, for they said, "He was a son of Jehoshaphat, who sought the LORD with all his heart." So there was no one in the house of Ahaziah powerful enough to retain the kingdom.

Athaliah and Joash

¹⁰When Athaliah the mother of Ahaziah saw that her son was dead, she proceeded to destroy the whole royal family of the house of Judah. ¹¹But Jehosheba,^f the daughter of King Jehoram, took Joash son of Ahaziah and stole him away from among the royal princes who were about to be murdered and put him and his nurse in a bedroom. Because Jehosheba,^f the daughter of King Jehoram and wife of the priest Jehoiada, was Ahaziah's sister, she hid the child from Athaliah so she could not kill him. ¹²He remained hidden with them at the temple of God for six years while Athaliah ruled the land.

23 In the seventh year Jehoiada showed his strength. He made a covenant with the commanders of units of a hundred: Azariah son of Jeroham, Ishmael son of Jehohanan, Azariah son of Obed, Maaseiah son of Adaiah, and Elishaphat son of Zicri. ²They went throughout Judah and gathered the Levites and the heads of Israelite families from all the towns. When they came to Jerusalem, ³the whole assembly made a covenant with the king at the temple of God.

Jehoiada said to them, "The king's son shall reign, as the LORD promised concerning the descendants of David. ⁴Now this is what you are to do: A third of you priests and Levites who are going on duty on the Sabbath are to keep watch at the doors, ⁵a third of you at the royal palace and a third at the Foundation Gate, and all the other men are to be in the courtyards of the temple of the LORD. ⁶No one is to enter the temple of the LORD except the priests and Levites on duty; they may enter because they are consecrated, but all the other men are to guard what the LORD has as-

---

^a 17 Hebrew *Jehoahaz*, a variant of *Ahaziah*   ^b 2 Some Septuagint manuscripts and Syriac (see also 2 Kings 8:26); Hebrew *forty-two*   ^c 5 Hebrew *Jehoram*, a variant of *Joram*; also in verses 6 and 7   ^d 6 Hebrew *Ramah*, a variant of *Ramoth*   ^e 6 Some Hebrew manuscripts, Septuagint, Vulgate and Syriac (see also 2 Kings 8:29); most Hebrew manuscripts *Azariah*   ^f 11 Hebrew *Jehoshabeath*, a variant of *Jehosheba*

mirror images

When Athaliah the mother of Ahaziah saw that her son was dead, she proceeded to destroy the whole royal family. 2 Kings 11:1

Athaliah—Grandmother of the Year

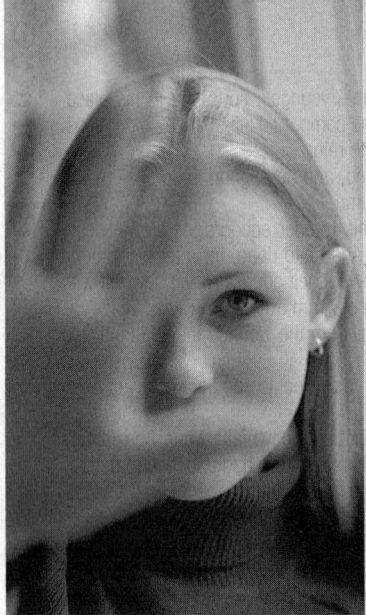

She wasn't exactly the sweet little grandmotherly type—pudgy cheeks, jolly eyes, baking cookies and giving you socks for your birthday. No, Grandma was cold and calculating, looking to get things her way. Her young son Ahaziah died in battle after being the king for only a year. So did she grieve and mourn the loss of her baby boy? No way! She started knocking off everyone else with a claim to the throne. She knew the competition would be stiff, so she killed everyone—her own family, particularly *her own grandchildren!*—anyone who stood between her and that coveted crown.

What is it that makes us go a little crazy in competition? In student elections and class debates, aren't we a little tempted to take some cheap personal shots at our opponents to make ourselves look better? There's no telling what we are secretly willing to do to our opponents when we're in tryouts or elections or races (especially when we think we won't get caught). How about if a good friend likes the same guy? Look out!

Those moments are when life begins to boil down to one thing—winning. That's temptation. And Satan entices us and lures us to take that one little step to get the lead. "Go ahead. You'll win if you eliminate your competition." But taking that one step means we compromise our own integrity. Winning the race yet losing God's blessing in the process is a high price to pay.

Look again at Athaliah. No one cares that she wore the crown of Judah for seven years; we only remember her because of the evil she did to get that crown. If you win something by eliminating your competition to get it, you still end up the loser.

Dear God, I know competition is a part of life, but help me not to be obsessed with winning. Lead me through it, so I won't give in to the temptation to try to win dishonorably. Amen.

To read the next Mirror Images profile, go to page 579.

>> Read more about evil Queen Athaliah in 2 Kings 11 (pages 448–449) and 2 Chronicles 22–23 (pages 537–539).

signed to them. *a* 7The Levites are to station themselves around the king, each man with his weapons in his hand. Anyone who enters the temple must be put to death. Stay close to the king wherever he goes."

8The Levites and all the men of Judah did just as Jehoiada the priest ordered. Each one took his men—those who were going on duty on the Sabbath and those who were going off duty—for Jehoiada the priest had not released any of the divisions. 9Then he gave the commanders of units of a hundred the spears and the large and small shields that had belonged to King David and that were in the temple of God. 10He stationed all the men, each with his weapon in his hand, around the king—near the altar and the temple, from the south side to the north side of the temple.

11Jehoiada and his sons brought out the king's son and put the crown on him; they presented him with a copy of the covenant and proclaimed him king. They anointed him and shouted, "Long live the king!"

12When Athaliah heard the noise of the people running and cheering the king, she went to them at the temple of the LORD. 13She looked, and there was the king, standing by his pillar at the entrance. The officers and the trumpeters were beside the king, and all the people of the land were rejoicing and blowing trumpets, and singers with musical instruments were leading the praises. Then Athaliah tore her robes and shouted, "Treason! Treason!"

14Jehoiada the priest sent out the commanders of units of a hundred, who were in charge of the troops, and said to them: "Bring her out between the ranks *b* and put to the sword anyone who follows her." For the priest had said, "Do not put her to death at the temple of the LORD." 15So they seized her as she reached the entrance of the Horse Gate on the palace grounds, and there they put her to death.

16Jehoiada then made a covenant that he and the people and the king *c* would be the LORD's people. 17All the people went to the temple of Baal and tore it down. They smashed the altars and idols and killed Mattan the priest of Baal in front of the altars.

18Then Jehoiada placed the oversight of the temple of the LORD in the hands of the priests, who were Levites, to whom David had made assignments in the temple, to present the burnt offerings of the LORD as written in the Law of Moses, with rejoicing and singing, as David had ordered. 19He also stationed doorkeepers at the gates of the LORD's temple so that no one who was in any way unclean might enter.

20He took with him the commanders of hundreds, the nobles, the rulers of the people and all the people of the land and brought the king down from the temple of the LORD. They went into the palace through the Upper Gate and seated the king on the royal throne, 21and all the people of the land rejoiced. And the city was quiet, because Athaliah had been slain with the sword.

Joash Repairs the Temple

24 Joash was seven years old when he became king, and he reigned in Jerusalem forty years. His mother's name was Zibiah; she was from Beersheba. 2Joash did what was right in the eyes of the LORD all the years of Jehoiada the priest. 3Jehoiada chose two wives for him, and he had sons and daughters.

4Some time later Joash decided to restore the temple of the LORD. 5He called together the priests and Levites and said to them, "Go to the towns of Judah and collect the money due annually from all Israel, to repair the temple of your God. Do it now." But the Levites did not act at once.

6Therefore the king summoned Jehoiada the chief priest and said to him, "Why haven't you required the Levites to bring in from Judah and Jerusalem the tax imposed by Moses the servant of the LORD and by the assembly of Israel for the Tent of the Testimony?"

7Now the sons of that wicked woman Athaliah had broken into the temple of God and had used even its sacred objects for the Baals.

8At the king's command, a chest was made and placed outside, at the gate of the temple of the LORD. 9A proclamation was then issued in Judah and Jerusalem that they should bring to the LORD the tax that Moses the servant of God had required of Israel in the desert. 10All the officials and all the people brought their contributions gladly, dropping them into the chest until it was full. 11Whenever the chest was brought in by the Levites to the king's officials and they saw that there was a

a 6 Or *to observe the LORD's command* ₁*not to enter*₁   *b 14* Or *out from the precincts*   *c 16* Or *covenant between* ₁*the LORD*₁ *and the people and the king that they* (see 2 Kings 11:17) large amount of money, the royal secretary and the officer of the chief priest would come and empty the chest and carry it back to its place. They did this regularly and collected a great amount of money. [12]The king and Jehoiada gave it to the men who carried out the work required for the temple of the LORD. They hired masons and carpenters to restore the LORD's temple, and also workers in iron and bronze to repair the temple.

[13]The men in charge of the work were diligent, and the repairs progressed under them. They rebuilt the temple of God according to its original design and reinforced it. [14]When they had finished, they brought the rest of the money to the king and Jehoiada, and with it were made articles for the LORD's temple: articles for the service and for the burnt offerings, and also dishes and other objects of gold and silver. As long as Jehoiada lived, burnt offerings were presented continually in the temple of the LORD.

[15]Now Jehoiada was old and full of years, and he died at the age of a hundred and thirty. [16]He was buried with the kings in the City of David, because of the good he had done in Israel for God and his temple.

genuine persistence »» 24:13

Think of something you could do all day with no problem. Got that fixed in your mind? Good. Would you keep on doing it if it started getting hard or boring? The men Joash hired to repair the temple kept at it until the work was completed. Repair work can be hard and tedious sometimes. (If you don't believe that, check out the next road construction site you pass.) That kind of work requires diligence—getting the job done regardless of how boring or tiresome it is. Having a diligence dilemma? Talk to God about it. Don't delay.

The Wickedness of Joash

[17]After the death of Jehoiada, the officials of Judah came and paid homage to the king, and he listened to them. [18]They abandoned the temple of the LORD, the God of their fathers, and worshiped Asherah poles and idols. Because of their guilt, God's anger came upon Judah and Jerusalem. [19]Although the LORD sent prophets to the people to bring them back to him, and though they testified against them, they would not listen.

[20]Then the Spirit of God came upon Zechariah son of Jehoiada the priest. He stood before the people and said, "This is what God says: 'Why do you disobey the LORD's commands? You will not prosper. Because you have forsaken the LORD, he has forsaken you.' "

[21]But they plotted against him, and by order of the king they stoned him to death in the courtyard of the LORD's temple. [22]King Joash did not remember the kindness Zechariah's father Jehoiada had shown him but killed his son, who said as he lay dying, "May the LORD see this and call you to account."

[23]At the turn of the year,[a] the army of Aram marched against Joash; it invaded Judah and Jerusalem and killed all the leaders of the people. They sent all the plunder to their king in Damascus. [24]Although the Aramean army had come with only a few men, the LORD delivered into their hands a much larger army. Because Judah had forsaken the LORD, the God of their fathers, judgment was executed on Joash. [25]When the Arameans withdrew, they left Joash severely wounded. His officials conspired against him for murdering the son of Jehoiada the priest, and they killed him in his bed. So he died and was buried in the City of David, but not in the tombs of the kings.

[26]Those who conspired against him were Zabad,[b] son of Shimeath an Ammonite woman, and Jehozabad, son of Shimrith[c] a Moabite woman. [27]The account of his sons, the many prophecies about him, and the record of the restoration of the temple of God are written in the annotations on the book of the kings. And Amaziah his son succeeded him as king.

a 23 Probably in the spring   b 26 A variant of Jozabad   c 26 A variant of Shomer

Amaziah King of Judah

25 Amaziah was twenty-five years old when he became king, and he reigned in Jerusalem twenty-nine years. His mother's name was Jehoaddin[a]; she was from Jerusalem. ²He did what was right in the eyes of the LORD, but not wholeheartedly. ³After the kingdom was firmly in his control, he executed the officials who had murdered his father the king. ⁴Yet he did not put their sons to death, but acted in accordance with what is written in the Law, in the Book of Moses, where the LORD commanded: "Fathers shall not be put to death for their children, nor children put to death for their fathers; each is to die for his own sins."[b]

⁵Amaziah called the people of Judah together and assigned them according to their families to commanders of thousands and commanders of hundreds for all Judah and Benjamin. He then mustered those twenty years old or more and found that there were three hundred thousand men ready for military service, able to handle the spear and shield. ⁶He also hired a hundred thousand fighting men from Israel for a hundred talents[c] of silver.

⁷But a man of God came to him and said, "O king, these troops from Israel must not march with you, for the LORD is not with Israel—not with any of the people of Ephraim. ⁸Even if you go and fight courageously in battle, God will overthrow you before the enemy, for God has the power to help or to overthrow."

⁹Amaziah asked the man of God, "But what about the hundred talents I paid for these Israelite troops?"

The man of God replied, "The LORD can give you much more than that."

¹⁰So Amaziah dismissed the troops who had come to him from Ephraim and sent them home. They were furious with Judah and left for home in a great rage.

¹¹Amaziah then marshaled his strength and led his army to the Valley of Salt, where he killed ten thousand men of Seir. ¹²The army of Judah also captured ten thousand men alive, took them to the top of a cliff and threw them down so that all were dashed to pieces.

¹³Meanwhile the troops that Amaziah had sent back and had not allowed to take part in the war raided Judean towns from Samaria to Beth Horon. They killed three thousand people and carried off great quantities of plunder.

¹⁴When Amaziah returned from slaughtering the Edomites, he brought back the gods of the people of Seir. He set them up as his own gods, bowed down to them and burned sacrifices to them. ¹⁵The anger of the LORD burned against Amaziah, and he sent a prophet to him, who said, "Why do you consult this people's gods, which could not save their own people from your hand?"

¹⁶While he was still speaking, the king said to him, "Have we appointed you an adviser to the king? Stop! Why be struck down?"

So the prophet stopped but said, "I know that God has determined to destroy you, because you have done this and have not listened to my counsel."

¹⁷After Amaziah king of Judah consulted his advisers, he sent this challenge to Jehoash[d] son of Jehoahaz, the son of Jehu, king of Israel: "Come, meet me face to face."

¹⁸But Jehoash king of Israel replied to Amaziah king of Judah: "A thistle in Lebanon sent a message to a cedar in Lebanon, 'Give your daughter to my son in marriage.' Then a wild beast in Lebanon came along and trampled the thistle underfoot. ¹⁹You say to yourself that you have defeated Edom, and now you are arrogant and proud. But stay at home! Why ask for trouble and cause your own downfall and that of Judah also?"

²⁰Amaziah, however, would not listen, for God so worked that he might hand them over to Jehoash, because they sought the gods of Edom. ²¹So Jehoash king of Israel attacked. He and Amaziah king of Judah faced each other at Beth Shemesh in Judah. ²²Judah was routed by Israel, and every man fled to his home. ²³Jehoash king of Israel captured Amaziah king of Judah, the son of Joash, the son of Ahaziah,[e] at Beth Shemesh. Then Jehoash brought him to Jerusalem and broke down the wall of Jerusalem from the Ephraim Gate to the Corner Gate—a section about six hundred feet[f] long. ²⁴He took all the gold and silver and all the articles found in the temple of God that had been in the care of Obed-Edom, together with the palace treasures and the hostages, and returned to Samaria.

---

a 1 Hebrew *Jehoaddan,* a variant of *Jehoaddin*   *b 4* Deut. 24:16   *c 6* That is, about 3 3/4 tons (about 3.4 metric tons); also in verse 9   *d 17* Hebrew *Joash,* a variant of *Jehoash*; also in verses 18, 21, 23 and 25   *e 23* Hebrew *Jehoahaz,* a variant of *Ahaziah*   *f 23* Hebrew *four hundred cubits* (about 180 meters)

²⁵Amaziah son of Joash king of Judah lived for fifteen years after the death of Jehoash son of Jehoahaz king of Israel. ²⁶As for the other events of Amaziah's reign, from beginning to end, are they not written in the book of the kings of Judah and Israel? ²⁷From the time that Amaziah turned away from following the LORD, they conspired against him in Jerusalem and he fled to Lachish, but they sent men after him to Lachish and killed him there. ²⁸He was brought back by horse and was buried with his fathers in the City of Judah.

Uzziah King of Judah

26 Then all the people of Judah took Uzziah,ᵃ who was sixteen years old, and made him king in place of his father Amaziah. ²He was the one who rebuilt Elath and restored it to Judah after Amaziah rested with his fathers.

³Uzziah was sixteen years old when he became king, and he reigned in Jerusalem fifty-two years. His mother's name was Jecoliah; she was from Jerusalem. ⁴He did what was right in the eyes of the LORD, just as his father Amaziah had done. ⁵He sought God during the days of Zechariah, who instructed him in the fearᵇ of God. As long as he sought the LORD, God gave him success.

⁶He went to war against the Philistines and broke down the walls of Gath, Jabneh and Ashdod. He then rebuilt towns near Ashdod and elsewhere among the Philistines. ⁷God helped him against the Philistines and against the Arabs who lived in Gur Baal and against the Meunites. ⁸The Ammonites brought tribute to Uzziah, and his fame spread as far as the border of Egypt, because he had become very powerful.

⁹Uzziah built towers in Jerusalem at the Corner Gate, at the Valley Gate and at the angle of the wall, and he fortified them. ¹⁰He also built towers in the desert and dug many cisterns, because he had much livestock in the foothills and in the plain. He had people working his fields and vineyards in the hills and in the fertile lands, for he loved the soil.

¹¹Uzziah had a well-trained army, ready to go out by divisions according to their numbers as mustered by Jeiel the secretary and Maaseiah the officer under the direction of Hananiah, one of the royal officials. ¹²The total number of family leaders over the fighting men was 2,600. ¹³Under their command was an army of 307,500 men trained for war, a powerful force to support the king against his enemies. ¹⁴Uzziah provided shields, spears, helmets, coats of armor, bows and slingstones for the entire army. ¹⁵In Jerusalem he made machines designed by skillful men for use on the towers and on the corner defenses to shoot arrows and hurl large stones. His fame spread far and wide, for he was greatly helped until he became powerful.

¹⁶But after Uzziah became powerful, his pride led to his downfall. He was unfaithful to the LORD his God, and entered the temple of the LORD to burn incense on the altar of incense. ¹⁷Azariah the priest with eighty other courageous priests of the LORD followed him in. ¹⁸They confronted him and said, "It is not right for you, Uzziah, to burn incense to the LORD. That is for the priests, the descendants of Aaron, who have been consecrated to burn incense. Leave the sanctuary, for you have been unfaithful; and you will not be honored by the LORD God."

¹⁹Uzziah, who had a censer in his hand ready to burn incense, became angry. While he was raging at the priests in their presence before the incense altar in the LORD's temple, leprosyᶜ broke out on his forehead. ²⁰When Azariah the chief priest and all the other priests looked at him, they saw that he had leprosy on his forehead, so they hurried him out. Indeed, he himself was eager to leave, because the LORD had afflicted him.

²¹King Uzziah had leprosy until the day he died. He lived in a separate houseᵈ—leprous, and excluded from the temple of the LORD. Jotham his son had charge of the palace and governed the people of the land.

---

truth or dare

So your prayers have been answered, and life is good. Don't let your attention wander now! Keep tight with God through the rough *and* smooth times.

26:5

ᵃ 1 Also called *Azariah*   ᵇ 5 Many Hebrew manuscripts, Septuagint and Syriac; other Hebrew manuscripts *vision*   ᶜ 19 The Hebrew word was used for various diseases affecting the skin—not necessarily leprosy; also in verses 20, 21 and 23.   ᵈ 21 Or *in a house where he was relieved of responsibilities*

[22]The other events of Uzziah's reign, from beginning to end, are recorded by the prophet Isaiah son of Amoz. [23]Uzziah rested with his fathers and was buried near them in a field for burial that belonged to the kings, for people said, "He had leprosy." And Jotham his son succeeded him as king.

Jotham King of Judah

27 Jotham was twenty-five years old when he became king, and he reigned in Jerusalem sixteen years. His mother's name was Jerusha daughter of Zadok. [2]He did what was right in the eyes of the LORD, just as his father Uzziah had done, but unlike him he did not enter the temple of the LORD. The people, however, continued their corrupt practices. [3]Jotham rebuilt the Upper Gate of the temple of the LORD and did extensive work on the wall at the hill of Ophel. [4]He built towns in the Judean hills and forts and towers in the wooded areas.

[5]Jotham made war on the king of the Ammonites and conquered them. That year the Ammonites paid him a hundred talents[a] of silver, ten thousand cors[b] of wheat and ten thousand cors of barley. The Ammonites brought him the same amount also in the second and third years.

[6]Jotham grew powerful because he walked steadfastly before the LORD his God.

[7]The other events in Jotham's reign, including all his wars and the other things he did, are written in the book of the kings of Israel and Judah. [8]He was twenty-five years old when he became king, and he reigned in Jerusalem sixteen years. [9]Jotham rested with his fathers and was buried in the City of David. And Ahaz his son succeeded him as king.

Ahaz King of Judah

28 Ahaz was twenty years old when he became king, and he reigned in Jerusalem sixteen years. Unlike David his father, he did not do what was right in the eyes of the LORD. [2]He walked in the ways of the kings of Israel and also made cast idols for worshiping the Baals. [3]He burned sacrifices in the Valley of Ben Hinnom and sacrificed his sons in the fire, following the detestable ways of the nations the LORD had driven out before the Israelites. [4]He offered sacrifices and burned incense at the high places, on the hilltops and under every spreading tree.

[5]Therefore the LORD his God handed him over to the king of Aram. The Arameans defeated him and took many of his people as prisoners and brought them to Damascus.

He was also given into the hands of the king of Israel, who inflicted heavy casualties on him. [6]In one day Pekah son of Remaliah killed a hundred and twenty thousand soldiers in Judah—because Judah had forsaken the LORD, the God of their fathers. [7]Zicri, an Ephraimite warrior, killed Maaseiah the king's son, Azrikam the officer in charge of the palace, and Elkanah, second to the king. [8]The Israelites took captive from their kinsmen two hundred thousand wives, sons and daughters. They also took a great deal of plunder, which they carried back to Samaria.

[9]But a prophet of the LORD named Oded was there, and he went out to meet the army when it returned to Samaria. He said to them, "Because the LORD, the God of your fathers, was angry with Judah, he gave them into your hand. But you have slaughtered them in a rage that reaches to heaven. [10]And now you intend to make the men and women of Judah and Jerusalem your slaves. But aren't you also guilty of sins against the LORD your God? [11]Now listen to me! Send back your fellow countrymen you have taken as prisoners, for the LORD's fierce anger rests on you."

[12]Then some of the leaders in Ephraim—Azariah son of Jehohanan, Berekiah son of Meshillemoth, Jehizkiah son of Shallum, and Amasa son of Hadlai—confronted those who were arriving from the war. [13]"You must not bring those prisoners here," they said, "or we will be guilty before the LORD. Do you intend to add to our sin and guilt? For our guilt is already great, and his fierce anger rests on Israel."

[14]So the soldiers gave up the prisoners and plunder in the presence of the officials and all the assembly. [15]The men designated by name took the prisoners, and from the plunder they clothed all who were naked. They provided them with clothes and sandals, food and drink, and healing balm. All those who were weak they put on donkeys. So they took them back to their fellow countrymen at Jericho, the City of Palms, and returned to Samaria.

[16]At that time King Ahaz sent to the king[c] of Assyria for help. [17]The Edomites had again come and attacked Judah and carried away prisoners, [18]while the Philistines had raided towns in the foot-

---

a 5 That is, about 3 3/4 tons (about 3.4 metric tons)   b 5 That is, probably about 62,000 bushels (about 2,200 kiloliters)
c 16 One Hebrew manuscript, Septuagint and Vulgate (see also 2 Kings 16:7); most Hebrew manuscripts kings

hills and in the Negev of Judah. They captured and occupied Beth Shemesh, Aijalon and Gederoth, as well as Soco, Timnah and Gimzo, with their surrounding villages. [19]The LORD had humbled Judah because of Ahaz king of Israel,[a] for he had promoted wickedness in Judah and had been most unfaithful to the LORD. [20]Tiglath-Pileser[b] king of Assyria came to him, but he gave him trouble instead of help. [21]Ahaz took some of the things from the temple of the LORD and from the royal palace and from the princes and presented them to the king of Assyria, but that did not help him.

[22]In his time of trouble King Ahaz became even more unfaithful to the LORD. [23]He offered sacrifices to the gods of Damascus, who had defeated him; for he thought, "Since the gods of the kings of Aram have helped them, I will sacrifice to them so they will help me." But they were his downfall and the downfall of all Israel.

[24]Ahaz gathered together the furnishings from the temple of God and took them away.[c] He shut the doors of the LORD's temple and set up altars at every street corner in Jerusalem. [25]In every town in Judah he built high places to burn sacrifices to other gods and provoked the LORD, the God of his fathers, to anger.

[26]The other events of his reign and all his ways, from beginning to end, are written in the book of the kings of Judah and Israel. [27]Ahaz rested with his fathers and was buried in the city of Jerusalem, but he was not placed in the tombs of the kings of Israel. And Hezekiah his son succeeded him as king.

Hezekiah Purifies the Temple

29 Hezekiah was twenty-five years old when he became king, and he reigned in Jerusalem twenty-nine years. His mother's name was Abijah daughter of Zechariah. [2]He did what was right in the eyes of the LORD, just as his father David had done.

[3]In the first month of the first year of his reign, he opened the doors of the temple of the LORD and repaired them. [4]He brought in the priests and the Levites, assembled them in the square on the east side [5]and said: "Listen to me, Levites! Consecrate yourselves now and consecrate the temple of the LORD, the God of your fathers. Remove all defilement from the sanctuary. [6]Our fathers were unfaithful; they did evil in the eyes of the LORD our God and forsook him. They turned their faces away from the LORD's dwelling place and turned their backs on him. [7]They also shut the doors of the portico and put out the lamps. They did not burn incense or present any burnt offerings at the sanctuary to the God of Israel. [8]Therefore, the anger of the LORD has fallen on Judah and Jerusalem; he has made them an object of dread and horror and scorn, as you can see with your own eyes. [9]This is why our fathers have fallen by the sword and why our sons and daughters and our wives are in captivity. [10]Now I intend to make a covenant with the LORD, the God of Israel, so that his fierce anger will turn away from us. [11]My sons, do not be negligent now, for the LORD has chosen you to stand before him and serve him, to minister before him and to burn incense."

[12]Then these Levites set to work:

from the Kohathites,

Mahath son of Amasai and Joel son of Azariah;

from the Merarites,

Kish son of Abdi and Azariah son of Jehallelel;

from the Gershonites,

Joah son of Zimmah and Eden son of Joah;

[13]from the descendants of Elizaphan,

Shimri and Jeiel;

from the descendants of Asaph,

Zechariah and Mattaniah;

truth or dare

"My life is filled with problems, so God must not care about me." Wrong assumption! When the going gets tough, really lean on God.

28:22

---

a 19 That is, Judah, as frequently in 2 Chronicles   b 20 Hebrew Tilgath-Pilneser, a variant of Tiglath-Pileser   c 24 Or and cut them up

Broken Promises

Today I called my older brother Ben at college and broke the news. "Mom's having an affair," I said quietly when he asked me what was wrong. Ben lit into me and asked me 20 questions about how I knew, and has Dad figured out and stuff like that. Then he told me not to mention it to anyone—the news would devastate Dad.

But this is one secret that probably won't last long. Mom and Dad aren't even speaking to each other. And a week ago, Mom had roses on her desk in the den. She said they were from a friend—and I believed her—until I did the laundry and found a note in her jeans pocket. All it said was, *I miss you every moment we're apart. We've got to find a way to be together all the time, love. Yours always, Thomas.*

I felt like I was going to throw up. I cried for an hour till Mom got home from work and found me sobbing in the kitchen. She saw the note crumpled up on the table and quickly tossed it in the trash. "Bethany," she said, "I love you, and I don't expect you to understand, but I hope you'll trust me. I'm your mother, and that's not going to change."

As much as I'd like to believe her, I can't. Everything *has* changed—and our family will never be the same.

adultery in focus

For more on adultery, see the link on www.TrueImagesBible.com

It's beautiful the way a husband and wife come together to love each other for life. But when they choose to set aside their marriage commitment, they cause a lot of pain. Adultery comes at a high price.

» When a husband and wife are married, they become one in God's eyes (see Matthew 19:5–6, page 1317).
» Adultery has devastating results (see Proverbs 6:20–29, pages 811-812).
» If your family is being torn apart by adultery, look to your perfect heavenly Father for help. You may want to consider Christian counseling; ask a trusted Christian adult for help.

For more on this topic, see the index on page 1656.

adultery

[14] from the descendants of Heman,
    Jehiel and Shimei;
from the descendants of Jeduthun,
    Shemaiah and Uzziel.

[15] When they had assembled their brothers and consecrated themselves, they went in to purify the temple of the LORD, as the king had ordered, following the word of the LORD. [16] The priests went into the sanctuary of the LORD to purify it. They brought out to the courtyard of the LORD's temple everything unclean that they found in the temple of the LORD. The Levites took it and carried it out to the Kidron Valley. [17] They began the consecration on the first day of the first month, and by the eighth day of the month they reached the portico of the LORD. For eight more days they consecrated the temple of the LORD itself, finishing on the sixteenth day of the first month.

[18]Then they went in to King Hezekiah and reported: "We have purified the entire temple of the Lord, the altar of burnt offering with all its utensils, and the table for setting out the consecrated bread, with all its articles. [19]We have prepared and consecrated all the articles that King Ahaz removed in his unfaithfulness while he was king. They are now in front of the Lord's altar."

[20]Early the next morning King Hezekiah gathered the city officials together and went up to the temple of the Lord. [21]They brought seven bulls, seven rams, seven male lambs and seven male goats as a sin offering for the kingdom, for the sanctuary and for Judah. The king commanded the priests, the descendants of Aaron, to offer these on the altar of the Lord. [22]So they slaughtered the bulls, and the priests took the blood and sprinkled it on the altar; next they slaughtered the rams and sprinkled their blood on the altar; then they slaughtered the lambs and sprinkled their blood on the altar. [23]The goats for the sin offering were brought before the king and the assembly, and they laid their hands on them. [24]The priests then slaughtered the goats and presented their blood on the altar for a sin offering to atone for all Israel, because the king had ordered the burnt offering and the sin offering for all Israel.

[25]He stationed the Levites in the temple of the Lord with cymbals, harps and lyres in the way prescribed by David and Gad the king's seer and Nathan the prophet; this was commanded by the Lord through his prophets. [26]So the Levites stood ready with David's instruments, and the priests with their trumpets.

[27]Hezekiah gave the order to sacrifice the burnt offering on the altar. As the offering began, singing to the Lord began also, accompanied by trumpets and the instruments of David king of Israel. [28]The whole assembly bowed in worship, while the singers sang and the trumpeters played. All this continued until the sacrifice of the burnt offering was completed.

[29]When the offerings were finished, the king and everyone present with him knelt down and worshiped. [30]King Hezekiah and his officials ordered the Levites to praise the Lord with the words of David and of Asaph the seer. So they sang praises with gladness and bowed their heads and worshiped.

[31]Then Hezekiah said, "You have now dedicated yourselves to the Lord. Come and bring sacrifices and thank offerings to the temple of the Lord." So the assembly brought sacrifices and thank offerings, and all whose hearts were willing brought burnt offerings.

[32]The number of burnt offerings the assembly brought was seventy bulls, a hundred rams and two hundred male lambs—all of them for burnt offerings to the Lord. [33]The animals consecrated as sacrifices amounted to six hundred bulls and three thousand sheep and goats. [34]The priests, however, were too few to skin all the burnt offerings; so their kinsmen the Levites helped them until the task was finished and until other priests had been consecrated, for the Levites had been more conscientious in consecrating themselves than the priests had been. [35]There were burnt offerings in abundance, together with the fat of the fellowship offerings[a] and the drink offerings that accompanied the burnt offerings.

So the service of the temple of the Lord was reestablished. [36]Hezekiah and all the people rejoiced at what God had brought about for his people, because it was done so quickly.

Hezekiah Celebrates the Passover

30 Hezekiah sent word to all Israel and Judah and also wrote letters to Ephraim and Manasseh, inviting them to come to the temple of the Lord in Jerusalem and celebrate the Passover to the Lord, the God of Israel. [2]The king and his officials and the whole assembly in Jerusalem decided to celebrate the Passover in the second month. [3]They had not been able to celebrate it at the regular time because not enough priests had consecrated themselves and the people had not assembled in Jerusalem. [4]The plan seemed right both to the king and to the whole assembly. [5]They decided to send a proclamation throughout Israel, from Beersheba to Dan, calling the people to come to Jerusalem and celebrate the Passover to the Lord, the God of Israel. It had not been celebrated in large numbers according to what was written.

[6]At the king's command, couriers went throughout Israel and Judah with letters from the king and from his officials, which read:

"People of Israel, return to the Lord, the God of Abraham, Isaac and Israel, that he may return to you who are left, who have escaped from the hand of the kings of Assyria. [7]Do not be like your fathers and brothers, who were unfaithful to the Lord, the God of their fathers, so that

a 35 Traditionally peace offerings

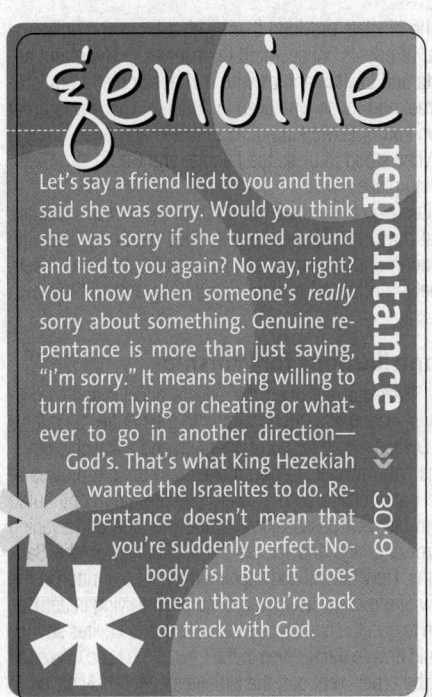

Genuine repentance

Let's say a friend lied to you and then said she was sorry. Would you think she was sorry if she turned around and lied to you again? No way, right? You know when someone's *really* sorry about something. Genuine repentance is more than just saying, "I'm sorry." It means being willing to turn from lying or cheating or whatever to go in another direction— God's. That's what King Hezekiah wanted the Israelites to do. Repentance doesn't mean that you're suddenly perfect. Nobody is! But it does mean that you're back on track with God.

» 30:9

he made them an object of horror, as you see. ⁸Do not be stiff-necked, as your fathers were; submit to the LORD. Come to the sanctuary, which he has consecrated forever. Serve the LORD your God, so that his fierce anger will turn away from you. ⁹If you return to the LORD, then your brothers and your children will be shown compassion by their captors and will come back to this land, for the LORD your God is gracious and compassionate. He will not turn his face from you if you return to him."

¹⁰The couriers went from town to town in Ephraim and Manasseh, as far as Zebulun, but the people scorned and ridiculed them. ¹¹Nevertheless, some men of Asher, Manasseh and Zebulun humbled themselves and went to Jerusalem. ¹²Also in Judah the hand of God was on the people to give them unity of mind to carry out what the king and his officials had ordered, following the word of the LORD.

¹³A very large crowd of people assembled in Jerusalem to celebrate the Feast of Unleavened Bread in the second month. ¹⁴They removed the altars in Jerusalem and cleared away the incense altars and threw them into the Kidron Valley.

¹⁵They slaughtered the Passover lamb on the fourteenth day of the second month. The priests and the Levites were ashamed and consecrated themselves and brought burnt offerings to the temple of the LORD. ¹⁶Then they took up their regular positions as prescribed in the Law of Moses the man of God. The priests sprinkled the blood handed to them by the Levites. ¹⁷Since many in the crowd had not consecrated themselves, the Levites had to kill the Passover lambs for all those who were not ceremonially clean and could not consecrate ˻their lambs˼ to the LORD. ¹⁸Although most of the many people who came from Ephraim, Manasseh, Issachar and Zebulun had not purified themselves, yet they ate the Passover, contrary to what was written. But Hezekiah prayed for them, saying, "May the LORD, who is good, pardon everyone ¹⁹who sets his heart on seeking God—the LORD, the God of his fathers—even if he is not clean according to the rules of the sanctuary." ²⁰And the LORD heard Hezekiah and healed the people.

²¹The Israelites who were present in Jerusalem celebrated the Feast of Unleavened Bread for seven days with great rejoicing, while the Levites and priests sang to the LORD every day, accompanied by the LORD's instruments of praise.ᵃ

²²Hezekiah spoke encouragingly to all the Levites, who showed good understanding of the service of the LORD. For the seven days they ate their assigned portion and offered fellowship offeringsᵇ and praised the LORD, the God of their fathers.

²³The whole assembly then agreed to celebrate the festival seven more days; so for another seven days they celebrated joyfully. ²⁴Hezekiah king of Judah provided a thousand bulls and seven thou-

truth or dare

"Good understanding of the service of the LORD" means that the Levites stuck to the book. God loves to see you pouring all your heart *and* ability into serving him!

30:22

ᵃ 21 Or *priests praised the* LORD *every day with resounding instruments belonging to the* LORD ᵇ 22 Traditionally *peace offerings* sand sheep and goats for the assembly, and the officials provided them with a thousand bulls and ten thousand sheep and goats. A great number of priests consecrated themselves. 25The entire assembly of Judah rejoiced, along with the priests and Levites and all who had assembled from Israel, including the aliens who had come from Israel and those who lived in Judah. 26There was great joy in Jerusalem, for since the days of Solomon son of David king of Israel there had been nothing like this in Jerusalem. 27The priests and the Levites stood to bless the people, and God heard them, for their prayer reached heaven, his holy dwelling place.

31 When all this had ended, the Israelites who were there went out to the towns of Judah, smashed the sacred stones and cut down the Asherah poles. They destroyed the high places and the altars throughout Judah and Benjamin and in Ephraim and Manasseh. After they had destroyed all of them, the Israelites returned to their own towns and to their own property.

truth or dare

When King Hezekiah brought back the old system of giving, the people responded immediately—and generously. What's *your* attitude towards giving?

31:2–8

Contributions for Worship

2Hezekiah assigned the priests and Levites to divisions—each of them according to their duties as priests or Levites—to offer burnt offerings and fellowship offerings,a to minister, to give thanks and to sing praises at the gates of the Lord's dwelling. 3The king contributed from his own possessions for the morning and evening burnt offerings and for the burnt offerings on the Sabbaths, New Moons and appointed feasts as written in the Law of the Lord. 4He ordered the people living in Jerusalem to give the portion due the priests and Levites so they could devote themselves to the Law of the Lord. 5As soon as the order went out, the Israelites generously gave the firstfruits of their grain, new wine, oil and honey and all that the fields produced. They brought a great amount, a tithe of everything. 6The men of Israel and Judah who lived in the towns of Judah also brought a tithe of their herds and flocks and a tithe of the holy things dedicated to the Lord their God, and they piled them in heaps. 7They began doing this in the third month and finished in the seventh month. 8When Hezekiah and his officials came and saw the heaps, they praised the Lord and blessed his people Israel.

9Hezekiah asked the priests and Levites about the heaps; 10and Azariah the chief priest, from the family of Zadok, answered, "Since the people began to bring their contributions to the temple of the Lord, we have had enough to eat and plenty to spare, because the Lord has blessed his people, and this great amount is left over."

11Hezekiah gave orders to prepare storerooms in the temple of the Lord, and this was done. 12Then they faithfully brought in the contributions, tithes and dedicated gifts. Conaniah, a Levite, was in charge of these things, and his brother Shimei was next in rank. 13Jehiel, Azaziah, Nahath, Asahel, Jerimoth, Jozabad, Eliel, Ismakiah, Mahath and Benaiah were supervisors under Conaniah and Shimei his brother, by appointment of King Hezekiah and Azariah the official in charge of the temple of God.

14Kore son of Imnah the Levite, keeper of the East Gate, was in charge of the freewill offerings given to God, distributing the contributions made to the Lord and also the consecrated gifts. 15Eden, Miniamin, Jeshua, Shemaiah, Amariah and Shecaniah assisted him faithfully in the towns of the priests, distributing to their fellow priests according to their divisions, old and young alike.

16In addition, they distributed to the males three years old or more whose names were in the genealogical records—all who would enter the temple of the Lord to perform the daily duties of their various tasks, according to their responsibilities and their divisions. 17And they distributed to the priests enrolled by their families in the genealogical records and likewise to the Levites twenty years old or more, according to their responsibilities and their divisions. 18They included all the little ones, the wives, and the sons and daughters of the whole community listed in these genealogical records. For they were faithful in consecrating themselves.

a 2 Traditionally *peace offerings*

¹⁹As for the priests, the descendants of Aaron, who lived on the farm lands around their towns or in any other towns, men were designated by name to distribute portions to every male among them and to all who were recorded in the genealogies of the Levites.

²⁰This is what Hezekiah did throughout Judah, doing what was good and right and faithful before the LORD his God. ²¹In everything that he undertook in the service of God's temple and in obedience to the law and the commands, he sought his God and worked wholeheartedly. And so he prospered.

Sennacherib Threatens Jerusalem

32 After all that Hezekiah had so faithfully done, Sennacherib king of Assyria came and invaded Judah. He laid siege to the fortified cities, thinking to conquer them for himself. ²When Hezekiah saw that Sennacherib had come and that he intended to make war on Jerusalem, ³he consulted with his officials and military staff about blocking off the water from the springs outside the city, and they helped him. ⁴A large force of men assembled, and they blocked all the springs and the stream that flowed through the land. "Why should the kings*a* of Assyria come and find plenty of water?" they said. ⁵Then he worked hard repairing all the broken sections of the wall and building towers on it. He built another wall outside that one and reinforced the supporting terraces*b* of the City of David. He also made large numbers of weapons and shields.

⁶He appointed military officers over the people and assembled them before him in the square at the city gate and encouraged them with these words: ⁷"Be strong and courageous. Do not be afraid or discouraged because of the king of Assyria and the vast army with him, for there is a greater power with us than with him. ⁸With him is only the arm of flesh, but with us is the LORD our God to help us and to fight our battles." And the people gained confidence from what Hezekiah the king of Judah said.

⁹Later, when Sennacherib king of Assyria and all his forces were laying siege to Lachish, he sent his officers to Jerusalem with this message for Hezekiah king of Judah and for all the people of Judah who were there:

truth or dare

Knowing God doesn't make the opposition disappear. It just means that no battle is too difficult to win with his strength.

32:6–8

¹⁰"This is what Sennacherib king of Assyria says: On what are you basing your confidence, that you remain in Jerusalem under siege? ¹¹When Hezekiah says, 'The LORD our God will save us from the hand of the king of Assyria,' he is misleading you, to let you die of hunger and thirst. ¹²Did not Hezekiah himself remove this god's high places and altars, saying to Judah and Jerusalem, 'You must worship before one altar and burn sacrifices on it'?

¹⁴"Do you not know what I and my fathers have done to all the peoples of the other lands? Were the gods of those nations ever able to deliver their land from my hand? ¹⁴Who of all the gods of these nations that my fathers destroyed has been able to save his people from me? How then can your god deliver you from my hand? ¹⁵Now do not let Hezekiah deceive you and mislead you like this. Do not believe him, for no god of any nation or kingdom has been able to deliver his people from my hand or the hand of my fathers. How much less will your god deliver you from my hand!"

¹⁶Sennacherib's officers spoke further against the LORD God and against his servant Hezekiah. ¹⁷The king also wrote letters insulting the LORD, the God of Israel, and saying this against him: "Just as the gods of the peoples of the other lands did not rescue their people from my hand, so the god of Hezekiah will not rescue his people from my hand." ¹⁸Then they called out in Hebrew to the people of Jerusalem who were on the wall, to terrify them and make them afraid in order to capture the city. ¹⁹They spoke about the God of Jerusalem as they did about the gods of the other peoples of the world—the work of men's hands.

²⁰King Hezekiah and the prophet Isaiah son of Amoz cried out in prayer to heaven about this. ²¹And the LORD sent an angel, who annihilated all the fighting men and the leaders and officers in

a 4 Hebrew; Septuagint and Syriac king   b 5 Or the Millo the camp of the Assyrian king. So he withdrew to his own land in disgrace. And when he went into the temple of his god, some of his sons cut him down with the sword. ²²So the LORD saved Hezekiah and the people of Jerusalem from the hand of Sennacherib king of Assyria and from the hand of all others. He took care of them[a] on every side. ²³Many brought offerings to Jerusalem for the LORD and valuable gifts for Hezekiah king of Judah. From then on he was highly regarded by all the nations.

Hezekiah's Pride, Success and Death

²⁴In those days Hezekiah became ill and was at the point of death. He prayed to the LORD, who answered him and gave him a miraculous sign. ²⁵But Hezekiah's heart was proud and he did not respond to the kindness shown him; therefore the LORD's wrath was on him and on Judah and Jerusalem. ²⁶Then Hezekiah repented of the pride of his heart, as did the people of Jerusalem; therefore the LORD's wrath did not come upon them during the days of Hezekiah.

²⁷Hezekiah had very great riches and honor, and he made treasuries for his silver and gold and for his precious stones, spices, shields and all kinds of valuables. ²⁸He also made buildings to store the harvest of grain, new wine and oil; and he made stalls for various kinds of cattle, and pens for the flocks. ²⁹He built villages and acquired great numbers of flocks and herds, for God had given him very great riches.

³⁰It was Hezekiah who blocked the upper outlet of the Gihon spring and channeled the water down to the west side of the City of David. He succeeded in everything he undertook. ³¹But when envoys were sent by the rulers of Babylon to ask him about the miraculous sign that had occurred in the land, God left him to test him and to know everything that was in his heart.

³²The other events of Hezekiah's reign and his acts of devotion are written in the vision of the prophet Isaiah son of Amoz in the book of the kings of Judah and Israel. ³³Hezekiah rested with his fathers and was buried on the hill where the tombs of David's descendants are. All Judah and the people of Jerusalem honored him when he died. And Manasseh his son succeeded him as king.

Manasseh King of Judah

33 Manasseh was twelve years old when he became king, and he reigned in Jerusalem fifty-five years. ²He did evil in the eyes of the LORD, following the detestable practices of the nations the LORD had driven out before the Israelites. ³He rebuilt the high places his father Hezekiah had demolished; he also erected altars to the Baals and made Asherah poles. He bowed down to all the starry hosts and worshiped them. ⁴He built altars in the temple of the LORD, of which the LORD had said, "My Name will remain in Jerusalem forever." ⁵In both courts of the temple of the LORD, he built altars to all the starry hosts. ⁶He sacrificed his sons in[b] the fire in the Valley of Ben Hinnom, practiced sorcery, divination and witchcraft, and consulted mediums and spiritists. He did much evil in the eyes of the LORD, provoking him to anger.

⁷He took the carved image he had made and put it in God's temple, of which God had said to David and to his son Solomon, "In this temple and in Jerusalem, which I have chosen out of all the tribes of Israel, I will put my Name forever. ⁸I will not again make the feet of the Israelites leave the land I assigned to your forefathers, if only they will be careful to do everything I commanded them concerning all the laws, decrees and ordinances given through Moses." ⁹But Manasseh led Judah and the people of Jerusalem astray, so that they did more evil than the nations the LORD had destroyed before the Israelites.

¹⁰The LORD spoke to Manasseh and his people, but they paid no attention. ¹¹So the LORD brought against them the army commanders of the king of Assyria, who took Manasseh prisoner, put a hook in his nose, bound him with bronze shackles and took him to Babylon. ¹²In his distress he sought the favor of the LORD his God and humbled himself greatly before the God of his fathers. ¹³And when he prayed to him, the

truth or dare

God uses a number of ways to get us to recognize and listen to him. What will it take for you to humble yourself and follow God?

33:10–13

a 22 Hebrew; Septuagint and Vulgate *He gave them rest*   b 6 Or *He made his sons pass through*

LORD was moved by his entreaty and listened to his plea; so he brought him back to Jerusalem and to his kingdom. Then Manasseh knew that the LORD is God.

[14]Afterward he rebuilt the outer wall of the City of David, west of the Gihon spring in the valley, as far as the entrance of the Fish Gate and encircling the hill of Ophel; he also made it much higher. He stationed military commanders in all the fortified cities in Judah.

[15]He got rid of the foreign gods and removed the image from the temple of the LORD, as well as all the altars he had built on the temple hill and in Jerusalem; and he threw them out of the city. [16]Then he restored the altar of the LORD and sacrificed fellowship offerings[a] and thank offerings on it, and told Judah to serve the LORD, the God of Israel. [17]The people, however, continued to sacrifice at the high places, but only to the LORD their God.

[18]The other events of Manasseh's reign, including his prayer to his God and the words the seers spoke to him in the name of the LORD, the God of Israel, are written in the annals of the kings of Israel.[b] [19]His prayer and how God was moved by his entreaty, as well as all his sins and unfaithfulness, and the sites where he built high places and set up Asherah poles and idols before he humbled himself—all are written in the records of the seers.[c] [20]Manasseh rested with his fathers and was buried in his palace. And Amon his son succeeded him as king.

Amon King of Judah

[21]Amon was twenty-two years old when he became king, and he reigned in Jerusalem two years. [22]He did evil in the eyes of the LORD, as his father Manasseh had done. Amon worshiped and offered sacrifices to all the idols Manasseh had made. [23]But unlike his father Manasseh, he did not humble himself before the LORD; Amon increased his guilt.

[24]Amon's officials conspired against him and assassinated him in his palace. [25]Then the people of the land killed all who had plotted against King Amon, and they made Josiah his son king in his place.

Josiah's Reforms

34 Josiah was eight years old when he became king, and he reigned in Jerusalem thirty-one years. [2]He did what was right in the eyes of the LORD and walked in the ways of his father David, not turning aside to the right or to the left.

[3]In the eighth year of his reign, while he was still young, he began to seek the God of his father David. In his twelfth year he began to purge Judah and Jerusalem of high places, Asherah poles, carved idols and cast images. [4]Under his direction the altars of the Baals were torn down; he cut to pieces the incense altars that were above them, and smashed the Asherah poles, the idols and the images. These he broke to pieces and scattered over the graves of those who had sacrificed to them. [5]He burned the bones of the priests on their altars, and so he purged Judah and Jerusalem. [6]In the towns of Manasseh, Ephraim and Simeon, as far as Naphtali, and in the ruins around them, [7]he tore down the altars and the Asherah poles and crushed the idols to powder and cut to pieces all the incense altars throughout Israel. Then he went back to Jerusalem.

[8]In the eighteenth year of Josiah's reign, to purify the land and the temple, he sent Shaphan son of Azaliah and Maaseiah the ruler of the city, with Joah son of Joahaz, the recorder, to repair the temple of the LORD his God.

[9]They went to Hilkiah the high priest and gave him the money that had been brought into the temple of God, which the Levites who were the doorkeepers had collected from the people of Manasseh, Ephraim and the entire remnant of Israel and from all the people of Judah and Benjamin and the inhabitants of Jerusalem. [10]Then they entrusted it to the men appointed to supervise the work on the LORD's temple. These men paid the workers who repaired and restored the temple. [11]They also gave money to the carpenters and builders to purchase dressed stone, and timber for joists and beams for the buildings that the kings of Judah had allowed to fall into ruin.

[12]The men did the work faithfully. Over them to direct them were Jahath and Obadiah, Levites descended from Merari, and Zechariah and Meshullam, descended from Kohath. The Levites—all who were skilled in playing musical instruments— [13]had charge of the laborers and supervised all the workers from job to job. Some of the Levites were secretaries, scribes and doorkeepers.

---

a 16 Traditionally *peace offerings*   b 18 That is, Judah, as frequently in 2 Chronicles   c 19 One Hebrew manuscript and Septuagint; most Hebrew manuscripts *of Hozai*

[14]While they were bringing out the money that had been taken into the temple of the LORD, Hilkiah the priest found the Book of the Law of the LORD that had been given through Moses. [15]Hilkiah said to Shaphan the secretary, "I have found the Book of the Law in the temple of the LORD." He gave it to Shaphan.

[16]Then Shaphan took the book to the king and reported to him: "Your officials are doing everything that has been committed to them. [17]They have paid out the money that was in the temple of the LORD and have entrusted it to the supervisors and workers." [18]Then Shaphan the secretary informed the king, "Hilkiah the priest has given me a book." And Shaphan read from it in the presence of the king.

[19]When the king heard the words of the Law, he tore his robes. [20]He gave these orders to Hilkiah, Ahikam son of Shaphan, Abdon son of Micah, *a* Shaphan the secretary and Asaiah the king's attendant: [21]"Go and inquire of the LORD for me and for the remnant in Israel and Judah about what is written in this book that has been found. Great is the LORD's anger that is poured out on us because our fathers have not kept the word of the LORD; they have not acted in accordance with all that is written in this book."

[22]Hilkiah and those the king had sent with him *b* went to speak to the prophetess Huldah, who was the wife of Shallum son of Tokhath, *c* the son of Hasrah, *d* keeper of the wardrobe. She lived in Jerusalem, in the Second District.

[23]She said to them, "This is what the LORD, the God of Israel, says: Tell the man who sent you to me, [24]'This is what the LORD says: I am going to bring disaster on this place and its people—all the curses written in the book that has been read in the presence of the king of Judah. [25]Because they have forsaken me and burned incense to other gods and provoked me to anger by all that their hands have made, *e* my anger will be poured out on this place and will not be quenched.' [26]Tell the king of Judah, who sent you to inquire of the LORD, 'This is what the LORD, the God of Israel, says concerning the words you heard: [27]Because your heart was responsive and you humbled yourself before God when you heard what he spoke against this place and its people, and because you humbled yourself before me and tore your robes and wept in my presence, I have heard you, declares the LORD. [28]Now I will gather you to your fathers, and you will be buried in peace. Your eyes will not see all the disaster I am going to bring on this place and on those who live here.' "

So they took her answer back to the king.

[29]Then the king called together all the elders of Judah and Jerusalem. [30]He went up to the temple of the LORD with the men of Judah, the people of Jerusalem, the priests and the Levites—all the people from the least to the greatest. He read in their hearing all the words of the Book of the Covenant, which had been found in the temple of the LORD. [31]The king stood by his pillar and renewed the covenant in the presence of the LORD—to follow the LORD and keep his commands, regulations and decrees with all his heart and all his soul, and to obey the words of the covenant written in this book.

[32]Then he had everyone in Jerusalem and Benjamin pledge themselves to it; the people of Jerusalem did this in accordance with the covenant of God, the God of their fathers.

[33]Josiah removed all the detestable idols from all the territory belonging to the Israelites, and he had all who were present in Israel serve the LORD their God. As long as he lived, they did not fail to follow the LORD, the God of their fathers.

Josiah Celebrates the Passover

35 Josiah celebrated the Passover to the LORD in Jerusalem, and the Passover lamb was slaughtered on the fourteenth day of the first month. [2]He appointed the priests to their duties and encouraged them in the service of the LORD's temple. [3]He said to the Levites, who instructed all Israel and who had been consecrated to the LORD: "Put the sacred ark in the temple that Solomon son of David king of Israel built. It is not to be carried about on your shoulders. Now serve the LORD your God and his people Israel. [4]Prepare yourselves by families in your divisions, according to the directions written by David king of Israel and by his son Solomon.

a 20 Also called *Acbor son of Micaiah*   *b* 22 One Hebrew manuscript, Vulgate and Syriac; most Hebrew manuscripts do not have *had sent with him.*   *c* 22 Also called *Tikvah*   *d* 22 Also called *Harhas*   *e* 25 Or *by everything they have done*

⁵"Stand in the holy place with a group of Levites for each subdivision of the families of your fellow countrymen, the lay people. ⁶Slaughter the Passover lambs, consecrate yourselves and prepare ⌐the lambs⌐ for your fellow countrymen, doing what the LORD commanded through Moses."

⁷Josiah provided for all the lay people who were there a total of thirty thousand sheep and goats for the Passover offerings, and also three thousand cattle—all from the king's own possessions.

⁸His officials also contributed voluntarily to the people and the priests and Levites. Hilkiah, Zechariah and Jehiel, the administrators of God's temple, gave the priests twenty-six hundred Passover offerings and three hundred cattle. ⁹Also Conaniah along with Shemaiah and Nethanel, his brothers, and Hashabiah, Jeiel and Jozabad, the leaders of the Levites, provided five thousand Passover offerings and five hundred head of cattle for the Levites.

¹⁰The service was arranged and the priests stood in their places with the Levites in their divisions as the king had ordered. ¹¹The Passover lambs were slaughtered, and the priests sprinkled the blood handed to them, while the Levites skinned the animals. ¹²They set aside the burnt offerings to give them to the subdivisions of the families of the people to offer to the LORD, as is written in the Book of Moses. They did the same with the cattle. ¹³They roasted the Passover animals over the fire as prescribed, and boiled the holy offerings in pots, caldrons and pans and served them quickly to all the people. ¹⁴After this, they made preparations for themselves and for the priests, because the priests, the descendants of Aaron, were sacrificing the burnt offerings and the fat portions until nightfall. So the Levites made preparations for themselves and for the Aaronic priests.

¹⁵The musicians, the descendants of Asaph, were in the places prescribed by David, Asaph, Heman and Jeduthun the king's seer. The gatekeepers at each gate did not need to leave their posts, because their fellow Levites made the preparations for them.

¹⁶So at that time the entire service of the LORD was carried out for the celebration of the Passover and the offering of burnt offerings on the altar of the LORD, as King Josiah had ordered. ¹⁷The Israelites who were present celebrated the Passover at that time and observed the Feast of Unleavened Bread for seven days. ¹⁸The Passover had not been observed like this in Israel since the days of the prophet Samuel; and none of the kings of Israel had ever celebrated such a Passover as did Josiah, with the priests, the Levites and all Judah and Israel who were there with the people of Jerusalem. ¹⁹This Passover was celebrated in the eighteenth year of Josiah's reign.

The Death of Josiah

²⁰After all this, when Josiah had set the temple in order, Neco king of Egypt went up to fight at Carchemish on the Euphrates, and Josiah marched out to meet him in bat-

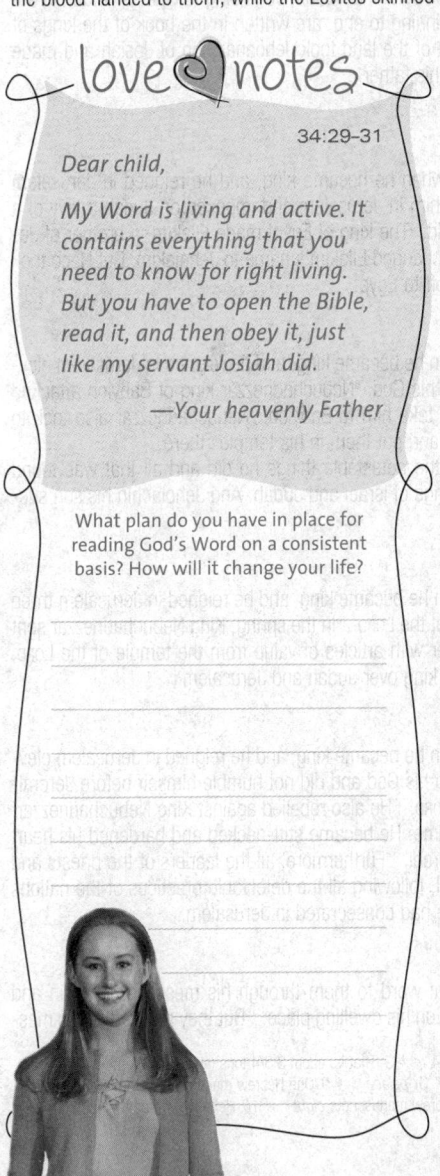

love notes

34:29–31

Dear child,

My Word is living and active. It contains everything that you need to know for right living. But you have to open the Bible, read it, and then obey it, just like my servant Josiah did.

—Your heavenly Father

What plan do you have in place for reading God's Word on a consistent basis? How will it change your life?

tle. [21]But Neco sent messengers to him, saying, "What quarrel is there between you and me, O king of Judah? It is not you I am attacking at this time, but the house with which I am at war. God has told me to hurry; so stop opposing God, who is with me, or he will destroy you."

[22]Josiah, however, would not turn away from him, but disguised himself to engage him in battle. He would not listen to what Neco had said at God's command but went to fight him on the plain of Megiddo.

[23]Archers shot King Josiah, and he told his officers, "Take me away; I am badly wounded." [24]So they took him out of his chariot, put him in the other chariot he had and brought him to Jerusalem, where he died. He was buried in the tombs of his fathers, and all Judah and Jerusalem mourned for him.

[25]Jeremiah composed laments for Josiah, and to this day all the men and women singers commemorate Josiah in the laments. These became a tradition in Israel and are written in the Laments.

[26]The other events of Josiah's reign and his acts of devotion, according to what is written in the Law of the LORD— [27]all the events, from beginning to end, are written in the book of the kings of Israel and Judah. [1]And the people of the land took Jehoahaz son of Josiah and made

36

him king in Jerusalem in place of his father.

Jehoahaz King of Judah

[2]Jehoahaz[a] was twenty-three years old when he became king, and he reigned in Jerusalem three months. [3]The king of Egypt dethroned him in Jerusalem and imposed on Judah a levy of a hundred talents[b] of silver and a talent[c] of gold. [4]The king of Egypt made Eliakim, a brother of Jehoahaz, king over Judah and Jerusalem and changed Eliakim's name to Jehoiakim. But Neco took Eliakim's brother Jehoahaz and carried him off to Egypt.

Jehoiakim King of Judah

[5]Jehoiakim was twenty-five years old when he became king, and he reigned in Jerusalem eleven years. He did evil in the eyes of the LORD his God. [6]Nebuchadnezzar king of Babylon attacked him and bound him with bronze shackles to take him to Babylon. [7]Nebuchadnezzar also took to Babylon articles from the temple of the LORD and put them in his temple[d] there.

[8]The other events of Jehoiakim's reign, the detestable things he did and all that was found against him, are written in the book of the kings of Israel and Judah. And Jehoiachin his son succeeded him as king.

Jehoiachin King of Judah

[9]Jehoiachin was eighteen[e] years old when he became king, and he reigned in Jerusalem three months and ten days. He did evil in the eyes of the LORD. [10]In the spring, King Nebuchadnezzar sent for him and brought him to Babylon, together with articles of value from the temple of the LORD, and he made Jehoiachin's uncle,[f] Zedekiah, king over Judah and Jerusalem.

Zedekiah King of Judah

[11]Zedekiah was twenty-one years old when he became king, and he reigned in Jerusalem eleven years. [12]He did evil in the eyes of the LORD his God and did not humble himself before Jeremiah the prophet, who spoke the word of the LORD. [13]He also rebelled against King Nebuchadnezzar, who had made him take an oath in God's name. He became stiff-necked and hardened his heart and would not turn to the LORD, the God of Israel. [14]Furthermore, all the leaders of the priests and the people became more and more unfaithful, following all the detestable practices of the nations and defiling the temple of the LORD, which he had consecrated in Jerusalem.

The Fall of Jerusalem

[15]The LORD, the God of their fathers, sent word to them through his messengers again and again, because he had pity on his people and on his dwelling place. [16]But they mocked God's mes-

a 2 Hebrew *Joahaz,* a variant of *Jehoahaz;* also in verse 4   *b 3* That is, about 3 3/4 tons (about 3.4 metric tons)   *c 3* That is, about 75 pounds (about 34 kilograms)   *d 7* Or *palace*   *e 9* One Hebrew manuscript, some Septuagint manuscripts and Syriac (see also 2 Kings 24:8); most Hebrew manuscripts *eight*   *f 10* Hebrew *brother,* that is, relative (see 2 Kings 24:17) sengers, despised his words and scoffed at his prophets until the wrath of the LORD was aroused against his people and there was no remedy. [17]He brought up against them the king of the Babylonians,[a] who killed their young men with the sword in the sanctuary, and spared neither young man nor young woman, old man or aged. God handed all of them over to Nebuchadnezzar. [18]He carried to Babylon all the articles from the temple of God, both large and small, and the treasures of the LORD's temple and the treasures of the king and his officials. [19]They set fire to God's temple and broke down the wall of Jerusalem; they burned all the palaces and destroyed everything of value there.

[20]He carried into exile to Babylon the remnant, who escaped from the sword, and they became servants to him and his sons until the kingdom of Persia came to power. [21]The land enjoyed its sabbath rests; all the time of its desolation it rested, until the seventy years were completed in fulfillment of the word of the LORD spoken by Jeremiah.

truth or dare

God is a patient God. He'll give you lots of chances, but he's also willing to punish you if you don't change. Testing God's patience is never cool.

36:15–21

[22]In the first year of Cyrus king of Persia, in order to fulfill the word of the LORD spoken by Jeremiah, the LORD moved the heart of Cyrus king of Persia to make a proclamation throughout his realm and to put it in writing:

[23]"This is what Cyrus king of Persia says:

" 'The LORD, the God of heaven, has given me all the kingdoms of the earth and he has appointed me to build a temple for him at Jerusalem in Judah. Anyone of his people among you—may the LORD his God be with him, and let him go up.' "

a 17 Or Chaldeans

author: Unknown, but possibly Ezra.

date: Written probably around 440 B.C.

setting: Some of the Israelites who had been exiled to Babylon return home and rebuild the temple.

verse to remember: For seven days they celebrated with joy the Feast of Unleavened Bread, because the LORD had filled them with joy by changing the attitude of the king of Assyria, so that he assisted them in the work on the house of God, the God of Israel (6:22).

theme to consider: God is always faithful to keep his word and to work out his plan.

ezra

unchanging truth

At some point in our lives, we've all faced the disappointment of the broken promise. Maybe it was the friend who promised to help you with a project but backed out at the last minute. Or a parent who promised to make your final game of the season and then had something come up suddenly.

Eventually, if the person disappoints us a few times, we find it difficult to believe anything that she or he says. In contrast, there are also people in our lives who are completely trustworthy and reliable. If they say they'll do something, we know it'll be done—and done well. If they say they'll be there, we know they will. We don't doubt it for an instant.

In the book of Ezra, we see how God continued to faithfully work out his plan for the Israelites despite tremendous obstacles. God made a way for the Jews to return to Jerusalem and rebuild the temple, even though they were captives in Babylon. He even used a pagan king to carry out his plan!

The book of Ezra shows God's faithfulness and how he always keeps his promises. He will never disappoint you or let you down. Count on it!

life lessons

1. God keeps his word. Nothing or no one stands in the way of God's plans for his followers (1:1–4).

2. God gives us the courage and strength to carry out his work (7:27–28).

3. We sin when we disobey God. But God is faithful and forgives us when we repent (9:6–9).

Cyrus Helps the Exiles to Return

1 In the first year of Cyrus king of Persia, in order to fulfill the word of the LORD spoken by Jeremiah, the LORD moved the heart of Cyrus king of Persia to make a proclamation throughout his realm and to put it in writing:

²"This is what Cyrus king of Persia says:

" 'The LORD, the God of heaven, has given me all the kingdoms of the earth and he has appointed me to build a temple for him at Jerusalem in Judah. ³Anyone of his people among you—may his God be with him, and let him go up to Jerusalem in Judah and build the temple of the LORD, the God of Israel, the God who is in Jerusalem. ⁴And the people of any place where survivors may now be living are to provide him with silver and gold, with goods and livestock, and with freewill offerings for the temple of God in Jerusalem.' "

⁵Then the family heads of Judah and Benjamin, and the priests and Levites—everyone whose heart God had moved—prepared to go up and build the house of the LORD in Jerusalem. ⁶All their neighbors assisted them with articles of silver and gold, with goods and livestock, and with valuable gifts, in addition to all the freewill offerings. ⁷Moreover, King Cyrus brought out the articles belonging to the temple of the LORD, which Nebuchadnezzar had carried away from Jerusalem and had placed in the temple of his god.ᵃ ⁸Cyrus king of Persia had them brought by Mithredath the treasurer, who counted them out to Sheshbazzar the prince of Judah.

⁹This was the inventory:

gold dishes	30
silver dishes	1,000
silver pansᵇ	29
¹⁰ gold bowls	30
matching silver bowls	410
other articles	1,000

¹¹In all, there were 5,400 articles of gold and of silver. Sheshbazzar brought all these along when the exiles came up from Babylon to Jerusalem.

The List of the Exiles Who Returned

2 Now these are the people of the province who came up from the captivity of the exiles, whom Nebuchadnezzar king of Babylon had taken captive to Babylon (they returned to Jerusalem and Judah, each to his own town, ²in company with Zerubbabel, Jeshua, Nehemiah, Seraiah, Reelaiah, Mordecai, Bilshan, Mispar, Bigvai, Rehum and Baanah):

The list of the men of the people of Israel:

³ the descendants of Parosh	2,172
⁴ of Shephatiah	372
⁵ of Arah	775
⁶ of Pahath-Moab (through the line of Jeshua and Joab)	2,812
⁷ of Elam	1,254
⁸ of Zattu	945
⁹ of Zaccai	760
¹⁰ of Bani	642
¹¹ of Bebai	623
¹² of Azgad	1,222

truth **or dare**

When God's on a mission, he can use anyone—even a hardhearted pagan ruler—to get the word out. Don't underestimate God's power in any situation!

1:1–4

ᵃ 7 Or *gods* ᵇ 9 The meaning of the Hebrew for this word is uncertain.

[13] of Adonikam	666
[14] of Bigvai	2,056
[15] of Adin	454
[16] of Ater (through Hezekiah)	98
[17] of Bezai	323
[18] of Jorah	112
[19] of Hashum	223
[20] of Gibbar	95
[21] the men of Bethlehem	123
[22] of Netophah	56
[23] of Anathoth	128
[24] of Azmaveth	42
[25] of Kiriath Jearim, [a] Kephirah and Beeroth	743
[26] of Ramah and Geba	621
[27] of Micmash	122
[28] of Bethel and Ai	223
[29] of Nebo	52
[30] of Magbish	156
[31] of the other Elam	1,254
[32] of Harim	320
[33] of Lod, Hadid and Ono	725
[34] of Jericho	345
[35] of Senaah	3,630

[36]The priests:

the descendants of Jedaiah (through the family of Jeshua)	973
[37] of Immer	1,052
[38] of Pashhur	1,247
[39] of Harim	1,017

[40]The Levites:

the descendants of Jeshua and Kadmiel (through the line of Hodaviah)	74

[41]The singers:

the descendants of Asaph	128

[42]The gatekeepers of the temple:

the descendants of Shallum, Ater, Talmon, Akkub, Hatita and Shobai	139

[43]The temple servants:

the descendants of
Ziha, Hasupha, Tabbaoth,
[44]Keros, Siaha, Padon,
[45]Lebanah, Hagabah, Akkub,
[46]Hagab, Shalmai, Hanan,
[47]Giddel, Gahar, Reaiah,
[48]Rezin, Nekoda, Gazzam,
[49]Uzza, Paseah, Besai,
[50]Asnah, Meunim, Nephusim,
[51]Bakbuk, Hakupha, Harhur,

[a] 25 See Septuagint (see also Neh. 7:29); Hebrew *Kiriath Arim*.

[52] Bazluth, Mehida, Harsha,
[53] Barkos, Sisera, Temah,
[54] Neziah and Hatipha

[55] The descendants of the servants of Solomon:

the descendants of
Sotai, Hassophereth, Peruda,
[56] Jaala, Darkon, Giddel,
[57] Shephatiah, Hattil,
Pokereth-Hazzebaim and Ami

[58] The temple servants and the descendants
of the servants of Solomon   392

[59] The following came up from the towns of Tel Melah, Tel Harsha, Kerub, Addon and Immer, but they could not show that their families were descended from Israel:

[60] The descendants of
Delaiah, Tobiah and Nekoda   652

[61] And from among the priests:

The descendants of
Hobaiah, Hakkoz and Barzillai (a man who had married a daughter of Barzillai the Gileadite and was called by that name).

[62] These searched for their family records, but they could not find them and so were excluded from the priesthood as unclean. [63] The governor ordered them not to eat any of the most sacred food until there was a priest ministering with the Urim and Thummim.

[64] The whole company numbered 42,360, [65] besides their 7,337 menservants and maidservants; and they also had 200 men and women singers. [66] They had 736 horses, 245 mules, [67] 435 camels and 6,720 donkeys.

[68] When they arrived at the house of the LORD in Jerusalem, some of the heads of the families gave freewill offerings toward the rebuilding of the house of God on its site. [69] According to their ability they gave to the treasury for this work 61,000 drachmas[a] of gold, 5,000 minas[b] of silver and 100 priestly garments.

[70] The priests, the Levites, the singers, the gatekeepers and the temple servants settled in their own towns, along with some of the other people, and the rest of the Israelites settled in their towns.

Rebuilding the Altar

3 When the seventh month came and the Israelites had settled in their towns, the people assembled as one man in Jerusalem. [2] Then Jeshua son of Jozadak and his fellow priests and Zerubbabel son of Shealtiel and his associates began to build the altar of the God of Israel to sacrifice burnt offerings on it, in accordance with what is written in the Law of Moses the

genuine
generosity » 2:68-69

What's the first thing you think to do with your cash? Save it? Spend it? (Two-for-one shoe sale, here I come!) Give it away? The first thing the Jewish family leaders did when they returned to Jerusalem after years of exile was to donate their family fortunes to the temple rebuilding project. There was no guilt trip attached. They gave "according to their ability." You got a lot? Give a lot! To the Israelites, being generous surely brought a genuine sense of joy. Have you ever experienced the joy of giving?

---

a 69 That is, about 1,100 pounds (about 500 kilograms)   *b 69* That is, about 3 tons (about 2.9 metric tons) man of God. ³Despite their fear of the peoples around them, they built the altar on its foundation and sacrificed burnt offerings on it to the Lᴏʀᴅ, both the morning and evening sacrifices. ⁴Then in accordance with what is written, they celebrated the Feast of Tabernacles with the required number of burnt offerings prescribed for each day. ⁵After that, they presented the regular burnt offerings, the New Moon sacrifices and the sacrifices for all the appointed sacred feasts of the Lᴏʀᴅ, as well as those brought as freewill offerings to the Lᴏʀᴅ. ⁶On the first day of the seventh month they began to offer burnt offerings to the Lᴏʀᴅ, though the foundation of the Lᴏʀᴅ's temple had not yet been laid.

Rebuilding the Temple

⁷Then they gave money to the masons and carpenters, and gave food and drink and oil to the people of Sidon and Tyre, so that they would bring cedar logs by sea from Lebanon to Joppa, as authorized by Cyrus king of Persia.

⁸In the second month of the second year after their arrival at the house of God in Jerusalem, Zerubbabel son of Shealtiel, Jeshua son of Jozadak and the rest of their brothers (the priests and the Levites and all who had returned from the captivity to Jerusalem) began the work, appointing Levites twenty years of age and older to supervise the building of the house of the Lᴏʀᴅ. ⁹Jeshua and his sons and brothers and Kadmiel and his sons (descendants of Hodaviah*ᵃ*) and the sons of Henadad and their sons and brothers—all Levites—joined together in supervising those working on the house of God.

¹⁰When the builders laid the foundation of the temple of the Lᴏʀᴅ, the priests in their vestments and with trumpets, and the Levites (the sons of Asaph) with cymbals, took their places to praise the Lᴏʀᴅ, as prescribed by David king of Israel. ¹¹With praise and thanksgiving they sang to the Lᴏʀᴅ:

> "He is good;
>   his love to Israel endures forever."

And all the people gave a great shout of praise to the Lᴏʀᴅ, because the foundation of the house of the Lᴏʀᴅ was laid. ¹²But many of the older priests and Levites and family heads, who had seen the former temple, wept aloud when they saw the foundation of this temple being laid, while many others shouted for joy. ¹³No one could distinguish the sound of the shouts of joy from the sound of weeping, because the people made so much noise. And the sound was heard far away.

Opposition to the Rebuilding

4 When the enemies of Judah and Benjamin heard that the exiles were building a temple for the Lᴏʀᴅ, the God of Israel, ²they came to Zerubbabel and to the heads of the families and said, "Let us help you build because, like you, we seek your God and have been sacrificing to him since the time of Esarhaddon king of Assyria, who brought us here."

³But Zerubbabel, Jeshua and the rest of the heads of the families of Israel answered, "You have no part with us in building a temple to our God. We alone will build it for the Lᴏʀᴅ, the God of Israel, as King Cyrus, the king of Persia, commanded us."

⁴Then the peoples around them set out to discourage the people of Judah and make them afraid to go on building.*ᵇ* ⁵They hired counselors to work against them and frustrate their plans during the entire reign of Cyrus king of Persia and down to the reign of Darius king of Persia.

truth or dare

Just as Israel discovered, following God means running into resentment from non-believers. Be ready for opposition by bracing your spirit with God's Word.

4:1–5

Later Opposition Under Xerxes and Artaxerxes

⁶At the beginning of the reign of Xerxes,*ᶜ* they lodged an accusation against the people of Judah and Jerusalem.

ᵃ 9 Hebrew *Yehudah*, probably a variant of *Hodaviah*   *ᵇ 4* Or *and troubled them as they built*   *ᶜ 6* Hebrew *Ahasuerus*, a variant of Xerxes' Persian name

[7]And in the days of Artaxerxes king of Persia, Bishlam, Mithredath, Tabeel and the rest of his associates wrote a letter to Artaxerxes. The letter was written in Aramaic script and in the Aramaic language.[a, b]

[8]Rehum the commanding officer and Shimshai the secretary wrote a letter against Jerusalem to Artaxerxes the king as follows:

[9]Rehum the commanding officer and Shimshai the secretary, together with the rest of their associates—the judges and officials over the men from Tripolis, Persia,[c] Erech and Babylon, the Elamites of Susa, [10]and the other people whom the great and honorable Ashurbanipal[d] deported and settled in the city of Samaria and elsewhere in Trans-Euphrates.

[11](This is a copy of the letter they sent him.)

To King Artaxerxes,

From your servants, the men of Trans-Euphrates:

[12]The king should know that the Jews who came up to us from you have gone to Jerusalem and are rebuilding that rebellious and wicked city. They are restoring the walls and repairing the foundations.

[13]Furthermore, the king should know that if this city is built and its walls are restored, no more taxes, tribute or duty will be paid, and the royal revenues will suffer. [14]Now since we are under obligation to the palace and it is not proper for us to see the king dishonored, we are sending this message to inform the king, [15]so that a search may be made in the archives of your predecessors. In these records you will find that this city is a rebellious city, troublesome to kings and provinces, a place of rebellion from ancient times. That is why this city was destroyed. [16]We inform the king that if this city is built and its walls are restored, you will be left with nothing in Trans-Euphrates.

[17]The king sent this reply:

To Rehum the commanding officer, Shimshai the secretary and the rest of their associates living in Samaria and elsewhere in Trans-Euphrates:

Greetings.

[18]The letter you sent us has been read and translated in my presence. [19]I issued an order and a search was made, and it was found that this city has a long history of revolt against kings and has been a place of rebellion and sedition. [20]Jerusalem has had powerful kings ruling over the whole of Trans-Euphrates, and taxes, tribute and duty were paid to them. [21]Now issue an order to these men to stop work, so that this city will not be rebuilt until I so order. [22]Be careful not to neglect this matter. Why let this threat grow, to the detriment of the royal interests?

[23]As soon as the copy of the letter of King Artaxerxes was read to Rehum and Shimshai the secretary and their associates, they went immediately to the Jews in Jerusalem and compelled them by force to stop.

[24]Thus the work on the house of God in Jerusalem came to a standstill until the second year of the reign of Darius king of Persia.

Tattenai's Letter to Darius

5 Now Haggai the prophet and Zechariah the prophet, a descendant of Iddo, prophesied to the Jews in Judah and Jerusalem in the name of the God of Israel, who was over them. [2]Then Zerubbabel son of Shealtiel and Jeshua son of Jozadak set to work to rebuild the house of God in Jerusalem. And the prophets of God were with them, helping them.

[3]At that time Tattenai, governor of Trans-Euphrates, and Shethar-Bozenai and their associates went to them and asked, "Who authorized you to rebuild this temple and restore this structure?"

---

a 7 Or written in Aramaic and translated   *b 7 The text of Ezra 4:8—6:18 is in Aramaic.*   *c 9 Or officials, magistrates*
and governors over the men from   *d 10 Aramaic Osnappar, a variant of Ashurbanipal*

Just Do It

Profile: **Natasha**

"**N**atasha, I dare you not to study for the physics final!" my best friend Summer yelled down the hall. Yeah, right! Like I'd risk getting a bad grade and pulling my GPA down my junior year. Summer has no concept of how tough the competition is for college scholarships.

Me? I've got a road mapped out for the future, and I'm going to do everything it takes to get there. Which is why I'm constantly running in a zillion directions, trying to cover all my bases. This semester I kept a 3.9 in all of my classes, including A.P. German. Which isn't bad, considering it was basketball season, and I had practice every day. (Did I mention I got MVP?)

Of course, extracurricular activities are a *must* if you really want to get into a good school, so I served as vice president for the environmental club and played piano for the jazz choir, too. For some reason, though, I didn't make the debate team. The coach said it was because he wanted people who could be committed and that I already had too much going. What does he know?

I'm the kind of girl who can handle a lot of pressure—I actually like it that way. What's wrong with doing it all, if I can do it well and feel good about myself?

For more on identity, check out the link on www.TrueImagesBible.com

identity in focus

Imagine if Natasha woke up one day and completely forgot how to study for her classes or how to play basketball? No doubt this girl would be devastated! That's what happens when we base our value on what we can *do* instead of on *who we are* in Christ. Everything else— talents, achievements, looks, family and possessions—is temporary. Remember . . .

» You're accepted because of God's grace—not because of anything you do (see Ephesians 2:8–10, page 1543).

» Jesus isn't looking for girls who think they've got it all together on their own; he longs for girls who know they need him (see Mark 2:17, page 1337).

For more on this topic, see the index on page 1656.

⁴They also asked, "What are the names of the men constructing this building?"*ᵃ* ⁵But the eye of their God was watching over the elders of the Jews, and they were not stopped until a report could go to Darius and his written reply be received.

⁶This is a copy of the letter that Tattenai, governor of Trans-Euphrates, and Shethar-Bozenai and their associates, the officials of Trans-Euphrates, sent to King Darius. ⁷The report they sent him read as follows:

ᵃ 4 See Septuagint; Aramaic *⁴We told them the names of the men constructing this building.*

To King Darius:

Cordial greetings.

⁸The king should know that we went to the district of Judah, to the temple of the great God. The people are building it with large stones and placing the timbers in the walls. The work is being carried on with diligence and is making rapid progress under their direction.

⁹We questioned the elders and asked them, "Who authorized you to rebuild this temple and restore this structure?" ¹⁰We also asked them their names, so that we could write down the names of their leaders for your information.

¹¹This is the answer they gave us:

"We are the servants of the God of heaven and earth, and we are rebuilding the temple that was built many years ago, one that a great king of Israel built and finished. ¹²But because our fathers angered the God of heaven, he handed them over to Nebuchadnezzar the Chaldean, king of Babylon, who destroyed this temple and deported the people to Babylon.

¹³"However, in the first year of Cyrus king of Babylon, King Cyrus issued a decree to rebuild this house of God. ¹⁴He even removed from the temple*a* of Babylon the gold and silver articles of the house of God, which Nebuchadnezzar had taken from the temple in Jerusalem and brought to the temple*a* in Babylon.

"Then King Cyrus gave them to a man named Sheshbazzar, whom he had appointed governor, ¹⁵and he told him, 'Take these articles and go and deposit them in the temple in Jerusalem. And rebuild the house of God on its site.' ¹⁶So this Sheshbazzar came and laid the foundations of the house of God in Jerusalem. From that day to the present it has been under construction but is not yet finished."

¹⁷Now if it pleases the king, let a search be made in the royal archives of Babylon to see if King Cyrus did in fact issue a decree to rebuild this house of God in Jerusalem. Then let the king send us his decision in this matter.

The Decree of Darius

6 King Darius then issued an order, and they searched in the archives stored in the treasury at Babylon. ²A scroll was found in the citadel of Ecbatana in the province of Media, and this was written on it:

Memorandum:

³In the first year of King Cyrus, the king issued a decree concerning the temple of God in Jerusalem:

Let the temple be rebuilt as a place to present sacrifices, and let its foundations be laid. It is to be ninety feet*b* high and ninety feet wide, ⁴with three courses of large stones and one of timbers. The costs are to be paid by the royal treasury. ⁵Also, the gold and silver articles of the house of God, which Nebuchadnezzar took from the temple in Jerusalem and brought to Babylon, are to be returned to their places in the temple in Jerusalem; they are to be deposited in the house of God.

⁶Now then, Tattenai, governor of Trans-Euphrates, and Shethar-Bozenai and you, their fellow officials of that province, stay away from there. ⁷Do not interfere with the work on this temple of God. Let the governor of the Jews and the Jewish elders rebuild this house of God on its site.

⁸Moreover, I hereby decree what you are to do for these elders of the Jews in the construction of this house of God:

The expenses of these men are to be fully paid out of the royal treasury, from the revenues of Trans-Euphrates, so that the work will not stop. ⁹Whatever is needed—young bulls, rams, male lambs for burnt offerings to the God of heaven, and wheat, salt, wine and oil, as requested by the priests in Jerusalem—must be given them daily without fail, ¹⁰so that they may offer sacrifices pleasing to the God of heaven and pray for the well-being of the king and his sons.

¹¹Furthermore, I decree that if anyone changes this edict, a beam is to be pulled from his house and he is to be lifted up and impaled on it. And for this crime his house is to be made a pile of rubble. ¹²May God, who has caused his Name to dwell there, overthrow any king or people who lifts a hand to change this decree or to destroy this temple in Jerusalem.

I Darius have decreed it. Let it be carried out with diligence.

Completion and Dedication of the Temple

¹³Then, because of the decree King Darius had sent, Tattenai, governor of Trans-Euphrates, and Shethar-Bozenai and their associates carried it out with diligence. ¹⁴So the elders of the Jews continued to build and prosper under the preaching of Haggai the prophet and Zechariah, a descendant of Iddo. They finished building the temple according to the command of the God of Israel and the decrees of Cyrus, Darius and Artaxerxes, kings of Persia. ¹⁵The temple was completed on the third day of the month Adar, in the sixth year of the reign of King Darius.

¹⁶Then the people of Israel—the priests, the Levites and the rest of the exiles—celebrated the dedication of the house of God with joy. ¹⁷For the dedication of this house of God they offered a hundred bulls, two hundred rams, four hundred male lambs and, as a sin offering for all Israel, twelve male goats, one for each of the tribes of Israel. ¹⁸And they installed the priests in their divisions and the Levites in their groups for the service of God at Jerusalem, according to what is written in the Book of Moses.

truth or dare

Have you ever given up on someone because you feel she's a lost cause? Keep praying daily for that person. God can soften the hardest of hearts.

6:22

The Passover

¹⁹On the fourteenth day of the first month, the exiles celebrated the Passover. ²⁰The priests and Levites had purified themselves and were all ceremonially clean. The Levites slaughtered the Passover lamb for all the exiles, for their brothers the priests and for themselves. ²¹So the Israelites who had returned from the exile ate it, together with all who had separated themselves from the unclean practices of their Gentile neighbors in order to seek the LORD, the God of Israel. ²²For seven days they celebrated with joy the Feast of Unleavened Bread, because the LORD had filled them with joy by changing the attitude of the king of Assyria, so that he assisted them in the work on the house of God, the God of Israel.

Ezra Comes to Jerusalem

7 After these things, during the reign of Artaxerxes king of Persia, Ezra son of Seraiah, the son of Azariah, the son of Hilkiah, ²the son of Shallum, the son of Zadok, the son of Ahitub, ³the son of Amariah, the son of Azariah, the son of Meraioth, ⁴the son of Zerahiah, the son of Uzzi, the son of Bukki, ⁵the son of Abishua, the son of Phinehas, the son of Eleazar, the son of Aaron the chief priest— ⁶this Ezra came up from Babylon. He was a teacher well versed in the Law of Moses, which the LORD, the God of Israel, had given. The king had granted him everything he asked, for the hand of the LORD his God was on him. ⁷Some of the Israelites, including priests, Levites, singers, gatekeepers and temple servants, also came up to Jerusalem in the seventh year of King Artaxerxes.

⁸Ezra arrived in Jerusalem in the fifth month of the seventh year of the king. ⁹He had begun his journey from Babylon on the first day of the first month, and he arrived in Jerusalem on the first day of the fifth month, for the gracious hand of his God was on him. ¹⁰For Ezra had devoted himself to the study and observance of the Law of the LORD, and to teaching its decrees and laws in Israel.

King Artaxerxes' Letter to Ezra

[11]This is a copy of the letter King Artaxerxes had given to Ezra the priest and teacher, a man learned in matters concerning the commands and decrees of the LORD for Israel:

[12 a] Artaxerxes, king of kings,

To Ezra the priest, a teacher of the Law of the God of heaven:

Greetings.

[13]Now I decree that any of the Israelites in my kingdom, including priests and Levites, who wish to go to Jerusalem with you, may go. [14]You are sent by the king and his seven advisers to inquire about Judah and Jerusalem with regard to the Law of your God, which is in your hand. [15]Moreover, you are to take with you the silver and gold that the king and his advisers have freely given to the God of Israel, whose dwelling is in Jerusalem, [16]together with all the silver and gold you may obtain from the province of Babylon, as well as the freewill offerings of the people and priests for the temple of their God in Jerusalem. [17]With this money be sure to buy bulls, rams and male lambs, together with their grain offerings and drink offerings, and sacrifice them on the altar of the temple of your God in Jerusalem.

[18]You and your brother Jews may then do whatever seems best with the rest of the silver and gold, in accordance with the will of your God. [19]Deliver to the God of Jerusalem all the articles entrusted to you for worship in the temple of your God. [20]And anything else needed for the temple of your God that you may have occasion to supply, you may provide from the royal treasury.

[21]Now I, King Artaxerxes, order all the treasurers of Trans-Euphrates to provide with diligence whatever Ezra the priest, a teacher of the Law of the God of heaven, may ask of you— [22]up to a hundred talents[b] of silver, a hundred cors[c] of wheat, a hundred baths[d] of wine, a hundred baths[d] of olive oil, and salt without limit. [23]Whatever the God of heaven has prescribed, let it be done with diligence for the temple of the God of heaven. Why should there be wrath against the realm of the king and of his sons? [24]You are also to know that you have no authority to impose taxes, tribute or duty on any of the priests, Levites, singers, gatekeepers, temple servants or other workers at this house of God.

[25]And you, Ezra, in accordance with the wisdom of your God, which you possess, appoint magistrates and judges to administer justice to all the people of Trans-Euphrates— all who know the laws of your God. And you are to teach any who do not know them. [26]Whoever does not obey the law of your God and the law of the king must surely be punished by death, banishment, confiscation of property, or imprisonment.

[27]Praise be to the LORD, the God of our fathers, who has put it into the king's heart to bring honor to the house of the LORD in Jerusalem in this way [28]and who has extended his good favor to me before the king and his advisers and all the king's powerful officials. Because the hand of the LORD my God was on me, I took courage and gathered leading men from Israel to go up with me.

List of the Family Heads Returning With Ezra

8 These are the family heads and those registered with them who came up with me from Babylon during the reign of King Artaxerxes:

[2]of the descendants of Phinehas, Gershom;
of the descendants of Ithamar, Daniel;
of the descendants of David, Hattush [3]of the descendants of Shecaniah;

of the descendants of Parosh, Zechariah, and with him were registered 150 men;
[4]of the descendants of Pahath-Moab, Eliehoenai son of Zerahiah, and with him 200 men;
[5]of the descendants of Zattu,[e] Shecaniah son of Jahaziel, and with him 300 men;
[6]of the descendants of Adin, Ebed son of Jonathan, and with him 50 men;

---

a 12 The text of Ezra 7:12-26 is in Aramaic.   *b 22* That is, about 3 3/4 tons (about 3.4 metric tons)   *c 22* That is, probably about 600 bushels (about 22 kiloliters)   *d 22* That is, probably about 600 gallons (about 2.2 kiloliters)
e 5 Some Septuagint manuscripts (also 1 Esdras 8:32); Hebrew does not have *Zattu*.

⁷of the descendants of Elam, Jeshaiah son of Athaliah, and with him 70 men;

⁸of the descendants of Shephatiah, Zebadiah son of Michael, and with him 80 men;

⁹of the descendants of Joab, Obadiah son of Jehiel, and with him 218 men;

¹⁰of the descendants of Bani,ᵃ Shelomith son of Josiphiah, and with him 160 men;

¹¹of the descendants of Bebai, Zechariah son of Bebai, and with him 28 men;

¹²of the descendants of Azgad, Johanan son of Hakkatan, and with him 110 men;

¹³of the descendants of Adonikam, the last ones, whose names were Eliphelet, Jeuel and Shemaiah, and with them 60 men;

¹⁴of the descendants of Bigvai, Uthai and Zaccur, and with them 70 men.

The Return to Jerusalem

¹⁵I assembled them at the canal that flows toward Ahava, and we camped there three days. When I checked among the people and the priests, I found no Levites there. ¹⁶So I summoned Eliezer, Ariel, Shemaiah, Elnathan, Jarib, Elnathan, Nathan, Zechariah and Meshullam, who were leaders, and Joiarib and Elnathan, who were men of learning, ¹⁷and I sent them to Iddo, the leader in Casiphia. I told them what to say to Iddo and his kinsmen, the temple servants in Casiphia, so that they might bring attendants to us for the house of our God. ¹⁸Because the gracious hand of our God was on us, they brought us Sherebiah, a capable man, from the descendants of Mahli son of Levi, the son of Israel, and Sherebiah's sons and brothers, 18 men; ¹⁹and Hashabiah, together with Jeshaiah from the descendants of Merari, and his brothers and nephews, 20 men. ²⁰They also brought 220 of the temple servants—a body that David and the officials had established to assist the Levites. All were registered by name.

²¹There, by the Ahava Canal, I proclaimed a fast, so that we might humble ourselves before our God and ask him for a safe journey for us and our children, with all our possessions. ²²I was ashamed to ask the king for soldiers and horsemen to protect us from enemies on the road, because we had told the king, "The gracious hand of our God is on everyone who looks to him, but his great anger is against all who forsake him." ²³So we fasted and petitioned our God about this, and he answered our prayer.

²⁴Then I set apart twelve of the leading priests, together with Sherebiah, Hashabiah and ten of their brothers, ²⁵and I weighed out to them the offering of silver and gold and the articles that the king, his advisers, his officials and all Israel present there had donated for the house of our God. ²⁶I weighed out to them 650 talentsᵇ of silver, silver articles weighing 100 talents,ᶜ 100 talentsᶜ of gold, ²⁷20 bowls of gold valued at 1,000 darics,ᵈ and two fine articles of polished bronze, as precious as gold.

²⁸I said to them, "You as well as these articles are consecrated to the LORD. The silver and gold are a freewill offering to the LORD, the God of your fathers. ²⁹Guard them carefully until you weigh them out in the chambers of the house of the LORD in Jerusalem before the leading priests and the Levites and the family heads of Israel." ³⁰Then the priests and Levites received the silver and gold and sacred articles that had been weighed out to be taken to the house of our God in Jerusalem.

genuine persistence » 8:21-23

How do you get prepared? Guess it depends on what you're preparing for, right? You prepare for a final exam by studying. You prepare for a marathon by running long distances. If you don't prepare, you fail. Ezra and the exiles prepared themselves for a long, dangerous journey by fasting and praying for God's protection. The Christian life is like a marathon. If you're not prepared, you'll never finish the race. Studying the Word, praying and fasting are three ways you can prepare for the daily challenges you face. How ready are you for the race ahead?

ᵃ 10 Some Septuagint manuscripts (also 1 Esdras 8:36); Hebrew does not have Bani.   ᵇ 26 That is, about 25 tons (about 22 metric tons)   ᶜ 26 That is, about 3 3/4 tons (about 3.4 metric tons)   ᵈ 27 That is, about 19 pounds (about 8.5 kilograms)

[31]On the twelfth day of the first month we set out from the Ahava Canal to go to Jerusalem. The hand of our God was on us, and he protected us from enemies and bandits along the way. [32]So we arrived in Jerusalem, where we rested three days.

[33]On the fourth day, in the house of our God, we weighed out the silver and gold and the sacred articles into the hands of Meremoth son of Uriah, the priest. Eleazar son of Phinehas was with him, and so were the Levites Jozabad son of Jeshua and Noadiah son of Binnui. [34]Everything was accounted for by number and weight, and the entire weight was recorded at that time.

[35]Then the exiles who had returned from captivity sacrificed burnt offerings to the God of Israel: twelve bulls for all Israel, ninety-six rams, seventy-seven male lambs and, as a sin offering, twelve male goats. All this was a burnt offering to the LORD. [36]They also delivered the king's orders to the royal satraps and to the governors of Trans-Euphrates, who then gave assistance to the people and to the house of God.

Ezra's Prayer About Intermarriage

9 After these things had been done, the leaders came to me and said, "The people of Israel, including the priests and the Levites, have not kept themselves separate from the neighboring peoples with their detestable practices, like those of the Canaanites, Hittites, Perizzites, Jebusites, Ammonites, Moabites, Egyptians and Amorites. [2]They have taken some of their daughters as wives for themselves and their sons, and have mingled the holy race with the peoples around them. And the leaders and officials have led the way in this unfaithfulness."

[3]When I heard this, I tore my tunic and cloak, pulled hair from my head and beard and sat down appalled. [4]Then everyone who trembled at the words of the God of Israel gathered around me because of this unfaithfulness of the exiles. And I sat there appalled until the evening sacrifice.

[5]Then, at the evening sacrifice, I rose from my self-abasement, with my tunic and cloak torn, and fell on my knees with my hands spread out to the LORD my God [6]and prayed:

truth or dare

Out with it. No excuses. Just confess, straight up, as Ezra did. Admitting your guilt saves you a lot of heartache in the long run.

9:5–15

"O my God, I am too ashamed and disgraced to lift up my face to you, my God, because our sins are higher than our heads and our guilt has reached to the heavens. [7]From the days of our forefathers until now, our guilt has been great. Because of our sins, we and our kings and our priests have been subjected to the sword and captivity, to pillage and humiliation at the hand of foreign kings, as it is today.

[8]"But now, for a brief moment, the LORD our God has been gracious in leaving us a remnant and giving us a firm place in his sanctuary, and so our God gives light to our eyes and a little relief in our bondage. [9]Though we are slaves, our God has not deserted us in our bondage. He has shown us kindness in the sight of the kings of Persia: He has granted us new life to rebuild the house of our God and repair its ruins, and he has given us a wall of protection in Judah and Jerusalem.

[10]"But now, O our God, what can we say after this? For we have disregarded the commands [11]you gave through your servants the prophets when you said: 'The land you are entering to possess is a land polluted by the corruption of its peoples. By their detestable practices they have filled it with their impurity from one end to the other. [12]Therefore, do not give your daughters in marriage to their sons or take their daughters for your sons. Do not seek a treaty of friendship with them at any time, that you may be strong and eat the good things of the land and leave it to your children as an everlasting inheritance.'

[13]"What has happened to us is a result of our evil deeds and our great guilt, and yet, our God, you have punished us less than our sins have deserved and have given us a remnant like this. [14]Shall we again break your commands and intermarry with the peoples who commit such detestable practices? Would you not be angry enough with us to destroy us, leaving us no remnant or survivor? [15]O LORD, God of Israel, you are righteous! We are left

this day as a remnant. Here we are before you in our guilt, though because of it not one of us can stand in your presence."

The People's Confession of Sin

10 While Ezra was praying and confessing, weeping and throwing himself down before the house of God, a large crowd of Israelites—men, women and children—gathered around him. They too wept bitterly. ²Then Shecaniah son of Jehiel, one of the descendants of Elam, said to Ezra, "We have been unfaithful to our God by marrying foreign women from the peoples around us. But in spite of this, there is still hope for Israel. ³Now let us make a covenant before our God to send away all these women and their children, in accordance with the counsel of my lord and of those who fear the commands of our God. Let it be done according to the Law. ⁴Rise up; this matter is in your hands. We will support you, so take courage and do it."

⁵So Ezra rose up and put the leading priests and Levites and all Israel under oath to do what had been suggested. And they took the oath. ⁶Then Ezra withdrew from before the house of God and went to the room of Jehohanan son of Eliashib. While he was there, he ate no food and drank no water, because he continued to mourn over the unfaithfulness of the exiles.

⁷A proclamation was then issued throughout Judah and Jerusalem for all the exiles to assemble in Jerusalem. ⁸Anyone who failed to appear within three days would forfeit all his property, in accordance with the decision of the officials and elders, and would himself be expelled from the assembly of the exiles.

⁹Within the three days, all the men of Judah and Benjamin had gathered in Jerusalem. And on the twentieth day of the ninth month, all the people were sitting in the square before the house of God, greatly distressed by the occasion and because of the rain. ¹⁰Then Ezra the priest stood up and said to them, "You have been unfaithful; you have married foreign women, adding to Israel's guilt. ¹¹Now make confession to the LORD, the God of your fathers, and do his will. Separate yourselves from the peoples around you and from your foreign wives."

¹²The whole assembly responded with a loud voice: "You are right! We must do as you say. ¹³But there are many people here and it is the rainy season; so we cannot stand outside. Besides, this matter cannot be taken care of in a day or two, because we have sinned greatly in this thing. ¹⁴Let our officials act for the whole assembly. Then let everyone in our towns who has married a foreign woman come at a set time, along with the elders and judges of each town, until the fierce anger of our God

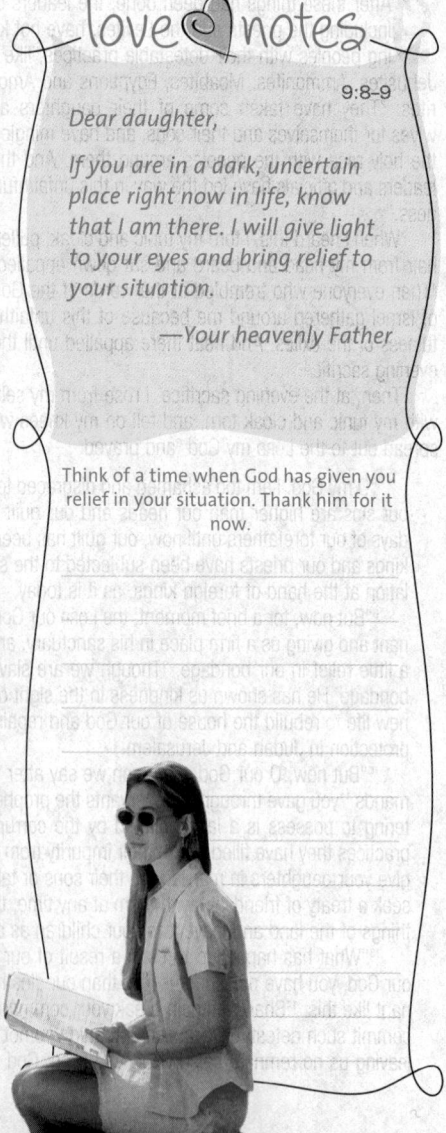

love notes

9:8–9

Dear daughter,

If you are in a dark, uncertain place right now in life, know that I am there. I will give light to your eyes and bring relief to your situation.

—Your heavenly Father

Think of a time when God has given you relief in your situation. Thank him for it now.

in this matter is turned away from us." [15]Only Jonathan son of Asahel and Jahzeiah son of Tikvah, supported by Meshullam and Shabbethai the Levite, opposed this.

[16]So the exiles did as was proposed. Ezra the priest selected men who were family heads, one from each family division, and all of them designated by name. On the first day of the tenth month they sat down to investigate the cases, [17]and by the first day of the first month they finished dealing with all the men who had married foreign women.

Those Guilty of Intermarriage

[18]Among the descendants of the priests, the following had married foreign women:

From the descendants of Jeshua son of Jozadak, and his brothers: Maaseiah, Eliezer, Jarib and Gedaliah. [19](They all gave their hands in pledge to put away their wives, and for their guilt they each presented a ram from the flock as a guilt offering.)
[20]From the descendants of Immer:
Hanani and Zebadiah.
[21]From the descendants of Harim:
Maaseiah, Elijah, Shemaiah, Jehiel and Uzziah.
[22]From the descendants of Pashhur:
Elioenai, Maaseiah, Ishmael, Nethanel, Jozabad and Elasah.

[23]Among the Levites:

Jozabad, Shimei, Kelaiah (that is, Kelita), Pethahiah, Judah and Eliezer.
[24]From the singers:
Eliashib.
From the gatekeepers:
Shallum, Telem and Uri.

[25]And among the other Israelites:

From the descendants of Parosh:
Ramiah, Izziah, Malkijah, Mijamin, Eleazar, Malkijah and Benaiah.
[26]From the descendants of Elam:
Mattaniah, Zechariah, Jehiel, Abdi, Jeremoth and Elijah.
[27]From the descendants of Zattu:
Elioenai, Eliashib, Mattaniah, Jeremoth, Zabad and Aziza.
[28]From the descendants of Bebai:
Jehohanan, Hananiah, Zabbai and Athlai.
[29]From the descendants of Bani:
Meshullam, Malluch, Adaiah, Jashub, Sheal and Jeremoth.
[30]From the descendants of Pahath-Moab:
Adna, Kelal, Benaiah, Maaseiah, Mattaniah, Bezalel, Binnui and Manasseh.
[31]From the descendants of Harim:
Eliezer, Ishijah, Malkijah, Shemaiah, Shimeon, [32]Benjamin, Malluch and Shemariah.
[33]From the descendants of Hashum:
Mattenai, Mattattah, Zabad, Eliphelet, Jeremai, Manasseh and Shimei.
[34]From the descendants of Bani:
Maadai, Amram, Uel, [35]Benaiah, Bedeiah, Keluhi, [36]Vaniah, Meremoth, Eliashib, [37]Mattaniah, Mattenai and Jaasu.
[38]From the descendants of Binnui:[a]
Shimei, [39]Shelemiah, Nathan, Adaiah, [40]Macnadebai, Shashai, Sharai, [41]Azarel, Shelemiah, Shemariah, [42]Shallum, Amariah and Joseph.
[43]From the descendants of Nebo:
Jeiel, Mattithiah, Zabad, Zebina, Jaddai, Joel and Benaiah.

[44]All these had married foreign women, and some of them had children by these wives. [b]

author: Unknown, but possibly Nehemiah or Ezra.

date: About 430 B.C.

setting: Nehemiah travels to Jerusalem to lead the Israelites in rebuilding the city's walls.

verse to remember: So the wall was completed on the twenty-fifth of Elul, in fifty-two days. When all our enemies heard about this, all the surrounding nations were afraid and lost their self-confidence, because they realized that this work had been done with the help of our God (6:15–16).

theme to consider: When we place our faith in God, he can help us overcome any opposition or obstacle—no matter how great.

nehemiah

unchanging truth

Wouldn't it be great if every day were perfect? No problems, no setbacks, no disappointments—just one great day after another! Ideal but totally unrealistic, right? You probably *do* have days that are almost perfect, but then there are those other days. You know, the ones when everything goes wrong. No matter what you try, there's always something getting in the way of what you want to do.

How do you react when you run up against one obstacle after another and you feel so frustrated? One tactic is to whine and complain. Typically, self-pity doesn't change anything, except that no one wants to be around you. A wiser move is to find a way around or over the obstacle.

The book of Nehemiah describes the activities of the exiles from Babylon who returned to Jerusalem to rebuild the city's walls. Talk about obstacles! The Jewish people were met with opposition to rebuilding the wall; seemingly insurmountable obstacles were thrown in their way. But they had an obstacle-breaker on their side—the God of Israel. Their faith in God helped them overcome the strong opposition and any obstacle put in their way. God can also help you overcome any obstacle thrown at you—no matter how great!

life lessons

1. Sometimes we face the most opposition when we're trying to do God's work. That's when we must rely on our faith (2:17–20).

2. Feel up to building a wall? God can use your gifts to serve him, just as Shallum's daughters used their gifts to help out with a construction project that is remembered ages later (3:12).

3. Angry and insulting words from others can make us doubt ourselves. But God is more powerful than any words (4:1–15).

Nehemiah's Prayer

1 The words of Nehemiah son of Hacaliah:

In the month of Kislev in the twentieth year, while I was in the citadel of Susa, ²Hanani, one of my brothers, came from Judah with some other men, and I questioned them about the Jewish remnant that survived the exile, and also about Jerusalem.

³They said to me, "Those who survived the exile and are back in the province are in great trouble and disgrace. The wall of Jerusalem is broken down, and its gates have been burned with fire."

⁴When I heard these things, I sat down and wept. For some days I mourned and fasted and prayed before the God of heaven. ⁵Then I said:

"O LORD, God of heaven, the great and awesome God, who keeps his covenant of love with those who love him and obey his commands, ⁶let your ear be attentive and your eyes open to hear the prayer your servant is praying before you day and night for your servants, the people of Israel. I confess the sins we Israelites, including myself and my father's house, have committed against you. ⁷We have acted very wickedly toward you. We have not obeyed the commands, decrees and laws you gave your servant Moses. ⁸"Remember the instruction you gave your servant Moses, saying, 'If you are unfaithful, I will scatter you among the nations, ⁹but if you return to me and obey my commands, then even if your exiled people are at the farthest horizon, I will gather them from there and bring them to the place I have chosen as a dwelling for my Name.'

¹⁰"They are your servants and your people, whom you redeemed by your great strength and your mighty hand. ¹¹O Lord, let your ear be attentive to the prayer of this your servant and to the prayer of your servants who delight in revering your name. Give your servant success today by granting him favor in the presence of this man."

I was cupbearer to the king.

Artaxerxes Sends Nehemiah to Jerusalem

2 In the month of Nisan in the twentieth year of King Artaxerxes, when wine was brought for him, I took the wine and gave it to the king. I had not been sad in his presence before; ²so the king asked me, "Why does your face look so sad when you are not ill? This can be nothing but sadness of heart."

I was very much afraid, ³but I said to the king, "May the king live forever! Why should my face not look sad when the city where my fathers are buried lies in ruins, and its gates have been destroyed by fire?"

⁴The king said to me, "What is it you want?"

Then I prayed to the God of heaven, ⁵and I answered the king, "If it pleases the king and if your servant has found favor in his sight, let him send me to the city in Judah where my fathers are buried so that I can rebuild it."

⁶Then the king, with the queen sitting beside him, asked me, "How long will your journey take,

genuine compassion « 1:14

What was the last thing that broke your heart—really touched you to the point of tears? The loss of a family member? Seeing a homeless woman out on the street? The suffering of a close friend? Nehemiah cried when he heard that his people were unprotected in Jerusalem. He didn't just cry, though. He also prayed. And then, after God made a way for him, he acted. Compassion is more than just tears. It moves you to act on someone else's behalf. Would you consider yourself a compassionate person? How do you show it?

and when will you get back?" It pleased the king to send me; so I set a time.

⁷I also said to him, "If it pleases the king, may I have letters to the governors of Trans-Euphrates, so that they will provide me safe-conduct until I arrive in Judah? ⁸And may I have a letter to Asaph, keeper of the king's forest, so he will give me timber to make beams for the gates of the citadel by the temple and for the city wall and for the residence I will occupy?" And because the gracious hand of my God was upon me, the king granted my requests. ⁹So I went to the governors of Trans-Euphrates and gave them the king's letters. The king had also sent army officers and cavalry with me.

¹⁰When Sanballat the Horonite and Tobiah the Ammonite official heard about this, they were very much disturbed that someone had come to promote the welfare of the Israelites.

truth or dare

Did Nehemiah's request seem cocky? Actually, he showed great boldness in stepping out and giving God a chance to work. Real faith means taking real risks.

2:4–5

Nehemiah Inspects Jerusalem's Walls

¹¹I went to Jerusalem, and after staying there three days ¹²I set out during the night with a few men. I had not told anyone what my God had put in my heart to do for Jerusalem. There were no mounts with me except the one I was riding on.

¹³By night I went out through the Valley Gate toward the Jackal ᵃ Well and the Dung Gate, examining the walls of Jerusalem, which had been broken down, and its gates, which had been destroyed by fire. ¹⁴Then I moved on toward the Fountain Gate and the King's Pool, but there was not enough room for my mount to get through; ¹⁵so I went up the valley by night, examining the wall. Finally, I turned back and reentered through the Valley Gate. ¹⁶The officials did not know where I had gone or what I was doing, because as yet I had said nothing to the Jews or the priests or nobles or officials or any others who would be doing the work.

¹⁷Then I said to them, "You see the trouble we are in: Jerusalem lies in ruins, and its gates have been burned with fire. Come, let us rebuild the wall of Jerusalem, and we will no longer be in disgrace." ¹⁸I also told them about the gracious hand of my God upon me and what the king had said to me.

They replied, "Let us start rebuilding." So they began this good work.

¹⁹But when Sanballat the Horonite, Tobiah the Ammonite official and Geshem the Arab heard about it, they mocked and ridiculed us. "What is this you are doing?" they asked. "Are you rebelling against the king?"

²⁰I answered them by saying, "The God of heaven will give us success. We his servants will start rebuilding, but as for you, you have no share in Jerusalem or any claim or historic right to it."

Builders of the Wall

3 Eliashib the high priest and his fellow priests went to work and rebuilt the Sheep Gate. They dedicated it and set its doors in place, building as far as the Tower of the Hundred, which they dedicated, and as far as the Tower of Hananel. ²The men of Jericho built the adjoining section, and Zaccur son of Imri built next to them.

³The Fish Gate was rebuilt by the sons of Hassenaah. They laid its beams and put its doors and bolts and bars in place. ⁴Meremoth son of Uriah, the son of Hakkoz, repaired the next section. Next to him Meshullam son of Berekiah, the son of Meshezabel, made repairs, and next to him Zadok son of Baana also made repairs. ⁵The next section was repaired by the men of Tekoa, but their nobles would not put their shoulders to the work under their supervisors. ᵇ

⁶The Jeshanah ᶜ Gate was repaired by Joiada son of Paseah and Meshullam son of Besodeiah. They laid its beams and put its doors and bolts and bars in place. ⁷Next to them, repairs were made by men from Gibeon and Mizpah—Melatiah of Gibeon and Jadon of Meronoth—places under the authority of the governor of Trans-Euphrates. ⁸Uzziel son of Harhaiah, one of the goldsmiths, repaired the next section; and Hananiah, one of the perfume-makers, made repairs next to that. They restored ᵈ

ᵃ 13 Or Serpent or Fig   ᵇ 5 Or their Lord or the governor   ᶜ 6 Or Old   ᵈ 8 Or They left out part of

Teacher Talk

focus Profile: **Marissa**

Mr. Quigley's the newest teacher at our school. Oh my word, he is so ugly! He's bald on top with the greasy comb-over, and he's got hair growing out of his nose and ears. And his potbelly hangs over his belt and jiggles around when he's in a hurry to get to the computer lab.

Alicia and Colleen are always making fun of how goofy he looks. I'm just afraid that one day he'll overhear some of their comments. "There goes jelly-belly." "Hey, Quigs—who do *you* call for hair removal?" One time Colleen even followed him down the hall, mimicking his fat, awkward walk. Good thing he was in too big of a hurry to notice.

Lately I've been thinking that maybe mocking Quigley isn't so harmless after all. This week in small group, our leader started talking about the damage we can do just by joking around. She read this verse that said the things we say can destroy like fire. I started feeling guilty, thinking how Mr. Quigley would feel if he overheard our comments. And when I started thinking about all the terrible things we've said about him, I wondered what Alicia and Colleen say about me when I'm not around. If they ever mocked me like they do Quigley, I'd feel horrible about myself. I feel like I should say something to them . . . but what?

---

slander in focus

Slander's like gossip—vicious, cruel words that hurt another's reputation. Slander is a dangerous thing—it hurts the other person, and it can also lead you into bad habits. Avoid slander by . . .

» *Saying something positive.* If you're in a conversation that takes a turn for the worse, say something nice about the person, then change the topic (see Ephesians 4:29, page 1546).

» *Staying away.* If one of your friends is constantly bashing others, avoid her but keep her in your prayers (see 1 Corinthians 15:33, page 1521).

» *Evaluating your own heart.* A person's words say a lot about her (see Matthew 12:34, page 1307). What do your words reveal about you?

For more on this topic, see the index on page 1656.

For more info, check out the Gossip Link on www.TrueImagesBible.com

slander

Jerusalem as far as the Broad Wall. [9]Rephaiah son of Hur, ruler of a half-district of Jerusalem, repaired the next section. [10]Adjoining this, Jedaiah son of Harumaph made repairs opposite his house, and Hattush son of Hashabneiah made repairs next to him. [11]Malkijah son of Harim and Hasshub son of Pahath-Moab repaired another section and the Tower of the Ovens. [12]Shallum son of Hallohesh, ruler of a half-district of Jerusalem, repaired the next section with the help of his daughters.

[13]The Valley Gate was repaired by Hanun and the residents of Zanoah. They rebuilt it and put its doors and bolts and bars in place. They also repaired five hundred yards*a* of the wall as far as the Dung Gate.

a 13 Hebrew a thousand cubits (about 450 meters)

[14]The Dung Gate was repaired by Malkijah son of Recab, ruler of the district of Beth Hakkerem. He rebuilt it and put its doors and bolts and bars in place.

[15]The Fountain Gate was repaired by Shallun son of Col-Hozeh, ruler of the district of Mizpah. He rebuilt it, roofing it over and putting its doors and bolts and bars in place. He also repaired the wall of the Pool of Siloam,[a] by the King's Garden, as far as the steps going down from the City of David. [16]Beyond him, Nehemiah son of Azbuk, ruler of a half-district of Beth Zur, made repairs up to a point opposite the tombs[b] of David, as far as the artificial pool and the House of the Heroes.

[17]Next to him, the repairs were made by the Levites under Rehum son of Bani. Beside him, Hashabiah, ruler of half the district of Keilah, carried out repairs for his district. [18]Next to him, the repairs were made by their countrymen under Binnui[c] son of Henadad, ruler of the other half-district of Keilah. [19]Next to him, Ezer son of Jeshua, ruler of Mizpah, repaired another section, from a point facing the ascent to the armory as far as the angle. [20]Next to him, Baruch son of Zabbai zealously repaired another section, from the angle to the entrance of the house of Eliashib the high priest. [21]Next to him, Meremoth son of Uriah, the son of Hakkoz, repaired another section, from the entrance of Eliashib's house to the end of it.

[22]The repairs next to him were made by the priests from the surrounding region. [23]Beyond them, Benjamin and Hasshub made repairs in front of their house; and next to them, Azariah son of Maaseiah, the son of Ananiah, made repairs beside his house. [24]Next to him, Binnui son of Henadad repaired another section, from Azariah's house to the angle and the corner, [25]and Palal son of Uzai worked opposite the angle and the tower projecting from the upper palace near the court of the guard. Next to him, Pedaiah son of Parosh [26]and the temple servants living on the hill of Ophel made repairs up to a point opposite the Water Gate toward the east and the projecting tower. [27]Next to them, the men of Tekoa repaired another section, from the great projecting tower to the wall of Ophel.

[28]Above the Horse Gate, the priests made repairs, each in front of his own house. [29]Next to them, Zadok son of Immer made repairs opposite his house. Next to him, Shemaiah son of Shecaniah, the guard at the East Gate, made repairs. [30]Next to him, Hananiah son of Shelemiah, and Hanun, the sixth son of Zalaph, repaired another section. Next to them, Meshullam son of Berekiah made repairs opposite his living quarters. [31]Next to him, Malkijah, one of the goldsmiths, made repairs as far as the house of the temple servants and the merchants, opposite the Inspection Gate, and as far as the room above the corner; [32]and between the room above the corner and the Sheep Gate the goldsmiths and merchants made repairs.

Opposition to the Rebuilding

4 When Sanballat heard that we were rebuilding the wall, he became angry and was greatly incensed. He ridiculed the Jews, [2]and in the presence of his associates and the army of Samaria, he said, "What are those feeble Jews doing? Will they restore their wall? Will they offer sacrifices? Will they finish in a day? Can they bring the stones back to life from those heaps of rubble—burned as they are?"

[3]Tobiah the Ammonite, who was at his side, said, "What they are building—if even a fox climbed up on it, he would break down their wall of stones!"

[4]Hear us, O our God, for we are despised. Turn their insults back on their own heads. Give them over as plunder in a land of captivity. [5]Do not cover up their guilt or blot out their sins from your sight, for they have thrown insults in the face of[d] the builders.

[6]So we rebuilt the wall till all of it reached half its height, for the people worked with all their heart.

truth or dare

Rejection hurts, especially when people mock you for your faith. Don't take it personally. Their hate is really aimed at God, so let it roll off your back and onto God.

4:4–5

---

a 15 Hebrew *Shelah*, a variant of *Shiloah*, that is, Siloam   b 16 Hebrew; Septuagint, some Vulgate manuscripts and Syriac *tomb*   c 18 Two Hebrew manuscripts and Syriac (see also Septuagint and verse 24); most Hebrew manuscripts *Bavvai*   d 5 Or *have provoked you to anger before*

⁷But when Sanballat, Tobiah, the Arabs, the Ammonites and the men of Ashdod heard that the repairs to Jerusalem's walls had gone ahead and that the gaps were being closed, they were very angry. ⁸They all plotted together to come and fight against Jerusalem and stir up trouble against it. ⁹But we prayed to our God and posted a guard day and night to meet this threat.

¹⁰Meanwhile, the people in Judah said, "The strength of the laborers is giving out, and there is so much rubble that we cannot rebuild the wall."

¹¹Also our enemies said, "Before they know it or see us, we will be right there among them and will kill them and put an end to the work."

¹²Then the Jews who lived near them came and told us ten times over, "Wherever you turn, they will attack us."

¹³Therefore I stationed some of the people behind the lowest points of the wall at the exposed places, posting them by families, with their swords, spears and bows. ¹⁴After I looked things over, I stood up and said to the nobles, the officials and the rest of the people, "Don't be afraid of them. Remember the Lord, who is great and awesome, and fight for your brothers, your sons and your daughters, your wives and your homes."

¹⁵When our enemies heard that we were aware of their plot and that God had frustrated it, we all returned to the wall, each to his own work.

¹⁶From that day on, half of my men did the work, while the other half were equipped with spears, shields, bows and armor. The officers posted themselves behind all the people of Judah ¹⁷who were building the wall. Those who carried materials did their work with one hand and held a weapon in the other, ¹⁸and each of the builders wore his sword at his side as he worked. But the man who sounded the trumpet stayed with me.

¹⁹Then I said to the nobles, the officials and the rest of the people, "The work is extensive and spread out, and we are widely separated from each other along the wall. ²⁰Wherever you hear the sound of the trumpet, join us there. Our God will fight for us!"

²¹So we continued the work with half the men holding spears, from the first light of dawn till the stars came out. ²²At that time I also said to the people, "Have every man and his helper stay inside Jerusalem at night, so they can serve us as guards by night and workmen by day." ²³Neither I nor my brothers nor my men nor the guards with me took off our clothes; each had his weapon, even when he went for water.ᵃ

Nehemiah Helps the Poor

5 Now the men and their wives raised a great outcry against their Jewish brothers. ²Some were saying, "We and our sons and daughters are numerous; in order for us to eat and stay alive, we must get grain."

³Others were saying, "We are mortgaging our fields, our vineyards and our homes to get grain during the famine."

⁴Still others were saying, "We have had to borrow money to pay the king's tax on our fields and vineyards. ⁵Although we are of the same flesh and blood as our countrymen and though our sons are as good as theirs, yet we have to subject our sons and daughters to slavery. Some of our

genuine

character » 4:15-18

Talk about resourceful! The construction workers on the Jerusalem wall were forced to be very creative because of threats of harm from their enemies. To defend themselves and to avoid losing valuable work time, they carried materials in one hand and a weapon in the other. While they trusted God to protect them, they also used all the resources he had given them—their weapons *and* their tools. A resourceful girl makes the most of every resource she has, rather than complaining about what she doesn't have. Does that sound like you?

ᵃ 23 The meaning of the Hebrew for this clause is uncertain.

daughters have already been enslaved, but we are powerless, because our fields and our vineyards belong to others."

[6]When I heard their outcry and these charges, I was very angry. [7]I pondered them in my mind and then accused the nobles and officials. I told them, "You are exacting usury from your own countrymen!" So I called together a large meeting to deal with them [8]and said: "As far as possible, we have bought back our Jewish brothers who were sold to the Gentiles. Now you are selling your brothers, only for them to be sold back to us!" They kept quiet, because they could find nothing to say.

[9]So I continued, "What you are doing is not right. Shouldn't you walk in the fear of our God to avoid the reproach of our Gentile enemies? [10]I and my brothers and my men are also lending the people money and grain. But let the exacting of usury stop! [11]Give back to them immediately their fields, vineyards, olive groves and houses, and also the usury you are charging them—the hundredth part of the money, grain, new wine and oil."

[12]"We will give it back," they said. "And we will not demand anything more from them. We will do as you say."

Then I summoned the priests and made the nobles and officials take an oath to do what they had promised. [13]I also shook out the folds of my robe and said, "In this way may God shake out of his house and possessions every man who does not keep this promise. So may such a man be shaken out and emptied!"

At this the whole assembly said, "Amen," and praised the LORD. And the people did as they had promised.

[14]Moreover, from the twentieth year of King Artaxerxes, when I was appointed to be their governor in the land of Judah, until his thirty-second year—twelve years—neither I nor my brothers ate the food allotted to the governor. [15]But the earlier governors—those preceding me—placed a heavy burden on the people and took forty shekels[a] of silver from them in addition to food and wine. Their assistants also lorded it over the people. But out of reverence for God I did not act like that. [16]Instead, I devoted myself to the work on this wall. All my men were assembled there for the work; we[b] did not acquire any land.

[17]Furthermore, a hundred and fifty Jews and officials ate at my table, as well as those who came to us from the surrounding nations. [18]Each day one ox, six choice sheep and some poultry were prepared for me, and every ten days an abundant supply of wine of all kinds. In spite of all this, I never demanded the food allotted to the governor, because the demands were heavy on these people.

[19]Remember me with favor, O my God, for all I have done for these people.

Further Opposition to the Rebuilding

6 When word came to Sanballat, Tobiah, Geshem the Arab and the rest of our enemies that I had rebuilt the wall and not a gap was left in it—though up to that time I had not set the doors in the gates— [2]Sanballat and Geshem sent me this message: "Come, let us meet together in one of the villages[c] on the plain of Ono."

truth or dare

Nehemiah didn't dish out rules that he wasn't willing to obey *himself*. If you're focusing on someone's imperfections, ask yourself—do you stick to the same high standards?

5:9-10

truth or dare

Intimidation is all about getting power. When someone pressures you to doubt what you believe, consider Nehemiah's solution to combat bullying. Truth is a powerful weapon.

6:1-14

---

[a] 15 That is, about 1 pound (about 0.5 kilogram)   [b] 16 Most Hebrew manuscripts; some Hebrew manuscripts, Septuagint, Vulgate and Syriac /   [c] 2 Or *in Kephirim*

But they were scheming to harm me; [3]so I sent messengers to them with this reply: "I am carrying on a great project and cannot go down. Why should the work stop while I leave it and go down to you?" [4]Four times they sent me the same message, and each time I gave them the same answer.

[5]Then, the fifth time, Sanballat sent his aide to me with the same message, and in his hand was an unsealed letter [6]in which was written:

"It is reported among the nations—and Geshem[a] says it is true—that you and the Jews are plotting to revolt, and therefore you are building the wall. Moreover, according to these reports you are about to become their king [7]and have even appointed prophets to make this proclamation about you in Jerusalem: 'There is a king in Judah!' Now this report will get back to the king; so come, let us confer together."

[8]I sent him this reply: "Nothing like what you are saying is happening; you are just making it up out of your head."

[9]They were all trying to frighten us, thinking, "Their hands will get too weak for the work, and it will not be completed."

⌊But I prayed,⌋ "Now strengthen my hands."

[10]One day I went to the house of Shemaiah son of Delaiah, the son of Mehetabel, who was shut in at his home. He said, "Let us meet in the house of God, inside the temple, and let us close the temple doors, because men are coming to kill you—by night they are coming to kill you."

genuine persistence » 6:1-16

When the going gets tough, what motivates you to keep going? Although vicious enemies continually interrupted Nehemiah and the people of Israel, they persevered and completed the rebuilding of the wall of Jerusalem in just 52 days. (Crazy construction schedule!) What obstacles are you facing these days? An enemy who's trying to discourage you? A task that seems impossibly big? Don't let the size of the task daunt you. If you're a believer, you've got a built-in Perseverance Coach, the Holy Spirit, who helps you to keep on keeping on. Keep at it, girl!

[11]But I said, "Should a man like me run away? Or should one like me go into the temple to save his life? I will not go!" [12]I realized that God had not sent him, but that he had prophesied against me because Tobiah and Sanballat had hired him. [13]He had been hired to intimidate me so that I would commit a sin by doing this, and then they would give me a bad name to discredit me.

[14]Remember Tobiah and Sanballat, O my God, because of what they have done; remember also the prophetess Noadiah and the rest of the prophets who have been trying to intimidate me.

The Completion of the Wall

[15]So the wall was completed on the twenty-fifth of Elul, in fifty-two days. [16]When all our enemies heard about this, all the surrounding nations were afraid and lost their self-confidence, because they realized that this work had been done with the help of our God.

[17]Also, in those days the nobles of Judah were sending many letters to Tobiah, and replies from Tobiah kept coming to them. [18]For many in Judah were under oath to him, since he was son-in-law to Shecaniah son of Arah, and his son Jehohanan had married the daughter of Meshullam son of Berekiah. [19]Moreover, they kept reporting to me his good deeds and then telling him what I said. And Tobiah sent letters to intimidate me.

7After the wall had been rebuilt and I had set the doors in place, the gatekeepers and the singers and the Levites were appointed. [2]I put in charge of Jerusalem my brother Hanani, along with[b] Hananiah the commander of the citadel, because he was a man of integrity and feared God more than most men do. [3]I said to them, "The gates of Jerusalem are not to be opened until the sun is hot. While the gatekeepers are still on duty, have them shut the doors and bar them. Also appoint residents of Jerusalem as guards, some at their posts and some near their own houses."

[a] 6 Hebrew *Gashmu,* a variant of *Geshem*   [b] 2 Or *Hanani, that is,*

The List of the Exiles Who Returned

[4]Now the city was large and spacious, but there were few people in it, and the houses had not yet been rebuilt. [5]So my God put it into my heart to assemble the nobles, the officials and the common people for registration by families. I found the genealogical record of those who had been the first to return. This is what I found written there:

[6]These are the people of the province who came up from the captivity of the exiles whom Nebuchadnezzar king of Babylon had taken captive (they returned to Jerusalem and Judah, each to his own town, [7]in company with Zerubbabel, Jeshua, Nehemiah, Azariah, Raamiah, Nahamani, Mordecai, Bilshan, Mispereth, Bigvai, Nehum and Baanah):

The list of the men of Israel:

[8]the descendants of Parosh	2,172
[9]of Shephatiah	372
[10]of Arah	652
[11]of Pahath-Moab (through the line of Jeshua and Joab)	2,818
[12]of Elam	1,254
[13]of Zattu	845
[14]of Zaccai	760
[15]of Binnui	648
[16]of Bebai	628
[17]of Azgad	2,322
[18]of Adonikam	667
[19]of Bigvai	2,067
[20]of Adin	655
[21]of Ater (through Hezekiah)	98
[22]of Hashum	328
[23]of Bezai	324
[24]of Hariph	112
[25]of Gibeon	95
[26]the men of Bethlehem and Netophah	188
[27]of Anathoth	128
[28]of Beth Azmaveth	42
[29]of Kiriath Jearim, Kephirah and Beeroth	743
[30]of Ramah and Geba	621
[31]of Micmash	122
[32]of Bethel and Ai	123
[33]of the other Nebo	52
[34]of the other Elam	1,254
[35]of Harim	320
[36]of Jericho	345
[37]of Lod, Hadid and Ono	721
[38]of Senaah	3,930

[39]The priests:

the descendants of Jedaiah (through the family of Jeshua)	973
[40]of Immer	1,052
[41]of Pashhur	1,247
[42]of Harim	1,017

[43]The Levites:

the descendants of Jeshua (through Kadmiel through the line of Hodaviah)	74

mirror images

But when [Jochebed] could hide him no longer, she got a papyrus basket for him and coated it with tar and pitch. Then she placed the child in it and put it among the reeds along the bank of the Nile. Exodus 2:3

Jochebed—Letting Go, Letting God

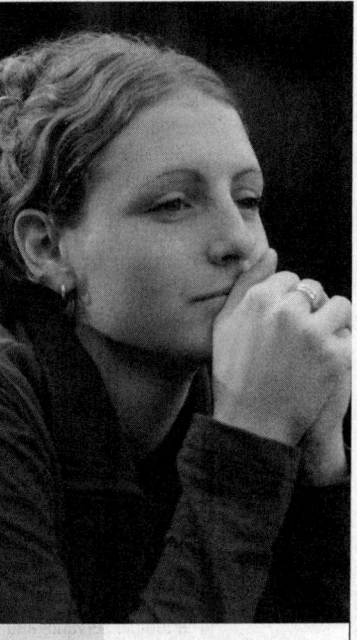

Moses' mom had zero good options. She'd already broken the law by keeping her Hebrew baby boy alive. Every day she ran the risk of someone hearing him cry, asking questions, finding out about her crime. The punishment could be terrible—seeing her baby killed and getting her whole family in trouble. But the alternative seemed unthinkable. How could she say good-bye to her baby?

But Jochebed had guts. She knew what she had to do—no matter how badly she didn't want to do it. She sent her young son downstream toward the Pharaoh's palace, hoping against hope to give him a chance at freedom. It worked. The bobbing bassinet grabbed the attention of the princess as she bathed. In fact, as it turned out, the princess unwittingly hired Moses' mom as his nanny (see 2:6–9). Moses grew up in the royal household, setting the stage for him to later lead the Israelites out of Egypt.

Where can one act of faith lead? Ask Jochebed. She could not have planned for things to happen the way they did. She acted in faith when she let her son go, and she let God do the rest. God proved himself faithful to Jochebed—orchestrating his perfect plan through impossible circumstances. Is there anything in your life you need to let go of and "send downstream" as an act of complete faith and trust?

Like Jochebed, we must be willing to let go of our preconceived ideas of how we want things to go in our lives—no matter how heartbreaking that may be—in order to see what God can do.

Dear God, help me let go of all my plans and hopes for my life and surrender to your perfect will. Show me how one act of faith can lead to a lifetime of blessing. Amen.

To read the next Mirror Images profile, go page 601.

Read more about Jochebed in Exodus 2:1–10 (pages 70–71) and Numbers 26:59 (page 195).

⁴⁴The singers:

the descendants of Asaph   148

⁴⁵The gatekeepers:

the descendants of
Shallum, Ater, Talmon, Akkub, Hatita
and Shobai   138

⁴⁶The temple servants:

the descendants of
Ziha, Hasupha, Tabbaoth,
⁴⁷Keros, Sia, Padon,
⁴⁸Lebana, Hagaba, Shalmai,
⁴⁹Hanan, Giddel, Gahar,
⁵⁰Reaiah, Rezin, Nekoda,
⁵¹Gazzam, Uzza, Paseah,
⁵²Besai, Meunim, Nephusim,
⁵³Bakbuk, Hakupha, Harhur,
⁵⁴Bazluth, Mehida, Harsha,
⁵⁵Barkos, Sisera, Temah,
⁵⁶Neziah and Hatipha

⁵⁷The descendants of the servants of Solomon:

the descendants of
Sotai, Sophereth, Perida,
⁵⁸Jaala, Darkon, Giddel,
⁵⁹Shephatiah, Hattil,
Pokereth-Hazzebaim and Amon

⁶⁰The temple servants and the descendants
of the servants of Solomon   392

⁶¹The following came up from the towns of Tel Melah, Tel Harsha, Kerub, Addon and Immer, but they could not show that their families were descended from Israel:

⁶²the descendants of
Delaiah, Tobiah and Nekoda   642

⁶³And from among the priests:

the descendants of
Hobaiah, Hakkoz and Barzillai (a man who had married a daughter of Barzillai
the Gileadite and was called by that name).

⁶⁴These searched for their family records, but they could not find them and so were excluded from the priesthood as unclean. ⁶⁵The governor, therefore, ordered them not to eat any of the most sacred food until there should be a priest ministering with the Urim and Thummim.

⁶⁶The whole company numbered 42,360, ⁶⁷besides their 7,337 menservants and maidservants; and they also had 245 men and women singers. ⁶⁸There were 736 horses, 245 mules, ᵃ ⁶⁹435 camels and 6,720 donkeys.

⁷⁰Some of the heads of the families contributed to the work. The governor gave to the treasury 1,000 drachmas ᵇ of gold, 50 bowls and 530 garments for priests. ⁷¹Some of the heads of the families gave to the treasury for the work 20,000 drachmas ᶜ of gold and

ᵃ 68 Some Hebrew manuscripts (see also Ezra 2:66); most Hebrew manuscripts do not have this verse.   ᵇ 70 That is, about 19 pounds (about 8.5 kilograms)   ᶜ 71 That is, about 375 pounds (about 170 kilograms); also in verse 72

2,200 minasᵃ of silver. ⁷²The total given by the rest of the people was 20,000 drachmas of gold, 2,000 minasᵇ of silver and 67 garments for priests.

⁷³The priests, the Levites, the gatekeepers, the singers and the temple servants, along with certain of the people and the rest of the Israelites, settled in their own towns.

Ezra Reads the Law

8 When the seventh month came and the Israelites had settled in their towns, ¹all the people assembled as one man in the square before the Water Gate. They told Ezra the scribe to bring out the Book of the Law of Moses, which the LORD had commanded for Israel.

²So on the first day of the seventh month Ezra the priest brought the Law before the assembly, which was made up of men and women and all who were able to understand. ³He read it aloud from daybreak till noon as he faced the square before the Water Gate in the presence of the men, women and others who could understand. And all the people listened attentively to the Book of the Law.

⁴Ezra the scribe stood on a high wooden platform built for the occasion. Beside him on his right stood Mattithiah, Shema, Anaiah, Uriah, Hilkiah and Maaseiah; and on his left were Pedaiah, Mishael, Malkijah, Hashum, Hashbaddanah, Zechariah and Meshullam.

⁵Ezra opened the book. All the people could see him because he was standing above them; and as he opened it, the people all stood up. ⁶Ezra praised the LORD, the great God; and all the people lifted their hands and responded, "Amen! Amen!" Then they bowed down and worshiped the LORD with their faces to the ground.

⁷The Levites—Jeshua, Bani, Sherebiah, Jamin, Akkub, Shabbethai, Hodiah, Maaseiah, Kelita, Azariah, Jozabad, Hanan and Pelaiah—instructed the people in the Law while the people were standing there. ⁸They read from the Book of the Law of God, making it clearᶜ and giving the meaning so that the people could understand what was being read.

⁹Then Nehemiah the governor, Ezra the priest and scribe, and the Levites who were instructing the people said to them all, "This day is sacred to the LORD your God. Do not mourn or weep." For all the people had been weeping as they listened to the words of the Law.

¹⁰Nehemiah said, "Go and enjoy choice food and sweet drinks, and send some to those who have nothing prepared. This day is sacred to our Lord. Do not grieve, for the joy of the LORD is your strength."

¹¹The Levites calmed all the people, saying, "Be still, for this is a sacred day. Do not grieve."

¹²Then all the people went away to eat and drink, to send portions of food and to celebrate with great joy, because they now understood the words that had been made known to them.

¹³On the second day of the month, the heads of all the families, along with the priests and the Levites, gathered around Ezra the scribe to give attention to the words of the Law. ¹⁴They found written in the Law, which the LORD had commanded through Moses, that the Israelites were to live in booths during the feast of the seventh month ¹⁵and that they should proclaim this word and spread it throughout their towns and in Jerusalem: "Go out into the hill country and bring back branches from olive and wild olive trees, and from myrtles, palms and shade trees, to make booths"—as it is written.ᵈ

¹⁶So the people went out and brought back branches and built themselves booths on their own roofs, in their courtyards, in the courts of the house of God and in the square by the Water Gate and the one by the Gate of Ephraim. ¹⁷The whole company that had returned from exile built booths and lived in them. From the days of Joshua son of Nun until that day, the Israelites had not celebrated it like this. And their joy was very great.

¹⁸Day after day, from the first day to the last, Ezra read from the Book of the Law of God. They

truth or dare

Some people think Christianity is just a straight-laced, guilt-trip religion. False! Knowing Jesus brings joy and strength to each day. **Do you celebrate your faith or always keep a poker face?**

8:9–12

ᵃ 71 That is, about 1 1/3 tons (about 1.2 metric tons)   ᵇ 72 That is, about 1 1/4 tons (about 1.1 metric tons)   ᶜ 8 Or God, translating it   ᵈ 15 See Lev. 23:37-40.

celebrated the feast for seven days, and on the eighth day, in accordance with the regulation, there was an assembly.

The Israelites Confess Their Sins

On the twenty-fourth day of the same month, the Israelites gathered together, fasting and wearing sackcloth and having dust on their heads. [2]Those of Israelite descent had separated themselves from all foreigners. They stood in their places and confessed their sins and the wickedness of their fathers. [3]They stood where they were and read from the Book of the Law of the Lord their God for a quarter of the day, and spent another quarter in confession and in worshiping the Lord their God. [4]Standing on the stairs were the Levites—Jeshua, Bani, Kadmiel, Shebaniah, Bunni, Sherebiah, Bani and Kenani—who called with loud voices to the Lord their God. [5]And the Levites—Jeshua, Kadmiel, Bani, Hashabneiah, Sherebiah, Hodiah, Shebaniah and Pethahiah—said: "Stand up and praise the Lord your God, who is from everlasting to everlasting. [a]"

"Blessed be your glorious name, and may it be exalted above all blessing and praise. [6]You alone are the Lord. You made the heavens, even the highest heavens, and all their starry host, the earth and all that is on it, the seas and all that is in them. You give life to everything, and the multitudes of heaven worship you.

[7]"You are the Lord God, who chose Abram and brought him out of Ur of the Chaldeans and named him Abraham. [8]You found his heart faithful to you, and you made a covenant with him to give to his descendants the land of the Canaanites, Hittites, Amorites, Perizzites, Jebusites and Girgashites. You have kept your promise because you are righteous.

[9]"You saw the suffering of our forefathers in Egypt; you heard their cry at the Red Sea. [b] [10]You sent miraculous signs and wonders against Pharaoh, against all his officials and all the people of his land, for you knew how arrogantly the Egyptians treated them. You made a name for yourself, which remains to this day. [11]You divided the sea before them, so that they passed through it on dry ground, but you hurled their pursuers into the depths, like a stone into mighty waters. [12]By day you led them with a pillar of cloud, and by night with a pillar of fire to give them light on the way they were to take.

[13]"You came down on Mount Sinai; you spoke to them from heaven. You gave them regulations and laws that are just and right, and decrees and commands that are good. [14]You made known to them your holy Sabbath and gave them commands, decrees and laws through your servant Moses. [15]In their hunger you gave them bread from heaven and in their thirst you brought them water from the rock; you told them to go in and take possession of the land you had sworn with uplifted hand to give them.

[16]"But they, our forefathers, became arrogant and stiff-necked, and did not obey your commands. [17]They refused to listen and failed to remember the miracles you performed among them. They became stiff-necked and in their rebellion appointed a leader in order to return to their slavery. But you are a forgiving God, gracious and compassionate, slow to anger and abounding in love. Therefore you did not desert them, [18]even when they cast for themselves an image of a calf and said, 'This is your god, who brought you up out of Egypt,' or when they committed awful blasphemies.

[19]"Because of your great compassion you did not abandon them in the desert. By day the pillar of cloud did not cease to guide them on their path, nor the pillar of fire by night to shine on the way they were to take. [20]You gave your good Spirit to instruct them. You did not withhold your manna from their mouths, and you gave them water for their thirst. [21]For forty years you sustained them in the desert; they lacked nothing, their clothes did not wear out nor did their feet become swollen.

[22]"You gave them kingdoms and nations, allotting to them even the remotest frontiers. They took over the country of Sihon[c] king of Heshbon and the country of Og king of Bashan. [23]You made their sons as numerous as the stars in the sky, and you brought them into the land that you told their fathers to enter and possess. [24]Their sons went in and took possession of the land. You subdued before them the Canaanites, who lived in the land; you handed the Canaanites over to them, along with their kings and the peoples of the land, to deal

a 5 Or God for ever and ever   b 9 Hebrew Yam Suph; that is, Sea of Reeds   c 22 One Hebrew manuscript and Septuagint; most Hebrew manuscripts Sihon, that is, the country of the with them as they pleased. ²⁵They captured fortified cities and fertile land; they took possession of houses filled with all kinds of good things, wells already dug, vineyards, olive groves and fruit trees in abundance. They ate to the full and were well-nourished; they reveled in your great goodness.

²⁶"But they were disobedient and rebelled against you; they put your law behind their backs. They killed your prophets, who had admonished them in order to turn them back to you; they committed awful blasphemies. ²⁷So you handed them over to their enemies, who oppressed them. But when they were oppressed they cried out to you. From heaven you heard them, and in your great compassion you gave them deliverers, who rescued them from the hand of their enemies.

²⁸"But as soon as they were at rest, they again did what was evil in your sight. Then you abandoned them to the hand of their enemies so that they ruled over them. And when they cried out to you again, you heard from heaven, and in your compassion you delivered them time after time.

²⁹"You warned them to return to your law, but they became arrogant and disobeyed your commands. They sinned against your ordinances, by which a man will live if he obeys them. Stubbornly they turned their backs on you, became stiff-necked and refused to listen. ³⁰For many years you were patient with them. By your Spirit you admonished them through your prophets. Yet they paid no attention, so you handed them over to the neighboring peoples. ³¹But in your great mercy you did not put an end to them or abandon them, for you are a gracious and merciful God.

³²"Now therefore, O our God, the great, mighty and awesome God, who keeps his covenant of love, do not let all this hardship seem trifling in your eyes—the hardship that has come upon us, upon our kings and leaders, upon our priests and prophets, upon our fathers and all your people, from the days of the kings of Assyria until today. ³³In all that has happened to us, you have been just; you have acted faithfully, while we did wrong. ³⁴Our kings, our leaders, our priests and our fathers did not follow your law; they did not pay attention to your commands or the warnings you gave them. ³⁵Even while they were in their kingdom, enjoying your great goodness to them in the spacious and fertile land you gave them, they did not serve you or turn from their evil ways.

³⁶"But see, we are slaves today, slaves in the land you gave our forefathers so they could eat its fruit and the other good things it produces. ³⁷Because of our sins, its abundant harvest goes to

love ♥ notes

9:16–21

My loved one,

Look at my people Israel in the desert. Even at their worst moments, I never abandoned them. Despite their rebellion, I cared for them, fed them and instructed them. The same holds true for you.

—Your patient Father

In what area of your life do you need God's patience the most?

the kings you have placed over us. They rule over our bodies and our cattle as they please. We are in great distress.

The Agreement of the People

38 "In view of all this, we are making a binding agreement, putting it in writing, and our leaders, our Levites and our priests are affixing their seals to it."

10

Those who sealed it were:

Nehemiah the governor, the son of Hacaliah.

Zedekiah, 2 Seraiah, Azariah, Jeremiah,
3 Pashhur, Amariah, Malkijah,
4 Hattush, Shebaniah, Malluch,
5 Harim, Meremoth, Obadiah,
6 Daniel, Ginnethon, Baruch,
7 Meshullam, Abijah, Mijamin,
8 Maaziah, Bilgai and Shemaiah.
These were the priests.

9 The Levites:

Jeshua son of Azaniah, Binnui of the sons of Henadad, Kadmiel,
10 and their associates: Shebaniah,
Hodiah, Kelita, Pelaiah, Hanan,
11 Mica, Rehob, Hashabiah,
12 Zaccur, Sherebiah, Shebaniah,
13 Hodiah, Bani and Beninu.

14 The leaders of the people:

Parosh, Pahath-Moab, Elam, Zattu, Bani,
15 Bunni, Azgad, Bebai,
16 Adonijah, Bigvai, Adin,
17 Ater, Hezekiah, Azzur,
18 Hodiah, Hashum, Bezai,
19 Hariph, Anathoth, Nebai,
20 Magpiash, Meshullam, Hezir,
21 Meshezabel, Zadok, Jaddua,
22 Pelatiah, Hanan, Anaiah,
23 Hoshea, Hananiah, Hasshub,
24 Hallohesh, Pilha, Shobek,
25 Rehum, Hashabnah, Maaseiah,
26 Ahiah, Hanan, Anan,
27 Malluch, Harim and Baanah.

28 "The rest of the people—priests, Levites, gatekeepers, singers, temple servants and all who separated themselves from the neighboring peoples for the sake of the Law of God, together

genuine
devotion » 10:28-29

Ever set your mind on something and really intentionally go after it? Maybe you're intentional about studying more or working out longer because of a bigger purpose (to get better grades or to be healthier physically). The people of Israel all made the same vow—to follow God's laws. They set out together to seriously keep God's commands. They really went after it. Do you take God's commands seriously? Seriously enough that you really work intentionally to keep them?

with their wives and all their sons and daughters who are able to understand— 29 all these now join their brothers the nobles, and bind themselves with a curse and an oath to follow the Law of God given through Moses the servant of God and to obey carefully all the commands, regulations and decrees of the LORD our Lord.

30 "We promise not to give our daughters in marriage to the peoples around us or take their daughters for our sons.

31 "When the neighboring peoples bring merchandise or grain to sell on the Sabbath, we

will not buy from them on the Sabbath or on any holy day. Every seventh year we will forgo working the land and will cancel all debts.

[32] "We assume the responsibility for carrying out the commands to give a third of a shekel[a] each year for the service of the house of our God: [33]for the bread set out on the table; for the regular grain offerings and burnt offerings; for the offerings on the Sabbaths, New Moon festivals and appointed feasts; for the holy offerings; for sin offerings to make atonement for Israel; and for all the duties of the house of our God.

[34] "We—the priests, the Levites and the people—have cast lots to determine when each of our families is to bring to the house of our God at set times each year a contribution of wood to burn on the altar of the LORD our God, as it is written in the Law.

[35] "We also assume responsibility for bringing to the house of the LORD each year the firstfruits of our crops and of every fruit tree.

[36] "As it is also written in the Law, we will bring the firstborn of our sons and of our cattle, of our herds and of our flocks to the house of our God, to the priests ministering there.

[37] "Moreover, we will bring to the storerooms of the house of our God, to the priests, the first of our ground meal, of our ˻grain˼ offerings, of the fruit of all our trees and of our new wine and oil. And we will bring a tithe of our crops to the Levites, for it is the Levites who collect the tithes in all the towns where we work. [38]A priest descended from Aaron is to accompany the Levites when they receive the tithes, and the Levites are to bring a tenth of the tithes up to the house of our God, to the storerooms of the treasury. [39]The people of Israel, including the Levites, are to bring their contributions of grain, new wine and oil to the storerooms where the articles for the sanctuary are kept and where the ministering priests, the gatekeepers and the singers stay.

"We will not neglect the house of our God."

The New Residents of Jerusalem

11 Now the leaders of the people settled in Jerusalem, and the rest of the people cast lots to bring one out of every ten to live in Jerusalem, the holy city, while the remaining nine were to stay in their own towns. [2]The people commended all the men who volunteered to live in Jerusalem.

[3]These are the provincial leaders who settled in Jerusalem (now some Israelites, priests, Levites, temple servants and descendants of Solomon's servants lived in the towns of Judah, each on his own property in the various towns, [4]while other people from both Judah and Benjamin lived in Jerusalem):

From the descendants of Judah:

Athaiah son of Uzziah, the son of Zechariah, the son of Amariah, the son of Shephatiah, the son of Mahalalel, a descendant of Perez; [5]and Maaseiah son of Baruch, the son of Col-Hozeh, the son of Hazaiah, the son of Adaiah, the son of Joiarib, the son of Zechariah, a descendant of Shelah. [6]The descendants of Perez who lived in Jerusalem totaled 468 able men.

[7]From the descendants of Benjamin:

Sallu son of Meshullam, the son of Joed, the son of Pedaiah, the son of Kolaiah, the son of Maaseiah, the son of Ithiel, the son of Jeshaiah, [8]and his followers, Gabbai and Sallai—928 men. [9]Joel son of Zicri was their chief officer, and Judah son of Hassenuah was over the Second District of the city.

[10]From the priests:

Jedaiah; the son of Joiarib; Jakin; [11]Seraiah son of Hilkiah, the son of Meshullam, the son of Zadok, the son of Meraioth, the son of Ahitub, supervisor in the house of God, [12]and their associates, who carried on work for the temple—822 men; Adaiah son of Jeroham, the son of Pelaliah, the son of Amzi, the son of Zechariah, the son of Pashhur, the son of Malkijah, [13]and his associates, who were heads of families—242 men; Amashsai son of Azarel, the son of Ahzai, the son of Meshillemoth, the son of Immer, [14]and his[b] associates, who were able men—128. Their chief officer was Zabdiel son of Haggedolim.

---

[a] 32 That is, about 1/8 ounce (about 4 grams) [b] 14 Most Septuagint manuscripts; Hebrew *their*

¹⁵From the Levites:

Shemaiah son of Hasshub, the son of Azrikam, the son of Hashabiah, the son of Bunni; ¹⁶Shabbethai and Jozabad, two of the heads of the Levites, who had charge of the outside work of the house of God; ¹⁷Mattaniah son of Mica, the son of Zabdi, the son of Asaph, the director who led in thanksgiving and prayer; Bakbukiah, second among his associates; and Abda son of Shammua, the son of Galal, the son of Jeduthun. ¹⁸The Levites in the holy city totaled 284.

¹⁹The gatekeepers:

Akkub, Talmon and their associates, who kept watch at the gates—172 men.

²⁰The rest of the Israelites, with the priests and Levites, were in all the towns of Judah, each on his ancestral property.

²¹The temple servants lived on the hill of Ophel, and Ziha and Gishpa were in charge of them.

²²The chief officer of the Levites in Jerusalem was Uzzi son of Bani, the son of Hashabiah, the son of Mattaniah, the son of Mica. Uzzi was one of Asaph's descendants, who were the singers responsible for the service of the house of God. ²³The singers were under the king's orders, which regulated their daily activity.

²⁴Pethahiah son of Meshezabel, one of the descendants of Zerah son of Judah, was the king's agent in all affairs relating to the people.

²⁵As for the villages with their fields, some of the people of Judah lived in Kiriath Arba and its surrounding settlements, in Dibon and its settlements, in Jekabzeel and its villages, ²⁶in Jeshua, in Moladah, in Beth Pelet, ²⁷in Hazar Shual, in Beersheba and its settlements, ²⁸in Ziklag, in Meconah and its settlements, ²⁹in En Rimmon, in Zorah, in Jarmuth, ³⁰Zanoah, Adullam and their villages, in Lachish and its fields, and in Azekah and its settlements. So they were living all the way from Beersheba to the Valley of Hinnom.

³¹The descendants of the Benjamites from Geba lived in Micmash, Aija, Bethel and its settlements, ³²in Anathoth, Nob and Ananiah, ³³in Hazor, Ramah and Gittaim, ³⁴in Hadid, Zeboim and Neballat, ³⁵in Lod and Ono, and in the Valley of the Craftsmen.

³⁶Some of the divisions of the Levites of Judah settled in Benjamin.

Priests and Levites

12 These were the priests and Levites who returned with Zerubbabel son of Shealtiel and with Jeshua:
Seraiah, Jeremiah, Ezra,
²Amariah, Malluch, Hattush,
³Shecaniah, Rehum, Meremoth,
⁴Iddo, Ginnethon,^a Abijah,
⁵Mijamin,^b Moadiah, Bilgah,
⁶Shemaiah, Joiarib, Jedaiah,
⁷Sallu, Amok, Hilkiah and Jedaiah.
These were the leaders of the priests and their associates in the days of Jeshua.

⁸The Levites were Jeshua, Binnui, Kadmiel, Sherebiah, Judah, and also Mattaniah, who, together with his associates, was in charge of the songs of thanksgiving. ⁹Bakbukiah and Unni, their associates, stood opposite them in the services.

¹⁰Jeshua was the father of Joiakim, Joiakim the father of Eliashib, Eliashib the father of Joiada, ¹¹Joiada the father of Jonathan, and Jonathan the father of Jaddua.

¹²In the days of Joiakim, these were the heads of the priestly families:
of Seraiah's family, Meraiah;
of Jeremiah's, Hananiah;
¹³of Ezra's, Meshullam;
of Amariah's, Jehohanan;
¹⁴of Malluch's, Jonathan;
of Shecaniah's,^c Joseph;

^a 4 Many Hebrew manuscripts and Vulgate (see also Neh. 12:16); most Hebrew manuscripts *Ginnethoi*   ^b 5 A variant of *Miniamin*   ^c 14 Very many Hebrew manuscripts, some Septuagint manuscripts and Syriac (see also Neh. 12:3); most Hebrew manuscripts *Shebaniah's*

Always the Girl "Friend"

Friday night. I'm sitting at home watching old *I Love Lucy* episodes with my little sister. I know what you must be thinking—*Get a life*. Every weekend it's the same thing: TV, homework, surf the net, paint my toenails and sit around waiting for a phone call that never comes.

I'm not sure when it happened, really. But suddenly all five of my closest girlfriends have boyfriends. Which makes me the odd girl out. When I turned sixteen, I figured I'd start dating, too. I guess I figured wrong. Last week, a cute guy from my physics class instant messaged me. I was hopeful . . . till I learned he was using my friend's laptop and got the wrong person. Why can't I be the *right* person?

Every guy I know thinks of me as his sister or his best bud. During biology I told my lab partner Miguel a joke. He laughed out loud, then said, "Sydnie, you're one funny girl!" Ever since then he's been calling me "funny girl." What's *that* supposed to mean?

Just for once, I'd like to have a killer weekend planned just like everyone else. I'd even settle for a girls' night out, just like we used to do. Pizza at Verino's, caramel lattes at Starbucks, then an all-night movie marathon. But no one's got time for that anymore. No one's got time for me.

loneliness in focus

We all go through seasons of loneliness. And there are no easy answers or quick solutions. Remember, though, that you're never truly alone. God longs to comfort you whenever you feel alone or rejected. Hebrews 13:5 says, "Never will I leave you; never will I forsake you."

If you're feeling like the odd girl out, consider this:

» Process your feelings. Write them in a journal, and then pour them out to God, as David the psalmist often did. A time of loneliness in life may actually deepen your relationship with God.

» Reach out to others. You're not the only one who feels alone and needs a friend. Find another girl who's lonely and make an effort to befriend her. Focusing on someone else's need helps lessen your own pain.

For more on this topic, see the index on page 1656.

For more ideas on overcoming loneliness, check out the link on www.TrueImagesBible.com

[15] of Harim's, Adna;
of Meremoth's,[a] Helkai;

[16] of Iddo's, Zechariah;
of Ginnethon's, Meshullam;

[17] of Abijah's, Zicri;
of Miniamin's and of Moadiah's, Piltai;

[18] of Bilgah's, Shammua;
of Shemaiah's, Jehonathan;

[19] of Joiarib's, Mattenai;

a 15 Some Septuagint manuscripts (see also Neh. 12:3); Hebrew *Meraioth's*

of Jedaiah's, Uzzi;
20 of Sallu's, Kallai;
of Amok's, Eber;
21 of Hilkiah's, Hashabiah;
of Jedaiah's, Nethanel.

22The family heads of the Levites in the days of Eliashib, Joiada, Johanan and Jaddua, as well as those of the priests, were recorded in the reign of Darius the Persian. 23The family heads among the descendants of Levi up to the time of Johanan son of Eliashib were recorded in the book of the annals. 24And the leaders of the Levites were Hashabiah, Sherebiah, Jeshua son of Kadmiel, and their associates, who stood opposite them to give praise and thanksgiving, one section responding to the other, as prescribed by David the man of God.

25Mattaniah, Bakbukiah, Obadiah, Meshullam, Talmon and Akkub were gatekeepers who guarded the storerooms at the gates. 26They served in the days of Joiakim son of Jeshua, the son of Jozadak, and in the days of Nehemiah the governor and of Ezra the priest and scribe.

Dedication of the Wall of Jerusalem

27At the dedication of the wall of Jerusalem, the Levites were sought out from where they lived and were brought to Jerusalem to celebrate joyfully the dedication with songs of thanksgiving and with the music of cymbals, harps and lyres. 28The singers also were brought together from the region around Jerusalem—from the villages of the Netophathites, 29from Beth Gilgal, and from the area of Geba and Azmaveth, for the singers had built villages for themselves around Jerusalem. 30When the priests and Levites had purified themselves ceremonially, they purified the people, the gates and the wall.

31I had the leaders of Judah go up on top*a* of the wall. I also assigned two large choirs to give thanks. One was to proceed on top*b* of the wall to the right, toward the Dung Gate. 32Hoshaiah and half the leaders of Judah followed them, 33along with Azariah, Ezra, Meshullam, 34Judah, Benjamin, Shemaiah, Jeremiah, 35as well as some priests with trumpets, and also Zechariah son of Jonathan, the son of Shemaiah, the son of Mattaniah, the son of Micaiah, the son of Zaccur, the son of Asaph, 36and his associates—Shemaiah, Azarel, Milalai, Gilalai, Maai, Nethanel, Judah and Hanani—with musical instruments ⌊prescribed by⌋ David the man of God. Ezra the scribe led the procession. 37At the Fountain Gate they continued directly up the steps of the City of David on the ascent to the wall and passed above the house of David to the Water Gate on the east.

38The second choir proceeded in the opposite direction. I followed them on top*c* of the wall, together with half the people—past the Tower of the Ovens to the Broad Wall, 39over the Gate of Ephraim, the Jeshanah*d* Gate, the Fish Gate, the Tower of Hananel and the Tower of the Hundred, as far as the Sheep Gate. At the Gate of the Guard they stopped.

40The two choirs that gave thanks then took their places in the house of God; so did I, together with half the officials, 41as well as the priests—Eliakim, Maaseiah, Miniamin, Micaiah, Elioenai, Zechariah and Hananiah with their trumpets— 42and also Maaseiah, Shemaiah, Eleazar, Uzzi, Jehohanan, Malkijah, Elam and Ezer. The choirs sang under the direction of Jezrahiah. 43And on that day they offered great sacrifices, rejoicing because God had given them great joy. The women and children also rejoiced. The sound of rejoicing in Jerusalem could be heard far away.

44At that time men were appointed to be in charge of the storerooms for the contributions, firstfruits and tithes. From the fields around the towns they were to bring into the storerooms the portions required by the Law for the priests and the Levites, for Judah was pleased with the ministering priests and Levites. 45They performed the service of their God and the service of purification, as did also the singers and gatekeepers, according to the commands of David and his son Solomon. 46For long ago, in the days of David and Asaph, there had been directors for the singers and for the songs of praise and thanksgiving to God. 47So in the days of Zerubbabel and of Nehemiah, all Israel contributed the daily portions for the singers and gatekeepers. They also set aside the portion for the other Levites, and the Levites set aside the portion for the descendants of Aaron.

a 31 Or go alongside   b 31 Or proceed alongside   c 38 Or them alongside   d 39 Or Old

Nehemiah's Final Reforms

13 On that day the Book of Moses was read aloud in the hearing of the people and there it was found written that no Ammonite or Moabite should ever be admitted into the assembly of God, ²because they had not met the Israelites with food and water but had hired Balaam to call a curse down on them. (Our God, however, turned the curse into a blessing.) ³When the people heard this law, they excluded from Israel all who were of foreign descent.

⁴Before this, Eliashib the priest had been put in charge of the storerooms of the house of our God. He was closely associated with Tobiah, ⁵and he had provided him with a large room formerly used to store the grain offerings and incense and temple articles, and also the tithes of grain, new wine and oil prescribed for the Levites, singers and gatekeepers, as well as the contributions for the priests.

⁶But while all this was going on, I was not in Jerusalem, for in the thirty-second year of Artaxerxes king of Babylon I had returned to the king. Some time later I asked his permission ⁷and came back to Jerusalem. Here I learned about the evil thing Eliashib had done in providing Tobiah a room in the courts of the house of God. ⁸I was greatly displeased and threw all Tobiah's household goods out of the room. ⁹I gave orders to purify the rooms, and then I put back into them the equipment of the house of God, with the grain offerings and the incense.

¹⁰I also learned that the portions assigned to the Levites had not been given to them, and that all the Levites and singers responsible for the service had gone back to their own fields. ¹¹So I rebuked the officials and asked them, "Why is the house of God neglected?" Then I called them together and stationed them at their posts.

¹²All Judah brought the tithes of grain, new wine and oil into the storerooms. ¹³I put Shelemiah the priest, Zadok the scribe, and a Levite named Pedaiah in charge of the storerooms and made Hanan son of Zaccur, the son of Mattaniah, their assistant, because these men were considered trustworthy. They were made responsible for distributing the supplies to their brothers.

¹⁴Remember me for this, O my God, and do not blot out what I have so faithfully done for the house of my God and its services.

¹⁵In those days I saw men in Judah treading winepresses on the Sabbath and bringing in grain and loading it on donkeys, together with wine, grapes, figs and all other kinds of loads. And they were bringing all this into Jerusalem on the Sabbath. Therefore I warned them against selling food on that day. ¹⁶Men from Tyre who lived in Jerusalem were bringing in fish and all kinds of merchandise and selling them in Jerusalem on the Sabbath to the people of Judah. ¹⁷I rebuked the nobles of Judah and said to them, "What is this wicked thing you are doing—desecrating the Sabbath day? ¹⁸Didn't

truth or dare

Old habits die hard. Deep-rooted sin is equally difficult to root out. Get weeding, girl! You'll be opening up room to grow into a happier, healthier you.

13:4–27

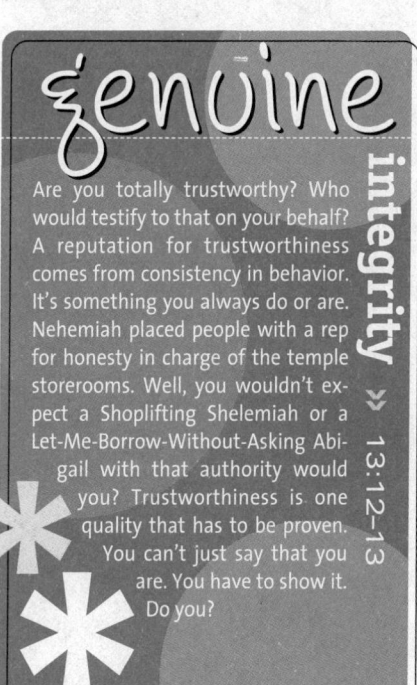

genuine

Are you totally trustworthy? Who would testify to that on your behalf? A reputation for trustworthiness comes from consistency in behavior. It's something you always do or are. Nehemiah placed people with a rep for honesty in charge of the temple storerooms. Well, you wouldn't expect a Shoplifting Shelemiah or a Let-Me-Borrow-Without-Asking Abigail with that authority would you? Trustworthiness is one quality that has to be proven. You can't just say that you are. You have to show it. Do you?

integrity » 13:12–13

your forefathers do the same things, so that our God brought all this calamity upon us and upon this city? Now you are stirring up more wrath against Israel by desecrating the Sabbath."

¹⁹When evening shadows fell on the gates of Jerusalem before the Sabbath, I ordered the doors to be shut and not opened until the Sabbath was over. I stationed some of my own men at the gates so that no load could be brought in on the Sabbath day. ²⁰Once or twice the merchants and sellers of all kinds of goods spent the night outside Jerusalem. ²¹But I warned them and said, "Why do you spend the night by the wall? If you do this again, I will lay hands on you." From that time on they no longer came on the Sabbath. ²²Then I commanded the Levites to purify themselves and go and guard the gates in order to keep the Sabbath day holy.

Remember me for this also, O my God, and show mercy to me according to your great love.

²³Moreover, in those days I saw men of Judah who had married women from Ashdod, Ammon and Moab. ²⁴Half of their children spoke the language of Ashdod or the language of one of the other peoples, and did not know how to speak the language of Judah. ²⁵I rebuked them and called curses down on them. I beat some of the men and pulled out their hair. I made them take an oath in God's name and said: "You are not to give your daughters in marriage to their sons, nor are you to take their daughters in marriage for your sons or for yourselves. ²⁶Was it not because of marriages like these that Solomon king of Israel sinned? Among the many nations there was no king like him. He was loved by his God, and God made him king over all Israel, but even he was led into sin by foreign women. ²⁷Must we hear now that you too are doing all this terrible wickedness and are being unfaithful to our God by marrying foreign women?"

²⁸One of the sons of Joiada son of Eliashib the high priest was son-in-law to Sanballat the Horonite. And I drove him away from me.

²⁹Remember them, O my God, because they defiled the priestly office and the covenant of the priesthood and of the Levites.

³⁰So I purified the priests and the Levites of everything foreign, and assigned them duties, each to his own task. ³¹I also made provision for contributions of wood at designated times, and for the firstfruits.

Remember me with favor, O my God.

author: Unknown.

date: Sometime after the events described, about 460 B.C.

setting: Susa, the capital of the Persian Empire.

verse to remember: "For if you remain silent at this time, relief and deliverance for the Jews will arise from another place, but you and your father's family will perish. And who knows but that you have come to royal position for such a time as this?" (4:14).

theme to consider: God uses ordinary people (like Esther and us!) to accomplish extraordinary things for his purposes.

esther

unchanging truth

Incredible but true stories. A mother lifts the car to free her trapped child. A "not very good" swimmer jumps into a swiftly moving river to rescue a drowning person. A middle-aged man bikes thousands of miles to make people aware of a rare disease and to raise money to help find a cure. You hear about them all the time—ordinary people doing extraordinary things.

Esther may have been considered "sub-ordinary" in the Persian culture. And if you'd asked her, she probably didn't think she was anything extraordinary. After all, she was a Jew (and her people had earlier been conquered and taken captive), and she was a woman! Of course, God didn't think of Esther as ordinary. He had extraordinary plans for his people, the Jews, and Esther was the one God chose to carry out his plans. Though Esther may have begun as a nobody, she became the queen of Persia. Then she played an instrumental role in saving all the Jews from annihilation. Nothing ordinary about that!

Think you're just average, an ordinary teen with an ordinary life doing ordinary things? Think again. When you allow God to use you for his purposes, the extraordinary happens.

life lessons

1 God uses even the most ordinary of people to accomplish his purposes. He makes sure the right person is in the right place at the right time (2:5–9,15–18).

2 Being afraid of taking a risk for God can have disastrous results for us and others (4:12–14).

3 Doing extraordinary things for and with God will be remembered for many generations (9:29–32).

Queen Vashti Deposed

1 This is what happened during the time of Xerxes,[a] the Xerxes who ruled over 127 provinces stretching from India to Cush[b]: [2]At that time King Xerxes reigned from his royal throne in the citadel of Susa, [3]and in the third year of his reign he gave a banquet for all his nobles and officials. The military leaders of Persia and Media, the princes, and the nobles of the provinces were present.

[4]For a full 180 days he displayed the vast wealth of his kingdom and the splendor and glory of his majesty. [5]When these days were over, the king gave a banquet, lasting seven days, in the enclosed garden of the king's palace, for all the people from the least to the greatest, who were in the citadel of Susa. [6]The garden had hangings of white and blue linen, fastened with cords of white linen and purple material to silver rings on marble pillars. There were couches of gold and silver on a mosaic pavement of porphyry, marble, mother-of-pearl and other costly stones. [7]Wine was served in goblets of gold, each one different from the other, and the royal wine was abundant, in keeping with the king's liberality. [8]By the king's command each guest was allowed to drink in his own way, for the king instructed all the wine stewards to serve each man what he wished.

[9]Queen Vashti also gave a banquet for the women in the royal palace of King Xerxes.

[10]On the seventh day, when King Xerxes was in high spirits from wine, he commanded the seven eunuchs who served him—Mehuman, Biztha, Harbona, Bigtha, Abagtha, Zethar and Carcas— [11]to bring before him Queen Vashti, wearing her royal crown, in order to display her beauty to the people and nobles, for she was lovely to look at. [12]But when the attendants delivered the king's command, Queen Vashti refused to come. Then the king became furious and burned with anger.

[13]Since it was customary for the king to consult experts in matters of law and justice, he spoke with the wise men who understood the times [14]and were closest to the king—Carshena, Shethar, Admatha, Tarshish, Meres, Marsena and Memucan, the seven nobles of Persia and Media who had special access to the king and were highest in the kingdom.

[15]"According to law, what must be done to Queen Vashti?" he asked. "She has not obeyed the command of King Xerxes that the eunuchs have taken to her."

[16]Then Memucan replied in the presence of the king and the nobles, "Queen Vashti has done wrong, not only against the king but also against all the nobles and the peoples of all the provinces of King Xerxes. [17]For the queen's conduct will become known to all the women, and so they will despise their husbands and say, 'King Xerxes commanded Queen Vashti to be brought before him, but she would not come.' [18]This very day the Persian and Median women of the nobility who have heard about the queen's conduct will respond to all the king's nobles in the same way. There will be no end of disrespect and discord.

[19]"Therefore, if it pleases the king, let him issue a royal decree and let it be written in the laws of Persia and Media, which cannot be repealed, that Vashti is never again to enter the presence of King Xerxes. Also let the king give her royal position to someone else who is better than she. [20]Then when the king's edict is proclaimed throughout all his vast realm, all the women will respect their husbands, from the least to the greatest."

[21]The king and his nobles were pleased with this advice, so the king did as Memucan proposed.

genuine character » 1:10-12

Let's take a minute for some good old soul-searching. Which do you think is more important: looks or character? Winning the Miss Congeniality award can seem less thrilling than being crowned Miss America. That's the way it was in Vashti's day. Her refusal to parade herself in front of her husband and his drunken buddies showed character. It also led to her being fired as queen. In a day when looks seem to be valued over character, many people are tempted to devalue character. But genuine character—inner beauty—never goes out of style with God.

---

a 1 Hebrew *Ahasuerus*, a variant of Xerxes' Persian name; here and throughout Esther   b 1 That is, the upper Nile region

²²He sent dispatches to all parts of the kingdom, to each province in its own script and to each people in its own language, proclaiming in each people's tongue that every man should be ruler over his own household.

Esther Made Queen

2 Later when the anger of King Xerxes had subsided, he remembered Vashti and what she had done and what he had decreed about her. ²Then the king's personal attendants proposed, "Let a search be made for beautiful young virgins for the king. ³Let the king appoint commissioners in every province of his realm to bring all these beautiful girls into the harem at the citadel of Susa. Let them be placed under the care of Hegai, the king's eunuch, who is in charge of the women; and let beauty treatments be given to them. ⁴Then let the girl who pleases the king be queen instead of Vashti." This advice appealed to the king, and he followed it.

⁵Now there was in the citadel of Susa a Jew of the tribe of Benjamin, named Mordecai son of Jair, the son of Shimei, the son of Kish, ⁶who had been carried into exile from Jerusalem by Nebuchadnezzar king of Babylon, among those taken captive with Jehoiachinᵃ king of Judah. ⁷Mordecai had a cousin named Hadassah, whom he had brought up because she had neither father nor mother. This girl, who was also known as Esther, was lovely in form and features, and Mordecai had taken her as his own daughter when her father and mother died.

⁸When the king's order and edict had been proclaimed, many girls were brought to the citadel of Susa and put under the care of Hegai. Esther also was taken to the king's palace and entrusted to Hegai, who had charge of the harem. ⁹The girl pleased him and won his favor. Immediately he provided her with her beauty treatments and special food. He assigned to her seven maids selected from the king's palace and moved her and her maids into the best place in the harem.

¹⁰Esther had not revealed her nationality and family background, because Mordecai had forbidden her to do so. ¹¹Every day he walked back and forth near the courtyard of the harem to find out how Esther was and what was happening to her.

¹²Before a girl's turn came to go in to King Xerxes, she had to complete twelve months of beauty treatments prescribed for the women, six months with oil of myrrh and six with perfumes and cosmetics. ¹³And this is how she would go to the king: Anything she wanted was given her to take with her from the harem to the king's palace. ¹⁴In the evening she would go there and in the morning return to another part of the harem to the care of Shaashgaz, the king's eunuch who was in charge of the concubines. She would not return to the king unless he was pleased with her and summoned her by name.

¹⁵When the turn came for Esther (the girl Mordecai had adopted, the daughter of his uncle Abihail) to go to the king, she asked for nothing other than what Hegai, the king's eunuch who was in charge of the harem, suggested. And Esther won the favor of everyone who saw her. ¹⁶She was taken to King Xerxes in the royal residence in the tenth month, the month of Tebeth, in the seventh year of his reign.

¹⁷Now the king was attracted to Esther more than to any of the other women, and she won his favor and approval more than any of the other virgins. So he set a royal crown on her head and made her queen instead of Vashti. ¹⁸And the king gave a great banquet, Esther's banquet, for all his nobles and officials. He proclaimed a holiday throughout the provinces and distributed gifts with royal liberality.

Mordecai Uncovers a Conspiracy

¹⁹When the virgins were assembled a second time, Mordecai was sitting at the king's gate. ²⁰But Esther had kept secret her family background and nationality just as Mordecai had told her

truth or dare

Openly sharing your faith is cool. Sometimes, though, it's wise to wait and let your *actions* do the talking. Once you've earned some trust, then you can share your message.

2:10,20

ᵃ 6 Hebrew *Jeconiah*, a variant of *Jehoiachin*

to do, for she continued to follow Mordecai's instructions as she had done when he was bringing her up.

²¹During the time Mordecai was sitting at the king's gate, Bigthana*a* and Teresh, two of the king's officers who guarded the doorway, became angry and conspired to assassinate King Xerxes. ²²But Mordecai found out about the plot and told Queen Esther, who in turn reported it to the king, giving credit to Mordecai. ²³And when the report was investigated and found to be true, the two officials were hanged on a gallows.*b* All this was recorded in the book of the annals in the presence of the king.

Haman's Plot to Destroy the Jews

3 After these events, King Xerxes honored Haman son of Hammedatha, the Agagite, elevating him and giving him a seat of honor higher than that of all the other nobles. ²All the royal officials at the king's gate knelt down and paid honor to Haman, for the king had commanded this concerning him. But Mordecai would not kneel down or pay him honor.

³Then the royal officials at the king's gate asked Mordecai, "Why do you disobey the king's command?" ⁴Day after day they spoke to him but he refused to comply. Therefore they told Haman about it to see whether Mordecai's behavior would be tolerated, for he had told them he was a Jew.

⁵When Haman saw that Mordecai would not kneel down or pay him honor, he was enraged. ⁶Yet having learned who Mordecai's people were, he scorned the idea of killing only Mordecai. Instead Haman looked for a way to destroy all Mordecai's people, the Jews, throughout the whole kingdom of Xerxes.

⁷In the twelfth year of King Xerxes, in the first month, the month of Nisan, they cast the *pur* (that is, the lot) in the presence of Haman to select a day and month. And the lot fell on*c* the twelfth month, the month of Adar.

⁸Then Haman said to King Xerxes, "There is a certain people dispersed and scattered among the peoples in all the provinces of your kingdom whose customs are different from those of all other people and who do not obey the king's laws; it is not in the king's best interest to tolerate them. ⁹If it pleases the king, let a decree be issued to destroy them, and I will put ten thousand talents*d* of silver into the royal treasury for the men who carry out this business."

¹⁰So the king took his signet ring from his finger and gave it to Haman son of Hammedatha, the Agagite, the enemy of the Jews. ¹¹"Keep the money," the king said to Haman, "and do with the people as you please."

---

love ♥ notes

2:17–18

Chosen one,

Just as I chose Esther to be queen to save my people from certain death, so I have chosen you for a specific purpose. It may not be clear to you yet, but trust me. I am in control.

—God over all things

How does knowing that God has a plan and purpose for you affect your feelings about your future?

_____

_____

_____

_____

_____

_____

_____

---

a 21 Hebrew *Bigthan*, a variant of *Bigthana*
b 23 Or *were hung* (or *impaled*) *on poles*; similarly elsewhere in Esther   *c* 7 Septuagint; Hebrew does not have *And the lot fell on.*   *d* 9 That is, about 375 tons (about 345 metric tons)

[12]Then on the thirteenth day of the first month the royal secretaries were summoned. They wrote out in the script of each province and in the language of each people all Haman's orders to the king's satraps, the governors of the various provinces and the nobles of the various peoples. These were written in the name of King Xerxes himself and sealed with his own ring. [13]Dispatches were sent by couriers to all the king's provinces with the order to destroy, kill and annihilate all the Jews—young and old, women and little children—on a single day, the thirteenth day of the twelfth month, the month of Adar, and to plunder their goods. [14]A copy of the text of the edict was to be issued as law in every province and made known to the people of every nationality so they would be ready for that day.

[15]Spurred on by the king's command, the couriers went out, and the edict was issued in the citadel of Susa. The king and Haman sat down to drink, but the city of Susa was bewildered.

Mordecai Persuades Esther to Help

4 When Mordecai learned of all that had been done, he tore his clothes, put on sackcloth and ashes, and went out into the city, wailing loudly and bitterly. [2]But he went only as far as the king's gate, because no one clothed in sackcloth was allowed to enter it. [3]In every province to which the edict and order of the king came, there was great mourning among the Jews, with fasting, weeping and wailing. Many lay in sackcloth and ashes.

[4]When Esther's maids and eunuchs came and told her about Mordecai, she was in great distress. She sent clothes for him to put on instead of his sackcloth, but he would not accept them. [5]Then Esther summoned Hathach, one of the king's eunuchs assigned to attend her, and ordered him to find out what was troubling Mordecai and why.

[6]So Hathach went out to Mordecai in the open square of the city in front of the king's gate. [7]Mordecai told him everything that had happened to him, including the exact amount of money Haman had promised to pay into the royal treasury for the destruction of the Jews. [8]He also gave him a copy of the text of the edict for their annihilation, which had been published in Susa, to show to Esther and explain it to her, and he told him to urge her to go into the king's presence to beg for mercy and plead with him for her people.

[9]Hathach went back and reported to Esther what Mordecai had said. [10]Then she instructed him to say to Mordecai, [11]"All the king's officials and the people of the royal provinces know that for any man or woman who approaches the king in the inner court without being summoned the king has but one law: that he be put to death. The only exception to this is for the king to extend the gold scepter to him and spare his life. But thirty days have passed since I was called to go to the king."

[12]When Esther's words were reported to Mordecai, [13]he sent back this answer: "Do not think that

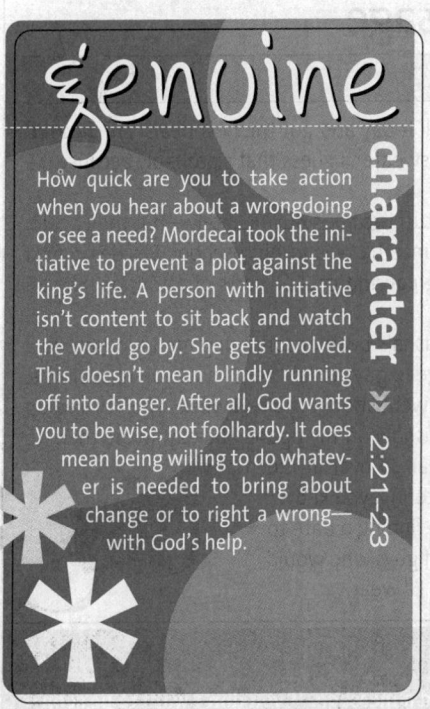

genuine

character » 2:21-23

How quick are you to take action when you hear about a wrongdoing or see a need? Mordecai took the initiative to prevent a plot against the king's life. A person with initiative isn't content to sit back and watch the world go by. She gets involved. This doesn't mean blindly running off into danger. After all, God wants you to be wise, not foolhardy. It does mean being willing to do whatever is needed to bring about change or to right a wrong—with God's help.

truth or dare

Every day, God gives you opportunities to act for him. But he'll never *force* you to take action. Sure you're scared of failure—but it's worse to not even try.

4:12-14

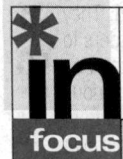

Sending a Message

Profile: **Isabel**

My cousin Sasha and I went to the mall today and got the best deals. I'm amazed at how much I saved on this little red sweater. I guess that's probably because it's so *little*.

My dad doesn't approve of the tighter stuff I've been buying lately—but then again, I'm his daughter, and it's been 20 years since he was in high school. Besides, Sasha wears this stuff every day, and she looks great and gets all sorts of attention. She always seems to have a date!

Since I've only been asked out twice, Sasha's been encouraging me to loosen up a little. She says you've got to send a message to guys to let them know you're available. And you know what? She's right. When we went shopping a few weeks ago, I picked up some tight jeans and a tank top that really show off my figure. The day I wore them to school, this guy who never talks to me walked over at lunch and started flirting big time. It was kind of flattering, you know?

A few months ago I was worried about finding a date to prom, but Sasha says she knows a couple of guys who would love to take me. Hmmm . . . I wonder what I'll wear.

For more on modesty, check out the link on www.TrueImagesBible.com

modesty in focus

When you dress sexy, you send a message. If you don't want to be seen as a sex object, then don't advertise your body by trying to get guys to want you sexually. Sound harsh? It's hardly meant to be. Remember . . .

» There's no harm in looking good, but Christians are supposed to focus on what's noble, right and pure (see Philippians 4:8, page 1553). Are you doing that—or obsessing about looks? Are you helping guys to focus on God—or contributing to them having impure thoughts?

» If you want to meet a quality guy who loves you for who you are, then don't settle for shallow attention.

» Think twice about what you're wearing, and develop the habit of seeking God's approval—not the stares of guys around you.

For more on this topic, see the index on page 1656.

because you are in the king's house you alone of all the Jews will escape. [14]For if you remain silent at this time, relief and deliverance for the Jews will arise from another place, but you and your father's family will perish. And who knows but that you have come to royal position for such a time as this?"

[15]Then Esther sent this reply to Mordecai: [16]"Go, gather together all the Jews who are in Susa, and fast for me. Do not eat or drink for three days, night or day. I and my maids will fast as you do. When this is done, I will go to the king, even though it is against the law. And if I perish, I perish."

[17]So Mordecai went away and carried out all of Esther's instructions.

Esther's Request to the King

5 On the third day Esther put on her royal robes and stood in the inner court of the palace, in front of the king's hall. The king was sitting on his royal throne in the hall, facing the entrance. [2]When he saw Queen Esther standing in the court, he was pleased with her and held

genuine

courage » 4:15–16

On a scale of 1 to 10 (with 10 being "courageous" and 1 being "wimpy"), how courageous are you? Esther risked her life to go before the king and speak on behalf of her people. That's about a 12 on a 10-point courage scale. You may not have to risk your life to prove your courage. But you might have to do something outside of your comfort zone—like speaking to your friends about God or not giving in to peer pressure even though everyone else is. Are you courageous enough?

out to her the gold scepter that was in his hand. So Esther approached and touched the tip of the scepter.

[3]Then the king asked, "What is it, Queen Esther? What is your request? Even up to half the kingdom, it will be given you."

[4]"If it pleases the king," replied Esther, "let the king, together with Haman, come today to a banquet I have prepared for him."

[5]"Bring Haman at once," the king said, "so that we may do what Esther asks."

So the king and Haman went to the banquet Esther had prepared. [6]As they were drinking wine, the king again asked Esther, "Now what is your petition? It will be given you. And what is your request? Even up to half the kingdom, it will be granted."

[7]Esther replied, "My petition and my request is this: [8]If the king regards me with favor and if it pleases the king to grant my petition and fulfill my request, let the king and Haman come tomorrow to the banquet I will prepare for them. Then I will answer the king's question."

Haman's Rage Against Mordecai

[9]Haman went out that day happy and in high spirits. But when he saw Mordecai at the king's gate and observed that he neither rose nor showed fear in his presence, he was filled with rage against Mordecai. [10]Nevertheless, Haman restrained himself and went home.

Calling together his friends and Zeresh, his wife, [11]Haman boasted to them about his vast wealth, his many sons, and all the ways the king had honored him and how he had elevated him above the other nobles and officials. [12]"And that's not all," Haman added. "I'm the only person Queen Esther invited to accompany the king to the banquet she gave. And she has invited me along with the king tomorrow. [13]But all this gives me no satisfaction as long as I see that Jew Mordecai sitting at the king's gate."

[14]His wife Zeresh and all his friends said to him, "Have a gallows built, seventy-five feet[a] high, and ask the king in the morning to have Mordecai hanged on it. Then go with the king to the dinner and be happy." This suggestion delighted Haman, and he had the gallows built.

Mordecai Honored

6 That night the king could not sleep; so he ordered the book of the chronicles, the record of his reign, to be brought in and read to him. [2]It was found recorded there that Mordecai had exposed Bigthana and Teresh, two of the king's officers who guarded the doorway, who had conspired to assassinate King Xerxes.

[3]"What honor and recognition has Mordecai received for this?" the king asked.

"Nothing has been done for him," his attendants answered.

truth or dare

Not seeing results from the seeds you've sown? Relax. God might be waiting for the perfect moment. Remember, in his book, there's no such thing as a coincidence.

6:1–3

[a] 14 Hebrew *fifty cubits* (about 23 meters)

[4]The king said, "Who is in the court?" Now Haman had just entered the outer court of the palace to speak to the king about hanging Mordecai on the gallows he had erected for him.

[5]His attendants answered, "Haman is standing in the court."

"Bring him in," the king ordered.

[6]When Haman entered, the king asked him, "What should be done for the man the king delights to honor?"

Now Haman thought to himself, "Who is there that the king would rather honor than me?" [7]So he answered the king, "For the man the king delights to honor, [8]have them bring a royal robe the king has worn and a horse the king has ridden, one with a royal crest placed on its head. [9]Then let the robe and horse be entrusted to one of the king's most noble princes. Let them robe the man the king delights to honor, and lead him on the horse through the city streets, proclaiming before him, 'This is what is done for the man the king delights to honor!' "

[10]"Go at once," the king commanded Haman. "Get the robe and the horse and do just as you have suggested for Mordecai the Jew, who sits at the king's gate. Do not neglect anything you have recommended."

[11]So Haman got the robe and the horse. He robed Mordecai, and led him on horseback through the city streets, proclaiming before him, "This is what is done for the man the king delights to honor!"

[12]Afterward Mordecai returned to the king's gate. But Haman rushed home, with his head covered in grief, [13]and told Zeresh his wife and all his friends everything that had happened to him.

His advisers and his wife Zeresh said to him, "Since Mordecai, before whom your downfall has started, is of Jewish origin, you cannot stand against him—you will surely come to ruin!" [14]While they were still talking with him, the king's eunuchs arrived and hurried Haman away to the banquet Esther had prepared.

Haman Hanged

7 So the king and Haman went to dine with Queen Esther, [2]and as they were drinking wine on that second day, the king again asked, "Queen Esther, what is your petition? It will be given you. What is your request? Even up to half the kingdom, it will be granted."

[3]Then Queen Esther answered, "If I have found favor with you, O king, and if it pleases your majesty, grant me my life—this is my petition. And spare my people—this is my request. [4]For I and my people have been sold for destruction and slaughter and annihilation. If we had merely been sold as male and female slaves, I would have kept quiet, because no such distress would justify disturbing the king.[a]"

[5]King Xerxes asked Queen Esther, "Who is he? Where is the man who has dared to do such a thing?"

[6]Esther said, "The adversary and enemy is this vile Haman."

Then Haman was terrified before the king and queen. [7]The king got up in a rage, left his wine and went out into the palace garden. But Haman, realizing that the king had already decided his fate, stayed behind to beg Queen Esther for his life.

[8]Just as the king returned from the palace garden to the banquet hall, Haman was falling on the couch where Esther was reclining.

The king exclaimed, "Will he even molest the queen while she is with me in the house?"

As soon as the word left the king's mouth, they covered Haman's face. [9]Then Harbona, one of the eunuchs attending the king, said, "A gallows seventy-five feet[b] high stands by Haman's house. He had it made for Mordecai, who spoke up to help the king."

The king said, "Hang him on it!" [10]So they hanged Haman on the gallows he had prepared for Mordecai. Then the king's fury subsided.

The King's Edict in Behalf of the Jews

8 That same day King Xerxes gave Queen Esther the estate of Haman, the enemy of the Jews. And Mordecai came into the presence of the king, for Esther had told how he was related to her. [2]The king took off his signet ring, which he had reclaimed from Haman, and presented it to Mordecai. And Esther appointed him over Haman's estate.

---

[a] 4 Or quiet, but the compensation our adversary offers cannot be compared with the loss the king would suffer
[b] 9 Hebrew fifty cubits (about 23 meters)

genuine

respect » 8:1-6

What would you do if a parent or teacher made a decision that clearly needed to be rethought? Would you have a "See, you don't know everything!" attitude or politely state your case? The king of Persia had been talked into making a terrible decree allowing every Jewish citizen in the kingdom to be murdered. But even though he'd made a bad decision, Esther didn't show disrespect. Instead, she worked with him on a plan to get around that law. Genuine respect doesn't mean dropping the subject when you disagree with someone in authority. You can still show respect, even when you have to say, "You're wrong."

³Esther again pleaded with the king, falling at his feet and weeping. She begged him to put an end to the evil plan of Haman the Agagite, which he had devised against the Jews. ⁴Then the king extended the gold scepter to Esther and she arose and stood before him.

⁵"If it pleases the king," she said, "and if he regards me with favor and thinks it the right thing to do, and if he is pleased with me, let an order be written overruling the dispatches that Haman son of Hammedatha, the Agagite, devised and wrote to destroy the Jews in all the king's provinces. ⁶For how can I bear to see disaster fall on my people? How can I bear to see the destruction of my family?"

⁷King Xerxes replied to Queen Esther and to Mordecai the Jew, "Because Haman attacked the Jews, I have given his estate to Esther, and they have hanged him on the gallows. ⁸Now write another decree in the king's name in behalf of the Jews as seems best to you, and seal it with the king's signet ring—for no document written in the king's name and sealed with his ring can be revoked."

⁹At once the royal secretaries were summoned—on the twenty-third day of the third month, the month of Sivan. They wrote out all Mordecai's orders to the Jews, and to the satraps, governors and nobles of the 127 provinces stretching from India to Cush.ᵃ These orders were written in the script of each province and the language of each people and also to the Jews in their own script and language. ¹⁰Mordecai wrote in the name of King Xerxes, sealed the dispatches with the king's signet ring, and sent them by mounted couriers, who rode fast horses especially bred for the king.

¹¹The king's edict granted the Jews in every city the right to assemble and protect themselves; to destroy, kill and annihilate any armed force of any nationality or province that might attack them and their women and children; and to plunder the property of their enemies. ¹²The day appointed for the Jews to do this in all the provinces of King Xerxes was the thirteenth day of the twelfth month, the month of Adar. ¹³A copy of the text of the edict was to be issued as law in every province and made known to the people of every nationality so that the Jews would be ready on that day to avenge themselves on their enemies.

¹⁴The couriers, riding the royal horses, raced out, spurred on by the king's command. And the edict was also issued in the citadel of Susa.

¹⁵Mordecai left the king's presence wearing royal garments of blue and white, a large crown of gold and a purple robe of fine linen. And the city of Susa held a joyous celebration. ¹⁶For the Jews it was a time of happiness and joy, gladness and honor. ¹⁷In every province and in every city, wherever the edict of the king went, there was joy and gladness among the Jews, with feasting and celebrating. And many people of other nationalities became Jews because fear of the Jews had seized them.

Triumph of the Jews

9 On the thirteenth day of the twelfth month, the month of Adar, the edict commanded by the king was to be carried out. On this day the enemies of the Jews had hoped to overpower them, but now the tables were turned and the Jews got the upper hand over those who hated them. ²The Jews assembled in their cities in all the provinces of King Xerxes to attack those

ᵃ *9* That is, the upper Nile region

seeking their destruction. No one could stand against them, because the people of all the other nationalities were afraid of them. ³And all the nobles of the provinces, the satraps, the governors and the king's administrators helped the Jews, because fear of Mordecai had seized them. ⁴Mordecai was prominent in the palace; his reputation spread throughout the provinces, and he became more and more powerful.

⁵The Jews struck down all their enemies with the sword, killing and destroying them, and they did what they pleased to those who hated them. ⁶In the citadel of Susa, the Jews killed and destroyed five hundred men. ⁷They also killed Parshandatha, Dalphon, Aspatha, ⁸Poratha, Adalia, Aridatha, ⁹Parmashta, Arisai, Aridai and Vaizatha, ¹⁰the ten sons of Haman son of Hammedatha, the enemy of the Jews. But they did not lay their hands on the plunder.

¹¹The number of those slain in the citadel of Susa was reported to the king that same day. ¹²The king said to Queen Esther, "The Jews have killed and destroyed five hundred men and the ten sons of Haman in the citadel of Susa. What have they done in the rest of the king's provinces? Now what is your petition? It will be given you. What is your request? It will also be granted."

¹³"If it pleases the king," Esther answered, "give the Jews in Susa permission to carry out this day's edict tomorrow also, and let Haman's ten sons be hanged on gallows."

¹⁴So the king commanded that this be done. An edict was issued in Susa, and they hanged the ten sons of Haman. ¹⁵The Jews in Susa came together on the fourteenth day of the month of Adar, and they put to death in Susa three hundred men, but they did not lay their hands on the plunder.

¹⁶Meanwhile, the remainder of the Jews who were in the king's provinces also assembled to protect themselves and get relief from their enemies. They killed seventy-five thousand of them but did not lay their hands on the plunder. ¹⁷This happened on the thirteenth day of the month of Adar, and on the fourteenth they rested and made it a day of feasting and joy.

Purim Celebrated

¹⁸The Jews in Susa, however, had assembled on the thirteenth and fourteenth, and then on the fifteenth they rested and made it a day of feasting and joy.

¹⁹That is why rural Jews—those living in villages—observe the fourteenth of the month of Adar as a day of joy and feasting, a day for giving presents to each other.

²⁰Mordecai recorded these events, and he sent letters to all the Jews throughout the provinces of King Xerxes, near and far, ²¹to have them celebrate annually the fourteenth and fifteenth days of the month of Adar ²²as the time when the Jews got relief from their enemies, and as the month when their sorrow was turned into joy and their mourning into a day of celebration. He wrote them to observe the days as days of feasting and joy and giving presents of food to one another and gifts to the poor.

²³So the Jews agreed to continue the celebration they had begun, doing what Mordecai had written to them. ²⁴For Haman son of Hammedatha, the Agagite, the enemy of all the Jews, had plotted against the Jews to destroy them and had cast the *pur* (that is, the lot) for their ruin and destruction. ²⁵But when the plot came to the king's attention,ᵃ he issued written orders that the evil scheme Haman had devised against the Jews should come back onto his own head, and that he and his sons should be hanged on the gallows. ²⁶(Therefore these days were called Purim, from the word *pur*.) Because of everything written in this letter and because of what they had seen and what had happened to them, ²⁷the Jews took it upon themselves to establish the custom that they and their descendants and all who join them should without fail observe these two days every year, in the way prescribed and at the time appointed. ²⁸These days should be remembered and observed in every generation by every family, and in every province and in every city. And these days of Purim should never cease to be celebrated by the Jews, nor should the memory of them die out among their descendants.

²⁹So Queen Esther, daughter of Abihail, along with Mordecai the Jew, wrote with full authority to confirm this second letter concerning Purim. ³⁰And Mordecai sent letters to all the Jews in the 127 provinces of the kingdom of Xerxes—words of goodwill and assurance— ³¹to establish these days of Purim at their designated times, as Mordecai the Jew and Queen Esther had decreed for them, and as they had established for themselves and their descendants in regard to their times of fasting and lamentation. ³²Esther's decree confirmed these regulations about Purim, and it was written down in the records.

ᵃ 25 Or *when Esther came before the king*

mirror images

"I will go to the king, even though it is against the law. And if I perish, I perish." Esther 4:16

Esther—Gutsy Girl

"**H**ow has it come down to this?" Esther wondered aloud as she stood in the king's palace, thinking back over her life. In some ways she'd lived a charmed life—winning the Miss Persia contest and marrying the king. But Esther wasn't feeling so lucky these days.

Esther had a secret: She was no Persian. She was a Jew.

When a Jew named Mordecai insulted the king's favorite noble, Haman, this scoundrel got the king's permission to destroy all the Jews in the empire. Another day, another decree—such was life in the empire.

But here's the catch. Mordecai was Esther's cousin, and because Esther's parents were dead, Mordecai had raised Esther. He encouraged her to change the king's mind. "Who knows?" he said. "Maybe God put you in a royal position for just this reason."

Pacing just outside the throne room, Esther took deep breaths, trying to calm herself. She knew she could be killed for the risk she was about to take. But she had to do it; the lives of millions of her own people were at stake. She mustered all her courage, closed her eyes, took one last deep breath, stepped up to the door . . . and took a chance.

Is it always worth it to do what is right? Just ask Esther. We can defend the girl others laugh at. We can refuse to give in to peer pressure. We can hold on to virginity. We can boldly tell people we believe in Christ. We may face ridicule or scorn, but we can remember what's at stake.

Esther risked her life, and God did incredible things through her. Do you have the chance to make an impact on your campus? Acting with courage is the difference between being a scared little kid and a gutsy girl. So, stop pacing. Muster your courage. Take a deep breath. And take that chance.

Dear God, in those moments when I feel afraid, give me the courage to do what is right and good. Help me to take a chance today. Amen.

dear God

To read the next Mirror Images profile, go to page 607.

» Read what happened as a result of Esther's courage in the book of Esther (pages 592–602).

The Greatness of Mordecai

10 King Xerxes imposed tribute throughout the empire, to its distant shores. [2]And all his acts of power and might, together with a full account of the greatness of Mordecai to which the king had raised him, are they not written in the book of the annals of the kings of Media and Persia? [3]Mordecai the Jew was second in rank to King Xerxes, preeminent among the Jews, and held in high esteem by his many fellow Jews, because he worked for the good of his people and spoke up for the welfare of all the Jews.

author:	Unknown.
date:	Unknown.
setting:	Job lived in the land of Uz, a large area east of Canaan.
verse to remember:	"Though he slay me, yet will I hope in him; I will surely defend my ways to his face" (13:15).
theme to consider:	We may never understand why there is suffering in our world, but we can learn the lesson Job learned. Even in tough circumstances, God is in complete control, and we can trust him.

unchanging truth

Reading the headlines in the newspaper or watching the news about bad things can stir up a lot of emotions—sadness, anger and fear, to name a few. These stories can also raise a lot of "why" questions in our minds. Why do thousands of children starve to death? Why are countless people killed in wars? Why are there so many diseases, accidents and senseless crimes?

You may even have some personal "why" questions. Why did someone I love suddenly die? Why did my mom lose her job? Why do I have to study so hard just to pass my classes? The truth is, life often *is* unfair—but it's never hopeless. God is in complete control, and you can trust him because he is good.

Job had many "why" questions. Why did he lose all his property, his livestock, even his children? Why did he break out with terrible sores? Why did he have to suffer when others were untouched? This book raises these questions as Job's friends attempt to help him find answers. But in the end, Job realizes he will not find answers to his sufferings this side of heaven. Instead of answers, Job is reassured that God is in complete control and can be trusted in the worst of circumstances.

When those "why" questions threaten to undermine your faith, remember Job. Turn to God and trust him completely with your situation.

life lessons

1. Even when terrible things happen to us, God is still in control and worthy of our trust (1:20–21).

2. No matter what happens, things are never hopeless. Our Redeemer lives, and someday in eternity he'll make everything right (19:25–27).

3. God loves us and has a plan for our lives. With God in control, we don't need to ask "why"; God knows what he's doing (42:1–3).

Prologue

1 In the land of Uz there lived a man whose name was Job. This man was blameless and upright; he feared God and shunned evil. ²He had seven sons and three daughters, ³and he owned seven thousand sheep, three thousand camels, five hundred yoke of oxen and five hundred donkeys, and had a large number of servants. He was the greatest man among all the people of the East.

⁴His sons used to take turns holding feasts in their homes, and they would invite their three sisters to eat and drink with them. ⁵When a period of feasting had run its course, Job would send and have them purified. Early in the morning he would sacrifice a burnt offering for each of them, thinking, "Perhaps my children have sinned and cursed God in their hearts." This was Job's regular custom.

Job's First Test

⁶One day the angels*ᵃ* came to present themselves before the Lᴏʀᴅ, and Satan*ᵇ* also came with them. ⁷The Lᴏʀᴅ said to Satan, "Where have you come from?"

Satan answered the Lᴏʀᴅ, "From roaming through the earth and going back and forth in it."

⁸Then the Lᴏʀᴅ said to Satan, "Have you considered my servant Job? There is no one on earth like him; he is blameless and upright, a man who fears God and shuns evil."

⁹"Does Job fear God for nothing?" Satan replied. ¹⁰"Have you not put a hedge around him and his household and everything he has? You have blessed the work of his hands, so that his flocks and herds are spread throughout the land. ¹¹But stretch out your hand and strike everything he has, and he will surely curse you to your face."

¹²The Lᴏʀᴅ said to Satan, "Very well, then, everything he has is in your hands, but on the man himself do not lay a finger."

Then Satan went out from the presence of the Lᴏʀᴅ.

¹³One day when Job's sons and daughters were feasting and drinking wine at the oldest brother's house, ¹⁴a messenger came to Job and said, "The oxen were plowing and the donkeys were grazing nearby, ¹⁵and the Sabeans attacked and carried them off. They put the servants to the sword, and I am the only one who has escaped to tell you!"

genuine
humility 1:20-22

Hard times reveal to the world what you're really made of. What do hard times reveal about you? A tendency to despair? To whine? Or to be humble? That's what hard times brought out in Job—humility. When horrible things happened, he didn't blame God or anyone else. He also didn't demand better treatment. Instead he acted humbly and *praised God*. Humility means yielding to God's leading instead of your own. The odd thing about humility is that you can't fake it. The moment you notice that you have it, well, it's not really there. It's something that only God can teach you.

¹⁶While he was still speaking, another messenger came and said, "The fire of God fell from the sky and burned up the sheep and the servants, and I am the only one who has escaped to tell you!"

¹⁷While he was still speaking, another messenger came and said, "The Chaldeans formed three raiding parties and swept down on your camels and carried them off. They put the servants to the sword, and I am the only one who has escaped to tell you!"

¹⁸While he was still speaking, yet another messenger came and said, "Your sons and daughters were feasting and drinking wine at the oldest brother's house, ¹⁹when suddenly a mighty wind swept in from the desert and struck the four corners of the house. It collapsed on them and they are dead, and I am the only one who has escaped to tell you!"

²⁰At this, Job got up and tore his robe and shaved his head. Then he fell to the ground in worship ²¹and said:

ᵃ 6 Hebrew *the sons of God*   *ᵇ 6 Satan* means *accuser.*

> "Naked I came from my mother's womb,
>   and naked I will depart. [a]
> The LORD gave and the LORD has taken away;
>   may the name of the LORD be praised."

²²In all this, Job did not sin by charging God with wrongdoing.

Job's Second Test

2 On another day the angels [b] came to present themselves before the LORD, and Satan also came with them to present himself before him. ²And the LORD said to Satan, "Where have you come from?"

Satan answered the LORD, "From roaming through the earth and going back and forth in it."

³Then the LORD said to Satan, "Have you considered my servant Job? There is no one on earth like him; he is blameless and upright, a man who fears God and shuns evil. And he still maintains his integrity, though you incited me against him to ruin him without any reason."

⁴"Skin for skin!" Satan replied. "A man will give all he has for his own life. ⁵But stretch out your hand and strike his flesh and bones, and he will surely curse you to your face."

⁶The LORD said to Satan, "Very well, then, he is in your hands; but you must spare his life."

⁷So Satan went out from the presence of the LORD and afflicted Job with painful sores from the soles of his feet to the top of his head. ⁸Then Job took a piece of broken pottery and scraped himself with it as he sat among the ashes.

⁹His wife said to him, "Are you still holding on to your integrity? Curse God and die!"

¹⁰He replied, "You are talking like a foolish [c] woman. Shall we accept good from God, and not trouble?"

In all this, Job did not sin in what he said.

Job's Three Friends

¹¹When Job's three friends, Eliphaz the Temanite, Bildad the Shuhite and Zophar the Naamathite, heard about all the troubles that had come upon him, they set out from their homes and met together by agreement to go and sympathize with him and comfort him. ¹²When they saw him from a distance, they could hardly recognize him; they began to weep aloud, and they tore their robes and sprinkled dust on their heads. ¹³Then they sat on the ground with him for seven days and seven nights. No one said a word to him, because they saw how great his suffering was.

Job Speaks

3 After this, Job opened his mouth and cursed the day of his birth. ²He said:

> ³ "May the day of my birth perish,
>   and the night it was said, 'A boy is born!'
> ⁴That day—may it turn to darkness;
>   may God above not care about it;
>   may no light shine upon it.

genuine integrity

2:7-10

How do you act when things aren't going your way? Does your personality change (hello, temper tantrum!), or do you act the same way regardless? When you have integrity, you do the right thing, even when you don't feel like it. After their children died and they lost just about everything, Job and his wife responded with two extremes. Job's wife advised him to curse God. But Job held on to his integrity and kept consistent, godly character even when life got hard. Which one are you more like—Job or his wife?

---

a 21 Or *will return there*   *b 1* Hebrew *the sons of God*   *c 10* The Hebrew word rendered *foolish* denotes moral deficiency.

⁵May darkness and deep shadowᵃ claim it once more;
>   may a cloud settle over it;
>   may blackness overwhelm its light.
⁶That night—may thick darkness seize it;
>   may it not be included among the days of the year
>   nor be entered in any of the months.
⁷May that night be barren;
>   may no shout of joy be heard in it.
⁸May those who curse daysᵇ curse that day,
>   those who are ready to rouse Leviathan.
⁹May its morning stars become dark;
>   may it wait for daylight in vain
>   and not see the first rays of dawn,
¹⁰for it did not shut the doors of the womb on me
>   to hide trouble from my eyes.

¹¹"Why did I not perish at birth,
>   and die as I came from the womb?
¹²Why were there knees to receive me
>   and breasts that I might be nursed?
¹³For now I would be lying down in peace;
>   I would be asleep and at rest
¹⁴with kings and counselors of the earth,
>   who built for themselves places now lying in ruins,
¹⁵with rulers who had gold,
>   who filled their houses with silver.
¹⁶Or why was I not hidden in the ground like a stillborn child,
>   like an infant who never saw the light of day?
¹⁷There the wicked cease from turmoil,
>   and there the weary are at rest.
¹⁸Captives also enjoy their ease;
>   they no longer hear the slave driver's shout.
¹⁹The small and the great are there,
>   and the slave is freed from his master.

²⁰"Why is light given to those in misery,
>   and life to the bitter of soul,
²¹to those who long for death that does not come,
>   who search for it more than for hidden treasure,
²²who are filled with gladness
>   and rejoice when they reach the grave?
²³Why is life given to a man
>   whose way is hidden,
>   whom God has hedged in?
²⁴For sighing comes to me instead of food;
>   my groans pour out like water.
²⁵What I feared has come upon me;
>   what I dreaded has happened to me.
²⁶I have no peace, no quietness;
>   I have no rest, but only turmoil."

Eliphaz

4 Then Eliphaz the Temanite replied:

²"If someone ventures a word with you, will you be impatient?
>   But who can keep from speaking?

ᵃ 5 Or *and the shadow of death*   ᵇ 8 Or *the sea*

mirror images

His wife said to him, "Are you still holding on to your integrity? Curse God and die!" Job 2:9

Job's Wife—Keepin' the Faith?

Job was rich, prosperous, powerful and godly, and that drove Satan crazy. So Satan started attacking Job to see if his faith was legit or if he just claimed he loved God because of his cushy lifestyle. First, Job lost everything he owned. Then his kids were killed (all ten of them). Then he got painful open sores all over his body, and everyone shunned him.

At this point, Job's wife said, "That's it! Forget God! He is ruining our lives, so I'm done with him!" She encouraged Job to tell God off and then die. And that's all we know about this woman. One comment. Maybe she was an all-around decent woman, but when the going got tough, she bailed on God and Job. Her faith fell short.

It's easy to love and serve God when everything in life is sunshine and smiley faces. If we score good grades, get the lead in the play and have money to spare, it's easy to be thankful. However, let reality come along and sometimes, like Job's wife, our faith falters.

Parents getting a divorce, the death of a friend, an illness, problems with drugs or alcohol in the family, acts of violence against our loved ones—these storms can shake our lives. In Job's wife's case, her faith was like a boat in port. Sure, it may have looked shiny and strong while it sat parked in calm waters, but its true test was in the storm. We often have no control over the storms in our lives—only our reactions to them. We can be like Job's wife, get ticked at God, pack up our "boat" and go home. Or we can acknowledge that bad things happen in life and look to God to keep us afloat. That's what it means to keep the faith.

To read the next Mirror Images profile, go to page 675.

Dear God, I confess that I sometimes want to blame you or get mad at you during storms in my life. Thank you for keeping me afloat and teaching me how to have faith instead. Amen.

dear God

>> **Read more about Job and his wife in the book of Job (pages 604-654).**

3 Think how you have instructed many,
how you have strengthened feeble hands.
4 Your words have supported those who stumbled;
you have strengthened faltering knees.
5 But now trouble comes to you, and you are discouraged;
it strikes you, and you are dismayed.
6 Should not your piety be your confidence
and your blameless ways your hope?

7 "Consider now: Who, being innocent, has ever perished?
Where were the upright ever
destroyed?
8 As I have observed, those who
plow evil
and those who sow trouble
reap it.
9 At the breath of God they are
destroyed;
at the blast of his anger they
perish.
10 The lions may roar and growl,
yet the teeth of the great lions
are broken.
11 The lion perishes for lack of prey,
and the cubs of the lioness are scattered.

12 "A word was secretly brought to me,
my ears caught a whisper of it.
13 Amid disquieting dreams in the night,
when deep sleep falls on men,
14 fear and trembling seized me
and made all my bones shake.
15 A spirit glided past my face,
and the hair on my body stood on end.
16 It stopped,
but I could not tell what it was.
A form stood before my eyes,
and I heard a hushed voice:
17 'Can a mortal be more righteous than God?
Can a man be more pure than his Maker?
18 If God places no trust in his servants,
if he charges his angels with error,
19 how much more those who live in houses of clay,
whose foundations are in the dust,
who are crushed more readily than a moth!
20 Between dawn and dusk they are broken to pieces;
unnoticed, they perish forever.
21 Are not the cords of their tent pulled up,
so that they die without wisdom?' a

5

"Call if you will, but who will answer you?
To which of the holy ones will you turn?
2 Resentment kills a fool,
and envy slays the simple.
3 I myself have seen a fool taking root,
but suddenly his house was cursed.

truth or dare

Eliphaz thought he could be exempted from the hard times by being good. Nope. Since the world is full of sin, bad things *will* happen to good people.

4:6–7

a 21 Some interpreters end the quotation after verse 17.

4 His children are far from safety,
  crushed in court without a defender.
5 The hungry consume his harvest,
  taking it even from among thorns,
  and the thirsty pant after his wealth.
6 For hardship does not spring from the soil,
  nor does trouble sprout from the ground.
7 Yet man is born to trouble
  as surely as sparks fly upward.

8 "But if it were I, I would appeal to God;
  I would lay my cause before him.
9 He performs wonders that cannot be fathomed,
  miracles that cannot be counted.
10 He bestows rain on the earth;
  he sends water upon the countryside.
11 The lowly he sets on high,
  and those who mourn are lifted to safety.
12 He thwarts the plans of the crafty,
  so that their hands achieve no success.
13 He catches the wise in their craftiness,
  and the schemes of the wily are swept away.
14 Darkness comes upon them in the daytime;
  at noon they grope as in the night.
15 He saves the needy from the sword in their mouth;
  he saves them from the clutches of the powerful.
16 So the poor have hope,
  and injustice shuts its mouth.

17 "Blessed is the man whom God corrects;
  so do not despise the discipline of the Almighty. *a*
18 For he wounds, but he also binds up;
  he injures, but his hands also heal.
19 From six calamities he will rescue you;
  in seven no harm will befall you.
20 In famine he will ransom you from death,
  and in battle from the stroke of the sword.
21 You will be protected from the lash of the tongue,
  and need not fear when destruction comes.
22 You will laugh at destruction and famine,
  and need not fear the beasts of the earth.
23 For you will have a covenant with the stones of the field,
  and the wild animals will be at peace with you.
24 You will know that your tent is secure;
  you will take stock of your property and find nothing missing.
25 You will know that your children will be many,
  and your descendants like the grass of the earth.
26 You will come to the grave in full vigor,
  like sheaves gathered in season.

27 "We have examined this, and it is true.
  So hear it and apply it to yourself."

a 17 Hebrew Shaddai; here and throughout Job

6

Then Job replied:

2 "If only my anguish could be weighed
  and all my misery be placed on the scales!
3 It would surely outweigh the sand
    of the seas—
  no wonder my words have
    been impetuous.
4 The arrows of the Almighty are in
    me,
  my spirit drinks in their
    poison;
  God's terrors are marshaled
    against me.
5 Does a wild donkey bray when it
    has grass,
  or an ox bellow when it has fodder?
6 Is tasteless food eaten without salt,
  or is there flavor in the white of an egg*?*
7 I refuse to touch it;
  such food makes me ill.

8 "Oh, that I might have my request,
  that God would grant what I hope for,
9 that God would be willing to crush me,
  to let loose his hand and cut me off!
10 Then I would still have this consolation—
  my joy in unrelenting pain—
  that I had not denied the words of the Holy One.

11 "What strength do I have, that I should still hope?
  What prospects, that I should be patient?
12 Do I have the strength of stone?
  Is my flesh bronze?
13 Do I have any power to help myself,
  now that success has been driven from me?

14 "A despairing man should have the devotion of his friends,
  even though he forsakes the fear of the Almighty.
15 But my brothers are as undependable as intermittent streams,
  as the streams that overflow
16 when darkened by thawing ice
  and swollen with melting snow,
17 but that cease to flow in the dry season,
  and in the heat vanish from their channels.
18 Caravans turn aside from their routes;
  they go up into the wasteland and perish.
19 The caravans of Tema look for water,
  the traveling merchants of Sheba look in hope.
20 They are distressed, because they had been confident;
  they arrive there, only to be disappointed.
21 Now you too have proved to be of no help;
  you see something dreadful and are afraid.
22 Have I ever said, 'Give something on my behalf,
  pay a ransom for me from your wealth,

truth or dare

Have you ever felt completely abandoned or mistreated by God, as Job did? Tell God how you're feeling. The sooner you spill, the sooner he can help you heal.

6:1–4

a 6 The meaning of the Hebrew for this phrase is uncertain.

²³ deliver me from the hand of the enemy,
        ransom me from the clutches of the ruthless'?

²⁴ "Teach me, and I will be quiet;
        show me where I have been wrong.
²⁵ How painful are honest words!
        But what do your arguments prove?
²⁶ Do you mean to correct what I say,
        and treat the words of a despairing man as wind?
²⁷ You would even cast lots for the fatherless
        and barter away your friend.

²⁸ "But now be so kind as to look at me.
        Would I lie to your face?
²⁹ Relent, do not be unjust;
        reconsider, for my integrity is at stake. ᵃ
³⁰ Is there any wickedness on my lips?
        Can my mouth not discern malice?

7

"Does not man have hard service on earth?
        Are not his days like those of a hired man?
² Like a slave longing for the evening shadows,
        or a hired man waiting eagerly for his wages,
³ so I have been allotted months of futility,
        and nights of misery have been assigned to me.
⁴ When I lie down I think, 'How long before I get up?'
        The night drags on, and I toss till dawn.
⁵ My body is clothed with worms and scabs,
        my skin is broken and festering.

⁶ "My days are swifter than a weaver's shuttle,
        and they come to an end without hope.
⁷ Remember, O God, that my life is but a breath;
        my eyes will never see happiness again.
⁸ The eye that now sees me will see me no longer;
        you will look for me, but I will be no more.
⁹ As a cloud vanishes and is gone,
        so he who goes down to the grave ᵇ does not return.
¹⁰ He will never come to his house again;
        his place will know him no more.

¹¹ "Therefore I will not keep silent;
        I will speak out in the anguish of my spirit,
        I will complain in the bitterness of my soul.
¹² Am I the sea, or the monster of the deep,
        that you put me under guard?
¹³ When I think my bed will comfort me
        and my couch will ease my complaint,
¹⁴ even then you frighten me with dreams
        and terrify me with visions,
¹⁵ so that I prefer strangling and death,
        rather than this body of mine.
¹⁶ I despise my life; I would not live forever.
        Let me alone; my days have no meaning.

¹⁷ "What is man that you make so much of him,
        that you give him so much attention,

ᵃ 29 Or *my righteousness still stands*   ᵇ 9 Hebrew *Sheol*

¹⁸ that you examine him every morning
and test him every moment?
¹⁹ Will you never look away from me,
or let me alone even for an instant?
²⁰ If I have sinned, what have I done to you,
O watcher of men?
Why have you made me your target?
Have I become a burden to you?^a
²¹ Why do you not pardon my offenses
and forgive my sins?
For I will soon lie down in the dust;
you will search for me, but I will be no more."

Bildad

8 Then Bildad the Shuhite replied:

² "How long will you say such things?
Your words are a blustering wind.
³ Does God pervert justice?
Does the Almighty pervert what is right?
⁴ When your children sinned against him,
he gave them over to the penalty of their sin.
⁵ But if you will look to God
and plead with the Almighty,
⁶ if you are pure and upright,
even now he will rouse himself on your behalf
and restore you to your rightful place.
⁷ Your beginnings will seem humble,
so prosperous will your future be.

⁸ "Ask the former generations
and find out what their fathers learned,
⁹ for we were born only yesterday and know nothing,
and our days on earth are but a shadow.
¹⁰ Will they not instruct you and tell you?
Will they not bring forth words from their understanding?
¹¹ Can papyrus grow tall where there is no marsh?
Can reeds thrive without water?
¹² While still growing and uncut,
they wither more quickly than grass.
¹³ Such is the destiny of all who forget God;
so perishes the hope of the godless.
¹⁴ What he trusts in is fragile^b;
what he relies on is a spider's web.
¹⁵ He leans on his web, but it gives way;
he clings to it, but it does not hold.
¹⁶ He is like a well-watered plant in the sunshine,
spreading its shoots over the garden;
¹⁷ it entwines its roots around a pile of rocks
and looks for a place among the stones.
¹⁸ But when it is torn from its spot,
that place disowns it and says, 'I never saw you.'
¹⁹ Surely its life withers away,
and^c from the soil other plants grow.

---

^a 20 A few manuscripts of the Masoretic Text, an ancient Hebrew scribal tradition and Septuagint; most manuscripts of the Masoretic Text *I have become a burden to myself.*   ^b 14 The meaning of the Hebrew for this word is uncertain.
^c 19 Or *Surely all the joy it has / is that*

20 "Surely God does not reject a blameless man
    or strengthen the hands of evildoers.
21 He will yet fill your mouth with laughter
    and your lips with shouts of joy.
22 Your enemies will be clothed in shame,
    and the tents of the wicked will be no more."

Job

9

Then Job replied:

2 "Indeed, I know that this is true.
    But how can a mortal be righteous before God?
3 Though one wished to dispute with him,
    he could not answer him one time out of a thousand.
4 His wisdom is profound, his power is vast.
    Who has resisted him and come out unscathed?
5 He moves mountains without their knowing it
    and overturns them in his anger.
6 He shakes the earth from its place
    and makes its pillars tremble.
7 He speaks to the sun and it does not shine;
    he seals off the light of the stars.
8 He alone stretches out the heavens
    and treads on the waves of the sea.
9 He is the Maker of the Bear and Orion,
    the Pleiades and the constellations of the south.
10 He performs wonders that cannot be fathomed,
    miracles that cannot be counted.
11 When he passes me, I cannot see him;
    when he goes by, I cannot perceive him.
12 If he snatches away, who can stop him?
    Who can say to him, 'What are you doing?'
13 God does not restrain his anger;
    even the cohorts of Rahab cowered at his feet.

14 "How then can I dispute with him?
    How can I find words to argue with him?
15 Though I were innocent, I could not answer him;
    I could only plead with my Judge for mercy.
16 Even if I summoned him and he responded,
    I do not believe he would give me a hearing.
17 He would crush me with a storm
    and multiply my wounds for no reason.
18 He would not let me regain my breath
    but would overwhelm me with misery.
19 If it is a matter of strength, he is mighty!
    And if it is a matter of justice, who will summon him[a]?
20 Even if I were innocent, my mouth would condemn me;
    if I were blameless, it would pronounce me guilty.

21 "Although I am blameless,
    I have no concern for myself;
    I despise my own life.
22 It is all the same; that is why I say,
    'He destroys both the blameless and the wicked.'

a 19 See Septuagint; Hebrew me.

²³ When a scourge brings sudden death,
    he mocks the despair of the innocent.
²⁴ When a land falls into the hands of the wicked,
    he blindfolds its judges.
    If it is not he, then who is it?

²⁵ "My days are swifter than a runner;
    they fly away without a glimpse of joy.
²⁶ They skim past like boats of papyrus,
    like eagles swooping down on their prey.
²⁷ If I say, 'I will forget my complaint,
    I will change my expression, and smile,'
²⁸ I still dread all my sufferings,
    for I know you will not hold me innocent.
²⁹ Since I am already found guilty,
    why should I struggle in vain?
³⁰ Even if I washed myself with soap *ᵃ*
    and my hands with washing soda,
³¹ you would plunge me into a slime pit
    so that even my clothes would detest me.

³² "He is not a man like me that I might answer him,
    that we might confront each other in court.
³³ If only there were someone to arbitrate between us,
    to lay his hand upon us both,
³⁴ someone to remove God's rod from me,
    so that his terror would frighten me no more.
³⁵ Then I would speak up without fear of him,
    but as it now stands with me, I cannot.

10

  "I loathe my very life;
    therefore I will give free rein to my complaint
    and speak out in the bitterness of my soul.
² I will say to God: Do not condemn
      me,
    but tell me what charges you
      have against me.
³ Does it please you to oppress me,
    to spurn the work of your
      hands,
    while you smile on the
      schemes of the wicked?
⁴ Do you have eyes of flesh?
    Do you see as a mortal sees?
⁵ Are your days like those of a
      mortal
    or your years like those of a man,
⁶ that you must search out my faults
    and probe after my sin—
⁷ though you know that I am not guilty
    and that no one can rescue me from your
      hand?

⁸ "Your hands shaped me and made me.
    Will you now turn and destroy me?
⁹ Remember that you molded me like clay.

truth or dare

Job started crossing the line between self-expression and self-pity. While it's healthy to unload your hurts and disappointments to God, don't cross over into bitterness.

10:1

ᵃ 30 Or snow

Will you now turn me to dust again?
¹⁰ Did you not pour me out like milk
and curdle me like cheese,
¹¹ clothe me with skin and flesh
and knit me together with bones and sinews?
¹² You gave me life and showed me kindness,
and in your providence watched over my spirit.

¹³ "But this is what you concealed in your heart,
and I know that this was in your mind:
¹⁴ If I sinned, you would be watching me
and would not let my offense go unpunished.
¹⁵ If I am guilty—woe to me!
Even if I am innocent, I cannot lift my head,
for I am full of shame
and drowned in *ᵃ* my affliction.
¹⁶ If I hold my head high, you stalk me like a lion
and again display your awesome power against me.
¹⁷ You bring new witnesses against me
and increase your anger toward me;
your forces come against me wave upon wave.

¹⁸ "Why then did you bring me out of the womb?
I wish I had died before any eye saw me.
¹⁹ If only I had never come into being,
or had been carried straight from the womb to the grave!
²⁰ Are not my few days almost over?
Turn away from me so I can have a moment's joy
²¹ before I go to the place of no return,
to the land of gloom and deep shadow, *ᵇ*
²² to the land of deepest night,
of deep shadow and disorder,
where even the light is like darkness."

Zophar

11 Then Zophar the Naamathite replied:

² "Are all these words to go unanswered?
Is this talker to be vindicated?
³ Will your idle talk reduce men to silence?
Will no one rebuke you when you mock?
⁴ You say to God, 'My beliefs are flawless
and I am pure in your sight.'
⁵ Oh, how I wish that God would speak,
that he would open his lips against you
⁶ and disclose to you the secrets of wisdom,
for true wisdom has two sides.
Know this: God has even forgotten some of your sin.

⁷ "Can you fathom the mysteries of God?
Can you probe the limits of the Almighty?
⁸ They are higher than the heavens—what can you do?
They are deeper than the depths of the grave *ᶜ*—what can you know?
⁹ Their measure is longer than the earth
and wider than the sea.

---

a 15 Or *and aware of*   *b 21* Or *and the shadow of death*; also in verse 22   *c 8* Hebrew *than Sheol*

¹⁰ "If he comes along and confines you in prison
and convenes a court, who can oppose him?
¹¹ Surely he recognizes deceitful men;
and when he sees evil, does he not take note?
¹² But a witless man can no more become wise
than a wild donkey's colt can be born a man. ^a

¹³ "Yet if you devote your heart to him
and stretch out your hands to him,
¹⁴ if you put away the sin that is in your hand
and allow no evil to dwell in your tent,
¹⁵ then you will lift up your face without shame;
you will stand firm and without fear.
¹⁶ You will surely forget your trouble,
recalling it only as waters gone by.
¹⁷ Life will be brighter than noonday,
and darkness will become like morning.
¹⁸ You will be secure, because there is hope;
you will look about you and take your rest in safety.
¹⁹ You will lie down, with no one to make you afraid,
and many will court your favor.
²⁰ But the eyes of the wicked will fail,
and escape will elude them;
their hope will become a dying gasp."

Job
12
Then Job replied:

² "Doubtless you are the people,
and wisdom will die with you!
³ But I have a mind as well as you;
I am not inferior to you.
Who does not know all these things?

⁴ "I have become a laughingstock to my friends,
though I called upon God and he answered—
a mere laughingstock, though righteous and blameless!
⁵ Men at ease have contempt for misfortune
as the fate of those whose feet are slipping.
⁶ The tents of marauders are undisturbed,
and those who provoke God are secure—
those who carry their god in their hands. ^b

⁷ "But ask the animals, and they will teach you,
or the birds of the air, and they will tell you;
⁸ or speak to the earth, and it will teach you,
or let the fish of the sea inform you.
⁹ Which of all these does not know
that the hand of the LORD has done this?
¹⁰ In his hand is the life of every creature
and the breath of all mankind.
¹¹ Does not the ear test words
as the tongue tastes food?
¹² Is not wisdom found among the aged?
Does not long life bring understanding?

^a 12 Or wild donkey can be born tame   ^b 6 Or secure / in what God's hand brings them

13 "To God belong wisdom and
power;
counsel and understanding
are his.
14 What he tears down cannot be
rebuilt;
the man he imprisons cannot
be released.
15 If he holds back the waters, there
is drought;
if he lets them loose, they
devastate the land.
16 To him belong strength and victory;
both deceived and deceiver are his.
17 He leads counselors away stripped
and makes fools of judges.
18 He takes off the shackles put on by kings
and ties a loincloth*a* around their waist.
19 He leads priests away stripped
and overthrows men long established.
20 He silences the lips of trusted advisers
and takes away the discernment of elders.
21 He pours contempt on nobles
and disarms the mighty.
22 He reveals the deep things of darkness
and brings deep shadows into the light.
23 He makes nations great, and destroys them;
he enlarges nations, and disperses them.
24 He deprives the leaders of the earth of their reason;
he sends them wandering through a trackless waste.
25 They grope in darkness with no light;
he makes them stagger like drunkards.

13

"My eyes have seen all this,
my ears have heard and understood it.
2 What you know, I also know;
I am not inferior to you.
3 But I desire to speak to the Almighty
and to argue my case with God.
4 You, however, smear me with lies;
you are worthless physicians, all of you!
5 If only you would be altogether silent!
For you, that would be wisdom.
6 Hear now my argument;
listen to the plea of my lips.
7 Will you speak wickedly on God's behalf?
Will you speak deceitfully for him?
8 Will you show him partiality?
Will you argue the case for God?
9 Would it turn out well if he examined you?
Could you deceive him as you might deceive men?
10 He would surely rebuke you
if you secretly showed partiality.
11 Would not his splendor terrify you?
Would not the dread of him fall on you?

truth or dare

If God says no to a relationship, a job or *anything*, you know it's the best answer for you. Rebelling against God's decision will only hurt you in the end.

12:13–14

a 18 Or shackles of kings / and ties a belt

¹²Your maxims are proverbs of ashes;
　　your defenses are defenses of clay.

¹³"Keep silent and let me speak;
　　then let come to me what may.
¹⁴Why do I put myself in jeopardy
　　and take my life in my hands?
¹⁵Though he slay me, yet will I hope in him;
　　I will surely^a defend my ways to his face.
¹⁶Indeed, this will turn out for my deliverance,
　　for no godless man would dare come before him!
¹⁷Listen carefully to my words;
　　let your ears take in what I say.
¹⁸Now that I have prepared my case,
　　I know I will be vindicated.
¹⁹Can anyone bring charges against me?
　　If so, I will be silent and die.

²⁰"Only grant me these two things, O God,
　　and then I will not hide from you:
²¹Withdraw your hand far from me,
　　and stop frightening me with your terrors.
²²Then summon me and I will answer,
　　or let me speak, and you reply.
²³How many wrongs and sins have I committed?
　　Show me my offense and my sin.
²⁴Why do you hide your face
　　and consider me your enemy?
²⁵Will you torment a windblown leaf?
　　Will you chase after dry chaff?
²⁶For you write down bitter things against me
　　and make me inherit the sins of my youth.
²⁷You fasten my feet in shackles;
　　you keep close watch on all my paths
　　by putting marks on the soles of my feet.

²⁸"So man wastes away like something rotten,
　　like a garment eaten by moths.

14

"Man born of woman
　　is of few days and full of trouble.
²He springs up like a flower and withers away;
　　like a fleeting shadow, he does not endure.
³Do you fix your eye on such a one?
　　Will you bring him^b before you for judgment?
⁴Who can bring what is pure from the impure?
　　No one!
⁵Man's days are determined;
　　you have decreed the number of his months
　　and have set limits he cannot exceed.
⁶So look away from him and let him alone,
　　till he has put in his time like a hired man.

⁷"At least there is hope for a tree:
　　If it is cut down, it will sprout again,
　　and its new shoots will not fail.
⁸Its roots may grow old in the ground

^a 15 Or *He will surely slay me; I have no hope — / yet I will*　　^b 3 Septuagint, Vulgate and Syriac; Hebrew *me*

and its stump die in the soil,
⁹ yet at the scent of water it will bud
   and put forth shoots like a
      plant.
¹⁰ But man dies and is laid low;
   he breathes his last and is no
      more.
¹¹ As water disappears from the sea
   or a riverbed becomes
      parched and dry,
¹² so man lies down and does not
   rise;
   till the heavens are no more, men will not
      awake
   or be roused from their sleep.

¹³ "If only you would hide me in the grave*ᵃ*
   and conceal me till your anger has passed!
 If only you would set me a time
   and then remember me!
¹⁴ If a man dies, will he live again?
   All the days of my hard service
   I will wait for my renewal*ᵇ* to come.
¹⁵ You will call and I will answer you;
   you will long for the creature your hands have made.
¹⁶ Surely then you will count my steps
   but not keep track of my sin.
¹⁷ My offenses will be sealed up in a bag;
   you will cover over my sin.

¹⁸ "But as a mountain erodes and crumbles
   and as a rock is moved from its place,
¹⁹ as water wears away stones
   and torrents wash away the soil,
   so you destroy man's hope.
²⁰ You overpower him once for all, and he is gone;
   you change his countenance and send him away.
²¹ If his sons are honored, he does not know it;
   if they are brought low, he does not see it.
²² He feels but the pain of his own body
   and mourns only for himself."

Eliphaz

15

Then Eliphaz the Temanite replied:

² "Would a wise man answer with empty notions
   or fill his belly with the hot east wind?
³ Would he argue with useless words,
   with speeches that have no value?
⁴ But you even undermine piety
   and hinder devotion to God.
⁵ Your sin prompts your mouth;
   you adopt the tongue of the crafty.
⁶ Your own mouth condemns you, not mine;
   your own lips testify against you.

truth or dare

From the moment you set foot on planet Earth, your days were numbered. So make the most out of every day God gives you. *Carpe diem!* Seize the day!

14:5

---

a 13 Hebrew *Sheol*   *b* 14 Or *release*

⁷ "Are you the first man ever born?
    Were you brought forth before the hills?
⁸ Do you listen in on God's council?
    Do you limit wisdom to yourself?
⁹ What do you know that we do not know?
    What insights do you have that we do not have?
¹⁰ The gray-haired and the aged are on our side,
    men even older than your father.
¹¹ Are God's consolations not enough for you,
    words spoken gently to you?
¹² Why has your heart carried you away,
    and why do your eyes flash,
¹³ so that you vent your rage against God
    and pour out such words from your mouth?

¹⁴ "What is man, that he could be pure,
    or one born of woman, that he could be righteous?
¹⁵ If God places no trust in his holy ones,
    if even the heavens are not pure in his eyes,
¹⁶ how much less man, who is vile and corrupt,
    who drinks up evil like water!

¹⁷ "Listen to me and I will explain to you;
    let me tell you what I have seen,
¹⁸ what wise men have declared,
    hiding nothing received from their fathers
¹⁹ (to whom alone the land was given
    when no alien passed among them):
²⁰ All his days the wicked man suffers torment,
    the ruthless through all the years stored up for him.
²¹ Terrifying sounds fill his ears;
    when all seems well, marauders attack him.
²² He despairs of escaping the darkness;
    he is marked for the sword.
²³ He wanders about—food for vultures ᵃ;
    he knows the day of darkness is at hand.
²⁴ Distress and anguish fill him with terror;
    they overwhelm him, like a king poised to attack,
²⁵ because he shakes his fist at God
    and vaunts himself against the Almighty,
²⁶ defiantly charging against him
    with a thick, strong shield.

²⁷ "Though his face is covered with fat
    and his waist bulges with flesh,
²⁸ he will inhabit ruined towns
    and houses where no one lives,
    houses crumbling to rubble.
²⁹ He will no longer be rich and his wealth will not endure,
    nor will his possessions spread over the land.
³⁰ He will not escape the darkness;
    a flame will wither his shoots,
    and the breath of God's mouth will carry him away.
³¹ Let him not deceive himself by trusting what is worthless,
    for he will get nothing in return.
³² Before his time he will be paid in full,

ᵃ 23 Or about, looking for food

Fire in My Bones

Profile: Reese

I have a temper. Always have. I'm getting better at hiding it. But my family sees that side of me all too often. Sometimes I wear this fake smile throughout the day, and then I come home and explode. The least little thing—like my dad asking me to pick up my schoolbooks—sends me into a scream-cry-and-throw-everything-in-sight rage.

For a long time I thought anger was a sin. I believed I was somehow less holy because I felt so much anger. So I kept it all inside. Then I heard my pastor talking about how holding anger in is just as dangerous as attacking people with it. So I started letting it out. The problem with me is that I can't find a balance. Either I'm stuffing my emotions inside and pretending like nothing's wrong, or I'm exploding and spewing out anger like scalding lava. What's my problem?

I've been praying that God would help me with this anger issue, but I don't see any progress in my life. I'm like two different people—the calm, easygoing girl that everyone knows and then the vicious girl who comes home and takes it all out on her family. I'm so frustrated with myself.

For more on dealing with anger, check out the Anger Link on www.TrueImagesBible.com

anger in focus

Reese is on the right track. She's learned that she can't hold her feelings of anger inside, but how she's reacting to her anger is wrong (see Ephesians 4:26, page 1545). When you feel anger rising inside you, choose to follow these guidelines:

»**A:** Accept anger as a normal emotion—the feeling itself isn't sin.
»**N:** Name the reason for your anger. Hurt? Jealousy? Injustice?
»**G:** Get moving toward a solution. Once you've identified the root cause, figure out a good way to deal with it.
»**E:** Embrace God's power. Anger is bigger than you are. But God is bigger than anger.
»**R:** Reach out for help. Ask someone you respect, like a parent or grandparent, to support you and help you find strategies for dealing with your anger.

For more on this topic, see the index on page 1656.

and his branches will not flourish.
33 He will be like a vine stripped of its unripe grapes,
    like an olive tree shedding its blossoms.
34 For the company of the godless will be barren,
    and fire will consume the tents of those who love bribes.
35 They conceive trouble and give birth to evil;
    their womb fashions deceit."

Job
16

Then Job replied:

2 "I have heard many things like these;
    miserable comforters are you all!

3 Will your long-winded speeches never end?
   What ails you that you keep on arguing?
4 I also could speak like you,
   if you were in my place;
 I could make fine speeches against you
   and shake my head at you.
5 But my mouth would encourage you;
   comfort from my lips would bring you relief.

6 "Yet if I speak, my pain is not relieved;
   and if I refrain, it does not go away.
7 Surely, O God, you have worn me out;
   you have devastated my entire household.
8 You have bound me—and it has become a witness;
   my gauntness rises up and testifies against me.
9 God assails me and tears me in his anger
   and gnashes his teeth at me;
   my opponent fastens on me his piercing eyes.
10 Men open their mouths to jeer at me;
   they strike my cheek in scorn
   and unite together against me.
11 God has turned me over to evil men
   and thrown me into the clutches of the wicked.
12 All was well with me, but he shattered me;
   he seized me by the neck and crushed me.

 He has made me his target;
13   his archers surround me.
 Without pity, he pierces my kidneys
   and spills my gall on the ground.
14 Again and again he bursts upon me;
   he rushes at me like a warrior.

15 "I have sewed sackcloth over my skin
   and buried my brow in the dust.
16 My face is red with weeping,
   deep shadows ring my eyes;
17 yet my hands have been free of violence
   and my prayer is pure.
18 "O earth, do not cover my blood;
   may my cry never be laid to rest!
19 Even now my witness is in heaven;
   my advocate is on high.
20 My intercessor is my friend[a]
   as my eyes pour out tears to God;
21 on behalf of a man he pleads with God
   as a man pleads for his friend.

22 "Only a few years will pass
   before I go on the journey of no return.

17

1 My spirit is broken,
   my days are cut short,
   the grave awaits me.
2 Surely mockers surround me;
   my eyes must dwell on their hostility.

3 "Give me, O God, the pledge you demand.

a 20 Or My friends treat me with scorn

Who else will put up security for me?
⁴You have closed their minds to understanding;
  therefore you will not let them triumph.
⁵If a man denounces his friends for reward,
  the eyes of his children will fail.

⁶"God has made me a byword to everyone,
  a man in whose face people spit.
⁷My eyes have grown dim with grief;
  my whole frame is but a shadow.
⁸Upright men are appalled at this;
  the innocent are aroused against the ungodly.
⁹Nevertheless, the righteous will hold to their ways,
      and those with clean hands
        will grow stronger.

¹⁰"But come on, all of you, try
        again!
  I will not find a wise man
        among you.
¹¹My days have passed, my plans
        are shattered,
  and so are the desires of my
        heart.
¹²These men turn night into day;
  in the face of darkness they
        say, 'Light is near.'
¹³If the only home I hope for is the
        grave,ᵃ
  if I spread out my bed in
        darkness,
¹⁴if I say to corruption, 'You are my
        father,'
  and to the worm, 'My mother'
        or 'My sister,'
¹⁵where then is my hope?
  Who can see any hope for
        me?
¹⁶Will it go down to the gates of
        deathᵃ?
  Will we descend together into
        the dust?"

Bildad

18 Then Bildad the Shuhite replied:

²"When will you end these
        speeches?
  Be sensible, and then we can
        talk.
³Why are we regarded as cattle
  and considered stupid in your
        sight?
⁴You who tear yourself to pieces
  in your anger,

---

love❤notes

16:19

Beloved,

*False accusations sting. But when
others accuse you and lie, remember that you have a witness
and advocate in heaven. I know
your innocence, and I will eventually restore your reputation.*

  —*Your heavenly Witness and
Advocate*

What does it mean to you that God is
on your side?

_____

_____

_____

_____

_____

_____

_____

_____

_____

_____

_____

ᵃ 13,16 Hebrew *Sheol*

is the earth to be abandoned for your sake?
Or must the rocks be moved from their place?

5 "The lamp of the wicked is snuffed out;
the flame of his fire stops burning.
6 The light in his tent becomes dark;
the lamp beside him goes out.
7 The vigor of his step is weakened;
his own schemes throw him down.
8 His feet thrust him into a net
and he wanders into its mesh.
9 A trap seizes him by the heel;
a snare holds him fast.
10 A noose is hidden for him on the ground;
a trap lies in his path.
11 Terrors startle him on every side
and dog his every step.
12 Calamity is hungry for him;
disaster is ready for him when he falls.
13 It eats away parts of his skin;
death's firstborn devours his limbs.
14 He is torn from the security of his tent
and marched off to the king of terrors.
15 Fire resides[a] in his tent;
burning sulfur is scattered over his dwelling.
16 His roots dry up below
and his branches wither above.
17 The memory of him perishes from the earth;
he has no name in the land.
18 He is driven from light into darkness
and is banished from the world.
19 He has no offspring or descendants among his people,
no survivor where once he lived.
20 Men of the west are appalled at his fate;
men of the east are seized with horror.
21 Surely such is the dwelling of an evil man;
such is the place of one who knows not God."

Job

19

Then Job replied:

2 "How long will you torment me
and crush me with words?
3 Ten times now you have reproached me;
shamelessly you attack me.
4 If it is true that I have gone astray,
my error remains my concern alone.
5 If indeed you would exalt yourselves above me
and use my humiliation against me,
6 then know that God has wronged me
and drawn his net around me.

7 "Though I cry, 'I've been wronged!' I get no response;
though I call for help, there is no justice.
8 He has blocked my way so I cannot pass;

a 15 Or *Nothing he had remains*

he has shrouded my paths in darkness.
⁹He has stripped me of my honor
and removed the crown from my head.
¹⁰He tears me down on every side till I am gone;
he uproots my hope like a tree.
¹¹His anger burns against me;
he counts me among his enemies.
¹²His troops advance in force;
they build a siege ramp against me
and encamp around my tent.

¹³"He has alienated my brothers from me;
my acquaintances are completely estranged from me.
¹⁴My kinsmen have gone away;
my friends have forgotten me.
¹⁵My guests and my maidservants count me a stranger;
they look upon me as an alien.
¹⁶I summon my servant, but he does not answer,
though I beg him with my own mouth.
¹⁷My breath is offensive to my wife;
I am loathsome to my own brothers.
¹⁸Even the little boys scorn me;
when I appear, they ridicule
me.
¹⁹All my intimate friends detest me;
those I love have turned
against me.
²⁰I am nothing but skin and bones;
I have escaped with only the
skin of my teeth. ᵃ

²¹"Have pity on me, my friends,
have pity,
for the hand of God has struck me.
²²Why do you pursue me as God does?
Will you never get enough of my flesh?

²³"Oh, that my words were recorded,
that they were written on a scroll,
²⁴that they were inscribed with an iron tool on ᵇ
lead,
or engraved in rock forever!
²⁵I know that my Redeemer ᶜ lives,
and that in the end he will stand upon the earth. ᵈ
²⁶And after my skin has been destroyed,
yet ᵉ in ᶠ my flesh I will see God;
²⁷I myself will see him
with my own eyes—I, and not another.
How my heart yearns within me!

²⁸"If you say, 'How we will hound him,
since the root of the trouble lies in him, ᵍ'
²⁹you should fear the sword yourselves;
for wrath will bring punishment by the sword,
and then you will know that there is judgment. ʰ"

truth or dare

Suffering isn't the worst thing that can happen to you. Losing hope is. Even in the awful times in life, you can have confidence that through Jesus, your living Redeemer, you are never without hope.

19:25

ᵃ 20 Or only my gums   ᵇ 24 Or and   ᶜ 25 Or defender   ᵈ 25 Or upon my grave   ᵉ 26 Or And after I awake, /
though this ⸤body⸥ has been destroyed, / then   ᶠ 26 Or / apart from   ᵍ 28 Many Hebrew manuscripts, Septuagint and
Vulgate; most Hebrew manuscripts me   ʰ 29 Or / that you may come to know the Almighty

20

Then Zophar the Naamathite replied:

2 "My troubled thoughts prompt me to answer
    because I am greatly disturbed.
3 I hear a rebuke that dishonors me,
    and my understanding inspires me to reply.

4 "Surely you know how it has been from of old,
    ever since man[a] was placed on the earth,
5 that the mirth of the wicked is brief,
    the joy of the godless lasts but a moment.
6 Though his pride reaches to the heavens
    and his head touches the clouds,
7 he will perish forever, like his
        own dung;
    those who have seen him will
        say, 'Where is he?'
8 Like a dream he flies away, no
        more to be found,
    banished like a vision of the
        night.
9 The eye that saw him will not see
        him again;
    his place will look on him no
        more.
10 His children must make amends to the poor;
    his own hands must give back his wealth.
11 The youthful vigor that fills his bones
    will lie with him in the dust.

12 "Though evil is sweet in his mouth
    and he hides it under his tongue,
13 though he cannot bear to let it go
    and keeps it in his mouth,
14 yet his food will turn sour in his stomach;
    it will become the venom of serpents within him.
15 He will spit out the riches he swallowed;
    God will make his stomach vomit them up.
16 He will suck the poison of serpents;
    the fangs of an adder will kill him.
17 He will not enjoy the streams,
    the rivers flowing with honey and cream.
18 What he toiled for he must give back uneaten;
    he will not enjoy the profit from his trading.
19 For he has oppressed the poor and left them destitute;
    he has seized houses he did not build.

20 "Surely he will have no respite from his craving;
    he cannot save himself by his treasure.
21 Nothing is left for him to devour;
    his prosperity will not endure.
22 In the midst of his plenty, distress will overtake him;
    the full force of misery will come upon him.
23 When he has filled his belly,

truth or dare

Let's face it—sin can be fun. If it wasn't fun, no one would do it. However, pleasure from sin is only *temporary*. The hard consequences can last forever.

20:4–5

a 4 Or Adam

God will vent his burning anger against him
and rain down his blows upon him.

²⁴ Though he flees from an iron weapon,
a bronze-tipped arrow pierces him.

²⁵ He pulls it out of his back,
the gleaming point out of his liver.
Terrors will come over him;

²⁶ total darkness lies in wait for his treasures.
A fire unfanned will consume him
and devour what is left in his tent.

²⁷ The heavens will expose his guilt;
the earth will rise up against him.

²⁸ A flood will carry off his house,
rushing waters ᵃ on the day of God's wrath.

²⁹ Such is the fate God allots the wicked,
the heritage appointed for them by God."

Job
21

Then Job replied:

² "Listen carefully to my words;
let this be the consolation you give me.

³ Bear with me while I speak,
and after I have spoken, mock on.

⁴ "Is my complaint directed to man?
Why should I not be impatient?

⁵ Look at me and be astonished;
clap your hand over your mouth.

⁶ When I think about this, I am terrified;
trembling seizes my body.

⁷ Why do the wicked live on,
growing old and increasing in power?

⁸ They see their children established around them,
their offspring before their eyes.

⁹ Their homes are safe and free from fear;
the rod of God is not upon them.

¹⁰ Their bulls never fail to breed;
their cows calve and do not miscarry.

¹¹ They send forth their children as a flock;
their little ones dance about.

¹² They sing to the music of tambourine and harp;
they make merry to the sound of the flute.

¹³ They spend their years in prosperity
and go down to the grave ᵇ in peace. ᶜ

¹⁴ Yet they say to God, 'Leave us alone!
We have no desire to know your ways.

¹⁵ Who is the Almighty, that we should serve him?
What would we gain by praying to him?'

¹⁶ But their prosperity is not in their own hands,
so I stand aloof from the counsel of the wicked.

¹⁷ "Yet how often is the lamp of the wicked snuffed out?
How often does calamity come upon them,
the fate God allots in his anger?

ᵃ 28 Or The possessions in his house will be carried off, / washed away   ᵇ 13 Hebrew Sheol   ᶜ 13 Or in an instant

¹⁸ How often are they like straw before the wind,
  like chaff swept away by a gale?
¹⁹ ⌊It is said,⌋ 'God stores up a man's punishment for his sons.'
  Let him repay the man himself, so that he will know it!
²⁰ Let his own eyes see his destruction;
  let him drink of the wrath of the Almighty.ᵃ
²¹ For what does he care about the family he leaves behind
  when his allotted months come to an end?

²² "Can anyone teach knowledge to God,
  since he judges even the highest?
²³ One man dies in full vigor,
  completely secure and at ease,
²⁴ his bodyᵇ well nourished,
  his bones rich with marrow.
²⁵ Another man dies in bitterness of soul,
  never having enjoyed anything good.
²⁶ Side by side they lie in the dust,
  and worms cover them both.

²⁷ "I know full well what you are thinking,
  the schemes by which you would wrong me.
²⁸ You say, 'Where now is the great man's house,
  the tents where wicked men lived?'
²⁹ Have you never questioned those who travel?
  Have you paid no regard to their accounts—
³⁰ that the evil man is spared from the day of calamity,
  that he is delivered fromᶜ the day of wrath?
³¹ Who denounces his conduct to his face?
  Who repays him for what he has done?
³² He is carried to the grave,
  and watch is kept over his tomb.
³³ The soil in the valley is sweet to him;
  all men follow after him,
  and a countless throng goesᵈ before him.

³⁴ "So how can you console me with your nonsense?
  Nothing is left of your answers but falsehood!"

Eliphaz

22 Then Eliphaz the Temanite replied:

² "Can a man be of benefit to God?
  Can even a wise man benefit him?
³ What pleasure would it give the Almighty if you were righteous?
  What would he gain if your ways were blameless?

⁴ "Is it for your piety that he rebukes you
  and brings charges against you?
⁵ Is not your wickedness great?
  Are not your sins endless?
⁶ You demanded security from your brothers for no reason;
  you stripped men of their clothing, leaving them naked.
⁷ You gave no water to the weary
  and you withheld food from the hungry,

ᵃ 17-20 Verses 17 and 18 may be taken as exclamations and 19 and 20 as declarations.   ᵇ 24 The meaning of the Hebrew for this word is uncertain.   ᶜ 30 Or man is reserved for the day of calamity, / that he is brought forth to   ᵈ 33 Or / as a countless throng went

8though you were a powerful man, owning land—
   an honored man, living on it.
9And you sent widows away empty-handed
   and broke the strength of the fatherless.
10That is why snares are all around you,
   why sudden peril terrifies you,
11why it is so dark you cannot see,
   and why a flood of water covers you.

12"Is not God in the heights of heaven?
   And see how lofty are the highest stars!
13Yet you say, 'What does God know?
   Does he judge through such darkness?
14Thick clouds veil him, so he does not see us
   as he goes about in the vaulted heavens.'
15Will you keep to the old path
   that evil men have trod?
16They were carried off before their time,
   their foundations washed away by a flood.
17They said to God, 'Leave us alone!
   What can the Almighty do to us?'
18Yet it was he who filled their houses with good things,
   so I stand aloof from the counsel of the wicked.

19"The righteous see their ruin and rejoice;
   the innocent mock them, saying,
20'Surely our foes are destroyed,
   and fire devours their wealth.'

21"Submit to God and be at peace with him;
   in this way prosperity will come to you.
22Accept instruction from his mouth
   and lay up his words in your heart.
23If you return to the Almighty, you will be restored:
   If you remove wickedness far from your tent
24and assign your nuggets to the dust,
   your gold of Ophir to the rocks in the ravines,
25then the Almighty will be your gold,
   the choicest silver for you.
26Surely then you will find delight in the Almighty
   and will lift up your face to God.
27You will pray to him, and he will hear you,
   and you will fulfill your vows.
28What you decide on will be done,
   and light will shine on your ways.
29When men are brought low and you say, 'Lift them up!'
   then he will save the downcast.
30He will deliver even one who is not innocent,
   who will be delivered through the cleanness of your hands."

Job

23

Then Job replied:

2"Even today my complaint is bitter;
   his hand*a* is heavy in spite of*b* my groaning.
3If only I knew where to find him;

a 2 Septuagint and Syriac; Hebrew / the hand on me   *b 2 Or heavy on me in*

if only I could go to his dwelling!
⁴I would state my case before him
and fill my mouth with arguments.
⁵I would find out what he would answer me,
and consider what he would say.
⁶Would he oppose me with great power?
No, he would not press charges against me.
⁷There an upright man could present his case before him,
and I would be delivered forever from my judge.

⁸"But if I go to the east, he is not there;
if I go to the west, I do not find him.
⁹When he is at work in the north, I do not see him;
when he turns to the south, I catch no glimpse of him.
¹⁰But he knows the way that I take;
when he has tested me, I will come forth as gold.
¹¹My feet have closely followed his steps;
I have kept to his way without turning aside.
¹²I have not departed from the commands of his lips;
I have treasured the words of his mouth more than my daily bread.

¹³"But he stands alone, and who can oppose him?
He does whatever he pleases.
¹⁴He carries out his decree against me,
and many such plans he still has in store.
¹⁵That is why I am terrified before him;
when I think of all this, I fear him.
¹⁶God has made my heart faint;
the Almighty has terrified me.
¹⁷Yet I am not silenced by the darkness,
by the thick darkness that covers my face.

24 "Why does the Almighty not set times for judgment?
Why must those who know him look in vain for such days?
²Men move boundary stones;
they pasture flocks they have stolen.
³They drive away the orphan's donkey

love notes

23:10

My girl,

Ever wish that life was just plain easier? I know your paths— where you've been, where you are, where you're going—and I'm making you into something beautiful through it all. Pure gold.

—Your good Father

In what ways is God making you into gold?

_____

_____

_____

_____

_____

_____

_____

_____

_____

_____

genuine

obedience »» 23:12

How high of a priority is obedience for you? Can you say with confidence, "Hey, I obey the rules"? Would you even want to? Job could confidently say that he kept God's commandments. He had the actions to prove it. Obedience wasn't a burden for Job—it was a lifestyle. Obeying God may not seem cool sometimes. It can seem like a burden when the focus is just on the rules themselves. But like Job, can you focus on the one who made the rules instead of just the rules themselves? Remembering who it's for can help make obedience a little easier.

and take the widow's ox in pledge.
⁴They thrust the needy from the path
and force all the poor of the land into hiding.
⁵Like wild donkeys in the desert, the poor go about their labor of foraging food;
the wasteland provides food for their children.
⁶They gather fodder in the fields and glean in the vineyards of the wicked.
⁷Lacking clothes, they spend the night naked;
they have nothing to cover themselves in the cold.
⁸They are drenched by mountain rains
and hug the rocks for lack of shelter.
⁹The fatherless child is snatched from the breast;
the infant of the poor is seized for a debt.
¹⁰Lacking clothes, they go about naked;
they carry the sheaves, but still go hungry.

¹¹They crush olives among the terraces ᵃ;
they tread the winepresses, yet suffer thirst.
¹²The groans of the dying rise from the city,
and the souls of the wounded cry out for help.
But God charges no one with wrongdoing.

¹³"There are those who rebel against the light,
who do not know its ways
or stay in its paths.
¹⁴When daylight is gone, the murderer rises up
and kills the poor and needy;
in the night he steals forth like a thief.
¹⁵The eye of the adulterer watches for dusk;
he thinks, 'No eye will see me,'
and he keeps his face concealed.
¹⁶In the dark, men break into houses,
but by day they shut themselves in;
they want nothing to do with the light.
¹⁷For all of them, deep darkness is their morning ᵇ;
they make friends with the terrors of darkness. ᶜ

¹⁸"Yet they are foam on the surface of the water;
their portion of the land is cursed,
so that no one goes to the vineyards.

ᵃ 11 Or *olives between the millstones*; the meaning of the Hebrew for this word is uncertain.   ᵇ 17 Or *them, their morning is like the shadow of death*   ᶜ 17 Or *of the shadow of death*

¹⁹As heat and drought snatch away the melted snow,
  so the grave^a snatches away those who have sinned.
²⁰The womb forgets them,
  the worm feasts on them;
evil men are no longer remembered
  but are broken like a tree.
²¹They prey on the barren and childless woman,
  and to the widow show no kindness.
²²But God drags away the mighty by his power;
  though they become established, they have no assurance of life.
²³He may let them rest in a feeling of security,
  but his eyes are on their ways.
²⁴For a little while they are exalted, and then they are gone;
  they are brought low and gathered up like all others;
  they are cut off like heads of grain.

²⁵"If this is not so, who can prove me false
  and reduce my words to nothing?"

Bildad

25

Then Bildad the Shuhite replied:

²"Dominion and awe belong to God;
  he establishes order in the heights of heaven.
³Can his forces be numbered?
  Upon whom does his light not rise?
⁴How then can a man be righteous before God?
  How can one born of woman be pure?
⁵If even the moon is not bright
  and the stars are not pure in his eyes,
⁶how much less man, who is but a maggot—
  a son of man, who is only a worm!"

Job

26

Then Job replied:

²"How you have helped the powerless!
  How you have saved the arm that is feeble!
³What advice you have offered to one without wisdom!
  And what great insight you have displayed!
⁴Who has helped you utter these words?
  And whose spirit spoke from your mouth?

⁵"The dead are in deep anguish,
  those beneath the waters and all that live in them.
⁶Death^a is naked before God;
  Destruction^b lies uncovered.
⁷He spreads out the northern ⌞skies⌟ over empty space;
  he suspends the earth over nothing.
⁸He wraps up the waters in his clouds,
  yet the clouds do not burst under their weight.
⁹He covers the face of the full moon,
  spreading his clouds over it.
¹⁰He marks out the horizon on the face of the waters
  for a boundary between light and darkness.

^a 19,6 Hebrew *Sheol*   ^b 6 Hebrew *Abaddon*

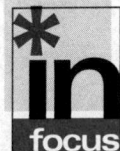

On a Mission

Jared and I have been dating for eleven months now. Everyone agrees we're perfect for each other. We have so much in common—we love sports, we listen to the same music and he's even been coming to church with me on Sundays.

I know he's not a perfect Christian or anything like that, but I think he's getting there. Once I asked him about a relationship with Jesus, and he shrugged and said, "All in good time." So when my aunt asked me whether or not Jared is saved, I told her he's in the process. He'll get there. I just have to be patient.

Of course, my aunt insists I shouldn't be dating someone who doesn't know Jesus. What she doesn't realize is that Jared's not your average guy. He's got a great heart, and I think he really loves me. And he lives a better life than a lot of Christian guys I know.

So why would I give up a great boyfriend just because he hasn't made the "big decision" for Jesus yet? Can you imagine what Jared would think if I told him I was throwing away our entire relationship because he's not spiritual enough? Besides, if I drop out of his life, who will lead him to Christ? And if my aunt really believes God answers our prayers, then she'll pray that I can help lead Jared to Christ. It's going to happen. All in good time.

---

dating in focus

When we're in love, we tend to rely on our feelings. That's when we need God's Word most of all. So ask yourself . . .

»*Why not?* Second Corinthians 6:14–18 (pages 1527–1528) tells us not to form binding relationships with unbelievers. It can only bring pain.

»*What for?* You wouldn't want a guy to do "the Jesus thing" only for you—he needs to do it for himself. Admit that sharing your life with someone who doesn't share your faith is a recipe for heartache.

For more on this topic, see the index on page 1656.

dating

---

¹¹ The pillars of the heavens quake,
aghast at his rebuke.
¹² By his power he churned up the sea;
by his wisdom he cut Rahab to pieces.
¹³ By his breath the skies became fair;
his hand pierced the gliding serpent.
¹⁴ And these are but the outer fringe of his works;
how faint the whisper we hear of him!
Who then can understand the thunder of his power?"

27

And Job continued his discourse:

2 "As surely as God lives, who has denied me justice,
the Almighty, who has made
me taste bitterness of
soul,
3 as long as I have life within me,
the breath of God in my
nostrils,
4 my lips will not speak wickedness,
and my tongue will utter no
deceit.
5 I will never admit you are in the
right;
till I die, I will not deny my
integrity.
6 I will maintain my righteousness and never let
go of it;
my conscience will not reproach me as
long as I live.

7 "May my enemies be like the wicked,
my adversaries like the unjust!
8 For what hope has the godless when he is cut off,
when God takes away his life?
9 Does God listen to his cry
when distress comes upon him?
10 Will he find delight in the Almighty?
Will he call upon God at all times?

11 "I will teach you about the power of God;
the ways of the Almighty I will not conceal.
12 You have all seen this yourselves.
Why then this meaningless talk?

13 "Here is the fate God allots to the wicked,
the heritage a ruthless man receives from the Almighty:
14 However many his children, their fate is the sword;
his offspring will never have enough to eat.
15 The plague will bury those who survive him,
and their widows will not weep for them.
16 Though he heaps up silver like dust
and clothes like piles of clay,
17 what he lays up the righteous will wear,
and the innocent will divide his silver.
18 The house he builds is like a moth's cocoon,
like a hut made by a watchman.
19 He lies down wealthy, but will do so no more;
when he opens his eyes, all is gone.
20 Terrors overtake him like a flood;
a tempest snatches him away in the night.
21 The east wind carries him off, and he is gone;
it sweeps him out of his place.
22 It hurls itself against him without mercy
as he flees headlong from its power.
23 It claps its hands in derision
and hisses him out of his place.

truth or dare

Job really saw God's power throughout his life. He could teach someone else about it because he'd experienced it personally. What could you teach a friend about God?

27:11

28

"There is a mine for silver
  and a place where gold is refined.
[2] Iron is taken from the earth,
  and copper is smelted from ore.
[3] Man puts an end to the darkness;
  he searches the farthest recesses
  for ore in the blackest darkness.
[4] Far from where people dwell he cuts a shaft,
  in places forgotten by the foot of man;
  far from men he dangles and sways.
[5] The earth, from which food comes,
  is transformed below as by fire;
[6] sapphires[a] come from its rocks,
  and its dust contains nuggets of gold.
[7] No bird of prey knows that hidden path,
  no falcon's eye has seen it.
[8] Proud beasts do not set foot on it,
  and no lion prowls there.
[9] Man's hand assaults the flinty rock
  and lays bare the roots of the mountains.
[10] He tunnels through the rock;
  his eyes see all its treasures.
[11] He searches[b] the sources of the rivers
  and brings hidden things to light.

[12] "But where can wisdom be found?
  Where does understanding dwell?
[13] Man does not comprehend its worth;
  it cannot be found in the land
  of the living.
[14] The deep says, 'It is not in me';
  the sea says, 'It is not with me.'
[15] It cannot be bought with the
    finest gold,
  nor can its price be weighed
    in silver.
[16] It cannot be bought with the gold
    of Ophir,
  with precious onyx or
    sapphires.
[17] Neither gold nor crystal can compare with it,
  nor can it be had for jewels of gold.
[18] Coral and jasper are not worthy of mention;
  the price of wisdom is beyond rubies.
[19] The topaz of Cush cannot compare with it;
  it cannot be bought with pure gold.

[20] "Where then does wisdom come from?
  Where does understanding dwell?
[21] It is hidden from the eyes of every living thing,
  concealed even from the birds of the air.
[22] Destruction[c] and Death say,
  'Only a rumor of it has reached our ears.'
[23] God understands the way to it
  and he alone knows where it dwells,

truth or dare

If you're asking people's advice 24/7 but never going straight to God, you're bound to bomb. Since all wisdom comes from God, why not go straight to the source?

28:12-13

a 6 Or lapis lazuli; also in verse 16   b 11 Septuagint, Aquila and Vulgate; Hebrew He dams up   c 22 Hebrew Abaddon

²⁴ for he views the ends of the earth
and sees everything under the heavens.
²⁵ When he established the force of the wind
and measured out the waters,
²⁶ when he made a decree for the rain
and a path for the thunderstorm,
²⁷ then he looked at wisdom and appraised it;
he confirmed it and tested it.
²⁸ And he said to man,
'The fear of the Lord—that is wisdom,
and to shun evil is understanding.' "

29

Job continued his discourse:

² "How I long for the months gone by,
for the days when God watched over me,
³ when his lamp shone upon my head
and by his light I walked through darkness!
⁴ Oh, for the days when I was in my prime,
when God's intimate friendship blessed my house,
⁵ when the Almighty was still with me
and my children were around me,
⁶ when my path was drenched with cream
and the rock poured out for me streams of olive oil.

⁷ "When I went to the gate of the city
and took my seat in the public square,
⁸ the young men saw me and stepped aside
and the old men rose to their feet;
⁹ the chief men refrained from speaking
and covered their mouths with their hands;
¹⁰ the voices of the nobles were hushed,
and their tongues stuck to the roof of their mouths.
¹¹ Whoever heard me spoke well of me,
and those who saw me commended me,
¹² because I rescued the poor who cried for help,
and the fatherless who had none to assist him.
¹³ The man who was dying blessed me;
I made the widow's heart sing.
¹⁴ I put on righteousness as my clothing;
justice was my robe and my turban.
¹⁵ I was eyes to the blind
and feet to the lame.
¹⁶ I was a father to the needy;
I took up the case of the stranger.
¹⁷ I broke the fangs of the wicked
and snatched the victims from their teeth.

¹⁸ "I thought, 'I will die in my own house,
my days as numerous as the grains of sand.
¹⁹ My roots will reach to the water,
and the dew will lie all night on my branches.
²⁰ My glory will remain fresh in me,
the bow ever new in my hand.'

²¹ "Men listened to me expectantly,
waiting in silence for my counsel.
²² After I had spoken, they spoke no more;
my words fell gently on their ears.

23 They waited for me as for showers
 and drank in my words as the spring rain.
24 When I smiled at them, they scarcely believed it;
 the light of my face was precious to them.*
25 I chose the way for them and sat as their chief;
 I dwelt as a king among his troops;
 I was like one who comforts mourners.

30

"But now they mock me,
 men younger than I,
whose fathers I would have disdained
 to put with my sheep dogs.
2 Of what use was the strength of their hands to me,
 since their vigor had gone from them?
3 Haggard from want and hunger,
 they roamed*b* the parched land
 in desolate wastelands at night.
4 In the brush they gathered salt herbs,
 and their food*c* was the root of the broom tree.
5 They were banished from their fellow men,
 shouted at as if they were thieves.
6 They were forced to live in the dry stream beds,
 among the rocks and in holes in the ground.
7 They brayed among the bushes
 and huddled in the undergrowth.
8 A base and nameless brood,
 they were driven out of the land.

9 "And now their sons mock me in song;
 I have become a byword among them.
10 They detest me and keep their distance;
 they do not hesitate to spit in my face.
11 Now that God has unstrung my bow and afflicted me,
 they throw off restraint in my presence.
12 On my right the tribe*d* attacks;
 they lay snares for my feet,
 they build their siege ramps against me.
13 They break up my road;
 they succeed in destroying me—
 without anyone's helping them.*e*
14 They advance as through a gaping breach;
 amid the ruins they come rolling in.
15 Terrors overwhelm me;
 my dignity is driven away as by the wind,
 my safety vanishes like a cloud.

16 "And now my life ebbs away;
 days of suffering grip me.
17 Night pierces my bones;
 my gnawing pains never rest.
18 In his great power ⌊God⌋ becomes like clothing to me*f*;
 he binds me like the neck of my garment.
19 He throws me into the mud,
 and I am reduced to dust and ashes.

---

a 24 The meaning of the Hebrew for this clause is uncertain. *b 3* Or *gnawed* *c 4* Or *fuel* *d 12* The meaning of the Hebrew for this word is uncertain. *e 13* Or *me. / 'No one can help him,' ⌊they say⌋.* *f 18* Hebrew; Septuagint ⌊*God*⌋ *grasps my clothing*

²⁰ "I cry out to you, O God, but you do not answer;
    I stand up, but you merely look at me.
²¹ You turn on me ruthlessly;
    with the might of your hand you attack me.
²² You snatch me up and drive me before the wind;
    you toss me about in the storm.
²³ I know you will bring me down to death,
    to the place appointed for all the living.

²⁴ "Surely no one lays a hand on a broken man
    when he cries for help in his distress.
²⁵ Have I not wept for those in trouble?
    Has not my soul grieved for the poor?
²⁶ Yet when I hoped for good, evil came;
    when I looked for light, then came darkness.
²⁷ The churning inside me never stops;
    days of suffering confront me.
²⁸ I go about blackened, but not by the sun;
    I stand up in the assembly and cry for help.
²⁹ I have become a brother of jackals,
    a companion of owls.
³⁰ My skin grows black and peels;
    my body burns with fever.
³¹ My harp is tuned to mourning,
    and my flute to the sound of wailing.

31

    "I made a covenant with my eyes
    not to look lustfully at a girl.
² For what is man's lot from God above,
    his heritage from the Almighty on high?
³ Is it not ruin for the wicked,
    disaster for those who do
        wrong?
⁴ Does he not see my ways
    and count my every step?

⁵ "If I have walked in falsehood
    or my foot has hurried after
        deceit—
⁶ let God weigh me in honest scales
    and he will know that I am
        blameless—
⁷ if my steps have turned from the path,
    if my heart has been led by my eyes,
    or if my hands have been defiled,
⁸ then may others eat what I have sown,
    and may my crops be uprooted.

⁹ "If my heart has been enticed by a woman,
    or if I have lurked at my neighbor's door,
¹⁰ then may my wife grind another man's grain,
    and may other men sleep with her.
¹¹ For that would have been shameful,
    a sin to be judged.
¹² It is a fire that burns to Destruction ᵃ;
    it would have uprooted my harvest.

truth or dare

Job knew his weaknesses. He even planned out his actions so he'd be ready to fight common temptations. What kind of strategy do you have to avoid sin?

31:1

ᵃ 12 Hebrew Abaddon

¹³ "If I have denied justice to my menservants and maidservants
  when they had a grievance against me,
¹⁴ what will I do when God confronts me?
  What will I answer when called to account?
¹⁵ Did not he who made me in the womb make them?
  Did not the same one form us both within our mothers?

¹⁶ "If I have denied the desires of the poor
  or let the eyes of the widow grow weary,
¹⁷ if I have kept my bread to myself,
  not sharing it with the fatherless—
¹⁸ but from my youth I reared him as would a father,
  and from my birth I guided the widow—
¹⁹ if I have seen anyone perishing for lack of clothing,
  or a needy man without a garment,
²⁰ and his heart did not bless me
  for warming him with the fleece from my sheep,
²¹ if I have raised my hand against the fatherless,
  knowing that I had influence in court,
²² then let my arm fall from the shoulder,
  let it be broken off at the joint.
²³ For I dreaded destruction from God,
  and for fear of his splendor I could not do such things.

²⁴ "If I have put my trust in gold
  or said to pure gold, 'You are my security,'
²⁵ if I have rejoiced over my great wealth,
  the fortune my hands had gained,
²⁶ if I have regarded the sun in its
    radiance
  or the moon moving in
    splendor,
²⁷ so that my heart was secretly
    enticed
  and my hand offered them a
    kiss of homage,
²⁸ then these also would be sins to
    be judged,
  for I would have been
    unfaithful to God on
    high.

²⁹ "If I have rejoiced at my enemy's
    misfortune
  or gloated over the trouble
    that came to him—
³⁰ I have not allowed my mouth to sin
  by invoking a curse against
    his life—
³¹ if the men of my household have
    never said,
  'Who has not had his fill of
    Job's meat?'—
³² but no stranger had to spend the
    night in the street,
  for my door was always open
    to the traveler—

genuine

speech » 31:30

Think about all of the products that have been invented for us to use so we won't gross each other out. Soap. Mouthwash. Mints. Perfume. Deodorant. There's nothing like a little Right Guard among friends. But there's no "Mouth Guard" product we can buy that helps us guard our words. Some words can be more offensive than b.o.! Job kept a guard over his words. He didn't want to offend others or God. Is that your desire as well? How will you be vigilant about your vocab today?

³³ if I have concealed my sin as men do, ^a
    by hiding my guilt in my heart
³⁴ because I so feared the crowd
    and so dreaded the contempt of the clans
    that I kept silent and would not go outside—

³⁵ ("Oh, that I had someone to hear me!
    I sign now my defense—let the Almighty answer me;
    let my accuser put his indictment in writing.
³⁶ Surely I would wear it on my shoulder,
    I would put it on like a crown.
³⁷ I would give him an account of my every step;
    like a prince I would approach him.)—

³⁸ "if my land cries out against me
    and all its furrows are wet with tears,
³⁹ if I have devoured its yield without payment
    or broken the spirit of its tenants,
⁴⁰ then let briers come up instead of wheat
    and weeds instead of barley."

The words of Job are ended.

Elihu

32 So these three men stopped answering Job, because he was righteous in his own eyes. ²But Elihu son of Barakel the Buzite, of the family of Ram, became very angry with Job for justifying himself rather than God. ³He was also angry with the three friends, because they had found no way to refute Job, and yet had condemned him. ^b ⁴Now Elihu had waited before speaking to Job because they were older than he. ⁵But when he saw that the three men had nothing more to say, his anger was aroused.

⁶So Elihu son of Barakel the Buzite said:

"I am young in years,
    and you are old;
    that is why I was fearful,
    not daring to tell you what I know.
⁷ I thought, 'Age should speak;
    advanced years should teach wisdom.'
⁸ But it is the spirit ^c in a man,
    the breath of the Almighty, that gives him understanding.
⁹ It is not only the old ^d who are wise,
    not only the aged who understand what is right.

¹⁰ "Therefore I say: Listen to me;
    I too will tell you what I know.
¹¹ I waited while you spoke,
    I listened to your reasoning;
    while you were searching for words,
¹²   I gave you my full attention.
    But not one of you has proved Job wrong;
    none of you has answered his arguments.
¹³ Do not say, 'We have found wisdom;
    let God refute him, not man.'
¹⁴ But Job has not marshaled his words against me,
    and I will not answer him with your arguments.

^a 33 Or as Adam did   ^b 3 Masoretic Text; an ancient Hebrew scribal tradition Job, and so had condemned God
^c 8 Or Spirit; also in verse 18   ^d 9 Or many; or great

¹⁵"They are dismayed and have no more to say;
    words have failed them.
¹⁶Must I wait, now that they are silent,
    now that they stand there with no reply?
¹⁷I too will have my say;
    I too will tell what I know.
¹⁸For I am full of words,
    and the spirit within me compels me;
¹⁹inside I am like bottled-up wine,
    like new wineskins ready to burst.
²⁰I must speak and find relief;
    I must open my lips and reply.
²¹I will show partiality to no one,
    nor will I flatter any man;
²²for if I were skilled in flattery,
    my Maker would soon take me away.

33 "But now, Job, listen to my words;
    pay attention to everything I say.
²I am about to open my mouth;
    my words are on the tip of my tongue.
³My words come from an upright heart;
    my lips sincerely speak what I know.
⁴The Spirit of God has made me;
    the breath of the Almighty gives me life.
⁵Answer me then, if you can;
    prepare yourself and confront me.
⁶I am just like you before God;
    I too have been taken from clay.
⁷No fear of me should alarm you,
    nor should my hand be heavy upon you.

⁸"But you have said in my hearing—
    I heard the very words—
⁹'I am pure and without sin;
    I am clean and free from guilt.
¹⁰Yet God has found fault with me;
    he considers me his enemy.
¹¹He fastens my feet in shackles;
    he keeps close watch on all my paths.'

¹²"But I tell you, in this you are not right,
    for God is greater than man.
¹³Why do you complain to him
    that he answers none of man's words^a?
¹⁴For God does speak—now one way, now another—
    though man may not perceive it.
¹⁵In a dream, in a vision of the night,
    when deep sleep falls on men
    as they slumber in their beds,
¹⁶he may speak in their ears
    and terrify them with warnings,
¹⁷to turn man from wrongdoing
    and keep him from pride,
¹⁸to preserve his soul from the pit,^b

^a 13 Or that he does not answer for any of his actions   ^b 18 Or preserve him from the grave

his life from perishing by the sword. ^a

¹⁹ Or a man may be chastened on a bed of pain
with constant distress in his bones,
²⁰ so that his very being finds food repulsive
and his soul loathes the choicest meal.
²¹ His flesh wastes away to nothing,
and his bones, once hidden, now stick out.
²² His soul draws near to the pit, ^b
and his life to the messengers of death. ^c

²³ "Yet if there is an angel on his side
as a mediator, one out of a thousand,
to tell a man what is right for him,
²⁴ to be gracious to him and say,
'Spare him from going down to the pit ^d;
I have found a ransom for him'—
²⁵ then his flesh is renewed like a child's;
it is restored as in the days of his youth.
²⁶ He prays to God and finds favor with him,
he sees God's face and shouts for joy;
he is restored by God to his righteous state.
²⁷ Then he comes to men and says,
'I sinned, and perverted what was right,
but I did not get what I deserved.
²⁸ He redeemed my soul from going down to the pit, ^e
and I will live to enjoy the light.'

²⁹ "God does all these things to a man—
twice, even three times—
³⁰ to turn back his soul from the pit, ^f
that the light of life may shine on him.

³¹ "Pay attention, Job, and listen to me;
be silent, and I will speak.
³² If you have anything to say, answer me;
speak up, for I want you to be cleared.
³³ But if not, then listen to me;
be silent, and I will teach you wisdom."

34 Then Elihu said:

² "Hear my words, you wise men;
listen to me, you men of learning.
³ For the ear tests words
as the tongue tastes food.
⁴ Let us discern for ourselves what is right;
let us learn together what is good.

⁵ "Job says, 'I am innocent,
but God denies me justice.
⁶ Although I am right,
I am considered a liar;
although I am guiltless,
his arrow inflicts an incurable wound.'
⁷ What man is like Job,
who drinks scorn like water?

^a 18 Or from crossing the River   ^b 22 Or He draws near to the grave   ^c 22 Or to the dead   ^d 24 Or grave
^e 28 Or redeemed me from going down to the grave   ^f 30 Or turn him back from the grave

⁸He keeps company with evildoers;
he associates with wicked men.
⁹For he says, 'It profits a man nothing
when he tries to please God.'

¹⁰ "So listen to me, you men of understanding.
Far be it from God to do evil,
from the Almighty to do wrong.
¹¹ He repays a man for what he has done;
he brings upon him what his conduct deserves.
¹² It is unthinkable that God would do wrong,
that the Almighty would pervert justice.
¹³ Who appointed him over the earth?
Who put him in charge of the whole world?
¹⁴ If it were his intention
and he withdrew his spirit[a] and breath,
¹⁵ all mankind would perish together
and man would return to the dust.

¹⁶ "If you have understanding, hear this;
listen to what I say.
¹⁷ Can he who hates justice govern?
Will you condemn the just and mighty One?
¹⁸ Is he not the One who says to kings, 'You are worthless,'
and to nobles, 'You are wicked,'
¹⁹ who shows no partiality to princes
and does not favor the rich over the poor,
for they are all the work of his hands?
²⁰ They die in an instant, in the middle of the night;
the people are shaken and they pass away;
the mighty are removed without human hand.

²¹ "His eyes are on the ways of men;
he sees their every step.
²² There is no dark place, no deep shadow,
where evildoers can hide.
²³ God has no need to examine men further,
that they should come before him for judgment.
²⁴ Without inquiry he shatters the mighty
and sets up others in their place.
²⁵ Because he takes note of their deeds,
he overthrows them in the night and they are crushed.
²⁶ He punishes them for their wickedness
where everyone can see them,
²⁷ because they turned from following him
and had no regard for any of his ways.
²⁸ They caused the cry of the poor to come before him,
so that he heard the cry of the needy.
²⁹ But if he remains silent, who can condemn him?
If he hides his face, who can see him?
Yet he is over man and nation alike,
³⁰ to keep a godless man from ruling,
from laying snares for the people.

³¹ "Suppose a man says to God,
'I am guilty but will offend no more.

---

a 14 Or *Spirit*

³²Teach me what I cannot see;
 if I have done wrong, I will not do so again.'
³³Should God then reward you on your terms,
 when you refuse to repent?
You must decide, not I;
 so tell me what you know.

³⁴"Men of understanding declare,
 wise men who hear me say to me,
³⁵'Job speaks without knowledge;
 his words lack insight.'
³⁶Oh, that Job might be tested to the utmost
 for answering like a wicked man!
³⁷To his sin he adds rebellion;
 scornfully he claps his hands among us
 and multiplies his words against God."

35

Then Elihu said:

²"Do you think this is just?
 You say, 'I will be cleared by God.'ᵃ
³Yet you ask him, 'What profit is it to me,ᵇ
 and what do I gain by not sinning?'

⁴"I would like to reply to you
 and to your friends with you.
⁵Look up at the heavens and see;
 gaze at the clouds so high above you.
⁶If you sin, how does that affect him?
 If your sins are many, what does that do to him?
⁷If you are righteous, what do you give to him,
 or what does he receive from your hand?
⁸Your wickedness affects only a man like yourself,
 and your righteousness only the sons of men.

⁹"Men cry out under a load of oppression;
 they plead for relief from the arm of the powerful.
¹⁰But no one says, 'Where is God my Maker,
 who gives songs in the night,
¹¹who teaches more to us than toᶜ the beasts of the earth
 and makes us wiser thanᵈ the birds of the air?'
¹²He does not answer when men cry out
 because of the arrogance of the wicked.
¹³Indeed, God does not listen to their empty plea;
 the Almighty pays no attention to it.
¹⁴How much less, then, will he listen
 when you say that you do not see him,
 that your case is before him
 and you must wait for him,
¹⁵and further, that his anger never punishes
 and he does not take the least notice of wickedness.ᵉ
¹⁶So Job opens his mouth with empty talk;
 without knowledge he multiplies words."

ᵃ 2 Or *My righteousness is more than God's*   ᵇ 3 Or *you*   ᶜ 11 Or *teaches us by*   ᵈ 11 Or *us wise by*
ᵉ 15 Symmachus, Theodotion and Vulgate; the meaning of the Hebrew for this word is uncertain.

36

² "Bear with me a little longer and I will show you
 that there is more to be said in God's behalf.
³ I get my knowledge from afar;
 I will ascribe justice to my Maker.
⁴ Be assured that my words are not false;
 one perfect in knowledge is with you.

⁵ "God is mighty, but does not despise men;
 he is mighty, and firm in his purpose.
⁶ He does not keep the wicked alive
 but gives the afflicted their rights.
⁷ He does not take his eyes off the righteous;
 he enthrones them with kings
 and exalts them forever.
⁸ But if men are bound in chains,
 held fast by cords of affliction,
⁹ he tells them what they have done—
 that they have sinned arrogantly.
¹⁰ He makes them listen to correction
 and commands them to repent of their evil.
¹¹ If they obey and serve him,
 they will spend the rest of their days in prosperity
 and their years in contentment.
¹² But if they do not listen,
 they will perish by the sword ᵃ
 and die without knowledge.

¹³ "The godless in heart harbor resentment;
 even when he fetters them, they do not cry for help.
¹⁴ They die in their youth,
 among male prostitutes of the shrines.
¹⁵ But those who suffer he delivers in their suffering;
 he speaks to them in their affliction.

¹⁶ "He is wooing you from the jaws of distress
 to a spacious place free from restriction,
 to the comfort of your table laden with choice food.
¹⁷ But now you are laden with the judgment due the wicked;
 judgment and justice have taken hold of you.
¹⁸ Be careful that no one entices you by riches;
 do not let a large bribe turn you aside.
¹⁹ Would your wealth
 or even all your mighty efforts
 sustain you so you would not be in distress?
²⁰ Do not long for the night,
 to drag people away from their homes. ᵇ
²¹ Beware of turning to evil,
 which you seem to prefer to affliction.

²² "God is exalted in his power.
 Who is a teacher like him?
²³ Who has prescribed his ways for him,
 or said to him, 'You have done wrong'?
²⁴ Remember to extol his work,
 which men have praised in song.

ᵃ 12 Or *will cross the River* ᵇ 20 The meaning of the Hebrew for verses 18-20 is uncertain.

36

²⁵ All mankind has seen it;
  men gaze on it from afar.
²⁶ How great is God—beyond our
    understanding!
  The number of his years is
    past finding out.

²⁷ "He draws up the drops of water,
  which distill as rain to the
    streams^a;
²⁸ the clouds pour down their
    moisture
  and abundant showers fall on mankind.
²⁹ Who can understand how he spreads out the
    clouds,
  how he thunders from his pavilion?
³⁰ See how he scatters his lightning about him,
  bathing the depths of the sea.
³¹ This is the way he governs^b the nations
  and provides food in abundance.
³² He fills his hands with lightning
  and commands it to strike its mark.
³³ His thunder announces the coming storm;
  even the cattle make known its approach.^c

37

  "At this my heart pounds
    and leaps from its place.
² Listen! Listen to the roar of his voice,
  to the rumbling that comes from his mouth.
³ He unleashes his lightning beneath the whole heaven
  and sends it to the ends of the earth.
⁴ After that comes the sound of his roar;
  he thunders with his majestic voice.
  When his voice resounds,
    he holds nothing back.
⁵ God's voice thunders in marvelous ways;
  he does great things beyond our understanding.
⁶ He says to the snow, 'Fall on the earth,'
  and to the rain shower, 'Be a mighty downpour.'
⁷ So that all men he has made may know his work,
  he stops every man from his labor.^d
⁸ The animals take cover;
  they remain in their dens.
⁹ The tempest comes out from its chamber,
  the cold from the driving winds.
¹⁰ The breath of God produces ice,
  and the broad waters become frozen.
¹¹ He loads the clouds with moisture;
  he scatters his lightning through them.
¹² At his direction they swirl around
  over the face of the whole earth
  to do whatever he commands them.
¹³ He brings the clouds to punish men,
  or to water his earth^e and show his love.

---

truth or dare

You'll never get your mind completely wrapped around God. And that's a good thing—it means he can know, help and love you more than you can even imagine!

36:26

---

^a 27 Or *distill from the mist as rain*   ^b 31 Or *nourishes*   ^c 33 Or *announces his coming— / the One zealous against evil*   ^d 7 Or / *he fills all men with fear by his power*   ^e 13 Or *to favor them*

¹⁴ "Listen to this, Job;
        stop and consider God's wonders.
¹⁵ Do you know how God controls the clouds
        and makes his lightning flash?
¹⁶ Do you know how the clouds hang poised,
        those wonders of him who is perfect in knowledge?
¹⁷ You who swelter in your clothes
        when the land lies hushed under the south wind,
¹⁸ can you join him in spreading out the skies,
        hard as a mirror of cast bronze?

¹⁹ "Tell us what we should say to him;
        we cannot draw up our case because of our darkness.
²⁰ Should he be told that I want to speak?
        Would any man ask to be swallowed up?
²¹ Now no one can look at the sun,
        bright as it is in the skies
        after the wind has swept them
        clean.
²² Out of the north he comes in
        golden splendor;
        God comes in awesome
        majesty.
²³ The Almighty is beyond our reach
        and exalted in power;
        in his justice and great
        righteousness, he does
        not oppress.
²⁴ Therefore, men revere him,
        for does he not have regard for all the
        wise in heart?ᵃ"

truth or dare

Power corrupts. That's usually true when you're talking about people. The *only* one who has ultimate power but stays fair and righteous is God.

37:23–24

The LORD Speaks

38

Then the LORD answered Job out of the storm. He said:

² "Who is this that darkens my counsel
        with words without knowledge?
³ Brace yourself like a man;
        I will question you,
        and you shall answer me.

⁴ "Where were you when I laid the earth's foundation?
        Tell me, if you understand.
⁵ Who marked off its dimensions? Surely you know!
        Who stretched a measuring line across it?
⁶ On what were its footings set,
        or who laid its cornerstone—
⁷ while the morning stars sang together
        and all the angelsᵇ shouted for joy?

⁸ "Who shut up the sea behind doors
        when it burst forth from the womb,
⁹ when I made the clouds its garment
        and wrapped it in thick darkness,
¹⁰ when I fixed limits for it
        and set its doors and bars in place,

ᵃ 24 Or *for he does not have regard for any who think they are wise.*   ᵇ 7 Hebrew *the sons of God*

¹¹ when I said, 'This far you may come and no farther;
  here is where your proud waves halt'?

¹² "Have you ever given orders to the morning,
  or shown the dawn its place,
¹³ that it might take the earth by the edges
  and shake the wicked out of it?
¹⁴ The earth takes shape like clay under a seal;
  its features stand out like those of a garment.
¹⁵ The wicked are denied their light,
  and their upraised arm is broken.

¹⁶ "Have you journeyed to the springs of the sea
  or walked in the recesses of the deep?
¹⁷ Have the gates of death been shown to you?
  Have you seen the gates of the shadow of death ᵃ?
¹⁸ Have you comprehended the vast expanses of the earth?
  Tell me, if you know all this.

¹⁹ "What is the way to the abode of light?
  And where does darkness reside?
²⁰ Can you take them to their places?
  Do you know the paths to their dwellings?
²¹ Surely you know, for you were already born!
  You have lived so many years!

²² "Have you entered the storehouses of the snow
  or seen the storehouses of the hail,
²³ which I reserve for times of trouble,
  for days of war and battle?
²⁴ What is the way to the place where the lightning is dispersed,
  or the place where the east winds are scattered over the earth?
²⁵ Who cuts a channel for the torrents of rain,
  and a path for the thunderstorm,
²⁶ to water a land where no man lives,
  a desert with no one in it,
²⁷ to satisfy a desolate wasteland
  and make it sprout with grass?
²⁸ Does the rain have a father?
  Who fathers the drops of dew?
²⁹ From whose womb comes the ice?
  Who gives birth to the frost from the heavens
³⁰ when the waters become hard as stone,
  when the surface of the deep is frozen?

³¹ "Can you bind the beautiful ᵇ Pleiades?
  Can you loose the cords of Orion?
³² Can you bring forth the constellations in their seasons ᶜ
  or lead out the Bear ᵈ with its cubs?
³³ Do you know the laws of the heavens?
  Can you set up ⌊God's ᵉ⌋ dominion over the earth?

³⁴ "Can you raise your voice to the clouds
  and cover yourself with a flood of water?
³⁵ Do you send the lightning bolts on their way?
  Do they report to you, 'Here we are'?

ᵃ 17 Or gates of deep shadows   ᵇ 31 Or the twinkling; or the chains of the   ᶜ 32 Or the morning star in its season
ᵈ 32 Or out Leo   ᵉ 33 Or his; or their

³⁶ Who endowed the heart ᵃ with wisdom
    or gave understanding to the mind ᵃ?
³⁷ Who has the wisdom to count the clouds?
    Who can tip over the water jars of the heavens
³⁸ when the dust becomes hard
    and the clods of earth stick together?

³⁹ "Do you hunt the prey for the lioness
    and satisfy the hunger of the lions
⁴⁰ when they crouch in their dens
    or lie in wait in a thicket?
⁴¹ Who provides food for the raven
    when its young cry out to God
    and wander about for lack of food?

39

  "Do you know when the mountain goats give birth?
    Do you watch when the doe bears her fawn?
² Do you count the months till they bear?
    Do you know the time they give birth?
³ They crouch down and bring forth their young;
    their labor pains are ended.
⁴ Their young thrive and grow strong in the wilds;
    they leave and do not return.

⁵ "Who let the wild donkey go free?
    Who untied his ropes?
⁶ I gave him the wasteland as his home,
    the salt flats as his habitat.
⁷ He laughs at the commotion in the town;
    he does not hear a driver's shout.
⁸ He ranges the hills for his pasture
    and searches for any green thing.

⁹ "Will the wild ox consent to serve you?
    Will he stay by your manger at night?
¹⁰ Can you hold him to the furrow with a harness?
    Will he till the valleys behind you?
¹¹ Will you rely on him for his great strength?
    Will you leave your heavy work to him?
¹² Can you trust him to bring in your grain
    and gather it to your threshing floor?

¹³ "The wings of the ostrich flap joyfully,
    but they cannot compare with the pinions and feathers of the stork.
¹⁴ She lays her eggs on the ground
    and lets them warm in the sand,
¹⁵ unmindful that a foot may crush them,
    that some wild animal may trample them.
¹⁶ She treats her young harshly, as if they were not hers;
    she cares not that her labor was in vain,
¹⁷ for God did not endow her with wisdom
    or give her a share of good sense.
¹⁸ Yet when she spreads her feathers to run,
    she laughs at horse and rider.

¹⁹ "Do you give the horse his strength
    or clothe his neck with a flowing mane?

ᵃ *36* The meaning of the Hebrew for this word is uncertain.

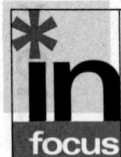

Drink Up

focus   Profile: **Fiona**

Drink Up. That's the slogan for the vending machine in the student lounge. But when people say it at our school, they always mean, "Party this weekend!" Since I'm only a freshman, I've been pretty shocked at how many people drink every weekend.

To tell you the truth, it's hard to find anyone who doesn't drink—or hasn't at least tried the stuff. And from what I've heard, most of them never get caught. I haven't figured out yet where they get their alcohol, but I know they always manage.

My friend Julia says it's no big deal for her to have a few drinks, but she swears she never gets wasted. And lately she's been pressuring me to go to her cousin's St. Patrick's Day party next weekend. She says her goal is to get me to at least drink a beer, so I can see how much it helps me relax and have more fun.

I feel so torn. I'm sure it's fun, and I'd meet a lot of people at the party. But that doesn't make it right. But what's the harm? Julia would be there with me. But why does she want me to try it so much anyway? She knows I'm a Christian—I wonder if that has something to do with it.

alcohol in focus

It doesn't take courage to give in to the pressure to drink. But it will take courage to say no. Before you're tempted, consider the following:

» *The damage.* Alcohol contributes to all of the leading causes of death among teens. That's a great reason to steer clear. Yet even more important is the damage it does to your Christian testimony. People are watching you to see if you'll live up to your faith.

» *The disobedience.* Not only would you be disobeying the law, and probably your parents, but you're also (and more importantly) disobeying God (see Romans 13:1, page 1500).

» *The dreams.* For many teens, a little alcohol turns into a habit and then an addiction. Read Proverbs 20:1 (page 832) and Ephesians 5:15–18 (page 1546).

For more on this topic, see the index on page 1656.

²⁰ Do you make him leap like a locust,
     striking terror with his proud snorting?
²¹ He paws fiercely, rejoicing in his strength,
     and charges into the fray.
²² He laughs at fear, afraid of nothing;
     he does not shy away from the sword.
²³ The quiver rattles against his side,
     along with the flashing spear and lance.
²⁴ In frenzied excitement he eats up the ground;
     he cannot stand still when the trumpet sounds.
²⁵ At the blast of the trumpet he snorts, 'Aha!'
     He catches the scent of battle from afar,
     the shout of commanders and the battle cry.

²⁶ "Does the hawk take flight by your wisdom
    and spread his wings toward the south?
²⁷ Does the eagle soar at your command
    and build his nest on high?
²⁸ He dwells on a cliff and stays there at night;
    a rocky crag is his stronghold.
²⁹ From there he seeks out his food;
    his eyes detect it from afar.
³⁰ His young ones feast on blood,
    and where the slain are, there is he."

40

The LORD said to Job:

² "Will the one who contends with the Almighty correct him?
    Let him who accuses God answer him!"

³ Then Job answered the LORD:

⁴ "I am unworthy—how can I reply to you?
    I put my hand over my mouth.
⁵ I spoke once, but I have no answer—
    twice, but I will say no more."

⁶ Then the LORD spoke to Job out of the storm:

⁷ "Brace yourself like a man;
    I will question you,
    and you shall answer me.

⁸ "Would you discredit my justice?
    Would you condemn me to
      justify yourself?
⁹ Do you have an arm like God's,
    and can your voice thunder
      like his?
¹⁰ Then adorn yourself with glory and splendor,
    and clothe yourself in honor and majesty.
¹¹ Unleash the fury of your wrath,
    look at every proud man and bring him low,
¹² look at every proud man and humble him,
    crush the wicked where they stand.
¹³ Bury them all in the dust together;
    shroud their faces in the grave.
¹⁴ Then I myself will admit to you
    that your own right hand can save you.

¹⁵ "Look at the behemoth, ^a
    which I made along with you
    and which feeds on grass like an ox.
¹⁶ What strength he has in his loins,
    what power in the muscles of his belly!
¹⁷ His tail ^b sways like a cedar;
    the sinews of his thighs are close-knit.
¹⁸ His bones are tubes of bronze,
    his limbs like rods of iron.
¹⁹ He ranks first among the works of God,
    yet his Maker can approach him with his sword.

truth or dare

God's actions are not open to public debate, especially from us. He is far superior to us in every way. How dare we question *God?*

40:8–14

---

^a 15 Possibly the hippopotamus or the elephant   ^b 17 Possibly trunk

²⁰ The hills bring him their produce,
and all the wild animals play nearby.
²¹ Under the lotus plants he lies,
hidden among the reeds in the marsh.
²² The lotuses conceal him in their shadow;
the poplars by the stream surround him.
²³ When the river rages, he is not alarmed;
he is secure, though the Jordan should surge against his mouth.
²⁴ Can anyone capture him by the eyes, ᵃ
or trap him and pierce his nose?

"Can you pull in the leviathan ᵇ with a fishhook
or tie down his tongue with a rope?
² Can you put a cord through his nose
or pierce his jaw with a hook?
³ Will he keep begging you for mercy?
Will he speak to you with gentle words?
⁴ Will he make an agreement with you
for you to take him as your slave for life?
⁵ Can you make a pet of him like a bird
or put him on a leash for your girls?
⁶ Will traders barter for him?
Will they divide him up among the merchants?
⁷ Can you fill his hide with harpoons
or his head with fishing spears?
⁸ If you lay a hand on him,
you will remember the struggle and never do it again!
⁹ Any hope of subduing him is false;
the mere sight of him is overpowering.
¹⁰ No one is fierce enough to rouse him.
Who then is able to stand against me?
¹¹ Who has a claim against me that I must pay?
Everything under heaven belongs to me.

¹² "I will not fail to speak of his limbs,
his strength and his graceful form.
¹³ Who can strip off his outer coat?
Who would approach him with a bridle?
¹⁴ Who dares open the doors of his mouth,
ringed about with his fearsome teeth?
¹⁵ His back has ᶜ rows of shields
tightly sealed together;
¹⁶ each is so close to the next
that no air can pass between.
¹⁷ They are joined fast to one another;
they cling together and cannot be parted.
¹⁸ His snorting throws out flashes of light;
his eyes are like the rays of dawn.
¹⁹ Firebrands stream from his mouth;
sparks of fire shoot out.
²⁰ Smoke pours from his nostrils
as from a boiling pot over a fire of reeds.
²¹ His breath sets coals ablaze,
and flames dart from his mouth.
²² Strength resides in his neck;

ᵃ 24 Or by a water hole   ᵇ 1 Possibly the crocodile   ᶜ 15 Or His pride is his dismay goes before him.

²³ The folds of his flesh are tightly joined;
they are firm and immovable.

²⁴ His chest is hard as rock,
hard as a lower millstone.

²⁵ When he rises up, the mighty are terrified;
they retreat before his thrashing.

²⁶ The sword that reaches him has no effect,
nor does the spear or the dart or the javelin.

²⁷ Iron he treats like straw
and bronze like rotten wood.

²⁸ Arrows do not make him flee;
slingstones are like chaff to him.

²⁹ A club seems to him but a piece of straw;
he laughs at the rattling of the lance.

³⁰ His undersides are jagged potsherds,
leaving a trail in the mud like a threshing sledge.

³¹ He makes the depths churn like a boiling caldron
and stirs up the sea like a pot of ointment.

³² Behind him he leaves a glistening wake;
one would think the deep had white hair.

³³ Nothing on earth is his equal—
a creature without fear.

³⁴ He looks down on all that are haughty;
he is king over all that are proud."

Job 42

Then Job replied to the Lord:

² "I know that you can do all things;
no plan of yours can be thwarted.

³ ˻You asked,˼ 'Who is this that obscures my counsel without knowledge?'
Surely I spoke of things I did not understand,
things too wonderful for me to know.

⁴ ˻You said,˼ 'Listen now, and I will speak;
I will question you,
and you shall answer me.'

⁵ My ears had heard of you
but now my eyes have seen you.

⁶ Therefore I despise myself
and repent in dust and ashes."

Epilogue

⁷ After the Lord had said these things to Job, he said to Eliphaz the Temanite, "I am angry with you and your two friends, because you have not spoken of me what is right, as my servant Job has. ⁸ So now take seven bulls and seven rams and go to my servant Job and sacrifice a burnt offering for yourselves. My servant Job will pray for you, and I will accept his prayer and not deal with you according to your folly. You have not spoken of me what is right, as my servant Job has." ⁹ So Eliphaz the Temanite, Bildad the Shuhite and Zophar the Naamathite did what the Lord told them; and the Lord accepted Job's prayer.

¹⁰ After Job had prayed for his friends, the Lord made him prosperous again and gave him twice as much as he had before. ¹¹ All his brothers and sisters and everyone who had known him before came and ate with him in his house. They comforted and consoled him over all the trouble the Lord had brought upon him, and each one gave him a piece of silver ᵃ and a gold ring.

ᵃ 11 Hebrew *him a kesitah*; a kesitah was a unit of money of unknown weight and value.

¹²The LORD blessed the latter part of Job's life more than the first. He had fourteen thousand sheep, six thousand camels, a thousand yoke of oxen and a thousand donkeys. ¹³And he also had seven sons and three daughters. ¹⁴The first daughter he named Jemimah, the second Keziah and the third Keren-Happuch. ¹⁵Nowhere in all the land were there found women as beautiful as Job's daughters, and their father granted them an inheritance along with their brothers.

¹⁶After this, Job lived a hundred and forty years; he saw his children and their children to the fourth generation. ¹⁷And so he died, old and full of years.

ξenuine

forgiveness » 42:8-10

For you, does forgiveness mean forgiving and forgetting? Or do you claim to forgive yet still hold a grudge? God promised to forgive the sin of Job's well-meaning but totally wrong friends. He didn't plan on reminding them about their sin later. Forgiveness is just like God says—it's not treating someone as he or she deserves. It also means wiping the slate completely clean. Is there someone who needs your forgiveness? How willing are you to totally forgive from the heart?

author: David, Asaph, the Sons of Korah, Solomon, Heman, Ethan and Moses.

date: The Psalms were written between the time of Moses (about 1440 B.C.) and the time following the Babylonian captivity (sometime after 538 B.C.).

setting: Many psalms were read or sung in Israelite worship in God's temple.

verse to remember: Let everything that has breath praise the LORD. Praise the LORD (150:6).

theme to consider: What are you feeling? Sorrow? Fear? Anger? Joy? You'll find it all expressed here in the writing of the psalmists, who poured out their hearts to God. Tell God whatever you're feeling. He wants to hear from you.

unchanging truth

psalms

"Hey, how are you?" "What's happening?" "How's it going?"

Undoubtedly you've heard these phrases. They've almost become substitutes for saying "hi." But do the speakers *really* want to know how you are and what's going on in your life? Probably not. Most people don't really want to take the time to find out what's making you happy or sad (or anything in between).

Real friends *do* listen to you, however. They want to know how you're feeling and what's happening in your life. They'll let you vent your anger, disappointment and fears. And your true friends want to celebrate with you when life is going great.

Every human—from Adam and Eve right up to you—has emotions and feelings. God planned it that way; it makes our lives interesting. But sometimes those emotions and feelings can feel overwhelming, and that can make our lives challenging. The writers of the book of Psalms knew all about the feelings that you have in your life, and they wrote about all of them, from joy and despair, to anger and sorrow. The psalmists talked to God about what they were feeling, and he listened. God's waiting to hear from you, too—he'll never be bothered or bored or too busy to listen.

How are you feeling right this minute? Happy, sad, angry, satisfied—talk to God about it.

life lessons

3

1 God is an amazing, awesome God and deserves our praise. Praise the Lord (100:1–5)!

2 Christians have a guidebook with answers to every important question in life. Following God's Word leads us on the right path (119:105).

3 The Lord made you exactly as you are and loves you more than you can imagine (139:1–16).

genuine

friendship »

1:1-3

Where a girl sits at lunch can be a big deal. In most schools, there's a "cool" table, a "studious" table, an "artsy" table, etc. It just so happens that God agrees that where you sit is important—not because of social status, but because your friendships affect you. Who are your closest friends? Do they strengthen your faith, or do they hinder your walk with Christ? While it's okay to have friends who aren't Christians, you need to be sure that your closest friends also love the Lord.

BOOK I

Psalms 1–41

Psalm 1

¹ Blessed is the man
　who does not walk in the
　　counsel of the wicked
or stand in the way of sinners
　or sit in the seat of mockers.
² But his delight is in the law of the
　LORD,
　and on his law he meditates
　　day and night.
³ He is like a tree planted by
　　streams of water,
　which yields its fruit in season
and whose leaf does not wither.
　Whatever he does prospers.

⁴ Not so the wicked!
　They are like chaff
　　that the wind blows away.
⁵ Therefore the wicked will not
　　stand in the judgment,
　nor sinners in the assembly of
　　the righteous.

⁶ For the LORD watches over the
　　way of the righteous,
　but the way of the wicked will
　　perish.

Psalm 2

¹ Why do the nations conspire*ᵃ*
　and the peoples plot in vain?
² The kings of the earth take their stand
　and the rulers gather together
against the LORD
　and against his Anointed One.*ᵇ*
³ "Let us break their chains," they say,
　"and throw off their fetters."

⁴ The One enthroned in heaven laughs;
　the Lord scoffs at them.
⁵ Then he rebukes them in his anger
　and terrifies them in his wrath, saying,
⁶ "I have installed my King*ᶜ*
　on Zion, my holy hill."

⁷ I will proclaim the decree of the LORD:

He said to me, "You are my Son*ᵈ*;
　today I have become your Father.*ᵉ*
⁸ Ask of me,
　and I will make the nations your inheritance,

ᵃ 1 Hebrew; Septuagint rage 　*ᵇ 2 Or anointed one* 　*ᶜ 6 Or king* 　*ᵈ 7 Or son; also in verse 12* 　*ᵉ 7 Or have begotten you*

the ends of the earth your
   possession.
⁹You will rule them with an iron
   scepter*;
  you will dash them to pieces
   like pottery."

¹⁰Therefore, you kings, be wise;
  be warned, you rulers of the
   earth.
¹¹Serve the Lord with fear
  and rejoice with trembling.
¹²Kiss the Son, lest he be angry
  and you be destroyed in your way,
for his wrath can flare up in a moment.
  Blessed are all who take refuge in him.

truth or dare

Some girls get so com-
fortable around God
that they forget who's
in charge. Yeah, he's a
friend, but above all
else, he's a holy God.

2:11

Psalm 3

A psalm of David. When he fled from his son Absalom.

¹O Lord, how many are my foes!
  How many rise up against me!
²Many are saying of me,
  "God will not deliver him."   *Selah*ᵇ

³But you are a shield around me, O Lord;
  you bestow glory on me and lift* up my head.
⁴To the Lord I cry aloud,
  and he answers me from his holy hill.   *Selah*

⁵I lie down and sleep;
  I wake again, because the Lord sustains me.
⁶I will not fear the tens of thousands
  drawn up against me on every side.

⁷Arise, O Lord!
  Deliver me, O my God!
Strike all my enemies on the jaw;
  break the teeth of the wicked.

⁸From the Lord comes deliverance.
  May your blessing be on your people.   *Selah*

Psalm 4

For the director of music. With stringed instruments. A psalm
of David.

¹Answer me when I call to you,
  O my righteous God.
Give me relief from my distress;
  be merciful to me and hear my prayer.

²How long, O men, will you turn my glory into shame*?
  How long will you love delusions and seek false gods*?   *Selah*
³Know that the Lord has set apart the godly for himself;
  the Lord will hear when I call to him.

a 9 Or will break them with a rod of iron b 2 A word of uncertain meaning, occurring frequently in the Psalms; possibly a musical term c 3 Or Lord, / my Glorious One, who lifts d 2 Or you dishonor my Glorious One e 2 Or seek lies

⁴In your anger do not sin;
 when you are on your beds,
 search your hearts and be silent.   *Selah*

⁵Offer right sacrifices
 and trust in the LORD.

⁶Many are asking, "Who can show us any good?"
 Let the light of your face shine upon us, O LORD.
⁷You have filled my heart with greater joy
 than when their grain and new wine abound.
⁸I will lie down and sleep in peace,
 for you alone, O LORD,
 make me dwell in safety.

love notes

4:8

My child,

*Next time you spend the night
tossing and turning, remember
this: You are safe with me. Close
your eyes. Find rest and peace in
me. Sweet dreams!*

—Your loving Father

What thoughts keep you awake at
night? Memorize this verse to combat
restless nights.

_____

_____

_____

_____

_____

_____

_____

Psalm 5

For the director of music. For flutes.
A psalm of David.

¹Give ear to my words, O LORD,
 consider my sighing.
²Listen to my cry for help,
 my King and my God,
 for to you I pray.
³In the morning, O LORD, you hear
 my voice;
 in the morning I lay my
 requests before you
 and wait in expectation.
⁴You are not a God who takes
 pleasure in evil;
 with you the wicked cannot
 dwell.
⁵The arrogant cannot stand in
 your presence;
 you hate all who do wrong.
⁶You destroy those who tell lies;
 bloodthirsty and deceitful men
 the LORD abhors.

truth or dare

Being angry isn't a sin.
It's what you *do* with
your anger that can get
you in trouble. When
you're fuming, don't re-
spond till after you've
calmed down.

4:4

⁷But I, by your great mercy,
      will come into your house;
   in reverence will I bow down
      toward your holy temple.
⁸Lead me, O Lord, in your righteousness
      because of my enemies—
   make straight your way before me.

⁹Not a word from their mouth can be trusted;
      their heart is filled with destruction.
   Their throat is an open grave;
      with their tongue they speak deceit.
¹⁰Declare them guilty, O God!
      Let their intrigues be their downfall.
   Banish them for their many sins,
      for they have rebelled against you.

¹¹But let all who take refuge in you be glad;
      let them ever sing for joy.
   Spread your protection over them,
      that those who love your name may rejoice in you.
¹²For surely, O Lord, you bless the righteous;
      you surround them with your favor as with a shield.

Psalm 6

For the director of music. With stringed instruments. According to
sheminith.ᵃ A psalm of David.

¹O Lord, do not rebuke me in your
      anger
   or discipline me in your wrath.
²Be merciful to me, Lord, for I am
      faint;
   O Lord, heal me, for my
      bones are in agony.
³My soul is in anguish.
   How long, O Lord, how long?

⁴Turn, O Lord, and deliver me;
   save me because of your
      unfailing love.
⁵No one remembers you when he
      is dead.
   Who praises you from the
      graveᵇ?

⁶I am worn out from groaning;
   all night long I flood my bed
      with weeping
   and drench my couch with
      tears.
⁷My eyes grow weak with sorrow;
   they fail because of all my
      foes.

⁸Away from me, all you who do
      evil,

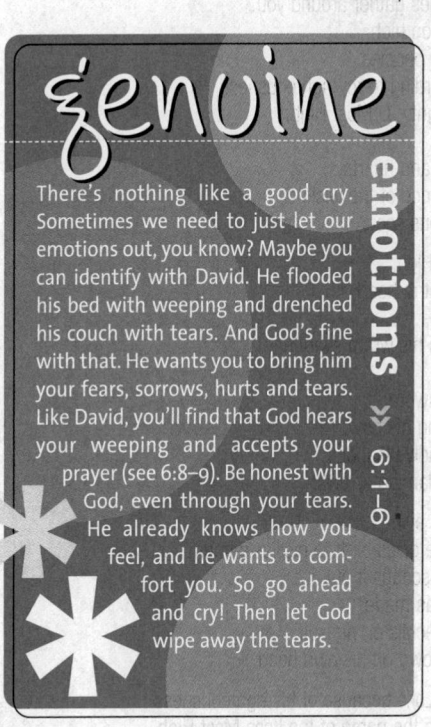

ǥenuine

emotions » 6:1-6

There's nothing like a good cry. Sometimes we need to just let our emotions out, you know? Maybe you can identify with David. He flooded his bed with weeping and drenched his couch with tears. And God's fine with that. He wants you to bring him your fears, sorrows, hurts and tears. Like David, you'll find that God hears your weeping and accepts your prayer (see 6:8–9). Be honest with God, even through your tears. He already knows how you feel, and he wants to comfort you. So go ahead and cry! Then let God wipe away the tears.

ᵃ Title: Probably a musical term   ᵇ 5 Hebrew *Sheol*

for the LORD has heard my weeping.
9 The LORD has heard my cry for mercy;
    the LORD accepts my prayer.
10 All my enemies will be ashamed and dismayed;
    they will turn back in sudden disgrace.

Psalm 7

A shiggaion[a] of David, which he sang to the LORD concerning Cush, a Benjamite.

1 O LORD my God, I take refuge in you;
    save and deliver me from all who pursue me,
2 or they will tear me like a lion
    and rip me to pieces with no one to rescue me.

3 O LORD my God, if I have done this
    and there is guilt on my hands—
4 if I have done evil to him who is at peace with me
    or without cause have robbed my foe—
5 then let my enemy pursue and overtake me;
    let him trample my life to the ground
    and make me sleep in the dust.   *Selah*

6 Arise, O LORD, in your anger;
    rise up against the rage of my enemies.
    Awake, my God; decree justice.
7 Let the assembled peoples gather around you.
    Rule over them from on high;
8   let the LORD judge the peoples.
    Judge me, O LORD, according to my righteousness,
    according to my integrity, O Most High.
9 O righteous God,
    who searches minds and hearts,
    bring to an end the violence of the wicked
    and make the righteous secure.

10 My shield[b] is God Most High,
    who saves the upright in heart.
11 God is a righteous judge,
    a God who expresses his wrath every day.
12 If he does not relent,
    he[c] will sharpen his sword;
    he will bend and string his bow.
13 He has prepared his deadly weapons;
    he makes ready his flaming arrows.

14 He who is pregnant with evil
    and conceives trouble gives birth to disillusionment.
15 He who digs a hole and scoops it out
    falls into the pit he has made.
16 The trouble he causes recoils on himself;
    his violence comes down on his own head.

17 I will give thanks to the LORD because of his righteousness
    and will sing praise to the name of the LORD Most High.

---

a Title: Probably a literary or musical term   *b* 10 Or *sovereign*   *c* 12 Or *If a man does not repent, / God*

Psalm 8

For the director of music. According to *gittith.*[a] A psalm of David.

¹O Lᴏʀᴅ, our Lord,
how majestic is your name in all the earth!

You have set your glory
above the heavens.
²From the lips of children and infants
you have ordained praise[b]
because of your enemies,
to silence the foe and the avenger.

³When I consider your heavens,
the work of your fingers,
the moon and the stars,
which you have set in place,
⁴what is man that you are mindful
of him,
the son of man that you care
for him?
⁵You made him a little lower than
the heavenly beings[c]
and crowned him with glory
and honor.
⁶You made him ruler over the
works of your hands;
you put everything under his
feet:
⁷all flocks and herds,
and the beasts of the field,
⁸the birds of the air,
and the fish of the sea,
all that swim the paths of the seas.

⁹O Lᴏʀᴅ, our Lord,
how majestic is your name in
all the earth!

Psalm 9[d]

For the director of music. To ⌞the tune of⌟
"The Death of the Son." A psalm of David.

¹I will praise you, O Lᴏʀᴅ, with all
my heart;
I will tell of all your wonders.
²I will be glad and rejoice in you;
I will sing praise to your
name, O Most High.

³My enemies turn back;
they stumble and perish
before you.

love ❤ notes

8:3–6

My valuable girl,

*When you were little, did you
ever dream about becoming a
princess? In my eyes, you are
better than a princess. See, I
have crowned you with my glory and honor! I have put you in
charge of the earth.*

—Your Creator

What does that mean to you—to be
crowned with God's glory and honor?

_____
_____
_____
_____
_____
_____
_____
_____
_____
_____
_____
_____
_____
_____
_____

a Title: Probably a musical term   *b* 2 Or *strength*
c 5 Or *than God*   *d* Psalms 9 and 10 may have been
originally a single acrostic poem, the stanzas of which
begin with the successive letters of the Hebrew
alphabet. In the Septuagint they constitute one psalm.

⁴ For you have upheld my right and
my cause;
you have sat on your throne,
judging righteously.
⁵ You have rebuked the nations
and destroyed the
wicked;
you have blotted out their
name for ever and ever.
⁶ Endless ruin has overtaken the
enemy,
you have uprooted their cities;
even the memory of them has perished.

⁷ The LORD reigns forever;
he has established his throne for
judgment.
⁸ He will judge the world in righteousness;
he will govern the peoples with justice.
⁹ The LORD is a refuge for the oppressed,
a stronghold in times of trouble.
¹⁰ Those who know your name will trust in you,
for you, LORD, have never forsaken those who seek you.

¹¹ Sing praises to the LORD, enthroned in Zion;
proclaim among the nations what he has done.
¹² For he who avenges blood remembers;
he does not ignore the cry of the afflicted.

¹³ O LORD, see how my enemies persecute me!
Have mercy and lift me up from the gates of death,
¹⁴ that I may declare your praises
in the gates of the Daughter of Zion
and there rejoice in your salvation.

¹⁵ The nations have fallen into the pit they have dug;
their feet are caught in the net they have hidden.
¹⁶ The LORD is known by his justice;
the wicked are ensnared by the work of their hands. *Higgaion.ᵃ Selah*
¹⁷ The wicked return to the grave,ᵇ
all the nations that forget God.
¹⁸ But the needy will not always be forgotten,
nor the hope of the afflicted ever perish.

¹⁹ Arise, O LORD, let not man triumph;
let the nations be judged in your presence.
²⁰ Strike them with terror, O LORD;
let the nations know they are but men. *Selah*

Psalm 10ᶜ

¹ Why, O LORD, do you stand far off?
Why do you hide yourself in times of trouble?

² In his arrogance the wicked man hunts down the weak,
who are caught in the schemes he devises.
³ He boasts of the cravings of his heart;

truth or dare

Have you ever been tempted to be an undercover Christian at school? While it may be easier, God needs fewer spies and more loudspeakers today. Be outspoken!
9:1

ᵃ *16* Or *Meditation*; possibly a musical notation   ᵇ *17* Hebrew *Sheol*   ᶜ Psalms 9 and 10 may have been originally a single acrostic poem, the stanzas of which begin with the successive letters of the Hebrew alphabet. In the Septuagint they constitute one psalm.

he blesses the greedy and
reviles the LORD.
4 In his pride the wicked does not
seek him;
in all his thoughts there is no
room for God.
5 His ways are always prosperous;
he is haughty and your laws
are far from him;
he sneers at all his enemies.
6 He says to himself, "Nothing will
shake me;
I'll always be happy and never have
trouble."
7 His mouth is full of curses and lies and threats;
trouble and evil are under his tongue.
8 He lies in wait near the villages;
from ambush he murders the innocent,
watching in secret for his victims.
9 He lies in wait like a lion in cover;
he lies in wait to catch the helpless;
he catches the helpless and drags them off in his net.
10 His victims are crushed, they collapse;
they fall under his strength.
11 He says to himself, "God has forgotten;
he covers his face and never sees."

12 Arise, LORD! Lift up your hand, O God.
Do not forget the helpless.
13 Why does the wicked man revile God?
Why does he say to himself,
"He won't call me to account"?
14 But you, O God, do see trouble and grief;
you consider it to take it in hand.
The victim commits himself to you;
you are the helper of the fatherless.
15 Break the arm of the wicked and evil man;
call him to account for his wickedness
that would not be found out.

16 The LORD is King for ever and ever;
the nations will perish from his land.
17 You hear, O LORD, the desire of the afflicted;
you encourage them, and you listen to their cry,
18 defending the fatherless and the oppressed,
in order that man, who is of the earth, may terrify no more.

Psalm 11

For the director of music. Of David.

1 In the LORD I take refuge.
How then can you say to me:
"Flee like a bird to your mountain.
2 For look, the wicked bend their bows;
they set their arrows against the strings
to shoot from the shadows
at the upright in heart.

truth or dare

Even David, a guy total-
ly in touch with God,
felt lonely and aban-
doned at times. Re-
member that your
emotions come and go,
but God will always be
by your side.

10:1

³When the foundations are being destroyed,
  what can the righteous do*?"

⁴The LORD is in his holy temple;
  the LORD is on his heavenly throne.
He observes the sons of men;
  his eyes examine them.
⁵The LORD examines the righteous,
  but the wicked ᵇ and those who love violence
  his soul hates.
⁶On the wicked he will rain
  fiery coals and burning sulfur;
  a scorching wind will be their lot.

⁷For the LORD is righteous,
  he loves justice;
  upright men will see his face.

Psalm 12

For the director of music. According to *sheminith.*ᶜ A psalm
of David.

¹Help, LORD, for the godly are no more;
  the faithful have vanished from among men.
²Everyone lies to his neighbor;
  their flattering lips speak with deception.

³May the LORD cut off all flattering lips
  and every boastful tongue
⁴that says, "We will triumph with our tongues;
  we own our lips ᵈ—who is our master?"

⁵"Because of the oppression of the weak
  and the groaning of the needy,
I will now arise," says the LORD.
  "I will protect them from those who malign them."
⁶And the words of the LORD are flawless,
  like silver refined in a furnace of clay,
  purified seven times.

⁷O LORD, you will keep us safe
  and protect us from such people forever.
⁸The wicked freely strut about
  when what is vile is honored among men.

Psalm 13

For the director of music. A psalm of David.

¹How long, O LORD? Will you forget me forever?
  How long will you hide your face from me?
²How long must I wrestle with my thoughts
  and every day have sorrow in my heart?
  How long will my enemy triumph over me?

³Look on me and answer, O LORD my God.
  Give light to my eyes, or I will sleep in death;

*a 3 Or what is the Righteous One doing b 5 Or The LORD, the Righteous One, examines the wicked, / c Title: Probably
a musical term d 4 Or / our lips are our plowshares*

Down in the Dumps

Profile: **Keri**

This morning my best friend Alexis told me I've been a real drag lately. And when my mom caught me crying while I practiced piano, she brought up the "d" word. (You know, "depression.") To top it off, my big brother snickered and said, "Hey, Keri, ever heard of Prozac?" That just made me cry even harder.

It's like no one understands me anymore. *I* don't even understand me. A few months ago I started feeling down in the dumps. Like numb and limp and not interested in life. I don't even care about food anymore—not even my favorite chocolate peanut butter ice cream. All I want is to curl up into a ball and sleep the day away. Maybe then I could forget how awful I feel. Mom and Dad are really going to flip out when they see my grades this quarter. I just can't concentrate anymore.

It's like the real Keri doesn't exist anymore. I'm trapped inside her body. I'm ready to drop out of student council. I just don't have the heart for it anymore. And I'm beginning to wonder if anyone really wants me around. Alexis was right—I am a drag.

I wonder what's wrong with me. This has to be my own fault. If I were really a good Christian, I wouldn't feel depressed. Now I'm wondering if God truly loves me anyway. And I wonder if I really love him. What is wrong with me?

For more on overcoming depression, check out www.TrueImagesBible.com

depression in focus

Ever feel hopeless like Keri? More than a million teens are suffering from depression right now, and many of them wrongly blame themselves. Depression isn't your "fault"; it's your body's cry for help. Remember . . .

»*There's help and hope.* If you feel depressed, a doctor may be able to help. Talk to your parents about seeing one, and try to meet with a youth worker, pastor or Christian counselor as well.

»*You are loved.* Remember that Jesus was overcome with sorrow and tears before he died. He understands your pain and longs to comfort you (see Psalm 62:5–8, page 713; Romans 8:38–39, page 1494).

For more on this topic, see the index on page 1656.

---

⁴my enemy will say, "I have overcome him,"
    and my foes will rejoice when I fall.

⁵But I trust in your unfailing love;
    my heart rejoices in your salvation.
⁶I will sing to the LORD,
    for he has been good to me.

Psalm 14

For the director of music. Of David.

[1] The fool[a] says in his heart,
   "There is no God."
They are corrupt, their deeds are
      vile;
   there is no one who does
      good.

[2] The LORD looks down from
      heaven
   on the sons of men
to see if there are any who
      understand,
   any who seek God.
[3] All have turned aside,
   they have together become
      corrupt;
there is no one who does good,
   not even one.

[4] Will evildoers never learn—
   those who devour my people as men eat bread
   and who do not call on the LORD?
[5] There they are, overwhelmed with dread,
   for God is present in the company of the righteous.
[6] You evildoers frustrate the plans of the poor,
   but the LORD is their refuge.

[7] Oh, that salvation for Israel would come out of Zion!
   When the LORD restores the fortunes of his people,
   let Jacob rejoice and Israel be glad!

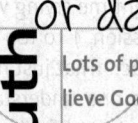

truth or dare

Lots of people today believe God doesn't exist. But God doesn't just vanish because a person believes he isn't there. In your heart, what do you believe?

14:1

Psalm 15

A psalm of David.

[1] LORD, who may dwell in your sanctuary?
   Who may live on your holy hill?

[2] He whose walk is blameless
   and who does what is righteous,
who speaks the truth from his heart
[3]   and has no slander on his tongue,
who does his neighbor no wrong
   and casts no slur on his fellowman,
[4] who despises a vile man
   but honors those who fear the LORD,
who keeps his oath
   even when it hurts,
[5] who lends his money without usury
   and does not accept a bribe against the innocent.

He who does these things
   will never be shaken.

a 1 The Hebrew words rendered fool in Psalms denote one who is morally deficient.

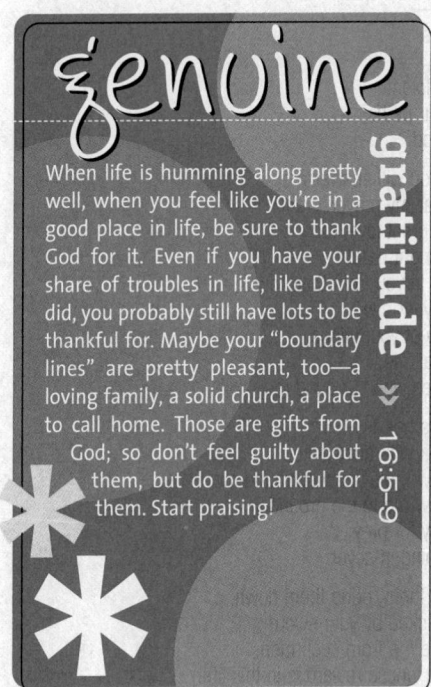

genuine

gratitude ≫ 16:5-9

When life is humming along pretty well, when you feel like you're in a good place in life, be sure to thank God for it. Even if you have your share of troubles in life, like David did, you probably still have lots to be thankful for. Maybe your "boundary lines" are pretty pleasant, too—a loving family, a solid church, a place to call home. Those are gifts from God; so don't feel guilty about them, but do be thankful for them. Start praising!

Psalm 16

A *miktam*ᵃ of David.

¹ Keep me safe, O God,
for in you I take refuge.

² I said to the LORD, "You are my Lord;
apart from you I have no good thing."
³ As for the saints who are in the land,
they are the glorious ones in whom is all my delight.ᵇ
⁴ The sorrows of those will increase who run after other gods.
I will not pour out their libations of blood
or take up their names on my lips.

⁵ LORD, you have assigned me my portion and my cup;
you have made my lot secure.
⁶ The boundary lines have fallen for me in pleasant places;
surely I have a delightful inheritance.

⁷ I will praise the LORD, who counsels me;
even at night my heart instructs me.
⁸ I have set the LORD always before me.
Because he is at my right hand,
I will not be shaken.

⁹ Therefore my heart is glad and my tongue rejoices;
my body also will rest secure,
¹⁰ because you will not abandon me to the grave,ᶜ
nor will you let your Holy Oneᵈ see decay.
¹¹ You have madeᵉ known to me the path of life;
you will fill me with joy in your presence,
with eternal pleasures at your right hand.

Psalm 17

A prayer of David.

¹ Hear, O LORD, my righteous plea;
listen to my cry.
Give ear to my prayer—
it does not rise from deceitful lips.
² May my vindication come from you;
may your eyes see what is right.

³ Though you probe my heart and examine me at night,
though you test me, you will find nothing;
I have resolved that my mouth will not sin.

ᵃ Title: Probably a literary or musical term   ᵇ 3 Or *As for the pagan priests who are in the land / and the nobles in whom all delight, I said:*   ᶜ 10 Hebrew *Sheol*   ᵈ 10 Or *your faithful one*   ᵉ 11 Or *You will make*

⁴As for the deeds of men—
by the word of your lips
I have kept myself
from the ways of the violent.
⁵My steps have held to your paths;
my feet have not slipped.

⁶I call on you, O God, for you will answer me;
give ear to me and hear my prayer.
⁷Show the wonder of your great love,
you who save by your right hand
those who take refuge in you from their foes.
⁸Keep me as the apple of your eye;
hide me in the shadow of your wings
⁹from the wicked who assail me,
from my mortal enemies who surround me.

¹⁰They close up their callous hearts,
and their mouths speak with arrogance.
¹¹They have tracked me down, they now surround me,
with eyes alert, to throw me to the ground.
¹²They are like a lion hungry for prey,
like a great lion crouching in cover.

¹³Rise up, O LORD, confront them, bring them down;
rescue me from the wicked by your sword.
¹⁴O LORD, by your hand save me from such men,
from men of this world whose reward is in this life.

You still the hunger of those you cherish;
their sons have plenty,
and they store up wealth for their children.
¹⁵And I—in righteousness I will see your face;
when I awake, I will be satisfied with seeing your likeness.

Psalm 18

For the director of music. Of David the servant of the LORD. He sang to the LORD the words of this song when the LORD delivered him from the hand of all his enemies and from the hand of Saul. He said:

¹I love you, O LORD, my strength.

²The LORD is my rock, my fortress
and my deliverer;
my God is my rock, in whom I
take refuge.
He is my shield and the horn^a
of my salvation, my
stronghold.
³I call to the LORD, who is worthy
of praise,
and I am saved from my
enemies.

⁴The cords of death entangled me;
the torrents of destruction overwhelmed
me.

truth or dare

As a teen girl, you know that life can seem downright crazy at times. Looking for something solid to lean on? Turn to the Rock.

18:2

^a 2 Horn here symbolizes strength.

⁵ The cords of the grave*ª* coiled around me;
    the snares of death confronted me.
⁶ In my distress I called to the Lᴏʀᴅ;
    I cried to my God for help.
From his temple he heard my voice;
    my cry came before him, into his ears.

⁷ The earth trembled and quaked,
    and the foundations of the mountains shook;
    they trembled because he was angry.
⁸ Smoke rose from his nostrils;
    consuming fire came from his mouth,
    burning coals blazed out of it.
⁹ He parted the heavens and came down;
    dark clouds were under his feet.
¹⁰ He mounted the cherubim and flew;
    he soared on the wings of the wind.
¹¹ He made darkness his covering, his canopy around him—
    the dark rain clouds of the sky.
¹² Out of the brightness of his presence clouds advanced,
    with hailstones and bolts of lightning.
¹³ The Lᴏʀᴅ thundered from heaven;
    the voice of the Most High resounded.*ᵇ*
¹⁴ He shot his arrows and scattered ⌊the enemies⌋,
    great bolts of lightning and routed them.
¹⁵ The valleys of the sea were exposed
    and the foundations of the earth laid bare
at your rebuke, O Lᴏʀᴅ,
    at the blast of breath from your nostrils.

¹⁶ He reached down from on high and took hold of me;
    he drew me out of deep waters.
¹⁷ He rescued me from my powerful enemy,
    from my foes, who were too strong for me.
¹⁸ They confronted me in the day of my disaster,
    but the Lᴏʀᴅ was my support.
¹⁹ He brought me out into a spacious place;
    he rescued me because he delighted in me.

²⁰ The Lᴏʀᴅ has dealt with me according to my righteousness;
    according to the cleanness of my hands he has rewarded me.
²¹ For I have kept the ways of the Lᴏʀᴅ;
    I have not done evil by turning from my God.
²² All his laws are before me;
    I have not turned away from his decrees.
²³ I have been blameless before him
    and have kept myself from sin.
²⁴ The Lᴏʀᴅ has rewarded me according to my righteousness,
    according to the cleanness of my hands in his sight.

²⁵ To the faithful you show yourself faithful,
    to the blameless you show yourself blameless,
²⁶ to the pure you show yourself pure,
    but to the crooked you show yourself shrewd.
²⁷ You save the humble

ª 5 Hebrew *Sheol*   *ᵇ 13* Some Hebrew manuscripts and Septuagint (see also 2 Samuel 22:14); most Hebrew
manuscripts *resounded, / amid hailstones and bolts of lightning*

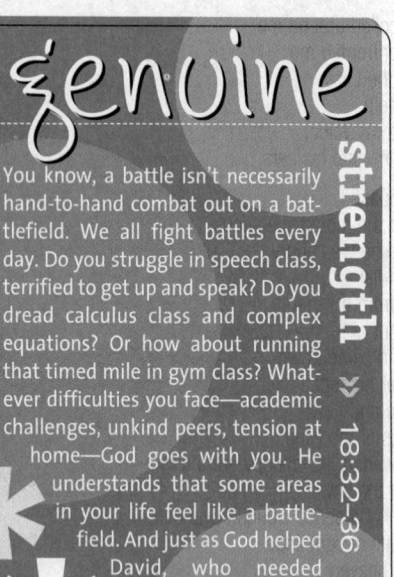

genuine

strength » 18:32-36

You know, a battle isn't necessarily hand-to-hand combat out on a battlefield. We all fight battles every day. Do you struggle in speech class, terrified to get up and speak? Do you dread calculus class and complex equations? Or how about running that timed mile in gym class? Whatever difficulties you face—academic challenges, unkind peers, tension at home—God goes with you. He understands that some areas in your life feel like a battlefield. And just as God helped David, who needed strength for the battle, he's ready and willing to help you, too.

but bring low those whose
    eyes are haughty.
²⁸ You, O LORD, keep my lamp
    burning;
  my God turns my darkness
    into light.
²⁹ With your help I can advance
    against a troop ᵃ;
  with my God I can scale a
    wall.

³⁰ As for God, his way is perfect;
  the word of the LORD is
    flawless.
  He is a shield
    for all who take refuge in him.
³¹ For who is God besides the
    LORD?
  And who is the Rock except
    our God?
³² It is God who arms me with
    strength
  and makes my way perfect.
³³ He makes my feet like the feet of
    a deer;
  he enables me to stand on
    the heights.
³⁴ He trains my hands for battle;
  my arms can bend a bow of bronze.
³⁵ You give me your shield of victory,
  and your right hand sustains me;
  you stoop down to make me great.
³⁶ You broaden the path beneath me,
  so that my ankles do not turn.

³⁷ I pursued my enemies and overtook them;
  I did not turn back till they were destroyed.
³⁸ I crushed them so that they could not rise;
  they fell beneath my feet.
³⁹ You armed me with strength for battle;
  you made my adversaries bow at my feet.
⁴⁰ You made my enemies turn their backs in flight,
  and I destroyed my foes.
⁴¹ They cried for help, but there was no one to save them—
  to the LORD, but he did not answer.
⁴² I beat them as fine as dust borne on the wind;
  I poured them out like mud in the streets.

⁴³ You have delivered me from the attacks of the people;
  you have made me the head of nations;
  people I did not know are subject to me.
⁴⁴ As soon as they hear me, they obey me;
  foreigners cringe before me.
⁴⁵ They all lose heart;
  they come trembling from their strongholds.

ᵃ 29 Or *can run through a barricade*

46 The LORD lives! Praise be to my Rock!
    Exalted be God my Savior!
47 He is the God who avenges me,
    who subdues nations under me,
48   who saves me from my enemies.
  You exalted me above my foes;
    from violent men you rescued me.
49 Therefore I will praise you among the nations, O LORD;
    I will sing praises to your name.
50 He gives his king great victories;
    he shows unfailing kindness to his anointed,
    to David and his descendants forever.

Psalm 19

For the director of music. A psalm of David.

1 The heavens declare the glory of God;
    the skies proclaim the work of his hands.
2 Day after day they pour forth speech;
    night after night they display knowledge.
3 There is no speech or language
    where their voice is not heard. *a*
4 Their voice *b* goes out into all the earth,
    their words to the ends of the world.

In the heavens he has pitched a tent for the sun,
5   which is like a bridegroom coming forth from his pavilion,
    like a champion rejoicing to run his course.
6 It rises at one end of the heavens
    and makes its circuit to the other;
    nothing is hidden from its heat.

7 The law of the LORD is perfect,
    reviving the soul.
  The statutes of the LORD are
      trustworthy,
    making wise the simple.
8 The precepts of the LORD are right,
    giving joy to the heart.
  The commands of the LORD are
      radiant,
    giving light to the eyes.
9 The fear of the LORD is pure,
    enduring forever.
  The ordinances of the LORD are sure
    and altogether righteous.
10 They are more precious than gold,
    than much pure gold;
  they are sweeter than honey,
    than honey from the comb.
11 By them is your servant warned;
    in keeping them there is great reward.

12 Who can discern his errors?
    Forgive my hidden faults.

truth or dare

Are you one of those girls who learns things the hard way? Save yourself some grief and give God's rules a chance.

19:7–8

a 3 Or *They have no speech, there are no words; / no sound is heard from them*   *b 4* Septuagint, Jerome and Syriac; Hebrew *line*

¹³Keep your servant also from willful sins;
    may they not rule over me.
Then will I be blameless,
    innocent of great transgression.

¹⁴May the words of my mouth and the meditation of my heart
    be pleasing in your sight,
    O LORD, my Rock and my Redeemer.

Psalm 20

For the director of music. A psalm of David.

¹May the LORD answer you when you are in distress;
    may the name of the God of Jacob protect you.
²May he send you help from the sanctuary
    and grant you support from Zion.
³May he remember all your sacrifices
    and accept your burnt offerings.   *Selah*
⁴May he give you the desire of your heart
    and make all your plans succeed.
⁵We will shout for joy when you are victorious
    and will lift up our banners in
        the name of our God.
May the LORD grant all your
        requests.

⁶Now I know that the LORD saves
        his anointed;
    he answers him from his holy
        heaven
    with the saving power of his
        right hand.
⁷Some trust in chariots and some
        in horses,
    but we trust in the name of the LORD our
        God.
⁸They are brought to their knees and fall,
    but we rise up and stand firm.

⁹O LORD, save the king!
    Answer^a us when we call!

truth or dare

Whether it's horses and chariots, or popularity and wealth, expecting anything (or *anyone*) other than God to give you joy and contentment will always lead to disappointment.

20:7

Psalm 21

For the director of music. A psalm of David.

¹O LORD, the king rejoices in your strength.
    How great is his joy in the victories you give!
²You have granted him the desire of his heart
    and have not withheld the request of his lips.   *Selah*
³You welcomed him with rich blessings
    and placed a crown of pure gold on his head.
⁴He asked you for life, and you gave it to him—
    length of days, for ever and ever.
⁵Through the victories you gave, his glory is great;
    you have bestowed on him splendor and majesty.
⁶Surely you have granted him eternal blessings

a 9 Or *save! / O King, answer

and made him glad with the joy of your presence.
7 For the king trusts in the LORD;
   through the unfailing love of the Most High
   he will not be shaken.

8 Your hand will lay hold on all your enemies;
   your right hand will seize your foes.
9 At the time of your appearing
   you will make them like a fiery furnace.
In his wrath the LORD will swallow them up,
   and his fire will consume them.
10 You will destroy their descendants from the earth,
   their posterity from mankind.
11 Though they plot evil against you
   and devise wicked schemes, they cannot succeed;
12 for you will make them turn their backs
   when you aim at them with drawn bow.

13 Be exalted, O LORD, in your strength;
   we will sing and praise your might.

Psalm 22

For the director of music. To ⌐the tune of⌐
"The Doe of the Morning." A psalm of David.

1 My God, my God, why have you forsaken me?
   Why are you so far from saving me,
   so far from the words of my groaning?
2 O my God, I cry out by day, but you do not answer,
   by night, and am not silent.

3 Yet you are enthroned as the Holy One;
   you are the praise of Israel. a
4 In you our fathers put their trust;
   they trusted and you delivered them.
5 They cried to you and were saved;
   in you they trusted and were not disappointed.

6 But I am a worm and not a man,
   scorned by men and despised by the people.
7 All who see me mock me;
   they hurl insults, shaking their heads:
8 "He trusts in the LORD;
   let the LORD rescue him.
Let him deliver him,
   since he delights in him."

9 Yet you brought me out of the womb;
   you made me trust in you
   even at my mother's breast.
10 From birth I was cast upon you;
   from my mother's womb you have been my God.
11 Do not be far from me,
   for trouble is near
   and there is no one to help.

12 Many bulls surround me;
   strong bulls of Bashan encircle me.

a 3 Or Yet you are holy, / enthroned on the praises of Israel

¹³Roaring lions tearing their prey
 open their mouths wide against me.
¹⁴I am poured out like water,
 and all my bones are out of joint.
 My heart has turned to wax;
 it has melted away within me.
¹⁵My strength is dried up like a potsherd,
 and my tongue sticks to the roof of my mouth;
 you lay me^a in the dust of death.
¹⁶Dogs have surrounded me;
 a band of evil men has encircled me,
 they have pierced^b my hands and my feet.
¹⁷I can count all my bones;
 people stare and gloat over me.
¹⁸They divide my garments among them
 and cast lots for my clothing.

¹⁹But you, O Lord, be not far off;
 O my Strength, come quickly to help me.
²⁰Deliver my life from the sword,
 my precious life from the power of the dogs.
²¹Rescue me from the mouth of the lions;
 save^c me from the horns of the wild oxen.

²²I will declare your name to my brothers;
 in the congregation I will praise you.
²³You who fear the Lord, praise him!
 All you descendants of Jacob, honor him!
 Revere him, all you descendants of Israel!
²⁴For he has not despised or disdained
 the suffering of the afflicted one;
 he has not hidden his face from him
 but has listened to his cry for help.

²⁵From you comes the theme of my praise in the great assembly;
 before those who fear you^d will I fulfill my vows.
²⁶The poor will eat and be satisfied;
 they who seek the Lord will praise him—
 may your hearts live forever!
²⁷All the ends of the earth
 will remember and turn to the Lord,
 and all the families of the nations
 will bow down before him,
²⁸for dominion belongs to the Lord
 and he rules over the nations.

²⁹All the rich of the earth will feast and worship;
 all who go down to the dust will kneel before him—
 those who cannot keep themselves alive.
³⁰Posterity will serve him;
 future generations will be told about the Lord.
³¹They will proclaim his righteousness
 to a people yet unborn—
 for he has done it.

^a 15 Or / I am laid   ^b 16 Some Hebrew manuscripts, Septuagint and Syriac; most Hebrew manuscripts / like the lion,
^c 21 Or / you have heard   ^d 25 Hebrew him

mirror images

David said to Abigail, "Praise be to the LORD, the God of Israel, who has sent you today to meet me. May you be blessed for your good judgment and for keeping me from bloodshed this day." 1 Samuel 25:32–33

Abigail—Smart Cookie

She was a quick thinker. Unfortunately for her, she was married to an idiot. Abigail's husband, Nabal, foolishly treated David badly. And nobody ever got away with that! David and about four hundred of his men grabbed their swords and set out to kill every male with any relation to Nabal. Fortunately, Abigail intercepted them before they arrived.

Abigail found herself caught between two men—one hot-headed soldier and one proud fool. The situation needed diplomacy and quick thinking. Abigail managed to keep the soldier from doing something he'd regret later and the fool from getting the beating he deserved.

Abigail offered David and his men food and gifts, asked for mercy and even accepted the blame for Nabal's stupidity. What a woman! And what a difficult life she must have had living with such a husband. When David saw Abigail's humility and wisdom, he praised her for keeping him from getting revenge and needlessly shedding blood.

Some might tell us to use our intelligence to manipulate people, make lots of money or get everything we want for ourselves. Others say it's nerdy to be smart. Yet God gives us the tool of intelligence for more than just getting A's in geometry and writing good book reports. He intends for us to use our gifts to glorify him. Having trouble with friends? Use your brain, not your brawn, to come up with a solution. Concerned about unfairness in your community? Worried about world issues? Put your mind to it—God may use you to make the world a better place. It would be so easy for us to use our sharp minds to cause problems for others or to brag about ourselves. But if we humble ourselves like Abigail, we can glorify God by finding wise solutions to problems we face.

To read the next Mirror Images profile, go to page 709.

Dear God, thank you for giving me a sharp mind. May I glorify you and not myself with it. Please grant me Abigail's wisdom and good judgment. Amen.

dear God

» Read more about Abigail in 1 Samuel 25 (pages 352–353).

Psalm 23

A psalm of David.

¹ The LORD is my shepherd, I shall not be in want.
² He makes me lie down in green pastures,
he leads me beside quiet waters,
³ he restores my soul.
He guides me in paths of righteousness
for his name's sake.
⁴ Even though I walk
through the valley of the shadow of death, *ᵃ*
I will fear no evil,
for you are with me;

your rod and your staff,
they comfort me.

⁵ You prepare a table before me
in the presence of my enemies.
You anoint my head with oil;
my cup overflows.
⁶ Surely goodness and love will follow me
all the days of my life,
and I will dwell in the house of
the LORD
forever.

love notes

23:1-6

Daughter,

I know you've read these words before. Read them again as if I'm talking directly to you. I'll give you everything you need. I'll guide you through life's toughest times. You'll live in my house . . . forever.

—Your good Shepherd

Spend some time thinking about the images in this psalm, then write out the feelings that this psalm evokes in your heart, knowing your good Shepherd is watching over you.

_____
_____
_____
_____
_____
_____
_____
_____
_____
_____
_____

Psalm 24

Of David. A psalm.

¹ The earth is the LORD'S, and
everything in it,
the world, and all who live in it;
² for he founded it upon the seas
and established it upon the
waters.

³ Who may ascend the hill of the
LORD?
Who may stand in his holy
place?
⁴ He who has clean hands and a
pure heart,
who does not lift up his soul
to an idol
or swear by what is false. *ᵇ*
⁵ He will receive blessing from the
LORD
and vindication from God his
Savior.
⁶ Such is the generation of those
who seek him,
who seek your face, O God of
Jacob. *ᶜ* *Selah*

ᵃ 4 Or *through the darkest valley* *ᵇ 4* Or *swear falsely* *ᶜ 6* Two Hebrew manuscripts and Syriac (see also Septuagint); most Hebrew manuscripts *face, Jacob*

⁷Lift up your heads, O you gates;
    be lifted up, you ancient
        doors,
    that the King of glory may
        come in.
⁸Who is this King of glory?
    The LORD strong and mighty,
    the LORD mighty in battle.
⁹Lift up your heads, O you gates;
    lift them up, you ancient
        doors,
    that the King of glory may
        come in.
¹⁰Who is he, this King of glory?
    The LORD Almighty—
    he is the King of glory.

Selah

truth or dare

Save the Planet. That's a great motto for all of us, not just for extremist tree-huggers. God owns the earth, but he loaned it to us to take care of.

24:1–2

Psalm 25 ᵃ

Of David.

¹To you, O LORD, I lift up my soul;
²   in you I trust, O my God.
Do not let me be put to shame,
    nor let my enemies triumph over me.
³No one whose hope is in you
    will ever be put to shame,
but they will be put to shame
    who are treacherous without excuse.

⁴Show me your ways, O LORD,
    teach me your paths;
⁵guide me in your truth and teach me,
    for you are God my Savior,
    and my hope is in you all day long.
⁶Remember, O LORD, your great mercy and love,
    for they are from of old.
⁷Remember not the sins of my youth
    and my rebellious ways;
according to your love remember me,
    for you are good, O LORD.

⁸Good and upright is the LORD;
    therefore he instructs sinners in his ways.
⁹He guides the humble in what is right
    and teaches them his way.
¹⁰All the ways of the LORD are loving and faithful
    for those who keep the demands of his covenant.
¹¹For the sake of your name, O LORD,
    forgive my iniquity, though it is great.
¹²Who, then, is the man that fears the LORD?
    He will instruct him in the way chosen for him.
¹³He will spend his days in prosperity,
    and his descendants will inherit the land.
¹⁴The LORD confides in those who fear him;
    he makes his covenant known to them.

ᵃ This psalm is an acrostic poem, the verses of which begin with the successive letters of the Hebrew alphabet.

¹⁵My eyes are ever on the LORD,
for only he will release my feet from the snare.

¹⁶Turn to me and be gracious to me,
for I am lonely and afflicted.

¹⁷The troubles of my heart have multiplied;
free me from my anguish.

¹⁸Look upon my affliction and my distress
and take away all my sins.

¹⁹See how my enemies have increased
and how fiercely they hate me!

²⁰Guard my life and rescue me;
let me not be put to shame,
for I take refuge in you.

²¹May integrity and uprightness protect me,
because my hope is in you.

²²Redeem Israel, O God,
from all their troubles!

Psalm 26

Of David.

¹Vindicate me, O LORD,
for I have led a blameless life;
I have trusted in the LORD
without wavering.

²Test me, O LORD, and try me,
examine my heart and my mind;

³for your love is ever before me,
and I walk continually in your truth.

⁴I do not sit with deceitful men,
nor do I consort with hypocrites;

⁵I abhor the assembly of evildoers
and refuse to sit with the wicked.

⁶I wash my hands in innocence,
and go about your altar, O LORD,

⁷proclaiming aloud your praise
and telling of all your wonderful deeds.

⁸I love the house where you live, O LORD,
the place where your glory dwells.

⁹Do not take away my soul along with sinners,
my life with bloodthirsty men,

¹⁰in whose hands are wicked schemes,
whose right hands are full of bribes.

¹¹But I lead a blameless life;
redeem me and be merciful to me.

¹²My feet stand on level ground;
in the great assembly I will praise the LORD.

Psalm 27

Of David.

¹The LORD is my light and my salvation—
whom shall I fear?
The LORD is the stronghold of my life—
of whom shall I be afraid?

genuine

comfort

Have you ever had a really bad, horrible, no good, very bad day? Some days all you want to do is curl up in bed and try to forget everything that happened. David had a few days like that—when evil men, enemies and armies were all coming after him. So how did he cope with the fear and stress? He kept his eyes on what mattered most to him: God. When your day takes a sharp turn for the worse, focus on God's faithfulness and power to overcome any problem. And after locking eyes with the Lord, you'll find that you can face the world again—unafraid.

» 27:1-5

² When evil men advance against me
to devour my flesh, *a*
when my enemies and my foes
attack me,
they will stumble and fall.
³ Though an army besiege me,
my heart will not fear;
though war break out against me,
even then will I be confident.

⁴ One thing I ask of the Lord,
this is what I seek:
that I may dwell in the house of
the Lord
all the days of my life,
to gaze upon the beauty of the Lord
and to seek him in his temple.
⁵ For in the day of trouble
he will keep me safe in his
dwelling;
he will hide me in the shelter of
his tabernacle
and set me high upon a rock.
⁶ Then my head will be exalted
above the enemies who
surround me;
at his tabernacle will I sacrifice
with shouts of joy;
I will sing and make music to the Lord.

⁷ Hear my voice when I call, O Lord;
be merciful to me and answer me.
⁸ My heart says of you, "Seek his *b* face!"
Your face, Lord, I will seek.
⁹ Do not hide your face from me,
do not turn your servant away
in anger;
you have been my helper.
Do not reject me or forsake me,
O God my Savior.
¹⁰ Though my father and mother
forsake me,
the Lord will receive me.
¹¹ Teach me your way, O Lord;
lead me in a straight path
because of my oppressors.
¹² Do not turn me over to the desire of my foes,
for false witnesses rise up against me,
breathing out violence.
¹³ I am still confident of this:
I will see the goodness of the Lord
in the land of the living.
¹⁴ Wait for the Lord;
be strong and take heart
and wait for the Lord.

truth or dare

Are you in dire need of some face-time with God? You don't need an invite. He's already said, "Come and talk with me. Let's get to know each other."

27:8

a 2 Or to slander me   *b 8 Or To you, O my heart, he has said, "Seek my*

Psalm 28

Of David.

¹To you I call, O LORD my Rock;
    do not turn a deaf ear to me.
For if you remain silent,
    I will be like those who have gone down to the pit.
²Hear my cry for mercy
    as I call to you for help,
as I lift up my hands
    toward your Most Holy Place.

³Do not drag me away with the wicked,
    with those who do evil,
who speak cordially with their neighbors
    but harbor malice in their hearts.
⁴Repay them for their deeds
    and for their evil work;
repay them for what their hands have done
    and bring back upon them what they deserve.
⁵Since they show no regard for the works of the LORD
    and what his hands have done,
he will tear them down
    and never build them up again.

⁶Praise be to the LORD,
    for he has heard my cry for mercy.
⁷The LORD is my strength and my shield;
    my heart trusts in him, and I am helped.
My heart leaps for joy
    and I will give thanks to him in song.

⁸The LORD is the strength of his people,
    a fortress of salvation for his anointed one.
⁹Save your people and bless your inheritance;
    be their shepherd and carry them forever.

Psalm 29

A psalm of David.

¹Ascribe to the LORD, O mighty ones,
    ascribe to the LORD glory and strength.
²Ascribe to the LORD the glory due his name;
    worship the LORD in the splendor of his ᵃ holiness.

³The voice of the LORD is over the waters;
    the God of glory thunders,
    the LORD thunders over the mighty waters.
⁴The voice of the LORD is powerful;
    the voice of the LORD is majestic.
⁵The voice of the LORD breaks the cedars;
    the LORD breaks in pieces the cedars of Lebanon.
⁶He makes Lebanon skip like a calf,
    Sirion ᵇ like a young wild ox.
⁷The voice of the LORD strikes
    with flashes of lightning.

ᵃ 2 Or LORD with the splendor of   ᵇ 6 That is, Mount Hermon

⁸The voice of the Lord shakes the desert;
　the Lord shakes the Desert of Kadesh.
⁹The voice of the Lord twists the oaks *a*
　and strips the forests bare.
And in his temple all cry, "Glory!"

¹⁰The Lord sits *b* enthroned over the flood;
　the Lord is enthroned as King forever.
¹¹The Lord gives strength to his people;
　the Lord blesses his people with peace.

Psalm 30

A psalm. A song. For the dedication of the temple. *c* Of David.

¹I will exalt you, O Lord,
　for you lifted me out of the depths
　and did not let my enemies gloat over me.
²O Lord my God, I called to you for help
　and you healed me.

³O Lord, you brought me up from
　　the grave *d*;
　you spared me from going
　　down into the pit.

⁴Sing to the Lord, you saints of his;
　praise his holy name.
⁵For his anger lasts only a
　　moment,
　but his favor lasts a lifetime;
weeping may remain for a night,
　but rejoicing comes in the
　　morning.

⁶When I felt secure, I said,
　"I will never be shaken."
⁷O Lord, when you favored me,
　you made my mountain *e*
　　stand firm;
but when you hid your face,
　I was dismayed.

⁸To you, O Lord, I called;
　to the Lord I cried for mercy:
⁹"What gain is there in my
　　destruction, *f*
　in my going down into the pit?
Will the dust praise you?
　Will it proclaim your
　　faithfulness?

¹⁰Hear, O Lord, and be merciful to me;
　O Lord, be my help."

¹¹You turned my wailing into dancing;
　you removed my sackcloth and clothed me with joy,
¹²that my heart may sing to you and not be silent.
　O Lord my God, I will give you thanks forever.

genuine
security » 30:6-7

What's the most traumatic thing that's ever happened to you—something that seemed to shake your world? Maybe your parents got divorced, or a friend was hurt, or someone you love died. Times like these can make you feel shaken, unsettled and out of control. What to do? You can't change what happened, but you can put your focus on God and trust him. Even though you can't control your circumstances, you can say with confidence, "Because God is with me, I will never be shaken."

a 9 Or Lord *makes the deer give birth*　*b 10* Or *sat*　*c* Title: Or *palace*　*d 3* Hebrew *Sheol*　*e 7* Or *hill country*
f 9 Or *there if I am silenced*

Psalm 31

For the director of music. A psalm of David.

[1] In you, O LORD, I have taken refuge;
    let me never be put to shame;
    deliver me in your righteousness.
[2] Turn your ear to me,
    come quickly to my rescue;
  be my rock of refuge,
    a strong fortress to save me.
[3] Since you are my rock and my fortress,
    for the sake of your name lead and guide me.
[4] Free me from the trap that is set for me,
    for you are my refuge.
[5] Into your hands I commit my spirit;
    redeem me, O LORD, the God of truth.

[6] I hate those who cling to worthless idols;
    I trust in the LORD.
[7] I will be glad and rejoice in your love,
    for you saw my affliction
    and knew the anguish of my soul.
[8] You have not handed me over to the enemy
    but have set my feet in a spacious place.

[9] Be merciful to me, O LORD, for I am in distress;
    my eyes grow weak with sorrow,
    my soul and my body with grief.
[10] My life is consumed by anguish
    and my years by groaning;
    my strength fails because of my affliction,[a]
    and my bones grow weak.
[11] Because of all my enemies,
    I am the utter contempt of my neighbors;
    I am a dread to my friends—
    those who see me on the street flee from me.
[12] I am forgotten by them as though I were dead;
    I have become like broken pottery.
[13] For I hear the slander of many;
    there is terror on every side;
    they conspire against me
    and plot to take my life.

[14] But I trust in you, O LORD;
    I say, "You are my God."
[15] My times are in your hands;
    deliver me from my enemies
    and from those who pursue
        me.
[16] Let your face shine on your
        servant;
    save me in your unfailing love.
[17] Let me not be put to shame, O LORD,
    for I have cried out to you;
    but let the wicked be put to shame
    and lie silent in the grave.[b]

truth or dare

Is it a girl's curse to fret over the future? You can trust that God's all over it, especially in those major choices up ahead. So don't worry. *Really.*

31:14–15

[a] 10 Or guilt   [b] 17 Hebrew *Sheol*

¹⁸ Let their lying lips be silenced,
  for with pride and contempt
  they speak arrogantly against the righteous.

¹⁹ How great is your goodness,
  which you have stored up for those who fear you,
  which you bestow in the sight of men
  on those who take refuge in you.

²⁰ In the shelter of your presence you hide them
  from the intrigues of men;
  in your dwelling you keep them safe
  from accusing tongues.

²¹ Praise be to the LORD,
  for he showed his wonderful love to me
  when I was in a besieged city.

²² In my alarm I said,
  "I am cut off from your sight!"
  Yet you heard my cry for mercy
  when I called to you for help.

²³ Love the LORD, all his saints!
  The LORD preserves the faithful,
  but the proud he pays back in full.

²⁴ Be strong and take heart,
  all you who hope in the LORD.

Psalm 32

Of David. A *maskil.*ᵃ

¹ Blessed is he
  whose transgressions are forgiven,
  whose sins are covered.

² Blessed is the man
  whose sin the LORD does not
  count against him
  and in whose spirit is no
  deceit.

³ When I kept silent,
  my bones wasted away
  through my groaning all day long.

⁴ For day and night
  your hand was heavy upon me;
  my strength was sapped
  as in the heat of summer.
  Selah

⁵ Then I acknowledged my sin to
  you
  and did not cover up my
  iniquity.
  I said, "I will confess
  my transgressions to the
  LORD"—
  and you forgave
  the guilt of my sin.   *Selah*

genuine

forgiveness » 32:1-2

If you're a follower of Christ, then these verses are about you. Your transgressions are forgiven, your sins are covered and the Lord does not hold your sin against you. Now does that mean you will never sin again after you become a Christian? Hardly! You already know that from experience. Dealing with sin is a struggle, and at times you will fail. But when you do sin, confess it and seek God's forgiveness. No worries—you're covered!

a Title: Probably a literary or musical term

⁶ Therefore let everyone who is godly pray to you
    while you may be found;
surely when the mighty waters rise,
    they will not reach him.
⁷ You are my hiding place;
    you will protect me from trouble
    and surround me with songs of deliverance.   *Selah*

⁸ I will instruct you and teach you in the way you should go;
    I will counsel you and watch over you.
⁹ Do not be like the horse or the mule,
    which have no understanding
but must be controlled by bit and bridle
    or they will not come to you.
¹⁰ Many are the woes of the wicked,
    but the Lord's unfailing love
    surrounds the man who trusts in him.

¹¹ Rejoice in the Lord and be glad, you righteous;
    sing, all you who are upright in heart!

Psalm 33

¹ Sing joyfully to the Lord, you righteous;
    it is fitting for the upright to praise him.
² Praise the Lord with the harp;
    make music to him on the ten-stringed lyre.
³ Sing to him a new song;
    play skillfully, and shout for joy.

⁴ For the word of the Lord is right and true;
    he is faithful in all he does.
⁵ The Lord loves righteousness and justice;
    the earth is full of his unfailing love.

⁶ By the word of the Lord were the heavens made,
    their starry host by the breath of his mouth.
⁷ He gathers the waters of the sea into jars*ᵃ*;
    he puts the deep into storehouses.
⁸ Let all the earth fear the Lord;
    let all the people of the world revere him.
⁹ For he spoke, and it came to be;
    he commanded, and it stood firm.
¹⁰ The Lord foils the plans of the nations;
    he thwarts the purposes of the peoples.
¹¹ But the plans of the Lord stand firm forever,
    the purposes of his heart through all generations.

¹² Blessed is the nation whose God is the Lord,
    the people he chose for his inheritance.
¹³ From heaven the Lord looks down
    and sees all mankind;
¹⁴ from his dwelling place he watches
    all who live on earth—
¹⁵ he who forms the hearts of all,
    who considers everything they do.
¹⁶ No king is saved by the size of his army;
    no warrior escapes by his great strength.

ᵃ 7 Or *sea as into a heap*

My So-Called Life

focus — Profile: **Halley**

I used to have a normal family. A mom and a dad who lived together. Family vacations. Movie nights with popcorn. The home I grew up in.

I used to have a lot of things together. Now, thanks to my parents, my life has basically fallen apart. Half my closet is at Mom's house. And half is at my dad's house. Half my life happens Monday through Friday at school, living with my dad. The other half happens on weekend visits to my mom's place in Orange County.

It didn't have to be like this. Mom didn't have to leave us. She didn't have to go and "find herself" in another town. If she'd stayed, none of this would have happened. My dad wouldn't have lost his job, and he wouldn't be sitting on the couch in his pajamas looking through the want ads. My mom wouldn't be seeing a shrink. And I wouldn't be serving detention at school again. Ever since my family bailed out, I've been a wreck at school. I can't focus, I lose my temper and I forget to turn in my homework.

My dad blames my friends for being a bad influence on me. I think he just needs someone else to blame for why I'm struggling at school. He and Mom won't face the fact that I'm continually snapping under the stress that they caused. My so-called life would be normal again if my parents hadn't messed it up.

Read more on bitterness at www.TrueImagesBible.com

bitterness in focus

Bad stuff is bound to happen—and it's often beyond your control. However, you can control your response to it. Something like divorce may hurt you deeply, but it doesn't have to ruin your life. God knows what you're feeling. He understands your pain. He can heal your hurts. But you have to let him.

» Don't make your personal pain an excuse for rebellious behavior. It's just not worth it.

» Deal with your pain—talk about it with a friend, family member or even a professional counselor. Keeping it inside will only cause bitterness to grow.

» God will uphold you even if and when you stumble (see Psalm 37:23–24, page 690). Just don't let go of his hand.

For more on this topic, see the index on page 1656.

¹⁷A horse is a vain hope for deliverance;
    despite all its great strength it cannot save.
¹⁸But the eyes of the Lord are on those who fear him,
    on those whose hope is in his unfailing love,
¹⁹to deliver them from death
    and keep them alive in famine.

²⁰We wait in hope for the Lord;
    he is our help and our shield.
²¹In him our hearts rejoice,
    for we trust in his holy name.

²² May your unfailing love rest upon us, O LORD,
even as we put our hope in you.

Psalm 34 ^a

Of David. When he pretended to be insane before Abimelech, who drove him away, and he left.

¹ I will extol the LORD at all times;
his praise will always be on my lips.
² My soul will boast in the LORD;
let the afflicted hear and rejoice.
³ Glorify the LORD with me;
let us exalt his name together.

⁴ I sought the LORD, and he answered me;
he delivered me from all my fears.
⁵ Those who look to him are radiant;
their faces are never covered with shame.
⁶ This poor man called, and the
LORD heard him;
he saved him out of all his
troubles.
⁷ The angel of the LORD encamps
around those who fear
him,
and he delivers them.

⁸ Taste and see that the LORD is
good;
blessed is the man who takes
refuge in him.
⁹ Fear the LORD, you his saints,
for those who fear him lack nothing.
¹⁰ The lions may grow weak and hungry,
but those who seek the LORD lack no good thing.

¹¹ Come, my children, listen to me;
I will teach you the fear of the LORD.
¹² Whoever of you loves life
and desires to see many good days,
¹³ keep your tongue from evil
and your lips from speaking lies.
¹⁴ Turn from evil and do good;
seek peace and pursue it.

¹⁵ The eyes of the LORD are on the righteous
and his ears are attentive to their cry;
¹⁶ the face of the LORD is against those who do evil,
to cut off the memory of them from the earth.

¹⁷ The righteous cry out, and the LORD hears them;
he delivers them from all their troubles.
¹⁸ The LORD is close to the brokenhearted
and saves those who are crushed in spirit.

¹⁹ A righteous man may have many troubles,
but the LORD delivers him from them all;

truth or dare

Try it—you'll like it! Once you get a taste of God's goodness, you're guaranteed to keep coming back for more.

34:8

^a This psalm is an acrostic poem, the verses of which begin with the successive letters of the Hebrew alphabet.

genuine peace » 34:14

Usually we think of peace as something that happens when nothing else is happening. In other words, no conflict plus no worries equals peace. But the Bible doesn't tell us to sit around and hope for peace. It tells us to seek peace and pursue it. Do you want peace in your life and relationships? Do something about it. Be calm and patient instead of argumentative and angry. Try to change a situation rather than complain about it. Peace isn't for passivists; it's for activists.

20 he protects all his bones,
  not one of them will be broken.

21 Evil will slay the wicked;
  the foes of the righteous will
    be condemned.
22 The LORD redeems his servants;
  no one will be condemned who
    takes refuge in him.

Psalm 35

Of David.

1 Contend, O LORD, with those who
    contend with me;
  fight against those who fight
    against me.
2 Take up shield and buckler;
  arise and come to my aid.
3 Brandish spear and javelin *a*
  against those who pursue me.
Say to my soul,
  "I am your salvation."

4 May those who seek my life
  be disgraced and put to
    shame;
  may those who plot my ruin
  be turned back in dismay.

5 May they be like chaff before the wind,
  with the angel of the LORD driving them away;
6 may their path be dark and slippery,
  with the angel of the LORD pursuing them.
7 Since they hid their net for me without cause
  and without cause dug a pit for me,
8 may ruin overtake them by surprise—
  may the net they hid entangle them,
  may they fall into the pit, to their ruin.
9 Then my soul will rejoice in the LORD
  and delight in his salvation.
10 My whole being will exclaim,
  "Who is like you, O LORD?
You rescue the poor from those too strong for them,
  the poor and needy from those who rob them."

11 Ruthless witnesses come forward;
  they question me on things I know nothing about.
12 They repay me evil for good
  and leave my soul forlorn.
13 Yet when they were ill, I put on sackcloth
  and humbled myself with fasting.
When my prayers returned to me unanswered,
14 I went about mourning
  as though for my friend or brother.
I bowed my head in grief
  as though weeping for my mother.

a 3 Or and block the way

¹⁵But when I stumbled, they gathered in glee;
    attackers gathered against me when I was unaware.
    They slandered me without ceasing.
¹⁶Like the ungodly they maliciously mocked^a;
    they gnashed their teeth at me.
¹⁷O Lord, how long will you look on?
    Rescue my life from their ravages,
    my precious life from these lions.
¹⁸I will give you thanks in the great assembly;
    among throngs of people I will praise you.

¹⁹Let not those gloat over me
    who are my enemies without cause;
    let not those who hate me without reason
    maliciously wink the eye.
²⁰They do not speak peaceably,
    but devise false accusations
    against those who live quietly in the land.
²¹They gape at me and say, "Aha! Aha!
    With our own eyes we have seen it."

²²O Lord, you have seen this; be not silent.
    Do not be far from me, O Lord.
²³Awake, and rise to my defense!
    Contend for me, my God and Lord.
²⁴Vindicate me in your righteousness, O Lord my God;
    do not let them gloat over me.
²⁵Do not let them think, "Aha, just what we wanted!"
    or say, "We have swallowed him up."

²⁶May all who gloat over my distress
    be put to shame and confusion;
    may all who exalt themselves over me
    be clothed with shame and disgrace.
²⁷May those who delight in my vindication
    shout for joy and gladness;
    may they always say, "The Lord be exalted,
    who delights in the well-being of his servant."
²⁸My tongue will speak of your righteousness
    and of your praises all day long.

Psalm 36

For the director of music. Of David the servant of the Lord.

¹An oracle is within my heart
    concerning the sinfulness of the wicked:^b
There is no fear of God
    before his eyes.
²For in his own eyes he flatters himself
    too much to detect or hate his sin.
³The words of his mouth are wicked and deceitful;
    he has ceased to be wise and to do good.
⁴Even on his bed he plots evil;
    he commits himself to a sinful course
    and does not reject what is wrong.

^a 16 Septuagint; Hebrew may mean *ungodly circle of mockers.*   ^b 1 Or *heart: / Sin proceeds from the wicked.*

The Perfect Date

(whether it's your 1st date or 50th!)

1 He asks you what you're up for on Saturday night. You say:
- A. Paintball—bring it on!
- B. Opening night at the Shakespeare theater.
- C. Chillin' at home—low key and fun!

2 You're staring at your closet wondering what to wear. Eureka! You grab:
- A. A tank top and your favorite baseball cap.
- B. The little black dress—it's a classic for a reason, sista!
- C. The sweater he gave you for your birthday.

3 Have a sip, baby. You order a . . .
- A. Healthy fruit shake with extra protein powder.
- B. Virgin pina colada.
- C. Chocolate peanut butter milkshake to share.

4 The perfect setting for a heart-to-heart:
- A. Nature trail in the forest preserve.
- B. A four-star gourmet restaurant.
- C. Two stuffed chairs at the local coffee shop.

5 Your date calls on his cell—what should he pick up for dinner?
- A. Ingredients for make-your-own pizzas
- B. Sushi with chop sticks
- C. Fajitas for two

6 The hair, the hair!—what to do?
- A. The sporty ponytail
- B. The classic messy bun
- C. Down and natural—his favorite

7 You can tell he's dyin' to hold your hand. You hope he . . .
- A. Reaches out and grabs it.
- B. Asks first, politely.
- C. When *isn't* he holding your hand?!

8 It's your turn to plan a romantic evening out. Your pick:
- A. Skeeball and pizza at Chuck E. Cheese.
- B. Candlelight dinner for two at a French restaurant.
- C. Make dinner together and go for a picnic.

9 Bummin'! The night's over. How do you say good-bye?
- A. Slap a high-five.
- B. The classic cheek-to-cheek peck.
- C. Classified info—I never kiss and tell.

10 If this guy wants to win your heart, he'd better call . . .
- A. What are you talking about? We hang out every day!
- B. Within 48 hours.
- C. As soon as he gets home.

11 Flowers are waiting for you when you get home. You secretly hope they are:
- A. Bright yellow daisies.
- B. Long-stemmed red roses.
- C. Doesn't matter as long as he picked them.

12 What do your P's really think of him?
- A. They're pumped for your double date next weekend!
- B. He's passed the written test; his interview is next week.
- C. He's already practically part of the family!

scoring

Mostly Ⓐ's—*Sporty Chick*

You're a girl who knows how to have a good time! You'd rather be out doing somethin' than stuck in a serious one-on-one. Guys like you because you're fun and make them feel relaxed, like they can be themselves around you.

> *Sisterly advice:* Even if you're best buds, make sure he treats you like a lady. You deserve it.

Mostly Ⓑ's—*Classy Lady*

Audrey Hepburn—Need we say more? You're a girl who appreciates the finer things in life. You'd rather be having an elegant dinner with your squeeze than sitting through another Monday night football game. Guys like your refined, feminine side and know you're somethin' special.

> *Sisterly advice:* You may seem a bit untouchable—even Audrey might grab a hot dog at the ball game.

Mostly Ⓒ's—*Mad about You*

You're a long-term relationship kind of girl. None of this fling stuff for you! You'd rather get deep with one guy than jump from boy to boy. Guys like you because they can tell you really care for them, and you're the kind of girl a guy would fall in love with.

> *Sisterly advice:* Don't settle for the first boy you come across—there are other fish in the sea!

reflections from the other side

question:
What makes you ask a girl out a second time?

answer:
If I went out with a girl and had fun and was able to hold an interesting/ funny conversation with her, then I would certainly ask her out again. Oh, and the whole "feeling attracted to her" thing would help.

Some Creative Dates

1» Grab your favorite cookie recipe, bake up a fresh batch and pig out together on warm cookies and ice cream.

2» Check out some of those random holidays like National Vienna Sausage Week or Groundhog Day and celebrate!

3» Symphony under the stars—fresh air for you sporty chicks, romantic tunes for you classy ladies and cuddling opps for you mad-about-you types.

4» Set up a scavenger hunt at the zoo—great for a double date, too!

5» Get your groove on! Sign up for a ballroom or swing dance class. Check out the local college or your parks and recreation department.

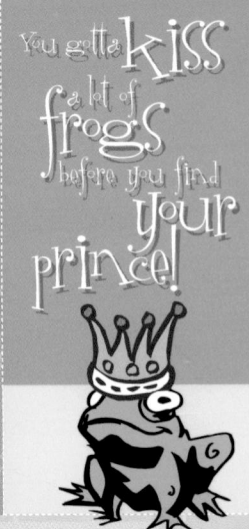

You gotta **KISS** a lot of **frogs** before you find **your** prince!

Remember Grandma's wisdom? "You can tell a lot about a guy by the way he treats old people, children and animals." Not bad, Granny!

How Well do you know your Best Bud?

How well do you know your best bud? No, *really!* You say you're the best of friends, but do you really know the depths of her soul? Are you surface-level friends or true soul mates? Fill in the following questions, and find out how well you really know her.

1. What's your best friend's middle name?

2. What does she want to be when she grows up?

3. Her favorite flower?

4. Her favorite color (and shade)?

5. Her gum of choice?

6. Her first crush?

7. Her favorite subject in school?

8. Her eye color?

9. Her favorite book of all time?

10. Her favorite movie?

11. Her favorite restaurant?

12. Braces or not?

13. Her siblings' names?

14. Her choice: beef, chicken or tofu?

15. Her major scars or birthmarks?

16. What does she want to name her firstborn?

17. Would she ever bungee jump?

18. Would she ever run a marathon?

19. Is she spontaneous enough to marry the first boy she fell in love with?

20. Would she walk up and introduce herself to the President if he walked into the room?

21. Would she rather have earrings from Tiffany's or a new mountain bike?

22. Chocolate or vanilla?

23. Her favorite season?

24. Her biggest prayer request?

25. Her greatest fear?

26. Her hidden talent?

27. Her dream vacation—city, beach or mountains?

28. Silver or gold?

29. Her biggest pet peeve?

30. Her deepest, darkest secret?

31. Her favorite junk food?

32. What embarrasses her?

33. Has she accepted Christ as her Savior? If so, when?

34. Does she bite her nails?

35. Her role model?

36. If she could go back in time and change one thing, what would it be?

37. The farthest she's traveled from home?

38. Coke or Pepsi?

(A) (B) (C) (?)

39. Night owl or morning person?

40. If she could have plastic surgery for free, would she do it?

41. If she could change one thing about her, what would it be?

42. Her favorite outfit: comfy or chic?

43. What brand of perfume does she wear (or does she)?

44. Procrastinator or Ms. Efficient?

45. Is she transparent or mysterious?

Well, does this give you some confirmation about your friendship, or does it make you realize you've got some work to do? If you don't know a lot of these answers, maybe you're a little too self-absorbed or aren't taking the time to invest in your friendship. If you do know most of the answers and feel closer to her than ever, think of ways to continue to build that friendship—don't take her for granted!

"A [girl] of many companions may come to ruin, but there is a friend who sticks closer than a [sister]" (Proverbs 18:24).

You can make more (and better!) friends in two months by being interested in others than you can in two years of trying to get others interested in you.

Five Ways to Get to Know Your G-Friend Better

① Take five minutes and *only listen*—let your best bud tell you whatever she wants during that time. No interrupting!

② Ask to see her photo albums from when she was growing up. Listen to the stories behind the pictures.

③ Write her a letter telling her how much you appreciate her. Be specific about what you value in her!

④ Show your support—go to her next game, performance, meet or competition.

⑤ Play Twenty Questions and ask her whatever you didn't know about her from the quiz.

⁵Your love, O Lord, reaches to the
heavens,
your faithfulness to the skies.
⁶Your righteousness is like the
mighty mountains,
your justice like the great deep.
O Lord, you preserve both man
and beast.
⁷   How priceless is your unfailing
love!
Both high and low among men
find*a* refuge in the shadow of
your wings.
⁸They feast on the abundance of your house;
you give them drink from your river of delights.
⁹For with you is the fountain of life;
in your light we see light.

¹⁰Continue your love to those who know you,
your righteousness to the upright in heart.
¹¹May the foot of the proud not come against me,
nor the hand of the wicked drive me away.
¹²See how the evildoers lie fallen—
thrown down, not able to rise!

truth or dare

God's love? Priceless.
And completely free.

36:7

genuine

desire » 37:3-4

Is this "desires of your heart" thing an open-ended offer for everything you could ever want? Well, not quite. See, there's one condition. First you have to *delight* yourself in the Lord—that means getting to know God, enjoying his presence and spending time with him. Once you get your joy tied to him, your desires just might change. Instead of a long wish list of *stuff*— clothes, popularity, a boyfriend and other things that don't last— you'll desire real, true, lasting satisfaction. What God offers is no fake, cheap, quick-fix happiness that lasts for a mo- ment. He offers you a fulfilling life that's way beyond what you can possibly imagine!

Psalm 37*b*

Of David.

¹Do not fret because of evil men
or be envious of those who do
wrong;
²for like the grass they will soon wither,
like green plants they will
soon die away.

³Trust in the Lord and do good;
dwell in the land and enjoy
safe pasture.
⁴Delight yourself in the Lord
and he will give you the
desires of your heart.

⁵Commit your way to the Lord;
trust in him and he will do this:
⁶He will make your righteousness
shine like the dawn,
the justice of your cause like
the noonday sun.

⁷Be still before the Lord and wait
patiently for him;
do not fret when men succeed
in their ways,
when they carry out their
wicked schemes.

---

a 7 Or *love, O God! / Men find*; or *love! / Both heavenly beings and men / find*   *b* This psalm is an acrostic poem, the
stanzas of which begin with the successive letters of the Hebrew alphabet.

⁸Refrain from anger and turn from wrath;
    do not fret—it leads only to evil.
⁹For evil men will be cut off,
    but those who hope in the LORD will inherit the land.

¹⁰A little while, and the wicked will be no more;
    though you look for them, they will not be found.
¹¹But the meek will inherit the land
    and enjoy great peace.

¹²The wicked plot against the righteous
    and gnash their teeth at them;
¹³but the Lord laughs at the wicked,
    for he knows their day is coming.

¹⁴The wicked draw the sword
    and bend the bow
to bring down the poor and needy,
    to slay those whose ways are upright.
¹⁵But their swords will pierce their own hearts,
    and their bows will be broken.

¹⁶Better the little that the righteous have
    than the wealth of many wicked;
¹⁷for the power of the wicked will be broken,
    but the LORD upholds the righteous.

¹⁸The days of the blameless are known to the LORD,
    and their inheritance will endure forever.
¹⁹In times of disaster they will not wither;
    in days of famine they will enjoy plenty.

²⁰But the wicked will perish:
    The LORD's enemies will be like the beauty of the fields,
    they will vanish—vanish like smoke.

²¹The wicked borrow and do not repay,
    but the righteous give generously;
²²those the LORD blesses will inherit the land,
    but those he curses will be cut off.

²³If the LORD delights in a man's
        way,
    he makes his steps firm;
²⁴though he stumble, he will not fall,
    for the LORD upholds him with
        his hand.

²⁵I was young and now I am old,
    yet I have never seen the
        righteous forsaken
    or their children begging
        bread.
²⁶They are always generous and
        lend freely;
    their children will be blessed.

²⁷Turn from evil and do good;
    then you will dwell in the land forever.
²⁸For the LORD loves the just
    and will not forsake his faithful ones.

truth or dare

If you're dead-set on disobedience, God isn't going to intervene to save you from a bad fall. Get a firm footing by walking with God.

37:23–24

They will be protected forever,
but the offspring of the wicked will be cut off;
²⁹ the righteous will inherit the land
and dwell in it forever.

³⁰ The mouth of the righteous man utters wisdom,
and his tongue speaks what is just.
³¹ The law of his God is in his heart;
his feet do not slip.

³² The wicked lie in wait for the righteous,
seeking their very lives;
³³ but the LORD will not leave them in their power
or let them be condemned when brought to trial.

³⁴ Wait for the LORD
and keep his way.
He will exalt you to inherit the land;
when the wicked are cut off, you will see it.

³⁵ I have seen a wicked and ruthless man
flourishing like a green tree in its native soil,
³⁶ but he soon passed away and was no more;
though I looked for him, he could not be found.

³⁷ Consider the blameless, observe the upright;
there is a future ᵃ for the man of peace.
³⁸ But all sinners will be destroyed;
the future ᵇ of the wicked will be cut off.

³⁹ The salvation of the righteous comes from the LORD;
he is their stronghold in time of trouble.
⁴⁰ The LORD helps them and delivers them;
he delivers them from the wicked and saves them,
because they take refuge in him.

Psalm 38

A psalm of David. A petition.

¹ O LORD, do not rebuke me in your anger
or discipline me in your wrath.
² For your arrows have pierced me,
and your hand has come down upon me.
³ Because of your wrath there is no health in my body;
my bones have no soundness because of my sin.
⁴ My guilt has overwhelmed me
like a burden too heavy to bear.

⁵ My wounds fester and are loathsome
because of my sinful folly.
⁶ I am bowed down and brought very low;
all day long I go about mourning.
⁷ My back is filled with searing pain;
there is no health in my body.
⁸ I am feeble and utterly crushed;
I groan in anguish of heart.

⁹ All my longings lie open before you, O Lord;

ᵃ 37 Or there will be posterity   ᵇ 38 Or posterity

my sighing is not hidden from you.
[10] My heart pounds, my strength fails me;
    even the light has gone from my eyes.
[11] My friends and companions avoid me because of my wounds;
    my neighbors stay far away.
[12] Those who seek my life set their traps,
    those who would harm me talk of my ruin;
    all day long they plot deception.

[13] I am like a deaf man, who cannot hear,
    like a mute, who cannot open his mouth;
[14] I have become like a man who does not hear,
    whose mouth can offer no reply.
[15] I wait for you, O LORD;
    you will answer, O Lord my God.
[16] For I said, "Do not let them gloat
    or exalt themselves over me when my foot slips."

[17] For I am about to fall,
    and my pain is ever with me.
[18] I confess my iniquity;
    I am troubled by my sin.
[19] Many are those who are my vigorous enemies;
    those who hate me without reason are numerous.
[20] Those who repay my good with evil
    slander me when I pursue what is good.

[21] O LORD, do not forsake me;
    be not far from me, O my God.
[22] Come quickly to help me,
    O Lord my Savior.

Psalm 39

For the director of music. For Jeduthun. A psalm of David.

[1] I said, "I will watch my ways
    and keep my tongue from sin;
I will put a muzzle on my mouth
    as long as the wicked are in
    my presence."
[2] But when I was silent and still,
    not even saying anything good,
    my anguish increased.
[3] My heart grew hot within me,
    and as I meditated, the fire
    burned;
then I spoke with my tongue:

[4] "Show me, O LORD, my life's end
    and the number of my days;
    let me know how fleeting is my life.
[5] You have made my days a mere
    handbreadth;
the span of my years is as nothing before you.
    Each man's life is but a breath.
[6] Man is a mere phantom as he goes to and fro:
    He bustles about, but only in vain;
    he heaps up wealth, not knowing who will get it.

truth or dare

Hopefully you won't have to resort to a muzzle! But David's idea wasn't too crazy, since some of the most hurtful things, like gossip and complaints, come from the mouth.

39:1

Selah

⁷ "But now, Lord, what do I look for?
  My hope is in you.
⁸ Save me from all my transgressions;
  do not make me the scorn of fools.
⁹ I was silent; I would not open my mouth,
  for you are the one who has done this.
¹⁰ Remove your scourge from me;
  I am overcome by the blow of your hand.
¹¹ You rebuke and discipline men for their sin;
  you consume their wealth like a moth—
  each man is but a breath.

Selah

¹² "Hear my prayer, O LORD,
  listen to my cry for help;
  be not deaf to my weeping.
For I dwell with you as an alien,
  a stranger, as all my fathers were.
¹³ Look away from me, that I may rejoice again
  before I depart and am no more."

Psalm 40

For the director of music. Of David. A psalm.

¹ I waited patiently for the LORD;
  he turned to me and heard my cry.

² He lifted me out of the slimy pit,
  out of the mud and mire;
  he set my feet on a rock
  and gave me a firm place to stand.
³ He put a new song in my mouth,
  a hymn of praise to our God.
Many will see and fear
  and put their trust in the LORD.

⁴ Blessed is the man
  who makes the LORD his trust,
who does not look to the proud,
  to those who turn aside to
  false gods. [a]
⁵ Many, O LORD my God,
  are the wonders you have done.
The things you planned for us
  no one can recount to you;
were I to speak and tell of them,
  they would be too many to
  declare.

⁶ Sacrifice and offering you did not
  desire,
  but my ears you have pierced [b, c];
burnt offerings and sin offerings
  you did not require.
⁷ Then I said, "Here I am, I have
  come—
  it is written about me in the scroll. [d]

genuine patience » 40:1-3

It's difficult to wait. You might even feel like you're becoming an expert at it—waiting to get your license, waiting for results from tryouts, waiting for test scores, waiting for that certain guy to notice you, waiting till you're old enough to be independent. Waiting is even worse when you're stuck in a difficult situation—a slimy pit that you need help escaping. So what's the quick fix? Sorry, Charlie, you've gotta wait it out. God knows your situation, but he has something for you to learn in the process. So keep waiting and start learning. Your patience will be rewarded. Guaranteed.

^a 4 Or to falsehood ^b 6 Hebrew; Septuagint but a body you have prepared for me (see also Symmachus and Theodotion)
^c 6 Or opened ^d 7 Or come / with the scroll written for me

8 I desire to do your will, O my God;
   your law is within my heart."

9 I proclaim righteousness in the great assembly;
   I do not seal my lips,
   as you know, O LORD.
10 I do not hide your righteousness in my heart;
   I speak of your faithfulness and salvation.
I do not conceal your love and your truth
   from the great assembly.

11 Do not withhold your mercy from me, O LORD;
   may your love and your truth always protect me.
12 For troubles without number surround me;
   my sins have overtaken me, and I cannot see.
They are more than the hairs of my head,
   and my heart fails within me.

13 Be pleased, O LORD, to save me;
   O LORD, come quickly to help me.
14 May all who seek to take my life
   be put to shame and confusion;
may all who desire my ruin
   be turned back in disgrace.
15 May those who say to me, "Aha! Aha!"
   be appalled at their own shame.
16 But may all who seek you
   rejoice and be glad in you;
may those who love your salvation always say,
   "The LORD be exalted!"

17 Yet I am poor and needy;
   may the Lord think of me.
You are my help and my deliverer;
   O my God, do not delay.

Psalm 41

For the director of music. A psalm of David.

1 Blessed is he who has regard for
      the weak;
   the LORD delivers him in times
      of trouble.
2 The LORD will protect him and
      preserve his life;
   he will bless him in the land
   and not surrender him to the
      desire of his foes.
3 The LORD will sustain him on his
      sickbed
   and restore him from his bed
      of illness.
4 I said, "O LORD, have mercy on me;
   heal me, for I have sinned against you."
5 My enemies say of me in malice,
   "When will he die and his name perish?"
6 Whenever one comes to see me,

truth or dare

It's an action with a
great reward. You
watch out for the weak
(like the unpopular kid
everyone makes fun of),
and God will watch out
for you.

41:1

he speaks falsely, while his heart gathers slander;
then he goes out and spreads it abroad.

⁷All my enemies whisper together against me;
they imagine the worst for me, saying,
⁸"A vile disease has beset him;
he will never get up from the place where he lies."
⁹Even my close friend, whom I trusted,
he who shared my bread,
has lifted up his heel against me.

¹⁰But you, O Lᴏʀᴅ, have mercy on me;
raise me up, that I may repay them.
¹¹I know that you are pleased with me,
for my enemy does not triumph over me.
¹²In my integrity you uphold me
and set me in your presence forever.

¹³Praise be to the Lᴏʀᴅ, the God of Israel,
from everlasting to everlasting.
Amen and Amen.

BOOK II

Psalms 42–72

Psalm 42ᵃ

For the director of music. A *maskil*ᵇ of the Sons of Korah.

¹As the deer pants for streams of water,
so my soul pants for you, O God.
²My soul thirsts for God, for the
living God.
When can I go and meet with
God?
³My tears have been my food
day and night,
while men say to me all day long,
"Where is your God?"
⁴These things I remember
as I pour out my soul:
how I used to go with the
multitude,
leading the procession to the house of God,
with shouts of joy and thanksgiving
among the festive throng.

⁵Why are you downcast, O my soul?
Why so disturbed within me?
Put your hope in God,
for I will yet praise him,
my Savior and ⁶my God.

Myᶜ soul is downcast within me;
therefore I will remember you

truth or dare

Spiritual thirst is kind of like physical thirst. No matter how much you chug, you're going to get thirsty again at some point unless you fill up with God. He's the only true thirst-quencher.

42:1

ᵃ In many Hebrew manuscripts Psalms 42 and 43 constitute one psalm. ᵇ Title: Probably a literary or musical term ᶜ 5,6 A few Hebrew manuscripts, Septuagint and Syriac; most Hebrew manuscripts *praise him for his saving help.* / ⁶O my God, my

from the land of the Jordan,
    the heights of Hermon—from Mount Mizar.
⁷Deep calls to deep
    in the roar of your waterfalls;
all your waves and breakers
    have swept over me.

⁸By day the LORD directs his love,
    at night his song is with me—
    a prayer to the God of my life.

⁹I say to God my Rock,
    "Why have you forgotten me?
Why must I go about mourning,
    oppressed by the enemy?"
¹⁰My bones suffer mortal agony
    as my foes taunt me,
saying to me all day long,
    "Where is your God?"

¹¹Why are you downcast, O my soul?
    Why so disturbed within me?
Put your hope in God,
    for I will yet praise him,
    my Savior and my God.

Psalm 43 *ᵃ*

¹Vindicate me, O God,
    and plead my cause against an ungodly nation;
    rescue me from deceitful and wicked men.
²You are God my stronghold.
    Why have you rejected me?
Why must I go about mourning,
    oppressed by the enemy?
³Send forth your light and your truth,
    let them guide me;
let them bring me to your holy mountain,
    to the place where you dwell.
⁴Then will I go to the altar of God,
    to God, my joy and my delight.
I will praise you with the harp,
    O God, my God.

⁵Why are you downcast, O my soul?
    Why so disturbed within me?
Put your hope in God,
    for I will yet praise him,
    my Savior and my God.

Psalm 44

For the director of music. Of the Sons of Korah. A *maskil.* *ᵇ*

¹We have heard with our ears, O God;
    our fathers have told us
what you did in their days,
    in days long ago.

ᵃ In many Hebrew manuscripts Psalms 42 and 43 constitute one psalm.   *ᵇ* Title: Probably a literary or musical term

The Urge to Curse

I don't know exactly when it started. I guess it was sort of a gradual thing. Everyone I hung out with swore a lot. Eventually I sort of slipped into it, too.

I used to be the only one who was good about *not* swearing. Everyone knew I was a Christian, so I tried to be an example to them. I felt like not swearing was a part of that. So when I did slip up, my friends noticed.

I guess it was good that I tried to set an example. But sometimes it just got so tiring. I always had to watch what I said. And sticking to words like "gosh" and "shoot" got old fast. Especially when everyone else got to say exactly what they wanted to say.

So at some point I just let down my guard. It was easier to express myself that way. And honestly, I felt like I sounded a little cooler, and even funnier, when I swore once in a while. Besides, everyone around me cursed a lot.

I know it's a bad habit. And now I do it without even thinking. It's a comfortable habit and such a minor thing. I mean, it's not like I'm into drinking or drugs or anything. Yet every now and then, I still feel a little pang of guilt.

For more on swearing and the power of your words, go to www.TrueImagesBible.com

swearing in focus

Liz's struggle with swearing is something that a lot of Christians deal with at one time or another. After all, it can be tiring trying to set an example for others in our speech. Sometimes we want the freedom to say whatever comes to mind—especially when we feel frustrated or angry.

Yes, it's a battle. But keep in mind . . .

»Jesus calls us to be the salt and light in a dark and desperate world (see Matthew 5:13–14, page 1295). We're supposed to be set apart, making a statement with our lives.

»Your words reveal what's going on inside your heart (see Luke 6:45, page 1374).

For more on this topic, see the index on page 1656.

²With your hand you drove out the nations
  and planted our fathers;
you crushed the peoples
  and made our fathers flourish.
³It was not by their sword that they won the land,
  nor did their arm bring them victory;
it was your right hand, your arm,
  and the light of your face, for you loved them.

⁴You are my King and my God,
  who decrees*ᵃ* victories for Jacob.
⁵Through you we push back our enemies;

ᵃ 4 Septuagint, Aquila and Syriac; Hebrew *King, O God; / command*

through your name we trample our foes.
⁶ I do not trust in my bow,
my sword does not bring me victory;
⁷ but you give us victory over our enemies,
you put our adversaries to shame.
⁸ In God we make our boast all day long,
and we will praise your name forever. *Selah*

⁹ But now you have rejected and humbled us;
you no longer go out with our armies.
¹⁰ You made us retreat before the enemy,
and our adversaries have plundered us.
¹¹ You gave us up to be devoured like sheep
and have scattered us among the nations.
¹² You sold your people for a pittance,
gaining nothing from their sale.

¹³ You have made us a reproach to our neighbors,
the scorn and derision of those around us.
¹⁴ You have made us a byword among the nations;
the peoples shake their heads at us.
¹⁵ My disgrace is before me all day long,
and my face is covered with shame
¹⁶ at the taunts of those who reproach and revile me,
because of the enemy, who is bent on revenge.

¹⁷ All this happened to us,
though we had not forgotten you
or been false to your covenant.
¹⁸ Our hearts had not turned back;
our feet had not strayed from your path.
¹⁹ But you crushed us and made us a haunt for jackals
and covered us over with deep darkness.

²⁰ If we had forgotten the name of our God
or spread out our hands to a foreign god,
²¹ would not God have discovered it,
since he knows the secrets of the heart?
²² Yet for your sake we face death all day long;
we are considered as sheep to be slaughtered.

²³ Awake, O Lord! Why do you sleep?
Rouse yourself! Do not reject us forever.
²⁴ Why do you hide your face
and forget our misery and oppression?

²⁵ We are brought down to the dust;
our bodies cling to the ground.
²⁶ Rise up and help us;
redeem us because of your unfailing love.

Psalm 45

For the director of music. To the tune of, "Lilies." Of the Sons
of Korah. A *maskil.*^a A wedding song.

¹ My heart is stirred by a noble theme
as I recite my verses for the king;
my tongue is the pen of a skillful writer.

^a Title: Probably a literary or musical term

²You are the most excellent of men
  and your lips have been anointed with grace,
  since God has blessed you forever.
³Gird your sword upon your side, O mighty one;
  clothe yourself with splendor and majesty.
⁴In your majesty ride forth victoriously
  in behalf of truth, humility and righteousness;
  let your right hand display awesome deeds.
⁵Let your sharp arrows pierce the hearts of the king's enemies;
  let the nations fall beneath your feet.
⁶Your throne, O God, will last for ever and ever;
  a scepter of justice will be the scepter of your kingdom.
⁷You love righteousness and hate wickedness;
  therefore God, your God, has set you above your companions
  by anointing you with the oil of joy.
⁸All your robes are fragrant with myrrh and aloes and cassia;
  from palaces adorned with ivory
  the music of the strings makes you glad.
⁹Daughters of kings are among your honored women;
  at your right hand is the royal bride in gold of Ophir.

¹⁰Listen, O daughter, consider and give ear:
  Forget your people and your father's house.
¹¹The king is enthralled by your beauty;
  honor him, for he is your lord.
¹²The Daughter of Tyre will come with a gift,ᵃ
  men of wealth will seek your favor.

¹³All glorious is the princess within ⌞her chamber⌟;
  her gown is interwoven with gold.
¹⁴In embroidered garments she is led to the king;
  her virgin companions follow her
  and are brought to you.
¹⁵They are led in with joy and gladness;
  they enter the palace of the king.

¹⁶Your sons will take the place of your fathers;
  you will make them princes throughout the land.
¹⁷I will perpetuate your memory through all generations;
  therefore the nations will praise you for ever and ever.

Psalm 46

For the director of music. Of the Sons of Korah. According
to *alamoth.*ᵇ A song.

¹God is our refuge and strength,
  an ever-present help in trouble.
²Therefore we will not fear, though the earth give way
  and the mountains fall into the heart of the sea,
³though its waters roar and foam
  and the mountains quake with their surging.   *Selah*

⁴There is a river whose streams make glad the city of God,
  the holy place where the Most High dwells.
⁵God is within her, she will not fall;
  God will help her at break of day.

ᵃ 12 Or *A Tyrian robe is among the gifts*   ᵇ Title: Probably a musical term

⁶ Nations are in uproar, kingdoms fall;
　　he lifts his voice, the earth melts.

⁷ The LORD Almighty is with us;
　　the God of Jacob is our fortress.　　　　*Selah*

⁸ Come and see the works of the LORD,
　　the desolations he has brought on the earth.
⁹ He makes wars cease to the ends of the earth;
　　he breaks the bow and shatters the spear,
　　he burns the shields *a* with fire.
¹⁰ "Be still, and know that I am God;
　　I will be exalted among the nations,
　　I will be exalted in the earth."

¹¹ The LORD Almighty is with us;
　　the God of Jacob is our
　　　fortress.　　　*Selah*

Psalm 47

For the director of music.
Of the Sons of Korah. A psalm.

¹ Clap your hands, all you nations;
　　shout to God with cries of joy.
² How awesome is the LORD Most
　　High,
　　the great King over all the
　　　earth!
³ He subdued nations under us,
　　peoples under our feet.
⁴ He chose our inheritance for us,
　　the pride of Jacob, whom he
　　　loved.　　　*Selah*

⁵ God has ascended amid shouts
　　of joy,
　　the LORD amid the sounding of
　　　trumpets.
⁶ Sing praises to God, sing praises;
　　sing praises to our King, sing
　　　praises.

⁷ For God is the King of all the
　　earth;
　　sing to him a psalm *b* of
　　　praise.
⁸ God reigns over the nations;
　　God is seated on his holy
　　　throne.
⁹ The nobles of the nations assemble
　　as the people of the God of
　　　Abraham,
　　for the kings *c* of the earth belong
　　　to God;
　　he is greatly exalted.

love♥notes

46:10

My girl,

Shut off the TV and hide the remote. Unplug the CD player and put away your headphones. Turn off your cell phone and close your bedroom door. Now come to me and be quiet. Do you hear me?

—Father God

Take time to be still and know God.
What is he telling you?

_____

_____

_____

_____

_____

_____

_____

_____

a 9 Or chariots　　*b 7 Or a maskil (probably a literary*
or musical term)　　*c 9 Or shields*

Psalm 48

A song. A psalm of the Sons of Korah.

[1] Great is the LORD, and most worthy of praise,
    in the city of our God, his holy mountain.
[2] It is beautiful in its loftiness,
    the joy of the whole earth.
  Like the utmost heights of Zaphon[a] is Mount Zion,
    the[b] city of the Great King.
[3] God is in her citadels;
    he has shown himself to be her fortress.

[4] When the kings joined forces,
    when they advanced together,
[5] they saw her and were astounded;
    they fled in terror.
[6] Trembling seized them there,
    pain like that of a woman in labor.
[7] You destroyed them like ships of Tarshish
    shattered by an east wind.

[8] As we have heard,
    so have we seen
  in the city of the LORD Almighty,
    in the city of our God:
  God makes her secure forever.   *Selah*

[9] Within your temple, O God,
    we meditate on your unfailing love.
[10] Like your name, O God,
    your praise reaches to the
      ends of the earth;
    your right hand is filled with
      righteousness.
[11] Mount Zion rejoices,
    the villages of Judah are glad
    because of your judgments.

[12] Walk about Zion, go around her,
    count her towers,
[13] consider well her ramparts,
    view her citadels,
    that you may tell of them to the next
      generation.
[14] For this God is our God for ever and ever;
    he will be our guide even to the end.

truth or dare

Once you're following Jesus, he's with you until the end. Sometimes you feel like you're alone, but it's an illusion. He's your forever guide.

48:14

Psalm 49

For the director of music. Of the Sons of Korah. A psalm.

[1] Hear this, all you peoples;
    listen, all who live in this world,
[2] both low and high,
    rich and poor alike:
[3] My mouth will speak words of wisdom;
    the utterance from my heart will give understanding.

---

a 2 Zaphon can refer to a sacred mountain or the direction north.   *b 2 Or earth, / Mount Zion, on the northern side / of the*

⁴I will turn my ear to a proverb;
    with the harp I will expound my riddle:

⁵Why should I fear when evil days come,
    when wicked deceivers surround me—
⁶those who trust in their wealth
    and boast of their great riches?
⁷No man can redeem the life of another
    or give to God a ransom for him—
⁸the ransom for a life is costly,
    no payment is ever enough—
⁹that he should live on forever
    and not see decay.

¹⁰For all can see that wise men die;
    the foolish and the senseless
      alike perish
    and leave their wealth to
      others.
¹¹Their tombs will remain their
    houses[a] forever,
    their dwellings for endless
      generations,
    though they had[b] named lands after
      themselves.

¹²But man, despite his riches, does not endure;
    he is[c] like the beasts that perish.

¹³This is the fate of those who trust in themselves,
    and of their followers, who approve their sayings.   *Selah*
¹⁴Like sheep they are destined for the grave,[d]
    and death will feed on them.
The upright will rule over them in the morning;
    their forms will decay in the grave,[d]
    far from their princely mansions.
¹⁵But God will redeem my life[e] from the grave;
    he will surely take me to himself.   *Selah*

¹⁶Do not be overawed when a man grows rich,
    when the splendor of his house increases;
¹⁷for he will take nothing with him when he dies,
    his splendor will not descend with him.
¹⁸Though while he lived he counted himself blessed—
    and men praise you when you prosper—
¹⁹he will join the generation of his fathers,
    who will never see the light ⌊of life⌋.

²⁰A man who has riches without understanding
    is like the beasts that perish.

truth or dare

Sure, girls can fork over $200 on the latest styles, but their jeans won't go with them when they die! Make sure your greatest investment is on eternal things.

49:16–17

Psalm 50

A psalm of Asaph.

¹The Mighty One, God, the LORD,
    speaks and summons the earth

a 11 Septuagint and Syriac; Hebrew *In their thoughts their houses will remain*   *b 11* Or */ for they have*   *c 12* Hebrew; Septuagint and Syriac read verse 12 the same as verse 20.   *d 14* Hebrew *Sheol*; also in verse 15   *e 15* Or *soul*

from the rising of the sun to the place where it sets.
2 From Zion, perfect in beauty,
God shines forth.
3 Our God comes and will not be silent;
a fire devours before him,
and around him a tempest rages.
4 He summons the heavens above,
and the earth, that he may judge his people:
5 "Gather to me my consecrated ones,
who made a covenant with me by sacrifice."
6 And the heavens proclaim his righteousness,
for God himself is judge. *Selah*

7 "Hear, O my people, and I will speak,
O Israel, and I will testify against you:
I am God, your God.
8 I do not rebuke you for your sacrifices
or your burnt offerings, which are ever before me.
9 I have no need of a bull from your stall
or of goats from your pens,
10 for every animal of the forest is mine,
and the cattle on a thousand hills.
11 I know every bird in the mountains,
and the creatures of the field are mine.
12 If I were hungry I would not tell you,
for the world is mine, and all that is in it.
13 Do I eat the flesh of bulls
or drink the blood of goats?
14 Sacrifice thank offerings to God,
fulfill your vows to the Most High,
15 and call upon me in the day of trouble;
I will deliver you, and you will honor me."

16 But to the wicked, God says:

"What right have you to recite my laws
or take my covenant on your lips?
17 You hate my instruction
and cast my words behind you.
18 When you see a thief, you join with him;
you throw in your lot with adulterers.
19 You use your mouth for evil
and harness your tongue to deceit.
20 You speak continually against your brother
and slander your own mother's son.
21 These things you have done and I kept silent;
you thought I was altogether *a* like you.
But I will rebuke you
and accuse you to your face.

22 "Consider this, you who forget God,
or I will tear you to pieces, with none to rescue:
23 He who sacrifices thank offerings honors me,
and he prepares the way
so that I may show him *b* the salvation of God."

a 21 Or *thought the 'I AM' was*   *b 23* Or *and to him who considers his way / I will show*

Psalm 51

For the director of music. A psalm of David. When the prophet Nathan came to him after David had committed adultery with Bathsheba.

¹Have mercy on me, O God,
  according to your unfailing love;
according to your great compassion
  blot out my transgressions.
²Wash away all my iniquity
  and cleanse me from my sin.

³For I know my transgressions,
  and my sin is always before me.
⁴Against you, you only, have I sinned
  and done what is evil in your sight,
so that you are proved right when you speak
  and justified when you judge.
⁵Surely I was sinful at birth,
  sinful from the time my
    mother conceived me.
⁶Surely you desire truth in the
    inner parts*ᵃ*;
  you teach*ᵇ* me wisdom in the
    inmost place.

⁷Cleanse me with hyssop, and I
    will be clean;
  wash me, and I will be whiter
    than snow.
⁸Let me hear joy and gladness;
  let the bones you have crushed rejoice.
⁹Hide your face from my sins
  and blot out all my iniquity.

¹⁰Create in me a pure heart, O God,
  and renew a steadfast spirit within me.
¹¹Do not cast me from your presence
  or take your Holy Spirit from me.
¹²Restore to me the joy of your salvation
  and grant me a willing spirit, to sustain me.

¹³Then I will teach transgressors your ways,
  and sinners will turn back to you.
¹⁴Save me from bloodguilt, O God,
  the God who saves me,
  and my tongue will sing of your righteousness.
¹⁵O Lord, open my lips,
  and my mouth will declare your praise.
¹⁶You do not delight in sacrifice, or I would bring it;
  you do not take pleasure in burnt offerings.
¹⁷The sacrifices of God are*ᶜ* a broken spirit;
  a broken and contrite heart,
  O God, you will not despise.

¹⁸In your good pleasure make Zion prosper;

truth or dare

Asking God to take a scrub brush to your heart isn't a one-time deal. Because you live in a fallen world, true spirit-cleansing is an on-going process. Are you due for a clean-up?

51:10

ᵃ 6 The meaning of the Hebrew for this phrase is uncertain.   *ᵇ 6* Or *you desired . . . ; / you taught*   *ᶜ 17* Or *My sacrifice, O God, is*

genuine

repentance »» 51:17

Imagine a conversation with your best friend. Without thinking, you slip and say something very hurtful to her. You apologize but it's too late—the damage has already been done. How do you feel? Pretty rotten, probably. Now what would happen if you apologized but then treated her that way again the next day? "I'm sorry" needs to be more than just words. The same holds true in your relationship with God. When you tell him you're sorry for sin, do you mean it? Do you feel bad over the way you've hurt and disappointed him? And do you try not to do it again?

build up the walls of
Jerusalem.
[19] Then there will be righteous
sacrifices,
whole burnt offerings to
delight you;
then bulls will be offered on
your altar.

Psalm 52

For the director of music. A *maskil*[a] of David.
When Doeg the Edomite had gone to Saul and
told him: "David has gone to the house
of Ahimelech."

[1] Why do you boast of evil, you
mighty man?
Why do you boast all day
long,
you who are a disgrace in the
eyes of God?
[2] Your tongue plots destruction;
it is like a sharpened razor,
you who practice deceit.
[3] You love evil rather than good,
falsehood rather than speaking
the truth.   *Selah*
[4] You love every harmful word,
O you deceitful tongue!

[5] Surely God will bring you down to everlasting ruin:
He will snatch you up and tear you from your tent;
he will uproot you from the land of the living.   *Selah*
[6] The righteous will see and fear;
they will laugh at him, saying,
[7] "Here now is the man
who did not make God his stronghold
but trusted in his great wealth
and grew strong by destroying others!"

[8] But I am like an olive tree
flourishing in the house of God;
I trust in God's unfailing love
for ever and ever.
[9] I will praise you forever for what you have done;
in your name I will hope, for your name is good.
I will praise you in the presence of your saints.

Psalm 53

For the director of music. According to *mahalath*.[b] A *maskil*[a]
of David.

[1] The fool says in his heart,
"There is no God."
They are corrupt, and their ways are vile;
there is no one who does good.

---

a Title: Probably a literary or musical term   *b* Title: Probably a musical term

²God looks down from heaven
on the sons of men
to see if there are any who
understand,
any who seek God.
³Everyone has turned away,
they have together become
corrupt;
there is no one who does good,
not even one.

⁴Will the evildoers never learn—
those who devour my people as men eat
bread
and who do not call on God?
⁵There they were, overwhelmed with dread,
where there was nothing to dread.
God scattered the bones of those who attacked you;
you put them to shame, for God despised them.

⁶Oh, that salvation for Israel would come out of Zion!
When God restores the fortunes of his people,
let Jacob rejoice and Israel be glad!

truth or dare

No one does good. Not even Mother Theresa. Our "good deeds" don't make us right in God's eyes. Only one thing will: Jesus.

53:2–3

Psalm 54

For the director of music. With stringed instruments. A *maskil*ᵃ of David. When the Ziphites had gone to Saul and said, "Is not David hiding among us?"

¹Save me, O God, by your name;
vindicate me by your might.
²Hear my prayer, O God;
listen to the words of my mouth.

³Strangers are attacking me;
ruthless men seek my life—
men without regard for God.   *Selah*

⁴Surely God is my help;
the Lord is the one who sustains me.

⁵Let evil recoil on those who slander me;
in your faithfulness destroy them.

⁶I will sacrifice a freewill offering to you;
I will praise your name, O LORD,
for it is good.
⁷For he has delivered me from all my troubles,
and my eyes have looked in triumph on my foes.

Psalm 55

For the director of music. With stringed instruments. A *maskil*ᵃ of David.

¹Listen to my prayer, O God,
do not ignore my plea;
²   hear me and answer me.
My thoughts trouble me and I am distraught

ᵃ Title: Probably a literary or musical term

³ at the voice of the enemy,
    at the stares of the wicked;
for they bring down suffering upon me
    and revile me in their anger.

⁴ My heart is in anguish within me;
    the terrors of death assail me.
⁵ Fear and trembling have beset me;
    horror has overwhelmed me.
⁶ I said, "Oh, that I had the wings of a dove!
    I would fly away and be at rest—
⁷ I would flee far away
    and stay in the desert;   *Selah*
⁸ I would hurry to my place of shelter,
    far from the tempest and storm."

⁹ Confuse the wicked, O Lord, confound their speech,
    for I see violence and strife in the city.
¹⁰ Day and night they prowl about on its walls;
    malice and abuse are within it.
¹¹ Destructive forces are at work in the city;
    threats and lies never leave its streets.

¹² If an enemy were insulting me,
    I could endure it;
if a foe were raising himself against me,
    I could hide from him.
¹³ But it is you, a man like myself,
    my companion, my close friend,
¹⁴ with whom I once enjoyed sweet fellowship
    as we walked with the throng at the house of God.

¹⁵ Let death take my enemies by surprise;
    let them go down alive to the grave,ᵃ
    for evil finds lodging among them.

¹⁶ But I call to God,
    and the Lᴏʀᴅ saves me.
¹⁷ Evening, morning and noon
    I cry out in distress,
    and he hears my voice.
¹⁸ He ransoms me unharmed
    from the battle waged against me,
    even though many oppose me.
¹⁹ God, who is enthroned forever,
    will hear them and afflict them—   *Selah*
men who never change their ways
    and have no fear of God.

²⁰ My companion attacks his friends;
    he violates his covenant.
²¹ His speech is smooth as butter,
    yet war is in his heart;
his words are more soothing than oil,
    yet they are drawn swords.

²² Cast your cares on the Lᴏʀᴅ
    and he will sustain you;
    he will never let the righteous fall.

ᵃ 15 Hebrew *Sheol*

²³ But you, O God, will bring down the wicked
     into the pit of corruption;
bloodthirsty and deceitful men
     will not live out half their days.

But as for me, I trust in you.

Psalm 56

For the director of music. To ⌊the tune of⌋
"A Dove on Distant Oaks." Of David. A *miktam.*ᵃ
When the Philistines had seized him in Gath.

¹ Be merciful to me, O God, for men hotly pursue me;
     all day long they press their attack.
² My slanderers pursue me all day long;
     many are attacking me in their pride.

³ When I am afraid,
     I will trust in you.
⁴ In God, whose word I praise,
     in God I trust; I will not be afraid.
     What can mortal man do to me?

⁵ All day long they twist my words;
     they are always plotting to
         harm me.
⁶ They conspire, they lurk,
     they watch my steps,
     eager to take my life.

⁷ On no account let them escape;
     in your anger, O God, bring
         down the nations.
⁸ Record my lament;
     list my tears on your scrollᵇ—
     are they not in your record?

⁹ Then my enemies will turn back
     when I call for help.
     By this I will know that God is for me.
¹⁰ In God, whose word I praise,
     in the LORD, whose word I praise—
¹¹ in God I trust; I will not be afraid.
     What can man do to me?

¹² I am under vows to you, O God;
     I will present my thank offerings to you.
¹³ For you have delivered meᶜ from death
     and my feet from stumbling,
that I may walk before God
     in the light of life.ᵈ

Psalm 57

For the director of music. ⌊To the tune of⌋ "Do Not Destroy." Of
David. A *miktam.*ᵃ When he had fled from Saul into the cave.

¹ Have mercy on me, O God, have mercy on me,
     for in you my soul takes refuge.

truth **or dare**

We girls often worry about the people or situations we care most about. Telling God about our worries puts these things in the best possible hands.

55:22

ᵃ Title: Probably a literary or musical term   ᵇ 8 Or *I put my tears in your wineskin*   ᶜ 13 Or *my soul*   ᵈ 13 Or *the land of the living*

mirror images

Then David sent messengers to get her. She came to him, and he slept with her. 2 Samuel 11:4

Bathsheba—A Life-Changing Night

I t's flattering when you catch the eye of the popular guy on the soccer team. Can you even imagine what it would be like to have someone famous interested in you, like an actor or a pro athlete? How about the king of the nation? Would you be flattered . . . or scared?

Bathsheba was minding her own business, washing off on a warm night when a messenger from King David's palace knocked at her door. He said that the king had seen her bathing from his rooftop and wanted to meet her.

Bathsheba may have been star-struck and jumped at the opportunity to meet the most powerful man in her land. Or she may have been frightened. *Can I dare refuse the king?* Bathsheba's husband was off fighting for David in the army. How could she refuse to go?

We don't know what Bathsheba was thinking, but we do know what happened that night. Bathsheba went to David; they slept together, and the result of that night of sin was a domino effect of tragic circumstances: Bathsheba got pregnant, David had her husband murdered, and then their newborn baby died. The course of Bathsheba's life changed in one night.

Our lives can change in an instant, too.

Maybe you've met your dream guy, and you're so infatuated that you make a bad decision about how far to go with him. Maybe you let a guy talk you into doing drugs. Or maybe you were out for a walk, minding your own business when someone did something terrible to you. And now everything about your life is changed. It can never go back.

No matter what's happened to you, God can still intervene in your life to bring about something good. For Bathsheba and David, their lives looked terrible, but David begged God for forgiveness. And God gave them a child who would become the wisest king who ever lived: King Solomon. What will God do in your life?

Dear God, help me remember that no matter what happens, you can bring great things out of bad situations. Amen.

dear God

To read the next Mirror Images profile, go to page 733.

>> **Read more about Bathsheba in 2 Samuel 11–12 (pages 373–376) and 1 Kings 1–2 (pages 397–400).**

I will take refuge in the shadow of your wings
   until the disaster has passed.
[2] I cry out to God Most High,
   to God, who fulfills ⌊his purpose⌋ for me.
[3] He sends from heaven and saves me,
   rebuking those who hotly pursue me;   *Selah*
   God sends his love and his faithfulness.

[4] I am in the midst of lions;
   I lie among ravenous beasts—
men whose teeth are spears and arrows,
   whose tongues are sharp swords.

[5] Be exalted, O God, above the heavens;
   let your glory be over all the earth.

[6] They spread a net for my feet—
   I was bowed down in distress.
They dug a pit in my path—
   but they have fallen into it themselves.   *Selah*

[7] My heart is steadfast, O God,
   my heart is steadfast;
   I will sing and make music.
[8] Awake, my soul!
   Awake, harp and lyre!
   I will awaken the dawn.

[9] I will praise you, O Lord, among the nations;
   I will sing of you among the peoples.
[10] For great is your love, reaching to the heavens;
   your faithfulness reaches to the skies.

[11] Be exalted, O God, above the heavens;
   let your glory be over all the earth.

Psalm 58

For the director of music. ⌊To the tune of⌋ "Do Not Destroy."
Of David. A *miktam.*[a]

[1] Do you rulers indeed speak justly?
   Do you judge uprightly among men?
[2] No, in your heart you devise injustice,
   and your hands mete out violence on the earth.
[3] Even from birth the wicked go astray;
   from the womb they are wayward and speak lies.
[4] Their venom is like the venom of a snake,
   like that of a cobra that has stopped its ears,
[5] that will not heed the tune of the charmer,
   however skillful the enchanter may be.

[6] Break the teeth in their mouths, O God;
   tear out, O LORD, the fangs of the lions!
[7] Let them vanish like water that flows away;
   when they draw the bow, let their arrows be blunted.
[8] Like a slug melting away as it moves along,
   like a stillborn child, may they not see the sun.

a Title: Probably a literary or musical term

⁹Before your pots can feel ⌊the heat of⌋ the thorns—
   whether they be green or dry—the wicked will be swept away.ᵃ
¹⁰The righteous will be glad when they are avenged,
   when they bathe their feet in the blood of the wicked.
¹¹Then men will say,
   "Surely the righteous still are rewarded;
   surely there is a God who judges the earth."

Psalm 59

For the director of music. ⌊To the tune of⌋ "Do Not Destroy." Of
David. A *miktam.*ᵇ When Saul had sent men to watch David's
house in order to kill him.

¹Deliver me from my enemies, O God;
   protect me from those who rise up against me.
²Deliver me from evildoers
   and save me from bloodthirsty men.

³See how they lie in wait for me!
   Fierce men conspire against me
   for no offense or sin of mine, O LORD.
⁴I have done no wrong, yet they are ready to attack me.
   Arise to help me; look on my plight!
⁵O LORD God Almighty, the God of Israel,
   rouse yourself to punish all the nations;
   show no mercy to wicked traitors.   *Selah*

⁶They return at evening,
   snarling like dogs,
   and prowl about the city.
⁷See what they spew from their mouths—
   they spew out swords from their lips,
   and they say, "Who can hear us?"
⁸But you, O LORD, laugh at them;
   you scoff at all those nations.

⁹O my Strength, I watch for you;
   you, O God, are my fortress, ¹⁰my loving God.

God will go before me
   and will let me gloat over those who slander me.
¹¹But do not kill them, O Lord our shield,ᶜ
   or my people will forget.
In your might make them wander about,
   and bring them down.
¹²For the sins of their mouths,
   for the words of their lips,
   let them be caught in their pride.
For the curses and lies they utter,
¹³   consume them in wrath,
   consume them till they are no more.
Then it will be known to the ends of the earth
   that God rules over Jacob.   *Selah*

¹⁴They return at evening,
   snarling like dogs,

ᵃ 9 The meaning of the Hebrew for this verse is uncertain.   ᵇ Title: Probably a literary or musical term
ᶜ 11 Or *sovereign*

and prowl about the city.
¹⁵ They wander about for food
and howl if not satisfied.
¹⁶ But I will sing of your strength,
in the morning I will sing of your love;
for you are my fortress,
my refuge in times of trouble.

¹⁷ O my Strength, I sing praise to you;
you, O God, are my fortress, my loving God.

Psalm 60

For the director of music. To ⌞the tune of⌟ "The Lily of the Covenant."
A *miktam*ᵃ of David. For teaching. When he fought Aram Naharaimᵇ
and Aram Zobah,ᶜ and when Joab returned and struck down twelve
thousand Edomites in the Valley of Salt.

¹ You have rejected us, O God, and burst forth upon us;
you have been angry—now restore us!
² You have shaken the land and torn it open;
mend its fractures, for it is quaking.
³ You have shown your people desperate times;
you have given us wine that makes us stagger.

⁴ But for those who fear you, you have raised a banner
to be unfurled against the bow.   *Selah*

⁵ Save us and help us with your right hand,
that those you love may be delivered.
⁶ God has spoken from his sanctuary:
"In triumph I will parcel out Shechem
and measure off the Valley of Succoth.
⁷ Gilead is mine, and Manasseh is mine;
Ephraim is my helmet,
Judah my scepter.
⁸ Moab is my washbasin,
upon Edom I toss my sandal;
over Philistia I shout in triumph."

⁹ Who will bring me to the fortified city?
Who will lead me to Edom?
¹⁰ Is it not you, O God, you who have rejected us
and no longer go out with our armies?
¹¹ Give us aid against the enemy,
for the help of man is worthless.
¹² With God we will gain the victory,
and he will trample down our enemies.

Psalm 61

For the director of music. With stringed instruments. Of David.

¹ Hear my cry, O God;
listen to my prayer.

² From the ends of the earth I call to you,
I call as my heart grows faint;
lead me to the rock that is higher than I.

ᵃ Title: Probably a literary or musical term   ᵇ Title: That is, Arameans of Northwest Mesopotamia   ᶜ Title: That is,
Arameans of central Syria

³For you have been my refuge,
    a strong tower against the foe.

⁴I long to dwell in your tent forever
    and take refuge in the shelter of your wings.   *Selah*
⁵For you have heard my vows, O God;
    you have given me the heritage of those who fear your name.

⁶Increase the days of the king's life,
    his years for many generations.
⁷May he be enthroned in God's presence forever;
    appoint your love and faithfulness to protect him.

⁸Then will I ever sing praise to your name
    and fulfill my vows day after day.

Psalm 62

For the director of music. For Jeduthun. A psalm of David.

¹My soul finds rest in God alone;
    my salvation comes from him.
²He alone is my rock and my salvation;
    he is my fortress, I will never be shaken.

³How long will you assault a man?
    Would all of you throw him down—
    this leaning wall, this tottering fence?
⁴They fully intend to topple him
    from his lofty place;
    they take delight in lies.
With their mouths they bless,
    but in their hearts they curse.   *Selah*

⁵Find rest, O my soul, in God alone;
    my hope comes from him.
⁶He alone is my rock and my salvation;
    he is my fortress, I will not be shaken.
⁷My salvation and my honor depend on God *ᵃ*;
    he is my mighty rock, my refuge.
⁸Trust in him at all times, O people;
    pour out your hearts to him,
    for God is our refuge.   *Selah*

⁹Lowborn men are but a breath,
    the highborn are but a lie;
if weighed on a balance, they are nothing;
    together they are only a breath.
¹⁰Do not trust in extortion
    or take pride in stolen goods;
though your riches increase,
    do not set your heart on them.

¹¹One thing God has spoken,
    two things have I heard:
that you, O God, are strong,
¹²   and that you, O Lord, are loving.
Surely you will reward each person
    according to what he has done.

ᵃ 7 Or I God Most High is my salvation and my honor

Psalm 63

A psalm of David. When he was in the Desert of Judah.

¹ O God, you are my God,
    earnestly I seek you;
my soul thirsts for you,
    my body longs for you,
in a dry and weary land
    where there is no water.

² I have seen you in the sanctuary
    and beheld your power and your glory.
³ Because your love is better than life,
    my lips will glorify you.
⁴ I will praise you as long as I live,
    and in your name I will lift up my hands.
⁵ My soul will be satisfied as with the richest of foods;
    with singing lips my mouth will praise you.

⁶ On my bed I remember you;
    I think of you through the watches of the night.
⁷ Because you are my help,
    I sing in the shadow of your wings.
⁸ My soul clings to you;
    your right hand upholds me.

⁹ They who seek my life will be destroyed;
    they will go down to the depths of the earth.
¹⁰ They will be given over to the sword
    and become food for jackals.

¹¹ But the king will rejoice in God;
    all who swear by God's name will praise him,
    while the mouths of liars will be silenced.

Psalm 64

For the director of music. A psalm of David.

¹ Hear me, O God, as I voice my complaint;
    protect my life from the threat of the enemy.
² Hide me from the conspiracy of the wicked,
    from that noisy crowd of evildoers.

³ They sharpen their tongues like swords
    and aim their words like deadly arrows.
⁴ They shoot from ambush at the innocent man;
    they shoot at him suddenly, without fear.

⁵ They encourage each other in evil plans,
    they talk about hiding their snares;
    they say, "Who will see them ᵃ?"
⁶ They plot injustice and say,
    "We have devised a perfect plan!"
    Surely the mind and heart of man are cunning.

⁷ But God will shoot them with arrows;
    suddenly they will be struck down.
⁸ He will turn their own tongues against them

ᵃ 5 Or us

and bring them to ruin;
   all who see them will shake their heads in scorn.

⁹All mankind will fear;
   they will proclaim the works of God
   and ponder what he has done.
¹⁰Let the righteous rejoice in the Lᴏʀᴅ
   and take refuge in him;
   let all the upright in heart praise him!

Psalm 65

For the director of music. A psalm of David. A song.

¹Praise awaits*ᵃ* you, O God, in Zion;
   to you our vows will be fulfilled.
²O you who hear prayer,
   to you all men will come.
³When we were overwhelmed by sins,
   you forgave*ᵇ* our transgressions.
⁴Blessed are those you choose
   and bring near to live in your courts!
We are filled with the good things of your house,
   of your holy temple.

⁵You answer us with awesome deeds of righteousness,
   O God our Savior,
the hope of all the ends of the earth
   and of the farthest seas,
⁶who formed the mountains by your power,
   having armed yourself with strength,
⁷who stilled the roaring of the seas,
   the roaring of their waves,
   and the turmoil of the nations.
⁸Those living far away fear your wonders;
   where morning dawns and evening fades
   you call forth songs of joy.

⁹You care for the land and water it;
   you enrich it abundantly.
The streams of God are filled with water
   to provide the people with grain,
   for so you have ordained it.*ᶜ*
¹⁰You drench its furrows
   and level its ridges;
you soften it with showers
   and bless its crops.
¹¹You crown the year with your bounty,
   and your carts overflow with abundance.
¹²The grasslands of the desert overflow;
   the hills are clothed with gladness.
¹³The meadows are covered with flocks
   and the valleys are mantled with grain;
   they shout for joy and sing.

ᵃ 1 Or *befits*; the meaning of the Hebrew for this word is uncertain.   *ᵇ 3* Or *made atonement for*   *ᶜ 9* Or *for that is how you prepare the land*

Psalm 66

For the director of music. A song. A psalm.

¹ Shout with joy to God, all the earth!
²   Sing the glory of his name;
    make his praise glorious!
³ Say to God, "How awesome are your deeds!
    So great is your power
    that your enemies cringe before you.
⁴ All the earth bows down to you;
    they sing praise to you,
    they sing praise to your name."   *Selah*

⁵ Come and see what God has done,
    how awesome his works in man's behalf!
⁶ He turned the sea into dry land,
    they passed through the waters on foot—
    come, let us rejoice in him.
⁷ He rules forever by his power,
    his eyes watch the nations—
    let not the rebellious rise up against him.   *Selah*

⁸ Praise our God, O peoples,
    let the sound of his praise be heard;
⁹ he has preserved our lives
    and kept our feet from slipping.
¹⁰ For you, O God, tested us;
    you refined us like silver.
¹¹ You brought us into prison
    and laid burdens on our backs.
¹² You let men ride over our heads;
    we went through fire and water,
    but you brought us to a place of abundance.

¹³ I will come to your temple with burnt offerings
    and fulfill my vows to you—
¹⁴ vows my lips promised and my mouth spoke
    when I was in trouble.
¹⁵ I will sacrifice fat animals to you
    and an offering of rams;
    I will offer bulls and goats.   *Selah*

¹⁶ Come and listen, all you who fear God;
    let me tell you what he has done for me.
¹⁷ I cried out to him with my mouth;
    his praise was on my tongue.
¹⁸ If I had cherished sin in my heart,
    the Lord would not have listened;
¹⁹ but God has surely listened
    and heard my voice in prayer.
²⁰ Praise be to God,
    who has not rejected my prayer
    or withheld his love from me!

*in focus

Am I Really Safe?

focus Profile: Mitra

From the stories my parents tell me about growing up in the Middle East, I'm glad I was born an American. But I really thought things would be different here. Like I'd feel safer. More at home. Now, with all the conflict in the world today, it doesn't seem like anywhere's safe.

My family moved here because of the promise of a new world. They were Christians in a very Muslim culture, and they wanted us to grow up with more freedom. In America, anything's possible. I didn't know that included the possibility of terrorist attacks, bio-terrorism, bombings and school shootings. This stuff isn't supposed to happen in America. It happens other places around the world but not here, right? Wrong.

Sometimes the future scares me; it's so uncertain. And with our olive skin and dark hair, my family and I are easy targets for some radical anti-Arab. Like last fall, my uncle got hate mail at his store. Why? He didn't do anything. It's like 99 percent of people are fine, but there's that 1 percent out there who are psycho. I told my mom about my fears, and she told me to pray about it. But what if there's a bomb threat the next time we're in an airport? What if some lunatic gets his hands on a biochemical weapon? What if? What if? What if? I just wish things felt more secure.

For more encouragement on facing an uncertain future, go to www.TrueImagesBible.com

fear in focus

At times the world can be a scary place. But we can't live in constant fear. Keep in mind:

»Jesus has already overcome the world and everything we fear. Conquered. Beaten. Won. And that gives us a great sense of comfort and peace because nothing we face is greater than he is (see John 16:33, page 1437).

»Don't let fear rule your life. Most of what you fear doesn't end up happening, and worrying about it doesn't make you any safer (see Matthew 6:27, page 1298).

»Prayer brings peace (see Philippians 4:6–7, page 1553)—and not a peace that glosses over problems and pretends everything's okay—a deep, inner peace that only God can give.

For more on this topic, see the index on page 1656.

fear

Psalm 67

For the director of music. With stringed instruments. A psalm.
A song.

¹ May God be gracious to us and bless us
    and make his face shine upon us,   *Selah*
² that your ways may be known on earth,
    your salvation among all nations.

³ May the peoples praise you, O God;
    may all the peoples praise you.

⁴May the nations be glad and sing for joy,
  for you rule the peoples justly
  and guide the nations of the earth.   *Selah*
⁵May the peoples praise you, O God;
  may all the peoples praise you.

⁶Then the land will yield its harvest,
  and God, our God, will bless us.
⁷God will bless us,
  and all the ends of the earth will fear him.

Psalm 68

For the director of music. Of David. A psalm. A song.

¹May God arise, may his enemies be scattered;
  may his foes flee before him.
²As smoke is blown away by the wind,
  may you blow them away;
as wax melts before the fire,
  may the wicked perish before God.
³But may the righteous be glad
  and rejoice before God;
  may they be happy and joyful.

⁴Sing to God, sing praise to his name,
  extol him who rides on the clouds ᵃ—
his name is the LORD—
  and rejoice before him.
⁵A father to the fatherless, a defender of widows,
  is God in his holy dwelling.
⁶God sets the lonely in families, ᵇ
  he leads forth the prisoners with singing;
  but the rebellious live in a sun-scorched land.

⁷When you went out before your people, O God,
  when you marched through the wasteland,   *Selah*
⁸the earth shook,
  the heavens poured down rain,
before God, the One of Sinai,
  before God, the God of Israel.
⁹You gave abundant showers, O God;
  you refreshed your weary inheritance.
¹⁰Your people settled in it,
  and from your bounty, O God, you provided for the poor.

¹¹The Lord announced the word,
  and great was the company of those who proclaimed it:
¹²"Kings and armies flee in haste;
  in the camps men divide the plunder.
¹³Even while you sleep among the campfires, ᶜ
  the wings of ⌐my⌐ dove are sheathed with silver,
  its feathers with shining gold."
¹⁴When the Almighty ᵈ scattered the kings in the land,
  it was like snow fallen on Zalmon.

¹⁵The mountains of Bashan are majestic mountains;
  rugged are the mountains of Bashan.

ᵃ 4 Or *I prepare the way for him who rides through the deserts*   ᵇ 6 Or *the desolate in a homeland*
ᶜ 13 Or *saddlebags*   ᵈ 14 Hebrew *Shaddai*

¹⁶Why gaze in envy, O rugged mountains,
　　at the mountain where God chooses to reign,
　　where the LORD himself will dwell forever?
¹⁷The chariots of God are tens of thousands
　　and thousands of thousands;
　　the Lord ⌐has come⌐ from Sinai into his sanctuary.
¹⁸When you ascended on high,
　　you led captives in your train;
　　you received gifts from men,
　even from^a the rebellious—
　　that you,^b O LORD God, might dwell there.

¹⁹Praise be to the Lord, to God our Savior,
　　who daily bears our burdens.　　　　　　　　　　　*Selah*
²⁰Our God is a God who saves;
　　from the Sovereign LORD comes escape from death.

²¹Surely God will crush the heads of his enemies,
　　the hairy crowns of those who go on in their sins.
²²The Lord says, "I will bring them from Bashan;
　　I will bring them from the depths of the sea,
²³that you may plunge your feet in the blood of your foes,
　　while the tongues of your dogs have their share."

²⁴Your procession has come into view, O God,
　　the procession of my God and King into the sanctuary.
²⁵In front are the singers, after them the musicians;
　　with them are the maidens playing tambourines.
²⁶Praise God in the great congregation;
　　praise the LORD in the assembly of Israel.
²⁷There is the little tribe of Benjamin, leading them,
　　there the great throng of Judah's princes,
　　and there the princes of Zebulun and of Naphtali.

²⁸Summon your power, O God^c;
　　show us your strength, O God, as you have done before.
²⁹Because of your temple at Jerusalem
　　kings will bring you gifts.
³⁰Rebuke the beast among the reeds,
　　the herd of bulls among the calves of the nations.
　Humbled, may it bring bars of silver.
　　Scatter the nations who delight in war.
³¹Envoys will come from Egypt;
　　Cush^d will submit herself to God.

³²Sing to God, O kingdoms of the earth,
　　sing praise to the Lord,　　　　　　　　　　　　*Selah*
³³to him who rides the ancient skies above,
　　who thunders with mighty voice.
³⁴Proclaim the power of God,
　　whose majesty is over Israel,
　　whose power is in the skies.
³⁵You are awesome, O God, in your sanctuary;
　　the God of Israel gives power and strength to his people.

　Praise be to God!

^a 18 Or *gifts for men, / even*　　^b 18 Or *they*　　^c 28 Many Hebrew manuscripts, Septuagint and Syriac; most Hebrew
manuscripts *Your God has summoned power for you*　　^d 31 That is, the upper Nile region

Psalm 69

For the director of music. To the tune of, "Lilies." Of David.

¹ Save me, O God,
   for the waters have come up to my neck.
² I sink in the miry depths,
   where there is no foothold.
 I have come into the deep waters;
   the floods engulf me.
³ I am worn out calling for help;
   my throat is parched.
 My eyes fail,
   looking for my God.
⁴ Those who hate me without reason
   outnumber the hairs of my head;
 many are my enemies without cause,
   those who seek to destroy me.
 I am forced to restore
   what I did not steal.

⁵ You know my folly, O God;
   my guilt is not hidden from
      you.

⁶ May those who hope in you
   not be disgraced because of
      me,
   O Lord, the LORD Almighty;
 may those who seek you
   not be put to shame because
      of me,
   O God of Israel.
⁷ For I endure scorn for your sake,
   and shame covers my face.
⁸ I am a stranger to my brothers,
   an alien to my own mother's sons;
⁹ for zeal for your house consumes me,
   and the insults of those who insult you fall on me.
¹⁰ When I weep and fast,
   I must endure scorn;
¹¹ when I put on sackcloth,
   people make sport of me.
¹² Those who sit at the gate mock me,
   and I am the song of the drunkards.

¹³ But I pray to you, O LORD,
   in the time of your favor;
 in your great love, O God,
   answer me with your sure salvation.
¹⁴ Rescue me from the mire,
   do not let me sink;
 deliver me from those who hate me,
   from the deep waters.
¹⁵ Do not let the floodwaters engulf me
   or the depths swallow me up
   or the pit close its mouth over me.
¹⁶ Answer me, O LORD, out of the goodness of your love;

truth or dare

What a noble request! "Lord, I'm not perfect. Please don't let my failures cause others to stumble. And don't let me bring a bad name to your family."

69:5–6

in your great mercy turn to me.
¹⁷ Do not hide your face from your servant;
    answer me quickly, for I am in trouble.
¹⁸ Come near and rescue me;
    redeem me because of my foes.

¹⁹ You know how I am scorned, disgraced and shamed;
    all my enemies are before you.
²⁰ Scorn has broken my heart
    and has left me helpless;
I looked for sympathy, but there was none,
    for comforters, but I found none.
²¹ They put gall in my food
    and gave me vinegar for my thirst.

²² May the table set before them become a snare;
    may it become retribution and ᵃ a trap.
²³ May their eyes be darkened so they cannot see,
    and their backs be bent forever.
²⁴ Pour out your wrath on them;
    let your fierce anger overtake them.
²⁵ May their place be deserted;
    let there be no one to dwell in their tents.
²⁶ For they persecute those you wound
    and talk about the pain of those you hurt.
²⁷ Charge them with crime upon crime;
    do not let them share in your salvation.
²⁸ May they be blotted out of the book of life
    and not be listed with the righteous.

²⁹ I am in pain and distress;
    may your salvation, O God, protect me.

³⁰ I will praise God's name in song
    and glorify him with thanksgiving.
³¹ This will please the LORD more than an ox,
    more than a bull with its horns and hoofs.
³² The poor will see and be glad—
    you who seek God, may your hearts live!
³³ The LORD hears the needy
    and does not despise his captive people.

³⁴ Let heaven and earth praise him,
    the seas and all that move in them,
³⁵ for God will save Zion
    and rebuild the cities of Judah.
Then people will settle there and possess it;
³⁶   the children of his servants will inherit it,
    and those who love his name will dwell there.

Psalm 70

For the director of music. Of David. A petition.

¹ Hasten, O God, to save me;
    O LORD, come quickly to help me.
² May those who seek my life
    be put to shame and confusion;

ᵃ 22 Or *snare / and their fellowship become*

may all who desire my ruin
be turned back in disgrace.
³May those who say to me, "Aha! Aha!"
turn back because of their shame.
⁴But may all who seek you
rejoice and be glad in you;
may those who love your salvation always say,
"Let God be exalted!"

⁵Yet I am poor and needy;
come quickly to me, O God.
You are my help and my deliverer;
O Lord, do not delay.

Psalm 71

¹In you, O Lord, I have taken refuge;
let me never be put to shame.
²Rescue me and deliver me in your righteousness;
turn your ear to me and save me.
³Be my rock of refuge,
to which I can always go;
give the command to save me,
for you are my rock and my fortress.
⁴Deliver me, O my God, from the hand of the wicked,
from the grasp of evil and cruel men.

⁵For you have been my hope,
O Sovereign Lord,
my confidence since my youth.
⁶From birth I have relied on you;
you brought me forth from my
mother's womb.
I will ever praise you.
⁷I have become like a portent to
many,
but you are my strong refuge.
⁸My mouth is filled with your praise,
declaring your splendor all day long.

⁹Do not cast me away when I am old;
do not forsake me when my strength is
gone.
¹⁰For my enemies speak against me;
those who wait to kill me conspire
together.
¹¹They say, "God has forsaken him;
pursue him and seize him,
for no one will rescue him."
¹²Be not far from me, O God;
come quickly, O my God, to help me.
¹³May my accusers perish in shame;
may those who want to harm me
be covered with scorn and disgrace.

¹⁴But as for me, I will always have hope;
I will praise you more and more.
¹⁵My mouth will tell of your righteousness,

truth or dare

Portent is just another word for example. David's awesome relationship with God had become a model for the people. What kind of example are you to others?

71:7–8

of your salvation all day long,
    though I know not its measure.
[16] I will come and proclaim your mighty acts, O Sovereign LORD;
    I will proclaim your righteousness, yours alone.
[17] Since my youth, O God, you have taught me,
    and to this day I declare your marvelous deeds.
[18] Even when I am old and gray,
    do not forsake me, O God,
till I declare your power to the next generation,
    your might to all who are to come.

[19] Your righteousness reaches to the skies, O God,
    you who have done great things.
    Who, O God, is like you?
[20] Though you have made me see troubles, many and bitter,
    you will restore my life again;
from the depths of the earth
    you will again bring me up.
[21] You will increase my honor
    and comfort me once again.

[22] I will praise you with the harp
    for your faithfulness, O my God;
I will sing praise to you with the lyre,
    O Holy One of Israel.
[23] My lips will shout for joy
    when I sing praise to you—
    I, whom you have redeemed.
[24] My tongue will tell of your righteous acts
    all day long,
for those who wanted to harm me
    have been put to shame and confusion.

Psalm 72

Of Solomon.

[1] Endow the king with your justice, O God,
    the royal son with your righteousness.
[2] He will*a* judge your people in righteousness,
    your afflicted ones with justice.
[3] The mountains will bring prosperity to the people,
    the hills the fruit of righteousness.
[4] He will defend the afflicted among the people
    and save the children of the needy;
    he will crush the oppressor.

[5] He will endure*b* as long as the sun,
    as long as the moon, through all generations.
[6] He will be like rain falling on a mown field,
    like showers watering the earth.
[7] In his days the righteous will flourish;
    prosperity will abound till the moon is no more.

[8] He will rule from sea to sea
    and from the River*c* to the ends of the earth.*d*

a 2 Or *May he*; similarly in verses 3-11 and 17   *b 5* Septuagint; Hebrew *You will be feared*   *c 8* That is, the Euphrates
d 8 Or *the end of the land*

⁶ Therefore pride is their necklace;
　　they clothe themselves with
　　　violence.
⁷ From their callous hearts comes
　　iniquity*ᵃ*;
　　the evil conceits of their minds
　　　know no limits.
⁸ They scoff, and speak with
　　malice;
　　in their arrogance they
　　　threaten oppression.
⁹ Their mouths lay claim to heaven,
　　and their tongues take possession of the
　　　earth.
¹⁰ Therefore their people turn to them
　　and drink up waters in abundance.*ᵇ*
¹¹ They say, "How can God know?
　　Does the Most High have knowledge?"

¹² This is what the wicked are like—
　　always carefree, they increase in wealth.

¹³ Surely in vain have I kept my heart pure;
　　in vain have I washed my hands in innocence.
¹⁴ All day long I have been plagued;
　　I have been punished every morning.

¹⁵ If I had said, "I will speak thus,"
　　I would have betrayed your children.
¹⁶ When I tried to understand all this,
　　it was oppressive to me
¹⁷ till I entered the sanctuary of God;
　　then I understood their final destiny.

¹⁸ Surely you place them on slippery ground;
　　you cast them down to ruin.
¹⁹ How suddenly are they destroyed,
　　completely swept away by terrors!
²⁰ As a dream when one awakes,
　　so when you arise, O Lord,
　　you will despise them as fantasies.

²¹ When my heart was grieved
　　and my spirit embittered,
²² I was senseless and ignorant;
　　I was a brute beast before you.

²³ Yet I am always with you;
　　you hold me by my right hand.
²⁴ You guide me with your counsel,
　　and afterward you will take me into glory.
²⁵ Whom have I in heaven but you?
　　And earth has nothing I desire besides you.
²⁶ My flesh and my heart may fail,
　　but God is the strength of my heart
　　and my portion forever.

truth or dare

Why do some of the most wicked girls become the most popular? The psalmist kept this "unfair" situation in perspective. Their final destiny will be very different than ours.

73:3,16–20

ᵃ 7 Syriac (see also Septuagint); Hebrew *Their eyes bulge with fat*　　*ᵇ 10* The meaning of the Hebrew for this verse is uncertain.

²⁷ Those who are far from you will perish;
you destroy all who are unfaithful to you.
²⁸ But as for me, it is good to be near God.
I have made the Sovereign Lord my refuge;
I will tell of all your deeds.

Psalm 74

A *maskil*^a of Asaph.

¹ Why have you rejected us forever, O God?
Why does your anger smolder against the sheep of your pasture?
² Remember the people you purchased of old,
the tribe of your inheritance, whom you redeemed—
Mount Zion, where you dwelt.
³ Turn your steps toward these everlasting ruins,
all this destruction the enemy has brought on the sanctuary.

⁴ Your foes roared in the place where you met with us;
they set up their standards as signs.
⁵ They behaved like men wielding axes
to cut through a thicket of trees.
⁶ They smashed all the carved paneling
with their axes and hatchets.
⁷ They burned your sanctuary to the ground;
they defiled the dwelling place of your Name.
⁸ They said in their hearts, "We will crush them completely!"
They burned every place where God was worshiped in the land.
⁹ We are given no miraculous signs;
no prophets are left,
and none of us knows how long this will be.

¹⁰ How long will the enemy mock you, O God?
Will the foe revile your name forever?
¹¹ Why do you hold back your hand, your right hand?
Take it from the folds of your garment and destroy them!

¹² But you, O God, are my king from of old;
you bring salvation upon the earth.
¹³ It was you who split open the sea by your power;
you broke the heads of the monster in the waters.
¹⁴ It was you who crushed the heads of Leviathan
and gave him as food to the creatures of the desert.
¹⁵ It was you who opened up springs and streams;
you dried up the ever flowing rivers.
¹⁶ The day is yours, and yours also the night;
you established the sun and moon.
¹⁷ It was you who set all the boundaries of the earth;
you made both summer and winter.

¹⁸ Remember how the enemy has mocked you, O Lord,
how foolish people have reviled your name.
¹⁹ Do not hand over the life of your dove to wild beasts;
do not forget the lives of your afflicted people forever.
²⁰ Have regard for your covenant,
because haunts of violence fill the dark places of the land.
²¹ Do not let the oppressed retreat in disgrace;
may the poor and needy praise your name.

a Title: Probably a literary or musical term

²² Rise up, O God, and defend your cause;
    remember how fools mock you all day long.
²³ Do not ignore the clamor of your adversaries,
    the uproar of your enemies, which rises continually.

Psalm 75

For the director of music. ⌊To the tune of⌋ "Do Not Destroy."
A psalm of Asaph. A song.

¹ We give thanks to you, O God,
    we give thanks, for your Name is near;
    men tell of your wonderful deeds.

² You say, "I choose the appointed time;
    it is I who judge uprightly.
³ When the earth and all its people quake,
    it is I who hold its pillars firm.   *Selah*
⁴ To the arrogant I say, 'Boast no more,'
    and to the wicked, 'Do not lift up your horns.
⁵ Do not lift your horns against heaven;
    do not speak with outstretched neck.' "

⁶ No one from the east or the west
    or from the desert can exalt a man.
⁷ But it is God who judges:
    He brings one down, he exalts another.
⁸ In the hand of the LORD is a cup
    full of foaming wine mixed with spices;
he pours it out, and all the wicked of the earth
    drink it down to its very dregs.

⁹ As for me, I will declare this forever;
    I will sing praise to the God of Jacob.
¹⁰ I will cut off the horns of all the wicked,
    but the horns of the righteous will be lifted up.

Psalm 76

For the director of music. With stringed instruments. A psalm
of Asaph. A song.

¹ In Judah God is known;
    his name is great in Israel.
² His tent is in Salem,
    his dwelling place in Zion.
³ There he broke the flashing arrows,
    the shields and the swords, the weapons of war.   *Selah*

⁴ You are resplendent with light,
    more majestic than mountains rich with game.
⁵ Valiant men lie plundered,
    they sleep their last sleep;
not one of the warriors
    can lift his hands.
⁶ At your rebuke, O God of Jacob,
    both horse and chariot lie still.
⁷ You alone are to be feared.
    Who can stand before you when you are angry?
⁸ From heaven you pronounced judgment,
    and the land feared and was quiet—

⁹when you, O God, rose up to judge,
　　to save all the afflicted of the land. *Selah*
¹⁰Surely your wrath against men brings you praise,
　　and the survivors of your wrath are restrained. *ᵃ*

¹¹Make vows to the LORD your God and fulfill them;
　　let all the neighboring lands
　　bring gifts to the One to be feared.
¹²He breaks the spirit of rulers;
　　he is feared by the kings of the earth.

Psalm 77

For the director of music. For Jeduthun. Of Asaph. A psalm.

¹I cried out to God for help;
　　I cried out to God to hear me.
²When I was in distress, I sought the Lord;
　　at night I stretched out untiring hands
　　and my soul refused to be comforted.

³I remembered you, O God, and I groaned;
　　I mused, and my spirit grew faint. *Selah*
⁴You kept my eyes from closing;
　　I was too troubled to speak.
⁵I thought about the former days,
　　the years of long ago.
⁶I remembered my songs in the night.
　　My heart mused and my spirit inquired:

⁷"Will the Lord reject forever?
　　Will he never show his favor
　　again?
⁸Has his unfailing love vanished
　　forever?
　　Has his promise failed for all
　　time?
⁹Has God forgotten to be merciful?
　　Has he in anger withheld his
　　compassion?" *Selah*

¹⁰Then I thought, "To this I will
　　appeal:
　　the years of the right hand of
　　the Most High."
¹¹I will remember the deeds of the
　　LORD;
　　yes, I will remember your
　　miracles of long ago.
¹²I will meditate on all your works
　　and consider all your mighty
　　deeds.

¹³Your ways, O God, are holy.
　　What god is so great as our
　　God?
¹⁴You are the God who performs
　　miracles;

genuine

hope »» 77:11-12

When you're in a tight spot, it's tough to wait for God to respond and save you. The best way to keep up your hope through a tough time is to *remember* what God has done for you in the past. Remembering all that God did for you in past crises can give you hope that he'll come through for you again. Preach it to yourself, sista! Remind yourself that even when you can't see God, he's at work. Even when you can't feel God, he's by your side. Even when you're unstable, he's constant. Memory is a powerful thing.

ᵃ 10 Or Surely the wrath of men brings you praise, / and with the remainder of wrath you arm yourself

you display your power among the peoples.
¹⁵ With your mighty arm you redeemed your people,
the descendants of Jacob and Joseph.   *Selah*

¹⁶ The waters saw you, O God,
the waters saw you and writhed;
the very depths were convulsed.
¹⁷ The clouds poured down water,
the skies resounded with thunder;
your arrows flashed back and forth.
¹⁸ Your thunder was heard in the whirlwind,
your lightning lit up the world;
the earth trembled and quaked.
¹⁹ Your path led through the sea,
your way through the mighty waters,
though your footprints were not seen.

²⁰ You led your people like a flock
by the hand of Moses and Aaron.

Psalm 78

A maskil[a] of Asaph.

¹ O my people, hear my teaching;
listen to the words of my mouth.
² I will open my mouth in parables,
I will utter hidden things, things from of old—
³ what we have heard and known,
what our fathers have told us.
⁴ We will not hide them from their children;
we will tell the next generation
the praiseworthy deeds of the LORD,
his power, and the wonders he has done.
⁵ He decreed statutes for Jacob
and established the law in Israel,
which he commanded our forefathers
to teach their children,
⁶ so the next generation would know them,
even the children yet to be born,
and they in turn would tell their children.
⁷ Then they would put their trust in God
and would not forget his deeds
but would keep his commands.
⁸ They would not be like their forefathers—
a stubborn and rebellious generation,
whose hearts were not loyal to God,
whose spirits were not faithful to him.

⁹ The men of Ephraim, though armed with bows,
turned back on the day of battle;
¹⁰ they did not keep God's covenant
and refused to live by his law.
¹¹ They forgot what he had done,
the wonders he had shown them.
¹² He did miracles in the sight of their fathers
in the land of Egypt, in the region of Zoan.

a Title: Probably a literary or musical term

¹³ He divided the sea and led them through;
    he made the water stand firm like a wall.
¹⁴ He guided them with the cloud by day
    and with light from the fire all night.
¹⁵ He split the rocks in the desert
    and gave them water as abundant as the seas;
¹⁶ he brought streams out of a rocky crag
    and made water flow down like rivers.

¹⁷ But they continued to sin against him,
    rebelling in the desert against the Most High.
¹⁸ They willfully put God to the test
    by demanding the food they craved.
¹⁹ They spoke against God, saying,
    "Can God spread a table in the desert?
²⁰ When he struck the rock, water gushed out,
    and streams flowed abundantly.
    But can he also give us food?
    Can he supply meat for his people?"
²¹ When the LORD heard them, he was very angry;
    his fire broke out against Jacob,
    and his wrath rose against Israel,
²² for they did not believe in God
    or trust in his deliverance.
²³ Yet he gave a command to the skies above
    and opened the doors of the heavens;
²⁴ he rained down manna for the people to eat,
    he gave them the grain of heaven.
²⁵ Men ate the bread of angels;
    he sent them all the food they could eat.
²⁶ He let loose the east wind from the heavens
    and led forth the south wind by his power.
²⁷ He rained meat down on them like dust,
    flying birds like sand on the seashore.
²⁸ He made them come down inside their camp,
    all around their tents.
²⁹ They ate till they had more than enough,
    for he had given them what they craved.
³⁰ But before they turned from the food they craved,
    even while it was still in their mouths,
³¹ God's anger rose against them;
    he put to death the sturdiest among them,
    cutting down the young men of Israel.

³² In spite of all this, they kept on sinning;
    in spite of his wonders, they did not believe.
³³ So he ended their days in futility
    and their years in terror.
³⁴ Whenever God slew them, they would seek him;
    they eagerly turned to him again.
³⁵ They remembered that God was their Rock,
    that God Most High was their Redeemer.
³⁶ But then they would flatter him with their mouths,
    lying to him with their tongues;
³⁷ their hearts were not loyal to him,
    they were not faithful to his covenant.
³⁸ Yet he was merciful;

he forgave their iniquities
    and did not destroy them.
Time after time he restrained his anger
    and did not stir up his full wrath.
³⁹ He remembered that they were but flesh,
    a passing breeze that does not return.

⁴⁰ How often they rebelled against him in the desert
    and grieved him in the wasteland!
⁴¹ Again and again they put God to the test;
    they vexed the Holy One of Israel.
⁴² They did not remember his power—
    the day he redeemed them from the oppressor,
⁴³ the day he displayed his miraculous signs in Egypt,
    his wonders in the region of Zoan.
⁴⁴ He turned their rivers to blood;
    they could not drink from their streams.
⁴⁵ He sent swarms of flies that devoured them,
    and frogs that devastated them.
⁴⁶ He gave their crops to the grasshopper,
    their produce to the locust.
⁴⁷ He destroyed their vines with hail
    and their sycamore-figs with sleet.
⁴⁸ He gave over their cattle to the hail,
    their livestock to bolts of lightning.
⁴⁹ He unleashed against them his hot anger,
    his wrath, indignation and hostility—
    a band of destroying angels.
⁵⁰ He prepared a path for his anger;
    he did not spare them from death
    but gave them over to the plague.
⁵¹ He struck down all the firstborn of Egypt,
    the firstfruits of manhood in the tents of Ham.
⁵² But he brought his people out like a flock;
    he led them like sheep through the desert.
⁵³ He guided them safely, so they were unafraid;
    but the sea engulfed their enemies.
⁵⁴ Thus he brought them to the border of his holy land,
    to the hill country his right hand had taken.
⁵⁵ He drove out nations before them
    and allotted their lands to them as an inheritance;
    he settled the tribes of Israel in their homes.

⁵⁶ But they put God to the test
    and rebelled against the Most High;
    they did not keep his statutes.
⁵⁷ Like their fathers they were disloyal and faithless,
    as unreliable as a faulty bow.
⁵⁸ They angered him with their high places;
    they aroused his jealousy with their idols.
⁵⁹ When God heard them, he was very angry;
    he rejected Israel completely.
⁶⁰ He abandoned the tabernacle of Shiloh,
    the tent he had set up among men.
⁶¹ He sent ⌊the ark of⌋ his might into captivity,
    his splendor into the hands of the enemy.
⁶² He gave his people over to the sword;

he was very angry with his inheritance.
⁶³Fire consumed their young men,
   and their maidens had no wedding songs;
⁶⁴their priests were put to the sword,
   and their widows could not weep.

⁶⁵Then the Lord awoke as from sleep,
   as a man wakes from the stupor of wine.
⁶⁶He beat back his enemies;
   he put them to everlasting shame.
⁶⁷Then he rejected the tents of Joseph,
   he did not choose the tribe of Ephraim;
⁶⁸but he chose the tribe of Judah,
   Mount Zion, which he loved.
⁶⁹He built his sanctuary like the heights,
   like the earth that he established forever.
⁷⁰He chose David his servant
   and took him from the sheep pens;
⁷¹from tending the sheep he brought him
   to be the shepherd of his people Jacob,
   of Israel his inheritance.
⁷²And David shepherded them with integrity of heart;
   with skillful hands he led them.

Psalm 79

A psalm of Asaph.

¹O God, the nations have invaded your inheritance;
   they have defiled your holy temple,
   they have reduced Jerusalem to rubble.
²They have given the dead bodies of your servants
   as food to the birds of the air,
   the flesh of your saints to the beasts of the earth.
³They have poured out blood like water
   all around Jerusalem,
   and there is no one to bury the dead.
⁴We are objects of reproach to our neighbors,
   of scorn and derision to those around us.

⁵How long, O LORD? Will you be angry forever?
   How long will your jealousy burn like fire?
⁶Pour out your wrath on the nations
   that do not acknowledge you,
on the kingdoms
   that do not call on your name;
⁷for they have devoured Jacob
   and destroyed his homeland.
⁸Do not hold against us the sins of the fathers;
   may your mercy come quickly to meet us,
   for we are in desperate need.

⁹Help us, O God our Savior,
   for the glory of your name;
deliver us and forgive our sins
   for your name's sake.
¹⁰Why should the nations say,
   "Where is their God?"

Zipporah—Can't Wait to Procrastinate

Meet Mrs. Moses. Shepherdess. Daughter of the famous priest of Midian. Wife of the (almost) fearless leader of God's people. Zipporah first met Moses when he rescued her and her sisters from some rowdy shepherds (see Exodus 2:15–20). And when he came to live with her family, her father decided he would make a good son-in-law.

Marrying Moses threw Zipporah into the limelight. She became like the First Lady of the Hebrew nation. That's a tough role for a girl who didn't grow up an Israelite. She was just as unfamiliar with God's laws as Moses was, since he hadn't lived in a Hebrew household since he was three months old. But she stepped up to her role and worked to support her husband. When Moses wanted to send word to his father-in-law of the successful exodus from Egypt, Zipporah readily went with the news (see Exodus 18:1–6).

However, Zipporah and Moses made a bad decision when they failed to circumcise their child. Their lack of obedience in this area almost cost Moses his life (see Exodus 4:24–26). It wasn't until the last life-threatening minute that Zipporah took action. Perhaps Moses and Zipporah didn't understand the importance of following God's command regarding circumcision. Whatever the cause, God demanded that they follow through on following him.

Do you know that God requires something of you, but you are procrastinating? Do you think that maybe it's just not a big deal? "Just a second." "Be right there." "Wait until this show is over." "I'll do it tomorrow." Reluctance to obey is not pure obedience. Even if we're doing what we're asked, *when* and *how* we do it show what's really in our hearts.

To read the next Mirror Images profile, go to page 782.

Dear God, sometimes I act like Zipporah. What I want to do comes first, even if means procrastinating on being helpful to my family. Help me to work wholeheartedly at being helpful. Amen.

Read more about Zipporah in Exodus 2:11–22 (page 71); 4:20–26 (page 74); 18:1–6 (page 91).

» 733

Before our eyes, make known among the nations
that you avenge the outpoured blood of your servants.
[11] May the groans of the prisoners come before you;
by the strength of your arm
preserve those condemned to die.

[12] Pay back into the laps of our neighbors seven times
the reproach they have hurled at you, O Lord.
[13] Then we your people, the sheep of your pasture,
will praise you forever;
from generation to generation
we will recount your praise.

Psalm 80

*For the director of music. To ʟthe tune ofʝ "The Lilies of the
Covenant." Of Asaph. A psalm.*

[1] Hear us, O Shepherd of Israel,
you who lead Joseph like a flock;
you who sit enthroned between the cherubim, shine forth
[2] before Ephraim, Benjamin and Manasseh.
Awaken your might;
come and save us.

[3] Restore us, O God;
make your face shine upon us,
that we may be saved.

[4] O LORD God Almighty,
how long will your anger smolder
against the prayers of your people?
[5] You have fed them with the bread of tears;
you have made them drink tears by the bowlful.
[6] You have made us a source of contention to our neighbors,
and our enemies mock us.

[7] Restore us, O God Almighty;
make your face shine upon us,
that we may be saved.

[8] You brought a vine out of Egypt;
you drove out the nations and planted it.
[9] You cleared the ground for it,
and it took root and filled the land.
[10] The mountains were covered with its shade,
the mighty cedars with its branches.
[11] It sent out its boughs to the Sea,[a]
its shoots as far as the River.[b]

[12] Why have you broken down its walls
so that all who pass by pick its grapes?
[13] Boars from the forest ravage it
and the creatures of the field feed on it.
[14] Return to us, O God Almighty!
Look down from heaven and see!
Watch over this vine,
[15] the root your right hand has planted,
the son[c] you have raised up for yourself.

a 11 Probably the Mediterranean   *b 11 That is, the Euphrates*   *c 15 Or branch*

16 Your vine is cut down, it is burned with fire;
    at your rebuke your people perish.
17 Let your hand rest on the man at your right hand,
    the son of man you have raised up for yourself.
18 Then we will not turn away from you;
    revive us, and we will call on your name.

19 Restore us, O LORD God Almighty;
    make your face shine upon us,
    that we may be saved.

Psalm 81

For the director of music. According to *gittith.* *a* Of Asaph.

1 Sing for joy to God our strength;
    shout aloud to the God of Jacob!
2 Begin the music, strike the tambourine,
    play the melodious harp and lyre.

3 Sound the ram's horn at the New Moon,
    and when the moon is full, on the day of our Feast;
4 this is a decree for Israel,
    an ordinance of the God of Jacob.
5 He established it as a statute for Joseph
    when he went out against Egypt,
    where we heard a language we did not understand. *b*

6 He says, "I removed the burden from their shoulders;
    their hands were set free from the basket.
7 In your distress you called and I rescued you,
    I answered you out of a thundercloud;
    I tested you at the waters of Meribah.   *Selah*

8 "Hear, O my people, and I will warn you—
    if you would but listen to me, O Israel!
9 You shall have no foreign god among you;
    you shall not bow down to an alien god.
10 I am the LORD your God,
    who brought you up out of Egypt.
    Open wide your mouth and I will fill it.

11 "But my people would not listen to me;
    Israel would not submit to me.
12 So I gave them over to their stubborn hearts
    to follow their own devices.

13 "If my people would but listen to me,
    if Israel would follow my ways,
14 how quickly would I subdue their enemies
    and turn my hand against their foes!
15 Those who hate the LORD would cringe before him,
    and their punishment would last forever.
16 But you would be fed with the finest of wheat;
    with honey from the rock I would satisfy you."

a Title: Probably a musical term   *b 5* Or *I and we heard a voice we had not known*

Psalm 82

A psalm of Asaph.

[1] God presides in the great assembly;
he gives judgment among the "gods":

[2] "How long will you[a] defend the unjust
and show partiality to the wicked?   *Selah*
[3] Defend the cause of the weak and fatherless;
maintain the rights of the poor and oppressed.
[4] Rescue the weak and needy;
deliver them from the hand of the wicked.

[5] "They know nothing, they understand nothing.
They walk about in darkness;
all the foundations of the earth are shaken.

[6] "I said, 'You are "gods";
you are all sons of the Most High.'
[7] But you will die like mere men;
you will fall like every other ruler."

[8] Rise up, O God, judge the earth,
for all the nations are your inheritance.

Psalm 83

A song. A psalm of Asaph.

[1] O God, do not keep silent;
be not quiet, O God, be not still.
[2] See how your enemies are astir,
how your foes rear their heads.
[3] With cunning they conspire against your people;
they plot against those you cherish.
[4] "Come," they say, "let us destroy them as a nation,
that the name of Israel be remembered no more."

[5] With one mind they plot together;
they form an alliance against you—
[6] the tents of Edom and the Ishmaelites,
of Moab and the Hagrites,
[7] Gebal,[b] Ammon and Amalek,
Philistia, with the people of Tyre.
[8] Even Assyria has joined them
to lend strength to the descendants of Lot.   *Selah*

[9] Do to them as you did to Midian,
as you did to Sisera and Jabin at the river Kishon,
[10] who perished at Endor
and became like refuse on the ground.
[11] Make their nobles like Oreb and Zeeb,
all their princes like Zebah and Zalmunna,
[12] who said, "Let us take possession
of the pasturelands of God."

[13] Make them like tumbleweed, O my God,
like chaff before the wind.
[14] As fire consumes the forest
or a flame sets the mountains ablaze,

a 2 The Hebrew is plural.   *b 7* That is, Byblos

¹⁵ so pursue them with your tempest
and terrify them with your storm.
¹⁶ Cover their faces with shame
so that men will seek your name, O Lᴏʀᴅ.

¹⁷ May they ever be ashamed and dismayed;
may they perish in disgrace.
¹⁸ Let them know that you, whose name is the Lᴏʀᴅ—
that you alone are the Most High over all the earth.

Psalm 84

For the director of music. According to *gittith.*ᵃ Of the Sons
of Korah. A psalm.

¹ How lovely is your dwelling place,
O Lᴏʀᴅ Almighty!
² My soul yearns, even faints,
for the courts of the Lᴏʀᴅ;
my heart and my flesh cry out
for the living God.

³ Even the sparrow has found a
home,
and the swallow a nest for
herself,
where she may have her
young—
a place near your altar,
O Lᴏʀᴅ Almighty, my King and
my God.
⁴ Blessed are those who dwell in
your house;
they are ever praising you.

Selah

⁵ Blessed are those whose
strength is in you,
who have set their hearts on
pilgrimage.
⁶ As they pass through the Valley
of Baca,
they make it a place of
springs;
the autumn rains also cover it
with pools.ᵇ
⁷ They go from strength to
strength,
till each appears before God
in Zion.

genuine life » 84:5

Welcome to the journey of life! Your destination is heaven. Your travel time is however long you're breathing. Your goal is eternity with God. Your job is to set your heart on pilgrimage. Say what?! Well, we aren't here to stay on this planet, are we? We're pilgrims, travelers, just passing through, so we'd better not get too attached to the stuff of this world. Instead we should set our hearts on home, our *real* home, not the hotels we happen to be livin' in right now. You get the drift, fellow drifter?

⁸ Hear my prayer, O Lᴏʀᴅ God Almighty;
listen to me, O God of Jacob.

Selah

⁹ Look upon our shield,ᶜ O God;
look with favor on your anointed one.

¹⁰ Better is one day in your courts
than a thousand elsewhere;

ᵃ Title: Probably a musical term   ᵇ 6 Or *blessings*   ᶜ 9 Or *sovereign*

I would rather be a doorkeeper in the house of my God
    than dwell in the tents of the wicked.
[11] For the LORD God is a sun and shield;
    the LORD bestows favor and honor;
no good thing does he withhold
    from those whose walk is blameless.

[12] O LORD Almighty,
    blessed is the man who trusts in you.

Psalm 85

For the director of music. Of the Sons of Korah. A psalm.

[1] You showed favor to your land, O LORD;
    you restored the fortunes of Jacob.
[2] You forgave the iniquity of your people
    and covered all their sins.   *Selah*
[3] You set aside all your wrath
    and turned from your fierce anger.

[4] Restore us again, O God our Savior,
    and put away your displeasure toward us.
[5] Will you be angry with us forever?
    Will you prolong your anger through all generations?
[6] Will you not revive us again,
    that your people may rejoice in
        you?
[7] Show us your unfailing love,
      O LORD,
    and grant us your salvation.

[8] I will listen to what God the LORD
      will say;
    he promises peace to his
        people, his saints—
    but let them not return to folly.
[9] Surely his salvation is near those who fear him,
    that his glory may dwell in our land.

[10] Love and faithfulness meet together;
    righteousness and peace kiss each other.
[11] Faithfulness springs forth from the earth,
    and righteousness looks down from
        heaven.
[12] The LORD will indeed give what is good,
    and our land will yield its harvest.
[13] Righteousness goes before him
    and prepares the way for his steps.

truth or **dare**

A lot of people think prayer's all about talking to God. Actually, prayer also involves God talking to you. Having trouble hearing him? Quiet down and *just listen.*

85:8

Psalm 86

A prayer of David.

[1] Hear, O LORD, and answer me,
    for I am poor and needy.
[2] Guard my life, for I am devoted to you.
    You are my God; save your servant
      who trusts in you.
[3] Have mercy on me, O Lord,

for I call to you all day long.
⁴Bring joy to your servant,
    for to you, O Lord,
    I lift up my soul.

⁵You are forgiving and good, O Lord,
    abounding in love to all who call to you.
⁶Hear my prayer, O Lᴏʀᴅ;
    listen to my cry for mercy.
⁷In the day of my trouble I will call to you,
    for you will answer me.

⁸Among the gods there is none like you, O Lord;
    no deeds can compare with yours.
⁹All the nations you have made
    will come and worship before you, O Lord;
    they will bring glory to your name.
¹⁰For you are great and do marvelous deeds;
    you alone are God.

¹¹Teach me your way, O Lᴏʀᴅ,
    and I will walk in your truth;
give me an undivided heart,
    that I may fear your name.
¹²I will praise you, O Lord my God, with all my heart;
    I will glorify your name forever.
¹³For great is your love toward me;
    you have delivered me from the depths of the grave.ᵃ

¹⁴The arrogant are attacking me, O God;
    a band of ruthless men seeks my life—
    men without regard for you.
¹⁵But you, O Lord, are a compassionate and gracious God,
    slow to anger, abounding in love and faithfulness.
¹⁶Turn to me and have mercy on me;
    grant your strength to your servant
    and save the son of your maidservant.ᵇ
¹⁷Give me a sign of your goodness,
    that my enemies may see it and be put to shame,
    for you, O Lᴏʀᴅ, have helped me and comforted me.

Psalm 87

Of the Sons of Korah. A psalm. A song.

¹He has set his foundation on the holy mountain;
²   the Lᴏʀᴅ loves the gates of Zion
    more than all the dwellings of Jacob.
³Glorious things are said of you,
    O city of God: *Selah*
⁴"I will record Rahabᶜ and Babylon
    among those who acknowledge me—
Philistia too, and Tyre, along with Cushᵈ—
    and will say, 'Thisᵉ one was born in Zion.' "

⁵Indeed, of Zion it will be said,
    "This one and that one were born in her,

ᵃ 13 Hebrew *Sheol*   ᵇ 16 Or *save your faithful son*   ᶜ 4 A poetic name for Egypt   ᵈ 4 That is, the upper Nile region
ᵉ 4 Or *"O Rahab and Babylon, / Philistia, Tyre and Cush, / I will record concerning those who acknowledge me: / 'This*

and the Most High himself will establish her."
⁶ The LORD will write in the register of the peoples:
"This one was born in Zion."   *Selah*
⁷ As they make music they will sing,
"All my fountains are in you."

Psalm 88

A song. A psalm of the Sons of Korah. For the director of music.
According to *mahalath leannoth.*ᵃ A *maskil*ᵇ of
Heman the Ezrahite.

¹ O LORD, the God who saves me,
day and night I cry out before you.
² May my prayer come before you;
turn your ear to my cry.

³ For my soul is full of trouble
and my life draws near the grave.ᶜ
⁴ I am counted among those who go down to the pit;
I am like a man without strength.
⁵ I am set apart with the dead,
like the slain who lie in the grave,
whom you remember no more,
who are cut off from your care.

⁶ You have put me in the lowest pit,
in the darkest depths.
⁷ Your wrath lies heavily upon me;
you have overwhelmed me with all your waves.   *Selah*
⁸ You have taken from me my closest friends
and have made me repulsive to them.
I am confined and cannot escape;
⁹   my eyes are dim with grief.

I call to you, O LORD, every day;
I spread out my hands to you.
¹⁰ Do you show your wonders to the dead?
Do those who are dead rise up and praise you?   *Selah*
¹¹ Is your love declared in the grave,
your faithfulness in Destructionᵈ?
¹² Are your wonders known in the place of darkness,
or your righteous deeds in the land of oblivion?

¹³ But I cry to you for help, O LORD;
in the morning my prayer comes before you.
¹⁴ Why, O LORD, do you reject me
and hide your face from me?

¹⁵ From my youth I have been afflicted and close to death;
I have suffered your terrors and am in despair.
¹⁶ Your wrath has swept over me;
your terrors have destroyed me.
¹⁷ All day long they surround me like a flood;
they have completely engulfed me.
¹⁸ You have taken my companions and loved ones from me;
the darkness is my closest friend.

ᵃ Title: Possibly a tune, "The Suffering of Affliction"   ᵇ Title: Probably a literary or musical term   ᶜ 3 Hebrew *Sheol*
ᵈ 11 Hebrew *Abaddon*

in focus

Breaking Stereotypes
Profile: Bryn

I didn't want to like her. After all, she's not like me. She's black. I'm white. I didn't have any friends like her. None of my friends had friends like her. We had our style. And they had theirs. We would never mix. Not like we purposely avoided them; it just worked best that way. At least that's what I used to think.

I didn't want to grow to appreciate the way she challenged me on my views about life. People. Music. Things. I used to think the way I was brought up—believing all the stereotypes about others—was fine.

Until she opened my eyes.

I hadn't planned to notice the way she loved her family—how connected they were. I wish my family was as tight as hers.

I didn't predict I'd end up admiring the way she dressed. She has an incredible sense of style that I wish I had.

There was no way we had anything in common—at least that's what I said at first. Then I found out she was a lot like me. She laughs. She loves. She cries. She lives life, just like me. How could someone so different be so much like me? How could I keep her out of my life just because of the color of her skin? How could people be so wrong about each other?

No, I didn't plan to like her. But it turns out, I did. Now she's my best friend.

Want more info about how to end prejudice in your heart and mind? Go online at www.TrueImagesBible.com

prejudice in focus

Prejudice is ugly—it talks ugly and thinks ugly thoughts. It doesn't look good on anyone—especially a Christian woman. God sees us all the same, regardless of race or background (see Galatians 3:28, page 1538).

» If you or someone you know is struggling with prejudice or racism, remember that it's a learned behavior—it doesn't change overnight. You can combat it with repentance, hard work, determination and the truth of God.

» Seek friendships with those who are different from you. You never know what surprises await you.

For more on this topic, see the index on page 1656.

Psalm 89

A *maskil*[a] of Ethan the Ezrahite.

¹I will sing of the Lord's great love forever;
with my mouth I will make your faithfulness known through all generations.

a Title: Probably a literary or musical term

²I will declare that your love stands firm forever,
that you established your faithfulness in heaven itself.

³You said, "I have made a covenant with my chosen one,
I have sworn to David my servant,

⁴'I will establish your line forever
and make your throne firm through all generations.'"   *Selah*

⁵The heavens praise your wonders, O LORD,
your faithfulness too, in the assembly of the holy ones.

⁶For who in the skies above can compare with the LORD?
Who is like the LORD among the heavenly beings?

⁷In the council of the holy ones God is greatly feared;
he is more awesome than all who surround him.

⁸O LORD God Almighty, who is like you?
You are mighty, O LORD, and your faithfulness surrounds you.

⁹You rule over the surging sea;
when its waves mount up, you still them.

¹⁰You crushed Rahab like one of the slain;
with your strong arm you scattered your enemies.

¹¹The heavens are yours, and yours also the earth;
you founded the world and all that is in it.

¹²You created the north and the south;
Tabor and Hermon sing for joy at your name.

¹³Your arm is endued with power;
your hand is strong, your right hand exalted.

¹⁴Righteousness and justice are the foundation of your throne;
love and faithfulness go before you.

¹⁵Blessed are those who have learned to acclaim you,
who walk in the light of your presence, O LORD.

¹⁶They rejoice in your name all day long;
they exult in your righteousness.

¹⁷For you are their glory and strength,
and by your favor you exalt our horn.ᵃ

¹⁸Indeed, our shieldᵇ belongs to the LORD,
our king to the Holy One of Israel.

¹⁹Once you spoke in a vision,
to your faithful people you said:
"I have bestowed strength on a warrior;
I have exalted a young man from among the people.

²⁰I have found David my servant;
with my sacred oil I have anointed him.

²¹My hand will sustain him;
surely my arm will strengthen him.

²²No enemy will subject him to tribute;
no wicked man will oppress him.

²³I will crush his foes before him
and strike down his adversaries.

²⁴My faithful love will be with him,
and through my name his hornᶜ will be exalted.

²⁵I will set his hand over the sea,
his right hand over the rivers.

²⁶He will call out to me, 'You are my Father,
my God, the Rock my Savior.'

ᵃ *17* *Horn* here symbolizes strong one.   ᵇ *18* Or *sovereign*   ᶜ *24* *Horn* here symbolizes strength.

²⁷I will also appoint him my firstborn,
the most exalted of the kings of the earth.
²⁸I will maintain my love to him forever,
and my covenant with him will never fail.
²⁹I will establish his line forever,
his throne as long as the heavens endure.

³⁰"If his sons forsake my law
and do not follow my statutes,
³¹if they violate my decrees
and fail to keep my commands,
³²I will punish their sin with the rod,
their iniquity with flogging;
³³but I will not take my love from him,
nor will I ever betray my faithfulness.
³⁴I will not violate my covenant
or alter what my lips have uttered.
³⁵Once for all, I have sworn by my holiness—
and I will not lie to David—
³⁶that his line will continue forever
and his throne endure before me like the sun;
³⁷it will be established forever like the moon,
the faithful witness in the sky."   *Selah*

³⁸But you have rejected, you have spurned,
you have been very angry with your anointed one.
³⁹You have renounced the covenant with your servant
and have defiled his crown in the dust.
⁴⁰You have broken through all his walls
and reduced his strongholds to ruins.
⁴¹All who pass by have plundered him;
he has become the scorn of his neighbors.
⁴²You have exalted the right hand of his foes;
you have made all his enemies rejoice.
⁴³You have turned back the edge of his sword
and have not supported him in battle.
⁴⁴You have put an end to his splendor
and cast his throne to the ground.
⁴⁵You have cut short the days of his youth;
you have covered him with a mantle of shame.   *Selah*

⁴⁶How long, O LORD? Will you hide yourself forever?
How long will your wrath burn like fire?
⁴⁷Remember how fleeting is my life.
For what futility you have created all men!
⁴⁸What man can live and not see death,
or save himself from the power of the grave*ᵃ*?   *Selah*
⁴⁹O Lord, where is your former great love,
which in your faithfulness you swore to David?
⁵⁰Remember, Lord, how your servant has*ᵇ* been mocked,
how I bear in my heart the taunts of all the nations,
⁵¹the taunts with which your enemies have mocked, O LORD,
with which they have mocked every step of your anointed one.

⁵²Praise be to the LORD forever!
Amen and Amen.

a 48 Hebrew *Sheol*   *b 50* Or *your servants have*

BOOK IV

Psalms 90–106

Psalm 90

A prayer of Moses the man of God.

¹ Lord, you have been our dwelling place
    throughout all generations.
² Before the mountains were born
    or you brought forth the earth and the world,
    from everlasting to everlasting you are God.

³ You turn men back to dust,
    saying, "Return to dust, O sons of men."
⁴ For a thousand years in your sight
    are like a day that has just gone by,
    or like a watch in the night.
⁵ You sweep men away in the sleep of death;
    they are like the new grass of the morning—
⁶ though in the morning it springs up new,
    by evening it is dry and withered.

⁷ We are consumed by your anger
    and terrified by your indignation.
⁸ You have set our iniquities before you,
    our secret sins in the light of your presence.
⁹ All our days pass away under your wrath;
    we finish our years with a moan.
¹⁰ The length of our days is seventy
    years—
    or eighty, if we have the strength;
    yet their span *ᵃ* is but trouble and
    sorrow,
    for they quickly pass, and we
    fly away.
¹¹ Who knows the power of your
    anger?
    For your wrath is as great as
    the fear that is due you.
¹² Teach us to number our days
    aright,
    that we may gain a heart of
    wisdom.
¹³ Relent, O LORD! How long will it be?
    Have compassion on your
    servants.
¹⁴ Satisfy us in the morning with
    your unfailing love,
    that we may sing for joy and
    be glad all our days.
¹⁵ Make us glad for as many days
    as you have afflicted us,
    for as many years as we have
    seen trouble.

genuine joy

» 90:14

What are you like when you first wake up in the morning? Do you drag your crabby self out of bed and snap at your mom and brother if they try to talk to you? Is it common knowledge that everyone should steer clear of you before 10:00 AM? How about changing your mindset? What would your day be like if your first thoughts were of God's unfailing love and your first words to him were thanks? Maybe that would ease your worries and get you excited for the day. Hmmm . . . maybe you could become a morning person after all!

ᵃ 10 Or yet the best of them

16 May your deeds be shown to your servants,
     your splendor to their children.

17 May the favor^a of the Lord our God rest upon us;
     establish the work of our hands for us—
     yes, establish the work of our hands.

Psalm 91

1 He who dwells in the shelter of the Most High
     will rest in the shadow of the Almighty.^b
2 I will say^c of the LORD, "He is my refuge and my fortress,
     my God, in whom I trust."

3 Surely he will save you from the
     fowler's snare
     and from the deadly pestilence.
4 He will cover you with his feathers,
     and under his wings you will
     find refuge;
     his faithfulness will be your
     shield and rampart.
5 You will not fear the terror of night,
     nor the arrow that flies by day,
6 nor the pestilence that stalks in
     the darkness,
     nor the plague that destroys
     at midday.
7 A thousand may fall at your side,
     ten thousand at your right hand,
     but it will not come near you.
8 You will only observe with your eyes
     and see the punishment of
     the wicked.

9 If you make the Most High your
     dwelling—
     even the LORD, who is my refuge—
10 then no harm will befall you,
     no disaster will come near
     your tent.
11 For he will command his angels
     concerning you
     to guard you in all your ways;
12 they will lift you up in their hands,
     so that you will not strike your
     foot against a stone.
13 You will tread upon the lion and
     the cobra;
     you will trample the great lion
     and the serpent.

14 "Because he loves me," says the
     LORD, "I will rescue him;
     I will protect him, for he
     acknowledges my name.

love ♥ notes

91:14–16

Beloved,

Trouble in this world comes in many different forms—sickness, accidents, rejection, failures. When you're in trouble, come to me. Because I love you, my daughter, I will be with you and save you.

—Your God and Protector

What troubles are you facing? Ask God for his help.

_____
_____
_____
_____
_____
_____
_____
_____
_____
_____

^a 17 Or beauty   ^b 1 Hebrew Shaddai   ^c 2 Or He says

¹⁵He will call upon me, and I will answer him;
   I will be with him in trouble,
   I will deliver him and honor him.
¹⁶With long life will I satisfy him
   and show him my salvation."

Psalm 92

A psalm. A song. For the Sabbath day.

¹It is good to praise the LORD
   and make music to your name, O Most High,
²to proclaim your love in the morning
   and your faithfulness at night,
³to the music of the ten-stringed lyre
   and the melody of the harp.

⁴For you make me glad by your deeds, O LORD;
   I sing for joy at the works of your hands.
⁵How great are your works, O LORD,
   how profound your thoughts!
⁶The senseless man does not
      know,
   fools do not understand,
⁷that though the wicked spring up
      like grass
   and all evildoers flourish,
they will be forever destroyed.

⁸But you, O LORD, are exalted
   forever.

⁹For surely your enemies, O LORD,
   surely your enemies will perish;
   all evildoers will be scattered.
¹⁰You have exalted my horn[a] like that of a wild
      ox;
   fine oils have been poured upon me.
¹¹My eyes have seen the defeat of my
      adversaries;
   my ears have heard the rout of my wicked foes.

¹²The righteous will flourish like a palm tree,
   they will grow like a cedar of Lebanon;
¹³planted in the house of the LORD,
   they will flourish in the courts of our God.
¹⁴They will still bear fruit in old age,
   they will stay fresh and green,
¹⁵proclaiming, "The LORD is upright;
   he is my Rock, and there is no wickedness in him."

Psalm 93

¹The LORD reigns, he is robed in majesty;
   the LORD is robed in majesty
   and is armed with strength.
The world is firmly established;
   it cannot be moved.

truth or dare

How do you express praise to God? Through singing? Writing? Art? However you get that awesome inner flame out to the world, do it for God and do it all the time!

92:1–4

^a 10 *Horn* here symbolizes strength.

² Your throne was established long ago;
   you are from all eternity.

³ The seas have lifted up, O Lord,
   the seas have lifted up their voice;
   the seas have lifted up their pounding waves.
⁴ Mightier than the thunder of the great waters,
   mightier than the breakers of the sea—
   the Lord on high is mighty.

⁵ Your statutes stand firm;
   holiness adorns your house
   for endless days, O Lord.

Psalm 94

¹ O Lord, the God who avenges,
   O God who avenges, shine forth.
² Rise up, O Judge of the earth;
   pay back to the proud what they deserve.
³ How long will the wicked, O Lord,
   how long will the wicked be jubilant?

⁴ They pour out arrogant words;
   all the evildoers are full of boasting.
⁵ They crush your people, O Lord;
   they oppress your inheritance.
⁶ They slay the widow and the alien;
   they murder the fatherless.
⁷ They say, "The Lord does not see;
   the God of Jacob pays no heed."

⁸ Take heed, you senseless ones among the people;
   you fools, when will you become wise?
⁹ Does he who implanted the ear not hear?
   Does he who formed the eye not see?
¹⁰ Does he who disciplines nations not punish?
   Does he who teaches man lack knowledge?
¹¹ The Lord knows the thoughts of man;
   he knows that they are futile.

¹² Blessed is the man you discipline, O Lord,
   the man you teach from your law;
¹³ you grant him relief from days of trouble,
   till a pit is dug for the wicked.
¹⁴ For the Lord will not reject his people;
   he will never forsake his inheritance.
¹⁵ Judgment will again be founded on righteousness,
   and all the upright in heart will follow it.

¹⁶ Who will rise up for me against the wicked?
   Who will take a stand for me against evildoers?
¹⁷ Unless the Lord had given me help,
   I would soon have dwelt in the silence of death.
¹⁸ When I said, "My foot is slipping,"
   your love, O Lord, supported me.
¹⁹ When anxiety was great within me,
   your consolation brought joy to my soul.

²⁰ Can a corrupt throne be allied with you—

one that brings on misery by its decrees?
²¹ They band together against the righteous
    and condemn the innocent to death.
²² But the LORD has become my fortress,
    and my God the rock in whom I take refuge.
²³ He will repay them for their sins
    and destroy them for their wickedness;
    the LORD our God will destroy them.

Psalm 95

¹ Come, let us sing for joy to the LORD;
    let us shout aloud to the Rock of our salvation.
² Let us come before him with thanksgiving
    and extol him with music and song.

³ For the LORD is the great God,
    the great King above all gods.
⁴ In his hand are the depths of the earth,
    and the mountain peaks belong to him.
⁵ The sea is his, for he made it,
    and his hands formed the dry land.

⁶ Come, let us bow down in worship,
    let us kneel before the LORD our Maker;
⁷ for he is our God
    and we are the people of his pasture,
    the flock under his care.

Today, if you hear his voice,
⁸   do not harden your hearts as you did at Meribah,ᵃ
    as you did that day at Massahᵇ in the desert,
⁹ where your fathers tested and tried me,
    though they had seen what I did.
¹⁰ For forty years I was angry with that generation;
    I said, "They are a people whose hearts go astray,
    and they have not known my ways."
¹¹ So I declared on oath in my anger,
    "They shall never enter my rest."

Psalm 96

¹ Sing to the LORD a new song;
    sing to the LORD, all the earth.
² Sing to the LORD, praise his name;
    proclaim his salvation day after day.
³ Declare his glory among the nations,
    his marvelous deeds among all peoples.

⁴ For great is the LORD and most worthy of praise;
    he is to be feared above all gods.
⁵ For all the gods of the nations are idols,
    but the LORD made the heavens.
⁶ Splendor and majesty are before him;
    strength and glory are in his sanctuary.

⁷ Ascribe to the LORD, O families of nations,
    ascribe to the LORD glory and strength.

ᵃ 8 Meribah means quarreling.   ᵇ 8 Massah means testing.

A Little Patience

Profile: Alyssa

Things aren't very good with me and my mom. She drives me crazy. It's like she's always on my back about *something*. Where I'm going, who I'm hanging out with, whether I'm getting my homework done, what I'm wearing . . . blah, blah, blah.

When she starts in on me, I feel this anger bubbling up in me, and I end up snapping back at her and telling her to leave me alone. I say whatever comes to mind. Sometimes I am so rude to her. I feel like I have to be to get my point across, but I do feel bad about that.

My dad says I have a serious patience problem. He says it's not just my mom that I talk to that way. I guess he may be right. I yell at my little brothers sometimes. And I've noticed I've been snapping at my friends when they say stuff that sets me off. My mouth starts going before my mind checks in.

I don't try to be harsh. I feel so frustrated, like I can't get through to people, and they won't listen till I really make my point. I've tried to be more patient, but it's hard for me. Besides, doesn't *everyone* lose her temper once in a while? It seems like a pretty natural reaction to me.

For more on patience, visit
www.TrueImagesBible.com

patience in focus

Got a patience problem? Or maybe you manage to control your temper all day but take out your impatience at home? Remember, anger and frustration are natural feelings, but what we do with those can either be healthy or destructive—to us and others.

»Words said impatiently can really hurt others and ruin a friendship (see Proverbs 13:3, page 820, and 25:18, page 841).
»God encourages us to be patient and think before we speak (see Proverbs 15:28, page 825).
»Love is patient (see 1 Corinthians 13:4, page 1519). When you feel like you're about to unleash on someone, just pause for a minute. Ask God to help you be patient and loving toward that person.

For more on this topic, see the index on page 1656.

⁸ Ascribe to the Lᴏʀᴅ the glory due his name;
  bring an offering and come into his courts.
⁹ Worship the Lᴏʀᴅ in the splendor of his*ᵃ* holiness;
  tremble before him, all the earth.

¹⁰ Say among the nations, "The Lᴏʀᴅ reigns."
  The world is firmly established, it cannot be moved;
  he will judge the peoples with equity.
¹¹ Let the heavens rejoice, let the earth be glad;
  let the sea resound, and all that is in it;
¹² let the fields be jubilant, and everything in them.
  Then all the trees of the forest will sing for joy;

---

a 9 Or Lᴏʀᴅ *with the splendor of*

¹³ they will sing before the LORD, for he comes,
he comes to judge the earth.
He will judge the world in righteousness
and the peoples in his truth.

Psalm 97

¹ The LORD reigns, let the earth be glad;
let the distant shores rejoice.
² Clouds and thick darkness surround him;
righteousness and justice are the foundation of his throne.
³ Fire goes before him
and consumes his foes on every side.
⁴ His lightning lights up the world;
the earth sees and trembles.
⁵ The mountains melt like wax before the LORD,
before the Lord of all the earth.
⁶ The heavens proclaim his righteousness,
and all the peoples see his glory.

⁷ All who worship images are put to shame,
those who boast in idols—
worship him, all you gods!
⁸ Zion hears and rejoices
and the villages of Judah are glad
because of your judgments, O LORD.
⁹ For you, O LORD, are the Most High over all the earth;
you are exalted far above all gods.

¹⁰ Let those who love the LORD hate evil,
for he guards the lives of his faithful ones
and delivers them from the hand of the wicked.
¹¹ Light is shed upon the righteous
and joy on the upright in heart.
¹² Rejoice in the LORD, you who are righteous,
and praise his holy name.

Psalm 98

A psalm.

¹ Sing to the LORD a new song,
for he has done marvelous things;
his right hand and his holy arm
have worked salvation for him.
² The LORD has made his salvation known
and revealed his righteousness to the nations.
³ He has remembered his love
and his faithfulness to the house of Israel;
all the ends of the earth have seen
the salvation of our God.

⁴ Shout for joy to the LORD, all the earth,
burst into jubilant song with music;
⁵ make music to the LORD with the harp,
with the harp and the sound of singing,
⁶ with trumpets and the blast of the ram's horn—
shout for joy before the LORD, the King.

⁷Let the sea resound, and everything in it,
    the world, and all who live in it.
⁸Let the rivers clap their hands,
    let the mountains sing together for joy;
⁹let them sing before the LORD,
    for he comes to judge the earth.
He will judge the world in righteousness
    and the peoples with equity.

Psalm 99

¹The LORD reigns,
    let the nations tremble;
he sits enthroned between the cherubim,
    let the earth shake.
²Great is the LORD in Zion;
    he is exalted over all the nations.
³Let them praise your great and awesome name—
    he is holy.

⁴The King is mighty, he loves justice—
    you have established equity;
in Jacob you have done
    what is just and right.
⁵Exalt the LORD our God
    and worship at his footstool;
    he is holy.

⁶Moses and Aaron were among his priests,
    Samuel was among those who called on his name;
they called on the LORD
    and he answered them.
⁷He spoke to them from the pillar of cloud;
    they kept his statutes and the decrees he gave them.

⁸O LORD our God,
    you answered them;
you were to Israel ᵃ a forgiving God,
    though you punished their misdeeds. ᵇ
⁹Exalt the LORD our God
    and worship at his holy mountain,
    for the LORD our God is holy.

Psalm 100

A psalm. For giving thanks.

¹Shout for joy to the LORD, all the earth.
²   Worship the LORD with gladness;
    come before him with joyful songs.
³Know that the LORD is God.
    It is he who made us, and we are his ᶜ;
    we are his people, the sheep of his pasture.

⁴Enter his gates with thanksgiving
    and his courts with praise;
    give thanks to him and praise his name.
⁵For the LORD is good and his love endures forever;
    his faithfulness continues through all generations.

ᵃ 8 Hebrew them   ᵇ 8 Or / an avenger of the wrongs done to them   ᶜ 3 Or and not we ourselves

genuine

worship » 100:4

Which one are you: worship-challenged or worshipful? The worship-challenged girl sits with her friends at church and passes notes during the sermon. She falls asleep because she thinks the pastor is boring and long-winded and the service isn't entertaining enough. In contrast, the worshipful girl asks what she can give God, not what the church has to offer her. The worshipful girl enters God's gates with thanksgiving in her heart and praise on her lips. She knows that God's looking at her heart and not her attendance record. So back to the question—which one are you?

Psalm 101

Of David. A psalm.

¹ I will sing of your love and justice;
  to you, O LORD, I will sing praise.
² I will be careful to lead a blameless life—
  when will you come to me?

I will walk in my house
  with blameless heart.
³ I will set before my eyes
  no vile thing.

The deeds of faithless men I hate;
  they will not cling to me.
⁴ Men of perverse heart shall be far from me;
  I will have nothing to do with evil.

⁵ Whoever slanders his neighbor in secret,
  him will I put to silence;
whoever has haughty eyes and a proud heart,
  him will I not endure.

⁶ My eyes will be on the faithful in the land,
  that they may dwell with me;
he whose walk is blameless
  will minister to me.

⁷ No one who practices deceit
  will dwell in my house;
no one who speaks falsely
  will stand in my presence.

⁸ Every morning I will put to silence
  all the wicked in the land;
I will cut off every evildoer
  from the city of the LORD.

Psalm 102

A prayer of an afflicted man. When he is faint and pours out his lament before the LORD.

¹ Hear my prayer, O LORD;
  let my cry for help come to you.
² Do not hide your face from me
  when I am in distress.
Turn your ear to me;
  when I call, answer me quickly.

³ For my days vanish like smoke;
  my bones burn like glowing embers.
⁴ My heart is blighted and withered like grass;

I forget to eat my food.
[5] Because of my loud groaning
I am reduced to skin and bones.
[6] I am like a desert owl,
like an owl among the ruins.
[7] I lie awake; I have become
like a bird alone on a roof.
[8] All day long my enemies taunt me;
those who rail against me use
my name as a curse.
[9] For I eat ashes as my food
and mingle my drink with tears
[10] because of your great wrath,
for you have taken me up and thrown me
aside.
[11] My days are like the evening shadow;
I wither away like grass.

[12] But you, O LORD, sit enthroned forever;
your renown endures through all generations.
[13] You will arise and have compassion on Zion,
for it is time to show favor to her;
the appointed time has come.
[14] For her stones are dear to your servants;
her very dust moves them to pity.
[15] The nations will fear the name of the LORD,
all the kings of the earth will revere your glory.
[16] For the LORD will rebuild Zion
and appear in his glory.
[17] He will respond to the prayer of the destitute;
he will not despise their plea.

[18] Let this be written for a future generation,
that a people not yet created may praise the LORD:
[19] "The LORD looked down from his sanctuary on high,
from heaven he viewed the earth,
[20] to hear the groans of the prisoners
and release those condemned to death."
[21] So the name of the LORD will be declared in Zion
and his praise in Jerusalem
[22] when the peoples and the kingdoms
assemble to worship the LORD.

[23] In the course of my life [a] he broke my strength;
he cut short my days.
[24] So I said:
"Do not take me away, O my God, in the midst of my days;
your years go on through all generations.
[25] In the beginning you laid the foundations of the earth,
and the heavens are the work of your hands.
[26] They will perish, but you remain;
they will all wear out like a garment.
Like clothing you will change them
and they will be discarded.
[27] But you remain the same,
and your years will never end.

truth *or dare*

Who says guys are the only visually-driven beings on the planet? If lately your thought life has picked up a less-than-holy vibe, think about what you've been looking at recently.

101:2–3

a 23 Or By his power

28 The children of your servants will live in your presence;
    their descendants will be established before you."

Psalm 103

Of David.

1 Praise the LORD, O my soul;
    all my inmost being, praise his holy name.
2 Praise the LORD, O my soul,
    and forget not all his benefits—
3 who forgives all your sins
    and heals all your diseases,
4 who redeems your life from the pit
    and crowns you with love and compassion,
5 who satisfies your desires with
        good things
    so that your youth is renewed
        like the eagle's.

6 The LORD works righteousness
    and justice for all the
        oppressed.

7 He made known his ways to
        Moses,
    his deeds to the people of
        Israel:
8 The LORD is compassionate and gracious,
    slow to anger, abounding in love.
9 He will not always accuse,
    nor will he harbor his anger forever;
10 he does not treat us as our sins deserve
    or repay us according to our iniquities.
11 For as high as the heavens are above the
        earth,
    so great is his love for those who fear him;
12 as far as the east is from the west,
    so far has he removed our transgressions from us.
13 As a father has compassion on his children,
    so the LORD has compassion on those who fear him;
14 for he knows how we are formed,
    he remembers that we are dust.
15 As for man, his days are like grass,
    he flourishes like a flower of the field;
16 the wind blows over it and it is gone,
    and its place remembers it no more.
17 But from everlasting to everlasting
    the LORD's love is with those who fear him,
    and his righteousness with their children's children—
18 with those who keep his covenant
    and remember to obey his precepts.

19 The LORD has established his throne in heaven,
    and his kingdom rules over all.

20 Praise the LORD, you his angels,
    you mighty ones who do his bidding,
    who obey his word.

truth or dare

News flash: Sin may seem glitzier than following Christ, but it doesn't have any of these benefits: forgiveness, healing, redemption, love and the total fulfillment of your desires.

103:1–5

²¹ Praise the LORD, all his heavenly hosts,
   you his servants who do his will.
²² Praise the LORD, all his works
   everywhere in his dominion.

Praise the LORD, O my soul.

Psalm 104

¹ Praise the LORD, O my soul.

O LORD my God, you are very great;
   you are clothed with splendor and majesty.
² He wraps himself in light as with a garment;

he stretches out the heavens
   like a tent
³ and lays the beams of his upper
   chambers on their
   waters.
He makes the clouds his chariot
   and rides on the wings of the
   wind.
⁴ He makes winds his
   messengers,ᵃ
   flames of fire his servants.

⁵ He set the earth on its
   foundations;
   it can never be moved.
⁶ You covered it with the deep as
   with a garment;
   the waters stood above the
   mountains.
⁷ But at your rebuke the waters fled,
   at the sound of your thunder
   they took to flight;
⁸ they flowed over the mountains,
   they went down into the
   valleys,
   to the place you assigned for
   them.
⁹ You set a boundary they cannot
   cross;
   never again will they cover the
   earth.

¹⁰ He makes springs pour water
   into the ravines;
   it flows between the mountains.
¹¹ They give water to all the beasts
   of the field;
   the wild donkeys quench their
   thirst.
¹² The birds of the air nest by the
   waters;
   they sing among the
   branches.

love ♥ notes

103:13-18

Dear loved one,

Don't kid yourself. I know all about you—everything! But even though I know all your weaknesses, my love for you will never fade. I'll never get tired of you. My love for you is forever. Promise.

—Your everlasting Love

What is the one thing about you that you're glad God knows and understands? Tell him!

ᵃ 4 Or *angels*

¹³ He waters the mountains from his upper chambers;
the earth is satisfied by the fruit of his work.
¹⁴ He makes grass grow for the cattle,
and plants for man to cultivate—
bringing forth food from the earth:
¹⁵ wine that gladdens the heart of man,
oil to make his face shine,
and bread that sustains his heart.
¹⁶ The trees of the LORD are well watered,
the cedars of Lebanon that he planted.
¹⁷ There the birds make their nests;
the stork has its home in the pine trees.
¹⁸ The high mountains belong to the wild goats;
the crags are a refuge for the coneys. ^a

¹⁹ The moon marks off the seasons,
and the sun knows when to go down.
²⁰ You bring darkness, it becomes night,
and all the beasts of the forest prowl.
²¹ The lions roar for their prey
and seek their food from God.
²² The sun rises, and they steal away;
they return and lie down in their dens.
²³ Then man goes out to his work,
to his labor until evening.

²⁴ How many are your works, O LORD!
In wisdom you made them all;
the earth is full of your creatures.
²⁵ There is the sea, vast and spacious,
teeming with creatures beyond number—
living things both large and small.
²⁶ There the ships go to and fro,
and the leviathan, which you formed to frolic there.

²⁷ These all look to you
to give them their food at the proper time.
²⁸ When you give it to them,
they gather it up;
when you open your hand,
they are satisfied with good things.
²⁹ When you hide your face,
they are terrified;
when you take away their breath,
they die and return to the dust.
³⁰ When you send your Spirit,
they are created,
and you renew the face of the earth.

³¹ May the glory of the LORD endure forever;
may the LORD rejoice in his works—
³² he who looks at the earth, and it trembles,
who touches the mountains, and they smoke.

³³ I will sing to the LORD all my life;
I will sing praise to my God as long as I live.
³⁴ May my meditation be pleasing to him,

^a 18 That is, the hyrax or rock badger

as I rejoice in the Lord.

35 But may sinners vanish from the earth
and the wicked be no more.

Praise the Lord, O my soul.

Praise the Lord. *a*

Psalm 105

1 Give thanks to the Lord, call on his name;
make known among the nations what he has done.
2 Sing to him, sing praise to him;
tell of all his wonderful acts.
3 Glory in his holy name;
let the hearts of those who seek the Lord rejoice.
4 Look to the Lord and his strength;
seek his face always.

5 Remember the wonders he has done,
his miracles, and the judgments he pronounced,
6 O descendants of Abraham his servant,
O sons of Jacob, his chosen ones.
7 He is the Lord our God;
his judgments are in all the earth.

8 He remembers his covenant forever,
the word he commanded, for a thousand generations,
9 the covenant he made with Abraham,
the oath he swore to Isaac.
10 He confirmed it to Jacob as a decree,
to Israel as an everlasting covenant:
11 "To you I will give the land of Canaan
as the portion you will inherit."

12 When they were but few in number,
few indeed, and strangers in it,
13 they wandered from nation to nation,
from one kingdom to another.
14 He allowed no one to oppress them;
for their sake he rebuked kings:
15 "Do not touch my anointed ones;
do my prophets no harm."

16 He called down famine on the land
and destroyed all their supplies of food;
17 and he sent a man before them—
Joseph, sold as a slave.
18 They bruised his feet with shackles,
his neck was put in irons,
19 till what he foretold came to pass,
till the word of the Lord proved him true.
20 The king sent and released him,
the ruler of peoples set him free.
21 He made him master of his household,
ruler over all he possessed,
22 to instruct his princes as he pleased
and teach his elders wisdom.

a 35 Hebrew *Hallelu Yah*; in the Septuagint this line stands at the beginning of Psalm 105.

²³ Then Israel entered Egypt;
   Jacob lived as an alien in the land of Ham.
²⁴ The LORD made his people very fruitful;
   he made them too numerous for their foes,
²⁵ whose hearts he turned to hate his people,
   to conspire against his servants.
²⁶ He sent Moses his servant,
   and Aaron, whom he had chosen.
²⁷ They performed his miraculous signs among them,
   his wonders in the land of Ham.
²⁸ He sent darkness and made the land dark—
   for had they not rebelled against his words?
²⁹ He turned their waters into blood,
   causing their fish to die.
³⁰ Their land teemed with frogs,
   which went up into the bedrooms of their rulers.
³¹ He spoke, and there came swarms of flies,
   and gnats throughout their country.
³² He turned their rain into hail,
   with lightning throughout their land;
³³ he struck down their vines and fig trees
   and shattered the trees of their country.
³⁴ He spoke, and the locusts came,
   grasshoppers without number;
³⁵ they ate up every green thing in their land,
   ate up the produce of their soil.
³⁶ Then he struck down all the firstborn in their land,
   the firstfruits of all their manhood.

³⁷ He brought out Israel, laden with silver and gold,
   and from among their tribes no one faltered.
³⁸ Egypt was glad when they left,
   because dread of Israel had fallen on them.
³⁹ He spread out a cloud as a covering,
   and a fire to give light at night.
⁴⁰ They asked, and he brought them quail
   and satisfied them with the bread of heaven.
⁴¹ He opened the rock, and water gushed out;
   like a river it flowed in the desert.

⁴² For he remembered his holy promise
   given to his servant Abraham.
⁴³ He brought out his people with rejoicing,
   his chosen ones with shouts of joy;
⁴⁴ he gave them the lands of the nations,
   and they fell heir to what others had toiled for—
⁴⁵ that they might keep his precepts
   and observe his laws.

   Praise the LORD. ᵃ

Psalm 106

¹ Praise the LORD. ᵇ

   Give thanks to the LORD, for he is good;
   his love endures forever.

ᵃ 45 Hebrew *Hallelu Yah*   ᵇ 1 Hebrew *Hallelu Yah*; also in verse 48

² Who can proclaim the mighty acts of the Lord
    or fully declare his praise?
³ Blessed are they who maintain justice,
    who constantly do what is right.

⁴ Remember me, O Lord, when you show favor to your people,
    come to my aid when you save them,
⁵ that I may enjoy the prosperity of your chosen ones,
    that I may share in the joy of your nation
    and join your inheritance in giving praise.

⁶ We have sinned, even as our fathers did;
    we have done wrong and acted wickedly.
⁷ When our fathers were in Egypt,
    they gave no thought to your miracles;
    they did not remember your many kindnesses,
    and they rebelled by the sea, the Red Sea.ᵃ
⁸ Yet he saved them for his name's sake,
    to make his mighty power known.
⁹ He rebuked the Red Sea, and it dried up;
    he led them through the depths as through a desert.
¹⁰ He saved them from the hand of the foe;
    from the hand of the enemy he redeemed them.
¹¹ The waters covered their adversaries;
    not one of them survived.
¹² Then they believed his promises
    and sang his praise.

¹³ But they soon forgot what he had done
    and did not wait for his counsel.
¹⁴ In the desert they gave in to their craving;
    in the wasteland they put God to the test.
¹⁵ So he gave them what they asked for,
    but sent a wasting disease upon them.

¹⁶ In the camp they grew envious of Moses
    and of Aaron, who was consecrated to the Lord.
¹⁷ The earth opened up and swallowed Dathan;
    it buried the company of Abiram.
¹⁸ Fire blazed among their followers;
    a flame consumed the wicked.

¹⁹ At Horeb they made a calf
    and worshiped an idol cast from metal.
²⁰ They exchanged their Glory
    for an image of a bull, which eats grass.
²¹ They forgot the God who saved them,
    who had done great things in Egypt,
²² miracles in the land of Ham
    and awesome deeds by the Red Sea.
²³ So he said he would destroy them—
    had not Moses, his chosen one,
    stood in the breach before him
    to keep his wrath from destroying them.

²⁴ Then they despised the pleasant land;
    they did not believe his promise.
²⁵ They grumbled in their tents

ᵃ 7 Hebrew *Yam Suph*; that is, Sea of Reeds; also in verses 9 and 22

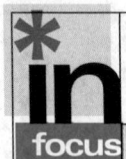

Mind Over Movie

focus Profile: **Morgan**

"*Stick It*—the summer's most hilarious teen movie. Edgy, dangerous, and everything your mother wouldn't approve of. Now playing in theaters everywhere." I can't believe Kendra and Jodi picked this movie for our Friday night out. I feel like I'm fighting this battle with them all the time.

I used to think that all Christians had certain standards when it came to movies. You know, not too much profanity, no sex scenes, not too much violence. But nothing seems to faze Kendra and Jodi. They only seem to care about whether it's funny or what hot guy's in it.

I think I'm an open-minded person, but I feel like you have to draw the line somewhere. It's starting to get to me. I know I'm putting thoughts in my mind that I can't get rid of. And the worst part is that our friends from school see us there, and it makes them think we're no different than they are. They think that if we watch it then it's definitely okay.

Anymore I find myself laughing at things that used to shock me. And when I told Kendra and Jodi that, they just rolled their eyes. "Lighten up, girl," Kendra said. "You're always ruining a good time."

For more ideas on how to maintain purity, go to www.TrueImagesBible.com

purity in focus

A godly mind is a terrible thing to waste. If you stuff it with needless sex and violence and tasteless jokes, then you'll have a hard time maintaining a pure thought life. Still, how do you tell when a movie crosses the line?

»*Make it personal.* Read Psalm 101:3 (page 1752) and ask yourself this question: Are my entertainment choices hurting my relationship with Jesus or my witness for him?

»*Confess your sin.* God is ready and waiting to forgive.

»*Stand firm.* If you take a stand on what goes into your mind, you're likely to lose a few friends. Prepare yourself by reading 2 Timothy 3:12–15 (page 1578), and fill your mind with God's Word.

For more on this topic, see the index on page 1656.

---

and did not obey the LORD.
²⁶ So he swore to them with uplifted hand
that he would make them fall in the desert,
²⁷ make their descendants fall among the nations
and scatter them throughout the lands.

²⁸ They yoked themselves to the Baal of Peor
and ate sacrifices offered to lifeless gods;
²⁹ they provoked the LORD to anger by their wicked deeds,
and a plague broke out among them.
³⁰ But Phinehas stood up and intervened,

and the plague was checked.
³¹ This was credited to him as righteousness
 for endless generations to come.

³² By the waters of Meribah they angered the LORD,
 and trouble came to Moses because of them;
³³ for they rebelled against the Spirit of God,
 and rash words came from Moses' lips.^a

³⁴ They did not destroy the peoples
 as the LORD had commanded them,
³⁵ but they mingled with the nations
 and adopted their customs.
³⁶ They worshiped their idols,
 which became a snare to them.
³⁷ They sacrificed their sons
 and their daughters to demons.
³⁸ They shed innocent blood,
 the blood of their sons and daughters,
whom they sacrificed to the idols of Canaan,
 and the land was desecrated by their blood.
³⁹ They defiled themselves by what they did;
 by their deeds they prostituted themselves.

⁴⁰ Therefore the LORD was angry with his people
 and abhorred his inheritance.
⁴¹ He handed them over to the nations,
 and their foes ruled over them.
⁴² Their enemies oppressed them
 and subjected them to their power.
⁴³ Many times he delivered them,
 but they were bent on rebellion
 and they wasted away in their sin.

⁴⁴ But he took note of their distress
 when he heard their cry;
⁴⁵ for their sake he remembered his covenant
 and out of his great love he relented.
⁴⁶ He caused them to be pitied
 by all who held them captive.

⁴⁷ Save us, O LORD our God,
 and gather us from the nations,
that we may give thanks to your holy name
 and glory in your praise.

⁴⁸ Praise be to the LORD, the God of Israel,
 from everlasting to everlasting.
Let all the people say, "Amen!"

Praise the LORD.

BOOK V

Psalms 107–150

Psalm 107

¹ Give thanks to the LORD, for he is good;
 his love endures forever.

---

^a *33* Or *against his spirit, / and rash words came from his lips*

²Let the redeemed of the LORD say this—
  those he redeemed from the hand of the foe,
³those he gathered from the lands,
  from east and west, from north and south. ᵃ

⁴Some wandered in desert wastelands,
  finding no way to a city where they could settle.
⁵They were hungry and thirsty,
  and their lives ebbed away.
⁶Then they cried out to the LORD in their trouble,
  and he delivered them from their distress.
⁷He led them by a straight way
  to a city where they could settle.

⁸Let them give thanks to the LORD
  for his unfailing love
  and his wonderful deeds for men,
⁹for he satisfies the thirsty
  and fills the hungry with good things.

¹⁰Some sat in darkness and the deepest gloom,
  prisoners suffering in iron chains,
¹¹for they had rebelled against the words of God
  and despised the counsel of the Most High.
¹²So he subjected them to bitter labor;
  they stumbled, and there was no one to help.
¹³Then they cried to the LORD in their trouble,
  and he saved them from their distress.
¹⁴He brought them out of darkness and the deepest gloom
  and broke away their chains.
¹⁵Let them give thanks to the LORD
  for his unfailing love
  and his wonderful deeds for men,
¹⁶for he breaks down gates of bronze
  and cuts through bars of iron.
¹⁷Some became fools through their rebellious ways
  and suffered affliction because of their iniquities.
¹⁸They loathed all food
  and drew near the gates of death.
¹⁹Then they cried to the LORD in their trouble,
  and he saved them from their distress.

love ♥ notes

107:8–9

My child,

This world offers you so many kinds of fake satisfaction— through accomplishments, education, relationships, enter- tainment. But if you want true *satisfaction, choose me. I'll pro- vide you with lasting, good things.*

—The One who satisfies

Be honest—where in your life do you try to find satisfaction apart from God? Ask God to help you choose him instead.

_____
_____
_____
_____
_____
_____
_____
_____
_____
_____

ᵃ 3 Hebrew *north and the sea*

²⁰ He sent forth his word and healed them;
he rescued them from the grave.
²¹ Let them give thanks to the Lord for his unfailing love
and his wonderful deeds for men.
²² Let them sacrifice thank offerings
and tell of his works with songs of joy.

²³ Others went out on the sea in ships;
they were merchants on the mighty waters.
²⁴ They saw the works of the Lord,
his wonderful deeds in the deep.
²⁵ For he spoke and stirred up a tempest
that lifted high the waves.
²⁶ They mounted up to the heavens and went down to the depths;
in their peril their courage melted away.
²⁷ They reeled and staggered like drunken men;
they were at their wits' end.
²⁸ Then they cried out to the Lord in their trouble,
and he brought them out of their distress.
²⁹ He stilled the storm to a whisper;
the waves of the sea were hushed.
³⁰ They were glad when it grew calm,
and he guided them to their desired haven.
³¹ Let them give thanks to the Lord for his unfailing love
and his wonderful deeds for men.
³² Let them exalt him in the assembly of the people
and praise him in the council of the elders.

³³ He turned rivers into a desert,
flowing springs into thirsty ground,
³⁴ and fruitful land into a salt waste,
because of the wickedness of those who lived there.
³⁵ He turned the desert into pools of water
and the parched ground into flowing springs;
³⁶ there he brought the hungry to live,
and they founded a city where they could settle.
³⁷ They sowed fields and planted vineyards
that yielded a fruitful harvest;
³⁸ he blessed them, and their numbers greatly increased,
and he did not let their herds diminish.

³⁹ Then their numbers decreased, and they were humbled
by oppression, calamity and sorrow;
⁴⁰ he who pours contempt on nobles
made them wander in a trackless waste.
⁴¹ But he lifted the needy out of their affliction
and increased their families like flocks.
⁴² The upright see and rejoice,
but all the wicked shut their mouths.

⁴³ Whoever is wise, let him heed these things
and consider the great love of the Lord.

Psalm 108

A song. A psalm of David.

¹ My heart is steadfast, O God;
I will sing and make music with all my soul.

² Awake, harp and lyre!
    I will awaken the dawn.
³ I will praise you, O LORD, among the nations;
    I will sing of you among the peoples.
⁴ For great is your love, higher than the heavens;
    your faithfulness reaches to the skies.
⁵ Be exalted, O God, above the heavens,
    and let your glory be over all the earth.

⁶ Save us and help us with your right hand,
    that those you love may be delivered.
⁷ God has spoken from his sanctuary:
    "In triumph I will parcel out Shechem
    and measure off the Valley of Succoth.
⁸ Gilead is mine, Manasseh is mine;
    Ephraim is my helmet,
    Judah my scepter.
⁹ Moab is my washbasin,
    upon Edom I toss my sandal;
    over Philistia I shout in triumph."

¹⁰ Who will bring me to the fortified city?
    Who will lead me to Edom?
¹¹ Is it not you, O God, you who have rejected us
    and no longer go out with our armies?
¹² Give us aid against the enemy,
    for the help of man is worthless.
¹³ With God we will gain the victory,
    and he will trample down our enemies.

Psalm 109

For the director of music. Of David. A psalm.

¹ O God, whom I praise,
    do not remain silent,
² for wicked and deceitful men
    have opened their mouths against me;
    they have spoken against me with lying tongues.
³ With words of hatred they surround me;
    they attack me without cause.
⁴ In return for my friendship they accuse me,
    but I am a man of prayer.
⁵ They repay me evil for good,
    and hatred for my friendship.

⁶ Appoint ᵃ an evil man ᵇ to oppose him;
    let an accuser ᶜ stand at his right hand.
⁷ When he is tried, let him be found guilty,
    and may his prayers condemn him.
⁸ May his days be few;
    may another take his place of leadership.
⁹ May his children be fatherless
    and his wife a widow.
¹⁰ May his children be wandering beggars;
    may they be driven ᵈ from their ruined homes.

ᵃ 6 Or ˌThey say:ˌ "Appoint (with quotation marks at the end of verse 19)   ᵇ 6 Or the Evil One   ᶜ 6 Or let Satan
ᵈ 10 Septuagint; Hebrew sought

¹¹ May a creditor seize all he has;
    may strangers plunder the fruits of his labor.
¹² May no one extend kindness to him
    or take pity on his fatherless children.
¹³ May his descendants be cut off,
    their names blotted out from the next generation.
¹⁴ May the iniquity of his fathers be remembered before the LORD;
    may the sin of his mother never be blotted out.
¹⁵ May their sins always remain before the LORD,
    that he may cut off the memory of them from the earth.

¹⁶ For he never thought of doing a kindness,
    but hounded to death the poor
    and the needy and the brokenhearted.
¹⁷ He loved to pronounce a curse—
    may it[a] come on him;
  he found no pleasure in blessing—
    may it be[b] far from him.
¹⁸ He wore cursing as his garment;
    it entered into his body like water,
    into his bones like oil.
¹⁹ May it be like a cloak wrapped about him,
    like a belt tied forever around him.
²⁰ May this be the LORD's payment
        to my accusers,
    to those who speak evil of me.

²¹ But you, O Sovereign LORD,
    deal well with me for your
        name's sake;
    out of the goodness of your
        love, deliver me.
²² For I am poor and needy,
    and my heart is wounded
        within me.
²³ I fade away like an evening shadow;
    I am shaken off like a locust.
²⁴ My knees give way from fasting;
    my body is thin and gaunt.
²⁵ I am an object of scorn to my accusers;
    when they see me, they shake their heads.

²⁶ Help me, O LORD my God;
    save me in accordance with your love.
²⁷ Let them know that it is your hand,
    that you, O LORD, have done it.
²⁸ They may curse, but you will bless;
    when they attack they will be put to shame,
    but your servant will rejoice.
²⁹ My accusers will be clothed with disgrace
    and wrapped in shame as in a cloak.

³⁰ With my mouth I will greatly extol the LORD;
    in the great throng I will praise him.
³¹ For he stands at the right hand of the needy one,
    to save his life from those who condemn him.

truth or dare

This guy was going through some major pain. Did God forget about him? Never!— God kept him safe throughout his heartache. He'll do the same for you. Just ask.

109:21–31

---

a 17 Or curse, / and it has   *b 17 Or blessing, / and it is*

Psalm 110

Of David. A psalm.

¹ The LORD says to my Lord:
 "Sit at my right hand
until I make your enemies
 a footstool for your feet."

² The LORD will extend your mighty scepter from Zion;
 you will rule in the midst of your enemies.
³ Your troops will be willing
 on your day of battle.
Arrayed in holy majesty,
 from the womb of the dawn
 you will receive the dew of your youth.ᵃ

⁴ The LORD has sworn
 and will not change his mind:
"You are a priest forever,
 in the order of Melchizedek."

⁵ The Lord is at your right hand;
 he will crush kings on the day of his wrath.
⁶ He will judge the nations, heaping up the dead
 and crushing the rulers of the whole earth.
⁷ He will drink from a brook beside the wayᵇ;
 therefore he will lift up his head.

Psalm 111ᶜ

¹ Praise the LORD.ᵈ

 I will extol the LORD with all my heart
 in the council of the upright and in the assembly.

² Great are the works of the LORD;
 they are pondered by all who delight in them.
³ Glorious and majestic are his deeds,
 and his righteousness endures forever.
⁴ He has caused his wonders to be remembered;
 the LORD is gracious and compassionate.
⁵ He provides food for those who fear him;
 he remembers his covenant forever.
⁶ He has shown his people the power of his works,
 giving them the lands of other nations.
⁷ The works of his hands are faithful and just;
 all his precepts are trustworthy.
⁸ They are steadfast for ever and ever,
 done in faithfulness and uprightness.
⁹ He provided redemption for his people;
 he ordained his covenant forever—
 holy and awesome is his name.

¹⁰ The fear of the LORD is the beginning of wisdom;
 all who follow his precepts have good understanding.
 To him belongs eternal praise.

ᵃ 3 Or *I / your young men will come to you like the dew* ᵇ 7 Or *I / The One who grants succession will set him in authority*
ᶜ This psalm is an acrostic poem, the lines of which begin with the successive letters of the Hebrew alphabet.
ᵈ 1 Hebrew *Hallelu Yah*

Psalm 112[a]

[1] Praise the LORD.[b]

Blessed is the man who fears the LORD,
    who finds great delight in his commands.

[2] His children will be mighty in the land;
    the generation of the upright will be blessed.
[3] Wealth and riches are in his house,
    and his righteousness endures forever.
[4] Even in darkness light dawns for the upright,
    for the gracious and compassionate and righteous man.[c]
[5] Good will come to him who is generous and lends freely,
    who conducts his affairs with justice.
[6] Surely he will never be shaken;
    a righteous man will be remembered forever.
[7] He will have no fear of bad news;
    his heart is steadfast, trusting in the LORD.
[8] His heart is secure, he will have no fear;
    in the end he will look in triumph on his foes.
[9] He has scattered abroad his gifts to the poor,
    his righteousness endures forever;
    his horn[d] will be lifted high in honor.

[10] The wicked man will see and be vexed,
    he will gnash his teeth and waste away;
    the longings of the wicked will come to nothing.

Psalm 113

[1] Praise the LORD.[e]

Praise, O servants of the LORD,
    praise the name of the LORD.
[2] Let the name of the LORD be praised,
    both now and forevermore.
[3] From the rising of the sun to the place where it sets,
    the name of the LORD is to be praised.

[4] The LORD is exalted over all the nations,
    his glory above the heavens.
[5] Who is like the LORD our God,
    the One who sits enthroned on high,
[6] who stoops down to look
    on the heavens and the earth?

[7] He raises the poor from the dust
    and lifts the needy from the ash heap;
[8] he seats them with princes,
    with the princes of their people.
[9] He settles the barren woman in her home
    as a happy mother of children.

Praise the LORD.

---

[a] This psalm is an acrostic poem, the lines of which begin with the successive letters of the Hebrew alphabet.
[b] 1 Hebrew *Hallelu Yah*   [c] 4 Or *for the LORD, is gracious and compassionate and righteous*   [d] 9 *Horn* here symbolizes dignity.   [e] 1 Hebrew *Hallelu Yah*; also in verse 9

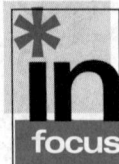

Stuck in Neutral

When it comes to spiritual growth, I think I'm a dud. I feel like I should be further along by now, but I just don't seem to be growing. I was practically born in the church nursery, spent years in Sunday School, did youth group, mission trips, choir. You'd think I'd be about as spiritual as they get. So what's my problem?

I feel kind of indifferent about my faith. I should "feel" like reading my Bible and praying, right? I never do. Whenever I try reading the Bible and writing in my prayer journal, I get distracted and bored. What kind of Christian is *that*? Maybe I am just not a spiritual person. Other girls really get into their faith—praying, witnessing and even leading Bible studies on campus. And then there's me. I can't even remember the last time I had a good quiet time.

It's not like I'm a bad person or anything. I'm a good daughter, good friend, good student. But there has to be more to it than just being good. Maybe I've outgrown my faith now that I'm older. I feel like I must have missed something along the way.

Need more encouragement? Go to www.TrueImagesBible.com

spiritual growth in focus

You can be a Christian all your life and still be a spiritual baby. Spiritual growth doesn't just happen naturally without any effort from you. You have to work at it over time. Philippians 2:13 (page 1552) says God alone gives us the desire and ability to grow in him.

»Don't feel like praying or reading God's Word? Be honest with God and ask him to give you the desire.

»Spiritual growth takes discipline. It's like exercise. How many girls wake up longing to go work out? Probably not many of us. Yet we make ourselves do it, knowing it's good for us.

»If you do the work, your heart will follow. At first your devotions may seem like a chore, but over time, you'll start to enjoy them and get to the place where you can't stand missing that time with God.

For more on this topic, see the index on page 1656.

Psalm 114

¹When Israel came out of Egypt,
　　the house of Jacob from a people of foreign tongue,
²Judah became God's sanctuary,
　　Israel his dominion.

³The sea looked and fled,
　　the Jordan turned back;
⁴the mountains skipped like rams,
　　the hills like lambs.

⁵Why was it, O sea, that you fled,
   O Jordan, that you turned back,
⁶you mountains, that you skipped like rams,
   you hills, like lambs?

⁷Tremble, O earth, at the presence of the Lord,
   at the presence of the God of Jacob,
⁸who turned the rock into a pool,
   the hard rock into springs of water.

Psalm 115

¹Not to us, O LORD, not to us
   but to your name be the glory,
   because of your love and faithfulness.

²Why do the nations say,
   "Where is their God?"
³Our God is in heaven;
   he does whatever pleases him.
⁴But their idols are silver and gold,
   made by the hands of men.
⁵They have mouths, but cannot speak,
   eyes, but they cannot see;
⁶they have ears, but cannot hear,
   noses, but they cannot smell;
⁷they have hands, but cannot feel,
   feet, but they cannot walk;
   nor can they utter a sound with their throats.
⁸Those who make them will be like them,
   and so will all who trust in them.

⁹O house of Israel, trust in the LORD—
   he is their help and shield.
¹⁰O house of Aaron, trust in the LORD—
   he is their help and shield.
¹¹You who fear him, trust in the LORD—
   he is their help and shield.

¹²The LORD remembers us and will bless us:
   He will bless the house of Israel,
   he will bless the house of Aaron,
¹³he will bless those who fear the LORD—
   small and great alike.

¹⁴May the LORD make you increase,
   both you and your children.
¹⁵May you be blessed by the LORD,
   the Maker of heaven and earth.

¹⁶The highest heavens belong to the LORD,
   but the earth he has given to man.
¹⁷It is not the dead who praise the LORD,
   those who go down to silence;
¹⁸it is we who extol the LORD,
   both now and forevermore.

Praise the LORD. ᵃ

ᵃ 18 Hebrew *Hallelu Yah*

Psalm 116

[1] I love the LORD, for he heard my voice;
　　he heard my cry for mercy.
[2] Because he turned his ear to me,
　　I will call on him as long as I live.

[3] The cords of death entangled me,
　　the anguish of the grave[a] came upon me;
　　I was overcome by trouble and sorrow.
[4] Then I called on the name of the LORD:
　　"O LORD, save me!"

[5] The LORD is gracious and righteous;
　　our God is full of compassion.
[6] The LORD protects the simplehearted;
　　when I was in great need, he saved me.

[7] Be at rest once more, O my soul,
　　for the LORD has been good to you.

[8] For you, O LORD, have delivered my soul from death,
　　my eyes from tears,
　　my feet from stumbling,
[9] that I may walk before the LORD
　　in the land of the living.
[10] I believed; therefore[b] I said,
　　"I am greatly afflicted."
[11] And in my dismay I said,
　　"All men are liars."

[12] How can I repay the LORD
　　for all his goodness to me?
[13] I will lift up the cup of salvation
　　and call on the name of the LORD.
[14] I will fulfill my vows to the LORD
　　in the presence of all his people.

[15] Precious in the sight of the LORD
　　is the death of his saints.
[16] O LORD, truly I am your servant;
　　I am your servant, the son of your maidservant[c];
　　you have freed me from my chains.

[17] I will sacrifice a thank offering to you
　　and call on the name of the LORD.
[18] I will fulfill my vows to the LORD
　　in the presence of all his people,
[19] in the courts of the house of the LORD—
　　in your midst, O Jerusalem.

Praise the LORD.[d]

truth or dare

Salvation is a *free* gift—no payment necessary. You should do good deeds as a way of thanking God, not to try to earn "bonus points." You can never repay him.

116:12–14

Psalm 117

[1] Praise the LORD, all you nations;
　　extol him, all you peoples.
[2] For great is his love toward us,
　　and the faithfulness of the LORD endures forever.

Praise the LORD.[d]

---

a 3 Hebrew *Sheol*　　*b 10* Or *believed even when*　　*c 16* Or *servant, your faithful son*　　*d 19,2* Hebrew *Hallelu Yah*

¹Give thanks to the LORD, for he is good;
  his love endures forever.

²Let Israel say:
  "His love endures forever."
³Let the house of Aaron say:
  "His love endures forever."
⁴Let those who fear the LORD say:
  "His love endures forever."

⁵In my anguish I cried to the LORD,
  and he answered by setting
    me free.
⁶The LORD is with me; I will not be
    afraid.
  What can man do to me?
⁷The LORD is with me; he is my helper.
  I will look in triumph on my enemies.

⁸It is better to take refuge in the LORD
  than to trust in man.
⁹It is better to take refuge in the LORD
  than to trust in princes.

¹⁰All the nations surrounded me,
  but in the name of the LORD I cut them off.
¹¹They surrounded me on every side,
  but in the name of the LORD I cut them off.
¹²They swarmed around me like bees,
  but they died out as quickly as burning thorns;
  in the name of the LORD I cut them off.

¹³I was pushed back and about to fall,
  but the LORD helped me.
¹⁴The LORD is my strength and my song;
  he has become my salvation.

¹⁵Shouts of joy and victory
  resound in the tents of the righteous:
  "The LORD's right hand has done mighty things!
¹⁶ The LORD's right hand is lifted high;
  the LORD's right hand has done mighty things!"

¹⁷I will not die but live,
  and will proclaim what the LORD has done.
¹⁸The LORD has chastened me severely,
  but he has not given me over to death.

¹⁹Open for me the gates of righteousness;
  I will enter and give thanks to the LORD.
²⁰This is the gate of the LORD
  through which the righteous may enter.
²¹I will give you thanks, for you answered me;
  you have become my salvation.

²²The stone the builders rejected
  has become the capstone;
²³the LORD has done this,
  and it is marvelous in our eyes.

truth or dare

Looking for the perfect friend? You may be setting yourself up for disappointment. Even your most faithful bud can let you down sometimes. Only God is 100 percent perfectly trustworthy.

118:8

²⁴ This is the day the LORD has made;
  let us rejoice and be glad in it.

²⁵ O LORD, save us;
  O LORD, grant us success.
²⁶ Blessed is he who comes in the name of the LORD.
  From the house of the LORD we bless you. ª
²⁷ The LORD is God,
  and he has made his light shine upon us.
With boughs in hand, join in the festal procession
  up ᵇ to the horns of the altar.

²⁸ You are my God, and I will give you thanks;
  you are my God, and I will exalt you.

²⁹ Give thanks to the LORD, for he is good;
  his love endures forever.

genuine

purity » 119:9

When was the last time you heard an actress discuss how important "purity" is to her (unless she's talking about her drinking water)? Purity is always very important to God, but how can a girl like you "keep your way pure"? By obeying God's Word. How will that help? God's Word will guide you as you make important decisions. God's Word will challenge you to do the right thing when the wrong thing might seem easier or more popular. So get to know God's Word. It will give you the courage to be pure in an impure world.

Psalm 119 ᶜ

א Aleph

¹ Blessed are they whose ways are
  blameless,
  who walk according to the law
  of the LORD.
² Blessed are they who keep his
  statutes
  and seek him with all their heart.
³ They do nothing wrong;
  they walk in his ways.
⁴ You have laid down precepts
  that are to be fully obeyed.
⁵ Oh, that my ways were steadfast
  in obeying your decrees!
⁶ Then I would not be put to shame
  when I consider all your
  commands.
⁷ I will praise you with an upright
  heart
  as I learn your righteous laws.
⁸ I will obey your decrees;
  do not utterly forsake me.

ב Beth

⁹ How can a young man keep his way pure?
  By living according to your word.
¹⁰ I seek you with all my heart;
  do not let me stray from your commands.
¹¹ I have hidden your word in my heart
  that I might not sin against you.
¹² Praise be to you, O LORD;
  teach me your decrees.
¹³ With my lips I recount

ª 26 The Hebrew is plural.   ᵇ 27 Or *Bind the festal sacrifice with ropes / and take it*   ᶜ This psalm is an acrostic poem;
the verses of each stanza begin with the same letter of the Hebrew alphabet.

all the laws that come from your mouth.
¹⁴ I rejoice in following your statutes
as one rejoices in great riches.
¹⁵ I meditate on your precepts
and consider your ways.
¹⁶ I delight in your decrees;
I will not neglect your word.

‎ Gimel

¹⁷ Do good to your servant, and I will live;
I will obey your word.
¹⁸ Open my eyes that I may see
wonderful things in your law.
¹⁹ I am a stranger on earth;
do not hide your commands from me.
²⁰ My soul is consumed with longing
for your laws at all times.
²¹ You rebuke the arrogant, who are cursed
and who stray from your commands.
²² Remove from me scorn and contempt,
for I keep your statutes.
²³ Though rulers sit together and slander me,
your servant will meditate on your decrees.
²⁴ Your statutes are my delight;
they are my counselors.

‎ Daleth

²⁵ I am laid low in the dust;
preserve my life according to your word.
²⁶ I recounted my ways and you answered me;
teach me your decrees.
²⁷ Let me understand the teaching of your precepts;
then I will meditate on your wonders.
²⁸ My soul is weary with sorrow;
strengthen me according to
your word.
²⁹ Keep me from deceitful ways;
be gracious to me through
your law.
³⁰ I have chosen the way of truth;
I have set my heart on your
laws.
³¹ I hold fast to your statutes,
O LORD;
do not let me be put to shame.
³² I run in the path of your
commands,
for you have set my heart free.

‎ He

³³ Teach me, O LORD, to follow your decrees;
then I will keep them to the end.
³⁴ Give me understanding, and I will keep your law
and obey it with all my heart.

truth or dare

What does the word *freedom* bring to mind? Adventure? Breaking the rules? So why would a free person stick to the path? True freedom comes from running on God's path.

119:32

³⁵ Direct me in the path of your commands,
   for there I find delight.
³⁶ Turn my heart toward your statutes
   and not toward selfish gain.
³⁷ Turn my eyes away from worthless things;
   preserve my life according to your word. ^a
³⁸ Fulfill your promise to your servant,
   so that you may be feared.
³⁹ Take away the disgrace I dread,
   for your laws are good.
⁴⁰ How I long for your precepts!
   Preserve my life in your righteousness.

ו Waw

⁴¹ May your unfailing love come to me, O LORD,
   your salvation according to your promise;
⁴² then I will answer the one who taunts me,
   for I trust in your word.
⁴³ Do not snatch the word of truth from my mouth,
   for I have put my hope in your laws.
⁴⁴ I will always obey your law,
   for ever and ever.
⁴⁵ I will walk about in freedom,
   for I have sought out your precepts.
⁴⁶ I will speak of your statutes before kings
   and will not be put to shame,
⁴⁷ for I delight in your commands
   because I love them.
⁴⁸ I lift up my hands to ^b your commands, which I love,
   and I meditate on your decrees.

ז Zayin

⁴⁹ Remember your word to your servant,
   for you have given me hope.
⁵⁰ My comfort in my suffering is this:
   Your promise preserves my life.
⁵¹ The arrogant mock me without restraint,
   but I do not turn from your law.
⁵² I remember your ancient laws, O LORD,
   and I find comfort in them.
⁵³ Indignation grips me because of the wicked,
   who have forsaken your law.
⁵⁴ Your decrees are the theme of my song
   wherever I lodge.
⁵⁵ In the night I remember your name, O LORD,
   and I will keep your law.
⁵⁶ This has been my practice:
   I obey your precepts.

ח Heth

⁵⁷ You are my portion, O LORD;
   I have promised to obey your words.
⁵⁸ I have sought your face with all my heart;

---

^a 37 Two manuscripts of the Masoretic Text and Dead Sea Scrolls; most manuscripts of the Masoretic Text *life in your way*
^b 48 Or *for*

be gracious to me according to your promise.
[59] I have considered my ways
and have turned my steps to your statutes.
[60] I will hasten and not delay
to obey your commands.
[61] Though the wicked bind me with ropes,
I will not forget your law.
[62] At midnight I rise to give you thanks
for your righteous laws.
[63] I am a friend to all who fear you,
to all who follow your precepts.
[64] The earth is filled with your love, O LORD;
teach me your decrees.

ט Teth

[65] Do good to your servant
according to your word, O LORD.
[66] Teach me knowledge and good judgment,
for I believe in your commands.
[67] Before I was afflicted I went astray,
but now I obey your word.
[68] You are good, and what you do is good;
teach me your decrees.
[69] Though the arrogant have smeared me with lies,
I keep your precepts with all my heart.
[70] Their hearts are callous and unfeeling,
but I delight in your law.
[71] It was good for me to be afflicted
so that I might learn your decrees.
[72] The law from your mouth is more precious to me
than thousands of pieces of silver and gold.

י Yodh

[73] Your hands made me and formed me;
give me understanding to learn your commands.
[74] May those who fear you rejoice when they see me,
for I have put my hope in your word.
[75] I know, O LORD, that your laws are righteous,
and in faithfulness you have afflicted me.
[76] May your unfailing love be my comfort,
according to your promise to your servant.
[77] Let your compassion come to me that I may live,
for your law is my delight.
[78] May the arrogant be put to shame for wronging me without cause;
but I will meditate on your precepts.
[79] May those who fear you turn to me,
those who understand your statutes.
[80] May my heart be blameless toward your decrees,
that I may not be put to shame.

כ Kaph

[81] My soul faints with longing for your salvation,
but I have put my hope in your word.
[82] My eyes fail, looking for your promise;

I say, "When will you comfort me?"
83 Though I am like a wineskin in the smoke,
    I do not forget your decrees.
84 How long must your servant wait?
    When will you punish my persecutors?
85 The arrogant dig pitfalls for me,
    contrary to your law.
86 All your commands are trustworthy;
    help me, for men persecute me without cause.
87 They almost wiped me from the earth,
    but I have not forsaken your precepts.
88 Preserve my life according to your love,
    and I will obey the statutes of your mouth.

ל Lamedh

89 Your word, O LORD, is eternal;
    it stands firm in the heavens.
90 Your faithfulness continues through all generations;
    you established the earth, and it endures.
91 Your laws endure to this day,
    for all things serve you.
92 If your law had not been my delight,
    I would have perished in my affliction.
93 I will never forget your precepts,
    for by them you have preserved my life.
94 Save me, for I am yours;
    I have sought out your precepts.
95 The wicked are waiting to destroy me,
    but I will ponder your statutes.
96 To all perfection I see a limit;
    but your commands are boundless.

מ Mem

97 Oh, how I love your law!
    I meditate on it all day long.
98 Your commands make me wiser than my enemies,
    for they are ever with me.
99 I have more insight than all my teachers,
    for I meditate on your statutes.
100 I have more understanding than the elders,
    for I obey your precepts.
101 I have kept my feet from every
        evil path
    so that I might obey your
        word.
102 I have not departed from your
        laws,
    for you yourself have taught
        me.
103 How sweet are your words to my
        taste,
    sweeter than honey to my
        mouth!
104 I gain understanding from your precepts;
    therefore I hate every wrong path.

truth or dare

Isn't meditation only for gurus? Nope. Christian meditation is different, though. The point is to be filled up with God's love, not emptied out.

119:97

׃ Nun

[105] Your word is a lamp to my feet
and a light for my path.
[106] I have taken an oath and confirmed it,
that I will follow your righteous laws.
[107] I have suffered much;
preserve my life, O LORD, according to your word.
[108] Accept, O LORD, the willing praise of my mouth,
and teach me your laws.
[109] Though I constantly take my life in my hands,
I will not forget your law.
[110] The wicked have set a snare for me,
but I have not strayed from your precepts.
[111] Your statutes are my heritage forever;
they are the joy of my heart.
[112] My heart is set on keeping your decrees
to the very end.

ס Samekh

[113] I hate double-minded men,
but I love your law.
[114] You are my refuge and my shield;
I have put my hope in your word.
[115] Away from me, you evildoers,
that I may keep the commands of my God!
[116] Sustain me according to your promise, and I will live;
do not let my hopes be dashed.
[117] Uphold me, and I will be delivered;
I will always have regard for your decrees.
[118] You reject all who stray from your decrees,
for their deceitfulness is in vain.
[119] All the wicked of the earth you discard like dross;
therefore I love your statutes.
[120] My flesh trembles in fear of you;
I stand in awe of your laws.

ע Ayin

[121] I have done what is righteous and just;
do not leave me to my oppressors.
[122] Ensure your servant's well-being;
let not the arrogant oppress me.
[123] My eyes fail, looking for your salvation,
looking for your righteous promise.
[124] Deal with your servant according to your love
and teach me your decrees.
[125] I am your servant; give me discernment
that I may understand your statutes.
[126] It is time for you to act, O LORD;
your law is being broken.
[127] Because I love your commands
more than gold, more than pure gold,
[128] and because I consider all your precepts right,
I hate every wrong path.

‫ﬤ‬ Pe

[129] Your statutes are wonderful;
  therefore I obey them.
[130] The unfolding of your words gives light;
  it gives understanding to the simple.
[131] I open my mouth and pant,
  longing for your commands.
[132] Turn to me and have mercy on me,
  as you always do to those who love your name.
[133] Direct my footsteps according to your word;
  let no sin rule over me.
[134] Redeem me from the oppression of men,
  that I may obey your precepts.
[135] Make your face shine upon your servant
  and teach me your decrees.
[136] Streams of tears flow from my eyes,
  for your law is not obeyed.

‫צ‬ Tsadhe

[137] Righteous are you, O Lord,
  and your laws are right.
[138] The statutes you have laid down are righteous;
  they are fully trustworthy.
[139] My zeal wears me out,
  for my enemies ignore your words.
[140] Your promises have been thoroughly tested,
  and your servant loves them.
[141] Though I am lowly and despised,
  I do not forget your precepts.
[142] Your righteousness is everlasting
  and your law is true.
[143] Trouble and distress have come upon me,
  but your commands are my delight.
[144] Your statutes are forever right;
  give me understanding that I may live.

‫ק‬ Qoph

[145] I call with all my heart; answer me, O Lord,
  and I will obey your decrees.
[146] I call out to you; save me
  and I will keep your statutes.
[147] I rise before dawn and cry for help;
  I have put my hope in your word.
[148] My eyes stay open through the watches of the night,
  that I may meditate on your promises.
[149] Hear my voice in accordance with your love;
  preserve my life, O Lord, according to your laws.
[150] Those who devise wicked schemes are near,
  but they are far from your law.
[151] Yet you are near, O Lord,
  and all your commands are true.
[152] Long ago I learned from your statutes
  that you established them to last forever.

ר Resh

¹⁵³ Look upon my suffering and deliver me,
    for I have not forgotten your law.
¹⁵⁴ Defend my cause and redeem me;
    preserve my life according to your promise.
¹⁵⁵ Salvation is far from the wicked,
    for they do not seek out your decrees.
¹⁵⁶ Your compassion is great, O LORD;
    preserve my life according to your laws.
¹⁵⁷ Many are the foes who persecute me,
    but I have not turned from your statutes.
¹⁵⁸ I look on the faithless with loathing,
    for they do not obey your word.
¹⁵⁹ See how I love your precepts;
    preserve my life, O LORD, according to your love.
¹⁶⁰ All your words are true;
    all your righteous laws are eternal.

ש Sin and Shin

¹⁶¹ Rulers persecute me without cause,
    but my heart trembles at your word.
¹⁶² I rejoice in your promise
    like one who finds great spoil.
¹⁶³ I hate and abhor falsehood
    but I love your law.
¹⁶⁴ Seven times a day I praise you
    for your righteous laws.
¹⁶⁵ Great peace have they who love
       your law,
    and nothing can make them
       stumble.
¹⁶⁶ I wait for your salvation, O LORD,
    and I follow your commands.
¹⁶⁷ I obey your statutes,
    for I love them greatly.
¹⁶⁸ I obey your precepts and your statutes,
    for all my ways are known to you.

truth or dare

Imagine being handed one of those big sweepstakes checks. You'd probably scream your head off. Finding God is an even greater prize, so celebrate!

119:162

ת Taw

¹⁶⁹ May my cry come before you, O LORD;
    give me understanding according to your word.
¹⁷⁰ May my supplication come before you;
    deliver me according to your promise.
¹⁷¹ May my lips overflow with praise,
    for you teach me your decrees.
¹⁷² May my tongue sing of your word,
    for all your commands are righteous.
¹⁷³ May your hand be ready to help me,
    for I have chosen your precepts.
¹⁷⁴ I long for your salvation, O LORD,
    and your law is my delight.
¹⁷⁵ Let me live that I may praise you,
    and may your laws sustain me.
¹⁷⁶ I have strayed like a lost sheep.
    Seek your servant,
    for I have not forgotten your commands.

Psalm 120

A song of ascents.

¹ I call on the LORD in my distress,
  and he answers me.
² Save me, O LORD, from lying lips
  and from deceitful tongues.

³ What will he do to you,
  and what more besides, O deceitful tongue?
⁴ He will punish you with a warrior's sharp arrows,
  with burning coals of the broom tree.

⁵ Woe to me that I dwell in Meshech,
  that I live among the tents of Kedar!
⁶ Too long have I lived
  among those who hate peace.
⁷ I am a man of peace;
  but when I speak, they are for war.

love notes

121:1-8

My daughter,

I never sleep. I never take a vacation or go on a break or ask for a substitute. I watch over you constantly. I see you come and go—I'm always caring, loving, protecting you 24/7.

—Eternal Father

Has there been a time when you felt that God was not there? How do these verses change your view of that situation?

_____
_____
_____
_____
_____
_____
_____
_____
_____
_____

Psalm 121

A song of ascents.

¹ I lift up my eyes to the hills—
  where does my help come from?
² My help comes from the LORD,
  the Maker of heaven and earth.

³ He will not let your foot slip—
  he who watches over you will not slumber;
⁴ indeed, he who watches over Israel
  will neither slumber nor sleep.

⁵ The LORD watches over you—
  the LORD is your shade at your right hand;
⁶ the sun will not harm you by day,
  nor the moon by night.

⁷ The LORD will keep you from all harm—
  he will watch over your life;
⁸ the LORD will watch over your coming and going
  both now and forevermore.

Psalm 122

A song of ascents. Of David.

¹ I rejoiced with those who said to me,
  "Let us go to the house of the LORD."
² Our feet are standing
  in your gates, O Jerusalem.

³ Jerusalem is built like a city
 that is closely compacted together.
⁴ That is where the tribes go up,
 the tribes of the Lord,
to praise the name of the Lord
 according to the statute given to Israel.
⁵ There the thrones for judgment stand,
 the thrones of the house of David.

⁶ Pray for the peace of Jerusalem:
 "May those who love you be secure.
⁷ May there be peace within your walls
 and security within your citadels."
⁸ For the sake of my brothers and friends,
 I will say, "Peace be within you."
⁹ For the sake of the house of the Lord our God,
 I will seek your prosperity.

Psalm 123

A song of ascents.

¹ I lift up my eyes to you,
 to you whose throne is in heaven.
² As the eyes of slaves look to the hand of their master,
 as the eyes of a maid look to the hand of her mistress,
so our eyes look to the Lord our God,
 till he shows us his mercy.

³ Have mercy on us, O Lord, have mercy on us,
 for we have endured much contempt.
⁴ We have endured much ridicule from the proud,
 much contempt from the arrogant.

Psalm 124

A song of ascents. Of David.

¹ If the Lord had not been on our side—
 let Israel say—
² if the Lord had not been on our side
 when men attacked us,
³ when their anger flared against us,
 they would have swallowed us alive;
⁴ the flood would have engulfed us,
 the torrent would have swept over us,
⁵ the raging waters
 would have swept us away.

⁶ Praise be to the Lord,
 who has not let us be torn by their teeth.
⁷ We have escaped like a bird
 out of the fowler's snare;
the snare has been broken,
 and we have escaped.
⁸ Our help is in the name of the Lord,
 the Maker of heaven and earth.

mirror images

Jael—In the Right Place at the Right Time

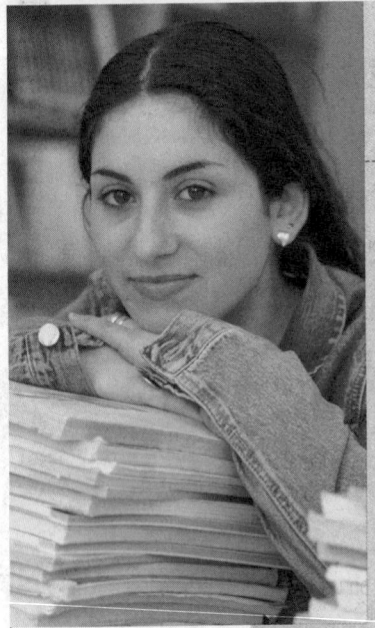

How gruesome! Jael's gory story sounds more like a slasher movie than a Bible story. She sneaked up on her sleeping victim and viciously finished him off.

Whose side was she on, anyway?

Jael's husband, Heber, an ironworker by trade and a longtime friend of the Israelites, probably aligned himself with Sisera, the commander of the Canaanite army, because of the dollar signs he saw when he considered all of Sisera's iron chariots. So Sisera had a good worker in Heber, but he didn't realize that not everyone in Heber's family was a Sisera-cheerleader. Although Jael had obediently moved with her husband to pitch a tent near the Canaanite army, her loyalty to Israel had not budged. Sisera didn't know it, but he would soon be sleeping with the enemy.

On the run from the Israelite army, Sisera came upon Jael's tent, accepted her hospitality and warm milk and fell fast asleep. That's when Jael seized the moment and nailed him with a tent peg—straight through his skull. Jael turned out to be the heroine that Judge Deborah had predicted would rise to fame (see Judges 4:9). Deborah's song of praise recounted Jael's bravery in gruesome detail and hailed her as a woman of great influence.

Jael knew she was in the right place at the right time, and she was willing to act on it. Has God placed you in the right place at the right time to do something for him? To witness at school? On the swim team? In band? On student council? Of course, the goal is not to go around "pegging" people, self-righteously thumping them over the head. The point is to use your position for the greatest good. As a student, you may never be in a position to witness to your generation like this again. Evangelists and youth ministers would give anything to have the influence you have on your campus. Ask God to show you how to use this time in your life for his glory.

To read the next Mirror Images profile, go to page 848.

Dear God, could it be you've put me in a position to witness for you? Give me the words and wisdom I need to say and do the right thing at the right time. Amen.

dear God

>> **Read more about Jael in Judges 4–5 (pages 288–291).**

Psalm 125

A song of ascents.

¹ Those who trust in the LORD are like Mount Zion,
  which cannot be shaken but endures forever.
² As the mountains surround Jerusalem,
  so the LORD surrounds his people
  both now and forevermore.

³ The scepter of the wicked will not remain
  over the land allotted to the righteous,
  for then the righteous might use
  their hands to do evil.

⁴ Do good, O LORD, to those who are good,
  to those who are upright in heart.
⁵ But those who turn to crooked ways
  the LORD will banish with the evildoers.

Peace be upon Israel.

Psalm 126

A song of ascents.

¹ When the LORD brought back the captives to ᵃ Zion,
  we were like men who dreamed. ᵇ
² Our mouths were filled with laughter,
  our tongues with songs of joy.
Then it was said among the
  nations,
  "The LORD has done great
  things for them."
³ The LORD has done great things
  for us,
  and we are filled with joy.

⁴ Restore our fortunes, ᶜ O LORD,
  like streams in the Negev.
⁵ Those who sow in tears
  will reap with songs of joy.
⁶ He who goes out weeping,
  carrying seed to sow,
will return with songs of joy,
  carrying sheaves with him.

truth or dare

Unless you're living for
God, it's all for naught,
sista! But with God in
your life, even the little
things take on new
meaning.

127:1

Psalm 127

A song of ascents. Of Solomon.

¹ Unless the LORD builds the house,
  its builders labor in vain.
Unless the LORD watches over the city,
  the watchmen stand guard in vain.
² In vain you rise early
  and stay up late,
toiling for food to eat—
  for he grants sleep to ᵈ those he loves.

ᵃ 1 Or LORD restored the fortunes of   ᵇ 1 Or men restored to health   ᶜ 4 Or Bring back our captives   ᵈ 2 Or eat— /
for while they sleep he provides for

³ Sons are a heritage from the Lord,
  children a reward from him.
⁴ Like arrows in the hands of a warrior
  are sons born in one's youth.
⁵ Blessed is the man
  whose quiver is full of them.
  They will not be put to shame
    when they contend with their enemies in the gate.

Psalm 128

A song of ascents.

¹ Blessed are all who fear the Lord,
  who walk in his ways.
² You will eat the fruit of your labor;
  blessings and prosperity will be yours.
³ Your wife will be like a fruitful vine
  within your house;
  your sons will be like olive shoots
    around your table.
⁴ Thus is the man blessed
  who fears the Lord.

⁵ May the Lord bless you from Zion
  all the days of your life;
  may you see the prosperity of Jerusalem,
⁶   and may you live to see your children's children.

Peace be upon Israel.

Psalm 129

A song of ascents.

¹ They have greatly oppressed me from my youth—
  let Israel say—
² they have greatly oppressed me from my youth,
  but they have not gained the victory over me.
³ Plowmen have plowed my back
  and made their furrows long.
⁴ But the Lord is righteous;
  he has cut me free from the cords of the wicked.

⁵ May all who hate Zion
  be turned back in shame.
⁶ May they be like grass on the roof,
  which withers before it can grow;
⁷ with it the reaper cannot fill his hands,
  nor the one who gathers fill his arms.
⁸ May those who pass by not say,
  "The blessing of the Lord be upon you;
  we bless you in the name of the Lord."

Psalm 130

A song of ascents.

¹ Out of the depths I cry to you, O Lord;
²   O Lord, hear my voice.

Let your ears be attentive
    to my cry for mercy.

³ If you, O Lᴏʀᴅ, kept a record of sins,
    O Lord, who could stand?
⁴ But with you there is forgiveness;
    therefore you are feared.

⁵ I wait for the Lᴏʀᴅ, my soul waits,
    and in his word I put my hope.
⁶ My soul waits for the Lord
    more than watchmen wait for the morning,
    more than watchmen wait for the morning.

⁷ O Israel, put your hope in the Lᴏʀᴅ,
    for with the Lᴏʀᴅ is unfailing love
    and with him is full redemption.
⁸ He himself will redeem Israel
    from all their sins.

Psalm 131

A song of ascents. Of David.

¹ My heart is not proud, O Lᴏʀᴅ,
    my eyes are not haughty;
I do not concern myself with great matters
    or things too wonderful for me.
² But I have stilled and quieted my soul;

like a weaned child with its
    mother,
like a weaned child is my soul
    within me.

³ O Israel, put your hope in the Lᴏʀᴅ
    both now and forevermore.

Psalm 132

A song of ascents.

¹ O Lᴏʀᴅ, remember David
    and all the hardships he
    endured.

² He swore an oath to the Lᴏʀᴅ
    and made a vow to the Mighty
    One of Jacob:
³ "I will not enter my house
    or go to my bed—
⁴ I will allow no sleep to my eyes,
    no slumber to my eyelids,
⁵ till I find a place for the Lᴏʀᴅ,
    a dwelling for the Mighty One
    of Jacob."

⁶ We heard it in Ephrathah,
    we came upon it in the fields
    of Jaar ᵃ: ᵇ

ǵenuine

humility »

Arrogance is an ugly trait. Have you ever met someone who looked down on everyone and constantly criticized other people in her conversations? That kind of arrogance is very hurtful. The psalmist told God that he wasn't about that, and he wanted instead to sit still and be quiet before the Lord. It just so happens that when you sit quietly and focus on God, you simply can't be proud and haughty. In quietness before God you find true humility. When you compare yourself to him, you realize that you're not the celebrity in the relationship.

131:1-2

ᵃ 6 That is, Kiriath Jearim   ᵇ 6 Or *heard of it in Ephrathah, / we found it in the fields of Jaar.* (And no quotes around verses 7-9)

7 "Let us go to his dwelling place;
  let us worship at his footstool—
8 arise, O Lord, and come to your resting place,
  you and the ark of your might.
9 May your priests be clothed with righteousness;
  may your saints sing for joy."

10 For the sake of David your servant,
  do not reject your anointed one.

11 The Lord swore an oath to David,
  a sure oath that he will not revoke:
"One of your own descendants
  I will place on your throne—
12 if your sons keep my covenant
  and the statutes I teach them,
then their sons will sit
  on your throne for ever and ever."

13 For the Lord has chosen Zion,
  he has desired it for his dwelling:
14 "This is my resting place for ever and ever;
  here I will sit enthroned, for I have desired it—
15 I will bless her with abundant provisions;
  her poor will I satisfy with food.
16 I will clothe her priests with salvation,
  and her saints will ever sing for joy.

17 "Here I will make a horn*a* grow for David
  and set up a lamp for my anointed one.
18 I will clothe his enemies with shame,
  but the crown on his head will be resplendent."

Psalm 133

A song of ascents. Of David.

1 How good and pleasant it is
  when brothers live together in
    unity!
2 It is like precious oil poured on
    the head,
  running down on the beard,
running down on Aaron's beard,
  down upon the collar of his
    robes.
3 It is as if the dew of Hermon
  were falling on Mount Zion.
For there the Lord bestows his blessing,
  even life forevermore.

Psalm 134

A song of ascents.

1 Praise the Lord, all you servants of the Lord
  who minister by night in the house of the
    Lord.

truth or dare

Unity doesn't mean you're a carbon copy of your friends! Real unity involves strengthening each other and overlooking faults. Don't let petty differences break your bond. Godly girls, unite!

133:1

a 17 Horn here symbolizes strong one, that is, king.

² Lift up your hands in the sanctuary
    and praise the LORD.

³ May the LORD, the Maker of heaven and earth,
    bless you from Zion.

Psalm 135

¹ Praise the LORD. *ᵃ*

Praise the name of the LORD;
    praise him, you servants of the LORD,
² you who minister in the house of the LORD,
    in the courts of the house of our God.

³ Praise the LORD, for the LORD is good;
    sing praise to his name, for that is pleasant.
⁴ For the LORD has chosen Jacob to be his own,
    Israel to be his treasured possession.

⁵ I know that the LORD is great,
    that our Lord is greater than all gods.
⁶ The LORD does whatever pleases him,
    in the heavens and on the earth,
    in the seas and all their depths.
⁷ He makes clouds rise from the ends of the earth;
    he sends lightning with the rain
    and brings out the wind from his storehouses.

⁸ He struck down the firstborn of Egypt,
    the firstborn of men and animals.
⁹ He sent his signs and wonders into your midst, O Egypt,
    against Pharaoh and all his servants.
¹⁰ He struck down many nations
    and killed mighty kings—
¹¹ Sihon king of the Amorites,
    Og king of Bashan
    and all the kings of Canaan—
¹² and he gave their land as an inheritance,
    an inheritance to his people Israel.

¹³ Your name, O LORD, endures forever,
    your renown, O LORD, through all generations.
¹⁴ For the LORD will vindicate his people
    and have compassion on his servants.

¹⁵ The idols of the nations are silver and gold,
    made by the hands of men.
¹⁶ They have mouths, but cannot speak,
    eyes, but they cannot see;
¹⁷ they have ears, but cannot hear,
    nor is there breath in their mouths.
¹⁸ Those who make them will be like them,
    and so will all who trust in them.

¹⁹ O house of Israel, praise the LORD;
    O house of Aaron, praise the LORD;
²⁰ O house of Levi, praise the LORD;
    you who fear him, praise the LORD.

ᵃ 1 Hebrew *Hallelu Yah*; also in verses 3 and 21

The Perfect Body

focus | Profile: **Geneva**

I'm so sick of all this dieting crap. One minute I'm eating celery and the next I'm gorging myself on Fritos. I just can't seem to stick with any weight loss plan.

Ever since cheerleading tryouts, I've been noticing the flab on my thighs. My mom says I look great—but c'mon, what does she know? Moms have to say nice things. Besides, she's 40. It takes a lot more to be popular and get noticed these days.

So I started trying something different. I know it's not great for me, but if I can get the poundage off, then I'll be done with it. I've known for a while that my friend Leslie is bulimic. It's one of those unspokens. She eats whatever she wants and then loses it. I imagined it would be awful sticking my finger down my throat to throw up, but if it works, I'm willing to try anything.

I'm just not good at starving myself. I get too hungry and kind of dizzy feeling. Plus it's a relief not to have to watch what I eat. And I'll be one step closer to having a perfect body like our captain, Erica. Don't worry—I'm not saying I'll do it forever. I just need a little help to get a few pounds off, like five or maybe ten.

bulimia in focus

For more on bulimia, go to
www.TrueImagesBible.com

It's amazing what a girl will do to get the "ideal" body—just ask the five to ten million girls and women who struggle with eating disorders. Purging your body of food can be a one-way ticket to destroying your health *and even your life*. If you or a friend is struggling . . .

»*Tell someone now.* Have the courage to tell a trusted adult who can help. Bulimia is a very serious issue and requires wise professional help.

»*Know that it doesn't work.* Bulimia won't make you healthy, thin or beautiful.

»*It's a trap.* Like many other addictive behaviors, it seems to offer a "quick and easy" solution to a problem. However, the more you do it, the easier it is to keep on doing it, and soon you can't stop.

»*Accept the way God made you.* The girl you see in the mirror was created by God and is beautiful in his sight (see 1 Samuel 16:7, page 340).

For more on this topic, see the index on page 1656.

²¹ Praise be to the LORD from Zion,
　　to him who dwells in Jerusalem.

Praise the LORD.

Psalm 136

¹ Give thanks to the LORD, for he is good.

His love endures forever.

² Give thanks to the God of gods.

His love endures forever.

³ Give thanks to the Lord of lords:

His love endures forever.

⁴to him who alone does great wonders,

His love endures forever.

⁵who by his understanding made the heavens,

His love endures forever.

⁶who spread out the earth upon the waters,

His love endures forever.

⁷who made the great lights—

His love endures forever.

⁸the sun to govern the day,

His love endures forever.

⁹the moon and stars to govern the night;

His love endures forever.

¹⁰to him who struck down the firstborn of Egypt
His love endures forever.
¹¹and brought Israel out from among them
His love endures forever.
¹²with a mighty hand and outstretched arm;
His love endures forever.

¹³to him who divided the Red Sea ᵃ asunder
His love endures forever.
¹⁴and brought Israel through the midst of it,
His love endures forever.
¹⁵but swept Pharaoh and his army into the Red Sea;
His love endures forever.

¹⁶to him who led his people through the desert,
His love endures forever.
¹⁷who struck down great kings,
His love endures forever.
¹⁸and killed mighty kings—
His love endures forever.
¹⁹Sihon king of the Amorites
His love endures forever.
²⁰and Og king of Bashan—
His love endures forever.
²¹and gave their land as an inheritance,
His love endures forever.
²²an inheritance to his servant Israel;
His love endures forever.

²³to the One who remembered us in our low estate
His love endures forever.
²⁴and freed us from our enemies,
His love endures forever.

ᵃ *13* Hebrew *Yam Suph*; that is, Sea of Reeds; also in verse 15

love ♥ notes

136:1–26

Beloved,

My love endures forever. *Do you know what that means? My forgiveness, my protection, my care, my kindness, my faithfulness, my promises—all of it will last forever. My love for you is endless.*

—Father God

Write your own "psalm" of thanks to God for his endless love.

²⁵ and who gives food to every creature.

His love endures forever.

²⁶ Give thanks to the God of heaven.

His love endures forever.

Psalm 137

¹ By the rivers of Babylon we sat and wept
    when we remembered Zion.
² There on the poplars
    we hung our harps,
³ for there our captors asked us for songs,
    our tormentors demanded songs of joy;
    they said, "Sing us one of the songs of Zion!"

⁴ How can we sing the songs of the LORD
    while in a foreign land?
⁵ If I forget you, O Jerusalem,
    may my right hand forget its skill.
⁶ May my tongue cling to the roof of my mouth
    if I do not remember you,
    if I do not consider Jerusalem
    my highest joy.

⁷ Remember, O LORD, what the Edomites did
    on the day Jerusalem fell.
"Tear it down," they cried,
    "tear it down to its foundations!"

⁸ O Daughter of Babylon, doomed to destruction,
    happy is he who repays you
    for what you have done to us—
⁹ he who seizes your infants
    and dashes them against the rocks.

Psalm 138

Of David.

¹ I will praise you, O LORD, with all my heart;
    before the "gods" I will sing your praise.
² I will bow down toward your holy temple
    and will praise your name
    for your love and your faithfulness,
for you have exalted above all things
    your name and your word.
³ When I called, you answered me;
    you made me bold and stouthearted.

⁴ May all the kings of the earth praise you, O LORD,
    when they hear the words of your mouth.
⁵ May they sing of the ways of the LORD,
    for the glory of the LORD is great.

⁶ Though the LORD is on high, he looks upon the lowly,
    but the proud he knows from afar.
⁷ Though I walk in the midst of trouble,
    you preserve my life;
    you stretch out your hand against the anger of my foes,

with your right hand you save
   me.
[8] The LORD will fulfill ⌐his purpose⌐
      for me;
   your love, O LORD, endures
      forever—
   do not abandon the works of
      your hands.

Psalm 139

For the director of music.
Of David. A psalm.

[1] O LORD, you have searched me
      and you know me.
[2] You know when I sit and when I
      rise;
   you perceive my thoughts
      from afar.
[3] You discern my going out and my
      lying down;
   you are familiar with all my
      ways.
[4] Before a word is on my tongue
   you know it completely, O LORD.

[5] You hem me in—behind and
      before;
   you have laid your hand upon
      me.

[6] Such knowledge is too wonderful for me,
      too lofty for me to attain.

[7] Where can I go from your Spirit?
   Where can I flee from your presence?
[8] If I go up to the heavens, you are there;
   if I make my bed in the depths,[a] you are there.
[9] If I rise on the wings of the dawn,
   if I settle on the far side of the sea,
[10] even there your hand will guide me,
   your right hand will hold me fast.

[11] If I say, "Surely the darkness will hide me
   and the light become night around me,"
[12] even the darkness will not be dark to you;
   the night will shine like the day,
   for darkness is as light to you.

[13] For you created my inmost being;
   you knit me together in my mother's womb.
[14] I praise you because I am fearfully and wonderfully made;
   your works are wonderful,
   I know that full well.
[15] My frame was not hidden from you
   when I was made in the secret place.
   When I was woven together in the depths of the earth,

---

a 8 Hebrew *Sheol*

¹⁶ your eyes saw my unformed body.
All the days ordained for me
were written in your book
before one of them came to be.

¹⁷ How precious to^a me are your
thoughts, O God!
How vast is the sum of them!
¹⁸ Were I to count them,
they would outnumber the
grains of sand.
When I awake,
I am still with you.

¹⁹ If only you would slay the wicked,
O God!
Away from me, you
bloodthirsty men!
²⁰ They speak of you with evil intent;
your adversaries misuse your
name.
²¹ Do I not hate those who hate
you, O LORD,
and abhor those who rise up
against you?
²² I have nothing but hatred for them;
I count them my enemies.

²³ Search me, O God, and know my
heart;
test me and know my anxious
thoughts.
²⁴ See if there is any offensive way
in me,
and lead me in the way everlasting.

genuine

worth »» 139:13-14

It can be painful to compare yourself to other girls. Some girls are prettier, some have cooler clothes, some are more athletic, some get better grades, some get all the guys. Of course, *those* girls are also looking around and seeing other girls who are prettier, more athletic, smarter and more popular. The truth is, there's *always* someone better than you at something. So how can you feel like you're of any value at all? Remember that you are "wonderfully made" by God—and God doesn't make mistakes. You are valuable because you are his!

Psalm 140

For the director of music. A psalm of David.

¹ Rescue me, O LORD, from evil men;
protect me from men of violence,
² who devise evil plans in their hearts
and stir up war every day.
³ They make their tongues as sharp as a serpent's;
the poison of vipers is on their lips.　　　　　　*Selah*

⁴ Keep me, O LORD, from the hands of the wicked;
protect me from men of violence
who plan to trip my feet.
⁵ Proud men have hidden a snare for me;
they have spread out the cords of their net
and have set traps for me along my path.　　　　　*Selah*

⁶ O LORD, I say to you, "You are my God."
Hear, O LORD, my cry for mercy.
⁷ O Sovereign LORD, my strong deliverer,
who shields my head in the day of battle—

a 17 Or *concerning*

⁸do not grant the wicked their desires, O Lᴏʀᴅ;
    do not let their plans succeed,
    or they will become proud.

    Selah

⁹Let the heads of those who surround me
    be covered with the trouble their lips have caused.
¹⁰Let burning coals fall upon them;
    may they be thrown into the fire,
    into miry pits, never to rise.
¹¹Let slanderers not be established in the land;
    may disaster hunt down men of violence.

¹²I know that the Lᴏʀᴅ secures justice for the poor
    and upholds the cause of the needy.
¹³Surely the righteous will praise your name
    and the upright will live before you.

Psalm 141

A psalm of David.

¹O Lᴏʀᴅ, I call to you; come quickly to me.
    Hear my voice when I call to you.
²May my prayer be set before you like incense;
    may the lifting up of my hands be like the evening sacrifice.

³Set a guard over my mouth, O Lᴏʀᴅ;
    keep watch over the door of my lips.
⁴Let not my heart be drawn to what is evil,
    to take part in wicked deeds
with men who are evildoers;
    let me not eat of their delicacies.

⁵Let a righteous man*ᵃ* strike me—
    it is a kindness;
    let him rebuke me—it is oil on
    my head.
    My head will not refuse it.

Yet my prayer is ever against the
    deeds of evildoers;
⁶   their rulers will be thrown
    down from the cliffs,
and the wicked will learn that
    my words were well
    spoken.
⁷⌊They will say,⌋ "As one plows
    and breaks up the earth,
so our bones have been scattered at the
    mouth of the grave.*ᵇ*"

⁸But my eyes are fixed on you, O Sovereign
    Lᴏʀᴅ;
    in you I take refuge—do not give me over to death.
⁹Keep me from the snares they have laid for me,
    from the traps set by evildoers.
¹⁰Let the wicked fall into their own nets,
    while I pass by in safety.

truth or dare

Sometimes the best thing to do in a conversation is to just be quiet. You can avoid a lot of hurt feelings and regrets if you just keep that mouth shut!

141:3

ᵃ 5 Or Let the Righteous One   *ᵇ 7 Hebrew Sheol*

Psalm 142

A *maskil*[a] of David. When he was in the cave. A prayer.

[1] I cry aloud to the LORD;
   I lift up my voice to the LORD for mercy.
[2] I pour out my complaint before him;
   before him I tell my trouble.

[3] When my spirit grows faint within me,
   it is you who know my way.
 In the path where I walk
   men have hidden a snare for me.
[4] Look to my right and see;
   no one is concerned for me.
 I have no refuge;
   no one cares for my life.

[5] I cry to you, O LORD;
   I say, "You are my refuge,
   my portion in the land of the living."
[6] Listen to my cry,
   for I am in desperate need;
 rescue me from those who pursue me,
   for they are too strong for me.
[7] Set me free from my prison,
   that I may praise your name.

 Then the righteous will gather about me
   because of your goodness to me.

Psalm 143

A psalm of David.

[1] O LORD, hear my prayer,
   listen to my cry for mercy;
 in your faithfulness and righteousness
   come to my relief.
[2] Do not bring your servant into judgment,
   for no one living is righteous before you.

[3] The enemy pursues me,
   he crushes me to the ground;
 he makes me dwell in darkness
   like those long dead.
[4] So my spirit grows faint within me;
   my heart within me is dismayed.

[5] I remember the days of long ago;
   I meditate on all your works
   and consider what your hands have done.
[6] I spread out my hands to you;
   my soul thirsts for you like a parched land.   *Selah*

[7] Answer me quickly, O LORD;
   my spirit fails.
 Do not hide your face from me
   or I will be like those who go down to the pit.

a Title: Probably a literary or musical term

Running Out of Excuses

focus | Profile: **Mia**

"Sure you guys can come over anytime … just not this weekend. My mom said she's having the carpets redone or something."

"I thought she did that like a month ago," Sam said and raised his eyebrows.

Kelly came to my rescue. "Whatever, Sam. Ms. Valdez said it's bad timing. Besides, I thought we were going to a movie this weekend." Kelly linked her arm through Sam's and gave me a reassuring look as we all walked to our next class. What a relief. Kelly's a good friend, all right. She swore she would keep my secret safe—and she always does.

Oh, the life of Mia Valdez. I'm a Chicano, which is not a big deal in a city like ours. But my parents are first-generation Chicano. They barely speak English. Like hardly at all. Do you know what it's like to have parents who can't even come to "Meet the Teacher" night because they can't understand her? How about trying to do homework on your own every night—no help with science projects, no proofreading my papers? They're not dumb. They're just different. That's so hard to explain to outsiders.

That's why I always avoid bringing my friends home. What would they think? We're illegal immigrants or something? My mom wants me to have friends over, but it's just not worth the trauma. I'm running out of excuses, though. Somebody is bound to find out.

immigration in focus

Everyone's embarrassed of their families for one reason or another. While you may be inwardly proud of your heritage and culture, sharing that with others can get complicated. If you're struggling with feelings of insecurity about your background, keep in mind …

»God doesn't make mistakes. He made you exactly as you are—unique and special (see Psalm 139:14, page 791).

»Usually what we fear our friends will say or think about us doesn't come true. You might be pleasantly surprised at your friends' reaction to what you find embarrassing about your family.

For more on this topic, see the index on page 1656.

⁸Let the morning bring me word of your unfailing love,
    for I have put my trust in you.
Show me the way I should go,
    for to you I lift up my soul.
⁹Rescue me from my enemies, O Lᴏʀᴅ,
    for I hide myself in you.
¹⁰Teach me to do your will,
    for you are my God;

may your good Spirit
 lead me on level ground.

[11] For your name's sake, O LORD, preserve my life;
 in your righteousness, bring me out of trouble.
[12] In your unfailing love, silence my enemies;
 destroy all my foes,
 for I am your servant.

Psalm 144

Of David.

[1] Praise be to the LORD my Rock,
 who trains my hands for war,
 my fingers for battle.
[2] He is my loving God and my fortress,
 my stronghold and my deliverer,
 my shield, in whom I take refuge,
 who subdues peoples[a] under me.

[3] O LORD, what is man that you care for him,
 the son of man that you think of him?
[4] Man is like a breath;
 his days are like a fleeting shadow.

[5] Part your heavens, O LORD, and come down;
 touch the mountains, so that they smoke.
[6] Send forth lightning and scatter ⌊the enemies⌋;
 shoot your arrows and rout them.
[7] Reach down your hand from on high;
 deliver me and rescue me
 from the mighty waters,
 from the hands of foreigners
[8] whose mouths are full of lies,
 whose right hands are deceitful.

[9] I will sing a new song to you, O God;
 on the ten-stringed lyre I will make music to you,
[10] to the One who gives victory to kings,
 who delivers his servant David from the deadly sword.

[11] Deliver me and rescue me
 from the hands of foreigners
 whose mouths are full of lies,
 whose right hands are deceitful.

[12] Then our sons in their youth
 will be like well-nurtured plants,
 and our daughters will be like pillars
 carved to adorn a palace.
[13] Our barns will be filled
 with every kind of provision.
 Our sheep will increase by thousands,
 by tens of thousands in our fields;
[14] our oxen will draw heavy loads.[b]
 There will be no breaching of walls,

---

a 2 Many manuscripts of the Masoretic Text, Dead Sea Scrolls, Aquila, Jerome and Syriac; most manuscripts of the Masoretic Text *subdues my people* b 14 Or *our chieftains will be firmly established*

no going into captivity,
no cry of distress in our streets.
¹⁵ Blessed are the people of whom this is true;
blessed are the people whose God is the Lord.

Psalm 145 ᵃ

A psalm of praise. Of David.

¹ I will exalt you, my God the King;
I will praise your name for ever and ever.
² Every day I will praise you
and extol your name for ever and ever.

³ Great is the Lord and most worthy of praise;
his greatness no one can fathom.
⁴ One generation will commend your works to another;
they will tell of your mighty acts.
⁵ They will speak of the glorious splendor of your majesty,
and I will meditate on your wonderful works. ᵇ
⁶ They will tell of the power of your awesome works,
and I will proclaim your great deeds.
⁷ They will celebrate your abundant goodness
and joyfully sing of your righteousness.

⁸ The Lord is gracious and compassionate,
slow to anger and rich in love.
⁹ The Lord is good to all;
he has compassion on all he has made.
¹⁰ All you have made will praise you, O Lord;
your saints will extol you.
¹¹ They will tell of the glory of your kingdom
and speak of your might,
¹² so that all men may know of your mighty acts
and the glorious splendor of your kingdom.
¹³ Your kingdom is an everlasting kingdom,
and your dominion endures through all generations.

The Lord is faithful to all his promises
and loving toward all he has made. ᶜ
¹⁴ The Lord upholds all those who fall
and lifts up all who are bowed down.
¹⁵ The eyes of all look to you,
and you give them their food at the proper time.
¹⁶ You open your hand
and satisfy the desires of every living thing.

¹⁷ The Lord is righteous in all his ways
and loving toward all he has made.
¹⁸ The Lord is near to all who call on him,
to all who call on him in truth.
¹⁹ He fulfills the desires of those who fear him;
he hears their cry and saves them.
²⁰ The Lord watches over all who love him,
but all the wicked he will destroy.

ᵃ This psalm is an acrostic poem, the verses of which (including verse 13b) begin with the successive letters of the Hebrew alphabet. ᵇ 5 Dead Sea Scrolls and Syriac (see also Septuagint); Masoretic Text *On the glorious splendor of your majesty / and on your wonderful works I will meditate* ᶜ 13 One manuscript of the Masoretic Text, Dead Sea Scrolls and Syriac (see also Septuagint); most manuscripts of the Masoretic Text do not have the last two lines of verse 13.

²¹ My mouth will speak in praise of the LORD.
   Let every creature praise his holy name
   for ever and ever.

Psalm 146

¹ Praise the LORD. ^a

Praise the LORD, O my soul.
² I will praise the LORD all my
     life;
  I will sing praise to my God as
     long as I live.

³ Do not put your trust in princes,
  in mortal men, who cannot
     save.
⁴ When their spirit departs, they
    return to the ground;
  on that very day their plans come to
    nothing.

⁵ Blessed is he whose help is the God of
    Jacob,
  whose hope is in the LORD his God,
⁶ the Maker of heaven and earth,
  the sea, and everything in them—
  the LORD, who remains faithful forever.
⁷ He upholds the cause of the oppressed
  and gives food to the hungry.
The LORD sets prisoners free,
⁸ the LORD gives sight to the blind,
the LORD lifts up those who are bowed down,
  the LORD loves the righteous.
⁹ The LORD watches over the alien
  and sustains the fatherless and the widow,
  but he frustrates the ways of the wicked.

¹⁰ The LORD reigns forever,
  your God, O Zion, for all generations.

Praise the LORD.

truth *or dare*

For a limited time only? No way! Praising God is for a lifetime! Make your relationship with God last for the long-haul by connecting with him throughout the day.

146:1–2

Psalm 147

¹ Praise the LORD. ^b

How good it is to sing praises to our God,
  how pleasant and fitting to praise him!

² The LORD builds up Jerusalem;
  he gathers the exiles of Israel.
³ He heals the brokenhearted
  and binds up their wounds.
⁴ He determines the number of the stars
  and calls them each by name.
⁵ Great is our Lord and mighty in power;
  his understanding has no limit.

^a 1 Hebrew *Hallelu Yah*; also in verse 10   ^b 1 Hebrew *Hallelu Yah*; also in verse 20

⁶ The Lᴏʀᴅ sustains the humble
   but casts the wicked to the ground.

⁷ Sing to the Lᴏʀᴅ with thanksgiving;
   make music to our God on the harp.
⁸ He covers the sky with clouds;
   he supplies the earth with rain
   and makes grass grow on the hills.
⁹ He provides food for the cattle
   and for the young ravens when they call.

¹⁰ His pleasure is not in the strength of the horse,
   nor his delight in the legs of a man;
¹¹ the Lᴏʀᴅ delights in those who fear him,
   who put their hope in his
      unfailing love.

¹² Extol the Lᴏʀᴅ, O Jerusalem;
   praise your God, O Zion,
¹³ for he strengthens the bars of
      your gates
   and blesses your people
      within you.
¹⁴ He grants peace to your borders
   and satisfies you with the
      finest of wheat.

¹⁵ He sends his command to the
      earth;
   his word runs swiftly.
¹⁶ He spreads the snow like wool
   and scatters the frost like
      ashes.
¹⁷ He hurls down his hail like
      pebbles.
   Who can withstand his icy
      blast?
¹⁸ He sends his word and melts
      them;
   he stirs up his breezes, and
      the waters flow.

¹⁹ He has revealed his word to
      Jacob,
   his laws and decrees to Israel.
²⁰ He has done this for no other nation;
   they do not know his laws.

   Praise the Lᴏʀᴅ.

Psalm 148

¹ Praise the Lᴏʀᴅ. ᵃ

   Praise the Lᴏʀᴅ from the
      heavens,
   praise him in the heights
      above.

ᵃ 1 Hebrew *Hallelu Yah*; also in verse 14

---

love ♥ notes

147:5

Loved one,

This time of your life can feel confusing—about what you want and feel, even about who you are. Focus on me. I understand you perfectly and will help you learn more about yourself.

—The One who understands you

In what area of life are you feeling most confused? Tell God, then ask him to give you understanding.

² Praise him, all his angels,
　　praise him, all his heavenly hosts.
³ Praise him, sun and moon,
　　praise him, all you shining stars.
⁴ Praise him, you highest heavens
　　and you waters above the skies.
⁵ Let them praise the name of the LORD,
　　for he commanded and they were created.
⁶ He set them in place for ever and ever;
　　he gave a decree that will never pass away.

⁷ Praise the LORD from the earth,
　　you great sea creatures and all ocean depths,
⁸ lightning and hail, snow and clouds,
　　stormy winds that do his bidding,
⁹ you mountains and all hills,
　　fruit trees and all cedars,
¹⁰ wild animals and all cattle,
　　small creatures and flying birds,
¹¹ kings of the earth and all nations,
　　you princes and all rulers on earth,
¹² young men and maidens,
　　old men and children.

¹³ Let them praise the name of the LORD,
　　for his name alone is exalted;
　　his splendor is above the earth and the heavens.
¹⁴ He has raised up for his people a horn, ^a
　　the praise of all his saints,
　　of Israel, the people close to his heart.

　　Praise the LORD.

Psalm 149

¹ Praise the LORD. ^b

Sing to the LORD a new song,
　　his praise in the assembly of the saints.

² Let Israel rejoice in their Maker;
　　let the people of Zion be glad in their King.
³ Let them praise his name with dancing
　　and make music to him with tambourine and harp.
⁴ For the LORD takes delight in his people;
　　he crowns the humble with salvation.
⁵ Let the saints rejoice in this honor
　　and sing for joy on their beds.

⁶ May the praise of God be in their mouths
　　and a double-edged sword in their hands,
⁷ to inflict vengeance on the nations
　　and punishment on the peoples,
⁸ to bind their kings with fetters,
　　their nobles with shackles of iron,
⁹ to carry out the sentence written against them.
　　This is the glory of all his saints.

　　Praise the LORD.

^a 14 *Horn* here symbolizes strong one, that is, king.　　^b 1 Hebrew *Hallelu Yah*; also in verse 9

Psalm 150

¹ Praise the Lord. [a]

Praise God in his sanctuary;
   praise him in his mighty heavens.
² Praise him for his acts of power;
   praise him for his surpassing greatness.
³ Praise him with the sounding of the trumpet,
   praise him with the harp and lyre,
⁴ praise him with tambourine and dancing,
   praise him with the strings and flute,
⁵ praise him with the clash of cymbals,
   praise him with resounding cymbals.

⁶ Let everything that has breath praise the Lord.

Praise the Lord.

a 1 Hebrew *Hallelu Yah*; also in verse 6

author: King Solomon primarily.

date: Solomon wrote the majority of these proverbs during his reign (970 to 930 B.C.), but the book wasn't fully compiled until around 700 B.C.

setting: Solomon was Israel's king during a time when the nation was faithful to God. Solomon wrote these wise sayings before he himself became caught up in materialism and idolatry.

verse to remember: The fear of the LORD is the beginning of knowledge, but fools despise wisdom and discipline (1:7).

theme to consider: Allow these wise sayings to help you develop attitudes and behaviors that are pleasing to God.

proverbs

unchanging truth

Life is full of either/or situations—*either* I can stay home and start studying for finals *or* I can go shopping with my friends and procrastinate on studying. *Either* I can speak up for the unpopular girl *or* I can go along with the crowd and ignore her. Either/or. What to do? Sometimes it can feel like a real struggle to make a wise decision.

So where do you go to find wisdom? The world says knowledge can be found in books and academics. But true wisdom means taking that knowledge and applying those facts to your life. According to Solomon, the author of most of the book of Proverbs, wisdom is found in knowing and honoring God (see 1:7).

The book of Proverbs is full of wise sayings. It contrasts the rewards of adopting godly attitudes and behaviors with the consequences of worldly attitudes and behaviors. The word *smart* isn't used in these proverbs because being smart is not the same as being wise. It doesn't matter if you're a 4.0 student with a 1600 SAT score. That may make you smart, but it doesn't make you wise. Being wise involves making good decisions with the knowledge you have. For Christians, that means making decisions based on knowing what pleases God.

What either/or situations are you facing? Go to the source for wisdom, God's Word, and learn what's pleasing to him.

life lessons

1. True wisdom—the kind that guides you through life—can only come from God (2:1–6).

2. Our words (or lack of them) have a great influence on others. Guard your mouth (10:18–21; 12:17–19)!

3. Love your friends and stick with them through the tough times (17:17; 18:24).

Prologue: Purpose and Theme

1 The proverbs of Solomon son of David, king of Israel:

² for attaining wisdom and discipline;
  for understanding words of
    insight;
³ for acquiring a disciplined and
    prudent life,
  doing what is right and just
    and fair;
⁴ for giving prudence to the simple,
  knowledge and discretion to
    the young—
⁵ let the wise listen and add to
    their learning,
  and let the discerning get
    guidance—
⁶ for understanding proverbs and parables,
  the sayings and riddles of the wise.

⁷ The fear of the LORD is the beginning of
    knowledge,
  but fools[a] despise wisdom and discipline.

truth or dare

God doesn't want you to be afraid of him. "Fearing the Lord" means respecting his power and authority. Show you fear God by giving him the R-E-S-P-E-C-T he deserves.

1:7

Exhortations to Embrace Wisdom

Warning Against Enticement

⁸ Listen, my son, to your father's instruction
  and do not forsake your mother's teaching.
⁹ They will be a garland to grace your head
  and a chain to adorn your neck.

¹⁰ My son, if sinners entice you,
  do not give in to them.
¹¹ If they say, "Come along with us;
  let's lie in wait for someone's blood,
  let's waylay some harmless soul;
¹² let's swallow them alive, like the grave,[b]
  and whole, like those who go down to the pit;
¹³ we will get all sorts of valuable things
  and fill our houses with plunder;
¹⁴ throw in your lot with us,
  and we will share a common purse"—
¹⁵ my son, do not go along with them,
  do not set foot on their paths;
¹⁶ for their feet rush into sin,
  they are swift to shed blood.
¹⁷ How useless to spread a net
  in full view of all the birds!
¹⁸ These men lie in wait for their own blood;
  they waylay only themselves!
¹⁹ Such is the end of all who go after ill-gotten gain;
  it takes away the lives of those who get it.

a 7 The Hebrew words rendered *fool* in Proverbs, and often elsewhere in the Old Testament, denote one who is morally deficient.   b 12 Hebrew *Sheol*

Warning Against Rejecting Wisdom

20 Wisdom calls aloud in the street,
   she raises her voice in the public squares;
21 at the head of the noisy streets*a* she cries out,
   in the gateways of the city she makes her speech:

22 "How long will you simple ones*b* love your simple ways?
   How long will mockers delight in mockery
   and fools hate knowledge?
23 If you had responded to my rebuke,
   I would have poured out my heart to you
   and made my thoughts known to you.
24 But since you rejected me when I called
   and no one gave heed when I stretched out my hand,
25 since you ignored all my advice
   and would not accept my rebuke,
26 I in turn will laugh at your disaster;
   I will mock when calamity overtakes you—
27 when calamity overtakes you like a storm,
   when disaster sweeps over you like a whirlwind,
   when distress and trouble overwhelm you.

28 "Then they will call to me but I will not answer;
   they will look for me but will not find me.
29 Since they hated knowledge
   and did not choose to fear the Lord,
30 since they would not accept my advice
   and spurned my rebuke,
31 they will eat the fruit of their ways
   and be filled with the fruit of their schemes.
32 For the waywardness of the simple will kill them,
   and the complacency of fools will destroy them;
33 but whoever listens to me will live in safety
   and be at ease, without fear of harm."

Moral Benefits of Wisdom

2
   My son, if you accept my words
   and store up my commands within you,
2 turning your ear to wisdom
   and applying your heart to understanding,
3 and if you call out for insight
   and cry aloud for understanding,
4 and if you look for it as for silver
   and search for it as for hidden treasure,
5 then you will understand the fear of the Lord
   and find the knowledge of God.
6 For the Lord gives wisdom,
   and from his mouth come knowledge and understanding.
7 He holds victory in store for the upright,
   he is a shield to those whose walk is blameless,
8 for he guards the course of the just
   and protects the way of his faithful ones.

9 Then you will understand what is right and just

a 21 Hebrew; Septuagint / *on the tops of the walls*   *b 22* The Hebrew word rendered *simple* in Proverbs generally denotes one without moral direction and inclined to evil.

genuine wisdom » 2:1-9

We often associate wisdom with old age, like the wise old owl and the wizened, white-haired professor. We make the mistake of thinking that we can't really be wise till we're way older. While it's true that wisdom often comes from experience, we can also become wise by doing several things: accepting advice from parents, following God's commands and actively seeking wisdom. The Lord promises to give wisdom to those who go after it (see James 1:5). Got wisdom?

and fair—every good path.
¹⁰ For wisdom will enter your heart,
and knowledge will be
pleasant to your soul.
¹¹ Discretion will protect you,
and understanding will guard
you.

¹² Wisdom will save you from the
ways of wicked men,
from men whose words are
perverse,
¹³ who leave the straight paths
to walk in dark ways,
¹⁴ who delight in doing wrong
and rejoice in the
perverseness of evil,
¹⁵ whose paths are crooked
and who are devious in their
ways.

¹⁶ It will save you also from the
adulteress,
from the wayward wife with
her seductive words,
¹⁷ who has left the partner of her
youth
and ignored the covenant she
made before God. ᵃ

¹⁸ For her house leads down to death
and her paths to the spirits of the dead.
¹⁹ None who go to her return
or attain the paths of life.

²⁰ Thus you will walk in the ways of good men
and keep to the paths of the righteous.
²¹ For the upright will live in the land,
and the blameless will remain in it;
²² but the wicked will be cut off from the land,
and the unfaithful will be torn from it.

Further Benefits of Wisdom

3 My son, do not forget my teaching,
but keep my commands in your heart,
² for they will prolong your life many years
and bring you prosperity.

³ Let love and faithfulness never leave you;
bind them around your neck,
write them on the tablet of your heart.
⁴ Then you will win favor and a good name
in the sight of God and man.

⁵ Trust in the Lᴏʀᴅ with all your heart
and lean not on your own understanding;
⁶ in all your ways acknowledge him,
and he will make your paths straight. ᵇ

ᵃ 17 Or *covenant of her God*   ᵇ 6 Or *will direct your paths*

⁷Do not be wise in your own eyes;
  fear the LORD and shun evil.
⁸This will bring health to your body
  and nourishment to your bones.

⁹Honor the LORD with your wealth,
  with the firstfruits of all your crops;
¹⁰then your barns will be filled to overflowing,
  and your vats will brim over with new wine.

¹¹My son, do not despise the LORD's discipline
  and do not resent his rebuke,
¹²because the LORD disciplines those he loves,
  as a father ᵃ the son he delights in.

¹³Blessed is the man who finds wisdom,
  the man who gains understanding,
¹⁴for she is more profitable than silver
  and yields better returns than gold.
¹⁵She is more precious than rubies;
  nothing you desire can compare with her.
¹⁶Long life is in her right hand;
  in her left hand are riches and honor.
¹⁷Her ways are pleasant ways,
  and all her paths are peace.
¹⁸She is a tree of life to those who embrace her;
  those who lay hold of her will be blessed.

¹⁹By wisdom the LORD laid the
    earth's foundations,
  by understanding he set the
    heavens in place;
²⁰by his knowledge the deeps were
    divided,
  and the clouds let drop the
    dew.

²¹My son, preserve sound judgment
    and discernment,
  do not let them out of your
    sight;
²²they will be life for you,
  an ornament to grace your
    neck.
²³Then you will go on your way in
    safety,
  and your foot will not stumble;
²⁴when you lie down, you will not
    be afraid;
  when you lie down, your sleep
    will be sweet.
²⁵Have no fear of sudden disaster
  or of the ruin that overtakes
    the wicked,
²⁶for the LORD will be your confidence
  and will keep your foot from
    being snared.

genuine

judgment » 3:21-24

You may get tired of hearing it, but it's true. The decisions you make today will affect your future. A decision to start doing drugs could lead to a lifetime of addiction. A decision to be sexually active could lead to pregnancy, which could affect your ability to go on to college or have the career of your choice. It's never too early to make good decisions because even "small" decisions can have a big effect on your future. Never underestimate the value of wise decisions; like the proverb says, they'll be life for you.

ᵃ 12 Hebrew; Septuagint / and he punishes

27 Do not withhold good from those
   who deserve it,
   when it is in your power to act.
28 Do not say to your neighbor,
   "Come back later; I'll give it
   tomorrow"—
   when you now have it with you.

29 Do not plot harm against your
   neighbor,
   who lives trustfully near you.
30 Do not accuse a man for no
   reason—
   when he has done you no harm.
31 Do not envy a violent man
   or choose any of his ways,
32 for the LORD detests a perverse man
   but takes the upright into his confidence.

33 The LORD's curse is on the house of the wicked,
   but he blesses the home of the righteous.
34 He mocks proud mockers
   but gives grace to the humble.
35 The wise inherit honor,
   but fools he holds up to shame.

truth or dare

Not doing something wrong isn't good enough! God loves to see you go the extra mile to assist a sister in need. What's really in your power, girl?

3:27

Wisdom Is Supreme

4
Listen, my sons, to a father's instruction;
   pay attention and gain understanding.
2 I give you sound learning,
   so do not forsake my teaching.
3 When I was a boy in my father's house,
   still tender, and an only child of my mother,
4 he taught me and said,
   "Lay hold of my words with all your heart;
   keep my commands and you will live.
5 Get wisdom, get understanding;
   do not forget my words or swerve from them.
6 Do not forsake wisdom, and she will protect you;
   love her, and she will watch over you.
7 Wisdom is supreme; therefore get wisdom.
   Though it cost all you have,ª get understanding.
8 Esteem her, and she will exalt you;
   embrace her, and she will honor you.
9 She will set a garland of grace on your head
   and present you with a crown of splendor."

10 Listen, my son, accept what I say,
   and the years of your life will be many.
11 I guide you in the way of wisdom
   and lead you along straight paths.
12 When you walk, your steps will not be hampered;
   when you run, you will not stumble.
13 Hold on to instruction, do not let it go;
   guard it well, for it is your life.

ª 7 Or Whatever else you get

¹⁴ Do not set foot on the path of the wicked
    or walk in the way of evil men.
¹⁵ Avoid it, do not travel on it;
    turn from it and go on your way.
¹⁶ For they cannot sleep till they do evil;
    they are robbed of slumber till they make someone fall.
¹⁷ They eat the bread of wickedness
    and drink the wine of violence.

¹⁸ The path of the righteous is like the first gleam of dawn,
    shining ever brighter till the full light of day.
¹⁹ But the way of the wicked is like deep darkness;
    they do not know what makes them stumble.

²⁰ My son, pay attention to what I say;
    listen closely to my words.
²¹ Do not let them out of your sight,
    keep them within your heart;
²² for they are life to those who find them
    and health to a man's whole body.
²³ Above all else, guard your heart,
    for it is the wellspring of life.
²⁴ Put away perversity from your mouth;
    keep corrupt talk far from your lips.
²⁵ Let your eyes look straight ahead,
    fix your gaze directly before you.
²⁶ Make level *a* paths for your feet
    and take only ways that are firm.
²⁷ Do not swerve to the right or the left;
    keep your foot from evil.

Warning Against Adultery

5 My son, pay attention to my wisdom,
    listen well to my words of insight,
² that you may maintain discretion
    and your lips may preserve knowledge.
³ For the lips of an adulteress drip honey,
    and her speech is smoother than oil;
⁴ but in the end she is bitter as gall,
    sharp as a double-edged sword.
⁵ Her feet go down to death;
    her steps lead straight to the grave. *b*
⁶ She gives no thought to the way of life;
    her paths are crooked, but she knows it not.

⁷ Now then, my sons, listen to me;
    do not turn aside from what I say.
⁸ Keep to a path far from her,
    do not go near the door of her house,
⁹ lest you give your best strength to others
    and your years to one who is cruel,
¹⁰ lest strangers feast on your wealth
    and your toil enrich another man's house.
¹¹ At the end of your life you will groan,
    when your flesh and body are spent.
¹² You will say, "How I hated discipline!

a 26 Or *Consider the*   *b 5* Hebrew *Sheol*

The Music Scene

"You can't be serious," Justine said condescendingly, as if she couldn't possibly believe what I was saying.

"Uh, actually I am." I was trying my best not to get defensive. "Let's just drop it. It's not a big deal." She shrugged okay, but I could tell that to her, it was a huge deal. I feel like I have this conversation all the time! Most of my Christian friends, like Justine, only listen to Christian music—which is fine. But they think it's a sign of true faith. And my non-Christian friends only listen to pop music. And me? Well, I'm somewhere in the middle. I like both kinds of music and have a mix of CDs. I'll listen to whatever, depending on who I'm with.

Some of my Christian friends are so sheltered. And why do they have to nag me about my music, as if it's their personal mission to change my lifestyle? It's so irritating! I mean, what's wrong with other music? I like the beat, the sound, the lyrics—well, most of the time. I try to tune out bad lyrics, but I guess I could be a little more strict with my limits.

This has actually been on my mind a lot lately. (Maybe because Justine gives me constant grief!) I wish God were a little more clear on this whole music thing.

For more on music, check out www.TrueImagesBible.com

music in focus

Ever wonder what God thinks of your music? God didn't give us clear-cut rules or tell us which bands have his stamp of approval. But he did leave us some guidelines. God's concerned with your heart and mind and what you put in them. When you're thinking about music, ask yourself:

»Are you guarding your heart (see Proverbs 4:23, page 808)?
»Does the music make you angry, depressed or distracted?
»Does it plant bad thoughts in your mind, like violence and sexual promiscuity?
»Are you respecting your parents' standards—even if you don't agree with them (see Ephesians 6:1, page 1548)?
»Does your music have a negative effect on your relationship with Jesus?
»Are you showing maturity, self-discipline and integrity in your choices (see 2 Timothy 2:22, page 1577)?

For more on this topic, see the index on page 1656.

> How my heart spurned correction!
> ¹³ I would not obey my teachers
>   or listen to my instructors.
> ¹⁴ I have come to the brink of utter ruin
>   in the midst of the whole assembly."
>
> ¹⁵ Drink water from your own cistern,
>   running water from your own well.
> ¹⁶ Should your springs overflow in the streets,
>   your streams of water in the public squares?
> ¹⁷ Let them be yours alone,

genuine

character » 5:21

What do you have stashed in the bottom drawer of your dresser or under your bed (besides some dirty clothes)? What things about yourself do you try to hide? What are your deepest, darkest secrets? While it's okay not to advertise your personal life to the outside world, it's not okay to try to hide it from God. It doesn't work. Your life is laid out for him to see in full view and living color, regardless of whether anyone else knows or not. He knows all your secrets. You're completely transparent in his eyes.

never to be shared with
strangers.
[18] May your fountain be blessed,
and may you rejoice in the
wife of your youth.
[19] A loving doe, a graceful deer—
may her breasts satisfy you
always,
may you ever be captivated by
her love.
[20] Why be captivated, my son, by
an adulteress?
Why embrace the bosom of
another man's wife?
[21] For a man's ways are in full view
of the LORD,
and he examines all his
paths.
[22] The evil deeds of a wicked man
ensnare him;
the cords of his sin hold him
fast.
[23] He will die for lack of discipline,
led astray by his own great
folly.

Warnings Against Folly

6 My son, if you have put up security for your neighbor,
if you have struck hands in pledge for another,
[2] if you have been trapped by what you said,
ensnared by the words of your mouth,
[3] then do this, my son, to free yourself,
since you have fallen into your neighbor's hands:
Go and humble yourself;
press your plea with your neighbor!
[4] Allow no sleep to your eyes,
no slumber to your eyelids.
[5] Free yourself, like a gazelle from the hand of the hunter,
like a bird from the snare of the fowler.

[6] Go to the ant, you sluggard;
consider its ways and be wise!
[7] It has no commander,
no overseer or ruler,
[8] yet it stores its provisions in summer
and gathers its food at harvest.

[9] How long will you lie there, you sluggard?
When will you get up from your sleep?
[10] A little sleep, a little slumber,
a little folding of the hands to rest—
[11] and poverty will come on you like a bandit
and scarcity like an armed man.[a]

a 11 Or *like a vagrant / and scarcity like a beggar*

genuine

teamwork » 6:6–11

Have you ever worked on a group project with someone who doesn't want to do any of the work? What a frustrating experience! Everyone else has to scramble to pick up the slack, and you all end up muttering about Lazy Lesley. The book of Proverbs talks a lot about lazy people and not in very flattering terms. Being lazy causes problems for everyone— both for Lesley and those she's "working" with. Are you guilty of being lazy sometimes— slacking off and not doing your fair share? Don't let laziness become a habit.

¹² A scoundrel and villain,
who goes about with a corrupt mouth,
¹³ who winks with his eye,
signals with his feet
and motions with his fingers,
¹⁴ who plots evil with deceit in his heart—
he always stirs up dissension.
¹⁵ Therefore disaster will overtake him in an instant;
he will suddenly be destroyed—without remedy.

¹⁶ There are six things the LORD hates,
seven that are detestable to him:
¹⁷ haughty eyes,
a lying tongue,
hands that shed innocent blood,
¹⁸ a heart that devises wicked schemes,
feet that are quick to rush into evil,
¹⁹ a false witness who pours out lies
and a man who stirs up dissension among brothers.

Warning Against Adultery

²⁰ My son, keep your father's commands
and do not forsake your mother's teaching.
²¹ Bind them upon your heart forever;
fasten them around your neck.
²² When you walk, they will guide you;
when you sleep, they will watch over you;
when you awake, they will speak to you.
²³ For these commands are a lamp,
this teaching is a light,
and the corrections of discipline are the way to life,
²⁴ keeping you from the immoral woman,
from the smooth tongue of the wayward wife.
²⁵ Do not lust in your heart after her beauty
or let her captivate you with her eyes,
²⁶ for the prostitute reduces you to a loaf of bread,
and the adulteress preys upon your very life.
²⁷ Can a man scoop fire into his lap
without his clothes being burned?
²⁸ Can a man walk on hot coals

truth or dare

Hate is a strong emotion. But that's just how God reacts towards things like lying, pride and wickedness. Do you hate the same things God hates?

6:16–19

without his feet being scorched?
²⁹ So is he who sleeps with another man's wife;
no one who touches her will go unpunished.

³⁰ Men do not despise a thief if he steals
to satisfy his hunger when he is starving.
³¹ Yet if he is caught, he must pay sevenfold,
though it costs him all the wealth of his house.
³² But a man who commits adultery lacks judgment;
whoever does so destroys himself.
³³ Blows and disgrace are his lot,
and his shame will never be wiped away;
³⁴ for jealousy arouses a husband's fury,
and he will show no mercy when he takes revenge.
³⁵ He will not accept any compensation;
he will refuse the bribe, however great it is.

Warning Against the Adulteress

7 My son, keep my words
and store up my commands within you.
² Keep my commands and you will live;
guard my teachings as the apple of your eye.
³ Bind them on your fingers;
write them on the tablet of your heart.
⁴ Say to wisdom, "You are my sister,"
and call understanding your kinsman;
⁵ they will keep you from the adulteress,
from the wayward wife with her seductive words.

⁶ At the window of my house
I looked out through the lattice.
⁷ I saw among the simple,
I noticed among the young men,
a youth who lacked judgment.
⁸ He was going down the street near her corner,
walking along in the direction of her house
⁹ at twilight, as the day was fading,
as the dark of night set in.

¹⁰ Then out came a woman to meet him,
dressed like a prostitute and with crafty intent.
¹¹ (She is loud and defiant,
her feet never stay at home;
¹² now in the street, now in the squares,
at every corner she lurks.)
¹³ She took hold of him and kissed him
and with a brazen face she said:

¹⁴ "I have fellowship offerings^a at home;
today I fulfilled my vows.
¹⁵ So I came out to meet you;
I looked for you and have found you!
¹⁶ I have covered my bed
with colored linens from Egypt.
¹⁷ I have perfumed my bed
with myrrh, aloes and cinnamon.

^a 14 Traditionally *peace offerings*

¹⁸ Come, let's drink deep of love till morning;
　　let's enjoy ourselves with love!
¹⁹ My husband is not at home;
　　he has gone on a long journey.
²⁰ He took his purse filled with money
　　and will not be home till full moon."

²¹ With persuasive words she led him astray;
　　she seduced him with her smooth talk.
²² All at once he followed her
　　like an ox going to the slaughter,
　like a deer ^a stepping into a noose ^b
²³ 　till an arrow pierces his liver,

　　like a bird darting into a snare,
　　little knowing it will cost him
　　　his life.

²⁴ Now then, my sons, listen to me;
　　pay attention to what I say.
²⁵ Do not let your heart turn to her
　　ways
　　or stray into her paths.
²⁶ Many are the victims she has
　　brought down;
　　her slain are a mighty throng.
²⁷ Her house is a highway to the
　　grave, ^c
　　leading down to the chambers
　　　of death.

Wisdom's Call

8 Does not wisdom call out?
　　Does not understanding raise her
　　　voice?
² On the heights along the way,
　　where the paths meet, she
　　　takes her stand;
³ beside the gates leading into the
　　city,
　　at the entrances, she cries
　　　aloud:
⁴ "To you, O men, I call out;
　　I raise my voice to all
　　　mankind.
⁵ You who are simple, gain
　　prudence;
　　you who are foolish, gain
　　　understanding.
⁶ Listen, for I have worthy things to
　　say;
　　I open my lips to speak what
　　　is right.

~ love ♥ notes ~

7:1–3

My child,

*I've given you the most valuable
thing you'll ever own—my
Word. It's your guide to living,
your key to success, your path to
a rich and full life. Write my
Word on your heart. You won't
be sorry.*

—*The living Word*

Think of several ways you can "write"
God's Word on your heart.

_____

_____

_____

_____

_____

_____

_____

_____

_____

_____

^a *22* Syriac (see also Septuagint); Hebrew *fool*
^b *22* The meaning of the Hebrew for this line is
uncertain.　　^c *27* Hebrew *Sheol*

⁷ My mouth speaks what is true,
　for my lips detest wickedness.
⁸ All the words of my mouth are just;
　none of them is crooked or perverse.
⁹ To the discerning all of them are right;
　they are faultless to those who have knowledge.
¹⁰ Choose my instruction instead of silver,
　knowledge rather than choice gold,
¹¹ for wisdom is more precious than rubies,
　and nothing you desire can compare with her.

¹² "I, wisdom, dwell together with prudence;
　I possess knowledge and discretion.
¹³ To fear the Lᴏʀᴅ is to hate evil;
　I hate pride and arrogance,
　evil behavior and perverse speech.
¹⁴ Counsel and sound judgment are mine;
　I have understanding and power.
¹⁵ By me kings reign
　and rulers make laws that are just;
¹⁶ by me princes govern,
　and all nobles who rule on earth.ᵃ
¹⁷ I love those who love me,
　and those who seek me find me.
¹⁸ With me are riches and honor,
　enduring wealth and prosperity.
¹⁹ My fruit is better than fine gold;
　what I yield surpasses choice silver.
²⁰ I walk in the way of righteousness,
　along the paths of justice,
²¹ bestowing wealth on those who love me
　and making their treasuries full.

²² "The Lᴏʀᴅ brought me forth as the first of his works,ᵇ,ᶜ
　before his deeds of old;
²³ I was appointedᵈ from eternity,
　from the beginning, before the world began.
²⁴ When there were no oceans, I was given birth,
　when there were no springs abounding with water;
²⁵ before the mountains were settled in place,
　before the hills, I was given birth,
²⁶ before he made the earth or its fields
　or any of the dust of the world.
²⁷ I was there when he set the heavens in place,
　when he marked out the horizon on the face of the deep,
²⁸ when he established the clouds above
　and fixed securely the fountains of the deep,
²⁹ when he gave the sea its boundary
　so the waters would not overstep his command,
　and when he marked out the foundations of the earth.
³⁰ 　Then I was the craftsman at his side.
　I was filled with delight day after day,
　rejoicing always in his presence,

ᵃ 16 Many Hebrew manuscripts and Septuagint; most Hebrew manuscripts *and nobles—all righteous rulers*
ᵇ 22 Or *way*; or *dominion*　ᶜ 22 Or *The Lᴏʀᴅ possessed me at the beginning of his work*; or *The Lᴏʀᴅ brought me forth at the beginning of his work*　ᵈ 23 Or *fashioned*

³¹ rejoicing in his whole world
    and delighting in mankind.

³² "Now then, my sons, listen to me;
    blessed are those who keep my ways.
³³ Listen to my instruction and be wise;
    do not ignore it.
³⁴ Blessed is the man who listens to me,
    watching daily at my doors,
    waiting at my doorway.
³⁵ For whoever finds me finds life
    and receives favor from the LORD.
³⁶ But whoever fails to find me harms himself;
    all who hate me love death."

Invitations of Wisdom and of Folly

9

Wisdom has built her house;
    she has hewn out its seven pillars.
² She has prepared her meat and mixed her wine;
    she has also set her table.
³ She has sent out her maids, and she calls
    from the highest point of the city.
⁴ "Let all who are simple come in here!"
    she says to those who lack judgment.
⁵ "Come, eat my food
    and drink the wine I have mixed.
⁶ Leave your simple ways and you will live;
    walk in the way of understanding.

⁷ "Whoever corrects a mocker invites insult;
    whoever rebukes a wicked man incurs abuse.
⁸ Do not rebuke a mocker or he will hate you;
    rebuke a wise man and he will love you.
⁹ Instruct a wise man and he will be wiser still;
    teach a righteous man and he will add to his learning.

¹⁰ "The fear of the LORD is the beginning of wisdom,
    and knowledge of the Holy One is understanding.
¹¹ For through me your days will be many,
    and years will be added to your life.
¹² If you are wise, your wisdom will reward you;
    if you are a mocker, you alone will suffer."

¹³ The woman Folly is loud;
    she is undisciplined and without knowledge.
¹⁴ She sits at the door of her house,
    on a seat at the highest point of the city,
¹⁵ calling out to those who pass by,
    who go straight on their way.
¹⁶ "Let all who are simple come in here!"
    she says to those who lack judgment.
¹⁷ "Stolen water is sweet;
    food eaten in secret is delicious!"
¹⁸ But little do they know that the dead are there,
    that her guests are in the depths of the grave. ^a

a 18 Hebrew *Sheol*

Proverbs of Solomon

10 The proverbs of Solomon:

A wise son brings joy to his father,
　but a foolish son grief to his mother.

[2] Ill-gotten treasures are of no value,
　but righteousness delivers from death.

[3] The LORD does not let the righteous go hungry
　but he thwarts the craving of the wicked.

[4] Lazy hands make a man poor,
　but diligent hands bring wealth.

[5] He who gathers crops in summer
　　is a wise son,
　but he who sleeps during
　　harvest is a disgraceful
　　son.

[6] Blessings crown the head of the
　　righteous,
　but violence overwhelms the
　　mouth of the wicked. [a]

[7] The memory of the righteous will be a
　　blessing,
　but the name of the wicked will rot.

[8] The wise in heart accept commands,
　but a chattering fool comes to ruin.

[9] The man of integrity walks securely,
　but he who takes crooked paths will be found out.

[10] He who winks maliciously causes grief,
　and a chattering fool comes to ruin.

[11] The mouth of the righteous is a fountain of life,
　but violence overwhelms the mouth of the wicked.

[12] Hatred stirs up dissension,
　but love covers over all wrongs.

[13] Wisdom is found on the lips of the discerning,
　but a rod is for the back of him who lacks judgment.

[14] Wise men store up knowledge,
　but the mouth of a fool invites ruin.

[15] The wealth of the rich is their fortified city,
　but poverty is the ruin of the poor.

[16] The wages of the righteous bring them life,
　but the income of the wicked brings them punishment.

[17] He who heeds discipline shows the way to life,
　but whoever ignores correction leads others astray.

[18] He who conceals his hatred has lying lips,
　and whoever spreads slander is a fool.

truth or dare

If you have an A+ in laziness, perhaps it's time to turn up the idle! God gives you many opportunities in life. Don't miss them by sleeping the day away.

10:4–5

a 6 Or but the mouth of the wicked conceals violence; also in verse 11

¹⁹When words are many, sin is not absent,
  but he who holds his tongue is wise.

²⁰The tongue of the righteous is choice silver,
  but the heart of the wicked is of little value.

²¹The lips of the righteous nourish many,
  but fools die for lack of judgment.

²²The blessing of the Lord brings wealth,
  and he adds no trouble to it.

²³A fool finds pleasure in evil conduct,
  but a man of understanding delights in wisdom.

²⁴What the wicked dreads will overtake him;
  what the righteous desire will be granted.

²⁵When the storm has swept by, the wicked are gone,
  but the righteous stand firm forever.

²⁶As vinegar to the teeth and smoke to the eyes,
  so is a sluggard to those who send him.

²⁷The fear of the Lord adds length to life,
  but the years of the wicked are cut short.

²⁸The prospect of the righteous is joy,
  but the hopes of the wicked come to nothing.

²⁹The way of the Lord is a refuge for the righteous,
  but it is the ruin of those who do evil.

³⁰The righteous will never be uprooted,
  but the wicked will not remain in the land.

³¹The mouth of the righteous brings forth wisdom,
  but a perverse tongue will be cut out.

³²The lips of the righteous know what is fitting,
  but the mouth of the wicked only what is perverse.

11

The Lord abhors dishonest scales,
  but accurate weights are his delight.

²When pride comes, then comes disgrace,
  but with humility comes wisdom.

³The integrity of the upright guides them,
  but the unfaithful are destroyed by their duplicity.

⁴Wealth is worthless in the day of wrath,
  but righteousness delivers from death.

⁵The righteousness of the blameless makes a straight way for them,
  but the wicked are brought down by their own wickedness.

⁶The righteousness of the upright delivers them,
  but the unfaithful are trapped by evil desires.

⁷When a wicked man dies, his hope perishes;
  all he expected from his power comes to nothing.

⁸The righteous man is rescued from trouble,
  and it comes on the wicked instead.

⁹With his mouth the godless destroys his neighbor,
  but through knowledge the righteous escape.

¹⁰ When the righteous prosper, the city rejoices;
   when the wicked perish, there are shouts of joy.

¹¹ Through the blessing of the upright a city is exalted,
   but by the mouth of the wicked it is destroyed.

¹² A man who lacks judgment
      derides his neighbor,
   but a man of understanding
      holds his tongue.

¹³ A gossip betrays a confidence,
   but a trustworthy man keeps a
      secret.

¹⁴ For lack of guidance a nation falls,
   but many advisers make
      victory sure.

¹⁵ He who puts up security for
      another will surely suffer,
   but whoever refuses to strike hands in
      pledge is safe.

¹⁶ A kindhearted woman gains respect,
   but ruthless men gain only wealth.

¹⁷ A kind man benefits himself,
   but a cruel man brings trouble on himself.

¹⁸ The wicked man earns deceptive wages,
   but he who sows righteousness reaps a sure reward.

¹⁹ The truly righteous man attains life,
   but he who pursues evil goes to his death.

²⁰ The LORD detests men of perverse heart
   but he delights in those whose ways are blameless.

²¹ Be sure of this: The wicked will not go unpunished,
   but those who are righteous will go free.

²² Like a gold ring in a pig's snout
   is a beautiful woman who shows no discretion.

²³ The desire of the righteous ends only in good,
   but the hope of the wicked only in wrath.

²⁴ One man gives freely, yet gains even more;
   another withholds unduly, but comes to poverty.

²⁵ A generous man will prosper;
   he who refreshes others will himself be refreshed.

²⁶ People curse the man who hoards grain,
   but blessing crowns him who is willing to sell.

²⁷ He who seeks good finds goodwill,
   but evil comes to him who searches for it.

²⁸ Whoever trusts in his riches will fall,
   but the righteous will thrive like a green leaf.

²⁹ He who brings trouble on his family will inherit only wind,
   and the fool will be servant to the wise.

truth or dare

Winning the award for being the goddess of gossip is never cool. Want to keep your friends? Keep your lips locked, and resist the daily gossip mill.
11:13

genuine beauty » 11:22

What a waste! A solid gold ring hooked through the snout of a stinky pig. That's how useful beauty is without good judgment to balance it out. Just think about the lives of some of the most beautiful super-models and movie stars in the world. While these chicks look beautiful on the outside, they're often confused and unhappy on the inside. Their beauty doesn't do much but ac-cessorize an otherwise ugly life. And in the end, even a pig with a nose ring is still just a pig. True beauty grows from the inside out, not the outside in.

---

30 The fruit of the righteous is a tree
    of life,
        and he who wins souls is
        wise.

31 If the righteous receive their due
    on earth,
        how much more the ungodly
        and the sinner!

12 Whoever loves discipline loves
        knowledge,
    but he who hates correction is
        stupid.

2 A good man obtains favor from
    the LORD,
        but the LORD condemns a
        crafty man.

3 A man cannot be established
        through wickedness,
    but the righteous cannot be
        uprooted.

4 A wife of noble character is her
        husband's crown,
    but a disgraceful wife is like
        decay in his bones.

5 The plans of the righteous are just,
        but the advice of the wicked is deceitful.

6 The words of the wicked lie in wait for blood,
        but the speech of the upright rescues them.

7 Wicked men are overthrown and are no more,
        but the house of the righteous stands firm.

8 A man is praised according to his wisdom,
        but men with warped minds
        are despised.

9 Better to be a nobody and yet
        have a servant
    than pretend to be somebody
        and have no food.

10 A righteous man cares for the
        needs of his animal,
    but the kindest acts of the
        wicked are cruel.

11 He who works his land will have
        abundant food,
    but he who chases fantasies lacks
        judgment.

12 The wicked desire the plunder of evil men,
        but the root of the righteous flourishes.

13 An evil man is trapped by his sinful talk,
        but a righteous man escapes trouble.

truth or dare

So someone's called you on your errors? Thank goodness! Discipline and criticism (creative or otherwise) can give you major insights. Wise women harness today's stumbles to get tomorrow's successes.

12:1

¹⁴ From the fruit of his lips a man is filled with good things
as surely as the work of his hands rewards him.

¹⁵ The way of a fool seems right to him,
but a wise man listens to advice.

¹⁶ A fool shows his annoyance at once,
but a prudent man overlooks an insult.

¹⁷ A truthful witness gives honest testimony,
but a false witness tells lies.

¹⁸ Reckless words pierce like a sword,
but the tongue of the wise brings healing.

¹⁹ Truthful lips endure forever,
but a lying tongue lasts only a moment.

²⁰ There is deceit in the hearts of those who plot evil,
but joy for those who promote peace.

²¹ No harm befalls the righteous,
but the wicked have their fill of trouble.

²² The LORD detests lying lips,
but he delights in men who are truthful.

²³ A prudent man keeps his knowledge to himself,
but the heart of fools blurts out folly.

²⁴ Diligent hands will rule,
but laziness ends in slave labor.

²⁵ An anxious heart weighs a man down,
but a kind word cheers him up.

²⁶ A righteous man is cautious in friendship, ^a
but the way of the wicked leads them astray.

²⁷ The lazy man does not roast ^b his game,
but the diligent man prizes his possessions.

²⁸ In the way of righteousness there is life;
along that path is immortality.

13

A wise son heeds his father's instruction,
but a mocker does not listen to rebuke.

² From the fruit of his lips a man enjoys good things,
but the unfaithful have a craving for violence.

³ He who guards his lips guards his life,
but he who speaks rashly will come to ruin.

⁴ The sluggard craves and gets nothing,
but the desires of the diligent are fully satisfied.

⁵ The righteous hate what is false,
but the wicked bring shame and disgrace.

⁶ Righteousness guards the man of integrity,
but wickedness overthrows the sinner.

⁷ One man pretends to be rich, yet has nothing;
another pretends to be poor, yet has great wealth.

^a 26 Or man is a guide to his neighbor   ^b 27 The meaning of the Hebrew for this word is uncertain.

God, Are You Listening?

Have you ever written a letter to God? Where would you address it to—the outer edges of the universe? But since my prayers seem to be going nowhere lately, I decided to do it . . . to write a letter to God in my journal, kind of like praying on paper . . .

Dear God,

It's Val—again. I've been praying for two weeks straight now and no response from you yet. I know I might seem impatient, but I have to make some big decisions for the fall. I think you care about where I end up at college. And with five choices, I really need some help narrowing things down.

If the future is as big a deal as everyone says it is, I just need a clue that I'm headed in the right direction. I mean, Christian college or state university? In state or out of state? Solid academics or more ministry opportunities?

Here's the thing. I never expected you to give me a flashing neon sign with the right answer. But now's the time for me to figure out what I'm supposed to be doing with my life. And if you've got it all figured out like my sister says you do, then I need some kind of signal. Something. Anything!

Everyday I'm afraid that I'm going to miss out on your will for me. So, please, don't leave me in the dark, okay?

Desperate,

Val

P.S. Only eight more days till my deadline to decide!

For more on how to deal with the future, go to www.TrueImagesBible.com

future in focus

Like Val, we don't always know what to do about the future. But God does give us some guidelines for making wise decisions. Here's a checklist to help you make the best choices:

» *Seek God* (see James 1:5–8, page 1602). Keep asking. God doesn't want you to give up after asking just once.

» *Seek wise counsel* (see Proverbs 15:22, page 825). Get advice from people you respect.

» *Make a decision.* Sometimes there's more than one good choice, and God may leave it to you to make a choice and stick with it.

For more on this topic, see the index on page 1656.

future

⁸ A man's riches may ransom his life,
   but a poor man hears no threat.

⁹ The light of the righteous shines brightly,
   but the lamp of the wicked is snuffed out.

¹⁰ Pride only breeds quarrels,
   but wisdom is found in those who take advice.

11 Dishonest money dwindles away,
    but he who gathers money little by little makes it grow.

12 Hope deferred makes the heart sick,
    but a longing fulfilled is a tree of life.

13 He who scorns instruction will pay for it,
    but he who respects a command is rewarded.

14 The teaching of the wise is a fountain of life,
    turning a man from the snares of death.

15 Good understanding wins favor,
    but the way of the unfaithful is hard. *a*

16 Every prudent man acts out of knowledge,
    but a fool exposes his folly.

17 A wicked messenger falls into trouble,
    but a trustworthy envoy brings healing.

18 He who ignores discipline comes to poverty and shame,
    but whoever heeds correction is honored.

19 A longing fulfilled is sweet to the soul,
    but fools detest turning from evil.

20 He who walks with the wise grows wise,
    but a companion of fools suffers harm.

21 Misfortune pursues the sinner,
    but prosperity is the reward of the righteous.

22 A good man leaves an inheritance for his children's children,
    but a sinner's wealth is stored up for the righteous.

23 A poor man's field may produce abundant food,
    but injustice sweeps it away.

24 He who spares the rod hates his son,
    but he who loves him is careful to discipline him.

25 The righteous eat to their hearts' content,
    but the stomach of the wicked goes hungry.

14

The wise woman builds her house,
    but with her own hands the foolish one tears hers down.

2 He whose walk is upright fears the LORD,
    but he whose ways are devious despises him.

3 A fool's talk brings a rod to his back,
    but the lips of the wise protect them.

4 Where there are no oxen, the manger is empty,
    but from the strength of an ox comes an abundant harvest.

5 A truthful witness does not deceive,
    but a false witness pours out lies.

6 The mocker seeks wisdom and finds none,
    but knowledge comes easily to the discerning.

7 Stay away from a foolish man,
    for you will not find knowledge on his lips.

a 15 Or unfaithful does not endure

8 The wisdom of the prudent is to
  give thought to their
  ways,
  but the folly of fools is
  deception.

9 Fools mock at making amends
  for sin,
  but goodwill is found among
  the upright.

10 Each heart knows its own
  bitterness,
  and no one else can share its joy.

11 The house of the wicked will be destroyed,
  but the tent of the upright will flourish.

12 There is a way that seems right to a man,
  but in the end it leads to death.

13 Even in laughter the heart may ache,
  and joy may end in grief.

14 The faithless will be fully repaid for their ways,
  and the good man rewarded for his.

15 A simple man believes anything,
  but a prudent man gives thought to his steps.

16 A wise man fears the LORD and shuns evil,
  but a fool is hotheaded and reckless.

17 A quick-tempered man does foolish things,
  and a crafty man is hated.

18 The simple inherit folly,
  but the prudent are crowned with knowledge.

19 Evil men will bow down in the presence of the good,
  and the wicked at the gates of the righteous.

20 The poor are shunned even by their neighbors,
  but the rich have many friends.

21 He who despises his neighbor sins,
  but blessed is he who is kind to the needy.

22 Do not those who plot evil go astray?
  But those who plan what is good find *a* love and
  faithfulness.

23 All hard work brings a profit,
  but mere talk leads only to poverty.

24 The wealth of the wise is their crown,
  but the folly of fools yields folly.

25 A truthful witness saves lives,
  but a false witness is deceitful.

26 He who fears the LORD has a secure fortress,
  and for his children it will be a refuge.

truth or dare

Why would anyone tear her own house down? Actually, it's easier than you think. Don't let bitterness, manipulation and selfishness rule (and ruin) your relationships.

14:1

proverbs 14:26

a 22 Or show

» 823

²⁷ The fear of the LORD is a fountain of life,
  turning a man from the snares of death.

²⁸ A large population is a king's glory,
  but without subjects a prince is ruined.

²⁹ A patient man has great understanding,
  but a quick-tempered man displays folly.

³⁰ A heart at peace gives life to the body,
  but envy rots the bones.

³¹ He who oppresses the poor shows contempt for their Maker,
  but whoever is kind to the needy honors God.

³² When calamity comes, the wicked are brought down,
  but even in death the righteous have a refuge.

³³ Wisdom reposes in the heart of the discerning
  and even among fools she lets herself be known. ᵃ

³⁴ Righteousness exalts a nation,
  but sin is a disgrace to any people.

³⁵ A king delights in a wise servant,
  but a shameful servant incurs his wrath.

15 A gentle answer turns away wrath,
  but a harsh word stirs up anger.

² The tongue of the wise commends knowledge,
  but the mouth of the fool gushes folly.

³ The eyes of the LORD are everywhere,
  keeping watch on the wicked and the good.

⁴ The tongue that brings healing is a tree of life,
  but a deceitful tongue crushes the spirit.

⁵ A fool spurns his father's discipline,
  but whoever heeds correction shows prudence.

⁶ The house of the righteous contains great treasure,
  but the income of the wicked brings them trouble.

⁷ The lips of the wise spread knowledge;
  not so the hearts of fools.

⁸ The LORD detests the sacrifice of the wicked,
  but the prayer of the upright pleases him.

genuine speech »» 15:2,4,7

You can tell a lot about a girl by listening to what she says and how she says it. What do your words reveal about you? Do you gush foolish words, say hurtful things and spread lies and gossip? Or do you speak the truth, say helpful things and spread kindness and encouragement? Every time you get ready to open that mouth of yours, think about what you're going to say . . . and what that says about you.

ᵃ 33 Hebrew; Septuagint and Syriac / but in the heart of fools she is not known

⁹ The LORD detests the way of the wicked
    but he loves those who pursue righteousness.

¹⁰ Stern discipline awaits him who leaves the path;
    he who hates correction will die.

¹¹ Death and Destruction*ᵃ* lie open before the LORD—
    how much more the hearts of men!

¹² A mocker resents correction;
    he will not consult the wise.

¹³ A happy heart makes the face cheerful,
    but heartache crushes the spirit.

¹⁴ The discerning heart seeks knowledge,
    but the mouth of a fool feeds on folly.

¹⁵ All the days of the oppressed are wretched,
    but the cheerful heart has a continual feast.

¹⁶ Better a little with the fear of the LORD
    than great wealth with turmoil.

¹⁷ Better a meal of vegetables where there is love
    than a fattened calf with hatred.

¹⁸ A hot-tempered man stirs up dissension,
    but a patient man calms a quarrel.

¹⁹ The way of the sluggard is blocked with thorns,
    but the path of the upright is a highway.

²⁰ A wise son brings joy to his father,
    but a foolish man despises his mother.

²¹ Folly delights a man who lacks judgment,
    but a man of understanding keeps a straight course.

²² Plans fail for lack of counsel,
    but with many advisers they succeed.

²³ A man finds joy in giving an apt reply—
    and how good is a timely word!

²⁴ The path of life leads upward for the wise
    to keep him from going down to the grave.*ᵇ*

²⁵ The LORD tears down the proud man's house
    but he keeps the widow's boundaries intact.

²⁶ The LORD detests the thoughts of the wicked,
    but those of the pure are pleasing to him.

²⁷ A greedy man brings trouble to his family,
    but he who hates bribes will live.

²⁸ The heart of the righteous weighs its answers,
    but the mouth of the wicked gushes evil.

²⁹ The LORD is far from the wicked
    but he hears the prayer of the righteous.

³⁰ A cheerful look brings joy to the heart,
    and good news gives health to the bones.

a 11 Hebrew *Sheol and Abaddon*   *b* 24 Hebrew *Sheol*

16

³¹ He who listens to a life-giving rebuke
will be at home among the wise.

³² He who ignores discipline despises himself,
but whoever heeds correction gains understanding.

³³ The fear of the LORD teaches a man wisdom,[a]
and humility comes before honor.

To man belong the plans of the heart,
but from the LORD comes the reply of the tongue.

² All a man's ways seem innocent to him,
but motives are weighed by the LORD.

³ Commit to the LORD whatever you do,
and your plans will succeed.

⁴ The LORD works out everything for his own ends—
even the wicked for a day of disaster.

⁵ The LORD detests all the proud of heart.
Be sure of this: They will not go unpunished.

⁶ Through love and faithfulness sin is atoned for;
through the fear of the LORD a man avoids evil.

⁷ When a man's ways are pleasing to the LORD,
he makes even his enemies live at peace with him.

⁸ Better a little with righteousness
than much gain with injustice.

⁹ In his heart a man plans his course,
but the LORD determines his steps.

¹⁰ The lips of a king speak as an oracle,
and his mouth should not betray justice.

¹¹ Honest scales and balances are from the LORD;
all the weights in the bag are of his making.

¹² Kings detest wrongdoing,
for a throne is established through righteousness.

¹³ Kings take pleasure in honest lips;
they value a man who speaks the truth.

¹⁴ A king's wrath is a messenger of death,
but a wise man will appease it.

¹⁵ When a king's face brightens, it means life;
his favor is like a rain cloud in spring.

¹⁶ How much better to get wisdom than gold,
to choose understanding rather than silver!

¹⁷ The highway of the upright avoids evil;
he who guards his way guards his life.

¹⁸ Pride goes before destruction,
a haughty spirit before a fall.

¹⁹ Better to be lowly in spirit and among the oppressed
than to share plunder with the proud.

a 33 Or Wisdom teaches the fear of the LORD

²⁰ Whoever gives heed to instruction prospers,
and blessed is he who trusts in the LORD.

²¹ The wise in heart are called discerning,
and pleasant words promote instruction.ᵃ

²² Understanding is a fountain of life to those who have it,
but folly brings punishment to fools.

²³ A wise man's heart guides his mouth,
and his lips promote instruction.ᵇ

²⁴ Pleasant words are a honeycomb,
sweet to the soul and healing to the bones.

²⁵ There is a way that seems right to a man,
but in the end it leads to death.

²⁶ The laborer's appetite works for him;
his hunger drives him on.

²⁷ A scoundrel plots evil,
and his speech is like a scorching fire.

²⁸ A perverse man stirs up dissension,
and a gossip separates close friends.

²⁹ A violent man entices his neighbor
and leads him down a path that is not good.

³⁰ He who winks with his eye is plotting perversity;
he who purses his lips is bent on evil.

³¹ Gray hair is a crown of splendor;
it is attained by a righteous life.

³² Better a patient man than a warrior,
a man who controls his temper than one who takes a city.

³³ The lot is cast into the lap,
but its every decision is from the LORD.

17

Better a dry crust with peace and quiet
than a house full of feasting,ᶜ with strife.

² A wise servant will rule over a disgraceful son,
and will share the inheritance as one of the brothers.

³ The crucible for silver and the furnace for gold,
but the LORD tests the heart.

⁴ A wicked man listens to evil lips;
a liar pays attention to a malicious tongue.

⁵ He who mocks the poor shows contempt for their Maker;
whoever gloats over disaster will not go unpunished.

⁶ Children's children are a crown to the aged,
and parents are the pride of their children.

⁷ Arrogantᵈ lips are unsuited to a fool—
how much worse lying lips to a ruler!

⁸ A bribe is a charm to the one who gives it;
wherever he turns, he succeeds.

ᵃ 21 Or words make a man persuasive   ᵇ 23 Or mouth / and makes his lips persuasive   ᶜ 1 Hebrew sacrifices
ᵈ 7 Or Eloquent

⁹He who covers over an offense promotes love,
but whoever repeats the matter separates close friends.

¹⁰A rebuke impresses a man of discernment
more than a hundred lashes a fool.

¹¹An evil man is bent only on rebellion;
a merciless official will be sent against him.

¹²Better to meet a bear robbed of her cubs
than a fool in his folly.

¹³If a man pays back evil for good,
evil will never leave his house.

¹⁴Starting a quarrel is like
breaching a dam;
so drop the matter before a
dispute breaks out.

¹⁵Acquitting the guilty and
condemning the
innocent—
the LORD detests them both.

¹⁶Of what use is money in the
hand of a fool,
since he has no desire to get
wisdom?

¹⁷A friend loves at all times,
and a brother is born for adversity.

¹⁸A man lacking in judgment
strikes hands in pledge
and puts up security for his
neighbor.

¹⁹He who loves a quarrel loves sin;
he who builds a high gate
invites destruction.

²⁰A man of perverse heart does not
prosper;
he whose tongue is deceitful
falls into trouble.

genuine friendship » 17:17

Your true friends are those you can count on even when you feel moody, even when you're not at your best, even when you're going through an ugly stage, even when you don't make the team or get the award. A true friend loves at all times. Some girls will only be "friends" with you if they think that your friendship will somehow help *them*. But friendship is about being there through the good times and the bad, and that's usually when you need your friends the most! What kind of friend are you?

²¹To have a fool for a son brings grief;
there is no joy for the father of a fool.

²²A cheerful heart is good medicine,
but a crushed spirit dries up the bones.

²³A wicked man accepts a bribe in secret
to pervert the course of justice.

²⁴A discerning man keeps wisdom in view,
but a fool's eyes wander to the ends of the earth.

²⁵A foolish son brings grief to his father
and bitterness to the one who bore him.

²⁶It is not good to punish an innocent man,
or to flog officials for their integrity.

18

²⁷ A man of knowledge uses words with restraint,
   and a man of understanding is even-tempered.

²⁸ Even a fool is thought wise if he keeps silent,
   and discerning if he holds his tongue.

An unfriendly man pursues selfish ends;
   he defies all sound judgment.

² A fool finds no pleasure in understanding
   but delights in airing his own opinions.

³ When wickedness comes, so does contempt,
   and with shame comes disgrace.

⁴ The words of a man's mouth are deep waters,
   but the fountain of wisdom is a bubbling brook.

⁵ It is not good to be partial to the wicked
   or to deprive the innocent of justice.

⁶ A fool's lips bring him strife,
   and his mouth invites a beating.

⁷ A fool's mouth is his undoing,
   and his lips are a snare to his soul.

⁸ The words of a gossip are like choice morsels;
   they go down to a man's inmost parts.

⁹ One who is slack in his work
   is brother to one who destroys.

¹⁰ The name of the LORD is a strong tower;
   the righteous run to it and are safe.

¹¹ The wealth of the rich is their fortified city;
   they imagine it an unscalable wall.

¹² Before his downfall a man's heart is proud,
   but humility comes before honor.

¹³ He who answers before listening—
   that is his folly and his shame.

¹⁴ A man's spirit sustains him in sickness,
   but a crushed spirit who can bear?

¹⁵ The heart of the discerning acquires knowledge;
   the ears of the wise seek it out.

¹⁶ A gift opens the way for the giver
   and ushers him into the presence of the great.

¹⁷ The first to present his case seems right,
   till another comes forward and questions him.

¹⁸ Casting the lot settles disputes
   and keeps strong opponents apart.

¹⁹ An offended brother is more unyielding than a fortified city,
   and disputes are like the barred gates of a citadel.

²⁰ From the fruit of his mouth a man's stomach is filled;
   with the harvest from his lips he is satisfied.

²¹ The tongue has the power of life and death,
   and those who love it will eat its fruit.

19

²² He who finds a wife finds what is
good
and receives favor from the
LORD.

²³ A poor man pleads for mercy,
but a rich man answers
harshly.

²⁴ A man of many companions may
come to ruin,
but there is a friend who sticks
closer than a brother.

Better a poor man whose walk is blameless
than a fool whose lips are perverse.

² It is not good to have zeal without knowledge,
nor to be hasty and miss the way.

³ A man's own folly ruins his life,
yet his heart rages against the LORD.

⁴ Wealth brings many friends,
but a poor man's friend deserts him.

⁵ A false witness will not go unpunished,
and he who pours out lies will not go free.

⁶ Many curry favor with a ruler,
and everyone is the friend of a man who gives gifts.

⁷ A poor man is shunned by all his relatives—
how much more do his friends avoid him!
Though he pursues them with pleading,
they are nowhere to be found. ^a

⁸ He who gets wisdom loves his own soul;
he who cherishes understanding prospers.

⁹ A false witness will not go unpunished,
and he who pours out lies will perish.

¹⁰ It is not fitting for a fool to live in luxury—
how much worse for a slave to rule over princes!

¹¹ A man's wisdom gives him patience;
it is to his glory to overlook an offense.

¹² A king's rage is like the roar of a lion,
but his favor is like dew on the grass.

¹³ A foolish son is his father's ruin,
and a quarrelsome wife is like a constant dripping.

¹⁴ Houses and wealth are inherited from parents,
but a prudent wife is from the LORD.

¹⁵ Laziness brings on deep sleep,
and the shiftless man goes hungry.

¹⁶ He who obeys instructions guards his life,
but he who is contemptuous of his ways will die.

truth or dare

Someday you'll have to face the consequences of your words, whether good or bad. Do you criticize your friends or compliment them? How encouraging is your input?

18:21

^a 7 The meaning of the Hebrew for this sentence is uncertain.

Remember Me?

Profile: Jane

Good things come in threes. You know, three-leaf clovers, triple fudge brownies . . . and girlfriends. That's the way it's always been—Jane, Beverly and Jackee—ever since freshman year. We were so inseparable that last year's class president only signed Bev's yearbook, laughing and saying he figured we were "all basically the same person."

Now the joke's on me. On Monday Jackee and Bev both showed up with new make-up. I felt so confused—I had no idea they had plans together over the weekend. "Oh, it's no big deal," Jackee said. "We just got makeovers on Saturday." She didn't make eye contact. All I could say was, "Oh." What I really wanted to say was, "Remember me? Your other friend?! Since when do we do stuff without all three of us? We've always done everything together!"

Every day they do something else that makes me want to scream. Bev's brother even let it slip that they have a double date this weekend. What makes it even worse is they both know I had a major crush on one of the guys, Adrian Douglass, just last semester. They are being so cruel!

I can't believe they're breaking up our threesome— I know for a fact I'd never dump them like this.

For more on friendship, go to www.TrueImagesBible.com

friendship in focus

Too bad every girl doesn't memorize this mantra: I know someday my friends will disappoint me. But God is my faithful friend, no matter what (see Psalm 62:5–8, page 713). Keep in mind . . .

»It's easy to get jealous when friends ignore you or choose to exclude you. In Romans 13:12–13 (page 1501), jealousy's called "a deed of darkness."

»Never pin all your hope on one human being. Never. You will be disappointed. It's valuable to open up your life to multiple girlfriends so that if one falls away, you still have friends.

»Ask God to teach you something valuable even from the painful experiences in your life. Being ditched by a friend hurts; now you know what it feels like, and you can make sure you never do that to your girlfriends. Let this experience make you a more compassionate and faithful friend.

For more on this topic, see the index on page 1656.

---

¹⁷He who is kind to the poor lends to the LORD,
and he will reward him for what he has done.

¹⁸Discipline your son, for in that there is hope;
do not be a willing party to his death.

¹⁹A hot-tempered man must pay the penalty;
if you rescue him, you will have to do it again.

²⁰Listen to advice and accept instruction,
and in the end you will be wise.

²¹ Many are the plans in a man's heart,
  but it is the LORD's purpose that prevails.

²² What a man desires is unfailing love*;
  better to be poor than a liar.

²³ The fear of the LORD leads to life:
  Then one rests content, untouched by trouble.

²⁴ The sluggard buries his hand in the dish;
  he will not even bring it back to his mouth!

²⁵ Flog a mocker, and the simple will learn prudence;
  rebuke a discerning man, and he will gain knowledge.

²⁶ He who robs his father and drives out his mother
  is a son who brings shame and disgrace.

²⁷ Stop listening to instruction, my son,
  and you will stray from the words of knowledge.

²⁸ A corrupt witness mocks at justice,
  and the mouth of the wicked gulps down evil.

²⁹ Penalties are prepared for mockers,
  and beatings for the backs of fools.

20

Wine is a mocker and beer a brawler;
  whoever is led astray by them is not wise.

² A king's wrath is like the roar of a lion;
  he who angers him forfeits his life.

³ It is to a man's honor to avoid strife,
  but every fool is quick to quarrel.

⁴ A sluggard does not plow in season;
  so at harvest time he looks but finds nothing.

⁵ The purposes of a man's heart are deep waters,
  but a man of understanding draws them out.

⁶ Many a man claims to have unfailing love,
  but a faithful man who can find?

⁷ The righteous man leads a blameless life;
  blessed are his children after him.

⁸ When a king sits on his throne to judge,
  he winnows out all evil with his eyes.

⁹ Who can say, "I have kept my heart pure;
  I am clean and without sin"?

¹⁰ Differing weights and differing measures—
  the LORD detests them both.

truth or dare

Drinking as a teen isn't only illegal; it's also dangerous. Alcohol lowers your defenses, makes a fool of you and leads you astray. Don't follow.

20:1

* 22 Or *A man's greed is his shame*

¹¹Even a child is known by his actions,
    by whether his conduct is pure and right.

¹²Ears that hear and eyes that see—
    the LORD has made them both.

¹³Do not love sleep or you will grow poor;
    stay awake and you will have food to spare.

¹⁴"It's no good, it's no good!" says the buyer;
    then off he goes and boasts about his purchase.

¹⁵Gold there is, and rubies in abundance,
    but lips that speak knowledge are a rare jewel.

¹⁶Take the garment of one who puts up security for a stranger;
    hold it in pledge if he does it for a wayward woman.

¹⁷Food gained by fraud tastes sweet to a man,
    but he ends up with a mouth full of gravel.

¹⁸Make plans by seeking advice;
    if you wage war, obtain guidance.

¹⁹A gossip betrays a confidence;
    so avoid a man who talks too much.

²⁰If a man curses his father or mother,
    his lamp will be snuffed out in pitch darkness.

²¹An inheritance quickly gained at the beginning
    will not be blessed at the end.

²²Do not say, "I'll pay you back for this wrong!"
    Wait for the LORD, and he will deliver you.

²³The LORD detests differing weights,
    and dishonest scales do not please him.

²⁴A man's steps are directed by the LORD.
    How then can anyone understand his own way?

²⁵It is a trap for a man to dedicate something rashly
    and only later to consider his vows.

²⁶A wise king winnows out the wicked;
    he drives the threshing wheel over them.

²⁷The lamp of the LORD searches the spirit of a man ᵃ;
    it searches out his inmost being.

²⁸Love and faithfulness keep a king safe;
    through love his throne is made secure.

²⁹The glory of young men is their strength,
    gray hair the splendor of the old.

³⁰Blows and wounds cleanse away evil,
    and beatings purge the inmost being.

21

The king's heart is in the hand of the LORD;
    he directs it like a watercourse wherever he pleases.

²All a man's ways seem right to him,
    but the LORD weighs the heart.

ᵃ 27 Or The spirit of man is the LORD's lamp

³ To do what is right and just
   is more acceptable to the LORD than sacrifice.

⁴ Haughty eyes and a proud heart,
   the lamp of the wicked, are sin!

⁵ The plans of the diligent lead to profit
   as surely as haste leads to poverty.

⁶ A fortune made by a lying tongue
   is a fleeting vapor and a deadly snare.ᵃ

⁷ The violence of the wicked will drag them away,
   for they refuse to do what is right.

⁸ The way of the guilty is devious,
   but the conduct of the
      innocent is upright.

⁹ Better to live on a corner of the
      roof
   than share a house with a
      quarrelsome wife.

¹⁰ The wicked man craves evil;
   his neighbor gets no mercy
      from him.

¹¹ When a mocker is punished, the
      simple gain wisdom;
   when a wise man is
      instructed, he gets
      knowledge.

¹² The Righteous Oneᵇ takes note
      of the house of the
      wicked
   and brings the wicked to ruin.

¹³ If a man shuts his ears to the cry
      of the poor,
   he too will cry out and not be
      answered.

¹⁴ A gift given in secret soothes
      anger,
   and a bribe concealed in the
      cloak pacifies great
      wrath.

¹⁵ When justice is done, it brings
      joy to the righteous
   but terror to evildoers.

¹⁶ A man who strays from the path
      of understanding
   comes to rest in the company
      of the dead.

love ♥ notes

21:2–3

Loved one,

Do you see what matters most
to me? It's not your offerings, or
the time you spend doing ministry. It's your heart. Is it totally
committed to me? Or are you
just going through the motions?

—Your Father in heaven

Do a heart check. How would you
answer those questions above?

_____

_____

_____

_____

_____

_____

_____

_____

_____

ᵃ 6 Some Hebrew manuscripts, Septuagint and
Vulgate; most Hebrew manuscripts *vapor for those who
seek death*   ᵇ 12 Or *The righteous man*

¹⁷ He who loves pleasure will become poor;
  whoever loves wine and oil will never be rich.

¹⁸ The wicked become a ransom for the righteous,
  and the unfaithful for the upright.

¹⁹ Better to live in a desert
  than with a quarrelsome and ill-tempered wife.

²⁰ In the house of the wise are stores of choice food and oil,
  but a foolish man devours all he has.

²¹ He who pursues righteousness and love
  finds life, prosperity *a* and honor.

²² A wise man attacks the city of the mighty
  and pulls down the stronghold in which they trust.

²³ He who guards his mouth and his tongue
  keeps himself from calamity.

²⁴ The proud and arrogant man—"Mocker" is his name;
  he behaves with overweening pride.

²⁵ The sluggard's craving will be the death of him,
  because his hands refuse to work.
²⁶ All day long he craves for more,
  but the righteous give without sparing.

²⁷ The sacrifice of the wicked is detestable—
  how much more so when brought with evil intent!

²⁸ A false witness will perish,
  and whoever listens to him will be destroyed forever. *b*

²⁹ A wicked man puts up a bold front,
  but an upright man gives thought to his ways.

³⁰ There is no wisdom, no insight, no plan
  that can succeed against the Lord.

³¹ The horse is made ready for the day of battle,
  but victory rests with the Lord.

22 A good name is more desirable than great riches;
  to be esteemed is better than silver or gold.

² Rich and poor have this in common:
  The Lord is the Maker of them all.

³ A prudent man sees danger and takes refuge,
  but the simple keep going and suffer for it.

⁴ Humility and the fear of the Lord
  bring wealth and honor and life.

⁵ In the paths of the wicked lie thorns and snares,
  but he who guards his soul stays far from them.

⁶ Train *c* a child in the way he should go,
  and when he is old he will not turn from it.

⁷ The rich rule over the poor,
  and the borrower is servant to the lender.

a 21 Or righteousness   *b 28 Or / but the words of an obedient man will live on*   *c 6 Or Start*

⁸ He who sows wickedness reaps trouble,
    and the rod of his fury will be destroyed.

⁹ A generous man will himself be blessed,
    for he shares his food with the poor.

¹⁰ Drive out the mocker, and out goes strife;
    quarrels and insults are ended.

¹¹ He who loves a pure heart and whose speech is gracious
    will have the king for his friend.

¹² The eyes of the LORD keep watch over knowledge,
    but he frustrates the words of the unfaithful.

¹³ The sluggard says, "There is a lion outside!"
    or, "I will be murdered in the streets!"

¹⁴ The mouth of an adulteress is a deep pit;
    he who is under the LORD's wrath will fall into it.

¹⁵ Folly is bound up in the heart of a child,
    but the rod of discipline will drive it far from him.

¹⁶ He who oppresses the poor to increase his wealth
    and he who gives gifts to the rich—both come to poverty.

Sayings of the Wise

¹⁷ Pay attention and listen to the sayings of the wise;
    apply your heart to what I teach,
¹⁸ for it is pleasing when you keep them in your heart
    and have all of them ready on your lips.
¹⁹ So that your trust may be in the LORD,
    I teach you today, even you.
²⁰ Have I not written thirty ᵃ sayings for you,
    sayings of counsel and knowledge,
²¹ teaching you true and reliable words,
    so that you can give sound answers
    to him who sent you?

²² Do not exploit the poor because they are poor
    and do not crush the needy in court,
²³ for the LORD will take up their case
    and will plunder those who plunder them.

²⁴ Do not make friends with a hot-tempered man,
    do not associate with one easily angered,
²⁵ or you may learn his ways
    and get yourself ensnared.

²⁶ Do not be a man who strikes hands in pledge
    or puts up security for debts;
²⁷ if you lack the means to pay,
    your very bed will be snatched from under you.

²⁸ Do not move an ancient boundary stone
    set up by your forefathers.

²⁹ Do you see a man skilled in his work?
    He will serve before kings;
    he will not serve before obscure men.

ᵃ 20 Or not formerly written; or not written excellent

When you sit to dine with a ruler,
note well what[a] is before you,
[2] and put a knife to your throat
if you are given to gluttony.
[3] Do not crave his delicacies,
for that food is deceptive.

[4] Do not wear yourself out to get rich;
have the wisdom to show restraint.
[5] Cast but a glance at riches, and they are gone,
for they will surely sprout wings
and fly off to the sky like an eagle.

[6] Do not eat the food of a stingy man,
do not crave his delicacies;
[7] for he is the kind of man
who is always thinking about the cost.[b]
"Eat and drink," he says to you,
but his heart is not with you.
[8] You will vomit up the little you have eaten
and will have wasted your compliments.

[9] Do not speak to a fool,
for he will scorn the wisdom of your words.

[10] Do not move an ancient boundary stone
or encroach on the fields of the fatherless,
[11] for their Defender is strong;
he will take up their case against you.

[12] Apply your heart to instruction
and your ears to words of knowledge.

[13] Do not withhold discipline from a child;
if you punish him with the rod, he will not die.
[14] Punish him with the rod
and save his soul from death.[c]

[15] My son, if your heart is wise,
then my heart will be glad;
[16] my inmost being will rejoice
when your lips speak what is right.

[17] Do not let your heart envy sinners,
but always be zealous for the fear of the LORD.
[18] There is surely a future hope for you,
and your hope will not be cut off.

[19] Listen, my son, and be wise,
and keep your heart on the right path.
[20] Do not join those who drink too much wine
or gorge themselves on meat,
[21] for drunkards and gluttons become poor,
and drowsiness clothes them in rags.

[22] Listen to your father, who gave you life,
and do not despise your mother when she is old.
[23] Buy the truth and do not sell it;
get wisdom, discipline and understanding.

---

a 1 Or who   *b 7 Or for as he thinks within himself, / so he is; or for as he puts on a feast, / so he is*   *c 14 Hebrew Sheol*

²⁴ The father of a righteous man has great joy;
     he who has a wise son delights in him.
²⁵ May your father and mother be glad;
     may she who gave you birth rejoice!

²⁶ My son, give me your heart
     and let your eyes keep to my ways,
²⁷ for a prostitute is a deep pit
     and a wayward wife is a narrow well.
²⁸ Like a bandit she lies in wait,
     and multiplies the unfaithful among men.

²⁹ Who has woe? Who has sorrow?
     Who has strife? Who has complaints?
     Who has needless bruises? Who has bloodshot eyes?
³⁰ Those who linger over wine,
     who go to sample bowls of mixed wine.
³¹ Do not gaze at wine when it is red,
     when it sparkles in the cup,
     when it goes down smoothly!
³² In the end it bites like a snake
     and poisons like a viper.
³³ Your eyes will see strange sights
     and your mind imagine confusing things.
³⁴ You will be like one sleeping on the high seas,
     lying on top of the rigging.
³⁵ "They hit me," you will say, "but I'm not hurt!
     They beat me, but I don't feel it!
     When will I wake up
     so I can find another drink?"

24

Do not envy wicked men,
     do not desire their company;
² for their hearts plot violence,
     and their lips talk about making trouble.

³ By wisdom a house is built,
     and through understanding it is established;
⁴ through knowledge its rooms are filled
     with rare and beautiful treasures.

⁵ A wise man has great power,
     and a man of knowledge increases strength;
⁶ for waging war you need guidance,
     and for victory many advisers.

⁷ Wisdom is too high for a fool;
     in the assembly at the gate he has nothing to say.

⁸ He who plots evil
     will be known as a schemer.
⁹ The schemes of folly are sin,
     and men detest a mocker.

¹⁰ If you falter in times of trouble,
     how small is your strength!

¹¹ Rescue those being led away to death;
     hold back those staggering toward slaughter.
¹² If you say, "But we knew nothing about this,"

does not he who weighs the
heart perceive it?
Does not he who guards your life
know it?
Will he not repay each person
according to what he
has done?

Eat honey, my son, for it is good;
honey from the comb is sweet
to your taste.

Know also that wisdom is sweet
to your soul;
if you find it, there is a future hope for
you,
and your hope will not be cut off.

Do not lie in wait like an outlaw against a
righteous man's house,
do not raid his dwelling place;

for though a righteous man falls seven times, he rises again,
but the wicked are brought down by calamity.

Do not gloat when your enemy falls;
when he stumbles, do not let your heart rejoice,

or the LORD will see and disapprove
and turn his wrath away from him.

Do not fret because of evil men
or be envious of the wicked,

for the evil man has no future hope,
and the lamp of the wicked will be snuffed out.

Fear the LORD and the king, my son,
and do not join with the rebellious,

for those two will send sudden destruction upon them,
and who knows what calamities they can bring?

Further Sayings of the Wise

23These also are sayings of the wise:

To show partiality in judging is not good:
24Whoever says to the guilty, "You are innocent"—
peoples will curse him and nations denounce him.
25But it will go well with those who convict the guilty,
and rich blessing will come upon them.

26An honest answer
is like a kiss on the lips.

27Finish your outdoor work
and get your fields ready;
after that, build your house.

28Do not testify against your neighbor without cause,
or use your lips to deceive.
29Do not say, "I'll do to him as he has done to me;
I'll pay that man back for what he did."

30I went past the field of the sluggard,
past the vineyard of the man who lacks judgment;

truth or dare

Welcome to spiritual boot camp! When you face problems, think of them as small obstacles that build your strength for the spiritual battles ahead.

24:10

proverbs 24:30

839

³¹ thorns had come up everywhere,
  the ground was covered with weeds,
  and the stone wall was in ruins.
³² I applied my heart to what I observed
  and learned a lesson from what I saw:
³³ A little sleep, a little slumber,
  a little folding of the hands to rest—
³⁴ and poverty will come on you like a bandit
  and scarcity like an armed man. ᵃ

More Proverbs of Solomon

25 These are more proverbs of Solomon, copied by the men of Hezekiah king of Judah:

² It is the glory of God to conceal a matter;
  to search out a matter is the glory of kings.

³ As the heavens are high and the earth is deep,
  so the hearts of kings are unsearchable.

⁴ Remove the dross from the silver,
  and out comes material for ᵇ the silversmith;
⁵ remove the wicked from the king's presence,
  and his throne will be established through righteousness.

⁶ Do not exalt yourself in the king's presence,
  and do not claim a place among great men;
⁷ it is better for him to say to you, "Come up here,"
  than for him to humiliate you before a nobleman.

What you have seen with your eyes
⁸   do not bring ᶜ hastily to court,
for what will you do in the end
  if your neighbor puts you to shame?

⁹ If you argue your case with a neighbor,
  do not betray another man's confidence,
¹⁰ or he who hears it may shame you
  and you will never lose your bad reputation.

¹¹ A word aptly spoken
  is like apples of gold in settings of silver.

¹² Like an earring of gold or an ornament of fine gold
  is a wise man's rebuke to a listening ear.

¹³ Like the coolness of snow at harvest time
  is a trustworthy messenger to those who send him;
  he refreshes the spirit of his masters.

¹⁴ Like clouds and wind without rain
  is a man who boasts of gifts he does not give.

¹⁵ Through patience a ruler can be persuaded,
  and a gentle tongue can break a bone.

¹⁶ If you find honey, eat just enough—
  too much of it, and you will vomit.
¹⁷ Seldom set foot in your neighbor's house—
  too much of you, and he will hate you.

ᵃ 34 Or *like a vagrant / and scarcity like a beggar*   ᵇ 4 Or *comes a vessel from*   ᶜ 7,8 Or *nobleman / on whom you had set your eyes. / ⁸Do not go*

¹⁸ Like a club or a sword or a sharp
arrow
is the man who gives false
testimony against his
neighbor.

¹⁹ Like a bad tooth or a lame foot
is reliance on the unfaithful in
times of trouble.

²⁰ Like one who takes away a
garment on a cold day,
or like vinegar poured on soda,
is one who sings songs to a heavy heart.

²¹ If your enemy is hungry, give him food to eat;
if he is thirsty, give him water to drink.

²² In doing this, you will heap burning coals on
his head,
and the LORD will reward you.

²³ As a north wind brings rain,
so a sly tongue brings angry looks.

²⁴ Better to live on a corner of the roof
than share a house with a quarrelsome wife.

²⁵ Like cold water to a weary soul
is good news from a distant land.

²⁶ Like a muddied spring or a polluted well
is a righteous man who gives way to the wicked.

²⁷ It is not good to eat too much honey,
nor is it honorable to seek one's own honor.

²⁸ Like a city whose walls are broken down
is a man who lacks self-control.

26

Like snow in summer or rain in harvest,
honor is not fitting for a fool.

² Like a fluttering sparrow or a darting swallow,
an undeserved curse does not come to rest.

³ A whip for the horse, a halter for the donkey,
and a rod for the backs of fools!

⁴ Do not answer a fool according to his folly,
or you will be like him yourself.

⁵ Answer a fool according to his folly,
or he will be wise in his own eyes.

⁶ Like cutting off one's feet or drinking violence
is the sending of a message by the hand of a fool.

⁷ Like a lame man's legs that hang limp
is a proverb in the mouth of a fool.

⁸ Like tying a stone in a sling
is the giving of honor to a fool.

⁹ Like a thornbush in a drunkard's hand
is a proverb in the mouth of a fool.

truth or dare

Having an unfaithful friend can be like walking through life with a painful limp. Don't depend on an untrustworthy girl! Remember, only God is 100 percent dependable.

25:19

¹⁰ Like an archer who wounds at random
    is he who hires a fool or any passer-by.

¹¹ As a dog returns to its vomit,
    so a fool repeats his folly.

¹² Do you see a man wise in his own eyes?
    There is more hope for a fool than for him.

¹³ The sluggard says, "There is a lion in the road,
    a fierce lion roaming the streets!"

¹⁴ As a door turns on its hinges,
    so a sluggard turns on his bed.

¹⁵ The sluggard buries his hand in the dish;
    he is too lazy to bring it back to his mouth.

¹⁶ The sluggard is wiser in his own eyes
    than seven men who answer discreetly.

¹⁷ Like one who seizes a dog by the ears
    is a passer-by who meddles in a quarrel not his own.

¹⁸ Like a madman shooting
    firebrands or deadly arrows
¹⁹ is a man who deceives his neighbor
    and says, "I was only joking!"

²⁰ Without wood a fire goes out;
    without gossip a quarrel dies down.

²¹ As charcoal to embers and as wood to fire,
    so is a quarrelsome man for kindling strife.

²² The words of a gossip are like choice morsels;
    they go down to a man's inmost parts.

²³ Like a coating of glaze *a* over earthenware
    are fervent lips with an evil heart.

²⁴ A malicious man disguises himself with his lips,
    but in his heart he harbors deceit.
²⁵ Though his speech is charming, do not believe him,
    for seven abominations fill his heart.
²⁶ His malice may be concealed by deception,
    but his wickedness will be exposed in the assembly.

²⁷ If a man digs a pit, he will fall into it;
    if a man rolls a stone, it will roll back on him.

²⁸ A lying tongue hates those it hurts,
    and a flattering mouth works ruin.

27

Do not boast about tomorrow,
    for you do not know what a day may bring forth.

² Let another praise you, and not your own mouth;
    someone else, and not your own lips.

³ Stone is heavy and sand a burden,
    but provocation by a fool is heavier than both.

⁴ Anger is cruel and fury overwhelming,
    but who can stand before jealousy?

a 23 With a different word division of the Hebrew; Masoretic Text *of silver dross*

ξenuine

humility »» 27:2

Have you ever been around someone who couldn't stop talking about herself? She tells you more than you ever wanted to know about her shopping, her diet, her makeup, her social life and her talents. Even if she deserves praise, you probably don't say anything because she's so full of herself she doesn't need to hear more. Take this lesson to heart—let someone else praise you. Do your best and then let your work speak for itself. Even if no one else notices, God does. And his praise is much better than your own.

⁵ Better is open rebuke
than hidden love.

⁶ Wounds from a friend can be
trusted,
but an enemy multiplies
kisses.

⁷ He who is full loathes honey,
but to the hungry even what is
bitter tastes sweet.

⁸ Like a bird that strays from its
nest
is a man who strays from his
home.

⁹ Perfume and incense bring joy to
the heart,
and the pleasantness of one's
friend springs from his
earnest counsel.

¹⁰ Do not forsake your friend and
the friend of your father,
and do not go to your
brother's house when
disaster strikes you—
better a neighbor nearby than
a brother far away.

¹¹ Be wise, my son, and bring joy to my heart;
then I can answer anyone who treats me with contempt.

¹² The prudent see danger and take refuge,
but the simple keep going and suffer for it.

¹³ Take the garment of one who
puts up security for a
stranger;
hold it in pledge if he does it
for a wayward woman.

¹⁴ If a man loudly blesses his
neighbor early in the
morning,
it will be taken as a curse.

¹⁵ A quarrelsome wife is like
a constant dripping on a rainy
day;
¹⁶ restraining her is like restraining the wind
or grasping oil with the hand.

¹⁷ As iron sharpens iron,
so one man sharpens another.

¹⁸ He who tends a fig tree will eat its fruit,
and he who looks after his master will be honored.

¹⁹ As water reflects a face,
so a man's heart reflects the man.

truth or dare

Close girlfriends can sometimes become complete clones of each other. Why don't you step out and share your faith with your buds to help them grow? It's sharpening time!

27:17

[20] Death and Destruction[a] are never satisfied,
  and neither are the eyes of man.

[21] The crucible for silver and the furnace for gold,
  but man is tested by the praise he receives.

[22] Though you grind a fool in a mortar,
  grinding him like grain with a pestle,
  you will not remove his folly from him.

[23] Be sure you know the condition of your flocks,
  give careful attention to your herds;
[24] for riches do not endure forever,
  and a crown is not secure for all generations.
[25] When the hay is removed and new growth appears
  and the grass from the hills is gathered in,
[26] the lambs will provide you with clothing,
  and the goats with the price of a field.
[27] You will have plenty of goats' milk
  to feed you and your family
  and to nourish your servant girls.

28

The wicked man flees though no one pursues,
  but the righteous are as bold as a lion.

[2] When a country is rebellious, it has many rulers,
  but a man of understanding and knowledge maintains order.

[3] A ruler[b] who oppresses the poor
  is like a driving rain that leaves no crops.

[4] Those who forsake the law praise the wicked,
  but those who keep the law resist them.

[5] Evil men do not understand justice,
  but those who seek the LORD understand it fully.

[6] Better a poor man whose walk is
    blameless
  than a rich man whose ways
    are perverse.

[7] He who keeps the law is a
    discerning son,
  but a companion of gluttons
    disgraces his father.

[8] He who increases his wealth by
    exorbitant interest
  amasses it for another, who
    will be kind to the poor.

[9] If anyone turns a deaf ear to the law,
  even his prayers are detestable.

[10] He who leads the upright along an evil path
  will fall into his own trap,
  but the blameless will receive a good inheritance.

[11] A rich man may be wise in his own eyes,
  but a poor man who has discernment sees through him.

truth or dare

Which would you prefer: Broke and honest, or rich and corrupt? Strong women choose to invest in integrity rather than chasing after cash.

28:6

[a] 20 Hebrew *Sheol and Abaddon*   [b] 3 Or *A poor man*

¹²When the righteous triumph, there is great elation;
    but when the wicked rise to power, men go into hiding.

¹³He who conceals his sins does not prosper,
    but whoever confesses and renounces them finds mercy.

¹⁴Blessed is the man who always fears the LORD,
    but he who hardens his heart falls into trouble.

¹⁵Like a roaring lion or a charging bear
    is a wicked man ruling over a helpless people.

¹⁶A tyrannical ruler lacks judgment,
    but he who hates ill-gotten gain will enjoy a long life.

¹⁷A man tormented by the guilt of murder
    will be a fugitive till death;
    let no one support him.

¹⁸He whose walk is blameless is kept safe,
    but he whose ways are perverse will suddenly fall.

¹⁹He who works his land will have abundant food,
    but the one who chases fantasies will have his fill of poverty.

²⁰A faithful man will be richly blessed,
    but one eager to get rich will not go unpunished.

²¹To show partiality is not good—
    yet a man will do wrong for a piece of bread.

²²A stingy man is eager to get rich
    and is unaware that poverty awaits him.

²³He who rebukes a man will in the end gain more favor
    than he who has a flattering tongue.

²⁴He who robs his father or mother
    and says, "It's not wrong"—
    he is partner to him who destroys.

²⁵A greedy man stirs up dissension,
    but he who trusts in the LORD will prosper.

²⁶He who trusts in himself is a fool,
    but he who walks in wisdom is kept safe.

²⁷He who gives to the poor will lack nothing,
    but he who closes his eyes to them receives many curses.

²⁸When the wicked rise to power, people go into hiding;
    but when the wicked perish, the righteous thrive.

29

A man who remains stiff-necked after many rebukes
    will suddenly be destroyed—without remedy.

²When the righteous thrive, the people rejoice;
    when the wicked rule, the people groan.

³A man who loves wisdom brings joy to his father,
    but a companion of prostitutes squanders his wealth.

⁴By justice a king gives a country stability,
    but one who is greedy for bribes tears it down.

⁵Whoever flatters his neighbor
    is spreading a net for his feet.

⁶An evil man is snared by his own sin,
  but a righteous one can sing and be glad.

⁷The righteous care about justice for the poor,
  but the wicked have no such concern.

⁸Mockers stir up a city,
  but wise men turn away anger.

⁹If a wise man goes to court with a fool,
  the fool rages and scoffs, and there is no peace.

¹⁰Bloodthirsty men hate a man of integrity
  and seek to kill the upright.

¹¹A fool gives full vent to his anger,
  but a wise man keeps himself
    under control.

¹²If a ruler listens to lies,
  all his officials become
    wicked.

¹³The poor man and the oppressor
  have this in common:
  The Lord gives sight to the
    eyes of both.

¹⁴If a king judges the poor with fairness,
  his throne will always be secure.

¹⁵The rod of correction imparts wisdom,
  but a child left to himself disgraces his
    mother.

¹⁶When the wicked thrive, so does sin,
  but the righteous will see their downfall.

¹⁷Discipline your son, and he will give you peace;
  he will bring delight to your soul.

¹⁸Where there is no revelation, the people cast off restraint;
  but blessed is he who keeps the law.

¹⁹A servant cannot be corrected by mere words;
  though he understands, he will not respond.

²⁰Do you see a man who speaks in haste?
  There is more hope for a fool than for him.

²¹If a man pampers his servant from youth,
  he will bring grief*ᵃ* in the end.

²²An angry man stirs up dissension,
  and a hot-tempered one commits many sins.

²³A man's pride brings him low,
  but a man of lowly spirit gains honor.

²⁴The accomplice of a thief is his own enemy;
  he is put under oath and dare not testify.

²⁵Fear of man will prove to be a snare,
  but whoever trusts in the Lord is kept safe.

truth or dare

Bag the PMS excuse—letting your temper fly never fixes a situation. While you can't control another person's actions, you can work on whipping your rage into shape.

29:11,22

ᵃ 21 The meaning of the Hebrew for this word is uncertain.

²⁶ Many seek an audience with a ruler,
    but it is from the LORD that man gets justice.

²⁷ The righteous detest the dishonest;
    the wicked detest the upright.

Sayings of Agur

30 The sayings of Agur son of Jakeh—an oracle ᵃ:

    This man declared to Ithiel,
      to Ithiel and to Ucal: ᵇ

² "I am the most ignorant of men;
    I do not have a man's understanding.
³ I have not learned wisdom,
    nor have I knowledge of the Holy One.
⁴ Who has gone up to heaven and come down?
    Who has gathered up the wind in the hollow of his hands?
Who has wrapped up the waters in his cloak?
    Who has established all the ends of the earth?
What is his name, and the name of his son?
    Tell me if you know!

⁵ "Every word of God is flawless;
    he is a shield to those who take refuge in him.
⁶ Do not add to his words,
    or he will rebuke you and prove you a liar.

⁷ "Two things I ask of you, O LORD;
    do not refuse me before I die:
⁸ Keep falsehood and lies far from me;
    give me neither poverty nor riches,
    but give me only my daily bread.
⁹ Otherwise, I may have too much and disown you
    and say, 'Who is the LORD?'
Or I may become poor and steal,
    and so dishonor the name of my God.

¹⁰ "Do not slander a servant to his master,
    or he will curse you, and you will pay for it.

¹¹ "There are those who curse their fathers
    and do not bless their mothers;
¹² those who are pure in their own eyes
    and yet are not cleansed of their filth;
¹³ those whose eyes are ever so haughty,
    whose glances are so disdainful;
¹⁴ those whose teeth are swords
    and whose jaws are set with knives
to devour the poor from the earth,
    the needy from among mankind.

¹⁵ "The leech has two daughters.
    'Give! Give!' they cry.

"There are three things that are never satisfied,
    four that never say, 'Enough!':

ᵃ 1 Or *Jakeh of Massa*   ᵇ 1 Masoretic Text; with a different word division of the Hebrew *declared,* "I am weary, O God; /
I am weary, O God, and faint.

mirror images

Charm is deceptive, and beauty is fleeting; but a woman who fears the LORD is to be praised. Proverbs 31:30

Proverbs 31 Woman—Godliness in the Real World

A noble girl is worth more than diamonds.

Her family can trust her because she's always trustworthy.

She gets home by her curfew, obeys her parents and keeps her word.

She's easy to be around, and she makes other people's lives better.

She expands her mind by being willing to learn different kinds of skills and subjects.

She gets up in the morning without being crabby and helps around the house even more than what's required of her.

She knows the value of money and doesn't waste it.

She works hard and does her best at school, never settling for "good enough."

Whatever she tries, she always has a good attitude and gives it her best shot.

She isn't lazy.

She is kind and compassionate to everyone, regardless of popularity or personality.

She looks for ways to help those who have less than she does.

She makes wise choices and thinks ahead so she won't have regrets later.

Her family is proud of the choices she makes.

She carries herself with strength and dignity, not making a fool of herself.

She doesn't gossip, gripe, lie, insult or offer unwanted opinions.

She reads God's Word and seeks him for wisdom.

Her beauty doesn't come from what she wears or how her hair looks.

Her personality is sincere, not self-gratifying and fake.

She is beautiful because she is filled with a passion for God.

To read the next Mirror Images profile, go to page 859.

Dear God, there are so many opportunities for me to serve you! As I read about being a godly woman, help me to choose to seek you in all the things that I do. Amen.

>> Read the poem about a godly woman in Proverbs 31:10–31 (pages 850-851).

16 the grave,^a the barren womb,
    land, which is never satisfied with water,
    and fire, which never says, 'Enough!'

17 "The eye that mocks a father,
    that scorns obedience to a mother,
will be pecked out by the ravens of the valley,
    will be eaten by the vultures.

18 "There are three things that are too amazing for me,
    four that I do not understand:
19 the way of an eagle in the sky,
    the way of a snake on a rock,
the way of a ship on the high seas,
    and the way of a man with a maiden.

20 "This is the way of an adulteress:
    She eats and wipes her mouth
    and says, 'I've done nothing wrong.'

21 "Under three things the earth trembles,
    under four it cannot bear up:
22 a servant who becomes king,
    a fool who is full of food,
23 an unloved woman who is married,
    and a maidservant who displaces her mistress.

24 "Four things on earth are small,
    yet they are extremely wise:
25 Ants are creatures of little strength,
    yet they store up their food in the summer;
26 coneys^b are creatures of little power,
    yet they make their home in the crags;
27 locusts have no king,
    yet they advance together in ranks;
28 a lizard can be caught with the hand,
    yet it is found in kings' palaces.

29 "There are three things that are stately in their stride,
    four that move with stately bearing:
30 a lion, mighty among beasts,
    who retreats before nothing;
31 a strutting rooster, a he-goat,
    and a king with his army around him.^c

32 "If you have played the fool and exalted yourself,
    or if you have planned evil,
    clap your hand over your mouth!
33 For as churning the milk produces butter,
    and as twisting the nose produces blood,
    so stirring up anger produces strife."

Sayings of King Lemuel

31 The sayings of King Lemuel—an oracle^d his mother taught him:

2 "O my son, O son of my womb,
    O son of my vows,^e

---

^a 16 Hebrew *Sheol*   ^b 26 That is, the hyrax or rock badger   ^c 31 Or *king secure against revolt*   ^d 1 Or *of Lemuel king of Massa, which*   ^e 2 Or / *the answer to my prayers*

³ do not spend your strength on women,
   your vigor on those who ruin kings.

⁴ "It is not for kings, O Lemuel—
   not for kings to drink wine,
   not for rulers to crave beer,
⁵ lest they drink and forget what the law decrees,
   and deprive all the oppressed of their rights.
⁶ Give beer to those who are perishing,
   wine to those who are in anguish;
⁷ let them drink and forget their poverty
   and remember their misery no more.

⁸ "Speak up for those who cannot speak for themselves,
   for the rights of all who are destitute.
⁹ Speak up and judge fairly;
   defend the rights of the poor and needy."

Epilogue: The Wife of Noble Character

¹⁰ ᵃ A wife of noble character who can find?
   She is worth far more than rubies.
¹¹ Her husband has full confidence in her
   and lacks nothing of value.
¹² She brings him good, not harm,
   all the days of her life.
¹³ She selects wool and flax
   and works with eager hands.
¹⁴ She is like the merchant ships,
   bringing her food from afar.
¹⁵ She gets up while it is still dark;
   she provides food for her family
   and portions for her servant
      girls.
¹⁶ She considers a field and buys it;
   out of her earnings she plants a vineyard.
¹⁷ She sets about her work vigorously;
   her arms are strong for her tasks.
¹⁸ She sees that her trading is profitable,
   and her lamp does not go out at night.
¹⁹ In her hand she holds the distaff
   and grasps the spindle with her fingers.
²⁰ She opens her arms to the poor
   and extends her hands to the needy.
²¹ When it snows, she has no fear for her household;
   for all of them are clothed in scarlet.
²² She makes coverings for her bed;
   she is clothed in fine linen and purple.
²³ Her husband is respected at the city gate,
   where he takes his seat among the elders of the land.
²⁴ She makes linen garments and sells them,
   and supplies the merchants with sashes.
²⁵ She is clothed with strength and dignity;
   she can laugh at the days to come.
²⁶ She speaks with wisdom,
   and faithful instruction is on her tongue.

truth or dare

Nobility hasn't been lost to the Dark Ages! God (and any great guy) judges a woman's worth by her strong, virtuous and dignified character (a.k.a. nobility), not her accessories.

31:10–19

ᵃ 10 Verses 10-31 are an acrostic, each verse beginning with a successive letter of the Hebrew alphabet.

genuine

How many eighty-year-old models do you see on magazine covers? Even the most beautiful women eventually get old and forgotten. No matter how beautiful they once were, their beauty just doesn't last. It's fleeting—going, going, gone. You probably spend a lot of time trying to look your best. That's fine, but you also need to spend time with God so that you develop lasting beauty—the kind of character that sets you apart and doesn't fade with time. It gets better and better, making you beautiful no matter how old you are.

[27] She watches over the affairs of her household
and does not eat the bread of idleness.

[28] Her children arise and call her blessed;
her husband also, and he praises her:

[29] "Many women do noble things, but you surpass them all."

[30] Charm is deceptive, and beauty is fleeting;
but a woman who fears the Lord is to be praised.

[31] Give her the reward she has earned,
and let her works bring her praise at the city gate.

author: Probably King Solomon.

date: Probably near the end of Solomon's life (930 B.C.)

setting: Solomon went through a time in his life when he was apart from God, experimenting with sins like idolatry and materialism. In the book of Ecclesiastes he reflects on his experiences.

verse to remember: Now all has been heard; here is the conclusion of the matter: Fear God and keep his commandments, for this is the whole duty of man (12:13).

theme to consider: Life is meaningless apart from a relationship with the Lord. Solomon found that power, popularity, prestige and pleasure really don't satisfy.

ecclesiastes

unchanging truth

Close your eyes and dream for a minute . . . Your life is perfect. You are gorgeous—perfect hair, perfect skin, perfect body. Oh, and not only that, you're fabulously rich! You have it all. . . .

Solomon, king of Israel, lived that dream. He was fabulously rich. He had power, popularity and prestige; he could enjoy any pleasure that he desired—and he did. He documents his quests in this book. The king pursued knowledge; he indulged in every possible pleasure that money could buy.

And do you know what he concluded? "Everything is meaningless."

That seems a little bit depressing for a book in the Bible, doesn't it? But that's not really the end of the story. You see, Solomon discovered that deep within him was a desire for something that could not be satisfied with all the riches and power in the world. That "something" had to do with a relationship with his Creator. God infuses everything we do for him with meaning and purpose. Without God, nothing will satisfy.

The only way to be fulfilled in life is not to chase after beauty, money or fame—for, as Solomon discovered, these are like chasing the wind. Instead, "Fear God and keep his commandments."

Now open your eyes . . . you already *are* living the dream. In your relationship with God, you have everything you need for a meaningful life.

life lessons

1. No matter what we can learn (1:13), enjoy (2:1–3) or attain (2:4–11), we will have nothing unless we have a personal relationship with God (1:2; 2:24–25).

2. Remember your Creator while you're young. If you stick with God *now*, while you're young, you'll have a head start on avoiding many painful mistakes and heartache in life (12:1).

3. The only way to have a meaningful life is to fear God and keep his commandments (12:13–14).

Everything Is Meaningless

1 The words of the Teacher,*ᵃ* son of David, king in Jerusalem:

²"Meaningless! Meaningless!"
　　says the Teacher.
"Utterly meaningless!
　　Everything is meaningless."

³What does man gain from all his labor
　　at which he toils under the sun?
⁴Generations come and generations go,
　　but the earth remains forever.
⁵The sun rises and the sun sets,
　　and hurries back to where it
　　　　rises.
⁶The wind blows to the south
　　and turns to the north;
round and round it goes,
　　ever returning on its course.
⁷All streams flow into the sea,
　　yet the sea is never full.
To the place the streams come
　　　　from,
　　there they return again.
⁸All things are wearisome,
　　more than one can say.
The eye never has enough of seeing,
　　nor the ear its fill of hearing.
⁹What has been will be again,
　　what has been done will be done again;
　　there is nothing new under the sun.
¹⁰Is there anything of which one can say,
　　"Look! This is something new"?
It was here already, long ago;
　　it was here before our time.
¹¹There is no remembrance of men of old,
　　and even those who are yet to come
will not be remembered
　　by those who follow.

truth or dare

Whoa! Was Solomon depressed or *what?* Actually, he was conducting a major life experiment. His conclusion? Without God, *everything* loses meaning.

1:2–3

Wisdom Is Meaningless

¹²I, the Teacher, was king over Israel in Jerusalem. ¹³I devoted myself to study and to explore by wisdom all that is done under heaven. What a heavy burden God has laid on men! ¹⁴I have seen all the things that are done under the sun; all of them are meaningless, a chasing after the wind.

¹⁵What is twisted cannot be straightened;
　　what is lacking cannot be counted.

¹⁶I thought to myself, "Look, I have grown and increased in wisdom more than anyone who has ruled over Jerusalem before me; I have experienced much of wisdom and knowledge." ¹⁷Then I applied myself to the understanding of wisdom, and also of madness and folly, but I learned that this, too, is a chasing after the wind.

¹⁸For with much wisdom comes much sorrow;
　　the more knowledge, the more grief.

ᵃ 1 Or leader of the assembly; also in verses 2 and 12

Pleasures Are Meaningless

2 I thought in my heart, "Come now, I will test you with pleasure to find out what is good." But that also proved to be meaningless. [2]"Laughter," I said, "is foolish. And what does pleasure accomplish?" [3]I tried cheering myself with wine, and embracing folly—my mind still guiding me with wisdom. I wanted to see what was worthwhile for men to do under heaven during the few days of their lives.

[4]I undertook great projects: I built houses for myself and planted vineyards. [5]I made gardens and parks and planted all kinds of fruit trees in them. [6]I made reservoirs to water groves of flourishing trees. [7]I bought male and female slaves and had other slaves who were born in my house. I also owned more herds and flocks than anyone in Jerusalem before me. [8]I amassed silver and gold for myself, and the treasure of kings and provinces. I acquired men and women singers, and a harem[a] as well—the delights of the heart of man. [9]I became greater by far than anyone in Jerusalem before me. In all this my wisdom stayed with me.

[10]I denied myself nothing my eyes desired;
    I refused my heart no pleasure.
My heart took delight in all my work,
    and this was the reward for all my labor.
[11]Yet when I surveyed all that my hands had done
    and what I had toiled to achieve,
everything was meaningless, a chasing after the wind;
    nothing was gained under the sun.

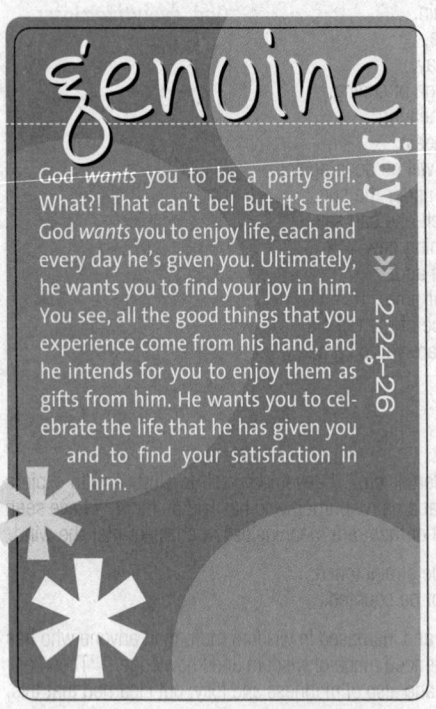

genuine joy » 2:24-26

God ~~wants~~ you to be a party girl. What?! That can't be! But it's true. God *wants* you to enjoy life, each and every day he's given you. Ultimately, he wants you to find your joy in him. You see, all the good things that you experience come from his hand, and he intends for you to enjoy them as gifts from him. He wants you to celebrate the life that he has given you and to find your satisfaction in him.

Wisdom and Folly Are Meaningless

[12]Then I turned my thoughts to
    consider wisdom,
    and also madness and folly.
What more can the king's
    successor do
    than what has already been
    done?
[13]I saw that wisdom is better than
    folly,
    just as light is better than
    darkness.
[14]The wise man has eyes in his
    head,
    while the fool walks in the
    darkness;
but I came to realize
    that the same fate overtakes
    them both.

[15]Then I thought in my heart,

"The fate of the fool will overtake
    me also.
    What then do I gain by being
    wise?"
I said in my heart,
    "This too is meaningless."
[16]For the wise man, like the fool, will not be long remembered;
    in days to come both will be forgotten.
Like the fool, the wise man too must die!

a 8 The meaning of the Hebrew for this phrase is uncertain.

Toil Is Meaningless

¹⁷So I hated life, because the work that is done under the sun was grievous to me. All of it is meaningless, a chasing after the wind. ¹⁸I hated all the things I had toiled for under the sun, because I must leave them to the one who comes after me. ¹⁹And who knows whether he will be a wise man or a fool? Yet he will have control over all the work into which I have poured my effort and skill under the sun. This too is meaningless. ²⁰So my heart began to despair over all my toilsome labor under the sun. ²¹For a man may do his work with wisdom, knowledge and skill, and then he must leave all he owns to someone who has not worked for it. This too is meaningless and a great misfortune. ²²What does a man get for all the toil and anxious striving with which he labors under the sun? ²³All his days his work is pain and grief; even at night his mind does not rest. This too is meaningless.

²⁴A man can do nothing better than to eat and drink and find satisfaction in his work. This too, I see, is from the hand of God, ²⁵for without him, who can eat or find enjoyment? ²⁶To the man who pleases him, God gives wisdom, knowledge and happiness, but to the sinner he gives the task of gathering and storing up wealth to hand it over to the one who pleases God. This too is meaningless, a chasing after the wind.

A Time for Everything

3 There is a time for everything,
and a season for every activity under heaven:

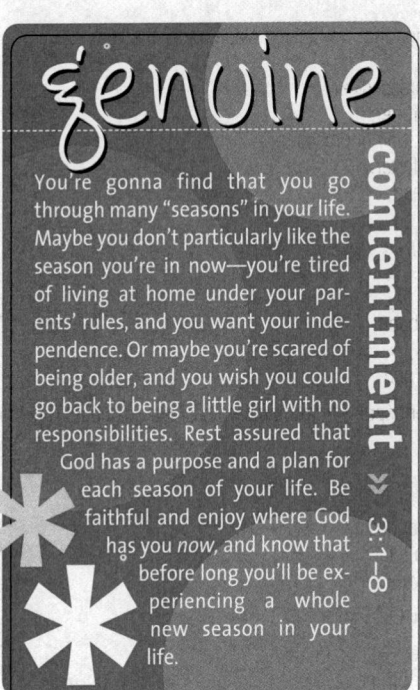

genuine

contentment » 3:1-8

You're gonna find that you go through many "seasons" in your life. Maybe you don't particularly like the season you're in now—you're tired of living at home under your parents' rules, and you want your independence. Or maybe you're scared of being older, and you wish you could go back to being a little girl with no responsibilities. Rest assured that God has a purpose and a plan for each season of your life. Be faithful and enjoy where God has you *now,* and know that before long you'll be experiencing a whole new season in your life.

²　a time to be born and a time to die,
　　a time to plant and a time to uproot,
³　a time to kill and a time to heal,
　　a time to tear down and a time to build,
⁴　a time to weep and a time to laugh,
　　a time to mourn and a time to dance,
⁵　a time to scatter stones and a time to gather them,
　　a time to embrace and a time to refrain,
⁶　a time to search and a time to give up,
　　a time to keep and a time to throw away,
⁷　a time to tear and a time to mend,
　　a time to be silent and a time to speak,
⁸　a time to love and a time to hate,
　　a time for war and a time for peace.

⁹What does the worker gain from his toil? ¹⁰I have seen the burden God has laid on men. ¹¹He has made everything beautiful in its time. He has also set eternity in the hearts of men; yet they cannot fathom what God has done from beginning to end. ¹²I know that there is nothing better for men than to be happy and do good while they live. ¹³That everyone may eat and drink, and find satisfaction in all his toil—this is the gift of God. ¹⁴I know that everything God does will endure forever; nothing can be added to it and nothing taken from it. God does it so that men will revere him.

¹⁵Whatever is has already been,
  and what will be has been before;
  and God will call the past to account.ᵃ

¹⁶And I saw something else under the sun:

  In the place of judgment—wickedness was there,
    in the place of justice—wickedness was there.

¹⁷I thought in my heart,

  "God will bring to judgment
    both the righteous and the wicked,
  for there will be a time for every activity,
    a time for every deed."

¹⁸I also thought, "As for men, God tests them so that they may see that they are like the animals. ¹⁹Man's fate is like that of the animals; the same fate awaits them both: As one dies, so dies the other. All have the same breathᵇ; man has no advantage over the animal. Everything is meaningless. ²⁰All go to the same place; all come from dust, and to dust all return. ²¹Who knows if the spirit of man rises upward and if the spirit of the animalᶜ goes down into the earth?"

²²So I saw that there is nothing better for a man than to enjoy his work, because that is his lot. For who can bring him to see what will happen after him?

Oppression, Toil, Friendlessness

4 Again I looked and saw all the oppression that was taking place under the sun:

  I saw the tears of the oppressed—
    and they have no comforter;
  power was on the side of their oppressors—
    and they have no comforter.
  ²And I declared that the dead,
    who had already died,
  are happier than the living,
    who are still alive.
  ³But better than both
    is he who has not yet been,
  who has not seen the evil
    that is done under the sun.

⁴And I saw that all labor and all achievement spring from man's envy of his neighbor. This too is meaningless, a chasing after the wind.

  ⁵The fool folds his hands
    and ruins himself.
  ⁶Better one handful with tranquillity
    than two handfuls with toil
    and chasing after the wind.

⁷Again I saw something meaningless under the sun:

  ⁸There was a man all alone;
    he had neither son nor brother.
  There was no end to his toil,
    yet his eyes were not content with his wealth.
  "For whom am I toiling," he asked,
    "and why am I depriving myself of enjoyment?"
  This too is meaningless—
    a miserable business!

ᵃ 15 Or *God calls back the past*   ᵇ 19 Or *spirit*   ᶜ 21 Or *Who knows the spirit of man, which rises upward, or the spirit of the animal, which*

genuine

friendship ≫ 4:9–12

Two really *are* better than one. Sometimes it's hard to believe this—especially when you've been hurt by a close friend and feel like you don't want to let anyone too close to you for a while. But God didn't design us to go through life on our own. A good friend can pick you up when you fall and make everything seem better just because she's there to share it with you. Do you want a friend like that? Are *you* a friend like that? Invest in your friendships, and you'll find that the return on your investment is priceless!

⁹Two are better than one,
  because they have a good
      return for their work:
¹⁰If one falls down,
    his friend can help him up.
But pity the man who falls
    and has no one to help him
      up!
¹¹Also, if two lie down together,
      they will keep warm.
  But how can one keep warm
      alone?
¹²Though one may be
      overpowered,
    two can defend themselves.
A cord of three strands is not
    quickly broken.

Advancement Is Meaningless

¹³Better a poor but wise youth than an old but foolish king who no longer knows how to take warning. ¹⁴The youth may have come from prison to the kingship, or he may have been born in poverty within his kingdom. ¹⁵I saw that all who lived and walked under the sun followed the youth, the king's successor. ¹⁶There was no end to all the people who were before them. But those who came later were not pleased with the successor. This too is meaningless, a chasing after the wind.

Stand in Awe of God

5 Guard your steps when you go to the house of God. Go near to listen rather than to offer the sacrifice of fools, who do not know that they do wrong.

²Do not be quick with your mouth,
    do not be hasty in your heart
      to utter anything before God.
  God is in heaven
      and you are on earth,
    so let your words be few.
³As a dream comes when there are many cares,
    so the speech of a fool when there are many words.

⁴When you make a vow to God, do not delay in fulfilling it. He has no pleasure in fools; fulfill your vow. ⁵It is better not to vow than to make a vow and not fulfill it. ⁶Do not let your mouth lead you into sin. And do not protest to the ⌞temple⌟ messenger, "My vow was a mistake." Why should God be angry at what you say and destroy the work of your hands? ⁷Much dreaming and many words are meaningless. Therefore stand in awe of God.

Riches Are Meaningless

⁸If you see the poor oppressed in a district, and justice and rights denied, do not be surprised at such things; for one official is eyed by a higher one, and over them both are others higher still. ⁹The increase from the land is taken by all; the king himself profits from the fields.

¹⁰Whoever loves money never has money enough;
    whoever loves wealth is never satisfied with his income.
    This too is meaningless.

¹¹ As goods increase,
so do those who consume
them.
And what benefit are they to the
owner
except to feast his eyes on
them?

¹² The sleep of a laborer is sweet,
whether he eats little or much,
but the abundance of a rich man
permits him no sleep.

¹³ I have seen a grievous evil under the sun:

wealth hoarded to the harm of its owner,
¹⁴   or wealth lost through some misfortune,
so that when he has a son
there is nothing left for him.
¹⁵ Naked a man comes from his mother's
womb,
and as he comes, so he departs.
He takes nothing from his labor
that he can carry in his hand.

¹⁶ This too is a grievous evil:

As a man comes, so he departs,
and what does he gain,
since he toils for the wind?
¹⁷ All his days he eats in darkness,
with great frustration, affliction and anger.

¹⁸ Then I realized that it is good and proper for a man to eat and drink, and to find satisfaction in his toilsome labor under the sun during the few days of life God has given him—for this is his lot. ¹⁹ Moreover, when God gives any man wealth and possessions, and enables him to enjoy them, to accept his lot and be happy in his work—this is a gift of God. ²⁰ He seldom reflects on the days of his life, because God keeps him occupied with gladness of heart.

6 I have seen another evil under the sun, and it weighs heavily on men: ²God gives a man wealth, possessions and honor, so that he lacks nothing his heart desires, but God does not enable him to enjoy them, and a stranger enjoys them instead. This is meaningless, a grievous evil.

³ A man may have a hundred children and live many years; yet no matter how long he lives, if he cannot enjoy his prosperity and does not receive proper burial, I say that a stillborn child is better off than he. ⁴ It comes without meaning, it departs in darkness, and in darkness its name is shrouded. ⁵ Though it never saw the sun or knew anything, it has more rest than does that man— ⁶ even if he lives a thousand years twice over but fails to enjoy his prosperity. Do not all go to the same place?

⁷ All man's efforts are for his mouth,
yet his appetite is never satisfied.
⁸ What advantage has a wise man
over a fool?
What does a poor man gain
by knowing how to conduct himself before others?
⁹ Better what the eye sees
than the roving of the appetite.
This too is meaningless,
a chasing after the wind.

¹⁰ Whatever exists has already been named,
and what man is has been known;

truth or dare

You can live quite happily with very little money. And some millionaires have taken their own lives because their $$$ didn't make them happy. The point? Live for more than money.

5:10

mirror images

With such nagging she prodded him day after day until he was tired to death. Judges 16:16

Delilah—Master Manipulator

She could have won an Emmy. She was that good of a performer. Delilah used her talents of charm and manipulation to get whatever she wanted. Pulling strings. Playing others' emotions. Wearing others down with her pleas. She knew every trick for getting her way.

When the hero of Israel, Samson, fell in love with Delilah, he didn't realize he'd met his match. Samson's enemies, the Philistines, played Delilah against him. With a little flattery and a pile of cash, they bribed her into tricking Samson to confess the secret to his incredible strength. So Delilah hounded Samson day and night to let her in on the scoop. She played games with his emotions until he confessed his secret.

You see, Samson had great hair. We're talking beautiful locks that had never been cut. His hair was a sign of his spiritual commitment and the source of his super-human strength. Cutting his hair would mean he had blown his commitment to God, and his strength would be gone. He thought he could keep his secret from Delilah. He was wrong.

Delilah betrayed Samson to the Philistines. She watched as a man shaved Samson's head while he slept. Then the Philistines rushed in to capture their weakened foe. They gouged his eyes and took him prisoner. Delilah was successful in getting Samson's secret.

Some of us are masters at getting what we want from others. Like Delilah, sometimes we use others. We think we know how things should be, so we orchestrate everything and play everyone to our liking. We nag our parents till they give us what we want—when it wasn't good for us in the first place. We manipulate our friends to try to get things our way—when it takes a heavy toll on our friendships.

Trying to control your own destiny may bring unintended consequences that you don't know how to handle. Delilah used her charms to harm others. What will you do with your talents?

> **dear God**
>
> Dear God, forgive me for the times I play people's emotions just to get what I want. Help me to appreciate the people I love, not misuse them for my own gain.

To read the next Mirror Images profile, go to page 897.

>> Read more about Delilah's story in Judges 16 (pages 304–306).

no man can contend
    with one who is stronger than he.
11 The more the words,
    the less the meaning,
    and how does that profit anyone?

12 For who knows what is good for a man in life, during the few and meaningless days he passes through like a shadow? Who can tell him what will happen under the sun after he is gone?

Wisdom

7

A good name is better than fine perfume,
    and the day of death better than the day of birth.
2 It is better to go to a house of mourning
    than to go to a house of feasting,
for death is the destiny of every man;
    the living should take this to heart.
3 Sorrow is better than laughter,
    because a sad face is good for the heart.
4 The heart of the wise is in the house of mourning,
    but the heart of fools is in the house of pleasure.
5 It is better to heed a wise man's rebuke
    than to listen to the song of
        fools.
6 Like the crackling of thorns under
        the pot,
    so is the laughter of fools.
    This too is meaningless.

7 Extortion turns a wise man into a
        fool,
    and a bribe corrupts the heart.

8 The end of a matter is better than
        its beginning,
    and patience is better than pride.
9 Do not be quickly provoked in your spirit,
    for anger resides in the lap of fools.

10 Do not say, "Why were the old days better
        than these?"
    For it is not wise to ask such questions.

11 Wisdom, like an inheritance, is a good thing
    and benefits those who see the sun.
12 Wisdom is a shelter
    as money is a shelter,
but the advantage of knowledge is this:
    that wisdom preserves the life of its possessor.

13 Consider what God has done:

Who can straighten
    what he has made crooked?
14 When times are good, be happy;
    but when times are bad, consider:
God has made the one
    as well as the other.
Therefore, a man cannot discover
    anything about his future.

truth or dare

This passage isn't as morbid as it sounds. Thinking about death actually puts life in the right perspective. What things in your life have you taken for granted?

7:2

¹⁵In this meaningless life of mine I have seen both of these:

> a righteous man perishing in his righteousness,
> and a wicked man living long in his wickedness.

¹⁶Do not be overrighteous,
neither be overwise—
why destroy yourself?
¹⁷Do not be overwicked,
and do not be a fool—
why die before your time?
¹⁸It is good to grasp the one
and not let go of the other.
The man who fears God will avoid all ⌊extremes⌋. *a*

¹⁹Wisdom makes one wise man more powerful
than ten rulers in a city.

²⁰There is not a righteous man on earth
who does what is right and never sins.

²¹Do not pay attention to every word people say,
or you may hear your servant cursing you—
²²for you know in your heart
that many times you yourself have cursed others.

²³All this I tested by wisdom and I said,

> "I am determined to be wise"—
> but this was beyond me.
> ²⁴Whatever wisdom may be,
> it is far off and most profound—
> who can discover it?
> ²⁵So I turned my mind to understand,
> to investigate and to search out wisdom and the scheme of things
> and to understand the stupidity of wickedness
> and the madness of folly.

²⁶I find more bitter than death
the woman who is a snare,
whose heart is a trap
and whose hands are chains.
The man who pleases God will escape her,
but the sinner she will ensnare.

²⁷"Look," says the Teacher, *b* "this is what I have discovered:

> "Adding one thing to another to discover the scheme of things—
> ²⁸ while I was still searching
> but not finding—
> I found one ⌊upright⌋ man among a thousand,
> but not one ⌊upright⌋ woman among them all.
> ²⁹This only have I found:
> God made mankind upright,
> but men have gone in search of many schemes."

8

> Who is like the wise man?
> Who knows the explanation of things?
> Wisdom brightens a man's face
> and changes its hard appearance.

a 18 Or *will follow them both*   *b 27* Or *leader of the assembly*

Obey the King

[2]Obey the king's command, I say, because you took an oath before God. [3]Do not be in a hurry to leave the king's presence. Do not stand up for a bad cause, for he will do whatever he pleases. [4]Since a king's word is supreme, who can say to him, "What are you doing?"

[5]Whoever obeys his command will come to no harm,
    and the wise heart will know the proper time and procedure.
[6]For there is a proper time and procedure for every matter,
    though a man's misery weighs heavily upon him.

[7]Since no man knows the future,
    who can tell him what is to come?
[8]No man has power over the wind to contain it[a];
    so no one has power over the day of his death.
As no one is discharged in time of war,
    so wickedness will not release those who practice it.

[9]All this I saw, as I applied my mind to everything done under the sun. There is a time when a man lords it over others to his own[b] hurt. [10]Then too, I saw the wicked buried—those who used to come and go from the holy place and receive praise[c] in the city where they did this. This too is meaningless.

[11]When the sentence for a crime is not quickly carried out, the hearts of the people are filled with schemes to do wrong. [12]Although a wicked man commits a hundred crimes and still lives a long time, I know that it will go better with God-fearing men, who are reverent before God. [13]Yet because the wicked do not fear God, it will not go well with them, and their days will not lengthen like a shadow.

[14]There is something else meaningless that occurs on earth: righteous men who get what the wicked deserve, and wicked men who get what the righteous deserve. This too, I say, is meaningless. [15]So I commend the enjoyment of life, because nothing is better for a man under the sun than to eat and drink and be glad. Then joy will accompany him in his work all the days of the life God has given him under the sun.

[16]When I applied my mind to know wisdom and to observe man's labor on earth—his eyes not seeing sleep day or night— [17]then I saw all that God has done. No one can comprehend what goes on under the sun. Despite all his efforts to search it out, man cannot discover its meaning. Even if a wise man claims he knows, he cannot really comprehend it.

A Common Destiny for All

9 So I reflected on all this and concluded that the righteous and the wise and what they do are in God's hands, but no man knows whether love or hate awaits him. [2]All share a common destiny—the righteous and the wicked, the good and the bad,[d] the clean and the unclean, those who offer sacrifices and those who do not.

As it is with the good man,
    so with the sinner;
as it is with those who take oaths,
    so with those who are afraid to take them.

[3]This is the evil in everything that happens under the sun: The same destiny overtakes all. The hearts of men, moreover, are full of evil and there is madness in their hearts while they live, and afterward they join the dead. [4]Anyone who is among the living has hope[e]—even a live dog is better off than a dead lion!

[5]For the living know that they will die,
    but the dead know nothing;
they have no further reward,
    and even the memory of them is forgotten.

a 8 Or over his spirit to retain it   b 9 Or to their   c 10 Some Hebrew manuscripts and Septuagint (Aquila); most Hebrew manuscripts and are forgotten   d 2 Septuagint (Aquila), Vulgate and Syriac; Hebrew does not have and the bad.   e 4 Or What then is to be chosen? With all who live, there is hope

⁶Their love, their hate
and their jealousy have long since vanished;
never again will they have a part
in anything that happens under the sun.

⁷Go, eat your food with gladness, and drink your wine with a joyful heart, for it is now that God favors what you do. ⁸Always be clothed in white, and always anoint your head with oil. ⁹Enjoy life with your wife, whom you love, all the days of this meaningless life that God has given you under the sun—all your meaningless days. For this is your lot in life and in your toilsome labor under the sun. ¹⁰Whatever your hand finds to do, do it with all your might, for in the grave,^a where you are going, there is neither working nor planning nor knowledge nor wisdom.

¹¹I have seen something else under the sun:

The race is not to the swift
or the battle to the strong,
nor does food come to the wise
or wealth to the brilliant
or favor to the learned;
but time and chance happen to
them all.

¹²Moreover, no man knows when his hour will come:

As fish are caught in a cruel net,
or birds are taken in a snare,
so men are trapped by evil times
that fall unexpectedly upon them.

truth or dare

Why does everyone expect life to be fair, when it rarely ever is? In this sinful world, life isn't always fair—your *response* to life is what matters most.

9:11

Wisdom Better Than Folly

¹³I also saw under the sun this example of wisdom that greatly impressed me: ¹⁴There was once a small city with only a few people in it. And a powerful king came against it, surrounded it and built huge siegeworks against it. ¹⁵Now there lived in that city a man poor but wise, and he saved the city by his wisdom. But nobody remembered that poor man. ¹⁶So I said, "Wisdom is better than strength." But the poor man's wisdom is despised, and his words are no longer heeded.

¹⁷The quiet words of the wise are more to be heeded
than the shouts of a ruler of fools.
¹⁸Wisdom is better than weapons of war,
but one sinner destroys much good.

10

As dead flies give perfume a bad smell,
so a little folly outweighs wisdom and honor.
²The heart of the wise inclines to the right,
but the heart of the fool to the left.
³Even as he walks along the road,
the fool lacks sense
and shows everyone how stupid he is.
⁴If a ruler's anger rises against you,
do not leave your post;
calmness can lay great errors to rest.
⁵There is an evil I have seen under the sun,
the sort of error that arises from a ruler:
⁶Fools are put in many high positions,
while the rich occupy the low ones.
⁷I have seen slaves on horseback,
while princes go on foot like slaves.

a 10 Hebrew *Sheol*

A Weed in God's Garden

Profile: **Ceil**

If I were a plant in God's garden, I think I'd be a weed. There's nothing special about weeds. They're a dime-a-dozen, and what are they good for? Nothing. That's me. There's nothing exceptional about me—not my looks, not my grades, not my personality—nothing. And everywhere I look I see gorgeous roses and bright daffodils—girls who seem to have it all. Charming smiles. That easy laugh. Bright eyes and a way about them that says, "Look at me!" Whatever it is they have, God ran out of it when it was time to create me.

Do you know how hard it is to get a guy to notice you? When there's nothing to notice? I do. I feel like I must be invisible most days.

Do you know what it's like to be in a group of talented friends? Knowing you don't have half the athletic ability, musical talent or intelligence they have?

I do. That's what I mean by feeling like a weed. I'm the anonymous girl who always gets overlooked. I'm one of the players on the bench the coach could just as easily do without. I'm one of the names on the school roster that will never show up on the Dean's list.

I feel like a weed in God's garden—but I dream of blooming someday.

Feeling better yet? Find even more encouragement by going online at www.TrueImagesBible.com

identity in focus

Who we are in Christ and the person we feel like are two different things. Our identity is not what we look like or what we do—our identity is in Christ. That means . . .

»You are beyond condemnation (see Romans 8:1, page 1493).
»You are close to God (see Ephesians 2:13, page 1544).
»You are perfect in his sight (see Hebrews 10:14, page 1595).
»You are God's child (see 1 John 3:1, page 1619).
»You have access to God at any moment (see Ephesians 2:18, page 1544).
»You will never be abandoned (see Hebrews 13:5, page 1599).

For more on this topic, see the index on page 1656.

identity

⁸ Whoever digs a pit may fall into it;
  whoever breaks through a wall may be bitten by a snake.
⁹ Whoever quarries stones may be injured by them;
  whoever splits logs may be endangered by them.

¹⁰ If the ax is dull
    and its edge unsharpened,
  more strength is needed
    but skill will bring success.

¹¹ If a snake bites before it is charmed,
    there is no profit for the charmer.

[12] Words from a wise man's mouth are gracious,
 but a fool is consumed by his own lips.
[13] At the beginning his words are folly;
 at the end they are wicked madness—
[14] and the fool multiplies words.

No one knows what is coming—
 who can tell him what will happen after him?

[15] A fool's work wearies him;
 he does not know the way to town.

[16] Woe to you, O land whose king was a servant[a]
 and whose princes feast in the morning.
[17] Blessed are you, O land whose king is of noble birth
 and whose princes eat at a proper time—
 for strength and not for drunkenness.

[18] If a man is lazy, the rafters sag;
 if his hands are idle, the house leaks.

[19] A feast is made for laughter,
 and wine makes life merry,
 but money is the answer for everything.

[20] Do not revile the king even in your thoughts,
 or curse the rich in your bedroom,
 because a bird of the air may carry your words,
 and a bird on the wing may report what you say.

Bread Upon the Waters

11 Cast your bread upon the waters,
 for after many days you will find it
 again.
[2] Give portions to seven, yes to eight,
 for you do not know what
 disaster may come
 upon the land.

[3] If clouds are full of water,
 they pour rain upon the earth.
Whether a tree falls to the south
 or to the north,
 in the place where it falls,
 there will it lie.
[4] Whoever watches the wind will
 not plant;
 whoever looks at the clouds
 will not reap.

[5] As you do not know the path of
 the wind,
 or how the body is formed[b] in
 a mother's womb,
so you cannot understand the
 work of God,
 the Maker of all things.

[6] Sow your seed in the morning,

genuine

character » 11:9

Life is sweet and meant to be enjoyed. And when you're young and have your whole life ahead of you, it's especially easy to feel carefree and wild. Fun seems to lie around every corner! But while enjoying all that today holds, it's also easy to forget about tomorrow. You've got to keep in mind that the choices you make today may affect you for eternity. Don't do anything now that you will be ashamed of later. Enjoy life in such a way that you will have no regrets when you come to the end of it.

---

a 16 Or king is a child   b 5 Or know how life (or the spirit) / enters the body being formed

and at evening let not your hands be idle,
for you do not know which will succeed,
whether this or that,
or whether both will do equally well.

Remember Your Creator While Young

7 Light is sweet,
and it pleases the eyes to see the sun.
8 However many years a man may live,
let him enjoy them all.
But let him remember the days of darkness,
for they will be many.
Everything to come is meaningless.

9 Be happy, young man, while you
are young,
and let your heart give you joy
in the days of your
youth.
Follow the ways of your heart
and whatever your eyes see,
but know that for all these things
God will bring you to
judgment.
10 So then, banish anxiety from your
heart
and cast off the troubles of
your body,
for youth and vigor are
meaningless.

love ♥ notes

11:9—12:1

Dear daughter,

*Enjoy each day to its fullest. This
is such an exciting time in life as
you're discovering and trying
new things. But remember—
what you do while you're young
does matter and has lasting effects on you. Keep me at the
center of your life.*

—Your Father

How can you keep God at the center of
your life?

12 Remember your Creator
in the days of your youth,
before the days of trouble
come
and the years approach when
you will say,
"I find no pleasure in them"—

truth or dare

"I'll make a decision
about God later." That
might be a painless deci-
sion, but it's also really
risky. You're not guaran-
teed you'll be around to-
morrow. Choose to
honor God today.

12:1

²before the sun and the light
        and the moon and the stars grow dark,
        and the clouds return after the rain;
³when the keepers of the house tremble,
        and the strong men stoop,
    when the grinders cease because they are few,
        and those looking through the windows grow dim;
⁴when the doors to the street are closed
        and the sound of grinding fades;
    when men rise up at the sound of birds,
        but all their songs grow faint;
⁵when men are afraid of heights
        and of dangers in the streets;
    when the almond tree blossoms
        and the grasshopper drags himself along
        and desire no longer is stirred.
    Then man goes to his eternal home
        and mourners go about the streets.

⁶Remember him—before the silver cord is severed,
        or the golden bowl is broken;
    before the pitcher is shattered at the spring,
        or the wheel broken at the well,
⁷and the dust returns to the ground it came from,
        and the spirit returns to God who gave it.

⁸"Meaningless! Meaningless!" says the Teacher.ᵃ
    "Everything is meaningless!"

The Conclusion of the Matter

⁹Not only was the Teacher wise, but also he imparted knowledge to the people. He pondered and searched out and set in order many proverbs. ¹⁰The Teacher searched to find just the right words, and what he wrote was upright and true.

¹¹The words of the wise are like goads, their collected sayings like firmly embedded nails—given by one Shepherd. ¹²Be warned, my son, of anything in addition to them.

Of making many books there is no end, and much study wearies the body.

¹³Now all has been heard;
        here is the conclusion of the
            matter:
    Fear God and keep his
            commandments,
        for this is the whole ⌐duty⌐ of
            man.
¹⁴For God will bring every deed into
            judgment,
        including every hidden thing,
        whether it is good or evil.

genuine

purpose » 12:13-14

When life doesn't make sense, do you ever find yourself thinking, *What's the point? What am I doing here anyway?* Are you searching for a purpose to your life? Well, here it is: You're supposed to "fear God and keep his commandments." *That's* what you're here for. Fearing God means honoring and respecting and being in awe of him at all times. And when you keep his commands— like loving him and loving others with all that you are—*then* life really starts to make sense.

ᵃ 8 Or *the leader of the assembly*; also in verses 9 and 10

at a glance

author: Probably King Solomon.

date: Probably early in Solomon's reign, around 965 B.C.

setting: Israel.

verse to remember: Many waters cannot quench love; rivers cannot wash it away. If one were to give all the wealth of his house for love, it would be utterly scorned (8:7).

theme to consider: Sex is God's amazing gift to a husband and wife. Song of Songs gives us a proper perspective of love between a man and a woman. The beauty of love in a marriage also represents God's love for his people.

song of songs

unchanging truth

Don't you love a good love story? There's nothing like getting together with girlfriends to watch a romantic movie, popcorn bowl on the left, box of tissues on the right. The story sweeps us off our feet as we watch the hero and heroine finally realize what we knew all along—they really *do* love each other! And when they finally have that passionate kiss, we wipe our tears in joy at the happy ending.

Well, did you know that the Bible includes a love story? Start reading the Song of Songs and you might find yourself blushing! The song recorded here is a beautiful poem that celebrates love, passion and yes—even sex—between and a bride and groom as they enjoy each other intensely.

The girl and the guy in this story meet (She's a peasant girl; he's a king—really, does it get any better than that?), fall in love and marry. They seem to face some fears (3:1) and some jealousy (8:6), but they continue to delight each other.

So why is this story in the Bible? On one level, this song celebrates that God created sex and wants married couples to enjoy each other. On another level, it pictures the overwhelming love God has for his people—faithful, true, unending, joyous. As you read this love story, pray that if God has a guy in your future, that he will love you this much—and set your heart on the God who already does.

life lessons

1. Don't rush to fall in love. Ask God to help you guard your heart so that feelings of love will come at the right time (2:7; 3:5; 8:4).

2. Pray that God will guide you to the man he has for you (if he does plan for you to get married). Pray that you will be a loving and refreshing part of your future husband's life (4:15).

3. Treasure your virginity. Decide not to be like a "door" (sexually active); instead, be like a "wall," and save yourself for your husband (8:8–12).

1

Solomon's Song of Songs.

Beloved [a]

²Let him kiss me with the kisses of his mouth—
for your love is more delightful
than wine.
³Pleasing is the fragrance of your
perfumes;
your name is like perfume
poured out.
No wonder the maidens love
you!
⁴Take me away with you—let us
hurry!
Let the king bring me into his
chambers.

Friends

We rejoice and delight in you [b];
we will praise your love more than wine.

Beloved

How right they are to adore you!

⁵Dark am I, yet lovely,
O daughters of Jerusalem,
dark like the tents of Kedar,
like the tent curtains of Solomon. [c]
⁶Do not stare at me because I am dark,
because I am darkened by the sun.
My mother's sons were angry with me
and made me take care of the vineyards;
my own vineyard I have neglected.
⁷Tell me, you whom I love, where you graze your flock
and where you rest your sheep at midday.
Why should I be like a veiled woman
beside the flocks of your friends?

Friends

⁸If you do not know, most beautiful of women,
follow the tracks of the sheep
and graze your young goats
by the tents of the shepherds.

Lover

⁹I liken you, my darling, to a mare
harnessed to one of the chariots of Pharaoh.
¹⁰Your cheeks are beautiful with earrings,
your neck with strings of jewels.
¹¹We will make you earrings of gold,
studded with silver.

truth or dare

God reserved a whole book of the Bible to talk about love and sex! Surprised? Sex is God's gift to married couples—it lets spiritually bonded couples become physically one.

1:1–4

^a Primarily on the basis of the gender of the Hebrew pronouns used, male and female speakers are indicated in the margins by the captions *Lover* and *Beloved* respectively. The words of others are marked *Friends*. In some instances the divisions and their captions are debatable.   ^b 4 The Hebrew is masculine singular.   ^c 5 Or *Salma*

Beloved

¹²While the king was at his table,
my perfume spread its fragrance.
¹³My lover is to me a sachet of myrrh
resting between my breasts.
¹⁴My lover is to me a cluster of henna blossoms
from the vineyards of En Gedi.

Lover

¹⁵How beautiful you are, my darling!
Oh, how beautiful!
Your eyes are doves.

Beloved

¹⁶How handsome you are, my lover!
Oh, how charming!
And our bed is verdant.

Lover

¹⁷The beams of our house are cedars;
our rafters are firs.

Beloved ᵃ

2

I am a rose ᵇ of Sharon,
a lily of the valleys.

Lover

²Like a lily among thorns
is my darling among the maidens.

Beloved

³Like an apple tree among the trees of the forest
is my lover among the young men.
I delight to sit in his shade,
and his fruit is sweet to my taste.
⁴He has taken me to the banquet hall,
and his banner over me is love.
⁵Strengthen me with raisins,
refresh me with apples,
for I am faint with love.
⁶His left arm is under my head,
and his right arm embraces me.
⁷Daughters of Jerusalem, I charge you
by the gazelles and by the does of the field:
Do not arouse or awaken love
until it so desires.

⁸Listen! My lover!
Look! Here he comes,
leaping across the mountains,
bounding over the hills.
⁹My lover is like a gazelle or a young stag.
Look! There he stands behind our wall,

ᵃ Or *Lover*   ᵇ 1 Possibly a member of the crocus family

genuine

love » 2:7

Do not arouse or awaken love until it so desires. What does *that* mean? It means letting love develop naturally. It means not forcing it, not manipulating circumstances to . speed things up. It means waiting for love and commitment to grow together. That is so hard for us gals to do! We tend to scheme and plot and finagle to get a guy to like us. We work hard to "catch that man." But that's not God's way. Doing it his way means concentrating on being a friend, without expectations, and waiting on God to see what he brings about naturally.

gazing through the windows,
   peering through the lattice.
[10] My lover spoke and said to me,
   "Arise, my darling,
     my beautiful one, and come
      with me.
[11] See! The winter is past;
   the rains are over and gone.
[12] Flowers appear on the earth;
   the season of singing has
     come,
the cooing of doves
   is heard in our land.
[13] The fig tree forms its early fruit;
   the blossoming vines spread
     their fragrance.
Arise, come, my darling;
   my beautiful one, come with me."

Lover

[14] My dove in the clefts of the rock,
   in the hiding places on the
     mountainside,
show me your face,
   let me hear your voice;
for your voice is sweet,
   and your face is lovely.

[15] Catch for us the foxes,
   the little foxes
that ruin the vineyards,
   our vineyards that are in bloom.

Beloved

[16] My lover is mine and I am his;
   he browses among the lilies.
[17] Until the day breaks
   and the shadows flee,
turn, my lover,
   and be like a gazelle
or like a young stag
   on the rugged hills. *[a]*

3 All night long on my bed
   I looked for the one my heart loves;
   I looked for him but did not find him.
[2] I will get up now and go about the city,
   through its streets and squares;
I will search for the one my heart loves.
   So I looked for him but did not find him.
[3] The watchmen found me
   as they made their rounds in the city.
   "Have you seen the one my heart loves?"
[4] Scarcely had I passed them
   when I found the one my heart loves.
I held him and would not let him go

a 17 Or the hills of Bether

till I had brought him to my
mother's house,
to the room of the one who
conceived me.
⁵ Daughters of Jerusalem, I charge
you
by the gazelles and by the
does of the field:
Do not arouse or awaken love
until it so desires.

⁶ Who is this coming up from the
desert

truth or dare

Love is like fire—once it's started, it's hard to put out. If you don't feel ready for a lifelong commitment, why play with fire? You *will* get badly burned.

3:5

like a column of smoke,
perfumed with myrrh and incense
made from all the spices of
the merchant?
⁷ Look! It is Solomon's carriage,
escorted by sixty warriors,
the noblest of Israel,
⁸ all of them wearing the sword,
all experienced in battle,
each with his sword at his side,
prepared for the terrors of the
night.
⁹ King Solomon made for himself
the carriage;
he made it of wood from Lebanon.
¹⁰ Its posts he made of silver,
its base of gold.
Its seat was upholstered with purple,
its interior lovingly inlaid
by ᵃ the daughters of Jerusalem.
¹¹ Come out, you daughters of Zion,
and look at King Solomon
wearing the crown,
the crown with which his
mother crowned him
on the day of his wedding,
the day his heart rejoiced.

Lover

4 How beautiful you are, my darling!
Oh, how beautiful!
Your eyes behind your veil are doves.
Your hair is like a flock of goats
descending from Mount Gilead.
² Your teeth are like a flock of
sheep just shorn,

love ❤ notes

4:1a,7

Beautiful one,

You are beautiful and flawless in my eyes. Do you believe that? Oh, there may be days when you look in the mirror and see nothing but flaws. But I only see you as beautiful, created in my image. You are beautiful. Believe it!

—Your Creator

Describe what you see in the mirror. Now describe what God sees.

_____
_____
_____
_____
_____
_____
_____
_____
_____
_____
_____

ᵃ 10 Or *its inlaid interior a gift of love / from*

genuine

purity »» 4:9-15

Wow! This guy is majorly in love—deep, passionate, lasting, head-over-heels, till-death-do-us-part love. You can see that he absolutely adores his bride. And isn't that what every girl dreams of? Now, if you look closely at the things he praises her for, you'll see that her virginity is one of them. He calls her a garden locked up, a spring enclosed, a sealed fountain—and he loves that about her! While some people may put you down for wanting to stay a virgin until marriage, the right guy—the one who really counts—will love that about you.

coming up from the washing.
Each has its twin;
    not one of them is alone.
³Your lips are like a scarlet ribbon;
    your mouth is lovely.
Your temples behind your veil
    are like the halves of a
        pomegranate.
⁴Your neck is like the tower of David,
    built with elegance ᵃ;
on it hang a thousand shields,
    all of them shields of warriors.
⁵Your two breasts are like two fawns,
    like twin fawns of a gazelle
        that browse among the lilies.
⁶Until the day breaks
    and the shadows flee,
I will go to the mountain of myrrh
    and to the hill of incense.
⁷All beautiful you are, my darling;
    there is no flaw in you.

⁸Come with me from Lebanon, my
        bride,
    come with me from Lebanon.
Descend from the crest of Amana,
    from the top of Senir, the
        summit of Hermon,
from the lions' dens
    and the mountain haunts of the leopards.
⁹You have stolen my heart, my sister, my bride;
    you have stolen my heart
with one glance of your eyes,
    with one jewel of your
        necklace.
¹⁰How delightful is your love, my
        sister, my bride!
    How much more pleasing is
        your love than wine,
    and the fragrance of your
        perfume than any spice!
¹¹Your lips drop sweetness as the
        honeycomb, my bride;
    milk and honey are under your tongue.
The fragrance of your garments is like that
        of Lebanon.
¹²You are a garden locked up, my sister, my
        bride;
    you are a spring enclosed, a sealed fountain.
¹³Your plants are an orchard of pomegranates
        with choice fruits,
        with henna and nard,
¹⁴   nard and saffron,
        calamus and cinnamon,
        with every kind of incense tree,

truth or dare

Sex isn't a ticket to win love. That never works! God intended your virginity to be an amazing gift to your husband, a guy *already* committed to you for life.

4:12

ᵃ 4 The meaning of the Hebrew for this word is uncertain.

with myrrh and aloes
and all the finest spices.
¹⁵ You are^a a garden fountain,
a well of flowing water
streaming down from Lebanon.

Beloved

¹⁶ Awake, north wind,
and come, south wind!
Blow on my garden,
that its fragrance may spread abroad.
Let my lover come into his garden
and taste its choice fruits.

Lover

5

I have come into my garden, my sister, my bride;
I have gathered my myrrh with my spice.
I have eaten my honeycomb and my honey;
I have drunk my wine and my milk.

Friends

Eat, O friends, and drink;
drink your fill, O lovers.

Beloved

² I slept but my heart was awake.
Listen! My lover is knocking:
"Open to me, my sister, my darling,
my dove, my flawless one.
My head is drenched with dew,
my hair with the dampness of the night."
³ I have taken off my robe—
must I put it on again?
I have washed my feet—
must I soil them again?
⁴ My lover thrust his hand through the latch-opening;
my heart began to pound for him.
⁵ I arose to open for my lover,
and my hands dripped with myrrh,
my fingers with flowing myrrh,
on the handles of the lock.
⁶ I opened for my lover,
but my lover had left; he was gone.
My heart sank at his departure.^b
I looked for him but did not find him.
I called him but he did not answer.
⁷ The watchmen found me
as they made their rounds in the city.
They beat me, they bruised me;
they took away my cloak,
those watchmen of the walls!
⁸ O daughters of Jerusalem, I charge you—
if you find my lover,
what will you tell him?
Tell him I am faint with love.

---

a 15 Or *I am* (spoken by the *Beloved*)   *b 6* Or *heart had gone out to him when he spoke*

Friends

⁹How is your beloved better than others,
    most beautiful of women?
How is your beloved better than others,
    that you charge us so?

Beloved

¹⁰My lover is radiant and ruddy,
    outstanding among ten thousand.
¹¹His head is purest gold;
    his hair is wavy
    and black as a raven.
¹²His eyes are like doves
    by the water streams,
washed in milk,
    mounted like jewels.
¹³His cheeks are like beds of spice
    yielding perfume.
His lips are like lilies
    dripping with myrrh.
¹⁴His arms are rods of gold
    set with chrysolite.
His body is like polished ivory
    decorated with sapphires. ^a
¹⁵His legs are pillars of marble
    set on bases of pure gold.
His appearance is like Lebanon,
    choice as its cedars.
¹⁶His mouth is sweetness itself;
    he is altogether lovely.
This is my lover, this my friend,
    O daughters of Jerusalem.

Friends

6

Where has your lover gone,
    most beautiful of women?
Which way did your lover turn,
    that we may look for him with you?

Beloved

²My lover has gone down to his garden,
    to the beds of spices,
to browse in the gardens
    and to gather lilies.
³I am my lover's and my lover is mine;
    he browses among the lilies.

Lover

⁴You are beautiful, my darling, as Tirzah,
    lovely as Jerusalem,
    majestic as troops with banners.
⁵Turn your eyes from me;
    they overwhelm me.
Your hair is like a flock of goats

---

^a 14 Or *lapis lazuli*

descending from Gilead.
⁶Your teeth are like a flock of sheep
    coming up from the washing.
Each has its twin,
    not one of them is alone.
⁷Your temples behind your veil
    are like the halves of a pomegranate.
⁸Sixty queens there may be,
    and eighty concubines,
    and virgins beyond number;
⁹but my dove, my perfect one, is unique,
    the only daughter of her mother,
    the favorite of the one who bore her.
The maidens saw her and called her blessed;
    the queens and concubines praised her.

Friends

¹⁰Who is this that appears like the dawn,
    fair as the moon, bright as the sun,
    majestic as the stars in procession?

Lover

¹¹I went down to the grove of nut trees
    to look at the new growth in the valley,
to see if the vines had budded
    or the pomegranates were in bloom.
¹²Before I realized it,
    my desire set me among the royal chariots of my people.ᵃ

Friends

¹³Come back, come back, O Shulammite;
    come back, come back, that we may gaze on you!

Lover

7

Why would you gaze on the Shulammite
    as on the dance of Mahanaim?

How beautiful your sandaled feet,
    O prince's daughter!
Your graceful legs are like jewels,
    the work of a craftsman's hands.
²Your navel is a rounded goblet
    that never lacks blended wine.
Your waist is a mound of wheat
    encircled by lilies.
³Your breasts are like two fawns,
    twins of a gazelle.
⁴Your neck is like an ivory tower.
Your eyes are the pools of Heshbon
    by the gate of Bath Rabbim.
Your nose is like the tower of Lebanon
    looking toward Damascus.
⁵Your head crowns you like Mount Carmel.
Your hair is like royal tapestry;
    the king is held captive by its tresses.

ᵃ 12 Or *among the chariots of Amminadab*; or *among the chariots of the people of the prince*

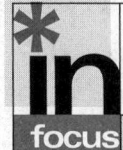

Something to Lose

focus Profile: **Taranda**

I'm still a virgin. My friends keep nagging me, asking me when I'm going to "get rid of it." I don't know why it's so important to them that I lose my virginity.

All of them have had sex. The funny thing is, none of them *act* like it was that great, even though they say it was. Sometimes they make me feel like a prude because I'm still a virgin. Some think I'm crazy to hang on to it. Others, like my friend Desiree, treat me like a little kid because I won't have sex before I'm married. She keeps telling me, "Girl, how do you expect to keep a guy if you won't do it?"

My friend Raven asked me, "Where in the Bible does it say you can't have sex?" She claims to be a Christian! When I couldn't just quote a verse off the top of my head, she said, "It's okay if two people are in love and committed to each other like you and Andre."

Andre is my boyfriend. I really like him—actually, I think I even love him. But I don't know if he's the man I'll wind up marrying. I mean, I just want to graduate right now and get into college.

Two years ago, Mama wanted me to promise that I wouldn't have sex till I got married. She bought me a promise ring and everything. It's beautiful. Sometimes I wonder if I made that promise just because I was afraid to make her sad or because I really wanted to.

For more information on virginity and premarital sex, check out the link on www.TrueImagesBible.com

virginity in focus

Your virginity is a precious gift God gave you to hand to your husband someday. Keep in mind . . .

»God has not changed his mind about premarital sex just because it seems "acceptable" today. The answer has been and always will be the same: *no*.

»Any guy who demands sex in order to be "kept" in a relationship isn't worth keeping.

»Ask yourself: what're your friends' motives for encouraging you to have sex? Is it for your good—or to make them feel better?

»What do you give up when you have sex? More than just your virginity. Your self-respect. Your peace of mind. Your obedience to God. And the incredible experience of having sex with your husband free of guilt, free of baggage, full of love, trust and joy. If you have sex now, you'll never have sex like that (see Genesis 2:24, page 4).

For more on this topic, see the index on page 1656.

⁶How beautiful you are and how pleasing,
    O love, with your delights!
⁷Your stature is like that of the palm,
    and your breasts like clusters of fruit.
⁸I said, "I will climb the palm tree;
    I will take hold of its fruit."
 May your breasts be like the clusters of the vine,
    the fragrance of your breath like apples,
⁹   and your mouth like the best wine.

Beloved

May the wine go straight to my lover,
    flowing gently over lips and teeth. [a]
[10] I belong to my lover,
    and his desire is for me.
[11] Come, my lover, let us go to the countryside,
    let us spend the night in the villages. [b]
[12] Let us go early to the vineyards
    to see if the vines have budded,
if their blossoms have opened,
    and if the pomegranates are in bloom—
there I will give you my love.
[13] The mandrakes send out their fragrance,
    and at our door is every delicacy,
both new and old,
    that I have stored up for you, my lover.

8

If only you were to me like a brother,
    who was nursed at my mother's breasts!
Then, if I found you outside,
    I would kiss you,
    and no one would despise me.
[2] I would lead you
    and bring you to my mother's house—
    she who has taught me.
I would give you spiced wine to drink,
    the nectar of my pomegranates.
[3] His left arm is under my head
    and his right arm embraces me.
[4] Daughters of Jerusalem, I charge you:
Do not arouse or awaken love
    until it so desires.

Friends

[5] Who is this coming up from the desert
    leaning on her lover?

Beloved

Under the apple tree I roused you;
    there your mother conceived you,
    there she who was in labor gave you birth.
[6] Place me like a seal over your heart,
    like a seal on your arm;
for love is as strong as death,
    its jealousy[c] unyielding as the grave. [d]
It burns like blazing fire,
    like a mighty flame. [e]
[7] Many waters cannot quench love;
    rivers cannot wash it away.
If one were to give
    all the wealth of his house for love,
    it[f] would be utterly scorned.

[a] 9 Septuagint, Aquila, Vulgate and Syriac; Hebrew *lips of sleepers*   [b] 11 Or *henna bushes*   [c] 6 Or *ardor*
[d] 6 Hebrew *Sheol*   [e] 6 Or / *like the very flame of the* Lord   [f] 7 Or *he*

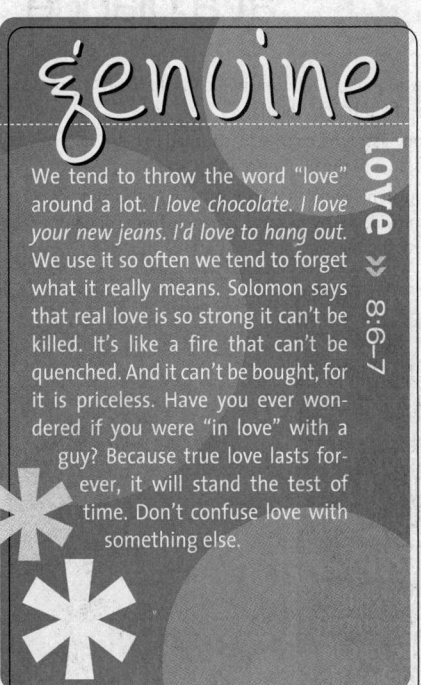

genuine

love » 8:6-7

We tend to throw the word "love" around a lot. *I love chocolate. I love your new jeans. I'd love to hang out.* We use it so often we tend to forget what it really means. Solomon says that real love is so strong it can't be killed. It's like a fire that can't be quenched. And it can't be bought, for it is priceless. Have you ever wondered if you were "in love" with a guy? Because true love lasts forever, it will stand the test of time. Don't confuse love with something else.

Friends

⁸We have a young sister,
and her breasts are not yet
grown.
What shall we do for our sister
for the day she is spoken for?
⁹If she is a wall,
we will build towers of silver
on her.
If she is a door,
we will enclose her with
panels of cedar.

Beloved

¹⁰I am a wall,
and my breasts are like
towers.
Thus I have become in his eyes
like one bringing contentment.
¹¹Solomon had a vineyard in Baal
Hamon;
he let out his vineyard to
tenants.
Each was to bring for its fruit
a thousand shekels *ᵃ* of silver.
¹²But my own vineyard is mine to
give;
the thousand shekels are for you, O Solomon,
and two hundred *ᵇ* are for those who tend its fruit.

Lover

¹³You who dwell in the gardens
with friends in attendance,
let me hear your voice!

Beloved

¹⁴Come away, my lover,
and be like a gazelle
or like a young stag
on the spice-laden mountains.

---

a 11 That is, about 25 pounds (about 11.5 kilograms); also in verse 12   *b 12* That is, about 5 pounds (about 2.3 kilograms)

at a glance

author:	Isaiah.
date:	Between 701 and 681 B.C.
setting:	Isaiah spoke to the people during a rough time in Judah when the Assyrians were becoming more of a threat to them.
verse to remember:	We all, like sheep, have gone astray, each of us has turned to his own way; and the LORD has laid on him the iniquity of us all (53:6).
theme to consider:	God, who is holy, must punish his people for their sin. But God is also compassionate, and he'll provide a way to save his people from condemnation through Jesus Christ, the Messiah.

isaiah

unchanging truth

Sometimes we are lucky enough to be forgiven even when we don't deserve it. Maybe you hurt a friend with an unkind comment. Then you realize what you did and rush to tell her you're sorry. When she smiles and says, "It's okay, forget about it," what a relief that is! You didn't deserve forgiveness, but your friend was gracious enough to give it anyway.

The people of Judah did not deserve forgiveness. They had turned from God and worshiped idols, so God sent special messengers—prophets—to speak his truth and turn the people back to him. Isaiah was one such prophet. He warned the people that if they did not change their ways, God would punish them. And that's exactly what happened. The people continued to ignore God, and eventually, they were carried off into captivity.

But the story does not end there. Because God is just, he must punish sin. But because he is also compassionate and merciful, he promises forgiveness and restoration. Isaiah saw not only the coming punishment of the people but also the eventual restoration of the people to their land. He saw many centuries into the future when God would invite *all people* to himself by mercifully sending his Son, Jesus Christ, to take the punishment we deserve for our sin through his death on the cross.

You have been forgiven. That's the ultimate joy and relief.

life lessons

1. No matter how deep the stain of our sin, Jesus' sacrifice is able to cleanse and purify us. We're never beyond God's forgiveness (1:18).

2. God longs to be gracious to us. All we must do is call out to him and ask for his forgiveness. He'll gladly give it (30:15,18–19).

3. Even though we deserve punishment, Jesus Christ took the punishment for our sins upon himself (53:1–12).

1 The vision concerning Judah and Jerusalem that Isaiah son of Amoz saw during the reigns of Uzziah, Jotham, Ahaz and Hezekiah, kings of Judah.

A Rebellious Nation

²Hear, O heavens! Listen, O earth!
    For the LORD has spoken:
"I reared children and brought them up,
    but they have rebelled against me.
³The ox knows his master,
    the donkey his owner's manger,
but Israel does not know,
    my people do not understand."

⁴Ah, sinful nation,
    a people loaded with guilt,
a brood of evildoers,
    children given to corruption!
They have forsaken the LORD;
    they have spurned the Holy One of Israel
    and turned their backs on him.

⁵Why should you be beaten anymore?
    Why do you persist in rebellion?
Your whole head is injured,
    your whole heart afflicted.
⁶From the sole of your foot to the top of your head
    there is no soundness—
only wounds and welts
    and open sores,
not cleansed or bandaged
    or soothed with oil.

⁷Your country is desolate,
    your cities burned with fire;
your fields are being stripped by
        foreigners
    right before you,
    laid waste as when overthrown
        by strangers.
⁸The Daughter of Zion is left
    like a shelter in a vineyard,
like a hut in a field of melons,
    like a city under siege.
⁹Unless the LORD Almighty
    had left us some survivors,
we would have become like
        Sodom,
    we would have been like Gomorrah.

¹⁰Hear the word of the LORD,
    you rulers of Sodom;
listen to the law of our God,
    you people of Gomorrah!
¹¹"The multitude of your sacrifices—
    what are they to me?" says the LORD.
"I have more than enough of burnt offerings,
    of rams and the fat of fattened animals;

truth or dare

Longwinded prayers and religious rituals don't win points with God. Above all else, he wants you to clean up your life and obey him. Are you all religion and no heart?

1:11–20

genuine

forgiveness » 1:18

Imagine spilling an entire bottle of fire engine red nail polish all over your new white sweater. Talk about disaster! No matter how hard you try, it's unlikely your sweater will ever be completely white again. Sin is like that bright red polish, and it has left you with a permanent stain that *you* can't get rid of. But God can. He is able to take your sin, no matter how bad it is, and remove it completely. He can make you white as snow. Confess your sin to him, and be confident that you will be made perfectly clean.

I have no pleasure
in the blood of bulls and
lambs and goats.
¹²When you come to appear before
me,
who has asked this of you,
this trampling of my courts?
¹³Stop bringing meaningless
offerings!
Your incense is detestable to me.
New Moons, Sabbaths and
convocations—
I cannot bear your evil
assemblies.
¹⁴Your New Moon festivals and
your appointed feasts
my soul hates.
They have become a burden to
me;
I am weary of bearing them.
¹⁵When you spread out your hands
in prayer,
I will hide my eyes from you;
even if you offer many prayers,
I will not listen.
Your hands are full of blood;
¹⁶ wash and make yourselves
clean.

Take your evil deeds
out of my sight!
Stop doing wrong,
¹⁷ learn to do right!
Seek justice,
encourage the oppressed. ᵃ
Defend the cause of the fatherless,
plead the case of the widow.

¹⁸ "Come now, let us reason together,"
says the LORD.
"Though your sins are like scarlet,
they shall be as white as snow;
though they are red as crimson,
they shall be like wool.
¹⁹If you are willing and obedient,
you will eat the best from the land;
²⁰but if you resist and rebel,
you will be devoured by the sword."
For the mouth of the LORD has spoken.

²¹ See how the faithful city
has become a harlot!
She once was full of justice;
righteousness used to dwell in her—
but now murderers!
²²Your silver has become dross,

a 17 Or / rebuke the oppressor

your choice wine is diluted with water.
²³ Your rulers are rebels,
  companions of thieves;
they all love bribes
  and chase after gifts.
They do not defend the cause of the fatherless;
  the widow's case does not come before them.
²⁴ Therefore the Lord, the LORD Almighty,
  the Mighty One of Israel, declares:
"Ah, I will get relief from my foes
  and avenge myself on my enemies.
²⁵ I will turn my hand against you;
  I will thoroughly purge away your dross
  and remove all your impurities.
²⁶ I will restore your judges as in days of old,
  your counselors as at the beginning.
Afterward you will be called
  the City of Righteousness,
  the Faithful City."

²⁷ Zion will be redeemed with justice,
  her penitent ones with righteousness.
²⁸ But rebels and sinners will both be broken,
  and those who forsake the LORD will perish.

²⁹ "You will be ashamed because of the sacred oaks
  in which you have delighted;
you will be disgraced because of the gardens
  that you have chosen.
³⁰ You will be like an oak with fading leaves,
  like a garden without water.
³¹ The mighty man will become tinder
  and his work a spark;
both will burn together,
  with no one to quench the fire."

The Mountain of the LORD

2 This is what Isaiah son of Amoz saw concerning Judah and Jerusalem:

² In the last days

the mountain of the LORD's temple
  will be established
  as chief among the mountains;
it will be raised above the hills,
  and all nations will stream to it.

³ Many peoples will come and say,

"Come, let us go up to the
  mountain of the LORD,
  to the house of the God of Jacob.
He will teach us his ways,
  so that we may walk in his paths."
The law will go out from Zion,
  the word of the LORD from Jerusalem.
⁴ He will judge between the nations
  and will settle disputes for many peoples.

truth or dare

God promises a future without war, where weapons will be turned into farm equipment! Don't wait passively for that day. Walk in God's light today.

2:4–5

They will beat their swords into plowshares
  and their spears into pruning hooks.
Nation will not take up sword against nation,
  nor will they train for war anymore.
⁵Come, O house of Jacob,
  let us walk in the light of the Lord.

The Day of the Lord

⁶You have abandoned your people,
  the house of Jacob.
They are full of superstitions from the East;
  they practice divination like the Philistines
  and clasp hands with pagans.
⁷Their land is full of silver and gold;
  there is no end to their treasures.
Their land is full of horses;
  there is no end to their chariots.
⁸Their land is full of idols;
  they bow down to the work of their hands,
  to what their fingers have made.
⁹So man will be brought low
  and mankind humbled—
  do not forgive them. ᵃ

¹⁰Go into the rocks,
  hide in the ground
from dread of the Lord
  and the splendor of his majesty!
¹¹The eyes of the arrogant man will be humbled
  and the pride of men brought low;
the Lord alone will be exalted in that day.

¹²The Lord Almighty has a day in store
  for all the proud and lofty,
  for all that is exalted
  (and they will be humbled),
¹³for all the cedars of Lebanon, tall and lofty,
  and all the oaks of Bashan,
¹⁴for all the towering mountains
  and all the high hills,
¹⁵for every lofty tower
  and every fortified wall,
¹⁶for every trading ship ᵇ
  and every stately vessel.
¹⁷The arrogance of man will be brought low
  and the pride of men humbled;
the Lord alone will be exalted in that day,
¹⁸ and the idols will totally disappear.

¹⁹Men will flee to caves in the rocks
  and to holes in the ground
from dread of the Lord
  and the splendor of his majesty,
  when he rises to shake the earth.
²⁰In that day men will throw away

ᵃ 9 Or not raise them up   ᵇ 16 Hebrew every ship of Tarshish

to the rodents and bats
their idols of silver and idols of
gold,
which they made to worship.
²¹ They will flee to caverns in the
rocks
and to the overhanging crags
from dread of the LORD
and the splendor of his majesty,
when he rises to shake the
earth.

²² Stop trusting in man,
who has but a breath in his nostrils.
Of what account is he?

Judgment on Jerusalem and Judah

3 See now, the Lord,
the LORD Almighty,
is about to take from Jerusalem and Judah
both supply and support:
all supplies of food and all supplies of water,
²   the hero and warrior,
the judge and prophet,
the soothsayer and elder,
³ the captain of fifty and man of rank,
the counselor, skilled craftsman and clever enchanter.

⁴ I will make boys their officials;
mere children will govern them.
⁵ People will oppress each other—
man against man, neighbor against neighbor.
The young will rise up against the old,
the base against the honorable.

⁶ A man will seize one of his brothers
at his father's home, and say,
"You have a cloak, you be our leader;
take charge of this heap of ruins!"
⁷ But in that day he will cry out,
"I have no remedy.
I have no food or clothing in my house;
do not make me the leader of the people."

⁸ Jerusalem staggers,
Judah is falling;
their words and deeds are against the LORD,
defying his glorious presence.
⁹ The look on their faces testifies against them;
they parade their sin like Sodom;
they do not hide it.
Woe to them!
They have brought disaster upon themselves.

¹⁰ Tell the righteous it will be well with them,
for they will enjoy the fruit of their deeds.
¹¹ Woe to the wicked! Disaster is upon them!
They will be paid back for what their hands have done.

truth or dare

Stop! Instead of searching once again for that one flawless guy, try trusting in a perfect God. Your chances of finding him are *much* better!

2:22

¹²Youths oppress my people,
women rule over them.
O my people, your guides lead you astray;
they turn you from the path.

¹³The LORD takes his place in court;
he rises to judge the people.
¹⁴The LORD enters into judgment
against the elders and leaders of his people:
"It is you who have ruined my vineyard;
the plunder from the poor is in your houses.
¹⁵What do you mean by crushing
my people
and grinding the faces of the
poor?"
declares the Lord,
the LORD Almighty.

¹⁶The LORD says,
"The women of Zion are
haughty,
walking along with outstretched
necks,
flirting with their eyes,
tripping along with mincing steps,
with ornaments jingling on
their ankles.
¹⁷Therefore the Lord will bring
sores on the heads of
the women of Zion;
the LORD will make their
scalps bald."

¹⁸In that day the Lord will snatch away their finery: the bangles and headbands and crescent necklaces, ¹⁹the earrings and bracelets and veils, ²⁰the headdresses and ankle chains and sashes, the perfume bottles and charms, ²¹the signet rings and nose rings, ²²the fine robes and the capes and cloaks, the purses ²³and mirrors, and the linen garments and tiaras and shawls.

genuine

beauty » 3:16-24

Does God have something against trendy clothes, great hair, jewelry and perfume? No way! The real problem with the Israelite women was their hearts—they were vain and conceited and self-centered. They cared more about their appearance than about honoring God. And because God refuses to take second place, he said he would strip them of the finery they were so proud of so that they would turn to him instead. While there's nothing wrong with caring about your appearance, keep it in perspective. Make sure you honor God with all you are—both inside and out.

²⁴Instead of fragrance there will be a stench;
instead of a sash, a rope;
instead of well-dressed hair, baldness;
instead of fine clothing, sackcloth;
instead of beauty, branding.
²⁵Your men will fall by the sword,
your warriors in battle.
²⁶The gates of Zion will lament and mourn;
destitute, she will sit on the ground.
In that day seven women
will take hold of one man
and say, "We will eat our own food
and provide our own clothes;
only let us be called by your name.
Take away our disgrace!"

4

Daddy's Gone

focus Profile: Kayla

Rainy, dreary, hopeless. I remember that day like it was yesterday. Mom tiptoed into my room with bloodshot eyes and gave me the news. "Your dad's gone, Kayla," she said, "And this time he's not coming back."

I cried for a few days, and then I got really mad. *How dare he do this to us!* I thought. *And what did I do that made Daddy want to leave?* That was a year ago. And Mom was right—he never came back.

Mom does her best to come to all of my volleyball games, but it's just not the same. Dad used to do this special whistle every time I scored. Sometimes I imagine I hear it again, but when I turn to look, he's never there.

My friend Brittany goes on fishing trips with her dad every summer, and the girl who lives next door to me is filling out college applications with her dad. Every time I see a girl doing something with her dad, I get so jealous. I wish I could change things back to normal. But things aren't normal, and they'll never be normal again.

The hardest part is that I used to believe Dad really loved me and my mom, that he'd always be there for us. If he ever comes around, I'll never let him know how much we miss him. I'll never let him hurt me again.

For more ideas on how to cope without a parent, check out the Parents Link on www.TrueImagesBible.com

parents in focus

It's a dad's job to help his daughter feel secure, loved and beautiful. So when a dad steps outside of God's plan, it's easy for us to lose our self-worth and to become bitter and angry. If your dad has checked out of your life . . .

»*Turn to your heavenly Father.* When dads disappoint, it's sometimes hard to understand God's unconditional love. Psalm 68:5 (page 718) tells us that God is "a father to the fatherless." He always has open arms for you, his precious daughter (see Romans 8:14–16, page 1493).

»*Don't be afraid to ask for help.* Those feelings of abandonment, bitterness and anger can have lasting effects on you. It's important to process your feelings. Talk to someone you trust, and seek out professional Christian counseling.

For more on this topic, see the index on page 1656.

The Branch of the Lord

²In that day the Branch of the Lord will be beautiful and glorious, and the fruit of the land will be the pride and glory of the survivors in Israel. ³Those who are left in Zion, who remain in Jerusalem, will be called holy, all who are recorded among the living in Jerusalem. ⁴The Lord will wash away the filth of the women of Zion; he will cleanse the bloodstains from Jerusalem by a spirit*ᵃ* of judgment and a spirit*ᵃ* of fire. ⁵Then the Lord will create over all of Mount Zion and over those who assemble there a cloud of smoke by day and a glow of flaming fire by night; over all the glory will be a canopy. ⁶It will be a shelter and shade from the heat of the day, and a refuge and hiding place from the storm and rain.

ᵃ 4 Or the Spirit

The Song of the Vineyard

5

I will sing for the one I love
    a song about his vineyard:
My loved one had a vineyard
    on a fertile hillside.
² He dug it up and cleared it of stones
    and planted it with the choicest vines.
He built a watchtower in it
    and cut out a winepress as well.
Then he looked for a crop of good grapes,
    but it yielded only bad fruit.

³ "Now you dwellers in Jerusalem and men of Judah,
    judge between me and my vineyard.
⁴ What more could have been done for my vineyard
    than I have done for it?
When I looked for good grapes,
    why did it yield only bad?
⁵ Now I will tell you
    what I am going to do to my vineyard:
I will take away its hedge,
    and it will be destroyed;
I will break down its wall,
    and it will be trampled.
⁶ I will make it a wasteland,
    neither pruned nor cultivated,
    and briers and thorns will grow there.
I will command the clouds
    not to rain on it."

⁷ The vineyard of the LORD Almighty
    is the house of Israel,
and the men of Judah
    are the garden of his delight.
And he looked for justice, but saw bloodshed;
    for righteousness, but heard cries of distress.

Woes and Judgments

⁸ Woe to you who add house to house
    and join field to field
till no space is left
    and you live alone in the land.

⁹ The LORD Almighty has declared in my hearing:

"Surely the great houses will become desolate,
    the fine mansions left without occupants.
¹⁰ A ten-acre ᵃ vineyard will produce only a bath ᵇ of wine,
    a homer ᶜ of seed only an ephah ᵈ of grain."

¹¹ Woe to those who rise early in the morning
    to run after their drinks,
who stay up late at night
    till they are inflamed with wine.
¹² They have harps and lyres at their banquets,

ᵃ 10 Hebrew *ten-yoke*, that is, the land plowed by 10 yoke of oxen in one day (about 22 liters)   ᶜ 10 That is, probably about 6 bushels (about 220 liters)   ᵇ 10 That is, probably about 6 gallons (about 22 liters)   ᵈ 10 That is, probably about 3/5 bushel (about 22 liters)

tambourines and flutes and
wine,
but they have no regard for the
deeds of the Lord,
no respect for the work of his
hands.
¹³ Therefore my people will go into
exile
for lack of understanding;
their men of rank will die of
hunger
and their masses will be
parched with thirst.
¹⁴ Therefore the grave^a enlarges its appetite
and opens its mouth without limit;
into it will descend their nobles and masses
with all their brawlers and revelers.
¹⁵ So man will be brought low
and mankind humbled,
the eyes of the arrogant humbled.
¹⁶ But the Lord Almighty will be exalted by his justice,
and the holy God will show himself holy by his righteousness.
¹⁷ Then sheep will graze as in their own pasture;
lambs will feed^b among the ruins of the rich.

¹⁸ Woe to those who draw sin along with cords of deceit,
and wickedness as with cart ropes,
¹⁹ to those who say, "Let God hurry,
let him hasten his work
so we may see it.
Let it approach,
let the plan of the Holy One of Israel come,
so we may know it."

²⁰ Woe to those who call evil good
and good evil,
who put darkness for light
and light for darkness,
who put bitter for sweet
and sweet for bitter.

²¹ Woe to those who are wise in their own eyes
and clever in their own sight.

²² Woe to those who are heroes at drinking wine
and champions at mixing drinks,
²³ who acquit the guilty for a bribe,
but deny justice to the innocent.
²⁴ Therefore, as tongues of fire lick up straw
and as dry grass sinks down in the flames,
so their roots will decay
and their flowers blow away like dust;
for they have rejected the law of the Lord Almighty
and spurned the word of the Holy One of Israel.
²⁵ Therefore the Lord's anger burns against his people;
his hand is raised and he strikes them down.

truth or dare

God's not against having fun. That's why he's given you life. But getting trashed doesn't please God because it's an avoidance of him and the life he's given you.

5:11–12

---

^a 14 Hebrew *Sheol*   ^b 17 Septuagint; Hebrew / *strangers will eat*

The mountains shake,
    and the dead bodies are like refuse in the streets.

Yet for all this, his anger is not turned away,
    his hand is still upraised.

²⁶ He lifts up a banner for the distant nations,
    he whistles for those at the ends of the earth.
Here they come,
    swiftly and speedily!
²⁷ Not one of them grows tired or stumbles,
    not one slumbers or sleeps;
not a belt is loosened at the waist,
    not a sandal thong is broken.
²⁸ Their arrows are sharp,
    all their bows are strung;
their horses' hoofs seem like flint,
    their chariot wheels like a whirlwind.
²⁹ Their roar is like that of the lion,
    they roar like young lions;
they growl as they seize their prey
    and carry it off with no one to rescue.
³⁰ In that day they will roar over it
    like the roaring of the sea.
And if one looks at the land,
    he will see darkness and distress;
    even the light will be darkened by the clouds.

Isaiah's Commission

6 In the year that King Uzziah died, I saw the Lord seated on a throne, high and exalted, and the train of his robe filled the temple. ²Above him were seraphs, each with six wings: With two wings they covered their faces, with two they covered their feet, and with two they were flying. ³And they were calling to one another:

"Holy, holy, holy is the Lᴏʀᴅ Almighty;
    the whole earth is full of his glory."

⁴At the sound of their voices the doorposts and thresholds shook and the temple was filled with smoke.

⁵"Woe to me!" I cried. "I am ruined! For I am a man of unclean lips, and I live among a people of unclean lips, and my eyes have seen the King, the Lᴏʀᴅ Almighty."

⁶Then one of the seraphs flew to me with a live coal in his hand, which he had taken with tongs from the altar. ⁷With it he touched my mouth and said, "See, this has touched your lips; your guilt is taken away and your sin atoned for."

⁸Then I heard the voice of the Lord saying, "Whom shall I send? And who will go for us?"

And I said, "Here am I. Send me!"

⁹He said, "Go and tell this people:

" 'Be ever hearing, but never understanding;
    be ever seeing, but never perceiving.'
¹⁰ Make the heart of this people calloused;
    make their ears dull
    and close their eyes. ᵃ
Otherwise they might see with their eyes,
    hear with their ears,
    understand with their hearts,
and turn and be healed."

ᵃ 9,10 Hebrew; Septuagint 'You will be ever hearing, but never understanding; / you will be ever seeing, but never perceiving.' / ¹⁰ This people's heart has become calloused; / they hardly hear with their ears, / and they have closed their eyes

[11]Then I said, "For how long, O Lord?" And he answered:

"Until the cities lie ruined
    and without inhabitant,
until the houses are left deserted
    and the fields ruined and
        ravaged,
[12]until the LORD has sent everyone
        far away
    and the land is utterly forsaken.
[13]And though a tenth remains in
        the land,
    it will again be laid waste.
But as the terebinth and oak
    leave stumps when they are
        cut down,
    so the holy seed will be the
        stump in the land."

The Sign of Immanuel

7 When Ahaz son of Jotham, the son of Uzziah, was king of Judah, King Rezin of Aram and Pekah son of Remaliah king of Israel marched up to fight against Jerusalem, but they could not overpower it. [2]Now the house of David was told, "Aram has allied itself with[a] Ephraim"; so the hearts of Ahaz and his people were shaken, as the trees of the forest are shaken by the wind.

[3]Then the LORD said to Isaiah, "Go out, you and your son Shear-Jashub,[b] to meet Ahaz at the end of the aqueduct of the Upper Pool, on the road to the Washerman's Field. [4]Say to him, 'Be careful, keep calm and don't be afraid. Do not lose heart because of these two smoldering stubs of firewood—because of the fierce anger of Rezin and Aram and of the son of Remaliah. [5]Aram, Ephraim and Remaliah's son have plotted your ruin, saying, [6]"Let us invade Judah; let us tear it apart and divide it among ourselves, and make the son of Tabeel king over it." [7]Yet this is what the Sovereign LORD says:

" 'It will not take place,
    it will not happen,
[8]for the head of Aram is Damascus,
    and the head of Damascus is only Rezin.
Within sixty-five years
    Ephraim will be too shattered to be a people.
[9]The head of Ephraim is Samaria,
    and the head of Samaria is only Remaliah's son.
If you do not stand firm in your faith,
    you will not stand at all.' "

[10]Again the LORD spoke to Ahaz, [11]"Ask the LORD your God for a sign, whether in the deepest depths or in the highest heights."

[12]But Ahaz said, "I will not ask; I will not put the LORD to the test."

[13]Then Isaiah said, "Hear now, you house of David! Is it not enough to try the patience of men? Will you try the patience of my God also? [14]Therefore the Lord himself will give you[c] a sign: The virgin will be with child and will give birth to a son, and[d] will call him Immanuel.[e] [15]He will eat curds and honey when he knows enough to reject the wrong and choose the right. [16]But before the boy knows

---

a 2 Or *has set up camp in*   *b 3 Shear-Jashub* means *a remnant will return.*   *c 14* The Hebrew is plural.
d 14 Masoretic Text; Dead Sea Scrolls *and he* or *and they*   *e 14 Immanuel* means *God with us.*

enough to reject the wrong and choose the right, the land of the two kings you dread will be laid waste. ¹⁷The LORD will bring on you and on your people and on the house of your father a time unlike any since Ephraim broke away from Judah—he will bring the king of Assyria."

¹⁸In that day the LORD will whistle for flies from the distant streams of Egypt and for bees from the land of Assyria. ¹⁹They will all come and settle in the steep ravines and in the crevices in the rocks, on all the thornbushes and at all the water holes. ²⁰In that day the Lord will use a razor hired from beyond the River*ᵃ—the king of Assyria—to shave your head and the hair of your legs, and to take off your beards also. ²¹In that day, a man will keep alive a young cow and two goats. ²²And because of the abundance of the milk they give, he will have curds to eat. All who remain in the land will eat curds and honey. ²³In that day, in every place where there were a thousand vines worth a thousand silver shekels,ᵇ there will be only briers and thorns. ²⁴Men will go there with bow and arrow, for the land will be covered with briers and thorns. ²⁵As for all the hills once cultivated by the hoe, you will no longer go there for fear of the briers and thorns; they will become places where cattle are turned loose and where sheep run.

Assyria, the LORD's Instrument

8 The LORD said to me, "Take a large scroll and write on it with an ordinary pen: Maher-Shalal-Hash-Baz.ᶜ ²And I will call in Uriah the priest and Zechariah son of Jeberekiah as reliable witnesses for me."

³Then I went to the prophetess, and she conceived and gave birth to a son. And the LORD said to me, "Name him Maher-Shalal-Hash-Baz. ⁴Before the boy knows how to say 'My father' or 'My mother,' the wealth of Damascus and the plunder of Samaria will be carried off by the king of Assyria."

⁵The LORD spoke to me again:

⁶ "Because this people has rejected
　　the gently flowing waters of Shiloah
　　and rejoices over Rezin
　　　and the son of Remaliah,
⁷ therefore the Lord is about to bring against them
　　the mighty floodwaters of the Riverᵃ—
　　the king of Assyria with all his pomp.
It will overflow all its channels,
　　run over all its banks
⁸ and sweep on into Judah, swirling over it,
　　passing through it and reaching up to the neck.
Its outspread wings will cover the breadth of your land,
　　O Immanuelᵈ!"

⁹ Raise the war cry,ᵉ you nations, and be shattered!
　　Listen, all you distant lands.
Prepare for battle, and be shattered!
　　Prepare for battle, and be shattered!
¹⁰ Devise your strategy, but it will be thwarted;
　　propose your plan, but it will not stand,
　　for God is with us.ᶠ

truth or dare

How patient are you? And how much do you think it would take to test God's patience? Everyone has a limit, even God. Quit messing around, and start obeying.

7:13

ᵃ 20,7 That is, the Euphrates　　ᵇ 23 That is, about 25 pounds (about 11.5 kilograms)　　ᶜ 1 Maher-Shalal-Hash-Baz means quick to the plunder, swift to the spoil; also in verse 3.　　ᵈ 8 Immanuel means God with us.　　ᵉ 9 Or Do your worst　　ᶠ 10 Hebrew Immanuel

genuine

obedience

Let's say you and your friends hatch a perfect plan for prom night. You have the dresses, the dates, the limo and even a hotel room. Problem is, your parents don't like the plan. You dread telling your friends that you have a curfew for prom night and a budget that ain't gonna cover all this. You're afraid of what your friends will say, so you're tempted to just blow off your parents and stick with the plan. But God says to obey your parents. *His* opinion should matter most to you—not your friends'.

» 8:13

isaiah 9:2 «

Fear God

[11] The LORD spoke to me with his strong hand upon me, warning me not to follow the way of this people. He said:

[12] "Do not call conspiracy
    everything that these people
        call conspiracy[a];
do not fear what they fear,
    and do not dread it.
[13] The LORD Almighty is the one you
        are to regard as holy,
he is the one you are to fear,
    he is the one you are to dread,
[14] and he will be a sanctuary;
    but for both houses of Israel
        he will be
a stone that causes men to
        stumble
    and a rock that makes them fall.
And for the people of Jerusalem
    he will be
a trap and a snare.
[15] Many of them will stumble;
    they will fall and be broken,
    they will be snared and
        captured."

[16] Bind up the testimony
    and seal up the law among my disciples.
[17] I will wait for the LORD,
    who is hiding his face from the house of Jacob.
    I will put my trust in him.

[18] Here am I, and the children the LORD has given me. We are signs and symbols in Israel from the LORD Almighty, who dwells on Mount Zion.

[19] When men tell you to consult mediums and spiritists, who whisper and mutter, should not a people inquire of their God? Why consult the dead on behalf of the living? [20] To the law and to the testimony! If they do not speak according to this word, they have no light of dawn. [21] Distressed and hungry, they will roam through the land; when they are famished, they will become enraged and, looking upward, will curse their king and their God. [22] Then they will look toward the earth and see only distress and darkness and fearful gloom, and they will be thrust into utter darkness.

To Us a Child Is Born

9 Nevertheless, there will be no more gloom for those who were in distress. In the past he humbled the land of Zebulun and the land of Naphtali, but in the future he will honor Galilee of the Gentiles, by the way of the sea, along the Jordan—

[2] The people walking in darkness
    have seen a great light;
on those living in the land of the shadow of
    death[b]

truth or dare

Spending all your time fantasizing about the future? Skip the horoscopes! Get all your guidance from God. He's just a prayer away.

8:19

---

[a] 12 Or *Do not call for a treaty / every time these people call for a treaty*   [b] 2 Or *land of darkness*

» 893

a light has dawned.
³You have enlarged the nation
and increased their joy;
they rejoice before you
as people rejoice at the harvest,
as men rejoice
when dividing the plunder.
⁴For as in the day of Midian's
defeat,
you have shattered
the yoke that burdens them,
the bar across their shoulders,
the rod of their oppressor.
⁵Every warrior's boot used in
battle
and every garment rolled in
blood
will be destined for burning,
will be fuel for the fire.
⁶For to us a child is born,
to us a son is given,
and the government will be on his
shoulders.
And he will be called
Wonderful Counselor,ᵃ Mighty God,
Everlasting Father, Prince of Peace.
⁷Of the increase of his government and peace
there will be no end.
He will reign on David's throne
and over his kingdom,
establishing and upholding it
with justice and righteousness
from that time on and forever.
The zeal of the LORD Almighty
will accomplish this.

The LORD's Anger Against Israel

⁸The Lord has sent a message against Jacob;
it will fall on Israel.
⁹All the people will know it—
Ephraim and the inhabitants of Samaria—
who say with pride
and arrogance of heart,
¹⁰"The bricks have fallen down,
but we will rebuild with dressed stone;
the fig trees have been felled,
but we will replace them with cedars."
¹¹But the LORD has strengthened Rezin's foes against them
and has spurred their enemies on.
¹²Arameans from the east and Philistines from the west
have devoured Israel with open mouth.

Yet for all this, his anger is not turned away,
his hand is still upraised.

truth or dare

And you thought these were just lyrics from a Christmas song! Hundreds of years before the life of Jesus, his birth was already big news.

9:6–7

ᵃ 6 Or *Wonderful, Counselor*

¹³ But the people have not returned to him who struck them,
  nor have they sought the LORD Almighty.
¹⁴ So the LORD will cut off from Israel both head and tail,
  both palm branch and reed in a single day;
¹⁵ the elders and prominent men are the head,
  the prophets who teach lies are the tail.
¹⁶ Those who guide this people mislead them,
  and those who are guided are led astray.
¹⁷ Therefore the Lord will take no pleasure in the young men,
  nor will he pity the fatherless and widows,
for everyone is ungodly and wicked,
  every mouth speaks vileness.

Yet for all this, his anger is not turned away,
  his hand is still upraised.

¹⁸ Surely wickedness burns like a fire;
  it consumes briers and thorns,
it sets the forest thickets ablaze,
  so that it rolls upward in a column of smoke.
¹⁹ By the wrath of the LORD Almighty
  the land will be scorched
and the people will be fuel for the fire;
  no one will spare his brother.
²⁰ On the right they will devour,
  but still be hungry;
on the left they will eat,
  but not be satisfied.
Each will feed on the flesh of his own offspring ᵃ:
²¹ Manasseh will feed on Ephraim, and Ephraim on Manasseh;
  together they will turn against Judah.

Yet for all this, his anger is not turned away,
  his hand is still upraised.

10 Woe to those who make unjust laws,
  to those who issue oppressive decrees,
² to deprive the poor of their rights
  and withhold justice from the oppressed of my people,
making widows their prey
  and robbing the fatherless.
³ What will you do on the day of reckoning,
  when disaster comes from afar?
To whom will you run for help?
  Where will you leave your riches?
⁴ Nothing will remain but to cringe among the captives
  or fall among the slain.

Yet for all this, his anger is not turned away,
  his hand is still upraised.

God's Judgment on Assyria

⁵ "Woe to the Assyrian, the rod of my anger,
  in whose hand is the club of my wrath!
⁶ I send him against a godless nation,
  I dispatch him against a people who anger me,

ᵃ 20 Or arm

to seize loot and snatch plunder,
and to trample them down like mud in the streets.
⁷ But this is not what he intends,
this is not what he has in mind;
his purpose is to destroy,
to put an end to many nations.
⁸ 'Are not my commanders all kings?' he says.
⁹ 'Has not Calno fared like Carchemish?
Is not Hamath like Arpad,
and Samaria like Damascus?
¹⁰ As my hand seized the kingdoms of the idols,
kingdoms whose images excelled those of Jerusalem and Samaria—
¹¹ shall I not deal with Jerusalem and her images
as I dealt with Samaria and her idols?' "

¹²When the Lord has finished all his work against Mount Zion and Jerusalem, he will say, "I will punish the king of Assyria for the willful pride of his heart and the haughty look in his eyes. ¹³For he says:

" 'By the strength of my hand I have done this,
and by my wisdom, because I have understanding.
I removed the boundaries of nations,
I plundered their treasures;
like a mighty one I subdued ᵃ their kings.
¹⁴ As one reaches into a nest,
so my hand reached for the wealth of the nations;
as men gather abandoned eggs,
so I gathered all the countries;
not one flapped a wing,
or opened its mouth to chirp.' "

¹⁵ Does the ax raise itself above him who swings it,
or the saw boast against him who uses it?
As if a rod were to wield him who lifts it up,
or a club brandish him who is not wood!
¹⁶ Therefore, the Lord, the Lord Almighty,
will send a wasting disease upon his sturdy warriors;
under his pomp a fire will be kindled
like a blazing flame.
¹⁷ The Light of Israel will become a fire,
their Holy One a flame;
in a single day it will burn and consume
his thorns and his briers.
¹⁸ The splendor of his forests and fertile fields
it will completely destroy,
as when a sick man wastes away.
¹⁹ And the remaining trees of his forests will be so few
that a child could write them down.

The Remnant of Israel

²⁰ In that day the remnant of Israel,
the survivors of the house of Jacob,
will no longer rely on him
who struck them down
but will truly rely on the Lord,
the Holy One of Israel.

ᵃ 13 Or / I subdued the mighty,

mirror images

Mary—Just Say "Yes"

I magine just for a minute that you're Mary, the teenager chosen to be the mother of Jesus. (That's right—she was almost certainly only a teen!) You're a follower of God and an all-around really nice girl. And since you've become engaged to the well-respected Joseph, life is looking comfortable and predictable. Until you get pregnant.

Think there's a stigma on unwed mothers today? It's nothing compared to the scandal an unwanted pregnancy must have caused back then. Engagement at that time was taken so seriously that it could only be broken by divorce. Matthew 1:19 says that, until God changed Joseph's mind, Joseph planned to "divorce her quietly" because he didn't want to expose Mary to "public disgrace." Sounds pretty serious.

Not only did Mary have to deal with the realization she was pregnant; she also had to come to terms with the idea of becoming pregnant by a miracle. You see, Mary was a virgin. She kept herself pure in anticipation of her wedding night. So she never had to worry about a skipped period or "how far is too far?" Mary knew she was on track with God and her man.

So when an angel told her she was going to be the mother of the Son of God, Mary was confused. "How will this be," she asked, "since I am a virgin?" When the angel told her the Holy Spirit would cause the pregnancy, Mary had another choice. She could have freaked out and told God no. She could have bargained with God. She could have at least grumbled. But Mary simply said, "May it be to me as you have said." What would you have said?

Saying "yes" to God, like Mary did, often requires sacrifice. When God brings an opportunity into our lives, we might lose friends, give up our plans or just be plain misunderstood. But just as Mary experienced, saying yes to God's plan is worth it. She was given the awesome privilege of being the mother of Jesus. Can you imagine how she would have felt if she'd said no?

When God gives you opportunities to say yes to him, remember the angel's final words to Mary: *"Nothing is impossible with God."*

Dear Jesus, sometimes I'm afraid of letting you have complete control of my life. Show me how to be a "yes" kind of girl, like Mary was, and use me to bring you to others. Amen.

To read the next Mirror Images profile, go to page 945.

» Read more about Mary in Matthew 1–2 (pages 1290–1292), Luke 1–2 (pages 1363–1367) and John 19:25–30 (page 1440).

21 A remnant will return,[a] a remnant of Jacob
   will return to the Mighty God.
22 Though your people, O Israel, be like the sand by the sea,
   only a remnant will return.
Destruction has been decreed,
   overwhelming and righteous.
23 The Lord, the LORD Almighty, will carry out
   the destruction decreed upon the whole land.

24 Therefore, this is what the Lord, the LORD Almighty, says:

"O my people who live in Zion,
   do not be afraid of the Assyrians,
who beat you with a rod
   and lift up a club against you, as Egypt did.
25 Very soon my anger against you will end
   and my wrath will be directed to their destruction."

26 The LORD Almighty will lash them with a whip,
   as when he struck down Midian at the rock of Oreb;
and he will raise his staff over the waters,
   as he did in Egypt.
27 In that day their burden will be lifted from your shoulders,
   their yoke from your neck;
the yoke will be broken
   because you have grown so fat.[b]

28 They enter Aiath;
   they pass through Migron;
   they store supplies at Micmash.
29 They go over the pass, and say,
   "We will camp overnight at Geba."
Ramah trembles;
   Gibeah of Saul flees.
30 Cry out, O Daughter of Gallim!
   Listen, O Laishah!
   Poor Anathoth!
31 Madmenah is in flight;
   the people of Gebim take cover.
32 This day they will halt at Nob;
   they will shake their fist
at the mount of the Daughter of Zion,
   at the hill of Jerusalem.

33 See, the Lord, the LORD Almighty,
   will lop off the boughs with great power.
The lofty trees will be felled,
   the tall ones will be brought low.
34 He will cut down the forest thickets with an ax;
   Lebanon will fall before the Mighty One.

The Branch From Jesse

11 A shoot will come up from the stump of Jesse;
   from his roots a Branch will bear fruit.
2 The Spirit of the LORD will rest on him—
   the Spirit of wisdom and of understanding,
   the Spirit of counsel and of power,

a 21 Hebrew shear-jashub; also in verse 22   b 27 Hebrew; Septuagint broken / from your shoulders

the Spirit of knowledge and of
the fear of the LORD—
³and he will delight in the fear of
the LORD.

He will not judge by what he sees
with his eyes,
or decide by what he hears
with his ears;
⁴but with righteousness he will
judge the needy,
with justice he will give
decisions for the poor of
the earth.
He will strike the earth with the rod of his
mouth;
with the breath of his lips he will slay the
wicked.
⁵Righteousness will be his belt
and faithfulness the sash around his waist.

⁶The wolf will live with the lamb,
the leopard will lie down with the goat,
the calf and the lion and the yearling*ᵃ together;
and a little child will lead them.
⁷The cow will feed with the bear,
their young will lie down together,
and the lion will eat straw like the ox.
⁸The infant will play near the hole of the cobra,
and the young child put his
hand into the viper's
nest.
⁹They will neither harm nor destroy
on all my holy mountain,
for the earth will be full of the
knowledge of the LORD
as the waters cover the sea.

¹⁰In that day the Root of Jesse will stand as a banner for the peoples; the nations will rally to him, and his
place of rest will be glorious. ¹¹In that day the Lord will
reach out his hand a second time to reclaim the remnant that is left of his people from Assyria, from Lower Egypt, from
Upper Egypt,ᵇ from Cush,ᶜ from Elam, from Babylonia,ᵈ from Hamath and from the islands of the sea.

¹²He will raise a banner for the nations
and gather the exiles of Israel;
he will assemble the scattered people of Judah
from the four quarters of the earth.
¹³Ephraim's jealousy will vanish,
and Judah's enemiesᵉ will be cut off;
Ephraim will not be jealous of Judah,
nor Judah hostile toward Ephraim.
¹⁴They will swoop down on the slopes of Philistia to the west;

truth or dare

If you want to be like
Jesus, follow his exam-
ple: 1) Judge others by
their hearts, not their
outer appearance.
2) Take special care of
the poor and needy.

11:1–5

truth or dare

Can you imagine get-
ting cozy with a lion or
letting a baby play with
a cobra? God promises
us a cool future, with-
out violence or death or
pain.

11:6–9

ᵃ 6 Hebrew; Septuagint *lion will feed*   *ᵇ 11* Hebrew *from Pathros*   *ᶜ 11* That is, the upper Nile region   *ᵈ 11* Hebrew
Shinar   *ᵉ 13* Or *hostility*

ɡenuine

strength ❯❯ 12:2

Surely. Of course. Certainly. Definitely. Unquestionably. Without a doubt. *Surely,* God is your salvation; you can trust him and not be afraid. What is your greatest fear? Not being accepted for who you are? Never finding true love? Getting raped? Getting shot? Are you afraid of heights? Afraid of public speaking? No matter what, you can trust God and not be afraid. Because no matter what happens to you, God will give you strength. His salvation means that you will spend all of eternity in heaven with him—and what can compare with that?!

together they will plunder the
people to the east.
They will lay hands on Edom and
Moab,
and the Ammonites will be
subject to them.
[15] The LORD will dry up
the gulf of the Egyptian sea;
with a scorching wind he will
sweep his hand
over the Euphrates River. [a]
He will break it up into seven
streams
so that men can cross over in
sandals.
[16] There will be a highway for the
remnant of his people
that is left from Assyria,
as there was for Israel
when they came up from
Egypt.

Songs of Praise

12 In that day you will say:

"I will praise you, O LORD.
Although you were angry with
me,
your anger has turned away
and you have comforted me.
[2] Surely God is my salvation;
I will trust and not be afraid.
The LORD, the LORD, is my strength and my song;
he has become my salvation."
[3] With joy you will draw water
from the wells of salvation.

[4] In that day you will say:

"Give thanks to the LORD, call on his name;
make known among the nations what he has done,
and proclaim that his name is exalted.
[5] Sing to the LORD, for he has done glorious things;
let this be known to all the world.
[6] Shout aloud and sing for joy, people of Zion,
for great is the Holy One of Israel among you."

A Prophecy Against Babylon

13 An oracle concerning Babylon that Isaiah son of Amoz saw:

[2] Raise a banner on a bare hilltop,
shout to them;
beckon to them
to enter the gates of the nobles.
[3] I have commanded my holy ones;

a 15 Hebrew *the River*

I have summoned my warriors to carry out my wrath—
    those who rejoice in my triumph.

⁴Listen, a noise on the mountains,
    like that of a great multitude!
Listen, an uproar among the kingdoms,
    like nations massing together!
The Lord Almighty is mustering
    an army for war.
⁵They come from faraway lands,
    from the ends of the heavens—
the Lord and the weapons of his wrath—
    to destroy the whole country.

⁶Wail, for the day of the Lord is near;
    it will come like destruction from the Almighty.ᵃ
⁷Because of this, all hands will go limp,
    every man's heart will melt.
⁸Terror will seize them,
    pain and anguish will grip them;
    they will writhe like a woman in labor.
They will look aghast at each other,
    their faces aflame.

⁹See, the day of the Lord is coming
    —a cruel day, with wrath and fierce anger—
to make the land desolate
    and destroy the sinners within it.
¹⁰The stars of heaven and their constellations
    will not show their light.
The rising sun will be darkened
    and the moon will not give its light.
¹¹I will punish the world for its evil,
    the wicked for their sins.
I will put an end to the arrogance of the haughty
    and will humble the pride of the ruthless.
¹²I will make man scarcer than pure gold,
    more rare than the gold of Ophir.
¹³Therefore I will make the heavens tremble;
    and the earth will shake from its place
at the wrath of the Lord Almighty,
    in the day of his burning anger.

¹⁴Like a hunted gazelle,
    like sheep without a shepherd,
each will return to his own people,
    each will flee to his native land.
¹⁵Whoever is captured will be thrust through;
    all who are caught will fall by the sword.
¹⁶Their infants will be dashed to pieces before their eyes;
    their houses will be looted and their wives ravished.

¹⁷See, I will stir up against them the Medes,
    who do not care for silver
    and have no delight in gold.
¹⁸Their bows will strike down the young men;
    they will have no mercy on infants

ᵃ *6* Hebrew *Shaddai*

nor will they look with compassion on children.
¹⁹Babylon, the jewel of kingdoms,
　the glory of the Babylonians'ᵃ pride,
will be overthrown by God
　like Sodom and Gomorrah.
²⁰She will never be inhabited
　or lived in through all
　　generations;
no Arab will pitch his tent there,
　no shepherd will rest his
　　flocks there.
²¹But desert creatures will lie there,
　jackals will fill her houses;
there the owls will dwell,
　and there the wild goats will
　　leap about.
²²Hyenas will howl in her strongholds,
　jackals in her luxurious palaces.
Her time is at hand,
　and her days will not be prolonged.

or dare

truth

Every great power must come to an end. Archaeologists back up God's message—Babylon *was* destroyed and to this day has never been rebuilt.

13:19–22

14

The LORD will have compassion on Jacob;
　once again he will choose Israel
　and will settle them in their own land.
Aliens will join them
　and unite with the house of Jacob.
²Nations will take them
　and bring them to their own place.
And the house of Israel will possess the nations
　as menservants and maidservants in the LORD's land.
They will make captives of their captors
　and rule over their oppressors.

³On the day the LORD gives you relief from suffering and turmoil and cruel bondage, ⁴you will take up this taunt against the king of Babylon:

How the oppressor has come to an end!
　How his furyᵇ has ended!
⁵The LORD has broken the rod of the wicked,
　the scepter of the rulers,
⁶which in anger struck down peoples
　with unceasing blows,
and in fury subdued nations
　with relentless aggression.
⁷All the lands are at rest and at peace;
　they break into singing.
⁸Even the pine trees and the cedars of Lebanon
　exult over you and say,
"Now that you have been laid low,
　no woodsman comes to cut us down."

⁹The graveᶜ below is all astir
　to meet you at your coming;
it rouses the spirits of the departed to greet you—
　all those who were leaders in the world;

ᵃ *19* Or *Chaldeans'*　ᵇ *4* Dead Sea Scrolls, Septuagint and Syriac; the meaning of the word in the Masoretic Text is uncertain.　ᶜ *9* Hebrew *Sheol*; also in verses 11 and 15

it makes them rise from their thrones—
all those who were kings over the nations.
[10] They will all respond,
they will say to you,
"You also have become weak, as we are;
you have become like us."
[11] All your pomp has been brought down to the grave,
along with the noise of your harps;
maggots are spread out beneath you
and worms cover you.

[12] How you have fallen from heaven,
O morning star, son of the dawn!
You have been cast down to the earth,
you who once laid low the nations!
[13] You said in your heart,
"I will ascend to heaven;
I will raise my throne
above the stars of God;
I will sit enthroned on the mount of assembly,
on the utmost heights of the sacred mountain. [a]
[14] I will ascend above the tops of
the clouds;
I will make myself like the
Most High."
[15] But you are brought down to the
grave,
to the depths of the pit.

[16] Those who see you stare at you,
they ponder your fate:
"Is this the man who shook the
earth
and made kingdoms tremble,
[17] the man who made the world a desert,
who overthrew its cities
and would not let his captives go home?"

[18] All the kings of the nations lie in state,
each in his own tomb.
[19] But you are cast out of your tomb
like a rejected branch;
you are covered with the slain,
with those pierced by the sword,
those who descend to the stones of the pit.
Like a corpse trampled underfoot,
[20]   you will not join them in burial,
for you have destroyed your land
and killed your people.

The offspring of the wicked
will never be mentioned again.
[21] Prepare a place to slaughter his sons
for the sins of their forefathers;
they are not to rise to inherit the land
and cover the earth with their cities.

truth or dare

These verses are an analogy of what happened to Satan. His pride led to his ruin—he wanted to be higher than God. Always keep God is his rightful place.

14:12–15

[a] 13 Or *the north;* Hebrew *Zaphon*

22 "I will rise up against them,"
  declares the LORD Almighty.
"I will cut off from Babylon her name and survivors,
  her offspring and descendants,"

declares the LORD.

23 "I will turn her into a place for owls
  and into swampland;
I will sweep her with the broom of destruction,"
  declares the LORD Almighty.

A Prophecy Against Assyria

24 The LORD Almighty has sworn,

"Surely, as I have planned, so it will be,
  and as I have purposed, so it will stand.
25 I will crush the Assyrian in my land;
  on my mountains I will trample him down.
His yoke will be taken from my
    people,
  and his burden removed from
    their shoulders."

26 This is the plan determined for
    the whole world;
  this is the hand stretched out
    over all nations.
27 For the LORD Almighty has
    purposed, and who can
    thwart him?
  His hand is stretched out, and
    who can turn it back?

truth or dare

Sure, you might have your future planned out to perfection. Be careful, though. God gets the last word.

14:26–27

A Prophecy Against the Philistines

28 This oracle came in the year King Ahaz died:

29 Do not rejoice, all you Philistines,
  that the rod that struck you is broken;
from the root of that snake will spring up a viper,
  its fruit will be a darting, venomous serpent.
30 The poorest of the poor will find pasture,
  and the needy will lie down in safety.
But your root I will destroy by famine;
  it will slay your survivors.

31 Wail, O gate! Howl, O city!
  Melt away, all you Philistines!
A cloud of smoke comes from the north,
  and there is not a straggler in its ranks.
32 What answer shall be given
  to the envoys of that nation?
"The LORD has established Zion,
  and in her his afflicted people will find refuge."

A Prophecy Against Moab

15
An oracle concerning Moab:

Ar in Moab is ruined,
  destroyed in a night!

Kir in Moab is ruined,
  destroyed in a night!
[2] Dibon goes up to its temple,
  to its high places to weep;
  Moab wails over Nebo and Medeba.
Every head is shaved
  and every beard cut off.
[3] In the streets they wear sackcloth;
  on the roofs and in the public squares
they all wail,
  prostrate with weeping.
[4] Heshbon and Elealeh cry out,
  their voices are heard all the way to Jahaz.
Therefore the armed men of Moab cry out,
  and their hearts are faint.

[5] My heart cries out over Moab;
  her fugitives flee as far as Zoar,
  as far as Eglath Shelishiyah.
They go up the way to Luhith,
  weeping as they go;
on the road to Horonaim
  they lament their destruction.
[6] The waters of Nimrim are dried up
  and the grass is withered;
the vegetation is gone
  and nothing green is left.
[7] So the wealth they have acquired and stored up
  they carry away over the Ravine of the Poplars.
[8] Their outcry echoes along the border of Moab;
  their wailing reaches as far as Eglaim,
  their lamentation as far as Beer Elim.
[9] Dimon's[a] waters are full of blood,
  but I will bring still more upon Dimon[a]—
a lion upon the fugitives of Moab
  and upon those who remain in the land.

16

Send lambs as tribute
  to the ruler of the land,
from Sela, across the desert,
  to the mount of the Daughter of Zion.
[2] Like fluttering birds
  pushed from the nest,
so are the women of Moab
  at the fords of the Arnon.

[3] "Give us counsel,
  render a decision.
Make your shadow like night—
  at high noon.
Hide the fugitives,
  do not betray the refugees.
[4] Let the Moabite fugitives stay with you;
  be their shelter from the destroyer."

---

a 9 Masoretic Text; Dead Sea Scrolls, some Septuagint manuscripts and Vulgate *Dibon*

The oppressor will come to an end,
and destruction will cease;
the aggressor will vanish from the land.
⁵In love a throne will be established;
in faithfulness a man will sit on it—
one from the house *ᵃ* of David—
one who in judging seeks justice
and speeds the cause of righteousness.

⁶We have heard of Moab's pride—
her overweening pride and conceit,
her pride and her insolence—
but her boasts are empty.
⁷Therefore the Moabites wail,
they wail together for Moab.
Lament and grieve
for the men *ᵇ* of Kir Hareseth.
⁸The fields of Heshbon wither,
the vines of Sibmah also.
The rulers of the nations
have trampled down the choicest vines,
which once reached Jazer
and spread toward the desert.
Their shoots spread out
and went as far as the sea.
⁹So I weep, as Jazer weeps,
for the vines of Sibmah.
O Heshbon, O Elealeh,
I drench you with tears!
The shouts of joy over your ripened fruit
and over your harvests have been stilled.
¹⁰Joy and gladness are taken away from the orchards;
no one sings or shouts in the vineyards;
no one treads out wine at the presses,
for I have put an end to the shouting.
¹¹My heart laments for Moab like a harp,
my inmost being for Kir Hareseth.
¹²When Moab appears at her high place,
she only wears herself out;
when she goes to her shrine to pray,
it is to no avail.

¹³This is the word the LORD has already spoken concerning Moab. ¹⁴But now the LORD says: "Within three years, as a servant bound by contract would count them, Moab's splendor and all her many people will be despised, and her survivors will be very few and feeble."

An Oracle Against Damascus

17 An oracle concerning Damascus:

"See, Damascus will no longer be a city
but will become a heap of ruins.
²The cities of Aroer will be deserted
and left to flocks, which will lie down,
with no one to make them afraid.
³The fortified city will disappear from Ephraim,

ᵃ 5 Hebrew *tent*   *ᵇ 7* Or *"raisin cakes,"* a wordplay

in focus

Standing Alone

Profile: Dana

I just got "employee of the month" at the coffee shop where I work. Please, don't congratulate me—all the people I work with rolled their eyes when they read my manager's comments: *Dana has a great attitude. She's always honest and helpful to anyone who comes her way. We need more employees like her.*

No one ever said anything to me, though, except Jenna. "Hey, it's our token Christian," she said. "Now where in the Bible does it say you're better than us?" That's just like Jenna to make a scene with everyone else around. My face turned bright red and I stammered, "It . . . it doesn't."

Another time Jenna cornered me and asked me why I believe God exists. I told her that all of his creation, including us, is living proof. She smiled slyly and said, "Okay, Dana—then who created God?" I was so stunned I didn't know what to say.

I hate to admit it, but every time I go to work I try to avoid you-know-who. If she's up front making drinks, then I volunteer to work in the back. It just seems like I don't have any answers to prove what I believe. And Jenna has an amazing way of making me feel stupid and naïve.

The truth is, Jenna needs Jesus as much as anybody. And while I'm sure somebody could answer all her big questions and help her see the truth, I'm pretty sure that somebody isn't me.

apologetics in focus

Dana can relax—after all, God's the only one with all the answers. Still, he somehow uses us to show others who he is. Remember to . . .

»*Be like Jesus.* What girls like Jenna need is someone who will love them unconditionally and set a good example (see 1 Peter 2:11–12, page 1609).

»*Don't bend.* Girls like Jenna will try to provoke you to see if you'll react. And even if they don't realize it, they're also testing you, seeing if you're for real.

»*Let God's Word sink in.* The more you study the Bible, the better prepared you are to talk about what you believe (see 1 Peter 3:15–16, page 1610). And if you don't know the answer, be honest.

For more on this topic, see the index on page 1656.

apologetics

For more apologetics ammo, check out the Apologetics Link on www.TrueImagesBible.com

and royal power from Damascus;
the remnant of Aram will be
like the glory of the Israelites,"

declares the LORD Almighty.

⁴ "In that day the glory of Jacob will fade;
the fat of his body will waste away.
⁵ It will be as when a reaper gathers the standing grain
and harvests the grain with his arm—

as when a man gleans heads of grain
    in the Valley of Rephaim.
[6]Yet some gleanings will remain,
    as when an olive tree is beaten,
leaving two or three olives on the topmost branches,
    four or five on the fruitful boughs,"
                declares the LORD, the God of Israel.

[7]In that day men will look to their Maker
    and turn their eyes to the Holy One of Israel.
[8]They will not look to the altars,
    the work of their hands,
and they will have no regard for the Asherah poles[a]
    and the incense altars their fingers have made.

[9]In that day their strong cities, which they left because of the Israelites, will be like places abandoned to thickets and undergrowth. And all will be desolation.

[10]You have forgotten God your Savior;
    you have not remembered the Rock, your fortress.
Therefore, though you set out the finest plants
    and plant imported vines,
[11]though on the day you set them
        out, you make them
        grow,
    and on the morning when you
        plant them, you bring
        them to bud,
yet the harvest will be as nothing
    in the day of disease and
        incurable pain.

[12]Oh, the raging of many nations—
    they rage like the raging sea!
Oh, the uproar of the peoples—
    they roar like the roaring of great waters!
[13]Although the peoples roar like the roar of
        surging waters,
    when he rebukes them they flee far away,
driven before the wind like chaff on the hills,
    like tumbleweed before a gale.
[14]In the evening, sudden terror!
    Before the morning, they are gone!
This is the portion of those who loot us,
    the lot of those who plunder us.

truth or dare

No matter what foolproof ideas you have or how talented you are, if you forget God, your plans will be worthless. Is he Lord over your schedule, your plans, your dreams?

17:10–11

A Prophecy Against Cush

18

Woe to the land of whirring wings[b]
    along the rivers of Cush,[c]
[2]which sends envoys by sea
    in papyrus boats over the water.

Go, swift messengers,
to a people tall and smooth-skinned,
    to a people feared far and wide,
an aggressive nation of strange speech,
    whose land is divided by rivers.

a 8 That is, symbols of the goddess Asherah   *b 1* Or *of locusts*   *c 1* That is, the upper Nile region

³All you people of the world,
  you who live on the earth,
when a banner is raised on the mountains,
  you will see it,
and when a trumpet sounds,
  you will hear it.
⁴This is what the LORD says to me:
  "I will remain quiet and will look on from my dwelling place,
like shimmering heat in the sunshine,
  like a cloud of dew in the heat of harvest."
⁵For, before the harvest, when the blossom is gone
  and the flower becomes a ripening grape,
he will cut off the shoots with pruning knives,
  and cut down and take away the spreading branches.
⁶They will all be left to the mountain birds of prey
  and to the wild animals;
the birds will feed on them all summer,
  the wild animals all winter.

⁷At that time gifts will be brought to the LORD Almighty

  from a people tall and smooth-skinned,
  from a people feared far and wide,
an aggressive nation of strange speech,
  whose land is divided by rivers—

the gifts will be brought to Mount Zion, the place of the Name of the LORD Almighty.

A Prophecy About Egypt

19 An oracle concerning Egypt:

  See, the LORD rides on a swift cloud
    and is coming to Egypt.
  The idols of Egypt tremble before him,
    and the hearts of the Egyptians melt within them.

²"I will stir up Egyptian against Egyptian—
    brother will fight against brother,
    neighbor against neighbor,
    city against city,
    kingdom against kingdom.
³The Egyptians will lose heart,
    and I will bring their plans to nothing;
they will consult the idols and the spirits of the dead,
    the mediums and the spiritists.
⁴I will hand the Egyptians over
    to the power of a cruel master,
and a fierce king will rule over them,"
    declares the Lord, the LORD Almighty.

⁵The waters of the river will dry up,
    and the riverbed will be parched and dry.
⁶The canals will stink;
    the streams of Egypt will dwindle and dry up.
The reeds and rushes will wither,
⁷   also the plants along the Nile,
    at the mouth of the river.
Every sown field along the Nile

will become parched, will blow away and be no more.

⁸ The fishermen will groan and lament,
   all who cast hooks into the Nile;
those who throw nets on the water
   will pine away.
⁹ Those who work with combed flax will despair,
   the weavers of fine linen will lose hope.
¹⁰ The workers in cloth will be dejected,
   and all the wage earners will be sick at heart.

¹¹ The officials of Zoan are nothing but fools;
   the wise counselors of Pharaoh give senseless advice.
How can you say to Pharaoh,
   "I am one of the wise men,
   a disciple of the ancient kings"?

¹² Where are your wise men now?
   Let them show you and make known
what the LORD Almighty
   has planned against Egypt.
¹³ The officials of Zoan have become fools,
   the leaders of Memphis*a* are deceived;
the cornerstones of her peoples
   have led Egypt astray.
¹⁴ The LORD has poured into them
   a spirit of dizziness;
they make Egypt stagger in all that she does,
   as a drunkard staggers around in his vomit.
¹⁵ There is nothing Egypt can do—
   head or tail, palm branch or reed.

¹⁶In that day the Egyptians will be like women. They will shudder with fear at the uplifted hand that the LORD Almighty raises against them. ¹⁷And the land of Judah will bring terror to the Egyptians; everyone to whom Judah is mentioned will be terrified, because of what the LORD Almighty is planning against them.

¹⁸In that day five cities in Egypt will speak the language of Canaan and swear allegiance to the LORD Almighty. One of them will be called the City of Destruction.*b*

¹⁹In that day there will be an altar to the LORD in the heart of Egypt, and a monument to the LORD at its border. ²⁰It will be a sign and witness to the LORD Almighty in the land of Egypt. When they cry out to the LORD because of their oppressors, he will send them a savior and defender, and he will rescue them. ²¹So the LORD will make himself known to the Egyptians, and in that day they will acknowledge the LORD. They will worship with sacrifices and grain offerings; they will make vows to the LORD and keep them. ²²The LORD will strike Egypt with a plague; he will strike them and heal them. They will turn to the LORD, and he will respond to their pleas and heal them.

²³In that day there will be a highway from Egypt to Assyria. The Assyrians will go to Egypt and the Egyptians to Assyria. The Egyptians and Assyrians will worship together. ²⁴In that day Israel will be the third, along with Egypt and Assyria, a blessing on the earth. ²⁵The LORD Almighty will bless them, saying, "Blessed be Egypt my people, Assyria my handiwork, and Israel my inheritance."

truth or dare

Did he say *Egypt* and *Assyria* would turn to God? Israel's longtime archenemies? Sounds kinda far-fetched. But God promises that in the future, *every* knee will bow to Jesus (see Philippians 2:9–11).

19:19–25

a 13 Hebrew *Noph*   *b 18* Most manuscripts of the Masoretic Text; some manuscripts of the Masoretic Text, Dead Sea Scrolls and Vulgate *City of the Sun* (that is, Heliopolis)

Rodeo

I saw her every day for a week. Ordinarily, I would never have run into this girl. We have different schedules. We're even in different grades. But she caught my eye every time I passed her in the hall. She was new—that much was obvious. She dressed as if she came straight off a farm. No kidding. Jeans. Boots. My friends nicknamed her "Rodeo." They didn't know her real name. They didn't care enough to ask.

"Did you see what Rodeo was wearing today?" Shelley asked at lunch.

"Yee haw! Got to get me some of them jeans!" Shenal said with her best country accent.

They laughed and walked away. I felt this heaviness in my heart. It was like I was sad, but I didn't know why. Finally, I figured out that God was trying to get my attention. I imagined what it must be like to be that new girl and wondered what Jesus would do about it. The new girl probably felt lonely. Out of place. Awkward. Maybe she didn't want to move here anyway.

I asked God to show me what he wanted me to do. "Just don't ask me to do anything extreme, God, okay? Like invite her to my party Friday." Famous last words. Those kinds of requests never seem to work with God.

Inviting her to my party was exactly what he wanted me to do. After all, isn't that what Jesus would do?

compassion in focus

Compassion comes in all different forms. Sometimes God wants us to pray for those in need. Sometimes he wants us to befriend others. You notice. God nudges. Then you have a choice—do I reach out to this person in need, or do I stay in my comfortable world without risking anything yet also missing out on God's reward for obedience? (See Proverbs 19:17, page 831.) If God gives you an opportunity to be compassionate . . .

»Remember Jesus' example (see John 8:1–11, pages 1422–1423)—compassion, not judgment.
»Reach out as if you're doing it for Jesus himself (see Matthew 25:34–40, pages 1326–1327)—you'll be greatly rewarded.

For more on this topic, see the index on page 1656.

A Prophecy Against Egypt and Cush

20 In the year that the supreme commander, sent by Sargon king of Assyria, came to Ashdod and attacked and captured it— ²at that time the LORD spoke through Isaiah son of Amoz. He said to him, "Take off the sackcloth from your body and the sandals from your feet." And he did so, going around stripped and barefoot.

³Then the LORD said, "Just as my servant Isaiah has gone stripped and barefoot for three years,

as a sign and portent against Egypt and Cush,ᵃ ⁴so the king of Assyria will lead away stripped and barefoot the Egyptian captives and Cushite exiles, young and old, with buttocks bared—to Egypt's shame. ⁵Those who trusted in Cush and boasted in Egypt will be afraid and put to shame. ⁶In that day the people who live on this coast will say, 'See what has happened to those we relied on, those we fled to for help and deliverance from the king of Assyria! How then can we escape?' "

A Prophecy Against Babylon

21

An oracle concerning the Desert by the Sea:

Like whirlwinds sweeping through the southland,
 an invader comes from the desert,
 from a land of terror.

²A dire vision has been shown to me:
 The traitor betrays, the looter takes loot.
 Elam, attack! Media, lay siege!
 I will bring to an end all the groaning she caused.

³At this my body is racked with pain,
 pangs seize me, like those of a woman in labor;
 I am staggered by what I hear,
 I am bewildered by what I see.
⁴My heart falters,
 fear makes me tremble;
 the twilight I longed for
 has become a horror to me.

⁵They set the tables,
 they spread the rugs,
 they eat, they drink!
 Get up, you officers,
 oil the shields!

⁶This is what the Lord says to me:

"Go, post a lookout
 and have him report what he sees.
⁷When he sees chariots
 with teams of horses,
 riders on donkeys
 or riders on camels,
 let him be alert,
 fully alert."

⁸And the lookoutᵇ shouted,

"Day after day, my lord, I stand on the watchtower;
 every night I stay at my post.
⁹Look, here comes a man in a chariot
 with a team of horses.
And he gives back the answer:
 'Babylon has fallen, has fallen!
All the images of its gods
 lie shattered on the ground!' "

¹⁰O my people, crushed on the threshing floor,
 I tell you what I have heard
from the Lord Almighty,
 from the God of Israel.

ᵃ 3 That is, the upper Nile region; also in verse 5   ᵇ 8 Dead Sea Scrolls and Syriac; Masoretic Text A lion

A Prophecy Against Edom

¹¹An oracle concerning Dumah*:*

> Someone calls to me from Seir,
>> "Watchman, what is left of the night?
>> Watchman, what is left of the night?"
> ¹²The watchman replies,
>> "Morning is coming, but also the night.
> If you would ask, then ask;
>> and come back yet again."

A Prophecy Against Arabia

¹³An oracle concerning Arabia:

> You caravans of Dedanites,
>> who camp in the thickets of Arabia,
>>> bring water for the thirsty;
> you who live in Tema,
>> bring food for the fugitives.
> ¹⁵They flee from the sword,
>> from the drawn sword,
> from the bent bow
>> and from the heat of battle.

¹⁶This is what the Lord says to me: "Within one year, as a servant bound by contract would count it, all the pomp of Kedar will come to an end. ¹⁷The survivors of the bowmen, the warriors of Kedar, will be few." The LORD, the God of Israel, has spoken.

A Prophecy About Jerusalem

22 An oracle concerning the Valley of Vision:

> What troubles you now,
>> that you have all gone up on the roofs,
> ²O town full of commotion,
>> O city of tumult and revelry?
> Your slain were not killed by the sword,
>> nor did they die in battle.
> ³All your leaders have fled together;
>> they have been captured without using the bow.
> All you who were caught were taken prisoner together,
>> having fled while the enemy was still far away.
> ⁴Therefore I said, "Turn away from me;
>> let me weep bitterly.
> Do not try to console me
>> over the destruction of my people."

> ⁵The Lord, the LORD Almighty, has a day
>> of tumult and trampling and terror
>> in the Valley of Vision,
> a day of battering down walls
>> and of crying out to the mountains.
> ⁶Elam takes up the quiver,
>> with her charioteers and horses;
>> Kir uncovers the shield.
> ⁷Your choicest valleys are full of chariots,

---

a 11 Dumah means *silence* or *stillness,* a wordplay on *Edom.*

and horsemen are posted at the city gates;
8   the defenses of Judah are stripped away.

And you looked in that day
    to the weapons in the Palace of the Forest;
9 you saw that the City of David
    had many breaches in its defenses;
you stored up water
    in the Lower Pool.
10 You counted the buildings in Jerusalem
    and tore down houses to strengthen the wall.
11 You built a reservoir between the
        two walls
    for the water of the Old Pool,
but you did not look to the One
        who made it,
    or have regard for the One
        who planned it long ago.

12 The Lord, the LORD Almighty,
        called you on that day
    to weep and to wail,
        to tear out your hair and put
            on sackcloth.
13 But see, there is joy and revelry,
    slaughtering of cattle and killing of sheep,
    eating of meat and drinking of wine!
"Let us eat and drink," you say,
    "for tomorrow we die!"

14 The LORD Almighty has revealed this in my hearing: "Till your dying day this sin will not be atoned for," says the Lord, the LORD Almighty.

15 This is what the Lord, the LORD Almighty, says:

"Go, say to this steward,
    to Shebna, who is in charge of the palace:
16 What are you doing here and who gave you permission
        to cut out a grave for yourself here,
    hewing your grave on the height
        and chiseling your resting place in the rock?

17 "Beware, the LORD is about to take firm hold of you
        and hurl you away, O you mighty man.
18 He will roll you up tightly like a ball
        and throw you into a large country.
There you will die
        and there your splendid chariots will remain—
    you disgrace to your master's house!
19 I will depose you from your office,
        and you will be ousted from your position.

20 "In that day I will summon my servant, Eliakim son of Hilkiah. 21 I will clothe him with your robe and fasten your sash around him and hand your authority over to him. He will be a father to those who live in Jerusalem and to the house of Judah. 22 I will place on his shoulder the key to the house of David; what he opens no one can shut, and what he shuts no one can open. 23 I will drive him like a peg into a firm place; he will be a seat*a* of honor for the house of his father. 24 All the glory of his family will hang on him: its offspring and offshoots—all its lesser vessels, from the bowls to all the jars.

a 23 Or *throne*

truth or dare

Look around you. You'll probably see tons of people doing things to escape life. They've lost their hope. But our lives are never hopeless. Jesus will always be our hope.

22:12-13

²⁵"In that day," declares the L ORD Almighty, "the peg driven into the firm place will give way; it will be sheared off and will fall, and the load hanging on it will be cut down." The L ORD has spoken.

A Prophecy About Tyre

23 An oracle concerning Tyre:

Wail, O ships of Tarshish!
For Tyre is destroyed
and left without house or harbor.
From the land of Cyprus ᵃ
word has come to them.

²Be silent, you people of the island
and you merchants of Sidon,
whom the seafarers have enriched.
³On the great waters
came the grain of the Shihor;
the harvest of the Nile ᵇ was the revenue of Tyre,
and she became the marketplace of the nations.

⁴Be ashamed, O Sidon, and you, O fortress of the sea,
for the sea has spoken:
"I have neither been in labor nor given birth;
I have neither reared sons nor brought up daughters."
⁵When word comes to Egypt,
they will be in anguish at the report from Tyre.

⁶Cross over to Tarshish;
wail, you people of the island.
⁷Is this your city of revelry,
the old, old city,
whose feet have taken her
to settle in far-off lands?
⁸Who planned this against Tyre,
the bestower of crowns,
whose merchants are princes,
whose traders are renowned in
the earth?
⁹The L ORD Almighty planned it,
to bring low the pride of all glory
and to humble all who are renowned on
the earth.

¹⁰Till ᶜ your land as along the Nile,
O Daughter of Tarshish,
for you no longer have a harbor.
¹¹The L ORD has stretched out his hand over the sea
and made its kingdoms tremble.
He has given an order concerning Phoenicia ᵈ
that her fortresses be destroyed.
¹²He said, "No more of your reveling,
O Virgin Daughter of Sidon, now crushed!

"Up, cross over to Cyprus ᵃ;
even there you will find no rest."

truth or dare

Tyre sounds like the first setting of *The Rich and the Famous.* Unfortunately, wealth and fame often lead to pride, and God has no tolerance for human pride.

23:8–9

ᵃ 1,12 Hebrew *Kittim*   ᵇ 2,3 Masoretic Text; one Dead Sea Scroll *Sidon, / who cross over the sea; / your envoys* ³*are on the great waters. / The grain of the Shihor, / the harvest of the Nile,*   ᶜ 10 Dead Sea Scrolls and some Septuagint manuscripts; Masoretic Text *Go through*   ᵈ 11 Hebrew *Canaan*

¹³Look at the land of the Babylonians,^a
this people that is now of no account!
The Assyrians have made it
a place for desert creatures;
they raised up their siege towers,
they stripped its fortresses bare
and turned it into a ruin.

¹⁴Wail, you ships of Tarshish;
your fortress is destroyed!

¹⁵At that time Tyre will be forgotten for seventy years, the span of a king's life. But at the end of these seventy years, it will happen to Tyre as in the song of the prostitute:

¹⁶"Take up a harp, walk through the city,
O prostitute forgotten;
play the harp well, sing many a song,
so that you will be remembered."

¹⁷At the end of seventy years, the LORD will deal with Tyre. She will return to her hire as a prostitute and will ply her trade with all the kingdoms on the face of the earth. ¹⁸Yet her profit and her earnings will be set apart for the LORD; they will not be stored up or hoarded. Her profits will go to those who live before the LORD, for abundant food and fine clothes.

The LORD's Devastation of the Earth

24
See, the LORD is going to lay waste the earth
and devastate it;
he will ruin its face
and scatter its inhabitants—
²it will be the same
for priest as for people,
for master as for servant,
for mistress as for maid,
for seller as for buyer,
for borrower as for lender,
for debtor as for creditor.
³The earth will be completely laid waste
and totally plundered.

The LORD has spoken this word.

⁴The earth dries up and withers,
the world languishes and withers,
the exalted of the earth languish.
⁵The earth is defiled by its people;
they have disobeyed the laws,
violated the statutes
and broken the everlasting covenant.
⁶Therefore a curse consumes the earth;
its people must bear their guilt.
Therefore earth's inhabitants are burned up,
and very few are left.
⁷The new wine dries up and the vine withers;
all the merrymakers groan.
⁸The gaiety of the tambourines is stilled,
the noise of the revelers has stopped,
the joyful harp is silent.
⁹No longer do they drink wine with a song;

^a 13 Or Chaldeans

the beer is bitter to its drinkers.
¹⁰ The ruined city lies desolate;
    the entrance to every house is barred.
¹¹ In the streets they cry out for wine;
    all joy turns to gloom,
    all gaiety is banished from the earth.
¹² The city is left in ruins,
    its gate is battered to pieces.
¹³ So will it be on the earth
    and among the nations,
as when an olive tree is beaten,
    or as when gleanings are left after the grape harvest.

¹⁴ They raise their voices, they shout for joy;
    from the west they acclaim the LORD's majesty.
¹⁵ Therefore in the east give glory to the LORD;
    exalt the name of the LORD, the God of Israel,
    in the islands of the sea.
¹⁶ From the ends of the earth we hear singing:
    "Glory to the Righteous One."

But I said, "I waste away, I waste away!
    Woe to me!
The treacherous betray!
    With treachery the treacherous betray!"
¹⁷ Terror and pit and snare await you,
    O people of the earth.
¹⁸ Whoever flees at the sound of terror
    will fall into a pit;
whoever climbs out of the pit
    will be caught in a snare.

The floodgates of the heavens are opened,
    the foundations of the earth shake.
¹⁹ The earth is broken up,
    the earth is split asunder,
    the earth is thoroughly shaken.
²⁰ The earth reels like a drunkard,
    it sways like a hut in the wind;
so heavy upon it is the guilt of its
        rebellion
    that it falls—never to rise
        again.

²¹ In that day the LORD will punish
    the powers in the heavens
        above
    and the kings on the earth below.
²² They will be herded together
    like prisoners bound in a dungeon;
they will be shut up in prison
    and be punished ᵃ after many days.
²³ The moon will be abashed, the sun ashamed;
    for the LORD Almighty will reign
on Mount Zion and in Jerusalem,
    and before its elders, gloriously.

truth or dare

It's a fact—there will be an actual "end of the world." Want a preview? The books of Isaiah and Revelation tell all the main events. The only question left is, are you ready?

24:1–23

ᵃ 22 Or released

Isaiah 25:1

25

O Lord, you are my God;
I will exalt you and praise your name,
for in perfect faithfulness
you have done marvelous things,
things planned long ago.
[2] You have made the city a heap of rubble,
the fortified town a ruin,
the foreigners' stronghold a city no more;
it will never be rebuilt.
[3] Therefore strong peoples will honor you;
cities of ruthless nations will revere you.

[4] You have been a refuge for the poor,
a refuge for the needy in his
distress,
a shelter from the storm
and a shade from the heat.
For the breath of the ruthless
is like a storm driving against
a wall
[5] and like the heat of the desert.
You silence the uproar of
foreigners;
as heat is reduced by the
shadow of a cloud,
so the song of the ruthless is
stilled.

[6] On this mountain the Lord
Almighty will prepare
a feast of rich food for all
peoples,
a banquet of aged wine—
the best of meats and the
finest of wines.
[7] On this mountain he will destroy
the shroud that enfolds all
peoples,
the sheet that covers all nations;
[8] he will swallow up death
forever.
The Sovereign Lord will wipe
away the tears
from all faces;
he will remove the disgrace of his
people
from all the earth.
The Lord has spoken.

[9] In that day they will say,

"Surely this is our God;
we trusted in him, and he
saved us.
This is the Lord, we trusted in him;
let us rejoice and be glad in
his salvation."

love notes

25:4

My child,

*I will be your shelter when you
are in distress—whether it's
about family problems or a broken friendship. I will protect you
when you are poor—whether
it's in academics or relationships
or finances. I am your safe
place—always.*

—Your caring Father

Write a prayer of response, telling God
that you trust him as your safe place in
a situation that is causing you worry.

¹⁰The hand of the Lord will rest on this mountain;
>> but Moab will be trampled under him
>> as straw is trampled down in the manure.
¹¹They will spread out their hands in it,
>> as a swimmer spreads out his hands to swim.
> God will bring down their pride
>> despite the cleverness^a of their hands.
¹²He will bring down your high fortified walls
>> and lay them low;
> he will bring them down to the ground,
>> to the very dust.

A Song of Praise

26

In that day this song will be sung in the land of Judah:

> We have a strong city;
> God makes salvation
>> its walls and ramparts.
> ²Open the gates
>> that the righteous nation may enter,
> the nation that keeps faith.
> ³You will keep in perfect peace
>> him whose mind is steadfast,
>> because he trusts in you.
> ⁴Trust in the Lord forever,
>> for the Lord, the Lord, is the Rock eternal.
> ⁵He humbles those who dwell on high,
>> he lays the lofty city low;
> he levels it to the ground
>> and casts it down to the dust.
> ⁶Feet trample it down—
>> the feet of the oppressed,
>> the footsteps of the poor.

> ⁷The path of the righteous is level;
>> O upright One, you make the
>> way of the righteous
>> smooth.
> ⁸Yes, Lord, walking in the way of
>> your laws,^b
> we wait for you;
> your name and renown
>> are the desire of our hearts.
> ⁹My soul yearns for you in the
>> night;
> in the morning my spirit longs for you.
> When your judgments come upon the earth,
>> the people of the world learn
>> righteousness.
> ¹⁰Though grace is shown to the wicked,
>> they do not learn righteousness;
> even in a land of uprightness they go on doing evil
>> and regard not the majesty of the Lord.
> ¹¹O Lord, your hand is lifted high,
>> but they do not see it.

truth or dare

If you're a Christian, you *always* have a reason to party. God has saved you! If everything else for the rest of your entire life goes wrong, you'll still be okay.

25:9

---

^a 11 The meaning of the Hebrew for this word is uncertain.   ^b 8 Or judgments

Let them see your zeal for your people and be put to shame;
let the fire reserved for your enemies consume them.

¹² LORD, you establish peace for us;
all that we have accomplished you have done for us.
¹³ O LORD, our God, other lords besides you have ruled over us,
but your name alone do we honor.
¹⁴ They are now dead, they live no more;
those departed spirits do not rise.
You punished them and brought them to ruin;
you wiped out all memory of them.
¹⁵ You have enlarged the nation, O LORD;
you have enlarged the nation.

You have gained glory for
yourself;
you have extended all the
borders of the land.

¹⁶ LORD, they came to you in their
distress;
when you disciplined them,
they could barely whisper a
prayer.ᵃ
¹⁷ As a woman with child and about
to give birth
writhes and cries out in her
pain,
so were we in your presence,
O LORD.
¹⁸ We were with child, we writhed
in pain,
but we gave birth to wind.
We have not brought salvation to
the earth;
we have not given birth to
people of the world.

¹⁹ But your dead will live;
their bodies will rise.
You who dwell in the dust,
wake up and shout for joy.

love ♥ notes

26:3-4

Beloved,

*In the midst of your crazy-busy
schedule, in the middle of all
your responsibilities and activities, you can find my peace.
Trust in me forever. I'll keep you
in my perfect peace.*

—The Rock Eternal

How is it possible to have peace, even
during busy or difficult times?

_____

_____

_____

_____

_____

_____

_____

_____

_____

truth or dare

Wait a second! If *you*
accomplish something,
then what does God
have to do with it?
Everything.

26:12

ᵃ 16 The meaning of the Hebrew for this clause is
uncertain.

Your dew is like the dew of the morning;
  the earth will give birth to her dead.

²⁰ Go, my people, enter your rooms
  and shut the doors behind you;
hide yourselves for a little while
  until his wrath has passed by.
²¹ See, the LORD is coming out of his dwelling
  to punish the people of the earth for their sins.
The earth will disclose the blood shed upon her;
  she will conceal her slain no longer.

Deliverance of Israel

27

In that day,

the LORD will punish with his sword,
  his fierce, great and powerful sword,
Leviathan the gliding serpent,
  Leviathan the coiling serpent;
he will slay the monster of the sea.

² In that day—

"Sing about a fruitful vineyard:
³   I, the LORD, watch over it;
    I water it continually.
I guard it day and night
  so that no one may harm it.
⁴   I am not angry.
If only there were briers and thorns confronting me!
  I would march against them in battle;
  I would set them all on fire.
⁵ Or else let them come to me for refuge;
  let them make peace with me,
  yes, let them make peace with me."

⁶ In days to come Jacob will take root,
  Israel will bud and blossom
  and fill all the world with fruit.

⁷ Has ⌊the LORD⌋ struck her
  as he struck down those who struck her?
Has she been killed
  as those were killed who killed her?
⁸ By warfare^a and exile you contend with her—
  with his fierce blast he drives her out,
  as on a day the east wind blows.
⁹ By this, then, will Jacob's guilt be atoned for,
  and this will be the full fruitage of the removal of his sin:
When he makes all the altar stones
  to be like chalk stones crushed to pieces,
no Asherah poles^b or incense altars
  will be left standing.
¹⁰ The fortified city stands desolate,
  an abandoned settlement, forsaken like the desert;
there the calves graze,
  there they lie down;

---

^a 8 See Septuagint; the meaning of the Hebrew for this word is uncertain.   ^b 9 That is, symbols of the goddess Asherah

Achy Breaky Heart

Profile: Taylor

I've never dated someone for a whole year—not until Josh. Everyone says we're perfect for each other. But deep down, I know things aren't as perfect as they seem.

I think Josh is cheating on me. That's why I've been avoiding him today. I'm afraid of what I would say, and I'm afraid of losing him, and I guess I'm afraid of knowing the truth. If he starts talking to me, I know I can't fake it with him and pretend nothing's wrong. And I have no idea what to say to him yet. I wish I could believe it's not true.

My friend Krysti thinks I'm being paranoid. But she doesn't know the whole story. There's this girl at our school named Cari, and I know she's been after Josh all year. She flirts with him whenever I'm not around. After Josh's last basketball game, he was talking to her when I walked up afterwards. "Well, see ya around," she said, not even looking at me. What Krysti doesn't know is that I checked Josh's palm pilot yesterday and found her name, phone number, email, everything.

Not to mention that he never called me last night, and he always calls me. Does he really think I don't have a clue? But I can't stand the thought of losing him. Maybe I should just keep on pretending. Josh might get over her, right? After all, he said he loved me.

dating in focus

No one said dating is easy, but God's Word gives us some principles for romance. Here are some guidelines:

»*Keep it in perspective.* Yeah, it feels like your heart is breaking, and yeah, it seems like he's the right guy for you. But you know what? God might have someone way better in mind for you. Don't settle for less.

»*Embrace honesty.* Proverbs 11:3 (page 818) shows us that people who do one thing but say another are destined for trouble. Avoiding the truth will only hurt you more in the long run. If he's been lying to you, then it's time *now* to make the tough choice to end the relationship.

For more on this topic, see the index on page 1656.

dating

they strip its branches bare.
11 When its twigs are dry, they are broken off
and women come and make fires with them.
For this is a people without understanding;
so their Maker has no compassion on them,
and their Creator shows them no favor.

12 In that day the LORD will thresh from the flowing Euphrates*a* to the Wadi of Egypt, and you, O Israelites, will be gathered up one by one. 13 And in that day a great trumpet will sound. Those who

a 12 Hebrew River

were perishing in Assyria and those who were exiled in Egypt will come and worship the LORD on the holy mountain in Jerusalem.

Woe to Ephraim

28 Woe to that wreath, the pride of Ephraim's drunkards,
    to the fading flower, his glorious beauty,
set on the head of a fertile valley—
    to that city, the pride of those laid low by wine!
[2] See, the Lord has one who is powerful and strong.
    Like a hailstorm and a destructive wind,
like a driving rain and a flooding downpour,
    he will throw it forcefully to the ground.
[3] That wreath, the pride of Ephraim's drunkards,
    will be trampled underfoot.
[4] That fading flower, his glorious beauty,
    set on the head of a fertile valley,
will be like a fig ripe before harvest—
    as soon as someone sees it and takes it in his hand,
    he swallows it.

[5] In that day the LORD Almighty
    will be a glorious crown,
a beautiful wreath
    for the remnant of his people.
[6] He will be a spirit of justice
    to him who sits in judgment,
a source of strength
    to those who turn back the battle at the gate.

[7] And these also stagger from wine
    and reel from beer:
Priests and prophets stagger from beer
    and are befuddled with wine;
they reel from beer,
    they stagger when seeing visions,
    they stumble when rendering decisions.
[8] All the tables are covered with vomit
    and there is not a spot without filth.

[9] "Who is it he is trying to teach?
    To whom is he explaining his message?
To children weaned from their milk,
    to those just taken from the breast?
[10] For it is:
    Do and do, do and do,
    rule on rule, rule on rule[a];
    a little here, a little there."

[11] Very well then, with foreign lips and strange tongues
    God will speak to this people,
[12] to whom he said,
    "This is the resting place, let the weary rest";
and, "This is the place of repose"—
    but they would not listen.
[13] So then, the word of the LORD to them will become:

Do and do, do and do,
rule on rule, rule on rule;
a little here, a little there—
so that they will go and fall backward,
be injured and snared and captured.

[14] Therefore hear the word of the LORD, you scoffers
who rule this people in Jerusalem.
[15] You boast, "We have entered into a covenant with death,
with the grave[a] we have made an agreement.
When an overwhelming scourge sweeps by,
it cannot touch us,
for we have made a lie our refuge
and falsehood[b] our hiding place."

[16] So this is what the Sovereign LORD says:

"See, I lay a stone in Zion,
a tested stone,
a precious cornerstone for a sure
foundation;
the one who trusts will never
be dismayed.
[17] I will make justice the measuring
line
and righteousness the plumb
line;
hail will sweep away your refuge, the lie,
and water will overflow your hiding place.
[18] Your covenant with death will be annulled;
your agreement with the grave will not
stand.
When the overwhelming scourge sweeps by,
you will be beaten down by it.
[19] As often as it comes it will carry you away;
morning after morning, by day and by night,
it will sweep through."

The understanding of this message
will bring sheer terror.
[20] The bed is too short to stretch out on,
the blanket too narrow to wrap around you.
[21] The LORD will rise up as he did at Mount Perazim,
he will rouse himself as in the Valley of Gibeon—
to do his work, his strange work,
and perform his task, his alien task.
[22] Now stop your mocking,
or your chains will become heavier;
the Lord, the LORD Almighty, has told me
of the destruction decreed against the whole land.

[23] Listen and hear my voice;
pay attention and hear what I say.
[24] When a farmer plows for planting, does he plow continually?
Does he keep on breaking up and harrowing the soil?
[25] When he has leveled the surface,
does he not sow caraway and scatter cummin?

truth or dare

The cornerstone is the most important part of a house's foundation. Who's your cornerstone? Is it God, the rock solid foundation? Or are you relying on your own flimsy strength?

28:16

a 15 Hebrew *Sheol*; also in verse 18   b 15 Or *false gods*

Does he not plant wheat in its place,[a]
   barley in its plot,[a]
   and spelt in its field?
[26] His God instructs him
   and teaches him the right way.

[27] Caraway is not threshed with a sledge,
   nor is a cartwheel rolled over cummin;
caraway is beaten out with a rod,
   and cummin with a stick.
[28] Grain must be ground to make bread;
   so one does not go on threshing it forever.
Though he drives the wheels of his threshing cart over it,
   his horses do not grind it.
[29] All this also comes from the LORD Almighty,
   wonderful in counsel and magnificent in wisdom.

Woe to David's City

29

Woe to you, Ariel, Ariel,
   the city where David settled!
Add year to year
   and let your cycle of festivals go on.
[2] Yet I will besiege Ariel;
   she will mourn and lament,
   she will be to me like an altar hearth.[b]
[3] I will encamp against you all around;
   I will encircle you with towers
   and set up my siege works against you.
[4] Brought low, you will speak from the ground;
   your speech will mumble out of the dust.
Your voice will come ghostlike from the earth;
   out of the dust your speech will whisper.

[5] But your many enemies will become like fine dust,
   the ruthless hordes like blown chaff.
Suddenly, in an instant,
[6]   the LORD Almighty will come
with thunder and earthquake and great noise,
   with windstorm and tempest and flames of a devouring fire.
[7] Then the hordes of all the nations that fight against Ariel,
   that attack her and her fortress and besiege her,
will be as it is with a dream,
   with a vision in the night—
[8] as when a hungry man dreams that he is eating,
   but he awakens, and his hunger remains;
as when a thirsty man dreams that he is drinking,
   but he awakens faint, with his thirst unquenched.
So will it be with the hordes of all the nations
   that fight against Mount Zion.

[9] Be stunned and amazed,
   blind yourselves and be sightless;
be drunk, but not from wine,
   stagger, but not from beer.
[10] The LORD has brought over you a deep sleep:

---

a 25 The meaning of the Hebrew for this word is uncertain.   b 2 The Hebrew for *altar hearth* sounds like the Hebrew for *Ariel.*

He has sealed your eyes (the prophets);
he has covered your heads (the seers).

[11] For you this whole vision is nothing but words sealed in a scroll. And if you give the scroll to someone who can read, and say to him, "Read this, please," he will answer, "I can't; it is sealed." [12] Or if you give the scroll to someone who cannot read, and say, "Read this, please," he will answer, "I don't know how to read."

[13] The Lord says:

"These people come near to me with their mouth
and honor me with their lips,
but their hearts are far from me.
Their worship of me
is made up only of rules taught by men." [a]

[14] Therefore once more I will
astound these people
with wonder upon wonder;
the wisdom of the wise will perish,
the intelligence of the
intelligent will vanish."
[15] Woe to those who go to great
depths
to hide their plans from the
Lord,
who do their work in darkness
and think,
"Who sees us? Who will
know?"
[16] You turn things upside down,
as if the potter were thought
to be like the clay!
Shall what is formed say to him
who formed it,
"He did not make me"?
Can the pot say of the potter,
"He knows nothing"?

[17] In a very short time, will not
Lebanon be turned into
a fertile field
and the fertile field seem like
a forest?
[18] In that day the deaf will hear the
words of the scroll,

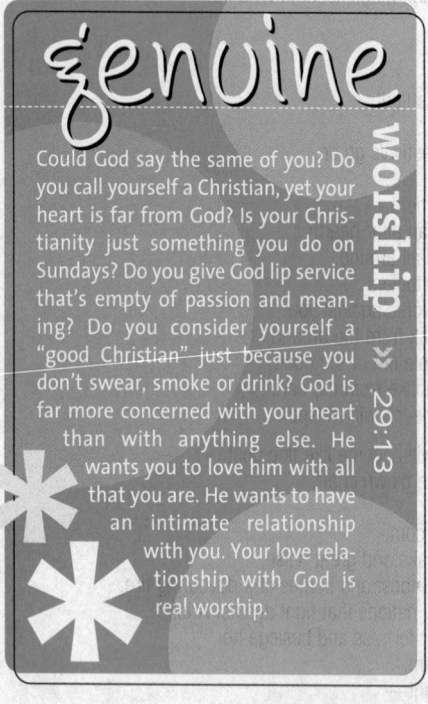

genuine worship » 29:13

Could God say the same of you? Do you call yourself a Christian, yet your heart is far from God? Is your Christianity just something you do on Sundays? Do you give God lip service that's empty of passion and meaning? Do you consider yourself a "good Christian" just because you don't swear, smoke or drink? God is far more concerned with your heart than with anything else. He wants you to love him with all that you are. He wants to have an intimate relationship with you. Your love relationship with God is real worship.

and out of gloom and darkness
the eyes of the blind will see.
[19] Once more the humble will rejoice in the Lord;
the needy will rejoice in the Holy One of Israel.
[20] The ruthless will vanish,
the mockers will disappear,
and all who have an eye for evil will be cut down—
[21] those who with a word make a man out to be guilty,
who ensnare the defender in court
and with false testimony deprive the innocent of justice.

[22] Therefore this is what the Lord, who redeemed Abraham, says to the house of Jacob:

[a] 13 Hebrew; Septuagint *They worship me in vain; / their teachings are but rules taught by men*

"No longer will Jacob be ashamed;
no longer will their faces grow pale.
[23] When they see among them their children,
the work of my hands,
they will keep my name holy;
they will acknowledge the holiness of the Holy One of Jacob,
and will stand in awe of the God of Israel.
[24] Those who are wayward in spirit will gain understanding;
those who complain will accept instruction."

Woe to the Obstinate Nation

30

"Woe to the obstinate children,"
declares the LORD,
"to those who carry out plans that are not mine,
forming an alliance, but not by my Spirit,
heaping sin upon sin;
[2] who go down to Egypt
without consulting me;
who look for help to Pharaoh's protection,
to Egypt's shade for refuge.
[3] But Pharaoh's protection will be to your shame,
Egypt's shade will bring you disgrace.
[4] Though they have officials in Zoan
and their envoys have arrived in Hanes,
[5] everyone will be put to shame
because of a people useless to them,
who bring neither help nor advantage,
but only shame and disgrace."

[6] An oracle concerning the animals of the Negev:

Through a land of hardship and distress,
of lions and lionesses,
of adders and darting snakes,
the envoys carry their riches on donkeys' backs,
their treasures on the humps of camels,
to that unprofitable nation,
[7]   to Egypt, whose help is utterly useless.
Therefore I call her
Rahab the Do-Nothing.

[8] Go now, write it on a tablet for them,
inscribe it on a scroll,
that for the days to come
it may be an everlasting witness.
[9] These are rebellious people, deceitful children,
children unwilling to listen to the LORD's instruction.
[10] They say to the seers,
"See no more visions!"
and to the prophets,
"Give us no more visions of what is right!
Tell us pleasant things,
prophesy illusions.
[11] Leave this way,
get off this path,
and stop confronting us
with the Holy One of Israel!"

[12]Therefore, this is what the Holy One of Israel says:

"Because you have rejected this message,
relied on oppression
and depended on deceit,
[13]this sin will become for you
like a high wall, cracked and bulging,
that collapses suddenly, in an instant.
[14]It will break in pieces like pottery,
shattered so mercilessly
that among its pieces not a fragment will be found
for taking coals from a hearth
or scooping water out of a cistern."

[15]This is what the Sovereign LORD, the Holy One of Israel, says:

"In repentance and rest is your salvation,
in quietness and trust is your strength,
but you would have none of it.
[16]You said, 'No, we will flee on horses.'
Therefore you will flee!
You said, 'We will ride off on
swift horses.'
Therefore your pursuers will
be swift!
[17]A thousand will flee
at the threat of one;
at the threat of five
you will all flee away,
till you are left
like a flagstaff on a
mountaintop,
like a banner on a hill."

[18]Yet the LORD longs to be gracious to you;
he rises to show you compassion.
For the LORD is a God of justice.
Blessed are all who wait for him!

truth *or dare*

As much as people joke, God really isn't waiting around to zap you with his handy lightning bolt. Actually, he'll go out of his way to show you compassion.

30:18

[19]O people of Zion, who live in Jerusalem, you will weep no more. How gracious he will be when you cry for help! As soon as he hears, he will answer you. [20]Although the Lord gives you the bread of adversity and the water of affliction, your teachers will be hidden no more; with your own eyes you will see them. [21]Whether you turn to the right or to the left, your ears will hear a voice behind you, saying, "This is the way; walk in it." [22]Then you will defile your idols overlaid with silver and your images covered with gold; you will throw them away like a menstrual cloth and say to them, "Away with you!"

[23]He will also send you rain for the seed you sow in the ground, and the food that comes from the land will be rich and plentiful. In that day your cattle will graze in broad meadows. [24]The oxen and donkeys that work the soil will eat fodder and mash, spread out with fork and shovel. [25]In the day of great slaughter, when the towers fall, streams of water will flow on every high mountain and every lofty hill. [26]The moon will shine like the sun, and the sunlight will be seven times brighter, like the light of seven full days, when the LORD binds up the bruises of his people and heals the wounds he inflicted.

[27]See, the Name of the LORD comes from afar,
with burning anger and dense clouds of smoke;
his lips are full of wrath,
and his tongue is a consuming fire.

²⁸ His breath is like a rushing torrent,
    rising up to the neck.
He shakes the nations in the sieve of destruction;
    he places in the jaws of the peoples
    a bit that leads them astray.
²⁹ And you will sing
    as on the night you celebrate a holy festival;
your hearts will rejoice
    as when people go up with flutes
to the mountain of the Lord,
    to the Rock of Israel.
³⁰ The Lord will cause men to hear his majestic voice
    and will make them see his arm coming down
with raging anger and consuming fire,
    with cloudburst, thunderstorm and hail.
³¹ The voice of the Lord will shatter Assyria;
    with his scepter he will strike them down.
³² Every stroke the Lord lays on them
    with his punishing rod
will be to the music of tambourines and harps,
    as he fights them in battle with the blows of his arm.
³³ Topheth has long been prepared;
    it has been made ready for the king.
Its fire pit has been made deep and wide,
    with an abundance of fire and wood;
the breath of the Lord,
    like a stream of burning sulfur,
    sets it ablaze.

Woe to Those Who Rely on Egypt

31 Woe to those who go down to Egypt for help,
    who rely on horses,
who trust in the multitude of their chariots
    and in the great strength of their horsemen,
but do not look to the Holy One of Israel,
    or seek help from the Lord.
² Yet he too is wise and can bring
      disaster;
    he does not take back his
      words.
He will rise up against the house
      of the wicked,
    against those who help
      evildoers.
³ But the Egyptians are men and
      not God;
    their horses are flesh and not
      spirit.
When the Lord stretches out his hand,
    he who helps will stumble,
    he who is helped will fall;
    both will perish together.

⁴ This is what the Lord says to me:

    "As a lion growls,
      a great lion over his prey—

truth or dare

Israel was begging for help from everyone *except* God! How often do you reserve God as your last alternative for help? Try calling him first.

31:1

and though a whole band of shepherds
is called together against him,
he is not frightened by their shouts
or disturbed by their clamor—
so the LORD Almighty will come down
to do battle on Mount Zion and on its heights.
⁵Like birds hovering overhead,
the LORD Almighty will shield Jerusalem;
he will shield it and deliver it,
he will 'pass over' it and will rescue it."

⁶Return to him you have so greatly revolted against, O Israelites. ⁷For in that day every one of you will reject the idols of silver and gold your sinful hands have made.

⁸"Assyria will fall by a sword that is not of man;
a sword, not of mortals, will devour them.
They will flee before the sword
and their young men will be put to forced labor.
⁹Their stronghold will fall because of terror;
at sight of the battle standard their commanders will panic,"
declares the LORD,
whose fire is in Zion,
whose furnace is in Jerusalem.

The Kingdom of Righteousness

32 See, a king will reign in righteousness
and rulers will rule with justice.
²Each man will be like a shelter from the wind
and a refuge from the storm,
like streams of water in the desert
and the shadow of a great rock in a thirsty land.

³Then the eyes of those who see will no longer be closed,
and the ears of those who hear will listen.
⁴The mind of the rash will know and understand,
and the stammering tongue will be fluent and clear.
⁵No longer will the fool be called noble
nor the scoundrel be highly respected.
⁶For the fool speaks folly,
his mind is busy with evil:
He practices ungodliness
and spreads error concerning the LORD;
the hungry he leaves empty
and from the thirsty he withholds water.
⁷The scoundrel's methods are wicked,
he makes up evil schemes
to destroy the poor with lies,
even when the plea of the needy is just.
⁸But the noble man makes noble plans,
and by noble deeds he stands.

The Women of Jerusalem

⁹You women who are so complacent,
rise up and listen to me;
you daughters who feel secure,
hear what I have to say!
¹⁰In little more than a year

you who feel secure will tremble;
the grape harvest will fail,
and the harvest of fruit will not come.

[11] Tremble, you complacent women;
shudder, you daughters who
feel secure!
Strip off your clothes,
put sackcloth around your waists.
[12] Beat your breasts for the
pleasant fields,
for the fruitful vines
[13] and for the land of my people,
a land overgrown with thorns
and briers—
yes, mourn for all houses of
merriment
and for this city of revelry.
[14] The fortress will be abandoned,
the noisy city deserted;
citadel and watchtower will become
a wasteland forever,
the delight of donkeys, a
pasture for flocks,
[15] till the Spirit is poured upon us
from on high,
and the desert becomes a
fertile field,
and the fertile field seems like
a forest.
[16] Justice will dwell in the desert
and righteousness live in the
fertile field.
[17] The fruit of righteousness will be peace;
the effect of righteousness will be quietness and confidence forever.
[18] My people will live in peaceful dwelling places,
in secure homes,
in undisturbed places of rest.
[19] Though hail flattens the forest
and the city is leveled completely,
[20] how blessed you will be,
sowing your seed by every stream,
and letting your cattle and donkeys range free.

genuine

confidence » 32:17

Do you ever wish you felt more sure of yourself? More confident? Maybe you decide to do something about it and get a little more assertive—your friends notice that you've started sportin' a little attitude. Problem solved? Not really. You see, that kind of confidence—talking louder and trying to get noticed—is just on the outside, and it doesn't last. Real confidence comes from righteousness— God's righteousness—at work in your heart. Real confidence comes from depending on him and not on you. And nothing can take *that* kind of confidence away—it's yours forever.

Distress and Help

33

Woe to you, O destroyer,
you who have not been destroyed!
Woe to you, O traitor,
you who have not been betrayed!
When you stop destroying,
you will be destroyed;
when you stop betraying,
you will be betrayed.

[2] O LORD, be gracious to us;
we long for you.
Be our strength every morning,

our salvation in time of distress.
³ At the thunder of your voice, the peoples flee;
    when you rise up, the nations scatter.
⁴ Your plunder, O nations, is harvested as by young locusts;
    like a swarm of locusts men
        pounce on it.

⁵ The LORD is exalted, for he dwells
        on high;
    he will fill Zion with justice and
        righteousness.
⁶ He will be the sure foundation for
        your times,
    a rich store of salvation and
        wisdom and knowledge;
    the fear of the LORD is the key
        to this treasure. ᵃ

⁷ Look, their brave men cry aloud in the
        streets;
    the envoys of peace weep bitterly.
⁸ The highways are deserted,
    no travelers are on the roads.
The treaty is broken,
    its witnesses ᵇ are despised,
    no one is respected.
⁹ The land mourns ᶜ and wastes away,
    Lebanon is ashamed and withers;
Sharon is like the Arabah,
    and Bashan and Carmel drop their leaves.

¹⁰ "Now will I arise," says the LORD.
    "Now will I be exalted;
    now will I be lifted up.
¹¹ You conceive chaff,
    you give birth to straw;
    your breath is a fire that consumes you.
¹² The peoples will be burned as if to lime;
    like cut thornbushes they will be set ablaze."

¹³ You who are far away, hear what I have done;
    you who are near, acknowledge my power!
¹⁴ The sinners in Zion are terrified;
    trembling grips the godless:
"Who of us can dwell with the consuming fire?
    Who of us can dwell with everlasting burning?"
¹⁵ He who walks righteously
    and speaks what is right,
who rejects gain from extortion
    and keeps his hand from accepting bribes,
who stops his ears against plots of murder
    and shuts his eyes against contemplating evil—
¹⁶ this is the man who will dwell on the heights,
    whose refuge will be the mountain fortress.
His bread will be supplied,
    and water will not fail him.

---

truth or dare

Do you have to drag your cranky, sleepy self out of bed every morning? Make this verse your personal morning mantra.

33:2

ᵃ 6 Or *is a treasure from him*   ᵇ 8 Dead Sea Scrolls; Masoretic Text / *the cities*   ᶜ 9 Or *dries up*

¹⁷ Your eyes will see the king in his beauty
and view a land that stretches afar.
¹⁸ In your thoughts you will ponder the former terror:
"Where is that chief officer?
Where is the one who took the revenue?
Where is the officer in charge of the towers?"
¹⁹ You will see those arrogant people no more,
those people of an obscure speech,
with their strange, incomprehensible tongue.

²⁰ Look upon Zion, the city of our festivals;
your eyes will see Jerusalem,
a peaceful abode, a tent that will not be moved;
its stakes will never be pulled up,
nor any of its ropes broken.
²¹ There the LORD will be our Mighty One.
It will be like a place of broad rivers and streams.
No galley with oars will ride them,
no mighty ship will sail them.
²² For the LORD is our judge,
the LORD is our lawgiver,
the LORD is our king;
it is he who will save us.

²³ Your rigging hangs loose:
The mast is not held secure,
the sail is not spread.
Then an abundance of spoils will be divided
and even the lame will carry off plunder.
²⁴ No one living in Zion will say, "I am ill";
and the sins of those who dwell there will be forgiven.

Judgment Against the Nations

34 Come near, you nations, and listen;
pay attention, you peoples!
Let the earth hear, and all that is in it,
the world, and all that comes out of it!
² The LORD is angry with all nations;
his wrath is upon all their armies.
He will totally destroy*ᵃ* them,
he will give them over to slaughter.
³ Their slain will be thrown out,
their dead bodies will send up a stench;
the mountains will be soaked with their blood.
⁴ All the stars of the heavens will be dissolved
and the sky rolled up like a scroll;
all the starry host will fall
like withered leaves from the vine,
like shriveled figs from the fig tree.

⁵ My sword has drunk its fill in the heavens;
see, it descends in judgment on Edom,
the people I have totally destroyed.
⁶ The sword of the LORD is bathed in blood,
it is covered with fat—

a 2 The Hebrew term refers to the irrevocable giving over of things or persons to the LORD, often by totally destroying them; also in verse 5.

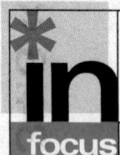

The Social Non-Drinker

Partying has always seemed like a side issue to me—some do, some don't, we're all still friends. But this year it's become *the* thing to do. And being the only Christian in a very public school, I feel like I stick out all the time.

Fine. I'm ready to take a stand for my faith. I just don't know where to stand. My friends know I don't drink, but they still invite me to their parties. I'm a social girl, so I've been going. I don't drink at all while I'm there. I just socialize and drive my wasted friends home. It's kind of funny being the only sober girl there. You see a very different side of people.

Yet I feel this twinge of guilt when I'm there. *Should I even be here? Am I really making a statement, or is it lost on these drunk friends of mine?* I know some Christians feel strongly that you shouldn't even be around that, especially because underage drinking is illegal and all. But how am I supposed to have an effect on my friends if I remove myself from their lives all the time? And what's the harm of showing up for awhile if I skip the beer? If I don't go, I'll sit at home all weekend, alone and bored. Not an attractive option.

fitting in in focus

How close can you get to the fire without being burned? When you're dying to fit in, it's easy to make compromises. Instead . . .

»*Ask for godly friends.* Proverbs 13:20 (page 822) says that if we spend time with wise friends, we'll become wise too. And 1 Corinthians 15:33 (page 1521) says "Do not be misled: 'Bad company corrupts good character.'" Ask God for a strong Christian friend who can encourage you.

»*Talk to your parents.* Yeah, they may be a bit removed from the social scene, but they really do have your best interests at heart. Ask for their guidance.

»*Guard your testimony.* You might know that you're not drinking, but what does everyone else assume? That the Christian girl is there and she's drinking, so it must be okay? You don't want even a hint of immorality associated with you (see Ephesians 5:3, page 1546).

For more on this topic, see the index on page 1656.

For more on fitting in, go to www.TrueImagesBible.com

the blood of lambs and goats,
    fat from the kidneys of rams.
For the LORD has a sacrifice in Bozrah
    and a great slaughter in Edom.
[7] And the wild oxen will fall with them,
    the bull calves and the great bulls.
Their land will be drenched with blood,
    and the dust will be soaked with fat.

[8] For the LORD has a day of vengeance,
    a year of retribution, to uphold Zion's cause.
[9] Edom's streams will be turned into pitch,
    her dust into burning sulfur;

her land will become blazing pitch!
[10] It will not be quenched night and day;
   its smoke will rise forever.
From generation to generation it will lie desolate;
   no one will ever pass through it again.
[11] The desert owl[a] and screech owl[a] will possess it;
   the great owl[a] and the raven will nest there.
God will stretch out over Edom
   the measuring line of chaos
   and the plumb line of desolation.
[12] Her nobles will have nothing there to be called a kingdom,
   all her princes will vanish away.
[13] Thorns will overrun her citadels,
   nettles and brambles her strongholds.
She will become a haunt for jackals,
   a home for owls.
[14] Desert creatures will meet with hyenas,
   and wild goats will bleat to each other;
there the night creatures will also repose
   and find for themselves places of rest.
[15] The owl will nest there and lay eggs,
   she will hatch them, and care for her young under the shadow of her wings;
there also the falcons will gather,
   each with its mate.

[16] Look in the scroll of the LORD and read:

None of these will be missing,
   not one will lack her mate.
For it is his mouth that has given the order,
   and his Spirit will gather them together.
[17] He allots their portions;
   his hand distributes them by measure.
They will possess it forever
   and dwell there from generation to generation.

Joy of the Redeemed

35

The desert and the parched land will be glad;
   the wilderness will rejoice and blossom.
Like the crocus, [2] it will burst into bloom;
   it will rejoice greatly and shout for joy.
The glory of Lebanon will be given to it,
   the splendor of Carmel and Sharon;
they will see the glory of the LORD,
   the splendor of our God.

[3] Strengthen the feeble hands,
   steady the knees that give way;
[4] say to those with fearful hearts,
   "Be strong, do not fear;
your God will come,
   he will come with vengeance;
with divine retribution
   he will come to save you."

---

a 11 The precise identification of these birds is uncertain.

⁵ Then will the eyes of the blind be opened
　　and the ears of the deaf unstopped.
⁶ Then will the lame leap like a deer,
　　and the mute tongue shout for joy.
　Water will gush forth in the
　　　wilderness
　　and streams in the desert.
⁷ The burning sand will become a
　　　pool,
　　the thirsty ground bubbling
　　　springs.
　In the haunts where jackals once
　　　lay,
　　grass and reeds and papyrus
　　　will grow.

⁸ And a highway will be there;
　　it will be called the Way of Holiness.
　The unclean will not journey on it;
　　it will be for those who walk in that Way;
　　wicked fools will not go about on it. *
⁹ No lion will be there,
　　nor will any ferocious beast get up on it;
　　they will not be found there.
　But only the redeemed will walk there,
¹⁰　and the ransomed of the LORD will return.
　They will enter Zion with singing;
　　everlasting joy will crown their heads.
　Gladness and joy will overtake them,
　　and sorrow and sighing will flee away.

truth or dare

Growing up with a disability is challenging. Feeling burned out? Even though the world isn't healed yet, someday all your imperfections will melt away, and God will make you perfectly whole.

35:5–6

Sennacherib Threatens Jerusalem

36 In the fourteenth year of King Hezekiah's reign, Sennacherib king of Assyria attacked all the fortified cities of Judah and captured them. ²Then the king of Assyria sent his field commander with a large army from Lachish to King Hezekiah at Jerusalem. When the commander stopped at the aqueduct of the Upper Pool, on the road to the Washerman's Field, ³Eliakim son of Hilkiah the palace administrator, Shebna the secretary, and Joah son of Asaph the recorder went out to him.

⁴The field commander said to them, "Tell Hezekiah,

" 'This is what the great king, the king of Assyria, says: On what are you basing this confidence of yours? ⁵You say you have strategy and military strength—but you speak only empty words. On whom are you depending, that you rebel against me? ⁶Look now, you are depending on Egypt, that splintered reed of a staff, which pierces a man's hand and wounds him if he leans on it! Such is Pharaoh king of Egypt to all who depend on him. ⁷And if you say to me, "We are depending on the LORD our God"—isn't he the one whose high places and altars Hezekiah removed, saying to Judah and Jerusalem, "You must worship before this altar"?

⁸" 'Come now, make a bargain with my master, the king of Assyria: I will give you two thousand horses—if you can put riders on them! ⁹How then can you repulse one officer of the least of my master's officials, even though you are depending on Egypt for chariots and horsemen? ¹⁰Furthermore, have I come to attack and destroy this land without the LORD? The LORD himself told me to march against this country and destroy it.' "

¹¹Then Eliakim, Shebna and Joah said to the field commander, "Please speak to your servants in Aramaic, since we understand it. Don't speak to us in Hebrew in the hearing of the people on the wall."

a 8 Or / *the simple will not stray from it*

[12]But the commander replied, "Was it only to your master and you that my master sent me to say these things, and not to the men sitting on the wall—who, like you, will have to eat their own filth and drink their own urine?"

[13]Then the commander stood and called out in Hebrew, "Hear the words of the great king, the king of Assyria! [14]This is what the king says: Do not let Hezekiah deceive you. He cannot deliver you! [15]Do not let Hezekiah persuade you to trust in the LORD when he says, 'The LORD will surely deliver us; this city will not be given into the hand of the king of Assyria.'

[16]"Do not listen to Hezekiah. This is what the king of Assyria says: Make peace with me and come out to me. Then every one of you will eat from his own vine and fig tree and drink water from his own cistern, [17]until I come and take you to a land like your own—a land of grain and new wine, a land of bread and vineyards.

[18]"Do not let Hezekiah mislead you when he says, 'The LORD will deliver us.' Has the god of any nation ever delivered his land from the hand of the king of Assyria? [19]Where are the gods of Hamath and Arpad? Where are the gods of Sepharvaim? Have they rescued Samaria from my hand? [20]Who of all the gods of these countries has been able to save his land from me? How then can the LORD deliver Jerusalem from my hand?"

[21]But the people remained silent and said nothing in reply, because the king had commanded, "Do not answer him."

[22]Then Eliakim son of Hilkiah the palace administrator, Shebna the secretary, and Joah son of Asaph the recorder went to Hezekiah, with their clothes torn, and told him what the field commander had said.

Jerusalem's Deliverance Foretold

37 When King Hezekiah heard this, he tore his clothes and put on sackcloth and went into the temple of the LORD. [2]He sent Eliakim the palace administrator, Shebna the secretary, and the leading priests, all wearing sackcloth, to the prophet Isaiah son of Amoz. [3]They told him, "This is what Hezekiah says: This day is a day of distress and rebuke and disgrace, as when children come to the point of birth and there is no strength to deliver them. [4]It may be that the LORD your God will hear the words of the field commander, whom his master, the king of Assyria, has sent to ridicule the living God, and that he will rebuke him for the words the LORD your God has heard. Therefore pray for the remnant that still survives."

[5]When King Hezekiah's officials came to Isaiah, [6]Isaiah said to them, "Tell your master, 'This is what the LORD says: Do not be afraid of what you have heard—those words with which the underlings of the king of Assyria have blasphemed me. [7]Listen! I am going to put a spirit in him so that when

love ♥ notes

35:8–10

Beloved,

I have a path for your life. It's a path of everlasting joy, an eternity without pain, worry or death. Follow my path, and I will never leave your side.

—Your heavenly Father

Describe the "Way of Holiness." Are you walking on it?

he hears a certain report, he will return to his own country, and there I will have him cut down with the sword.' "

⁸When the field commander heard that the king of Assyria had left Lachish, he withdrew and found the king fighting against Libnah.

⁹Now Sennacherib received a report that Tirhakah, the Cushite[a] king of Egypt, was marching out to fight against him. When he heard it, he sent messengers to Hezekiah with this word: ¹⁰"Say to Hezekiah king of Judah: Do not let the god you depend on deceive you when he says, 'Jerusalem will not be handed over to the king of Assyria.' ¹¹Surely you have heard what the kings of Assyria have done to all the countries, destroying them completely. And will you be delivered? ¹²Did the gods of the nations that were destroyed by my forefathers deliver them—the gods of Gozan, Haran, Rezeph and the people of Eden who were in Tel Assar? ¹³Where is the king of Hamath, the king of Arpad, the king of the city of Sepharvaim, or of Hena or Ivvah?"

Hezekiah's Prayer

¹⁴Hezekiah received the letter from the messengers and read it. Then he went up to the temple of the LORD and spread it out before the LORD. ¹⁵And Hezekiah prayed to the LORD: ¹⁶"O LORD Almighty, God of Israel, enthroned between the cherubim, you alone are God over all the kingdoms of the earth. You have made heaven and earth. ¹⁷Give ear, O LORD, and hear; open your eyes, O LORD, and see; listen to all the words Sennacherib has sent to insult the living God.

¹⁸"It is true, O LORD, that the Assyrian kings have laid waste all these peoples and their lands. ¹⁹They have thrown their gods into the fire and destroyed them, for they were not gods but only wood and stone, fashioned by human hands. ²⁰Now, O LORD our God, deliver us from his hand, so that all kingdoms on earth may know that you alone, O LORD, are God.[b]"

Sennacherib's Fall

²¹Then Isaiah son of Amoz sent a message to Hezekiah: "This is what the LORD, the God of Israel, says: Because you have prayed to me concerning Sennacherib king of Assyria, ²²this is the word the LORD has spoken against him:

> "The Virgin Daughter of Zion
>   despises and mocks you.
> The Daughter of Jerusalem
>   tosses her head as you flee.
> ²³Who is it you have insulted and blasphemed?
>   Against whom have you raised your voice
> and lifted your eyes in pride?
>   Against the Holy One of Israel!
> ²⁴By your messengers
>   you have heaped insults on the Lord.
> And you have said,
>   'With my many chariots
> I have ascended the heights of the mountains,

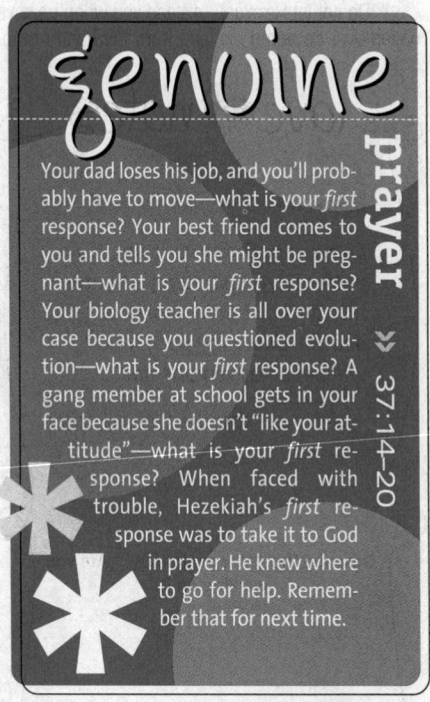

genuine » prayer » 37:14-20

Your dad loses his job, and you'll probably have to move—what is your *first* response? Your best friend comes to you and tells you she might be pregnant—what is your *first* response? Your biology teacher is all over your case because you questioned evolution—what is your *first* response? A gang member at school gets in your face because she doesn't "like your attitude"—what is your *first* response? When faced with trouble, Hezekiah's *first* response was to take it to God in prayer. He knew where to go for help. Remember that for next time.

---

a 9 That is, from the upper Nile region   *b 20* Dead Sea Scrolls (see also 2 Kings 19:19); Masoretic Text *alone are the LORD*

the utmost heights of Lebanon.
I have cut down its tallest cedars,
the choicest of its pines.
I have reached its remotest heights,
the finest of its forests.
²⁵ I have dug wells in foreign lands ᵃ
and drunk the water there.
With the soles of my feet
I have dried up all the streams of Egypt.'

²⁶ "Have you not heard?
Long ago I ordained it.
In days of old I planned it;
now I have brought it to pass,
that you have turned fortified cities
into piles of stone.
²⁷ Their people, drained of power,
are dismayed and put to shame.
They are like plants in the field,
like tender green shoots,
like grass sprouting on the roof,
scorched ᵇ before it grows up.

²⁸ "But I know where you stay
and when you come and go
and how you rage against me.
²⁹ Because you rage against me
and because your insolence has reached my ears,
I will put my hook in your nose
and my bit in your mouth,
and I will make you return
by the way you came.

³⁰ "This will be the sign for you, O Hezekiah:

"This year you will eat what grows by itself,
and the second year what springs from that.
But in the third year sow and reap,
plant vineyards and eat their fruit.
³¹ Once more a remnant of the house of Judah
will take root below and bear fruit above.
³² For out of Jerusalem will come a remnant,
and out of Mount Zion a band of survivors.
The zeal of the LORD Almighty
will accomplish this.

³³ "Therefore this is what the LORD says concerning the king of Assyria:

"He will not enter this city
or shoot an arrow here.
He will not come before it with shield
or build a siege ramp against it.
³⁴ By the way that he came he will return;
he will not enter this city,"

declares the LORD.

ᵃ 25 Dead Sea Scrolls (see also 2 Kings 19:24); Masoretic Text does not have in foreign lands.   ᵇ 27 Some manuscripts of the Masoretic Text, Dead Sea Scrolls and some Septuagint manuscripts (see also 2 Kings 19:26); most manuscripts of the Masoretic Text roof / and terraced fields

> [35] "I will defend this city and save it,
>   for my sake and for the sake of David my servant!"

[36] Then the angel of the LORD went out and put to death a hundred and eighty-five thousand men in the Assyrian camp. When the people got up the next morning—there were all the dead bodies! [37] So Sennacherib king of Assyria broke camp and withdrew. He returned to Nineveh and stayed there.

[38] One day, while he was worshiping in the temple of his god Nisroch, his sons Adrammelech and Sharezer cut him down with the sword, and they escaped to the land of Ararat. And Esarhaddon his son succeeded him as king.

Hezekiah's Illness

38 In those days Hezekiah became ill and was at the point of death. The prophet Isaiah son of Amoz went to him and said, "This is what the LORD says: Put your house in order, because you are going to die; you will not recover."

[2] Hezekiah turned his face to the wall and prayed to the LORD, [3] "Remember, O LORD, how I have walked before you faithfully and with wholehearted devotion and have done what is good in your eyes." And Hezekiah wept bitterly.

[4] Then the word of the LORD came to Isaiah: [5] "Go and tell Hezekiah, 'This is what the LORD, the God of your father David, says: I have heard your prayer and seen your tears; I will add fifteen years to your life. [6] And I will deliver you and this city from the hand of the king of Assyria. I will defend this city.

[7] " 'This is the LORD's sign to you that the LORD will do what he has promised: [8] I will make the shadow cast by the sun go back the ten steps it has gone down on the stairway of Ahaz.' " So the sunlight went back the ten steps it had gone down.

[9] A writing of Hezekiah king of Judah after his illness and recovery:

> [10] I said, "In the prime of my life
>   must I go through the gates of death[a]
>   and be robbed of the rest of my years?"
> [11] I said, "I will not again see the LORD,
>   the LORD, in the land of the living;
> no longer will I look on mankind,
>   or be with those who now dwell in this world.[b]
> [12] Like a shepherd's tent my house
>   has been pulled down and taken from me.
> Like a weaver I have rolled up my life,
>   and he has cut me off from the loom;
>   day and night you made an end of me.
> [13] I waited patiently till dawn,
>   but like a lion he broke all my bones;
>   day and night you made an end of me.
> [14] I cried like a swift or thrush,
>   I moaned like a mourning dove.
> My eyes grew weak as I looked to the heavens.
>   I am troubled; O Lord, come to my aid!"
>
> [15] But what can I say?
>   He has spoken to me, and he himself has done this.
> I will walk humbly all my years
>   because of this anguish of my soul.
> [16] Lord, by such things men live;
>   and my spirit finds life in them too.
> You restored me to health
>   and let me live.

a 10 Hebrew *Sheol*   *b 11* A few Hebrew manuscripts; most Hebrew manuscripts *in the place of cessation*

¹⁷ Surely it was for my benefit
    that I suffered such anguish.
In your love you kept me
    from the pit of destruction;
you have put all my sins
    behind your back.
¹⁸ For the grave^a cannot praise you,
    death cannot sing your praise;
those who go down to the pit
    cannot hope for your faithfulness.
¹⁹ The living, the living—they praise you,
    as I am doing today;
fathers tell their children
    about your faithfulness.

²⁰ The LORD will save me,
    and we will sing with stringed instruments
all the days of our lives
    in the temple of the LORD.

²¹ Isaiah had said, "Prepare a poultice of figs and apply it to the boil, and he will recover."
²² Hezekiah had asked, "What will be the sign that I will go up to the temple of the LORD?"

Envoys From Babylon

39 At that time Merodach-Baladan son of Baladan king of Babylon sent Hezekiah letters and a gift, because he had heard of his illness and recovery. ² Hezekiah received the envoys gladly and showed them what was in his storehouses—the silver, the gold, the spices, the fine oil, his entire armory and everything found among his treasures. There was nothing in his palace or in all his kingdom that Hezekiah did not show them.

³ Then Isaiah the prophet went to King Hezekiah and asked, "What did those men say, and where did they come from?"

"From a distant land," Hezekiah replied. "They came to me from Babylon."

⁴ The prophet asked, "What did they see in your palace?"

"They saw everything in my palace," Hezekiah said. "There is nothing among my treasures that I did not show them."

⁵ Then Isaiah said to Hezekiah, "Hear the word of the LORD Almighty: ⁶ The time will surely come when everything in your palace, and all that your fathers have stored up until this day, will be carried off to Babylon. Nothing will be left, says the LORD. ⁷ And some of your descendants, your own flesh and blood who will be born to you, will be taken away, and they will become eunuchs in the palace of the king of Babylon."

⁸ "The word of the LORD you have spoken is good," Hezekiah replied. For he thought, "There will be peace and security in my lifetime."

Comfort for God's People

40 Comfort, comfort my people,
    says your God.
² Speak tenderly to Jerusalem,
    and proclaim to her
that her hard service has been completed,
    that her sin has been paid for,
that she has received from the LORD's hand
    double for all her sins.

³ A voice of one calling:
"In the desert prepare
    the way for the LORD^b;

^a 18 Hebrew *Sheol*   ^b 3 Or *A voice of one calling in the desert: / "Prepare the way for the LORD*

make straight in the wilderness
  a highway for our God.[a]
[4] Every valley shall be raised up,
  every mountain and hill made low;
the rough ground shall become level,
  the rugged places a plain.
[5] And the glory of the LORD will be revealed,
  and all mankind together will see it.
      For the mouth of the LORD has spoken."

[6] A voice says, "Cry out."
  And I said, "What shall I cry?"

"All men are like grass,
  and all their glory is like the flowers of the field.
[7] The grass withers and the flowers fall,
  because the breath of the LORD blows on them.
  Surely the people are grass.
[8] The grass withers and the flowers fall,
  but the word of our God stands forever."

[9] You who bring good tidings to Zion,
  go up on a high mountain.
You who bring good tidings to Jerusalem,[b]
  lift up your voice with a shout,
lift it up, do not be afraid;
  say to the towns of Judah,
  "Here is your God!"
[10] See, the Sovereign LORD comes with power,
  and his arm rules for him.
See, his reward is with him,
  and his recompense accompanies him.
[11] He tends his flock like a shepherd:
  He gathers the lambs in his arms
and carries them close to his heart;
  he gently leads those that have young.

[12] Who has measured the waters in the hollow of his hand,
  or with the breadth of his hand marked off the heavens?
Who has held the dust of the earth in a basket,
  or weighed the mountains on the scales
  and the hills in a balance?
[13] Who has understood the mind[c] of the LORD,
  or instructed him as his counselor?
[14] Whom did the LORD consult to enlighten him,
  and who taught him the right way?
Who was it that taught him knowledge
  or showed him the path of understanding?

[15] Surely the nations are like a drop in a bucket;
  they are regarded as dust on the scales;
  he weighs the islands as though they were fine dust.
[16] Lebanon is not sufficient for altar fires,
  nor its animals enough for burnt offerings.
[17] Before him all the nations are as nothing;

---

a 3 Hebrew; Septuagint *make straight the paths of our God*   *b 9* Or *O Zion, bringer of good tidings, / go up on a high mountain. / O Jerusalem, bringer of good tidings*   *c 13* Or *Spirit*; or *spirit*

they are regarded by him as worthless
and less than nothing.

¹⁸ To whom, then, will you compare God?
What image will you compare him to?
¹⁹ As for an idol, a craftsman casts it,
and a goldsmith overlays it with gold
and fashions silver chains for it.
²⁰ A man too poor to present such an offering
selects wood that will not rot.
He looks for a skilled craftsman
to set up an idol that will not topple.

²¹ Do you not know?
Have you not heard?
Has it not been told you from the beginning?
Have you not understood since the earth was founded?
²² He sits enthroned above the circle of the earth,
and its people are like grasshoppers.
He stretches out the heavens like a canopy,
and spreads them out like a tent to live in.
²³ He brings princes to naught
and reduces the rulers of this world to nothing.
²⁴ No sooner are they planted,
no sooner are they sown,
no sooner do they take root in the ground,
than he blows on them and they wither,
and a whirlwind sweeps them away like chaff.

²⁵ "To whom will you compare me?
Or who is my equal?" says the Holy One.
²⁶ Lift your eyes and look to the heavens:
Who created all these?
He who brings out the starry host one by one,
and calls them each by name.
Because of his great power and mighty strength,
not one of them is missing.

²⁷ Why do you say, O Jacob,
and complain, O Israel,
"My way is hidden from the LORD;
my cause is disregarded by my God"?
²⁸ Do you not know?
Have you not heard?
The LORD is the everlasting God,
the Creator of the ends of the earth.
He will not grow tired or weary,
and his understanding no one can fathom.
²⁹ He gives strength to the weary
and increases the power of the weak.
³⁰ Even youths grow tired and weary,
and young men stumble and fall;
³¹ but those who hope in the LORD
will renew their strength.
They will soar on wings like eagles;
they will run and not grow weary,
they will walk and not be faint.

41

"Be silent before me, you islands!
  Let the nations renew their strength!
Let them come forward and speak;
  let us meet together at the place of judgment.

2 "Who has stirred up one from the east,
    calling him in righteousness to his service[a]?
He hands nations over to him
    and subdues kings before him.
He turns them to dust with his sword,
    to windblown chaff with his bow.
3 He pursues them and moves on unscathed,
    by a path his feet have not
      traveled before.
4 Who has done this and carried it
      through,
    calling forth the generations
      from the beginning?
I, the LORD—with the first of
  them
    and with the last—I am he."

5 The islands have seen it and fear;
    the ends of the earth tremble.
They approach and come
      forward;
6   each helps the other
    and says to his brother, "Be
      strong!"
7 The craftsman encourages the
      goldsmith,
    and he who smooths with the
      hammer
  spurs on him who strikes the
      anvil.
He says of the welding, "It is
      good."
    He nails down the idol so it
      will not topple.

8 "But you, O Israel, my servant,
    Jacob, whom I have chosen,
    you descendants of Abraham
      my friend,
9 I took you from the ends of the
      earth,
    from its farthest corners I
      called you.
I said, 'You are my servant';
    I have chosen you and have
      not rejected you.
10 So do not fear, for I am with you;
    do not be dismayed, for I am
      your God.

40:29–31

My daughter,

Need an energy boost? When you're feeling worn out and beaten down, come to me. I will refresh you so that you can walk, run, even soar with renewed strength!

—Your Hope and Strength

What do these verses say you have to do in order to get renewed strength? What does that mean?

_____

_____

_____

_____

_____

_____

_____

_____

_____

_____

_____

_____

a 2 Or / whom victory meets at every step

What's your Spiritual Gift?

Ever wondered about spiritual gifts? Every Christian has at least one, sometimes more (so if you're a Christian, read on!). There are lots of different gifts, but they're all equal in God's eyes. Realizing what gifts you have helps you learn who you are and what you do best.

Ready to start discovering how God has uniquely gifted you? For each answer you choose, circle the letter(s) next to it or write them on a separate piece of paper. You'll keep score that way.

1 If you were asked to do something at church, you'd pick . . .
A. Teaching a children's Sunday school class **T**
B. Doing behind-the-scenes tasks, like cleaning **S**
C. Being a greeter on Sunday mornings, welcoming people **H**
D. Organizing things **A**

2 Recently you had a fulfilling experience . . .
A. Encouraging someone who was hurting. **En**
B. Organizing a fun night for your friends. **A**
C. Giving to someone in need. **G**
D. Having your friends over at your house. **H**

3 At your youth group or school, you're usually asked to . . .
A. Lead a small group or be in charge of a committee. **L**
B. Help new people feel welcome. **H**
C. Do tasks like folding bulletins or serving food. **S**
D. Help plan activities or make things happen (set-up, calling people, recruiting volunteers, making sure that people have what they need). **A**

4 Which of the following do you find yourself doing, almost without thinking about it?
A. Feeling a deep sorrow over people who suffer. **M**
B. Cheering up people who are discouraged. **En**
C. Helping out without complaining about it. **S**
D. Believing that God can do the impossible. **F**

5 As you think about the future, you could easily see yourself . . .
A. Doing whatever you have to do to help the hurting. **M**
B. Teaching. **T**
C. Trusting God to do great things. **F**
D. Being in charge. **L**

6 Others have told you that . . .
A. You have a gift for helping people understand the truth about Jesus. **Ev**
B. You're always giving to people (money, time, etc.). **G**
C. You're definitely a leader. **L**
D. You're very compassionate. **M**

7 You looooove to . . .
A. Invite people to hang out at your home. **H**
B. Keep things organized (desk, locker, life). **A**
C. Talk with people about Jesus. **Ev**
D. Get everyone to rally around a cause. **L**

8 You don't usually have trouble . . .
A. Deciding whether to give sacrificially. **G**
B. Believing that God has a plan for you. **F**
C. Taking the time to make friends with the new girl. **En**
D. Setting goals and helping others follow those goals. **L**

9 In what area would you most like to grow?

A. Faith **F**
B. Leadership skills **L**
C. Creative ways to encourage others **En**
D. Teaching methods **T**

10 When you think about what you're passionate about, you think of . . .

A. How many people are hurting and in need around the world. **M**
B. How many people don't know Jesus. **Ev**
C. Helping people in their quest to learn. **T**
D. Growing in your faith. **F**

11 You've often felt an urgency to . . .

A. Give over and above what you usually give. **G**
B. Encourage someone in his or her faith. **En**
C. Share the good news about Jesus with a friend. **Ev**
D. Influence your friends for good. **L**

12 When you think about your environment (your room, your locker, your computer desktop—whatever), you think about . . .

A. How cool your place is and how you'd like to invite people over to enjoy it. **H**
B. How organized everything is. **A**
C. How much stuff you have that you'd like to give away. **G**
D. How many poor people don't have the advantages you have. **M**

13 What is the one fact you'd like to impress upon your friends?

A. The importance of having a place for everything and everything in its place. **A**
B. That there are so many hurting people in the world. **M**
C. That Jesus is the way, the truth and the life. **Ev**
D. That your home is always open to them. **H**

14 Which of the following makes you angry?

A. To see people in need. **G**
B. When people don't have the right resources to help them learn. **T**
C. When people ignore what needs to be done at home, church or school. **S**
D. Lack of faith in God. (You can so easily see the great things God does). **F**

to:
My daughter
from:
God
xoxo

15 This week you'd like to . . .

A. Help someone with a task he or she thinks is totally trivial. (You don't, though). **S**
B. Study the Bible to find just the right verse to use when telling someone about Jesus. **Ev**
C. Build up a friend who needs a little pick-me-up. **En**
D. Invite someone new to your home. **H**

16 Okay, what is one gift you've always wanted God to develop in you?

A. Teaching **T**
B. Administration **A**
C. Encouragement **En**
D. Other (see list) _____

17 What gift do you totally see at work in your life right now?

A. Giving **G**
B. Hospitality **H**
C. Faith **F**
D. Other (see list) _____

18 In order to be truly effective in the profession you'd like to choose (someday), what gift(s) do you think are needed?

A. Mercy **M**
B. Evangelism **Ev**
C. Serving **S**
D. Other (see list) _____

(A) (B) (C) (?)

Now count the letters you've circled and place that number(s) next to the corresponding gift(s) below. A higher number indicates that you may have that gift.

	A	Administration (see 1 Corinthians 12:28)
	EN	Encouragement (see Romans 12:8)
	EV	Evangelism (see Ephesians 4:11)
	F	Faith (see 1 Corinthians 12:9; Hebrews 11)
	G	Giving (see Romans 12:8; 2 Corinthians 8:1–5)
	H	Hospitality (see 1 Peter 4:9)
	M	Mercy (see Romans 12:8)
	L	Leadership (see Romans 12:8)
	S	Serving (see Romans 12:7)
	T	Teaching (see Romans 12:7; Ephesians 4:11)

Check out Romans 12:3–8, 1 Corinthians 12:1–31, Ephesians 4:7–13 and 1 Peter 4:7–11 for lists of the spiritual gifts.

Spiritual Gifts Tips

- **Stay connected with Jesus.** "No branch can bear fruit by itself; it must remain in the vine. Neither can you bear fruit unless you remain in me" (John 15:4).

- **Use your gifts to build up Christ's body, the church.** "So in Christ we who are many form one body, and each member belongs to all the others" (Romans 12:5).

- **Realize that no spiritual gift is better than another.** "There are different kinds of gifts, but the same Spirit" (1 Corinthians 12:4).

- **Use 'em with love—don't flaunt your gifts or be arrogant about them.** "If I speak in the tongues of men and of angels, but have not love, I am only a resounding gong or a clanging cymbal" (1 Corinthians 13:1).

- **Accept the gifts God gave *you* rather than seeking after those you think are "cool."** "Each one should use whatever gift he has received to serve others, faithfully administering God's grace in its various forms" (1 Peter 4:10).

Gifts @ Work

Check out these biblical examples of people using their spiritual gifts:

- Abraham's gifts of hospitality and faith (Genesis 18:1–15; 22:1–19)
- Joseph's gifts of administration and leadership (Genesis 41)
- Moses' gift of leadership (Exodus—Deuteronomy)
- Deborah's gift of leadership (Judges 4)
- Daniel's gift of administration (Daniel 6)
- Mary's gift of faith (Luke 1:26–38)
- Peter's and John's gifts of mercy and evangelism (Acts 3)
- Barnabas's gift of encouragement (Acts 4:36)
- Philip's gift of evangelism (Acts 8:26–40)
- Dorcas's gifts of serving and giving (Acts 9:36–41)
- Paul's gifts of teaching and leadership (Acts 13—28)
- Lydia's gift of hospitality (Acts 16:13–15)
- Philippian believers' gift of giving (Philippians 4:10–19)
- Timothy's gifts of teaching and leadership (1 Timothy 4:11–14)

The Ultimate Model Looking for the perfect model on using the gifts of the Spirit?

Look no further than Jesus! Yeah, we know. He was the perfect Son of God. How could you possibly be expected to live up to his example?! But don't forget that he was also human—like you. Want a gift-filled life? Stay connected to Christ, the true vine, and you'll bear much fruit (see John 15:1–17).

Personality 101

1 You love to . . .
- A. Plan events like holiday parties, school dances, ultimate sleepovers, etc.
- B. Go to events like holiday parties, school dances, ultimate sleepovers, etc.
- C. Spend one-on-one time with a friend.

2 A perfect day for you involves . . .
- A. "Ace"-ing a test, winning the lead in the school play or finally completing an assignment that took forever.
- B. A half-day of school, a movie or two with friends then out for coffee.
- C. Fresh air, sunshine and time to just *be*.

3 During a big holiday get-together with friends or family you usually . . .
- A. Help cook, serve or clean.
- B. Have fun and help out when you're needed.
- C. Hang out and talk.

4 In your mind, a satisfying time with God would be . . .
- A. Serving in some way, like helping out at a homeless shelter or organizing a youth group activity.
- B. Reading a Bible passage or singing praise songs with your small group.
- C. Taking a nature walk to check out the magnificence of God's creation.

5 What pushes your frantic button?
- A. Too much down time
- B. Too much to do, too little time
- C. Not enough chill time

6 At school, you're usually . . .
- A. Busy, busy, busy—juggling classes, friends and several extracurricular activities, like yearbook, sports, clubs (you get the picture!).
- B. Trying to get to class and be with your friends at the same time.
- C. Just doing stuff that floats your boat— whether it's trying out for the school play, being in art club or playing a sport.

7 What makes you feel down?
- A. When your efforts aren't appreciated
- B. Bad news of any kind
- C. When you feel like you can't be yourself around someone

8 Besides your relationship with Jesus (Okay, we're taking this for granted!), what do you treasure most?
- A. Your reputation or GPA
- B. Life and health . . . and cool stuff you own
- C. Times spent hanging out with family and friends

scoring

Are you like Mary? Martha? Or somewhere in between? Add up your points and see! Give yourself 1 point for every A, 2 points for every B and 3 points for every C.

Martha (8 to 13)
You're an "A student" because you're an *achiever*. Although you're a big-time doer, you don't always take time to chill and just be. It's okay to stop and smell the roses with God every once in a while. Check out a quick sketch of Martha in Luke 10:38–42.

In Between (14 to 18)
You're a "B student." In this case, B is for *balanced*. You seem pretty laidback about life. You know when to work and when to chill. But does your balanced life include both time with God and working for him?

Mary (19 to 24)
You're a "C student"—*calm, cool* and *collected*. You like the emphasis on being who you are. You know when to slow down and enjoy God, life and people. However, there's value in helping out sometimes, too! Check out a quick sketch of Mary in Luke 10:38–42.

mirror images

But they had no children, because Elizabeth was barren; and they were both well along in years. Luke 1:7

Elizabeth—Waiting It Out

Unexpected surprises can be the best kind. The gift you never thought you'd get under the Christmas tree. Being named most valuable player on your team. Seeing God answer your request for your best friend to get well.

Meet the aging Elizabeth, the queen of waiting. Sadly, she and her hubby Zechariah were childless and growing older, and back then, that reflected very poorly on Elizabeth. At that time a woman's worth was judged by her ability to have children.

Surprise #1 came when the angel Gabriel told Zechariah his wife would become pregnant. When Elizabeth had her first bout of morning sickness, she knew the angel's words were true.

Then came the day her relative, Mary, came to visit. Welcome, surprise #2. As soon as Mary opened her mouth, Elizabeth's baby took notice. "The baby in my womb leaped for joy," cried Elizabeth. And instantly Elizabeth blessed Mary, confirming that she was pregnant with the child who was the Messiah.

Elizabeth was walking so closely with God that she believed in even the most impossible surprises. A child at her age? Mary, a virgin, pregnant with the Savior? Sounds improbable—but if God said it, Elizabeth believed it. And her faith led to joy in her old age. As her son John grew up, he paved the way for Mary's baby. Elizabeth was blessed with a life of wonderful surprises.

Our disappointments over broken relationships, unfulfilled dreams or uncomfortable circumstances can leave us frustrated and unhappy. But God knows our losses, and he sees our broken hearts. He wants us to wait on him, as Elizabeth did, even when that means waiting for a long time without seeing the result. Regardless of what's happening to you or around you, don't lose hope. Keep your eyes focused on the one who can bless you beyond your wildest dreams.

Dear Jesus, I'd love to have joy like Elizabeth. But sometimes I get so wrapped up in my own problems, and I get impatient for the solution. Help me to see you in unexpected blessings and to wait for your timing. Amen.

To read the next Mirror Images profile, go to page 984.

»» Read more about Elizabeth in Luke 1:5-80 (pages 1363–1365).

I will strengthen you and help you;
    I will uphold you with my righteous right hand.

11 "All who rage against you
    will surely be ashamed and disgraced;
those who oppose you
    will be as nothing and perish.
12 Though you search for your enemies,
    you will not find them.
Those who wage war against you
    will be as nothing at all.
13 For I am the LORD, your God,
    who takes hold of your right hand
and says to you, Do not fear;
    I will help you.
14 Do not be afraid, O worm Jacob,
    O little Israel,
for I myself will help you," declares the LORD,
    your Redeemer, the Holy One of Israel.
15 "See, I will make you into a threshing sledge,
    new and sharp, with many teeth.
You will thresh the mountains and crush them,
    and reduce the hills to chaff.
16 You will winnow them, the wind will pick them up,
    and a gale will blow them away.
But you will rejoice in the LORD
    and glory in the Holy One of Israel.

17 "The poor and needy search for water,
    but there is none;
    their tongues are parched with thirst.
But I the LORD will answer them;
    I, the God of Israel, will not forsake them.
18 I will make rivers flow on barren heights,
    and springs within the valleys.
I will turn the desert into pools of water,
    and the parched ground into springs.
19 I will put in the desert
    the cedar and the acacia, the myrtle and the olive.
I will set pines in the wasteland,
    the fir and the cypress together,
20 so that people may see and know,
    may consider and understand,
that the hand of the LORD has done this,
    that the Holy One of Israel has created it.

21 "Present your case," says the LORD.
    "Set forth your arguments," says Jacob's King.
22 "Bring in ˛your idols˛ to tell us
    what is going to happen.
Tell us what the former things were,
    so that we may consider them
    and know their final outcome.
Or declare to us the things to come,
23   tell us what the future holds,
    so we may know that you are gods.
Do something, whether good or bad,

so that we will be dismayed and filled with fear.
24 But you are less than nothing
and your works are utterly worthless;
he who chooses you is detestable.

25 "I have stirred up one from the north, and he comes—
one from the rising sun who calls on my name.
He treads on rulers as if they were mortar,
as if he were a potter treading the clay.
26 Who told of this from the beginning, so we could know,
or beforehand, so we could say, 'He was right'?
No one told of this,
no one foretold it,
no one heard any words from you.
27 I was the first to tell Zion, 'Look, here they are!'
I gave to Jerusalem a messenger of good tidings.
28 I look but there is no one—
no one among them to give counsel,
no one to give answer when I ask them.
29 See, they are all false!
Their deeds amount to nothing;
their images are but wind and confusion.

The Servant of the LORD

42 "Here is my servant, whom I uphold,
my chosen one in whom I delight;
I will put my Spirit on him
and he will bring justice to the nations.
2 He will not shout or cry out,
or raise his voice in the streets.
3 A bruised reed he will not break,
and a smoldering wick he will not snuff out.
In faithfulness he will bring forth justice;
4   he will not falter or be discouraged
till he establishes justice on earth.
In his law the islands will put their hope."

5 This is what God the LORD says—
he who created the heavens and stretched them out,
who spread out the earth and all that comes out of it,
who gives breath to its people,
and life to those who walk on it:
6 "I, the LORD, have called you in righteousness;
I will take hold of your hand.
I will keep you and will make you
to be a covenant for the people
and a light for the Gentiles,
7 to open eyes that are blind,
to free captives from prison
and to release from the dungeon those who sit in darkness.

8 "I am the LORD; that is my name!
I will not give my glory to another
or my praise to idols.
9 See, the former things have taken place,
and new things I declare;
before they spring into being
I announce them to you."

Song of Praise to the LORD

¹⁰ Sing to the LORD a new song,
  his praise from the ends of the earth,
you who go down to the sea, and all that is in it,
  you islands, and all who live in them.
¹¹ Let the desert and its towns raise their voices;
  let the settlements where Kedar lives rejoice.
Let the people of Sela sing for joy;
  let them shout from the mountaintops.
¹² Let them give glory to the LORD
  and proclaim his praise in the islands.
¹³ The LORD will march out like a mighty man,
  like a warrior he will stir up his zeal;
with a shout he will raise the battle cry
  and will triumph over his enemies.

¹⁴ "For a long time I have kept silent,
  I have been quiet and held myself back.
But now, like a woman in childbirth,
  I cry out, I gasp and pant.
¹⁵ I will lay waste the mountains and hills
  and dry up all their vegetation;
I will turn rivers into islands
  and dry up the pools.
¹⁶ I will lead the blind by ways they have not known,
  along unfamiliar paths I will guide them;
I will turn the darkness into light before them
  and make the rough places smooth.
These are the things I will do;
  I will not forsake them.
¹⁷ But those who trust in idols,
  who say to images, 'You are our gods,'
  will be turned back in utter shame.

Israel Blind and Deaf

¹⁸ "Hear, you deaf;
  look, you blind, and see!
¹⁹ Who is blind but my servant,
  and deaf like the messenger I send?
Who is blind like the one committed to me,
  blind like the servant of the LORD?
²⁰ You have seen many things, but have paid no attention;
  your ears are open, but you hear nothing."
²¹ It pleased the LORD
  for the sake of his righteousness
  to make his law great and glorious.
²² But this is a people plundered and looted,
  all of them trapped in pits
  or hidden away in prisons.
They have become plunder,
  with no one to rescue them;
they have been made loot,
  with no one to say, "Send them back."

²³ Which of you will listen to this
  or pay close attention in time to come?

²⁴Who handed Jacob over to become loot,
and Israel to the plunderers?
Was it not the LORD,
against whom we have sinned?
For they would not follow his ways;
they did not obey his law.
²⁵So he poured out on them his burning anger,
the violence of war.
It enveloped them in flames, yet they did not understand;
it consumed them, but they did not take it to heart.

Israel's Only Savior

43 But now, this is what the LORD says—
he who created you,
O Jacob,
he who formed you, O Israel:
"Fear not, for I have redeemed
you;
I have summoned you by
name; you are mine.
²When you pass through the
waters,
I will be with you;
and when you pass through the
rivers,
they will not sweep over you.
When you walk through the fire,
you will not be burned;
the flames will not set you
ablaze.
³For I am the LORD, your God,
the Holy One of Israel, your
Savior;
I give Egypt for your ransom,
Cush ᵃ and Seba in your
stead.
⁴Since you are precious and
honored in my sight,
and because I love you,
I will give men in exchange for
you,
and people in exchange for
your life.
⁵Do not be afraid, for I am with
you;
I will bring your children from
the east
and gather you from the west.
⁶I will say to the north, 'Give them
up!'
and to the south, 'Do not hold
them back.'
Bring my sons from afar

love ♥ notes

43:1-2

Precious one,

No matter what difficulties you're facing, we will walk through them together. No matter how intense the situation, you won't be forever destroyed. Because you are special to me, I will always watch over you.

—Your Protector

Have you ever walked through the waters or fire with God? Describe that experience.

ᵃ 3 That is, the upper Nile region

genuine

purpose

» 43:5-7

When you think about your future—picking a college, pursuing a career, maybe getting married and starting a family—do you ever wonder what life is all about? What's the purpose? It seems like such a big, complicated question. But the answer is very simple: God created you for his glory. That's it. That's all there is to it. And you will find the truest joy and peace and satisfaction in life when you fulfill that purpose. As you make decisions about your future, remember that you were created to bring God glory—*that's* what it's all about.

and my daughters from the ends of the earth—
⁷everyone who is called by my name,
whom I created for my glory,
whom I formed and made."

⁸Lead out those who have eyes but are blind,
who have ears but are deaf.
⁹All the nations gather together and the peoples assemble.
Which of them foretold this and proclaimed to us the former things?
Let them bring in their witnesses to prove they were right,
so that others may hear and say, "It is true."
¹⁰"You are my witnesses," declares the LORD,
"and my servant whom I have chosen,
so that you may know and believe me
and understand that I am he.
Before me no god was formed, nor will there be one after me.

¹¹I, even I, am the LORD,
and apart from me there is no savior.
¹²I have revealed and saved and proclaimed—
I, and not some foreign god among you.
You are my witnesses," declares the LORD, "that I am God.
¹³ Yes, and from ancient days I am he.
No one can deliver out of my hand.
When I act, who can reverse it?"

God's Mercy and Israel's Unfaithfulness

¹⁴This is what the LORD says—
your Redeemer, the Holy One of Israel:
"For your sake I will send to Babylon
and bring down as fugitives all the Babylonians,ᵃ
in the ships in which they took pride.
¹⁵I am the LORD, your Holy One,
Israel's Creator, your King."

truth or dare

It's not up to you to *convince* others of the truth (that's up to the Holy Spirit). But you are to be a witness and testify that there's only one Savior.

43:10–11

ᵃ 14 Or *Chaldeans*

¹⁶ This is what the Lord says—
he who made a way through the sea,
a path through the mighty waters,
¹⁷ who drew out the chariots and horses,
the army and reinforcements together,
and they lay there, never to rise again,
extinguished, snuffed out like a wick:
¹⁸ "Forget the former things;
do not dwell on the past.
¹⁹ See, I am doing a new thing!
Now it springs up; do you not perceive it?
I am making a way in the desert
and streams in the wasteland.
²⁰ The wild animals honor me,
the jackals and the owls,
because I provide water in the desert
and streams in the wasteland,
to give drink to my people, my chosen,
²¹ the people I formed for myself
that they may proclaim my praise.

²² "Yet you have not called upon me, O Jacob,
you have not wearied yourselves for me, O Israel.
²³ You have not brought me sheep for burnt offerings,
nor honored me with your sacrifices.
I have not burdened you with grain offerings
nor wearied you with demands for incense.
²⁴ You have not bought any fragrant calamus for me,
or lavished on me the fat of your sacrifices.
But you have burdened me with your sins
and wearied me with your offenses.

²⁵ "I, even I, am he who blots out
your transgressions, for my own sake,
and remembers your sins no more.
²⁶ Review the past for me,
let us argue the matter together;
state the case for your innocence.
²⁷ Your first father sinned;
your spokesmen rebelled against me.
²⁸ So I will disgrace the dignitaries of your temple,
and I will consign Jacob to destruction^a
and Israel to scorn.

Israel the Chosen

44

"But now listen, O Jacob, my servant,
Israel, whom I have chosen.
² This is what the Lord says—
he who made you, who formed you in the womb,
and who will help you:
Do not be afraid, O Jacob, my servant,
Jeshurun, whom I have chosen.
³ For I will pour water on the thirsty land,

^a 28 The Hebrew term refers to the irrevocable giving over of things or persons to the Lord, often by totally destroying them.

and streams on the dry ground;
I will pour out my Spirit on your offspring,
    and my blessing on your descendants.
⁴ They will spring up like grass in a meadow,
    like poplar trees by flowing streams.
⁵ One will say, 'I belong to the LORD';
    another will call himself by the name of Jacob;
still another will write on his hand, 'The LORD's,'
    and will take the name Israel.

The LORD, Not Idols

⁶ "This is what the LORD says—
    Israel's King and Redeemer, the LORD Almighty:
I am the first and I am the last;
    apart from me there is no God.
⁷ Who then is like me? Let him proclaim it.
    Let him declare and lay out before me
what has happened since I established my ancient people,
    and what is yet to come—
    yes, let him foretell what will come.
⁸ Do not tremble, do not be afraid.
    Did I not proclaim this and foretell it long ago?
You are my witnesses. Is there any God besides me?
    No, there is no other Rock; I know not one."

⁹ All who make idols are nothing,
    and the things they treasure are worthless.
Those who would speak up for them are blind;
    they are ignorant, to their own shame.
¹⁰ Who shapes a god and casts an idol,
    which can profit him nothing?
¹¹ He and his kind will be put to shame;
    craftsmen are nothing but men.
Let them all come together and take their stand;
    they will be brought down to terror and infamy.

¹² The blacksmith takes a tool
    and works with it in the coals;
he shapes an idol with hammers,
    he forges it with the might of his arm.
He gets hungry and loses his strength;
    he drinks no water and grows faint.
¹³ The carpenter measures with a line
    and makes an outline with a marker;
he roughs it out with chisels
    and marks it with compasses.
He shapes it in the form of man,
    of man in all his glory,
    that it may dwell in a shrine.
¹⁴ He cut down cedars,
    or perhaps took a cypress or oak.
He let it grow among the trees of the forest,
    or planted a pine, and the rain made it grow.
¹⁵ It is man's fuel for burning;
    some of it he takes and warms himself,
    he kindles a fire and bakes bread.
But he also fashions a god and worships it;

he makes an idol and bows down to it.
16 Half of the wood he burns in the fire;
over it he prepares his meal,
he roasts his meat and eats his fill.
He also warms himself and says,
"Ah! I am warm; I see the fire."
17 From the rest he makes a god,
his idol;
he bows down to it and
worships.
He prays to it and says,
"Save me; you are my god."
18 They know nothing, they
understand nothing;
their eyes are plastered over
so they cannot see,
and their minds closed so they
cannot understand.
19 No one stops to think,
no one has the knowledge or
understanding to say,
"Half of it I used for fuel;
I even baked bread over its coals,
I roasted meat and I ate.
Shall I make a detestable thing from what is
left?
Shall I bow down to a block of wood?"
20 He feeds on ashes, a deluded heart misleads him;
he cannot save himself, or say,
"Is not this thing in my right hand a lie?"

21 "Remember these things, O Jacob,
for you are my servant, O Israel.
I have made you, you are my servant;
O Israel, I will not forget you.
22 I have swept away your offenses like a cloud,
your sins like the morning mist.
Return to me,
for I have redeemed you."

23 Sing for joy, O heavens, for the LORD has done this;
shout aloud, O earth beneath.
Burst into song, you mountains,
you forests and all your trees,
for the LORD has redeemed Jacob,
he displays his glory in Israel.

Jerusalem to Be Inhabited

24 "This is what the LORD says—
your Redeemer, who formed you in the womb:

I am the LORD,
who has made all things,
who alone stretched out the heavens,
who spread out the earth by myself,

25 who foils the signs of false prophets
and makes fools of diviners,

truth or dare

Many girls start obsessing over false gods (like popularity, money or appearance) without even thinking. And that's the main problem. Think about what those things are—they're just *things*.

44:16–19

who overthrows the learning of the wise
and turns it into nonsense,
²⁶ who carries out the words of his servants
and fulfills the predictions of his messengers,

who says of Jerusalem, 'It shall be inhabited,'
of the towns of Judah, 'They shall be built,'
and of their ruins, 'I will restore them,'
²⁷ who says to the watery deep, 'Be dry,
and I will dry up your streams,'
²⁸ who says of Cyrus, 'He is my shepherd
and will accomplish all that I please;
he will say of Jerusalem, "Let it be rebuilt,"
and of the temple, "Let its foundations be laid." '

45 "This is what the LORD says to his anointed,
to Cyrus, whose right hand I take hold of
to subdue nations before him
and to strip kings of their armor,
to open doors before him
so that gates will not be shut:
² I will go before you
and will level the mountains⁰;
I will break down gates of bronze
and cut through bars of iron.
³ I will give you the treasures of darkness,
riches stored in secret places,

so that you may know that I am
the LORD,
the God of Israel, who
summons you by name.
⁴ For the sake of Jacob my servant,
of Israel my chosen,
I summon you by name
and bestow on you a title of honor,
though you do not
acknowledge me.
⁵ I am the LORD, and there is no other;
apart from me there is no God.
I will strengthen you,
though you have not
acknowledged me,
⁶ so that from the rising of the sun
to the place of its setting
men may know there is none
besides me.
I am the LORD, and there is no
other.
⁷ I form the light and create darkness,
I bring prosperity and create
disaster;
I, the LORD, do all these things.

⁸ "You heavens above, rain down
righteousness;

genuine faith » 45:5-9

Apart from me there is no God. That means that God is God, and *you* are not. He has the right to call the shots in your life because he's the Potter, and you are the clay. The clay doesn't get to say, "I wish you'd made me prettier . . . I wish you'd given me different parents . . . I wish I lived anywhere but here!" The clay's job is to trust and submit to the Potter. God knows what he's doing as he's shaping you. Trust him with the outcome.

---

a 2 Dead Sea Scrolls and Septuagint; the meaning of the word in the Masoretic Text is uncertain.

let the clouds shower it down.
Let the earth open wide,
   let salvation spring up,
let righteousness grow with it;
   I, the LORD, have created it.

⁹ "Woe to him who quarrels with his Maker,
   to him who is but a potsherd among the potsherds on the ground.
Does the clay say to the potter,
   'What are you making?'
Does your work say,
   'He has no hands'?
¹⁰ Woe to him who says to his father,
   'What have you begotten?'
or to his mother,
   'What have you brought to birth?'

¹¹ "This is what the LORD says—
   the Holy One of Israel, and its Maker:
Concerning things to come,
   do you question me about my children,
   or give me orders about the work of my hands?
¹² It is I who made the earth
   and created mankind upon it.
My own hands stretched out the heavens;
   I marshaled their starry hosts.
¹³ I will raise up Cyrus[a] in my righteousness:
   I will make all his ways straight.
He will rebuild my city
   and set my exiles free,
but not for a price or reward,
   says the LORD Almighty."

¹⁴ This is what the LORD says:

"The products of Egypt and the merchandise of Cush,[b]
   and those tall Sabeans—
they will come over to you
   and will be yours;
they will trudge behind you,
   coming over to you in chains.
They will bow down before you
   and plead with you, saying,
'Surely God is with you, and there is no other;
   there is no other god.' "

¹⁵ Truly you are a God who hides himself,
   O God and Savior of Israel.
¹⁶ All the makers of idols will be put to shame and disgraced;
   they will go off into disgrace together.
¹⁷ But Israel will be saved by the LORD
   with an everlasting salvation;
you will never be put to shame or disgraced,
   to ages everlasting.

¹⁸ For this is what the LORD says—
   he who created the heavens,

---

a 13 Hebrew *him*   *b 14* That is, the upper Nile region

he is God;
he who fashioned and made the earth,
he founded it;
he did not create it to be empty,
but formed it to be inhabited—
he says:
"I am the LORD,
and there is no other.
¹⁹I have not spoken in secret,
from somewhere in a land of darkness;
I have not said to Jacob's descendants,
'Seek me in vain.'
I, the LORD, speak the truth;
I declare what is right.

²⁰ "Gather together and come;
assemble, you fugitives from the nations.
Ignorant are those who carry about idols of wood,
who pray to gods that cannot save.
²¹ Declare what is to be, present it—
let them take counsel together.
Who foretold this long ago,
who declared it from the distant past?
Was it not I, the LORD?
And there is no God apart from me,
a righteous God and a Savior;
there is none but me.

²² "Turn to me and be saved,
all you ends of the earth;
for I am God, and there is no other.
²³ By myself I have sworn,
my mouth has uttered in all integrity
a word that will not be revoked:
Before me every knee will bow;
by me every tongue will swear.
²⁴ They will say of me, 'In the LORD alone
are righteousness and strength.' "
All who have raged against him
will come to him and be put to shame.
²⁵ But in the LORD all the descendants of Israel
will be found righteous and will exult.

Gods of Babylon

46

Bel bows down, Nebo stoops low;
their idols are borne by beasts of burden. ^a
The images that are carried about are burdensome,
a burden for the weary.
² They stoop and bow down together;
unable to rescue the burden,
they themselves go off into captivity.

³ "Listen to me, O house of Jacob,
all you who remain of the house of Israel,
you whom I have upheld since you were conceived,
and have carried since your birth.

---

^a 1 Or are but beasts and cattle

⁴Even to your old age and gray hairs
  I am he, I am he who will sustain you.
I have made you and I will carry you;
  I will sustain you and I will rescue you.

⁵"To whom will you compare me or count me equal?
  To whom will you liken me that we may be compared?
⁶Some pour out gold from their bags
  and weigh out silver on the scales;
they hire a goldsmith to make it into a god,
  and they bow down and worship it.
⁷They lift it to their shoulders and carry it;
  they set it up in its place, and there it stands.
  From that spot it cannot move.
Though one cries out to it, it does not answer;
  it cannot save him from his troubles.

⁸"Remember this, fix it in mind,
  take it to heart, you rebels.
⁹Remember the former things, those of long ago;
  I am God, and there is no other;
  I am God, and there is none like me.
¹⁰I make known the end from the beginning,
  from ancient times, what is still to come.
I say: My purpose will stand,
  and I will do all that I please.
¹¹From the east I summon a bird of prey;
  from a far-off land, a man to fulfill my purpose.
What I have said, that will I bring about;
  what I have planned, that will I do.
¹²Listen to me, you stubborn-hearted,
  you who are far from righteousness.
¹³I am bringing my righteousness near,
  it is not far away;
  and my salvation will not be delayed.
I will grant salvation to Zion,
  my splendor to Israel.

The Fall of Babylon

47 "Go down, sit in the dust,
  Virgin Daughter of Babylon;
sit on the ground without a throne,
  Daughter of the Babylonians. ᵃ
No more will you be called
  tender or delicate.
²Take millstones and grind flour;
  take off your veil.
Lift up your skirts, bare your legs,
  and wade through the streams.
³Your nakedness will be exposed
  and your shame uncovered.
I will take vengeance;
  I will spare no one."

⁴Our Redeemer—the LORD Almighty is his name—
  is the Holy One of Israel.

ᵃ 1 Or *Chaldeans*; also in verse 5

Horoscopes: Harmless or Harmful?

Profile: Sage

This month is supposed to be my special month of love. That is, according to my horoscope.

I check it maybe once a week. (I'm a Libra.) I'm not as into it as some of my friends. One girl, Maria, lives her entire life by her horoscope. She'll break up with her boyfriend if her horoscope tells her to do it. Not me!

My small group leader told us that reading horoscopes, even just for fun, is wrong. She says they're a doorway into the occult or something. It's not like I'm going to a psychic or am ready to stop being a Christian. I still believe in God. To me horoscopes are harmless fun like the Magic 8 ball.

Sometimes, though, my horoscope seems true. Like the time it told me that a really, really shy guy I've been thinking about was finally going to make a move. That was so like Andy. (He's a Gemini. He's totally hot.) I kept hoping he'd ask me out, and he finally did!

There's nothing wrong with wanting to know what's up, is there? Sometimes God seems so far away, y'know? I've prayed about stuff and waited forever on answers. Who says God can't speak through horoscopes? I'm just keeping all of my options open.

For more ideas on how to deal with horoscopes, check out www.TrueImagesBible.com

horoscopes in focus

You don't have to look very far to find a horoscope—just check a newspaper, most teen magazines or the Web. Like Sage, are you or your friends wondering about horoscopes? Here's some fast truth:

» A horoscope seems like harmless fun. But in reality, it's a foot-in-the-door technique the enemy (aka Satan) uses to wear down your standards.

» If you're seeking knowledge and confidence about the future, that's great. But God wants you to seek him—not your horoscope or local psychic—for answers (see Isaiah 47:13–15, page 959).

» "Astrology is no big deal. It's just for fun." That line doesn't go far with God. God is crystal clear about these kinds of methods of gaining personal guidance apart from him—he hates them (see Deuteronomy 18:10–12, pages 229–230). This isn't a gray area. Don't compromise.

For more on this topic, see the index on page 1656.

5 "Sit in silence, go into darkness,
    Daughter of the Babylonians;
no more will you be called
    queen of kingdoms.
6 I was angry with my people
    and desecrated my inheritance;
I gave them into your hand,
    and you showed them no mercy.
Even on the aged
    you laid a very heavy yoke.

[7] You said, 'I will continue forever—
the eternal queen!'
But you did not consider these things
or reflect on what might happen.

[8] "Now then, listen, you wanton creature,
lounging in your security
and saying to yourself,
'I am, and there is none besides me.
I will never be a widow
or suffer the loss of children.'
[9] Both of these will overtake you
in a moment, on a single day:
loss of children and widowhood.
They will come upon you in full measure,
in spite of your many sorceries
and all your potent spells.
[10] You have trusted in your wickedness
and have said, 'No one sees me.'
Your wisdom and knowledge mislead you
when you say to yourself,
'I am, and there is none besides me.'
[11] Disaster will come upon you,
and you will not know how to conjure it away.
A calamity will fall upon you
that you cannot ward off with a ransom;
a catastrophe you cannot foresee
will suddenly come upon you.

[12] "Keep on, then, with your magic spells
and with your many sorceries,
which you have labored at since childhood.
Perhaps you will succeed,
perhaps you will cause terror.
[13] All the counsel you have received has only worn you out!
Let your astrologers come forward,
those stargazers who make predictions month by month,
let them save you from what is coming upon you.
[14] Surely they are like stubble;
the fire will burn them up.
They cannot even save themselves
from the power of the flame.
Here are no coals to warm anyone;
here is no fire to sit by.
[15] That is all they can do for you—
these you have labored with
and trafficked with since childhood.
Each of them goes on in his error;
there is not one that can save you.

Stubborn Israel

48

"Listen to this, O house of Jacob,
you who are called by the name of Israel
and come from the line of Judah,
you who take oaths in the name of the LORD
and invoke the God of Israel—
but not in truth or righteousness—

²you who call yourselves citizens of the holy city
    and rely on the God of Israel—
    the Lord Almighty is his name:
³I foretold the former things long ago,
    my mouth announced them and I made them known;
    then suddenly I acted, and they came to pass.
⁴For I knew how stubborn you were;
    the sinews of your neck were iron,
    your forehead was bronze.
⁵Therefore I told you these things long ago;
    before they happened I announced them to you
so that you could not say,
    'My idols did them;
    my wooden image and metal god ordained them.'
⁶You have heard these things; look at them all.
    Will you not admit them?

"From now on I will tell you of new things,
    of hidden things unknown to you.
⁷They are created now, and not long ago;
    you have not heard of them before today.
So you cannot say,
    'Yes, I knew of them.'
⁸You have neither heard nor understood;
    from of old your ear has not been open.
Well do I know how treacherous you are;
    you were called a rebel from birth.
⁹For my own name's sake I delay my wrath;
    for the sake of my praise I hold it back from you,
    so as not to cut you off.
¹⁰See, I have refined you, though not as silver;
    I have tested you in the furnace of affliction.
¹¹For my own sake, for my own sake, I do this.
    How can I let myself be defamed?
    I will not yield my glory to another.

Israel Freed

¹²"Listen to me, O Jacob,
    Israel, whom I have called:
I am he;
    I am the first and I am the last.
¹³My own hand laid the foundations of the earth,
    and my right hand spread out the heavens;
when I summon them,
    they all stand up together.

¹⁴"Come together, all of you, and listen:
    Which of ⌐the idols¬ has foretold these things?
The Lord's chosen ally
    will carry out his purpose against Babylon;
    his arm will be against the Babylonians. ͣ
¹⁵I, even I, have spoken;
    yes, I have called him.
I will bring him,
    and he will succeed in his mission.

ͣ 14 Or Chaldeans; also in verse 20

16 "Come near me and listen to this:

"From the first announcement I have not spoken in secret;
at the time it happens, I am there."

And now the Sovereign LORD has sent me,
with his Spirit.

17 This is what the LORD says—
your Redeemer, the Holy One of Israel:
"I am the LORD your God,
who teaches you what is best for you,
who directs you in the way you should go.
18 If only you had paid attention to my commands,
your peace would have been like a river,
your righteousness like the
waves of the sea.
19 Your descendants would have
been like the sand,
your children like its
numberless grains;
their name would never be cut off
nor destroyed from before
me."

20 Leave Babylon,
flee from the Babylonians!
Announce this with shouts of joy
and proclaim it.
Send it out to the ends of the earth;
say, "The LORD has redeemed his servant
Jacob."
21 They did not thirst when he led them through the deserts;
he made water flow for them from the rock;
he split the rock
and water gushed out.

22 "There is no peace," says the LORD, "for the wicked."

truth or dare

Do you often find your-
self wondering "if
only"? Paying attention
to God *today* means
skipping a load of re-
grets in the future.

48:18

The Servant of the LORD

49

Listen to me, you islands;
hear this, you distant nations:
Before I was born the LORD called me;
from my birth he has made mention of my name.
2 He made my mouth like a sharpened sword,
in the shadow of his hand he hid me;
he made me into a polished arrow
and concealed me in his quiver.
3 He said to me, "You are my servant,
Israel, in whom I will display my splendor."
4 But I said, "I have labored to no purpose;
I have spent my strength in vain and for nothing.
Yet what is due me is in the LORD's hand,
and my reward is with my God."

5 And now the LORD says—
he who formed me in the womb to be his servant
to bring Jacob back to him
and gather Israel to himself,

for I am honored in the eyes of the Lord
    and my God has been my strength—
⁶he says:
"It is too small a thing for you to
    be my servant
to restore the tribes of Jacob
    and bring back those of Israel
    I have kept.
I will also make you a light for the
    Gentiles,
that you may bring my
    salvation to the ends of
    the earth."

⁷This is what the Lord says—
    the Redeemer and Holy One of Israel—
to him who was despised and abhorred by
    the nation,
to the servant of rulers:
"Kings will see you and rise up,
    princes will see and bow down,
because of the Lord, who is faithful,
    the Holy One of Israel, who has chosen you."

Restoration of Israel

⁸This is what the Lord says:

"In the time of my favor I will answer you,
    and in the day of salvation I will help you;
I will keep you and will make you
    to be a covenant for the people,
to restore the land
    and to reassign its desolate inheritances,
⁹to say to the captives, 'Come out,'
    and to those in darkness, 'Be free!'

"They will feed beside the roads
    and find pasture on every barren hill.
¹⁰They will neither hunger nor thirst,
    nor will the desert heat or the sun beat upon them.
He who has compassion on them will guide them
    and lead them beside springs of water.
¹¹I will turn all my mountains into roads,
    and my highways will be raised up.
¹²See, they will come from afar—
    some from the north, some from the west,
    some from the region of Aswan.ᵃ"

¹³Shout for joy, O heavens;
    rejoice, O earth;
    burst into song, O mountains!
For the Lord comforts his people
    and will have compassion on his afflicted ones.

¹⁴But Zion said, "The Lord has forsaken me,
    the Lord has forgotten me."

truth or dare

Jesus is an equal opportunity Savior, bringing salvation both to the Jews, God's chosen people, and to the Gentiles (a.k.a. everyone else). Whatever your heritage, Jesus died for you.

49:6

ᵃ 12 Dead Sea Scrolls; Masoretic Text *Sinim*

¹⁵ "Can a mother forget the baby at her breast
and have no compassion on the child she has borne?
Though she may forget,
I will not forget you!

¹⁶ See, I have engraved you on the
palms of my hands;
your walls are ever before me.
¹⁷ Your sons hasten back,
and those who laid you waste
depart from you.
¹⁸ Lift up your eyes and look
around;
all your sons gather and come
to you.
As surely as I live," declares the
LORD,
"you will wear them all as
ornaments;
you will put them on, like a
bride.

¹⁹ "Though you were ruined and
made desolate
and your land laid waste,
now you will be too small for your
people,
and those who devoured you
will be far away.
²⁰ The children born during your
bereavement
will yet say in your hearing,
'This place is too small for us;
give us more space to live in.'

²¹ Then you will say in your heart,
'Who bore me these?
I was bereaved and barren;
I was exiled and rejected.
Who brought these up?
I was left all alone,
but these—where have they come from?' "

²² This is what the Sovereign LORD says:

"See, I will beckon to the Gentiles,
I will lift up my banner to the peoples;
they will bring your sons in their arms
and carry your daughters on their shoulders.
²³ Kings will be your foster fathers,
and their queens your nursing mothers.
They will bow down before you with their faces to the ground;
they will lick the dust at your feet.
Then you will know that I am the LORD;
those who hope in me will not be disappointed."

²⁴ Can plunder be taken from warriors,
or captives rescued from the fierce^a?

---

genuine

security » 49:15-16

Most girls grow up knowing that their moms love them deeply. Even if she doesn't always show it, well, your mom loves you—that's what moms are meant to do. And even if she gets caught up in her job or her own issues, she's still thinking about you—she never forgets you. And you want to know something cool? God loves you even more than your mom does! Even if your mom were to forget you—God never does. You can find security knowing he thinks of you constantly and loves you deeply.

---

^a 24 Dead Sea Scrolls, Vulgate and Syriac (see also Septuagint and verse 25); Masoretic Text *righteous*

²⁵But this is what the LORD says:

> "Yes, captives will be taken from warriors,
>> and plunder retrieved from the fierce;
> I will contend with those who contend with you,
>> and your children I will save.
> ²⁶I will make your oppressors eat their own flesh;
>> they will be drunk on their own blood, as with wine.
> Then all mankind will know
>> that I, the LORD, am your Savior,
>> your Redeemer, the Mighty One of Jacob."

Israel's Sin and the Servant's Obedience

50 This is what the LORD says:

> "Where is your mother's certificate of divorce
>> with which I sent her away?
> Or to which of my creditors
>> did I sell you?
> Because of your sins you were sold;
>> because of your transgressions your mother was sent away.
> ²When I came, why was there no one?
>> When I called, why was there no one to answer?
> Was my arm too short to ransom you?
>> Do I lack the strength to rescue you?
> By a mere rebuke I dry up the sea,
>> I turn rivers into a desert;
> their fish rot for lack of water
>> and die of thirst.
> ³I clothe the sky with darkness
>> and make sackcloth its covering."

> ⁴The Sovereign LORD has given me an instructed tongue,
>> to know the word that sustains the weary.
> He wakens me morning by morning,
>> wakens my ear to listen like one being taught.
> ⁵The Sovereign LORD has opened my ears,
>> and I have not been rebellious;
>> I have not drawn back.
> ⁶I offered my back to those who beat me,
>> my cheeks to those who pulled out my beard;
> I did not hide my face
>> from mocking and spitting.
> ⁷Because the Sovereign LORD helps me,
>> I will not be disgraced.
> Therefore have I set my face like flint,
>> and I know I will not be put to shame.
> ⁸He who vindicates me is near.
>> Who then will bring charges against me?
>> Let us face each other!
> Who is my accuser?
>> Let him confront me!
> ⁹It is the Sovereign LORD who helps me.
>> Who is he that will condemn me?
> They will all wear out like a garment;
>> the moths will eat them up.

[10] Who among you fears the LORD
and obeys the word of his servant?
Let him who walks in the dark,
who has no light,
trust in the name of the LORD
and rely on his God.
[11] But now, all you who light fires
and provide yourselves with
flaming torches,
go, walk in the light of your fires
and of the torches you have
set ablaze.
This is what you shall receive
from my hand:
You will lie down in torment.

Everlasting Salvation for Zion

51 "Listen to me, you who pursue
righteousness
and who seek the LORD:
Look to the rock from which you
were cut
and to the quarry from which
you were hewn;
[2] look to Abraham, your father,
and to Sarah, who gave you birth.
When I called him he was but
one,
and I blessed him and made
him many.

[3] The LORD will surely comfort Zion
and will look with compassion on all her ruins;
he will make her deserts like Eden,
her wastelands like the garden of the LORD.
Joy and gladness will be found in her,
thanksgiving and the sound of singing.

[4] "Listen to me, my people;
hear me, my nation:
The law will go out from me;
my justice will become a light to the nations.
[5] My righteousness draws near speedily,
my salvation is on the way,
and my arm will bring justice to the nations.
The islands will look to me
and wait in hope for my arm.
[6] Lift up your eyes to the heavens,
look at the earth beneath;
the heavens will vanish like smoke,
the earth will wear out like a garment
and its inhabitants die like flies.
But my salvation will last forever,
my righteousness will never fail.

[7] "Hear me, you who know what is right,
you people who have my law in your hearts:
Do not fear the reproach of men

---

genuine

faith »» 50:10-11

Do you ever feel like you're stumbling through life in the dark? Like you're trying to find your way and you can't see where to go? It's hard to figure out who you are and what you want out of life. It's tough to decide what's important to you and to sort through what you really believe. Don't try to find your way on your own, to provide *yourself* with light in the darkness—that will only cause you pain. Instead, trust in God to show you the way through life. Rely on him, and *he* will light up the darkness.

or be terrified by their insults.
⁸For the moth will eat them up like a garment;
the worm will devour them like wool.
But my righteousness will last forever,
my salvation through all generations."

⁹Awake, awake! Clothe yourself
with strength,
O arm of the LORD;
awake, as in days gone by,
as in generations of old.
Was it not you who cut Rahab to
pieces,
who pierced that monster
through?
¹⁰Was it not you who dried up the sea,
the waters of the great deep,
who made a road in the depths
of the sea
so that the redeemed might
cross over?
¹¹The ransomed of the LORD will return.
They will enter Zion with singing;
everlasting joy will crown their
heads.
Gladness and joy will overtake them,
and sorrow and sighing will
flee away.

¹²"I, even I, am he who comforts you.
Who are you that you fear
mortal men,
the sons of men, who are but
grass,
¹³that you forget the LORD your
Maker,

genuine obedience » 51:7-8

If you're a believer, then you have God's law in your heart—you know what's right and what's not. And God wants you to do the right thing without fear of being criticized by others or being scared of their insults. So, even if the people at school make fun of you for being a virgin or mock you for talking about Jesus or ridicule you for not going along with the crowd—don't give in! *You* keep doing the right thing, and know that God will deal with *them* in his own time.

who stretched out the heavens
and laid the foundations of the earth,
that you live in constant terror every day
because of the wrath of the oppressor,
who is bent on destruction?
For where is the wrath of the oppressor?
¹⁴ The cowering prisoners will soon be set free;
they will not die in their dungeon,
nor will they lack bread.
¹⁵For I am the LORD your God,
who churns up the sea so that its waves roar—
the LORD Almighty is his name.
¹⁶I have put my words in your mouth
and covered you with the shadow of my hand—
I who set the heavens in place,
who laid the foundations of the earth,
and who say to Zion, 'You are my people.' "

The Cup of the LORD's Wrath

¹⁷Awake, awake!
Rise up, O Jerusalem,

you who have drunk from the hand of the Lord
    the cup of his wrath,
you who have drained to its dregs
    the goblet that makes men stagger.
¹⁸Of all the sons she bore
    there was none to guide her;
of all the sons she reared
    there was none to take her by the hand.
¹⁹These double calamities have come upon you—
    who can comfort you?—
ruin and destruction, famine and sword—
    who can *a* console you?
²⁰Your sons have fainted;
    they lie at the head of every street,
    like antelope caught in a net.
They are filled with the wrath of the Lord
    and the rebuke of your God.
²¹Therefore hear this, you afflicted one,
    made drunk, but not with wine.
²²This is what your Sovereign Lord says,
    your God, who defends his people:
"See, I have taken out of your hand
    the cup that made you stagger;
from that cup, the goblet of my wrath,
    you will never drink again.
²³I will put it into the hands of your tormentors,
    who said to you,
    'Fall prostrate that we may walk over you.'
And you made your back like the ground,
    like a street to be walked over."

52

Awake, awake, O Zion,
    clothe yourself with strength.
Put on your garments of splendor,
    O Jerusalem, the holy city.
The uncircumcised and defiled
    will not enter you again.
²Shake off your dust;
    rise up, sit enthroned, O Jerusalem.
Free yourself from the chains on your neck,
    O captive Daughter of Zion.

³For this is what the Lord says:

"You were sold for nothing,
    and without money you will be redeemed."

⁴For this is what the Sovereign Lord says:

"At first my people went down to Egypt to live;
    lately, Assyria has oppressed them.

⁵"And now what do I have here?" declares the Lord.

"For my people have been taken away for nothing,
    and those who rule them mock, *b*"

                   declares the Lord.

a 19 Dead Sea Scrolls, Septuagint, Vulgate and Syriac; Masoretic Text *how can I*   *b 5* Dead Sea Scrolls and Vulgate;
Masoretic Text *wail*

"And all day long
my name is constantly blasphemed.
[6] Therefore my people will know my name;
therefore in that day they will know
that it is I who foretold it.
Yes, it is I."

[7] How beautiful on the mountains
are the feet of those who bring good news,
who proclaim peace,
who bring good tidings,
who proclaim salvation,

ǥenuine

evangelism »» 52:7

You want to have beautiful feet? Spiritually speaking, a pedicure just won't do it. Nope, the way to beautiful feet is through taking them to different places and sharing the good news about Jesus. Take them to your classes, to cheerleading practice, to work, to the mall, to the movies, to the coffee house, to your aunt's house, to your friend's house, to *your* house . . . Being able to share God's message of love and mercy to the lost is a beautiful thing. So get walking!

who say to Zion,
"Your God reigns!"
[8] Listen! Your watchmen lift up
their voices;
together they shout for joy.
When the Lord returns to Zion,
they will see it with their own
eyes.
[9] Burst into songs of joy together,
you ruins of Jerusalem,
for the Lord has comforted his people,
he has redeemed Jerusalem.
[10] The Lord will lay bare his holy arm
in the sight of all the nations,
and all the ends of the earth will
see
the salvation of our God.

[11] Depart, depart, go out from there!
Touch no unclean thing!
Come out from it and be pure,
you who carry the vessels of
the Lord.
[12] But you will not leave in haste
or go in flight;
for the Lord will go before you,
the God of Israel will be your
rear guard.

The Suffering and Glory of the Servant

[13] See, my servant will act wisely[a];
he will be raised and lifted up and highly exalted.
[14] Just as there were many who were appalled at him[b]—
his appearance was so disfigured beyond that of any man
and his form marred beyond human likeness—
[15] so will he sprinkle many nations,[c]
and kings will shut their mouths because of him.
For what they were not told, they will see,
and what they have not heard, they will understand.

53

Who has believed our message
and to whom has the arm of the Lord been revealed?
[2] He grew up before him like a tender shoot,
and like a root out of dry ground.

a 13 Or will prosper   *b 14 Hebrew you*   *c 15 Hebrew; Septuagint so will many nations marvel at him*

He had no beauty or majesty to attract us to him,
nothing in his appearance that we should desire him.

³ He was despised and rejected by
men,
a man of sorrows, and
familiar with suffering.
Like one from whom men hide
their faces
he was despised, and we
esteemed him not.

⁴ Surely he took up our infirmities
and carried our sorrows,
yet we considered him stricken
by God,
smitten by him, and afflicted.

⁵ But he was pierced for our
transgressions,
he was crushed for our
iniquities;
the punishment that brought us
peace was upon him,
and by his wounds we are
healed.

⁶ We all, like sheep, have gone astray,
each of us has turned to his
own way;
and the LORD has laid on him
the iniquity of us all.

⁷ He was oppressed and afflicted,
yet he did not open his mouth;

genuine

beauty » 53:2

How important is appearance to you? Come on—tell the truth. If we're honest, most of us will admit that we're drawn to good-looking people. A hot guy is going to get your attention a lot faster than someone you're not attracted to! This verse says that Jesus was not particularly attractive, that there was nothing in his appearance that was appealing. Maybe God made him that way so that no one would follow him just for his good looks. His followers were drawn to his heart. Would you have written Jesus off just because he wasn't handsome?

he was led like a lamb to the slaughter,
and as a sheep before her shearers is silent,
so he did not open his mouth.

⁸ By oppression ᵃ and judgment he was taken away.
And who can speak of his descendants?
For he was cut off from the land of the living;
for the transgression of my
people he was stricken. ᵇ

⁹ He was assigned a grave with the
wicked,
and with the rich in his death,
though he had done no violence,
nor was any deceit in his
mouth.

¹⁰ Yet it was the LORD's will to crush
him and cause him to
suffer,
and though the LORD makes ᶜ
his life a guilt offering,
he will see his offspring and prolong his days,
and the will of the LORD will prosper in his
hand.

truth or dare

This is one of clearest prophecies of Jesus in the Old Testament—a "must-read" that tells who Jesus was and what he did for us. Check it out!

53:4–12

ᵃ 8 Or From arrest   ᵇ 8 Or away. / Yet who of his generation considered / that he was cut off from the land of the living /
for the transgression of my people, / to whom the blow was due?   ᶜ 10 Hebrew though you make

[11] After the suffering of his soul,
    he will see the light ˌof lifeˌ*ᵃ* and be satisfied*ᵇ*;
by his knowledge*ᶜ* my righteous servant will justify many,
    and he will bear their iniquities.
[12] Therefore I will give him a portion among the great,*ᵈ*
    and he will divide the spoils with the strong,*ᵉ*
because he poured out his life unto death,
    and was numbered with the transgressors.
For he bore the sin of many,
    and made intercession for the transgressors.

The Future Glory of Zion

54

"Sing, O barren woman,
    you who never bore a child;
burst into song, shout for joy,
    you who were never in labor;
because more are the children of the desolate woman
    than of her who has a husband,"

                says the LORD.

[2] "Enlarge the place of your tent,
    stretch your tent curtains wide,
    do not hold back;
lengthen your cords,
    strengthen your stakes.
[3] For you will spread out to the right and to the left;
    your descendants will dispossess nations
    and settle in their desolate cities.

[4] "Do not be afraid; you will not suffer shame.
    Do not fear disgrace; you will not be humiliated.
You will forget the shame of your youth
    and remember no more the reproach of your widowhood.
[5] For your Maker is your husband—
    the LORD Almighty is his name—
the Holy One of Israel is your Redeemer;
    he is called the God of all the earth.
[6] The LORD will call you back
    as if you were a wife deserted and distressed in spirit—
a wife who married young,
    only to be rejected," says your God.
[7] "For a brief moment I abandoned you,
    but with deep compassion I will bring you back.
[8] In a surge of anger
    I hid my face from you for a moment,
but with everlasting kindness
    I will have compassion on you,"
    says the LORD your Redeemer.

[9] "To me this is like the days of Noah,
    when I swore that the waters of Noah would never again cover the
    earth.
So now I have sworn not to be angry with you,
    never to rebuke you again.

ᵃ 11 Dead Sea Scrolls (see also Septuagint); Masoretic Text does not have *the light ˌof lifeˌ*.   *ᵇ 11* Or (with Masoretic Text) *11He will see the result of the suffering of his soul / and be satisfied*   *ᶜ 11* Or *by knowledge of him*   *ᵈ 12* Or *many*   *ᵉ 12* Or *numerous*

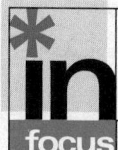

A Fond Farewell

focus Profile: Chenai

Lately I've been crying every night when I go to bed. I can't numb the pain with distractions and busyness; as soon as I lie still, I'm left alone with my thoughts. I'm so used to crying now that I just let the tears stream down my face and soak my pillowcase. Eventually I fall asleep. In the morning I have a few peaceful seconds before I remember the way things are, and then I have to face it all over again and try to make it through another day pretending everything is okay.

But nothing is okay. Last October Mom came home from a "routine doctor visit" and told us about the lump in her breast and the cancer that had spread to her lungs. Dad couldn't say anything, and my little brother Travis just stared at Mom. I hugged her and told her everything would be okay, even though I knew it wouldn't be.

Then came the chemotherapy. And the oxygen when she couldn't breathe well enough for herself. And the news that she only had two to three months to live. What a way to spend my sixteenth birthday—sitting by Mom's bed, looking at her skinny body and her weak smile, reading her favorite psalm.

I just can't keep going like this. It hurts too much—and besides, Travis and Dad need me to be strong. But those times at night, when I can't escape my thoughts any longer, I keep wondering why God allowed this if he truly had the power to heal her. Why did he let her suffer? And my tears are both sad and angry, till I finally fall asleep again.

For more ideas on how to deal with grief, check out the link on www.TrueImagesBible.com

grief in focus

The truth is, we know everyone will die someday (see Isaiah 57:1–2, pages 974-975, and Hebrews 9:27, page 1594). But when we face the death of someone we love, we're never ready for it. The shock and pain can leave us feeling overwhelmed and even angry. That's normal.

»*Face the pain and the truth.* It may be painful, but grieving for the person you lose is important. Don't be afraid to shed tears, and be honest about your emotions with God and others (see Matthew 5:4, page 1295).

»*Turn to God, not away from him.* He's strong enough to handle your questions, your grief, your anger. Ignoring him won't help, but unloading your burdens on him will.

»*Keep a journal.* This may sound like the last thing you want to do, but many people find it a helpful place to put their thoughts, feelings and pain.

For more on this topic, see the index on page 1656.

---

[10]Though the mountains be shaken
and the hills be removed,
yet my unfailing love for you will not be shaken
nor my covenant of peace be removed,"
says the LORD, who has compassion on you.

¹¹ "O afflicted city, lashed by storms and not comforted,
I will build you with stones of turquoise,^a
your foundations with sapphires.^b
¹² I will make your battlements of rubies,
your gates of sparkling jewels,
and all your walls of precious stones.
¹³ All your sons will be taught by the LORD,
and great will be your children's peace.
¹⁴ In righteousness you will be established:
Tyranny will be far from you;
you will have nothing to fear.
Terror will be far removed;
it will not come near you.
¹⁵ If anyone does attack you, it will not be my doing;
whoever attacks you will surrender to you.

¹⁶ "See, it is I who created the blacksmith
who fans the coals into flame
and forges a weapon fit for its work.
And it is I who have created the destroyer to work havoc;
¹⁷ no weapon forged against you will prevail,
and you will refute every tongue that accuses you.
This is the heritage of the servants of the LORD,
and this is their vindication from me,"

declares the LORD.

Invitation to the Thirsty

55 "Come, all you who are thirsty,
come to the waters;
and you who have no money,
come, buy and eat!
Come, buy wine and milk
without money and without
cost.
² Why spend money on what is not
bread,
and your labor on what does
not satisfy?
Listen, listen to me, and eat what
is good,
and your soul will delight in
the richest of fare.
³ Give ear and come to me;
hear me, that your soul may
live.
I will make an everlasting
covenant with you,
my faithful love promised to
David.
⁴ See, I have made him a witness
to the peoples,
a leader and commander of
the peoples.
⁵ Surely you will summon nations
you know not,

genuine

contentment » 55:1-2

Imagine being able to eat all the lobster and steak, Godiva chocolates, imported truffles and sparkling water you want—without it costing you a cent! Would you still go out and spend your own money on Ramen noodles and TV dinners? No way! Well, God offers you the richest of food and drink for your soul—he freely offers you a relationship with him through Jesus. No matter how hard you try, *you* won't be able to satisfy your soul. Accept what God offers, and you'll find that your "soul will delight in the richest of fare."

^a 11 The meaning of the Hebrew for this word is uncertain.   ^b 11 Or *lapis lazuli*

and nations that do not know you will hasten to you,
because of the LORD your God,
    the Holy One of Israel,
    for he has endowed you with splendor."

6 Seek the LORD while he may be found;
    call on him while he is near.
7 Let the wicked forsake his way
    and the evil man his thoughts.
Let him turn to the LORD, and he will have mercy on him,
    and to our God, for he will freely pardon.

8 "For my thoughts are not your thoughts,
    neither are your ways my ways,"
                declares the LORD.
9 "As the heavens are higher than the earth,
    so are my ways higher than your ways
    and my thoughts than your thoughts.
10 As the rain and the snow
    come down from heaven,
and do not return to it
    without watering the earth
and making it bud and flourish,
    so that it yields seed for the sower and bread for the eater,
11 so is my word that goes out from my mouth:
    It will not return to me empty,
but will accomplish what I desire
    and achieve the purpose for which I sent it.
12 You will go out in joy
    and be led forth in peace;
the mountains and hills
    will burst into song before you,
and all the trees of the field
    will clap their hands.
13 Instead of the thornbush will grow the pine tree,
    and instead of briers the myrtle will grow.
This will be for the LORD's renown,
    for an everlasting sign,
    which will not be destroyed."

Salvation for Others

56

This is what the LORD says:

"Maintain justice
    and do what is right,
for my salvation is close at hand
    and my righteousness will soon be revealed.
2 Blessed is the man who does this,
    the man who holds it fast,
who keeps the Sabbath without desecrating it,
    and keeps his hand from doing any evil."

3 Let no foreigner who has bound himself to the LORD say,
    "The LORD will surely exclude me from his people."
And let not any eunuch complain,
    "I am only a dry tree."

4For this is what the LORD says:

"To the eunuchs who keep my Sabbaths,
who choose what pleases me
and hold fast to my covenant—
5to them I will give within my temple and its walls
a memorial and a name
better than sons and daughters;
I will give them an everlasting name
that will not be cut off.
6And foreigners who bind themselves to the LORD
to serve him,
to love the name of the LORD,
and to worship him,
all who keep the Sabbath without desecrating it
and who hold fast to my covenant—
7these I will bring to my holy mountain
and give them joy in my house of prayer.
Their burnt offerings and sacrifices
will be accepted on my altar;
for my house will be called
a house of prayer for all nations."
8The Sovereign LORD declares—
he who gathers the exiles of Israel:
"I will gather still others to them
besides those already gathered."

God's Accusation Against the Wicked

9Come, all you beasts of the field,
come and devour, all you beasts of the forest!
10Israel's watchmen are blind,
they all lack knowledge;
they are all mute dogs,
they cannot bark;
they lie around and dream,
they love to sleep.
11They are dogs with mighty
appetites;
they never have enough.
They are shepherds who lack
understanding;
they all turn to their own way,
each seeks his own gain.
12"Come," each one cries, "let me
get wine!
Let us drink our fill of beer!
And tomorrow will be like today,
or even far better."

57

The righteous perish,
and no one ponders it in his heart;
devout men are taken away,
and no one understands
that the righteous are taken away
to be spared from evil.
2Those who walk uprightly

truth or dare

Most of us are afraid of death. It's scary and unknown. Yet when we're God's children, death takes on a whole different meaning.

57:1–2

enter into peace;
they find rest as they lie in death.

[3] "But you—come here, you sons of a sorceress,
you offspring of adulterers and prostitutes!
[4] Whom are you mocking?
At whom do you sneer
and stick out your tongue?
Are you not a brood of rebels,
the offspring of liars?
[5] You burn with lust among the oaks
and under every spreading tree;
you sacrifice your children in the ravines
and under the overhanging crags.
[6] ⌞The idols⌟ among the smooth stones of the ravines are your portion;
they, they are your lot.
Yes, to them you have poured out drink offerings
and offered grain offerings.
In the light of these things, should I relent?
[7] You have made your bed on a high and lofty hill;
there you went up to offer your sacrifices.
[8] Behind your doors and your doorposts
you have put your pagan symbols.
Forsaking me, you uncovered your bed,
you climbed into it and opened it wide;
you made a pact with those whose beds you love,
and you looked on their nakedness.
[9] You went to Molech[a] with olive oil
and increased your perfumes.
You sent your ambassadors[b] far away;
you descended to the grave[c] itself!
[10] You were wearied by all your ways,
but you would not say, 'It is hopeless.'
You found renewal of your strength,
and so you did not faint.

[11] "Whom have you so dreaded and feared
that you have been false to me,
and have neither remembered me
nor pondered this in your hearts?
Is it not because I have long been silent
that you do not fear me?
[12] I will expose your righteousness and your works,
and they will not benefit you.
[13] When you cry out for help,
let your collection ⌞of idols⌟ save you!
The wind will carry all of them off,
a mere breath will blow them away.
But the man who makes me his refuge
will inherit the land
and possess my holy mountain."

Comfort for the Contrite

[14] And it will be said:

"Build up, build up, prepare the road!
Remove the obstacles out of the way of my people."

[a] 9 Or *to the king*   [b] 9 Or *idols*   [c] 9 Hebrew *Sheol*

¹⁵ For this is what the high and lofty One says—
  he who lives forever, whose name is holy:
"I live in a high and holy place,

but also with him who is contrite
    and lowly in spirit,
to revive the spirit of the lowly
  and to revive the heart of the
    contrite.
¹⁶ I will not accuse forever,
  nor will I always be angry,
for then the spirit of man would
    grow faint before me—
  the breath of man that I have
    created.
¹⁷ I was enraged by his sinful greed;
  I punished him, and hid my
    face in anger,
  yet he kept on in his willful ways.
¹⁸ I have seen his ways, but I will
    heal him;
  I will guide him and restore
    comfort to him,
¹⁹ creating praise on the lips of
    the mourners in Israel.
Peace, peace, to those far and
    near,"
  says the LORD. "And I will heal
    them."
²⁰ But the wicked are like the
    tossing sea,
  which cannot rest,
  whose waves cast up mire
    and mud.

²¹ "There is no peace," says my God, "for the wicked."

genuine

humility » 57:15

Most women want to be considered anything but common. Or ordinary. Or simple. We want others to see us as complex, sophisticated and extraordinary. But God values the ordinary, simple, modest heart. He has a special relationship with those who are humble before him. Amazingly, the high and lofty God chooses to walk with, love and encourage his people—who are lowly and humble before him.

True Fasting

58

"Shout it aloud, do not hold back.
  Raise your voice like a trumpet.
Declare to my people their rebellion
  and to the house of Jacob their sins.
² For day after day they seek me out;
  they seem eager to know my ways,
as if they were a nation that does what is right
  and has not forsaken the commands of its God.
They ask me for just decisions
  and seem eager for God to come near them.
³ 'Why have we fasted,' they say,
  'and you have not seen it?
Why have we humbled ourselves,
  and you have not noticed?'

"Yet on the day of your fasting, you do as you please
  and exploit all your workers.
⁴ Your fasting ends in quarreling and strife,
  and in striking each other with wicked fists.
You cannot fast as you do today

and expect your voice to be heard on high.
⁵ Is this the kind of fast I have chosen,
    only a day for a man to humble himself?
Is it only for bowing one's head like a reed
    and for lying on sackcloth and ashes?
Is that what you call a fast,
    a day acceptable to the Lord?

⁶ "Is not this the kind of fasting I have chosen:
to loose the chains of injustice
    and untie the cords of the yoke,
to set the oppressed free
    and break every yoke?
⁷ Is it not to share your food with the hungry
    and to provide the poor wanderer with shelter—
when you see the naked, to clothe him,
    and not to turn away from your own flesh and blood?
⁸ Then your light will break forth like the dawn,
    and your healing will quickly appear;
then your righteousness ᵃ will go before you,
    and the glory of the Lord will be your rear guard.
⁹ Then you will call, and the Lord will answer;
    you will cry for help, and he will say: Here am I.

"If you do away with the yoke of oppression,
    with the pointing finger and malicious talk,
¹⁰ and if you spend yourselves in behalf of the hungry
    and satisfy the needs of the oppressed,
then your light will rise in the darkness,
    and your night will become like the noonday.
¹¹ The Lord will guide you always;
    he will satisfy your needs in a sun-scorched land
    and will strengthen your frame.
You will be like a well-watered garden,
    like a spring whose waters never fail.
¹² Your people will rebuild the
        ancient ruins
    and will raise up the age-old
        foundations;
you will be called Repairer of
        Broken Walls,
        Restorer of Streets with
        Dwellings.

¹³ "If you keep your feet from
        breaking the Sabbath
    and from doing as you please
        on my holy day,
if you call the Sabbath a delight
    and the Lord's holy day honorable,
and if you honor it by not going your own way
    and not doing as you please or speaking idle words,
¹⁴ then you will find your joy in the Lord,
    and I will cause you to ride on the heights of the land
    and to feast on the inheritance of your father Jacob."
        The mouth of the Lord has spoken.

truth or dare

Think you've got it all figured out? How satisfied are you so far doing things in life *your* way? Dare you to follow a better guide!

58:11

ᵃ 8 Or *your righteous One*

59

Surely the arm of the LORD is not too short to save,
nor his ear too dull to hear.
² But your iniquities have separated
you from your God;
your sins have hidden his face from you,
so that he will not hear.
³ For your hands are stained with blood,
your fingers with guilt.
Your lips have spoken lies,
and your tongue mutters wicked things.
⁴ No one calls for justice;
no one pleads his case with integrity.
They rely on empty arguments and speak lies;
they conceive trouble and give birth to evil.
⁵ They hatch the eggs of vipers
and spin a spider's web.
Whoever eats their eggs will die,
and when one is broken, an adder is hatched.
⁶ Their cobwebs are useless for clothing;
they cannot cover themselves with what they make.
Their deeds are evil deeds,
and acts of violence are in their hands.
⁷ Their feet rush into sin;
they are swift to shed innocent blood.
Their thoughts are evil thoughts;
ruin and destruction mark their ways.
⁸ The way of peace they do not know;
there is no justice in their paths.
They have turned them into crooked roads;
no one who walks in them will know peace.

⁹ So justice is far from us,
and righteousness does not reach us.
We look for light, but all is darkness;
for brightness, but we walk in deep shadows.
¹⁰ Like the blind we grope along the wall,
feeling our way like men without eyes.
At midday we stumble as if it were twilight;
among the strong, we are like the dead.
¹¹ We all growl like bears;
we moan mournfully like doves.
We look for justice, but find none;
for deliverance, but it is far away.

¹² For our offenses are many in your sight,
and our sins testify against us.
Our offenses are ever with us,
and we acknowledge our iniquities:
¹³ rebellion and treachery against the LORD,
turning our backs on our God,
fomenting oppression and revolt,
uttering lies our hearts have conceived.
¹⁴ So justice is driven back,
and righteousness stands at a distance;
truth has stumbled in the streets,

honesty cannot enter.
¹⁵ Truth is nowhere to be found,
and whoever shuns evil becomes a prey.

The LORD looked and was displeased
that there was no justice.
¹⁶ He saw that there was no one,
he was appalled that there was no one to intervene;
so his own arm worked salvation for him,
and his own righteousness sustained him.
¹⁷ He put on righteousness as his breastplate,
and the helmet of salvation on his head;
he put on the garments of vengeance
and wrapped himself in zeal as in a cloak.
¹⁸ According to what they have done,
so will he repay
wrath to his enemies
and retribution to his foes;
he will repay the islands their due.
¹⁹ From the west, men will fear the name of the LORD,
and from the rising of the sun, they will revere his glory.
For he will come like a pent-up flood
that the breath of the LORD drives along. ^a

²⁰ "The Redeemer will come to Zion,
to those in Jacob who repent of their sins,"

declares the LORD.

²¹ "As for me, this is my covenant with them," says the LORD. "My Spirit, who is on you, and my words that I have put in your mouth will not depart from your mouth, or from the mouths of your children, or from the mouths of their descendants from this time on and forever," says the LORD.

The Glory of Zion

60

"Arise, shine, for your light has come,
and the glory of the LORD rises upon you.
² See, darkness covers the earth
and thick darkness is over the peoples,
but the LORD rises upon you
and his glory appears over you.
³ Nations will come to your light,
and kings to the brightness of your dawn.

⁴ "Lift up your eyes and look about you:
All assemble and come to you;
your sons come from afar,
and your daughters are carried on the arm.
⁵ Then you will look and be radiant,
your heart will throb and swell with joy;
the wealth on the seas will be brought to you,
to you the riches of the nations will come.
⁶ Herds of camels will cover your land,
young camels of Midian and Ephah.
And all from Sheba will come,
bearing gold and incense
and proclaiming the praise of the LORD.
⁷ All Kedar's flocks will be gathered to you,

^a 19 Or *When the enemy comes in like a flood, / the Spirit of the LORD will put him to flight*

the rams of Nebaioth will serve you;
they will be accepted as offerings on my altar,
and I will adorn my glorious temple.

8 "Who are these that fly along like clouds,
like doves to their nests?
9 Surely the islands look to me;
in the lead are the ships of Tarshish,[a]
bringing your sons from afar,
with their silver and gold,
to the honor of the LORD your God,
the Holy One of Israel,
for he has endowed you with splendor.

10 "Foreigners will rebuild your walls,
and their kings will serve you.
Though in anger I struck you,
in favor I will show you compassion.
11 Your gates will always stand open,
they will never be shut, day or night,
so that men may bring you the wealth of the nations—
their kings led in triumphal procession.
12 For the nation or kingdom that will not serve you will perish;
it will be utterly ruined.

13 "The glory of Lebanon will come to you,
the pine, the fir and the cypress together,
to adorn the place of my sanctuary;
and I will glorify the place of my feet.
14 The sons of your oppressors will come bowing before you;
all who despise you will bow down at your feet
and will call you the City of the LORD,
Zion of the Holy One of Israel.

15 "Although you have been forsaken and hated,
with no one traveling through,
I will make you the everlasting pride
and the joy of all generations.
16 You will drink the milk of nations
and be nursed at royal breasts.
Then you will know that I, the LORD, am your Savior,
your Redeemer, the Mighty One of Jacob.
17 Instead of bronze I will bring you gold,
and silver in place of iron.
Instead of wood I will bring you bronze,
and iron in place of stones.
I will make peace your governor
and righteousness your ruler.
18 No longer will violence be heard in your land,
nor ruin or destruction within your borders,
but you will call your walls Salvation
and your gates Praise.
19 The sun will no more be your light by day,
nor will the brightness of the moon shine on you,
for the LORD will be your everlasting light,
and your God will be your glory.

a 9 Or the trading ships

²⁰Your sun will never set again,
    and your moon will wane no more;
the LORD will be your everlasting light,
    and your days of sorrow will end.
²¹Then will all your people be righteous
    and they will possess the land forever.
They are the shoot I have planted,
    the work of my hands,
    for the display of my splendor.
²²The least of you will become a thousand,
    the smallest a mighty nation.
I am the LORD;
    in its time I will do this swiftly."

The Year of the LORD's Favor

61

The Spirit of the Sovereign LORD is on me,
    because the LORD has anointed me
    to preach good news to the poor.
He has sent me to bind up the brokenhearted,
    to proclaim freedom for the captives
    and release from darkness for the prisoners, ᵃ
²to proclaim the year of the LORD's favor
    and the day of vengeance of our God,
to comfort all who mourn,
³   and provide for those who grieve in Zion—
to bestow on them a crown of beauty
    instead of ashes,
the oil of gladness
    instead of mourning,
and a garment of praise
    instead of a spirit of despair.
They will be called oaks of righteousness,
    a planting of the LORD
    for the display of his splendor.

⁴They will rebuild the ancient ruins
    and restore the places long devastated;
they will renew the ruined cities
    that have been devastated for generations.
⁵Aliens will shepherd your flocks;
    foreigners will work your fields and vineyards.
⁶And you will be called priests of the LORD,
    you will be named ministers of our God.
You will feed on the wealth of nations,
    and in their riches you will boast.

⁷Instead of their shame
    my people will receive a double portion,
and instead of disgrace
    they will rejoice in their inheritance;
and so they will inherit a double portion in their land,
    and everlasting joy will be theirs.

⁸"For I, the LORD, love justice;
    I hate robbery and iniquity.
In my faithfulness I will reward them

ᵃ 1 Hebrew; Septuagint the blind

and make an everlasting covenant with them.
⁹Their descendants will be known among the nations
  and their offspring among the peoples.
All who see them will acknowledge
  that they are a people the LORD has blessed."

¹⁰I delight greatly in the LORD;
  my soul rejoices in my God.
For he has clothed me with garments of salvation
  and arrayed me in a robe of righteousness,
as a bridegroom adorns his head like a priest,
  and as a bride adorns herself with her jewels.
¹¹For as the soil makes the sprout come up
  and a garden causes seeds to grow,
so the Sovereign LORD will make righteousness and praise
  spring up before all nations.

Zion's New Name

62

For Zion's sake I will not keep silent,
  for Jerusalem's sake I will not remain quiet,
till her righteousness shines out like the dawn,
  her salvation like a blazing torch.

²The nations will see your
    righteousness,
  and all kings your glory;
you will be called by a new name
  that the mouth of the LORD will
    bestow.
³You will be a crown of splendor
    in the LORD's hand,
  a royal diadem in the hand of
    your God.
⁴No longer will they call you
    Deserted,
  or name your land Desolate.
But you will be called
    Hephzibah,ᵃ
  and your land Beulahᵇ;
for the LORD will take delight in you,
  and your land will be married.
⁵As a young man marries a
    maiden,
  so will your sonsᶜ marry you;
as a bridegroom rejoices over his
    bride,
  so will your God rejoice over you.

⁶I have posted watchmen on your
    walls, O Jerusalem;
  they will never be silent day or
    night.

ġenuine righteousness » 61:10

What's your favorite "feel-good" outfit? You know, the one you wear when you want to impress a guy or have to do a presentation in class. Sometimes, wearing the right outfit just makes all the difference, doesn't it? Well, if you're a believer, then you should know you have a fantastic wardrobe from God. You have been clothed with "garments of salvation" and dressed in a "robe of righteousness." When God looks at you, he doesn't see your sin, your failure, your weaknesses. He sees the perfect righteousness of Jesus.

You who call on the LORD,
  give yourselves no rest,
⁷and give him no rest till he establishes Jerusalem
  and makes her the praise of the earth.

ᵃ 4 *Hephzibah* means *my delight is in her.*   ᵇ 4 *Beulah* means *married.*   ᶜ 5 Or *Builder*

⁸The LORD has sworn by his right hand
    and by his mighty arm:
"Never again will I give your grain
    as food for your enemies,
and never again will foreigners drink the new wine
    for which you have toiled;
⁹but those who harvest it will eat it
    and praise the LORD,
and those who gather the grapes will drink it
    in the courts of my sanctuary."

¹⁰Pass through, pass through the gates!
    Prepare the way for the people.
Build up, build up the highway!
    Remove the stones.
Raise a banner for the nations.

¹¹The LORD has made proclamation
    to the ends of the earth:
"Say to the Daughter of Zion,
    'See, your Savior comes!
See, his reward is with him,
    and his recompense accompanies him.' "
¹²They will be called the Holy People,
    the Redeemed of the LORD;
and you will be called Sought After,
    the City No Longer Deserted.

God's Day of Vengeance and Redemption

63
Who is this coming from Edom,
    from Bozrah, with his garments stained crimson?
Who is this, robed in splendor,
    striding forward in the greatness of his strength?

"It is I, speaking in righteousness,
    mighty to save."

²Why are your garments red,
    like those of one treading the winepress?

³"I have trodden the winepress alone;
    from the nations no one was with me.
I trampled them in my anger
    and trod them down in my wrath;
their blood spattered my garments,
    and I stained all my clothing.
⁴For the day of vengeance was in my heart,
    and the year of my redemption has come.
⁵I looked, but there was no one to help,
    I was appalled that no one gave support;
so my own arm worked salvation for me,
    and my own wrath sustained me.
⁶I trampled the nations in my anger;
    in my wrath I made them drunk
    and poured their blood on the ground."

Praise and Prayer

⁷I will tell of the kindnesses of the LORD,
    the deeds for which he is to be praised,

mirror images

But Ruth replied, "Don't urge me to leave you or to turn back from you. Where you go I will go, and where you stay I will stay. Your people will be my people and your God my God." Ruth 1:16

Naomi—Going Public

She probably didn't feel very godly at the time. To tell the truth, Naomi probably wondered what trusting God had done for her anyway. She had lost her husband. She had lost her sons. She was living in a foreign land with no means of financial support. She figured God had forgotten all about her—except to send heartache her way. She even told others that God had made her life "bitter" (see Ruth 1:20).

Sure, Naomi knew that she and her daughter-in-law Ruth had a close relationship. However, she probably thought that Ruth was disappointed with her faltering faith in God. Naomi didn't realize she was making an incredible spiritual impact on Ruth simply by being real. In reality, Ruth wanted what she saw in Naomi and willingly committed herself to Naomi's God (see Ruth 1:16).

Although Naomi wasn't a perfect witness (who is?), she showed what it meant to have faith during the tough times, when it really counts. Even when she went through heartache and her hope faltered, she kept her faith. Others, including Ruth, could tell her relationship with God was real—sustaining her through one crisis after another.

Are you ready to "go public" with your faith like Naomi did? Going public means you're not putting on a show, trying to be the "perfect Christian." It means you're willing to publicly live out your relationship with Christ, come what may. You don't have to have it all together spiritually to be a good witness. Like Naomi, you never know how choosing to hang onto your faith during heartache will affect others. Are you going through a challenging time? "Plastic" Christians who fake their way through life don't often touch others' lives. If you want to start making an impact for Christ among your friends, start by getting real.

Dear Jesus, I want to be a real witness for you—not a fake Christian who follows you in the good times only. Remind me that others are watching the difference you make in my life, especially during the hard times. Amen.

To read the next Mirror Images profile, go to page 1021.

Read more about Naomi in the book of Ruth (pages 314–319).

984

according to all the LORD has done for us—
yes, the many good things he has done
for the house of Israel,
according to his compassion and many kindnesses.
[8] He said, "Surely they are my people,
sons who will not be false to me";
and so he became their Savior.
[9] In all their distress he too was distressed,
and the angel of his presence saved them.
In his love and mercy he redeemed them;
he lifted them up and carried them
all the days of old.
[10] Yet they rebelled
and grieved his Holy Spirit.
So he turned and became their enemy
and he himself fought against them.

[11] Then his people recalled[a] the days of old,
the days of Moses and his people—
where is he who brought them through the sea,
with the shepherd of his flock?
Where is he who set
his Holy Spirit among them,
[12] who sent his glorious arm of power
to be at Moses' right hand,
who divided the waters before them,
to gain for himself everlasting renown,
[13] who led them through the depths?
Like a horse in open country,
they did not stumble;
[14] like cattle that go down to the plain,
they were given rest by the Spirit of the LORD.
This is how you guided your people
to make for yourself a glorious name.

[15] Look down from heaven and see
from your lofty throne, holy and glorious.
Where are your zeal and your might?
Your tenderness and compassion are withheld from us.
[16] But you are our Father,
though Abraham does not know us
or Israel acknowledge us;
you, O LORD, are our Father,
our Redeemer from of old is your name.
[17] Why, O LORD, do you make us wander from your ways
and harden our hearts so we do not revere you?
Return for the sake of your servants,
the tribes that are your inheritance.
[18] For a little while your people possessed your holy place,
but now our enemies have trampled down your sanctuary.
[19] We are yours from of old;
but you have not ruled over them,
they have not been called by your name.[b]

[a] 11 Or But may he recall   [b] 19 Or We are like those you have never ruled, / like those never called by your name

Oh, that you would rend the heavens and come down,
that the mountains would tremble before you!
²As when fire sets twigs ablaze
and causes water to boil,
come down to make your name known to your enemies
and cause the nations to quake before you!
³For when you did awesome things that we did not expect,
you came down, and the mountains trembled before you.
⁴Since ancient times no one has
heard,
no ear has perceived,
no eye has seen any God besides you,
who acts on behalf of those
who wait for him.
⁵You come to the help of those
who gladly do right,
who remember your ways.
But when we continued to sin
against them,
you were angry.
How then can we be saved?
⁶All of us have become like one
who is unclean,
and all our righteous acts are
like filthy rags;
we all shrivel up like a leaf,
and like the wind our sins
sweep us away.
⁷No one calls on your name
or strives to lay hold of you;
for you have hidden your face
from us
and made us waste away
because of our sins.

⁸Yet, O LORD, you are our Father.
We are the clay, you are the
potter;

we are all the work of your
hand.
⁹Do not be angry beyond measure,
O LORD;
do not remember our sins
forever.
Oh, look upon us, we pray,
for we are all your people.
¹⁰Your sacred cities have become a
desert;
even Zion is a desert,
Jerusalem a desolation.
¹¹Our holy and glorious temple, where our
fathers praised you,
has been burned with fire,
and all that we treasured lies in ruins.
¹²After all this, O LORD, will you hold yourself back?
Will you keep silent and punish us beyond measure?

genuine

purity »
64:6

No matter how good you think you are—you're not. Not exactly what anybody wants to hear, is it? God says that even the *good* things you do are like filthy rags. And we're not talking any old dirty rags here—these were the rags used by women on their periods. Yuck! As sinners, no matter how hard we try, we aren't clean before God. But God washes our hearts clean through Jesus. You can't be made pure through your own efforts, but you can be through his. Which is great to hear, isn't it?!

truth or dare

Nothing about you is an accident—you were made by the very talented Potter. How willing are you to let him continue to mold your life?

64:8

Judgment and Salvation

65

"I revealed myself to those who did not ask for me;
 I was found by those who did not seek me.
To a nation that did not call on my name,
 I said, 'Here am I, here am I.'
[2] All day long I have held out my hands
 to an obstinate people,
who walk in ways not good,
 pursuing their own imaginations—
[3] a people who continually provoke me
 to my very face,
offering sacrifices in gardens
 and burning incense on altars of brick;
[4] who sit among the graves
 and spend their nights keeping secret vigil;
who eat the flesh of pigs,
 and whose pots hold broth of unclean meat;
[5] who say, 'Keep away; don't come near me,
 for I am too sacred for you!'
Such people are smoke in my nostrils,
 a fire that keeps burning all day.

[6] "See, it stands written before me:
 I will not keep silent but will pay back in full;
 I will pay it back into their laps—
[7] both your sins and the sins of your fathers,"
 says the LORD.
"Because they burned sacrifices on the mountains
 and defied me on the hills,
I will measure into their laps
 the full payment for their former deeds."

[8] This is what the LORD says:

"As when juice is still found in a cluster of grapes
 and men say, 'Don't destroy it,
 there is yet some good in it,'
so will I do in behalf of my servants;
 I will not destroy them all.
[9] I will bring forth descendants from Jacob,
 and from Judah those who will possess my mountains;
my chosen people will inherit them,
 and there will my servants live.
[10] Sharon will become a pasture for flocks,
 and the Valley of Achor a resting place for herds,
 for my people who seek me.

[11] "But as for you who forsake the LORD
 and forget my holy mountain,
who spread a table for Fortune
 and fill bowls of mixed wine for Destiny,
[12] I will destine you for the sword,
 and you will all bend down for the slaughter;
for I called but you did not answer,
 I spoke but you did not listen.
You did evil in my sight
 and chose what displeases me."

¹³Therefore this is what the Sovereign Lᴏʀᴅ says:

"My servants will eat,
  but you will go hungry;
my servants will drink,
  but you will go thirsty;
my servants will rejoice,
  but you will be put to shame.
¹⁴My servants will sing
  out of the joy of their hearts,
but you will cry out
  from anguish of heart
  and wail in brokenness of spirit.

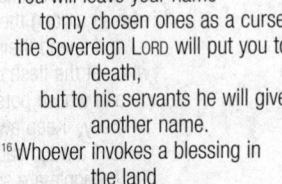

love notes

65:17–25

My daughter,

At times this world may seem like a violent, unlovely place to live. Don't be discouraged. One day I will prepare a new earth and a new heaven where you will live with me in peace and safety forever.

—Your Father

Underline the words in this passage that give you the most comfort. Thank God for the future he's promised you.

¹⁵You will leave your name
    to my chosen ones as a curse;
  the Sovereign Lᴏʀᴅ will put you to
    death,
  but to his servants he will give
    another name.
¹⁶Whoever invokes a blessing in
    the land
  will do so by the God of truth;
he who takes an oath in the land
  will swear by the God of truth.
For the past troubles will be
    forgotten
  and hidden from my eyes.

New Heavens and a New Earth

¹⁷"Behold, I will create
    new heavens and a new
    earth.
The former things will not be
    remembered,
  nor will they come to mind.
¹⁸But be glad and rejoice forever
    in what I will create,
for I will create Jerusalem to be a
    delight
  and its people a joy.
¹⁹I will rejoice over Jerusalem
    and take delight in my people;
the sound of weeping and of
    crying
  will be heard in it no more.

²⁰"Never again will there be in it
    an infant who lives but a few
    days,
  or an old man who does not
    live out his years;
he who dies at a hundred
  will be thought a mere youth;
he who fails to reach ᵃ a hundred
  will be considered accursed.

ᵃ 20 Or I the sinner who reaches

²¹ They will build houses and dwell in them;
　　they will plant vineyards and eat their fruit.
²² No longer will they build houses and others live in them,
　　or plant and others eat.
For as the days of a tree,
　　so will be the days of my people;
my chosen ones will long enjoy
　　the works of their hands.
²³ They will not toil in vain
　　or bear children doomed to misfortune;
for they will be a people blessed by the LORD,
　　they and their descendants with them.
²⁴ Before they call I will answer;
　　while they are still speaking I will hear.
²⁵ The wolf and the lamb will feed together,
　　and the lion will eat straw like the ox,
　　but dust will be the serpent's food.
They will neither harm nor destroy
　　on all my holy mountain,"

　　　　　　　　　　　　　　　　　　　　　　says the LORD.

Judgment and Hope

66 This is what the LORD says:

"Heaven is my throne,
　　and the earth is my footstool.
Where is the house you will build for me?
　　Where will my resting place be?
² Has not my hand made all these things,
　　and so they came into being?"

　　　　　　　　　　　　　　　　　　　　　　declares the LORD.

"This is the one I esteem:
　　he who is humble and contrite in spirit,
　　and trembles at my word.
³ But whoever sacrifices a bull
　　is like one who kills a man,
and whoever offers a lamb,
　　like one who breaks a dog's neck;
whoever makes a grain offering
　　is like one who presents pig's blood,
and whoever burns memorial incense,
　　like one who worships an idol.
They have chosen their own ways,
　　and their souls delight in their abominations;
⁴ so I also will choose harsh treatment for them
　　and will bring upon them what they dread.
For when I called, no one answered,
　　when I spoke, no one listened.
They did evil in my sight
　　and chose what displeases me."

⁵ Hear the word of the LORD,
　　you who tremble at his word:
"Your brothers who hate you,
　　and exclude you because of my name, have said,
'Let the LORD be glorified,

that we may see your joy!'
Yet they will be put to shame.
⁶ Hear that uproar from the city,
hear that noise from the temple!
It is the sound of the LORD
repaying his enemies all they deserve.

⁷ "Before she goes into labor,
she gives birth;
before the pains come upon her,
she delivers a son.
⁸ Who has ever heard of such a thing?
Who has ever seen such things?
Can a country be born in a day
or a nation be brought forth in a moment?
Yet no sooner is Zion in labor
than she gives birth to her children.
⁹ Do I bring to the moment of birth
and not give delivery?" says the LORD.
"Do I close up the womb
when I bring to delivery?" says your God.
¹⁰ "Rejoice with Jerusalem and be glad for her,
all you who love her;
rejoice greatly with her,
all you who mourn over her.
¹¹ For you will nurse and be satisfied
at her comforting breasts;
you will drink deeply
and delight in her overflowing abundance."

¹² For this is what the LORD says:

"I will extend peace to her like a river,
and the wealth of nations like a flooding stream;
you will nurse and be carried on her arm
and dandled on her knees.
¹³ As a mother comforts her child,
so will I comfort you;
and you will be comforted over Jerusalem."

¹⁴ When you see this, your heart will rejoice
and you will flourish like grass;
the hand of the LORD will be made known to his servants,
but his fury will be shown to his foes.
¹⁵ See, the LORD is coming with fire,
and his chariots are like a whirlwind;
he will bring down his anger with fury,
and his rebuke with flames of fire.
¹⁶ For with fire and with his sword
the LORD will execute judgment upon all men,
and many will be those slain by the LORD.

¹⁷ "Those who consecrate and purify themselves to go into the gardens, following the one in the midst of ᵃ those who eat the flesh of pigs and rats and other abominable things—they will meet their end together," declares the LORD.

¹⁸ "And I, because of their actions and their imaginations, am about to come ᵇ and gather all nations and tongues, and they will come and see my glory.

ᵃ 17 Or *gardens behind one of your temples, and*   ᵇ 18 The meaning of the Hebrew for this clause is uncertain.

[19]"I will set a sign among them, and I will send some of those who survive to the nations—to Tarshish, to the Libyans[a] and Lydians (famous as archers), to Tubal and Greece, and to the distant islands that have not heard of my fame or seen my glory. They will proclaim my glory among the nations. [20]And they will bring all your brothers, from all the nations, to my holy mountain in Jerusalem as an offering to the LORD—on horses, in chariots and wagons, and on mules and camels," says the LORD. "They will bring them, as the Israelites bring their grain offerings, to the temple of the LORD in ceremonially clean vessels. [21]And I will select some of them also to be priests and Levites," says the LORD.

[22]"As the new heavens and the new earth that I make will endure before me," declares the LORD, "so will your name and descendants endure. [23]From one New Moon to another and from one Sabbath to another, all mankind will come and bow down before me," says the LORD. [24]"And they will go out and look upon the dead bodies of those who rebelled against me; their worm will not die, nor will their fire be quenched, and they will be loathsome to all mankind."

---

[a] 19 Some Septuagint manuscripts Put (Libyans); Hebrew Pul

author:	Jeremiah.
date:	Jeremiah wrote during his years of ministry, which began in 626 B.C. and ended sometime after the fall of Jerusalem in 586 B.C.
setting:	Jeremiah spoke to the people of Judah during the reigns of Josiah, Jehoahaz, Jehoiakim, Jehoiachin and Zedekiah, the last five kings.
verse to remember:	"Obey me, and I will be your God and you will be my people" (7:23–24).
theme to consider:	Judah was dying spiritually, and Jeremiah was sent to plead with the people to stop sinning and return to God. Because they wouldn't listen, they were sent as captives to Babylon.

jeremiah

unchanging truth

Sometimes people can be just plain stubborn and hardheaded. They should know better than to do or say something, but they do it anyway. Have you ever been like that?

Stubbornness can get you into a lot of trouble. For example, you may know that you need to study for a test, but because you dislike the class or the teacher, you stubbornly refuse. But you know the funny thing about stubbornness? As much as you may think it puts you in control, it really only hurts *you*.

The people of Judah had been stubborn. God had sent many prophets to warn them to turn from their evil ways. If they would repent, God would protect them—yet they continued to stubbornly refuse. The prophet Jeremiah was given the unenviable job of telling the people that their time was up. Their stubbornness would result in punishment. They may have thought they were in control, but they were about to learn otherwise. Jeremiah suffered greatly for the message of tough truth that God had called him to deliver.

Yet Jeremiah also had good news for those who gave up their stubborn ways, repented and called out to God—they would eventually be restored and blessed. In the meantime, however, they had to pay a heavy price.

The lesson for you? Avoid stubbornness. Seek instead to obey God. It could save you a lot of trouble.

life lessons

1 Before we were even born, God knew us and had a plan for our lives, just as he did for Jeremiah (1:5).

2 God knows everything about us—even things we think we have hidden deep in our hearts (17:9–10).

3 God will punish sin, but he also promises restoration and healing (32:36–44).

1 The words of Jeremiah son of Hilkiah, one of the priests at Anathoth in the territory of Benjamin. [2]The word of the LORD came to him in the thirteenth year of the reign of Josiah son of Amon king of Judah, [3]and through the reign of Jehoiakim son of Josiah king of Judah, down to the fifth month of the eleventh year of Zedekiah son of Josiah king of Judah, when the people of Jerusalem went into exile.

The Call of Jeremiah

[4]The word of the LORD came to me, saying,

> [5]"Before I formed you in the womb I knew[a] you,
>> before you were born I set you apart;
>> I appointed you as a prophet to the nations."

[6]"Ah, Sovereign LORD," I said, "I do not know how to speak; I am only a child."

[7]But the LORD said to me, "Do not say, 'I am only a child.' You must go to everyone I send you to and say whatever I command you. [8]Do not be afraid of them, for I am with you and will rescue you," declares the LORD.

[9]Then the LORD reached out his hand and touched my mouth and said to me, "Now, I have put my words in your mouth. [10]See, today I appoint you over nations and kingdoms to uproot and tear down, to destroy and overthrow, to build and to plant."

[11]The word of the LORD came to me: "What do you see, Jeremiah?"

"I see the branch of an almond tree," I replied.

[12]The LORD said to me, "You have seen correctly, for I am watching[b] to see that my word is fulfilled."

[13]The word of the LORD came to me again: "What do you see?"

love ♥ notes

1:5

Loved one,

You are not an afterthought. I've known you and loved you from your very beginning. When you feel discouraged, remember that I value you. I have a purpose in mind for you.

—Your Creator

What do you like and dislike about yourself? How does knowing that God has always thought of you as valuable affect your view of yourself?

truth or dare

Jeremiah wasn't exactly thrilled with being picked as God's spokesperson. Despite his lack of confidence, God turned him into a great prophet. God can do great things in and through you, too!

1:6–7

a 5 Or *chose*   *b 12* The Hebrew for *watching* sounds like the Hebrew for *almond tree*.

genuine courage ≫ 1:17-19

It can be pretty scary sometimes to stand up for what you believe in. You don't generally win popularity points by speaking out against abortion or defending sexual purity or saying that Jesus Christ is the only way to get to heaven. You may even find that you make some enemies in the process. But don't be afraid to take a stand. Because just as God was with Jeremiah, so he is with you, and he will triumph in the end.

"I see a boiling pot, tilting away from the north," I answered.

¹⁴The LORD said to me, "From the north disaster will be poured out on all who live in the land. ¹⁵I am about to summon all the peoples of the northern kingdoms," declares the LORD.

"Their kings will come and set up
their thrones
in the entrance of the gates of
Jerusalem;
they will come against all her
surrounding walls
and against all the towns of Judah.
¹⁶I will pronounce my judgments
on my people
because of their wickedness
in forsaking me,
in burning incense to other gods
and in worshiping what their
hands have made.

¹⁷"Get yourself ready! Stand up and say to them whatever I command you. Do not be terrified by them, or I will terrify you before them. ¹⁸Today I have made you a fortified city, an iron pillar and a bronze wall to stand against the whole land—against the kings of Judah, its officials, its priests and the people of the land. ¹⁹They will fight against you but will not overcome you, for I am with you and will rescue you," declares the LORD.

Israel Forsakes God

2 The word of the LORD came to me: ²"Go and proclaim in the hearing of Jerusalem:

" 'I remember the devotion of your youth,
how as a bride you loved me
and followed me through the desert,
through a land not sown.
³Israel was holy to the LORD,
the firstfruits of his harvest;
all who devoured her were held guilty,
and disaster overtook them,' "

declares the LORD.

⁴Hear the word of the LORD, O house of Jacob,
all you clans of the house of Israel.

⁵This is what the LORD says:

"What fault did your fathers find in me,
that they strayed so far from me?
They followed worthless idols
and became worthless themselves.
⁶They did not ask, 'Where is the LORD,
who brought us up out of Egypt
and led us through the barren wilderness,
through a land of deserts and rifts,

a land of drought and darkness,[a]
    a land where no one travels and no one lives?'
[7]I brought you into a fertile land
    to eat its fruit and rich produce.
But you came and defiled my land
    and made my inheritance detestable.
[8]The priests did not ask,
    'Where is the LORD?'
Those who deal with the law did not know me;
    the leaders rebelled against me.
The prophets prophesied by Baal,
    following worthless idols.

[9]"Therefore I bring charges against you again,"
                          declares the LORD.
    "And I will bring charges against your children's children.
[10]Cross over to the coasts of Kittim[b] and look,
    send to Kedar[c] and observe closely;
    see if there has ever been anything like this:
[11]Has a nation ever changed its gods?
    (Yet they are not gods at all.)
But my people have exchanged their[d] Glory
    for worthless idols.
[12]Be appalled at this, O heavens,
    and shudder with great horror,"
                          declares the LORD.

[13]"My people have committed two sins:
They have forsaken me,
    the spring of living water,
and have dug their own cisterns,
    broken cisterns that cannot hold water.
[14]Is Israel a servant, a slave by birth?
    Why then has he become
        plunder?
[15]Lions have roared;
    they have growled at him.
They have laid waste his land;
    his towns are burned and
        deserted.
[16]Also, the men of Memphis[e] and
        Tahpanhes
    have shaved the crown of your
        head.[f]
[17]Have you not brought this on
        yourselves
    by forsaking the LORD your God
    when he led you in the way?
[18]Now why go to Egypt
    to drink water from the Shihor[g]?
And why go to Assyria
    to drink water from the River[h]?
[19]Your wickedness will punish you;
    your backsliding will rebuke you.

truth or dare

God's punishment isn't the only reason for avoiding wrongdoing. Sin has a ton of *natural consequences* like physical harm, jail and even death.

2:19

---

a 6 Or *and the shadow of death*   b 10 That is, Cyprus and western coastlands   c 10 The home of Bedouin tribes in the Syro-Arabian desert   d 11 Masoretic Text; an ancient Hebrew scribal tradition *my*   e 16 Hebrew *Noph*
f 16 Or *have cracked your skull*   g 18 That is, a branch of the Nile   h 18 That is, the Euphrates

≫ 995

Consider then and realize
    how evil and bitter it is for you
when you forsake the LORD your God
    and have no awe of me,"
                                declares the Lord, the LORD Almighty.

20 "Long ago you broke off your yoke
    and tore off your bonds;
    you said, 'I will not serve you!'
Indeed, on every high hill
    and under every spreading tree
    you lay down as a prostitute.
21 I had planted you like a choice vine
    of sound and reliable stock.
How then did you turn against me
    into a corrupt, wild vine?
22 Although you wash yourself with soda
    and use an abundance of soap,
    the stain of your guilt is still before me,"
                                declares the Sovereign LORD.

23 "How can you say, 'I am not defiled;
    I have not run after the Baals'?
See how you behaved in the valley;
    consider what you have done.
You are a swift she-camel
    running here and there,
24 a wild donkey accustomed to the desert,
    sniffing the wind in her craving—
    in her heat who can restrain her?
Any males that pursue her need not tire themselves;
    at mating time they will find her.
25 Do not run until your feet are bare
    and your throat is dry.
But you said, 'It's no use!
    I love foreign gods,
    and I must go after them.'

26 "As a thief is disgraced when he is caught,
    so the house of Israel is disgraced—
they, their kings and their officials,
    their priests and their prophets.
27 They say to wood, 'You are my father,'
    and to stone, 'You gave me birth.'
They have turned their backs to me
    and not their faces;
yet when they are in trouble, they say,
    'Come and save us!'
28 Where then are the gods you made for yourselves?
    Let them come if they can save you
    when you are in trouble!
For you have as many gods
    as you have towns, O Judah.

29 "Why do you bring charges against me?
    You have all rebelled against me,"
                                declares the LORD.

30 "In vain I punished your people;

they did not respond to correction.
Your sword has devoured your prophets
like a ravening lion.

[31] "You of this generation, consider the word of the LORD:

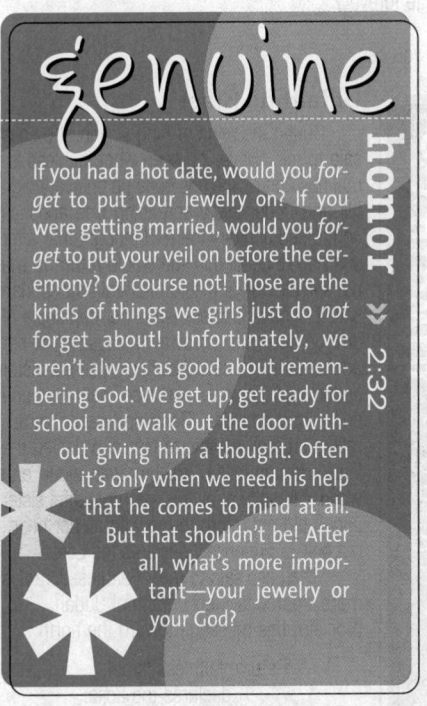

genuine

honor » 2:32

If you had a hot date, would you *forget* to put your jewelry on? If you were getting married, would you *forget* to put your veil on before the ceremony? Of course not! Those are the kinds of things we girls just do *not* forget about! Unfortunately, we aren't always as good about remembering God. We get up, get ready for school and walk out the door without giving him a thought. Often it's only when we need his help that he comes to mind at all. But that shouldn't be! After all, what's more important—your jewelry or your God?

"Have I been a desert to Israel
or a land of great darkness?
Why do my people say, 'We are
free to roam;
we will come to you no more'?
[32] Does a maiden forget her jewelry,
a bride her wedding
ornaments?
Yet my people have forgotten me,
days without number.
[33] How skilled you are at pursuing
love!
Even the worst of women can
learn from your ways.
[34] On your clothes men find
the lifeblood of the innocent
poor,
though you did not catch
them breaking in.
Yet in spite of all this
[35]   you say, 'I am innocent;
he is not angry with me.'
But I will pass judgment on you
because you say, 'I have not
sinned.'
[36] Why do you go about so much,
changing your ways?
You will be disappointed by Egypt
as you were by Assyria.
[37] You will also leave that place
with your hands on your head,
for the LORD has rejected those you trust;
you will not be helped by them.

3 "If a man divorces his wife
and she leaves him and marries another man,
should he return to her again?
Would not the land be completely defiled?
But you have lived as a prostitute with many lovers—
would you now return to me?"

declares the LORD.

[2] "Look up to the barren heights and see.
Is there any place where you have not been ravished?
By the roadside you sat waiting for lovers,
sat like a nomad[a] in the desert.
You have defiled the land
with your prostitution and wickedness.
[3] Therefore the showers have been withheld,
and no spring rains have fallen.

---

[a] 2 Or an Arab

Yet you have the brazen look of a prostitute;
you refuse to blush with shame.
⁴Have you not just called to me:
'My Father, my friend from my youth,
⁵will you always be angry?
Will your wrath continue forever?'
This is how you talk,
but you do all the evil you can."

genuine

growth » 3:6–10

Because the people of Israel committed spiritual "adultery" by pursuing other gods, they were exiled. The people of Judah should have learned from Israel's mistakes. But they didn't. So, God had to teach them the hard way. How about you? Do you learn from others' mistakes? Do you take to heart what happens to your friends when they make certain choices? Do you take seriously the lessons illustrated in the lives of those in the Bible? You can be sure that God *will* teach you. Don't make him do it the hard way.

Unfaithful Israel

⁶During the reign of King Josiah, the LORD said to me, "Have you seen what faithless Israel has done? She has gone up on every high hill and under every spreading tree and has committed adultery there. ⁷I thought that after she had done all this she would return to me but she did not, and her unfaithful sister Judah saw it. ⁸I gave faithless Israel her certificate of divorce and sent her away because of all her adulteries. Yet I saw that her unfaithful sister Judah had no fear; she also went out and committed adultery. ⁹Because Israel's immorality mattered so little to her, she defiled the land and committed adultery with stone and wood. ¹⁰In spite of all this, her unfaithful sister Judah did not return to me with all her heart, but only in pretense," declares the LORD.

¹¹The LORD said to me, "Faithless Israel is more righteous than unfaithful Judah. ¹²Go, proclaim this message toward the north:

" 'Return, faithless Israel,'
declares the LORD,
'I will frown on you no longer,
for I am merciful,' declares the
LORD,
'I will not be angry forever.

¹³Only acknowledge your guilt—
you have rebelled against the LORD your God,
you have scattered your favors to foreign gods
under every spreading tree,
and have not obeyed me,' "

declares the LORD.

¹⁴"Return, faithless people," declares the LORD, "for I am your husband. I will choose you—one from a town and two from a clan—and bring you to Zion. ¹⁵Then I will give you shepherds after my own heart, who will lead you with knowledge and understanding. ¹⁶In those days, when your numbers have increased greatly in the land," declares the LORD, "men will no longer say, 'The ark of the covenant of the LORD.' It will never enter their minds or be remembered; it will not be missed, nor will another one be made. ¹⁷At that time they will call Jerusalem The Throne of the LORD, and all nations will gather in Jerusalem to honor the name of the LORD. No longer will they follow the stubbornness of their evil hearts. ¹⁸In those days the house of Judah will join the house of Israel, and together they will come from a northern land to the land I gave your forefathers as an inheritance.

¹⁹"I myself said,

" 'How gladly would I treat you like sons
and give you a desirable land,

the most beautiful inheritance of any nation.'
I thought you would call me 'Father'
and not turn away from following me.
²⁰ But like a woman unfaithful to her husband,
so you have been unfaithful to me, O house of Israel,"

declares the LORD.

²¹ A cry is heard on the barren heights,
the weeping and pleading of the people of Israel,
because they have perverted their ways
and have forgotten the LORD their God.

²² "Return, faithless people;
I will cure you of backsliding."

"Yes, we will come to you,
for you are the LORD our God.
²³ Surely the ⌊idolatrous⌋ commotion on the hills
and mountains is a deception;
surely in the LORD our God
is the salvation of Israel.
²⁴ From our youth shameful gods have consumed
the fruits of our fathers' labor—
their flocks and herds,
their sons and daughters.
²⁵ Let us lie down in our shame,
and let our disgrace cover us.
We have sinned against the LORD our God,
both we and our fathers;
from our youth till this day
we have not obeyed the LORD our God."

4

"If you will return, O Israel,
return to me,"

declares the LORD.

"If you put your detestable idols out of my sight
and no longer go astray,
² and if in a truthful, just and righteous way
you swear, 'As surely as the LORD lives,'
then the nations will be blessed by him
and in him they will glory."

³ This is what the LORD says to the men of Judah and to Jerusalem:

"Break up your unplowed ground
and do not sow among thorns.
⁴ Circumcise yourselves to the LORD,
circumcise your hearts,
you men of Judah and people of Jerusalem,
or my wrath will break out and burn like fire
because of the evil you have done—
burn with no one to quench it.

Disaster From the North

⁵ "Announce in Judah and proclaim in Jerusalem and say:
'Sound the trumpet throughout the land!'
Cry aloud and say:
'Gather together!

Let us flee to the fortified cities!'
⁶Raise the signal to go to Zion!
    Flee for safety without delay!
For I am bringing disaster from the north,
    even terrible destruction."

⁷A lion has come out of his lair;
    a destroyer of nations has set out.
He has left his place
    to lay waste your land.
Your towns will lie in ruins
    without inhabitant.
⁸So put on sackcloth,
    lament and wail,
for the fierce anger of the LORD
    has not turned away from us.

⁹"In that day," declares the LORD,
    "the king and the officials will lose heart,
the priests will be horrified,
    and the prophets will be appalled."

¹⁰Then I said, "Ah, Sovereign LORD, how completely you have deceived this people and Jerusalem by saying, 'You will have peace,' when the sword is at our throats."

¹¹At that time this people and Jerusalem will be told, "A scorching wind from the barren heights in the desert blows toward my people, but not to winnow or cleanse; ¹²a wind too strong for that comes from me.ᵃ Now I pronounce my judgments against them."

¹³Look! He advances like the clouds,
    his chariots come like a whirlwind,
his horses are swifter than eagles.
    Woe to us! We are ruined!
¹⁴O Jerusalem, wash the evil from your heart and be saved.
    How long will you harbor wicked thoughts?
¹⁵A voice is announcing from Dan,
    proclaiming disaster from the hills of Ephraim.
¹⁶"Tell this to the nations,
    proclaim it to Jerusalem:
'A besieging army is coming from a distant land,
    raising a war cry against the cities of Judah.
¹⁷They surround her like men guarding a field,
    because she has rebelled against me,' "

                                        declares the LORD.

¹⁸"Your own conduct and actions
    have brought this upon you.
This is your punishment.
    How bitter it is!
    How it pierces to the heart!"

¹⁹Oh, my anguish, my anguish!
    I writhe in pain.
Oh, the agony of my heart!
    My heart pounds within me,
    I cannot keep silent.
For I have heard the sound of the trumpet;
    I have heard the battle cry.
²⁰Disaster follows disaster;

ᵃ 12 Or comes at my command

One Big Happy Family?

focus **Profile: Christina**

My parents got divorced when I was eight. That was six years ago. My dad got married less than a year after they divorced. (Guess that's why they got divorced.) Anyway, for awhile it was just Mom and me. Well, not anymore. Mom's getting married again.

She wants me to be happy for her. But how *can* I be? Everything's awful. She's marrying Bill, this guy from our church. I've got nothing against him. It's just his family I have a hard time getting along with. He's got a son who's seventeen and thinks he's God's gift to women or something. (News flash, Nelson. You're not.) We don't speak unless we have to. Bill's got a thirteen-year-old daughter who's obnoxious. Her name is Catherine, but she calls herself Cay. Whatever.

We might have to move out of our house into their house. I don't want to move! If I have to share a room with Catherine *(Cay!!)*, I will freak. She'd better not touch my stuff.

Mom wants us together all the time before the wedding, so we can get to know each other. I think we already know more than enough about each other.

I finally got used to Dad's new family. (I have a stepsister who's four.) Now this has to happen. I don't even know what to call Bill. I think he's hoping I'll call him Dad. No thanks. I already have a dad.

Sometimes I wish I had a less complicated family.

For more ideas on how to deal with blended families, check out the link on www.TrueImagesBible.com

blended families in focus

With the high divorce rate today, many families are changing and blending. Has that been your experience? If so, you already know that blending families isn't always easy. If you're in a blended family . . .

»Keep the lines of communication open between you and your parent and potential (or actual) stepparent. If talking is difficult, write your thoughts out first, and then talk them over together.

»Your parent is excited about a new chapter in life. Its okay if you're not quite there yet. Be honest and ask your family for patience as you get used to the changes.

»"Pray continually" (1 Thessalonians 5:17, page 1564).

»Make Ephesians 4:29–32 (page 1546) your personal motto.

»Try to find common ground. Maybe your new stepsister likes the same music you do. Maybe your stepdad likes to hike just as much as you do.

For more on this topic, see the index on page 1656.

the whole land lies in ruins.
In an instant my tents are destroyed,
    my shelter in a moment.
²¹ How long must I see the battle standard
    and hear the sound of the trumpet?

²² "My people are fools;
    they do not know me.
They are senseless children;
    they have no understanding.

They are skilled in doing evil;
    they know not how to do good."

²³ I looked at the earth,
    and it was formless and empty;
and at the heavens,
    and their light was gone.
²⁴ I looked at the mountains,
    and they were quaking;
    all the hills were swaying.
²⁵ I looked, and there were no people;
    every bird in the sky had flown away.
²⁶ I looked, and the fruitful land was a desert;
    all its towns lay in ruins
    before the LORD, before his fierce anger.

²⁷ This is what the LORD says:

"The whole land will be ruined,
    though I will not destroy it completely.
²⁸ Therefore the earth will mourn
    and the heavens above grow dark,
because I have spoken and will not relent,
    I have decided and will not turn back."

²⁹ At the sound of horsemen and archers
    every town takes to flight.
Some go into the thickets;
    some climb up among the rocks.
All the towns are deserted;
    no one lives in them.

³⁰ What are you doing, O devastated one?
    Why dress yourself in scarlet
    and put on jewels of gold?
Why shade your eyes with paint?
    You adorn yourself in vain.
Your lovers despise you;
    they seek your life.

³¹ I hear a cry as of a woman in labor,
    a groan as of one bearing her first child—
the cry of the Daughter of Zion gasping for breath,
    stretching out her hands and saying,
"Alas! I am fainting;
    my life is given over to murderers."

Not One Is Upright

5 "Go up and down the streets of Jerusalem,
    look around and consider,
    search through her squares.
If you can find but one person
    who deals honestly and seeks the truth,
    I will forgive this city.
² Although they say, 'As surely as the LORD lives,'
    still they are swearing falsely."

³ O LORD, do not your eyes look for truth?
    You struck them, but they felt no pain;

you crushed them, but they refused correction.
They made their faces harder than stone
    and refused to repent.
⁴ I thought, "These are only the poor;
    they are foolish,
for they do not know the way of the LORD,
    the requirements of their God.
⁵ So I will go to the leaders
    and speak to them;
surely they know the way of the LORD,
    the requirements of their God."
But with one accord they too had broken off the yoke
    and torn off the bonds.
⁶ Therefore a lion from the forest will attack them,
    a wolf from the desert will ravage them,
a leopard will lie in wait near their towns
    to tear to pieces any who venture out,
for their rebellion is great
    and their backslidings many.

⁷ "Why should I forgive you?
    Your children have forsaken me
    and sworn by gods that are not gods.
I supplied all their needs,
    yet they committed adultery
    and thronged to the houses of prostitutes.
⁸ They are well-fed, lusty stallions,
    each neighing for another man's wife.
⁹ Should I not punish them for this?"
    declares the LORD.
"Should I not avenge myself
    on such a nation as this?

¹⁰ "Go through her vineyards and ravage them,
    but do not destroy them completely.
Strip off her branches,
    for these people do not belong to the LORD.
¹¹ The house of Israel and the house of Judah
    have been utterly unfaithful to me,"

declares the LORD.

¹² They have lied about the LORD;
    they said, "He will do nothing!
No harm will come to us;
    we will never see sword or famine.
¹³ The prophets are but wind
    and the word is not in them;
    so let what they say be done to them."

¹⁴ Therefore this is what the LORD God Almighty says:

"Because the people have spoken these words,
    I will make my words in your mouth a fire
    and these people the wood it consumes.
¹⁵ O house of Israel," declares the LORD,
    "I am bringing a distant nation against you—
an ancient and enduring nation,
    a people whose language you do not know,

whose speech you do not understand.
¹⁶ Their quivers are like an open grave;
all of them are mighty warriors.
¹⁷ They will devour your harvests and food,
devour your sons and daughters;
they will devour your flocks and herds,
devour your vines and fig trees.
With the sword they will destroy
the fortified cities in which you trust.

¹⁸"Yet even in those days," declares the LORD, "I will not destroy you completely. ¹⁹And when the people ask, 'Why has the LORD our God done all this to us?' you will tell them, 'As you have forsaken me and served foreign gods in your own land, so now you will serve foreigners in a land not your own.'

²⁰ "Announce this to the house of Jacob
and proclaim it in Judah:
²¹ Hear this, you foolish and senseless people,
who have eyes but do not see,
who have ears but do not hear:
²² Should you not fear me?" declares the LORD.
"Should you not tremble in my presence?
I made the sand a boundary for the sea,
an everlasting barrier it cannot cross.
The waves may roll, but they cannot prevail;
they may roar, but they cannot cross it.
²³ But these people have stubborn and rebellious hearts;
they have turned aside and gone away.
²⁴ They do not say to themselves,
'Let us fear the LORD our God,
who gives autumn and spring rains in season,
who assures us of the regular weeks of harvest.'
²⁵ Your wrongdoings have kept these away;
your sins have deprived you of good.

²⁶ "Among my people are wicked men
who lie in wait like men who snare birds
and like those who set traps to catch men.
²⁷ Like cages full of birds,
their houses are full of deceit;
they have become rich and powerful
²⁸ and have grown fat and sleek.
Their evil deeds have no limit;
they do not plead the case of the fatherless to win it,
they do not defend the rights of the poor.
²⁹ Should I not punish them for this?"
declares the LORD.
"Should I not avenge myself
on such a nation as this?

³⁰ "A horrible and shocking thing
has happened in the land:
³¹ The prophets prophesy lies,
the priests rule by their own authority,
and my people love it this way.
But what will you do in the end?

6

"Flee for safety, people of Benjamin!
  Flee from Jerusalem!
Sound the trumpet in Tekoa!
  Raise the signal over Beth Hakkerem!
For disaster looms out of the north,
  even terrible destruction.
[2] I will destroy the Daughter of Zion,
  so beautiful and delicate.
[3] Shepherds with their flocks will come against her;
  they will pitch their tents around her,
  each tending his own portion."

[4] "Prepare for battle against her!
  Arise, let us attack at noon!
But, alas, the daylight is fading,
  and the shadows of evening grow long.
[5] So arise, let us attack at night
  and destroy her fortresses!"

[6] This is what the LORD Almighty says:

"Cut down the trees
  and build siege ramps against Jerusalem.
This city must be punished;
  it is filled with oppression.
[7] As a well pours out its water,
  so she pours out her wickedness.
Violence and destruction resound in her;
  her sickness and wounds are ever before me.
[8] Take warning, O Jerusalem,
  or I will turn away from you
and make your land desolate
  so no one can live in it."

[9] This is what the LORD Almighty says:

"Let them glean the remnant of Israel
  as thoroughly as a vine;
pass your hand over the
      branches again,
  like one gathering grapes."

[10] To whom can I speak and give
      warning?
  Who will listen to me?
Their ears are closed [a]
  so they cannot hear.
The word of the LORD is offensive
      to them;
  they find no pleasure in it.
[11] But I am full of the wrath of the LORD,
  and I cannot hold it in.

"Pour it out on the children in the street
  and on the young men gathered together;
both husband and wife will be caught in it,

truth or dare

God's Word makes people uncomfortable—it shows them that they're imperfect and demands they make a change. Don't be surprised when people get offended by the truth.

6:10

---

[a] 10 Hebrew *uncircumcised*

and the old, those weighed down with years.
¹² Their houses will be turned over to others,
together with their fields and their wives,
when I stretch out my hand
against those who live in the land,"

declares the LORD.

¹³ "From the least to the greatest,
all are greedy for gain;
prophets and priests alike,
all practice deceit.
¹⁴ They dress the wound of my people
as though it were not serious.
'Peace, peace,' they say,
when there is no peace.
¹⁵ Are they ashamed of their loathsome conduct?
No, they have no shame at all;
they do not even know how to blush.
So they will fall among the fallen;
they will be brought down when I punish them,"

says the LORD.

¹⁶ This is what the LORD says:

"Stand at the crossroads and look;
ask for the ancient paths,
ask where the good way is, and
walk in it,
and you will find rest for your
souls.
But you said, 'We will not
walk in it.'
¹⁷ I appointed watchmen over you
and said,
'Listen to the sound of the
trumpet!'
But you said, 'We will not listen.'
¹⁸ Therefore hear, O nations;
observe, O witnesses,
what will happen to them.
¹⁹ Hear, O earth:
I am bringing disaster on this
people,
the fruit of their schemes,
because they have not listened to
my words
and have rejected my law.
²⁰ What do I care about incense
from Sheba
or sweet calamus from a
distant land?

genuine peace » 6:16

Contemporary furniture, the latest fashions, the most modern technology . . . looking for new innovations is a way of life for most of us. But there's one area where looking for something *new* will definitely not lead to finding something *better*— and that's in your approach to life and salvation. God laid out the best way to live a long, long time ago and decided before he even made the world how he would save it. Look for the good way (even though it's ancient) and walk in it, and you will find peace and satisfaction for your soul.

Your burnt offerings are not acceptable;
your sacrifices do not please me."

²¹ Therefore this is what the LORD says:

"I will put obstacles before this people.
Fathers and sons alike will stumble over them;
neighbors and friends will perish."

²²This is what the LORD says:

"Look, an army is coming
　　from the land of the north;
a great nation is being stirred up
　　from the ends of the earth.
²³They are armed with bow and spear;
　　they are cruel and show no mercy.
They sound like the roaring sea
　　as they ride on their horses;
they come like men in battle formation
　　to attack you, O Daughter of Zion."

²⁴We have heard reports about them,
　　and our hands hang limp.
Anguish has gripped us,
　　pain like that of a woman in labor.
²⁵Do not go out to the fields
　　or walk on the roads,
for the enemy has a sword,
　　and there is terror on every side.
²⁶O my people, put on sackcloth
　　and roll in ashes;
mourn with bitter wailing
　　as for an only son,
for suddenly the destroyer
　　will come upon us.

²⁷"I have made you a tester of metals
　　and my people the ore,
that you may observe
　　and test their ways.
²⁸They are all hardened rebels,
　　going about to slander.
They are bronze and iron;
　　they all act corruptly.
²⁹The bellows blow fiercely
　　to burn away the lead with fire,
but the refining goes on in vain;
　　the wicked are not purged out.
³⁰They are called rejected silver,
　　because the LORD has rejected them."

False Religion Worthless

7 This is the word that came to Jeremiah from the LORD: ²"Stand at the gate of the LORD's house and there proclaim this message:

" 'Hear the word of the LORD, all you people of Judah who come through these gates to worship the LORD. ³This is what the LORD Almighty, the God of Israel, says: Reform your ways and your actions, and I will let you live in this place. ⁴Do not trust in deceptive words and say, "This is the temple of the LORD, the temple of the LORD, the temple of the LORD!" ⁵If you really change your ways and your actions and deal with each other justly, ⁶if you do not oppress the alien, the fatherless or the widow and do not shed innocent blood in this place, and if you do not follow other gods to your own harm, ⁷then I will let you live in this place, in the land I gave your forefathers for ever and ever. ⁸But look, you are trusting in deceptive words that are worthless.

⁹" 'Will you steal and murder, commit adultery and perjury,ᵃ burn incense to Baal and follow other gods you have not known, ¹⁰and then come and stand before me in this house, which bears

ᵃ 9 Or *and swear by false gods*

my Name, and say, "We are safe"—safe to do all these detestable things? ¹¹Has this house, which bears my Name, become a den of robbers to you? But I have been watching! declares the LORD.

¹²" 'Go now to the place in Shiloh where I first made a dwelling for my Name, and see what I did to it because of the wickedness of my people Israel. ¹³While you were doing all these things, declares the LORD, I spoke to you again and again, but you did not listen; I called you, but you did not answer. ¹⁴Therefore, what I did to Shiloh I will now do to the house that bears my Name, the temple you trust in, the place I gave to you and your fathers. ¹⁵I will thrust you from my presence, just as I did all your brothers, the people of Ephraim.'

¹⁶"So do not pray for this people nor offer any plea or petition for them; do not plead with me, for I will not listen to you. ¹⁷Do you not see what they are doing in the towns of Judah and in the streets of Jerusalem? ¹⁸The children gather wood, the fathers light the fire, and the women knead the dough and make cakes of bread for the Queen of Heaven. They pour out drink offerings to other gods to provoke me to anger. ¹⁹But am I the one they are provoking? declares the LORD. Are they not rather harming themselves, to their own shame?

²⁰" 'Therefore this is what the Sovereign LORD says: My anger and my wrath will be poured out on this place, on man and beast, on the trees of the field and on the fruit of the ground, and it will burn and not be quenched.

²¹" 'This is what the LORD Almighty, the God of Israel, says: Go ahead, add your burnt offerings to your other sacrifices and eat the meat yourselves! ²²For when I brought your forefathers out of Egypt and spoke to them, I did not just give them commands about burnt offerings and sacrifices, ²³but I gave them this command: Obey me, and I will be your God and you will be my people. Walk in all the ways I command you, that it may go well with you. ²⁴But they did not listen or pay attention; instead, they followed the stubborn inclinations of their evil hearts. They went backward and not forward. ²⁵From the time your forefathers left Egypt until now, day after day, again and again I sent you my servants the prophets. ²⁶But they did not listen to me or pay attention. They were stiff-necked and did more evil than their forefathers.'

²⁷"When you tell them all this, they will not listen to you; when you call to them, they will not answer. ²⁸Therefore say to them, 'This is the nation that has not obeyed the LORD its God or responded to correction. Truth has perished; it has vanished from their lips. ²⁹Cut off your hair and throw it away; take up a lament on the barren heights, for the LORD has rejected and abandoned this generation that is under his wrath.

genuine obedience » 7:22-23

To you, is Christianity a "Sunday thing"? Do the drill: go to church, sing the songs, bow for prayer, say amen, endure the sermon ... then do whatever you feel like doing the rest of the week? If so, then you are on a dangerous path. God wants you to obey him in everything, all the time. He wants to have a relationship that affects you every minute of every day. And he makes this promise: When you walk in all the ways he has commanded you, it will go well with you—because you walk together.

The Valley of Slaughter

³⁰" 'The people of Judah have done evil in my eyes, declares the LORD. They have set up their detestable idols in the house that bears my Name and have defiled it. ³¹They have built the high places of Topheth in the Valley of Ben Hinnom to burn their sons and daughters in the fire—something I did not command, nor did it enter my mind. ³²So beware, the days are coming, declares the LORD, when people will no longer call it Topheth or the Valley of Ben Hinnom, but the Valley of Slaughter, for they will bury the dead in Topheth until there is no more room. ³³Then the carcasses of this people will become food for the birds of the air and the beasts of the earth, and there will be no one to frighten them away. ³⁴I will bring an end to the sounds of joy and gladness and

to the voices of bride and bridegroom in the towns of Judah and the streets of Jerusalem, for the land will become desolate.

8 " 'At that time, declares the LORD, the bones of the kings and officials of Judah, the bones of the priests and prophets, and the bones of the people of Jerusalem will be removed from their graves. ²They will be exposed to the sun and the moon and all the stars of the heavens, which they have loved and served and which they have followed and consulted and worshiped. They will not be gathered up or buried, but will be like refuse lying on the ground. ³Wherever I banish them, all the survivors of this evil nation will prefer death to life, declares the LORD Almighty.'

Sin and Punishment

⁴"Say to them, 'This is what the LORD says:

> " 'When men fall down, do they not get up?
>   When a man turns away, does he not return?
> ⁵Why then have these people turned away?
>   Why does Jerusalem always turn away?
> They cling to deceit;
>   they refuse to return.
> ⁶I have listened attentively,
>   but they do not say what is right.
> No one repents of his wickedness,
>   saying, "What have I done?"
> Each pursues his own course
>   like a horse charging into battle.
> ⁷Even the stork in the sky
>   knows her appointed seasons,
> and the dove, the swift and the thrush
>   observe the time of their migration.
> But my people do not know
>   the requirements of the LORD.
>
> ⁸" 'How can you say, "We are wise,
>   for we have the law of the LORD,"
> when actually the lying pen of the scribes
>   has handled it falsely?
> ⁹The wise will be put to shame;
>   they will be dismayed and trapped.
> Since they have rejected the word of the LORD,
>   what kind of wisdom do they have?
> ¹⁰Therefore I will give their wives to other men
>   and their fields to new owners.
> From the least to the greatest,
>   all are greedy for gain;
> prophets and priests alike,
>   all practice deceit.
> ¹¹They dress the wound of my people
>   as though it were not serious.
> "Peace, peace," they say,
>   when there is no peace.
> ¹²Are they ashamed of their loathsome conduct?
>   No, they have no shame at all;
>   they do not even know how to blush.
> So they will fall among the fallen;
>   they will be brought down when they are punished,
>   says the LORD.

¹³ " 'I will take away their harvest,

declares the LORD.

There will be no grapes on the vine.
There will be no figs on the tree,
    and their leaves will wither.
What I have given them
    will be taken from them.^a ' "

¹⁴ "Why are we sitting here?
    Gather together!
Let us flee to the fortified cities
    and perish there!
For the LORD our God has doomed us to perish
    and given us poisoned water to drink,
    because we have sinned against him.
¹⁵ We hoped for peace
    but no good has come,
for a time of healing
    but there was only terror.
¹⁶ The snorting of the enemy's horses
    is heard from Dan;
at the neighing of their stallions
    the whole land trembles.
They have come to devour
    the land and everything in it,
    the city and all who live there."

¹⁷ "See, I will send venomous snakes among you,
    vipers that cannot be charmed,
    and they will bite you,"

declares the LORD.

¹⁸ O my Comforter^b in sorrow,
    my heart is faint within me.
¹⁹ Listen to the cry of my people
    from a land far away:
"Is the LORD not in Zion?
    Is her King no longer there?"

"Why have they provoked me to anger with their images,
    with their worthless foreign idols?"

²⁰ "The harvest is past,
    the summer has ended,
    and we are not saved."

²¹ Since my people are crushed, I am crushed;
    I mourn, and horror grips me.
²² Is there no balm in Gilead?
    Is there no physician there?
Why then is there no healing
    for the wound of my people?
¹ Oh, that my head were a spring of water
    and my eyes a fountain of tears!
I would weep day and night
    for the slain of my people.

^a 13 The meaning of the Hebrew for this sentence is uncertain.   ^b 18 The meaning of the Hebrew for this word is uncertain.

²Oh, that I had in the desert
    a lodging place for travelers,
so that I might leave my people
    and go away from them;
for they are all adulterers,
    a crowd of unfaithful people.

³"They make ready their tongue
    like a bow, to shoot lies;
it is not by truth
    that they triumph *a* in the land.
They go from one sin to another;
    they do not acknowledge me,"

                declares the LORD.

⁴"Beware of your friends;
    do not trust your brothers.
For every brother is a deceiver, *b*
    and every friend a slanderer.
⁵Friend deceives friend,
    and no one speaks the truth.
They have taught their tongues to lie;
    they weary themselves with sinning.
⁶You *c* live in the midst of deception;
    in their deceit they refuse to acknowledge me,"

                declares the LORD.

⁷Therefore this is what the LORD Almighty says:

"See, I will refine and test them,
    for what else can I do
because of the sin of my people?
⁸Their tongue is a deadly arrow;
    it speaks with deceit.
With his mouth each speaks cordially to his neighbor,
    but in his heart he sets a trap for him.
⁹Should I not punish them for this?"
    declares the LORD.
"Should I not avenge myself
    on such a nation as this?"

¹⁰I will weep and wail for the mountains
    and take up a lament concerning the desert pastures.
They are desolate and untraveled,
    and the lowing of cattle is not heard.
The birds of the air have fled
    and the animals are gone.

¹¹"I will make Jerusalem a heap of ruins,
    a haunt of jackals;
and I will lay waste the towns of Judah
    so no one can live there."

¹²What man is wise enough to understand this? Who has been instructed by the LORD and can explain it? Why has the land been ruined and laid waste like a desert that no one can cross?
¹³The LORD said, "It is because they have forsaken my law, which I set before them; they have not obeyed me or followed my law. ¹⁴Instead, they have followed the stubbornness of their hearts; they have followed the Baals, as their fathers taught them." ¹⁵Therefore, this is what the LORD Al-

---

a 3 Or lies; / they are not valiant for truth   *b 4 Or a deceiving Jacob*   *c 6 That is, Jeremiah (the Hebrew is singular)* mighty, the God of Israel, says: "See, I will make this people eat bitter food and drink poisoned water. [16]I will scatter them among nations that neither they nor their fathers have known, and I will pursue them with the sword until I have destroyed them."

[17]This is what the LORD Almighty says:

"Consider now! Call for the wailing women to come;
    send for the most skillful of them.
[18]Let them come quickly
    and wail over us
till our eyes overflow with tears
    and water streams from our eyelids.
[19]The sound of wailing is heard from Zion:
    'How ruined we are!
    How great is our shame!
We must leave our land
    because our houses are in ruins.' "

[20]Now, O women, hear the word of the LORD;
    open your ears to the words of his mouth.
Teach your daughters how to wail;
    teach one another a lament.

[21]Death has climbed in through our
        windows
    and has entered our fortresses;
it has cut off the children from
        the streets
    and the young men from the
        public squares.

[22]Say, "This is what the LORD declares:

" 'The dead bodies of men will lie
    like refuse on the open field,
like cut grain behind the reaper,
    with no one to gather them.' "

[23]This is what the LORD says:

"Let not the wise man boast of
        his wisdom
    or the strong man boast of his
        strength
    or the rich man boast of his riches,
[24]but let him who boasts boast
        about this:
    that he understands and
        knows me,
that I am the LORD, who exercises
        kindness,
    justice and righteousness on
        earth,
for in these I delight,"
        declares the LORD.

genuine relationship » 9:23-24

Do you have brains? Do you have a great personality? Do you have an unlimited cash flow? If you answered "yes" to any of those, that's great. But what's even better is answering "yes" to this question: Do you know God? You see, being smart or charming or rich doesn't matter in the end. What matters is having a relationship with God. It's okay to be glad that you can ace a test or out-dribble your opponent on the soccer field or have a hefty clothing budget. But it's more important to be glad that you know God—because that's what counts.

[25]"The days are coming," declares the LORD, "when I will punish all who are circumcised only in the flesh— [26]Egypt, Judah, Edom, Ammon, Moab and all who live in the desert in distant places.[a] For all these nations are really uncircumcised, and even the whole house of Israel is uncircumcised in heart."

a 26 Or desert and who clip the hair by their foreheads

God and Idols

10

Hear what the LORD says to you, O house of Israel. ²This is what the LORD says:

> "Do not learn the ways of the nations
>   or be terrified by signs in the sky,
>   though the nations are terrified by them.
> ³For the customs of the peoples are worthless;
>   they cut a tree out of the forest,
>   and a craftsman shapes it with his chisel.
> ⁴They adorn it with silver and gold;
>   they fasten it with hammer
>   and nails
>   so it will not totter.
> ⁵Like a scarecrow in a melon
>   patch,
>   their idols cannot speak;
> they must be carried
>   because they cannot walk.
> Do not fear them;
>   they can do no harm
>   nor can they do any good."

> ⁶No one is like you, O LORD;
>   you are great,
>   and your name is mighty in power.
> ⁷Who should not revere you,
>   O King of the nations?
>   This is your due.
> Among all the wise men of the nations
>   and in all their kingdoms,
>   there is no one like you.
> ⁸They are all senseless and foolish;
>   they are taught by worthless wooden idols.
> ⁹Hammered silver is brought from Tarshish
>   and gold from Uphaz.
> What the craftsman and goldsmith have made
>   is then dressed in blue and purple—
>   all made by skilled workers.
> ¹⁰But the LORD is the true God;
>   he is the living God, the eternal King.
> When he is angry, the earth trembles;
>   the nations cannot endure his wrath.

¹¹"Tell them this: 'These gods, who did not make the heavens and the earth, will perish from the earth and from under the heavens.' " *ᵃ*

> ¹²But God made the earth by his power;
>   he founded the world by his wisdom
>   and stretched out the heavens by his understanding.
> ¹³When he thunders, the waters in the heavens roar;
>   he makes clouds rise from the ends of the earth.
> He sends lightning with the rain
>   and brings out the wind from his storehouses.

> ¹⁴Everyone is senseless and without knowledge;
>   every goldsmith is shamed by his idols.

ᵃ 11 The text of this verse is in Aramaic.

---

truth or dare

You can dress it, paint it and worship it, but it still won't be God. Have you idolized things in the past? Jesus is the real thing. Accept no substitutes.

10:6–10

His images are a fraud;
    they have no breath in them.
¹⁵ They are worthless, the objects of mockery;
    when their judgment comes, they will perish.
¹⁶ He who is the Portion of Jacob is not like these,
    for he is the Maker of all things,
including Israel, the tribe of his inheritance—
    the LORD Almighty is his name.

Coming Destruction

¹⁷ Gather up your belongings to leave the land,
    you who live under siege.
¹⁸ For this is what the LORD says:

"At this time I will hurl out
    those who live in this land;
I will bring distress on them
    so that they may be captured."

¹⁹ Woe to me because of my injury!
    My wound is incurable!
Yet I said to myself,
    "This is my sickness, and I must endure it."
²⁰ My tent is destroyed;
    all its ropes are snapped.
My sons are gone from me and are no more;
    no one is left now to pitch my tent
    or to set up my shelter.
²¹ The shepherds are senseless
    and do not inquire of the LORD;
so they do not prosper
    and all their flock is scattered.
²² Listen! The report is coming—
    a great commotion from the land of the north!
It will make the towns of Judah desolate,
    a haunt of jackals.

Jeremiah's Prayer

²³ I know, O LORD, that a man's life is not his own;
    it is not for man to direct his steps.
²⁴ Correct me, LORD, but only with justice—
    not in your anger,
    lest you reduce me to nothing.
²⁵ Pour out your wrath on the nations
    that do not acknowledge you,
    on the peoples who do not call on your name.
For they have devoured Jacob;
    they have devoured him completely
    and destroyed his homeland.

The Covenant Is Broken

11 This is the word that came to Jeremiah from the LORD: ²"Listen to the terms of this covenant and tell them to the people of Judah and to those who live in Jerusalem. ³Tell them that this is what the LORD, the God of Israel, says: 'Cursed is the man who does not obey the terms of this covenant— ⁴the terms I commanded your forefathers when I brought them out of Egypt, out of the iron-smelting furnace.' I said, 'Obey me and do everything I command you, and you will be my people, and I will be your God. ⁵Then I will fulfill the oath I

Don't Leave Me Lonely

focus | **Profile: Paige**

"You always have to have a boyfriend, don't you?" Vanessa asked with a smile. She's my best friend and seems to know me better than I know myself.

"Yeah, Paige, have you *ever* gone without some guy in your life?" Sarah chimed in.

"That is so not true, you guys. Remember, Austin and I broke up for two whole days last year!" I joked as I tossed my trash into the bin and walked back to the lunch table.

My friends were only kidding me. But their words hit home—more than they knew. They're right. I've always had a guy in my life. So what does that say about me? That I'm like psycho-dependent or something? I don't know.

Right now, I'm scared *not* to be with Austin. He'd go nuts. I tried breaking up with him before, and he freaked out on me. He called me on my cell phone and cussed me out, saying he was going to hurt himself if we didn't get back together. Then he came by my house—I could hear his car driving by, back and forth all night, and he kept calling my cell and hanging up. But the next day he was so sweet. He was sorry for all that. He'd just "lost his head," that's all. He said we were meant for each other and that he loved me. We're back together and everything, but sometimes I'm still not sure he's right for me. But without him I'd be alone.

To learn more about healthy dating relationships, bookmark the information at www.TrueImagesBible.com

dependency in focus

Relationships are great—as long as the other person suppports your growth as an individual. Constantly being in relationships so you don't have to deal with who you are is a sign of dependency and an unhealthy relationship.

»Girls who are overly dependent on guys are usually attracted to the rebel types. Helping "solve" the guy's problems is one more way these girls can avoid their own.

»Are you truly compatible? Ask yourself the tough questions about your relationship: Is he a Christian? If not—see ya (2 Corinthians 6:14, page 1527)! Is he strengthening your faith or dragging you down to his level (see 1 Corinthians 15:33, page 1521)? Every relationship has an effect on you—is it for good or for bad?

For more on this topic, see the index on page 1656.

swore to your forefathers, to give them a land flowing with milk and honey'—the land you possess today."

I answered, "Amen, Lord."

6The Lord said to me, "Proclaim all these words in the towns of Judah and in the streets of Jerusalem: 'Listen to the terms of this covenant and follow them. 7From the time I brought your forefathers up from Egypt until today, I warned them again and again, saying, "Obey me." 8But they did not listen or pay attention; instead, they followed the stubbornness of their evil hearts. So I brought on them all the curses of the covenant I had commanded them to follow but that they did not keep.' "

9Then the Lord said to me, "There is a conspiracy among the people of Judah and those who live in Jerusalem. [10]They have returned to the sins of their forefathers, who refused to listen to my words. They have followed other gods to serve them. Both the house of Israel and the house of Judah have broken the covenant I made with their forefathers. [11]Therefore this is what the LORD says: 'I will bring on them a disaster they cannot escape. Although they cry out to me, I will not listen to them. [12]The towns of Judah and the people of Jerusalem will go and cry out to the gods to whom they burn incense, but they will not help them at all when disaster strikes. [13]You have as many gods as you have towns, O Judah; and the altars you have set up to burn incense to that shameful god Baal are as many as the streets of Jerusalem.'

[14]"Do not pray for this people nor offer any plea or petition for them, because I will not listen when they call to me in the time of their distress.

> [15]"What is my beloved doing in my temple
>   as she works out her evil schemes with many?
>   Can consecrated meat avert ⌞your punishment⌟?
> When you engage in your wickedness,
>   then you rejoice.[a]"

> [16]The LORD called you a thriving olive tree
>   with fruit beautiful in form.
> But with the roar of a mighty storm
>   he will set it on fire,
>   and its branches will be broken.

[17]The LORD Almighty, who planted you, has decreed disaster for you, because the house of Israel and the house of Judah have done evil and provoked me to anger by burning incense to Baal.

Plot Against Jeremiah

[18]Because the LORD revealed their plot to me, I knew it, for at that time he showed me what they were doing. [19]I had been like a gentle lamb led to the slaughter; I did not realize that they had plotted against me, saying,

> "Let us destroy the tree and its fruit;
>   let us cut him off from the land of the living,
>   that his name be remembered no more."
> [20]But, O LORD Almighty, you who judge righteously
>   and test the heart and mind,
> let me see your vengeance upon them,
>   for to you I have committed my cause.

[21]"Therefore this is what the LORD says about the men of Anathoth who are seeking your life and saying, 'Do not prophesy in the name of the LORD or you will die by our hands'— [22]therefore this is what the LORD Almighty says: 'I will punish them. Their young men will die by the sword, their sons and daughters by famine. [23]Not even a remnant will be left to them, because I will bring disaster on the men of Anathoth in the year of their punishment.' "

Jeremiah's Complaint

12

> You are always righteous, O LORD,
>   when I bring a case before you.
> Yet I would speak with you about your justice:
>   Why does the way of the wicked prosper?
>   Why do all the faithless live at ease?
> [2]You have planted them, and they have taken root;
>   they grow and bear fruit.
> You are always on their lips
>   but far from their hearts.
> [3]Yet you know me, O LORD;
>   you see me and test my thoughts about you.

a 15 Or Could consecrated meat avert your punishment? / Then you would rejoice

Drag them off like sheep to be butchered!
  Set them apart for the day of slaughter!
⁴How long will the land lie parched[a]
  and the grass in every field be withered?
Because those who live in it are wicked,
  the animals and birds have perished.
Moreover, the people are saying,
  "He will not see what happens to us."

God's Answer

⁵"If you have raced with men on foot
  and they have worn you out,
    how can you compete with horses?
If you stumble in safe country,[b]
  how will you manage in the thickets by[c] the Jordan?
⁶Your brothers, your own family—
  even they have betrayed you;
  they have raised a loud cry against you.
Do not trust them,
  though they speak well of you.

⁷"I will forsake my house,
  abandon my inheritance;
I will give the one I love
  into the hands of her enemies.
⁸My inheritance has become to me
  like a lion in the forest.
She roars at me;
  therefore I hate her.
⁹Has not my inheritance become to me
  like a speckled bird of prey
  that other birds of prey surround and attack?
Go and gather all the wild beasts;
  bring them to devour.
¹⁰Many shepherds will ruin my vineyard
  and trample down my field;
they will turn my pleasant field
  into a desolate wasteland.
¹¹It will be made a wasteland,
  parched and desolate before me;
the whole land will be laid waste
  because there is no one who cares.
¹²Over all the barren heights in the desert
  destroyers will swarm,
for the sword of the LORD will devour
  from one end of the land to the other;
  no one will be safe.
¹³They will sow wheat but reap thorns;
  they will wear themselves out but gain nothing.
So bear the shame of your harvest
  because of the LORD's fierce anger."

¹⁴This is what the LORD says: "As for all my wicked neighbors who seize the inheritance I gave my people Israel, I will uproot them from their lands and I will uproot the house of Judah from among them. ¹⁵But after I uproot them, I will again have compassion and will bring each of them

a 4 Or *land mourn*   b 5 Or *If you put your trust in a land of safety*   c 5 Or *the flooding of* back to his own inheritance and his own country. [16]And if they learn well the ways of my people and swear by my name, saying, 'As surely as the LORD lives'—even as they once taught my people to swear by Baal—then they will be established among my people. [17]But if any nation does not listen, I will completely uproot and destroy it," declares the LORD.

A Linen Belt

13 This is what the LORD said to me: "Go and buy a linen belt and put it around your waist, but do not let it touch water." [2]So I bought a belt, as the LORD directed, and put it around my waist.

[3]Then the word of the LORD came to me a second time: [4]"Take the belt you bought and are wearing around your waist, and go now to Perath[a] and hide it there in a crevice in the rocks." [5]So I went and hid it at Perath, as the LORD told me.

[6]Many days later the LORD said to me, "Go now to Perath and get the belt I told you to hide there." [7]So I went to Perath and dug up the belt and took it from the place where I had hidden it, but now it was ruined and completely useless.

[8]Then the word of the LORD came to me: [9]"This is what the LORD says: 'In the same way I will ruin the pride of Judah and the great pride of Jerusalem. [10]These wicked people, who refuse to listen to my words, who follow the stubbornness of their hearts and go after other gods to serve and worship them, will be like this belt—completely useless! [11]For as a belt is bound around a man's waist, so I bound the whole house of Israel and the whole house of Judah to me,' declares the LORD, 'to be my people for my renown and praise and honor. But they have not listened.'

Wineskins

[12]"Say to them: 'This is what the LORD, the God of Israel, says: Every wineskin should be filled with wine.' And if they say to you, 'Don't we know that every wineskin should be filled with wine?' [13]then tell them, 'This is what the LORD says: I am going to fill with drunkenness all who live in this land, including the kings who sit on David's throne, the priests, the prophets and all those living in Jerusalem. [14]I will smash them one against the other, fathers and sons alike, declares the LORD. I will allow no pity or mercy or compassion to keep me from destroying them.' "

Threat of Captivity

[15]Hear and pay attention,
    do not be arrogant,
    for the LORD has spoken.
[16]Give glory to the LORD your God
    before he brings the darkness,
before your feet stumble
    on the darkening hills.
You hope for light,
    but he will turn it to thick darkness
    and change it to deep gloom.
[17]But if you do not listen,
    I will weep in secret
    because of your pride;
my eyes will weep bitterly,
    overflowing with tears,
    because the LORD's flock will be taken captive.

[18]Say to the king and to the queen mother,
    "Come down from your thrones,
    for your glorious crowns
    will fall from your heads."
[19]The cities in the Negev will be shut up,
    and there will be no one to open them.

---

a 4 Or possibly the Euphrates; also in verses 5-7

All Judah will be carried into exile,
　　carried completely away.

20 Lift up your eyes and see
　　those who are coming from the north.
Where is the flock that was entrusted to you,
　　the sheep of which you boasted?
21 What will you say when ⌊the Lord⌋ sets over you
　　those you cultivated as your special allies?
Will not pain grip you
　　like that of a woman in labor?
22 And if you ask yourself,
　　"Why has this happened to me?"—
it is because of your many sins
　　that your skirts have been torn off
　　and your body mistreated.
23 Can the Ethiopian[a] change his skin
　　or the leopard its spots?
Neither can you do good
　　who are accustomed to doing evil.

24 "I will scatter you like chaff
　　driven by the desert wind.
25 This is your lot,
　　the portion I have decreed for you,"

　　　　　　　　　　　　　　　　　declares the Lord,

"because you have forgotten me
　　and trusted in false gods.
26 I will pull up your skirts over your face
　　that your shame may be seen—
27 your adulteries and lustful neighings,
　　your shameless prostitution!
I have seen your detestable acts
　　on the hills and in the fields.
Woe to you, O Jerusalem!
　　How long will you be unclean?"

Drought, Famine, Sword

14 This is the word of the Lord to Jeremiah concerning the drought:

2 "Judah mourns,
　　her cities languish;
they wail for the land,
　　and a cry goes up from Jerusalem.
3 The nobles send their servants for water;
　　they go to the cisterns
　　but find no water.
They return with their jars unfilled;
　　dismayed and despairing,
　　they cover their heads.
4 The ground is cracked
　　because there is no rain in the land;
the farmers are dismayed
　　and cover their heads.
5 Even the doe in the field

a 23 Hebrew *Cushite* (probably a person from the upper Nile region)

deserts her newborn fawn
because there is no grass.
⁶Wild donkeys stand on the barren heights
and pant like jackals;
their eyesight fails
for lack of pasture."

⁷Although our sins testify against us,
O LORD, do something for the sake of your name.
For our backsliding is great;
we have sinned against you.
⁸O Hope of Israel,
its Savior in times of distress,
why are you like a stranger in the land,
like a traveler who stays only a night?
⁹Why are you like a man taken by surprise,
like a warrior powerless to save?
You are among us, O LORD,
and we bear your name;
do not forsake us!

¹⁰This is what the LORD says about this people:

"They greatly love to wander;
they do not restrain their feet.
So the LORD does not accept them;
he will now remember their wickedness
and punish them for their sins."

¹¹Then the LORD said to me, "Do not pray for the well-being of this people. ¹²Although they fast, I will not listen to their cry; though they offer burnt offerings and grain offerings, I will not accept them. Instead, I will destroy them with the sword, famine and plague."

¹³But I said, "Ah, Sovereign LORD, the prophets keep telling them, 'You will not see the sword or suffer famine. Indeed, I will give you lasting peace in this place.' "

¹⁴Then the LORD said to me, "The prophets are prophesying lies in my name. I have not sent them or appointed them or spoken to them. They are prophesying to you false visions, divinations, idolatries ᵃ and the delusions of their own minds. ¹⁵Therefore, this is what the LORD says about the prophets who are prophesying in my name: I did not send them, yet they are saying, 'No sword or famine will touch this land.' Those same prophets will perish by sword and famine. ¹⁶And the people they are prophesying to will be thrown out into the streets of Jerusalem because of the famine and sword. There will be no one to bury them or their wives, their sons or their daughters. I will pour out on them the calamity they deserve.

¹⁷"Speak this word to them:

" 'Let my eyes overflow with tears
night and day without ceasing;
for my virgin daughter—my people—
has suffered a grievous wound,
a crushing blow.
¹⁸If I go into the country,
I see those slain by the sword;
if I go into the city,
I see the ravages of famine.
Both prophet and priest
have gone to a land they know not.' "

¹⁹Have you rejected Judah completely?

ᵃ 14 Or visions, worthless divinations

mirror images

And because the LORD had closed her womb, her rival kept provoking her in order to irritate her. 1 Samuel 1:6

Peninnah—Rubbing It In

Not only did Peninnah have to share her husband, Elkanah, with his other wife, Hannah, but she also had to face the fact that he loved Hannah more. Even though Peninnah had given him many sons and daughters, she couldn't win his favor. Hannah still had his heart—even though she couldn't have any children.

So what did Peninnah do? She could have looked to God for her strength. She could have befriended Hannah to fill the void her husband left in her heart. But Peninnah chose a different path. She resorted to some classic girl-fight tactics. She tried to cut down Hannah, picked on her for being childless and insulted her, never letting her forget her pain. Peninnah tormented Hannah at every opportunity.

Peninnah was downright jealous, and she let her feelings of loss and pain turn ugly.

The truth is, there will always be some girl who seems to be getting more than you. You think she's more popular, prettier or more talented. Maybe she's the guys' favorite, the teacher's pet or a sister who can do no wrong.

Our natural instinct is to try to lift ourselves up by putting others down. We feel that if we can't be the most popular, at least we can trash the one who is. That may be what we naturally want to do, but there's no place for this kind of attitude in a Christian's life.

What glory is there for the girl who keeps pointing out she is smarter than the "dumb blonde" cheerleader? Maybe that cheerleader has learning problems. Maybe she's deeply embarrassed because of her difficulty in school. Peninnah's story reminds us that even the girls who seem to have more than we do still need friendship and encouragement. Her efforts to lift herself up by stepping on Hannah actually backfired—her jealousy said more about her own shortcomings than Hannah's. In the same way, how we treat others shows either that we are self-confident enough to lift others up or that we are just jealous little girls.

Dear God, I don't want to hurt others to try to get ahead. Help me to lift others up—even the ones who don't seem like they need it. Amen.

dear God

To read the next Mirror Images profile, go to page 1083.

» **Read more about Peninnah in 1 Samuel 1:1–8 (page 321).**

Do you despise Zion?
Why have you afflicted us
    so that we cannot be healed?
We hoped for peace
    but no good has come,
for a time of healing
    but there is only terror.
²⁰ O Lord, we acknowledge our wickedness
    and the guilt of our fathers;
    we have indeed sinned against you.
²¹ For the sake of your name do not despise us;
    do not dishonor your glorious throne.
Remember your covenant with us
    and do not break it.
²² Do any of the worthless idols of the nations bring rain?
    Do the skies themselves send down showers?
No, it is you, O Lord our God.
    Therefore our hope is in you,
    for you are the one who does all this.

15

Then the Lord said to me: "Even if Moses and Samuel were to stand before me, my heart would not go out to this people. Send them away from my presence! Let them go! ² And if they ask you, 'Where shall we go?' tell them, 'This is what the Lord says:

" 'Those destined for death, to death;
those for the sword, to the sword;
those for starvation, to starvation;
those for captivity, to captivity.'

³"I will send four kinds of destroyers against them," declares the Lord, "the sword to kill and the dogs to drag away and the birds of the air and the beasts of the earth to devour and destroy. ⁴I will make them abhorrent to all the kingdoms of the earth because of what Manasseh son of Hezekiah king of Judah did in Jerusalem.

⁵ "Who will have pity on you, O Jerusalem?
    Who will mourn for you?
    Who will stop to ask how you are?
⁶ You have rejected me," declares the Lord.
    "You keep on backsliding.
So I will lay hands on you and destroy you;
    I can no longer show compassion.
⁷ I will winnow them with a winnowing fork
    at the city gates of the land.
I will bring bereavement and destruction on my people,
    for they have not changed their ways.
⁸ I will make their widows more numerous
    than the sand of the sea.
At midday I will bring a destroyer
    against the mothers of their young men;
suddenly I will bring down on them
    anguish and terror.
⁹ The mother of seven will grow faint
    and breathe her last.
Her sun will set while it is still day;
    she will be disgraced and humiliated.
I will put the survivors to the sword
    before their enemies,"

                                        declares the Lord.

¹⁰Alas, my mother, that you gave me birth,
    a man with whom the whole land strives and contends!
I have neither lent nor borrowed,
    yet everyone curses me.

¹¹The Lord said,

    "Surely I will deliver you for a good purpose;
    surely I will make your enemies plead with you
        in times of disaster and times of distress.

¹²"Can a man break iron—
    iron from the north—or bronze?
¹³Your wealth and your treasures
    I will give as plunder, without charge,
because of all your sins
    throughout your country.
¹⁴I will enslave you to your enemies
    in ^a a land you do not know,
for my anger will kindle a fire
    that will burn against you."

¹⁵You understand, O Lord;
    remember me and care for
        me.
Avenge me on my
        persecutors.
You are long-suffering—do not
        take me away;
think of how I suffer reproach
        for your sake.
¹⁶When your words came, I ate them;
    they were my joy and my
        heart's delight,
for I bear your name,
    O Lord God Almighty.
¹⁷I never sat in the company of
        revelers,
    never made merry with them;
I sat alone because your hand
        was on me
and you had filled me with
        indignation.
¹⁸Why is my pain unending
    and my wound grievous and
        incurable?
Will you be to me like a
        deceptive brook,
like a spring that fails?

¹⁹Therefore this is what the Lord says:

    "If you repent, I will restore you
        that you may serve me;
    if you utter worthy, not worthless, words,
        you will be my spokesman.

genuine
respect »» 15:16

Do you trust in Jesus? If so, then you "bear his name." And one of the things that marks you as a "name-bearer" is that you cherish and respect the things he has to say. You can find joy and delight in what God has shared in his Word. If you don't, maybe it's because you've never taken the time and effort to dig into the Bible. Once you get started, you may find yourself starting to hang on his every word.

^a 14 Some Hebrew manuscripts, Septuagint and Syriac (see also Jer. 17:4); most Hebrew manuscripts *I will cause your enemies to bring you / into*

Let this people turn to you,
  but you must not turn to them.
²⁰I will make you a wall to this people,
  a fortified wall of bronze;
they will fight against you
  but will not overcome you,
for I am with you
  to rescue and save you,"

declares the LORD.

²¹ "I will save you from the hands of the wicked
  and redeem you from the grasp of the cruel."

Day of Disaster

16 Then the word of the LORD came to me: ²"You must not marry and have sons or daughters in this place." ³For this is what the LORD says about the sons and daughters born in this land and about the women who are their mothers and the men who are their fathers: ⁴"They will die of deadly diseases. They will not be mourned or buried but will be like refuse lying on the ground. They will perish by sword and famine, and their dead bodies will become food for the birds of the air and the beasts of the earth."

⁵For this is what the LORD says: "Do not enter a house where there is a funeral meal; do not go to mourn or show sympathy, because I have withdrawn my blessing, my love and my pity from this people," declares the LORD. ⁶"Both high and low will die in this land. They will not be buried or mourned, and no one will cut himself or shave his head for them. ⁷No one will offer food to comfort those who mourn for the dead—not even for a father or a mother—nor will anyone give them a drink to console them.

⁸"And do not enter a house where there is feasting and sit down to eat and drink. ⁹For this is what the LORD Almighty, the God of Israel, says: Before your eyes and in your days I will bring an end to the sounds of joy and gladness and to the voices of bride and bridegroom in this place.

¹⁰"When you tell these people all this and they ask you, 'Why has the LORD decreed such a great disaster against us? What wrong have we done? What sin have we committed against the LORD our God?' ¹¹then say to them, 'It is because your fathers forsook me,' declares the LORD, 'and followed other gods and served and worshiped them. They forsook me and did not keep my law. ¹²But you have behaved more wickedly than your fathers. See how each of you is following the stubbornness of his evil heart instead of obeying me. ¹³So I will throw you out of this land into a land neither you nor your fathers have known, and there you will serve other gods day and night, for I will show you no favor.'

¹⁴"However, the days are coming," declares the LORD, "when men will no longer say, 'As surely as the LORD lives, who brought the Israelites up out of Egypt,' ¹⁵but they will say, 'As surely as the LORD lives, who brought the Israelites up out of the land of the north and out of all the countries where he had banished them.' For I will restore them to the land I gave their forefathers.

¹⁶"But now I will send for many fishermen," declares the LORD, "and they will catch them. After that I will send for many hunters, and they will hunt them down on every mountain and hill and from the crevices of the rocks. ¹⁷My eyes are on all their ways; they are not hidden from me, nor is their sin concealed from my eyes. ¹⁸I will repay them double for their wickedness and their sin, because they have defiled my land with the lifeless forms of their vile images and have filled my inheritance with their detestable idols."

¹⁹O LORD, my strength and my fortress,
  my refuge in time of distress,

truth or dare

In case you've just tuned in, God's summing up the main events in this passage: "Hey Judah: I loved you; you rejected me; I'm punishing you; but I'll restore you!"

16:10–15

to you the nations will come
from the ends of the earth and say,
"Our fathers possessed nothing but false gods,
worthless idols that did them no good.
²⁰Do men make their own gods?
Yes, but they are not gods!"

²¹"Therefore I will teach them—
this time I will teach them
my power and might.
Then they will know
that my name is the LORD.

17

"Judah's sin is engraved with an iron tool,
inscribed with a flint point,
on the tablets of their hearts
and on the horns of their altars.
²Even their children remember
their altars and Asherah poles^a
beside the spreading trees
and on the high hills.
³My mountain in the land
and your^b wealth and all your treasures
I will give away as plunder,
together with your high places,
because of sin throughout your country.
⁴Through your own fault you will lose
the inheritance I gave you.
I will enslave you to your enemies
in a land you do not know,
for you have kindled my anger,
and it will burn forever."

⁵This is what the LORD says:

"Cursed is the one who trusts in man,
who depends on flesh for his strength
and whose heart turns away from the LORD.
⁶He will be like a bush in the wastelands;
he will not see prosperity when it comes.
He will dwell in the parched places of the desert,
in a salt land where no one lives.

⁷"But blessed is the man who trusts in the LORD,
whose confidence is in him.
⁸He will be like a tree planted by the water
that sends out its roots by the stream.
It does not fear when heat comes;
its leaves are always green.
It has no worries in a year of drought
and never fails to bear fruit."

⁹The heart is deceitful above all things
and beyond cure.
Who can understand it?

¹⁰"I the LORD search the heart
and examine the mind,

---

^a 2 That is, symbols of the goddess Asherah   ^b 2,3 Or hills / ³and the mountains of the land. / Your

to reward a man according to his conduct,
according to what his deeds deserve."

¹¹ Like a partridge that hatches eggs it did not lay
is the man who gains riches by unjust means.
When his life is half gone, they will desert him,
and in the end he will prove to be a fool.

¹² A glorious throne, exalted from the beginning,
is the place of our sanctuary.
¹³ O LORD, the hope of Israel,
all who forsake you will be put to shame.
Those who turn away from you will be written in the dust
because they have forsaken the LORD,
the spring of living water.

¹⁴ Heal me, O LORD, and I will be
healed;
save me and I will be saved,
for you are the one I praise.
¹⁵ They keep saying to me,
"Where is the word of the
LORD?
Let it now be fulfilled!"
¹⁶ I have not run away from being
your shepherd;
you know I have not desired
the day of despair.
What passes my lips is open
before you.
¹⁷ Do not be a terror to me;
you are my refuge in the day
of disaster.
¹⁸ Let my persecutors be put to
shame,
but keep me from shame;
let them be terrified,
but keep me from terror.
Bring on them the day of
disaster;
destroy them with double
destruction.

love ❤ notes

17:7–8

My daughter,

*If you trust in me, you'll grow
like a well-watered, healthy
tree. Your roots will be strong,
and you won't be shaken by
anything. You will never wilt
under pressure or lack anything
you need.*

—God

What kind of tree are you? Healthy and
well-watered?

_____

_____

_____

_____

_____

_____

_____

_____

_____

Keeping the Sabbath Holy

¹⁹ This is what the LORD said to me: "Go
and stand at the gate of the people,
through which the kings of Judah go in and
out; stand also at all the other gates of Jerusalem. ²⁰ Say to them, 'Hear the word of
the LORD, O kings of Judah and all people of
Judah and everyone living in Jerusalem
who come through these gates. ²¹ This is
what the LORD says: Be careful not to carry
a load on the Sabbath day or bring it
through the gates of Jerusalem. ²² Do not
bring a load out of your houses or do any
work on the Sabbath, but keep the Sabbath

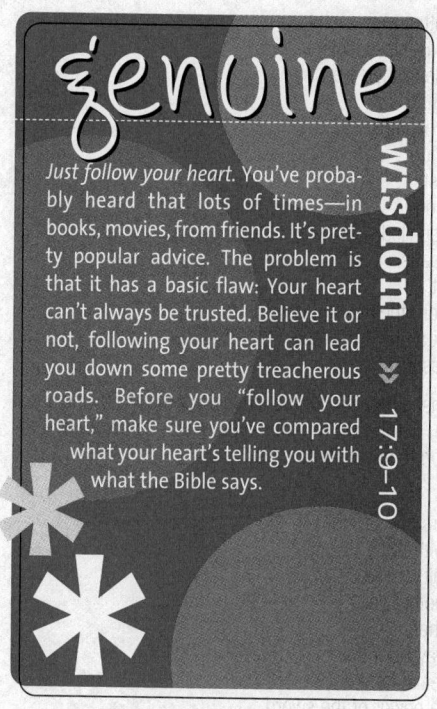

day holy, as I commanded your forefathers. [23]Yet they did not listen or pay attention; they were stiff-necked and would not listen or respond to discipline. [24]But if you are careful to obey me, declares the LORD, and bring no load through the gates of this city on the Sabbath, but keep the Sabbath day holy by not doing any work on it, [25]then kings who sit on David's throne will come through the gates of this city with their officials. They and their officials will come riding in chariots and on horses, accompanied by the men of Judah and those living in Jerusalem, and this city will be inhabited forever. [26]People will come from the towns of Judah and the villages around Jerusalem, from the territory of Benjamin and the western foothills, from the hill country and the Negev, bringing burnt offerings and sacrifices, grain offerings, incense and thank offerings to the house of the LORD. [27]But if you do not obey me to keep the Sabbath day holy by not carrying any load as you come through the gates of Jerusalem on the Sabbath day, then I will kindle an unquenchable fire in the gates of Jerusalem that will consume her fortresses.' "

At the Potter's House

18 This is the word that came to Jeremiah from the LORD: [2]"Go down to the potter's house, and there I will give you my message." [3]So I went down to the potter's house, and I saw him working at the wheel. [4]But the pot he was shaping from the clay was marred in his hands; so the potter formed it into another pot, shaping it as seemed best to him.

[5]Then the word of the LORD came to me: [6]"O house of Israel, can I not do with you as this potter does?" declares the LORD. "Like clay in the hand of the potter, so are you in my hand, O house of Israel. [7]If at any time I announce that a nation or kingdom is to be uprooted, torn down and destroyed, [8]and if that nation I warned repents of its evil, then I will relent and not inflict on it the disaster I had planned. [9]And if at another time I announce that a nation or kingdom is to be built up and planted, [10]and if it does evil in my sight and does not obey me, then I will reconsider the good I had intended to do for it.

[11]"Now therefore say to the people of Judah and those living in Jerusalem, 'This is what the LORD says: Look! I am preparing a disaster for you and devising a plan against you. So turn from your evil ways, each one of you, and reform your ways and your actions.' [12]But they will reply, 'It's no use. We will continue with our own plans; each of us will follow the stubbornness of his evil heart.' "

[13]Therefore this is what the LORD says:

> "Inquire among the nations:
>   Who has ever heard anything like this?
> A most horrible thing has been done
>   by Virgin Israel.
> [14]Does the snow of Lebanon
>   ever vanish from its rocky slopes?
> Do its cool waters from distant sources
>   ever cease to flow? [a]

---

[a] 14 The meaning of the Hebrew for this sentence is uncertain.

¹⁵Yet my people have forgotten me;
they burn incense to worthless idols,
which made them stumble in their ways
and in the ancient paths.
They made them walk in bypaths
and on roads not built up.
¹⁶Their land will be laid waste,
an object of lasting scorn;
all who pass by will be appalled
and will shake their heads.
¹⁷Like a wind from the east,
I will scatter them before their enemies;
I will show them my back and not my face
in the day of their disaster."

¹⁸They said, "Come, let's make plans against Jeremiah; for the teaching of the law by the priest will not be lost, nor will counsel from the wise, nor the word from the prophets. So come, let's attack him with our tongues and pay no attention to anything he says."

¹⁹Listen to me, O Lord;
hear what my accusers are saying!
²⁰Should good be repaid with evil?
Yet they have dug a pit for me.
Remember that I stood before you
and spoke in their behalf
to turn your wrath away from them.
²¹So give their children over to famine;
hand them over to the power of the sword.
Let their wives be made childless and widows;
let their men be put to death,
their young men slain by the sword in battle.
²²Let a cry be heard from their houses
when you suddenly bring invaders against them,
for they have dug a pit to capture me
and have hidden snares for my feet.
²³But you know, O Lord,
all their plots to kill me.
Do not forgive their crimes
or blot out their sins from your sight.
Let them be overthrown before you;
deal with them in the time of your anger.

19 This is what the Lord says: "Go and buy a clay jar from a potter. Take along some of the elders of the people and of the priests ²and go out to the Valley of Ben Hinnom, near the entrance of the Potsherd Gate. There proclaim the words I tell you, ³and say, 'Hear the word of the Lord, O kings of Judah and people of Jerusalem. This is what the Lord Almighty, the God of Israel, says: Listen! I am going to bring a disaster on this place that will make the ears of everyone who hears of it tingle. ⁴For they have forsaken me and made this a place of foreign gods; they have burned sacrifices in it to gods that neither they nor their fathers nor the kings of Judah ever knew, and they have filled this place with the blood of the innocent. ⁵They have built the high places of Baal to burn their sons in the fire as offerings to Baal—something I did not command or mention, nor did it enter my mind. ⁶So beware, the days are coming, declares the Lord, when people will no longer call this place Topheth or the Valley of Ben Hinnom, but the Valley of Slaughter.

⁷" 'In this place I will ruin^a the plans of Judah and Jerusalem. I will make them fall by the sword

---

^a 7 The Hebrew for *ruin* sounds like the Hebrew for *jar* (see verses 1 and 10).

before their enemies, at the hands of those who seek their lives, and I will give their carcasses as food to the birds of the air and the beasts of the earth. [8]I will devastate this city and make it an object of scorn; all who pass by will be appalled and will scoff because of all its wounds. [9]I will make them eat the flesh of their sons and daughters, and they will eat one another's flesh during the stress of the siege imposed on them by the enemies who seek their lives.'

[10]"Then break the jar while those who go with you are watching, [11]and say to them, 'This is what the LORD Almighty says: I will smash this nation and this city just as this potter's jar is smashed and cannot be repaired. They will bury the dead in Topheth until there is no more room. [12]This is what I will do to this place and to those who live here, declares the LORD. I will make this city like Topheth. [13]The houses in Jerusalem and those of the kings of Judah will be defiled like this place, Topheth—all the houses where they burned incense on the roofs to all the starry hosts and poured out drink offerings to other gods.' "

[14]Jeremiah then returned from Topheth, where the LORD had sent him to prophesy, and stood in the court of the LORD's temple and said to all the people, [15]"This is what the LORD Almighty, the God of Israel, says: 'Listen! I am going to bring on this city and the villages around it every disaster I pronounced against them, because they were stiff-necked and would not listen to my words.' "

Jeremiah and Pashhur

20 When the priest Pashhur son of Immer, the chief officer in the temple of the LORD, heard Jeremiah prophesying these things, [2]he had Jeremiah the prophet beaten and put in the stocks at the Upper Gate of Benjamin at the LORD's temple. [3]The next day, when Pashhur released him from the stocks, Jeremiah said to him, "The LORD's name for you is not Pashhur, but Magor-Missabib. *a* [4]For this is what the LORD says: 'I will make you a terror to yourself and to all your friends; with your own eyes you will see them fall by the sword of their enemies. I will hand all Judah over to the king of Babylon, who will carry them away to Babylon or put them to the sword. [5]I will hand over to their enemies all the wealth of this city—all its products, all its valuables and all the treasures of the kings of Judah. They will take it away as plunder and carry it off to Babylon. [6]And you, Pashhur, and all who live in your house will go into exile to Babylon. There you will die and be buried, you and all your friends to whom you have prophesied lies.' "

Jeremiah's Complaint

[7]O LORD, you deceived[b] me, and I was deceived[b];
    you overpowered me and prevailed.
I am ridiculed all day long;
    everyone mocks me.
[8]Whenever I speak, I cry out
    proclaiming violence and destruction.
So the word of the LORD has brought me
    insult and reproach all day long.
[9]But if I say, "I will not mention him
    or speak any more in his name,"
his word is in my heart like a fire,
    a fire shut up in my bones.
I am weary of holding it in;
    indeed, I cannot.
[10]I hear many whispering,
    "Terror on every side!
    Report him! Let's report him!"
All my friends
    are waiting for me to slip, saying,
"Perhaps he will be deceived;
    then we will prevail over him
    and take our revenge on him."

[11]But the LORD is with me like a mighty warrior;

---

a 3 Magor-Missabib means *terror on every side.*   *b 7* Or *persuaded*

so my persecutors will stumble and not prevail.
They will fail and be thoroughly disgraced;
their dishonor will never be forgotten.

¹²O LORD Almighty, you who examine the righteous
and probe the heart and mind,
let me see your vengeance upon them,
for to you I have committed my cause.

¹³Sing to the LORD!
Give praise to the LORD!
He rescues the life of the needy
from the hands of the wicked.

¹⁴Cursed be the day I was born!
May the day my mother bore me not be blessed!
¹⁵Cursed be the man who brought my father the news,
who made him very glad, saying,
"A child is born to you—a son!"
¹⁶May that man be like the towns
the LORD overthrew without pity.
May he hear wailing in the morning,
a battle cry at noon.
¹⁷For he did not kill me in the womb,
with my mother as my grave,
her womb enlarged forever.
¹⁸Why did I ever come out of the womb
to see trouble and sorrow
and to end my days in shame?

God Rejects Zedekiah's Request

21 The word came to Jeremiah from the LORD when King Zedekiah sent to him Pashhur son of Malkijah and the priest Zephaniah son of Maaseiah. They said: ²"Inquire now of the LORD for us because Nebuchadnezzar*ᵃ* king of Babylon is attacking us. Perhaps the LORD will perform wonders for us as in times past so that he will withdraw from us."

³But Jeremiah answered them, "Tell Zedekiah, ⁴'This is what the LORD, the God of Israel, says: I am about to turn against you the weapons of war that are in your hands, which you are using to fight the king of Babylon and the Babylonians*ᵇ* who are outside the wall besieging you. And I will gather them inside this city. ⁵I myself will fight against you with an outstretched hand and a mighty arm in anger and fury and great wrath. ⁶I will strike down those who live in this city—both men and animals—and they will die of a terrible plague. ⁷After that, declares the LORD, I will hand over Zedekiah king of Judah, his officials and the people in this city who survive the plague, sword and famine, to Nebuchadnezzar king of Babylon and to their enemies who seek their lives. He will put them to the sword; he will show them no mercy or pity or compassion.'

⁸"Furthermore, tell the people, 'This is what the LORD says: See, I am setting before you the way of life and the way of death. ⁹Whoever stays in this city will die by the sword, famine or plague. But whoever goes out and surrenders to the Babylonians who are besieging you will live; he will escape with his life. ¹⁰I have determined to do this city harm and not good, declares the LORD. It will be given into the hands of the king of Babylon, and he will destroy it with fire.'

¹¹"Moreover, say to the royal house of Judah, 'Hear the word of the LORD; ¹²O house of David, this is what the LORD says:

" 'Administer justice every morning;
rescue from the hand of his oppressor
the one who has been robbed,
or my wrath will break out and burn like fire

ᵃ 2 Hebrew *Nebuchadrezzar*, of which *Nebuchadnezzar* is a variant; here and often in Jeremiah and Ezekiel
ᵇ 4 Or *Chaldeans*; also in verse 9

Alone and "Ann"onymous

focus | **Profile: Anna**

You can describe most girls at our school with one word. Musician. Jock. Cheerleader. Brain. Dork. Popular. Artsy. Whatever. Then there's *me*. I don't feel like I fit in anywhere. I'm the kind of girl who knows a lot of people and can kind of roam from group to group—yet I'm not really close with anyone. Every day at school I feel like a misfit.

I'm not a brainiac like my brother. I'm definitely not a rebel. I'm not Miss Prim-and-Proper either, though. I'm kind of on the fringes of the popular crowd, but I don't really belong.

I'm too blunt sometimes. I have my own sense of style (I guess you'd call it that) and am not afraid to show up at school wearing sweats and no makeup. Most of the girls hold me at a distance since I'm not like them. If you asked the people I hang out with about me, they'd probably say I'm nice and all, but they don't really know the real me.

I am in student council. I love everything about it—speaking, community service projects, planning events. It's awesome. I've been told that I'm a good speaker. But is that my high school identity: "Anna Ferguson, Public Speaker"? Yeah right. Like that's gonna win me any friends.

For more on friendship and fitting in, check out the links on www.TrueImagesBible.com

fitting in in focus

Ever feel like you know a lot of people but you don't quite belong anywhere? That's especially hard for girls. Girls tend to travel in packs, and girls are notorious for getting catty or turning on each other. How do you cope with the ups and downs of trying to fit in?

»*Be yourself*. If you don't fit neatly into any of those one-word categories, don't try. Eventually you'll find a friend who loves you just the way you are. Be patient.

»*You may not be the only one who feels this way*. Look for other girls around you who may be struggling to fit in, and who knows—you might be just what they need, and vice versa.

»*At the end of the day, there is one best friend who is always there—Jesus Christ*. He'll never turn his back on you. You belong perfectly with him (see Matthew 28:20, page 1333).

For more on this topic, see the index on page 1656.

because of the evil you have done—
        burn with no one to quench it.
¹³ I am against you, ⌊Jerusalem,⌋
        you who live above this valley
        on the rocky plateau,

                                                        declares the LORD—
    you who say, "Who can come against us?
        Who can enter our refuge?"
¹⁴ I will punish you as your deeds deserve,

                                                        declares the LORD.
    I will kindle a fire in your forests
        that will consume everything around you.' "

Judgment Against Evil Kings

22 This is what the LORD says: "Go down to the palace of the king of Judah and proclaim this message there: 2 Hear the word of the LORD, O king of Judah, you who sit on David's throne—you, your officials and your people who come through these gates. 3 This is what the LORD says: Do what is just and right. Rescue from the hand of his oppressor the one who has been robbed. Do no wrong or violence to the alien, the fatherless or the widow, and do not shed innocent blood in this place. 4 For if you are careful to carry out these commands, then kings who sit on David's throne will come through the gates of this palace, riding in chariots and on horses, accompanied by their officials and their people. 5 But if you do not obey these commands, declares the LORD, I swear by myself that this palace will become a ruin.' "

6 For this is what the LORD says about the palace of the king of Judah:

truth or dare

God gives you a choice whether to obey him or not. If you break the rules, you have to face up to the consequences. Bypass future heartache—follow God today.

22:1–5

"Though you are like Gilead to me,
    like the summit of Lebanon,
I will surely make you like a desert,
    like towns not inhabited.
7 I will send destroyers against you,
    each man with his weapons,
and they will cut up your fine cedar beams
    and throw them into the fire.

8 "People from many nations will pass by this city and will ask one another, 'Why has the LORD done such a thing to this great city?' 9 And the answer will be: 'Because they have forsaken the covenant of the LORD their God and have worshiped and served other gods.' "

10 Do not weep for the dead ⌊king⌋ or mourn his loss;
    rather, weep bitterly for him who is exiled,
because he will never return
    nor see his native land again.

11 For this is what the LORD says about Shallum[a] son of Josiah, who succeeded his father as king of Judah but has gone from this place: "He will never return. 12 He will die in the place where they have led him captive; he will not see this land again."

13 "Woe to him who builds his palace by unrighteousness,
    his upper rooms by injustice,
making his countrymen work for nothing,
    not paying them for their labor.
14 He says, 'I will build myself a great palace
    with spacious upper rooms.'
So he makes large windows in it,
    panels it with cedar
    and decorates it in red.

15 "Does it make you a king
    to have more and more cedar?
Did not your father have food and drink?
    He did what was right and just,
    so all went well with him.
16 He defended the cause of the poor and needy,

a 11 Also called Jehoahaz

and so all went well.
Is that not what it means to know me?"
    declares the LORD.
¹⁷ "But your eyes and your heart
    are set only on dishonest gain,
on shedding innocent blood
    and on oppression and extortion."

¹⁸ Therefore this is what the LORD says about Jehoiakim son of Josiah king of Judah:

"They will not mourn for him:
    'Alas, my brother! Alas, my sister!'
They will not mourn for him:
    'Alas, my master! Alas, his splendor!'
¹⁹ He will have the burial of a donkey—
    dragged away and thrown
    outside the gates of Jerusalem."

²⁰ "Go up to Lebanon and cry out,
    let your voice be heard in Bashan,
cry out from Abarim,
    for all your allies are crushed.
²¹ I warned you when you felt secure,
    but you said, 'I will not listen!'
This has been your way from your youth;
    you have not obeyed me.
²² The wind will drive all your shepherds away,
    and your allies will go into exile.
Then you will be ashamed and disgraced
    because of all your wickedness.
²³ You who live in 'Lebanon,'ᵃ
    who are nestled in cedar buildings,
how you will groan when pangs come upon you,
    pain like that of a woman in labor!

²⁴ "As surely as I live," declares the LORD, "even if you, Jehoiachinᵇ son of Jehoiakim king of Judah, were a signet ring on my right hand, I would still pull you off. ²⁵ I will hand you over to those who seek your life, those you fear—to Nebuchadnezzar king of Babylon and to the Babylonians.ᶜ ²⁶ I will hurl you and the mother who gave you birth into another country, where neither of you was born, and there you both will die. ²⁷ You will never come back to the land you long to return to."

²⁸ Is this man Jehoiachin a despised, broken pot,
    an object no one wants?
Why will he and his children be hurled out,
    cast into a land they do not know?
²⁹ O land, land, land,
    hear the word of the LORD!
³⁰ This is what the LORD says:
"Record this man as if childless,
    a man who will not prosper in his lifetime,
for none of his offspring will prosper,
    none will sit on the throne of David
    or rule anymore in Judah."

ᵃ 23 That is, the palace in Jerusalem (see 1 Kings 7:2)   ᵇ 24 Hebrew Coniah, a variant of Jehoiachin; also in verse 28
ᶜ 25 Or Chaldeans

The Righteous Branch

23 "Woe to the shepherds who are destroying and scattering the sheep of my pasture!" declares the LORD. ²Therefore this is what the LORD, the God of Israel, says to the shepherds who tend my people: "Because you have scattered my flock and driven them away and have not bestowed care on them, I will bestow punishment on you for the evil you have done," declares the LORD. ³"I myself will gather the remnant of my flock out of all the countries where I have driven them and will bring them back to their pasture, where they will be fruitful and increase in number. ⁴I will place shepherds over them who will tend them, and they will no longer be afraid or terrified, nor will any be missing," declares the LORD.

⁵"The days are coming," declares the LORD,
    "when I will raise up to David ᵃ a righteous
      Branch,
  a King who will reign wisely
      and do what is just and right in the land.
⁶ In his days Judah will be saved
      and Israel will live in safety.
  This is the name by which he will be called:
      The LORD Our Righteousness.

⁷"So then, the days are coming," declares the LORD, "when people will no longer say, 'As surely as the LORD lives, who brought the Israelites up out of Egypt,' ⁸but they will say, 'As surely as the LORD lives, who brought the descendants of Israel up out of the land of the north and out of all the countries where he had banished them.' Then they will live in their own land."

Lying Prophets

⁹Concerning the prophets:

  My heart is broken within me;
      all my bones tremble.
  I am like a drunken man,
      like a man overcome by wine,
  because of the LORD
      and his holy words.
¹⁰ The land is full of adulterers;
      because of the curse ᵇ the land lies parched ᶜ
      and the pastures in the desert are withered.
  The ⌊prophets⌋ follow an evil course
      and use their power unjustly.

¹¹ "Both prophet and priest are godless;
      even in my temple I find their wickedness,"
                                    declares the LORD.

¹² "Therefore their path will become slippery;
      they will be banished to darkness
      and there they will fall.
  I will bring disaster on them
      in the year they are punished,"
                                    declares the LORD.

truth or dare

The shepherds for God's people totally abused their positions. Have you been hurt by those who were supposed to care for you? The real Shepherd will comfort and guide you.

23:1–6

ᵃ 5 Or up from David's line   ᵇ 10 Or because of these things   ᶜ 10 Or land mourns

¹³ "Among the prophets of Samaria
    I saw this repulsive thing:
They prophesied by Baal
    and led my people Israel astray.
¹⁴ And among the prophets of Jerusalem
    I have seen something horrible:
They commit adultery and live a lie.
They strengthen the hands of evildoers,
    so that no one turns from his wickedness.
They are all like Sodom to me;
    the people of Jerusalem are like Gomorrah."

¹⁵Therefore, this is what the LORD Almighty says concerning the prophets:

"I will make them eat bitter food
    and drink poisoned water,
because from the prophets of Jerusalem
    ungodliness has spread throughout the land."

¹⁶This is what the LORD Almighty says:

"Do not listen to what the prophets are prophesying to you;
    they fill you with false hopes.
They speak visions from their own minds,
    not from the mouth of the LORD.
¹⁷ They keep saying to those who despise me,
    'The LORD says: You will have peace.'
And to all who follow the stubbornness of their hearts
    they say, 'No harm will come to you.'
¹⁸ But which of them has stood in the council of the LORD
    to see or to hear his word?
Who has listened and heard his word?
¹⁹ See, the storm of the LORD
    will burst out in wrath,
a whirlwind swirling down
    on the heads of the wicked.
²⁰ The anger of the LORD will not turn back
    until he fully accomplishes
    the purposes of his heart.
In days to come
    you will understand it clearly.
²¹ I did not send these prophets,
    yet they have run with their message;
I did not speak to them,
    yet they have prophesied.
²² But if they had stood in my council,
    they would have proclaimed my words to my people
and would have turned them from their evil ways
    and from their evil deeds.

²³ "Am I only a God nearby,"

                  declares the LORD,

"and not a God far away?
²⁴ Can anyone hide in secret places
    so that I cannot see him?"

                  declares the LORD.

"Do not I fill heaven and earth?"

                  declares the LORD.

25"I have heard what the prophets say who prophesy lies in my name. They say, 'I had a dream! I had a dream!' 26How long will this continue in the hearts of these lying prophets, who prophesy the delusions of their own minds? 27They think the dreams they tell one another will make my people forget my name, just as their fathers forgot my name through Baal worship. 28Let the prophet who has a dream tell his dream, but let the one who has my word speak it faithfully. For what has straw to do with grain?" declares the LORD. 29"Is not my word like fire," declares the LORD, "and like a hammer that breaks a rock in pieces?

30"Therefore," declares the LORD, "I am against the prophets who steal from one another words supposedly from me. 31Yes," declares the LORD, "I am against the prophets who wag their own tongues and yet declare, 'The LORD declares.' 32Indeed, I am against those who prophesy false dreams," declares the LORD. "They tell them and lead my people astray with their reckless lies, yet I did not send or appoint them. They do not benefit these people in the least," declares the LORD.

False Oracles and False Prophets

33"When these people, or a prophet or a priest, ask you, 'What is the oracle*a* of the LORD?' say to them, 'What oracle?*b* I will forsake you, declares the LORD.' 34If a prophet or a priest or anyone else claims, 'This is the oracle of the LORD,' I will punish that man and his household. 35This is what each of you keeps on saying to his friend or relative: 'What is the LORD's answer?' or 'What has the LORD spoken?' 36But you must not mention 'the oracle of the LORD' again, because every man's own word becomes his oracle and so you distort the words of the living God, the LORD Almighty, our God. 37This is what you keep saying to a prophet: 'What is the LORD's answer to you?' or 'What has the LORD spoken?' 38Although you claim, 'This is the oracle of the LORD,' this is what the LORD says: You used the words, 'This is the oracle of the LORD,' even though I told you that you must not claim, 'This is the oracle of the LORD.' 39Therefore, I will surely forget you and cast you out of my presence along with the city I gave to you and your fathers. 40I will bring upon you everlasting disgrace—everlasting shame that will not be forgotten."

Two Baskets of Figs

24 After Jehoiachin*c* son of Jehoiakim king of Judah and the officials, the craftsmen and the artisans of Judah were carried into exile from Jerusalem to Babylon by Nebuchadnezzar king of Babylon, the LORD showed me two baskets of figs placed in front of the temple of the LORD. 2One basket had very good figs, like those that ripen early; the other basket had very poor figs, so bad they could not be eaten.

3Then the LORD asked me, "What do you see, Jeremiah?"

"Figs," I answered. "The good ones are very good, but the poor ones are so bad they cannot be eaten."

truth or dare

Which kind of fig are you? A bad fig, ignoring God and what he's trying to teach you? Or a good fig with a teachable heart that learns from God's discipline?

24:1–10

4Then the word of the LORD came to me: 5"This is what the LORD, the God of Israel, says: 'Like these good figs, I regard as good the exiles from Judah, whom I sent away from this place to the land of the Babylonians.*d* 6My eyes will watch over them for their good, and I will bring them back to this land. I will build them up and not tear them down; I will plant them and not uproot them. 7I will give them a heart to know me, that I am the LORD. They will be my people, and I will be their God, for they will return to me with all their heart.

8" 'But like the poor figs, which are so bad they cannot be eaten,' says the LORD, 'so will I deal with Zedekiah king of Judah, his officials and the survivors from Jerusalem, whether they remain in this land or live in Egypt. 9I will make them abhorrent and an offense to all the kingdoms of the earth, a reproach and a byword, an object of ridicule and cursing, wherever I banish them. 10I will send the sword, famine and plague against them until they are destroyed from the land I gave to them and their fathers.' "

a 33 Or *burden* (see Septuagint and Vulgate)   *b 33* Hebrew; Septuagint and Vulgate *'You are the burden.* (The Hebrew for *oracle* and *burden* is the same.)   *c 1* Hebrew *Jeconiah,* a variant of *Jehoiachin*   *d 5* Or *Chaldeans*

Seventy Years of Captivity

25 The word came to Jeremiah concerning all the people of Judah in the fourth year of Jehoiakim son of Josiah king of Judah, which was the first year of Nebuchadnezzar king of Babylon. [2]So Jeremiah the prophet said to all the people of Judah and to all those living in Jerusalem: [3]For twenty-three years—from the thirteenth year of Josiah son of Amon king of Judah until this very day—the word of the LORD has come to me and I have spoken to you again and again, but you have not listened.

[4]And though the LORD has sent all his servants the prophets to you again and again, you have not listened or paid any attention. [5]They said, "Turn now, each of you, from your evil ways and your evil practices, and you can stay in the land the LORD gave to you and your fathers for ever and ever. [6]Do not follow other gods to serve and worship them; do not provoke me to anger with what your hands have made. Then I will not harm you."

[7]"But you did not listen to me," declares the LORD, "and you have provoked me with what your hands have made, and you have brought harm to yourselves."

[8]Therefore the LORD Almighty says this: "Because you have not listened to my words, [9]I will summon all the peoples of the north and my servant Nebuchadnezzar king of Babylon," declares the LORD, "and I will bring them against this land and its inhabitants and against all the surrounding nations. I will completely destroy[a] them and make them an object of horror and scorn, and an everlasting ruin. [10]I will banish from them the sounds of joy and gladness, the voices of bride and bridegroom, the sound of millstones and the light of the lamp. [11]This whole country will become a desolate wasteland, and these nations will serve the king of Babylon seventy years.

[12]"But when the seventy years are fulfilled, I will punish the king of Babylon and his nation, the land of the Babylonians,[b] for their guilt," declares the LORD, "and will make it desolate forever. [13]I will bring upon that land all the things I have spoken against it, all that are written in this book and prophesied by Jeremiah against all the nations. [14]They themselves will be enslaved by many nations and great kings; I will repay them according to their deeds and the work of their hands."

The Cup of God's Wrath

[15]This is what the LORD, the God of Israel, said to me: "Take from my hand this cup filled with the wine of my wrath and make all the nations to whom I send you drink it. [16]When they drink it, they will stagger and go mad because of the sword I will send among them."

[17]So I took the cup from the LORD's hand and made all the nations to whom he sent me drink it: [18]Jerusalem and the towns of Judah, its kings and officials, to make them a ruin and an object of horror and scorn and cursing, as they are today; [19]Pharaoh king of Egypt, his attendants, his officials and all his people, [20]and all the foreign people there; all the kings of Uz; all the kings of the Philistines (those of Ashkelon, Gaza, Ekron, and the people left at Ashdod); [21]Edom, Moab and Ammon; [22]all the kings of Tyre and Sidon; the kings of the coastlands across the sea; [23]Dedan, Tema, Buz and all who are in distant places[c]; [24]all the kings of Arabia and all the kings of the foreign people who live in the desert; [25]all the kings of Zimri, Elam and Media; [26]and all the kings of the north, near and far, one after the other—all the kingdoms on the face of the earth. And after all of them, the king of Sheshach[d] will drink it too.

[27]"Then tell them, 'This is what the LORD Almighty, the God of Israel, says: Drink, get drunk and vomit, and fall to rise no more because of the sword I will send among you.' [28]But if they refuse to take the cup from your hand and drink, tell them, 'This is what the LORD Almighty says: You must drink it! [29]See, I am beginning to bring disaster on the city that bears my Name, and will you indeed go unpunished? You will not go unpunished, for I am calling down a sword upon all who live on the earth, declares the LORD Almighty.'

[30]"Now prophesy all these words against them and say to them:

> " 'The LORD will roar from on high;
>   he will thunder from his holy dwelling
>   and roar mightily against his land.
> He will shout like those who tread the grapes,

---

a 9 The Hebrew term refers to the irrevocable giving over of things or persons to the LORD, often by totally destroying them.   *b 12* Or *Chaldeans*   *c 23* Or *who clip the hair by their foreheads*   *d 26 Sheshach* is a cryptogram for Babylon.

shout against all who live on the earth.'
³¹ The tumult will resound to the ends of the earth,
    for the LORD will bring charges against the nations;
he will bring judgment on all mankind
    and put the wicked to the sword,' "

declares the LORD.

³² This is what the LORD Almighty says:

"Look! Disaster is spreading
    from nation to nation;
a mighty storm is rising
    from the ends of the earth."

³³ At that time those slain by the LORD will be everywhere—from one end of the earth to the other. They will not be mourned or gathered up or buried, but will be like refuse lying on the ground.

³⁴ Weep and wail, you shepherds;
    roll in the dust, you leaders of the flock.
For your time to be slaughtered has come;
    you will fall and be shattered like fine pottery.
³⁵ The shepherds will have nowhere to flee,
    the leaders of the flock no place to escape.
³⁶ Hear the cry of the shepherds,
    the wailing of the leaders of the flock,
    for the LORD is destroying their pasture.
³⁷ The peaceful meadows will be laid waste
    because of the fierce anger of the LORD.
³⁸ Like a lion he will leave his lair,
    and their land will become desolate
because of the sword^a of the oppressor
    and because of the LORD's fierce anger.

Jeremiah Threatened With Death

26 Early in the reign of Jehoiakim son of Josiah king of Judah, this word came from the LORD: ² "This is what the LORD says: Stand in the courtyard of the LORD's house and speak to all the people of the towns of Judah who come to worship in the house of the LORD. Tell them everything I command you; do not omit a word. ³ Perhaps they will listen and each will turn from his evil way. Then I will relent and not bring on them the disaster I was planning because of the evil they have done. ⁴ Say to them, 'This is what the LORD says: If you do not listen to me and follow my law, which I have set before you, ⁵ and if you do not listen to the words of my servants the prophets, whom I have sent to you again and again (though you have not listened), ⁶ then I will make this house like Shiloh and this city an object of cursing among all the nations of the earth.' "

⁷ The priests, the prophets and all the people heard Jeremiah speak these words in the house of the LORD. ⁸ But as soon as Jeremiah finished telling all the people everything the LORD had commanded him to say, the priests, the prophets and all the people seized him and said, "You must die! ⁹ Why do you prophesy in the LORD's name that this house will be like Shiloh and this city will be desolate and deserted?" And all the people crowded around Jeremiah in the house of the LORD.

¹⁰ When the officials of Judah heard about these things, they went up from the royal palace to the house of the LORD and took their places at the entrance of the New Gate of the LORD's house. ¹¹ Then the priests and the prophets said to the officials and all the people, "This man should be sentenced to death because he has prophesied against this city. You have heard it with your own ears!"

¹² Then Jeremiah said to all the officials and all the people: "The LORD sent me to prophesy against this house and this city all the things you have heard. ¹³ Now reform your ways and your actions and obey the LORD your God. Then the LORD will relent and not bring the disaster he has pronounced against you. ¹⁴ As for me, I am in your hands; do with me whatever you think is good and

---

^a 38 Some Hebrew manuscripts and Septuagint (see also Jer. 46:16 and 50:16); most Hebrew manuscripts *anger*

right. [15]Be assured, however, that if you put me to death, you will bring the guilt of innocent blood on yourselves and on this city and on those who live in it, for in truth the LORD has sent me to you to speak all these words in your hearing."

[16]Then the officials and all the people said to the priests and the prophets, "This man should not be sentenced to death! He has spoken to us in the name of the LORD our God."

[17]Some of the elders of the land stepped forward and said to the entire assembly of people, [18]"Micah of Moresheth prophesied in the days of Hezekiah king of Judah. He told all the people of Judah, 'This is what the LORD Almighty says:

" 'Zion will be plowed like a field,
Jerusalem will become a heap of rubble,
the temple hill a mound overgrown with thickets.'[a]

[19]"Did Hezekiah king of Judah or anyone else in Judah put him to death? Did not Hezekiah fear the LORD and seek his favor? And did not the LORD relent, so that he did not bring the disaster he pronounced against them? We are about to bring a terrible disaster on ourselves!"

[20](Now Uriah son of Shemaiah from Kiriath Jearim was another man who prophesied in the name of the LORD; he prophesied the same things against this city and this land as Jeremiah did. [21]When King Jehoiakim and all his officers and officials heard his words, the king sought to put him to death. But Uriah heard of it and fled in fear to Egypt. [22]King Jehoiakim, however, sent Elnathan son of Acbor to Egypt, along with some other men. [23]They brought Uriah out of Egypt and took him to King Jehoiakim, who had him struck down with a sword and his body thrown into the burial place of the common people.)

[24]Furthermore, Ahikam son of Shaphan supported Jeremiah, and so he was not handed over to the people to be put to death.

Judah to Serve Nebuchadnezzar

27 Early in the reign of Zedekiah[b] son of Josiah king of Judah, this word came to Jeremiah from the LORD: [2]This is what the LORD said to me: "Make a yoke out of straps and crossbars and put it on your neck. [3]Then send word to the kings of Edom, Moab, Ammon, Tyre and Sidon through the envoys who have come to Jerusalem to Zedekiah king of Judah. [4]Give them a message for their masters and say, 'This is what the LORD Almighty, the God of Israel, says: "Tell this to your masters: [5]With my great power and outstretched arm I made the earth and its people and the animals that are on it, and I give it to anyone I please. [6]Now I will hand all your countries over to my servant Nebuchadnezzar king of Babylon; I will make even the wild animals subject to him. [7]All nations will serve him and his son and his grandson until the time for his land comes; then many nations and great kings will subjugate him.

[8]" ' "If, however, any nation or kingdom will not serve Nebuchadnezzar king of Babylon or bow its neck under his yoke, I will punish that nation with the sword, famine and plague, declares the LORD, until I destroy it by his hand. [9]So do not listen to your prophets, your diviners, your interpreters of dreams, your mediums or your sorcerers who tell you, 'You will not serve the king of Babylon.' [10]They prophesy lies to you that will only serve to remove you far from your lands; I will banish you and you will perish. [11]But if any nation will bow its neck under the yoke of the king of Babylon and serve him, I will let that nation remain in its own land to till it and to live there, declares the LORD." ' "

[12]I gave the same message to Zedekiah king of Judah. I said, "Bow your neck under the yoke of the king of Babylon; serve him and his people, and you will live. [13]Why will you and your people die by the sword, famine and plague with which the LORD has threatened any nation that will not serve the king of Babylon? [14]Do not listen to the words of the prophets who say to you, 'You will not serve the king of Babylon,' for they are prophesying lies to you. [15]'I have not sent them,' declares the LORD. 'They are prophesying lies in my name. Therefore, I will banish you and you will perish, both you and the prophets who prophesy to you.' "

[16]Then I said to the priests and all these people, "This is what the LORD says: Do not listen to the prophets who say, 'Very soon now the articles from the LORD's house will be brought back from Babylon.' They are prophesying lies to you. [17]Do not listen to them. Serve the king of Babylon, and

a 18 Micah 3:12   *b 1* A few Hebrew manuscripts and Syriac (see also Jer. 27:3,12 and 28:1); most Hebrew manuscripts *Jehoiakim* (Most Septuagint manuscripts do not have this verse.)

you will live. Why should this city become a ruin? [18]If they are prophets and have the word of the LORD, let them plead with the LORD Almighty that the furnishings remaining in the house of the LORD and in the palace of the king of Judah and in Jerusalem not be taken to Babylon. [19]For this is what the LORD Almighty says about the pillars, the Sea, the movable stands and the other furnishings that are left in this city, [20]which Nebuchadnezzar king of Babylon did not take away when he carried Jehoiachin[a] son of Jehoiakim king of Judah into exile from Jerusalem to Babylon, along with all the nobles of Judah and Jerusalem— [21]yes, this is what the LORD Almighty, the God of Israel, says about the things that are left in the house of the LORD and in the palace of the king of Judah and in Jerusalem: [22]'They will be taken to Babylon and there they will remain until the day I come for them,' declares the LORD. 'Then I will bring them back and restore them to this place.' "

The False Prophet Hananiah

28 In the fifth month of that same year, the fourth year, early in the reign of Zedekiah king of Judah, the prophet Hananiah son of Azzur, who was from Gibeon, said to me in the house of the LORD in the presence of the priests and all the people: [2]"This is what the LORD Almighty, the God of Israel, says: 'I will break the yoke of the king of Babylon. [3]Within two years I will bring back to this place all the articles of the LORD's house that Nebuchadnezzar king of Babylon removed from here and took to Babylon. [4]I will also bring back to this place Jehoiachin[a] son of Jehoiakim king of Judah and all the other exiles from Judah who went to Babylon,' declares the LORD, 'for I will break the yoke of the king of Babylon.' "

[5]Then the prophet Jeremiah replied to the prophet Hananiah before the priests and all the people who were standing in the house of the LORD. [6]He said, "Amen! May the LORD do so! May the LORD fulfill the words you have prophesied by bringing the articles of the LORD's house and all the exiles back to this place from Babylon. [7]Nevertheless, listen to what I have to say in your hearing and in the hearing of all the people: [8]From early times the prophets who preceded you and me have prophesied war, disaster and plague against many countries and great kingdoms. [9]But the prophet who prophesies peace will be recognized as one truly sent by the LORD only if his prediction comes true."

[10]Then the prophet Hananiah took the yoke off the neck of the prophet Jeremiah and broke it, [11]and he said before all the people, "This is what the LORD says: 'In the same way will I break the yoke of Nebuchadnezzar king of Babylon off the neck of all the nations within two years.' " At this, the prophet Jeremiah went on his way.

[12]Shortly after the prophet Hananiah had broken the yoke off the neck of the prophet Jeremiah, the word of the LORD came to Jeremiah: [13]"Go and tell Hananiah, 'This is what the LORD says: You have broken a wooden yoke, but in its place you will get a yoke of iron. [14]This is what the LORD Almighty, the God of Israel, says: I will put an iron yoke on the necks of all these nations to make them serve Nebuchadnezzar king of Babylon, and they will serve him. I will even give him control over the wild animals.' "

[15]Then the prophet Jeremiah said to Hananiah the prophet, "Listen, Hananiah! The LORD has not sent you, yet you have persuaded this nation to trust in lies. [16]Therefore, this is what the LORD says: 'I am about to remove you from the face of the earth. This very year you are going to die, because you have preached rebellion against the LORD.' "

[17]In the seventh month of that same year, Hananiah the prophet died.

A Letter to the Exiles

29 This is the text of the letter that the prophet Jeremiah sent from Jerusalem to the surviving elders among the exiles and to the priests, the prophets and all the other people Nebuchadnezzar had carried into exile from Jerusalem to Babylon. [2](This was after King Jehoiachin[a] and the queen mother, the court officials and the leaders of Judah and Jerusalem, the craftsmen and the artisans had gone into exile from Jerusalem.) [3]He entrusted the letter to Elasah son of Shaphan and to Gemariah son of Hilkiah, whom Zedekiah king of Judah sent to King Nebuchadnezzar in Babylon. It said:

[4]This is what the LORD Almighty, the God of Israel, says to all those I carried into exile from Jerusalem to Babylon: [5]"Build houses and settle down; plant gardens and eat what

a 20,4 Hebrew Jeconiah, a variant of Jehoiachin

Where's the Love?

I love hanging out with my friends. I don't have to psych myself up to hang out with them. I just do it because I like being with them. We never run out of things to say or do (or laugh about!). But with God, I always feel like I have to make an effort.

I feel so guilty! I'm supposed to love God, right? But sometimes I'm not so sure that I do. I mean, I don't *feel* anything toward him. It's kind of hard with him being invisible and all.

I've been a Christian since I was twelve. So, it's been five years. I know we're supposed to go to church, read the Bible, pray and tell others about Jesus to show our love for him. I try to do all of that. But I don't enjoy any of it. I read the Bible because I know I should, not because I'm dying to. And sometimes church is boring. (Okay, yeah, I've fallen asleep a few times.) And praying? I never think to pray unless I've got something big going on. And so far I don't think I've told anybody about Jesus! Every time I have a chance to say something, I freeze up.

Last night, I tried to read the Bible just before I went to bed. Well, next thing I knew, I was waking up three hours later, drooling on the book of Jeremiah.

Are we supposed to fake it with God?

For more ideas on loving God, check out the link on www.TrueImagesBible.com

loving God in focus

We're called to love God with our whole heart and mind (see Matthew 22:37, page 1323). Think you can do that on your own? No one can—not even the most strong-willed girl out there! You can't *fake* that kind of devotion. We love him because he loved us first (see 1 John 4:19, page 1621). A genuine love for God can flow when you . . .

» Take time to be honest with God about everything you're feeling. Sometimes anger or other emotions toward God can make you "feel" like you're just going through the motions.

» Realize that you won't always "feel" love for God (see 2 Corinthians 5:7, page 1527).

» Accept God's unconditional love and stop trying to earn or repay it.

For more on this topic, see the index on page 1656.

they produce. [6]Marry and have sons and daughters; find wives for your sons and give your daughters in marriage, so that they too may have sons and daughters. Increase in number there; do not decrease. [7]Also, seek the peace and prosperity of the city to which I have carried you into exile. Pray to the LORD for it, because if it prospers, you too will prosper." [8]Yes, this is what the LORD Almighty, the God of Israel, says: "Do not let the prophets and diviners among you deceive you. Do not listen to the dreams you encourage them to have. [9]They are prophesying lies to you in my name. I have not sent them," declares the LORD.

[10]This is what the LORD says: "When seventy years are completed for Babylon, I will come to you and fulfill my gracious promise to bring you back to this place. [11]For I know the plans I have for you," declares the LORD, "plans to prosper you and not to harm you, plans to give

you hope and a future. ¹²Then you will call upon me and come and pray to me, and I will listen to you. ¹³You will seek me and find me when you seek me with all your heart. ¹⁴I will be found by you," declares the LORD, "and will bring you back from captivity.ᵃ I will gather you from all the nations and places where I have banished you," declares the LORD, "and will bring you back to the place from which I carried you into exile."

¹⁵You may say, "The LORD has raised up prophets for us in Babylon," ¹⁶but this is what the LORD says about the king who sits on David's throne and all the people who remain in this city, your countrymen who did not go with you into exile— ¹⁷yes, this is what the LORD Almighty says: "I will send the sword, famine and plague against them and I will make them like poor figs that are so bad they cannot be eaten. ¹⁸I will pursue them with the sword, famine and plague and will make them abhorrent to all the kingdoms of the earth and an object of cursing and horror, of scorn and reproach, among all the nations where I drive them. ¹⁹For they have not listened to my words," declares the LORD, "words that I sent to them again and again by my servants the prophets. And you exiles have not listened either," declares the LORD.

²⁰Therefore, hear the word of the LORD, all you exiles whom I have sent away from Jerusalem to Babylon. ²¹This is what the LORD Almighty, the God of Israel, says about Ahab son of Kolaiah and Zedekiah son of Maaseiah, who are prophesying lies to you in my name: "I will hand them over to Nebuchadnezzar king of Babylon, and he will put them to death before your very eyes. ²²Because of them, all the exiles from Judah who are in Babylon will use this curse: 'The LORD treat you like Zedekiah and Ahab, whom the king of Babylon burned in the fire.' ²³For they have done outrageous things in Israel; they have committed adultery with their neighbors' wives and in my name have spoken lies, which I did not tell them to do. I know it and am a witness to it," declares the LORD.

Message to Shemaiah

²⁴Tell Shemaiah the Nehelamite, ²⁵"This is what the LORD Almighty, the God of Israel, says: You sent letters in your own name to all the people in Jerusalem, to Zephaniah son of Maaseiah the priest, and to all the other priests. You said to Zephaniah, ²⁶'The LORD has appointed you priest in place of Jehoiada to be in charge of the house of the LORD; you should put any madman who acts like a prophet into the stocks and neck-irons. ²⁷So why have you not reprimanded Jeremiah from Anathoth, who poses as a prophet among you? ²⁸He has sent this message to us in Babylon: It will be a long time. Therefore build houses and settle down; plant gardens and eat what they produce.' "

²⁹Zephaniah the priest, however, read the letter to Jeremiah the prophet. ³⁰Then the word of the LORD came to Jeremiah: ³¹"Send this message to all the exiles: 'This is what the LORD says about Shemaiah the Nehelamite: Because Shemaiah has prophesied to you, even though I did not send him, and has led you to believe a lie, ³²this is what the LORD says: I will surely punish Shemaiah the Nehelamite and his descendants. He will have no one left among this people, nor will he see the good things I will do for my people, declares the LORD, because he has preached rebellion against me.' "

genuine purpose » 29:11

When you're having a bad day—you arrive late for school, with bad hair and last year's outfit, to discover that you have a pop quiz on a book you haven't read, and the guy you had a crush on asked out another girl instead—you might wonder, *Is God out to get me?* No way! God's plans for his people are for good, not bad. God had a hope and a future planned for Israel, and he has the same for you. No matter how bad the day, remember that God has good things in store for you.

ᵃ 14 Or *will restore your fortunes*

Restoration of Israel

30 This is the word that came to Jeremiah from the Lord: ²"This is what the Lord, the God of Israel, says: 'Write in a book all the words I have spoken to you. ³The days are coming,' declares the Lord, 'when I will bring my people Israel and Judah back from captivity[a] and restore them to the land I gave their forefathers to possess,' says the Lord."

⁴These are the words the Lord spoke concerning Israel and Judah: ⁵"This is what the Lord says:

" 'Cries of fear are heard—
terror, not peace.
⁶ Ask and see:
Can a man bear children?
Then why do I see every strong
man
with his hands on his stomach
like a woman in labor,
every face turned deathly
pale?
⁷ How awful that day will be!
None will be like it.
It will be a time of trouble for Jacob,
but he will be saved out of it.

⁸ " 'In that day,' declares the Lord Almighty,
'I will break the yoke off their necks
and will tear off their bonds;
no longer will foreigners enslave them.
⁹ Instead, they will serve the Lord their God
and David their king,
whom I will raise up for them.

¹⁰ " 'So do not fear, O Jacob my servant;
do not be dismayed, O Israel,'

declares the Lord.

'I will surely save you out of a distant place,
your descendants from the land of their exile.
Jacob will again have peace and security,
and no one will make him afraid.
¹¹ I am with you and will save you,'
declares the Lord.
'Though I completely destroy all the nations
among which I scatter you,
I will not completely destroy you.
I will discipline you but only with justice;
I will not let you go entirely unpunished.'

¹²"This is what the Lord says:

" 'Your wound is incurable,
your injury beyond healing.
¹³ There is no one to plead your cause,
no remedy for your sore,
no healing for you.
¹⁴ All your allies have forgotten you;
they care nothing for you.
I have struck you as an enemy would
and punished you as would the cruel,

---

[a] 3 Or *will restore the fortunes of my people Israel and Judah*

because your guilt is so great
and your sins so many.
¹⁵ Why do you cry out over your wound,
your pain that has no cure?
Because of your great guilt and many sins
I have done these things to you.

¹⁶ " 'But all who devour you will be devoured;
all your enemies will go into exile.
Those who plunder you will be plundered;
all who make spoil of you I will despoil.
¹⁷ But I will restore you to health
and heal your wounds,'

declares the LORD,

'because you are called an outcast,
Zion for whom no one cares.'

¹⁸ "This is what the LORD says:

" 'I will restore the fortunes of Jacob's tents
and have compassion on his dwellings;
the city will be rebuilt on her ruins,
and the palace will stand in its proper place.
¹⁹ From them will come songs of thanksgiving
and the sound of rejoicing.
I will add to their numbers,
and they will not be decreased;
I will bring them honor,
and they will not be disdained.
²⁰ Their children will be as in days of old,
and their community will be established before me;
I will punish all who oppress them.
²¹ Their leader will be one of their own;
their ruler will arise from among them.
I will bring him near and he will come close to me,
for who is he who will devote himself
to be close to me?'

declares the LORD.

²² " 'So you will be my people,
and I will be your God.' "

²³ See, the storm of the LORD
will burst out in wrath,
a driving wind swirling down
on the heads of the wicked.
²⁴ The fierce anger of the LORD will not turn back
until he fully accomplishes
the purposes of his heart.
In days to come
you will understand this.

31 "At that time," declares the LORD, "I will be the God of all the clans of Israel, and they will be my people."
² This is what the LORD says:

"The people who survive the sword
will find favor in the desert;
I will come to give rest to Israel."

[3] The LORD appeared to us in the past,[a] saying:

"I have loved you with an everlasting love;
    I have drawn you with loving-kindness.
[4] I will build you up again
    and you will be rebuilt, O Virgin Israel.
Again you will take up your tambourines
    and go out to dance with the joyful.
[5] Again you will plant vineyards
    on the hills of Samaria;
the farmers will plant them
    and enjoy their fruit.
[6] There will be a day when watchmen cry out
    on the hills of Ephraim,
'Come, let us go up to Zion,
    to the LORD our God.' "

[7] This is what the LORD says:

"Sing with joy for Jacob;
    shout for the foremost of the
        nations.
Make your praises heard, and say,
    'O LORD, save your people,
    the remnant of Israel.'
[8] See, I will bring them from the
        land of the north
    and gather them from the
        ends of the earth.
Among them will be the blind
        and the lame,
    expectant mothers and
        women in labor;
    a great throng will return.
[9] They will come with weeping;
    they will pray as I bring them
        back.
I will lead them beside streams of
        water
    on a level path where they will
        not stumble,
because I am Israel's father,
    and Ephraim is my firstborn son.

[10] "Hear the word of the LORD,
        O nations;
    proclaim it in distant
        coastlands:
'He who scattered Israel will
        gather them
    and will watch over his flock
        like a shepherd.'
[11] For the LORD will ransom Jacob
    and redeem them from the
        hand of those stronger
        than they.

love ❤ notes

31:3

Beloved,

Never doubt this. I want only the very best for you. I will do whatever it takes to get your attention, to draw you closer to me and to wrap you in my everlasting love. You are my child, my chosen one.

—Your loving Father

Think of three ways you can draw
nearer to God.

[a] *3 Or LORD has appeared to us from afar*

¹² They will come and shout for joy on the heights of Zion;
  they will rejoice in the bounty of the LORD—
the grain, the new wine and the oil,
  the young of the flocks and herds.
They will be like a well-watered garden,
  and they will sorrow no more.
¹³ Then maidens will dance and be glad,
  young men and old as well.
I will turn their mourning into gladness;
  I will give them comfort and joy instead of sorrow.
¹⁴ I will satisfy the priests with abundance,
  and my people will be filled with my bounty,"

  declares the LORD.

¹⁵ This is what the LORD says:

  "A voice is heard in Ramah,
    mourning and great weeping,
  Rachel weeping for her children
    and refusing to be comforted,
    because her children are no more."

¹⁶ This is what the LORD says:

  "Restrain your voice from
      weeping
    and your eyes from tears,
  for your work will be rewarded,"
      declares the LORD.
  "They will return from the land
      of the enemy.
¹⁷ So there is hope for your future,"
      declares the LORD.
  "Your children will return to
      their own land.

¹⁸ "I have surely heard Ephraim's
      moaning:
  'You disciplined me like an
      unruly calf,
    and I have been disciplined.
  Restore me, and I will return,
    because you are the LORD my
      God.
¹⁹ After I strayed,
    I repented;
  after I came to understand,
    I beat my breast.
  I was ashamed and humiliated
    because I bore the disgrace of
      my youth.'

genuine repentance » 31:19

Have you ever thought about what *repentance* means? It's not just offering God a quick "I'm sorry," said without much thought and no real intention of change. No, it's much deeper than that. True repentance over your sin will penetrate your heart and result in a change in your life. So, the next time you sin—by bad-mouthing a friend or letting slip that not-so-nice comment about another girl or deceiving your parents by only telling them part of the story—what will you do? Will you throw out a shallow "I'm sorry, God"? Or will you truly repent?

²⁰ Is not Ephraim my dear son,
  the child in whom I delight?
Though I often speak against him,
  I still remember him.
Therefore my heart yearns for him;
  I have great compassion for him,"

  declares the LORD.

²¹ "Set up road signs;
    put up guideposts.
Take note of the highway,
    the road that you take.
Return, O Virgin Israel,
    return to your towns.
²² How long will you wander,
    O unfaithful daughter?
The LORD will create a new thing on earth—
    a woman will surround*ᵃ* a man."

²³This is what the LORD Almighty, the God of Israel, says: "When I bring them back from captivity,*ᵇ* the people in the land of Judah and in its towns will once again use these words: 'The LORD bless you, O righteous dwelling, O sacred mountain.' ²⁴People will live together in Judah and all its towns—farmers and those who move about with their flocks. ²⁵I will refresh the weary and satisfy the faint."

²⁶At this I awoke and looked around. My sleep had been pleasant to me.

²⁷"The days are coming," declares the LORD, "when I will plant the house of Israel and the house of Judah with the offspring of men and of animals. ²⁸Just as I watched over them to uproot and tear down, and to overthrow, destroy and bring disaster, so I will watch over them to build and to plant," declares the LORD. ²⁹"In those days people will no longer say,

'The fathers have eaten sour grapes,
    and the children's teeth are set on edge.'

³⁰Instead, everyone will die for his own sin; whoever eats sour grapes—his own teeth will be set on edge.

³¹ "The time is coming," declares the LORD,
    "when I will make a new covenant
with the house of Israel
    and with the house of Judah.
³² It will not be like the covenant
    I made with their forefathers
when I took them by the hand
    to lead them out of Egypt,
because they broke my covenant,
    though I was a husband to*ᶜ*
    them,*ᵈ*"
        declares the LORD.
³³ "This is the covenant I will make
    with the house of Israel
    after that time," declares the
        LORD.
"I will put my law in their minds
    and write it on their hearts.
I will be their God,
    and they will be my people.
³⁴No longer will a man teach his neighbor,
    or a man his brother, saying, 'Know the
        LORD,'
because they will all know me,
    from the least of them to the greatest,"
        declares the LORD.

"For I will forgive their wickedness
    and will remember their sins no more."

truth or dare

MAJOR PRESS RELEASE: God Announces New Covenant! It's a revolutionary new plan based on Jesus. It's not written on stone tablets but on our hearts. And now, we can know God personally.

31:31–34

ᵃ 22 Or will go about seeking; or will protect   ᵇ 23 Or I restore their fortunes   ᶜ 32 Hebrew; Septuagint and Syriac / and I turned away from   ᵈ 32 Or was their master

³⁵This is what the LORD says,

> he who appoints the sun
> > to shine by day,
> who decrees the moon and stars
> > to shine by night,
> who stirs up the sea
> > so that its waves roar—
> > the LORD Almighty is his name:
> > ³⁶"Only if these decrees vanish from my sight,"
> > declares the LORD,
> "will the descendants of Israel ever cease
> > to be a nation before me."

³⁷This is what the LORD says:

> "Only if the heavens above can be measured
> > and the foundations of the earth below be searched out
> will I reject all the descendants of Israel
> > because of all they have done,"

> > > > > declares the LORD.

³⁸"The days are coming," declares the LORD, "when this city will be rebuilt for me from the Tower of Hananel to the Corner Gate. ³⁹The measuring line will stretch from there straight to the hill of Gareb and then turn to Goah. ⁴⁰The whole valley where dead bodies and ashes are thrown, and all the terraces out to the Kidron Valley on the east as far as the corner of the Horse Gate, will be holy to the LORD. The city will never again be uprooted or demolished."

Jeremiah Buys a Field

32 This is the word that came to Jeremiah from the LORD in the tenth year of Zedekiah king of Judah, which was the eighteenth year of Nebuchadnezzar. ²The army of the king of Babylon was then besieging Jerusalem, and Jeremiah the prophet was confined in the courtyard of the guard in the royal palace of Judah.

³Now Zedekiah king of Judah had imprisoned him there, saying, "Why do you prophesy as you do? You say, 'This is what the LORD says: I am about to hand this city over to the king of Babylon, and he will capture it. ⁴Zedekiah king of Judah will not escape out of the hands of the Babylonians^a but will certainly be handed over to the king of Babylon, and will speak with him face to face and see him with his own eyes. ⁵He will take Zedekiah to Babylon, where he will remain until I deal with him, declares the LORD. If you fight against the Babylonians, you will not succeed.' "

⁶Jeremiah said, "The word of the LORD came to me: ⁷Hanamel son of Shallum your uncle is going to come to you and say, 'Buy my field at Anathoth, because as nearest relative it is your right and duty to buy it.'

⁸"Then, just as the LORD had said, my cousin Hanamel came to me in the courtyard of the guard and said, 'Buy my field at Anathoth in the territory of Benjamin. Since it is your right to redeem it and possess it, buy it for yourself.'

"I knew that this was the word of the LORD; ⁹so I bought the field at Anathoth from my cousin Hanamel and weighed out for him seventeen shekels^b of silver. ¹⁰I signed and sealed the deed, had it witnessed, and weighed out the silver on the scales. ¹¹I took the deed of purchase—the sealed copy containing the terms and conditions, as well as the unsealed copy— ¹²and I gave this deed to Baruch son of Neriah, the son of Mahseiah, in the presence of my cousin Hanamel and of the witnesses who had signed the deed and of all the Jews sitting in the courtyard of the guard.

¹³"In their presence I gave Baruch these instructions: ¹⁴'This is what the LORD Almighty, the God of Israel, says: Take these documents, both the sealed and unsealed copies of the deed of purchase, and put them in a clay jar so they will last a long time. ¹⁵For this is what the LORD Almighty, the God of Israel, says: Houses, fields and vineyards will again be bought in this land.'

¹⁶"After I had given the deed of purchase to Baruch son of Neriah, I prayed to the LORD:

---

^a 4 Or *Chaldeans*; also in verses 5, 24, 25, 28, 29 and 43   ^b 9 That is, about 7 ounces (about 200 grams)

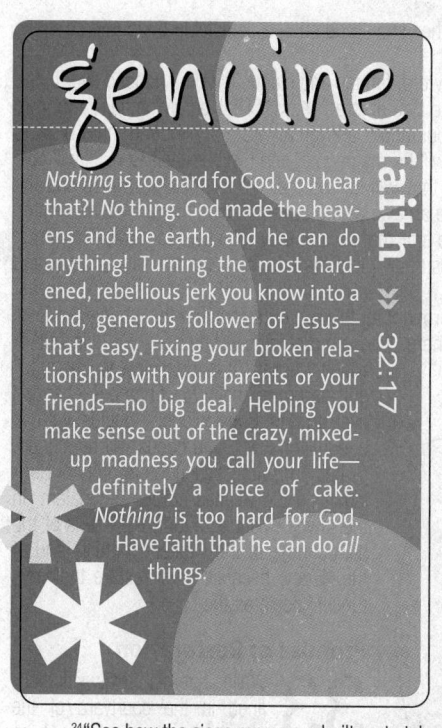

genuine

faith »» 32:17

Nothing is too hard for God. You hear that?! *No* thing. God made the heavens and the earth, and he can do anything! Turning the most hardened, rebellious jerk you know into a kind, generous follower of Jesus— that's easy. Fixing your broken relationships with your parents or your friends—no big deal. Helping you make sense out of the crazy, mixed-up madness you call your life— definitely a piece of cake. *Nothing* is too hard for God. Have faith that he can do *all* things.

[17] "Ah, Sovereign LORD, you have made the heavens and the earth by your great power and outstretched arm. Nothing is too hard for you. [18] You show love to thousands but bring the punishment for the fathers' sins into the laps of their children after them. O great and powerful God, whose name is the LORD Almighty, [19] great are your purposes and mighty are your deeds. Your eyes are open to all the ways of men; you reward everyone according to his conduct and as his deeds deserve. [20] You performed miraculous signs and wonders in Egypt and have continued them to this day, both in Israel and among all mankind, and have gained the renown that is still yours. [21] You brought your people Israel out of Egypt with signs and wonders, by a mighty hand and an outstretched arm and with great terror. [22] You gave them this land you had sworn to give their forefathers, a land flowing with milk and honey. [23] They came in and took possession of it, but they did not obey you or follow your law; they did not do what you commanded them to do. So you brought all this disaster upon them.

[24] "See how the siege ramps are built up to take the city. Because of the sword, famine and plague, the city will be handed over to the Babylonians who are attacking it. What you said has happened, as you now see. [25] And though the city will be handed over to the Babylonians, you, O Sovereign LORD, say to me, 'Buy the field with silver and have the transaction witnessed.' "

[26] Then the word of the LORD came to Jeremiah: [27] "I am the LORD, the God of all mankind. Is anything too hard for me? [28] Therefore, this is what the LORD says: I am about to hand this city over to the Babylonians and to Nebuchadnezzar king of Babylon, who will capture it. [29] The Babylonians who are attacking this city will come in and set it on fire; they will burn it down, along with the houses where the people provoked me to anger by burning incense on the roofs to Baal and by pouring out drink offerings to other gods.

[30] "The people of Israel and Judah have done nothing but evil in my sight from their youth; indeed, the people of Israel have done nothing but provoke me with what their hands have made, declares the LORD. [31] From the day it was built until now, this city has so aroused my anger and wrath that I must remove it from my sight. [32] The people of Israel and Judah have provoked me by all the evil they have done—they, their kings and officials, their priests and prophets, the men of Judah and the people of Jerusalem. [33] They turned their backs to me and not their faces; though I taught them again and again, they would not listen or respond to discipline. [34] They set up their abominable idols in the house that bears my Name and defiled it. [35] They built high places for Baal in the Valley of Ben Hinnom to sacrifice their sons and daughters[a] to Molech, though I never

truth or dare

Although things might seem impossible right now, nothing's too hard for God. Your greatest heartbreak, God can mend. Your greatest storm, God can calm.

32:26,36–41

---

[a] 35 Or *to make their sons and daughters pass through the fire*

commanded, nor did it enter my mind, that they should do such a detestable thing and so make Judah sin.

³⁶"You are saying about this city, 'By the sword, famine and plague it will be handed over to the king of Babylon'; but this is what the LORD, the God of Israel, says: ³⁷I will surely gather them from all the lands where I banish them in my furious anger and great wrath; I will bring them back to this place and let them live in safety. ³⁸They will be my people, and I will be their God. ³⁹I will give them singleness of heart and action, so that they will always fear me for their own good and the good of their children after them. ⁴⁰I will make an everlasting covenant with them: I will never stop doing good to them, and I will inspire them to fear me, so that they will never turn away from me. ⁴¹I will rejoice in doing them good and will assuredly plant them in this land with all my heart and soul.

⁴²"This is what the LORD says: As I have brought all this great calamity on this people, so I will give them all the prosperity I have promised them. ⁴³Once more fields will be bought in this land of which you say, 'It is a desolate waste, without men or animals, for it has been handed over to the Babylonians.' ⁴⁴Fields will be bought for silver, and deeds will be signed, sealed and witnessed in the territory of Benjamin, in the villages around Jerusalem, in the towns of Judah and in the towns of the hill country, of the western foothills and of the Negev, because I will restore their fortunes,ᵃ declares the LORD."

love notes

33:3

Dear daughter,

Don't set your expectations too low for me. Don't just give me easy, surface-level questions. Bring me your biggest problems, your toughest challenges, your deepest questions. I'll answer you—and I'll blow your mind in the process.

—Your all-powerful Father

What concerns and questions do you have? Write a prayer to God and tell him about them.

Promise of Restoration

33 While Jeremiah was still confined in the courtyard of the guard, the word of the LORD came to him a second time: ²"This is what the LORD says, he who made the earth, the LORD who formed it and established it—the LORD is his name: ³'Call to me and I will answer you and tell you great and unsearchable things you do not know.' ⁴For this is what the LORD, the God of Israel, says about the houses in this city and the royal palaces of Judah that have been torn down to be used against the siege ramps and the sword ⁵in the fight with the Babyloniansᵇ: 'They will be filled with the dead bodies of the men I will slay in my anger and wrath. I will hide my face from this city because of all its wickedness.

⁶" 'Nevertheless, I will bring health and healing to it; I will heal my people and will let them enjoy abundant peace and security. ⁷I will bring Judah and Israel back from captivityᶜ and will rebuild them as they were before. ⁸I will cleanse them from all the sin they have committed against me and will forgive all their sins of rebellion against me. ⁹Then this city will bring me renown, joy, praise and honor before all nations on earth

ᵃ 44 Or will bring them back from captivity
ᵇ 5 Or Chaldeans   ᶜ 7 Or will restore the fortunes of Judah and Israel

that hear of all the good things I do for it; and they will be in awe and will tremble at the abundant prosperity and peace I provide for it.'

[10]"This is what the LORD says: 'You say about this place, "It is a desolate waste, without men or animals." Yet in the towns of Judah and the streets of Jerusalem that are deserted, inhabited by neither men nor animals, there will be heard once more [11]the sounds of joy and gladness, the voices of bride and bridegroom, and the voices of those who bring thank offerings to the house of the LORD, saying,

> "Give thanks to the LORD
> Almighty,
> for the LORD is good;
> his love endures forever."

For I will restore the fortunes of the land as they were before,' says the LORD.

[12]"This is what the LORD Almighty says: 'In this place, desolate and without men or animals—in all its towns there will again be pastures for shepherds to rest their flocks. [13]In the towns of the hill country, of the western foothills and of the Negev, in the territory of Benjamin, in the villages around Jerusalem and in the towns of Judah, flocks will again pass under the hand of the one who counts them,' says the LORD.

[14]" 'The days are coming,' declares the LORD, 'when I will fulfill the gracious promise I made to the house of Israel and to the house of Judah.

> [15]" 'In those days and at that time
> I will make a righteous Branch sprout from David's line;
> he will do what is just and right in the land.
> [16]In those days Judah will be saved
> and Jerusalem will live in safety.
> This is the name by which it[a] will be called:
> The LORD Our Righteousness.'

[17]For this is what the LORD says: 'David will never fail to have a man to sit on the throne of the house of Israel, [18]nor will the priests, who are Levites, ever fail to have a man to stand before me continually to offer burnt offerings, to burn grain offerings and to present sacrifices.' "

[19]The word of the LORD came to Jeremiah: [20]"This is what the LORD says: 'If you can break my covenant with the day and my covenant with the night, so that day and night no longer come at their appointed time, [21]then my covenant with David my servant—and my covenant with the Levites who are priests ministering before me—can be broken and David will no longer have a descendant to reign on his throne. [22]I will make the descendants of David my servant and the Levites who minister before me as countless as the stars of the sky and as measureless as the sand on the seashore.' "

[23]The word of the LORD came to Jeremiah: [24]"Have you not noticed that these people are saying, 'The LORD has rejected the two kingdoms[b] he chose'? So they despise my people and no longer regard them as a nation. [25]This is what the LORD says: 'If I have not established my covenant with day and night and the fixed laws of heaven and earth, [26]then I will reject the descendants of Jacob and David my servant and will not choose one of his sons to rule over the descendants of Abraham, Isaac and Jacob. For I will restore their fortunes[c] and have compassion on them.' "

Warning to Zedekiah

34

While Nebuchadnezzar king of Babylon and all his army and all the kingdoms and peoples in the empire he ruled were fighting against Jerusalem and all its surrounding towns, this word came to Jeremiah from the LORD: [2]"This is what the LORD, the God of Israel, says: Go to Zedekiah king of Judah and tell him, 'This is what the LORD says: I am about to

truth or dare

There's never a reason to give up hope. What areas in your life do you feel are dead and useless? Add a little faith. God can bring new life.

33:10–11

---

[a] 16 Or he   [b] 24 Or families   [c] 26 Or will bring them back from captivity

hand this city over to the king of Babylon, and he will burn it down. ³You will not escape from his grasp but will surely be captured and handed over to him. You will see the king of Babylon with your own eyes, and he will speak with you face to face. And you will go to Babylon.

⁴" 'Yet hear the promise of the LORD, O Zedekiah king of Judah. This is what the LORD says concerning you: You will not die by the sword; ⁵you will die peacefully. As people made a funeral fire in honor of your fathers, the former kings who preceded you, so they will make a fire in your honor and lament, "Alas, O master!" I myself make this promise, declares the LORD.' "

⁶Then Jeremiah the prophet told all this to Zedekiah king of Judah, in Jerusalem, ⁷while the army of the king of Babylon was fighting against Jerusalem and the other cities of Judah that were still holding out—Lachish and Azekah. These were the only fortified cities left in Judah.

Freedom for Slaves

⁸The word came to Jeremiah from the LORD after King Zedekiah had made a covenant with all the people in Jerusalem to proclaim freedom for the slaves. ⁹Everyone was to free his Hebrew slaves, both male and female; no one was to hold a fellow Jew in bondage. ¹⁰So all the officials and people who entered into this covenant agreed that they would free their male and female slaves and no longer hold them in bondage. They agreed, and set them free. ¹¹But afterward they changed their minds and took back the slaves they had freed and enslaved them again.

¹²Then the word of the LORD came to Jeremiah: ¹³"This is what the LORD, the God of Israel, says: I made a covenant with your forefathers when I brought them out of Egypt, out of the land of slavery. I said, ¹⁴'Every seventh year each of you must free any fellow Hebrew who has sold himself to you. After he has served you six years, you must let him go free.'ᵃ Your fathers, however, did not listen to me or pay attention to me. ¹⁵Recently you repented and did what is right in my sight: Each of you proclaimed freedom to his countrymen. You even made a covenant before me in the house that bears my Name. ¹⁶But now you have turned around and profaned my name; each of you has taken back the male and female slaves you had set free to go where they wished. You have forced them to become your slaves again.

¹⁷"Therefore, this is what the LORD says: You have not obeyed me; you have not proclaimed freedom for your fellow countrymen. So I now proclaim 'freedom' for you, declares the LORD— 'freedom' to fall by the sword, plague and famine. I will make you abhorrent to all the kingdoms of the earth. ¹⁸The men who have violated my covenant and have not fulfilled the terms of the covenant they made before me, I will treat like the calf they cut in two and then walked between its pieces. ¹⁹The leaders of Judah and Jerusalem, the court officials, the priests and all the people of the land who walked between the pieces of the calf, ²⁰I will hand over to their enemies who seek their lives. Their dead bodies will become food for the birds of the air and the beasts of the earth.

²¹"I will hand Zedekiah king of Judah and his officials over to their enemies who seek their lives, to the army of the king of Babylon, which has withdrawn from you. ²²I am going to give the order, declares the LORD, and I will bring them back to this city. They will fight against it, take it and burn it down. And I will lay waste the towns of Judah so no one can live there."

The Recabites

35 This is the word that came to Jeremiah from the LORD during the reign of Jehoiakim son of Josiah king of Judah: ²"Go to the Recabite family and invite them to come to one of the side rooms of the house of the LORD and give them wine to drink."

³So I went to get Jaazaniah son of Jeremiah, the son of Habazziniah, and his brothers and all his sons—the whole family of the Recabites. ⁴I brought them into the house of the LORD, into the room of the sons of Hanan son of Igdaliah the man of God. It was next to the room of the officials, which was over that of Maaseiah son of Shallum the doorkeeper. ⁵Then I set bowls full of wine and some cups before the men of the Recabite family and said to them, "Drink some wine."

⁶But they replied, "We do not drink wine, because our forefather Jonadab son of Recab gave us this command: 'Neither you nor your descendants must ever drink wine. ⁷Also you must never build houses, sow seed or plant vineyards; you must never have any of these things, but must always live in tents. Then you will live a long time in the land where you are nomads.' ⁸We have obeyed everything our forefather Jonadab son of Recab commanded us. Neither we nor our wives nor our sons

ᵃ 14 Deut. 15:12

Call Me Supergirl

focus Profile: Leanne

This morning when my palm pilot beeped, I realized I'd scheduled two meetings before school. I had to blow off studying for chemistry with my friend Tracy because I knew my English teacher needed to talk with me about the after-school poetry reading. I hope Tracy understands I didn't ditch her on purpose.

The other day she muttered something under her breath about my being an "imaginary friend," but I pretended I didn't hear her. What does she expect me to do? With soccer, the school newspaper, working at the mall, and being class president, I'm just about maxed out. Whenever Tracy calls or asks if I can go rollerblading or something, I'm always tied up trying to keep my life under control.

Lately, my dad says the only time he sees me is when I whiz by the breakfast table on my way to school. I guess that's why he started calling me "supergirl." Kind of embarrassing when he says it in front of my friends!

Yesterday our athletic director asked me if I'd be willing to coach a little kids' soccer team this spring. For some reason, I said yes. I know I've got too much going, and I feel like I can't concentrate on anything anymore—but how could I say no to that? It'll be a good experience and look good on my college applications, and besides, those little kids are so cute.

Still, some days I find myself daydreaming about having a normal life, whatever that means.

For more ideas on how to deal with overcommitment, check out the link on www.TrueImagesBible.com

overcommitment in focus

So many girls out there are overcommitted. Are you? Are you sleep-deprived because you have so much going on? Do you feel worn thin by rushing around from one thing to the next? Do you feel like everyone wants a piece of you—your family, your friends, your teachers, your coaches—and there's just not enough of you to go around? Remember . . .

»Busyness is dangerous because it makes us lose sight of God's best plan for our lives (see Matthew 6:33, page 1298).
»Spend time with God and ask him where you should focus your energy (see Psalm 46:10, page 700).
»Prioritize what's most important. Don't shortchange the things that matter most, like devotions, sleep and homework.
»Choose to focus on fewer things, and do those things well.

For more on this topic, see the index on page 1656.

and daughters have ever drunk wine [9]or built houses to live in or had vineyards, fields or crops. [10]We have lived in tents and have fully obeyed everything our forefather Jonadab commanded us. [11]But when Nebuchadnezzar king of Babylon invaded this land, we said, 'Come, we must go to Jerusalem to escape the Babylonian[a] and Aramean armies.' So we have remained in Jerusalem."

[12]Then the word of the LORD came to Jeremiah, saying: [13]"This is what the LORD Almighty, the God of Israel, says: Go and tell the men of Judah and the people of Jerusalem, 'Will you not learn

a 11 Or Chaldean

a lesson and obey my words?' declares the LORD. ¹⁴Jonadab son of Recab ordered his sons not to drink wine and this command has been kept. To this day they do not drink wine, because they obey their forefather's command. But I have spoken to you again and again, yet you have not obeyed me. ¹⁵Again and again I sent all my servants the prophets to you. They said, "Each of you must turn from your wicked ways and reform your actions; do not follow other gods to serve them. Then you will live in the land I have given to you and your fathers." But you have not paid attention or listened to me. ¹⁶The descendants of Jonadab son of Recab have carried out the command their forefather gave them, but these people have not obeyed me.'

¹⁷"Therefore, this is what the LORD God Almighty, the God of Israel, says: 'Listen! I am going to bring on Judah and on everyone living in Jerusalem every disaster I pronounced against them. I spoke to them, but they did not listen; I called to them, but they did not answer.' "

¹⁸Then Jeremiah said to the family of the Recabites, "This is what the LORD Almighty, the God of Israel, says: 'You have obeyed the command of your forefather Jonadab and have followed all his instructions and have done everything he ordered.' ¹⁹Therefore, this is what the LORD Almighty, the God of Israel, says: 'Jonadab son of Recab will never fail to have a man to serve me.' "

Jehoiakim Burns Jeremiah's Scroll

36 In the fourth year of Jehoiakim son of Josiah king of Judah, this word came to Jeremiah from the LORD: ²"Take a scroll and write on it all the words I have spoken to you concerning Israel, Judah and all the other nations from the time I began speaking to you in the reign of Josiah till now. ³Perhaps when the people of Judah hear about every disaster I plan to inflict on them, each of them will turn from his wicked way; then I will forgive their wickedness and their sin."

⁴So Jeremiah called Baruch son of Neriah, and while Jeremiah dictated all the words the LORD had spoken to him, Baruch wrote them on the scroll. ⁵Then Jeremiah told Baruch, "I am restricted; I cannot go to the LORD's temple. ⁶So you go to the house of the LORD on a day of fasting and read to the people from the scroll the words of the LORD that you wrote as I dictated. Read them to all the people of Judah who come in from their towns. ⁷Perhaps they will bring their petition before the LORD, and each will turn from his wicked ways, for the anger and wrath pronounced against this people by the LORD are great."

⁸Baruch son of Neriah did everything Jeremiah the prophet told him to do; at the LORD's temple he read the words of the LORD from the scroll. ⁹In the ninth month of the fifth year of Jehoiakim son of Josiah king of Judah, a time of fasting before the LORD was proclaimed for all the people in Jerusalem and those who had come from the towns of Judah. ¹⁰From the room of Gemariah son of Shaphan the secretary, which was in the upper courtyard at the entrance of the New Gate of the temple, Baruch read to all the people at the LORD's temple the words of Jeremiah from the scroll.

¹¹When Micaiah son of Gemariah, the son of Shaphan, heard all the words of the LORD from the scroll, ¹²he went down to the secretary's room in the royal palace, where all the officials were sitting: Elishama the secretary, Delaiah son of Shemaiah, Elnathan son of Acbor, Gemariah son of Shaphan, Zedekiah son of Hananiah, and all the other officials. ¹³After Micaiah told them everything he had heard Baruch read to the people from the scroll, ¹⁴all the officials sent Jehudi son of Nethaniah, the son of Shelemiah, the son of Cushi, to say to Baruch, "Bring the scroll from which you have read to the people and come." So Baruch son of Neriah went to them with the scroll in his hand. ¹⁵They said to him, "Sit down, please, and read it to us."

So Baruch read it to them. ¹⁶When they heard all these words, they looked at each other in fear and said to Baruch, "We must report all these words to the king." ¹⁷Then they asked Baruch, "Tell us, how did you come to write all this? Did Jeremiah dictate it?"

¹⁸"Yes," Baruch replied, "he dictated all these words to me, and I wrote them in ink on the scroll."

truth or dare

King Jehoiakim might have been a Bible burner, but he couldn't destroy the Word of God. It always has been and will be preserved. Forever.

36:1–3,20–28

¹⁹Then the officials said to Baruch, "You and Jeremiah, go and hide. Don't let anyone know where you are."

²⁰After they put the scroll in the room of Elishama the secretary, they went to the king in the courtyard and reported everything to him. ²¹The king sent Jehudi to get the scroll, and Jehudi brought it from the room of Elishama the secretary and read it to the king and all the officials standing beside him. ²²It was the ninth month and the king was sitting in the winter apartment, with a fire burning in the firepot in front of him. ²³Whenever Jehudi had read three or four columns of the scroll, the king cut them off with a scribe's knife and threw them into the firepot, until the entire scroll was burned in the fire. ²⁴The king and all his attendants who heard all these words showed no fear, nor did they tear their clothes. ²⁵Even though Elnathan, Delaiah and Gemariah urged the king not to burn the scroll, he would not listen to them. ²⁶Instead, the king commanded Jerahmeel, a son of the king, Seraiah son of Azriel and Shelemiah son of Abdeel to arrest Baruch the scribe and Jeremiah the prophet. But the Lord had hidden them.

²⁷After the king burned the scroll containing the words that Baruch had written at Jeremiah's dictation, the word of the Lord came to Jeremiah: ²⁸"Take another scroll and write on it all the words that were on the first scroll, which Jehoiakim king of Judah burned up. ²⁹Also tell Jehoiakim king of Judah, 'This is what the Lord says: You burned that scroll and said, "Why did you write on it that the king of Babylon would certainly come and destroy this land and cut off both men and animals from it?" ³⁰Therefore, this is what the Lord says about Jehoiakim king of Judah: He will have no one to sit on the throne of David; his body will be thrown out and exposed to the heat by day and the frost by night. ³¹I will punish him and his children and his attendants for their wickedness; I will bring on them and those living in Jerusalem and the people of Judah every disaster I pronounced against them, because they have not listened.' "

³²So Jeremiah took another scroll and gave it to the scribe Baruch son of Neriah, and as Jeremiah dictated, Baruch wrote on it all the words of the scroll that Jehoiakim king of Judah had burned in the fire. And many similar words were added to them.

Jeremiah in Prison

37 Zedekiah son of Josiah was made king of Judah by Nebuchadnezzar king of Babylon; he reigned in place of Jehoiachin*a* son of Jehoiakim. ²Neither he nor his attendants nor the people of the land paid any attention to the words the Lord had spoken through Jeremiah the prophet.

³King Zedekiah, however, sent Jehucal son of Shelemiah with the priest Zephaniah son of Maaseiah to Jeremiah the prophet with this message: "Please pray to the Lord our God for us."

⁴Now Jeremiah was free to come and go among the people, for he had not yet been put in prison. ⁵Pharaoh's army had marched out of Egypt, and when the Babylonians*b* who were besieging Jerusalem heard the report about them, they withdrew from Jerusalem.

⁶Then the word of the Lord came to Jeremiah the prophet: ⁷"This is what the Lord, the God of Israel, says: Tell the king of Judah, who sent you to inquire of me, 'Pharaoh's army, which has marched out to support you, will go back to its own land, to Egypt. ⁸Then the Babylonians will return and attack this city; they will capture it and burn it down.'

⁹"This is what the Lord says: Do not deceive yourselves, thinking, 'The Babylonians will surely leave us.' They will not! ¹⁰Even if you were to defeat the entire Babylonian*c* army that is attacking you and only wounded men were left in their tents, they would come out and burn this city down."

¹¹After the Babylonian army had withdrawn from Jerusalem because of Pharaoh's army, ¹²Jeremiah started to leave the city to go to the territory of Benjamin to get his share of the property among the people there. ¹³But when he reached the Benjamin Gate, the captain of the guard, whose name was Irijah son of Shelemiah, the son of Hananiah, arrested him and said, "You are deserting to the Babylonians!"

¹⁴"That's not true!" Jeremiah said. "I am not deserting to the Babylonians." But Irijah would not listen to him; instead, he arrested Jeremiah and brought him to the officials. ¹⁵They were angry with Jeremiah and had him beaten and imprisoned in the house of Jonathan the secretary, which they had made into a prison.

a 1 Hebrew *Coniah,* a variant of *Jehoiachin*   *b 5* Or *Chaldeans*; also in verses 8, 9, 13 and 14   *c 10* Or *Chaldean*; also in verse 11

¹⁶Jeremiah was put into a vaulted cell in a dungeon, where he remained a long time. ¹⁷Then King Zedekiah sent for him and had him brought to the palace, where he asked him privately, "Is there any word from the LORD?"

"Yes," Jeremiah replied, "you will be handed over to the king of Babylon."

¹⁸Then Jeremiah said to King Zedekiah, "What crime have I committed against you or your officials or this people, that you have put me in prison? ¹⁹Where are your prophets who prophesied to you, 'The king of Babylon will not attack you or this land'? ²⁰But now, my lord the king, please listen. Let me bring my petition before you: Do not send me back to the house of Jonathan the secretary, or I will die there."

²¹King Zedekiah then gave orders for Jeremiah to be placed in the courtyard of the guard and given bread from the street of the bakers each day until all the bread in the city was gone. So Jeremiah remained in the courtyard of the guard.

Jeremiah Thrown Into a Cistern

38 Shephatiah son of Mattan, Gedaliah son of Pashhur, Jehucal*ᵃ* son of Shelemiah, and Pashhur son of Malkijah heard what Jeremiah was telling all the people when he said, ²"This is what the LORD says: 'Whoever stays in this city will die by the sword, famine or plague, but whoever goes over to the Babylonians*ᵇ* will live. He will escape with his life; he will live.' ³And this is what the LORD says: 'This city will certainly be handed over to the army of the king of Babylon, who will capture it.' "

⁴Then the officials said to the king, "This man should be put to death. He is discouraging the soldiers who are left in this city, as well as all the people, by the things he is saying to them. This man is not seeking the good of these people but their ruin."

⁵"He is in your hands," King Zedekiah answered. "The king can do nothing to oppose you."

⁶So they took Jeremiah and put him into the cistern of Malkijah, the king's son, which was in the courtyard of the guard. They lowered Jeremiah by ropes into the cistern; it had no water in it, only mud, and Jeremiah sank down into the mud.

genuine character »» 38:1-13

Ebed-Melech took a chance. He went out on a limb when he stood up for Jeremiah. Everyone else seemed to want Jeremiah dead, but that didn't stop Ebed-Melech from doing the right thing. And because he trusted in God and took that risk, he was spared when Jerusalem fell. When you see someone being bullied or made fun of, when others decide to play a mean prank or a nasty trick on someone else, will you go out on a limb for that person? Will you do the right thing even if everyone else hates you for it?

⁷But Ebed-Melech, a Cushite,*ᶜ* an official*ᵈ* in the royal palace, heard that they had put Jeremiah into the cistern. While the king was sitting in the Benjamin Gate, ⁸Ebed-Melech went out of the palace and said to him, ⁹"My lord the king, these men have acted wickedly in all they have done to Jeremiah the prophet. They have thrown him into a cistern, where he will starve to death when there is no longer any bread in the city."

¹⁰Then the king commanded Ebed-Melech the Cushite, "Take thirty men from here with you and lift Jeremiah the prophet out of the cistern before he dies."

¹¹So Ebed-Melech took the men with him and went to a room under the treasury in the palace. He took some old rags and worn-out clothes from there and let them down with ropes to Jeremiah in the cistern. ¹²Ebed-Melech the Cushite said to Jeremiah, "Put these old rags and worn-out clothes under your arms to pad the ropes." Jeremiah did so, ¹³and they pulled him up with the ropes and lifted him out of the cistern. And Jeremiah remained in the courtyard of the guard.

ᵃ 1 Hebrew *Jucal,* a variant of *Jehucal*   *ᵇ 2* Or *Chaldeans;* also in verses 18, 19 and 23   *ᶜ 7* Probably from the upper Nile region   *ᵈ 7* Or *a eunuch*

Zedekiah Questions Jeremiah Again

[14]Then King Zedekiah sent for Jeremiah the prophet and had him brought to the third entrance to the temple of the LORD. "I am going to ask you something," the king said to Jeremiah. "Do not hide anything from me."

[15]Jeremiah said to Zedekiah, "If I give you an answer, will you not kill me? Even if I did give you counsel, you would not listen to me."

[16]But King Zedekiah swore this oath secretly to Jeremiah: "As surely as the LORD lives, who has given us breath, I will neither kill you nor hand you over to those who are seeking your life."

[17]Then Jeremiah said to Zedekiah, "This is what the LORD God Almighty, the God of Israel, says: 'If you surrender to the officers of the king of Babylon, your life will be spared and this city will not be burned down; you and your family will live. [18]But if you will not surrender to the officers of the king of Babylon, this city will be handed over to the Babylonians and they will burn it down; you yourself will not escape from their hands.' "

[19]King Zedekiah said to Jeremiah, "I am afraid of the Jews who have gone over to the Babylonians, for the Babylonians may hand me over to them and they will mistreat me."

[20]"They will not hand you over," Jeremiah replied. "Obey the LORD by doing what I tell you. Then it will go well with you, and your life will be spared. [21]But if you refuse to surrender, this is what the LORD has revealed to me: [22]All the women left in the palace of the king of Judah will be brought out to the officials of the king of Babylon. Those women will say to you:

> " 'They misled you and overcame you—
>   those trusted friends of yours.
> Your feet are sunk in the mud;
>   your friends have deserted you.'

[23]"All your wives and children will be brought out to the Babylonians. You yourself will not escape from their hands but will be captured by the king of Babylon; and this city will*ᵃ* be burned down."

[24]Then Zedekiah said to Jeremiah, "Do not let anyone know about this conversation, or you may die. [25]If the officials hear that I talked with you, and they come to you and say, 'Tell us what you said to the king and what the king said to you; do not hide it from us or we will kill you,' [26]then tell them, 'I was pleading with the king not to send me back to Jonathan's house to die there.' "

[27]All the officials did come to Jeremiah and question him, and he told them everything the king had ordered him to say. So they said no more to him, for no one had heard his conversation with the king.

[28]And Jeremiah remained in the courtyard of the guard until the day Jerusalem was captured.

truth or **dare**

Sometimes holding on to a dream (like Zedekiah did) can interfere with God's plan. Pray for the wisdom to know which goals to pursue and which ones to let go.

38:14–28

The Fall of Jerusalem

39 This is how Jerusalem was taken: [1]In the ninth year of Zedekiah king of Judah, in the tenth month, Nebuchadnezzar king of Babylon marched against Jerusalem with his whole army and laid siege to it. [2]And on the ninth day of the fourth month of Zedekiah's eleventh year, the city wall was broken through. [3]Then all the officials of the king of Babylon came and took seats in the Middle Gate: Nergal-Sharezer of Samgar, Nebo-Sarsekim*ᵇ* a chief officer, Nergal-Sharezer a high official and all the other officials of the king of Babylon. [4]When Zedekiah king of Judah and all the soldiers saw them, they fled; they left the city at night by way of the king's garden, through the gate between the two walls, and headed toward the Arabah.*ᶜ*

[5]But the Babylonian*ᵈ* army pursued them and overtook Zedekiah in the plains of Jericho. They captured him and took him to Nebuchadnezzar king of Babylon at Riblah in the land of Hamath,

---

ᵃ 23 Or and you will cause this city to   *ᵇ 3 Or Nergal-Sharezer, Samgar-Nebo, Sarsekim*   *ᶜ 4 Or the Jordan Valley*
ᵈ 5 Or Chaldean

where he pronounced sentence on him. [6]There at Riblah the king of Babylon slaughtered the sons of Zedekiah before his eyes and also killed all the nobles of Judah. [7]Then he put out Zedekiah's eyes and bound him with bronze shackles to take him to Babylon.

[8]The Babylonians[a] set fire to the royal palace and the houses of the people and broke down the walls of Jerusalem. [9]Nebuzaradan commander of the imperial guard carried into exile to Babylon the people who remained in the city, along with those who had gone over to him, and the rest of the people. [10]But Nebuzaradan the commander of the guard left behind in the land of Judah some of the poor people, who owned nothing; and at that time he gave them vineyards and fields.

[11]Now Nebuchadnezzar king of Babylon had given these orders about Jeremiah through Nebuzaradan commander of the imperial guard: [12]"Take him and look after him; don't harm him but do for him whatever he asks." [13]So Nebuzaradan the commander of the guard, Nebushazban a chief officer, Nergal-Sharezer a high official and all the other officers of the king of Babylon [14]sent and had Jeremiah taken out of the courtyard of the guard. They turned him over to Gedaliah son of Ahikam, the son of Shaphan, to take him back to his home. So he remained among his own people.

[15]While Jeremiah had been confined in the courtyard of the guard, the word of the LORD came to him: [16]"Go and tell Ebed-Melech the Cushite, 'This is what the LORD Almighty, the God of Israel, says: I am about to fulfill my words against this city through disaster, not prosperity. At that time they will be fulfilled before your eyes. [17]But I will rescue you on that day, declares the LORD; you will not be handed over to those you fear. [18]I will save you; you will not fall by the sword but will escape with your life, because you trust in me, declares the LORD.' "

Jeremiah Freed

40 The word came to Jeremiah from the LORD after Nebuzaradan commander of the imperial guard had released him at Ramah. He had found Jeremiah bound in chains among all the captives from Jerusalem and Judah who were being carried into exile to Babylon. [2]When the commander of the guard found Jeremiah, he said to him, "The LORD your God decreed this disaster for this place. [3]And now the LORD has brought it about; he has done just as he said he would. All this happened because you people sinned against the LORD and did not obey him. [4]But today I am freeing you from the chains on your wrists. Come with me to Babylon, if you like, and I will look after you; but if you do not want to, then don't come. Look, the whole country lies before you; go wherever you please." [5]However, before Jeremiah turned to go,[b] Nebuzaradan added, "Go back to Gedaliah son of Ahikam, the son of Shaphan, whom the king of Babylon has appointed over the towns of Judah, and live with him among the people, or go anywhere else you please."

Then the commander gave him provisions and a present and let him go. [6]So Jeremiah went to Gedaliah son of Ahikam at Mizpah and stayed with him among the people who were left behind in the land.

Gedaliah Assassinated

[7]When all the army officers and their men who were still in the open country heard that the king of Babylon had appointed Gedaliah son of Ahikam as governor over the land and had put him in charge of the men, women and children who were the poorest in the land and who had not been carried into exile to Babylon, [8]they came to Gedaliah at Mizpah—Ishmael son of Nethaniah, Johanan and Jonathan the sons of Kareah, Seraiah son of Tanhumeth, the sons of Ephai the Netophathite, and Jaazaniah[c] the son of the Maacathite, and their men. [9]Gedaliah son of Ahikam, the son of Shaphan, took an oath to reassure them and their men. "Do not be afraid to serve the Babylonians,[d]" he said. "Settle down in the land and serve the king of Babylon, and it will go well with you. [10]I myself will stay at Mizpah to represent you before the Babylonians who come to us, but you are to harvest the wine, summer fruit and oil, and put them in your storage jars, and live in the towns you have taken over."

[11]When all the Jews in Moab, Ammon, Edom and all the other countries heard that the king of Babylon had left a remnant in Judah and had appointed Gedaliah son of Ahikam, the son of Shaphan, as governor over them, [12]they all came back to the land of Judah, to Gedaliah at Mizpah,

---

a 8 Or *Chaldeans*   *b 5* Or *Jeremiah answered*   *c 8* Hebrew *Jezaniah,* a variant of *Jaazaniah*   *d 9* Or *Chaldeans;* also in verse 10 from all the countries where they had been scattered. And they harvested an abundance of wine and summer fruit.

[13]Johanan son of Kareah and all the army officers still in the open country came to Gedaliah at Mizpah [14]and said to him, "Don't you know that Baalis king of the Ammonites has sent Ishmael son of Nethaniah to take your life?" But Gedaliah son of Ahikam did not believe them.

[15]Then Johanan son of Kareah said privately to Gedaliah in Mizpah, "Let me go and kill Ishmael son of Nethaniah, and no one will know it. Why should he take your life and cause all the Jews who are gathered around you to be scattered and the remnant of Judah to perish?"

[16]But Gedaliah son of Ahikam said to Johanan son of Kareah, "Don't do such a thing! What you are saying about Ishmael is not true."

41

In the seventh month Ishmael son of Nethaniah, the son of Elishama, who was of royal blood and had been one of the king's officers, came with ten men to Gedaliah son of Ahikam at Mizpah. While they were eating together there, [2]Ishmael son of Nethaniah and the ten men who were with him got up and struck down Gedaliah son of Ahikam, the son of Shaphan, with the sword, killing the one whom the king of Babylon had appointed as governor over the land. [3]Ishmael also killed all the Jews who were with Gedaliah at Mizpah, as well as the Babylonian[a] soldiers who were there.

[4]The day after Gedaliah's assassination, before anyone knew about it, [5]eighty men who had shaved off their beards, torn their clothes and cut themselves came from Shechem, Shiloh and Samaria, bringing grain offerings and incense with them to the house of the LORD. [6]Ishmael son of Nethaniah went out from Mizpah to meet them, weeping as he went. When he met them, he said, "Come to Gedaliah son of Ahikam." [7]When they went into the city, Ishmael son of Nethaniah and the men who were with him slaughtered them and threw them into a cistern. [8]But ten of them said to Ishmael, "Don't kill us! We have wheat and barley, oil and honey, hidden in a field." So he let them alone and did not kill them with the others. [9]Now the cistern where he threw all the bodies of the men he had killed along with Gedaliah was the one King Asa had made as part of his defense against Baasha king of Israel. Ishmael son of Nethaniah filled it with the dead.

[10]Ishmael made captives of all the rest of the people who were in Mizpah—the king's daughters along with all the others who were left there, over whom Nebuzaradan commander of the imperial guard had appointed Gedaliah son of Ahikam. Ishmael son of Nethaniah took them captive and set out to cross over to the Ammonites.

[11]When Johanan son of Kareah and all the army officers who were with him heard about all the crimes Ishmael son of Nethaniah had committed, [12]they took all their men and went to fight Ishmael son of Nethaniah. They caught up with him near the great pool in Gibeon. [13]When all the people Ishmael had with him saw Johanan son of Kareah and the army officers who were with him, they were glad. [14]All the people Ishmael had taken captive at Mizpah turned and went over to Johanan son of Kareah. [15]But Ishmael son of Nethaniah and eight of his men escaped from Johanan and fled to the Ammonites.

Flight to Egypt

[16]Then Johanan son of Kareah and all the army officers who were with him led away all the survivors from Mizpah whom he had recovered from Ishmael son of Nethaniah after he had assassinated Gedaliah son of Ahikam: the soldiers, women, children and court officials he had brought from Gibeon. [17]And they went on, stopping at Geruth Kimham near Bethlehem on their way to Egypt [18]to escape the Babylonians.[b] They were afraid of them because Ishmael son of Nethaniah had killed Gedaliah son of Ahikam, whom the king of Babylon had appointed as governor over the land.

42

Then all the army officers, including Johanan son of Kareah and Jezaniah[c] son of Hoshaiah, and all the people from the least to the greatest approached [2]Jeremiah the prophet and said to him, "Please hear our petition and pray to the LORD your God for this entire remnant. For as you now see, though we were once many, now only a few are left. [3]Pray that the LORD your God will tell us where we should go and what we should do."

[4]"I have heard you," replied Jeremiah the prophet. "I will certainly pray to the LORD your God as you have requested; I will tell you everything the LORD says and will keep nothing back from you."

[5]Then they said to Jeremiah, "May the LORD be a true and faithful witness against us if we do

---

[a] 3 Or Chaldean   [b] 18 Or Chaldeans   [c] 1 Hebrew; Septuagint (see also 43:2) Azariah

Dad's Little Secret

Profile: Lorraine

Dad and I have always been close. We talk about everything. Well, almost everything. We haven't talked about what I found in the basement two days ago: *Playboy* and *Penthouse* magazines.

I couldn't believe it when I found the box. Those horrible magazines! I found them behind the furnace of all places. Maybe if they had been just ten inches to the right—actually *in* the furnace—that would've been better.

They had to be Dad's. My brother Chris wouldn't have left anything like this around. He's not into leaving a paper trail or evidence of any kind.

All I could think was, *My own father looks at this stuff. How long has he been doing this? What would Mom think? Does she know?*

I know that some porn is considered more "hard-core" than *Playboy*. Chris told me that after I caught him looking at some stuff on the Internet. He told me that guys who look at hard-core pornography *really* have a problem. Like that makes looking at *Playboy* okay?? All of it makes me sick!

I couldn't even look at my dad after I found it. It's like he wasn't the same person anymore.

Maybe he knows something's wrong. He keeps asking me if I'm okay. I can't understand why he'd do this. My dad's a Christian! Yet he's got this porn stash. It's like he's got this secret life.

I wish I knew what to do.

For more ideas on how to deal with pornography, check out the link on www.TrueImagesBible.com

pornography in focus

It's everywhere. Pornography, that is. It's on the Internet, on television, at bookstores. Frequent exposure to pornography can lead to feelings of alienation and some changes in personality. If you know someone who struggles with pornography addiction . . .

»Talk with a trusted Christian adult about the issue. Pray together, and come up with a plan for what to do next.

»Just telling a person to "stop" won't bring about lasting change. Pornography addiction is a bondage that is difficult but not impossible to break.. The Holy Spirit can bring freedom. (See John 8:32, page 1424; Galatians 5:1,16,22–25, pages 1539–1540.)

»Show God's love to the person and work with other adults to confront the person in a nonjudgmental way.

»Be prepared for denial or rationalization.

For more on this topic, see the index on page 1656.

not act in accordance with everything the Lᴏʀᴅ your God sends you to tell us. [6]Whether it is favorable or unfavorable, we will obey the Lᴏʀᴅ our God, to whom we are sending you, so that it will go well with us, for we will obey the Lᴏʀᴅ our God."

[7]Ten days later the word of the Lᴏʀᴅ came to Jeremiah. [8]So he called together Johanan son of Kareah and all the army officers who were with him and all the people from the least to the greatest. [9]He said to them, "This is what the Lᴏʀᴅ, the God of Israel, to whom you sent me to present your petition, says: [10]'If you stay in this land, I will build you up and not tear you down; I will plant

you and not uproot you, for I am grieved over the disaster I have inflicted on you. [11]Do not be afraid of the king of Babylon, whom you now fear. Do not be afraid of him, declares the LORD, for I am with you and will save you and deliver you from his hands. [12]I will show you compassion so that he will have compassion on you and restore you to your land.'

[13]"However, if you say, 'We will not stay in this land,' and so disobey the LORD your God, [14]and if you say, 'No, we will go and live in Egypt, where we will not see war or hear the trumpet or be hungry for bread,' [15]then hear the word of the LORD, O remnant of Judah. This is what the LORD Almighty, the God of Israel, says: 'If you are determined to go to Egypt and you do go to settle there, [16]then the sword you fear will overtake you there, and the famine you dread will follow you into Egypt, and there you will die. [17]Indeed, all who are determined to go to Egypt to settle there will die by the sword, famine and plague; not one of them will survive or escape the disaster I will bring on them.' [18]This is what the LORD Almighty, the God of Israel, says: 'As my anger and wrath have been poured out on those who lived in Jerusalem, so will my wrath be poured out on you when you go to Egypt. You will be an object of cursing and horror, of condemnation and reproach; you will never see this place again.'

[19]"O remnant of Judah, the LORD has told you, 'Do not go to Egypt.' Be sure of this: I warn you today [20]that you made a fatal mistake[a] when you sent me to the LORD your God and said, 'Pray to the LORD our God for us; tell us everything he says and we will do it.' [21]I have told you today, but you still have not obeyed the LORD your God in all he sent me to tell you. [22]So now, be sure of this: You will die by the sword, famine and plague in the place where you want to go to settle."

43

When Jeremiah finished telling the people all the words of the LORD their God—everything the LORD had sent him to tell them— [2]Azariah son of Hoshaiah and Johanan son of Kareah and all the arrogant men said to Jeremiah, "You are lying! The LORD our God has not sent you to say, 'You must not go to Egypt to settle there.' [3]But Baruch son of Neriah is inciting you against us to hand us over to the Babylonians,[b] so they may kill us or carry us into exile to Babylon."

[4]So Johanan son of Kareah and all the army officers and all the people disobeyed the LORD's command to stay in the land of Judah. [5]Instead, Johanan son of Kareah and all the army officers led away all the remnant of Judah who had come back to live in the land of Judah from all the nations where they had been scattered. [6]They also led away all the men, women and children and the king's daughters whom Nebuzaradan commander of the imperial guard had left with Gedaliah son of Ahikam, the son of Shaphan, and Jeremiah the prophet and Baruch son of Neriah. [7]So they entered Egypt in disobedience to the LORD and went as far as Tahpanhes.

[8]In Tahpanhes the word of the LORD came to Jeremiah: [9]"While the Jews are watching, take some large stones with you and bury them in clay in the brick pavement at the entrance to Pharaoh's palace in Tahpanhes. [10]Then say to them, 'This is what the LORD Almighty, the God of Israel, says: I will send for my servant Nebuchadnezzar king of Babylon, and I will set his throne over these stones I have buried here; he will spread his royal canopy above them. [11]He will come and attack Egypt, bringing death to those destined for death, captivity to those destined for captivity, and the sword to those destined for the sword. [12]He[c] will set fire to the temples of the gods of Egypt; he will burn their temples and take their gods captive. As a shepherd wraps his garment around him, so will he wrap Egypt around himself and depart from there unscathed. [13]There in the temple of the sun[d] in Egypt he will demolish the sacred pillars and will burn down the temples of the gods of Egypt.' "

Disaster Because of Idolatry

44

This word came to Jeremiah concerning all the Jews living in Lower Egypt—in Migdol, Tahpanhes and Memphis[e]—and in Upper Egypt[f]: [2]"This is what the LORD Almighty, the God of Israel, says: You saw the great disaster I brought on Jerusalem and on all the towns of Judah. Today they lie deserted and in ruins [3]because of the evil they have done. They provoked me to anger by burning incense and by worshiping other gods that neither they nor you nor your fathers ever knew. [4]Again and again I sent my servants the prophets, who said, 'Do not do this detestable thing that I hate!' [5]But they did not listen or pay attention; they did not turn

---

a 20 Or you erred in your hearts   b 3 Or Chaldeans   c 12 Or I   d 13 Or in Heliopolis   e 1 Hebrew Noph
f 1 Hebrew in Pathros

from their wickedness or stop burning incense to other gods. ⁶Therefore, my fierce anger was poured out; it raged against the towns of Judah and the streets of Jerusalem and made them the desolate ruins they are today.

⁷"Now this is what the LORD God Almighty, the God of Israel, says: Why bring such great disaster on yourselves by cutting off from Judah the men and women, the children and infants, and so leave yourselves without a remnant? ⁸Why provoke me to anger with what your hands have made, burning incense to other gods in Egypt, where you have come to live? You will destroy yourselves and make yourselves an object of cursing and reproach among all the nations on earth. ⁹Have you forgotten the wickedness committed by your fathers and by the kings and queens of Judah and the wickedness committed by you and your wives in the land of Judah and the streets of Jerusalem? ¹⁰To this day they have not humbled themselves or shown reverence, nor have they followed my law and the decrees I set before you and your fathers.

¹¹"Therefore, this is what the LORD Almighty, the God of Israel, says: I am determined to bring disaster on you and to destroy all Judah. ¹²I will take away the remnant of Judah who were determined to go to Egypt to settle there. They will all perish in Egypt; they will fall by the sword or die from famine. From the least to the greatest, they will die by sword or famine. They will become an object of cursing and horror, of condemnation and reproach. ¹³I will punish those who live in Egypt with the sword, famine and plague, as I punished Jerusalem. ¹⁴None of the remnant of Judah who have gone to live in Egypt will escape or survive to return to the land of Judah, to which they long to return and live; none will return except a few fugitives."

¹⁵Then all the men who knew that their wives were burning incense to other gods, along with all the women who were present—a large assembly—and all the people living in Lower and Upper Egypt,ᵃ said to Jeremiah, ¹⁶"We will not listen to the message you have spoken to us in the name of the LORD! ¹⁷We will certainly do everything we said we would: We will burn incense to the Queen of Heaven and will pour out drink offerings to her just as we and our fathers, our kings and our officials did in the towns of Judah and in the streets of Jerusalem. At that time we had plenty of food and were well off and suffered no harm. ¹⁸But ever since we stopped burning incense to the Queen of Heaven and pouring out drink offerings to her, we have had nothing and have been perishing by sword and famine."

¹⁹The women added, "When we burned incense to the Queen of Heaven and poured out drink offerings to her, did not our husbands know that we were making cakes like her image and pouring out drink offerings to her?"

²⁰Then Jeremiah said to all the people, both men and women, who were answering him, ²¹"Did not the LORD remember and think about the incense burned in the towns of Judah and the streets of Jerusalem by you and your fathers, your kings and your officials and the people of the land? ²²When the LORD could no longer endure your wicked actions and the detestable things you did, your land became an object of cursing and a desolate waste without inhabitants, as it is today. ²³Because you have burned incense and have sinned against the LORD and have not obeyed him or followed his law or his decrees or his stipulations, this disaster has come upon you, as you now see."

²⁴Then Jeremiah said to all the people, including the women, "Hear the word of the LORD, all you people of Judah in Egypt. ²⁵This is what the LORD Almighty, the God of Israel, says: You and your wives have shown by your actions what you promised when you said, 'We will certainly carry out the vows we made to burn incense and pour out drink offerings to the Queen of Heaven.'

"Go ahead then, do what you promised! Keep your vows! ²⁶But hear the word of the LORD, all Jews living in Egypt: 'I swear by my great name,' says the LORD, 'that no one from Judah living anywhere in Egypt will ever again invoke my name or swear, "As surely as the Sovereign LORD lives."' ²⁷For I am watching over them for harm, not for good; the Jews in Egypt will perish by sword and

truth or dare

When you're plagued by problems, do you immediately assume you know the reason? Sometimes we miss the point because we refuse to hear what God's trying to tell us.

44:15–18

ᵃ 15 Hebrew *in Egypt and Pathros*

famine until they are all destroyed. 28Those who escape the sword and return to the land of Judah from Egypt will be very few. Then the whole remnant of Judah who came to live in Egypt will know whose word will stand—mine or theirs.

29" 'This will be the sign to you that I will punish you in this place,' declares the LORD, 'so that you will know that my threats of harm against you will surely stand.' 30This is what the LORD says: 'I am going to hand Pharaoh Hophra king of Egypt over to his enemies who seek his life, just as I handed Zedekiah king of Judah over to Nebuchadnezzar king of Babylon, the enemy who was seeking his life.' "

A Message to Baruch

45 This is what Jeremiah the prophet told Baruch son of Neriah in the fourth year of Jehoiakim son of Josiah king of Judah, after Baruch had written on a scroll the words Jeremiah was then dictating: 2"This is what the LORD, the God of Israel, says to you, Baruch: 3You said, 'Woe to me! The LORD has added sorrow to my pain; I am worn out with groaning and find no rest.' "

4The LORD said, "Say this to him: 'This is what the LORD says: I will overthrow what I have built and uproot what I have planted, throughout the land. 5Should you then seek great things for yourself? Seek them not. For I will bring disaster on all people, declares the LORD, but wherever you go I will let you escape with your life.' "

truth or dare

Do you want great things for yourself? Don't. That was good advice then and still is now. Don't focus only on yourself. Life's not all about you.

45:5

A Message About Egypt

46 This is the word of the LORD that came to Jeremiah the prophet concerning the nations:

2Concerning Egypt:

This is the message against the army of Pharaoh Neco king of Egypt, which was defeated at Carchemish on the Euphrates River by Nebuchadnezzar king of Babylon in the fourth year of Jehoiakim son of Josiah king of Judah:

> 3"Prepare your shields, both large and small,
> and march out for battle!
> 4Harness the horses,
> mount the steeds!
> Take your positions
> with helmets on!
> Polish your spears,
> put on your armor!
> 5What do I see?
> They are terrified,
> they are retreating,
> their warriors are defeated.
> They flee in haste
> without looking back,
> and there is terror on every side,"

declares the LORD.

> 6"The swift cannot flee
> nor the strong escape.
> In the north by the River Euphrates
> they stumble and fall.
> 7"Who is this that rises like the Nile,

like rivers of surging waters?
[8] Egypt rises like the Nile,
  like rivers of surging waters.
She says, 'I will rise and cover the earth;
  I will destroy cities and their people.'
[9] Charge, O horses!
  Drive furiously, O charioteers!
March on, O warriors—
  men of Cush[a] and Put who carry shields,
  men of Lydia who draw the bow.
[10] But that day belongs to the Lord, the LORD Almighty—
  a day of vengeance, for vengeance on his foes.
The sword will devour till it is satisfied,
  till it has quenched its thirst with blood.
For the Lord, the LORD Almighty, will offer sacrifice
  in the land of the north by the River Euphrates.

[11] "Go up to Gilead and get balm,
  O Virgin Daughter of Egypt.
But you multiply remedies in vain;
  there is no healing for you.
[12] The nations will hear of your shame;
  your cries will fill the earth.
One warrior will stumble over another;
  both will fall down together."

[13] This is the message the LORD spoke to Jeremiah the prophet about the coming of Nebuchadnezzar king of Babylon to attack Egypt:

[14] "Announce this in Egypt, and proclaim it in Migdol;
  proclaim it also in Memphis[b] and Tahpanhes:
'Take your positions and get ready,
  for the sword devours those around you.'
[15] Why will your warriors be laid low?
  They cannot stand, for the LORD will push them down.
[16] They will stumble repeatedly;
  they will fall over each other.
They will say, 'Get up, let us go back
  to our own people and our native lands,
  away from the sword of the oppressor.'
[17] There they will exclaim,
  'Pharaoh king of Egypt is only a loud noise;
  he has missed his opportunity.'

[18] "As surely as I live," declares the King,
  whose name is the LORD Almighty,
"one will come who is like Tabor among the mountains,
  like Carmel by the sea.
[19] Pack your belongings for exile,
  you who live in Egypt,
for Memphis will be laid waste
  and lie in ruins without inhabitant.

[20] "Egypt is a beautiful heifer,
  but a gadfly is coming
  against her from the north.
[21] The mercenaries in her ranks

a 9 That is, the upper Nile region b 14 Hebrew Noph; also in verse 19

are like fattened calves.
They too will turn and flee together,
    they will not stand their ground,
for the day of disaster is coming upon them,
    the time for them to be punished.
²²Egypt will hiss like a fleeing serpent
    as the enemy advances in force;
they will come against her with axes,
    like men who cut down trees.
²³They will chop down her forest,"

declares the LORD,

"dense though it be.
They are more numerous than locusts,
    they cannot be counted.
²⁴The Daughter of Egypt will be put to shame,
    handed over to the people of the north."

²⁵The LORD Almighty, the God of Israel, says: "I am about to bring punishment on Amon god of Thebes,^a on Pharaoh, on Egypt and her gods and her kings, and on those who rely on Pharaoh. ²⁶I will hand them over to those who seek their lives, to Nebuchadnezzar king of Babylon and his officers. Later, however, Egypt will be inhabited as in times past," declares the LORD.

²⁷"Do not fear, O Jacob my servant;
    do not be dismayed, O Israel.
I will surely save you out of a distant place,
    your descendants from the land of their exile.
Jacob will again have peace and security,
    and no one will make him afraid.
²⁸Do not fear, O Jacob my servant,
    for I am with you," declares the LORD.
"Though I completely destroy all the nations
    among which I scatter you,
    I will not completely destroy you.
I will discipline you but only with justice;
    I will not let you go entirely unpunished."

A Message About the Philistines

47 This is the word of the LORD that came to Jeremiah the prophet concerning the Philistines before Pharaoh attacked Gaza:

²This is what the LORD says:

"See how the waters are rising in the north;
    they will become an overflowing torrent.
They will overflow the land and everything in it,
    the towns and those who live in them.
The people will cry out;
    all who dwell in the land will wail
³at the sound of the hoofs of galloping steeds,
    at the noise of enemy chariots
    and the rumble of their wheels.
Fathers will not turn to help their children;
    their hands will hang limp.
⁴For the day has come
    to destroy all the Philistines
and to cut off all survivors

^a 25 Hebrew *No*

who could help Tyre and Sidon.
The LORD is about to destroy the Philistines,
    the remnant from the coasts of Caphtor.[a]
[5]Gaza will shave her head in mourning;
    Ashkelon will be silenced.
O remnant on the plain,
    how long will you cut yourselves?

[6]" 'Ah, sword of the LORD,' you cry,
    'how long till you rest?
Return to your scabbard;
    cease and be still.'
[7]But how can it rest
    when the LORD has commanded it,
when he has ordered it
    to attack Ashkelon and the coast?"

A Message About Moab

48
Concerning Moab:

This is what the LORD Almighty, the God of Israel, says:

"Woe to Nebo, for it will be ruined.
    Kiriathaim will be disgraced and captured;
    the stronghold[b] will be disgraced and shattered.
[2]Moab will be praised no more;
    in Heshbon[c] men will plot her downfall:
    'Come, let us put an end to that nation.'
You too, O Madmen,[d] will be silenced;
    the sword will pursue you.
[3]Listen to the cries from Horonaim,
    cries of great havoc and destruction.
[4]Moab will be broken;
    her little ones will cry out.[e]
[5]They go up the way to Luhith,
    weeping bitterly as they go;
on the road down to Horonaim
    anguished cries over the destruction are heard.
[6]Flee! Run for your lives;
    become like a bush[f] in the desert.
[7]Since you trust in your deeds and riches,
    you too will be taken captive,
and Chemosh will go into exile,
    together with his priests and officials.
[8]The destroyer will come against every town,
    and not a town will escape.
The valley will be ruined
    and the plateau destroyed,
    because the LORD has spoken.
[9]Put salt on Moab,
    for she will be laid waste[g];

---

a 4 That is, Crete   *b 1* Or */ Misgab*   *c 2* The Hebrew for *Heshbon* sounds like the Hebrew for *plot.*   *d 2* The name of the Moabite town Madmen sounds like the Hebrew for *be silenced.*   *e 4* Hebrew; Septuagint */ proclaim it to Zoar* *f 6* Or *like Aroer*   *g 9* Or *Give wings to Moab, / for she will fly away*

Shirk the Work?

Profile: Whitney

At my church, everybody's always going on and on about serving. You gotta serve on the missions team. You gotta teach Sunday school. It's like the focus is so on "do this, do that."

It's not like I don't wanna serve. It's just that all of the old people at my church won't let us do anything. They look at us like we're poison or something. Or maybe they think we're too dumb to know what we're doing.

Like in the church nursery. I volunteered to help out once a month with the babies after my mama nagged me to "do something" at church. I love babies, so I really didn't mind. So, I'd go there and do my thing. But every time I made a move, one of the primary caregivers (that's what they call the nursery supervisors) would say, "Hold the baby like this, Whitney." Like I didn't know you're supposed to support a baby's head with your hand. Or, she'd make me clean the room while she got to play with the babies.

After three months of that, I stopped helping out. I'd rather hang out with my friends in the church atrium.

Anyway, I thought the main thing about Christianity was believing in Jesus. Well, I believe in him. I'm real cool with God. So what's all this about serving? Isn't that *works*?

For more on serving and discovering your spiritual gifts, check out the link on www.TrueImagesBible.com

serving others in focus

Think you're exempt from serving? Not if you wanna have real faith. "In the same way, faith by itself, if it is not accompanied by action, is dead. . . . Show me your faith without deeds, and I will show you my faith by what I do" (James 2:17–18, page 1603). Serving helps you to . . .

»Be God's hands and feet (see Matthew 25:34–40, pages 1326–1327).
»Jumpstart your faith.
»Express your love for God—*not* earn your salvation (see Ephesians 2:8–10, page 1543).
»Focus on others rather than on yourself.

Serving others takes time, persistence and humility. It involves knowing where your passions and abilities lie. Bottom line? It involves really wanting to do stuff for others.

For more on this topic, see the index on page 1656.

---

her towns will become desolate,
with no one to live in them.

¹⁰ "A curse on him who is lax in doing the Lord's work!
A curse on him who keeps his sword from bloodshed!

¹¹ "Moab has been at rest from youth,
like wine left on its dregs,
not poured from one jar to another—
she has not gone into exile.
So she tastes as she did,

and her aroma is unchanged.
¹² But days are coming,"
    declares the LORD,
  "when I will send men who pour from jars,
    and they will pour her out;
  they will empty her jars
    and smash her jugs.
¹³ Then Moab will be ashamed of Chemosh,
    as the house of Israel was ashamed
    when they trusted in Bethel.

¹⁴ "How can you say, 'We are warriors,
    men valiant in battle'?
¹⁵ Moab will be destroyed and her towns invaded;
    her finest young men will go down in the slaughter,"
    declares the King, whose name is the LORD Almighty.
¹⁶ "The fall of Moab is at hand;
    her calamity will come quickly.
¹⁷ Mourn for her, all who live around her,
    all who know her fame;
  say, 'How broken is the mighty scepter,
    how broken the glorious staff!'

¹⁸ "Come down from your glory
    and sit on the parched ground,
    O inhabitants of the Daughter of Dibon,
  for he who destroys Moab
    will come up against you
    and ruin your fortified cities.
¹⁹ Stand by the road and watch,
    you who live in Aroer.
  Ask the man fleeing and the woman escaping,
    ask them, 'What has happened?'
²⁰ Moab is disgraced, for she is shattered.
    Wail and cry out!
  Announce by the Arnon
    that Moab is destroyed.
²¹ Judgment has come to the plateau—
    to Holon, Jahzah and Mephaath,
²²   to Dibon, Nebo and Beth Diblathaim,
²³   to Kiriathaim, Beth Gamul and Beth Meon,
²⁴   to Kerioth and Bozrah—
    to all the towns of Moab, far and near.
²⁵ Moab's horn^a is cut off;
    her arm is broken,"

                                        declares the LORD.

²⁶ "Make her drunk,
    for she has defied the LORD.
  Let Moab wallow in her vomit;
    let her be an object of ridicule.
²⁷ Was not Israel the object of your ridicule?
    Was she caught among thieves,
  that you shake your head in scorn
    whenever you speak of her?
²⁸ Abandon your towns and dwell among the rocks,

---

^a 25 Horn here symbolizes strength.

you who live in Moab.
Be like a dove that makes its nest
    at the mouth of a cave.

²⁹ "We have heard of Moab's pride—
    her overweening pride and conceit,
her pride and arrogance
    and the haughtiness of her heart.
³⁰ I know her insolence but it is futile,"

declares the LORD,

    "and her boasts accomplish nothing.
³¹ Therefore I wail over Moab,
    for all Moab I cry out,
    I moan for the men of Kir Hareseth.
³² I weep for you, as Jazer weeps,
    O vines of Sibmah.
Your branches spread as far as the sea;
    they reached as far as the sea of Jazer.
The destroyer has fallen
    on your ripened fruit and grapes.
³³ Joy and gladness are gone
    from the orchards and fields of Moab.
I have stopped the flow of wine from the presses;
    no one treads them with shouts of joy.
Although there are shouts,
    they are not shouts of joy.

³⁴ "The sound of their cry rises
    from Heshbon to Elealeh and Jahaz,
from Zoar as far as Horonaim and Eglath Shelishiyah,
    for even the waters of Nimrim are dried up.
³⁵ In Moab I will put an end
    to those who make offerings on the high places
    and burn incense to their gods,"

declares the LORD.

³⁶ "So my heart laments for Moab like a flute;
    it laments like a flute for the men of Kir Hareseth.
    The wealth they acquired is gone.
³⁷ Every head is shaved
    and every beard cut off;
every hand is slashed
    and every waist is covered with sackcloth.
³⁸ On all the roofs in Moab
    and in the public squares
there is nothing but mourning,
    for I have broken Moab
    like a jar that no one wants,"

declares the LORD.

³⁹ "How shattered she is! How they wail!
    How Moab turns her back in shame!
Moab has become an object of ridicule,
    an object of horror to all those around her."

⁴⁰ This is what the LORD says:

    "Look! An eagle is swooping down,
        spreading its wings over Moab.

⁴¹ Kerioth ᵃ will be captured
    and the strongholds taken.
In that day the hearts of Moab's warriors
    will be like the heart of a woman in labor.
⁴² Moab will be destroyed as a nation
    because she defied the LORD.
⁴³ Terror and pit and snare await you,
    O people of Moab,"

declares the LORD.

⁴⁴ "Whoever flees from the terror
    will fall into a pit,
whoever climbs out of the pit
    will be caught in a snare;
for I will bring upon Moab
    the year of her punishment,"

declares the LORD.

⁴⁵ "In the shadow of Heshbon
    the fugitives stand helpless,
for a fire has gone out from Heshbon,
    a blaze from the midst of Sihon;
it burns the foreheads of Moab,
    the skulls of the noisy boasters.
⁴⁶ Woe to you, O Moab!
    The people of Chemosh are destroyed;
your sons are taken into exile
    and your daughters into captivity.

⁴⁷ "Yet I will restore the fortunes of Moab
    in days to come,"

declares the LORD.

Here ends the judgment on Moab.

A Message About Ammon

49

Concerning the Ammonites:

This is what the LORD says:

"Has Israel no sons?
    Has she no heirs?
Why then has Molech ᵇ taken possession of Gad?
    Why do his people live in its towns?
² But the days are coming,"
    declares the LORD,
"when I will sound the battle cry
    against Rabbah of the Ammonites;
it will become a mound of ruins,
    and its surrounding villages will be set on fire.
Then Israel will drive out
    those who drove her out,"

says the LORD.

³ "Wail, O Heshbon, for Ai is destroyed!
    Cry out, O inhabitants of Rabbah!
Put on sackcloth and mourn;
    rush here and there inside the walls,

ᵃ 41 Or The cities   ᵇ 1 Or their king; Hebrew malcam; also in verse 3

for Molech will go into exile,
together with his priests and officials.
⁴Why do you boast of your valleys,
boast of your valleys so fruitful?
O unfaithful daughter,
you trust in your riches and say,
'Who will attack me?'
⁵I will bring terror on you
from all those around you,"

declares the Lord, the LORD Almighty.

"Every one of you will be driven away,
and no one will gather the fugitives.

⁶"Yet afterward, I will restore the fortunes of the Ammonites,"

declares the LORD.

A Message About Edom

⁷Concerning Edom:

This is what the LORD Almighty says:

"Is there no longer wisdom in Teman?
Has counsel perished from the prudent?
Has their wisdom decayed?
⁸Turn and flee, hide in deep caves,
you who live in Dedan,
for I will bring disaster on Esau
at the time I punish him.
⁹If grape pickers came to you,
would they not leave a few grapes?
If thieves came during the night,
would they not steal only as much as they wanted?
¹⁰But I will strip Esau bare;
I will uncover his hiding places,
so that he cannot conceal himself.
His children, relatives and neighbors will perish,
and he will be no more.
¹¹Leave your orphans; I will protect their lives.
Your widows too can trust in me."

¹²This is what the LORD says: "If those who do not deserve to drink the cup must drink it, why should you go unpunished? You will not go unpunished, but must drink it. ¹³I swear by myself," declares the LORD, "that Bozrah will become a ruin and an object of horror, of reproach and of cursing; and all its towns will be in ruins forever."

¹⁴I have heard a message from the LORD:
An envoy was sent to the nations to say,
"Assemble yourselves to attack it!
Rise up for battle!"

¹⁵"Now I will make you small among the nations,
despised among men.
¹⁶The terror you inspire
and the pride of your heart have deceived you,
you who live in the clefts of the rocks,
who occupy the heights of the hill.
Though you build your nest as high as the eagle's,
from there I will bring you down,"

declares the LORD.

¹⁷ "Edom will become an object of horror;
     all who pass by will be appalled and will scoff
         because of all its wounds.
¹⁸ As Sodom and Gomorrah were overthrown,
     along with their neighboring towns,"

                                                    says the LORD,

     "so no one will live there;
         no man will dwell in it.

¹⁹ "Like a lion coming up from Jordan's thickets
     to a rich pastureland,
 I will chase Edom from its land in an instant.
     Who is the chosen one I will appoint for this?
 Who is like me and who can challenge me?
     And what shepherd can stand against me?"
²⁰ Therefore, hear what the LORD has planned against Edom,
     what he has purposed against those who live in Teman:
 The young of the flock will be dragged away;
     he will completely destroy their pasture because of them.
²¹ At the sound of their fall the earth will tremble;
     their cry will resound to the Red Sea. *
²² Look! An eagle will soar and swoop down,
     spreading its wings over Bozrah.
 In that day the hearts of Edom's warriors
     will be like the heart of a woman in labor.

A Message About Damascus

²³ Concerning Damascus:

     "Hamath and Arpad are dismayed,
         for they have heard bad news.
     They are disheartened,
         troubled like ᵇ the restless sea.
²⁴ Damascus has become feeble,
         she has turned to flee
         and panic has gripped her;
     anguish and pain have seized her,
         pain like that of a woman in labor.
²⁵ Why has the city of renown not been abandoned,
         the town in which I delight?
²⁶ Surely, her young men will fall in the streets;
         all her soldiers will be silenced in that day,"

                                        declares the LORD Almighty.

²⁷ "I will set fire to the walls of Damascus;
         it will consume the fortresses of Ben-Hadad."

A Message About Kedar and Hazor

²⁸ Concerning Kedar and the kingdoms of Hazor, which Nebuchadnezzar king of Babylon attacked:

This is what the LORD says:

     "Arise, and attack Kedar
         and destroy the people of the East.
²⁹ Their tents and their flocks will be taken;
         their shelters will be carried off

a 21 Hebrew *Yam Suph*; that is, Sea of Reeds   *b 23* Hebrew *on* or *by*

with all their goods and camels.
Men will shout to them,
        'Terror on every side!'

30 "Flee quickly away!
        Stay in deep caves, you who live in Hazor,"

declares the Lord.

"Nebuchadnezzar king of Babylon has plotted against you;
        he has devised a plan against you.

31 "Arise and attack a nation at ease,
        which lives in confidence,"

declares the Lord,

"a nation that has neither gates nor bars;
        its people live alone.
32 Their camels will become plunder,
        and their large herds will be booty.
I will scatter to the winds those who are in distant places [a]
        and will bring disaster on them from every side,"

declares the Lord.

33 "Hazor will become a haunt of jackals,
        a desolate place forever.
No one will live there;
        no man will dwell in it."

A Message About Elam

34 This is the word of the Lord that came to Jeremiah the prophet concerning Elam, early in the reign of Zedekiah king of Judah:

35 This is what the Lord Almighty says:

"See, I will break the bow of Elam,
        the mainstay of their might.
36 I will bring against Elam the four winds
        from the four quarters of the heavens;
I will scatter them to the four winds,
        and there will not be a nation
        where Elam's exiles do not go.
37 I will shatter Elam before their foes,
        before those who seek their lives;
I will bring disaster upon them,
        even my fierce anger,"

declares the Lord.

"I will pursue them with the sword
        until I have made an end of them.
38 I will set my throne in Elam
        and destroy her king and officials,"

declares the Lord.

39 "Yet I will restore the fortunes of Elam
        in days to come,"

declares the Lord.

A Message About Babylon

50 This is the word the Lord spoke through Jeremiah the prophet concerning Babylon and the land of the Babylonians [b]:

a 32 Or who clip the hair by their foreheads   b 1 Or Chaldeans; also in verses 8, 25, 35 and 45

2 "Announce and proclaim among
the nations,
lift up a banner and proclaim
it;
keep nothing back, but say,
'Babylon will be captured;
Bel will be put to shame,
Marduk filled with terror.
Her images will be put to shame
and her idols filled with terror.'
3 A nation from the north will
attack her
and lay waste her land.
No one will live in it;
both men and animals will flee away.

4 "In those days, at that time,"
declares the Lord,
"the people of Israel and the people of Judah
together
will go in tears to seek the Lord their God.
5 They will ask the way to Zion
and turn their faces toward it.
They will come and bind themselves to the Lord
in an everlasting covenant
that will not be forgotten.

6 "My people have been lost sheep;
their shepherds have led them astray
and caused them to roam on the mountains.
They wandered over mountain and hill
and forgot their own resting place.
7 Whoever found them devoured them;
their enemies said, 'We are not guilty,
for they sinned against the Lord, their true pasture,
the Lord, the hope of their fathers.'

8 "Flee out of Babylon;
leave the land of the Babylonians,
and be like the goats that lead the flock.
9 For I will stir up and bring against Babylon
an alliance of great nations from the land of the north.
They will take up their positions against her,
and from the north she will be captured.
Their arrows will be like skilled warriors
who do not return empty-handed.
10 So Babylonia a will be plundered;
all who plunder her will have their fill,"

declares the Lord.

11 "Because you rejoice and are glad,
you who pillage my inheritance,
because you frolic like a heifer threshing grain
and neigh like stallions,
12 your mother will be greatly ashamed;
she who gave you birth will be disgraced.

truth or dare

During its time, Babylon was *the* leading nation on earth. But Jeremiah, speaking via God, had the audacity to declare Babylon's doom. Would you have dared to believe him?

50:1–3

a 10 Or *Chaldea*

She will be the least of the nations—
    a wilderness, a dry land, a desert.
¹³Because of the LORD's anger she will not be inhabited
    but will be completely desolate.
All who pass Babylon will be horrified and scoff
    because of all her wounds.

¹⁴"Take up your positions around Babylon,
    all you who draw the bow.
Shoot at her! Spare no arrows,
    for she has sinned against the LORD.
¹⁵Shout against her on every side!
    She surrenders, her towers fall,
    her walls are torn down.
Since this is the vengeance of the LORD,
    take vengeance on her;
    do to her as she has done to others.
¹⁶Cut off from Babylon the sower,
    and the reaper with his sickle at harvest.
Because of the sword of the oppressor
    let everyone return to his own people,
    let everyone flee to his own land.

¹⁷"Israel is a scattered flock
    that lions have chased away.
The first to devour him
    was the king of Assyria;
the last to crush his bones
    was Nebuchadnezzar king of Babylon."

¹⁸Therefore this is what the LORD Almighty, the God of Israel, says:

"I will punish the king of Babylon and his land
    as I punished the king of Assyria.
¹⁹But I will bring Israel back to his own pasture
    and he will graze on Carmel and Bashan;
his appetite will be satisfied
    on the hills of Ephraim and Gilead.
²⁰In those days, at that time,"
    declares the LORD,
"search will be made for Israel's guilt,
    but there will be none,
and for the sins of Judah,
    but none will be found,
    for I will forgive the remnant I spare.

²¹"Attack the land of Merathaim
    and those who live in Pekod.
Pursue, kill and completely destroy*ᵃ* them,"
                            declares the LORD.
"Do everything I have commanded you.
²²The noise of battle is in the land,
    the noise of great destruction!
²³How broken and shattered
    is the hammer of the whole earth!
How desolate is Babylon

---

a 21 The Hebrew term refers to the irrevocable giving over of things or persons to the LORD, often by totally destroying them; also in verse 26.

among the nations!

²⁴ I set a trap for you, O Babylon,
　　and you were caught before you knew it;
you were found and captured
　　because you opposed the LORD.
²⁵ The LORD has opened his arsenal
　　and brought out the weapons of his wrath,
for the Sovereign LORD Almighty has work to do
　　in the land of the Babylonians.
²⁶ Come against her from afar.
　　Break open her granaries;
　　pile her up like heaps of grain.
Completely destroy her
　　and leave her no remnant.
²⁷ Kill all her young bulls;
　　let them go down to the slaughter!
Woe to them! For their day has come,
　　the time for them to be punished.
²⁸ Listen to the fugitives and refugees from Babylon
　　declaring in Zion
how the LORD our God has taken vengeance,
　　vengeance for his temple.

²⁹ "Summon archers against Babylon,
　　all those who draw the bow.
Encamp all around her;
　　let no one escape.
Repay her for her deeds;
　　do to her as she has done.
For she has defied the LORD,
　　the Holy One of Israel.
³⁰ Therefore, her young men will fall in the streets;
　　all her soldiers will be silenced in that day,"

declares the LORD.

³¹ "See, I am against you, O arrogant one,"
　　declares the Lord, the LORD Almighty,
"for your day has come,
　　the time for you to be punished.
³² The arrogant one will stumble and fall
　　and no one will help her up;
I will kindle a fire in her towns
　　that will consume all who are around her."

³³ This is what the LORD Almighty says:

"The people of Israel are oppressed,
　　and the people of Judah as well.
All their captors hold them fast,
　　refusing to let them go.
³⁴ Yet their Redeemer is strong;
　　the LORD Almighty is his name.
He will vigorously defend their cause
　　so that he may bring rest to their land,
　　but unrest to those who live in Babylon.

³⁵ "A sword against the Babylonians!"
　　declares the LORD—
"against those who live in Babylon

and against her officials and wise men!
[36] A sword against her false prophets!
They will become fools.
A sword against her warriors!
They will be filled with terror.
[37] A sword against her horses and chariots
and all the foreigners in her ranks!
They will become women.
A sword against her treasures!
They will be plundered.
[38] A drought on[a] her waters!
They will dry up.
For it is a land of idols,
idols that will go mad with terror.

[39] "So desert creatures and hyenas will live there,
and there the owl will dwell.
It will never again be inhabited
or lived in from generation to generation.
[40] As God overthrew Sodom and Gomorrah
along with their neighboring towns,"

declares the LORD,

"so no one will live there;
no man will dwell in it.

[41] "Look! An army is coming from the north;
a great nation and many kings
are being stirred up from the ends of the earth.
[42] They are armed with bows and spears;
they are cruel and without mercy.
They sound like the roaring sea
as they ride on their horses;
they come like men in battle formation
to attack you, O Daughter of Babylon.
[43] The king of Babylon has heard reports about them,
and his hands hang limp.
Anguish has gripped him,
pain like that of a woman in labor.
[44] Like a lion coming up from Jordan's thickets
to a rich pastureland,
I will chase Babylon from its land in an instant.
Who is the chosen one I will appoint for this?
Who is like me and who can challenge me?
And what shepherd can stand against me?"
[45] Therefore, hear what the LORD has planned against Babylon,
what he has purposed against the land of the Babylonians:
The young of the flock will be dragged away;
he will completely destroy their pasture because of them.
[46] At the sound of Babylon's capture the earth will tremble;
its cry will resound among the nations.

51

This is what the LORD says:

"See, I will stir up the spirit of a destroyer
against Babylon and the people of Leb Kamai.[b]

a 38 Or *A sword against*   *b 1 Leb Kamai* is a cryptogram for Chaldea, that is, Babylonia.

[2] I will send foreigners to Babylon
    to winnow her and to devastate her land;
they will oppose her on every side
    in the day of her disaster.
[3] Let not the archer string his bow,
    nor let him put on his armor.
Do not spare her young men;
    completely destroy[a] her army.
[4] They will fall down slain in Babylon,[b]
    fatally wounded in her streets.
[5] For Israel and Judah have not been forsaken
    by their God, the LORD Almighty,
though their land[c] is full of guilt
    before the Holy One of Israel.

[6] "Flee from Babylon!
    Run for your lives!
    Do not be destroyed because of her sins.
It is time for the LORD's vengeance;
    he will pay her what she deserves.
[7] Babylon was a gold cup in the LORD's hand;
    she made the whole earth drunk.
The nations drank her wine;
    therefore they have now gone mad.
[8] Babylon will suddenly fall and be broken.
    Wail over her!
Get balm for her pain;
    perhaps she can be healed.

[9] " 'We would have healed Babylon,
    but she cannot be healed;
let us leave her and each go to his own land,
    for her judgment reaches to the skies,
    it rises as high as the clouds.'

[10] " 'The LORD has vindicated us;
    come, let us tell in Zion
    what the LORD our God has done.'

[11] "Sharpen the arrows,
    take up the shields!
The LORD has stirred up the kings of the Medes,
    because his purpose is to destroy Babylon.
The LORD will take vengeance,
    vengeance for his temple.
[12] Lift up a banner against the walls of Babylon!
    Reinforce the guard,
station the watchmen,
    prepare an ambush!
The LORD will carry out his purpose,
    his decree against the people of Babylon.
[13] You who live by many waters
    and are rich in treasures,
your end has come,
    the time for you to be cut off.

a 3 The Hebrew term refers to the irrevocable giving over of things or persons to the LORD, often by totally destroying them.
b 4 Or Chaldea   c 5 Or / and the land of the Babylonians,

[14] The LORD Almighty has sworn by
  himself:
 I will surely fill you with men,
   as with a swarm of
   locusts,
 and they will shout in triumph
  over you.

[15] "He made the earth by his power;
 he founded the world by his
  wisdom
 and stretched out the heavens
  by his understanding.
[16] When he thunders, the waters in the heavens
  roar;
 he makes clouds rise from the ends of the
  earth.
He sends lightning with the rain
 and brings out the wind from his storehouses.

[17] "Every man is senseless and without knowledge;
 every goldsmith is shamed by his idols.
His images are a fraud;
 they have no breath in them.
[18] They are worthless, the objects of mockery;
 when their judgment comes, they will perish.
[19] He who is the Portion of Jacob is not like these,
 for he is the Maker of all things,
including the tribe of his inheritance—
 the LORD Almighty is his name.

[20] "You are my war club,
 my weapon for battle—
with you I shatter nations,
 with you I destroy kingdoms,
[21] with you I shatter horse and rider,
 with you I shatter chariot and driver,
[22] with you I shatter man and woman,
 with you I shatter old man and youth,
 with you I shatter young man and maiden,
[23] with you I shatter shepherd and flock,
 with you I shatter farmer and oxen,
 with you I shatter governors and officials.

[24] "Before your eyes I will repay Babylon and all who live in Babylonia[a] for all the wrong they
have done in Zion," declares the LORD.

[25] "I am against you, O destroying mountain,
 you who destroy the whole earth,"

          declares the LORD.

"I will stretch out my hand against you,
 roll you off the cliffs,
 and make you a burned-out mountain.
[26] No rock will be taken from you for a cornerstone,
 nor any stone for a foundation,
 for you will be desolate forever,"

          declares the LORD.

truth or dare

Ever doubt God's greatness? Just compare what God makes (e.g, humans, the universe) to what people make (e.g., replicas, idols). The difference is huge.

51:15–19

_a 24_ Or _Chaldea;_ also in verse 35

²⁷ "Lift up a banner in the land!
    Blow the trumpet among the nations!
Prepare the nations for battle against her;
    summon against her these kingdoms:
    Ararat, Minni and Ashkenaz.
Appoint a commander against her;
    send up horses like a swarm of locusts.
²⁸ Prepare the nations for battle against her—
    the kings of the Medes,
their governors and all their officials,
    and all the countries they rule.
²⁹ The land trembles and writhes,
    for the LORD's purposes against Babylon stand—
to lay waste the land of Babylon
    so that no one will live there.
³⁰ Babylon's warriors have stopped fighting;
    they remain in their strongholds.
Their strength is exhausted;
    they have become like women.
Her dwellings are set on fire;
    the bars of her gates are broken.
³¹ One courier follows another
    and messenger follows messenger
to announce to the king of Babylon
    that his entire city is captured,
³² the river crossings seized,
    the marshes set on fire,
    and the soldiers terrified."

³³ This is what the LORD Almighty, the God of Israel, says:

"The Daughter of Babylon is like a threshing floor
    at the time it is trampled;
    the time to harvest her will soon come."

³⁴ "Nebuchadnezzar king of Babylon has devoured us,
    he has thrown us into confusion,
    he has made us an empty jar.
Like a serpent he has swallowed us
    and filled his stomach with our delicacies,
    and then has spewed us out.
³⁵ May the violence done to our flesh^a be upon Babylon,"
    say the inhabitants of Zion.
"May our blood be on those who live in Babylonia,"
    says Jerusalem.

³⁶ Therefore, this is what the LORD says:

"See, I will defend your cause
    and avenge you;
I will dry up her sea
    and make her springs dry.
³⁷ Babylon will be a heap of ruins,
    a haunt of jackals,
an object of horror and scorn,
    a place where no one lives.
³⁸ Her people all roar like young lions,

---

^a 35 Or done to us and to our children

they growl like lion cubs.
³⁹ But while they are aroused,
    I will set out a feast for them
    and make them drunk,
so that they shout with laughter—
    then sleep forever and not awake,"
declares the LORD.

⁴⁰ "I will bring them down
    like lambs to the slaughter,
    like rams and goats.

⁴¹ "How Sheshach ^a will be captured,
    the boast of the whole earth seized!
What a horror Babylon will be
    among the nations!
⁴² The sea will rise over Babylon;
    its roaring waves will cover her.
⁴³ Her towns will be desolate,
    a dry and desert land,
a land where no one lives,
    through which no man travels.
⁴⁴ I will punish Bel in Babylon
    and make him spew out what he has swallowed.
The nations will no longer stream to him.
    And the wall of Babylon will fall.

⁴⁵ "Come out of her, my people!
    Run for your lives!
    Run from the fierce anger of the LORD.
⁴⁶ Do not lose heart or be afraid
    when rumors are heard in the land;
one rumor comes this year, another the next,
    rumors of violence in the land
    and of ruler against ruler.
⁴⁷ For the time will surely come
    when I will punish the idols of Babylon;
her whole land will be disgraced
    and her slain will all lie fallen within her.
⁴⁸ Then heaven and earth and all that is in them
    will shout for joy over Babylon,
for out of the north
    destroyers will attack her,"
declares the LORD.

⁴⁹ "Babylon must fall because of Israel's slain,
    just as the slain in all the earth
    have fallen because of Babylon.
⁵⁰ You who have escaped the sword,
    leave and do not linger!
Remember the LORD in a distant land,
    and think on Jerusalem."

⁵¹ "We are disgraced,
    for we have been insulted
    and shame covers our faces,
because foreigners have entered
    the holy places of the LORD's house."

---

^a 41 *Sheshach* is a cryptogram for Babylon.

⁵²"But days are coming," declares the LORD,
    "when I will punish her idols,
and throughout her land
    the wounded will groan.
⁵³Even if Babylon reaches the sky
    and fortifies her lofty stronghold,
    I will send destroyers against her,"
                        declares the LORD.

⁵⁴"The sound of a cry comes from Babylon,
    the sound of great destruction
    from the land of the Babylonians.^a
⁵⁵The LORD will destroy Babylon;
    he will silence her noisy din.
Waves ⌊of enemies⌋ will rage like great waters;
    the roar of their voices will resound.
⁵⁶A destroyer will come against Babylon;
    her warriors will be captured,
    and their bows will be broken.
For the LORD is a God of retribution;
    he will repay in full.
⁵⁷I will make her officials and wise men drunk,
    her governors, officers and warriors as well;
they will sleep forever and not awake,"
    declares the King, whose name is the LORD Almighty.

⁵⁸This is what the LORD Almighty says:

"Babylon's thick wall will be leveled
    and her high gates set on fire;
the peoples exhaust themselves for nothing,
    the nations' labor is only fuel for the flames."

⁵⁹This is the message Jeremiah gave to the staff officer Seraiah son of Neriah, the son of Mahseiah, when he went to Babylon with Zedekiah king of Judah in the fourth year of his reign. ⁶⁰Jeremiah had written on a scroll about all the disasters that would come upon Babylon—all that had been recorded concerning Babylon. ⁶¹He said to Seraiah, "When you get to Babylon, see that you read all these words aloud. ⁶²Then say, 'O LORD, you have said you will destroy this place, so that neither man nor animal will live in it; it will be desolate forever.' ⁶³When you finish reading this scroll, tie a stone to it and throw it into the Euphrates. ⁶⁴Then say, 'So will Babylon sink to rise no more because of the disaster I will bring upon her. And her people will fall.' "

The words of Jeremiah end here.

The Fall of Jerusalem

52 Zedekiah was twenty-one years old when he became king, and he reigned in Jerusalem eleven years. His mother's name was Hamutal daughter of Jeremiah; she was from Libnah. ²He did evil in the eyes of the LORD, just as Jehoiakim had done. ³It was because of the LORD's anger that all this happened to Jerusalem and Judah, and in the end he thrust them from his presence.

Now Zedekiah rebelled against the king of Babylon.

⁴So in the ninth year of Zedekiah's reign, on the tenth day of the tenth month, Nebuchadnezzar king of Babylon marched against Jerusalem with his whole army. They camped outside the city and built siege works all around it. ⁵The city was kept under siege until the eleventh year of King Zedekiah.

⁶By the ninth day of the fourth month the famine in the city had become so severe that there was no food for the people to eat. ⁷Then the city wall was broken through, and the whole army fled.

^a 54 Or Chaldeans

"Don't, my brother!" she said to him. "Don't force me. Such a thing should not be done in Israel! Don't do this wicked thing. What about me? Where could I get rid of my disgrace?" 2 Samuel 13:12–13

Tamar—When Heartbreak Happens

She was terrified. She never realized how strong her half brother was—until the moment she realized she could not fight him off.

Many girls are victims of sexual assault, incest, rape or molestation. Even Tamar, the princess daughter of the mighty King David, was not safe from the threat of being abused. She pleaded as she struggled with Amnon, giving every reason she could think of for him not to rape her. But he chose to ignore her pleas.

Amnon had thought he was in love with Tamar. First Samuel 13:2 says that Amnon was "frustrated to the point of illness." Not exactly a description of someone really in love. In fact, Amnon wasn't in love with Tamar at all. He was in lust. Lust is ugly, selfish and violent. True love never hurts others or forces others to do things against their will.

Amnon's rape of Tamar had nothing to do with love. Rape is a violent crime against an innocent victim, and Tamar did nothing to deserve it. Not only did the rape hurt Tamar physically, but it also crushed her spirit and broke her heart. She carried that pain with her the rest of her life. Many girls carry the same emotional scars. They feel as if they should have done something different to avoid what happened, or that they are now damaged goods. But if Christ has set us free from our sins, can't he also free us from the disgrace of others' sins against us? Yes—he can; he will; he does. In him, we are free from shame and hopelessness. Free from anger and feelings of false guilt. Free to live joyfully, powerfully and victoriously in Christ.

Letting go of our pain doesn't mean what happened to us was okay. It makes *us* okay—big difference. Due to customs of the time, Tamar couldn't marry another man after she lost her virginity. That's why she protested to Amnon, "Sending me away would be a greater wrong than what you have already done to me" (13:16). Fortunately, girls today don't have to live with that same stigma. Tamar was never able to let go of her sadness and shame, and it shaped the rest of her life. Ask God to help you let go of anything holding you back today.

Dear God, I give you my heartbreak today, so it won't hold me back tomorrow. Set me free from shame, and give me the power to move forward. Amen.

dear God

To read the next Mirror Images profile, go to page 1105.

>> Read more about Tamar in 2 Samuel 13 (pages 376–378).

They left the city at night through the gate between the two walls near the king's garden, though the Babylonians*a* were surrounding the city. They fled toward the Arabah,*b* 8but the Babylonian*c* army pursued King Zedekiah and overtook him in the plains of Jericho. All his soldiers were separated from him and scattered, 9and he was captured.

He was taken to the king of Babylon at Riblah in the land of Hamath, where he pronounced sentence on him. 10There at Riblah the king of Babylon slaughtered the sons of Zedekiah before his eyes; he also killed all the officials of Judah. 11Then he put out Zedekiah's eyes, bound him with bronze shackles and took him to Babylon, where he put him in prison till the day of his death.

12On the tenth day of the fifth month, in the nineteenth year of Nebuchadnezzar king of Babylon, Nebuzaradan commander of the imperial guard, who served the king of Babylon, came to Jerusalem. 13He set fire to the temple of the LORD, the royal palace and all the houses of Jerusalem. Every important building he burned down. 14The whole Babylonian army under the commander of the imperial guard broke down all the walls around Jerusalem. 15Nebuzaradan the commander of the guard carried into exile some of the poorest people and those who remained in the city, along with the rest of the craftsmen*d* and those who had gone over to the king of Babylon. 16But Nebuzaradan left behind the rest of the poorest people of the land to work the vineyards and fields.

17The Babylonians broke up the bronze pillars, the movable stands and the bronze Sea that were at the temple of the LORD and they carried all the bronze to Babylon. 18They also took away the pots, shovels, wick trimmers, sprinkling bowls, dishes and all the bronze articles used in the temple service. 19The commander of the imperial guard took away the basins, censers, sprinkling bowls, pots, lampstands, dishes and bowls used for drink offerings—all that were made of pure gold or silver.

20The bronze from the two pillars, the Sea and the twelve bronze bulls under it, and the movable stands, which King Solomon had made for the temple of the LORD, was more than could be weighed. 21Each of the pillars was eighteen cubits high and twelve cubits in circumference*e*; each was four fingers thick, and hollow. 22The bronze capital on top of the one pillar was five cubits*f* high and was decorated with a network and pomegranates of bronze all around. The other pillar, with its pomegranates, was similar. 23There were ninety-six pomegranates on the sides; the total number of pomegranates above the surrounding network was a hundred.

24The commander of the guard took as prisoners Seraiah the chief priest, Zephaniah the priest next in rank and the three doorkeepers. 25Of those still in the city, he took the officer in charge of the fighting men, and seven royal advisers. He also took the secretary who was chief officer in charge of conscripting the people of the land and sixty of his men who were found in the city. 26Nebuzaradan the commander took them all and brought them to the king of Babylon at Riblah. 27There at Riblah, in the land of Hamath, the king had them executed.

So Judah went into captivity, away from her land. 28This is the number of the people Nebuchadnezzar carried into exile:

in the seventh year, 3,023 Jews;
29in Nebuchadnezzar's eighteenth year,
  832 people from Jerusalem;
30in his twenty-third year,
  745 Jews taken into exile by Nebuzaradan the commander of the imperial guard.
  There were 4,600 people in all.

Jehoiachin Released

31In the thirty-seventh year of the exile of Jehoiachin king of Judah, in the year Evil-Merodach*g* became king of Babylon, he released Jehoiachin king of Judah and freed him from prison on the twenty-fifth day of the twelfth month. 32He spoke kindly to him and gave him a seat of honor higher than those of the other kings who were with him in Babylon. 33So Jehoiachin put aside his prison clothes and for the rest of his life ate regularly at the king's table. 34Day by day the king of Babylon gave Jehoiachin a regular allowance as long as he lived, till the day of his death.

a 7 Or *Chaldeans;* also in verse 17   *b 7* Or *the Jordan Valley*   *c 8* Or *Chaldean;* also in verse 14   *d 15* Or *populace*   *e 21* That is, about 27 feet (about 8.1 meters) high and 18 feet (about 5.4 meters) in circumference   *f 22* That is, about 7 1/2 feet (about 2.3 meters)   *g 31* Also called *Amel-Marduk*

author:	Jeremiah.
date:	Shortly after the fall of Jerusalem in 586 B.C.
setting:	Jerusalem had been utterly destroyed by the Babylonians. The people were killed, tortured or taken as prisoners.
verse to remember:	Because of the LORD's great love we are not consumed, for his compassions never fail. They are new every morning; great is your faithfulness (3:22–23).
theme to consider:	In the midst of hopelessness, Jeremiah had faith in God's character and in his promise to bring his people back to himself someday.

unchanging truth

Ever have a time in your life when you cried so hard for so long that you literally ran out of tears? Perhaps you felt hurt, afraid, sad or hopeless.

The prophet Jeremiah experienced a time like that, but he knew all too well the reason for his tears (2:11). He had spent years pleading with his nation to turn from their sinful ways. But they had refused. God had brought the promised punishment on the land—the nation was devastated, the temple destroyed, the people exiled. It seemed like all of God's promises for blessings had disappeared with the smoke that rose from the city. The people deserved this punishment, but that didn't make it any easier to take. So Jeremiah wept.

Through his tears, however, Jeremiah found a glimmer of hope. He knew that God does not forget his promises. He knew that God *loves* his people. In fact, he loved them enough to discipline them, cleanse them and bring them back to himself. Because of the Lord's compassion, the people hadn't been completely destroyed. So Jeremiah settled down to hope in the Lord, to "wait quietly for the salvation of the LORD" (3:26).

God sees your tears and shares your pain. When you are in the darkest moments, ask him to show you his glimmer of hope—his great love, compassion and faithfulness that are new every morning. Then wait quietly for him.

lamentations

life lessons

3

1. When you're hurting, honestly tell your feelings to God. He can take it (1:20–22).

2. No matter how hopeless a situation seems, you can always find hope in God (3:19–23).

3. God promises to answer you, but you may have to wait patiently for him to work your situation out in his way, in his time (3:24–26).

⌃

^aHow deserted lies the city,
  once so full of people!
How like a widow is she,
  who once was great among the nations!
She who was queen among the provinces
  has now become a slave.

² Bitterly she weeps at night,
  tears are upon her cheeks.
Among all her lovers
  there is none to comfort her.
All her friends have betrayed her;
  they have become her enemies.

³ After affliction and harsh labor,
  Judah has gone into exile.
She dwells among the nations;
  she finds no resting place.
All who pursue her have overtaken her
  in the midst of her distress.

⁴ The roads to Zion mourn,
  for no one comes to her appointed feasts.
All her gateways are desolate,
  her priests groan,
her maidens grieve,
  and she is in bitter anguish.

⁵ Her foes have become her masters;
  her enemies are at ease.
The LORD has brought her grief
  because of her many sins.
Her children have gone into exile,
  captive before the foe.

⁶ All the splendor has departed
  from the Daughter of Zion.
Her princes are like deer
  that find no pasture;
in weakness they have fled
  before the pursuer.

⁷ In the days of her affliction and wandering
  Jerusalem remembers all the treasures
  that were hers in days of old.
When her people fell into enemy hands,
  there was no one to help her.
Her enemies looked at her
  and laughed at her destruction.

⁸ Jerusalem has sinned greatly
  and so has become unclean.
All who honored her despise her,
  for they have seen her nakedness;
she herself groans
  and turns away.

⁹ Her filthiness clung to her skirts;

---

^a This chapter is an acrostic poem, the verses of which begin with the successive letters of the Hebrew alphabet.

she did not consider her future.
Her fall was astounding;
  there was none to comfort her.
"Look, O LORD, on my affliction,
  for the enemy has triumphed."

¹⁰ The enemy laid hands
  on all her treasures;
she saw pagan nations
  enter her sanctuary—
those you had forbidden
  to enter your assembly.

¹¹ All her people groan
  as they search for bread;
they barter their treasures for food
  to keep themselves alive.
"Look, O LORD, and consider,
  for I am despised."

¹² "Is it nothing to you, all you who pass by?
  Look around and see.
Is any suffering like my suffering
  that was inflicted on me,
that the LORD brought on me
  in the day of his fierce anger?

¹³ "From on high he sent fire,
  sent it down into my bones.
He spread a net for my feet
  and turned me back.
He made me desolate,
  faint all the day long.

¹⁴ "My sins have been bound into a
    yoke *a* ;
  by his hands they were woven together.
They have come upon my neck
  and the Lord has sapped my strength.
He has handed me over
  to those I cannot withstand.

¹⁵ "The Lord has rejected
  all the warriors in my midst;
he has summoned an army against me
  to *b* crush my young men.
In his winepress the Lord has trampled
  the Virgin Daughter of Judah.

¹⁶ "This is why I weep
  and my eyes overflow with tears.
No one is near to comfort me,
  no one to restore my spirit.
My children are destitute
  because the enemy has prevailed."

¹⁷ Zion stretches out her hands,
  but there is no one to comfort her.

truth or dare

Sin often promises us freedom from the rules. But here's a reality check—sin actually ties you down and takes away your freedom. Are you falling for the sin trap?

1:14

---

a 14 Most Hebrew manuscripts; Septuagint *He kept watch over my sins*   *b* 15 Or *has set a time for me / when he will*

The LORD has decreed for Jacob
    that his neighbors become his foes;
Jerusalem has become
    an unclean thing among them.

18 "The LORD is righteous,
    yet I rebelled against his command.
Listen, all you peoples;
    look upon my suffering.
My young men and maidens
    have gone into exile.

19 "I called to my allies
    but they betrayed me.
My priests and my elders
    perished in the city
while they searched for food
    to keep themselves alive.

20 "See, O LORD, how distressed I am!
    I am in torment within,
and in my heart I am disturbed,
    for I have been most rebellious.
Outside, the sword bereaves;
    inside, there is only death.

21 "People have heard my groaning,
    but there is no one to comfort me.
All my enemies have heard of my distress;
    they rejoice at what you have done.
May you bring the day you have announced
    so they may become like me.

22 "Let all their wickedness come before you;
    deal with them
as you have dealt with me
    because of all my sins.
My groans are many
    and my heart is faint."

2

a How the Lord has covered the Daughter of Zion
    with the cloud of his anger *b*!
He has hurled down the splendor of Israel
    from heaven to earth;
he has not remembered his footstool
    in the day of his anger.

2 Without pity the Lord has swallowed up
    all the dwellings of Jacob;
in his wrath he has torn down
    the strongholds of the Daughter of Judah.
He has brought her kingdom and its princes
    down to the ground in dishonor.

3 In fierce anger he has cut off
    every horn *c* of Israel.

---

a This chapter is an acrostic poem, the verses of which begin with the successive letters of the Hebrew alphabet.
b 1 Or *How the Lord in his anger / has treated the Daughter of Zion with contempt*   *c* 3 Or / *all the strength*; or *every king*; *horn* here symbolizes strength.

He has withdrawn his right hand
    at the approach of the enemy.
He has burned in Jacob like a flaming fire
    that consumes everything around it.

⁴Like an enemy he has strung his bow;
    his right hand is ready.
Like a foe he has slain
    all who were pleasing to the eye;
he has poured out his wrath like fire
    on the tent of the Daughter of Zion.

⁵The Lord is like an enemy;
    he has swallowed up Israel.
He has swallowed up all her palaces
    and destroyed her strongholds.
He has multiplied mourning and lamentation
    for the Daughter of Judah.

⁶He has laid waste his dwelling like a garden;
    he has destroyed his place of meeting.
The LORD has made Zion forget
    her appointed feasts and her Sabbaths;
in his fierce anger he has spurned
    both king and priest.

⁷The Lord has rejected his altar
    and abandoned his sanctuary.
He has handed over to the enemy
    the walls of her palaces;
they have raised a shout in the house of the LORD
    as on the day of an appointed feast.

⁸The LORD determined to tear down
    the wall around the Daughter of Zion.
He stretched out a measuring line
    and did not withhold his hand from destroying.
He made ramparts and walls lament;
    together they wasted away.

⁹Her gates have sunk into the ground;
    their bars he has broken and destroyed.
Her king and her princes are exiled among the nations,
    the law is no more,
and her prophets no longer find
    visions from the LORD.

¹⁰The elders of the Daughter of Zion
    sit on the ground in silence;
they have sprinkled dust on their heads
    and put on sackcloth.
The young women of Jerusalem
    have bowed their heads to the ground.

¹¹My eyes fail from weeping,
    I am in torment within,
my heart is poured out on the ground
    because my people are destroyed,
because children and infants faint
    in the streets of the city.

12 They say to their mothers,
    "Where is bread and wine?"
as they faint like wounded men
    in the streets of the city,
as their lives ebb away
    in their mothers' arms.

13 What can I say for you?
    With what can I compare you,
    O Daughter of Jerusalem?
To what can I liken you,
    that I may comfort you,
    O Virgin Daughter of Zion?
Your wound is as deep as the sea.
    Who can heal you?

14 The visions of your prophets
    were false and worthless;
they did not expose your sin
    to ward off your captivity.
The oracles they gave you
    were false and misleading.

15 All who pass your way
    clap their hands at you;
they scoff and shake their heads
    at the Daughter of Jerusalem:
"Is this the city that was called
    the perfection of beauty,
    the joy of the whole earth?"

16 All your enemies open their mouths
    wide against you;
they scoff and gnash their teeth
    and say, "We have swallowed her up.
This is the day we have waited for;
    we have lived to see it."

17 The LORD has done what he planned;
    he has fulfilled his word,
    which he decreed long ago.
He has overthrown you without pity,
    he has let the enemy gloat over you,
    he has exalted the horn*a* of your foes.

18 The hearts of the people
    cry out to the Lord.
O wall of the Daughter of Zion,
    let your tears flow like a river
    day and night;
give yourself no relief,
    your eyes no rest.

19 Arise, cry out in the night,
    as the watches of the night begin;
pour out your heart like water
    in the presence of the Lord.
Lift up your hands to him

a 17 Horn here symbolizes strength.

Moody Blues

focus — Profile: Jazmyne

If I start crying at a cheesy commercial, just ignore me, okay? I don't know what's wrong with me! These days I just tear up for no good reason. It doesn't take much to get me started—the littlest thing can set me off, and I'm sobbing.

I told my mom I must be going through menopause or something. My hormones are whacked out. She just laughed and said that's part of puberty. (By the way, I hate that word; don't you?) Unfortunately, my parents think I'm emotionally unstable these days, so anything unusual I do is automatically chalked up to either puberty or PMS. Speaking of periods, mine is so irregular. It's like on a month, off a month. Maybe that's my problem.

My mom said that it's normal for girls to feel like they're on an emotional roller coaster sometimes. Well, get me off this ride! I get so angry and lose my cool over the littlest things. It's as if the whole world is on my last nerve. Sometimes I feel so worn out at the end of a day that I just crash. No wonder I feel like sleeping till noon everyday. Not to mention the stress of seeing my face break out like this. My poor chin. Aughhhh!

Sometimes I feel fine, but other days I feel so emotional ✶ that I just want to die. God, when you invented *puberty*, what were you thinking?!

Body and emotion questions? Check out the links on www.TrueImagesBible.com

emotions in focus

Emotions aren't bad. They're part of God's design. Figuring out how to control them is the key. Proverbs 17:27 (page 829) describes a person with emotional maturity as being even-tempered. Now that's not gonna happen overnight, but you can work on it.

»Physically speaking, while you're a teen, your body releases hormones that help you develop into a woman's mature body. Side effects? Acne, emotional flare-ups, irregular periods. You've gotta take the good with the bad, though.

»Hormones can run wild right before you start your period. Face it—you may be more moody. Irregular periods are not unusual for a teen, although you may want to check things out with your doctor if you're really irregular or have exceptionally painful periods.

»You can often control PMS symptoms with diet and exercise.

For more on this topic, see the index on page 1656.

for the lives of your children,
who faint from hunger
at the head of every street.

²⁰ "Look, O LORD, and consider:
Whom have you ever treated like this?
Should women eat their offspring,
the children they have cared for?
Should priest and prophet be killed
in the sanctuary of the Lord?

21 "Young and old lie together
   in the dust of the streets;
my young men and maidens
   have fallen by the sword.
You have slain them in the day of your anger;
   you have slaughtered them without pity.

22 "As you summon to a feast day,
   so you summoned against me terrors on every side.
In the day of the LORD's anger
   no one escaped or survived;
those I cared for and reared,
   my enemy has destroyed."

*a*I am the man who has seen affliction
   by the rod of his wrath.
2 He has driven me away and made me walk
   in darkness rather than light;
3 indeed, he has turned his hand against me
   again and again, all day long.

4 He has made my skin and my
      flesh grow old
   and has broken my bones.
5 He has besieged me and
      surrounded me
   with bitterness and hardship.
6 He has made me dwell in
      darkness
   like those long dead.

7 He has walled me in so I cannot
      escape;
   he has weighed me down with chains.
8 Even when I call out or cry for help,
   he shuts out my prayer.
9 He has barred my way with blocks of stone;
   he has made my paths crooked.

10 Like a bear lying in wait,
   like a lion in hiding,
11 he dragged me from the path and mangled me
   and left me without help.
12 He drew his bow
   and made me the target for his arrows.

13 He pierced my heart
   with arrows from his quiver.
14 I became the laughingstock of all my people;
   they mock me in song all day long.
15 He has filled me with bitter herbs
   and sated me with gall.

16 He has broken my teeth with gravel;
   he has trampled me in the dust.
17 I have been deprived of peace;

truth or dare

They didn't call this book "Lamentations" for nothing! Have you ever felt completely alone and forgotten by God? Take comfort in the verses following this lament (3:21–24).

3:1–20

a This chapter is an acrostic poem; the verses of each stanza begin with the successive letters of the Hebrew alphabet, and the verses within each stanza begin with the same letter.

I have forgotten what prosperity is.
¹⁸ So I say, "My splendor is gone
and all that I had hoped from the LORD."

¹⁹ I remember my affliction and my wandering,
the bitterness and the gall.
²⁰ I well remember them,
and my soul is downcast within me.
²¹ Yet this I call to mind
and therefore I have hope:

²² Because of the LORD's great love we are not consumed,
for his compassions never fail.
²³ They are new every morning;
great is your faithfulness.
²⁴ I say to myself, "The LORD is my portion;
therefore I will wait for him."

²⁵ The LORD is good to those whose hope is in him,
to the one who seeks him;
²⁶ it is good to wait quietly
for the salvation of the LORD.
²⁷ It is good for a man to bear the yoke
while he is young.

²⁸ Let him sit alone in silence,
for the LORD has laid it on him.

²⁹ Let him bury his face in the
dust—
there may yet be hope.
³⁰ Let him offer his cheek to one
who would strike him,
and let him be filled with
disgrace.

³¹ For men are not cast off
by the Lord forever.
³² Though he brings grief, he will
show compassion,
so great is his unfailing love.
³³ For he does not willingly bring
affliction
or grief to the children of men.

³⁴ To crush underfoot
all prisoners in the land,
³⁵ to deny a man his rights
before the Most High,
³⁶ to deprive a man of justice—
would not the Lord see such
things?

³⁷ Who can speak and have it
happen
if the Lord has not decreed it?
³⁸ Is it not from the mouth of the
Most High
that both calamities and good
things come?

genuine

hope »» 3:19-23

Few people go through life on planet Earth without feeling the blues every now and then. Can you relate? What was the last thing that made you feel down in the dumps? Because of his people's sin and their punishment, Jeremiah felt very depressed and hopeless. But remembering God's faithfulness turned his hopelessness into hope. Feeling hopeless? How has God been faithful to you in the past? Since you know he helped you in the past, do you think that he'll let you down now?

³⁹ Why should any living man complain
  when punished for his sins?
⁴⁰ Let us examine our ways and test them,
  and let us return to the Lᴏʀᴅ.
⁴¹ Let us lift up our hearts and our hands
  to God in heaven, and say:
⁴² "We have sinned and rebelled
  and you have not forgiven.

⁴³ "You have covered yourself with anger and pursued us;
  you have slain without pity.
⁴⁴ You have covered yourself with a cloud
  so that no prayer can get through.

love notes
3:22-23

Child,

Just as the dawn brings with it
the promise of a new day, so too
does each new day bring with it
the promise of my love and
faithfulness. Let each morning
be a reminder of my care and
kindness toward you.

—Your compassionate Father

Write out a response to each phrase in
these verses.

⁴⁵ You have made us scum and
  refuse
  among the nations.

⁴⁶ "All our enemies have opened
  their mouths
  wide against us.
⁴⁷ We have suffered terror and
  pitfalls,
  ruin and destruction."
⁴⁸ Streams of tears flow from my
  eyes
  because my people are
  destroyed.

⁴⁹ My eyes will flow unceasingly,
  without relief,
⁵⁰ until the Lᴏʀᴅ looks down
  from heaven and sees.
⁵¹ What I see brings grief to my
  soul
  because of all the women of
  my city.

⁵² Those who were my enemies
  without cause
  hunted me like a bird.
⁵³ They tried to end my life in a pit
  and threw stones at me;
⁵⁴ the waters closed over my head,
  and I thought I was about to
  be cut off.

⁵⁵ I called on your name, O Lᴏʀᴅ,
  from the depths of the pit.
⁵⁶ You heard my plea: "Do not close
  your ears
  to my cry for relief."
⁵⁷ You came near when I called
  you,
  and you said, "Do not fear."

⁵⁸ O Lord, you took up my
  case;
  you redeemed my life.

⁵⁹You have seen, O Lᴏʀᴅ, the wrong done to me.
　　Uphold my cause!
⁶⁰You have seen the depth of their vengeance,
　　all their plots against me.

⁶¹O Lᴏʀᴅ, you have heard their insults,
　　all their plots against me—
⁶²what my enemies whisper and mutter
　　against me all day long.
⁶³Look at them! Sitting or standing,
　　they mock me in their songs.

⁶⁴Pay them back what they deserve, O Lᴏʀᴅ,
　　for what their hands have done.
⁶⁵Put a veil over their hearts,
　　and may your curse be on them!
⁶⁶Pursue them in anger and destroy them
　　from under the heavens of the Lᴏʀᴅ.

4

ᵃHow the gold has lost its luster,
　　the fine gold become dull!
The sacred gems are scattered
　　at the head of every street.

²How the precious sons of Zion,
　　once worth their weight in gold,
are now considered as pots of clay,
　　the work of a potter's hands!

³Even jackals offer their breasts
　　to nurse their young,
but my people have become heartless
　　like ostriches in the desert.

⁴Because of thirst the infant's tongue
　　sticks to the roof of its mouth;
the children beg for bread,
　　but no one gives it to them.

⁵Those who once ate delicacies
　　are destitute in the streets.
Those nurtured in purple
　　now lie on ash heaps.

⁶The punishment of my people
　　is greater than that of Sodom,
which was overthrown in a moment
　　without a hand turned to help her.

⁷Their princes were brighter than snow
　　and whiter than milk,
their bodies more ruddy than rubies,
　　their appearance like sapphires.ᵇ

⁸But now they are blacker than soot;
　　they are not recognized in the streets.
Their skin has shriveled on their bones;
　　it has become as dry as a stick.

---

a This chapter is an acrostic poem, the verses of which begin with the successive letters of the Hebrew alphabet.
b 7 Or *lapis lazuli*

⁹ Those killed by the sword are better off
    than those who die of famine;
racked with hunger, they waste away
    for lack of food from the field.

¹⁰ With their own hands compassionate women
    have cooked their own children,
who became their food
    when my people were destroyed.

¹¹ The LORD has given full vent to his wrath;
    he has poured out his fierce anger.
He kindled a fire in Zion
    that consumed her foundations.

¹² The kings of the earth did not believe,
    nor did any of the world's people,
that enemies and foes could enter
    the gates of Jerusalem.

¹³ But it happened because of the sins of her prophets
    and the iniquities of her priests,
who shed within her
    the blood of the righteous.

¹⁴ Now they grope through the streets
    like men who are blind.
They are so defiled with blood
    that no one dares to touch their garments.

¹⁵ "Go away! You are unclean!" men cry to them.
    "Away! Away! Don't touch us!"
When they flee and wander about,
    people among the nations say,
    "They can stay here no longer."

¹⁶ The LORD himself has scattered them;
    he no longer watches over them.
The priests are shown no honor,
    the elders no favor.

¹⁷ Moreover, our eyes failed,
    looking in vain for help;
from our towers we watched
    for a nation that could not save us.

¹⁸ Men stalked us at every step,
    so we could not walk in our streets.
Our end was near, our days were numbered,
    for our end had come.

¹⁹ Our pursuers were swifter
    than eagles in the sky;
they chased us over the mountains
    and lay in wait for us in the desert.

²⁰ The LORD's anointed, our very life breath,
    was caught in their traps.
We thought that under his shadow
    we would live among the nations.

²¹ Rejoice and be glad, O Daughter of Edom,

you who live in the land of Uz.
But to you also the cup will be passed;
you will be drunk and stripped naked.

²² O Daughter of Zion, your punishment will end;
he will not prolong your exile.
But, O Daughter of Edom, he will punish your sin
and expose your wickedness.

5

Remember, O Lᴏʀᴅ, what has happened to us;
look, and see our disgrace.
² Our inheritance has been turned over to aliens,
our homes to foreigners.
³ We have become orphans and fatherless,
our mothers like widows.
⁴ We must buy the water we drink;
our wood can be had only at a price.
⁵ Those who pursue us are at our heels;
we are weary and find no rest.
⁶ We submitted to Egypt and Assyria
to get enough bread.
⁷ Our fathers sinned and are no more,
and we bear their punishment.
⁸ Slaves rule over us,
and there is none to free us from their hands.
⁹ We get our bread at the risk of our lives
because of the sword in the desert.
¹⁰ Our skin is hot as an oven,
feverish from hunger.

¹¹ Women have been ravished in
Zion,
and virgins in the towns of
Judah.
¹² Princes have been hung up by
their hands;
elders are shown no respect.
¹³ Young men toil at the millstones;
boys stagger under loads of
wood.
¹⁴ The elders are gone from the city
gate;
the young men have stopped
their music.
¹⁵ Joy is gone from our hearts;
our dancing has turned to
mourning.
¹⁶ The crown has fallen from our
head.
Woe to us, for we have sinned!
¹⁷ Because of this our hearts are
faint,
because of these things our
eyes grow dim
¹⁸ for Mount Zion, which lies
desolate,
with jackals prowling over it.

genuine prayer » 5:1-22

What do you think prayer is? A list of "thees" and "thous"? Perfectly polished speeches? When Jeremiah poured out his heart to God about his people, he didn't try to impress God with fancy words. Yet his pleas were heartfelt—he rattled off a list of every care and concern on his mind. And he never resorted to whining or disrespect. Believe it or not, God finds that kind of prayer pretty refreshing. He wants you to come to him as you are—not as you think you should be. He wants real communication from the real you. Really.

¹⁹You, O LORD, reign forever;
  your throne endures from generation to generation.
²⁰Why do you always forget us?
  Why do you forsake us so long?
²¹Restore us to yourself, O LORD, that we may return;
  renew our days as of old
²²unless you have utterly rejected us
  and are angry with us beyond measure.

author:	Ezekiel.
date:	Between 593 and 571 B.C.
setting:	Ezekiel the priest prophesied to his fellow Jews, who were taken as prisoners to Babylon in 597 B.C.
verse to remember:	"I will give you a new heart and put a new spirit in you; I will remove from you your heart of stone and give you a heart of flesh" (36:26).
theme to consider:	In part 1 of the book, Ezekiel warns God will punish the people for their sins. Later in the book (after that first part came true!), Ezekiel comforts the people by assuring them that God will someday bring them back to Jerusalem and restore the temple.

ezekiel

unchanging truth

For girls, getting clean is more than just scrubbing with soap and water. We don't just shower or bathe; we *indulge*. Indeed, we have made "getting clean" an art form.

No matter how much we scrub, however, our cleansing only goes skin deep (literally). When we need cleansing from sin, we need far more than a scented bubble bath.

The Israelites needed to get clean. They had dirtied themselves with sin and idolatry; many of them had been taken away into captivity in faraway Babylon. At the same time Jeremiah was telling the people in Jerusalem about the coming destruction of their beloved city, Ezekiel was giving the same message to those already in captivity. You see, the people were certain that because God loved Jerusalem, the city would never fall to a foreign nation. What they didn't understand was that God was willing to let the nation fall in order to teach his people an important lesson about *their* sin and *his* holiness.

God also gave Ezekiel a message of hope. One day, God would gather his people back and cleanse them right to their hearts. He would give them a new spirit and a new heart to love and serve him.

After you shower once, are you clean forever? Nope. In the same way, you need to keep coming back to God, asking him to cleanse you from sin.

life lessons

1 Speak out for God, whether others respond or not (2:3–7).

2 God will punish sin, but his goal is always to draw us back to himself so that we'll know that he is "the LORD" (6:7,10,13–14; 12:15–16,20).

3 God promises us a future with him in a glorious kingdom beside a life-giving river (47:6–12; see also Revelation 22:1–5).

The Living Creatures and the Glory of the LORD

In the[a] thirtieth year, in the fourth month on the fifth day, while I was among the exiles by the Kebar River, the heavens were opened and I saw visions of God.

²On the fifth of the month—it was the fifth year of the exile of King Jehoiachin— ³the word of the LORD came to Ezekiel the priest, the son of Buzi,[b] by the Kebar River in the land of the Babylonians.[c] There the hand of the LORD was upon him.

⁴I looked, and I saw a windstorm coming out of the north—an immense cloud with flashing lightning and surrounded by brilliant light. The center of the fire looked like glowing metal, ⁵and in the fire was what looked like four living creatures. In appearance their form was that of a man, ⁶but each of them had four faces and four wings. ⁷Their legs were straight; their feet were like those of a calf and gleamed like burnished bronze. ⁸Under their wings on their four sides they had the hands of a man. All four of them had faces and wings, ⁹and their wings touched one another. Each one went straight ahead; they did not turn as they moved.

¹⁰Their faces looked like this: Each of the four had the face of a man, and on the right side each had the face of a lion, and on the left the face of an ox; each also had the face of an eagle. ¹¹Such were their faces. Their wings were spread out upward; each had two wings, one touching the wing of another creature on either side, and two wings covering its body. ¹²Each one went straight ahead. Wherever the spirit would go, they would go, without turning as they went. ¹³The appearance of the living creatures was like burning coals of fire or like torches. Fire moved back and forth among the creatures; it was bright, and lightning flashed out of it. ¹⁴The creatures sped back and forth like flashes of lightning.

¹⁵As I looked at the living creatures, I saw a wheel on the ground beside each creature with its four faces. ¹⁶This was the appearance and structure of the wheels: They sparkled like chrysolite, and all four looked alike. Each appeared to be made like a wheel intersecting a wheel. ¹⁷As they moved, they would go in any one of the four directions the creatures faced; the wheels did not turn about[d] as the creatures went. ¹⁸Their rims were high and awesome, and all four rims were full of eyes all around.

¹⁹When the living creatures moved, the wheels beside them moved; and when the living creatures rose from the ground, the wheels also rose. ²⁰Wherever the spirit would go, they would go, and the wheels would rise along with them, because the spirit of the living creatures was in the wheels. ²¹When the creatures moved, they also moved; when the creatures stood still, they also stood still; and when the creatures rose from the ground, the wheels rose along with them, because the spirit of the living creatures was in the wheels.

²²Spread out above the heads of the living creatures was what looked like an expanse, sparkling like ice, and awesome. ²³Under the expanse their wings were stretched out one toward the other, and each had two wings covering its body. ²⁴When the creatures moved, I heard the sound of their wings, like the roar of rushing waters, like the voice of the Almighty,[e] like the tumult of an army. When they stood still, they lowered their wings.

²⁵Then there came a voice from above the expanse over their heads as they stood with lowered wings. ²⁶Above the expanse over their heads was what looked like a throne of sapphire,[f] and high above on the throne was a figure like that of a man. ²⁷I saw that from what appeared to be his waist up he looked like glowing metal, as if full of fire, and that from there down he looked like fire; and brilliant light surrounded him. ²⁸Like the appearance of a rainbow in the clouds on a rainy day, so was the radiance around him.

This was the appearance of the likeness of the glory of the LORD. When I saw it, I fell facedown, and I heard the voice of one speaking.

truth or dare

Ever had an *indescribable* experience that left you absolutely speechless? Imagine Ezekiel . . . seeing the glory of God and falling facedown. Think you'd react the same way?

1:25–28

---

a 1 Or *my*, b 3 Or *Ezekiel son of Buzi the priest* c 3 Or *Chaldeans* d 17 Or *aside* e 24 Hebrew *Shaddai* f 26 Or *lapis lazuli*

Ezekiel's Call

2 He said to me, "Son of man, stand up on your feet and I will speak to you." ²As he spoke, the Spirit came into me and raised me to my feet, and I heard him speaking to me.

³He said: "Son of man, I am sending you to the Israelites, to a rebellious nation that has rebelled against me; they and their fathers have been in revolt against me to this very day. ⁴The people to whom I am sending you are obstinate and stubborn. Say to them, 'This is what the Sovereign LORD says.' ⁵And whether they listen or fail to listen—for they are a rebellious house—they will know that a prophet has been among them. ⁶And you, son of man, do not be afraid of them or their words. Do not be afraid, though briers and thorns are all around you and you live among scorpions. Do not be afraid of what they say or terrified by them, though they are a rebellious house. ⁷You must speak my words to them, whether they listen or fail to listen, for they are rebellious. ⁸But you, son of man, listen to what I say to you. Do not rebel like that rebellious house; open your mouth and eat what I give you."

⁹Then I looked, and I saw a hand stretched out to me. In it was a scroll, ¹⁰which he unrolled before me. On both sides of it were written words of lament and mourning and woe.

3 And he said to me, "Son of man, eat what is before you, eat this scroll; then go and speak to the house of Israel." ²So I opened my mouth, and he gave me the scroll to eat.

³Then he said to me, "Son of man, eat this scroll I am giving you and fill your stomach with it." So I ate it, and it tasted as sweet as honey in my mouth.

⁴He then said to me: "Son of man, go now to the house of Israel and speak my words to them. ⁵You are not being sent to a people of obscure speech and difficult language, but to the house of Israel— ⁶not to many peoples of obscure speech and difficult language, whose words you cannot understand. Surely if I had sent you to them, they would have listened to you. ⁷But the house of Israel is not willing to listen to you because they are not willing to listen to me, for the whole house of Israel is hardened and obstinate. ⁸But I will make you as unyielding and hardened as they are. ⁹I will make your forehead like the hardest stone, harder than flint. Do not be afraid of them or terrified by them, though they are a rebellious house."

¹⁰And he said to me, "Son of man, listen carefully and take to heart all the words I speak to you. ¹¹Go now to your countrymen in exile and speak to them. Say to them, 'This is what the Sovereign LORD says,' whether they listen or fail to listen."

¹²Then the Spirit lifted me up, and I heard behind me a loud rumbling sound—May the glory of the LORD be praised in his dwelling place!— ¹³the sound of the wings of the living creatures brushing against each other and the sound of the wheels beside them, a loud rumbling sound. ¹⁴The Spirit then lifted me up and took me away, and I went in bitterness and in the anger of my spirit, with

---

genuine success ≫ 2:1–7

What's your definition of success? Gaining popularity? Being beautiful and getting lots of attention? Getting into the right college? According to God's math, 1 believer + obedience = success. Obedience didn't earn Ezekiel any friends, nor did it help him influence people. The people of Israel refused to listen to him and thought he was ... well ... weird. Yet he was pretty successful in God's eyes. Sometimes, following God can make you seem like a loser to the world. But to God, you've earned an A+.

---

truth or dare

It's true. God dumped Ezekiel into the deep end for his first assignment, but he prepared Zeke so he'd survive the job. God gives us whatever "swimming lessons" we need, too.

3:4–9

the strong hand of the Lᴏʀᴅ upon me. ¹⁵I came to the exiles who lived at Tel Abib near the Kebar River. And there, where they were living, I sat among them for seven days—overwhelmed.

Warning to Israel

¹⁶At the end of seven days the word of the Lᴏʀᴅ came to me: ¹⁷"Son of man, I have made you a watchman for the house of Israel; so hear the word I speak and give them warning from me. ¹⁸When I say to a wicked man, 'You will surely die,' and you do not warn him or speak out to dissuade him from his evil ways in order to save his life, that wicked man will die forᵃ his sin, and I will hold you accountable for his blood. ¹⁹But if you do warn the wicked man and he does not turn from his wickedness or from his evil ways, he will die for his sin; but you will have saved yourself.

²⁰"Again, when a righteous man turns from his righteousness and does evil, and I put a stumbling block before him, he will die. Since you did not warn him, he will die for his sin. The righteous things he did will not be remembered, and I will hold you accountable for his blood. ²¹But if you do warn the righteous man not to sin and he does not sin, he will surely live because he took warning, and you will have saved yourself."

²²The hand of the Lᴏʀᴅ was upon me there, and he said to me, "Get up and go out to the plain, and there I will speak to you." ²³So I got up and went out to the plain. And the glory of the Lᴏʀᴅ was standing there, like the glory I had seen by the Kebar River, and I fell facedown.

²⁴Then the Spirit came into me and raised me to my feet. He spoke to me and said: "Go, shut yourself inside your house. ²⁵And you, son of man, they will tie with ropes; you will be bound so that you cannot go out among the people. ²⁶I will make your tongue stick to the roof of your mouth so that you will be silent and unable to rebuke them, though they are a rebellious house. ²⁷But when I speak to you, I will open your mouth and you shall say to them, 'This is what the Sovereign Lᴏʀᴅ says.' Whoever will listen let him listen, and whoever will refuse let him refuse; for they are a rebellious house.

Siege of Jerusalem Symbolized

4 "Now, son of man, take a clay tablet, put it in front of you and draw the city of Jerusalem on it. ²Then lay siege to it: Erect siege works against it, build a ramp up to it, set up camps against it and put battering rams around it. ³Then take an iron pan, place it as an iron wall between you and the city and turn your face toward it. It will be under siege, and you shall besiege it. This will be a sign to the house of Israel.

⁴"Then lie on your left side and put the sin of the house of Israel upon yourself.ᵇ You are to bear their sin for the number of days you lie on your side. ⁵I have assigned you the same number of days as the years of their sin. So for 390 days you will bear the sin of the house of Israel.

⁶"After you have finished this, lie down again, this time on your right side, and bear the sin of the house of Judah. I have assigned you 40 days, a day for each year. ⁷Turn your face toward the siege of Jerusalem and with bared arm prophesy against her. ⁸I will tie you up with ropes so that you cannot turn from one side to the other until you have finished the days of your siege.

⁹"Take wheat and barley, beans and lentils, millet and spelt; put them in a storage jar and use

genuine

courage » 3:16-19

Ever feel uncomfortable at the thought of telling someone from the popular crowd about God or about confronting a friend about her life-threatening habit? God warned Ezekiel that he—*Ezekiel!*—would be held responsible for not telling the people of Israel about their sin and punishment. How could it be Ezekiel's fault if someone else was rebelling against God?! Genuine courage means telling others the truth. Pointing out a problem to someone never feels good. But that's what you'd do to save her life, wouldn't you?

---

a 18 Or *in*; also in verses 19 and 20   *b 4* Or *your side* them to make bread for yourself. You are to eat it during the 390 days you lie on your side. ¹⁰Weigh out twenty shekels*ᵃ* of food to eat each day and eat it at set times. ¹¹Also measure out a sixth of a hin*ᵇ* of water and drink it at set times. ¹²Eat the food as you would a barley cake; bake it in the sight of the people, using human excrement for fuel." ¹³The Lᴏʀᴅ said, "In this way the people of Israel will eat defiled food among the nations where I will drive them."

¹⁴Then I said, "Not so, Sovereign Lᴏʀᴅ! I have never defiled myself. From my youth until now I have never eaten anything found dead or torn by wild animals. No unclean meat has ever entered my mouth."

¹⁵"Very well," he said, "I will let you bake your bread over cow manure instead of human excrement."

¹⁶He then said to me: "Son of man, I will cut off the supply of food in Jerusalem. The people will eat rationed food in anxiety and drink rationed water in despair, ¹⁷for food and water will be scarce. They will be appalled at the sight of each other and will waste away because of*ᶜ* their sin.

5 "Now, son of man, take a sharp sword and use it as a barber's razor to shave your head and your beard. Then take a set of scales and divide up the hair. ²When the days of your siege come to an end, burn a third of the hair with fire inside the city. Take a third and strike it with the sword all around the city. And scatter a third to the wind. For I will pursue them with drawn sword. ³But take a few strands of hair and tuck them away in the folds of your garment. ⁴Again, take a few of these and throw them into the fire and burn them up. A fire will spread from there to the whole house of Israel.

⁵"This is what the Sovereign Lᴏʀᴅ says: This is Jerusalem, which I have set in the center of the nations, with countries all around her. ⁶Yet in her wickedness she has rebelled against my laws and decrees more than the nations and countries around her. She has rejected my laws and has not followed my decrees.

⁷"Therefore this is what the Sovereign Lᴏʀᴅ says: You have been more unruly than the nations around you and have not followed my decrees or kept my laws. You have not even*ᵈ* conformed to the standards of the nations around you.

⁸"Therefore this is what the Sovereign Lᴏʀᴅ says: I myself am against you, Jerusalem, and I will inflict punishment on you in the sight of the nations. ⁹Because of all your detestable idols, I will do to you what I have never done before and will never do again. ¹⁰Therefore in your midst fathers will eat their children, and children will eat their fathers. I will inflict punishment on you and will scatter all your survivors to the winds. ¹¹Therefore as surely as I live, declares the Sovereign Lᴏʀᴅ, because you have defiled my sanctuary with all your vile images and detestable practices, I myself will withdraw my favor; I will not look on you with pity or spare you. ¹²A third of your people will die of the plague or perish by famine inside you; a third will fall by the sword outside your walls; and a third I will scatter to the winds and pursue with drawn sword.

¹³"Then my anger will cease and my wrath against them will subside, and I will be avenged. And when I have spent my wrath upon them, they will know that I the Lᴏʀᴅ have spoken in my zeal.

¹⁴"I will make you a ruin and a reproach

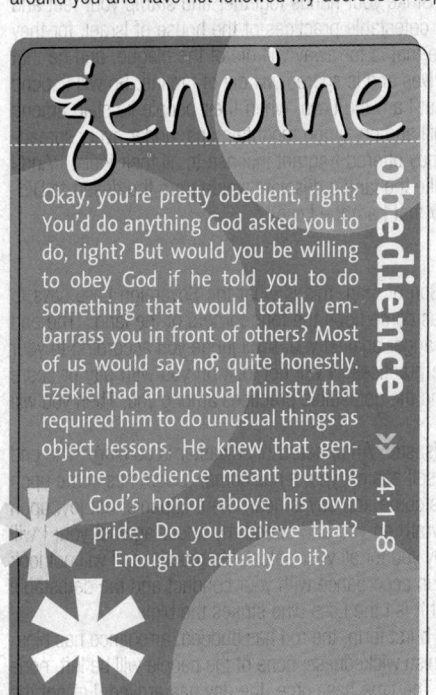

genuine *obedience* » 4:1–8

Okay, you're pretty obedient, right? You'd do anything God asked you to do, right? But would you be willing to obey God if he told you to do something that would totally embarrass you in front of others? Most of us would say no, quite honestly. Ezekiel had an unusual ministry that required him to do unusual things as object lessons. He knew that genuine obedience meant putting God's honor above his own pride. Do you believe that? Enough to actually do it?

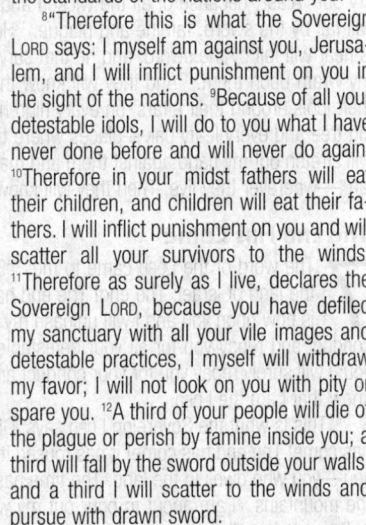

ᵃ 10 That is, about 8 ounces (about 0.2 kilogram)   *ᵇ 11* That is, about 2/3 quart (about 0.6 liter)   *ᶜ 17* Or *away in*
ᵈ 7 Most Hebrew manuscripts; some Hebrew manuscripts and Syriac *You have*

among the nations around you, in the sight of all who pass by. ¹⁵You will be a reproach and a taunt, a warning and an object of horror to the nations around you when I inflict punishment on you in anger and in wrath and with stinging rebuke. I the LORD have spoken. ¹⁶When I shoot at you with my deadly and destructive arrows of famine, I will shoot to destroy you. I will bring more and more famine upon you and cut off your supply of food. ¹⁷I will send famine and wild beasts against you, and they will leave you childless. Plague and bloodshed will sweep through you, and I will bring the sword against you. I the LORD have spoken."

A Prophecy Against the Mountains of Israel

6 The word of the LORD came to me: ²"Son of man, set your face against the mountains of Israel; prophesy against them ³and say: 'O mountains of Israel, hear the word of the Sovereign LORD. This is what the Sovereign LORD says to the mountains and hills, to the ravines and valleys: I am about to bring a sword against you, and I will destroy your high places. ⁴Your altars will be demolished and your incense altars will be smashed; and I will slay your people in front of your idols. ⁵I will lay the dead bodies of the Israelites in front of their idols, and I will scatter your bones around your altars. ⁶Wherever you live, the towns will be laid waste and the high places demolished, so that your altars will be laid waste and devastated, your idols smashed and ruined, your incense altars broken down, and what you have made wiped out. ⁷Your people will fall slain among you, and you will know that I am the LORD.

⁸" 'But I will spare some, for some of you will escape the sword when you are scattered among the lands and nations. ⁹Then in the nations where they have been carried captive, those who escape will remember me—how I have been grieved by their adulterous hearts, which have turned away from me, and by their eyes, which have lusted after their idols. They will loathe themselves for the evil they have done and for all their detestable practices. ¹⁰And they will know that I am the LORD; I did not threaten in vain to bring this calamity on them.

¹¹" 'This is what the Sovereign LORD says: Strike your hands together and stamp your feet and cry out "Alas!" because of all the wicked and detestable practices of the house of Israel, for they will fall by the sword, famine and plague. ¹²He that is far away will die of the plague, and he that is near will fall by the sword, and he that survives and is spared will die of famine. So will I spend my wrath upon them. ¹³And they will know that I am the LORD, when their people lie slain among their idols around their altars, on every high hill and on all the mountaintops, under every spreading tree and every leafy oak—places where they offered fragrant incense to all their idols. ¹⁴And I will stretch out my hand against them and make the land a desolate waste from the desert to Diblah*ª*—wherever they live. Then they will know that I am the LORD.' "

The End Has Come

7 The word of the LORD came to me: ²"Son of man, this is what the Sovereign LORD says to the land of Israel: The end! The end has come upon the four corners of the land. ³The end is now upon you and I will unleash my anger against you. I will judge you according to your conduct and repay you for all your detestable practices. ⁴I will not look on you with pity or spare you; I will surely repay you for your conduct and the detestable practices among you. Then you will know that I am the LORD.

⁵"This is what the Sovereign LORD says: Disaster! An unheard-of*ᵇ* disaster is coming. ⁶The end has come! The end has come! It has roused itself against you. It has come! ⁷Doom has come upon you—you who dwell in the land. The time has come, the day is near; there is panic, not joy, upon the mountains. ⁸I am about to pour out my wrath on you and spend my anger against you; I will judge you according to your conduct and repay you for all your detestable practices. ⁹I will not look on you with pity or spare you; I will repay you in accordance with your conduct and the detestable practices among you. Then you will know that it is I the LORD who strikes the blow.

¹⁰"The day is here! It has come! Doom has burst forth, the rod has budded, arrogance has blossomed! ¹¹Violence has grown into*ᶜ* a rod to punish wickedness; none of the people will be left, none of that crowd—no wealth, nothing of value. ¹²The time has come, the day has arrived. Let not the buyer rejoice nor the seller grieve, for wrath is upon the whole crowd. ¹³The seller will not recover

---

ª 14 Most Hebrew manuscripts; a few Hebrew manuscripts *Riblah*   *ᵇ 5* Most Hebrew manuscripts; some Hebrew manuscripts and Syriac *Disaster after*   *ᶜ 11* Or *The violent one has become*

mirror images

The Canaanite Woman—Never Give Up

Word was out. A Jewish healer was here in Gentile territory. And no matter what it took, she was going to hunt him down. Normally she wouldn't have been so pushy, so absolutely desperate. But she remembered her daughter's cries, small arms lashing out, hair in dark tangles against her head—possessed by a demon!

This woman would do *anything* to get help. Barging into the house where Jesus was, she begged for help. Jesus' disciples urged him to show the crazed woman the exit, but instead, Jesus gave this cryptic reply: "I was sent only to the lost sheep of Israel." And this woman was for sure a non-Israelite.

Freeze.

What?! What did the Lord mean? That all non-Jews were out of luck? That he didn't care about this woman's need? Or was he testing her?

Rather than head for the door, the woman persisted. No giving up, no turning back. She knew that in front of her stood her only hope, so she scrambled quickly for a reply. She suggested she would be glad to take just his leftovers, or the "crumbs" from the table.

That was the right answer. Jesus was waiting for the expression of wholehearted faith in him. Jesus wanted to know that this woman believed that even an ounce of his attention and power would solve her problems. So Jesus granted her request, and her daughter was instantly healed.

Have you ever done this? Thrown everything to the wind and begged the Lord to solve your problem instead of trying to do it on your own? Most of us girls tend to hold onto our pride, to work hard to find our own solutions. But try as we might, only one solution satisfies: Jesus. He will help us through any problem, no matter how big or small. It's a promise given to any girl who comes to God with faith.

dear Jesus

Lord Jesus, I'm used to handling my problems on my own. But, like the Canaanite woman, I need to turn to you for help. Show me how to humble my heart, and teach me to trust you more. Amen.

To read the next Mirror Images profile, go to page 1153.

Read more about the Canaanite woman in Matthew 15:21–28 (pages 1311–1313) and Mark 7:24–30 (pages 1344–1345).

the land he has sold as long as both of them live, for the vision concerning the whole crowd will not be reversed. Because of their sins, not one of them will preserve his life. ¹⁴Though they blow the trumpet and get everything ready, no one will go into battle, for my wrath is upon the whole crowd.

¹⁵"Outside is the sword, inside are plague and famine; those in the country will die by the sword, and those in the city will be devoured by famine and plague. ¹⁶All who survive and escape will be in the mountains, moaning like doves of the valleys, each because of his sins. ¹⁷Every hand will go limp, and every knee will become as weak as water. ¹⁸They will put on sackcloth and be clothed with terror. Their faces will be covered with shame and their heads will be shaved. ¹⁹They will throw their silver into the streets, and their gold will be an unclean thing. Their silver and gold will not be able to save them in the day of the LORD's wrath. They will not satisfy their hunger or fill their stomachs with it, for it has made them stumble into sin. ²⁰They were proud of their beautiful jewelry and used it to make their detestable idols and vile images. Therefore I will turn these into an unclean thing for them. ²¹I will hand it all over as plunder to foreigners and as loot to the wicked of the earth, and they will defile it. ²²I will turn my face away from them, and they will desecrate my treasured place; robbers will enter it and desecrate it.

²³"Prepare chains, because the land is full of bloodshed and the city is full of violence. ²⁴I will bring the most wicked of the nations to take possession of their houses; I will put an end to the pride of the mighty, and their sanctuaries will be desecrated. ²⁵When terror comes, they will seek peace, but there will be none. ²⁶Calamity upon calamity will come, and rumor upon rumor. They will try to get a vision from the prophet; the teaching of the law by the priest will be lost, as will the counsel of the elders. ²⁷The king will mourn, the prince will be clothed with despair, and the hands of the people of the land will tremble. I will deal with them according to their conduct, and by their own standards I will judge them. Then they will know that I am the LORD."

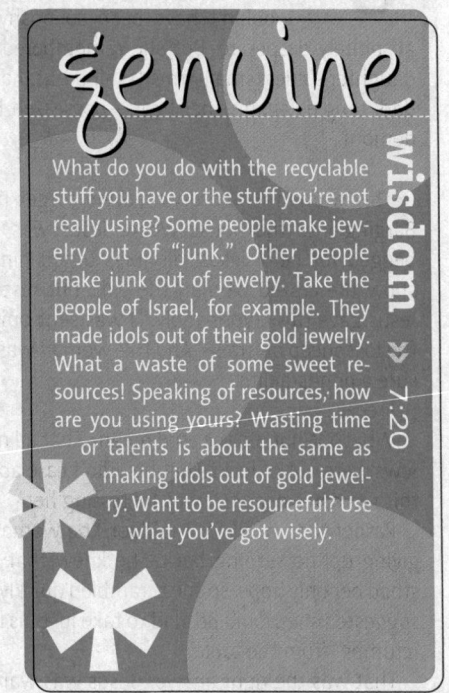

genuine wisdom » 7:20

What do you do with the recyclable stuff you have or the stuff you're not really using? Some people make jewelry out of "junk." Other people make junk out of jewelry. Take the people of Israel, for example. They made idols out of their gold jewelry. What a waste of some sweet resources! Speaking of resources, how are you using yours? Wasting time or talents is about the same as making idols out of gold jewelry. Want to be resourceful? Use what you've got wisely.

Idolatry in the Temple

8 In the sixth year, in the sixth month on the fifth day, while I was sitting in my house and the elders of Judah were sitting before me, the hand of the Sovereign LORD came upon me there. ²I looked, and I saw a figure like that of a man.ᵃ From what appeared to be his waist down he was like fire, and from there up his appearance was as bright as glowing metal. ³He stretched out what looked like a hand and took me by the hair of my head. The Spirit lifted me up between earth and heaven and in visions of God he took me to Jerusalem, to the entrance to the north gate of the inner court, where the idol that provokes to jealousy stood. ⁴And there before me was the glory of the God of Israel, as in the vision I had seen in the plain.

⁵Then he said to me, "Son of man, look toward the north." So I looked, and in the entrance north of the gate of the altar I saw this idol of jealousy.

⁶And he said to me, "Son of man, do you see what they are doing—the utterly detestable things the house of Israel is doing here, things that will drive me far from my sanctuary? But you will see things that are even more detestable."

⁷Then he brought me to the entrance to the court. I looked, and I saw a hole in the wall. ⁸He said to me, "Son of man, now dig into the wall." So I dug into the wall and saw a doorway there.

ᵃ 2 Or saw a fiery figure

⁹And he said to me, "Go in and see the wicked and detestable things they are doing here." ¹⁰So I went in and looked, and I saw portrayed all over the walls all kinds of crawling things and detestable animals and all the idols of the house of Israel. ¹¹In front of them stood seventy elders of the house of Israel, and Jaazaniah son of Shaphan was standing among them. Each had a censer in his hand, and a fragrant cloud of incense was rising.

¹²He said to me, "Son of man, have you seen what the elders of the house of Israel are doing in the darkness, each at the shrine of his own idol? They say, 'The LORD does not see us; the LORD has forsaken the land.' " ¹³Again, he said, "You will see them doing things that are even more detestable."

¹⁴Then he brought me to the entrance to the north gate of the house of the LORD, and I saw women sitting there, mourning for Tammuz. ¹⁵He said to me, "Do you see this, son of man? You will see things that are even more detestable than this."

¹⁶He then brought me into the inner court of the house of the LORD, and there at the entrance to the temple, between the portico and the altar, were about twenty-five men. With their backs toward the temple of the LORD and their faces toward the east, they were bowing down to the sun in the east.

¹⁷He said to me, "Have you seen this, son of man? Is it a trivial matter for the house of Judah to do the detestable things they are doing here? Must they also fill the land with violence and continually provoke me to anger? Look at them putting the branch to their nose! ¹⁸Therefore I will deal with them in anger; I will not look on them with pity or spare them. Although they shout in my ears, I will not listen to them."

Idolaters Killed

9 Then I heard him call out in a loud voice, "Bring the guards of the city here, each with a weapon in his hand." ²And I saw six men coming from the direction of the upper gate, which faces north, each with a deadly weapon in his hand. With them was a man clothed in linen who had a writing kit at his side. They came in and stood beside the bronze altar.

³Now the glory of the God of Israel went up from above the cherubim, where it had been, and moved to the threshold of the temple. Then the LORD called to the man clothed in linen who had the writing kit at his side ⁴and said to him, "Go throughout the city of Jerusalem and put a mark on the foreheads of those who grieve and lament over all the detestable things that are done in it."

⁵As I listened, he said to the others, "Follow him through the city and kill, without showing pity or compassion. ⁶Slaughter old men, young men and maidens, women and children, but do not touch anyone who has the mark. Begin at my sanctuary." So they began with the elders who were in front of the temple.

⁷Then he said to them, "Defile the temple and fill the courts with the slain. Go!" So they went

genuine

holiness » 8:1-18

Ever do something that you thought no one would ever see? You're not the only one. God showed Ezekiel all of the scandalous stuff people thought they were getting away with. The sad part is that these things were going on in the *temple*— the most holy place in Israel. Perhaps the people thought they could take time off from being holy. But holiness isn't just for Sundays or when people can see what you're doing. Holiness is a decision you make every day of your life. It's not something to turn on or off. Got the holiness habit?

truth or dare

Wondering how you should feel about the sin you see around you? Sorry, that's how! God notices those who are genuinely sorry about sin.

9:3–4

out and began killing throughout the city. [8]While they were killing and I was left alone, I fell face-down, crying out, "Ah, Sovereign Lord! Are you going to destroy the entire remnant of Israel in this outpouring of your wrath on Jerusalem?"

[9]He answered me, "The sin of the house of Israel and Judah is exceedingly great; the land is full of bloodshed and the city is full of injustice. They say, 'The Lord has forsaken the land; the Lord does not see.' [10]So I will not look on them with pity or spare them, but I will bring down on their own heads what they have done."

[11]Then the man in linen with the writing kit at his side brought back word, saying, "I have done as you commanded."

The Glory Departs From the Temple

10 I looked, and I saw the likeness of a throne of sapphire[a] above the expanse that was over the heads of the cherubim. [2]The Lord said to the man clothed in linen, "Go in among the wheels beneath the cherubim. Fill your hands with burning coals from among the cherubim and scatter them over the city." And as I watched, he went in.

[3]Now the cherubim were standing on the south side of the temple when the man went in, and a cloud filled the inner court. [4]Then the glory of the Lord rose from above the cherubim and moved to the threshold of the temple. The cloud filled the temple, and the court was full of the radiance of the glory of the Lord. [5]The sound of the wings of the cherubim could be heard as far away as the outer court, like the voice of God Almighty[b] when he speaks.

[6]When the Lord commanded the man in linen, "Take fire from among the wheels, from among the cherubim," the man went in and stood beside a wheel. [7]Then one of the cherubim reached out his hand to the fire that was among them. He took up some of it and put it into the hands of the man in linen, who took it and went out. [8](Under the wings of the cherubim could be seen what looked like the hands of a man.)

[9]I looked, and I saw beside the cherubim four wheels, one beside each of the cherubim; the wheels sparkled like chrysolite. [10]As for their appearance, the four of them looked alike; each was like a wheel intersecting a wheel. [11]As they moved, they would go in any one of the four directions the cherubim faced; the wheels did not turn about[c] as the cherubim went. The cherubim went in whatever direction the head faced, without turning as they went. [12]Their entire bodies, including their backs, their hands and their wings, were completely full of eyes, as were their four wheels. [13]I heard the wheels being called "the whirling wheels." [14]Each of the cherubim had four faces: One face was that of a cherub, the second the face of a man, the third the face of a lion, and the fourth the face of an eagle.

[15]Then the cherubim rose upward. These were the living creatures I had seen by the Kebar River. [16]When the cherubim moved, the wheels beside them moved; and when the cherubim spread their wings to rise from the ground, the wheels did not leave their side. [17]When the cherubim stood still, they also stood still; and when the cherubim rose, they rose with them, because the spirit of the living creatures was in them.

[18]Then the glory of the Lord departed from over the threshold of the temple and stopped above the cherubim. [19]While I watched, the cherubim spread their wings and rose from the ground, and as they went, the wheels went with them. They stopped at the entrance to the east gate of the Lord's house, and the glory of the God of Israel was above them.

[20]These were the living creatures I had seen beneath the God of Israel by the Kebar River, and I realized that they were cherubim. [21]Each had four faces and four wings, and under their wings was what looked like the hands of a man. [22]Their faces had the same appearance as those I had seen by the Kebar River. Each one went straight ahead.

Judgment on Israel's Leaders

11 Then the Spirit lifted me up and brought me to the gate of the house of the Lord that faces east. There at the entrance to the gate were twenty-five men, and I saw among them Jaazaniah son of Azzur and Pelatiah son of Benaiah, leaders of the people. [2]The Lord said to me, "Son of man, these are the men who are plotting evil and giving wicked advice in

---

a 1 Or *lapis lazuli*   *b 5* Hebrew *El-Shaddai*   *c 11* Or *aside* this city. [3]They say, 'Will it not soon be time to build houses?[a] This city is a cooking pot, and we are the meat.' [4]Therefore prophesy against them; prophesy, son of man."

[5]Then the Spirit of the LORD came upon me, and he told me to say: "This is what the LORD says: That is what you are saying, O house of Israel, but I know what is going through your mind. [6]You have killed many people in this city and filled its streets with the dead.

[7]"Therefore this is what the Sovereign LORD says: The bodies you have thrown there are the meat and this city is the pot, but I will drive you out of it. [8]You fear the sword, and the sword is what I will bring against you, declares the Sovereign LORD. [9]I will drive you out of the city and hand you over to foreigners and inflict punishment on you. [10]You will fall by the sword, and I will execute judgment on you at the borders of Israel. Then you will know that I am the LORD. [11]This city will not be a pot for you, nor will you be the meat in it; I will execute judgment on you at the borders of Israel. [12]And you will know that I am the LORD, for you have not followed my decrees or kept my laws but have conformed to the standards of the nations around you."

love notes

11:19-20

Loved one,

When others are pulling you in different directions, urging you to come and follow them, remember my promise. I will give you an undivided heart, a focus and purpose that will not lead you astray.

—Your loving Father

What does it mean to have an undivided heart for God?

[13]Now as I was prophesying, Pelatiah son of Benaiah died. Then I fell facedown and cried out in a loud voice, "Ah, Sovereign LORD! Will you completely destroy the remnant of Israel?"

[14]The word of the LORD came to me: [15]"Son of man, your brothers—your brothers who are your blood relatives[b] and the whole house of Israel—are those of whom the people of Jerusalem have said, 'They are[c] far away from the LORD; this land was given to us as our possession.'

Promised Return of Israel

[16]"Therefore say: 'This is what the Sovereign LORD says: Although I sent them far away among the nations and scattered them among the countries, yet for a little while I have been a sanctuary for them in the countries where they have gone.'

[17]"Therefore say: 'This is what the Sovereign LORD says: I will gather you from the nations and bring you back from the countries where you have been scattered, and I will give you back the land of Israel again.'

[18]"They will return to it and remove all its vile images and detestable idols. [19]I will give them an undivided heart and put a new spirit in them; I will remove from them their heart of stone and give them a heart of flesh. [20]Then they will follow my decrees and be careful to keep my laws. They will be my people, and I will be their God. [21]But as for those whose hearts are devoted to their vile images and detestable idols, I will bring down on their own heads what they have done, declares the Sovereign LORD."

[22]Then the cherubim, with the wheels beside them, spread their wings, and the

---

[a] 3 Or This is not the time to build houses.
[b] 15 Or are in exile with you (see Septuagint and Syriac)   [c] 15 Or those to whom the people of Jerusalem have said, 'Stay

glory of the God of Israel was above them. ²³The glory of the LORD went up from within the city and stopped above the mountain east of it. ²⁴The Spirit lifted me up and brought me to the exiles in Babylonia ᵃ in the vision given by the Spirit of God.

Then the vision I had seen went up from me, ²⁵and I told the exiles everything the LORD had shown me.

The Exile Symbolized

12 The word of the LORD came to me: ²"Son of man, you are living among a rebellious people. They have eyes to see but do not see and ears to hear but do not hear, for they are a rebellious people.

³"Therefore, son of man, pack your belongings for exile and in the daytime, as they watch, set out and go from where you are to another place. Perhaps they will understand, though they are a rebellious house. ⁴During the daytime, while they watch, bring out your belongings packed for exile. Then in the evening, while they are watching, go out like those who go into exile. ⁵While they watch, dig through the wall and take your belongings out through it. ⁶Put them on your shoulder as they are watching and carry them out at dusk. Cover your face so that you cannot see the land, for I have made you a sign to the house of Israel."

⁷So I did as I was commanded. During the day I brought out my things packed for exile. Then in the evening I dug through the wall with my hands. I took my belongings out at dusk, carrying them on my shoulders while they watched.

⁸In the morning the word of the LORD came to me: ⁹"Son of man, did not that rebellious house of Israel ask you, 'What are you doing?'

¹⁰"Say to them, 'This is what the Sovereign LORD says: This oracle concerns the prince in Jerusalem and the whole house of Israel who are there.' ¹¹Say to them, 'I am a sign to you.'

"As I have done, so it will be done to them. They will go into exile as captives.

¹²"The prince among them will put his things on his shoulder at dusk and leave, and a hole will be dug in the wall for him to go through. He will cover his face so that he cannot see the land. ¹³I will spread my net for him, and he will be caught in my snare; I will bring him to Babylonia, the land of the Chaldeans, but he will not see it, and there he will die. ¹⁴I will scatter to the winds all those around him—his staff and all his troops—and I will pursue them with drawn sword.

¹⁵"They will know that I am the LORD, when I disperse them among the nations and scatter them through the countries. ¹⁶But I will spare a few of them from the sword, famine and plague, so that in the nations where they go they may acknowledge all their detestable practices. Then they will know that I am the LORD."

¹⁷The word of the LORD came to me: ¹⁸"Son of man, tremble as you eat your food, and shudder in fear as you drink your water. ¹⁹Say to the people of the land: 'This is what the Sovereign LORD says about those living in Jerusalem and in the land of Israel: They will eat their food in anxiety and drink their water in despair, for their land will be stripped of everything in it because of the violence of all who live there. ²⁰The inhabited towns will be laid waste and the land will be desolate. Then you will know that I am the LORD.' "

²¹The word of the LORD came to me: ²²"Son of man, what is this proverb you have in the land of Israel: 'The days go by and every vision comes to nothing'? ²³Say to them, 'This is what the Sovereign LORD says: I am going to put an end to this proverb, and they will no longer quote it in Israel.' Say to them, 'The days are near when every vision will be fulfilled. ²⁴For there will be no more false visions or flattering divinations among the people of Israel. ²⁵But I the LORD will speak what I will, and it shall be fulfilled without delay. For in your days, you rebellious house, I will fulfill whatever I say, declares the Sovereign LORD.' "

²⁶The word of the LORD came to me: ²⁷"Son of man, the house of Israel is saying, 'The vision he sees is for many years from now, and he prophesies about the distant future.'

²⁸"Therefore say to them, 'This is what the Sovereign LORD says: None of my words will be delayed any longer; whatever I say will be fulfilled, declares the Sovereign LORD.' "

ᵃ 24 Or *Chaldea*

The Melting Pot

Profile: Hayden

I watched from the front seat of my mom's car as masses of very white kids walked through the front doors of my school. I did *not* want to get out of the car. I have to say that I felt a little like Ruby Bridges—the first African-American to go to an all-white elementary school. There she was in 1960, a little six-year old girl, escorted by the marshals to school her first day. Here I was in the twenty-first century, escorted by my mom and still feeling like an outcast . . . as if I was from another planet and dropped into this pasty white high school.

Why did my parents make me transfer here? This is a very white, very rich, very homogeneous school. I'm African-American.

Well, my parents are upper-middle class, and they want me to have the best education. They felt my old school wasn't strong enough academically. That's why I'm here.

It's not like I'm scared to go to this school. I have friends that are white. It's just that it's hard not to feel like you stick out when you're the only one in a crowded classroom who looks different. Whose family is different. Whose background is different.

If we were all created equal, then why do I see people looking at my skin color and making judgment calls about me? They don't even know me. Some of them just look curious. Others look condescending. For all the talk about diversity in America, I can tell you that my high school still needs a lot of work.

To learn more about diversity, go online at www.TrueImagesBible.com

diversity in focus

Schools can work on transforming their educational system, but it's individuals who make the real difference. Whether you're a minority student or in the majority at your school, you can hold high the standard for diversity in your friendships and in your attitudes. Lead through your example. Remember . . .

» God hates prejudice based on race, gender or background. See Acts 10:34–35 (page 1460) and Galatians 3:28 (page 1538).

» As a nation, we still don't have true diversity and equality yet, but make it *your* goal to bring peace between all kinds of people (see Romans 12:18, page 1500).

For more on this topic, see the index on page 1656.

diversity

False Prophets Condemned

13 The word of the LORD came to me: [2]"Son of man, prophesy against the prophets of Israel who are now prophesying. Say to those who prophesy out of their own imagination: 'Hear the word of the LORD! [3]This is what the Sovereign LORD says: Woe to the foolish[a] prophets who follow their own spirit and have seen nothing! [4]Your prophets, O Israel, are like jackals among ruins. [5]You have not gone up to the breaks in the wall to repair it for the house

---

a 3 Or wicked

of Israel so that it will stand firm in the battle on the day of the Lord. ⁶Their visions are false and their divinations a lie. They say, "The Lord declares," when the Lord has not sent them; yet they expect their words to be fulfilled. ⁷Have you not seen false visions and uttered lying divinations when you say, "The Lord declares," though I have not spoken?

⁸" 'Therefore this is what the Sovereign Lord says: Because of your false words and lying visions, I am against you, declares the Sovereign Lord. ⁹My hand will be against the prophets who see false visions and utter lying divinations. They will not belong to the council of my people or be listed in the records of the house of Israel, nor will they enter the land of Israel. Then you will know that I am the Sovereign Lord.

¹⁰" 'Because they lead my people astray, saying, "Peace," when there is no peace, and because, when a flimsy wall is built, they cover it with whitewash, ¹¹therefore tell those who cover it with whitewash that it is going to fall. Rain will come in torrents, and I will send hailstones hurtling down, and violent winds will burst forth.

truth or dare

A fresh paint job may hide a poorly constructed wall for awhile, but it doesn't change the fact that the wall is flimsy. It's better to be honest about rotten situations than to pretend they don't exist.

13:10–12

¹²When the wall collapses, will people not ask you, "Where is the whitewash you covered it with?"

¹³" 'Therefore this is what the Sovereign Lord says: In my wrath I will unleash a violent wind, and in my anger hailstones and torrents of rain will fall with destructive fury. ¹⁴I will tear down the wall you have covered with whitewash and will level it to the ground so that its foundation will be laid bare. When it* falls, you will be destroyed in it; and you will know that I am the Lord. ¹⁵So I will spend my wrath against the wall and against those who covered it with whitewash. I will say to you, "The wall is gone and so are those who whitewashed it, ¹⁶those prophets of Israel who prophesied to Jerusalem and saw visions of peace for her when there was no peace, declares the Sovereign Lord." '

¹⁷"Now, son of man, set your face against the daughters of your people who prophesy out of their own imagination. Prophesy against them ¹⁸and say, 'This is what the Sovereign Lord says: Woe to the women who sew magic charms on all their wrists and make veils of various lengths for their heads in order to ensnare people. Will you ensnare the lives of my people but preserve your own? ¹⁹You have profaned me among my people for a few handfuls of barley and scraps of bread. By lying to my people, who listen to lies, you have killed those who should not have died and have spared those who should not live.

²⁰" 'Therefore this is what the Sovereign Lord says: I am against your magic charms with which you ensnare people like birds and I will tear them from your arms; I will set free the people that you ensnare like birds. ²¹I will tear off your veils and save my people from your hands, and they will no longer fall prey to your power. Then you will know that I am

genuine power » 13:17-23

Forget what you see in the movies. Witchcraft is anything but glamorous. During Ezekiel's day, some women sold spells and magic charms. Perhaps they promised power to those who bought their charms. Or, maybe they put fear into the people by claiming power over them. God made his point crystal clear in Exodus 22:18: "Do not allow a sorceress to live." Does death sound glamorous? Hardly. Having power can seem cool. But with great power, great wisdom is needed. God has all of that. Feeling powerless? You're not, really. If you trust God, you have access to the greatest power source in the universe—God himself.

*14 Or the city

the LORD. ²²Because you disheartened the righteous with your lies, when I had brought them no grief, and because you encouraged the wicked not to turn from their evil ways and so save their lives, ²³therefore you will no longer see false visions or practice divination. I will save my people from your hands. And then you will know that I am the LORD.' "

Idolaters Condemned

14 Some of the elders of Israel came to me and sat down in front of me. ²Then the word of the LORD came to me: ³"Son of man, these men have set up idols in their hearts and put wicked stumbling blocks before their faces. Should I let them inquire of me at all? ⁴Therefore speak to them and tell them, 'This is what the Sovereign LORD says: When any Israelite sets up idols in his heart and puts a wicked stumbling block before his face and then goes to a prophet, I the LORD will answer him myself in keeping with his great idolatry. ⁵I will do this to recapture the hearts of the people of Israel, who have all deserted me for their idols.'

⁶"Therefore say to the house of Israel, 'This is what the Sovereign LORD says: Repent! Turn from your idols and renounce all your detestable practices!

⁷" 'When any Israelite or any alien living in Israel separates himself from me and sets up idols in his heart and puts a wicked stumbling block before his face and then goes to a prophet to inquire of me, I the LORD will answer him myself. ⁸I will set my face against that man and make him an example and a byword. I will cut him off from my people. Then you will know that I am the LORD.

⁹" 'And if the prophet is enticed to utter a prophecy, I the LORD have enticed that prophet, and I will stretch out my hand against him and destroy him from among my people Israel. ¹⁰They will bear their guilt—the prophet will be as guilty as the one who consults him. ¹¹Then the people of Israel will no longer stray from me, nor will they defile themselves anymore with all their sins. They will be my people, and I will be their God, declares the Sovereign LORD.' "

Judgment Inescapable

¹²The word of the LORD came to me: ¹³"Son of man, if a country sins against me by being unfaithful and I stretch out my hand against it to cut off its food supply and send famine upon it and kill its men and their animals, ¹⁴even if these three men—Noah, Daniel ᵃ and Job—were in it, they could save only themselves by their righteousness, declares the Sovereign LORD.

¹⁵"Or if I send wild beasts through that country and they leave it childless and it becomes desolate so that no one can pass through it because of the beasts, ¹⁶as surely as I live, declares the Sovereign LORD, even if these three men were in it, they could not save their own sons or daughters. They alone would be saved, but the land would be desolate.

¹⁷"Or if I bring a sword against that country and say, 'Let the sword pass throughout the land,' and I kill its men and their animals, ¹⁸as surely as I live, declares the Sovereign LORD, even if these three men were in it, they could not save their own sons or daughters. They alone would be saved.

¹⁹"Or if I send a plague into that land and pour out my wrath upon it through bloodshed, killing its men and their animals, ²⁰as surely as I live, declares the Sovereign LORD, even if Noah, Daniel and Job were in it, they could save neither son nor daughter. They would save only themselves by their righteousness.

²¹"For this is what the Sovereign LORD says: How much worse will it be when I send against Jerusalem my four dreadful judgments—sword and famine and wild beasts and plague—to kill its men and their animals! ²²Yet there will be some survivors—sons and daughters who will be brought out of it. They will come to you, and when you see their conduct and their actions, you will be consoled regarding the disaster I have brought upon Jerusalem—every disaster I have brought upon it. ²³You will be consoled when you see their conduct and their actions, for you will know that I have done nothing in it without cause, declares the Sovereign LORD."

Jerusalem, A Useless Vine

15 The word of the LORD came to me: ²"Son of man, how is the wood of a vine better than that of a branch on any of the trees in the forest? ³Is wood ever taken from it to make anything useful? Do they make pegs from it to hang things on? ⁴And after it is thrown on the fire as fuel and the fire burns both ends and chars the middle, is it then useful for anything?

ᵃ 14 Or *Daniel*; the Hebrew spelling may suggest a person other than the prophet Daniel; also in verse 20.

⁵If it was not useful for anything when it was whole, how much less can it be made into something useful when the fire has burned it and it is charred?

⁶"Therefore this is what the Sovereign LORD says: As I have given the wood of the vine among the trees of the forest as fuel for the fire, so will I treat the people living in Jerusalem. ⁷I will set my face against them. Although they have come out of the fire, the fire will yet consume them. And when I set my face against them, you will know that I am the LORD. ⁸I will make the land desolate because they have been unfaithful, declares the Sovereign LORD."

An Allegory of Unfaithful Jerusalem

16 The word of the LORD came to me: ²"Son of man, confront Jerusalem with her detestable practices ³and say, 'This is what the Sovereign LORD says to Jerusalem: Your ancestry and birth were in the land of the Canaanites; your father was an Amorite and your mother a Hittite. ⁴On the day you were born your cord was not cut, nor were you washed with water to make you clean, nor were you rubbed with salt or wrapped in cloths. ⁵No one looked on you with pity or had compassion enough to do any of these things for you. Rather, you were thrown out into the open field, for on the day you were born you were despised.

⁶" 'Then I passed by and saw you kicking about in your blood, and as you lay there in your blood I said to you, "Live!" ᵃ ⁷I made you grow like a plant of the field. You grew up and developed and became the most beautiful of jewels. ᵇ Your breasts were formed and your hair grew, you who were naked and bare.

⁸" 'Later I passed by, and when I looked at you and saw that you were old enough for love, I spread the corner of my garment over you and covered your nakedness. I gave you my solemn oath and entered into a covenant with you, declares the Sovereign LORD, and you became mine.

⁹" 'I bathedᶜ you with water and washed the blood from you and put ointments on you. ¹⁰I clothed you with an embroidered dress and put leather sandals on you. I dressed you in fine linen and covered you with costly garments. ¹¹I adorned you with jewelry: I put bracelets on your arms and a necklace around your neck, ¹²and I put a ring on your nose, earrings on your ears and a beautiful crown on your head. ¹³So you were adorned with gold and silver; your clothes were of fine linen and costly fabric and embroidered cloth. Your food was fine flour, honey and olive oil. You became very beautiful and rose to be a queen. ¹⁴And your fame spread among the nations on account of your beauty, because the splendor I had given you made your beauty perfect, declares the Sovereign LORD.

¹⁵" 'But you trusted in your beauty and used your fame to become a prostitute. You lavished your favors on anyone who passed

genuine beauty » 16:6–29

Everywhere you look you can find the most current images of beauty. Magazine articles tell you how to use what you've got to your advantage.

The Bible tells us that God symbolically entered into a marriage covenant with Israel and made her his beautiful bride. But unfaithful Israel turned her affections toward false gods and pursued alliances with other nations, just as a prostitute lures men. Genuine beauty is a purity that shines from within. Only God can provide this kind of beauty—a beauty that will never fade. You've got that glow, girl!

truth or dare

God had given the Israelites so much—beauty and fame—yet they forgot him completely. Don't trust in your gifts. Trust in the Giver.

16:15

ᵃ 6 A few Hebrew manuscripts, Septuagint and Syriac; most Hebrew manuscripts "Live!" And as you lay there in your blood I said to you, "Live!"   ᵇ 7 Or became mature   ᶜ 9 Or I had bathed by and your beauty became his. *a* ¹⁶You took some of your garments to make gaudy high places, where you carried on your prostitution. Such things should not happen, nor should they ever occur. ¹⁷You also took the fine jewelry I gave you, the jewelry made of my gold and silver, and you made for yourself male idols and engaged in prostitution with them. ¹⁸And you took your embroidered clothes to put on them, and you offered my oil and incense before them. ¹⁹Also the food I provided for you—the fine flour, olive oil and honey I gave you to eat—you offered as fragrant incense before them. That is what happened, declares the Sovereign LORD.

²⁰ 'And you took your sons and daughters whom you bore to me and sacrificed them as food to the idols. Was your prostitution not enough? ²¹You slaughtered my children and sacrificed them *b* to the idols. ²²In all your detestable practices and your prostitution you did not remember the days of your youth, when you were naked and bare, kicking about in your blood.

²³ " 'Woe! Woe to you, declares the Sovereign LORD. In addition to all your other wickedness, ²⁴you built a mound for yourself and made a lofty shrine in every public square. ²⁵At the head of every street you built your lofty shrines and degraded your beauty, offering your body with increasing promiscuity to anyone who passed by. ²⁶You engaged in prostitution with the Egyptians, your lustful neighbors, and provoked me to anger with your increasing promiscuity. ²⁷So I stretched out my hand against you and reduced your territory; I gave you over to the greed of your enemies, the daughters of the Philistines, who were shocked by your lewd conduct. ²⁸You engaged in prostitution with the Assyrians too, because you were insatiable; and even after that, you still were not satisfied. ²⁹Then you increased your promiscuity to include Babylonia, *c* a land of merchants, but even with this you were not satisfied.

³⁰ " 'How weak-willed you are, declares the Sovereign LORD, when you do all these things, acting like a brazen prostitute! ³¹When you built your mounds at the head of every street and made your lofty shrines in every public square, you were unlike a prostitute, because you scorned payment.

³² " 'You adulterous wife! You prefer strangers to your own husband! ³³Every prostitute receives a fee, but you give gifts to all your lovers, bribing them to come to you from everywhere for your illicit favors. ³⁴So in your prostitution you are the opposite of others; no one runs after you for your favors. You are the very opposite, for you give payment and none is given to you.

³⁵ " 'Therefore, you prostitute, hear the word of the LORD! ³⁶This is what the Sovereign LORD says: Because you poured out your wealth *d* and exposed your nakedness in your promiscuity with your lovers, and because of all your detestable idols, and because you gave them your children's blood, ³⁷therefore I am going to gather all your lovers, with whom you found pleasure, those you loved as well as those you hated. I will gather them against you from all around and will strip you in front of them, and they will see all your nakedness. ³⁸I will sentence you to the punishment of women who commit adultery and who shed blood; I will bring upon you the blood vengeance of my wrath and jealous anger. ³⁹Then I will hand you over to your lovers, and they will tear down your mounds and destroy your lofty shrines. They will strip you of your clothes and take your fine jewelry and leave you naked and bare. ⁴⁰They will bring a mob against you, who will stone you and hack you to pieces with their swords. ⁴¹They will burn down your houses and inflict punishment on you in the sight of many women. I will put a stop to your prostitution, and you will no longer pay your lovers. ⁴²Then my wrath against you will subside and my jealous anger will turn away from you; I will be calm and no longer angry.

⁴³ " 'Because you did not remember the days of your youth but enraged me with all these things, I will surely bring down on your head what you have done, declares the Sovereign LORD. Did you not add lewdness to all your other detestable practices?

⁴⁴ " 'Everyone who quotes proverbs will quote this proverb about you: "Like mother, like daughter." ⁴⁵You are a true daughter of your mother, who despised her husband and her children; and you are a true sister of your sisters, who despised their husbands and their children. Your mother was a Hittite and your father an Amorite. ⁴⁶Your older sister was Samaria, who lived to the north of you with her daughters; and your younger sister, who lived to the south of you with her daughters, was Sodom. ⁴⁷You not only walked in their ways and copied their detestable practices, but in all your ways you soon became more depraved than they. ⁴⁸As surely as I live, declares the Sovereign LORD, your sister Sodom and her daughters never did what you and your daughters have done.

---

a 15 Most Hebrew manuscripts; one Hebrew manuscript (see some Septuagint manuscripts) *by. Such a thing should not happen*   *b 21* Or *and made them pass through the fire*   *c 29* Or *Chaldea*   *d 36* Or *lust*

⁴⁹" 'Now this was the sin of your sister Sodom: She and her daughters were arrogant, overfed and unconcerned; they did not help the poor and needy. ⁵⁰They were haughty and did detestable things before me. Therefore I did away with them as you have seen. ⁵¹Samaria did not commit half the sins you did. You have done more detestable things than they, and have made your sisters seem righteous by all these things you have done. ⁵²Bear your disgrace, for you have furnished some justification for your sisters. Because your sins were more vile than theirs, they appear more righteous than you. So then, be ashamed and bear your disgrace, for you have made your sisters appear righteous.

⁵³" 'However, I will restore the fortunes of Sodom and her daughters and of Samaria and her daughters, and your fortunes along with them, ⁵⁴so that you may bear your disgrace and be ashamed of all you have done in giving them comfort. ⁵⁵And your sisters, Sodom with her daughters and Samaria with her daughters, will return to what they were before; and you and your daughters will return to what you were before. ⁵⁶You would not even mention your sister Sodom in the day of your pride, ⁵⁷before your wickedness was uncovered. Even so, you are now scorned by the daughters of Edom ᵃ and all her neighbors and the daughters of the Philistines—all those around you who despise you. ⁵⁸You will bear the consequences of your lewdness and your detestable practices, declares the Lᴏʀᴅ.

⁵⁹" 'This is what the Sovereign Lᴏʀᴅ says: I will deal with you as you deserve, because you have despised my oath by breaking the covenant. ⁶⁰Yet I will remember the covenant I made with you in the days of your youth, and I will establish an everlasting covenant with you. ⁶¹Then you will remember your ways and be ashamed when you receive your sisters, both those who are older than you and those who are younger. I will give them to you as daughters, but not on the basis of my covenant with you. ⁶²So I will establish my covenant with you, and you will know that I am the Lᴏʀᴅ. ⁶³Then, when I make atonement for you for all you have done, you will remember and be ashamed and never again open your mouth because of your humiliation, declares the Sovereign Lᴏʀᴅ.' "

Two Eagles and a Vine

17 The word of the Lᴏʀᴅ came to me: ²"Son of man, set forth an allegory and tell the house of Israel a parable. ³Say to them, 'This is what the Sovereign Lᴏʀᴅ says: A great eagle with powerful wings, long feathers and full plumage of varied colors came to Lebanon. Taking hold of the top of a cedar, ⁴he broke off its topmost shoot and carried it away to a land of merchants, where he planted it in a city of traders.

⁵" 'He took some of the seed of your land and put it in fertile soil. He planted it like a willow by abundant water, ⁶and it sprouted and became a low, spreading vine. Its branches turned toward him, but its roots remained under it. So it became a vine and produced branches and put out leafy boughs.

⁷" 'But there was another great eagle with powerful wings and full plumage. The vine now sent out its roots toward him from the plot where it was planted and stretched out its branches to him for water. ⁸It had been planted in good soil by abundant water so that it would produce branches, bear fruit and become a splendid vine.'

⁹"Say to them, 'This is what the Sovereign Lᴏʀᴅ says: Will it thrive? Will it not be uprooted and stripped of its fruit so that it withers? All its new growth will wither. It will not take a strong arm or many people to pull it up by the roots. ¹⁰Even if it is transplanted, will it thrive? Will it not wither completely when the east wind strikes it—wither away in the plot where it grew?' "

¹¹Then the word of the Lᴏʀᴅ came to me: ¹²"Say to this rebellious house, 'Do you not know what these things mean?' Say to them: 'The king of Babylon went to Jerusalem and carried off her king and her nobles, bringing them back with him to Babylon. ¹³Then he took a member of the royal family and made a treaty with him, putting him under oath. He also carried away the leading men of the land, ¹⁴so that the kingdom would be brought low, unable to rise again, surviving only by keeping his treaty. ¹⁵But the king rebelled against him by sending his envoys to Egypt to get horses and a large army. Will he succeed? Will he who does such things escape? Will he break the treaty and yet escape?

¹⁶" 'As surely as I live, declares the Sovereign Lᴏʀᴅ, he shall die in Babylon, in the land of the king who put him on the throne, whose oath he despised and whose treaty he broke. ¹⁷Pharaoh

ᵃ 57 Many Hebrew manuscripts and Syriac; most Hebrew manuscripts, Septuagint and Vulgate Aram with his mighty army and great horde will be of no help to him in war, when ramps are built and siege works erected to destroy many lives. ¹⁸He despised the oath by breaking the covenant. Because he had given his hand in pledge and yet did all these things, he shall not escape.

¹⁹" 'Therefore this is what the Sovereign LORD says: As surely as I live, I will bring down on his head my oath that he despised and my covenant that he broke. ²⁰I will spread my net for him, and he will be caught in my snare. I will bring him to Babylon and execute judgment upon him there because he was unfaithful to me. ²¹All his fleeing troops will fall by the sword, and the survivors will be scattered to the winds. Then you will know that I the LORD have spoken.

²²" 'This is what the Sovereign LORD says: I myself will take a shoot from the very top of a cedar and plant it; I will break off a tender sprig from its topmost shoots and plant it on a high and lofty mountain. ²³On the mountain heights of Israel I will plant it; it will produce branches and bear fruit and become a splendid cedar. Birds of every kind will nest in it; they will find shelter in the shade of its branches. ²⁴All the trees of the field will know that I the LORD bring down the tall tree and make the low tree grow tall. I dry up the green tree and make the dry tree flourish.

" 'I the LORD have spoken, and I will do it.' "

truth or dare

Catch the hidden meaning? The tender shoot—that's Christ. As predicted, Jesus is a shelter for any who come to him.

17:22–23

The Soul Who Sins Will Die

18 The word of the LORD came to me: ²"What do you people mean by quoting this proverb about the land of Israel:

> " 'The fathers eat sour grapes,
> and the children's teeth are
> set on edge'?

³"As surely as I live, declares the Sovereign LORD, you will no longer quote this proverb in Israel. ⁴For every living soul belongs to me, the father as well as the son—both alike belong to me. The soul who sins is the one who will die.

> ⁵"Suppose there is a righteous
> man
> who does what is just and
> right.
> ⁶He does not eat at the mountain
> shrines
> or look to the idols of the
> house of Israel.
> He does not defile his neighbor's
> wife
> or lie with a woman during
> her period.
> ⁷He does not oppress anyone,
> but returns what he took in
> pledge for a loan.
> He does not commit robbery
> but gives his food to the
> hungry
> and provides clothing for the
> naked.
> ⁸He does not lend at usury

genuine judgment

Ever feel judged for the mistakes of others? For example, you might be forced to live down your older brother's reputation with a certain teacher. Or maybe you fear that you'll follow in the footsteps of a parent with a problem, such as a family pattern of alcoholism. The good news is that God judges people for their own actions rather than anyone else's. He doesn't put false guilt on people. That's reassuring! A family's cycle of sin can be broken by trust in God. In the end, you're accountable for just one person—*you*.

» 18:1–21

> or take excessive interest. *ª*
> He withholds his hand from doing wrong
>   and judges fairly between man and man.
> ⁹He follows my decrees
>   and faithfully keeps my laws.
> That man is righteous;
>   he will surely live,

declares the Sovereign LORD.

¹⁰"Suppose he has a violent son, who sheds blood or does any of these other things *ᵇ* ¹¹(though the father has done none of them):

> "He eats at the mountain shrines.
> He defiles his neighbor's wife.
> ¹²He oppresses the poor and needy.
> He commits robbery.
> He does not return what he took in pledge.
> He looks to the idols.
> He does detestable things.
> ¹³He lends at usury and takes excessive interest.

Will such a man live? He will not! Because he has done all these detestable things, he will surely be put to death and his blood will be on his own head.

¹⁴"But suppose this son has a son who sees all the sins his father commits, and though he sees them, he does not do such things:

> ¹⁵"He does not eat at the mountain shrines
>   or look to the idols of the house of Israel.
> He does not defile his neighbor's wife.
> ¹⁶He does not oppress anyone
>   or require a pledge for a loan.
> He does not commit robbery
>   but gives his food to the hungry
>   and provides clothing for the naked.
> ¹⁷He withholds his hand from sin *ᶜ*
>   and takes no usury or excessive interest.
> He keeps my laws and follows my decrees.

He will not die for his father's sin; he will surely live. ¹⁸But his father will die for his own sin, because he practiced extortion, robbed his brother and did what was wrong among his people.

¹⁹"Yet you ask, 'Why does the son not share the guilt of his father?' Since the son has done what is just and right and has been careful to keep all my decrees, he will surely live. ²⁰The soul who sins is the one who will die. The son will not share the guilt of the father, nor will the father share the guilt of the son. The righteousness of the righteous man will be credited to him, and the wickedness of the wicked will be charged against him.

²¹"But if a wicked man turns away from all the sins he has committed and keeps all my decrees and does what is just and right, he will surely live; he will not die. ²²None of the offenses he has committed will be remembered against him. Because of the righteous things he has done, he will live. ²³Do I take any pleasure in the death of the wicked? declares the Sovereign LORD. Rather, am I not pleased when they turn from their ways and live?

²⁴"But if a righteous man turns from his righteousness and commits sin and does the same detestable things the wicked man does, will he live? None of the righteous things he has done will be remembered. Because of the unfaithfulness he is guilty of and because of the sins he has committed, he will die.

²⁵"Yet you say, 'The way of the Lord is not just.' Hear, O house of Israel: Is my way unjust? Is it not your ways that are unjust? ²⁶If a righteous man turns from his righteousness and commits

---

ª 8 Or *take interest*; similarly in verses 13 and 17   *ᵇ 10* Or *things to a brother*   *ᶜ 17* Septuagint (see also verse 8); Hebrew *from the poor* sin, he will die for it; because of the sin he has committed he will die. ²⁷But if a wicked man turns away from the wickedness he has committed and does what is just and right, he will save his life. ²⁸Because he considers all the offenses he has committed and turns away from them, he will surely live; he will not die. ²⁹Yet the house of Israel says, 'The way of the Lord is not just.' Are my ways unjust, O house of Israel? Is it not your ways that are unjust?

³⁰"Therefore, O house of Israel, I will judge you, each one according to his ways, declares the Sovereign Lord. Repent! Turn away from all your offenses; then sin will not be your downfall. ³¹Rid yourselves of all the offenses you have committed, and get a new heart and a new spirit. Why will you die, O house of Israel? ³²For I take no pleasure in the death of anyone, declares the Sovereign Lord. Repent and live!

A Lament for Israel's Princes

19 "Take up a lament concerning the princes of Israel ²and say:

" 'What a lioness was your mother
among the lions!
She lay down among the young lions
and reared her cubs.
³She brought up one of her cubs,
and he became a strong lion.
He learned to tear the prey
and he devoured men.
⁴The nations heard about him,
and he was trapped in their pit.
They led him with hooks
to the land of Egypt.

⁵" 'When she saw her hope unfulfilled,
her expectation gone,
she took another of her cubs
and made him a strong lion.
⁶He prowled among the lions,
for he was now a strong lion.
He learned to tear the prey
and he devoured men.
⁷He broke down ᵃ their strongholds
and devastated their towns.
The land and all who were in it
were terrified by his roaring.
⁸Then the nations came against him,
those from regions round about.
They spread their net for him,
and he was trapped in their pit.
⁹With hooks they pulled him into a cage
and brought him to the king of Babylon.
They put him in prison,
so his roar was heard no longer
on the mountains of Israel.

ᵃ 7 Targum (see Septuagint); Hebrew *He knew*

¹⁰ " 'Your mother was like a vine in your vineyard^a
>   planted by the water;
> it was fruitful and full of branches
>   because of abundant water.
> ¹¹ Its branches were strong,
>   fit for a ruler's scepter.
> It towered high
>   above the thick foliage,
> conspicuous for its height
>   and for its many branches.
> ¹² But it was uprooted in fury
>   and thrown to the ground.
> The east wind made it shrivel,
>   it was stripped of its fruit;
> its strong branches withered
>   and fire consumed them.
> ¹³ Now it is planted in the desert,
>   in a dry and thirsty land.
> ¹⁴ Fire spread from one of its main^b branches
>   and consumed its fruit.
> No strong branch is left on it
>   fit for a ruler's scepter.'

This is a lament and is to be used as a lament."

Rebellious Israel

20 In the seventh year, in the fifth month on the tenth day, some of the elders of Israel came to inquire of the LORD, and they sat down in front of me.
²Then the word of the LORD came to me: ³"Son of man, speak to the elders of Israel and say to them, 'This is what the Sovereign LORD says: Have you come to inquire of me? As surely as I live, I will not let you inquire of me, declares the Sovereign LORD.'

⁴"Will you judge them? Will you judge them, son of man? Then confront them with the detestable practices of their fathers ⁵and say to them: 'This is what the Sovereign LORD says: On the day I chose Israel, I swore with uplifted hand to the descendants of the house of Jacob and revealed myself to them in Egypt. With uplifted hand I said to them, "I am the LORD your God." ⁶On that day I swore to them that I would bring them out of Egypt into a land I had searched out for them, a land flowing with milk and honey, the most beautiful of all lands. ⁷And I said to them, "Each of you, get rid of the vile images you have set your eyes on, and do not defile yourselves with the idols of Egypt. I am the LORD your God."

⁸" 'But they rebelled against me and would not listen to me; they did not get rid of the vile images they had set their eyes on, nor did they forsake the idols of Egypt. So I said I would pour out my wrath on them and spend my anger against them in Egypt. ⁹But for the sake of my name I did what would keep it from being profaned in the eyes of the nations they lived among and in whose sight I had revealed myself to the Israelites by bringing them out of Egypt. ¹⁰Therefore I led them out of Egypt and brought them into the desert. ¹¹I gave them my decrees and made known to them my laws, for the man who obeys them will live by them. ¹²Also I gave them my Sabbaths as a sign between us, so they would know that I the LORD made them holy.

¹³" 'Yet the people of Israel rebelled against me in the desert. They did not follow my decrees but rejected my laws—although the

truth or dare

Are your Sundays usually packed with things to do and people to see? Don't forget that God gave you that day as a gift—to rest and remember him.

20:12

---

^a 10 Two Hebrew manuscripts; most Hebrew manuscripts *your blood*   ^b 14 Or *from under its*

What Do I Say When My Friend Is Gay?

Profile: Roselyn

Sean is gay. He told me so himself last week. I felt numb inside when he told me. He said he's been afraid to tell me. He's known about this for awhile, though. Guess he would.

I've known Sean since we were both three years old. He's my second best friend. Now that I think about it, I must say Sean is really cute. He's always been like a "husband back-up" for Melanie, my first best friend, and me. Mel and I decided that one of us would marry Sean if nobody else asked us. Guess neither of us will get him now. What a waste.

I still can't believe it. I'm not sure what to do. He says he's tried the straight life, and it didn't really fit him. He's happy now. That's funny because I'm miserable. I feel like I've lost one of my closest friends.

I told Sean that the Bible says that homosexuality is wrong. That sounded lame as soon as I said it, especially since I couldn't think of any Scriptures to use. Plus, Sean knows way more Scriptures than I do. He told me that if I can't accept him the way he is, we can't be friends. "And I would hate that," he said, which made me feel worse.

He also said he's still a Christian. That part of him hasn't changed. But how can he be gay and a Christian at the same time?

I keep reading about a gay gene—that people are born gay. I'm wondering if that's true in Sean's case. Does that mean it's okay with God that he's gay?

---

homosexuality in focus

Now that the 21st century is well underway, do you ever wonder if some things are okay now? Take homosexuality, for example. Many people have come out of the closet and feel empowered by expressing their sexual preference. Does that make it okay?

» Leviticus 18:22; 20:13 (pages 141,144), Romans 1:26–27 (page 1487) and 1 Corinthians 6:9–11 (page 1511) say no, it's still not okay. Also, contrary to popular belief, God doesn't "make" anyone gay. Homosexuality is a human choice.

» Know someone who is struggling with this choice? He or she still needs your love, even if you don't agree with the choice he or she has made.

For more on this topic, see the index on page 1656.

homosexuality

---

man who obeys them will live by them—and they utterly desecrated my Sabbaths. So I said I would pour out my wrath on them and destroy them in the desert. [14]But for the sake of my name I did what would keep it from being profaned in the eyes of the nations in whose sight I had brought them out. [15]Also with uplifted hand I swore to them in the desert that I would not bring them into the land I had given them—a land flowing with milk and honey, most beautiful of all lands— [16]because they rejected my laws and did not follow my decrees and desecrated my Sabbaths. For their hearts were devoted to their idols. [17]Yet I looked on them with pity and did not destroy them or put an end to them in the desert. [18]I said to their children in the desert, "Do not follow the statutes of your fathers or keep their laws or defile yourselves with their idols. ¹⁹I am the LORD your God; follow my decrees and be careful to keep my laws. ²⁰Keep my Sabbaths holy, that they may be a sign between us. Then you will know that I am the LORD your God."

²¹" 'But the children rebelled against me: They did not follow my decrees, they were not careful to keep my laws—although the man who obeys them will live by them—and they desecrated my Sabbaths. So I said I would pour out my wrath on them and spend my anger against them in the desert. ²²But I withheld my hand, and for the sake of my name I did what would keep it from being profaned in the eyes of the nations in whose sight I had brought them out. ²³Also with uplifted hand I swore to them in the desert that I would disperse them among the nations and scatter them through the countries, ²⁴because they had not obeyed my laws but had rejected my decrees and desecrated my Sabbaths, and their eyes ˌlustedˌ after their fathers' idols. ²⁵I also gave them over to statutes that were not good and laws they could not live by; ²⁶I let them become defiled through their gifts—the sacrifice of every firstborn ᵃ—that I might fill them with horror so they would know that I am the LORD.'

²⁷"Therefore, son of man, speak to the people of Israel and say to them, 'This is what the Sovereign LORD says: In this also your fathers blasphemed me by forsaking me: ²⁸When I brought them into the land I had sworn to give them and they saw any high hill or any leafy tree, there they offered their sacrifices, made offerings that provoked me to anger, presented their fragrant incense and poured out their drink offerings. ²⁹Then I said to them: What is this high place you go to?' " (It is called Bamah ᵇ to this day.)

Judgment and Restoration

³⁰"Therefore say to the house of Israel: 'This is what the Sovereign LORD says: Will you defile yourselves the way your fathers did and lust after their vile images? ³¹When you offer your gifts—the sacrifice of your sons in ᶜ the fire—you continue to defile yourselves with all your idols to this day. Am I to let you inquire of me, O house of Israel? As surely as I live, declares the Sovereign LORD, I will not let you inquire of me.

³²" 'You say, "We want to be like the nations, like the peoples of the world, who serve wood and stone." But what you have in mind will never happen. ³³As surely as I live, declares the Sovereign LORD, I will rule over you with a mighty hand and an outstretched arm and with outpoured wrath. ³⁴I will bring you from the nations and gather you from the countries where you have been scattered—with a mighty hand and an outstretched arm and with outpoured wrath. ³⁵I will bring you into the desert of the nations and there, face to face, I will execute judgment upon you. ³⁶As I judged your fathers in the desert of the land of Egypt, so I will judge you, declares the Sovereign LORD. ³⁷I will take note of you as you pass under my rod, and I will bring you into the bond of the covenant. ³⁸I will purge you of those who revolt and rebel against me. Although I will bring them out of the land where they are living, yet they will not enter the land of Israel. Then you will know that I am the LORD.

³⁹" 'As for you, O house of Israel, this is what the Sovereign LORD says: Go and serve your idols, every one of you! But afterward you will surely listen to me and no longer profane my holy name with your gifts and idols. ⁴⁰For on my holy mountain, the high mountain of Israel, declares the Sovereign LORD, there in the land the entire house of Israel will serve me, and there I will accept them. There I will require your offerings and your choice gifts, ᵈ along with all your holy sacrifices. ⁴¹I will accept you as fragrant incense when I bring you out from the nations and gather you from the countries where you have been scattered, and I will show myself holy among you in the sight of the nations. ⁴²Then you will know that I am the LORD, when I bring you into the land of Israel, the land I had sworn with uplifted hand to give to your fathers. ⁴³There you will remember your conduct and all the actions by which you have defiled yourselves, and you will loathe yourselves for all the evil you have done. ⁴⁴You will know that I am the LORD, when I deal with you for my name's sake and not according to your evil ways and your corrupt practices, O house of Israel, declares the Sovereign LORD.' "

Prophecy Against the South

⁴⁵The word of the LORD came to me: ⁴⁶"Son of man, set your face toward the south; preach against the south and prophesy against the forest of the southland. ⁴⁷Say to the southern forest:

ᵃ 26 Or —making every firstborn pass through ˌthe fire,ˌ   ᵇ 29 Bamah means high place.   ᶜ 31 Or —making your sons pass through   ᵈ 40 Or and the gifts of your firstfruits

'Hear the word of the LORD. This is what the Sovereign LORD says: I am about to set fire to you, and it will consume all your trees, both green and dry. The blazing flame will not be quenched, and every face from south to north will be scorched by it. ⁴⁸Everyone will see that I the LORD have kindled it; it will not be quenched.' "

⁴⁹Then I said, "Ah, Sovereign LORD! They are saying of me, 'Isn't he just telling parables?' "

Babylon, God's Sword of Judgment

21 The word of the LORD came to me: ²"Son of man, set your face against Jerusalem and preach against the sanctuary. Prophesy against the land of Israel ³and say to her: 'This is what the LORD says: I am against you. I will draw my sword from its scabbard and cut off from you both the righteous and the wicked. ⁴Because I am going to cut off the righteous and the wicked, my sword will be unsheathed against everyone from south to north. ⁵Then all people will know that I the LORD have drawn my sword from its scabbard; it will not return again.'

⁶"Therefore groan, son of man! Groan before them with broken heart and bitter grief. ⁷And when they ask you, 'Why are you groaning?' you shall say, 'Because of the news that is coming. Every heart will melt and every hand go limp; every spirit will become faint and every knee become as weak as water.' It is coming! It will surely take place, declares the Sovereign LORD."

⁸The word of the LORD came to me: ⁹"Son of man, prophesy and say, 'This is what the Lord says:

> " 'A sword, a sword,
> sharpened and polished—
> ¹⁰sharpened for the slaughter,
> polished to flash like lightning!

" 'Shall we rejoice in the scepter of my son ˻Judah˼? The sword despises every such stick.

> ¹¹ " 'The sword is appointed to be polished,
> to be grasped with the hand;
> it is sharpened and polished,
> made ready for the hand of the slayer.
> ¹²Cry out and wail, son of man,
> for it is against my people;
> it is against all the princes of Israel.
> They are thrown to the sword
> along with my people.
> Therefore beat your breast.

¹³" 'Testing will surely come. And what if the scepter ˻of Judah˼, which the sword despises, does not continue? declares the Sovereign LORD.'

> ¹⁴"So then, son of man, prophesy
> and strike your hands together.
> Let the sword strike twice,
> even three times.
> It is a sword for slaughter—
> a sword for great slaughter,
> closing in on them from every side.
> ¹⁵So that hearts may melt
> and the fallen be many,
> I have stationed the sword for slaughter*
> at all their gates.
> Oh! It is made to flash like lightning,
> it is grasped for slaughter.
> ¹⁶O sword, slash to the right,
> then to the left,
> wherever your blade is turned.

---

a 15 Septuagint; the meaning of the Hebrew for this word is uncertain.

¹⁷I too will strike my hands together,
    and my wrath will subside.
    I the LORD have spoken."

¹⁸The word of the LORD came to me: ¹⁹"Son of man, mark out two roads for the sword of the king of Babylon to take, both starting from the same country. Make a signpost where the road branches off to the city. ²⁰Mark out one road for the sword to come against Rabbah of the Ammonites and another against Judah and fortified Jerusalem. ²¹For the king of Babylon will stop at the fork in the road, at the junction of the two roads, to seek an omen: He will cast lots with arrows, he will consult his idols, he will examine the liver. ²²Into his right hand will come the lot for Jerusalem, where he is to set up battering rams, to give the command to slaughter, to sound the battle cry, to set battering rams against the gates, to build a ramp and to erect siege works. ²³It will seem like a false omen to those who have sworn allegiance to him, but he will remind them of their guilt and take them captive.

²⁴"Therefore this is what the Sovereign LORD says: 'Because you people have brought to mind your guilt by your open rebellion, revealing your sins in all that you do—because you have done this, you will be taken captive.

²⁵" 'O profane and wicked prince of Israel, whose day has come, whose time of punishment has reached its climax, ²⁶this is what the Sovereign LORD says: Take off the turban, remove the crown. It will not be as it was: The lowly will be exalted and the exalted will be brought low. ²⁷A ruin! A ruin! I will make it a ruin! It will not be restored until he comes to whom it rightfully belongs; to him I will give it.'

²⁸"And you, son of man, prophesy and say, 'This is what the Sovereign LORD says about the Ammonites and their insults:

" 'A sword, a sword,
    drawn for the slaughter,
polished to consume
    and to flash like lightning!
²⁹Despite false visions concerning you
    and lying divinations about you,
it will be laid on the necks
    of the wicked who are to be slain,
whose day has come,
    whose time of punishment has reached its climax.
³⁰Return the sword to its scabbard.
    In the place where you were created,
    in the land of your ancestry,
    I will judge you.
³¹I will pour out my wrath upon you
    and breathe out my fiery anger against you;
I will hand you over to brutal men,
    men skilled in destruction.
³²You will be fuel for the fire,
    your blood will be shed in your land,
you will be remembered no more;
    for I the LORD have spoken.' "

Jerusalem's Sins

22 The word of the LORD came to me: ²"Son of man, will you judge her? Will you judge this city of bloodshed? Then confront her with all her detestable practices ³and say: 'This is what the Sovereign LORD says: O city that brings on herself doom by shedding blood in her midst and defiles herself by making idols, ⁴you have become guilty because of the blood you have shed and have become defiled by the idols you have made. You have brought your days to a close, and the end of your years has come. Therefore I will make you an object of scorn to the nations and a laughingstock to all the countries. ⁵Those who are near and those who are far away will mock you, O infamous city, full of turmoil.

⁶" 'See how each of the princes of Israel who are in you uses his power to shed blood. ⁷In you

they have treated father and mother with contempt; in you they have oppressed the alien and mistreated the fatherless and the widow. ⁸You have despised my holy things and desecrated my Sabbaths. ⁹In you are slanderous men bent on shedding blood; in you are those who eat at the mountain shrines and commit lewd acts. ¹⁰In you are those who dishonor their fathers' bed; in you are those who violate women during their period, when they are ceremonially unclean. ¹¹In you one man commits a detestable offense with his neighbor's wife, another shamefully defiles his daughter-in-law, and another violates his sister, his own father's daughter. ¹²In you men accept bribes to shed blood; you take usury and excessive interest ͣ and make unjust gain from your neighbors by extortion. And you have forgotten me, declares the Sovereign LORD.

¹³"'I will surely strike my hands together at the unjust gain you have made and at the blood you have shed in your midst. ¹⁴Will your courage endure or your hands be strong in the day I deal with you? I the LORD have spoken, and I will do it. ¹⁵I will disperse you among the nations and scatter you through the countries; and I will put an end to your uncleanness. ¹⁶When you have been defiled ͣ in the eyes of the nations, you will know that I am the LORD.'"

¹⁷Then the word of the LORD came to me: ¹⁸"Son of man, the house of Israel has become dross to me; all of them are the copper, tin, iron and lead left inside a furnace. They are but the dross of silver. ¹⁹Therefore this is what the Sovereign LORD says: 'Because you have all become dross, I will gather you into Jerusalem. ²⁰As men gather silver, copper, iron, lead and tin into a furnace to melt it with a fiery blast, so will I gather you in my anger and my wrath and put you inside the city and melt you. ²¹I will gather you and I will blow on you with my fiery wrath, and you will be melted inside her. ²²As silver is melted in a furnace, so you will be melted inside her, and you will know that I the LORD have poured out my wrath upon you.'"

²³Again the word of the LORD came to me: ²⁴"Son of man, say to the land, 'You are a land that has had no rain or showers ͨ in the day of wrath.' ²⁵There is a conspiracy of her princes ͩ within her like a roaring lion tearing its prey; they devour people, take treasures and precious things and make many widows within her. ²⁶Her priests do violence to my law and profane my holy things; they do not distinguish between the holy and the common; they teach that there is no difference between the unclean and the clean; and they shut their eyes to the keeping of my Sabbaths, so that I am profaned among them. ²⁷Her officials within her are like wolves tearing their prey; they shed blood and kill people to make unjust gain. ²⁸Her prophets whitewash these deeds for them by false visions and lying divinations. They say, 'This is what the Sovereign LORD says'—when the LORD has not spoken. ²⁹The people of the land practice extortion and commit robbery; they oppress the poor and needy and mistreat the alien, denying them justice.

³⁰"I looked for a man among them who would build up the wall and stand before me in the gap on behalf of the land so I would not have to destroy it, but I found none. ³¹So I will pour out my wrath on them and consume them with my fiery anger, bringing down on their own heads all they have done, declares the Sovereign LORD."

Two Adulterous Sisters

23 The word of the LORD came to me: ²"Son of man, there were two women, daughters of the same mother. ³They became prostitutes in Egypt, engaging in prostitution from their youth. In that land their breasts were fondled and their virgin bosoms caressed. ⁴The older was named Oholah, and her sister was Oholibah. They were mine and gave birth to sons and daughters. Oholah is Samaria, and Oholibah is Jerusalem.

⁵"Oholah engaged in prostitution while she was still mine; and she lusted after her lovers, the

truth or dare

How could God rank murder and disrespecting your parents at the same level? God takes how we treat our parents seriously, in these verses *and* in the Ten Commandments.

22:6–8

ͣ 12 Or *usury and interest* ͣ 16 Or *When I have allotted you your inheritance* ͨ 24 Septuagint; Hebrew *has not been cleansed or rained on* ͩ 25 Septuagint; Hebrew *prophets*

Assyrians—warriors [6]clothed in blue, governors and commanders, all of them handsome young men, and mounted horsemen. [7]She gave herself as a prostitute to all the elite of the Assyrians and defiled herself with all the idols of everyone she lusted after. [8]She did not give up the prostitution she began in Egypt, when during her youth men slept with her, caressed her virgin bosom and poured out their lust upon her.

[9]"Therefore I handed her over to her lovers, the Assyrians, for whom she lusted. [10]They stripped her naked, took away her sons and daughters and killed her with the sword. She became a byword among women, and punishment was inflicted on her.

[11]"Her sister Oholibah saw this, yet in her lust and prostitution she was more depraved than her sister. [12]She too lusted after the Assyrians—governors and commanders, warriors in full dress, mounted horsemen, all handsome young men. [13]I saw that she too defiled herself; both of them went the same way.

[14]"But she carried her prostitution still further. She saw men portrayed on a wall, figures of Chaldeans[a] portrayed in red, [15]with belts around their waists and flowing turbans on their heads; all of them looked like Babylonian chariot officers, natives of Chaldea.[b] [16]As soon as she saw them, she lusted after them and sent messengers to them in Chaldea. [17]Then the Babylonians came to her, to the bed of love, and in their lust they defiled her. After she had been defiled by them, she turned away from them in disgust. [18]When she carried on her prostitution openly and exposed her nakedness, I turned away from her in disgust, just as I had turned away from her sister. [19]Yet she became more and more promiscuous as she recalled the days of her youth, when she was a prostitute in Egypt. [20]There she lusted after her lovers, whose genitals were like those of donkeys and whose emission was like that of horses. [21]So you longed for the lewdness of your youth, when in Egypt your bosom was caressed and your young breasts fondled.[c]

[22]"Therefore, Oholibah, this is what the Sovereign LORD says: I will stir up your lovers against you, those you turned away from in disgust, and I will bring them against you from every side— [23]the Babylonians and all the Chaldeans, the men of Pekod and Shoa and Koa, and all the Assyrians with them, handsome young men, all of them governors and commanders, chariot officers and men of high rank, all mounted on horses. [24]They will come against you with weapons,[d] chariots and wagons and with a throng of people; they will take up positions against you on every side with large and small shields and with helmets. I will turn you over to them for punishment, and they will punish you according to their standards. [25]I will direct my jealous anger against you, and they will deal with you in fury. They will cut off your noses and your ears, and those of you who are left will fall by the sword. They will take away your sons and daughters, and those of you who are left will be consumed by fire. [26]They will also strip you of your clothes and take your fine jewelry. [27]So I will put a stop to the lewdness and prostitution you began in Egypt. You will not look on these things with longing or remember Egypt anymore.

[28]"For this is what the Sovereign LORD says: I am about to hand you over to those you hate, to those you turned away from in disgust. [29]They will deal with you in hatred and take away every-

genuine

character »» 22:30

Think about the problems that a gap causes. No, we're not talking about the store. We're talking about a real live *gap*. A gap between your teeth. A gap between your defenders in sports. In Bible times, a gap in a city wall could be way more disastrous. Enemies could enter and destroy a city. It would take great courage for someone to stand in the gap and battle the enemy. God told Ezekiel that he was looking for followers to stand in the gap spiritually—in other words, to faithfully resist and fight evil. Are you willing to stand in the gap?

a 14 Or *Babylonians of your young breasts* *b 15* Or *Babylonia*; also in verse 16 *c 21* Syriac (see also verse 3); Hebrew *caressed because* *d 24* The meaning of the Hebrew for this word is uncertain.

So, What Does Your Dad Do?

"So, what does your dad do?" the girls asked nonchalantly as we walked to class. I'd been dreading that question. Yet I knew it would come up sooner or later. I was just hoping it would be later. In the split-second between their question and my answer, a thousand options came to mind:

My dad? Oh, my dad is an engineer at Compaq . . .

What does my father do? He has a family law practice with my grandfather . . .

My dad? He's the vice president of a software company, actually . . .

The lies came to mind way before the truth ever did. After all, I was the new girl—no one knew me from beans—I could be anyone I wanted. It felt like inventing my identity from scratch. And I knew I didn't want to be the poor minister's kid, driving a beater car, living in the church parsonage. It was going to be hard enough getting along with these girls. They were way out of my league. The cars they drove. The clothes they wore. There's no way my dad would ever be able to buy me stuff like that. Who was I kidding? I'd always be scraping it together as long as my dad was in the ministry.

But for one brief moment, I had the opportunity to be just like all of them. To have money. A big house. Everything I'd dreamed of having. So, when they asked me what my dad did for a living, I lied.

"My dad? He's in pharmaceutical sales . . ."

And for a moment, I almost believed it myself.

materialism in focus

Whether your parents are in the ministry or your family just doesn't have much money, it's tough to feel like you have so much less than everyone else around you. While everyone else is taking family vacations to Maui, that day-trip to the water park just doesn't seem to cut it. Yet God promises a special blessing for those who are willing to follow him, rich or poor.

»God promises to fulfill all our needs (see Philippians 4:19, page 1554): Notice that God doesn't offer to supply all our *wants*—big difference!

»Feel like you're sacrificing a lot for the Lord? He promises to reward you with a hundred times as much in this life (not necessarily with big bucks, of course!) and through eternity (see Mark 10:29–30, page 1349). How's that for a trade?

For more on this topic, see the index on page 1656.

thing you have worked for. They will leave you naked and bare, and the shame of your prostitution will be exposed. Your lewdness and promiscuity [30]have brought this upon you, because you lusted after the nations and defiled yourself with their idols. [31]You have gone the way of your sister; so I will put her cup into your hand.

[32]"This is what the Sovereign LORD says:

"You will drink your sister's cup,
    a cup large and deep;

it will bring scorn and derision,
for it holds so much.
³³You will be filled with drunkenness and sorrow,
the cup of ruin and desolation,
the cup of your sister Samaria.
³⁴You will drink it and drain it dry;
you will dash it to pieces
and tear your breasts.

I have spoken, declares the Sovereign LORD.

³⁵"Therefore this is what the Sovereign LORD says: Since you have forgotten me and thrust me behind your back, you must bear the consequences of your lewdness and prostitution."

³⁶The LORD said to me: "Son of man, will you judge Oholah and Oholibah? Then confront them with their detestable practices, ³⁷for they have committed adultery and blood is on their hands. They committed adultery with their idols; they even sacrificed their children, whom they bore to me,^a as food for them. ³⁸They have also done this to me: At that same time they defiled my sanctuary and desecrated my Sabbaths. ³⁹On the very day they sacrificed their children to their idols, they entered my sanctuary and desecrated it. That is what they did in my house.

⁴⁰"They even sent messengers for men who came from far away, and when they arrived you bathed yourself for them, painted your eyes and put on your jewelry. ⁴¹You sat on an elegant couch, with a table spread before it on which you had placed the incense and oil that belonged to me.

⁴²"The noise of a carefree crowd was around her; Sabeans^b were brought from the desert along with men from the rabble, and they put bracelets on the arms of the woman and her sister and beautiful crowns on their heads. ⁴³Then I said about the one worn out by adultery, 'Now let them use her as a prostitute, for that is all she is.' ⁴⁴And they slept with her. As men sleep with a prostitute, so they slept with those lewd women, Oholah and Oholibah. ⁴⁵But righteous men will sentence them to the punishment of women who commit adultery and shed blood, because they are adulterous and blood is on their hands.

⁴⁶"This is what the Sovereign LORD says: Bring a mob against them and give them over to terror and plunder. ⁴⁷The mob will stone them and cut them down with their swords; they will kill their sons and daughters and burn down their houses.

⁴⁸"So I will put an end to lewdness in the land, that all women may take warning and not imitate you. ⁴⁹You will suffer the penalty for your lewdness and bear the consequences of your sins of idolatry. Then you will know that I am the Sovereign LORD."

The Cooking Pot

24 In the ninth year, in the tenth month on the tenth day, the word of the LORD came to me: ²"Son of man, record this date, this very date, because the king of Babylon has laid siege to Jerusalem this very day. ³Tell this rebellious house a parable and say to them: 'This is what the Sovereign LORD says:

" 'Put on the cooking pot; put it on
and pour water into it.
⁴Put into it the pieces of meat,
all the choice pieces—the leg and the shoulder.
Fill it with the best of these bones;
⁵   take the pick of the flock.
Pile wood beneath it for the bones;
bring it to a boil
and cook the bones in it.

⁶" 'For this is what the Sovereign LORD says:

" 'Woe to the city of bloodshed,
to the pot now encrusted,
whose deposit will not go away!

^a 37 Or even made the children they bore to me pass through the fire   ^b 42 Or drunkards

Empty it piece by piece
without casting lots for them.

[7] " 'For the blood she shed is in her midst:
She poured it on the bare rock;
she did not pour it on the ground,
where the dust would cover it.
[8] To stir up wrath and take revenge
I put her blood on the bare rock,
so that it would not be covered.

[9] " 'Therefore this is what the Sovereign LORD says:

" 'Woe to the city of bloodshed!
I, too, will pile the wood high.
[10] So heap on the wood
and kindle the fire.
Cook the meat well,
mixing in the spices;
and let the bones be charred.
[11] Then set the empty pot on the coals
till it becomes hot and its copper glows
so its impurities may be melted
and its deposit burned away.
[12] It has frustrated all efforts;
its heavy deposit has not been removed,
not even by fire.

[13] " 'Now your impurity is lewdness. Because I tried to cleanse you but you would not be cleansed from your impurity, you will not be clean again until my wrath against you has subsided.

[14] " 'I the LORD have spoken. The time has come for me to act. I will not hold back; I will not have pity, nor will I relent. You will be judged according to your conduct and your actions, declares the Sovereign LORD.' "

Ezekiel's Wife Dies

[15] The word of the LORD came to me: [16] "Son of man, with one blow I am about to take away from you the delight of your eyes. Yet do not lament or weep or shed any tears. [17] Groan quietly; do not mourn for the dead. Keep your turban fastened and your sandals on your feet; do not cover the lower part of your face or eat the customary food [of mourners]."

[18] So I spoke to the people in the morning, and in the evening my wife died. The next morning I did as I had been commanded.

[19] Then the people asked me, "Won't you tell us what these things have to do with us?"

[20] So I said to them, "The word of the LORD came to me: [21] Say to the house of Israel, 'This is what the Sovereign LORD says: I am about to desecrate my sanctuary—the

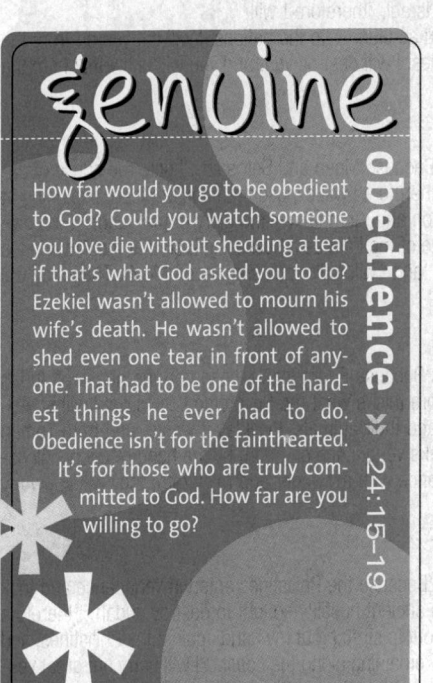

ğenuine

obedience » 24:15-19

How far would you go to be obedient to God? Could you watch someone you love die without shedding a tear if that's what God asked you to do? Ezekiel wasn't allowed to mourn his wife's death. He wasn't allowed to shed even one tear in front of anyone. That had to be one of the hardest things he ever had to do. Obedience isn't for the fainthearted. It's for those who are truly committed to God. How far are you willing to go?

stronghold in which you take pride, the delight of your eyes, the object of your affection. The sons and daughters you left behind will fall by the sword. ²²And you will do as I have done. You will not cover the lower part of your face or eat the customary food ˻of mourners˼. ²³You will keep your turbans on your heads and your sandals on your feet. You will not mourn or weep but will waste away because of ᵃ your sins and groan among yourselves. ²⁴Ezekiel will be a sign to you; you will do just as he has done. When this happens, you will know that I am the Sovereign LORD.'

²⁵"And you, son of man, on the day I take away their stronghold, their joy and glory, the delight of their eyes, their heart's desire, and their sons and daughters as well— ²⁶on that day a fugitive will come to tell you the news. ²⁷At that time your mouth will be opened; you will speak with him and will no longer be silent. So you will be a sign to them, and they will know that I am the LORD."

A Prophecy Against Ammon

25 The word of the LORD came to me: ²"Son of man, set your face against the Ammonites and prophesy against them. ³Say to them, 'Hear the word of the Sovereign LORD. This is what the Sovereign LORD says: Because you said "Aha!" over my sanctuary when it was desecrated and over the land of Israel when it was laid waste and over the people of Judah when they went into exile, ⁴therefore I am going to give you to the people of the East as a possession. They will set up their camps and pitch their tents among you; they will eat your fruit and drink your milk. ⁵I will turn Rabbah into a pasture for camels and Ammon into a resting place for sheep. Then you will know that I am the LORD. ⁶For this is what the Sovereign LORD says: Because you have clapped your hands and stamped your feet, rejoicing with all the malice of your heart against the land of Israel, ⁷therefore I will stretch out my hand against you and give you as plunder to the nations. I will cut you off from the nations and exterminate you from the countries. I will destroy you, and you will know that I am the LORD.' "

truth or dare

Four historical nations. All had sinned against God. All were completely wiped out forever, just as God said. He's true to his word.

25:1-17

A Prophecy Against Moab

⁸"This is what the Sovereign LORD says: 'Because Moab and Seir said, "Look, the house of Judah has become like all the other nations," ⁹therefore I will expose the flank of Moab, beginning at its frontier towns—Beth Jeshimoth, Baal Meon and Kiriathaim—the glory of that land. ¹⁰I will give Moab along with the Ammonites to the people of the East as a possession, so that the Ammonites will not be remembered among the nations; ¹¹and I will inflict punishment on Moab. Then they will know that I am the LORD.' "

A Prophecy Against Edom

¹²"This is what the Sovereign LORD says: 'Because Edom took revenge on the house of Judah and became very guilty by doing so, ¹³therefore this is what the Sovereign LORD says: I will stretch out my hand against Edom and kill its men and their animals. I will lay it waste, and from Teman to Dedan they will fall by the sword. ¹⁴I will take vengeance on Edom by the hand of my people Israel, and they will deal with Edom in accordance with my anger and my wrath; they will know my vengeance, declares the Sovereign LORD.' "

A Prophecy Against Philistia

¹⁵"This is what the Sovereign LORD says: 'Because the Philistines acted in vengeance and took revenge with malice in their hearts, and with ancient hostility sought to destroy Judah, ¹⁶therefore this is what the Sovereign LORD says: I am about to stretch out my hand against the Philistines, and I will cut off the Kerethites and destroy those remaining along the coast. ¹⁷I will carry out great ven-

ᵃ 23 Or away in

geance on them and punish them in my wrath. Then they will know that I am the LORD, when I take vengeance on them.' "

A Prophecy Against Tyre

26 In the eleventh year, on the first day of the month, the word of the LORD came to me: [2]"Son of man, because Tyre has said of Jerusalem, 'Aha! The gate to the nations is broken, and its doors have swung open to me; now that she lies in ruins I will prosper,' [3]therefore this is what the Sovereign LORD says: I am against you, O Tyre, and I will bring many nations against you, like the sea casting up its waves. [4]They will destroy the walls of Tyre and pull down her towers; I will scrape away her rubble and make her a bare rock. [5]Out in the sea she will become a place to spread fishnets, for I have spoken, declares the Sovereign LORD. She will become plunder for the nations, [6]and her settlements on the mainland will be ravaged by the sword. Then they will know that I am the LORD.

[7]"For this is what the Sovereign LORD says: From the north I am going to bring against Tyre Nebuchadnezzar[a] king of Babylon, king of kings, with horses and chariots, with horsemen and a great army. [8]He will ravage your settlements on the mainland with the sword; he will set up siege works against you, build a ramp up to your walls and raise his shields against you. [9]He will direct the blows of his battering rams against your walls and demolish your towers with his weapons. [10]His horses will be so many that they will cover you with dust. Your walls will tremble at the noise of the war horses, wagons and chariots when he enters your gates as men enter a city whose walls have been broken through. [11]The hoofs of his horses will trample all your streets; he will kill your people with the sword, and your strong pillars will fall to the ground. [12]They will plunder your wealth and loot your merchandise; they will break down your walls and demolish your fine houses and throw your stones, timber and rubble into the sea. [13]I will put an end to your noisy songs, and the music of your harps will be heard no more. [14]I will make you a bare rock, and you will become a place to spread fishnets. You will never be rebuilt, for I the LORD have spoken, declares the Sovereign LORD.

[15]"This is what the Sovereign LORD says to Tyre: Will not the coastlands tremble at the sound of your fall, when the wounded groan and the slaughter takes place in you? [16]Then all the princes of the coast will step down from their thrones and lay aside their robes and take off their embroidered garments. Clothed with terror, they will sit on the ground, trembling every moment, appalled at you. [17]Then they will take up a lament concerning you and say to you:

> " 'How you are destroyed, O city
>   of renown,
>   peopled by men of the sea!
> You were a power on the seas,
>   you and your citizens;
> you put your terror
>   on all who lived there.
> [18]Now the coastlands tremble
>   on the day of your fall;
> the islands in the sea
>   are terrified at your collapse.'

truth or dare

God wasn't shooting in the dark when he prophesied about the city of Tyre. The city fell exactly as God said it would and was never rebuilt.

26:7–14

[19]"This is what the Sovereign LORD says: When I make you a desolate city, like cities no longer inhabited, and when I bring the ocean depths over you and its vast waters cover you, [20]then I will bring you down with those who go down to the pit, to the people of long ago. I will make you dwell in the earth below, as in ancient ruins, with those who go down to the pit, and you will not return or take your place[b] in the land of the living. [21]I will bring you to a horrible end and you will be no more. You will be sought, but you will never again be found, declares the Sovereign LORD."

---

[a] 7 Hebrew *Nebuchadrezzar*, of which *Nebuchadnezzar* is a variant; here and often in Ezekiel and Jeremiah
[b] 20 Septuagint; Hebrew *return, and I will give glory*

27

The word of the LORD came to me: ²"Son of man, take up a lament concerning Tyre. ³Say to Tyre, situated at the gateway to the sea, merchant of peoples on many coasts, 'This is what the Sovereign LORD says:

" 'You say, O Tyre,
    "I am perfect in beauty."
⁴Your domain was on the high seas;
    your builders brought your beauty to perfection.
⁵They made all your timbers
    of pine trees from Senir ᵃ;
they took a cedar from Lebanon
    to make a mast for you.
⁶Of oaks from Bashan
    they made your oars;
of cypress wood ᵇ from the coasts of Cyprus ᶜ
    they made your deck, inlaid with ivory.
⁷Fine embroidered linen from Egypt was your sail
    and served as your banner;
your awnings were of blue and purple
    from the coasts of Elishah.
⁸Men of Sidon and Arvad were your oarsmen;
    your skilled men, O Tyre, were aboard as your seamen.
⁹Veteran craftsmen of Gebal ᵈ were on board
    as shipwrights to caulk your seams.
All the ships of the sea and their sailors
    came alongside to trade for your wares.

¹⁰ " 'Men of Persia, Lydia and Put
    served as soldiers in your army.
They hung their shields and helmets on your walls,
    bringing you splendor.
¹¹Men of Arvad and Helech
    manned your walls on every side;
men of Gammad
    were in your towers.
They hung their shields around your walls;
    they brought your beauty to perfection.

¹²" 'Tarshish did business with you because of your great wealth of goods; they exchanged silver, iron, tin and lead for your merchandise.

¹³" 'Greece, Tubal and Meshech traded with you; they exchanged slaves and articles of bronze for your wares.

¹⁴" 'Men of Beth Togarmah exchanged work horses, war horses and mules for your merchandise.

¹⁵" 'The men of Rhodes ᵉ traded with you, and many coastlands were your customers; they paid you with ivory tusks and ebony.

¹⁶" 'Aram ᶠ did business with you because of your many products; they exchanged turquoise, purple fabric, embroidered work, fine linen, coral and rubies for your merchandise.

¹⁷" 'Judah and Israel traded with you; they exchanged wheat from Minnith and confections, ᵍ honey, oil and balm for your wares.

¹⁸" 'Damascus, because of your many products and great wealth of goods, did business with you in wine from Helbon and wool from Zahar.

¹⁹" 'Danites and Greeks from Uzal bought your merchandise; they exchanged wrought iron, cassia and calamus for your wares.

ᵃ 5 That is, Hermon   ᵇ 6 Targum; the Masoretic Text has a different division of the consonants.   ᶜ 6 Hebrew Kittim
ᵈ 9 That is, Byblos   ᵉ 15 Septuagint; Hebrew Dedan   ᶠ 16 Most Hebrew manuscripts; some Hebrew manuscripts and Syriac Edom   ᵍ 17 The meaning of the Hebrew for this word is uncertain.

20 " 'Dedan traded in saddle blankets with you.

21 " 'Arabia and all the princes of Kedar were your customers; they did business with you in lambs, rams and goats.

22 " 'The merchants of Sheba and Raamah traded with you; for your merchandise they exchanged the finest of all kinds of spices and precious stones, and gold.

23 " 'Haran, Canneh and Eden and merchants of Sheba, Asshur and Kilmad traded with you. 24In your marketplace they traded with you beautiful garments, blue fabric, embroidered work and multicolored rugs with cords twisted and tightly knotted.

> 25 " 'The ships of Tarshish serve
>   as carriers for your wares.
> You are filled with heavy cargo
>   in the heart of the sea.
> 26 Your oarsmen take you
>   out to the high seas.
> But the east wind will break you to pieces
>   in the heart of the sea.
> 27 Your wealth, merchandise and wares,
>   your mariners, seamen and shipwrights,
> your merchants and all your soldiers,
>   and everyone else on board
> will sink into the heart of the sea
>   on the day of your shipwreck.
> 28 The shorelands will quake
>   when your seamen cry out.
> 29 All who handle the oars
>   will abandon their ships;
> the mariners and all the seamen
>   will stand on the shore.
> 30 They will raise their voice
>   and cry bitterly over you;
> they will sprinkle dust on their heads
>   and roll in ashes.
> 31 They will shave their heads because of you
>   and will put on sackcloth.
> They will weep over you with anguish of soul
>   and with bitter mourning.
> 32 As they wail and mourn over you,
>   they will take up a lament concerning you:
> "Who was ever silenced like Tyre,
>   surrounded by the sea?"
> 33 When your merchandise went out on the seas,
>   you satisfied many nations;
> with your great wealth and your wares
>   you enriched the kings of the earth.
> 34 Now you are shattered by the sea
>   in the depths of the waters;
> your wares and all your company
>   have gone down with you.
> 35 All who live in the coastlands
>   are appalled at you;
> their kings shudder with horror
>   and their faces are distorted with fear.
> 36 The merchants among the nations hiss at you;
>   you have come to a horrible end
>   and will be no more.' "

A Prophecy Against the King of Tyre

28

The word of the LORD came to me: [2]"Son of man, say to the ruler of Tyre, 'This is what the Sovereign LORD says:

> " 'In the pride of your heart
>> you say, "I am a god;
> I sit on the throne of a god
>> in the heart of the seas."
> But you are a man and not a god,
>> though you think you are as wise as a god.
> [3] Are you wiser than Daniel[a]?
>> Is no secret hidden from you?
> [4] By your wisdom and understanding
>> you have gained wealth for yourself
> and amassed gold and silver
>> in your treasuries.
> [5] By your great skill in trading
>> you have increased your wealth,
> and because of your wealth
>> your heart has grown proud.

[6]" 'Therefore this is what the Sovereign LORD says:

> " 'Because you think you are wise,
>> as wise as a god,
> [7] I am going to bring foreigners against you,
>> the most ruthless of nations;
> they will draw their swords against your beauty and wisdom
>> and pierce your shining splendor.
> [8] They will bring you down to the pit,
>> and you will die a violent death
>> in the heart of the seas.
> [9] Will you then say, "I am a god,"
>> in the presence of those who kill you?
> You will be but a man, not a god,
>> in the hands of those who slay you.
> [10] You will die the death of the uncircumcised
>> at the hands of foreigners.

I have spoken, declares the Sovereign LORD.' "

[11] The word of the LORD came to me: [12]"Son of man, take up a lament concerning the king of Tyre and say to him: 'This is what the Sovereign LORD says:

> " 'You were the model of perfection,
>> full of wisdom and perfect in beauty.
> [13] You were in Eden,
>> the garden of God;
> every precious stone adorned you:
>> ruby, topaz and emerald,
>> chrysolite, onyx and jasper,
>> sapphire,[b] turquoise and beryl.[c]
> Your settings and mountings[d] were made of gold;
>> on the day you were created they were prepared.
> [14] You were anointed as a guardian cherub,

---

[a] 3 Or Danel; the Hebrew spelling may suggest a person other than the prophet Daniel.   [b] 13 Or lapis lazuli
[c] 13 The precise identification of some of these precious stones is uncertain.   [d] 13 The meaning of the Hebrew for this phrase is uncertain.

for so I ordained you.
You were on the holy mount of
God;
you walked among the fiery
stones.
¹⁵ You were blameless in your ways
from the day you were
created
till wickedness was found in
you.
¹⁶ Through your widespread trade
you were filled with violence,
and you sinned.
So I drove you in disgrace from
the mount of God,
and I expelled you, O guardian
cherub,
from among the fiery stones.
¹⁷ Your heart became proud
on account of your beauty,
and you corrupted your wisdom
because of your splendor.
So I threw you to the earth;
I made a spectacle of you
before kings.
¹⁸ By your many sins and dishonest
trade
you have desecrated your sanctuaries.
So I made a fire come out from you,
and it consumed you,
and I reduced you to ashes on the ground
in the sight of all who were watching.
¹⁹ All the nations who knew you
are appalled at you;
you have come to a horrible end
and will be no more.' "

A Prophecy Against Sidon

²⁰ The word of the LORD came to me: ²¹ "Son of man, set your face against Sidon; prophesy against her ²² and say: 'This is what the Sovereign LORD says:

" 'I am against you, O Sidon,
and I will gain glory within you.
They will know that I am the LORD,
when I inflict punishment on her
and show myself holy within her.
²³ I will send a plague upon her
and make blood flow in her streets.
The slain will fall within her,
with the sword against her on every side.
Then they will know that I am the LORD.

²⁴ " 'No longer will the people of Israel have malicious neighbors who are painful briers and sharp thorns. Then they will know that I am the Sovereign LORD.

²⁵ " 'This is what the Sovereign LORD says: When I gather the people of Israel from the nations where they have been scattered, I will show myself holy among them in the sight of the nations. Then they will live in their own land, which I gave to my servant Jacob. ²⁶ They will live there in safe-

ty and will build houses and plant vineyards; they will live in safety when I inflict punishment on all their neighbors who maligned them. Then they will know that I am the LORD their God.' "

A Prophecy Against Egypt

29 In the tenth year, in the tenth month on the twelfth day, the word of the LORD came to me: [2]"Son of man, set your face against Pharaoh king of Egypt and prophesy against him and against all Egypt. [3]Speak to him and say: 'This is what the Sovereign LORD says:

" 'I am against you, Pharaoh king of Egypt,
    you great monster lying among your streams.
You say, "The Nile is mine;
    I made it for myself."
[4]But I will put hooks in your jaws
    and make the fish of your streams stick to your scales.
I will pull you out from among your streams,
    with all the fish sticking to your scales.
[5]I will leave you in the desert,
    you and all the fish of your streams.
You will fall on the open field
    and not be gathered or picked up.
I will give you as food
    to the beasts of the earth and the birds of the air.

[6]Then all who live in Egypt will know that I am the LORD.

" 'You have been a staff of reed for the house of Israel. [7]When they grasped you with their hands, you splintered and you tore open their shoulders; when they leaned on you, you broke and their backs were wrenched.[a]

[8]" 'Therefore this is what the Sovereign LORD says: I will bring a sword against you and kill your men and their animals. [9]Egypt will become a desolate wasteland. Then they will know that I am the LORD.

" 'Because you said, "The Nile is mine; I made it," [10]therefore I am against you and against your streams, and I will make the land of Egypt a ruin and a desolate waste from Migdol to Aswan, as far as the border of Cush.[b] [11]No foot of man or animal will pass through it; no one will live there for forty years. [12]I will make the land of Egypt desolate among devastated lands, and her cities will lie desolate forty years among ruined cities. And I will disperse the Egyptians among the nations and scatter them through the countries.

[13]" 'Yet this is what the Sovereign LORD says: At the end of forty years I will gather the Egyptians from the nations where they were scattered. [14]I will bring them back from captivity and return them to Upper Egypt,[c] the land of their ancestry. There they will be a lowly kingdom. [15]It will be the lowliest of kingdoms and will never again exalt itself above the other nations. I will make it so weak that it will never again rule over the nations. [16]Egypt will no longer be a source of confidence for the people of Israel but will be a reminder of their sin in turning to her for help. Then they will know that I am the Sovereign LORD.' "

[17]In the twenty-seventh year, in the first month on the first day, the word of the LORD came to me: [18]"Son of man, Nebuchadnezzar king of Babylon drove his army in a hard campaign against Tyre; every head was rubbed bare and every shoulder made raw. Yet he and his army got no reward from the campaign he led against Tyre. [19]Therefore this is what the Sovereign LORD says: I am going to give Egypt to Nebuchadnezzar king of Babylon, and he will carry off its wealth. He will loot and plunder the land as pay for his army. [20]I have given him Egypt as a reward for his efforts because he and his army did it for me, declares the Sovereign LORD.

[21]"On that day I will make a horn[d] grow for the house of Israel, and I will open your mouth among them. Then they will know that I am the LORD."

[a] 7 Syriac (see also Septuagint and Vulgate); Hebrew *and you caused their backs to stand*   [b] 10 That is, the upper Nile region   [c] 14 Hebrew *to Pathros*   [d] 21 *Horn* here symbolizes strength.

A Lament for Egypt

30 The word of the LORD came to me: ²"Son of man, prophesy and say: 'This is what the Sovereign LORD says:

> " 'Wail and say,
>> "Alas for that day!"
> ³For the day is near,
>> the day of the LORD is near—
> a day of clouds,
>> a time of doom for the nations.
> ⁴A sword will come against Egypt,
>> and anguish will come upon Cush.ᵃ
> When the slain fall in Egypt,
>> her wealth will be carried away
>> and her foundations torn down.

⁵Cush and Put, Lydia and all Arabia, Libyaᵇ and the people of the covenant land will fall by the sword along with Egypt.

⁶" 'This is what the LORD says:

> " 'The allies of Egypt will fall
>> and her proud strength will fail.
> From Migdol to Aswan
>> they will fall by the sword within her,
>>> declares the Sovereign LORD.

> ⁷" 'They will be desolate
>> among desolate lands,
> and their cities will lie
>> among ruined cities.
> ⁸Then they will know that I am the LORD,
>> when I set fire to Egypt
>> and all her helpers are crushed.

⁹" 'On that day messengers will go out from me in ships to frighten Cush out of her complacency. Anguish will take hold of them on the day of Egypt's doom, for it is sure to come.

¹⁰" 'This is what the Sovereign LORD says:

> " 'I will put an end to the hordes of Egypt
>> by the hand of Nebuchadnezzar king of Babylon.
> ¹¹He and his army—the most ruthless of nations—
>> will be brought in to destroy the land.
> They will draw their swords against Egypt
>> and fill the land with the slain.
> ¹²I will dry up the streams of the Nile
>> and sell the land to evil men;
> by the hand of foreigners
>> I will lay waste the land and everything in it.

I the LORD have spoken.

¹³" 'This is what the Sovereign LORD says:

> " 'I will destroy the idols
>> and put an end to the images in Memphis.ᶜ
> No longer will there be a prince in Egypt,
>> and I will spread fear throughout the land.

ᵃ *4* That is, the upper Nile region; also in verses 5 and 9   ᵇ *5* Hebrew *Cub*   ᶜ *13* Hebrew *Noph*; also in verse 16

A Silent Cry

Profile: Daray

I cut myself sometimes. I don't know why exactly. I can't help it. When I feel sad or overwhelmed or something, I just take a razor and do it. I don't really think about it. Sometimes I don't even realize what I've done till I look down and see blood on my arm.

Jeff just dumped me. I really loved him. I don't know why people think that someone 15 can't love someone else deeply. I went into the bathroom today and started thinking about Jeff and wondering why he doesn't still love me even after I gave myself totally to him. Next thing I knew, I had done it. Cut myself, I mean.

My mom didn't even ask me why I have a bandage on my arm. Both of my parents are so clueless. Sometimes I just want to scream, "Look at me! Look at what I've done!" But I don't think they'd care. They're so wrapped up in their own lives. Mom's too busy working. Dad's got a new girlfriend—a different one from the one he had when Mom filed for a divorce. (I live with my mom.)

My friend Rain saw the cuts on my arm and asked me about them. (I'm still amazed that she did. I had on a long-sleeved shirt.) She goes to my church, and I wondered if I should tell her that I'm always worried. I don't know if she'd understand. I just don't know what to do.

self-injury in focus

Millions of teens practice some form of self-injury (cutting, burning, etc.). If you or someone you know engages in self-injury . . .

»Know that some self-injury is in response to intense feelings of anger, sadness, self-hatred or helplessness. It is a silent but serious cry for help. Many people who cut themselves have trouble expressing their pain in other ways. This pain is very real, but there are better ways to express it.

»Encourage your friend to talk with a professional. If you injure yourself, seek out a school counselor, pastor, or Christian counselor.

»Don't expect your friend to "snap out of it" quickly and stop doing this to herself. This behavior is a symptom of a deeper emotional need that takes time to heal. And sometimes, once a person starts using self-injury to cope, it ends up being the only way to cope, and the person becomes addicted.

»You can start the healing process by praying for her (see James 5:16, page 1606).

For more on this topic, see the index on page 1656.

[14] I will lay waste Upper Egypt, [a]
  set fire to Zoan
  and inflict punishment on Thebes. [b]
[15] I will pour out my wrath on Pelusium, [c]
  the stronghold of Egypt,
  and cut off the hordes of Thebes.
[16] I will set fire to Egypt;
  Pelusium will writhe in agony.

[a] 14 Hebrew *waste Pathros*   [b] 14 Hebrew *No*; also in verses 15 and 16   [c] 15 Hebrew *Sin*; also in verse 16

Thebes will be taken by storm;
    Memphis will be in constant distress.
¹⁷The young men of Heliopolis*ᵃ* and Bubastis*ᵇ*
    will fall by the sword,
    and the cities themselves will go into captivity.
¹⁸Dark will be the day at Tahpanhes
    when I break the yoke of Egypt;
    there her proud strength will come to an end.
She will be covered with clouds,
    and her villages will go into captivity.
¹⁹So I will inflict punishment on Egypt,
    and they will know that I am the Lord.' "

²⁰In the eleventh year, in the first month on the seventh day, the word of the Lord came to me: ²¹"Son of man, I have broken the arm of Pharaoh king of Egypt. It has not been bound up for healing or put in a splint so as to become strong enough to hold a sword. ²²Therefore this is what the Sovereign Lord says: I am against Pharaoh king of Egypt. I will break both his arms, the good arm as well as the broken one, and make the sword fall from his hand. ²³I will disperse the Egyptians among the nations and scatter them through the countries. ²⁴I will strengthen the arms of the king of Babylon and put my sword in his hand, but I will break the arms of Pharaoh, and he will groan before him like a mortally wounded man. ²⁵I will strengthen the arms of the king of Babylon, but the arms of Pharaoh will fall limp. Then they will know that I am the Lord, when I put my sword into the hand of the king of Babylon and he brandishes it against Egypt. ²⁶I will disperse the Egyptians among the nations and scatter them through the countries. Then they will know that I am the Lord."

A Cedar in Lebanon

31 In the eleventh year, in the third month on the first day, the word of the Lord came to me: ²"Son of man, say to Pharaoh king of Egypt and to his hordes:

" 'Who can be compared with you in majesty?
³Consider Assyria, once a cedar in Lebanon,
    with beautiful branches overshadowing the forest;
it towered on high,
    its top above the thick foliage.
⁴The waters nourished it,
    deep springs made it grow tall;
their streams flowed
    all around its base
and sent their channels
    to all the trees of the field.
⁵So it towered higher
    than all the trees of the field;
its boughs increased
    and its branches grew long,
    spreading because of abundant waters.
⁶All the birds of the air
    nested in its boughs,
all the beasts of the field
    gave birth under its branches;
all the great nations
    lived in its shade.
⁷It was majestic in beauty,
    with its spreading boughs,
for its roots went down
    to abundant waters.

ᵃ 17 Hebrew *Awen* (or *On*)   *ᵇ* 17 Hebrew *Pi Beseth*

> [8] The cedars in the garden of God
> could not rival it,
> nor could the pine trees
> equal its boughs,
> nor could the plane trees
> compare with its branches—
> no tree in the garden of God
> could match its beauty.
> [9] I made it beautiful
> with abundant branches,
> the envy of all the trees of Eden
> in the garden of God.

[10] " 'Therefore this is what the Sovereign Lord says: Because it towered on high, lifting its top above the thick foliage, and because it was proud of its height, [11] I handed it over to the ruler of the nations, for him to deal with according to its wickedness. I cast it aside, [12] and the most ruthless of foreign nations cut it down and left it. Its boughs fell on the mountains and in all the valleys; its branches lay broken in all the ravines of the land. All the nations of the earth came out from under its shade and left it. [13] All the birds of the air settled on the fallen tree, and all the beasts of the field were among its branches. [14] Therefore no other trees by the waters are ever to tower proudly on high, lifting their tops above the thick foliage. No other trees so well-watered are ever to reach such a height; they are all destined for death, for the earth below, among mortal men, with those who go down to the pit.

[15] " 'This is what the Sovereign Lord says: On the day it was brought down to the grave[a] I covered the deep springs with mourning for it; I held back its streams, and its abundant waters were restrained. Because of it I clothed Lebanon with gloom, and all the trees of the field withered away. [16] I made the nations tremble at the sound of its fall when I brought it down to the grave with those who go down to the pit. Then all the trees of Eden, the choicest and best of Lebanon, all the trees that were well-watered, were consoled in the earth below. [17] Those who lived in its shade, its allies among the nations, had also gone down to the grave with it, joining those killed by the sword.

[18] " 'Which of the trees of Eden can be compared with you in splendor and majesty? Yet you, too, will be brought down with the trees of Eden to the earth below; you will lie among the uncircumcised, with those killed by the sword.

" 'This is Pharaoh and all his hordes, declares the Sovereign Lord.' "

A Lament for Pharaoh

32 In the twelfth year, in the twelfth month on the first day, the word of the Lord came to me: [2] "Son of man, take up a lament concerning Pharaoh king of Egypt and say to him:

> " 'You are like a lion among the nations;
> you are like a monster in the seas
> thrashing about in your streams,
> churning the water with your feet
> and muddying the streams.

[3] " 'This is what the Sovereign Lord says:

> " 'With a great throng of people
> I will cast my net over you,
> and they will haul you up in my net.
> [4] I will throw you on the land
> and hurl you on the open field.
> I will let all the birds of the air settle on you
> and all the beasts of the earth gorge themselves on you.
> [5] I will spread your flesh on the mountains
> and fill the valleys with your remains.

a 15 Hebrew Sheol; also in verses 16 and 17

⁶I will drench the land with your flowing blood
    all the way to the mountains,
    and the ravines will be filled with your flesh.
⁷When I snuff you out, I will cover the heavens
    and darken their stars;
I will cover the sun with a cloud,
    and the moon will not give its light.
⁸All the shining lights in the heavens
    I will darken over you;
I will bring darkness over your land,
                 declares the Sovereign LORD.
⁹I will trouble the hearts of many peoples
    when I bring about your destruction among the nations,
    among^a lands you have not known.
¹⁰I will cause many peoples to be appalled at you,
    and their kings will shudder with horror because of you
    when I brandish my sword before them.
On the day of your downfall
    each of them will tremble
    every moment for his life.

¹¹" 'For this is what the Sovereign LORD says:

" 'The sword of the king of Babylon
    will come against you.
¹²I will cause your hordes to fall
    by the swords of mighty men—
    the most ruthless of all nations.
They will shatter the pride of Egypt,
    and all her hordes will be overthrown.
¹³I will destroy all her cattle
    from beside abundant waters
no longer to be stirred by the foot of man
    or muddied by the hoofs of cattle.
¹⁴Then I will let her waters settle
    and make her streams flow like oil,
                 declares the Sovereign LORD.
¹⁵When I make Egypt desolate
    and strip the land of everything in it,
when I strike down all who live there,
    then they will know that I am the LORD.'

¹⁶"This is the lament they will chant for her. The daughters of the nations will chant it; for Egypt and all her hordes they will chant it, declares the Sovereign LORD."

¹⁷In the twelfth year, on the fifteenth day of the month, the word of the LORD came to me: ¹⁸"Son of man, wail for the hordes of Egypt and consign to the earth below both her and the daughters of mighty nations, with those who go down to the pit. ¹⁹Say to them, 'Are you more favored than others? Go down and be laid among the uncircumcised.' ²⁰They will fall among those killed by the sword. The sword is drawn; let her be dragged off with all her hordes. ²¹From within the grave^b the mighty leaders will say of Egypt and her allies, 'They have come down and they lie with the uncircumcised, with those killed by the sword.'

²²"Assyria is there with her whole army; she is surrounded by the graves of all her slain, all who have fallen by the sword. ²³Their graves are in the depths of the pit and her army lies around her grave. All who had spread terror in the land of the living are slain, fallen by the sword.

²⁴"Elam is there, with all her hordes around her grave. All of them are slain, fallen by the sword.

^a 9 Hebrew; Septuagint *bring you into captivity among the nations,* / *to*   ^b 21 Hebrew *Sheol;* also in verse 27

All who had spread terror in the land of the living went down uncircumcised to the earth below. They bear their shame with those who go down to the pit. ²⁵A bed is made for her among the slain, with all her hordes around her grave. All of them are uncircumcised, killed by the sword. Because their terror had spread in the land of the living, they bear their shame with those who go down to the pit; they are laid among the slain.

²⁶"Meshech and Tubal are there, with all their hordes around their graves. All of them are uncircumcised, killed by the sword because they spread their terror in the land of the living. ²⁷Do they not lie with the other uncircumcised warriors who have fallen, who went down to the grave with their weapons of war, whose swords were placed under their heads? The punishment for their sins rested on their bones, though the terror of these warriors had stalked through the land of the living.

²⁸"You too, O Pharaoh, will be broken and will lie among the uncircumcised, with those killed by the sword.

²⁹"Edom is there, her kings and all her princes; despite their power, they are laid with those killed by the sword. They lie with the uncircumcised, with those who go down to the pit.

³⁰"All the princes of the north and all the Sidonians are there; they went down with the slain in disgrace despite the terror caused by their power. They lie uncircumcised with those killed by the sword and bear their shame with those who go down to the pit.

³¹"Pharaoh—he and all his army—will see them and he will be consoled for all his hordes that were killed by the sword, declares the Sovereign LORD. ³²Although I had him spread terror in the land of the living, Pharaoh and all his hordes will be laid among the uncircumcised, with those killed by the sword, declares the Sovereign LORD."

Ezekiel a Watchman

33 The word of the LORD came to me: ²"Son of man, speak to your countrymen and say to them: 'When I bring the sword against a land, and the people of the land choose one of their men and make him their watchman, ³and he sees the sword coming against the land and blows the trumpet to warn the people, ⁴then if anyone hears the trumpet but does not take warning and the sword comes and takes his life, his blood will be on his own head. ⁵Since he heard the sound of the trumpet but did not take warning, his blood will be on his own head. If he had taken warning, he would have saved himself. ⁶But if the watchman sees the sword coming and does not blow the trumpet to warn the people and the sword comes and takes the life of one of them, that man will be taken away because of his sin, but I will hold the watchman accountable for his blood.'

⁷"Son of man, I have made you a watchman for the house of Israel; so hear the word I speak and give them warning from me. ⁸When I say to the wicked, 'O wicked man, you will surely die,' and you do not speak out to dissuade him from his ways, that wicked man will die forᵃ his sin, and I will hold you accountable for his blood. ⁹But if you do warn the wicked man to turn from his ways and he does not do so, he will die for his sin, but you will have saved yourself.

¹⁰"Son of man, say to the house of Israel, 'This is what you are saying: "Our offenses and sins weigh us down, and we are wasting away because ofᵇ them. How then can we live?" ' ¹¹Say to them, 'As surely as I live, declares the Sovereign LORD, I take no pleasure in the death of the wicked, but rather that they turn from their ways and live. Turn! Turn from your evil ways! Why will you die, O house of Israel?'

¹²"Therefore, son of man, say to your countrymen, 'The righteousness of the righteous man will not save him when he disobeys, and the wickedness of the wicked man will not cause him to fall when he turns from it. The righteous man, if he sins, will not be allowed to live because of his former righteousness.' ¹³If I tell the righteous man that he will surely live, but then he trusts in his righ-

truth or dare

Fill in your name:

_____,

the watchman (or watch-girl, if you prefer). *You* have a responsibility to warn others against sin. You can't control their response, but you're responsible to speak up.

33:1–9

ᵃ 8 Or *in*; also in verse 9   ᵇ 10 Or *away in*

teousness and does evil, none of the righteous things he has done will be remembered; he will die for the evil he has done. [14]And if I say to the wicked man, 'You will surely die,' but he then turns away from his sin and does what is just and right— [15]if he gives back what he took in pledge for a loan, returns what he has stolen, follows the decrees that give life, and does no evil, he will surely live; he will not die. [16]None of the sins he has committed will be remembered against him. He has done what is just and right; he will surely live.

[17]"Yet your countrymen say, 'The way of the Lord is not just.' But it is their way that is not just. [18]If a righteous man turns from his righteousness and does evil, he will die for it. [19]And if a wicked man turns away from his wickedness and does what is just and right, he will live by doing so. [20]Yet, O house of Israel, you say, 'The way of the Lord is not just.' But I will judge each of you according to his own ways."

Jerusalem's Fall Explained

[21]In the twelfth year of our exile, in the tenth month on the fifth day, a man who had escaped from Jerusalem came to me and said, "The city has fallen!" [22]Now the evening before the man arrived, the hand of the LORD was upon me, and he opened my mouth before the man came to me in the morning. So my mouth was opened and I was no longer silent.

[23]Then the word of the LORD came to me: [24]"Son of man, the people living in those ruins in the land of Israel are saying, 'Abraham was only one man, yet he possessed the land. But we are many; surely the land has been given to us as our possession.' [25]Therefore say to them, 'This is what the Sovereign LORD says: Since you eat meat with the blood still in it and look to your idols and shed blood, should you then possess the land? [26]You rely on your sword, you do detestable things, and each of you defiles his neighbor's wife. Should you then possess the land?'

[27]"Say this to them: 'This is what the Sovereign LORD says: As surely as I live, those who are left in the ruins will fall by the sword, those out in the country I will give to the wild animals to be devoured, and those in strongholds and caves will die of a plague. [28]I will make the land a desolate waste, and her proud strength will come to an end, and the mountains of Israel will become desolate so that no one will cross them. [29]Then they will know that I am the LORD, when I have made the land a desolate waste because of all the detestable things they have done.'

[30]"As for you, son of man, your countrymen are talking together about you by the walls and at the doors of the houses, saying to each other, 'Come and hear the message that has come from the LORD.' [31]My people come to you, as they usually do, and sit before you to listen to your words, but they do not put them into practice. With their mouths they express devotion, but their hearts are greedy for unjust gain. [32]Indeed, to them you are nothing more than one who sings love songs with a beautiful voice and plays an instrument well, for they hear your words but do not put them into practice.

[33]"When all this comes true—and it surely will—then they will know that a prophet has been among them."

Shepherds and Sheep

34 The word of the LORD came to me: [2]"Son of man, prophesy against the shepherds of Israel; prophesy and say to them: 'This is what the Sovereign LORD says: Woe to the shepherds of Israel who only take care of themselves! Should not shepherds take care of the flock? [3]You eat the curds, clothe yourselves with the wool and slaughter the choice animals, but you do not take care of the flock. [4]You have not strengthened the weak or healed the sick or bound up the injured. You have not brought back the strays or searched for the lost. You have ruled them harshly and brutally. [5]So they were scattered because there was no shepherd, and when they were scattered they became food for all the wild animals. [6]My sheep wandered over all the mountains and on every high hill. They were scattered over the whole earth, and no one searched or looked for them.

[7]" 'Therefore, you shepherds, hear the word of the LORD: [8]As surely as I live, declares the Sovereign LORD, because my flock lacks a shepherd and so has been plundered and has become food for all the wild animals, and because my shepherds did not search for my flock but cared for themselves rather than for my flock, [9]therefore, O shepherds, hear the word of the LORD: [10]This is what the Sovereign LORD says: I am against the shepherds and will hold them accountable for my flock. I will remove them from tending the flock so that the shepherds can no longer feed themselves. I will rescue my flock from their mouths, and it will no longer be food for them.

11" 'For this is what the Sovereign LORD says: I myself will search for my sheep and look after them. 12As a shepherd looks after his scattered flock when he is with them, so will I look after my sheep. I will rescue them from all the places where they were scattered on a day of clouds and darkness. 13I will bring them out from the nations and gather them from the countries, and I will bring them into their own land. I will pasture them on the mountains of Israel, in the ravines and in all the settlements in the land. 14I will tend them in a good pasture, and the mountain heights of Israel will be their grazing land. There they will lie down in good grazing land, and there they will feed in a rich pasture on the mountains of Israel. 15I myself will tend my sheep and have them lie down, declares the Sovereign LORD. 16I will search for the lost and bring back the strays. I will bind up the injured and strengthen the weak, but the sleek and the strong I will destroy. I will shepherd the flock with justice.

17" 'As for you, my flock, this is what the Sovereign LORD says: I will judge between one sheep and another, and between rams and goats. 18Is it not enough for you to feed on the good pasture? Must you also trample the rest of your pasture with your feet? Is it not enough for you to drink clear water? Must you also muddy the rest with your feet? 19Must my flock feed on what you have trampled and drink what you have muddied with your feet?

20" 'Therefore this is what the Sovereign LORD says to them: See, I myself will judge between the fat sheep and the lean sheep. 21Because you shove with flank and shoulder, butting all the weak sheep with your horns until you have driven them away, 22I will save my flock, and they will no longer be plundered. I will judge between one sheep and another. 23I will place over them one shepherd, my servant David, and he will tend them; he will tend them and be their shepherd. 24I the LORD will be their God, and my servant David will be prince among them. I the LORD have spoken.

25" 'I will make a covenant of peace with them and rid the land of wild beasts so that they may live in the desert and sleep in the forests in safety. 26I will bless them and the places surrounding my hill.ª I will send down showers in season; there will be showers of blessing. 27The trees of the field will yield their fruit and the ground will yield its crops; the people will be secure in their land. They will know that I am the LORD, when I break the bars of their yoke and rescue them from the hands of those who enslaved them. 28They will no longer be plundered by the nations, nor will wild animals devour them. They will live in safety, and no one will make them afraid. 29I will provide for them a land renowned for its crops, and they will no longer be victims of famine in the land or bear the scorn of the nations. 30Then they will know that I, the LORD their God, am with

love ❤ notes

34:11–12

My daughter,

It's easy to feel lost in this fast-paced, get-it-done-now, what-have-you-done-for-me-lately world. When you are feeling lost or overwhelmed, remember that I am your shepherd. I will search for you myself and offer you safekeeping. Count on it.

—Your good Shepherd

How does knowing God will search for you himself comfort you in times of uncertainty?

_____

_____

_____

_____

_____

_____

_____

_____

_____

_____

ª 26 Or I will make them and the places surrounding my hill a blessing them and that they, the house of Israel, are my people, declares the Sovereign LORD. ³¹You my sheep, the sheep of my pasture, are people, and I am your God, declares the Sovereign LORD.' "

A Prophecy Against Edom

35 The word of the LORD came to me: ²"Son of man, set your face against Mount Seir; prophesy against it ³and say: 'This is what the Sovereign LORD says: I am against you, Mount Seir, and I will stretch out my hand against you and make you a desolate waste. ⁴I will turn your towns into ruins and you will be desolate. Then you will know that I am the LORD.

⁵" 'Because you harbored an ancient hostility and delivered the Israelites over to the sword at the time of their calamity, the time their punishment reached its climax, ⁶therefore as surely as I live, declares the Sovereign LORD, I will give you over to bloodshed and it will pursue you. Since you did not hate bloodshed, bloodshed will pursue you. ⁷I will make Mount Seir a desolate waste and cut off from it all who come and go. ⁸I will fill your mountains with the slain; those killed by the sword will fall on your hills and in your valleys and in all your ravines. ⁹I will make you desolate forever; your towns will not be inhabited. Then you will know that I am the LORD.

¹⁰" 'Because you have said, "These two nations and countries will be ours and we will take possession of them," even though I the LORD was there, ¹¹therefore as surely as I live, declares the Sovereign LORD, I will treat you in accordance with the anger and jealousy you showed in your hatred of them and I will make myself known among them when I judge you. ¹²Then you will know that I the LORD have heard all the contemptible things you have said against the mountains of Israel. You said, "They have been laid waste and have been given over to us to devour." ¹³You boasted against me and spoke against me without restraint, and I heard it. ¹⁴This is what the Sovereign LORD says: While the whole earth rejoices, I will make you desolate. ¹⁵Because you rejoiced when the inheritance of the house of Israel became desolate, that is how I will treat you. You will be desolate, O Mount Seir, you and all of Edom. Then they will know that I am the LORD.' "

---

love ❤ notes

34:25

Beloved,

I promise to give you peace— not just escape from conflict or turmoil in your life, but a deep inner peace that comes from finding your contentment, security and fulfillment in me. Rest in my perfect peace.

—Your God

Take time now to thank God and ask him for his peace in the unsettled areas of your life.

---

truth or dare

It's pretty hard to stay completely dry in a rain shower. When God decides to shower you with blessings—watch out! You're gonna get drenched!

34:25–31

Blindsided

I never saw it coming. I thought everything was going great between us. I spent almost a year of my life with this guy. We did everything together. His family loved me, and my family was crazy about him. It's not like we were talking about getting married any- time soon or anything. Still, we talked about our futures. We dreamed of what it would be like if we were together someday. Everyone said we were the perfect couple—even his mom. I thought so, too. That is, until tonight.

"I'm not sure I can do this anymore . . . " he said quietly as we sat in his car.

"Do what?" I asked. I didn't have a clue what was coming. Was I oblivious? Or just too trusting?

"*Us*. It's not working out anymore," he said with a tone that suddenly sounded so cold. Like he was some sort of robot. No expression. Nothing.

I don't remember what all we said next. It's kind of a blur. I remember I started cry- ing—I was fighting so hard to stay composed—and he just sort of sat there. Like he felt sorry for me but just wanted to leave as fast as possible.

And the worst part is that it's not a relationship he's tired of. It's *me*. I'm sure he'll start dating some other girl soon. He has no intentions of being single. That's what hurts. It's as if he took the best I had to offer and decided, "Thanks, but no thanks."

rejection in focus

We're alive and go through the motions of the day—but inside our heart is dying. That's how rejection feels. One of the first things the Bible tells us about Jesus is that he knows how it feels to be rejected. Isaiah 53:3 (page 969) says that Jesus was rejected. He understands our pain (Hebrews 4:14–16, pages 1588–1590).

»As hard as it is to believe, rejection is not the end of the story. Sometimes some- thing better is waiting for us just down the road.

»Pour out your heart and feelings to God (see Psalm 62:8, page 713). You can be perfectly honest with him.

»Forgive. It's easy to let anger and hurt feelings turn into resentment, bitterness and hatred. In the long run, that only hurts you, and it keeps you from healing and happiness in the future.

For more on this topic, see the index on page 1656.

Want more info about dealing with rejection? Go online at www.TrueImagesBible.com

A Prophecy to the Mountains of Israel

36 "Son of man, prophesy to the mountains of Israel and say, 'O mountains of Israel, hear the word of the LORD. ²This is what the Sovereign LORD says: The enemy said of you, "Aha! The ancient heights have become our possession." ' ³Therefore prophesy and say, 'This is what the Sovereign LORD says: Because they ravaged and hounded you from every side so that you became the possession of the rest of the nations and the object of people's malicious talk and slander, ⁴therefore, O mountains of Israel, hear the word of the Sovereign LORD: This is what the Sovereign LORD says to the mountains and hills, to the ravines and valleys, to the deso- late ruins and the deserted towns that have been plundered and ridiculed by the rest of the nations around you— [5]this is what the Sovereign LORD says: In my burning zeal I have spoken against the rest of the nations, and against all Edom, for with glee and with malice in their hearts they made my land their own possession so that they might plunder its pastureland.' [6]Therefore prophesy concerning the land of Israel and say to the mountains and hills, to the ravines and valleys: 'This is what the Sovereign LORD says: I speak in my jealous wrath because you have suffered the scorn of the nations. [7]Therefore this is what the Sovereign LORD says: I swear with uplifted hand that the nations around you will also suffer scorn.

[8]" 'But you, O mountains of Israel, will produce branches and fruit for my people Israel, for they will soon come home. [9]I am concerned for you and will look on you with favor; you will be plowed and sown, [10]and I will multiply the number of people upon you, even the whole house of Israel. The towns will be inhabited and the ruins rebuilt. [11]I will increase the number of men and animals upon you, and they will be fruitful and become numerous. I will settle people on you as in the past and will make you prosper more than before. Then you will know that I am the LORD. [12]I will cause people, my people Israel, to walk upon you. They will possess you, and you will be their inheritance; you will never again deprive them of their children.

[13]" 'This is what the Sovereign LORD says: Because people say to you, "You devour men and deprive your nation of its children," [14]therefore you will no longer devour men or make your nation childless, declares the Sovereign LORD. [15]No longer will I make you hear the taunts of the nations, and no longer will you suffer the scorn of the peoples or cause your nation to fall, declares the Sovereign LORD.' "

[16]Again the word of the LORD came to me: [17]"Son of man, when the people of Israel were living in their own land, they defiled it by their conduct and their actions. Their conduct was like a woman's monthly uncleanness in my sight. [18]So I poured out my wrath on them because they had shed blood in the land and because they had defiled it with their idols. [19]I dispersed them among the nations, and they were scattered through the countries; I judged them according to their conduct and their actions. [20]And wherever they went among the nations they profaned my holy name, for it was said of them, 'These are the LORD's people, and yet they had to leave his land.' [21]I had concern for my holy name, which the house of Israel profaned among the nations where they had gone.

[22]"Therefore say to the house of Israel, 'This is what the Sovereign LORD says: It is not for your sake, O house of Israel, that I am going to do these things, but for the sake of my holy name, which you have profaned among the nations where you have gone. [23]I will show the holiness of my great name, which has been profaned among the nations, the name you have profaned among them. Then the nations will know that I am the

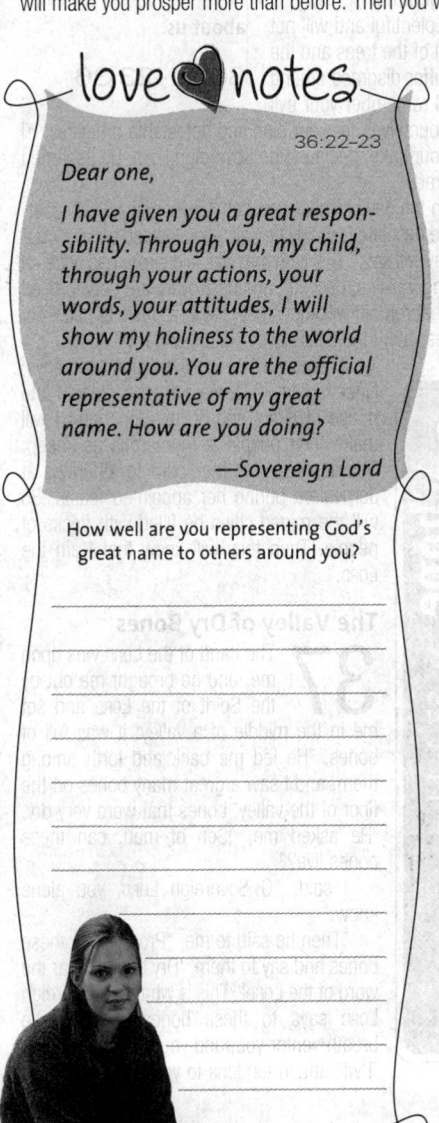

love ♥ notes

36:22–23

Dear one,

I have given you a great responsibility. Through you, my child, through your actions, your words, your attitudes, I will show my holiness to the world around you. You are the official representative of my great name. How are you doing?

—Sovereign Lord

How well are you representing God's great name to others around you?

_____

_____

_____

_____

_____

_____

_____

_____

LORD, declares the Sovereign LORD, when I show myself holy through you before their eyes.

²⁴ 'For I will take you out of the nations; I will gather you from all the countries and bring you back into your own land. ²⁵I will sprinkle clean water on you, and you will be clean; I will cleanse you from all your impurities and from all your idols. ²⁶I will give you a new heart and put a new spirit in you; I will remove from you your heart of stone and give you a heart of flesh. ²⁷And I will put my Spirit in you and move you to follow my decrees and be careful to keep my laws. ²⁸You will live in the land I gave your forefathers; you will be my people, and I will be your God. ²⁹I will save you from all your uncleanness. I will call for the grain and make it plentiful and will not bring famine upon you. ³⁰I will increase the fruit of the trees and the crops of the field, so that you will no longer suffer disgrace among the nations because of famine. ³¹Then you will remember your evil ways and wicked deeds, and you will loathe yourselves for your sins and detestable practices. ³²I want you to know that I am not doing this for your sake, declares the Sovereign LORD. Be ashamed and disgraced for your conduct, O house of Israel!

³³ 'This is what the Sovereign LORD says: On the day I cleanse you from all your sins, I will resettle your towns, and the ruins will be rebuilt. ³⁴The desolate land will be cultivated instead of lying desolate in the sight of all who pass through it. ³⁵They will say, "This land that was laid waste has become like the garden of Eden; the cities that were lying in ruins, desolate and destroyed, are now fortified and inhabited." ³⁶Then the nations around you that remain will know that I the LORD have rebuilt what was destroyed and have replanted what was desolate. I the LORD have spoken, and I will do it.'

³⁷"This is what the Sovereign LORD says: Once again I will yield to the plea of the house of Israel and do this for them: I will make their people as numerous as sheep, ³⁸as numerous as the flocks for offerings at Jerusalem during her appointed feasts. So will the ruined cities be filled with flocks of people. Then they will know that I am the LORD."

The Valley of Dry Bones

37 The hand of the LORD was upon me, and he brought me out by the Spirit of the LORD and set me in the middle of a valley; it was full of bones. ²He led me back and forth among them, and I saw a great many bones on the floor of the valley, bones that were very dry. ³He asked me, "Son of man, can these bones live?"

I said, "O Sovereign LORD, you alone know."

⁴Then he said to me, "Prophesy to these bones and say to them, 'Dry bones, hear the word of the LORD! ⁵This is what the Sovereign LORD says to these bones: I will make breath*ᵃ* enter you, and you will come to life. ⁶I will attach tendons to you and make flesh

---

truth or dare

God does things for the sake of his holy name. When he blesses us, it's for his glory because he's God. Ultimately, it's all about HIM, not about us.

36:21–23,36

---

genuine

hope » 37:1-14

Any kind of death is painful. Ever have a dream or a relationship die? That can cause as much heartache as when someone you love dies. Spiritual death—separation from God due to unbelief or sin—is the kind of death that especially makes God sad. He gave life to some skeletons in a valley to show the life he can bring to the spiritually dead. Only God, the source of all life, can give life to dead dreams, relationships and bodies. He adds that breath of life that can't be faked or found anywhere else. Feeling like a dry heap of bones? Turn to God.

ᵃ 5 The Hebrew for this word can also mean wind or spirit (see verses 6-14).

come upon you and cover you with skin; I will put breath in you, and you will come to life. Then you will know that I am the LORD.' "

[7]So I prophesied as I was commanded. And as I was prophesying, there was a noise, a rattling sound, and the bones came together, bone to bone. [8]I looked, and tendons and flesh appeared on them and skin covered them, but there was no breath in them.

[9]Then he said to me, "Prophesy to the breath; prophesy, son of man, and say to it, 'This is what the Sovereign LORD says: Come from the four winds, O breath, and breathe into these slain, that they may live.' " [10]So I prophesied as he commanded me, and breath entered them; they came to life and stood up on their feet—a vast army.

[11]Then he said to me: "Son of man, these bones are the whole house of Israel. They say, 'Our bones are dried up and our hope is gone; we are cut off.' [12]Therefore prophesy and say to them: 'This is what the Sovereign LORD says: O my people, I am going to open your graves and bring you up from them; I will bring you back to the land of Israel. [13]Then you, my people, will know that I am the LORD, when I open your graves and bring you up from them. [14]I will put my Spirit in you and you will live, and I will settle you in your own land. Then you will know that I the LORD have spoken, and I have done it, declares the LORD.' "

One Nation Under One King

[15]The word of the LORD came to me: [16]"Son of man, take a stick of wood and write on it, 'Belonging to Judah and the Israelites associated with him.' Then take another stick of wood, and write on it, 'Ephraim's stick, belonging to Joseph and all the house of Israel associated with him.' [17]Join them together into one stick so that they will become one in your hand.

[18]"When your countrymen ask you, 'Won't you tell us what you mean by this?' [19]say to them, 'This is what the Sovereign LORD says: I am going to take the stick of Joseph—which is in Ephraim's hand—and of the Israelite tribes associated with him, and join it to Judah's stick, making them a single stick of wood, and they will become one in my hand.' [20]Hold before their eyes the sticks you have written on [21]and say to them, 'This is what the Sovereign LORD says: I will take the Israelites out of the nations where they have gone. I will gather them from all around and bring them back into their own land. [22]I will make them one nation in the land, on the mountains of Israel. There will be one king over all of them and they will never again be two nations or be divided into two kingdoms. [23]They will no longer defile themselves with their idols and vile images or with any of their offenses, for I will save them from all their sinful backsliding,[a] and I will cleanse them. They will be my people, and I will be their God.

[24]" 'My servant David will be king over them, and they will all have one shepherd. They will follow my laws and be careful to keep my decrees. [25]They will live in the land I gave to my servant Jacob, the land where your fathers lived. They and their children and their children's children will live there forever, and David my servant will be their prince forever. [26]I will make a covenant of peace with them; it will be an everlasting covenant. I will establish them and increase their numbers, and I will put my sanctuary among them forever. [27]My dwelling place will be with them; I will be their God, and they will be my people. [28]Then the nations will know that I the LORD make Israel holy, when my sanctuary is among them forever.' "

A Prophecy Against Gog

38 The word of the LORD came to me: [2]"Son of man, set your face against Gog, of the land of Magog, the chief prince of[b] Meshech and Tubal; prophesy against him [3]and say: 'This is what the Sovereign LORD says: I am against you, O Gog, chief prince of[c]

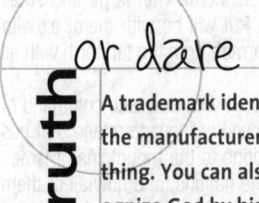

truth or dare

A trademark identifies the manufacturer of a thing. You can also recognize God by his trademark—wherever there's everlasting peace and holiness, God's had a hand in its creation.

37:26–28

---

[a] 23 Many Hebrew manuscripts (see also Septuagint); most Hebrew manuscripts *all their dwelling places where they sinned*
[b] 2 Or *the prince of Rosh,* [c] 3 Or *Gog, prince of Rosh,*

Meshech and Tubal. [4]I will turn you around, put hooks in your jaws and bring you out with your whole army—your horses, your horsemen fully armed, and a great horde with large and small shields, all of them brandishing their swords. [5]Persia, Cush[a] and Put will be with them, all with shields and helmets, [6]also Gomer with all its troops, and Beth Togarmah from the far north with all its troops—the many nations with you.

[7]" 'Get ready; be prepared, you and all the hordes gathered about you, and take command of them. [8]After many days you will be called to arms. In future years you will invade a land that has recovered from war, whose people were gathered from many nations to the mountains of Israel, which had long been desolate. They had been brought out from the nations, and now all of them live in safety. [9]You and all your troops and the many nations with you will go up, advancing like a storm; you will be like a cloud covering the land.

[10]" 'This is what the Sovereign Lord says: On that day thoughts will come into your mind and you will devise an evil scheme. [11]You will say, "I will invade a land of unwalled villages; I will attack a peaceful and unsuspecting people—all of them living without walls and without gates and bars. [12]I will plunder and loot and turn my hand against the resettled ruins and the people gathered from the nations, rich in livestock and goods, living at the center of the land." [13]Sheba and Dedan and the merchants of Tarshish and all her villages[b] will say to you, "Have you come to plunder? Have you gathered your hordes to loot, to carry off silver and gold, to take away livestock and goods and to seize much plunder?" '

[14]"Therefore, son of man, prophesy and say to Gog: 'This is what the Sovereign Lord says: In that day, when my people Israel are living in safety, will you not take notice of it? [15]You will come from your place in the far north, you and many nations with you, all of them riding on horses, a great horde, a mighty army. [16]You will advance against my people Israel like a cloud that covers the land. In days to come, O Gog, I will bring you against my land, so that the nations may know me when I show myself holy through you before their eyes.

[17]" 'This is what the Sovereign Lord says: Are you not the one I spoke of in former days by my servants the prophets of Israel? At that time they prophesied for years that I would bring you against them. [18]This is what will happen in that day: When Gog attacks the land of Israel, my hot anger will be aroused, declares the Sovereign Lord. [19]In my zeal and fiery wrath I declare that at that time there shall be a great earthquake in the land of Israel. [20]The fish of the sea, the birds of the air, the beasts of the field, every creature that moves along the ground, and all the people on the face of the earth will tremble at my presence. The mountains will be overturned, the cliffs will crumble and every wall will fall to the ground. [21]I will summon a sword against Gog on all my mountains, declares the Sovereign Lord. Every man's sword will be against his brother. [22]I will execute judgment upon him with plague and bloodshed; I will pour down torrents of rain, hailstones and burning sulfur on him and on his troops and on the many nations with him. [23]And so I will show my greatness and my holiness, and I will make myself known in the sight of many nations. Then they will know that I am the Lord.'

39 "Son of man, prophesy against Gog and say: 'This is what the Sovereign Lord says: I am against you, O Gog, chief prince of[c] Meshech and Tubal. [2]I will turn you around and drag you along. I will bring you from the far north and send you against the mountains of Israel. [3]Then I will strike your bow from your left hand and make your arrows drop from your right hand. [4]On the mountains of Israel you will fall, you and all your troops and the nations with you. I will give you as food to all kinds of carrion birds and to the wild animals. [5]You will fall in the open field, for I have spoken, declares the Sovereign Lord. [6]I will send fire on Magog and on those who live in safety in the coastlands, and they will know that I am the Lord.

[7]" 'I will make known my holy name among my people Israel. I will no longer let my holy name be profaned, and the nations will know that I the Lord am the Holy One in Israel. [8]It is coming! It will surely take place, declares the Sovereign Lord. This is the day I have spoken of.

[9]" 'Then those who live in the towns of Israel will go out and use the weapons for fuel and burn them up—the small and large shields, the bows and arrows, the war clubs and spears. For seven years they will use them for fuel. [10]They will not need to gather wood from the fields or cut it from the forests, because they will use the weapons for fuel. And they will plunder those who plundered them and loot those who looted them, declares the Sovereign Lord.

---

[a] 5 That is, the upper Nile region   [b] 13 Or *her strong lions*   [c] 1 Or *Gog, prince of Rosh,*

[11] " 'On that day I will give Gog a burial place in Israel, in the valley of those who travel east to-ward[a] the Sea.[b] It will block the way of travelers, because Gog and all his hordes will be buried there. So it will be called the Valley of Hamon Gog.[c]

[12] " 'For seven months the house of Israel will be burying them in order to cleanse the land. [13]All the people of the land will bury them, and the day I am glorified will be a memorable day for them, declares the Sovereign LORD.

[14] " 'Men will be regularly employed to cleanse the land. Some will go throughout the land and, in addition to them, others will bury those that remain on the ground. At the end of the seven months they will begin their search. [15]As they go through the land and one of them sees a human bone, he will set up a marker beside it until the gravediggers have buried it in the Valley of Hamon Gog. [16](Also a town called Hamonah[d] will be there.) And so they will cleanse the land.'

[17]"Son of man, this is what the Sovereign LORD says: Call out to every kind of bird and all the wild animals: 'Assemble and come together from all around to the sacrifice I am preparing for you, the great sacrifice on the mountains of Israel. There you will eat flesh and drink blood. [18]You will eat the flesh of mighty men and drink the blood of the princes of the earth as if they were rams and lambs, goats and bulls—all of them fattened animals from Bashan. [19]At the sacrifice I am pre-paring for you, you will eat fat till you are glutted and drink blood till you are drunk. [20]At my table you will eat your fill of horses and riders, mighty men and soldiers of every kind,' declares the Sov-ereign LORD.

[21]"I will display my glory among the nations, and all the nations will see the punishment I inflict and the hand I lay upon them. [22]From that day forward the house of Israel will know that I am the LORD their God. [23]And the nations will know that the people of Israel went into exile for their sin, be-cause they were unfaithful to me. So I hid my face from them and handed them over to their ene-mies, and they all fell by the sword. [24]I dealt with them according to their uncleanness and their offenses, and I hid my face from them.

[25]"Therefore this is what the Sovereign LORD says: I will now bring Jacob back from captivity[e] and will have compassion on all the people of Israel, and I will be zealous for my holy name. [26]They will forget their shame and all the unfaithfulness they showed toward me when they lived in safety in their land with no one to make them afraid. [27]When I have brought them back from the nations and have gathered them from the countries of their enemies, I will show myself holy through them in the sight of many nations. [28]Then they will know that I am the LORD their God, for though I sent them into exile among the nations, I will gather them to their own land, not leaving any behind. [29]I will no longer hide my face from them, for I will pour out my Spirit on the house of Israel, declares the Sovereign LORD."

The New Temple Area

40 In the twenty-fifth year of our exile, at the beginning of the year, on the tenth of the month, in the fourteenth year after the fall of the city—on that very day the hand of the LORD was upon me and he took me there. [2]In visions of God he took me to the land of Israel and set me on a very high mountain, on whose south side were some buildings that looked like a city. [3]He took me there, and I saw a man whose appearance was like bronze; he was stand-ing in the gateway with a linen cord and a measuring rod in his hand. [4]The man said to me, "Son of man, look with your eyes and hear with your ears and pay attention to everything I am going to show you, for that is why you have been brought here. Tell the house of Israel everything you see."

The East Gate to the Outer Court

[5]I saw a wall completely surrounding the temple area. The length of the measuring rod in the man's hand was six long cubits, each of which was a cubit[f] and a handbreadth.[g] He measured the wall; it was one measuring rod thick and one rod high.

[6]Then he went to the gate facing east. He climbed its steps and measured the threshold of the gate; it was one rod deep.[h] [7]The alcoves for the guards were one rod long and one rod wide, and the projecting walls between the alcoves were five cubits thick. And the threshold of the gate next to the portico facing the temple was one rod deep.

---

a 11 Or of   b 11 That is, the Dead Sea   c 11 Hamon Gog means hordes of Gog.   d 16 Hamonah means horde.
e 25 Or now restore the fortunes of Jacob   f 5 The common cubit was about 1 1/2 feet (about 0.5 meter).   g 5 That
is, about 3 inches (about 8 centimeters)   h 6 Septuagint; Hebrew deep, the first threshold, one rod deep

[8]Then he measured the portico of the gateway; [9]it[a] was eight cubits deep and its jambs were two cubits thick. The portico of the gateway faced the temple.

[10]Inside the east gate were three alcoves on each side; the three had the same measurements, and the faces of the projecting walls on each side had the same measurements. [11]Then he measured the width of the entrance to the gateway; it was ten cubits and its length was thirteen cubits. [12]In front of each alcove was a wall one cubit high, and the alcoves were six cubits square. [13]Then he measured the gateway from the top of the rear wall of one alcove to the top of the opposite one; the distance was twenty-five cubits from one parapet opening to the opposite one. [14]He measured along the faces of the projecting walls all around the inside of the gateway—sixty cubits. The measurement was up to the portico[b] facing the courtyard.[c] [15]The distance from the entrance of the gateway to the far end of its portico was fifty cubits. [16]The alcoves and the projecting walls inside the gateway were surmounted by narrow parapet openings all around, as was the portico; the openings all around faced inward. The faces of the projecting walls were decorated with palm trees.

The Outer Court

[17]Then he brought me into the outer court. There I saw some rooms and a pavement that had been constructed all around the court; there were thirty rooms along the pavement. [18]It abutted the sides of the gateways and was as wide as they were long; this was the lower pavement. [19]Then he measured the distance from the inside of the lower gateway to the outside of the inner court; it was a hundred cubits on the east side as well as on the north.

The North Gate

[20]Then he measured the length and width of the gate facing north, leading into the outer court. [21]Its alcoves—three on each side—its projecting walls and its portico had the same measurements as those of the first gateway. It was fifty cubits long and twenty-five cubits wide. [22]Its openings, its portico and its palm tree decorations had the same measurements as those of the gate facing east. Seven steps led up to it, with its portico opposite them. [23]There was a gate to the inner court facing the north gate, just as there was on the east. He measured from one gate to the opposite one; it was a hundred cubits.

The South Gate

[24]Then he led me to the south side and I saw a gate facing south. He measured its jambs and its portico, and they had the same measurements as the others. [25]The gateway and its portico had narrow openings all around, like the openings of the others. It was fifty cubits long and twenty-five cubits wide. [26]Seven steps led up to it, with its portico opposite them; it had palm tree decorations on the faces of the projecting walls on each side. [27]The inner court also had a gate facing south, and he measured from this gate to the outer gate on the south side; it was a hundred cubits.

Gates to the Inner Court

[28]Then he brought me into the inner court through the south gate, and he measured the south gate; it had the same measurements as the others. [29]Its alcoves, its projecting walls and its portico had the same measurements as the others. The gateway and its portico had openings all around. It was fifty cubits long and twenty-five cubits wide. [30](The porticoes of the gateways around the inner court were twenty-five cubits wide and five cubits deep.) [31]Its portico faced the outer court; palm trees decorated its jambs, and eight steps led up to it.

[32]Then he brought me to the inner court on the east side, and he measured the gateway; it had the same measurements as the others. [33]Its alcoves, its projecting walls and its portico had the same measurements as the others. The gateway and its portico had openings all around. It was fifty cubits long and twenty-five cubits wide. [34]Its portico faced the outer court; palm trees decorated the jambs on either side, and eight steps led up to it.

[35]Then he brought me to the north gate and measured it. It had the same measurements as

[a] 8,9 Many Hebrew manuscripts, Septuagint, Vulgate and Syriac; most Hebrew manuscripts *gateway facing the temple; it was one rod deep.* [9]*Then he measured the portico of the gateway; it*   [b] 14 Septuagint; Hebrew *projecting wall*   [c] 14 The meaning of the Hebrew for this verse is uncertain.

mirror images

She said, "Grant that one of these two sons of mine may sit at your right and the other at your left in your kingdom."
"You don't know what you are asking," Jesus said. Matthew 20:21–22

Salome—The Heart of a Servant

Ever asked the wrong question? How about asking your lab partner how the softball season's going—only to discover she got cut from the team?

Ouch! There's nothing comfortable about sticking your foot in your mouth. If you've ever been humiliated like that, you'll probably feel sorry for Salome. After all, she was just trying to help out her kids when she asked the day's most inappropriate question.

Since her feisty sons James and John had become Jesus-followers, they had become two of the Master's closest friends. He even nicknamed them "the sons of thunder." What would be the harm of asking Jesus to show her precious boys a favor? When she asked the Master to let her sons sit at his right and left in his kingdom, she must have been embarrassed at his reply. "You don't know what you're asking, Salome. You shouldn't desire recognition for you or your family. If you want greatness, you must become a servant."

Salome may have been startled and hurt as she learned that Jesus desires followers who are servant leaders—not the kind who look for fame and special privileges. But Salome proved through her ministry that she took his words to heart. In Mark 15, she's mentioned as one of three women who followed Jesus through the towns of Galilee, caring for his needs. Salome learned how to serve by watching the greatest Servant of all—Jesus Christ.

We can improve our "serve" by taking our focus off of the clothes, popularity and possessions most girls crave. When we focus on Jesus, we find the energy to help and care for others. And, like Salome, we'll discover that true greatness does come from servanthood.

To read the next Mirror Images profile, go to page 1178.

Dear Jesus, serving you is hardly popular. But even when no one else is doing it, help me to be faithful like Salome was. Show me at least one way I can serve someone else today, and help others to see you in me. Amen.

Read more about Salome in Matthew 20:20–28 (pages 1318–1319) and Mark 15:40–41 and 16:1–8 (pages 1359–1360).

the others, [36]as did its alcoves, its projecting walls and its portico, and it had openings all around. It was fifty cubits long and twenty-five cubits wide. [37]Its portico[a] faced the outer court; palm trees decorated the jambs on either side, and eight steps led up to it.

The Rooms for Preparing Sacrifices

[38]A room with a doorway was by the portico in each of the inner gateways, where the burnt offerings were washed. [39]In the portico of the gateway were two tables on each side, on which the burnt offerings, sin offerings and guilt offerings were slaughtered. [40]By the outside wall of the portico of the gateway, near the steps at the entrance to the north gateway were two tables, and on the other side of the steps were two tables. [41]So there were four tables on one side of the gateway and four on the other—eight tables in all—on which the sacrifices were slaughtered. [42]There were also four tables of dressed stone for the burnt offerings, each a cubit and a half long, a cubit and a half wide and a cubit high. On them were placed the utensils for slaughtering the burnt offerings and the other sacrifices. [43]And double-pronged hooks, each a handbreadth long, were attached to the wall all around. The tables were for the flesh of the offerings.

Rooms for the Priests

[44]Outside the inner gate, within the inner court, were two rooms, one[b] at the side of the north gate and facing south, and another at the side of the south[c] gate and facing north. [45]He said to me, "The room facing south is for the priests who have charge of the temple, [46]and the room facing north is for the priests who have charge of the altar. These are the sons of Zadok, who are the only Levites who may draw near to the LORD to minister before him."

[47]Then he measured the court: It was square—a hundred cubits long and a hundred cubits wide. And the altar was in front of the temple.

The Temple

[48]He brought me to the portico of the temple and measured the jambs of the portico; they were five cubits wide on either side. The width of the entrance was fourteen cubits and its projecting walls were[d] three cubits wide on either side. [49]The portico was twenty cubits wide, and twelve[e] cubits from front to back. It was reached by a flight of stairs,[f] and there were pillars on each side of the jambs.

41 Then the man brought me to the outer sanctuary and measured the jambs; the width of the jambs was six cubits[g] on each side.[h] [2]The entrance was ten cubits wide, and the projecting walls on each side of it were five cubits wide. He also measured the outer sanctuary; it was forty cubits long and twenty cubits wide.

[3]Then he went into the inner sanctuary and measured the jambs of the entrance; each was two cubits wide. The entrance was six cubits wide, and the projecting walls on each side of it were seven cubits wide. [4]And he measured the length of the inner sanctuary; it was twenty cubits, and its width was twenty cubits across the end of the outer sanctuary. He said to me, "This is the Most Holy Place."

[5]Then he measured the wall of the temple; it was six cubits thick, and each side room around the temple was four cubits wide. [6]The side rooms were on three levels, one above another, thirty on each level. There were ledges all around the wall of the temple to serve as supports for the side rooms, so that the supports were not inserted into the wall of the temple. [7]The side rooms all around the temple were wider at each successive level. The structure surrounding the temple was built in ascending stages, so that the rooms widened as one went upward. A stairway went up from the lowest floor to the top floor through the middle floor.

[8]I saw that the temple had a raised base all around it, forming the foundation of the side rooms. It was the length of the rod, six long cubits. [9]The outer wall of the side rooms was five cubits thick. The open area between the side rooms of the temple [10]and the ⌐priests'⌐ rooms was twenty cubits wide all around the temple. [11]There were entrances to the side rooms from the open area, one on

---

a 37 Septuagint (see also verses 31 and 34); Hebrew *jambs*   b 44 Septuagint; Hebrew *were rooms for singers, which were*   c 44 Septuagint; Hebrew *east*   d 48 Septuagint; Hebrew *entrance was*   e 49 Septuagint; Hebrew *eleven* f 49 Hebrew; Septuagint *Ten steps led up to it*   g 1 The common cubit was about 1 1/2 feet (about 0.5 meter). h 1 One Hebrew manuscript and Septuagint; most Hebrew manuscripts *side, the width of the tent* the north and another on the south; and the base adjoining the open area was five cubits wide all around.

¹²The building facing the temple courtyard on the west side was seventy cubits wide. The wall of the building was five cubits thick all around, and its length was ninety cubits.

¹³Then he measured the temple; it was a hundred cubits long, and the temple courtyard and the building with its walls were also a hundred cubits long. ¹⁴The width of the temple courtyard on the east, including the front of the temple, was a hundred cubits.

¹⁵Then he measured the length of the building facing the courtyard at the rear of the temple, including its galleries on each side; it was a hundred cubits.

The outer sanctuary, the inner sanctuary and the portico facing the court, ¹⁶as well as the thresholds and the narrow windows and galleries around the three of them—everything beyond and including the threshold was covered with wood. The floor, the wall up to the windows, and the windows were covered. ¹⁷In the space above the outside of the entrance to the inner sanctuary and on the walls at regular intervals all around the inner and outer sanctuary ¹⁸were carved cherubim and palm trees. Palm trees alternated with cherubim. Each cherub had two faces: ¹⁹the face of a man toward the palm tree on one side and the face of a lion toward the palm tree on the other. They were carved all around the whole temple. ²⁰From the floor to the area above the entrance, cherubim and palm trees were carved on the wall of the outer sanctuary.

²¹The outer sanctuary had a rectangular doorframe, and the one at the front of the Most Holy Place was similar. ²²There was a wooden altar three cubits high and two cubits square*ᵃ*; its corners, its base*ᵇ* and its sides were of wood. The man said to me, "This is the table that is before the Lord." ²³Both the outer sanctuary and the Most Holy Place had double doors. ²⁴Each door had two leaves—two hinged leaves for each door. ²⁵And on the doors of the outer sanctuary were carved cherubim and palm trees like those carved on the walls, and there was a wooden overhang on the front of the portico. ²⁶On the sidewalls of the portico were narrow windows with palm trees carved on each side. The side rooms of the temple also had overhangs.

Rooms for the Priests

42 Then the man led me northward into the outer court and brought me to the rooms opposite the temple courtyard and opposite the outer wall on the north side. ²The building whose door faced north was a hundred cubits*ᶜ* long and fifty cubits wide. ³Both in the section twenty cubits from the inner court and in the section opposite the pavement of the outer court, gallery faced gallery at the three levels. ⁴In front of the rooms was an inner passageway ten cubits wide and a hundred cubits*ᵈ* long. Their doors were on the north. ⁵Now the upper rooms were narrower, for the galleries took more space from them than from the rooms on the lower and middle floors of the building. ⁶The rooms on the third floor had no pillars, as the courts had; so they were smaller in floor space than those on the lower and middle floors. ⁷There was an outer wall parallel to the rooms and the outer court; it extended in front of the rooms for fifty cubits. ⁸While the row of rooms on the side next to the outer court was fifty cubits long, the row on the side nearest the sanctuary was a hundred cubits long. ⁹The lower rooms had an entrance on the east side as one enters them from the outer court.

¹⁰On the south side*ᵉ* along the length of the wall of the outer court, adjoining the temple courtyard and opposite the outer wall, were rooms ¹¹with a passageway in front of them. These were like the rooms on the north; they had the same length and width, with similar exits and dimensions. Similar to the doorways on the north ¹²were the doorways of the rooms on the south. There was a doorway at the beginning of the passageway that was parallel to the corresponding wall extending eastward, by which one enters the rooms.

¹³Then he said to me, "The north and south rooms facing the temple courtyard are the priests' rooms, where the priests who approach the Lord will eat the most holy offerings. There they will put the most holy offerings—the grain offerings, the sin offerings and the guilt offerings—for the place is holy. ¹⁴Once the priests enter the holy precincts, they are not to go into the outer court until they leave behind the garments in which they minister, for these are holy. They are to put on other clothes before they go near the places that are for the people."

ᵃ 22 Septuagint; Hebrew long   *ᵇ 22 Septuagint; Hebrew length*   *ᶜ 2 The common cubit was about 1 1/2 feet (about 0.5 meter).*   *ᵈ 4 Septuagint and Syriac; Hebrew and one cubit*   *ᵉ 10 Septuagint; Hebrew Eastward*

15When he had finished measuring what was inside the temple area, he led me out by the east gate and measured the area all around: 16He measured the east side with the measuring rod; it was five hundred cubits. *a* 17He measured the north side; it was five hundred cubits *b* by the measuring rod. 18He measured the south side; it was five hundred cubits by the measuring rod. 19Then he turned to the west side and measured; it was five hundred cubits by the measuring rod. 20So he measured the area on all four sides. It had a wall around it, five hundred cubits long and five hundred cubits wide, to separate the holy from the common.

The Glory Returns to the Temple

43 Then the man brought me to the gate facing east, 2and I saw the glory of the God of Israel coming from the east. His voice was like the roar of rushing waters, and the land was radiant with his glory. 3The vision I saw was like the vision I had seen when he *c* came to destroy the city and like the visions I had seen by the Kebar River, and I fell facedown. 4The glory of the LORD entered the temple through the gate facing east. 5Then the Spirit lifted me up and brought me into the inner court, and the glory of the LORD filled the temple.

6While the man was standing beside me, I heard someone speaking to me from inside the temple. 7He said: "Son of man, this is the place of my throne and the place for the soles of my feet. This is where I will live among the Israelites forever. The house of Israel will never again defile my holy name—neither they nor their kings—by their prostitution *d* and the lifeless idols *e* of their kings at their high places. 8When they placed their threshold next to my threshold and their doorposts beside my doorposts, with only a wall between me and them, they defiled my holy name by their detestable practices. So I destroyed them in my anger. 9Now let them put away from me their prostitution and the lifeless idols of their kings, and I will live among them forever.

10"Son of man, describe the temple to the people of Israel, that they may be ashamed of their sins. Let them consider the plan, 11and if they are ashamed of all they have done, make known to them the design of the temple—its arrangement, its exits and entrances—its whole design and all its regulations *f* and laws. Write these down before them so that they may be faithful to its design and follow all its regulations.

12"This is the law of the temple: All the surrounding area on top of the mountain will be most holy. Such is the law of the temple.

truth or dare

God doesn't want to share you with other loves and desires. He only fits into a life that has been offered to him fully. What're you still holding on to?

43:9

The Altar

13"These are the measurements of the altar in long cubits, that cubit being a cubit *g* and a handbreadth *h*: Its gutter is a cubit deep and a cubit wide, with a rim of one span *i* around the edge. And this is the height of the altar: 14From the gutter on the ground up to the lower ledge it is two cubits high and a cubit wide, and from the smaller ledge up to the larger ledge it is four cubits high and a cubit wide. 15The altar hearth is four cubits high, and four horns project upward from the hearth. 16The altar hearth is square, twelve cubits long and twelve cubits wide. 17The upper ledge also is square, fourteen cubits long and fourteen cubits wide, with a rim of half a cubit and a gutter of a cubit all around. The steps of the altar face east."

18Then he said to me, "Son of man, this is what the Sovereign LORD says: These will be the regulations for sacrificing burnt offerings and sprinkling blood upon the altar when it is built: 19You are to give a young bull as a sin offering to the priests, who are Levites, of the family of Zadok, who come near to minister before me, declares the Sovereign LORD. 20You are to take some of its blood and put it on the four horns of the altar and on the four corners of the upper ledge and all around

a 16 See Septuagint of verse 17; Hebrew *rods*; also in verses 18 and 19.   *b 17* Septuagint; Hebrew *rods*   *c 3* Some Hebrew manuscripts and Vulgate; most Hebrew manuscripts *I*   *d 7* Or *their spiritual adultery*; also in verse 9   *e 7* Or *the corpses*; also in verse 9   *f 11* Some Hebrew manuscripts and Septuagint; most Hebrew manuscripts *regulations and its whole design*   *g 13* The common cubit was about 1 1/2 feet (about 0.5 meter).   *h 13* That is, about 3 inches (about 8 centimeters)   *i 13* That is, about 9 inches (about 22 centimeters) the rim, and so purify the altar and make atonement for it. [21]You are to take the bull for the sin offering and burn it in the designated part of the temple area outside the sanctuary.

[22]"On the second day you are to offer a male goat without defect for a sin offering, and the altar is to be purified as it was purified with the bull. [23]When you have finished purifying it, you are to offer a young bull and a ram from the flock, both without defect. [24]You are to offer them before the LORD, and the priests are to sprinkle salt on them and sacrifice them as a burnt offering to the LORD.

[25]"For seven days you are to provide a male goat daily for a sin offering; you are also to provide a young bull and a ram from the flock, both without defect. [26]For seven days they are to make atonement for the altar and cleanse it; thus they will dedicate it. [27]At the end of these days, from the eighth day on, the priests are to present your burnt offerings and fellowship offerings[a] on the altar. Then I will accept you, declares the Sovereign LORD."

The Prince, the Levites, the Priests

44 Then the man brought me back to the outer gate of the sanctuary, the one facing east, and it was shut. [2]The LORD said to me, "This gate is to remain shut. It must not be opened; no one may enter through it. It is to remain shut because the LORD, the God of Israel, has entered through it. [3]The prince himself is the only one who may sit inside the gateway to eat in the presence of the LORD. He is to enter by way of the portico of the gateway and go out the same way."

[4]Then the man brought me by way of the north gate to the front of the temple. I looked and saw the glory of the LORD filling the temple of the LORD, and I fell facedown.

[5]The LORD said to me, "Son of man, look carefully, listen closely and give attention to everything I tell you concerning all the regulations regarding the temple of the LORD. Give attention to the entrance of the temple and all the exits of the sanctuary. [6]Say to the rebellious house of Israel, 'This is what the Sovereign LORD says: Enough of your detestable practices, O house of Israel! [7]In addition to all your other detestable practices, you brought foreigners uncircumcised in heart and flesh into my sanctuary, desecrating my temple while you offered me food, fat and blood, and you broke my covenant. [8]Instead of carrying out your duty in regard to my holy things, you put others in charge of my sanctuary. [9]This is what the Sovereign LORD says: No foreigner uncircumcised in heart and flesh is to enter my sanctuary, not even the foreigners who live among the Israelites.

[10]" 'The Levites who went far from me when Israel went astray and who wandered from me after their idols must bear the consequences of their sin. [11]They may serve in my sanctuary, having charge of the gates of the temple and serving in it; they may slaughter the burnt offerings and sacrifices for the people and stand before the people and serve them. [12]But because they served them in the presence of their idols and made the house of Israel fall into sin, therefore I have sworn with uplifted hand that they must bear the consequences of their sin, declares the Sovereign LORD. [13]They are not to come near to serve me as priests or come near any of my holy things or my most holy offerings; they must bear the shame of their detestable practices. [14]Yet I will put them in charge of the duties of the temple and all the work that is to be done in it.

[15]" 'But the priests, who are Levites and descendants of Zadok and who faithfully carried out the duties of my sanctuary when the Israelites went astray from me, are to come near to minister before me; they are to stand before me to offer sacrifices of fat and blood, declares the Sovereign LORD. [16]They alone are to enter my sanctuary; they alone are to come near my table to minister before me and perform my service.

[17]" 'When they enter the gates of the inner court, they are to wear linen clothes; they must not wear any woolen garment while ministering at the gates of the inner court or inside the temple. [18]They are to wear linen turbans on their heads and linen undergarments around their waists. They must not wear anything that makes them perspire. [19]When they go out into the outer court where the people are, they are to take off the clothes they have been ministering in and are to leave them in the sacred rooms, and put on other clothes, so that they do not consecrate the people by means of their garments.

[20]" 'They must not shave their heads or let their hair grow long, but they are to keep the hair of their heads trimmed. [21]No priest is to drink wine when he enters the inner court. [22]They must not marry widows or divorced women; they may marry only virgins of Israelite descent or widows of

---

a 27 Traditionally *peace offerings*

priests. ²³They are to teach my people the difference between the holy and the common and show them how to distinguish between the unclean and the clean.

²⁴'In any dispute, the priests are to serve as judges and decide it according to my ordinances. They are to keep my laws and my decrees for all my appointed feasts, and they are to keep my Sabbaths holy.

²⁵'A priest must not defile himself by going near a dead person; however, if the dead person was his father or mother, son or daughter, brother or unmarried sister, then he may defile himself. ²⁶After he is cleansed, he must wait seven days. ²⁷On the day he goes into the inner court of the sanctuary to minister in the sanctuary, he is to offer a sin offering for himself, declares the Sovereign Lord.

²⁸'I am to be the only inheritance the priests have. You are to give them no possession in Israel; I will be their possession. ²⁹They will eat the grain offerings, the sin offerings and the guilt offerings; and everything in Israel devoted*ᵃ* to the Lord will belong to them. ³⁰The best of all the firstfruits and of all your special gifts will belong to the priests. You are to give them the first portion of your ground meal so that a blessing may rest on your household. ³¹The priests must not eat anything, bird or animal, found dead or torn by wild animals.

Division of the Land

45 "'When you allot the land as an inheritance, you are to present to the Lord a portion of the land as a sacred district, 25,000 cubits long and 20,000*ᵇ* cubits wide; the entire area will be holy. ²Of this, a section 500 cubits square is to be for the sanctuary, with 50 cubits around it for open land. ³In the sacred district, measure off a section 25,000 cubits*ᶜ* long and 10,000 cubits*ᵈ* wide. In it will be the sanctuary, the Most Holy Place. ⁴It will be the sacred portion of the land for the priests, who minister in the sanctuary and who draw near to minister before the Lord. It will be a place for their houses as well as a holy place for the sanctuary. ⁵An area 25,000 cubits long and 10,000 cubits wide will belong to the Levites, who serve in the temple, as their possession for towns to live in.*ᵉ*

⁶"'You are to give the city as its property an area 5,000 cubits wide and 25,000 cubits long, adjoining the sacred portion; it will belong to the whole house of Israel.

⁷"'The prince will have the land bordering each side of the area formed by the sacred district and the property of the city. It will extend westward from the west side and eastward from the east side, running lengthwise from the western to the eastern border parallel to one of the tribal portions. ⁸This land will be his possession in Israel. And my princes will no longer oppress my people but will allow the house of Israel to possess the land according to their tribes.

⁹"'This is what the Sovereign Lord says: You have gone far enough, O princes of Israel! Give up your violence and oppression and do what is just and right. Stop dispossessing my people, declares the Sovereign Lord. ¹⁰You are to use accurate scales, an accurate ephah*ᶠ* and an accurate bath.*ᵍ* ¹¹The ephah and the bath are to be the same size, the bath containing a tenth of a homer*ʰ* and the ephah a tenth of a homer; the homer is to be the standard measure for both. ¹²The shekel*ⁱ* is to consist of twenty gerahs. Twenty shekels plus twenty-five shekels plus fifteen shekels equal one mina.*ʲ*

Offerings and Holy Days

¹³"'This is the special gift you are to offer: a sixth of an ephah from each homer of wheat and a sixth of an ephah from each homer of barley. ¹⁴The prescribed portion of oil, measured by the bath, is a tenth of a bath from each cor (which consists of ten baths or one homer, for ten baths are equivalent to a homer). ¹⁵Also one sheep is to be taken from every flock of two hundred from the well-watered pastures of Israel. These will be used for the grain offerings, burnt offerings and fellowship offerings*ᵏ* to make atonement for the people, declares the Sovereign Lord. ¹⁶All the people of the land will participate in this special gift for the use of the prince in Israel. ¹⁷It will be the

---

a 29 The Hebrew term refers to the irrevocable giving over of things or persons to the Lord.   *b 1* Septuagint (see also verses 3 and 5 and 48:9); Hebrew *10,000*   *c 3* That is, about 7 miles (about 12 kilometers)   *d 3* That is, about 3 miles (about 5 kilometers)   *e 5* Septuagint; Hebrew *temple; they will have as their possession 20 rooms*   *f 10* An ephah was a dry measure.   *g 10* A bath was a liquid measure.   *h 11* A homer was a dry measure.   *i 12* A shekel weighed about 2/5 ounce (about 11.5 grams).   *j 12* That is, 60 shekels; the common mina was 50 shekels.   *k 15* Traditionally *peace offerings*; also in verse 17

Why Am I So Unhappy?

focus — **Profile: Kristen**

"You have the perfect life," my friends always tell me. "What more could a girl want?"

I wish I knew the answer to that question. I can't figure it out. From the outside looking in, I do have the so-called "perfect life." My parents have been married for 27 years, and they're still crazy about each other. I've lived in the same two-story house all my life. I do well in school—even math comes easy to me. I have good friends who are always there for me.

"You have it so good," my friends tell me, with that little bit of jealousy in their eyes. They're right. I'm sure of it. I know all I have to do is say the word, and my parents would do anything for me. When something good happens, I'm happy for awhile. Then that feeling goes away, and it's not long before I start feeling restless again. Like there's something missing in my life. Like I want something more, something different, but I'm not sure what it is. Just something.

I don't expect anyone to feel sorry for me—the girl who has it all yet feels like she has nothing. I know I sound like a spoiled brat. Believe me, I don't *say* any of this to my friends. It's just how I feel. I guess I should just be thankful or whatever for what I have, yet I can't ignore this nagging feeling inside.

thankfulness in focus

Ever get that gnawing feeling of discontentment? Maybe like Kristen, you know you have it good, yet you still don't feel satisfied with your life. Sometimes the reason is because you're taking the good things in life for granted and failing to praise God for his gifts. Boost your thankfulness by trying one of the following ideas:

»Write a song of thanks (see Psalm 28:7, page 680).
»Go to a peaceful place, like a park or by a lake, and write down a list of what you're thankful for—from the shoes on your feet to the sky above.
»Give yourself a little reminder to stay current on your thanks to God—a sticker on your watch or a note on your mirror can remind you to thank him throughout the day.

For more on this topic, see the index on page 1656.

Want to learn more about developing thankfulness? Go to www.TrueImagesBible.com

duty of the prince to provide the burnt offerings, grain offerings and drink offerings at the festivals, the New Moons and the Sabbaths—at all the appointed feasts of the house of Israel. He will provide the sin offerings, grain offerings, burnt offerings and fellowship offerings to make atonement for the house of Israel.

¹⁸" 'This is what the Sovereign Lord says: In the first month on the first day you are to take a young bull without defect and purify the sanctuary. ¹⁹The priest is to take some of the blood of the sin offering and put it on the doorposts of the temple, on the four corners of the upper ledge of the altar and on the gateposts of the inner court. ²⁰You are to do the same on the seventh day of the month for anyone who sins unintentionally or through ignorance; so you are to make atonement for the temple.

²¹" 'In the first month on the fourteenth day you are to observe the Passover, a feast lasting seven days, during which you shall eat bread made without yeast. ²²On that day the prince is to provide a bull as a sin offering for himself and for all the people of the land. ²³Every day during the seven days of the Feast he is to provide seven bulls and seven rams without defect as a burnt offering to the LORD, and a male goat for a sin offering. ²⁴He is to provide as a grain offering an ephah for each bull and an ephah for each ram, along with a hin ᵃ of oil for each ephah.

²⁵" 'During the seven days of the Feast, which begins in the seventh month on the fifteenth day, he is to make the same provision for sin offerings, burnt offerings, grain offerings and oil.

46

" 'This is what the Sovereign LORD says: The gate of the inner court facing east is to be shut on the six working days, but on the Sabbath day and on the day of the New Moon it is to be opened. ²The prince is to enter from the outside through the portico of the gateway and stand by the gatepost. The priests are to sacrifice his burnt offering and his fellowship offerings. ᵇ He is to worship at the threshold of the gateway and then go out, but the gate will not be shut until evening. ³On the Sabbaths and New Moons the people of the land are to worship in the presence of the LORD at the entrance to that gateway. ⁴The burnt offering the prince brings to the LORD on the Sabbath day is to be six male lambs and a ram, all without defect. ⁵The grain offering given with the ram is to be an ephah, ᶜ and the grain offering with the lambs is to be as much as he pleases, along with a hin ᵃ of oil for each ephah. ⁶On the day of the New Moon he is to offer a young bull, six lambs and a ram, all without defect. ⁷He is to provide as a grain offering one ephah with the bull, one ephah with the ram, and with the lambs as much as he wants to give, along with a hin of oil with each ephah. ⁸When the prince enters, he is to go in through the portico of the gateway, and he is to come out the same way.

⁹" 'When the people of the land come before the LORD at the appointed feasts, whoever enters by the north gate to worship is to go out the south gate; and whoever enters by the south gate is to go out the north gate. No one is to return through the gate by which he entered, but each is to go out the opposite gate. ¹⁰The prince is to be among them, going in when they go in and going out when they go out.

¹¹" 'At the festivals and the appointed feasts, the grain offering is to be an ephah with a bull, an ephah with a ram, and with the lambs as much as one pleases, along with a hin of oil for each ephah. ¹²When the prince provides a freewill offering to the LORD—whether a burnt offering or fellowship offerings—the gate facing east is to be opened for him. He shall offer his burnt offering or his fellowship offerings as he does on the Sabbath day. Then he shall go out, and after he has gone out, the gate will be shut.

¹³" 'Every day you are to provide a year-old lamb without defect for a burnt offering to the LORD; morning by morning you shall provide it. ¹⁴You are also to provide with it morning by morning a grain offering, consisting of a sixth of an ephah with a third of a hin of oil to moisten the flour. The presenting of this grain offering to the LORD is a lasting ordinance. ¹⁵So the lamb and the grain offering and the oil shall be provided morning by morning for a regular burnt offering.

¹⁶" 'This is what the Sovereign LORD says: If the prince makes a gift from his inheritance to one of his sons, it will also belong to his descendants; it is to be their property by inheritance. ¹⁷If, however, he makes a gift from his inheritance to one of his servants, the servant may keep it until the year of freedom; then it will revert to the prince. His inheritance belongs to his sons only; it is theirs. ¹⁸The prince must not take any of the inheritance of the people, driving them off their property. He is to give his sons their inheritance out of his own property, so that none of my people will be separated from his property.' "

¹⁹Then the man brought me through the entrance at the side of the gate to the sacred rooms facing north, which belonged to the priests, and showed me a place at the western end. ²⁰He said to me, "This is the place where the priests will cook the guilt offering and the sin offering and bake the grain offering, to avoid bringing them into the outer court and consecrating the people."

²¹He then brought me to the outer court and led me around to its four corners, and I saw in each corner another court. ²²In the four corners of the outer court were enclosed ᵈ courts, forty cubits long and thirty cubits wide; each of the courts in the four corners was the same size. ²³Around the inside of each of the four courts was a ledge of stone, with places for fire built all around un-

---

ᵃ 24,5 That is, probably about 4 quarts (about 4 liters)   ᵇ 2 Traditionally *peace offerings*; also in verse 12   ᶜ 5 That is, probably about 3/5 bushel (about 22 liters)   ᵈ 22 The meaning of the Hebrew for this word is uncertain.

der the ledge. [24]He said to me, "These are the kitchens where those who minister at the temple will cook the sacrifices of the people."

The River From the Temple

47

The man brought me back to the entrance of the temple, and I saw water coming out from under the threshold of the temple toward the east (for the temple faced east). The water was coming down from under the south side of the temple, south of the altar. [2]He then brought me out through the north gate and led me around the outside to the outer gate facing east, and the water was flowing from the south side.

[3]As the man went eastward with a measuring line in his hand, he measured off a thousand cubits[a] and then led me through water that was ankle-deep. [4]He measured off another thousand cubits and led me through water that was knee-deep. He measured off another thousand and led me through water that was up to the waist. [5]He measured off another thousand, but now it was a river that I could not cross, because the water had risen and was deep enough to swim in—a river that no one could cross. [6]He asked me, "Son of man, do you see this?"

Then he led me back to the bank of the river. [7]When I arrived there, I saw a great number of trees on each side of the river. [8]He said to me, "This water flows toward the eastern region and goes down into the Arabah,[b] where it enters the Sea.[c] When it empties into the Sea,[c] the water there becomes fresh. [9]Swarms of living creatures will live wherever the river flows. There will be large numbers of fish, because this water flows there and makes the salt water fresh; so where the river flows everything will live. [10]Fishermen will stand along the shore; from En Gedi to En Eglaim there will be places for spreading nets. The fish will be of many kinds—like the fish of the Great Sea.[d] [11]But the swamps and marshes will not become fresh; they will be left for salt. [12]Fruit trees of all kinds will grow on both banks of the river. Their leaves will not wither, nor will their fruit fail. Every month they will bear, because the water from the sanctuary flows to them. Their fruit will serve for food and their leaves for healing."

truth or dare

Besides telling us that God's a nature lover, these verses describe the river of life. This living water symbolizes the eternal life you can have in Christ. Thirsty?

47:6–12

The Boundaries of the Land

[13]This is what the Sovereign LORD says: "These are the boundaries by which you are to divide the land for an inheritance among the twelve tribes of Israel, with two portions for Joseph. [14]You are to divide it equally among them. Because I swore with uplifted hand to give it to your forefathers, this land will become your inheritance.

[15]"This is to be the boundary of the land:

"On the north side it will run from the Great Sea by the Hethlon road past Lebo[e] Hamath to Zedad, [16]Berothah[f] and Sibraim (which lies on the border between Damascus and Hamath), as far as Hazer Hatticon, which is on the border of Hauran. [17]The boundary will extend from the sea to Hazar Enan,[g] along the northern border of Damascus, with the border of Hamath to the north. This will be the north boundary.

[18]"On the east side the boundary will run between Hauran and Damascus, along the Jordan between Gilead and the land of Israel, to the eastern sea and as far as Tamar.[h] This will be the east boundary.

[19]"On the south side it will run from Tamar as far as the waters of Meribah Kadesh, then along the Wadi of Egypt to the Great Sea. This will be the south boundary.

a 3 That is, about 1,500 feet (about 450 meters)   b 8 Or the Jordan Valley   c 8 That is, the Dead Sea   d 10 That is, the Mediterranean; also in verses 15, 19 and 20   e 15 Or past the entrance to   f 15,16 See Septuagint and Ezekiel 48:1; Hebrew road to go into Zedad, 16Hamath, Berothah   g 17 Hebrew Enon, a variant of Enan   h 18 Septuagint and Syriac; Hebrew Israel. You will measure to the eastern sea

20 "On the west side, the Great Sea will be the boundary to a point opposite Lebo[a] Hamath. This will be the west boundary.

21 "You are to distribute this land among yourselves according to the tribes of Israel. 22 You are to allot it as an inheritance for yourselves and for the aliens who have settled among you and who have children. You are to consider them as native-born Israelites; along with you they are to be allotted an inheritance among the tribes of Israel. 23 In whatever tribe the alien settles, there you are to give him his inheritance," declares the Sovereign Lord.

The Division of the Land

48 "These are the tribes, listed by name: At the northern frontier, Dan will have one portion; it will follow the Hethlon road to Lebo[b] Hamath; Hazar Enan and the northern border of Damascus next to Hamath will be part of its border from the east side to the west side.

2 "Asher will have one portion; it will border the territory of Dan from east to west.

3 "Naphtali will have one portion; it will border the territory of Asher from east to west.

4 "Manasseh will have one portion; it will border the territory of Naphtali from east to west.

5 "Ephraim will have one portion; it will border the territory of Manasseh from east to west.

6 "Reuben will have one portion; it will border the territory of Ephraim from east to west.

7 "Judah will have one portion; it will border the territory of Reuben from east to west.

8 "Bordering the territory of Judah from east to west will be the portion you are to present as a special gift. It will be 25,000 cubits[c] wide, and its length from east to west will equal one of the tribal portions; the sanctuary will be in the center of it.

9 "The special portion you are to offer to the Lord will be 25,000 cubits long and 10,000 cubits[d] wide. 10 This will be the sacred portion for the priests. It will be 25,000 cubits long on the north side, 10,000 cubits wide on the west side, 10,000 cubits wide on the east side and 25,000 cubits long on the south side. In the center of it will be the sanctuary of the Lord. 11 This will be for the consecrated priests, the Zadokites, who were faithful in serving me and did not go astray as the Levites did when the Israelites went astray. 12 It will be a special gift to them from the sacred portion of the land, a most holy portion, bordering the territory of the Levites.

13 "Alongside the territory of the priests, the Levites will have an allotment 25,000 cubits long and 10,000 cubits wide. Its total length will be 25,000 cubits and its width 10,000 cubits. 14 They must not sell or exchange any of it. This is the best of the land and must not pass into other hands, because it is holy to the Lord.

15 "The remaining area, 5,000 cubits wide and 25,000 cubits long, will be for the common use of the city, for houses and for pastureland. The city will be in the center of it 16 and will have these measurements: the north side 4,500 cubits, the south side 4,500 cubits, the east side 4,500 cubits, and the west side 4,500 cubits. 17 The pastureland for the city will be 250 cubits on the north, 250 cubits on the south, 250 cubits on the east, and 250 cubits on the west. 18 What remains of the area, bordering on the sacred portion and running the length of it, will be 10,000 cubits on the east side and 10,000 cubits on the west side. Its produce will supply food for the workers of the city. 19 The workers from the city who farm it will come from all the tribes of Israel. 20 The entire portion will be a square, 25,000 cubits on each side. As a special gift you will set aside the sacred portion, along with the property of the city.

21 "What remains on both sides of the area formed by the sacred portion and the city property will belong to the prince. It will extend eastward from the 25,000 cubits of the sacred portion to the eastern border, and westward from the 25,000 cubits to the western border. Both these areas running the length of the tribal portions will belong to the prince, and the sacred portion with the temple sanctuary will be in the center of them. 22 So the property of the Levites and the property of the city will lie in the center of the area that belongs to the prince. The area belonging to the prince will lie between the border of Judah and the border of Benjamin.

23 "As for the rest of the tribes: Benjamin will have one portion; it will extend from the east side to the west side.

24 "Simeon will have one portion; it will border the territory of Benjamin from east to west.

a 20 Or opposite the entrance to   b 1 Or to the entrance to   c 8 That is, about 7 miles (about 12 kilometers)
d 9 That is, about 3 miles (about 5 kilometers)

²⁵"Issachar will have one portion; it will border the territory of Simeon from east to west.

²⁶"Zebulun will have one portion; it will border the territory of Issachar from east to west.

²⁷"Gad will have one portion; it will border the territory of Zebulun from east to west.

²⁸"The southern boundary of Gad will run south from Tamar to the waters of Meribah Kadesh, then along the Wadi ⌐of Egypt⌐ to the Great Sea.ᵃ

²⁹"This is the land you are to allot as an inheritance to the tribes of Israel, and these will be their portions," declares the Sovereign LORD.

The Gates of the City

³⁰"These will be the exits of the city: Beginning on the north side, which is 4,500 cubits long, ³¹the gates of the city will be named after the tribes of Israel. The three gates on the north side will be the gate of Reuben, the gate of Judah and the gate of Levi.

³²"On the east side, which is 4,500 cubits long, will be three gates: the gate of Joseph, the gate of Benjamin and the gate of Dan.

³³"On the south side, which measures 4,500 cubits, will be three gates: the gate of Simeon, the gate of Issachar and the gate of Zebulun.

³⁴"On the west side, which is 4,500 cubits long, will be three gates: the gate of Gad, the gate of Asher and the gate of Naphtali.

³⁵"The distance all around will be 18,000 cubits.

"And the name of the city from that time on will be:

THE LORD IS THERE."

ᵃ 28 That is, the Mediterranean

at a glance

author:	Daniel.
date:	About 535 B.C.
setting:	Daniel, a Jew, was taken captive to Babylon in 605 B.C. He served in the government of Babylon, and then Persia, for nearly 70 years.
verse to remember:	"Praise be to the name of God for ever and ever; wisdom and power are his. He changes times and seasons; he sets up kings and deposes them. He gives wisdom to the wise and knowledge to the discerning" (2:20–22).
theme to consider:	God is in control over everything—nature, nations and his people. Because of this, we can trust him completely.

daniel

unchanging truth

Palm readers. Tarot cards. Ouija boards. Want to know the future? Want answers to some of your most pressing questions? Well, plunk down a few bucks and hold out your palm. The answers are there, if only you know how to read them . . .

Or at least that's what some would have you believe.

The desire to understand powers beyond ourselves is nothing new. When the powerful king of Babylon had a mysterious dream, who did he call for? His astrologers. Of course, if he had told them his dream, they might have been able to make up an interpretation. So the king demanded that they tell him both the dream *and* what it meant. Finally, even the astrologers admitted, "No one can reveal it to the king except the gods" (2:11) . . . or God.

And that's where Daniel comes in. Daniel was a young Jew who had been taken captive from Judah to Babylon. He and several others served in Nebuchadnezzar's court yet continued to worship their God. When the king needed to know both his dream and what it meant, God gave Daniel the answer.

Daniel understood that God is in complete control. When you want to know how to handle your future, talk to God. When you have big questions, ask him. You'll always get exactly what you need—an answer to guide you and complete truth—not a magical hoax.

life lessons

1 You can maintain a Christian witness, no matter how difficult the people around you try to make it for you (3:8–30; 6:1–23).

2 Powerful leaders are only in authority because God wills it. He raises up leaders and brings them down. No one is outside of his ultimate authority (4:28–37; 5:25–30).

3 God has all of the future in his hands. Nothing happens that surprises him (7:1—8:27; 9:20—12:4).

Daniel's Training in Babylon

1 In the third year of the reign of Jehoiakim king of Judah, Nebuchadnezzar king of Babylon came to Jerusalem and besieged it. [2]And the Lord delivered Jehoiakim king of Judah into his hand, along with some of the articles from the temple of God. These he carried off to the temple of his god in Babylonia[a] and put in the treasure house of his god.

[3]Then the king ordered Ashpenaz, chief of his court officials, to bring in some of the Israelites from the royal family and the nobility— [4]young men without any physical defect, handsome, showing aptitude for every kind of learning, well informed, quick to understand, and qualified to serve in the king's palace. He was to teach them the language and literature of the Babylonians.[b] [5]The king assigned them a daily amount of food and wine from the king's table. They were to be trained for three years, and after that they were to enter the king's service.

[6]Among these were some from Judah: Daniel, Hananiah, Mishael and Azariah. [7]The chief official gave them new names: to Daniel, the name Belteshazzar; to Hananiah, Shadrach; to Mishael, Meshach; and to Azariah, Abednego.

[8]But Daniel resolved not to defile himself with the royal food and wine, and he asked the chief official for permission not to defile himself this way. [9]Now God had caused the official to show favor and sympathy to Daniel, [10]but the official told Daniel, "I am afraid of my lord the king, who has assigned your[c] food and drink. Why should he see you looking worse than the other young men your age? The king would then have my head because of you."

[11]Daniel then said to the guard whom the chief official had appointed over Daniel, Hananiah, Mishael and Azariah, [12]"Please test your servants for ten days: Give us nothing but vegetables to eat and water to drink. [13]Then compare our appearance with that of the young men who eat the royal food, and treat your servants in accordance with what you see." [14]So he agreed to this and tested them for ten days.

[15]At the end of the ten days they looked healthier and better nourished than any of the young men who ate the royal food. [16]So the guard took away their choice food and the wine they were to drink and gave them vegetables instead.

[17]To these four young men God gave knowledge and understanding of all kinds of literature and learning. And Daniel could understand visions and dreams of all kinds.

[18]At the end of the time set by the king to bring them in, the chief official presented them to Nebuchadnezzar. [19]The king talked with them, and he found none equal to Daniel, Hananiah, Mishael and Azariah; so they entered the king's service. [20]In every matter of

genuine

integrity

daniel 1:20

Your character really shows through in a crisis. When bad things happen, do you try to put your best face forward? Or do you put the sulky face forward? Daniel and his friends were captives in a foreign land—not an ideal situation, right? Yet they didn't complain or turn into mindless zombies. Instead they kept their cool and their integrity. When you face a tough situation—being cut from the team, getting strict rules from your parents, being dumped by a guy or left out by your friends—do you sulk or stay strong?

1:1-21

or dare

truth

To Daniel, this was more about obedience than nutrition. God had told the Israelites not to eat certain foods, so Daniel and his buds didn't. When your beliefs butt heads with society, what do you do?

1:8–16

---

[a] 2 Hebrew *Shinar*   [b] 4 Or *Chaldeans*   [c] 10 The Hebrew for *your* and *you* in this verse is plural.

wisdom and understanding about which the king questioned them, he found them ten times better than all the magicians and enchanters in his whole kingdom.

²¹And Daniel remained there until the first year of King Cyrus.

Nebuchadnezzar's Dream

2 In the second year of his reign, Nebuchadnezzar had dreams; his mind was troubled and he could not sleep. ²So the king summoned the magicians, enchanters, sorcerers and astrologers *a* to tell him what he had dreamed. When they came in and stood before the king, ³he said to them, "I have had a dream that troubles me and I want to know what it means. *b*"

⁴Then the astrologers answered the king in Aramaic, *c* "O king, live forever! Tell your servants the dream, and we will interpret it."

⁵The king replied to the astrologers, "This is what I have firmly decided: If you do not tell me what my dream was and interpret it, I will have you cut into pieces and your houses turned into piles of rubble. ⁶But if you tell me the dream and explain it, you will receive from me gifts and rewards and great honor. So tell me the dream and interpret it for me."

⁷Once more they replied, "Let the king tell his servants the dream, and we will interpret it."

⁸Then the king answered, "I am certain that you are trying to gain time, because you realize that this is what I have firmly decided: ⁹If you do not tell me the dream, there is just one penalty for you. You have conspired to tell me misleading and wicked things, hoping the situation will change. So then, tell me the dream, and I will know that you can interpret it for me."

¹⁰The astrologers answered the king, "There is not a man on earth who can do what the king asks! No king, however great and mighty, has ever asked such a thing of any magician or enchanter or astrologer. ¹¹What the king asks is too difficult. No one can reveal it to the king except the gods, and they do not live among men."

¹²This made the king so angry and furious that he ordered the execution of all the wise men of Babylon. ¹³So the decree was issued to put the wise men to death, and men were sent to look for Daniel and his friends to put them to death.

¹⁴When Arioch, the commander of the king's guard, had gone out to put to death the wise men of Babylon, Daniel spoke to him with wisdom and tact. ¹⁵He asked the king's officer, "Why did the king issue such a harsh decree?" Arioch then explained the matter to Daniel. ¹⁶At this, Daniel went in to the king and asked for time, so that he might interpret the dream for him.

¹⁷Then Daniel returned to his house and explained the matter to his friends Hananiah, Mishael and Azariah. ¹⁸He urged them to plead for mercy from the God of heaven concerning this mystery, so that he and his friends might not be executed with the rest of the wise men of Babylon. ¹⁹During the night the mystery was revealed to Daniel in a vision. Then Daniel praised the God of heaven ²⁰and said:

> "Praise be to the name of God for ever and ever;
> wisdom and power are his.
> ²¹He changes times and seasons;
> he sets up kings and deposes them.
> He gives wisdom to the wise
> and knowledge to the discerning.
> ²²He reveals deep and hidden things;
> he knows what lies in darkness,
> and light dwells with him.
> ²³I thank and praise you, O God of my fathers:
> You have given me wisdom and power,
> you have made known to me what we asked of you,
> you have made known to us the dream of the king."

Daniel Interprets the Dream

²⁴Then Daniel went to Arioch, whom the king had appointed to execute the wise men of Babylon, and said to him, "Do not execute the wise men of Babylon. Take me to the king, and I will interpret his dream for him."

---

a 2 Or *Chaldeans*; also in verses 4, 5 and 10   *b 3* Or *was*   *c 4* The text from here through chapter 7 is in Aramaic.

To Each Her Own?

"Jesus, Buddha, Mohammed—they were all great teachers who taught basically the same thing," Gracie tossed out as we sat around the lunch table, waiting on the bell and discussing last period's world religions class with Mr. Sanchez.

"Right," I nodded in agreement with the others. Only I was actually thinking something different. *Yeah right! They only differ when it comes to what they teach about creation, sin, salvation, heaven, hell and God. Other than those little details, it's hard to tell them apart.*

"I agree with Mr. Sanchez. I'm not going to force my religion on someone else—whatever someone wants to believe is fine," said Maggie, drawing approving looks from the others.

"Exactly," I nodded, not wanting to seem to disagree. Except I did disagree. I'd always learned in church that we ought to share our Christian faith. *Is that the same as forcing your religion on someone?* I wondered.

"You know, Buddhists take their religion as seriously as any Christian I've seen. Who are we to say they're wrong?" Kapree asked. "Everybody finds their own way to God. The important thing is to find one that works for you."

"Preach it, girl," I joked, hoping desperately the topic would change. My heart was racing for some reason. I knew I should say something about my Christian beliefs, yet I was afraid to disagree.

My joke worked. The topic changed. The bell rang. And we went to our next class.

pluralism in focus

What's *pluralism*? A dictionary definition goes something like this: "the belief that multiple religions or secular worldviews are legitimate and valid. Each is true when viewed from within its own culture."

»*Translation?* According to pluralism, Christianity is up for grabs—along with every other worldview. There's no such thing as absolute truth.

»*What's wrong with pluralism?* You can't treat all religions equally. Their messages are actually contradictory. For example, Jesus excluded the possibility of "many paths to heaven" when he said he was the way, the truth and the life. No one can come to God apart from him (see John 14:6, page 1433).

»*Say what?* Yeah, God wants you to speak up. We're supposed to defend the faith with "gentleness and respect" (1 Peter 3:15, page 1610). Disagree, but do it lovingly.

For more on this topic, see the index on page 1656.

For more on what distinguishes Christianity from other religions, check out the Pluralism Link on www.TrueImagesBible.com

²⁵Arioch took Daniel to the king at once and said, "I have found a man among the exiles from Judah who can tell the king what his dream means."

²⁶The king asked Daniel (also called Belteshazzar), "Are you able to tell me what I saw in my dream and interpret it?"

²⁷Daniel replied, "No wise man, enchanter, magician or diviner can explain to the king the mystery he has asked about, ²⁸but there is a God in heaven who reveals mysteries. He has shown King

Nebuchadnezzar what will happen in days to come. Your dream and the visions that passed through your mind as you lay on your bed are these:

²⁹"As you were lying there, O king, your mind turned to things to come, and the revealer of mysteries showed you what is going to happen. ³⁰As for me, this mystery has been revealed to me, not because I have greater wisdom than other living men, but so that you, O king, may know the interpretation and that you may understand what went through your mind.

³¹"You looked, O king, and there before you stood a large statue—an enormous, dazzling statue, awesome in appearance. ³²The head of the statue was made of pure gold, its chest and arms of silver, its belly and thighs of bronze, ³³its legs of iron, its feet partly of iron and partly of baked clay. ³⁴While you were watching, a rock was cut out, but not by human hands. It struck the statue on its feet of iron and clay and smashed them. ³⁵Then the iron, the clay, the bronze, the silver and the gold were broken to pieces at the same time and became like chaff on a threshing floor in the summer. The wind swept them away without leaving a trace. But the rock that struck the statue became a huge mountain and filled the whole earth.

³⁶"This was the dream, and now we will interpret it to the king. ³⁷You, O king, are the king of kings. The God of heaven has given you dominion and power and might and glory; ³⁸in your hands he has placed mankind and the beasts of the field and the birds of the air. Wherever they live, he has made you ruler over them all. You are that head of gold.

³⁹"After you, another kingdom will rise, inferior to yours. Next, a third kingdom, one of bronze, will rule over the whole earth. ⁴⁰Finally, there will be a fourth kingdom, strong as iron—for iron breaks and smashes everything—and as iron breaks things to pieces, so it will crush and break all the others. ⁴¹Just as you saw that the feet and toes were partly of baked clay and partly of iron, so this will be a divided kingdom; yet it will have some of the strength of iron in it, even as you saw iron mixed with clay. ⁴²As the toes were partly iron and partly clay, so this kingdom will be partly strong and partly brittle. ⁴³And just as you saw the iron mixed with baked clay, so the people will be a mixture and will not remain united, any more than iron mixes with clay.

⁴⁴"In the time of those kings, the God of heaven will set up a kingdom that will never be destroyed, nor will it be left to another people. It will crush all those kingdoms and bring them to an end, but it will itself endure forever. ⁴⁵This is the meaning of the vision of the rock cut out of a mountain, but not by human hands—a rock that broke the iron, the bronze, the clay, the silver and the gold to pieces.

"The great God has shown the king what will take place in the future. The dream is true and the interpretation is trustworthy."

⁴⁶Then King Nebuchadnezzar fell prostrate before Daniel and paid him honor and ordered that an offering and incense be presented to him. ⁴⁷The king said to Daniel, "Surely your God is the God of gods and the Lord of kings and a revealer of mysteries, for you were able to reveal this mystery."

⁴⁸Then the king placed Daniel in a high position and lavished many gifts on him. He made him ruler over the entire province of Babylon and placed him in charge of all its wise men. ⁴⁹Moreover, at Daniel's request the king appointed Shadrach, Meshach and Abednego administrators over the province of Babylon, while Daniel himself remained at the royal court.

The Image of Gold and the Fiery Furnace

3 King Nebuchadnezzar made an image of gold, ninety feet high and nine feet*ᵃ* wide, and set it up on the plain of Dura in the province of Babylon. ²He then summoned the satraps, prefects, governors, advisers, treasurers, judges, magistrates and all the other provincial officials to come to the dedication of the image he had set up. ³So the satraps, prefects, governors, advisers, treasurers, judges, magistrates and all the other provincial officials assembled for the dedication of the image that King Nebuchadnezzar had set up, and they stood before it.

⁴Then the herald loudly proclaimed, "This is what you are commanded to do, O peoples, nations and men of every language: ⁵As soon as you hear the sound of the horn, flute, zither, lyre, harp, pipes and all kinds of music, you must fall down and worship the image of gold that King Nebuchadnezzar has set up. ⁶Whoever does not fall down and worship will immediately be thrown into a blazing furnace."

» *a 1* Aramaic *sixty cubits high and six cubits wide* (about 27 meters high and 2.7 meters wide)

⁷Therefore, as soon as they heard the sound of the horn, flute, zither, lyre, harp and all kinds of music, all the peoples, nations and men of every language fell down and worshiped the image of gold that King Nebuchadnezzar had set up.

⁸At this time some astrologers*ᵃ* came forward and denounced the Jews. ⁹They said to King Nebuchadnezzar, "O king, live forever! ¹⁰You have issued a decree, O king, that everyone who hears the sound of the horn, flute, zither, lyre, harp, pipes and all kinds of music must fall down and worship the image of gold, ¹¹and that whoever does not fall down and worship will be thrown into a blazing furnace. ¹²But there are some Jews whom you have set over the affairs of the province of Babylon—Shadrach, Meshach and Abednego—who pay no attention to you, O king. They neither serve your gods nor worship the image of gold you have set up."

¹³Furious with rage, Nebuchadnezzar summoned Shadrach, Meshach and Abednego. So these men were brought before the king, ¹⁴and Nebuchadnezzar said to them, "Is it true, Shadrach, Meshach and Abednego, that you do not serve my gods or worship the image of gold I have set up? ¹⁵Now when you hear the sound of the horn, flute, zither, lyre, harp, pipes and all kinds of music, if you are ready to fall down and worship the image I made, very good. But if you do not worship it, you will be thrown immediately into a blazing furnace. Then what god will be able to rescue you from my hand?"

¹⁶Shadrach, Meshach and Abednego replied to the king, "O Nebuchadnezzar, we do not need to defend ourselves before you in this matter. ¹⁷If we are thrown into the blazing furnace, the God we serve is able to save us from it, and he will rescue us from your hand, O king. ¹⁸But even if he does not, we want you to know, O king, that we will not serve your gods or worship the image of gold you have set up."

¹⁹Then Nebuchadnezzar was furious with Shadrach, Meshach and Abednego, and his attitude toward them changed. He ordered the furnace heated seven times hotter than usual ²⁰and commanded some of the strongest soldiers in his army to tie up Shadrach, Meshach and Abednego and throw them into the blazing furnace. ²¹So these men, wearing their robes, trousers, turbans and other clothes, were bound and thrown into the blazing furnace. ²²The king's command was so urgent and the furnace so hot that the flames of the fire killed the soldiers who took up Shadrach, Meshach and Abednego, ²³and these three men, firmly tied, fell into the blazing furnace.

²⁴Then King Nebuchadnezzar leaped to his feet in amazement and asked his advisers, "Weren't there three men that we tied up and threw into the fire?"

They replied, "Certainly, O king."

²⁵He said, "Look! I see four men walking around in the fire, unbound and unharmed, and the fourth looks like a son of the gods."

²⁶Nebuchadnezzar then approached the

truth or dare

These three guys faced a pretty hard choice: deny God by worshiping an idol, or get burned (literally). When opposition gets fiery hot, do you stand firm or start fumbling?

3:10–12

genuine

trust » 3:13–30

Would you trust God with your *life*? Or do you, like most of us, just *talk* about that kind of trust? Shadrach, Meshach and Abednego didn't just talk about trusting God. They proved it by their obedience, which nearly cost them their lives. You may never have to make a decision like theirs. But are you prepared to do so, regardless? It takes a lot of trust to walk into a hot furnace. A hot furnace for you might be walking into your school and sharing the gospel. Or it might mean risking your reputation instead of following the crowd. Are you ready?

ᵃ 8 Or *Chaldeans*

opening of the blazing furnace and shouted, "Shadrach, Meshach and Abednego, servants of the Most High God, come out! Come here!"

So Shadrach, Meshach and Abednego came out of the fire, ²⁷and the satraps, prefects, governors and royal advisers crowded around them. They saw that the fire had not harmed their bodies, nor was a hair of their heads singed; their robes were not scorched, and there was no smell of fire on them.

²⁸Then Nebuchadnezzar said, "Praise be to the God of Shadrach, Meshach and Abednego, who has sent his angel and rescued his servants! They trusted in him and defied the king's command and were willing to give up their lives rather than serve or worship any god except their own God. ²⁹Therefore I decree that the people of any nation or language who say anything against the God of Shadrach, Meshach and Abednego be cut into pieces and their houses be turned into piles of rubble, for no other god can save in this way."

³⁰Then the king promoted Shadrach, Meshach and Abednego in the province of Babylon.

Nebuchadnezzar's Dream of a Tree

4 King Nebuchadnezzar,

To the peoples, nations and men of every language, who live in all the world:

May you prosper greatly!

²It is my pleasure to tell you about the miraculous signs and wonders that the Most High God has performed for me.

³How great are his signs,
how mighty his wonders!
His kingdom is an eternal kingdom;
his dominion endures from generation to generation.

⁴I, Nebuchadnezzar, was at home in my palace, contented and prosperous. ⁵I had a dream that made me afraid. As I was lying in my bed, the images and visions that passed through my mind terrified me. ⁶So I commanded that all the wise men of Babylon be brought before me to interpret the dream for me. ⁷When the magicians, enchanters, astrologers^a and diviners came, I told them the dream, but they could not interpret it for me. ⁸Finally, Daniel came into my presence and I told him the dream. (He is called Belteshazzar, after the name of my god, and the spirit of the holy gods is in him.)

⁹I said, "Belteshazzar, chief of the magicians, I know that the spirit of the holy gods is in you, and no mystery is too difficult for you. Here is my dream; interpret it for me. ¹⁰These are the visions I saw while lying in my bed: I looked, and there before me stood a tree in the middle of the land. Its height was enormous. ¹¹The tree grew large and strong and its top touched the sky; it was visible to the ends of the earth. ¹²Its leaves were beautiful, its fruit abundant, and on it was food for all. Under it the beasts of the field found shelter, and the birds of the air lived in its branches; from it every creature was fed.

¹³"In the visions I saw while lying in my bed, I looked, and there before me was a messenger,^b a holy one, coming down from heaven. ¹⁴He called in a loud voice: 'Cut down the tree and trim off its branches; strip off its leaves and scatter its fruit. Let the animals flee from under it and the birds from its branches. ¹⁵But let the stump and its roots, bound with iron and bronze, remain in the ground, in the grass of the field.

" 'Let him be drenched with the dew of heaven, and let him live with the animals among the plants of the earth. ¹⁶Let his mind be changed from that of a man and let him be given the mind of an animal, till seven times^c pass by for him.

¹⁷" 'The decision is announced by messengers, the holy ones declare the verdict, so that the living may know that the Most High is sovereign over the kingdoms of men and gives them to anyone he wishes and sets over them the lowliest of men.'

¹⁸"This is the dream that I, King Nebuchadnezzar, had. Now, Belteshazzar, tell me what it means, for none of the wise men in my kingdom can interpret it for me. But you can, because the spirit of the holy gods is in you."

» ^a 7 Or Chaldeans   ^b 13 Or watchman; also in verses 17 and 23   ^c 16 Or years; also in verses 23, 25 and 32

Daniel Interprets the Dream

[19]Then Daniel (also called Belteshazzar) was greatly perplexed for a time, and his thoughts terrified him. So the king said, "Belteshazzar, do not let the dream or its meaning alarm you."

Belteshazzar answered, "My lord, if only the dream applied to your enemies and its meaning to your adversaries! [20]The tree you saw, which grew large and strong, with its top touching the sky, visible to the whole earth, [21]with beautiful leaves and abundant fruit, providing food for all, giving shelter to the beasts of the field, and having nesting places in its branches for the birds of the air— [22]you, O king, are that tree! You have become great and strong; your greatness has grown until it reaches the sky, and your dominion extends to distant parts of the earth.

[23]"You, O king, saw a messenger, a holy one, coming down from heaven and saying, 'Cut down the tree and destroy it, but leave the stump, bound with iron and bronze, in the grass of the field, while its roots remain in the ground. Let him be drenched with the dew of heaven; let him live like the wild animals, until seven times pass by for him.'

[24]"This is the interpretation, O king, and this is the decree the Most High has issued against my lord the king: [25]You will be driven away from people and will live with the wild animals; you will eat grass like cattle and be drenched with the dew of heaven. Seven times will pass by for you until you acknowledge that the Most High is sovereign over the kingdoms of men and gives them to anyone he wishes. [26]The command to leave the stump of the tree with its roots means that your kingdom will be restored to you when you acknowledge that Heaven rules. [27]Therefore, O king, be pleased to accept my advice: Renounce your sins by doing what is right, and your wickedness by being kind to the oppressed. It may be that then your prosperity will continue."

truth or dare

When ol' Neb decided to play truth or dare with God, he was asking for trouble. Don't learn the hard way. Search and destroy pride *before* it destroys you.

4:24–33

The Dream Is Fulfilled

[28]All this happened to King Nebuchadnezzar. [29]Twelve months later, as the king was walking on the roof of the royal palace of Babylon, [30]he said, "Is not this the great Babylon I have built as the royal residence, by my mighty power and for the glory of my majesty?"

[31]The words were still on his lips when a voice came from heaven, "This is what is decreed for you, King Nebuchadnezzar: Your royal authority has been taken from you. [32]You will be driven away from people and will live with the wild animals; you will eat grass like cattle. Seven times will pass by for you until you acknowledge that the Most High is sovereign over the kingdoms of men and gives them to anyone he wishes."

[33]Immediately what had been said about Nebuchadnezzar was fulfilled. He was driven away from people and ate grass like cattle. His body was drenched with the dew of heaven until his hair grew like the feathers of an eagle and his nails like the claws of a bird.

[34]At the end of that time, I, Nebuchadnezzar, raised my eyes toward heaven, and my sanity was restored. Then I praised the Most High; I honored and glorified him who lives forever.

> His dominion is an eternal dominion;
> his kingdom endures from generation to generation.
> [35]All the peoples of the earth
> are regarded as nothing.
> He does as he pleases
> with the powers of heaven
> and the peoples of the earth.
> No one can hold back his hand
> or say to him: "What have you done?"

[36]At the same time that my sanity was restored, my honor and splendor were returned to me for the glory of my kingdom. My advisers and nobles sought me out, and I was restored to my throne and became even greater than before. [37]Now I, Nebuchadnezzar, praise and exalt and glorify the King of heaven, because everything he does is right and all his ways are just. And those who walk in pride he is able to humble.

The Writing on the Wall

5 King Belshazzar gave a great banquet for a thousand of his nobles and drank wine with them. [2]While Belshazzar was drinking his wine, he gave orders to bring in the gold and silver goblets that Nebuchadnezzar his father[a] had taken from the temple in Jerusalem, so that the king and his nobles, his wives and his concubines might drink from them. [3]So they brought in the gold goblets that had been taken from the temple of God in Jerusalem, and the king and his nobles, his wives and his concubines drank from them. [4]As they drank the wine, they praised the gods of gold and silver, of bronze, iron, wood and stone.

[5]Suddenly the fingers of a human hand appeared and wrote on the plaster of the wall, near the lampstand in the royal palace. The king watched the hand as it wrote. [6]His face turned pale and he was so frightened that his knees knocked together and his legs gave way.

[7]The king called out for the enchanters, astrologers[b] and diviners to be brought and said to these wise men of Babylon, "Whoever reads this writing and tells me what it means will be clothed in purple and have a gold chain placed around his neck, and he will be made the third highest ruler in the kingdom."

[8]Then all the king's wise men came in, but they could not read the writing or tell the king what it meant. [9]So King Belshazzar became even more terrified and his face grew more pale. His nobles were baffled.

[10]The queen,[c] hearing the voices of the king and his nobles, came into the banquet hall. "O king, live forever!" she said. "Don't be alarmed! Don't look so pale! [11]There is a man in your kingdom who has the spirit of the holy gods in him. In the time of your father he was found to have insight and intelligence and wisdom like that of the gods. King Nebuchadnezzar your father—your father the king, I say—appointed him chief of the magicians, enchanters, astrologers and diviners. [12]This man Daniel, whom the king called Belteshazzar, was found to have a keen mind and knowledge and understanding, and also the ability to interpret dreams, explain riddles and solve difficult problems. Call for Daniel, and he will tell you what the writing means."

[13]So Daniel was brought before the king, and the king said to him, "Are you Daniel, one of the exiles my father the king brought from Judah? [14]I have heard that the spirit of the gods is in you and that you have insight, intelligence and outstanding wisdom. [15]The wise men and enchanters were brought before me to read this writing and tell me what it means, but they could not explain it. [16]Now I have heard that you are able to give interpretations and to solve difficult problems. If you can read this writing and tell me what it means, you will be clothed in purple and have a gold chain placed around your neck, and you will be made the third highest ruler in the kingdom."

[17]Then Daniel answered the king, "You may keep your gifts for yourself and give your rewards to someone else. Nevertheless, I will read the writing for the king and tell him what it means.

[18]"O king, the Most High God gave your father Nebuchadnezzar sovereignty and greatness and glory and splendor. [19]Because of the high position he gave him, all the peoples and nations and men of every language dreaded and feared him. Those the king wanted to put to death, he put to death; those he wanted to spare, he spared; those he wanted to promote, he promoted; and those he wanted to humble, he humbled. [20]But when his heart became arrogant and hardened with pride, he was deposed from his royal throne and stripped of his glory. [21]He was driven away from people and given the mind of an animal; he lived with the wild donkeys and ate grass like cattle; and his body was drenched with the dew of heaven, until he acknowledged that the Most High God is sovereign over the kingdoms of men and sets over them anyone he wishes.

[22]"But you his son,[d] O Belshazzar, have not humbled yourself, though you knew all this. [23]Instead, you have set yourself up against the Lord of heaven. You had the goblets from his temple brought to you, and you and your nobles, your wives and your concubines drank wine from them.

a 2 Or ancestor; or predecessor; also in verses 11, 13 and 18   b 7 Or Chaldeans; also in verse 11   c 10 Or queen mother   d 22 Or descendant; or successor

Follow Me?

Profile: MacKenzie

I couldn't believe it. Five minutes into our rehearsal, and everything was up for grabs. One girl didn't like the song that we'd chosen, another girl didn't want to wear blue and a few others were arguing about something totally unrelated! How were we ever going to get ready for the talent show audition?

I walked over to the piano and plunked down a key. "Hey! If we want to get something done, we're all going to have to work together here." At least *that* got their attention! From there, we were able to discuss the pros and cons of the song (the selection was okay since, as I pointed out, it fit so many of our voices), agree on what we were going to wear (blue, it turned out, was actually fine) and even get in some actual rehearsing.

As I was getting ready to leave, one of the girls walked over to me. "MacKenzie, thanks for helping us get our act together today. I don't know what we would have done if you hadn't taken control of the rehearsal."

I was a bit stunned at what she said. I didn't feel like I had "taken control." I just tried to keep us focused and offered some suggestions on what I thought we might want to do. The others just seemed to follow my lead.

You know, this isn't the first time that someone has mentioned my ability to "take control" or lead, or whatever you want to call it. Maybe there's something to this leadership thing . . .

leadership in focus

For more on leadership, log onto www.TrueImagesBible.com

Maybe you, like MacKenzie, have stepped up to take control of a group or meeting. Or maybe you've been asked to be a class rep or leader for your small group. Either way—whether you're a natural-born leader or you're not—being a leader is a huge responsibility.

»Remember that you have greater accountability for your decisions because they influence others so much.

»Read more about the high-profile women leaders in the Bible in the "Mirror Images" profiles. Check out Deborah and Esther, for example. See the index on page vi.

»Keep in mind that leadership has nothing to do with age. Set a good example now (see 1 Timothy 4:12, page 1572).

»Sometimes being a leader requires you to take a stand for what's right, as Daniel did (see Daniel 6, pages 1174–1175). Daniel's faithful leadership influenced a whole nation.

For more on this topic, see the index on page 1656.

You praised the gods of silver and gold, of bronze, iron, wood and stone, which cannot see or hear or understand. But you did not honor the God who holds in his hand your life and all your ways. [24]Therefore he sent the hand that wrote the inscription.

[25]"This is the inscription that was written:

MENE, MENE, TEKEL, PARSIN[a]

a 25 Aramaic *UPARSIN* (that is, *AND PARSIN*)

[26]"This is what these words mean:

> *Mene*[a]: God has numbered the days of your reign and brought it to an end.
> [27] *Tekel*[b]: You have been weighed on the scales and found wanting.
> [28] *Peres*[c]: Your kingdom is divided and given to the Medes and Persians."

[29]Then at Belshazzar's command, Daniel was clothed in purple, a gold chain was placed around his neck, and he was proclaimed the third highest ruler in the kingdom.

[30]That very night Belshazzar, king of the Babylonians,[d] was slain, [31]and Darius the Mede took over the kingdom, at the age of sixty-two.

Daniel in the Den of Lions

6 It pleased Darius to appoint 120 satraps to rule throughout the kingdom, [2]with three administrators over them, one of whom was Daniel. The satraps were made accountable to them so that the king might not suffer loss. [3]Now Daniel so distinguished himself among the administrators and the satraps by his exceptional qualities that the king planned to set him over the whole kingdom. [4]At this, the administrators and the satraps tried to find grounds for charges against Daniel in his conduct of government affairs, but they were unable to do so. They could find no corruption in him, because he was trustworthy and neither corrupt nor negligent. [5]Finally these men said, "We will never find any basis for charges against this man Daniel unless it has something to do with the law of his God."

[6]So the administrators and the satraps went as a group to the king and said: "O King Darius, live forever! [7]The royal administrators, prefects, satraps, advisers and governors have all agreed that the king should issue an edict and enforce the decree that anyone who prays to any god or man during the next thirty days, except to you, O king, shall be thrown into the lions' den. [8]Now, O king, issue the decree and put it in writing so that it cannot be altered—in accordance with the laws of the Medes and Persians, which cannot be repealed." [9]So King Darius put the decree in writing.

[10]Now when Daniel learned that the decree had been published, he went home to his upstairs room where the windows opened toward Jerusalem. Three times a day he got down on his knees and prayed, giving thanks to his God, just as he had done before. [11]Then these men went as a group and found Daniel praying and asking God for help. [12]So they went to the king and spoke to him about his royal decree: "Did you not publish a decree that during the next thirty days anyone who prays to any god or man except to you, O king, would be thrown into the lions' den?"

The king answered, "The decree stands—in accordance with the laws of the Medes and Persians, which cannot be repealed."

[13]Then they said to the king, "Daniel, who is one of the exiles from Judah, pays no attention to you, O king, or to the decree you put in writing. He still prays three times a day." [14]When the king heard this, he was greatly distressed; he was determined to rescue Daniel and made every effort until sundown to save him.

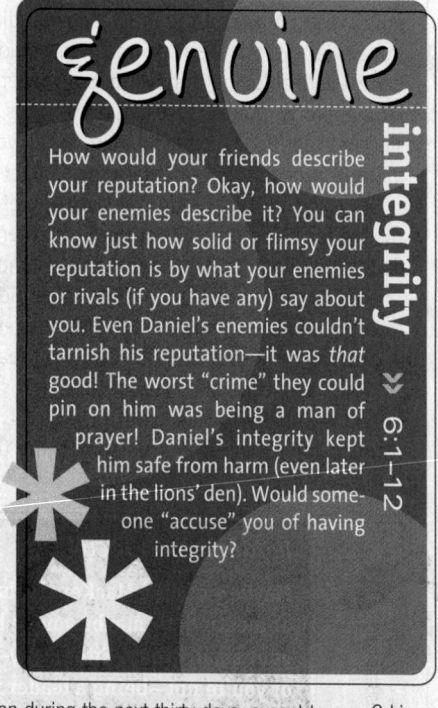

genuine integrity » 6:1-12

How would your friends describe your reputation? Okay, how would your enemies describe it? You can know just how solid or flimsy your reputation is by what your enemies or rivals (if you have any) say about you. Even Daniel's enemies couldn't tarnish his reputation—it was *that* good! The worst "crime" they could pin on him was being a man of prayer! Daniel's integrity kept him safe from harm (even later in the lions' den). Would someone "accuse" you of having integrity?

---

a 26 Mene can mean *numbered* or *mina* (a unit of money).   *b 27 Tekel* can mean *weighed* or *shekel*.   *c 28 Peres* (the singular of *Parsin*) can mean *divided* or *Persia* or *a half mina* or *a half shekel*.   *d 30* Or *Chaldeans*

¹⁵Then the men went as a group to the king and said to him, "Remember, O king, that according to the law of the Medes and Persians no decree or edict that the king issues can be changed."

¹⁶So the king gave the order, and they brought Daniel and threw him into the lions' den. The king said to Daniel, "May your God, whom you serve continually, rescue you!"

¹⁷A stone was brought and placed over the mouth of the den, and the king sealed it with his own signet ring and with the rings of his nobles, so that Daniel's situation might not be changed. ¹⁸Then the king returned to his palace and spent the night without eating and without any entertainment being brought to him. And he could not sleep.

¹⁹At the first light of dawn, the king got up and hurried to the lions' den. ²⁰When he came near the den, he called to Daniel in an anguished voice, "Daniel, servant of the living God, has your God, whom you serve continually, been able to rescue you from the lions?"

²¹Daniel answered, "O king, live forever! ²²My God sent his angel, and he shut the mouths of the lions. They have not hurt me, because I was found innocent in his sight. Nor have I ever done any wrong before you, O king."

²³The king was overjoyed and gave orders to lift Daniel out of the den. And when Daniel was lifted from the den, no wound was found on him, because he had trusted in his God.

²⁴At the king's command, the men who had falsely accused Daniel were brought in and thrown into the lions' den, along with their wives and children. And before they reached the floor of the den, the lions overpowered them and crushed all their bones.

²⁵Then King Darius wrote to all the peoples, nations and men of every language throughout the land:

"May you prosper greatly!

²⁶"I issue a decree that in every part of my kingdom people must fear and reverence the God of Daniel.

"For he is the living God
    and he endures forever;
his kingdom will not be destroyed,
    his dominion will never end.
²⁷He rescues and he saves;
    he performs signs and wonders
    in the heavens and on the earth.
He has rescued Daniel
    from the power of the lions."

²⁸So Daniel prospered during the reign of Darius and the reign of Cyrus*a* the Persian.

Daniel's Dream of Four Beasts

7 In the first year of Belshazzar king of Babylon, Daniel had a dream, and visions passed through his mind as he was lying on his bed. He wrote down the substance of his dream. ²Daniel said: "In my vision at night I looked, and there before me were the four winds of heaven churning up the great sea. ³Four great beasts, each different from the others, came up out of the sea.

⁴"The first was like a lion, and it had the wings of an eagle. I watched until its wings were torn off and it was lifted from the ground so that it stood on two feet like a man, and the heart of a man was given to it.

⁵"And there before me was a second beast, which looked like a bear. It was raised up on one

truth or dare

What do you do when you're facing ravenous lions who're eyeing you like a snack? Okay, so *that* may never happen, but this just goes to show that God can get you through *anything*.

6:15–23

a 28 Or Darius, that is, the reign of Cyrus

of its sides, and it had three ribs in its mouth between its teeth. It was told, 'Get up and eat your fill of flesh!'

⁶"After that, I looked, and there before me was another beast, one that looked like a leopard. And on its back it had four wings like those of a bird. This beast had four heads, and it was given authority to rule.

⁷"After that, in my vision at night I looked, and there before me was a fourth beast—terrifying and frightening and very powerful. It had large iron teeth; it crushed and devoured its victims and trampled underfoot whatever was left. It was different from all the former beasts, and it had ten horns.

⁸"While I was thinking about the horns, there before me was another horn, a little one, which came up among them; and three of the first horns were uprooted before it. This horn had eyes like the eyes of a man and a mouth that spoke boastfully.

⁹"As I looked,

> "thrones were set in place,
>   and the Ancient of Days took his seat.
> His clothing was as white as snow;
>   the hair of his head was white like wool.
> His throne was flaming with fire,
>   and its wheels were all ablaze.
> ¹⁰A river of fire was flowing,
>   coming out from before him.
> Thousands upon thousands attended him;
>   ten thousand times ten thousand stood before him.
> The court was seated,
>   and the books were opened.

¹¹"Then I continued to watch because of the boastful words the horn was speaking. I kept looking until the beast was slain and its body destroyed and thrown into the blazing fire. ¹²(The other beasts had been stripped of their authority, but were allowed to live for a period of time.)

¹³"In my vision at night I looked, and there before me was one like a son of man, coming with the clouds of heaven. He approached the Ancient of Days and was led into his presence. ¹⁴He was given authority, glory and sovereign power; all peoples, nations and men of every language worshiped him. His dominion is an everlasting dominion that will not pass away, and his kingdom is one that will never be destroyed.

The Interpretation of the Dream

¹⁵"I, Daniel, was troubled in spirit, and the visions that passed through my mind disturbed me. ¹⁶I approached one of those standing there and asked him the true meaning of all this.

"So he told me and gave me the interpretation of these things: ¹⁷'The four great beasts are four kingdoms that will rise from the earth. ¹⁸But the saints of the Most High will receive the kingdom and will possess it forever—yes, for ever and ever.'

¹⁹"Then I wanted to know the true meaning of the fourth beast, which was different from all the others and most terrifying, with its iron teeth and bronze claws—the beast that crushed and devoured its victims and trampled underfoot whatever was left. ²⁰I also wanted to know about the ten horns on its head and about the other horn that came up, before which three of them fell—the horn that looked more imposing than the others and that had eyes and a mouth that spoke boastfully. ²¹As I watched, this horn was waging war against the saints and defeating them, ²²until the Ancient of Days came and pronounced judgment in favor of the saints of the Most High, and the time came when they possessed the kingdom.

²³"He gave me this explanation: 'The fourth beast is a fourth kingdom that will appear on earth. It will be different from all the other kingdoms and will devour the whole earth, trampling it down and crushing it. ²⁴The ten horns are ten kings who will come from this kingdom. After them another king will arise, different from the earlier ones; he will subdue three kings. ²⁵He will speak against the Most High and oppress his saints and try to change the set times and the laws. The saints will be handed over to him for a time, times and half a time. ᵃ

ᵃ 25 Or *for a year, two years and half a year*

²⁶" 'But the court will sit, and his power will be taken away and completely destroyed forever. ²⁷Then the sovereignty, power and greatness of the kingdoms under the whole heaven will be handed over to the saints, the people of the Most High. His kingdom will be an everlasting kingdom, and all rulers will worship and obey him.'

²⁸"This is the end of the matter. I, Daniel, was deeply troubled by my thoughts, and my face turned pale, but I kept the matter to myself."

Daniel's Vision of a Ram and a Goat

8 In the third year of King Belshazzar's reign, I, Daniel, had a vision, after the one that had already appeared to me. ²In my vision I saw myself in the citadel of Susa in the province of Elam; in the vision I was beside the Ulai Canal. ³I looked up, and there before me was a ram with two horns, standing beside the canal, and the horns were long. One of the horns was longer than the other but grew up later. ⁴I watched the ram as he charged toward the west and the north and the south. No animal could stand against him, and none could rescue from his power. He did as he pleased and became great.

⁵As I was thinking about this, suddenly a goat with a prominent horn between his eyes came from the west, crossing the whole earth without touching the ground. ⁶He came toward the two-horned ram I had seen standing beside the canal and charged at him in great rage. ⁷I saw him attack the ram furiously, striking the ram and shattering his two horns. The ram was powerless to stand against him; the goat knocked him to the ground and trampled on him, and none could rescue the ram from his power. ⁸The goat became very great, but at the height of his power his large horn was broken off, and in its place four prominent horns grew up toward the four winds of heaven.

⁹Out of one of them came another horn, which started small but grew in power to the south and to the east and toward the Beautiful Land. ¹⁰It grew until it reached the host of the heavens, and it threw some of the starry host down to the earth and trampled on them. ¹¹It set itself up to be as great as the Prince of the host; it took away the daily sacrifice from him, and the place of his sanctuary was brought low. ¹²Because of rebellion, the host ⌊of the saints⌋^a and the daily sacrifice were given over to it. It prospered in everything it did, and truth was thrown to the ground.

¹³Then I heard a holy one speaking, and another holy one said to him, "How long will it take for the vision to be fulfilled—the vision concerning the daily sacrifice, the rebellion that causes desolation, and the surrender of the sanctuary and of the host that will be trampled underfoot?"

¹⁴He said to me, "It will take 2,300 evenings and mornings; then the sanctuary will be reconsecrated."

The Interpretation of the Vision

¹⁵While I, Daniel, was watching the vision and trying to understand it, there before me stood one who looked like a man. ¹⁶And I heard a man's voice from the Ulai calling, "Gabriel, tell this man the meaning of the vision."

¹⁷As he came near the place where I was standing, I was terrified and fell prostrate. "Son of man," he said to me, "understand that the vision concerns the time of the end."

¹⁸While he was speaking to me, I was in a deep sleep, with my face to the ground. Then he touched me and raised me to my feet.

¹⁹He said: "I am going to tell you what will happen later in the time of wrath, because the vision concerns the appointed time of the end.^b ²⁰The two-horned ram that you saw represents the kings of Media and Persia. ²¹The shaggy goat is the king of Greece, and the large horn between his eyes is the first king. ²²The four horns that replaced the one that was broken off represent four kingdoms that will emerge from his nation but will not have the same power.

²³"In the latter part of their reign, when rebels have become completely wicked, a stern-faced king, a master of intrigue, will arise. ²⁴He will become very strong, but not by his own power. He will cause astounding devastation and will succeed in whatever he does. He will destroy the mighty men and the holy people. ²⁵He will cause deceit to prosper, and he will consider himself superior. When they feel secure, he will destroy many and take his stand against the Prince of princes. Yet he will be destroyed, but not by human power.

---

^a 12 Or rebellion, the armies   ^b 19 Or because the end will be at the appointed time

mirror images

Peter knocked at the outer entrance, and a servant girl named Rhoda came to answer the door. When she recognized Peter's voice, she was so overjoyed she ran back without opening it. Acts 12:13–14

Rhoda—Answered Prayer

A soft knock. Then a little louder. A voice whispers loudly, "Hey, let me in already." And then, "Oh for Peter's sake, would you just open up!" Okay, so maybe those weren't the *exact* words the Apostle Peter used in Acts 12, but you get the idea.

A group of Christians had gathered together in the middle of the night to pray for Peter to be released from prison. When the servant girl Rhoda ran to answer a knock at the door, she had the shock of her life. She heard Peter's voice on the other side! For a minute, she was so shocked that she forgot poor old Peter and ran to share the good news. She must have been bouncing with all the enthusiasm of Tigger. "Hey, guess what! It's Peter. Wow—he's at the door. This is amazing! It's really him!"

While Peter kept knocking, waiting for his skeptical friends to realize that their prayers were really answered, the friends insisted Rhoda was crazy. They kept arguing that it must be Peter's angel at the door. But as the knocking continued, the group finally decided to see who was at the door. When they saw it was Peter, their jaws dropped in astonishment that he was free.

What a funny way to pray—asking God to do something miraculous without actually believing he'll do it. Here was Peter out of jail, the very thing they'd been asking for—you'd think they'd believe right away. Only Rhoda believed instantly—and the sound of Peter's voice was all the excuse she needed to start praising God for his answer!

So which way do you pray? Do you tell God your concerns, half-hoping he's listening in? Maybe you say the words because you know you should, but you don't really believe he'll grant your request. Or perhaps, like Rhoda, you pray in faith, believing that our good and powerful God will answer you. Don't be surprised if he chooses to answer your prayers. In fact, expect it.

> Dear Jesus, I want to believe with all the faith Rhoda had. Help me to pray, believing that you want to answer. And when you answer, remind me to give you all the thanks you deserve. Amen.

To read the next Mirror Images profile, go to page 1189.

Read more about Rhoda in Acts 12:1–17 (pages 1461–1462).

²⁶"The vision of the evenings and mornings that has been given you is true, but seal up the vision, for it concerns the distant future."

²⁷I, Daniel, was exhausted and lay ill for several days. Then I got up and went about the king's business. I was appalled by the vision; it was beyond understanding.

Daniel's Prayer

9 In the first year of Darius son of Xerxes*ᵃ* (a Mede by descent), who was made ruler over the Babylonian*ᵇ* kingdom— ²in the first year of his reign, I, Daniel, understood from the Scriptures, according to the word of the LORD given to Jeremiah the prophet, that the desolation of Jerusalem would last seventy years. ³So I turned to the Lord God and pleaded with him in prayer and petition, in fasting, and in sackcloth and ashes.

⁴I prayed to the LORD my God and confessed:

"O Lord, the great and awesome God, who keeps his covenant of love with all who love him and obey his commands, ⁵we have sinned and done wrong. We have been wicked and have rebelled; we have turned away from your commands and laws. ⁶We have not listened to your servants the prophets, who spoke in your name to our kings, our princes and our fathers, and to all the people of the land.

⁷"Lord, you are righteous, but this day we are covered with shame—the men of Judah and people of Jerusalem and all Israel, both near and far, in all the countries where you have scattered us because of our unfaithfulness to you. ⁸O LORD, we and our kings, our princes and our fathers are covered with shame because we have sinned against you. ⁹The Lord our God is merciful and forgiving, even though we have rebelled against him; ¹⁰we have not obeyed the LORD our God or kept the laws he gave us through his servants the prophets. ¹¹All Israel has transgressed your law and turned away, refusing to obey you.

"Therefore the curses and sworn judgments written in the Law of Moses, the servant of God, have been poured out on us, because we have sinned against you. ¹²You have fulfilled the words spoken against us and against our rulers by bringing upon us great disaster. Under the whole heaven nothing has ever been done like what has been done to Jerusalem. ¹³Just as it is written in the Law of Moses, all this disaster has come upon us, yet we have not sought the favor of the LORD our God by turning from our sins and giving attention to your truth. ¹⁴The LORD did not hesitate to bring the disaster upon us, for the LORD our God is righteous in everything he does; yet we have not obeyed him.

¹⁵"Now, O Lord our God, who brought your people out of Egypt with a mighty hand and who made for yourself a name that endures to this day, we have sinned, we have done wrong. ¹⁶O Lord, in keeping with all your righteous acts, turn away your anger and your wrath from Jerusalem, your city, your holy hill. Our sins and the iniquities of our fathers have made Jerusalem and your people an object of scorn to all those around us.

¹⁷"Now, our God, hear the prayers and petitions of your servant. For your sake, O Lord, look with favor on your desolate sanctuary. ¹⁸Give ear, O God, and hear; open your eyes and see the desolation of the city that bears your Name. We do not make requests of you because we are righteous, but because of your great mercy. ¹⁹O Lord, listen! O Lord, forgive! O Lord, hear and act! For your sake, O my God, do not delay, because your city and your people bear your Name."

The Seventy "Sevens"

²⁰While I was speaking and praying, confessing my sin and the sin of my people Israel and making my request to the LORD my God for his holy hill— ²¹while I was still in prayer, Gabriel, the man

truth or dare

If you're like Daniel, you care a lot about your country. Time to get involved, girl! Start making a difference at the grassroots level—pray Daniel's prayer for your nation.

9:4–19

ᵃ 1 Hebrew *Ahasuerus*   *ᵇ 1* Or *Chaldean*

I had seen in the earlier vision, came to me in swift flight about the time of the evening sacrifice. [22]He instructed me and said to me, "Daniel, I have now come to give you insight and understanding. [23]As soon as you began to pray, an answer was given, which I have come to tell you, for you are highly esteemed. Therefore, consider the message and understand the vision:

[24]"Seventy 'sevens' [a] are decreed for your people and your holy city to finish [b] transgression, to put an end to sin, to atone for wickedness, to bring in everlasting righteousness, to seal up vision and prophecy and to anoint the most holy. [c]

[25]"Know and understand this: From the issuing of the decree [d] to restore and rebuild Jerusalem until the Anointed One, [e] the ruler, comes, there will be seven 'sevens,' and sixty-two 'sevens.' It will be rebuilt with streets and a trench, but in times of trouble. [26]After the sixty-two 'sevens,' the Anointed One will be cut off and will have nothing. [f] The people of the ruler who will come will destroy the city and the sanctuary. The end will come like a flood: War will continue until the end, and desolations have been decreed. [27]He will confirm a covenant with many for one 'seven.' [g] In the middle of the 'seven' [g] he will put an end to sacrifice and offering. And on a wing ⌊of the temple⌋ he will set up an abomination that causes desolation, until the end that is decreed is poured out on him." [i]

Daniel's Vision of a Man

10
In the third year of Cyrus king of Persia, a revelation was given to Daniel (who was called Belteshazzar). Its message was true and it concerned a great war. [j] The understanding of the message came to him in a vision.

[2]At that time I, Daniel, mourned for three weeks. [3]I ate no choice food; no meat or wine touched my lips; and I used no lotions at all until the three weeks were over.

[4]On the twenty-fourth day of the first month, as I was standing on the bank of the great river, the Tigris, [5]I looked up and there before me was a man dressed in linen, with a belt of the finest gold around his waist. [6]His body was like chrysolite, his face like lightning, his eyes like flaming torches, his arms and legs like the gleam of burnished bronze, and his voice like the sound of a multitude.

[7]I, Daniel, was the only one who saw the vision; the men with me did not see it, but such terror overwhelmed them that they fled and hid themselves. [8]So I was left alone, gazing at this great vision; I had no strength left, my face turned deathly pale and I was helpless. [9]Then I heard him speaking, and as I listened to him, I fell into a deep sleep, my face to the ground.

[10]A hand touched me and set me trembling on my hands and knees. [11]He said, "Daniel, you who are highly esteemed, consider carefully the words I am about to speak to you, and stand up, for I have now been sent to you." And when he said this to me, I stood up trembling.

[12]Then he continued, "Do not be afraid, Daniel. Since the first day that you set your mind to gain understanding and to humble yourself before your God, your words were heard, and I have come in response to them. [13]But the prince of the Persian kingdom resisted me twenty-one days. Then Michael, one of the chief princes, came to help me, because I was detained there with the king of Persia. [14]Now I have come to explain to you what will happen to your people in the future, for the vision concerns a time yet to come."

[15]While he was saying this to me, I bowed with my face toward the ground and was speechless. [16]Then one who looked like a man [k] touched my lips, and I opened my mouth and began to

truth or dare

Doubt God hears your prayers? Check out Daniel's proof that God was with him from day one. *God is listening.* So what are you saying to him?

10:4–12

---

a 24 Or *'weeks';* also in verses 25 and 26   *b 24* Or *restrain*   *c 24* Or *Most Holy Place*; or *most holy One*
d 25 Or *word*   *e 25* Or *an anointed one*; also in verse 26   *f 26* Or *off and will have no one*; or *off, but not for himself*
g 27 Or *'week'*   *h 27* Or *it*   *i 27* Or *And one who causes desolation will come upon the pinnacle of the abominable ⌊temple⌋, until the end that is decreed is poured out on the desolated ⌊city⌋*   *j 1* Or *true and burdensome*   *k 16* Most
manuscripts of the Masoretic Text; one manuscript of the Masoretic Text, Dead Sea Scrolls and Septuagint *Then something
that looked like a man's hand*

speak. I said to the one standing before me, "I am overcome with anguish because of the vision, my lord, and I am helpless. ¹⁷How can I, your servant, talk with you, my lord? My strength is gone and I can hardly breathe."

¹⁸Again the one who looked like a man touched me and gave me strength. ¹⁹"Do not be afraid, O man highly esteemed," he said. "Peace! Be strong now; be strong."

When he spoke to me, I was strengthened and said, "Speak, my lord, since you have given me strength."

²⁰So he said, "Do you know why I have come to you? Soon I will return to fight against the prince of Persia, and when I go, the prince of Greece will come; ²¹but first I will tell you what is written in the Book of Truth. (No one supports me against them except Michael, your prince. ¹And in the first year of Darius the Mede, I took my stand to support and protect him.)

The Kings of the South and the North

²"Now then, I tell you the truth: Three more kings will appear in Persia, and then a fourth, who will be far richer than all the others. When he has gained power by his wealth, he will stir up everyone against the kingdom of Greece. ³Then a mighty king will appear, who will rule with great power and do as he pleases. ⁴After he has appeared, his empire will be broken up and parceled out toward the four winds of heaven. It will not go to his descendants, nor will it have the power he exercised, because his empire will be uprooted and given to others.

⁵"The king of the South will become strong, but one of his commanders will become even stronger than he and will rule his own kingdom with great power. ⁶After some years, they will become allies. The daughter of the king of the South will go to the king of the North to make an alliance, but she will not retain her power, and he and his power *a* will not last. In those days she will be handed over, together with her royal escort and her father *b* and the one who supported her.

⁷"One from her family line will arise to take her place. He will attack the forces of the king of the North and enter his fortress; he will fight against them and be victorious. ⁸He will also seize their gods, their metal images and their valuable articles of silver and gold and carry them off to Egypt. For some years he will leave the king of the North alone. ⁹Then the king of the North will invade the realm of the king of the South but will retreat to his own country. ¹⁰His sons will prepare for war and assemble a great army, which will sweep on like an irresistible flood and carry the battle as far as his fortress.

¹¹"Then the king of the South will march out in a rage and fight against the king of the North, who will raise a large army, but it will be defeated. ¹²When the army is carried off, the king of the South will be filled with pride and will slaughter many thousands, yet he will not remain triumphant. ¹³For the king of the North will muster another army, larger than the first; and after several years, he will advance with a huge army fully equipped.

¹⁴"In those times many will rise against the king of the South. The violent men among your own people will rebel in fulfillment of the vision, but without success. ¹⁵Then the king of the North will come and build up siege ramps and will capture a fortified city. The forces of the South will be powerless to resist; even their best troops will not have the strength to stand. ¹⁶The invader will do as he pleases; no one will be able to stand against him. He will establish himself in the Beautiful Land and will have the power to destroy it. ¹⁷He will determine to come with the might of his entire kingdom and will make an alliance with the king of the South. And he will give him a daughter in marriage in order to overthrow the kingdom, but his plans *c* will not succeed or help him. ¹⁸Then he will turn his attention to the coastlands and will take many of them, but a commander will put an end to his insolence and will turn his insolence back upon him. ¹⁹After this, he will turn back toward the fortresses of his own country but will stumble and fall, to be seen no more.

²⁰"His successor will send out a tax collector to maintain the royal splendor. In a few years, however, he will be destroyed, yet not in anger or in battle.

²¹"He will be succeeded by a contemptible person who has not been given the honor of royalty. He will invade the kingdom when its people feel secure, and he will seize it through intrigue. ²²Then an overwhelming army will be swept away before him; both it and a prince of the covenant will be destroyed. ²³After coming to an agreement with him, he will act deceitfully, and with only a

a 6 Or *offspring*   *b 6* Or *child* (see Vulgate and Syriac)   *c 17* Or *but she* few people he will rise to power. ²⁴When the richest provinces feel secure, he will invade them and will achieve what neither his fathers nor his forefathers did. He will distribute plunder, loot and wealth among his followers. He will plot the overthrow of fortresses—but only for a time.

²⁵"With a large army he will stir up his strength and courage against the king of the South. The king of the South will wage war with a large and very powerful army, but he will not be able to stand because of the plots devised against him. ²⁶Those who eat from the king's provisions will try to destroy him; his army will be swept away, and many will fall in battle. ²⁷The two kings, with their hearts bent on evil, will sit at the same table and lie to each other, but to no avail, because an end will still come at the appointed time. ²⁸The king of the North will return to his own country with great wealth, but his heart will be set against the holy covenant. He will take action against it and then return to his own country.

²⁹"At the appointed time he will invade the South again, but this time the outcome will be different from what it was before. ³⁰Ships of the western coastlands ᵃ will oppose him, and he will lose heart. Then he will turn back and vent his fury against the holy covenant. He will return and show favor to those who forsake the holy covenant.

³¹"His armed forces will rise up to desecrate the temple fortress and will abolish the daily sacrifice. Then they will set up the abomination that causes desolation. ³²With flattery he will corrupt those who have violated the covenant, but the people who know their God will firmly resist him.

³³"Those who are wise will instruct many, though for a time they will fall by the sword or be burned or captured or plundered. ³⁴When they fall, they will receive a little help, and many who are not sincere will join them. ³⁵Some of the wise will stumble, so that they may be refined, purified and made spotless until the time of the end, for it will still come at the appointed time.

truth or dare

The Bible gives lots of warnings about imposters during the end times. How can you stay free from phonies? Make *knowing God* your number one priority.

11:32

The King Who Exalts Himself

³⁶"The king will do as he pleases. He will exalt and magnify himself above every god and will say unheard-of things against the God of gods. He will be successful until the time of wrath is completed, for what has been determined must take place. ³⁷He will show no regard for the gods of his fathers or for the one desired by women, nor will he regard any god, but will exalt himself above them all. ³⁸Instead of them, he will honor a god of fortresses; a god unknown to his fathers he will honor with gold and silver, with precious stones and costly gifts. ³⁹He will attack the mightiest fortresses with the help of a foreign god and will greatly honor those who acknowledge him. He will make them rulers over many people and will distribute the land at a price. ᵇ

⁴⁰"At the time of the end the king of the South will engage him in battle, and the king of the North will storm out against him with chariots and cavalry and a great fleet of ships. He will invade many countries and sweep through them like a flood. ⁴¹He will also invade the Beautiful Land. Many countries will fall, but Edom, Moab and the leaders of Ammon will be delivered from his hand. ⁴²He will extend his power over many countries; Egypt will not escape. ⁴³He will gain control of the treasures of gold and silver and all the riches of Egypt, with the Libyans and Nubians in submission. ⁴⁴But reports from the east and the north will alarm him, and he will set out in a great rage to destroy and annihilate many. ⁴⁵He will pitch his royal tents between the seas at ᶜ the beautiful holy mountain. Yet he will come to his end, and no one will help him.

The End Times

12 "At that time Michael, the great prince who protects your people, will arise. There will be a time of distress such as has not happened from the beginning of nations until then. But at that time your people—everyone whose name is found written in the book—will be delivered. ²Multitudes who sleep in the dust of the earth will awake: some to ever-

ᵃ 30 Hebrew of Kittim   ᵇ 39 Or land for a reward   ᶜ 45 Or the sea and lasting life, others to shame and everlasting contempt. [3]Those who are wise[a] will shine like the brightness of the heavens, and those who lead many to righteousness, like the stars for ever and ever. [4]But you, Daniel, close up and seal the words of the scroll until the time of the end. Many will go here and there to increase knowledge."

[5]Then I, Daniel, looked, and there before me stood two others, one on this bank of the river and one on the opposite bank. [6]One of them said to the man clothed in linen, who was above the waters of the river, "How long will it be before these astonishing things are fulfilled?"

[7]The man clothed in linen, who was above the waters of the river, lifted his right hand and his left hand toward heaven, and I heard him swear by him who lives forever, saying, "It will be for a time, times and half a time.[b] When the power of the holy people has been finally broken, all these things will be completed."

[8]I heard, but I did not understand. So I asked, "My lord, what will the outcome of all this be?"

[9]He replied, "Go your way, Daniel, because the words are closed up and sealed until the time of the end. [10]Many will be purified, made spotless and refined, but the wicked will continue to be wicked. None of the wicked will understand, but those who are wise will understand.

[11]"From the time that the daily sacrifice is abolished and the abomination that causes desolation is set up, there will be 1,290 days. [12]Blessed is the one who waits for and reaches the end of the 1,335 days.

[13]"As for you, go your way till the end. You will rest, and then at the end of the days you will rise to receive your allotted inheritance."

love notes

12:3

Treasured one,

Your world is filled with so-called "stars"—people who earn a brief moment of fame for their achievements or talents or looks. But true "stars"—those who are wise in my ways and who guide others to me—will shine forever!

—Your heavenly Father

In what ways have you been a "star" for God?

_____

_____

_____

_____

_____

_____

_____

_____

_____

_____

a 3 Or who impart wisdom   b 7 Or a year, two years and half a year author: Hosea.

date: About 715 B.C.

setting: Hosea lived during the time of the end of the northern kingdom, which fell to the Assyrians in 722 B.C.

verse to remember: But you must return to your God; maintain love and justice, and wait for your God always (12:6).

theme to consider: Even though Israel committed spiritual adultery by worshiping other gods, God was loyal to his people by loving them and offering them forgiveness.

at a glance

hosea

unchanging truth

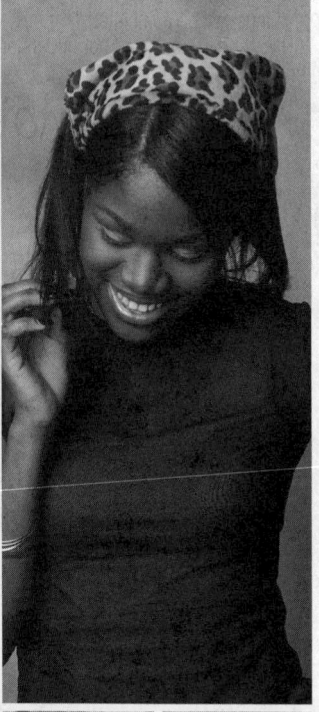

There's no getting around it—*adultery* is an ugly word. You don't hear it a whole lot, even though it happens all too frequently in our society. Adultery is number seven on the Ten Commandments (see Exodus 20:14). God knows how much adultery damages people's lives, so he expressly forbids it.

Perhaps you know firsthand the hurt of a marriage torn apart when one partner is unfaithful to the other—maybe your own parents, maybe those of a friend. No matter how glamorous it may seem in the movies or in romance novels, adultery destroys everyone and everything in its path.

God's prophet Hosea experienced the pain of adultery. God told Hosea to marry a woman who would be unfaithful to him. Hosea experienced the terrible pain of dealing with an adulterous wife.

Hosea's real-life experience was actually a word picture to help God's people understand what they were doing. When they worshiped other gods, they were committing "spiritual adultery"—being unfaithful to God. God used Hosea's devastating pain to show us, in no uncertain terms, the pain that he feels when we sin against him.

And here's the unbelievable part: God told Hosea to go and bring his wife back and to love her again. Why? Because that's exactly what God does for us! He brings us back and loves us, even though we hurt him deeply. Don't let anything ever keep you from running back into the loving arms of God.

life lessons

1 God loves us and draws us to himself. His desire is always to give us his very best (2:14–23).

2 Even though God punishes sin, he always seeks to restore us (11:8–11).

3 Through repentance, we can return to God and be forgiven (14:1–9).

1

The word of the LORD that came to Hosea son of Beeri during the reigns of Uzziah, Jotham, Ahaz and Hezekiah, kings of Judah, and during the reign of Jeroboam son of Jehoash[a] king of Israel:

Hosea's Wife and Children

[2]When the LORD began to speak through Hosea, the LORD said to him, "Go, take to yourself an adulterous wife and children of unfaithfulness, because the land is guilty of the vilest adultery in departing from the LORD." [3]So he married Gomer daughter of Diblaim, and she conceived and bore him a son.

[4]Then the LORD said to Hosea, "Call him Jezreel, because I will soon punish the house of Jehu for the massacre at Jezreel, and I will put an end to the kingdom of Israel. [5]In that day I will break Israel's bow in the Valley of Jezreel."

[6]Gomer conceived again and gave birth to a daughter. Then the LORD said to Hosea, "Call her Lo-Ruhamah,[b] for I will no longer show love to the house of Israel, that I should at all forgive them. [7]Yet I will show love to the house of Judah; and I will save them—not by bow, sword or battle, or by horses and horsemen, but by the LORD their God."

[8]After she had weaned Lo-Ruhamah, Gomer had another son. [9]Then the LORD said, "Call him Lo-Ammi,[c] for you are not my people, and I am not your God.

[10]"Yet the Israelites will be like the sand on the seashore, which cannot be measured or counted. In the place where it was said to them, 'You are not my people,' they will be called 'sons of the living God.' [11]The people of Judah and the people of Israel will be reunited, and they will appoint one leader and will come up out of the land, for great will be the day of Jezreel.

2

"Say of your brothers, 'My people,' and of your sisters, 'My loved one.'

truth or dare

You know the kinds of things that hurt your feelings. But what about *God's* feelings? Hosea's life shows us the deep pain God feels over our unfaithfulness.

1:2

Israel Punished and Restored

[2]"Rebuke your mother, rebuke her,
    for she is not my wife,
    and I am not her husband.
Let her remove the adulterous look from her face
    and the unfaithfulness from between her breasts.
[3]Otherwise I will strip her naked
    and make her as bare as on the day she was born;
I will make her like a desert,
    turn her into a parched land,
    and slay her with thirst.
[4]I will not show my love to her children,
    because they are the children of adultery.
[5]Their mother has been unfaithful
    and has conceived them in disgrace.
She said, 'I will go after my lovers,
    who give me my food and my water,
    my wool and my linen, my oil and my drink.'
[6]Therefore I will block her path with thornbushes;
    I will wall her in so that she cannot find her way.
[7]She will chase after her lovers but not catch them;
    she will look for them but not find them.
Then she will say,
    'I will go back to my husband as at first,
    for then I was better off than now.'

---

a 1 Hebrew *Joash,* a variant of *Jehoash*   *b 6 Lo-Ruhamah* means *not loved.*   *c 9 Lo-Ammi* means *not my people.*

⁸She has not acknowledged that I was the one
    who gave her the grain, the new wine and oil,
who lavished on her the silver and gold—
    which they used for Baal.

⁹"Therefore I will take away my grain when it ripens,
    and my new wine when it is ready.
I will take back my wool and my linen,
    intended to cover her nakedness.
¹⁰So now I will expose her lewdness
    before the eyes of her lovers;
    no one will take her out of my hands.
¹¹I will stop all her celebrations:

her yearly festivals, her New
        Moons,
    her Sabbath days—all her
        appointed feasts.
¹²I will ruin her vines and her fig
        trees,
    which she said were her pay
        from her lovers;
I will make them a thicket,
    and wild animals will devour
        them.
¹³I will punish her for the days
    she burned incense to the
        Baals;
she decked herself with rings
    and jewelry,
    and went after her lovers,
    but me she forgot,"
        declares the LORD.

¹⁴"Therefore I am now going to
        allure her;
    I will lead her into the desert
    and speak tenderly to her.
¹⁵There I will give her back her
        vineyards,
    and will make the Valley of
        Achorᵃ a door of hope.
There she will singᵇ as in the
        days of her youth,
    as in the day she came up out
        of Egypt.

¹⁶"In that day," declares the LORD,
    "you will call me 'my
        husband';
    you will no longer call me 'my
        master.'ᶜ
¹⁷I will remove the names of the
        Baals from her lips;
    no longer will their names be
        invoked.

love notes

2:19–20

Beloved,

I pledge myself to you forever. I
am your God, and you are mine.
You belong to me, and I will
never leave you. You have my
pledge.

        Eternally yours,

            —God

Thank God for his faithfulness and his
promise to be with you forever.

_____

_____

_____

_____

_____

_____

_____

_____

_____

_____

ᵃ 15 Achor means trouble.   ᵇ 15 Or respond
ᶜ 16 Hebrew baal

¹⁸In that day I will make a covenant for them
    with the beasts of the field and the birds of the air
    and the creatures that move along the ground.
Bow and sword and battle
    I will abolish from the land,
    so that all may lie down in safety.
¹⁹I will betroth you to me forever;
    I will betroth you in^a righteousness and justice,
    in^b love and compassion.
²⁰I will betroth you in faithfulness,
    and you will acknowledge the LORD.

²¹"In that day I will respond,"
    declares the LORD—
"I will respond to the skies,
    and they will respond to the earth;
²²and the earth will respond to the grain,
    the new wine and oil,
    and they will respond to Jezreel.^c
²³I will plant her for myself in the land;
    I will show my love to the one I called 'Not my loved one.'^d
I will say to those called 'Not my people,^e' 'You are my people';
    and they will say, 'You are my God.' "

Hosea's Reconciliation With His Wife

3 The LORD said to me, "Go, show your love to your wife again, though she is loved by another and is an adulteress. Love her as the LORD loves the Israelites, though they turn to other gods and love the sacred raisin cakes."

²So I bought her for fifteen shekels^f of silver and about a homer and a lethek^g of barley. ³Then I told her, "You are to live with^h me many days; you must not be a prostitute or be intimate with any man, and I will live with^h you."

⁴For the Israelites will live many days without king or prince, without sacrifice or sacred stones, without ephod or idol. ⁵Afterward the Israelites will return and seek the LORD their God and David their king. They will come trembling to the LORD and to his blessings in the last days.

The Charge Against Israel

4 Hear the word of the LORD, you Israelites,
    because the LORD has a charge to bring
    against you who live in the land:
"There is no faithfulness, no love,
    no acknowledgment of God in the land.
²There is only cursing,ⁱ lying and murder,
    stealing and adultery;
they break all bounds,
    and bloodshed follows bloodshed.
³Because of this the land mourns,^j
    and all who live in it waste away;

truth or dare

How easy would it be to forgive someone who's cheated on you? Revenge seems like a *much* easier option. But forgiving others reminds us of how much God has forgiven us.

3:1

---

^a 19 Or with; also in verse 20   ^b 19 Or with   ^c 22 Jezreel means God plants.   ^d 23 Hebrew Lo-Ruhamah
^e 23 Hebrew Lo-Ammi   ^f 2 That is, about 6 ounces (about 170 grams)   ^g 2 That is, probably about 10 bushels (about
330 liters)   ^h 3 Or wait for   ⁱ 2 That is, to pronounce a curse upon   ^j 3 Or dries up

the beasts of the field and the birds of the air
and the fish of the sea are dying.

4 "But let no man bring a charge,
let no man accuse another,
for your people are like those
who bring charges against a priest.
5 You stumble day and night,
and the prophets stumble with you.
So I will destroy your mother—
6 my people are destroyed from lack of knowledge.

"Because you have rejected knowledge,
I also reject you as my priests;
because you have ignored the law of your God,
I also will ignore your children.
7 The more the priests increased,
the more they sinned against me;
they exchanged[a] their[b] Glory for something disgraceful.
8 They feed on the sins of my people
and relish their wickedness.
9 And it will be: Like people, like priests.
I will punish both of them for their ways
and repay them for their deeds.

10 "They will eat but not have enough;
they will engage in prostitution but not increase,
because they have deserted the LORD
to give themselves 11 to prostitution,
to old wine and new,
which take away the understanding 12 of my people.
They consult a wooden idol
and are answered by a stick of wood.
A spirit of prostitution leads them astray;
they are unfaithful to their God.
13 They sacrifice on the mountaintops
and burn offerings on the hills,
under oak, poplar and terebinth,
where the shade is pleasant.
Therefore your daughters turn to prostitution
and your daughters-in-law to adultery.

14 "I will not punish your daughters
when they turn to prostitution,
nor your daughters-in-law
when they commit adultery,
because the men themselves consort with harlots
and sacrifice with shrine prostitutes—
a people without understanding will come to ruin!

15 "Though you commit adultery, O Israel,
let not Judah become guilty.

"Do not go to Gilgal;
do not go up to Beth Aven.[c]
And do not swear, 'As surely as the LORD lives!'

a 7 Syriac and an ancient Hebrew scribal tradition; Masoretic Text *I will exchange*   b 7 Masoretic Text; an ancient Hebrew scribal tradition *my*   c 15 *Beth Aven* means *house of wickedness* (a name for Bethel, which means *house of God*).

mirror images

The LORD said to me, "Go, show your love to your wife again, though she is loved by another and is an adulteress." Hosea 3:1

Gomer—A Before and After Story

I t's not like she tried to hide her sins. She flaunted them, living like a prostitute and sleeping with anyone who would buy her something pretty. She was the town tramp—so why did God tell his chosen prophet to marry *her*?

But God did tell Hosea to marry Gomer, and he used this marriage to draw a before-and-after picture for us. Gomer's sinfulness led her to a life of slavery, and it was Hosea's right to get rid of her for her adultery. But God instructed Hosea to do something unusual. Hosea bought Gomer back from slavery, and then he lovingly invited her back into his home as his wife, treating her just as wonderfully as if she were his new, beautiful, virgin bride. After Gomer had treated him in cruel ways he didn't deserve, Hosea gave her mercy and grace she didn't deserve. Why?

To show how God loves us. Our sin against him is as hurtful as Gomer's sins were against Hosea. We may not think our sin is all that bad, but each "little" sin is an insult to our perfect God. He bought us with the greatest price ever paid—his own blood—and then, instead of treating us like slaves, he welcomed us into his kingdom as his beloved princesses. Before, we were bound by sin, incapable of love. Afterward, we were free to love and be loved.

Like Gomer, do you struggle to remain faithful? Does your attention wander to other people and other things? Is your heart divided between God and the world? The shocking thing about this story is not the audacity of Gomer's unfaithfulness. It's Hosea's persistence. Before and after Gomer's waywardness, Hosea's love remained unaltered. Regardless of your own unfaithfulness, remember—God will always be faithful to you.

To read the next Mirror Images profile, go to page 1243.

Dear God, please forgive me for being unfaithful to you. You have always been faithful to me, and I thank you and praise you for your love. Amen.

dear God

Read more about Gomer's before and after story in Hosea 1–3 (pages 1185–1187).

16 The Israelites are stubborn,
 like a stubborn heifer.
How then can the LORD pasture them
 like lambs in a meadow?
17 Ephraim is joined to idols;
 leave him alone!
18 Even when their drinks are gone,
 they continue their prostitution;
 their rulers dearly love shameful ways.
19 A whirlwind will sweep them away,
 and their sacrifices will bring them shame.

Judgment Against Israel

5 "Hear this, you priests!
 Pay attention, you Israelites!
Listen, O royal house!
 This judgment is against you:
You have been a snare at Mizpah,
 a net spread out on Tabor.
2 The rebels are deep in slaughter.
 I will discipline all of them.
3 I know all about Ephraim;
 Israel is not hidden from me.
Ephraim, you have now turned to
  prostitution;
 Israel is corrupt.

4 "Their deeds do not permit them
 to return to their God.
A spirit of prostitution is in their heart;
 they do not acknowledge the LORD.
5 Israel's arrogance testifies against them;
 the Israelites, even Ephraim, stumble in their sin;
 Judah also stumbles with them.
6 When they go with their flocks and herds
 to seek the LORD,
they will not find him;
 he has withdrawn himself from them.
7 They are unfaithful to the LORD;
 they give birth to illegitimate children.
Now their New Moon festivals
 will devour them and their fields.

8 "Sound the trumpet in Gibeah,
 the horn in Ramah.
Raise the battle cry in Beth Aven ᵃ;
 lead on, O Benjamin.
9 Ephraim will be laid waste
 on the day of reckoning.
Among the tribes of Israel
 I proclaim what is certain.
10 Judah's leaders are like those
 who move boundary stones.
I will pour out my wrath on them
 like a flood of water.

---

truth or dare

Sinful actions are like concrete to the soul. After awhile, your heart becomes hard and heavy, preventing you from turning to God for help. What sin is blocking you from God?

5:4

ᵃ 8 *Beth Aven* means *house of wickedness* (a name for Bethel, which means *house of God*).

¹¹Ephraim is oppressed,
   trampled in judgment,
   intent on pursuing idols. ^a
¹²I am like a moth to Ephraim,
   like rot to the people of Judah.

¹³ "When Ephraim saw his sickness,
   and Judah his sores,
then Ephraim turned to Assyria,
   and sent to the great king for
     help.
But he is not able to cure you,
   not able to heal your sores.
¹⁴For I will be like a lion to Ephraim,
   like a great lion to Judah.
I will tear them to pieces and go away;
   I will carry them off, with no one to rescue
     them.
¹⁵Then I will go back to my place
   until they admit their guilt.
And they will seek my face;
   in their misery they will earnestly seek me."

Israel Unrepentant

6 "Come, let us return to the LORD.
   He has torn us to pieces
     but he will heal us;

he has injured us
   but he will bind up our wounds.
²After two days he will revive us;
   on the third day he will restore
     us,
   that we may live in his presence.
³Let us acknowledge the LORD;
   let us press on to
     acknowledge him.
As surely as the sun rises,
   he will appear;
he will come to us like the winter
     rains,
   like the spring rains that water
     the earth."

⁴ "What can I do with you,
     Ephraim?
   What can I do with you, Judah?
Your love is like the morning
     mist,
   like the early dew that disappears.
⁵Therefore I cut you in pieces with
     my prophets,
I killed you with the words of
     my mouth;
   my judgments flashed like
     lightning upon you.

---

truth or dare

Modern culture is virtually designed to distract us from God. That's why it's important to acknowledge him in thought and action. How do you keep your focus on him each day?

6:3

---

genuine love » 6:4

To what could your love for (or faithfulness to) God be compared? Something permanent like ink stains? Semi-permanent like a marker? Something that quickly fades like a light pencil mark? Would God agree with you? During Hosea's day, God compared the love of the people of Israel to the morning mist. In other words, it was temporary. Ouch. They weren't very faithful to God! This was obvious in their lack of sorrow over their sin. How deep is your love? If your love is "leaded" (get it—pencil lead?), why not ask the Lord to make it deeper and richer?

---

^a 11 The meaning of the Hebrew for this word is uncertain.

⁶ For I desire mercy, not sacrifice,
and acknowledgment of God rather than burnt offerings.
⁷ Like Adam,^a they have broken the covenant—
they were unfaithful to me there.
⁸ Gilead is a city of wicked men,
stained with footprints of blood.
⁹ As marauders lie in ambush for a man,
so do bands of priests;
they murder on the road to Shechem,
committing shameful crimes.
¹⁰ I have seen a horrible thing
in the house of Israel.
There Ephraim is given to prostitution
and Israel is defiled.

¹¹ "Also for you, Judah,
a harvest is appointed.

"Whenever I would restore the fortunes of my people,
¹   whenever I would heal Israel,
the sins of Ephraim are exposed
and the crimes of Samaria revealed.
They practice deceit,
thieves break into houses,
bandits rob in the streets;
² but they do not realize
that I remember all their evil deeds.
Their sins engulf them;
they are always before me.

³ "They delight the king with their wickedness,
the princes with their lies.
⁴ They are all adulterers,
burning like an oven
whose fire the baker need not stir
from the kneading of the dough till it rises.
⁵ On the day of the festival of our king
the princes become inflamed with wine,
and he joins hands with the mockers.
⁶ Their hearts are like an oven;
they approach him with intrigue.
Their passion smolders all night;
in the morning it blazes like a flaming fire.
⁷ All of them are hot as an oven;
they devour their rulers.
All their kings fall,
and none of them calls on me.

⁸ "Ephraim mixes with the nations;
Ephraim is a flat cake not turned over.
⁹ Foreigners sap his strength,
but he does not realize it.
His hair is sprinkled with gray,
but he does not notice.
¹⁰ Israel's arrogance testifies against him,
but despite all this

^a 7 Or As at Adam; or Like men

he does not return to the LORD his God
or search for him.

¹¹ "Ephraim is like a dove,
easily deceived and senseless—
now calling to Egypt,
now turning to Assyria.
¹² When they go, I will throw my net over them;
I will pull them down like birds of the air.
When I hear them flocking together,
I will catch them.
¹³ Woe to them,
because they have strayed from me!
Destruction to them,
because they have rebelled against me!
I long to redeem them
but they speak lies against me.
¹⁴ They do not cry out to me from their hearts
but wail upon their beds.
They gather together^a for grain and new wine
but turn away from me.
¹⁵ I trained them and strengthened them,
but they plot evil against me.
¹⁶ They do not turn to the Most High;
they are like a faulty bow.
Their leaders will fall by the sword
because of their insolent words.
For this they will be ridiculed
in the land of Egypt.

Israel to Reap the Whirlwind

8 "Put the trumpet to your lips!
An eagle is over the house of the LORD
because the people have broken my covenant
and rebelled against my law.
² Israel cries out to me,
'O our God, we acknowledge you!'
³ But Israel has rejected what is good;
an enemy will pursue him.
⁴ They set up kings without my consent;
they choose princes without my approval.
With their silver and gold
they make idols for themselves
to their own destruction.
⁵ Throw out your calf-idol, O Samaria!
My anger burns against them.
How long will they be incapable of purity?
⁶ They are from Israel!
This calf—a craftsman has made it;
it is not God.
It will be broken in pieces,
that calf of Samaria.

⁷ "They sow the wind
and reap the whirlwind.

a 14 Most Hebrew manuscripts; some Hebrew manuscripts and Septuagint They slash themselves

The stalk has no head;
   it will produce no flour.
Were it to yield grain,
   foreigners would swallow it up.
8 Israel is swallowed up;
   now she is among the nations
   like a worthless thing.
9 For they have gone up to Assyria
   like a wild donkey wandering alone.
   Ephraim has sold herself to lovers.
10 Although they have sold themselves among the nations,
   I will now gather them together.
They will begin to waste away
   under the oppression of the mighty king.

11 "Though Ephraim built many altars for sin offerings,
   these have become altars for sinning.
12 I wrote for them the many things of my law,
   but they regarded them as something alien.
13 They offer sacrifices given to me
   and they eat the meat,
   but the Lord is not pleased with them.
Now he will remember their wickedness
   and punish their sins:
   They will return to Egypt.
14 Israel has forgotten his Maker
   and built palaces;
   Judah has fortified many towns.
But I will send fire upon their cities
   that will consume their fortresses."

Punishment for Israel

9 Do not rejoice, O Israel;
   do not be jubilant like the other nations.
For you have been unfaithful to your God;
   you love the wages of a prostitute
   at every threshing floor.
2 Threshing floors and winepresses will not feed the people;
   the new wine will fail them.
3 They will not remain in the Lord's land;
   Ephraim will return to Egypt
   and eat unclean a food in Assyria.
4 They will not pour out wine offerings to the Lord,
   nor will their sacrifices please him.
Such sacrifices will be to them like the bread of mourners;
   all who eat them will be unclean.
This food will be for themselves;
   it will not come into the temple of the Lord.

5 What will you do on the day of your appointed feasts,
   on the festival days of the Lord?
6 Even if they escape from destruction,
   Egypt will gather them,
   and Memphis will bury them.
Their treasures of silver will be taken over by briers,

a 3 That is, ceremonially unclean

and thorns will overrun their tents.
7 The days of punishment are coming,
    the days of reckoning are at hand.
    Let Israel know this.
Because your sins are so many
    and your hostility so great,
the prophet is considered a fool,
    the inspired man a maniac.
8 The prophet, along with my God,
    is the watchman over Ephraim, [a]
yet snares await him on all his paths,
    and hostility in the house of his God.
9 They have sunk deep into corruption,
    as in the days of Gibeah.
God will remember their wickedness
    and punish them for their sins.

10 "When I found Israel,
    it was like finding grapes in the desert;
when I saw your fathers,
    it was like seeing the early fruit on the fig tree.
But when they came to Baal Peor,
    they consecrated themselves to that shameful idol
    and became as vile as the thing they loved.
11 Ephraim's glory will fly away like a bird—
    no birth, no pregnancy, no conception.
12 Even if they rear children,
    I will bereave them of every one.
Woe to them
    when I turn away from them!
13 I have seen Ephraim, like Tyre,
    planted in a pleasant place.
But Ephraim will bring out
    their children to the slayer."

14 Give them, O LORD—
    what will you give them?
Give them wombs that miscarry
    and breasts that are dry.

15 "Because of all their wickedness in Gilgal,
    I hated them there.
Because of their sinful deeds,
    I will drive them out of my house.
I will no longer love them;
    all their leaders are rebellious.
16 Ephraim is blighted,
    their root is withered,
    they yield no fruit.
Even if they bear children,
    I will slay their cherished offspring."

17 My God will reject them
    because they have not obeyed him;
    they will be wanderers among the nations.

a 8 Or The prophet is the watchman over Ephraim, / the people of my God

10

Israel was a spreading vine;
    he brought forth fruit for himself.
As his fruit increased,
    he built more altars;
as his land prospered,
    he adorned his sacred stones.
² Their heart is deceitful,
    and now they must bear their guilt.
The LORD will demolish their altars
    and destroy their sacred stones.

³ Then they will say, "We have no king
    because we did not revere the LORD.
But even if we had a king,
    what could he do for us?"

⁴ They make many promises,
    take false oaths
    and make agreements;
therefore lawsuits spring up
    like poisonous weeds in a
        plowed field.
⁵ The people who live in Samaria
    fear
    for the calf-idol of Beth Aven.ᵃ
Its people will mourn over it,
    and so will its idolatrous
        priests,
those who had rejoiced over its
        splendor,
    because it is taken from them
        into exile.
⁶ It will be carried to Assyria
    as tribute for the great king.
Ephraim will be disgraced;
    Israel will be ashamed of its
        wooden idols.ᵇ
⁷ Samaria and its king will float away
    like a twig on the surface of
        the waters.
⁸ The high places of wickednessᶜ
    will be destroyed—
    it is the sin of Israel.
Thorns and thistles will grow up
    and cover their altars.
Then they will say to the mountains, "Cover us!"
    and to the hills, "Fall on us!"

⁹ "Since the days of Gibeah, you have sinned, O Israel,
    and there you have remained.ᵈ
Did not war overtake
    the evildoers in Gibeah?
¹⁰ When I please, I will punish them;
    nations will be gathered against them
    to put them in bonds for their double sin.

---

genuine
devotion » 10:4

Think about the last thing you heard that struck you as insincere. Maybe someone complimented you, then quickly asked you for a favor. Makes the compliment seem suspicious rather than sincere, doesn't it? Or, maybe someone told you she would always be your friend but talked about you behind your back. You can usually tell insincerity by a person's empty words or broken promises. That was why God's insincerity meter pointed to the people of Israel. Their promises of loyalty meant nothing. What would God say about the sincerity of your loyalty to others, as well as to him?

ᵃ 5 Beth Aven means house of wickedness (a name for Bethel, which means house of God).   ᵇ 6 Or its counsel
ᶜ 8 Hebrew aven, a reference to Beth Aven (a derogatory name for Bethel)   ᵈ 9 Or there a stand was taken

¹¹ Ephraim is a trained heifer
      that loves to thresh;
so I will put a yoke
      on her fair neck.
I will drive Ephraim,
      Judah must plow,
      and Jacob must break up the ground.
¹² Sow for yourselves righteousness,
      reap the fruit of unfailing love,
and break up your unplowed ground;
      for it is time to seek the LORD,
until he comes
      and showers righteousness on you.
¹³ But you have planted wickedness,
      you have reaped evil,
      you have eaten the fruit of deception.
Because you have depended on your own strength
      and on your many warriors,
¹⁴ the roar of battle will rise against your people,
      so that all your fortresses will be devastated—
as Shalman devastated Beth Arbel on the day of battle,
      when mothers were dashed to the ground with their children.
¹⁵ Thus will it happen to you, O Bethel,
      because your wickedness is great.
When that day dawns,
      the king of Israel will be completely destroyed.

God's Love for Israel

11
      "When Israel was a child, I loved him,
      and out of Egypt I called my son.
² But the more I ᵃ called Israel,
      the further they went from me. ᵇ
They sacrificed to the Baals
      and they burned incense to
            images.
³ It was I who taught Ephraim to
            walk,
      taking them by the arms;
but they did not realize
      it was I who healed them.
⁴ I led them with cords of human
            kindness,
      with ties of love;
I lifted the yoke from their neck
      and bent down to feed them.

⁵ "Will they not return to Egypt
      and will not Assyria rule over them
      because they refuse to repent?
⁶ Swords will flash in their cities,
      will destroy the bars of their gates
      and put an end to their plans.
⁷ My people are determined to turn from me.
      Even if they call to the Most High,
      he will by no means exalt them.

truth or dare

God loved Israel as a parent loves a child. But, like a lot of kids, Israel loved independence more than God. Do you ever reject God's love in favor of independence?

11:1–11

ᵃ 2 Some Septuagint manuscripts; Hebrew *they*   ᵇ 2 Septuagint; Hebrew *them*

8 "How can I give you up, Ephraim?
How can I hand you over, Israel?
How can I treat you like Admah?
How can I make you like Zeboiim?
My heart is changed within me;
all my compassion is aroused.
9 I will not carry out my fierce anger,
nor will I turn and devastate Ephraim.
For I am God, and not man—
the Holy One among you.
I will not come in wrath. *ᵃ*
10 They will follow the LORD;
he will roar like a lion.
When he roars,
his children will come trembling from the west.
11 They will come trembling
like birds from Egypt,
like doves from Assyria.
I will settle them in their homes,"
declares the LORD.

Israel's Sin

12 Ephraim has surrounded me with lies,
the house of Israel with deceit.
And Judah is unruly against God,
even against the faithful Holy One.

12

1 Ephraim feeds on the wind;
he pursues the east wind all day
and multiplies lies and violence.
He makes a treaty with Assyria
and sends olive oil to Egypt.
2 The LORD has a charge to bring against Judah;
he will punish Jacob *ᵇ* according to his ways
and repay him according to his deeds.
3 In the womb he grasped his brother's heel;
as a man he struggled with God.
4 He struggled with the angel and overcame him;
he wept and begged for his favor.
He found him at Bethel
and talked with him there—
5 the LORD God Almighty,
the LORD is his name of renown!
6 But you must return to your God;
maintain love and justice,
and wait for your God always.

7 The merchant uses dishonest scales;
he loves to defraud.
8 Ephraim boasts,
"I am very rich; I have become wealthy.
With all my wealth they will not find in me
any iniquity or sin."

9 "I am the LORD your God,
⌊who brought you⌋ out of *ᶜ* Egypt;

ᵃ 9 Or *come against any city*   *ᵇ 2 Jacob* means *he grasps the heel* (figuratively, *he deceives*).   *ᶜ 9* Or *God / ever since you were in*

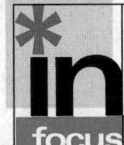

Shameless

Profile: Tania

Who says good girls don't show a little skin now and then? While I'm still young and fit, I'm going for it, girl! I figure this is God's reward for making me endure the pains of puberty all through middle school—like getting my first period at the seventh grade dance, the attack-of-the-acne and having to shave before other girls even owned a razor. Gross! Now that I've got some cleavage, I'm not ashamed to show it off.

My mom needs to get a life. It's like all she has time to think about is how short my skirt is. My mom's like every other mom—we fight about everything in my closet. But she doesn't understand that everyone dresses this way at my school. And, besides, it gets me where I've always wanted to be—*in* with the popular guys. Remind me again . . . *why* would I give that up? I've worked too hard to become the girl every guy wants to hook up with on Friday nights. I'll give the guys almost anything they want as long as I get what I want in return—popularity, attention, a date to every dance. It's all a game, and for once, I'm winning.

I know people talk about me behind my back. I hear the rumors. But that's okay. Those girls are just jealous.

flirting in focus

To flirt or not to flirt—that is the question (and a tough one, too). Read more on flirting at www.TrueImagesBible.com

There's a fine line between trying to look attractive and trying to look seductive. How do you know the difference?

»Like anything else, the difference is in your heart. Jesus said our actions come from our hearts (see Matthew 15:19, page 1311). What's your motive for wanting attention?

»Wanting a guy to notice you is no crime. It's part of how God created you. However, if your motive is wrong and you're compromising your integrity (or a guy's) in the way you dress, act or talk, you're off track (see Ephesians 5:3, page 1546).

»Getting a guy's attention and getting the *right* guy's attention are two very different goals. If you're looking for Mr. Right (a solid Christian guy), shameless flirting will not catch his eye. Godly guys are looking for godly girls—or they're not really godly guys. Are they overlooking you?

For more on this topic, see the index on page 1656.

I will make you live in tents again,
  as in the days of your appointed feasts.
[10] I spoke to the prophets,
  gave them many visions
  and told parables through them."

[11] Is Gilead wicked?
  Its people are worthless!
Do they sacrifice bulls in Gilgal?
  Their altars will be like piles of stones
  on a plowed field.

¹² Jacob fled to the country of Aram ᵃ;
    Israel served to get a wife,
    and to pay for her he tended sheep.
¹³ The LORD used a prophet to bring Israel up from Egypt,
    by a prophet he cared for him.
¹⁴ But Ephraim has bitterly provoked him to anger;
    his Lord will leave upon him the guilt of his bloodshed
    and will repay him for his contempt.

The LORD's Anger Against Israel

13

When Ephraim spoke, men trembled;
    he was exalted in Israel.
    But he became guilty of Baal worship and died.
² Now they sin more and more;
    they make idols for themselves from their silver,
cleverly fashioned images,
    all of them the work of craftsmen.
It is said of these people,
    "They offer human sacrifice
    and kiss ᵇ the calf-idols."
³ Therefore they will be like the morning mist,
    like the early dew that disappears,
    like chaff swirling from a threshing floor,
    like smoke escaping through a window.

⁴ "But I am the LORD your God,
    ⌞who brought you⌟ out of ᶜ Egypt.
You shall acknowledge no God but me,
    no Savior except me.
⁵ I cared for you in the desert,
    in the land of burning heat.
⁶ When I fed them, they were satisfied;
    when they were satisfied, they became proud;
    then they forgot me.
⁷ So I will come upon them like a lion,
    like a leopard I will lurk by the path.
⁸ Like a bear robbed of her cubs,
    I will attack them and rip them open.
Like a lion I will devour them;
    a wild animal will tear them apart.

⁹ "You are destroyed, O Israel,
    because you are against me, against your helper.
¹⁰ Where is your king, that he may save you?
    Where are your rulers in all your towns,
of whom you said,
    'Give me a king and princes'?
¹¹ So in my anger I gave you a king,
    and in my wrath I took him away.
¹² The guilt of Ephraim is stored up,
    his sins are kept on record.
¹³ Pains as of a woman in childbirth come to him,
    but he is a child without wisdom;
when the time arrives,
    he does not come to the opening of the womb.

ᵃ 12 That is, Northwest Mesopotamia   ᵇ 2 Or "Men who sacrifice / kiss   ᶜ 4 Or God / ever since you were in

DiVa, Doormat, or Dream Date?

Whether you have a boyfriend or not, you can still find out how you rate as a girlfriend. Are you a demanding diva? A docile doormat? Or would you make the all-time list of dream dates? Check it out!

1 When it comes down to spending time with you, your boyfriend . . .
- A. Hangs out with you whenever you want.
- B. Lets you know when he wants to hang out.
- C. Hangs with you some, hangs with his boys some.

2 If your guy told you about a problem he faced, you would . . .
- A. Jump right in and solve it.
- B. Give him some space till he gets over it.
- C. Offer your help but wait till he accepts your offer before doing anything.

3 When your birthday rolls around, you'd be happy if your boy . . .
- A. Gave you expensive gifts and lots of 'em, baby!
- B. Gave you whatever crumbs (time or gifts) he's willing to throw your way.
- C. Did something fun and thoughtful.

4 You catch your B.F. checking out another girl. You . . .
- A. Read him the riot act, then give him the silent treatment.
- B. Do nothing. Boys will be boys.
- C. Ask him what's up.

5 Let's say you're a Christian, and your boyfriend isn't sure what he believes (very bad scenario, by the way). Would you . . .
- A. Insist that he go to your church or you'll kick him to the curb?
- B. Keep your Christian beliefs to yourself to avoid making him feel uncomfortable?
- C. Tell him what you believe and why your faith is important to you, then suggest you take a break from dating but tell him you'd love to talk about it more?

6 Think about your B.F. and what's cool or quirky about him. What, if anything, would you change?
- A. Everything, starting with his friends, the way he dresses and his car. Definitely his car (or lack thereof).
- B. Nada. He's perfect as is.
- C. He bugs me sometimes, but changing him is up to God.

7 Whenever you and your boyfriend have a disagreement, you . . .
- A. Insist on getting your way.
- B. Give in and let him have his way.
- C. Work toward a compromise or agree to disagree.

8 If your boy had to break a date because some relatives arrived in town unexpectedly, you would . . .
- A. Freak out! How dare he?!
- B. Wait by the phone, hoping he'd invite you to hang out with his fam.
- C. Say, "No prob," and make plans to hang out with the girls.

9 You're still not done with a paper due Monday, and it's the weekend. Translation: you can't go to an amusement park with all your friends and B.F.—a trip you'd planned weeks ago. Your B.F. is still dyin' to go. You . . .
- A. Demand that he stay & help you with your paper.
- B. Say you're okay with him going but call him on his cell every two hours just to "check in" (i.e., let him know how miserable you are).
- C. Are disappointed but don't want him to miss going on your account.

10 When it comes to paying for dates, your motto is . . .
- A. The guy always pays—no exceptions.
- B. Whatever he needs me to do, I'll do. If I have to pay, I'll pay.
- C. If he asks, he pays; if I ask, I pay. Share and share alike.

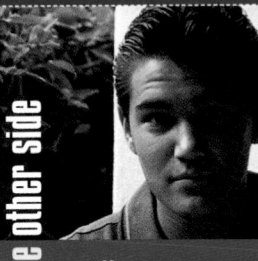

Mostly **A**'s—*Demanding Diva*

Girl, you're a straight-up diva. You know what you want and aren't afraid to be assertive. But maybe you come on too strong. It's your way or the highway, right? Hmmm. It doesn't always have to be about you, though. Remember the Golden Rule (Luke 6:31)? A relationship isn't about what *you* can get out of it and what *he* can give. It involves what you both bring to the table—a sincere desire to serve one another in Christ.

Mostly **B**'s—*Docile Doormat*

You try to please your guy, but bending over backward isn't the best way to keep him—or any other friend. Don't be passive or conform to who you think he wants you to be—be yourself. As Jesus once said, "Love your neighbor as yourself" (Matthew 22:39). Note the words *as yourself*. Ya gotta love yourself, girl, the way that God loves you. Now run, don't walk, to the "Stuck on him or God" sidebar.

Mostly **C**'s—*Dream Date*

You're the girl with something extra—respect for yourself and for your guy. That's pretty cool. Here's the pat on the back that you deserve. (Pat, pat!) Wanna keep building your dream date potential? Ask God to show you an older Christian girl who has this dating thing well balanced in her life, and take notes on her methods.

reflections from the other side

question:
What qualities do you look for as you consider a relationship with a girl?

answer:
At the risk of sounding shallow, one quality I consider is physical appearance. Of course, people often seem more attractive once you know them better; but for me there does have to be a threshold level in order to have any chemistry. Plus, it's the first thing you notice. Then I would consider Christian commitment—important because it shapes your goals. Then sense of humor, particularly an appreciation for sarcastic/edgy humor. I think relationships have a tough time working if people don't find the same type of stuff funny.

Stuck on him or God

Stuck on your guy? Cool. But does he edge out God in the heart sweepstakes? Not sure? Watch out for these warning signs:

1 » You think about pleasing him more than you think about pleasing God.

2 » You're willing to compromise your beliefs just to stay on his good side.

3 » You seek his opinion first, before checking out God's.

God wants your *whole* heart, not just the leftovers. Take a tip from Corrie ten Boom: "Whatever you treasure in life, hold it very loosely so that it doesn't hurt when God has to pry your fingers open to take it away." God does not delight in prying things out of our hands. He delights in watching us grow. Is your relationship helping you grow or holding you back?

GIRLFRIEND TIP:
Don't settle for less than God's best!

» Check out these biblical women who had the love and respect of the men in their lives.
Deborah (Judges 4), Hannah (1 Samuel 1), Abigail (1 Samuel 25), Esther (Esther 2:17; 5:1–3), Mary, the mother of Jesus (Matthew 1:18–25), Mary, the sister of Martha (Luke 10:38–42).

Who's Your Role Model?

1 Your friends have been naggin' you to run for class government. You run for . . .
- ○ A. Class President (Put me in control and give me a challenge!)
- ○ B. School Board Rep (Public speaking? Yeah, baby!)
- ○ C. Class Treasurer (Behind the scenes is more my thing!)

2 You're fillin' out your college apps. Who do you give your recommendations to?
- ○ A. Your coach—he loves your diehard mentality.
- ○ B. Your music teacher—you've always been a star performer.
- ○ C. Your small group leader—you're the kind of girl every leader loves: consistent and helpful.

3 Your friend comes to you when . . .
- ○ A. She needs some backup in an argument—there's no messing with you.
- ○ B. She's choosing a homecoming dress—you've got a killer eye for style.
- ○ C. She's lonely—you're always there for her.

4 You've got issues with a friend. How do you deal with it?
- ○ A. Face it—just take it head-on.
- ○ B. Smooth it over tactfully.
- ○ C. What conflict? You're never one to fight.

5 Your friends describe you as . . .
- ○ A. The go-to person. You lead by example and make things happen.
- ○ B. Always put together. Your hair and your homework are always done.
- ○ C. The best friend ever. You're comfortable to be around.

6 When you were a little girl, what did you want to be when you grew up?
- ○ A. High-powered lawyer
- ○ B. Miss America with a message
- ○ C. Elementary school teacher

7 Saturday afternoon. You're chillin' at home, wearing . . .
- ○ A. Shorts and a classic t-shirt—stylish but sporty.
- ○ B. A pretty sundress—with your toenails painted to match, of course.
- ○ C. Linen capris—casual but cute.

8 You'd most likely be voted . . .
- ○ A. Most Likely to Be President
- ○ B. Most Likely to Succeed
- ○ C. Best Marriage Material

(A)   (B)   (C)   (?)

scoring

(A) (B) (C)　　(?)

Mostly (A)'s

Remember Deborah, the famous leader, warrior and judge? Just like her, you're a cross between Joan of Arc and Mia Hamm. You're tough as nails, you take charge in a group, you like a challenge and you don't mind being a woman in a man's world. Deborah was a complex, multi-talented girl— warrior/judge by day, singer/song-writer by night. Don't be afraid to develop the softer facets of your personality.

Mostly (B)'s

Hello, Queen Esther, beauty pageant winner and public speaker extraordinaire! You're a cross between the elegant Princess Diana and the poised and lovely Laura Bush. You're a refined, high-profile, P.R. kind of girl who thinks fast on her feet and gives "eloquent" a whole new meaning. While being a charming beauty queen, you're also clever, respectful, resourceful and self-confident. Remember that the real key to Esther's success was her humility and love for others—not her drop-dead looks.

Mostly (C)'s

You take your cues from girls like Ruth. You're a cross between Martha Stewart and Mother Teresa—artsy, sweet, soft-spoken, compassionate, loyal. You're not the up-front person, but there's more than one way to lead in life, as seen in your hard-working, behind-the-scenes style. You're a true blue, stick to ya like glue kind of friend, and you're no non-sense with the task at hand. You have a deep beauty and charm that shine through you in an almost exotic, intriguing kind of way.

reflections from the other side

question:
What comes to mind when you think of Deborah, Esther and Ruth?

answer:
I guess Deborah had the whole leader thing going for her, and Esther had enough guts to save her peeps. Ruth was a faithful friend who'd stick with you through anything.

Build Your Ruth Factor:

» Volunteer @ the hospital or help out @ the church nursery.
» Stick close to a girlfriend who's going through a tough time in life.

Hey, All You Esther Wannabes!

» Don't be afraid to speak up, but always season your words with grace.
» Seek advice from mentors (like Mordecai; see Esther 2:7,20).
» Realizing that you don't know everything shows wisdom in and of itself.

Destined to Be a Deborah Dynamo?

» Don't shy away from a challenge. Never underestimate what God can do through you!
» Don't forget to thank God for your victories.

¹⁴"I will ransom them from the power of the grave^a;
  I will redeem them from death.
Where, O death, are your plagues?
  Where, O grave,^a is your destruction?

"I will have no compassion,
¹⁵ even though he thrives among his brothers.
An east wind from the LORD will come,
  blowing in from the desert;
his spring will fail
  and his well dry up.
His storehouse will be plundered
  of all its treasures.
¹⁶The people of Samaria must bear their guilt,
  because they have rebelled against their God.
They will fall by the sword;
  their little ones will be dashed to the ground,
  their pregnant women ripped open."

Repentance to Bring Blessing

14 Return, O Israel, to the LORD your God.
  Your sins have been your downfall!
²Take words with you
  and return to the LORD.
Say to him:
  "Forgive all our sins
  and receive us graciously,
that we may offer the fruit of
  our lips.^b
³Assyria cannot save us;
  we will not mount war-horses.
We will never again say 'Our gods'
  to what our own hands have
    made,
for in you the fatherless find
  compassion."

⁴"I will heal their waywardness
  and love them freely,
for my anger has turned away
  from them.
⁵I will be like the dew to Israel;
  he will blossom like a lily.
Like a cedar of Lebanon
  he will send down his roots;
⁶ his young shoots will grow.
His splendor will be like an olive
    tree,
  his fragrance like a cedar of
    Lebanon.
⁷Men will dwell again in his shade.
  He will flourish like the grain.
He will blossom like a vine,
  and his fame will be like the
    wine from Lebanon.

genuine success » 14:9

When you're hiking, how do you know the right paths to take? Duh. That's an easy one. The right paths are either the marked paths or the ones your guide takes you on. A wise hiker wouldn't set out on an unmarked path. Otherwise, she might stumble on something and fall or get hopelessly lost in the woods. It's the same way in life. God's ways *are* the right paths. You won't stumble or stray if you're going his way. As you're hiking through life, follow the ultimate Trailblazer—Jesus, the best hiking guide in the universe.

^a 14 Hebrew *Sheol*   ^b 2 Or *offer our lips as sacrifices of bulls*

⁸O Ephraim, what more have I[a] to do with idols?
  I will answer him and care for him.
I am like a green pine tree;
  your fruitfulness comes from me."

⁹Who is wise? He will realize these things.
  Who is discerning? He will understand them.
The ways of the LORD are right;
  the righteous walk in them,
  but the rebellious stumble in them.

[a] 8 Or *What more has Ephraim*

author:	Joel.
date:	Probably about 835 B.C.
setting:	The people of Judah had become wealthy and complacent. They stopped relying on God and instead worshiped idols.
verse to remember:	"And everyone who calls on the name of the Lord will be saved" (2:32).
theme to consider:	Joel warned the people of Judah that God would judge them by sending a locust plague against them. He urged them to turn to God and repent so they would be saved on the day of judgment.

Joel

unchanging truth

The words "I'm sorry" have a lot of power. Have you ever been really mad at someone and then that person came to you and said, "I'm sorry"? What a difference those two words can make! It means a lot to know that the person recognizes the pain he or she caused you and wants to apologize for it.

Those words make a big difference with God, too. A whole life can be changed when someone comes to God and sincerely says, "I'm sorry." That's actually the first step of salvation—recognizing your sin and your need for God to forgive you.

That's the message the prophet Joel brought to the southern kingdom of Judah. The people were not following God, so God sent Joel to tell the people that a plague of locusts would come upon them as punishment. Joel urged them to repent before even greater punishment occurred.

While God wanted the people to recognize their sin, he also required a change of heart. Suppose that person who apologized to you turned around and hurt you again. You wouldn't think much of the apology, would you? Repentance requires a change in our behavior. It means nothing if we say we're sorry only to go back and sin against God in the same way. You see, more than our words, God wants our hearts. And we are able to return to him because "he is gracious and compassionate, slow to anger and abounding in love" (2:13).

3 life lessons

1. God promised to pour out his Spirit on his people. Jesus fulfilled this promise when he sent the Holy Spirit to his followers—just as the Holy Spirit comes to us when we believe (2:28–29; see John 16:7; Acts 2:1–4,16–21).

2. Anyone who calls on the Lord will be saved (2:32).

3. In the future is coming a "day of the Lord" when God will judge all people—bringing the righteous into his everlasting kingdom and sending the evil ones away (3:12–16; see Revelation 14:14–20).

1

The word of the LORD that came to Joel son of Pethuel.

An Invasion of Locusts

² Hear this, you elders;
　　listen, all who live in the land.
Has anything like this ever happened in your days
　　or in the days of your forefathers?
³ Tell it to your children,
　　and let your children tell it to their children,
　　and their children to the next
　　　　generation.
⁴ What the locust swarm has left
　　the great locusts have eaten;
what the great locusts have left
　　the young locusts have eaten;
what the young locusts have left
　　other locusts ᵃ have eaten.

⁵ Wake up, you drunkards, and
　　　weep!
　　Wail, all you drinkers of wine;
wail because of the new wine,
　　for it has been snatched from your lips.
⁶ A nation has invaded my land,
　　powerful and without number;
it has the teeth of a lion,
　　the fangs of a lioness.
⁷ It has laid waste my vines
　　and ruined my fig trees.
It has stripped off their bark
　　and thrown it away,
　　leaving their branches white.

⁸ Mourn like a virgin ᵇ in sackcloth
　　grieving for the husband ᶜ of her youth.
⁹ Grain offerings and drink offerings
　　are cut off from the house of the LORD.
The priests are in mourning,
　　those who minister before the LORD.
¹⁰ The fields are ruined,
　　the ground is dried up ᵈ;
the grain is destroyed,
　　the new wine is dried up,
　　the oil fails.
¹¹ Despair, you farmers,
　　wail, you vine growers;
grieve for the wheat and the barley,
　　because the harvest of the field is destroyed.
¹² The vine is dried up
　　and the fig tree is withered;
the pomegranate, the palm and the apple tree—
　　all the trees of the field—are dried up.

---

truth or dare

Ask your grandparents to tell you their life story. You'll see how God has worked in their lives and learn from their mistakes. What will you be able to tell *your* grandchildren?

1:3

ᵃ 4 The precise meaning of the four Hebrew words used here for locusts is uncertain.　ᵇ 8 Or *young woman*
ᶜ 8 Or *betrothed*　ᵈ 10 Or *ground mourns*

Surely the joy of mankind
is withered away.

A Call to Repentance

¹³ Put on sackcloth, O priests, and mourn;
wail, you who minister before the altar.
Come, spend the night in sackcloth,
you who minister before my God;
for the grain offerings and drink offerings
are withheld from the house of your God.
¹⁴ Declare a holy fast;
call a sacred assembly.
Summon the elders
and all who live in the land
to the house of the LORD your God,
and cry out to the LORD.

¹⁵ Alas for that day!
For the day of the LORD is near;
it will come like destruction from the Almighty.^a

¹⁶ Has not the food been cut off
before our very eyes—
joy and gladness
from the house of our God?
¹⁷ The seeds are shriveled
beneath the clods.^b
The storehouses are in ruins,
the granaries have been broken down,
for the grain has dried up.
¹⁸ How the cattle moan!
The herds mill about
because they have no pasture;
even the flocks of sheep are suffering.

¹⁹ To you, O LORD, I call,
for fire has devoured the open pastures
and flames have burned up all the trees of the field.
²⁰ Even the wild animals pant for you;
the streams of water have dried up
and fire has devoured the open pastures.

An Army of Locusts

2 Blow the trumpet in Zion;
sound the alarm on my holy hill.
Let all who live in the land tremble,
for the day of the LORD is coming.
It is close at hand—
²   a day of darkness and gloom,
a day of clouds and blackness.
Like dawn spreading across the mountains
a large and mighty army comes,
such as never was of old
nor ever will be in ages to come.

³ Before them fire devours,

^a 15 Hebrew *Shaddai*   ^b 17 The meaning of the Hebrew for this word is uncertain.

behind them a flame blazes.
Before them the land is like the garden of Eden,
behind them, a desert waste—
nothing escapes them.
⁴They have the appearance of horses;
they gallop along like cavalry.
⁵With a noise like that of chariots
they leap over the mountaintops,
like a crackling fire consuming stubble,
like a mighty army drawn up for battle.

⁶At the sight of them, nations are in anguish;
every face turns pale.
⁷They charge like warriors;
they scale walls like soldiers.
They all march in line,
not swerving from their course.
⁸They do not jostle each other;
each marches straight ahead.
They plunge through defenses
without breaking ranks.
⁹They rush upon the city;
they run along the wall.
They climb into the houses;
like thieves they enter through the windows.

¹⁰Before them the earth shakes,
the sky trembles,
the sun and moon are darkened,
and the stars no longer shine.
¹¹The LORD thunders
at the head of his army;
his forces are beyond number,
and mighty are those who
obey his command.
The day of the LORD is great;
it is dreadful.
Who can endure it?

Rend Your Heart

¹²"Even now," declares the LORD,
"return to me with all your
heart,
with fasting and weeping and
mourning."

¹³Rend your heart
and not your garments.
Return to the LORD your God,
for he is gracious and
compassionate,
slow to anger and abounding in
love,
and he relents from sending
calamity.

genuine repentance » 2:12-13

Nothing's more irritating than someone who claims to be sorry for something but doesn't act like it. Wouldn't you agree? Maybe a friend claims to be sorry for something she did but later does the same thing again. Or maybe you get an apology that just doesn't sound very sincere. God told the prophet Joel that he wanted the kind of sorrow over sin that moved a person to want to change. It's not just empty tears (anyone can work those up), but actual hatred of sin. Sincerely sorry over sin? You've just made God's day!

¹⁴Who knows? He may turn and have pity
and leave behind a blessing—

grain offerings and drink offerings
    for the LORD your God.

¹⁵Blow the trumpet in Zion,
    declare a holy fast,
    call a sacred assembly.
¹⁶Gather the people,
    consecrate the assembly;
bring together the elders,
    gather the children,
    those nursing at the breast.
Let the bridegroom leave his room
    and the bride her chamber.
¹⁷Let the priests, who minister before the LORD,
    weep between the temple porch and the altar.
Let them say, "Spare your people, O LORD.
    Do not make your inheritance an object of scorn,
    a byword among the nations.
Why should they say among the peoples,
    'Where is their God?' "

The LORD's Answer

¹⁸Then the LORD will be jealous for his land
    and take pity on his people.
¹⁹The LORD will reply^a to them:

    "I am sending you grain, new wine and oil,
        enough to satisfy you fully;
    never again will I make you
        an object of scorn to the nations.

²⁰"I will drive the northern army far from you,
    pushing it into a parched and barren land,
with its front columns going into the eastern sea^b
    and those in the rear into the western sea.^c
And its stench will go up;
    its smell will rise."

Surely he has done great things.^d
²¹   Be not afraid, O land;
    be glad and rejoice.
Surely the LORD has done great things.
²²   Be not afraid, O wild animals,
    for the open pastures are becoming green.
The trees are bearing their fruit;
    the fig tree and the vine yield their riches.
²³Be glad, O people of Zion,
    rejoice in the LORD your God,
for he has given you
    the autumn rains in righteousness.^e
He sends you abundant showers,
    both autumn and spring rains, as before.
²⁴The threshing floors will be filled with grain;
    the vats will overflow with new wine and oil.

^a 18,19 Or LORD was jealous . . . / and took pity . . . / ¹⁹The LORD replied   ^b 20 That is, the Dead Sea   ^c 20 That is,
the Mediterranean   ^d 20 Or rise. / Surely it has done great things."   ^e 23 Or / the teacher for righteousness:

²⁵"I will repay you for the years the locusts have eaten—
    the great locust and the young locust,
    the other locusts and the locust swarm*—
my great army that I sent among you.
²⁶You will have plenty to eat, until you are full,
    and you will praise the name of the LORD your God,
    who has worked wonders for you;
never again will my people be shamed.
²⁷Then you will know that I am in Israel,
    that I am the LORD your God,
    and that there is no other;
never again will my people be shamed.

The Day of the LORD

²⁸"And afterward,
    I will pour out my Spirit on all people.
Your sons and daughters will prophesy,
    your old men will dream dreams,
    your young men will see visions.
²⁹Even on my servants, both men and women,
    I will pour out my Spirit in those days.
³⁰I will show wonders in the heavens
    and on the earth,
    blood and fire and billows of smoke.
³¹The sun will be turned to darkness
    and the moon to blood
    before the coming of the great
        and dreadful day of the
        LORD.
³²And everyone who calls
    on the name of the LORD will
        be saved;
    for on Mount Zion and in
        Jerusalem
    there will be deliverance,
    as the LORD has said,
among the survivors
    whom the LORD calls.

truth or dare

Wow! What a promise—no magic words, no strings attached—just respond to Jesus in faith, and you'll be saved.

2:32

The Nations Judged

3 "In those days and at that time,
    when I restore the fortunes of Judah and Jerusalem,
²I will gather all nations
    and bring them down to the Valley of Jehoshaphat.*
There I will enter into judgment against them
    concerning my inheritance, my people Israel,
for they scattered my people among the nations
    and divided up my land.
³They cast lots for my people
    and traded boys for prostitutes;
they sold girls for wine
    that they might drink.

⁴"Now what have you against me, O Tyre and Sidon and all you regions of Philistia? Are you

---

ᵃ 25 The precise meaning of the four Hebrew words used here for locusts is uncertain.   ᵇ 2 Jehoshaphat means the
LORD judges; also in verse 12.

repaying me for something I have done? If you are paying me back, I will swiftly and speedily return on your own heads what you have done. [5]For you took my silver and my gold and carried off my finest treasures to your temples. [6]You sold the people of Judah and Jerusalem to the Greeks, that you might send them far from their homeland.

[7]"See, I am going to rouse them out of the places to which you sold them, and I will return on your own heads what you have done. [8]I will sell your sons and daughters to the people of Judah, and they will sell them to the Sabeans, a nation far away." The LORD has spoken.

[9]Proclaim this among the nations:
    Prepare for war!
  Rouse the warriors!
    Let all the fighting men draw near and attack.
[10]Beat your plowshares into swords
    and your pruning hooks into spears.
  Let the weakling say,
    "I am strong!"
[11]Come quickly, all you nations from every side,
    and assemble there.

  Bring down your warriors, O LORD!

[12]"Let the nations be roused;
    let them advance into the Valley of Jehoshaphat,
  for there I will sit
    to judge all the nations on every side.
[13]Swing the sickle,
    for the harvest is ripe.
  Come, trample the grapes,
    for the winepress is full
    and the vats overflow—
  so great is their wickedness!"

[14]Multitudes, multitudes
    in the valley of decision!
  For the day of the LORD is near
    in the valley of decision.
[15]The sun and moon will be darkened,
    and the stars no longer shine.
[16]The LORD will roar from Zion
    and thunder from Jerusalem;
    the earth and the sky will tremble.
  But the LORD will be a refuge for his people,
    a stronghold for the people of Israel.

Blessings for God's People

[17]"Then you will know that I, the LORD your God,
    dwell in Zion, my holy hill.
  Jerusalem will be holy;
    never again will foreigners invade her.

[18]"In that day the mountains will drip new wine,
    and the hills will flow with milk;
    all the ravines of Judah will run with water.
  A fountain will flow out of the LORD's house
    and will water the valley of acacias. [a]
[19]But Egypt will be desolate,
    Edom a desert waste,

a 18 Or Valley of Shittim

because of violence done to the people of Judah,
in whose land they shed innocent blood.
²⁰ Judah will be inhabited forever
and Jerusalem through all generations.
²¹ Their bloodguilt, which I have not pardoned,
I will pardon."

The LORD dwells in Zion!

author:	Amos, a shepherd and fig-grower.
date:	About 760–750 B.C.
setting:	Some wealthy people in Israel were oppressing the poor.
verse to remember:	Hear this word the LORD has spoken against you, O people of Israel—against the whole family I brought up out of Egypt: "You only have I chosen of all the families of the earth; therefore I will punish you for all your sins" (3:1–2).
theme to consider:	Amos prophesied God's judgment on Israel for their sins of idolatry and the oppression of the poor.

unchanging truth

When you see a commercial or ad asking for money to help poor, starving people in other parts of the world, what do you feel? Perhaps you have some homeless people in your town who beg for money. You're not sure what to do or how to really help them.

God is concerned for the poor. Many of his laws focused on how his people should treat those less fortunate. They were never to take advantage of the poor.

Unfortunately, God's people were not following his laws. The prophet Amos was sent from Judah to speak to the northern kingdom of Israel. The wealthy were oppressing the poor—trampling on them, denying them justice. These rich Israelites had forgotten their own history—that their ancestors at one time had been destitute slaves in Egypt. Amos told these rich oppressors that they would again become slaves in a nation that would conquer them because of their sins.

No matter how much God has blessed you, he asks that you always have compassion for others. The poor girl at school who can't afford nice clothes is not to be teased, but befriended and treated kindly. The poor family in your neighborhood is not to be laughed at, but shown respect. There may be ways for you to help by giving money—but begin by learning to treat all people with fairness and respect. That is what God requires.

amos

life lessons

1 God has a plan for all nations of the earth. He rules over all (1:3—2:16).

2 God longs to show mercy to those who repent and return to him (5:4–6,14–15).

3 If God has blessed you, don't become arrogant and uncaring toward others. God judges such complacency (6:1–7).

⌃

1 The words of Amos, one of the shepherds of Tekoa—what he saw concerning Israel two years before the earthquake, when Uzziah was king of Judah and Jeroboam son of Jehoash[a] was king of Israel. [2]He said:

> "The LORD roars from Zion
>   and thunders from Jerusalem;
> the pastures of the shepherds dry up,[b]
>   and the top of Carmel withers."

Judgment on Israel's Neighbors

[3]This is what the LORD says:

> "For three sins of Damascus,
>   even for four, I will not turn back ⌐my wrath⌐.
> Because she threshed Gilead
>   with sledges having iron teeth,
> [4]I will send fire upon the house of Hazael
>   that will consume the fortresses of Ben-Hadad.
> [5]I will break down the gate of Damascus;
>   I will destroy the king who is in[c] the Valley of Aven[d]
> and the one who holds the scepter in Beth Eden.
>   The people of Aram will go into exile to Kir,"

says the LORD.

[6]This is what the LORD says:

> "For three sins of Gaza,
>   even for four, I will not turn back ⌐my wrath⌐.
> Because she took captive whole communities
>   and sold them to Edom,
> [7]I will send fire upon the walls of Gaza
>   that will consume her fortresses.
> [8]I will destroy the king[e] of Ashdod
>   and the one who holds the scepter in Ashkelon.
> I will turn my hand against Ekron,
>   till the last of the Philistines is dead,"

says the Sovereign LORD.

[9]This is what the LORD says:

> "For three sins of Tyre,
>   even for four, I will not turn back ⌐my wrath⌐.
> Because she sold whole communities of captives to Edom,
>   disregarding a treaty of brotherhood,
> [10]I will send fire upon the walls of Tyre
>   that will consume her fortresses."

[11]This is what the LORD says:

> "For three sins of Edom,
>   even for four, I will not turn back ⌐my wrath⌐.
> Because he pursued his brother with a sword,
>   stifling all compassion,[f]
> because his anger raged continually
>   and his fury flamed unchecked,
> [12]I will send fire upon Teman
>   that will consume the fortresses of Bozrah."

a 1 Hebrew Joash, a variant of Jehoash   b 2 Or shepherds mourn   c 5 Or the inhabitants of   d 5 Aven means wickedness.   e 8 Or inhabitants   f 11 Or sword / and destroyed his allies

¹³This is what the LORD says:

"For three sins of Ammon,
    even for four, I will not turn back ⌞my wrath⌟.
Because he ripped open the pregnant women of Gilead
    in order to extend his borders,
¹⁴I will set fire to the walls of Rabbah
    that will consume her fortresses
amid war cries on the day of battle,
    amid violent winds on a stormy day.
¹⁵Her king*ᵃ* will go into exile,
    he and his officials together,"

says the LORD.

2 This is what the LORD says:

"For three sins of Moab,
    even for four, I will not turn back ⌞my wrath⌟.
Because he burned, as if to lime,
    the bones of Edom's king,
²I will send fire upon Moab
    that will consume the fortresses of Kerioth.ᵇ
Moab will go down in great tumult
    amid war cries and the blast of the trumpet.
³I will destroy her ruler
    and kill all her officials with him,"

says the LORD.

⁴This is what the LORD says:

"For three sins of Judah,
    even for four, I will not turn
        back ⌞my wrath⌟.
Because they have rejected the
    law of the LORD
    and have not kept his decrees,
because they have been led
        astray by false gods,ᶜ
    the godsᵈ their ancestors
        followed,
⁵I will send fire upon Judah
    that will consume the
        fortresses of Jerusalem."

truth or dare

Think God overlooks the sins of his very favorite people? Nope. God requires repentance from all of us.

2:4–16

Judgment on Israel

⁶This is what the LORD says:

"For three sins of Israel,
    even for four, I will not turn back ⌞my wrath⌟.
They sell the righteous for silver,
    and the needy for a pair of sandals.
⁷They trample on the heads of the poor
    as upon the dust of the ground
    and deny justice to the oppressed.
Father and son use the same girl
    and so profane my holy name.
⁸They lie down beside every altar

ᵃ 15 Or *I / Molech*; Hebrew *malcam*   *ᵇ 2* Or *of her cities*   *ᶜ 4* Or *by lies*   *ᵈ 4* Or *lies*

on garments taken in pledge.
In the house of their god
they drink wine taken as fines.

⁹ "I destroyed the Amorite before them,
though he was tall as the cedars
and strong as the oaks.
I destroyed his fruit above
and his roots below.

¹⁰ "I brought you up out of Egypt,
and I led you forty years in the desert
to give you the land of the Amorites.

¹¹ I also raised up prophets from among your sons
and Nazirites from among your young men.
Is this not true, people of Israel?"

declares the LORD.

¹² "But you made the Nazirites drink wine
and commanded the prophets not to prophesy.

¹³ "Now then, I will crush you
as a cart crushes when loaded with grain.

¹⁴ The swift will not escape,
the strong will not muster their strength,
and the warrior will not save his life.

¹⁵ The archer will not stand his ground,
the fleet-footed soldier will not get away,
and the horseman will not save his life.

¹⁶ Even the bravest warriors
will flee naked on that day,"

declares the LORD.

Witnesses Summoned Against Israel

3 Hear this word the LORD has spoken against you, O people of Israel—against the whole family I brought up out of Egypt:

² "You only have I chosen
of all the families of the earth;
therefore I will punish you
for all your sins."

³ Do two walk together
unless they have agreed to do so?

⁴ Does a lion roar in the thicket
when he has no prey?
Does he growl in his den
when he has caught nothing?

⁵ Does a bird fall into a trap on the ground
where no snare has been set?
Does a trap spring up from the earth
when there is nothing to catch?

⁶ When a trumpet sounds in a city,
do not the people tremble?
When disaster comes to a city,
has not the LORD caused it?

⁷ Surely the Sovereign LORD does nothing
without revealing his plan
to his servants the prophets.

Going Public

"Let's skip class and go hang out at my house," Peter suggested. Everyone nodded in agreement. Then they looked at me.

"Ummm, actually I can't. I have a test next period," I said firmly (I hoped).

That didn't faze them at all. "So? Tell your mom to write you a note and say you were sick. My mom does it all the time," Rochelle said nonchalantly.

Yeah, well my *mom doesn't,* I thought to myself. Convincing Mom to let me transfer from a private Christian school to a public school was already a quantum leap for her. Like this conversation would go over well. "By the way, Mom, can you write a note to my advisor and tell her I had a doctor's appointment yesterday? I skipped class and need to cover for it." Yeah right! She'd flip out and launch into her speech again about public school and peer pressure . . .

But if I don't go with them, they'll stop asking me. And then I'll be all alone, walking to class and eating lunch all by myself. My new friends are really into partying (not *my* usual style), but so far they've left me alone when I've passed on the alcohol. Last weekend I even left their party early and made my curfew. No one gave me grief over leaving early, and Mom stayed happy (phew!).

It's getting harder and harder to stretch between them, though. I want to show Mom I can handle being on my own at a public school, while at the same time I want to fit in with the new friends I've made. I know I'm going to disappoint one of them eventually.

fitting in in focus

Who doesn't want to fit in? It's natural. However, if you compromise who you are in order to fit in, that's a problem.

»Sure, Jesus socialized with lots of different people (see Matthew 9:10–11, page 1302), yet he never changed who he was around them.

»Jesus' closest friends were his disciples—he "fit in" best with those who shared his love for God. Are you trying to fit in where a Christian doesn't belong?

»Sometimes you'll have to stand alone in order to stand for what's right (see Psalm 1:1, page 656).

For more on this topic, see the index on page 1656.

To learn more about friendship and fitting in, go to www.TrueImagesBible.com

[8]The lion has roared—
who will not fear?
The Sovereign LORD has spoken—
who can but prophesy?

⁹Proclaim to the fortresses of Ashdod
   and to the fortresses of Egypt:
"Assemble yourselves on the mountains of Samaria;
   see the great unrest within her
   and the oppression among her people."

¹⁰"They do not know how to do right," declares the LORD,
   "who hoard plunder and loot in their fortresses."

¹¹Therefore this is what the Sovereign LORD says:

"An enemy will overrun the land;
   he will pull down your strongholds
   and plunder your fortresses."

¹²This is what the LORD says:

"As a shepherd saves from the lion's mouth
   only two leg bones or a piece of an ear,
   so will the Israelites be saved,
those who sit in Samaria
   on the edge of their beds
   and in Damascus on their couches.ᵃ"

¹³"Hear this and testify against the house of Jacob," declares the Lord, the LORD God Almighty.

¹⁴"On the day I punish Israel for her sins,
   I will destroy the altars of Bethel;
the horns of the altar will be cut off
   and fall to the ground.
¹⁵I will tear down the winter house
   along with the summer house;
the houses adorned with ivory will be destroyed
   and the mansions will be demolished,"

declares the LORD.

Israel Has Not Returned to God

4 Hear this word, you cows of Bashan on Mount Samaria,
   you women who oppress the poor and crush the needy
   and say to your husbands, "Bring us some drinks!"
²The Sovereign LORD has sworn by his holiness:
   "The time will surely come
when you will be taken away with hooks,
   the last of you with fishhooks.
³You will each go straight out
   through breaks in the wall,
   and you will be cast out toward Harmon,ᵇ"

declares the LORD.

⁴"Go to Bethel and sin;
   go to Gilgal and sin yet more.
Bring your sacrifices every morning,
   your tithes every three years.ᶜ
⁵Burn leavened bread as a thank offering
   and brag about your freewill offerings—
boast about them, you Israelites,
   for this is what you love to do,"

declares the Sovereign LORD.

ᵃ 12 The meaning of the Hebrew for this line is uncertain.   ᵇ 3 Masoretic Text; with a different word division of the Hebrew (see Septuagint) out, O mountain of oppression   ᶜ 4 Or tithes on the third day

⁶"I gave you empty stomachs[a] in
every city
and lack of bread in every
town,
yet you have not returned to
me,"
declares the LORD.

⁷"I also withheld rain from you
when the harvest was still
three months away.
I sent rain on one town,
but withheld it from another.
One field had rain;
another had none and dried up.
⁸People staggered from town to town for water
but did not get enough to drink,
yet you have not returned to me,"
declares the LORD.

⁹"Many times I struck your gardens and
vineyards,
I struck them with blight and mildew.
Locusts devoured your fig and olive trees,
yet you have not returned to me,"

declares the LORD.

¹⁰"I sent plagues among you
as I did to Egypt.
I killed your young men with the sword,
along with your captured horses.
I filled your nostrils with the stench of your camps,
yet you have not returned to me,"

declares the LORD.

¹¹"I overthrew some of you
as I[b] overthrew Sodom and Gomorrah.
You were like a burning stick snatched from the fire,
yet you have not returned to me,"

declares the LORD.

¹²"Therefore this is what I will do to you, Israel,
and because I will do this to you,
prepare to meet your God, O Israel."

¹³He who forms the mountains,
creates the wind,
and reveals his thoughts to man,
he who turns dawn to darkness,
and treads the high places of the earth—
the LORD God Almighty is his name.

A Lament and Call to Repentance

5 Hear this word, O house of Israel, this lament I take up concerning you:

²"Fallen is Virgin Israel,
never to rise again,

truth or dare

If the fridge is empty, you look somewhere else for food, right? The Israelites were starving both physically and spiritually—yet they stubbornly kept going their own way and missed God's nourishment.

4:6–11

---

^a 6 Hebrew *you cleanness of teeth*   ^b 11 Hebrew *God*

deserted in her own land,
    with no one to lift her up."

[3] This is what the Sovereign Lord says:

"The city that marches out a thousand strong for Israel
    will have only a hundred left;
the town that marches out a hundred strong
    will have only ten left."

[4] This is what the Lord says to the house of Israel:

"Seek me and live;
[5]   do not seek Bethel,
do not go to Gilgal,

love notes

5:4

Dear daughter,

When you are hurting, come to me. When you are lonely or depressed, seek me. When your struggles threaten to overwhelm you, there is only one solution: Seek me and live! I alone am the answer to your problems.

—Father God

In what areas of your life do you most need to seek God?

_____

_____

_____

_____

_____

_____

_____

do not journey to Beersheba.
For Gilgal will surely go into exile,
    and Bethel will be reduced to
        nothing. [a]"
[6] Seek the Lord and live,
    or he will sweep through the
        house of Joseph like a fire;
it will devour,
    and Bethel will have no one to
        quench it.

[7] You who turn justice into
        bitterness
    and cast righteousness to the
        ground
[8] (he who made the Pleiades and
        Orion,
    who turns blackness into dawn
    and darkens day into night,
who calls for the waters of the
        sea
    and pours them out over the
        face of the land—
    the Lord is his name—
[9] he flashes destruction on the
        stronghold
    and brings the fortified city to
        ruin),
[10] you hate the one who reproves in
        court
    and despise him who tells the
        truth.

[11] You trample on the poor
    and force him to give you grain.
Therefore, though you have built
        stone mansions,
    you will not live in them;
though you have planted lush
        vineyards,
    you will not drink their wine.

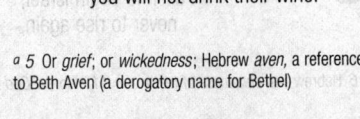

a 5 Or *grief*; or *wickedness*; Hebrew *aven*, a reference to Beth Aven (a derogatory name for Bethel)

¹²For I know how many are your offenses
and how great your sins.

You oppress the righteous and take bribes
and you deprive the poor of justice in the courts.
¹³Therefore the prudent man keeps quiet in such times,
for the times are evil.

¹⁴Seek good, not evil,
that you may live.
Then the LORD God Almighty will be with you,
just as you say he is.
¹⁵Hate evil, love good;
maintain justice in the courts.
Perhaps the LORD God Almighty will have mercy
on the remnant of Joseph.

¹⁶Therefore this is what the Lord, the LORD God Almighty, says:

"There will be wailing in all the streets
and cries of anguish in every public square.
The farmers will be summoned to weep
and the mourners to wail.
¹⁷There will be wailing in all the vineyards,
for I will pass through your midst,"

says the LORD.

The Day of the LORD

¹⁸Woe to you who long
for the day of the LORD!
Why do you long for the day of
the LORD?
That day will be darkness, not
light.
¹⁹It will be as though a man fled
from a lion
only to meet a bear,
as though he entered his house
and rested his hand on the
wall
only to have a snake bite him.
²⁰Will not the day of the LORD be
darkness, not light—
pitch-dark, without a ray of
brightness?

²¹"I hate, I despise your religious
feasts;
I cannot stand your
assemblies.
²²Even though you bring me burnt
offerings and grain
offerings,
I will not accept them.
Though you bring choice
fellowship offerings, ᵃ
I will have no regard for them.

genuine

worship ◀◀ 5:21-24

You know when someone's a phony, right? Yeah, you can spot one a mile away. Like someone who constantly flatters a teacher only to get a good grade. Or like Israel's religious practices. God had only one word for Israel's empty worship: Yucko. (Okay, that's a paraphrase of God's actual response.) Their disobedience made their sacrifices and other worship practices fake and therefore gross to God. Genuine worship involves a heart connection—yours to God's. It also involves being right with God. So here's one more paraphrase for you: Get your worship right, girl!

ᵃ 22 Traditionally *peace offerings*

²³ Away with the noise of your songs!
   I will not listen to the music of your harps.
²⁴ But let justice roll on like a river,
   righteousness like a never-failing stream!

²⁵ "Did you bring me sacrifices and offerings
   forty years in the desert, O house of Israel?
²⁶ You have lifted up the shrine of your king,
   the pedestal of your idols,
   the star of your god*—
   which you made for yourselves.
²⁷ Therefore I will send you into exile beyond Damascus,"
   says the LORD, whose name is God Almighty.

Woe to the Complacent

6 Woe to you who are complacent in Zion,
   and to you who feel secure on Mount Samaria,
you notable men of the foremost nation,
   to whom the people of Israel come!
² Go to Calneh and look at it;
   go from there to great
      Hamath,
   and then go down to Gath in
      Philistia.
Are they better off than your two
      kingdoms?
   Is their land larger than yours?
³ You put off the evil day
   and bring near a reign of
      terror.
⁴ You lie on beds inlaid with ivory
   and lounge on your couches.
You dine on choice lambs
   and fattened calves.
⁵ You strum away on your harps like David
   and improvise on musical instruments.
⁶ You drink wine by the bowlful
   and use the finest lotions,
   but you do not grieve over the ruin of Joseph.
⁷ Therefore you will be among the first to go into exile;
   your feasting and lounging will end.

truth or dare

Complacency is getting into a nice, comfortable rut in life. Don't get lulled into a false sense of security and ignore others' needs. You'll be the first to fall.

6:1,4–7

The LORD Abhors the Pride of Israel

⁸ The Sovereign LORD has sworn by himself—the LORD God Almighty declares:

"I abhor the pride of Jacob
   and detest his fortresses;
I will deliver up the city
   and everything in it."

⁹ If ten men are left in one house, they too will die. ¹⁰ And if a relative who is to burn the bodies comes to carry them out of the house and asks anyone still hiding there, "Is anyone with you?" and he says, "No," then he will say, "Hush! We must not mention the name of the LORD."

¹¹ For the LORD has given the command,

a 26 Or *lifted up Sakkuth your king / and Kaiwan your idols, / your star-gods*; Septuagint *lifted up the shrine of Molech / and the star of your god Rephan, / their idols*

and he will smash the great house into pieces
　　and the small house into bits.

[12]Do horses run on the rocky crags?
　　Does one plow there with oxen?
But you have turned justice into poison
　　and the fruit of righteousness into bitterness—
[13]you who rejoice in the conquest of Lo Debar*a*
　　and say, "Did we not take Karnaim*b* by our own strength?"

[14]For the LORD God Almighty declares,
　　"I will stir up a nation against you, O house of Israel,
that will oppress you all the way
　　from Lebo*c* Hamath to the valley of the Arabah."

Locusts, Fire and a Plumb Line

7 This is what the Sovereign LORD showed me: He was preparing swarms of locusts after the king's share had been harvested and just as the second crop was coming up. [2]When they had stripped the land clean, I cried out, "Sovereign LORD, forgive! How can Jacob survive? He is so small!"

[3]So the LORD relented.

"This will not happen," the LORD said.

[4]This is what the Sovereign LORD showed me: The Sovereign LORD was calling for judgment by fire; it dried up the great deep and devoured the land. [5]Then I cried out, "Sovereign LORD, I beg you, stop! How can Jacob survive? He is so small!"

[6]So the LORD relented.

"This will not happen either," the Sovereign LORD said.

[7]This is what he showed me: The Lord was standing by a wall that had been built true to plumb, with a plumb line in his hand. [8]And the LORD asked me, "What do you see, Amos?"

"A plumb line," I replied.

Then the Lord said, "Look, I am setting a plumb line among my people Israel; I will spare them no longer.

[9]"The high places of Isaac will be destroyed
　　and the sanctuaries of Israel will be ruined;
　　with my sword I will rise against the house of Jeroboam."

Amos and Amaziah

[10]Then Amaziah the priest of Bethel sent a message to Jeroboam king of Israel: "Amos is raising a conspiracy against you in the very heart of Israel. The land cannot bear all his words. [11]For this is what Amos is saying:

　　" 'Jeroboam will die by the sword,
　　　　and Israel will surely go into exile,
　　　　away from their native land.' "

[12]Then Amaziah said to Amos, "Get out, you seer! Go back to the land of Judah. Earn your bread there and do your prophesying there. [13]Don't prophesy anymore at Bethel, because this is the king's sanctuary and the temple of the kingdom."

[14]Amos answered Amaziah, "I was neither a prophet nor a prophet's son, but I was a shepherd, and I also took care of sycamore-fig trees. [15]But the LORD took me from tending the flock and said to me, 'Go, prophesy to my people Israel.' [16]Now then, hear the word of the LORD. You say,

　　" 'Do not prophesy against Israel,
　　　　and stop preaching against the house of Isaac.'

---

a 13 Lo Debar means nothing.　　　*b 13 Karnaim means horns; horn here symbolizes strength.*　　　*c 14 Or from the entrance to*

¹⁷"Therefore this is what the LORD says:

" 'Your wife will become a prostitute in the city,
   and your sons and daughters will fall by the sword.
Your land will be measured and divided up,
   and you yourself will die in a pagan*a* country.
And Israel will certainly go into exile,
   away from their native land.' "

A Basket of Ripe Fruit

8 This is what the Sovereign LORD showed me: a basket of ripe fruit. ²"What do you see, Amos?" he asked.

"A basket of ripe fruit," I answered.

Then the LORD said to me, "The time is ripe for my people Israel; I will spare them no longer.

³"In that day," declares the Sovereign LORD, "the songs in the temple will turn to wailing.*b* Many, many bodies—flung everywhere! Silence!"

genuine

trust » 7:14-15

You're pretty cool, aren't you? Pretty smart too, huh? Feel qualified to go out and change the entire world? No, you say? But you are—with God's help, of course! Amos could have felt underqualified. He knew how to be a shepherd and how to care for sycamore trees. (How's that for a random profession?) But God called him to be a prophet—a job no one in his family had held. Sometimes God gives us huge tasks to keep us dependent on him. When God gives you an assignment, he also gives you the know-how to do it. You just need to be willing.

⁴Hear this, you who trample the needy
   and do away with the poor of the land,

⁵saying,

"When will the New Moon be over
   that we may sell grain,
and the Sabbath be ended
   that we may market wheat?"—
skimping the measure,
   boosting the price
   and cheating with dishonest scales,
⁶buying the poor with silver
   and the needy for a pair of sandals,
   selling even the sweepings with the wheat.

⁷The LORD has sworn by the Pride of Jacob: "I will never forget anything they have done.

⁸"Will not the land tremble for this,
   and all who live in it mourn?
The whole land will rise like the Nile;

it will be stirred up and then sink
   like the river of Egypt.

⁹"In that day," declares the Sovereign LORD,

"I will make the sun go down at noon
   and darken the earth in broad daylight.
¹⁰I will turn your religious feasts into mourning
   and all your singing into weeping.
I will make all of you wear sackcloth

a 17 Hebrew *an unclean*   *b 3* Or *"the temple singers will wail"*

and shave your heads.
I will make that time like mourning for an only son
and the end of it like a bitter day.

[11] "The days are coming," declares the Sovereign Lord,
"when I will send a famine through the land—
not a famine of food or a thirst for water,
but a famine of hearing the words of the Lord.
[12] Men will stagger from sea to sea
and wander from north to east,
searching for the word of the Lord,
but they will not find it.

[13]"In that day

"the lovely young women and strong young men
will faint because of thirst.
[14] They who swear by the shame[a] of Samaria,
or say, 'As surely as your god lives, O Dan,'
or, 'As surely as the god[b] of Beersheba lives'—
they will fall,
never to rise again."

Israel to Be Destroyed

9 I saw the Lord standing by the altar, and he said:

"Strike the tops of the pillars
so that the thresholds shake.
Bring them down on the heads of all the people;
those who are left I will kill with the sword.
Not one will get away,
none will escape.
[2] Though they dig down to the depths of the grave,[c]
from there my hand will take them.
Though they climb up to the heavens,
from there I will bring them down.
[3] Though they hide themselves on the top of Carmel,
there I will hunt them down and seize them.
Though they hide from me at the bottom of the sea,
there I will command the serpent to bite them.
[4] Though they are driven into exile by their enemies,
there I will command the sword to slay them.
I will fix my eyes upon them
for evil and not for good."

[5] The Lord, the Lord Almighty,
he who touches the earth and it melts,
and all who live in it mourn—
the whole land rises like the Nile,
then sinks like the river of Egypt—
[6] he who builds his lofty palace[d] in the heavens
and sets its foundation[e] on the earth,
who calls for the waters of the sea
and pours them out over the face of the land—
the Lord is his name.

---

a 14 Or *by Ashima; or by the idol*   *b 14* Or *power*   *c 2* Hebrew *to Sheol*   *d 6* The meaning of the Hebrew for this phrase is uncertain.   *e 6* The meaning of the Hebrew for this word is uncertain.

7 "Are not you Israelites
　the same to me as the Cushites[a]?"

　　　　　　　　　　　　　declares the LORD.

"Did I not bring Israel up from Egypt,
　the Philistines from Caphtor[b]
　and the Arameans from Kir?

8 "Surely the eyes of the Sovereign LORD
　are on the sinful kingdom.
I will destroy it
　from the face of the earth—
yet I will not totally destroy
　the house of Jacob,"

　　　　　　　　　　　　　declares the LORD.

9 "For I will give the command,
　and I will shake the house of
　　Israel
　among all the nations
as grain is shaken in a sieve,
　and not a pebble will reach
　　the ground.
10 All the sinners among my people
　will die by the sword,
all those who say,
　'Disaster will not overtake or
　　meet us.'

Israel's Restoration

11 "In that day I will restore
　David's fallen tent.
I will repair its broken places,
　restore its ruins,
　and build it as it used to be,
12 so that they may possess the remnant of Edom
　and all the nations that bear my name,[c]"
　　　　　　declares the LORD, who will do these things.

13 "The days are coming," declares the LORD,

"when the reaper will be overtaken by the plowman
　and the planter by the one treading grapes.
New wine will drip from the mountains
　and flow from all the hills.
14 I will bring back my exiled[d] people Israel;
　they will rebuild the ruined cities and live in them.
They will plant vineyards and drink their wine;
　they will make gardens and eat their fruit.
15 I will plant Israel in their own land,
　never again to be uprooted
　from the land I have given them,"

　　　　　　　　　　　　says the LORD your God.

truth or dare

Don't get stuck on the harsh part. Yeah, God promised punishment for Israel's sin, yet he also promised them future blessings. Even though he disciplines us, he doesn't desert us.

9:9–15

---

a 7 That is, people from the upper Nile region　　b 7 That is, Crete　　c 12 Hebrew; Septuagint so that the remnant of
men / and all the nations that bear my name may seek ﹂the Lord�　　d 14 Or will restore the fortunes of my

author: Obadiah.

date: Probably during the Babylonian attacks on Jerusalem (605–586 B.C.)

setting: The Edomites, who were descendants of Esau and related to the Israelites, had constantly harassed the people of Israel.

verse to remember: "Because of the violence against your brother Jacob, you will be covered with shame; you will be destroyed forever" (10).

theme to consider: God will judge those who oppress his people. Obadiah prophesied the destruction of Edom because of their cruelty to Judah.

unchanging truth

obadiah

You probably get frustrated with your parents at times. They discipline you and make you do chores. (That's part of their job description.) But you can count on them if someone comes along who threatens to hurt you.

In the prophetic books in the Old Testament, God threatens to discipline his children by sending them into captivity because of their sin. And then he does just that! God reserved the right to punish his people—and to use pagan nations to do so.

But those nations would themselves be punished. The little book of Obadiah is a prophecy against a nation that had been hurting God's children— Edom. The Edomites were related to the Israelites. Their ancestor, Esau, and Israel's ancestor, Jacob, were *brothers*. But when Israel faced destruction, the Edomites rejoiced.

And God got plenty angry that the Edomites were hurting his kids—and enjoying it.

So he sent Obadiah with a message of judgment. Although the people lived in invincible clefts in the rocks and thought no enemy could take them, God would bring them down. He said that they "will be destroyed forever" (10). If you look at a map today, you won't find a nation of Edom. It no longer exists—just as God said.

You are God's special child. If anyone tries to mess with you, they will have *him* to deal with. Trust him to take care of you.

life lessons

1 God hates pride. Those who proudly trust in themselves will eventually fall (3–4).

2 When others are hurting, show them love (12).

3 God will keep his promises. You can count on it (17–21).

¹The vision of Obadiah.

This is what the Sovereign Lord says about Edom—

We have heard a message from the Lord:
An envoy was sent to the nations to say,
"Rise, and let us go against her for battle"—

² "See, I will make you small among the nations;
you will be utterly despised.
³ The pride of your heart has deceived you,
you who live in the clefts of the rocks^a
and make your home on the heights,
you who say to yourself,
'Who can bring me down to the ground?'
⁴ Though you soar like the eagle
and make your nest among the stars,
from there I will bring you down,"

declares the Lord.

⁵ "If thieves came to you,
if robbers in the night—
Oh, what a disaster awaits you—
would they not steal only as much as they wanted?
If grape pickers came to you,
would they not leave a few grapes?
⁶ But how Esau will be ransacked,
his hidden treasures pillaged!
⁷ All your allies will force you to the border;
your friends will deceive and overpower you;
those who eat your bread will set a trap for you,^b
but you will not detect it.

⁸ "In that day," declares the Lord,
"will I not destroy the wise men of Edom,
men of understanding in the mountains of Esau?
⁹ Your warriors, O Teman, will be terrified,
and everyone in Esau's mountains
will be cut down in the slaughter.
¹⁰ Because of the violence against your brother Jacob,
you will be covered with
shame;
you will be destroyed forever.
¹¹ On the day you stood aloof
while strangers carried off his
wealth
and foreigners entered his gates
and cast lots for Jerusalem,
you were like one of them.
¹² You should not look down on your
brother
in the day of his misfortune,
nor rejoice over the people of
Judah
in the day of their destruction,
nor boast so much
in the day of their trouble.

truth or dare

When an enemy gets it, do you secretly celebrate? No matter what she did, God wants you to show her love and mercy—especially when she's struggling.

12–15

^a 3 Or of Sela   ^b 7 The meaning of the Hebrew for this clause is uncertain.

¹³ You should not march through the gates of my people
    in the day of their disaster,
nor look down on them in their calamity
    in the day of their disaster,
nor seize their wealth
    in the day of their disaster.
¹⁴ You should not wait at the crossroads
    to cut down their fugitives,
nor hand over their survivors
    in the day of their trouble.

¹⁵ "The day of the Lord is near
    for all nations.
As you have done, it will be done to you;
    your deeds will return upon your own head.
¹⁶ Just as you drank on my holy hill,
    so all the nations will drink continually;
they will drink and drink
    and be as if they had never been.
¹⁷ But on Mount Zion will be deliverance;
    it will be holy,
and the house of Jacob
    will possess its inheritance.
¹⁸ The house of Jacob will be a fire
    and the house of Joseph a flame;
the house of Esau will be stubble,
    and they will set it on fire and consume it.
There will be no survivors
    from the house of Esau."

        The Lord has spoken.

¹⁹ People from the Negev will occupy
    the mountains of Esau,
and people from the foothills will possess
    the land of the Philistines.
They will occupy the fields of Ephraim and Samaria,
    and Benjamin will possess Gilead.
²⁰ This company of Israelite exiles who are in Canaan
    will possess ⌊the land⌋ as far as Zarephath;
the exiles from Jerusalem who are in Sepharad
    will possess the towns of the Negev.
²¹ Deliverers will go up on^a Mount Zion
    to govern the mountains of Esau.
And the kingdom will be the Lord's.

^a 21 Or *from*

author: Jonah.

date: Probably about 785–750 B.C.

setting: Jonah is sent to Nineveh, the most important city in Assyria, to tell the people to repent.

verse to remember: "O LORD, is this not what I said when I was still at home? . . . I knew that you are a gracious and compassionate God, slow to anger and abounding in love, a God who relents from sending calamity" (4:12).

theme to consider: Jonah's story brings us the encouraging message that no one is beyond hope. God's grace and mercy extend to all who seek his forgiveness.

jonah

unchanging truth

Hate crimes. Murders. Wars. Senseless violence. So much suffering in the world. But you don't have to read the newspaper to know that. Maybe you've experienced suffering firsthand. Perhaps your story isn't horrible enough to appear on the front page of the paper. But it hurt just the same.

Ever take comfort in the fact that the one who hurt you will get punished someday? Sweet, right?

But . . . suppose that person dramatically changes and expresses regret for what she did? Would that be a cause for celebration for you?

Jonah faced this dilemma from the moment God told him to warn the people of Nineveh to change their evil ways or they'd face destruction. The destruction part was easy for Jonah to swallow. After all, the Assyrians were some of Israel's worst enemies. They had a long history of cruelty. But Jonah knew that God's mercy was a definite possibility if the Ninevites turned from their sin. He didn't feel that they deserved God's forgiveness and grace. That's why he wanted no part of God's mission.

Can you relate? Many of us, if we're honest, have a hard time seeing an enemy through the eyes of a compassionate God. That's why the book of Jonah isn't just a fish story for kids. It's our story, too.

Like Jonah, do you feel like running when you think about showing compassion toward an enemy? You can run, but you can't hide. Just ask Jonah.

life lessons

1 When you disobey God, the consequences have a ripple effect on the people around you (1:4–17).

2 God is ready to hear and answer your prayers when you turn to him for help (2:1–10).

3 God's mercy extends to everyone—even the most "undeserving" (3:1–10).

Jonah Flees From the Lord

1 The word of the Lord came to Jonah son of Amittai: ²"Go to the great city of Nineveh and preach against it, because its wickedness has come up before me."

³But Jonah ran away from the Lord and headed for Tarshish. He went down to Joppa, where he found a ship bound for that port. After paying the fare, he went aboard and sailed for Tarshish to flee from the Lord.

⁴Then the Lord sent a great wind on the sea, and such a violent storm arose that the ship threatened to break up. ⁵All the sailors were afraid and each cried out to his own god. And they threw the cargo into the sea to lighten the ship.

But Jonah had gone below deck, where he lay down and fell into a deep sleep. ⁶The captain went to him and said, "How can you sleep? Get up and call on your god! Maybe he will take notice of us, and we will not perish."

⁷Then the sailors said to each other, "Come, let us cast lots to find out who is responsible for this calamity." They cast lots and the lot fell on Jonah.

⁸So they asked him, "Tell us, who is responsible for making all this trouble for us? What do you do? Where do you come from? What is your country? From what people are you?"

⁹He answered, "I am a Hebrew and I worship the Lord, the God of heaven, who made the sea and the land."

¹⁰This terrified them and they asked, "What have you done?" (They knew he was running away from the Lord, because he had already told them so.)

¹¹The sea was getting rougher and rougher. So they asked him, "What should we do to you to make the sea calm down for us?"

¹²"Pick me up and throw me into the sea," he replied, "and it will become calm. I know that it is my fault that this great storm has come upon you."

¹³Instead, the men did their best to row back to land. But they could not, for the sea grew even wilder than before. ¹⁴Then they cried to the Lord, "O Lord, please do not let us die for taking this man's life. Do not hold us accountable for killing an innocent man, for you, O Lord, have done as you pleased." ¹⁵Then they took Jonah and threw him overboard, and the raging sea grew calm. ¹⁶At this the men greatly feared the Lord, and they offered a sacrifice to the Lord and made vows to him.

¹⁷But the Lord provided a great fish to swallow Jonah, and Jonah was inside the fish three days and three nights.

Jonah's Prayer

2 From inside the fish Jonah prayed to the Lord his God. ²He said:

> "In my distress I called to the Lord,
>   and he answered me.
> From the depths of the grave ᵃ I called for help,
>   and you listened to my cry.

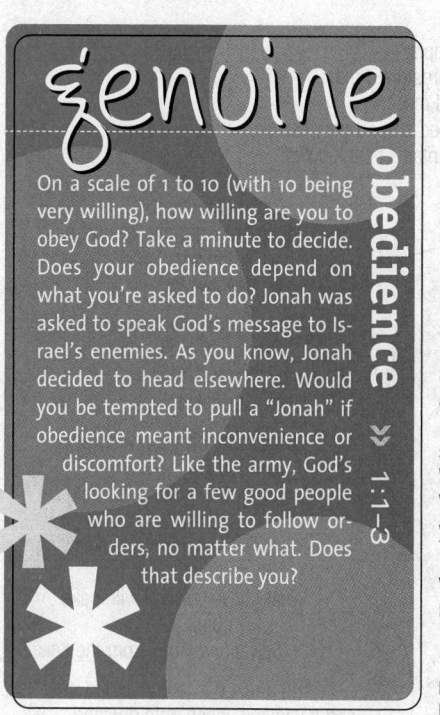

genuine

obedience » 1:1–3

On a scale of 1 to 10 (with 10 being very willing), how willing are you to obey God? Take a minute to decide. Does your obedience depend on what you're asked to do? Jonah was asked to speak God's message to Israel's enemies. As you know, Jonah decided to head elsewhere. Would you be tempted to pull a "Jonah" if obedience meant inconvenience or discomfort? Like the army, God's looking for a few good people who are willing to follow orders, no matter what. Does that describe you?

ᵃ 2 Hebrew *Sheol*

³You hurled me into the deep,
   into the very heart of the seas,
   and the currents swirled about me;
  all your waves and breakers
   swept over me.
⁴I said, 'I have been banished
   from your sight;
  yet I will look again
   toward your holy temple.'
⁵The engulfing waters threatened me,ᵃ
   the deep surrounded me;
  seaweed was wrapped around my head.
⁶To the roots of the mountains I sank down;
   the earth beneath barred me
    in forever.
  But you brought my life up from
    the pit,
   O LORD my God.

⁷"When my life was ebbing away,
   I remembered you, LORD,
  and my prayer rose to you,
   to your holy temple.

⁸"Those who cling to worthless
    idols
   forfeit the grace that could be
    theirs.
⁹But I, with a song of thanksgiving,
   will sacrifice to you.
  What I have vowed I will make
    good.
   Salvation comes from the LORD."

¹⁰And the LORD commanded the fish, and it vomited Jonah onto dry land.

Jonah Goes to Nineveh

3 Then the word of the LORD came to Jonah a second time: ²"Go to the great city of Nineveh and proclaim to it the message I give you."

³Jonah obeyed the word of the LORD and went to Nineveh. Now Nineveh was a very important city—a visit required three days. ⁴On the first day, Jonah started into the city. He proclaimed: "Forty more days and Nineveh will be overturned." ⁵The Ninevites believed God. They declared a fast, and all of them, from the greatest to the least, put on sackcloth.

⁶When the news reached the king of Nineveh, he rose from his throne, took off his royal robes, covered himself with sackcloth and sat down in the dust. ⁷Then he issued a proclamation in Nineveh:

---

love ❤ notes

2:1–2

My child,

There is no place you can go
that I will not be there. There is
no problem or struggle so great
that I can't help you. When
you've lost all hope, cry out to
me as Jonah did. I will hear you.

—Your heavenly Dad

Tell God your deepest needs. He knows them already. He can help.

ᵃ 5 Or *waters were at my throat*

"By the decree of the king and his nobles:

Do not let any man or beast, herd or flock, taste anything; do not let them eat or drink. [8]But let man and beast be covered with sackcloth. Let everyone call urgently on God. Let them give up their evil ways and their violence. [9]Who knows? God may yet relent and with compassion turn from his fierce anger so that we will not perish."

[10]When God saw what they did and how they turned from their evil ways, he had compassion and did not bring upon them the destruction he had threatened.

Jonah's Anger at the LORD's Compassion

4 But Jonah was greatly displeased and became angry. [2]He prayed to the LORD, "O LORD, is this not what I said when I was still at home? That is why I was so quick to flee to Tarshish. I knew that you are a gracious and compassionate God, slow to anger and abounding in love, a God who relents from sending calamity. [3]Now, O LORD, take away my life, for it is better for me to die than to live."

[4]But the LORD replied, "Have you any right to be angry?"

[5]Jonah went out and sat down at a place east of the city. There he made himself a shelter, sat in its shade and waited to see what would happen to the city. [6]Then the LORD God provided a vine and made it grow up over Jonah to give shade for his head to ease his discomfort, and Jonah was very happy about the vine. [7]But at dawn the next day God provided a worm, which chewed the vine so that it withered. [8]When the sun rose, God provided a scorching east wind, and the sun blazed on Jonah's head so that he grew faint. He wanted to die, and said, "It would be better for me to die than to live."

[9]But God said to Jonah, "Do you have a right to be angry about the vine?"

"I do," he said. "I am angry enough to die."

[10]But the LORD said, "You have been concerned about this vine, though you did not tend it or make it grow. It sprang up overnight and died overnight. [11]But Nineveh has more than a hundred and twenty thousand people who cannot tell their right hand from their left, and many cattle as well. Should I not be concerned about that great city?"

truth or dare

Does a chipped nail wreck your entire day? Jonah's dead vine ruined his. Time to crank up the compassion level! Is your heart broken over what breaks the heart of God?

4:5–11

author:	Micah.
date:	Likely written between 742 and 687 B.C., during the reigns of Jotham, Ahaz and Hezekiah.
setting:	Micah lived during the time of Isaiah and Hosea.
verse to remember:	"Who is a God like you, who pardons sin and forgives the transgression of the remnant of his inheritance? You do not stay angry forever but delight to show mercy" (7:18).
theme to consider:	Micah makes it clear what God hates—unkindness, idolatry, injustice and empty worship.

micah

unchanging truth

Do you hate anything? To most of us, *hate* is a dirty word. We feel guilty about hating something. Yet, if we're honest, we might own up to *occasionally* hating the actions of others. Still, hatred seems like a glib response these days. "I hate her haircut. I hate that song. I hate brussels sprouts."

Does it surprise you to learn that God hates some things? As he explained to the prophet Micah, God hates sins like pride and disregard for others. He hates it when people don't make him their highest priority. Most of all, he hates empty religion—worship that only goes through the motions. But hatred isn't an idle emotion for God. Nor is it sinful. He's always working to change things for the good.

God told Micah to warn the people of Israel about their upcoming punishment for their sins.

News flash from God: They were in for it. All of their phony acts of worship wouldn't shield them from the conquering army. But even with that message of doom, God reminded Micah of what he loved. He loved his people and loved to forgive them.

Maybe you feel like you've messed up beyond God's ability or desire to forgive. Maybe you're afraid you've earned God's hatred toward you. (You can't, by the way. He hates *sin*, not people.) Trust that God loves you enough to forgive any wrong you've ever done.

life lessons

3

1 Wrong actions can trigger God's wrath (1:1—2:11; 3). God is never a pushover when it comes to sin.

2 When our dreams seem shattered, God provides hope for the future (2:12–13; 4–5).

3 Even though he occasionally has to discipline his people, God still desires to forgive them (7:8–20).

1 The word of the LORD that came to Micah of Moresheth during the reigns of Jotham, Ahaz and Hezekiah, kings of Judah—the vision he saw concerning Samaria and Jerusalem.

> [2] Hear, O peoples, all of you,
>   listen, O earth and all who are in it,
> that the Sovereign LORD may witness against you,
>   the Lord from his holy temple.

Judgment Against Samaria and Jerusalem

> [3] Look! The LORD is coming from his dwelling place;
>   he comes down and treads the high places of the earth.
> [4] The mountains melt beneath him
>   and the valleys split apart,
> like wax before the fire,
>   like water rushing down a slope.
> [5] All this is because of Jacob's transgression,
>   because of the sins of the house of Israel.
> What is Jacob's transgression?
>   Is it not Samaria?
> What is Judah's high place?
>   Is it not Jerusalem?

> [6] "Therefore I will make Samaria a heap of rubble,
>   a place for planting vineyards.
> I will pour her stones into the valley
>   and lay bare her foundations.
> [7] All her idols will be broken to pieces;
>   all her temple gifts will be burned with fire;
>   I will destroy all her images.
> Since she gathered her gifts from the wages of prostitutes,
>   as the wages of prostitutes they will again be used."

Weeping and Mourning

> [8] Because of this I will weep and wail;
>   I will go about barefoot and naked.
> I will howl like a jackal
>   and moan like an owl.
> [9] For her wound is incurable;
>   it has come to Judah.
> It[a] has reached the very gate of my people,
>   even to Jerusalem itself.
> [10] Tell it not in Gath[b];
>   weep not at all.[c]
> In Beth Ophrah[d]
>   roll in the dust.
> [11] Pass on in nakedness and shame,
>   you who live in Shaphir.[e]
> Those who live in Zaanan[f]
>   will not come out.
> Beth Ezel is in mourning;
>   its protection is taken from you.
> [12] Those who live in Maroth[g] writhe in pain,
>   waiting for relief,

---

a 9 Or *He*   *b 10 Gath* sounds like the Hebrew for *tell*.   *c 10* Hebrew; Septuagint may suggest *not in Acco*. The Hebrew for *in Acco* sounds like the Hebrew for *weep*.   *d 10 Beth Ophrah* means *house of dust*.   *e 11 Shaphir* means *pleasant*. *f 11 Zaanan* sounds like the Hebrew for *come out*.   *g 12 Maroth* sounds like the Hebrew for *bitter*.

because disaster has come from the LORD,
    even to the gate of Jerusalem.
¹³You who live in Lachish,*ᵃ*
    harness the team to the chariot.
You were the beginning of sin
    to the Daughter of Zion,
for the transgressions of Israel
    were found in you.
¹⁴Therefore you will give parting gifts
    to Moresheth Gath.
The town of Aczib*ᵇ* will prove deceptive
    to the kings of Israel.
¹⁵I will bring a conqueror against you
    who live in Mareshah.*ᶜ*
He who is the glory of Israel
    will come to Adullam.
¹⁶Shave your heads in mourning
    for the children in whom you delight;
make yourselves as bald as the vulture,
    for they will go from you into exile.

Man's Plans and God's

2 Woe to those who plan iniquity,
    to those who plot evil on their beds!
At morning's light they carry it out
    because it is in their power to do it.
²They covet fields and seize them,
    and houses, and take them.
They defraud a man of his home,
    a fellowman of his inheritance.

³Therefore, the LORD says:

"I am planning disaster against
    this people,
from which you cannot save
    yourselves.
You will no longer walk proudly,
    for it will be a time of
    calamity.
⁴In that day men will ridicule you;
    they will taunt you with this mournful
    song:
'We are utterly ruined;
    my people's possession is divided up.
He takes it from me!
    He assigns our fields to traitors.' "

⁵Therefore you will have no one in the assembly of the LORD
    to divide the land by lot.

False Prophets

⁶"Do not prophesy," their prophets say.
    "Do not prophesy about these things;
    disgrace will not overtake us."

truth or dare

You've been planning the perfect revenge for days. Your plot keeps running through your head. Pause . . . What do your thoughts reveal about you? Don't do it, and don't even think it.

2:1–2

ᵃ 13 Lachish sounds like the Hebrew for *team.*   *ᵇ 14 Aczib* means *deception.*   *ᶜ 15 Mareshah* sounds like the Hebrew for *conqueror.*

⁷Should it be said, O house of Jacob:
"Is the Spirit of the LORD angry?
Does he do such things?"

"Do not my words do good
to him whose ways are upright?
⁸Lately my people have risen up
like an enemy.
You strip off the rich robe
from those who pass by without a care,
like men returning from battle.
⁹You drive the women of my people
from their pleasant homes.
You take away my blessing
from their children forever.
¹⁰Get up, go away!
For this is not your resting place,
because it is defiled,
it is ruined, beyond all remedy.
¹¹If a liar and deceiver comes and says,
'I will prophesy for you plenty of wine and beer,'
he would be just the prophet for this people!

Deliverance Promised

¹²"I will surely gather all of you, O Jacob;
I will surely bring together the remnant of Israel.
I will bring them together like sheep in a pen,
like a flock in its pasture;
the place will throng with people.
¹³One who breaks open the way will go up before them;
they will break through the gate and go out.
Their king will pass through before them,
the LORD at their head."

Leaders and Prophets Rebuked

3 Then I said,

"Listen, you leaders of Jacob,
you rulers of the house of Israel.
Should you not know justice,
²   you who hate good and love evil;
who tear the skin from my people
and the flesh from their bones;
³who eat my people's flesh,
strip off their skin
and break their bones in pieces;
who chop them up like meat for the pan,
like flesh for the pot?"

⁴Then they will cry out to the LORD,
but he will not answer them.
At that time he will hide his face from them
because of the evil they have done.

⁵This is what the LORD says:

"As for the prophets
who lead my people astray,

Bad Attitude

Profile: Lucy

As soon as I paid for lunch, I saw her sitting at the table. *Oh no! How am I going to make it through another lunch listening to her complain about her classes, her parents, her life?* I looked around the lunchroom and spotted all my other friends sitting at other tables, happily talking and laughing.

At the beginning of the year, we all sat together. Not anymore. One by one, Blair and her negative attitude chased everyone away. Nobody wanted to sit with her. No one.

So why do I put myself through this misery every lunch hour? I guess it's because I feel sorry for her. She just doesn't get it. No one wants to listen to an endless stream of complaints, gripes, whines and put-downs. Blair never has anything positive to say about anything.

Taking a deep breath, I smiled and walked over to the table. "Hi, Blair," I said brightly. "How's it going?" Wrong question. For the next twenty minutes, she talked about how boring her chem class is, how dumb her French teacher is, how she hates to go to chorus any more because all they sing is dorky songs . . . Twenty minutes!

When she finally stopped to take a bite of her sandwich, I couldn't help myself. I blurted out, "Don't you have anything good to say about *anything*?" Blair's mouth dropped open. She looked at me in total shock.

Now Blair avoids me like the plague. She eats alone because, well, I already told you why. She just doesn't get it.

pessimism in focus

Do you tend to look at the negatives rather than the positives in your life? Your attitude—how you view life—is huge. Once you start sliding into pessimism, it carries over into your whole outlook on life—relationships included! Need to remedy a bad attitude?

»Find something that interests you. So maybe you find all your classes dull as mud. What's *your* passion? God wired everyone with passions, so find yours— drawing, music, working with kids, running, drama, etc.

»Choose to focus on the good in life. Attitude is a choice (see Philippians 2:14, page 1552).

»Help others. When you're involved in someone else's life, there's little time left to dwell on your own situation. Get your eyes off yourself and your problems and help someone else.

For more on this topic, see the index on page 1656.

For more on attitude, go to www.TrueImagesBible.com

if one feeds them,
 they proclaim 'peace';
if he does not,
 they prepare to wage war against him.
[6] Therefore night will come over you, without visions,
 and darkness, without divination.
The sun will set for the prophets,

and the day will go dark for them.
⁷ The seers will be ashamed
and the diviners disgraced.
They will all cover their faces
because there is no answer from God."

⁸ But as for me, I am filled with power,
with the Spirit of the LORD,
and with justice and might,
to declare to Jacob his transgression,
to Israel his sin.
⁹ Hear this, you leaders of the house of Jacob,
you rulers of the house of Israel,
who despise justice
and distort all that is right;
¹⁰ who build Zion with bloodshed,
and Jerusalem with wickedness.
¹¹ Her leaders judge for a bribe,
her priests teach for a price,
and her prophets tell fortunes for money.
Yet they lean upon the LORD and say,
"Is not the LORD among us?
No disaster will come upon us."
¹² Therefore because of you,
Zion will be plowed like a field,
Jerusalem will become a heap of rubble,
the temple hill a mound overgrown with thickets.

The Mountain of the LORD

4 In the last days

the mountain of the LORD's temple
will be established
as chief among the
mountains;
it will be raised above the hills,
and peoples will stream to it.

² Many nations will come and say,

"Come, let us go up to the
mountain of the LORD,
to the house of the God of Jacob.
He will teach us his ways,
so that we may walk in his paths."
The law will go out from Zion,
the word of the LORD from
Jerusalem.
³ He will judge between many peoples
and will settle disputes for strong
nations far and wide.
They will beat their swords into
plowshares
and their spears into pruning
hooks.
Nation will not take up sword
against nation,

genuine
wisdom » 4:1-5

When are you truly teachable? You're teachable when you make the effort to learn something. It's more than just skating by at school or being brain dead till the bell rings. It means having a yearnin' for learnin'. (Yeeehaaa!) In some future time, Micah predicted that people would come from far and near to be taught God's ways. They'll want to hang out in his house and live lives that please him. When it comes to God's laws, is your mind open and ready to learn?

nor will they train for war
    anymore.
⁴Every man will sit under his own
    vine
and under his own fig tree,
and no one will make them
    afraid,
    for the LORD Almighty has
    spoken.
⁵All the nations may walk
    in the name of their gods;
we will walk in the name of the
    LORD
    our God for ever and ever.

The LORD's Plan

⁶"In that day," declares the LORD,

"I will gather the lame;
    I will assemble the exiles
and those I have brought to grief.
⁷I will make the lame a remnant,
    those driven away a strong nation.
The LORD will rule over them in Mount Zion
    from that day and forever.
⁸As for you, O watchtower of the flock,
    O stronghold*ᵃ* of the Daughter of Zion,
the former dominion will be restored to you;
    kingship will come to the Daughter of Jerusalem."

⁹Why do you now cry aloud—
    have you no king?
Has your counselor perished,
    that pain seizes you like that of a woman in labor?
¹⁰Writhe in agony, O Daughter of Zion,
    like a woman in labor,
for now you must leave the city
    to camp in the open field.
You will go to Babylon;
    there you will be rescued.
There the LORD will redeem you
    out of the hand of your enemies.

¹¹But now many nations
    are gathered against you.
They say, "Let her be defiled,
    let our eyes gloat over Zion!"
¹²But they do not know
    the thoughts of the LORD;
they do not understand his plan,
    he who gathers them like sheaves to the threshing floor.

¹³"Rise and thresh, O Daughter of Zion,
    for I will give you horns of iron;
I will give you hoofs of bronze
    and you will break to pieces many nations."

truth or dare

Someday . . . war will end. No more killing or fighting or bloodshed. We'll convert our weapons into farm equipment and live in perfect peace. Someday, when God reigns over all . . .

4:3

ᵃ *8 Or hill*

You will devote their ill-gotten gains to the Lord,
their wealth to the Lord of all the earth.

A Promised Ruler From Bethlehem

5 Marshal your troops, O city of troops,[a]
for a siege is laid against us.
They will strike Israel's ruler
on the cheek with a rod.

2 "But you, Bethlehem Ephrathah,
though you are small among the clans[b] of Judah,
out of you will come for me
one who will be ruler over Israel,
whose origins[c] are from of old,
from ancient times.[d]"

3 Therefore Israel will be abandoned
until the time when she who is in labor gives birth
and the rest of his brothers return
to join the Israelites.

4 He will stand and shepherd his flock
in the strength of the Lord,
in the majesty of the name of the Lord his God.
And they will live securely, for then his greatness
will reach to the ends of the earth.
5 And he will be their peace.

Deliverance and Destruction

When the Assyrian invades our land
and marches through our fortresses,
we will raise against him seven shepherds,
even eight leaders of men.
6 They will rule[e] the land of Assyria with the sword,
the land of Nimrod with drawn sword.[f]
He will deliver us from the Assyrian
when he invades our land
and marches into our borders.

7 The remnant of Jacob will be
in the midst of many peoples
like dew from the Lord,
like showers on the grass,
which do not wait for man
or linger for mankind.
8 The remnant of Jacob will be among the nations,
in the midst of many peoples,
like a lion among the beasts of the forest,
like a young lion among flocks of sheep,
which mauls and mangles as it goes,
and no one can rescue.
9 Your hand will be lifted up in triumph over your enemies,
and all your foes will be destroyed.

10 "In that day," declares the Lord,

a 1 Or *Strengthen your walls, O walled city*   b 2 Or *rulers*   c 2 Hebrew *goings out*   d 2 Or *from days of eternity*
e 6 Or *crush*   f 6 Or *Nimrod in its gates*

"I will destroy your horses from among you
and demolish your chariots.
[11] I will destroy the cities of your land
and tear down all your strongholds.
[12] I will destroy your witchcraft
and you will no longer cast spells.
[13] I will destroy your carved images
and your sacred stones from among you;
you will no longer bow down
to the work of your hands.
[14] I will uproot from among you your Asherah poles[a]
and demolish your cities.
[15] I will take vengeance in anger and wrath
upon the nations that have not obeyed me."

The LORD's Case Against Israel

6

Listen to what the LORD says:

"Stand up, plead your case before the mountains;
let the hills hear what you have to say.
[2] Hear, O mountains, the LORD's accusation;
listen, you everlasting foundations of the earth.
For the LORD has a case against his people;
he is lodging a charge against Israel.

[3] "My people, what have I done to you?
How have I burdened you? Answer me.
[4] I brought you up out of Egypt
and redeemed you from the land of slavery.
I sent Moses to lead you,
also Aaron and Miriam.
[5] My people, remember
what Balak king of Moab counseled
and what Balaam son of Beor answered.
Remember ⌊your journey⌋ from Shittim to Gilgal,
that you may know the righteous acts of the LORD."

[6] With what shall I come before the LORD
and bow down before the exalted God?
Shall I come before him with burnt offerings,
with calves a year old?
[7] Will the LORD be pleased with thousands of rams,
with ten thousand rivers of oil?
Shall I offer my firstborn for my transgression,
the fruit of my body for the sin of my soul?
[8] He has showed you, O man, what is good.
And what does the LORD require of you?
To act justly and to love mercy
and to walk humbly with your God.

Israel's Guilt and Punishment

[9] Listen! The LORD is calling to the city—
and to fear your name is wisdom—
"Heed the rod and the One who appointed it.[b]
[10] Am I still to forget, O wicked house,

a 14 That is, symbols of the goddess Asherah   b 9 The meaning of the Hebrew for this line is uncertain.

genuine

purpose » 6:8

What do you think God requires of you? To make a large sacrifice? To witness to thousands and thousands of people? To give up every dream you have in order to be a missionary in Africa? To scale Mt. Everest? (We just threw that last one in.) Would it surprise you to know that God simply wants you to treat others fairly and mercifully and to walk humbly with him? Yep. Doesn't sound too hard, does it? But it can be a challenge sometimes. Will you say yea or nay to his way to obey?

your ill-gotten treasures
and the short ephah, [a] which
is accursed?
[11] Shall I acquit a man with
dishonest scales,
with a bag of false weights?
[12] Her rich men are violent;
her people are liars
and their tongues speak
deceitfully.
[13] Therefore, I have begun to
destroy you,
to ruin you because of your
sins.
[14] You will eat but not be satisfied;
your stomach will still be
empty. [b]
You will store up but save
nothing,
because what you save I will
give to the sword.
[15] You will plant but not harvest;
you will press olives but not
use the oil on
yourselves,
you will crush grapes but not
drink the wine.

[16] You have observed the statutes of Omri
and all the practices of Ahab's house,
and you have followed their traditions.
Therefore I will give you over to ruin
and your people to derision;
you will bear the scorn of the nations. [c]"

Israel's Misery

7

What misery is mine!
I am like one who gathers summer fruit
at the gleaning of the vineyard;
there is no cluster of grapes to eat,
none of the early figs that I crave.
[2] The godly have been swept from the land;
not one upright man remains.
All men lie in wait to shed blood;
each hunts his brother with a net.
[3] Both hands are skilled in doing evil;
the ruler demands gifts,
the judge accepts bribes,
the powerful dictate what they desire—
they all conspire together.
[4] The best of them is like a brier,
the most upright worse than a thorn hedge.
The day of your watchmen has come,
the day God visits you.

[a] 10 An ephah was a dry measure.   [b] 14 The meaning of the Hebrew for this word is uncertain.   [c] 16 Septuagint; Hebrew *scorn due my people*

Now is the time of their confusion.
⁵Do not trust a neighbor;
  put no confidence in a friend.
Even with her who lies in your embrace
  be careful of your words.
⁶For a son dishonors his father,
  a daughter rises up against her mother,
  a daughter-in-law against her mother-in-law—
  a man's enemies are the members of his own household.

⁷But as for me, I watch in hope for the LORD,
  I wait for God my Savior;
  my God will hear me.

Israel Will Rise

⁸Do not gloat over me, my enemy!
  Though I have fallen, I will rise.
Though I sit in darkness,
  the LORD will be my light.
⁹Because I have sinned against him,
  I will bear the LORD's wrath,
until he pleads my case
  and establishes my right.
He will bring me out into the light;
  I will see his righteousness.
¹⁰Then my enemy will see it
  and will be covered with shame,
she who said to me,
  "Where is the LORD your God?"
My eyes will see her downfall;
  even now she will be trampled underfoot
  like mire in the streets.

¹¹The day for building your walls will come,
  the day for extending your boundaries.
¹²In that day people will come to you
  from Assyria and the cities of Egypt,
even from Egypt to the Euphrates
  and from sea to sea
  and from mountain to mountain.
¹³The earth will become desolate because of its inhabitants,
  as the result of their deeds.

Prayer and Praise

¹⁴Shepherd your people with your staff,
  the flock of your inheritance,
which lives by itself in a forest,
  in fertile pasturelands. ᵃ
Let them feed in Bashan and Gilead
  as in days long ago.

¹⁵"As in the days when you came out of Egypt,
  I will show them my wonders."

¹⁶Nations will see and be ashamed,
  deprived of all their power.

ᵃ 14 Or in the middle of Carmel

mirror images

The Twelve were with him, and also some women who had been cured of evil spirits and diseases: . . . Joanna the wife of Cuza, the manager of Herod's household. Luke 8:1–3

Joanna—A Noble Choice

Hers is a reverse Cinderella story. Instead of ascending from the ashes to the palace, Joanna descended from a life of luxury to a life of servanthood. It's not often that we hear of someone willingly giving up the good life to serve others.

It's unusual, but it happens. Being the wife of King Herod's steward (or right-hand man), Joanna was used to the good life. No doubt she attended parties in the palace, knew the king's peculiar habits and enjoyed the best food and drink Galilee had to offer. At the time Joanna joined Jesus' ragtag band of followers, she was something of a celebrity.

But in the eyes of Jesus, Joanna was simply a woman who gave freely and served faithfully. Out of her abundance, Joanna gave money to provide for the needs of Jesus and his disciples. While other women in her position may have enjoyed the royal treatment, she was out following Jesus. She was present at the empty tomb on Easter morning and heard the angels announce that Jesus had risen from the dead. Imagine the impact of her testimony on Jesus' followers, the servants in the palace and even the king himself.

If Joanna had chosen to live her comfortable life of luxury, do you think we'd be reading about her today? No way! Her life would have been a quick, anonymous blip on the historical screen. Yet because of what she gave up to serve her true King, Joanna's name goes down in history as a faithful, life-giving woman.

Every day you face a similar set of choices. Do you pursue popularity, or do you serve Jesus by befriending the outcast? Do you invest all your time and money in your looks, or do you use your gifts to serve the Lord? Are you seeking recognition for your talents and accomplishments, or are you seeking glory for him? What you choose today determines how you'll be remembered forever.

To read the next Mirror Images profile, go to page 1283.

Dear Jesus, in my heart I know serving you brings real joy. But I get distracted by the things the world offers. Purify my heart, and help me to make choices that count for your kingdom. Amen.

dear Jesus

» Read more about Joanna in Luke 8:1–3 (page 1377) and 23:55—24:10 (pages 1406–1407).

They will lay their hands on their mouths
 and their ears will become deaf.
¹⁷ They will lick dust like a snake,
 like creatures that crawl on the ground.
They will come trembling out of their dens;
 they will turn in fear to the Lᴏʀᴅ our God
 and will be afraid of you.
¹⁸ Who is a God like you,
 who pardons sin and forgives the transgression
 of the remnant of his inheritance?
You do not stay angry forever
 but delight to show mercy.
¹⁹ You will again have compassion on us;
 you will tread our sins underfoot
 and hurl all our iniquities into the depths of the sea.
²⁰ You will be true to Jacob,
 and show mercy to Abraham,
 as you pledged on oath to our fathers
 in days long ago.

author:	Nahum.
date:	Probably shortly before 612 B.C.
setting:	The prophecy takes place after the fall of the Egyptian city of Thebes in 663 B.C. (see 3:8–10) and before the fall of Nineveh in 612 B.C.
verse to remember:	The LORD is good, a refuge in times of trouble. He cares for those who trust in him, but with an overwhelming flood he will make an end of Nineveh; he will pursue his foes into darkness (1:7–8).
theme to consider:	Read the book of Nahum and take heart. Injustice, rebellion, cruelty and disobedience will not go unpunished.

nahum

unchanging truth

You've probably seen a game where it all came down to the final minute. Maybe your team was down by several points but in the last seconds pulled ahead and won. Or maybe your team was ahead but was then stunned by a loss.

Life is full of upsets. You're a winner one day and a loser the next. Think of the "upsets" in your life. Maybe you had the popularity of a pebble in grade school but blossomed into "Miss Popularity" in junior high.

The prophet Nahum predicted an upset for the city of Nineveh. You remember Nineveh—the city Jonah tried to avoid going to and wound up as temporary fish food. Through Jonah, God had promised to destroy the city because of the cruelty of the Assyrians. But because the people of Nineveh had expressed regret for what they did wrong, God forgave them. Now the sunny days were over. The rain was coming.

This sudden overturn wasn't a whim of God. He had watched the Assyrians over time and took note of their sinful attitudes. A just and holy God could not—and does not—let evil go unpunished.

Perhaps you're hoping for a sudden upset in your life. Maybe a persistent problem has you wondering whether God even notices. You're not in the final quarter of the game yet. Your just and holy God is still in control. Trust him for the right outcome.

life lessons 3

1 God will deal with our enemies. Rest in the security of his love (1:12–15).

2 God is just and thorough when he punishes people (1:3; 2:1—3:7).

3 We cannot find true security in the power, money or status of people here on earth. Only God is all-powerful and worthy of our trust (1:7–8; 3:12–19).

1

An oracle concerning Nineveh. The book of the vision of Nahum the Elkoshite.

The LORD's Anger Against Nineveh

² The LORD is a jealous and
avenging God;
the LORD takes vengeance and
is filled with wrath.
The LORD takes vengeance on his
foes
and maintains his wrath
against his enemies.
³ The LORD is slow to anger and
great in power;
the LORD will not leave the
guilty unpunished.
His way is in the whirlwind and the storm,
and clouds are the dust of his feet.
⁴ He rebukes the sea and dries it up;
he makes all the rivers run dry.
Bashan and Carmel wither
and the blossoms of Lebanon fade.
⁵ The mountains quake before him
and the hills melt away.
The earth trembles at his presence,
the world and all who live in it.
⁶ Who can withstand his
indignation?
Who can endure his fierce
anger?
His wrath is poured out like fire;
the rocks are shattered before
him.

⁷ The LORD is good,
a refuge in times of trouble.
He cares for those who trust in
him,
⁸ but with an overwhelming
flood
he will make an end of ⌊Nineveh⌋;
he will pursue his foes into
darkness.

⁹ Whatever they plot against the
LORD
he ᵃ will bring to an end;
trouble will not come a
second time.
¹⁰ They will be entangled among
thorns
and drunk from their wine;
they will be consumed like dry
stubble. ᵇ

truth or dare

Is your view of God skewed? In your mind, is he a merciful pushover or a mean punisher? He's neither one. He's a perfect balance between justice and mercy.

1:2–3

genuine security

What makes you feel most secure? The locks on your doors? Your family's finances? Your looks? Your ability to create stunning beauty with just the right makeup? Your GPA? Here in the middle of Nahum's message of God's judgment on evildoers are four words that can help you feel the ultimate security: "The LORD is good." For those who trust in him, he's a safe place to run to in times of trouble. Unlike beauty, finances or even a deadbolt on your door, God's power and love for you will never fade or fail.

1:7–8

ᵃ 9 Or What do you foes plot against the LORD? / He   ᵇ 10 The meaning of the Hebrew for this verse is uncertain.

¹¹From you, ⌞O Nineveh,⌟ has one come forth
    who plots evil against the Lᴏʀᴅ
    and counsels wickedness.

¹²This is what the Lᴏʀᴅ says:

"Although they have allies and are numerous,
    they will be cut off and pass away.
Although I have afflicted you, ⌞O Judah,⌟
    I will afflict you no more.
¹³Now I will break their yoke from your neck
    and tear your shackles away."

¹⁴The Lᴏʀᴅ has given a command concerning you, ⌞Nineveh⌟:
    "You will have no descendants to bear your name.
I will destroy the carved images and cast idols
    that are in the temple of your gods.
I will prepare your grave,
    for you are vile."

¹⁵Look, there on the mountains,
    the feet of one who brings good news,
    who proclaims peace!
Celebrate your festivals, O Judah,
    and fulfill your vows.
No more will the wicked invade you;
    they will be completely destroyed.

Nineveh to Fall

2

An attacker advances against you, ⌞Nineveh⌟.
    Guard the fortress,
    watch the road,
    brace yourselves,
    marshal all your strength!

²The Lᴏʀᴅ will restore the splendor of Jacob
    like the splendor of Israel,
though destroyers have laid them waste
    and have ruined their vines.

³The shields of his soldiers are
        red;
    the warriors are clad in
        scarlet.
The metal on the chariots flashes
    on the day they are made
        ready;
    the spears of pine are
        brandished. ᵃ
⁴The chariots storm through the
        streets,
    rushing back and forth through the
        squares.
They look like flaming torches;
    they dart about like lightning.

⁵He summons his picked troops,
    yet they stumble on their way.

truth *or dare*

Your life can *never* reach a point where God cannot bring you back and bless you. Remember this when you feel like the world's crashing down. You're never beyond hope.

2:2

ᵃ 3 Hebrew; Septuagint and Syriac / *the horsemen rush to and fro*

They dash to the city wall;
the protective shield is put in place.
⁶ The river gates are thrown open
and the palace collapses.
⁷ It is decreed* that ˌthe cityˌ
be exiled and carried away.
Its slave girls moan like doves
and beat upon their breasts.
⁸ Nineveh is like a pool,
and its water is draining away.
"Stop! Stop!" they cry,
but no one turns back.
⁹ Plunder the silver!
Plunder the gold!
The supply is endless,
the wealth from all its treasures!
¹⁰ She is pillaged, plundered, stripped!
Hearts melt, knees give way,
bodies tremble, every face grows pale.

¹¹ Where now is the lions' den,
the place where they fed their young,
where the lion and lioness went,
and the cubs, with nothing to fear?
¹² The lion killed enough for his cubs
and strangled the prey for his mate,
filling his lairs with the kill
and his dens with the prey.

¹³ "I am against you,"
declares the LORD Almighty.
"I will burn up your chariots in smoke,
and the sword will devour your young lions.
I will leave you no prey on the earth.
The voices of your messengers
will no longer be heard."

Woe to Nineveh

3 Woe to the city of blood,
full of lies,
full of plunder,
never without victims!
² The crack of whips,
the clatter of wheels,
galloping horses
and jolting chariots!
³ Charging cavalry,
flashing swords
and glittering spears!
Many casualties,
piles of dead,
bodies without number,
people stumbling over the corpses—
⁴ all because of the wanton lust of a harlot,
alluring, the mistress of sorceries,

a 7 The meaning of the Hebrew for this word is uncertain.

who enslaved nations by her prostitution
and peoples by her witchcraft.
⁵"I am against you," declares the LORD Almighty.
"I will lift your skirts over your face.
I will show the nations your nakedness
and the kingdoms your shame.
⁶I will pelt you with filth,
I will treat you with contempt
and make you a spectacle.
⁷All who see you will flee from you and say,
'Nineveh is in ruins—who will mourn for her?'
Where can I find anyone to comfort you?"

⁸Are you better than Thebes,ᵃ
situated on the Nile,
with water around her?
The river was her defense,
the waters her wall.
⁹Cushᵇ and Egypt were her boundless strength;
Put and Libya were among her allies.
¹⁰Yet she was taken captive
and went into exile.
Her infants were dashed to pieces
at the head of every street.
Lots were cast for her nobles,
and all her great men were put in chains.
¹¹You too will become drunk;
you will go into hiding
and seek refuge from the enemy.

¹²All your fortresses are like fig trees
with their first ripe fruit;
when they are shaken,
the figs fall into the mouth of the eater.
¹³Look at your troops—
they are all women!
The gates of your land
are wide open to your enemies;
fire has consumed their bars.

¹⁴Draw water for the siege,
strengthen your defenses!
Work the clay,
tread the mortar,
repair the brickwork!
¹⁵There the fire will devour you;
the sword will cut you down
and, like grasshoppers, consume you.
Multiply like grasshoppers,
multiply like locusts!
¹⁶You have increased the number of your merchants
till they are more than the stars of the sky,
but like locusts they strip the land
and then fly away.
¹⁷Your guards are like locusts,

ᵃ 8 Hebrew No Amon   ᵇ 9 That is, the upper Nile region

your officials like swarms of locusts
that settle in the walls on a cold day—
but when the sun appears they fly away,
and no one knows where.

18 O king of Assyria, your shepherds[a] slumber;
your nobles lie down to rest.
Your people are scattered on the mountains
with no one to gather them.
19 Nothing can heal your wound;
your injury is fatal.
Everyone who hears the news about you
claps his hands at your fall,
for who has not felt
your endless cruelty?

a 18 Or rulers

author:	Habakkuk.
date:	Around 605 B.C.
setting:	Babylon was about to destroy Judah.
verse to remember:	Though the fig tree does not bud and there are no grapes on the vines, though the olive crop fails and the fields produce no food, though there are no sheep in the pen and no cattle in the stalls, yet I will rejoice in the LORD, I will be joyful in God my Savior (3:17–18).
theme to consider:	Habbakkuk wondered why it appeared that evil was winning. After questioning God, Habakkuk concluded that God *is* in control; judgment *will* come; so praise God!

unchanging truth

habakkuk

What are you waiting for? To get your driver's license? For the guy you like to finally ask you out, let alone notice that you exist? To get into the right high school or college?

We spend a good percentage of our lives waiting for something to happen. Waiting is particularly difficult when you're in emotional pain. When a relationship ends or something else happens that hurts you, you wonder when the pain will ever go away. Maybe you even wonder whether God notices how you feel.

At times like that, have you ever cried out, "Lord, how long will you allow this?" That was the cry of the prophet Habakkuk. He wondered how long God planned to stand by and watch the wrongdoings of the wicked.

See, Habakkuk thought God was just idly standing by. He thought God might have forgotten or overlooked the actions of the wicked.

Not at all. God's answers to Habakkuk's questions show that he had indeed noticed what was going on. He even had a plan to deal with the wrongdoers—in *his* time. And those who did right would be rescued and protected.

Do you believe that God is still working on your behalf even when you can't see him at work and even when it feels like it's been forever? Let the message of Habakkuk fill you with hope.

life lessons

3

1. God answers our questions and cries for justice with the truth of his character (1:1—2:17).

2. Trusting in anything other than God is a foolish waste of time (2:18–20).

3. Remembering God's faithfulness is helpful during hard times (3:1–19).

1

The oracle that Habakkuk the prophet received.

Habakkuk's Complaint

²How long, O LORD, must I call for help,
    but you do not listen?
Or cry out to you, "Violence!"
    but you do not save?
³Why do you make me look at injustice?
    Why do you tolerate wrong?
Destruction and violence are
      before me;
    there is strife, and conflict
      abounds.
⁴Therefore the law is paralyzed,
    and justice never prevails.
The wicked hem in the righteous,
    so that justice is perverted.

The LORD's Answer

⁵"Look at the nations and
      watch—
    and be utterly amazed.
For I am going to do something in your days
    that you would not believe,
      even if you were told.
⁶I am raising up the Babylonians,^a
    that ruthless and impetuous people,
who sweep across the whole earth
    to seize dwelling places not their own.
⁷They are a feared and dreaded people;
    they are a law to themselves
    and promote their own honor.
⁸Their horses are swifter than leopards,
    fiercer than wolves at dusk.
Their cavalry gallops headlong;
    their horsemen come from afar.
They fly like a vulture swooping to devour;
⁹   they all come bent on violence.
Their hordes^b advance like a desert wind
    and gather prisoners like sand.
¹⁰They deride kings
    and scoff at rulers.
They laugh at all fortified cities;
    they build earthen ramps and capture them.
¹¹Then they sweep past like the wind and go on—
    guilty men, whose own strength is their god."

Habakkuk's Second Complaint

¹²O LORD, are you not from everlasting?
    My God, my Holy One, we will not die.
O LORD, you have appointed them to execute judgment;
    O Rock, you have ordained them to punish.

---

truth or dare

You've probably heard Habakkuk's vent session before: How can a *holy* God tolerate such a messed-up world? Actually, God's *patience* with us is what keeps his justice at bay.

1:2–4

---

^a 6 Or *Chaldeans*   ^b 9 The meaning of the Hebrew for this word is uncertain.

¹³Your eyes are too pure to look on evil;
 you cannot tolerate wrong.
Why then do you tolerate the treacherous?
 Why are you silent while the wicked
 swallow up those more righteous than themselves?
¹⁴You have made men like fish in the sea,
 like sea creatures that have no ruler.
¹⁵The wicked foe pulls all of them up with hooks,
 he catches them in his net,
he gathers them up in his dragnet;
 and so he rejoices and is glad.
¹⁶Therefore he sacrifices to his net
 and burns incense to his dragnet,
for by his net he lives in luxury
 and enjoys the choicest food.
¹⁷Is he to keep on emptying his net,
 destroying nations without mercy?

2

I will stand at my watch
 and station myself on the ramparts;
I will look to see what he will say to me,
 and what answer I am to give to this complaint.^a

The LORD's Answer

²Then the LORD replied:

"Write down the revelation
 and make it plain on tablets
 so that a herald^b may run with it.
³For the revelation awaits an appointed time;
 it speaks of the end
 and will not prove false.
Though it linger, wait for it;
 it^c will certainly come and will not delay.

⁴"See, he is puffed up;
 his desires are not upright—
 but the righteous will live by his faith^d—
⁵indeed, wine betrays him;
 he is arrogant and never at rest.
Because he is as greedy as the grave^e
 and like death is never satisfied,
he gathers to himself all the nations
 and takes captive all the peoples.

⁶"Will not all of them taunt him with ridicule and scorn, saying,

" 'Woe to him who piles up stolen goods
 and makes himself wealthy by extortion!
 How long must this go on?'
⁷Will not your debtors^f suddenly arise?
 Will they not wake up and make you tremble?
 Then you will become their victim.
⁸Because you have plundered many nations,
 the peoples who are left will plunder you.

a 1 Or and what to answer when I am rebuked   b 2 Or so that whoever reads it   c 3 Or Though he linger, wait for him; / he   d 4 Or faithfulness   e 5 Hebrew Sheol   f 7 Or creditors

For you have shed man's blood;
　　you have destroyed lands and cities and everyone in them.

⁹ "Woe to him who builds his realm by unjust gain
　　to set his nest on high,
　　to escape the clutches of ruin!
¹⁰ You have plotted the ruin of many peoples,
　　shaming your own house and forfeiting your life.
¹¹ The stones of the wall will cry out,
　　and the beams of the woodwork will echo it.

¹² "Woe to him who builds a city with bloodshed
　　and establishes a town by crime!
¹³ Has not the Lord Almighty determined
　　that the people's labor is only fuel for the fire,
　　that the nations exhaust themselves for nothing?
¹⁴ For the earth will be filled with the knowledge of the glory of the Lord,
　　as the waters cover the sea.

¹⁵ "Woe to him who gives drink to his neighbors,
　　pouring it from the wineskin till they are drunk,
　　so that he can gaze on their naked bodies.
¹⁶ You will be filled with shame instead of glory.
　　Now it is your turn! Drink and be exposed*!
The cup from the Lord's right hand is coming around to you,
　　and disgrace will cover your glory.
¹⁷ The violence you have done to Lebanon will overwhelm you,
　　and your destruction of animals will terrify you.
For you have shed man's blood;
　　you have destroyed lands and cities and everyone in them.

¹⁸ "Of what value is an idol, since a man has carved it?
　　Or an image that teaches lies?
For he who makes it trusts in his own creation;
　　he makes idols that cannot speak.
¹⁹ Woe to him who says to wood, 'Come to life!'
　　Or to lifeless stone, 'Wake up!'
Can it give guidance?
　　It is covered with gold and silver;
　　there is no breath in it.
²⁰ But the Lord is in his holy temple;
　　let all the earth be silent before him."

Habakkuk's Prayer

3 A prayer of Habakkuk the prophet. On *shigionoth*.ᵇ

² Lord, I have heard of your fame;
　　I stand in awe of your deeds, O Lord.
Renew them in our day,
　　in our time make them known;
　　in wrath remember mercy.

³ God came from Teman,
　　the Holy One from Mount Paran.　　　　　　　*Selah*ᶜ
His glory covered the heavens
　　and his praise filled the earth.

Lonely in a Crowd

Profile: Mickey

"WHAT?! I can't hear you! Talk louder!!" I shouted above the noise of the crowd and the music blaring from the back of some guy's pickup.

"I said . . . DO YOU . . . WANT . . . ANOTHER . . . COKE?" Lana asked as she dramatically attempted to emphasize each syllable, her own can of Coke sloshing to the ground as she talked.

"No thanks!" I yelled, gluing a fake smile to my face. "I'll let you know when I finish this one!" I could tell she didn't really hear me anyway. Oh well. I held up my can and smiled like I was having the time of my life.

I actually didn't feel like being at the party at all, though. At that moment, all I really wanted to do was to curl up on my couch at home and cry myself to sleep. I felt alone, even though I was in the middle of what was supposed to be one of the greatest parties of the year. My best friends were all there having a good time. On the surface I was even laughing and joking with them. But inside I felt like dying. It was the strangest feeling—being with everyone yet feeling like I was on some deserted island. No one knew how I felt. No one could even see my pain.

I tried talking to my mom about it once, but she wanted to take me to counseling—like I was a social misfit or something. I just told her, "It's all good. I know it will pass"—hoping she would forget I mentioned it.

loneliness in focus

The Bible is full of stories of people who were highly committed, outspoken heroes of the faith—yet they suffered from loneliness and depression. See 1 Kings 19:3–10 (page 425) and 2 Corinthians 1:8–9 (page 1524). Loneliness and depression are not sins.

»Some girls try to blunt the pain of loneliness with things like relationships with guys, drugs or alcohol. That won't solve the problem of loneliness; it'll just give you a new set of problems.

»Loneliness rarely gets better by focusing exclusively on yourself. Reach out to someone else who seems lonely and see how your own loneliness disappears.

»Consider Christian counseling. Despite what you might think, counseling is not for "psychos." It's for smart people who want to understand themselves better (see Psalm 139:13–14, page 791).

For more on this topic, see the index on page 1656.

⁴ His splendor was like the sunrise;
    rays flashed from his hand,
    where his power was hidden.
⁵ Plague went before him;
    pestilence followed his steps.
⁶ He stood, and shook the earth;
    he looked, and made the nations tremble.

The ancient mountains crumbled
and the age-old hills collapsed.
His ways are eternal.
7 I saw the tents of Cushan in distress,
the dwellings of Midian in anguish.

8 Were you angry with the rivers, O LORD?
Was your wrath against the streams?
Did you rage against the sea
when you rode with your horses
and your victorious chariots?
9 You uncovered your bow,
you called for many arrows.   *Selah*
You split the earth with rivers;
10 the mountains saw you and writhed.
Torrents of water swept by;
the deep roared
and lifted its waves on high.

11 Sun and moon stood still in the heavens
at the glint of your flying arrows,
at the lightning of your flashing spear.
12 In wrath you strode through the earth
and in anger you threshed the nations.
13 You came out to deliver your people,
to save your anointed one.
You crushed the leader of the land of wickedness,
you stripped him from head to foot.   *Selah*
14 With his own spear you pierced his head
when his warriors stormed out to scatter us,
gloating as though about to devour
the wretched who were in hiding.
15 You trampled the sea with your horses,
churning the great waters.

16 I heard and my heart pounded,
my lips quivered at the sound;
decay crept into my bones,
and my legs trembled.
Yet I will wait patiently for the day
of calamity
to come on the nation invading us.
17 Though the fig tree does not bud
and there are no grapes on
the vines,
though the olive crop fails
and the fields produce no food,
though there are no sheep in the pen
and no cattle in the stalls,
18 yet I will rejoice in the LORD,
I will be joyful in God my Savior.

19 The Sovereign LORD is my strength;
he makes my feet like the feet
of a deer,
he enables me to go on the heights.

For the director of music. On my
stringed instruments.

genuine

trust » 3:16-18

What do hard times inspire within you? Complaining? Bitterness? How about joy? Not likely, unless your trust is 100 percent in God, as Habakkuk's was. Even though God planned to allow an invading army to conquer Judah, Habakkuk's trust kept him praising God. You can't manufacture this level of trust. It comes from sticking with God, in good times and in bad. When your life's going great and when it just plain stinks. Do you have that level of trust? If not, are you willing to ask for it? It won't guarantee you trouble-free days. It will guarantee you the ride of your life.

at a glance ⌄

author:	Zephaniah.
date:	As 1:1 states, during the reign of King Josiah (640–609 B.C.), probably near the beginning of Josiah's reign.
setting:	King Josiah tried to make changes for the good in Judah.
verse to remember:	Seek the LORD, all you humble of the land, you who do what he commands. Seek righteousness, seek humility; perhaps you will be sheltered on the day of the LORD's anger (2:3).
theme to consider:	Zephaniah declares the coming of God's stern judgment, but the flip side of his message was that someday the people would repent and return to God.

unchanging truth

At times you can feel like you're just drowning in bad news. Who can forget the horror of watching the events of 9/11 unfold on TV and then seeing the same awful images replayed hour after hour?

War. Terrorism. Diseases. Broken marriages. Strained relationships. Gang violence. Drugs. Depressing, isn't it? It's especially depressing when our own actions help to usher in hard times.

The people of Judah probably felt as though they were drowning in bad news when the prophet Zephaniah spoke about the coming "day of the LORD." But their evil acts and those of other nations had earned them God's anger and impending punishment. Two kings of Judah (Manasseh and Amon) had led Judah in wrongdoing. So God planned to allow enemy nations to destroy their land.

Although the people of Judah may have felt overwhelmed, there was a lifeline. God invited them to turn from evil and turn back to him. One day he would give back to them what had been taken away (land, crops, etc.). Most of all, he would give them back their joy and hope.

Feeling like you're in that same sinking boat, awaiting the consequences of your poor choices? Or maybe you've seen the sorrow that others have experienced because of their sins. There's good news still. The Savior still cares. He doesn't delight in punishing. He delights in restoring.

zephaniah

life lessons

1. Although God is slow to anger, sin triggers his wrath and judgment (1:2–18). He never ignores sin.

2. God offers the hope of a new life when we return to him (2:1–3).

3. God still has good plans for his people—even those he disciplines (3:8–20).

1

The word of the LORD that came to Zephaniah son of Cushi, the son of Gedaliah, the son of Amariah, the son of Hezekiah, during the reign of Josiah son of Amon king of Judah:

Warning of Coming Destruction

² "I will sweep away everything
from the face of the earth,"

declares the LORD.

³ "I will sweep away both men and animals;
I will sweep away the birds of the air
and the fish of the sea.
The wicked will have only heaps of rubble^a
when I cut off man from the face of the earth,"

declares the LORD.

Against Judah

⁴ "I will stretch out my hand against Judah
and against all who live in Jerusalem.
I will cut off from this place every remnant of Baal,
the names of the pagan and the idolatrous priests—
⁵ those who bow down on the roofs
to worship the starry host,
those who bow down and swear by the LORD
and who also swear by Molech,^b
⁶ those who turn back from following the LORD
and neither seek the LORD nor inquire of him.
⁷ Be silent before the Sovereign LORD,
for the day of the LORD is near.
The LORD has prepared a sacrifice;
he has consecrated those he has invited.
⁸ On the day of the LORD's sacrifice
I will punish the princes
and the king's sons
and all those clad
in foreign clothes.
⁹ On that day I will punish
all who avoid stepping on the
threshold,^c
who fill the temple of their gods
with violence and deceit.

¹⁰ "On that day," declares the LORD,
"a cry will go up from the Fish
Gate,
wailing from the New Quarter,
and a loud crash from the
hills.
¹¹ Wail, you who live in the market
district^d;
all your merchants will be wiped out,
all who trade with^e silver will be ruined.
¹² At that time I will search Jerusalem with
lamps
and punish those who are complacent,

truth or dare

Indifference to God (a.k.a. thinking that "dear old God wouldn't *really* punish us for our sins") may be popular, but it sure isn't safe. Are you falling into the complacency trap?

1:12

^a 3 The meaning of the Hebrew for this line is uncertain.   ^b 5 Hebrew *Malcam*, that is, Milcom   ^c 9 See 1 Samuel 5:5.
^d 11 Or *the Mortar*   ^e 11 Or *in*

who are like wine left on its dregs,
who think, 'The LORD will do nothing,
  either good or bad.'
[13] Their wealth will be plundered,
  their houses demolished.
They will build houses
  but not live in them;
they will plant vineyards
  but not drink the wine.

The Great Day of the LORD

[14] "The great day of the LORD is near—
  near and coming quickly.
Listen! The cry on the day of the LORD will be bitter,
  the shouting of the warrior there.
[15] That day will be a day of wrath,
  a day of distress and anguish,
a day of trouble and ruin,
  a day of darkness and gloom,
  a day of clouds and blackness,
[16] a day of trumpet and battle cry
  against the fortified cities
  and against the corner towers.
[17] I will bring distress on the people
  and they will walk like blind men,
because they have sinned against the LORD.
Their blood will be poured out like dust
  and their entrails like filth.
[18] Neither their silver nor their gold
  will be able to save them
  on the day of the LORD's wrath.
In the fire of his jealousy
  the whole world will be consumed,
for he will make a sudden end
  of all who live in the earth."

2 Gather together, gather together,
  O shameful nation,
[2] before the appointed time arrives
  and that day sweeps on like
    chaff,
before the fierce anger of the
    LORD comes upon you,
before the day of the LORD's
    wrath comes upon you.
[3] Seek the LORD, all you humble of
    the land,
  you who do what he
    commands.
Seek righteousness, seek humility;
  perhaps you will be sheltered
  on the day of the LORD's anger.

truth or dare

Tick, tock. The clock *is* ticking, and the Lord will return any day now. How are you using the time you've got to prepare for his coming?

2:1–3

Against Philistia

[4] Gaza will be abandoned
  and Ashkelon left in ruins.

genuine comfort

2:6-7

How do you spell *relax*? S-E-R-T-A? There's nothing like a good mattress for some quality sleep. But how about rest from the weariness and stress of life? Even the best mattress can't take care of that. Only one brand name provides that type of rest: God. The faithful people of Judah would agree. God promised to give them land and provide for their needs. Now *that's* quality rest! In need of some genuine rest? Lean back and put the whole weight of your cares on God.

At midday Ashdod will be
emptied
and Ekron uprooted.
⁵ Woe to you who live by the sea,
O Kerethite people;
the word of the LORD is against you,
O Canaan, land of the Philistines.

"I will destroy you,
and none will be left."

⁶ The land by the sea, where the
Kerethites ᵃ dwell,
will be a place for shepherds
and sheep pens.
⁷ It will belong to the remnant of
the house of Judah;
there they will find pasture.
In the evening they will lie down
in the houses of Ashkelon.
The LORD their God will care for
them;
he will restore their fortunes. ᵇ

Against Moab and Ammon

⁸ "I have heard the insults of Moab
and the taunts of the
Ammonites,
who insulted my people
and made threats against their land.
⁹ Therefore, as surely as I live,"
declares the LORD Almighty, the God of Israel,
"surely Moab will become like Sodom,
the Ammonites like Gomorrah—
a place of weeds and salt pits,
a wasteland forever.
The remnant of my people will plunder them;
the survivors of my nation will inherit their land."

¹⁰ This is what they will get in return for their pride,
for insulting and mocking the people of the LORD Almighty.
¹¹ The LORD will be awesome to them
when he destroys all the gods of the land.
The nations on every shore will worship him,
every one in its own land.

Against Cush

¹² "You too, O Cushites, ᶜ
will be slain by my sword."

Against Assyria

¹³ He will stretch out his hand against the north
and destroy Assyria,
leaving Nineveh utterly desolate
and dry as the desert.

ᵃ 6 The meaning of the Hebrew for this word is uncertain.   *ᵇ 7* Or *will bring back their captives*   *ᶜ 12* That is, people from the upper Nile region

¹⁴Flocks and herds will lie down there,
    creatures of every kind.
The desert owl and the screech owl
    will roost on her columns.
Their calls will echo through the windows,
    rubble will be in the doorways,
    the beams of cedar will be exposed.
¹⁵This is the carefree city
    that lived in safety.
She said to herself,
    "I am, and there is none besides me."
What a ruin she has become,
    a lair for wild beasts!
All who pass by her scoff
    and shake their fists.

The Future of Jerusalem

3 Woe to the city of oppressors,
    rebellious and defiled!
²She obeys no one,
    she accepts no correction.
She does not trust in the LORD,
    she does not draw near to her God.
³Her officials are roaring lions,
    her rulers are evening wolves,
    who leave nothing for the morning.
⁴Her prophets are arrogant;
    they are treacherous men.
Her priests profane the sanctuary
    and do violence to the law.
⁵The LORD within her is righteous;
    he does no wrong.
Morning by morning he dispenses his justice,
    and every new day he does not fail,
    yet the unrighteous know no shame.

⁶"I have cut off nations;
    their strongholds are demolished.
I have left their streets deserted,
    with no one passing through.
Their cities are destroyed;
    no one will be left—no one at all.
⁷I said to the city,
    'Surely you will fear me
    and accept correction!'
Then her dwelling would not be cut off,
    nor all my punishments come upon her.
But they were still eager
    to act corruptly in all they did.
⁸Therefore wait for me," declares the LORD,
    "for the day I will stand up to testify.^a
I have decided to assemble the nations,
    to gather the kingdoms
and to pour out my wrath on them—
    all my fierce anger.

^a 8 Septuagint and Syriac; Hebrew *will rise up to plunder*

The whole world will be consumed
by the fire of my jealous anger.

9 "Then will I purify the lips of the peoples,
that all of them may call on the name of the LORD
and serve him shoulder to shoulder.
10 From beyond the rivers of Cush[a]
my worshipers, my scattered people,
will bring me offerings.
11 On that day you will not be put to shame
for all the wrongs you have done to me,
because I will remove from this city
those who rejoice in their pride.

love ♥ notes

3:17

Loved one,

This is my love song for you. I delight in you! I will calm your fears. I am strong enough to save and protect you. I will spend eternity singing over you.

—The One who loves you

Why do you think God delights in you? Write a prayer of response for the promise of his love.

_____

_____

_____

_____

_____

_____

_____

_____

_____

Never again will you be haughty
on my holy hill.
12 But I will leave within you
the meek and humble,
who trust in the name of the
LORD.
13 The remnant of Israel will do no
wrong;
they will speak no lies,
nor will deceit be found in
their mouths.
They will eat and lie down
and no one will make them
afraid."

14 Sing, O Daughter of Zion;
shout aloud, O Israel!
Be glad and rejoice with all your
heart,
O Daughter of Jerusalem!
15 The LORD has taken away your
punishment,
he has turned back your
enemy.
The LORD, the King of Israel, is
with you;
never again will you fear any
harm.
16 On that day they will say to
Jerusalem,
"Do not fear, O Zion;
do not let your hands hang
limp.
17 The LORD your God is with you,
he is mighty to save.
He will take great delight in you,
he will quiet you with his love,
he will rejoice over you with
singing."
18 "The sorrows for the appointed
feasts
I will remove from you;

a 10 That is, the upper Nile region

they are a burden and a reproach to you. [a]

19 At that time I will deal
    with all who oppressed you;
I will rescue the lame
    and gather those who have been scattered.
I will give them praise and honor
    in every land where they were put to shame.
20 At that time I will gather you;
    at that time I will bring you home.
I will give you honor and praise
    among all the peoples of the earth
when I restore your fortunes [b]
    before your very eyes,"

says the LORD.

---

[a] 18 Or "I will gather you who mourn for the appointed feasts; / your reproach is a burden to you   [b] 20 Or I bring back your captives

author:	Haggai.
date:	520 B.C.
setting:	The Persian King Cyrus had allowed the Jews to return to Jerusalem to rebuild the temple. The people began, but opposition from their neighbors and their own apathy caused them to abandon the project.
verse to remember:	Then the word of the LORD came through the prophet Haggai: "Is it a time for you yourselves to be living in your paneled houses, while this house remains a ruin?" (1:3–4).
theme to consider:	The situation in the book of Haggai is a challenging reminder to take inventory of our lives and reorder our priorities to reflect God's will.

haggai

unchanging truth

If you have ever witnessed the destruction of someone's reputation, it's not a pretty sight. Something as small as a whispered rumor can really wreck a reputation, especially if everyone believes the rumor is true.

If that's ever happened to you, sooner or later you have to think about rebuilding your reputation and your life. But how do you rebuild a reputation after it has been destroyed?

Or maybe you've moved to a new school and need to establish a reputation there. Perhaps you want to totally ditch your old identity and come out strong in the new school. Where do you begin?

The people of Judah had to begin again after returning to their land. Their long years of exile had finally ended. God gave them a good place to start: rebuilding the temple. Unfortunately, the temple was a low priority on their "to-do" list. They had put all their energy into their own homes instead. But putting God last was what got the people in trouble in the first place!

Through the prophet Haggai, God encouraged them to keep working at the temple. He reminded them of their lack of essentials—like crops and clothing—because they had ignored him.

Need to start over? Where is God on your "to-do" list? Make sure he's at the top of the list before you begin your own building projects.

life lessons

1 God wants first priority in our lives. He's never content with second place (1:1–15).

2 We are not to dwell on or rest in the glories of the past. Instead we are to do what God wants us to do today (2:1–9).

3 God encourages and equips his people to do his work (2:20–23).

A Call to Build the House of the LORD

1 In the second year of King Darius, on the first day of the sixth month, the word of the LORD came through the prophet Haggai to Zerubbabel son of Shealtiel, governor of Judah, and to Joshua*ᵃ* son of Jehozadak, the high priest:

²This is what the LORD Almighty says: "These people say, 'The time has not yet come for the LORD's house to be built.' "

³Then the word of the LORD came through the prophet Haggai: ⁴"Is it a time for you yourselves to be living in your paneled houses, while this house remains a ruin?"

⁵Now this is what the LORD Almighty says: "Give careful thought to your ways. ⁶You have planted much, but have harvested little. You eat, but never have enough. You drink, but never have your fill. You put on clothes, but are not warm. You earn wages, only to put them in a purse with holes in it."

⁷This is what the LORD Almighty says: "Give careful thought to your ways. ⁸Go up into the mountains and bring down timber and build the house, so that I may take pleasure in it and be honored," says the LORD. ⁹"You expected much, but see, it turned out to be little. What you brought home, I blew away. Why?" declares the LORD Almighty. "Because of my house, which remains a ruin, while each of you is busy with his own house. ¹⁰Therefore, because of you the heavens have withheld their dew and the earth its crops. ¹¹I called for a drought on the fields and the mountains, on the grain, the new wine, the oil and whatever the ground produces, on men and cattle, and on the labor of your hands."

truth *or dare*

"Busy with his own house" sounds a lot like "busy with her own life." Have you forgotten about God and his family while putting yourself and your shopping list in the spotlight?

1:9

¹²Then Zerubbabel son of Shealtiel, Joshua son of Jehozadak, the high priest, and the whole remnant of the people obeyed the voice of the LORD their God and the message of the prophet Haggai, because the LORD their God had sent him. And the people feared the LORD.

¹³Then Haggai, the LORD's messenger, gave this message of the LORD to the people: "I am with you," declares the LORD. ¹⁴So the LORD stirred up the spirit of Zerubbabel son of Shealtiel, governor of Judah, and the spirit of Joshua son of Jehozadak, the high priest, and the spirit of the whole remnant of the people. They came and began to work on the house of the LORD Almighty, their God, ¹⁵on the twenty-fourth day of the sixth month in the second year of King Darius.

The Promised Glory of the New House

2 On the twenty-first day of the seventh month, the word of the LORD came through the prophet Haggai: ²"Speak to Zerubbabel son of Shealtiel, governor of Judah, to Joshua son of Jehozadak, the high priest, and to the remnant of the people. Ask them, ³'Who of you is left who saw this house in its former glory? How does it look to you now? Does it not seem to you like nothing? ⁴But now be strong, O Zerubbabel,' declares the LORD. 'Be strong, O Joshua son of Jehozadak, the high priest. Be strong, all you people of the land,' declares the LORD, 'and work. For I am with you,' declares the LORD Almighty. ⁵'This is what I covenanted with you when you came out of Egypt. And my Spirit remains among you. Do not fear.'

⁶"This is what the LORD Almighty says: 'In a little while I will once more shake the heavens and the earth, the sea and the dry land. ⁷I will shake all nations, and the desired of all nations will come, and I will fill this house with glory,' says the LORD Almighty. ⁸'The silver is mine and the gold is mine,' declares the LORD Almighty. ⁹'The glory of this present house will be greater than the glory of the former house,' says the LORD Almighty. 'And in this place I will grant peace,' declares the LORD Almighty."

Blessings for a Defiled People

¹⁰On the twenty-fourth day of the ninth month, in the second year of Darius, the word of the LORD came to the prophet Haggai: ¹¹"This is what the LORD Almighty says: 'Ask the priests what the

ᵃ 1 A variant of Jeshua; here and elsewhere in Haggai

law says: [12]If a person carries consecrated meat in the fold of his garment, and that fold touches some bread or stew, some wine, oil or other food, does it become consecrated?' "

The priests answered, "No."

[13]Then Haggai said, "If a person defiled by contact with a dead body touches one of these things, does it become defiled?"

"Yes," the priests replied, "it becomes defiled."

[14]Then Haggai said, " 'So it is with this people and this nation in my sight,' declares the LORD. 'Whatever they do and whatever they offer there is defiled.

[15]" 'Now give careful thought to this from this day on*—consider how things were before one stone was laid on another in the LORD's temple. [16]When anyone came to a heap of twenty measures, there were only ten. When anyone went to a wine vat to draw fifty measures, there were only twenty. [17]I struck all the work of your hands with blight, mildew and hail, yet you did not turn to me,' declares the LORD. [18]'From this day on, from this twenty-fourth day of the ninth month, give careful thought to the day when the foundation of the LORD's temple was laid. Give careful thought: [19]Is there yet any seed left in the barn? Until now, the vine and the fig tree, the pomegranate and the olive tree have not borne fruit.

" 'From this day on I will bless you.' "

Zerubbabel the LORD's Signet Ring

[20]The word of the LORD came to Haggai a second time on the twenty-fourth day of the month: [21]"Tell Zerubbabel governor of Judah that I will shake the heavens and the earth. [22]I will overturn royal thrones and shatter the power of the foreign kingdoms. I will overthrow chariots and their drivers; horses and their riders will fall, each by the sword of his brother.

[23]" 'On that day,' declares the LORD Almighty, 'I will take you, my servant Zerubbabel son of Shealtiel,' declares the LORD, 'and I will make you like my signet ring, for I have chosen you,' declares the LORD Almighty."

a 15 Or to the days past

author:	Zechariah.
date:	Between about 520 and 480 B.C.
setting:	Zechariah, like Haggai, encouraged the exiles who had returned to Jerusalem from Babylon to complete the rebuilding of the temple.
verse to remember:	Rejoice greatly, O Daughter of Zion! Shout, Daughter of Jerusalem! See, your king comes to you, righteous and having salvation, gentle and riding on a donkey, on a colt, the foal of a donkey (9:9).
theme to consider:	Zechariah challenges his fellow Israelites to finish the work of rebuilding their temple. He also offers a glimpse of events that would take place five hundred years later—the coming of the Messiah!

zechariah

unchanging truth

It's tempting to wish that life were like a fairy tale—happy endings, handsome (and extremely rich) prince, defeated enemies. Is that how you'd want your story to play out?

All stories have an ending of some kind—some end happily, some unhappily. We all hope for happy endings, yet when something bad happens, it's hard to imagine how that story could possibly end well. Ever felt like that? What would you choose to change about the present to give you a happier future?

In order to change their future, the Jewish people first had to understand the past. Because of Judah's sin, the nation had been conquered and the people forced into captivity. They had abandoned God, which made the present seem bleak, even after they returned to their land. The once-destroyed temple had not been completely rebuilt. Enemies still threatened them. But through the prophet Zechariah, God promised Israel a happy ending, better than that of any fairy tale. Into Israel's story the ultimate hero—a King—would come, riding on a donkey. This was one of Zechariah's many prophecies of a coming Savior.

Israel's story is our story. Jesus promises to return to earth and take us happily off into the sunset. Until he does, he wants us to stick with God—to want what he wants.

life lessons

3

1 God invites us to repent from our sins and turn back to him. Then he'll be with us and act on our behalf (1:2—2:13).

2 God prefers our mercy and fairness toward others rather than our empty acts of worship (7:4–14).

3 The Savior is the only one who can provide the ultimate hope for the future. Only he can completely cleanse us from sin (6:12–13; 9:9—14:21).

A Call to Return to the Lord

1 In the eighth month of the second year of Darius, the word of the Lord came to the prophet Zechariah son of Iddo:

²"The Lord was very angry with your forefathers. ³Therefore tell the people: This is what the Lord Almighty says: 'Return to me,' declares the Lord Almighty, 'and I will return to you,' says the Lord Almighty. ⁴Do not be like your forefathers, to whom the earlier prophets proclaimed: This is what the Lord Almighty says: 'Turn from your evil ways and your evil practices.' But they would not listen or pay attention to me, declares the Lord. ⁵Where are your forefathers now? And the prophets, do they live forever? ⁶But did not my words and my decrees, which I commanded my servants the prophets, overtake your forefathers?

"Then they repented and said, 'The Lord Almighty has done to us what our ways and practices deserve, just as he determined to do.'"

The Man Among the Myrtle Trees

⁷On the twenty-fourth day of the eleventh month, the month of Shebat, in the second year of Darius, the word of the Lord came to the prophet Zechariah son of Berekiah, the son of Iddo.

⁸During the night I had a vision—and there before me was a man riding a red horse! He was standing among the myrtle trees in a ravine. Behind him were red, brown and white horses.

⁹I asked, "What are these, my lord?"

The angel who was talking with me answered, "I will show you what they are."

¹⁰Then the man standing among the myrtle trees explained, "They are the ones the Lord has sent to go throughout the earth."

¹¹And they reported to the angel of the Lord, who was standing among the myrtle trees, "We have gone throughout the earth and found the whole world at rest and in peace."

¹²Then the angel of the Lord said, "Lord Almighty, how long will you withhold mercy from Jerusalem and from the towns of Judah, which you have been angry with these seventy years?" ¹³So the Lord spoke kind and comforting words to the angel who talked with me.

¹⁴Then the angel who was speaking to me said, "Proclaim this word: This is what the Lord Almighty says: 'I am very jealous for Jerusalem and Zion, ¹⁵but I am very angry with the nations that feel secure. I was only a little angry, but they added to the calamity.'

¹⁶"Therefore, this is what the Lord says: 'I will return to Jerusalem with mercy, and there my house will be rebuilt. And the measuring line will be stretched out over Jerusalem,' declares the Lord Almighty.

¹⁷"Proclaim further: This is what the Lord Almighty says: 'My towns will again overflow with prosperity, and the Lord will again comfort Zion and choose Jerusalem.'"

Four Horns and Four Craftsmen

¹⁸Then I looked up—and there before me were four horns! ¹⁹I asked the angel who was speaking to me, "What are these?"

He answered me, "These are the horns that scattered Judah, Israel and Jerusalem."

²⁰Then the Lord showed me four craftsmen. ²¹I asked, "What are these coming to do?"

He answered, "These are the horns that scattered Judah so that no one could raise his head, but the craftsmen have come to terrify them and throw down these horns of the nations who lifted up their horns against the land of Judah to scatter its people."

A Man With a Measuring Line

2 Then I looked up—and there before me was a man with a measuring line in his hand! ²I asked, "Where are you going?"

He answered me, "To measure Jerusalem, to find out how wide and how long it is."

³Then the angel who was speaking to me left, and another angel came to meet him ⁴and said to him: "Run, tell that young man, 'Jerusalem will be a city without walls because of the great number of men and livestock in it. ⁵And I myself will be a wall of fire around it,' declares the Lord, 'and I will be its glory within.'

⁶"Come! Come! Flee from the land of the north," declares the Lord, "for I have scattered you to the four winds of heaven," declares the Lord.

⁷"Come, O Zion! Escape, you who live in the Daughter of Babylon!" ⁸For this is what the Lord Almighty says: "After he has honored me and has sent me against the nations that have plundered you—for whoever touches you touches the apple of his eye— ⁹I will surely raise my hand against them so that their slaves will plunder them.ᵃ Then you will know that the Lord Almighty has sent me.

¹⁰"Shout and be glad, O Daughter of Zion. For I am coming, and I will live among you," declares the Lord. ¹¹"Many nations will be joined with the Lord in that day and will become my people. I will live among you and you will know that the Lord Almighty has sent me to you. ¹²The Lord will inherit Judah as his portion in the holy land and will again choose Jerusalem. ¹³Be still before the Lord, all mankind, because he has roused himself from his holy dwelling."

Clean Garments for the High Priest

3 Then he showed me Joshuaᵇ the high priest standing before the angel of the Lord, and Satanᶜ standing at his right side to accuse him. ²The Lord said to Satan, "The Lord rebuke you, Satan! The Lord, who has chosen Jerusalem, rebuke you! Is not this man a burning stick snatched from the fire?"

³Now Joshua was dressed in filthy clothes as he stood before the angel. ⁴The angel said to those who were standing before him, "Take off his filthy clothes."

Then he said to Joshua, "See, I have taken away your sin, and I will put rich garments on you."

⁵Then I said, "Put a clean turban on his head." So they put a clean turban on his head and clothed him, while the angel of the Lord stood by.

⁶The angel of the Lord gave this charge to Joshua: ⁷"This is what the Lord Almighty says: 'If you will walk in my ways and keep my requirements, then you will govern my house and have charge of my courts, and I will give you a place among these standing here.

⁸" 'Listen, O high priest Joshua and your associates seated before you, who are men symbolic of things to come: I am going to

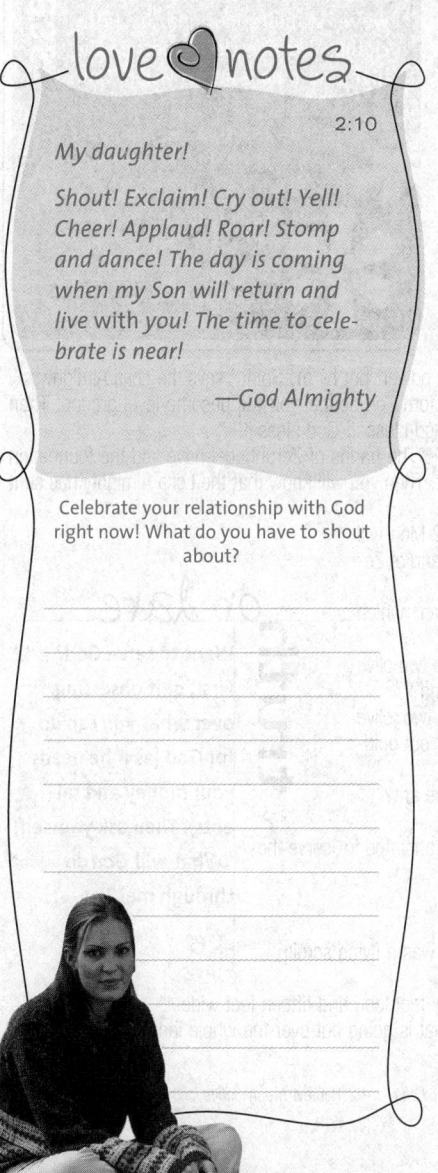

love notes

2:10

My daughter!

Shout! Exclaim! Cry out! Yell! Cheer! Applaud! Roar! Stomp and dance! The day is coming when my Son will return and live with you! The time to celebrate is near!

—God Almighty

Celebrate your relationship with God right now! What do you have to shout about?

ᵃ 8,9 Or *says after . . . eye:* ⁹"*I . . . plunder them.*"
ᵇ 1 A variant of *Jeshua*; here and elsewhere in Zechariah   ᶜ 1 *Satan* means *accuser.*

bring my servant, the Branch. ⁹See, the stone I have set in front of Joshua! There are seven eyes ᵃ on that one stone, and I will engrave an inscription on it,' says the LORD Almighty, 'and I will remove the sin of this land in a single day.

¹⁰ "In that day each of you will invite his neighbor to sit under his vine and fig tree,' declares the LORD Almighty."

The Gold Lampstand and the Two Olive Trees

4 Then the angel who talked with me returned and wakened me, as a man is wakened from his sleep. ²He asked me, "What do you see?"

I answered, "I see a solid gold lampstand with a bowl at the top and seven lights on it, with seven channels to the lights. ³Also there are two olive trees by it, one on the right of the bowl and the other on its left."

⁴I asked the angel who talked with me, "What are these, my lord?"

⁵He answered, "Do you not know what these are?"

"No, my lord," I replied.

⁶So he said to me, "This is the word of the LORD to Zerubbabel: 'Not by might nor by power, but by my Spirit,' says the LORD Almighty.

⁷"What ᵇ are you, O mighty mountain? Before Zerubbabel you will become level ground. Then he will bring out the capstone to shouts of 'God bless it! God bless it!' "

⁸Then the word of the LORD came to me: ⁹"The hands of Zerubbabel have laid the foundation of this temple; his hands will also complete it. Then you will know that the LORD Almighty has sent me to you.

¹⁰"Who despises the day of small things? Men will rejoice when they see the plumb line in the hand of Zerubbabel.

"(These seven are the eyes of the LORD, which range throughout the earth.)"

¹¹Then I asked the angel, "What are these two olive trees on the right and the left of the lampstand?"

¹²Again I asked him, "What are these two olive branches beside the two gold pipes that pour out golden oil?"

¹³He replied, "Do you not know what these are?"

"No, my lord," I said.

¹⁴So he said, "These are the two who are anointed to ᶜ serve the Lord of all the earth."

The Flying Scroll

5 I looked again—and there before me was a flying scroll! ²He asked me, "What do you see?"

I answered, "I see a flying scroll, thirty feet long and fifteen feet wide. ᵈ"

³And he said to me, "This is the curse that is going out over the whole land; for according to

---

genuine

forgiveness ›› 3:3-5

Ahh, there's nothing like a long, hot shower to make you feel clean. But there are some things you can't get clean from, no matter how many showers you take. The wrong things we do leave stains that can't be scrubbed away or hidden. It's like we're standing around in filthy clothes, like the clothes Joshua the high priest wore in this vision. Only God's method of stain removal can do the trick. He not only cleans us up, but he also provides a new wardrobe for us. Ready to get rid of some old rags? Confess your sins, and ask for God's cleansing.

---

truth or dare

Want to serve God? First, quit obsessing over what *you* can do for God (as if he needs your money and talents). Then ask yourself, "What will *God* do through me?"

4:6

ᵃ 9 Or *facets*   ᵇ 7 Or *Who*   ᶜ 14 Or *two who bring oil and*   ᵈ 2 Hebrew *twenty cubits long and ten cubits wide* (about 9 meters long and 4.5 meters wide) what it says on one side, every thief will be banished, and according to what it says on the other, everyone who swears falsely will be banished. ⁴The Lᴏʀᴅ Almighty declares, 'I will send it out, and it will enter the house of the thief and the house of him who swears falsely by my name. It will remain in his house and destroy it, both its timbers and its stones.' "

The Woman in a Basket

⁵Then the angel who was speaking to me came forward and said to me, "Look up and see what this is that is appearing."

⁶I asked, "What is it?"

He replied, "It is a measuring basket.ᵃ" And he added, "This is the iniquityᵇ of the people throughout the land."

⁷Then the cover of lead was raised, and there in the basket sat a woman! ⁸He said, "This is wickedness," and he pushed her back into the basket and pushed the lead cover down over its mouth.

⁹Then I looked up—and there before me were two women, with the wind in their wings! They had wings like those of a stork, and they lifted up the basket between heaven and earth.

¹⁰"Where are they taking the basket?" I asked the angel who was speaking to me.

¹¹He replied, "To the country of Babyloniaᶜ to build a house for it. When it is ready, the basket will be set there in its place."

Four Chariots

6 I looked up again—and there before me were four chariots coming out from between two mountains—mountains of bronze! ²The first chariot had red horses, the second black, ³the third white, and the fourth dappled—all of them powerful. ⁴I asked the angel who was speaking to me, "What are these, my lord?"

⁵The angel answered me, "These are the four spiritsᵈ of heaven, going out from standing in the presence of the Lord of the whole world. ⁶The one with the black horses is going toward the north country, the one with the white horses toward the west,ᵉ and the one with the dappled horses toward the south."

⁷When the powerful horses went out, they were straining to go throughout the earth. And he said, "Go throughout the earth!" So they went throughout the earth.

⁸Then he called to me, "Look, those going toward the north country have given my Spiritᶠ rest in the land of the north."

A Crown for Joshua

⁹The word of the Lᴏʀᴅ came to me: ¹⁰"Take ∟silver and gold∟ from the exiles Heldai, Tobijah and Jedaiah, who have arrived from Babylon. Go the same day to the house of Josiah son of Zephaniah. ¹¹Take the silver and gold and make a crown, and set it on the head of the high priest, Joshua son of Jehozadak. ¹²Tell him this is what the Lᴏʀᴅ Almighty says: 'Here is the man whose name is the Branch, and he will branch out from his place and build the temple of the Lᴏʀᴅ. ¹³It is he who will build the temple of the Lᴏʀᴅ, and he will be clothed with majesty and will sit and rule on his throne. And he will be a priest on his throne. And there will be harmony between the two.' ¹⁴The crown will be given to Heldai,ᵍ Tobijah, Jedaiah and Henʰ son of Zephaniah as a memorial in the temple of the Lᴏʀᴅ. ¹⁵Those who are far away will come and help to build the temple of the Lᴏʀᴅ, and you will know that the Lᴏʀᴅ Almighty has sent me to you. This will happen if you diligently obey the Lᴏʀᴅ your God."

Justice and Mercy, Not Fasting

7 In the fourth year of King Darius, the word of the Lᴏʀᴅ came to Zechariah on the fourth day of the ninth month, the month of Kislev. ²The people of Bethel had sent Sharezer and Regem-Melech, together with their men, to entreat the Lᴏʀᴅ ³by asking the priests of the house of the Lᴏʀᴅ Almighty and the prophets, "Should I mourn and fast in the fifth month, as I have done for so many years?"

ᵃ 6 Hebrew an ephah; also in verses 7-11   ᵇ 6 Or appearance   ᶜ 11 Hebrew Shinar   ᵈ 5 Or winds
ᵉ 6 Or horses after them   ᶠ 8 Or spirit   ᵍ 14 Syriac; Hebrew Helem   ʰ 14 Or and the gracious one, the

⁴Then the word of the Lord Almighty came to me: ⁵"Ask all the people of the land and the priests, 'When you fasted and mourned in the fifth and seventh months for the past seventy years, was it really for me that you fasted? ⁶And when you were eating and drinking, were you not just feasting for yourselves? ⁷Are these not the words the Lord proclaimed through the earlier prophets when Jerusalem and its surrounding towns were at rest and prosperous, and the Negev and the western foothills were settled?' "

⁸And the word of the Lord came again to Zechariah: ⁹"This is what the Lord Almighty says: 'Administer true justice; show mercy and compassion to one another. ¹⁰Do not oppress the widow or the fatherless, the alien or the poor. In your hearts do not think evil of each other.'

¹¹"But they refused to pay attention; stubbornly they turned their backs and stopped up their ears. ¹²They made their hearts as hard as flint and would not listen to the law or to the words that the Lord Almighty had sent by his Spirit through the earlier prophets. So the Lord Almighty was very angry.

¹³" 'When I called, they did not listen; so when they called, I would not listen,' says the Lord Almighty. ¹⁴'I scattered them with a whirlwind among all the nations, where they were strangers. The land was left so desolate behind them that no one could come or go. This is how they made the pleasant land desolate.' "

The Lord Promises to Bless Jerusalem

8 Again the word of the Lord Almighty came to me. ²This is what the Lord Almighty says: "I am very jealous for Zion; I am burning with jealousy for her."

³This is what the Lord says: "I will return to Zion and dwell in Jerusalem. Then Jerusalem will be called the City of Truth, and the mountain of the Lord Almighty will be called the Holy Mountain."

⁴This is what the Lord Almighty says: "Once again men and women of ripe old age will sit in the streets of Jerusalem, each with cane in hand because of his age. ⁵The city streets will be filled with boys and girls playing there."

⁶This is what the Lord Almighty says: "It may seem marvelous to the remnant of this people at that time, but will it seem marvelous to me?" declares the Lord Almighty.

⁷This is what the Lord Almighty says: "I will save my people from the countries of the east and the west. ⁸I will bring them back to live in Jerusalem; they will be my people, and I will be faithful and righteous to them as their God."

⁹This is what the Lord Almighty says: "You who now hear these words spoken by the prophets who were there when the foundation was laid for the house of the Lord Almighty, let your hands be strong so that the temple may be built. ¹⁰Before that time there were no wages for man or beast. No one could go about his business safely because of his enemy, for I had turned every man against his neighbor. ¹¹But now I will not deal with the remnant of this people as I did in the past," declares the Lord Almighty.

¹²"The seed will grow well, the vine will yield its fruit, the ground will produce its crops, and the heavens will drop their dew. I will give all these things as an inheritance to the remnant of this people. ¹³As you have been an object of cursing among the nations, O Judah and Israel, so will I save you, and you will be a blessing. Do not be afraid, but let your hands be strong."

¹⁴This is what the Lord Almighty says: "Just as I had determined to bring disaster upon you and showed no pity when your fathers angered me," says the Lord Almighty, ¹⁵"so now I have determined to do good again to Jerusalem and Judah. Do not be afraid. ¹⁶These are the things you are to do: Speak the truth to each other, and render true and sound judgment in your courts; ¹⁷do not plot evil against your neighbor, and do not love to swear falsely. I hate all this," declares the Lord.

¹⁸Again the word of the Lord Almighty came to me. ¹⁹This is what the Lord Almighty says: "The fasts of the fourth, fifth, seventh and tenth months will become joyful and glad occasions and happy festivals for Judah. Therefore love truth and peace."

truth or dare

"If I don't hurt anyone, can't I *think* whatever I want?" Actually, bitterness and bad thoughts can do serious internal damage. That's why God stresses not to think badly of others.

7:8–10

20This is what the LORD Almighty says: "Many peoples and the inhabitants of many cities will yet come, 21and the inhabitants of one city will go to another and say, 'Let us go at once to entreat the LORD and seek the LORD Almighty. I myself am going.' 22And many peoples and powerful nations will come to Jerusalem to seek the LORD Almighty and to entreat him."

23This is what the LORD Almighty says: "In those days ten men from all languages and nations will take firm hold of one Jew by the hem of his robe and say, 'Let us go with you, because we have heard that God is with you.' "

Judgment on Israel's Enemies

An Oracle

9 The word of the LORD is against the land of Hadrach
    and will rest upon Damascus—
for the eyes of men and all the tribes of Israel
    are on the LORD—a
2and upon Hamath too, which borders on it,
    and upon Tyre and Sidon, though they are very skillful.
3Tyre has built herself a stronghold;
    she has heaped up silver like dust,
    and gold like the dirt of the streets.
4But the Lord will take away her possessions
    and destroy her power on the sea,
    and she will be consumed by fire.
5Ashkelon will see it and fear;
    Gaza will writhe in agony,
    and Ekron too, for her hope will wither.
Gaza will lose her king
    and Ashkelon will be deserted.
6Foreigners will occupy Ashdod,
    and I will cut off the pride of the Philistines.
7I will take the blood from their mouths,
    the forbidden food from between their teeth.
Those who are left will belong to our God
    and become leaders in Judah,
    and Ekron will be like the Jebusites.
8But I will defend my house
    against marauding forces.
Never again will an oppressor
      overrun my people,
    for now I am keeping watch.

The Coming of Zion's King

9Rejoice greatly, O Daughter of
    Zion!
Shout, Daughter of Jerusalem!
See, your kingb comes to you,
    righteous and having
      salvation,
    gentle and riding on a donkey,
    on a colt, the foal of a donkey.
10I will take away the chariots from Ephraim
    and the war-horses from Jerusalem,
    and the battle bow will be broken.
He will proclaim peace to the nations.
    His rule will extend from sea to sea

truth or dare

Who knew Jesus' little trek into Jerusalem on a donkey was significant enough to be mentioned hundreds of years before it happened? Check out Matthew 21:4–5 and John 12:14–15.

9:9

a 1 Or Damascus. / For the eye of the LORD is on all mankind, / as well as on the tribes of Israel,   b 9 Or King and from the River^a to the ends of the earth.^b

¹¹As for you, because of the blood of my covenant with you,
I will free your prisoners from the waterless pit.
¹²Return to your fortress, O prisoners of hope;
even now I announce that I will restore twice as much to you.
¹³I will bend Judah as I bend my bow
and fill it with Ephraim.
I will rouse your sons, O Zion,
against your sons, O Greece,
and make you like a warrior's sword.

The LORD Will Appear

¹⁴Then the LORD will appear over them;
his arrow will flash like
lightning.
The Sovereign LORD will sound
the trumpet;
he will march in the storms of
the south,
¹⁵and the LORD Almighty will
shield them.
They will destroy
and overcome with
slingstones.
They will drink and roar as with
wine;
they will be full like a bowl
used for sprinkling^c the
corners of the altar.
¹⁶The LORD their God will save
them on that day
as the flock of his people.
They will sparkle in his land
like jewels in a crown.
¹⁷How attractive and beautiful they
will be!
Grain will make the young
men thrive,
and new wine the young
women.

genuine

beauty

Ever thought of yourself as a pearl or an opal? (If your name is Pearl or Opal, well, enough said.) How about a sparkling diamond? To God, you're as beautiful as a jewel in a queen's crown. His love for you and the good plans he has for your life, like the plans he had for Israel, make you beautiful in his eyes. While this kind of beauty may not put you on the cover of *Cosmo* or *Vogue*, it does make you pretty cool with God.

9:16–17

The LORD Will Care for Judah

10 Ask the LORD for rain in the springtime;
it is the LORD who makes the storm clouds.
He gives showers of rain to men,
and plants of the field to everyone.
²The idols speak deceit,
diviners see visions that lie;
they tell dreams that are false,
they give comfort in vain.
Therefore the people wander like sheep
oppressed for lack of a shepherd.

³"My anger burns against the shepherds,
and I will punish the leaders;

^a 10 That is, the Euphrates   ^b 10 Or *the end of the land*   ^c 15 Or *bowl, / like*

for the Lord Almighty will care
for his flock, the house of Judah,
and make them like a proud horse in battle.
⁴ From Judah will come the cornerstone,
from him the tent peg,
from him the battle bow,
from him every ruler.
⁵ Together they*ᵃ will be like mighty men
trampling the muddy streets in battle.
Because the Lord is with them,
they will fight and overthrow the horsemen.

⁶ "I will strengthen the house of Judah
and save the house of Joseph.
I will restore them
because I have compassion on them.
They will be as though
I had not rejected them,
for I am the Lord their God
and I will answer them.
⁷ The Ephraimites will become like mighty men,
and their hearts will be glad as with wine.
Their children will see it and be joyful;
their hearts will rejoice in the Lord.
⁸ I will signal for them
and gather them in.
Surely I will redeem them;
they will be as numerous as before.
⁹ Though I scatter them among the peoples,
yet in distant lands they will remember me.
They and their children will survive,
and they will return.
¹⁰ I will bring them back from Egypt
and gather them from Assyria.
I will bring them to Gilead and Lebanon,
and there will not be room enough for them.
¹¹ They will pass through the sea of trouble;
the surging sea will be subdued
and all the depths of the Nile will dry up.
Assyria's pride will be brought down
and Egypt's scepter will pass away.
¹² I will strengthen them in the Lord
and in his name they will walk,"

declares the Lord.

11 Open your doors, O Lebanon,
so that fire may devour your cedars!
² Wail, O pine tree, for the cedar has fallen;
the stately trees are ruined!
Wail, oaks of Bashan;
the dense forest has been cut down!
³ Listen to the wail of the shepherds;
their rich pastures are destroyed!
Listen to the roar of the lions;
the lush thicket of the Jordan is ruined!

ᵃ 4,5 Or ruler, all of them together. / ⁵They

Crossroads

I'm at the crossroads of the biggest decision of my life. Our lives. My baby and me. Even as I sit here in the clinic, I can't believe I'm actually carrying a baby. It's only the size of a speck, but it's already filled my whole heart. It's weird to think I'm old enough to have a legal abortion. My school can't even give me an aspirin without my parents' permission, but I can have an abortion on my own. Without anyone in my family ever knowing.

That's what Rod wants me to do. He says I might as well do it now before I start showing. He says he loves me. That in a few years after he graduates and gets back from the Navy we can get married and have a baby together. But that's *there* and *then*. I'm stuck in the here and now, by myself at the abortion clinic. Rod wouldn't come with me. He said it would be too uncomfortable for him.

But what about me? I'm the one who actually has to go through with it. Even now, I'm trying to remind myself of all the reasons I decided to have an abortion—before the nurse calls my name off the list. *I wouldn't have to drop out of school. I wouldn't have to burden my family with the expense of a baby. I wouldn't have to go through the trauma of giving it up for adoption. I wouldn't lose Rod. I wouldn't disappoint my parents.* Okay. Deep breath. If I can just get through the next few hours, well, everything will be fine. Right?

"Laura Jones? The doctor will see you now . . ."

abortion in focus

Get as much advice as possible before making a decision about abortion. It cannot be reversed. If you decide to carry your child to term, you'll certainly endure some heartache, criticism and stress. But you'll also know you've done the right thing.

» Do you feel alone? You're not. God will never leave you (see Hebrews 13:5, page 1599). Contact a church or a Crisis Pregnancy Center and ask for support. *You are not alone.*

» Is an unborn child alive? Yes. God knit you together in your mother's womb, and he knew you before you were born. He knows your baby, too.

» Abortion can have devastating physical effects, and always has devastating emotional effects. *Deep emotional depression is often a* lifelong *consequence of abortion.*

» If you've already had an abortion and you're feeling the consequences of regret and guilt, know that God can and will forgive you (see 1 John 1:9, page 1618). Seek out a pastor and/or a Christian counselor to help you begin the healing process.

For more on this topic, see the index on page 1656.

Two Shepherds

⁴This is what the Lᴏʀᴅ my God says: "Pasture the flock marked for slaughter. ⁵Their buyers slaughter them and go unpunished. Those who sell them say, 'Praise the Lᴏʀᴅ, I am rich!' Their own shepherds do not spare them. ⁶For I will no longer have pity on the people of the land," declares the Lᴏʀᴅ. "I will hand everyone over to his neighbor and his king. They will oppress the land, and I will not rescue them from their hands."

⁷So I pastured the flock marked for slaughter, particularly the oppressed of the flock. Then I took two staffs and called one Favor and the other Union, and I pastured the flock. ⁸In one month I got rid of the three shepherds.

The flock detested me, and I grew weary of them ⁹and said, "I will not be your shepherd. Let the dying die, and the perishing perish. Let those who are left eat one another's flesh."

¹⁰Then I took my staff called Favor and broke it, revoking the covenant I had made with all the nations. ¹¹It was revoked on that day, and so the afflicted of the flock who were watching me knew it was the word of the LORD.

¹²I told them, "If you think it best, give me my pay; but if not, keep it." So they paid me thirty pieces of silver.

¹³And the LORD said to me, "Throw it to the potter"—the handsome price at which they priced me! So I took the thirty pieces of silver and threw them into the house of the LORD to the potter.

¹⁴Then I broke my second staff called Union, breaking the brotherhood between Judah and Israel.

¹⁵Then the LORD said to me, "Take again the equipment of a foolish shepherd. ¹⁶For I am going to raise up a shepherd over the land who will not care for the lost, or seek the young, or heal the injured, or feed the healthy, but will eat the meat of the choice sheep, tearing off their hoofs.

> ¹⁷"Woe to the worthless shepherd,
>   who deserts the flock!
> May the sword strike his arm and his right eye!
> May his arm be completely withered,
>   his right eye totally blinded!"

Jerusalem's Enemies to Be Destroyed

An Oracle

12 This is the word of the LORD concerning Israel. The LORD, who stretches out the heavens, who lays the foundation of the earth, and who forms the spirit of man within him, declares: ²"I am going to make Jerusalem a cup that sends all the surrounding peoples reeling. Judah will be besieged as well as Jerusalem. ³On that day, when all the nations of the earth are gathered against her, I will make Jerusalem an immovable rock for all the nations. All who try to move it will injure themselves. ⁴On that day I will strike every horse with panic and its rider with madness," declares the LORD. "I will keep a watchful eye over the house of Judah, but I will blind all the horses of the nations. ⁵Then the leaders of Judah will say in their hearts, 'The people of Jerusalem are strong, because the LORD Almighty is their God.'

⁶"On that day I will make the leaders of Judah like a firepot in a woodpile, like a flaming torch among sheaves. They will consume right and left all the surrounding peoples, but Jerusalem will remain intact in her place.

⁷"The LORD will save the dwellings of Judah first, so that the honor of the house of David and of Jerusalem's inhabitants may not be greater than that of Judah. ⁸On that day the LORD will shield those who live in Jerusalem, so that the feeblest among them will be like David, and the house of David will be like God, like the Angel of the LORD going before them. ⁹On that day I will set out to destroy all the nations that attack Jerusalem.

Mourning for the One They Pierced

¹⁰"And I will pour out on the house of David and the inhabitants of Jerusalem a spirit*a* of grace and supplication. They will look on*b* me, the one they have pierced, and they will mourn for him as one mourns for an only child, and grieve bitterly for him as one grieves for a firstborn son. ¹¹On that day the weeping in Jerusalem will be great, like the weeping of Hadad Rimmon in the plain of Megiddo. ¹²The land will mourn, each clan by itself, with their wives by themselves: the clan of the house of David and their wives, the clan of the house of Nathan and their wives, ¹³the clan of the house of Levi and their wives, the clan of Shimei and their wives, ¹⁴and all the rest of the clans and their wives.

a 10 Or *the Spirit*   *b 10* Or *to*

Cleansing From Sin

13

¹"On that day a fountain will be opened to the house of David and the inhabitants of Jerusalem, to cleanse them from sin and impurity.

²"On that day, I will banish the names of the idols from the land, and they will be remembered no more," declares the LORD Almighty. "I will remove both the prophets and the spirit of impurity from the land. ³And if anyone still prophesies, his father and mother, to whom he was born, will say to him, 'You must die, because you have told lies in the LORD's name.' When he prophesies, his own parents will stab him.

genuine purity « 13:9

Gold and silver don't come out of the earth completely pure and ready for jewelry. Both have to be refined—made pure. You need fire to do that. Fire burns away the worthless stuff and purifies the precious metal. Guess what? That's the same process for spiritual purity. The heat of hard times and other situations burns away worthless stuff like self-sufficiency and the "it's all about me" attitudes that contaminate our lives. When God puts you through the fire, you'll come out like gold. Since you're already precious to him, could he do any less?

⁴"On that day every prophet will be ashamed of his prophetic vision. He will not put on a prophet's garment of hair in order to deceive. ⁵He will say, 'I am not a prophet. I am a farmer; the land has been my livelihood since my youth.ᵃ' ⁶If someone asks him, 'What are these wounds on your bodyᵇ?' he will answer, 'The wounds I was given at the house of my friends.'

The Shepherd Struck, the Sheep Scattered

⁷"Awake, O sword, against my
⠀⠀shepherd,
⠀⠀⠀against the man who is close
⠀⠀⠀⠀to me!"
⠀⠀declares the LORD Almighty.
"Strike the shepherd,
⠀⠀and the sheep will be scattered,
⠀⠀and I will turn my hand
⠀⠀⠀against the little ones.
⁸In the whole land," declares the
⠀⠀LORD,
⠀⠀"two-thirds will be struck
⠀⠀⠀down and perish;
⠀⠀yet one-third will be left in it.
⁹This third I will bring into the fire;
⠀⠀I will refine them like silver
⠀⠀and test them like gold.

They will call on my name
⠀⠀and I will answer them;
I will say, 'They are my people,'
⠀⠀and they will say, 'The LORD is our God.' "

The LORD Comes and Reigns

14

A day of the LORD is coming when your plunder will be divided among you. ²I will gather all the nations to Jerusalem to fight against it; the city will be captured, the houses ransacked, and the women raped. Half of the city will go into exile, but the rest of the people will not be taken from the city.

³Then the LORD will go out and fight against those nations, as he fights in the day of battle. ⁴On that day his feet will stand on the Mount of Olives, east of Jerusalem, and the Mount of Olives will be split in two from east to west, forming a great valley, with half of the mountain moving north and half moving south. ⁵You will flee by my mountain valley, for it will extend to Azel. You will flee as you fled from the earthquakeᶜ in the days of Uzziah king of Judah. Then the LORD my God will come, and all the holy ones with him.

ᵃ 5 Or *farmer; a man sold me in my youth*⠀⠀ᵇ 6 Or *wounds between your hands*⠀⠀ᶜ 5 Or *⁵My mountain valley will be blocked and will extend to Azel. It will be blocked as it was blocked because of the earthquake*

⁶On that day there will be no light, no cold or frost. ⁷It will be a unique day, without daytime or nighttime—a day known to the Lord. When evening comes, there will be light.

⁸On that day living water will flow out from Jerusalem, half to the eastern sea ᵃ and half to the western sea, ᵇ in summer and in winter.

⁹The Lord will be king over the whole earth. On that day there will be one Lord, and his name the only name.

¹⁰The whole land, from Geba to Rimmon, south of Jerusalem, will become like the Arabah. But Jerusalem will be raised up and remain in its place, from the Benjamin Gate to the site of the First Gate, to the Corner Gate, and from the Tower of Hananel to the royal winepresses. ¹¹It will be inhabited; never again will it be destroyed. Jerusalem will be secure.

¹²This is the plague with which the Lord will strike all the nations that fought against Jerusalem: Their flesh will rot while they are still standing on their feet, their eyes will rot in their sockets, and their tongues will rot in their mouths. ¹³On that day men will be stricken by the Lord with great panic. Each man will seize the hand of another, and they will attack each other. ¹⁴Judah too will fight at Jerusalem. The wealth of all the surrounding nations will be collected—great quantities of gold and silver and clothing. ¹⁵A similar plague will strike the horses and mules, the camels and donkeys, and all the animals in those camps.

¹⁶Then the survivors from all the nations that have attacked Jerusalem will go up year after year to worship the King, the Lord Almighty, and to celebrate the Feast of Tabernacles. ¹⁷If any of the peoples of the earth do not go up to Jerusalem to worship the King, the Lord Almighty, they will have no rain. ¹⁸If the Egyptian people do not go up and take part, they will have no rain. The Lord ᶜ will bring on them the plague he inflicts on the nations that do not go up to celebrate the Feast of Tabernacles. ¹⁹This will be the punishment of Egypt and the punishment of all the nations that do not go up to celebrate the Feast of Tabernacles.

²⁰On that day HOLY TO THE LORD will be inscribed on the bells of the horses, and the cooking pots in the Lord's house will be like the sacred bowls in front of the altar. ²¹Every pot in Jerusalem and Judah will be holy to the Lord Almighty, and all who come to sacrifice will take some of the pots and cook in them. And on that day there will no longer be a Canaanite ᵈ in the house of the Lord Almighty.

author:	Malachi.
date:	About 430 B.C.
setting:	The temple in Jerusalem had been rebuilt, and the city walls had been restored. But the Jews were discouraged, so they didn't worship or obey God wholeheartedly.
verse to remember:	"Return to me, and I will return to you," says the LORD Almighty (3:7).
theme to consider:	Don't let apathy and indifference prevent you from enjoying the full benefits of God's love for you.

malachi

unchanging truth

How are you feeling right now about life in general? Good? Bad? Indifferent?

Some Christians feel indifferent about their faith. According to a survey by Barna Research,* only four out of ten teens are excited about being active in a church. Yet some of these teens admitted that they weren't sure they would continue being involved in a church in the future. Only one out of four teens admitted to being committed to Christianity. Would you agree with these statistics? Where would you fall in the survey results?

Sometimes waiting for something that never seems to come lulls us into indifference. In Malachi's day, many of the people of Israel seemed indifferent. They stopped giving God a percentage of their crops or income. They were tired of waiting for the wonderful future predicted by the prophets of the past.

God wanted to break through the wall of indifference and unite the people's hearts with his. Once more he promised that a Savior was indeed coming. The people would know him by the Elijah-like prophet who pointed him out. But they would have to wait for his arrival.

Feeling good, bad or indifferent toward God? Will you wait on him to restore your spiritual passion?

*Survey information: "Teenagers Embrace Religion but Are Not Excited About Christianity" at http://www.barna.org/cgi-bin/PagePressRelease.asp?PressReleaseID=45&Reference=D

life lessons

1. In the midst of our indifference, God comes to reassure us of his love (1:2–5).
2. A holy God demands that his name be honored (1:6—3:5).
3. We are encouraged to give generously to the work of God's kingdom (3:6–12).

1

An oracle: The word of the Lord to Israel through Malachi. *a*

Jacob Loved, Esau Hated

²"I have loved you," says the Lord.

"But you ask, 'How have you loved us?'

"Was not Esau Jacob's brother?" the Lord says. "Yet I have loved Jacob, ³but Esau I have hated, and I have turned his mountains into a wasteland and left his inheritance to the desert jackals."

⁴Edom may say, "Though we have been crushed, we will rebuild the ruins."

But this is what the Lord Almighty says: "They may build, but I will demolish. They will be called the Wicked Land, a people always under the wrath of the Lord. ⁵You will see it with your own eyes and say, 'Great is the Lord—even beyond the borders of Israel!'

Blemished Sacrifices

⁶"A son honors his father, and a servant his master. If I am a father, where is the honor due me? If I am a master, where is the respect due me?" says the Lord Almighty. "It is you, O priests, who show contempt for my name.

"But you ask, 'How have we shown contempt for your name?'

⁷"You place defiled food on my altar.

"But you ask, 'How have we defiled you?'

"By saying that the Lord's table is contemptible. ⁸When you bring blind animals for sacrifice, is that not wrong? When you sacrifice crippled or diseased animals, is that not wrong? Try offering them to your governor! Would he be pleased with you? Would he accept you?" says the Lord Almighty.

⁹"Now implore God to be gracious to us. With such offerings from your hands, will he accept you?"—says the Lord Almighty. ¹⁰"Oh, that one of you would shut the temple doors, so that you would not light useless fires on my altar! I am not pleased with you," says the Lord Almighty, "and I will accept no offering from your hands. ¹¹My name will be great among the nations, from the rising to the setting of the sun. In every place incense and pure offerings will be brought to my name, because my name will be great among the nations," says the Lord Almighty.

¹²"But you profane it by saying of the Lord's table, 'It is defiled,' and of its food, 'It is contemptible.' ¹³And you say, 'What a burden!' and you sniff at it contemptuously," says the Lord Almighty.

"When you bring injured, crippled or diseased animals and offer them as sacrifices, should I accept them from your hands?" says the Lord. ¹⁴"Cursed is the cheat who has an acceptable male in his flock and vows to give it, but then sacrifices a blemished animal to the Lord. For I am a great king," says the Lord Almighty, "and my name is to be feared among the nations.

genuine

respect »» 1:14

Who do you respect? The President? The lead singer of your favorite band? Your team MVP? How do you show your respect? According to Malachi, God's status as king is proof enough that he deserves our respect. What we offer God reveals just how much we truly respect him. Do you offer God the best in your life or your leftovers? The first cut of your paycheck or allowance, or whatever you have left after your shopping spree? Your most awake time for devotions or the last few drowsy minutes before you fall asleep? Giving God the best you have is the ultimate sign of respect.

a 1 Malachi means *my messenger*.

Admonition for the Priests

2 "And now this admonition is for you, O priests. ²If you do not listen, and if you do not set your heart to honor my name," says the LORD Almighty, "I will send a curse upon you, and I will curse your blessings. Yes, I have already cursed them, because you have not set your heart to honor me.

³"Because of you I will rebuke *a* your descendants *b*; I will spread on your faces the offal from your festival sacrifices, and you will be carried off with it. ⁴And you will know that I have sent you this admonition so that my covenant with Levi may continue," says the LORD Almighty. ⁵"My covenant was with him, a covenant of life and peace, and I gave them to him; this called for reverence and he revered me and stood in awe of my name. ⁶True instruction was in his mouth and nothing false was found on his lips. He walked with me in peace and uprightness, and turned many from sin.

⁷"For the lips of a priest ought to preserve knowledge, and from his mouth men should seek instruction—because he is the messenger of the LORD Almighty. ⁸But you have turned from the way and by your teaching have caused many to stumble; you have violated the covenant with Levi," says the LORD Almighty. ⁹"So I have caused you to be despised and humiliated before all the people, because you have not followed my ways but have shown partiality in matters of the law."

Judah Unfaithful

¹⁰Have we not all one Father *c*? Did not one God create us? Why do we profane the covenant of our fathers by breaking faith with one another?

¹¹Judah has broken faith. A detestable thing has been committed in Israel and in Jerusalem: Judah has desecrated the sanctuary the LORD loves, by marrying the daughter of a foreign god. ¹²As for the man who does this, whoever he may be, may the LORD cut him off from the tents of Jacob *d*—even though he brings offerings to the LORD Almighty.

¹³Another thing you do: You flood the LORD's altar with tears. You weep and wail because he no longer pays attention to your offerings or accepts them with pleasure from your hands. ¹⁴You ask, "Why?" It is because the LORD is acting as the witness between you and the wife of your youth, because you have broken faith with her, though she is your partner, the wife of your marriage covenant.

¹⁵Has not ⌊the LORD⌋ made them one? In flesh and spirit they are his. And why one? Because he was seeking godly offspring. *e* So guard yourself in your spirit, and do not break faith with the wife of your youth.

¹⁶"I hate divorce," says the LORD God of Israel, "and I hate a man's covering himself *f* with violence as well as with his garment," says the LORD Almighty.

So guard yourself in your spirit, and do not break faith.

The Day of Judgment

¹⁷You have wearied the LORD with your words.

"How have we wearied him?" you ask.

By saying, "All who do evil are good in the eyes of the LORD, and he is pleased with them" or "Where is the God of justice?"

3 "See, I will send my messenger, who will prepare the way before me. Then suddenly the Lord you are seeking will come to his temple; the messenger of the covenant, whom you desire, will come," says the LORD Almighty.

²But who can endure the day of his coming? Who can stand when he appears? For he will be like a refiner's fire or a launderer's soap. ³He will sit as a refiner and purifier of silver; he will purify the Levites and refine them like gold and silver. Then the LORD will have men who will bring offerings in righteousness, ⁴and the offerings of Judah and Jerusalem will be acceptable to the LORD, as in days gone by, as in former years.

⁵"So I will come near to you for judgment. I will be quick to testify against sorcerers, adulterers and perjurers, against those who defraud laborers of their wages, who oppress the widows and the fatherless, and deprive aliens of justice, but do not fear me," says the LORD Almighty.

a 3 Or cut off (see Septuagint)   b 3 Or will blight your grain   c 10 Or father   d 12 Or ¹²May the LORD cut off from the tents of Jacob anyone who gives testimony in behalf of the man who does this   e 15 Or ¹⁵But the one ⌊who is our father⌋ did not do this, not as long as life remained in him. And what was he seeking? An offspring from God   f 16 Or his wife

mirror images

The Twelve were with him, and also some women who had been cured of evil spirits and diseases: . . . Susanna; and many others. These women were helping to support them out of their own means. Luke 8:1–3

Susanna—A Giving Spirit

Once there was a woman who suffered from an unknown pain, living out her uncomfortable existence in the area surrounding Jerusalem. No modern medical miracle could cure her. Undoubtedly she felt desperate and alone, in a society so male-centered that the men thanked God they were not born as women! Susanna must have felt pretty worthless. Why should she even go on?

But the depth of her pain was no match for the Master. The day Susanna met this teacher they called Jesus, she was instantly healed. Relieved of her suffering. Set free. And what freedom she experienced, as the Master encouraged her to follow him along with his disciples. While the Jewish rabbis insisted women were not fit to be instructed in the Scriptures, Jesus welcomed her openly. For the first time in her life, she understood that she was valuable in God's eyes.

Not only did Susanna open her life to Jesus, but she also opened something else—her checkbook. Susanna's gifts of money helped ensure that Jesus and his disciples had food on the table and clothes to wear. And Susanna didn't give out of blind duty, like those who flaunted their tithes in the temple. In contrast, Susanna's love offerings came from a heart overflowing with gratitude.

What a good motivation for giving—gratitude. Have you ever felt so thankful you couldn't help but give back? Or do you find yourself avoiding the offering at church and making excuses about how little money you have? Proverbs 3:9 tells us God wants us to give part of our money to him *first*—before we rush out and buy that "to-die-for" dress or spend it on lattes and late-night pizza runs. Next time you're tempted to keep your money for yourself, remember Susanna—and discover the joy that comes from giving to Jesus first, out of a grateful heart.

Dear Jesus, thank you for giving me so much. Show me the joy Susanna felt as I give back to you just a part of what you've already given me. Amen.

dear Jesus

To read the next Mirror Images profile, go to page 1312.

» Read Susanna's story in Luke 8:1–3 (page 1377).

» 1283

Robbing God

[6]"I the LORD do not change. So you, O descendants of Jacob, are not destroyed. [7]Ever since the time of your forefathers you have turned away from my decrees and have not kept them. Return to me, and I will return to you," says the LORD Almighty.

"But you ask, 'How are we to return?'

[8]"Will a man rob God? Yet you rob me.

"But you ask, 'How do we rob you?'

"In tithes and offerings. [9]You are under a curse—the whole nation of you—because you are robbing me. [10]Bring the whole tithe into the storehouse, that there may be food in my house. Test me in this," says the LORD Almighty, "and see if I will not throw open the floodgates of heaven and pour out so much blessing that you will not have room enough for it. [11]I will prevent pests from devouring your crops, and the vines in your fields will not cast their fruit," says the LORD Almighty.

[12]"Then all the nations will call you blessed, for yours will be a delightful land," says the LORD Almighty.

[13]"You have said harsh things against me," says the LORD.

"Yet you ask, 'What have we said against you?'

[14]"You have said, 'It is futile to serve God. What did we gain by carrying out his requirements and going about like mourners before the LORD Almighty? [15]But now we call the arrogant blessed. Certainly the evildoers prosper, and even those who challenge God escape.' "

[16]Then those who feared the LORD talked with each other, and the LORD listened and heard. A scroll of remembrance was written in his presence concerning those who feared the LORD and honored his name.

[17]"They will be mine," says the LORD Almighty, "in the day when I make up my treasured possession.[a] I will spare them, just as in compassion a man spares his son who serves him. [18]And you will again see

love♥notes

3:17

Dear one,

Look around you at the beautiful and wonderful world I have created. But do you know what? Of all the wonders of this world and the heavens beyond it, you are my most treasured possession. Believe it.

—Your loving Father

When you consider how much God loves you, how do you respond?

_____

_____

_____

_____

_____

_____

_____

_____

truth or dare

This is the only thing in the Bible that God openly invites you to test him on. If you're willing to give God the first and best of your $$$, he'll flood you with blessings.

3:8–10

[a] 17 Or Almighty, "my treasured possession, in the day when I act

For the Best?

focus **Profile: Katie**

"Hey, Katie, how's it going?" Todd asked me.

It was an innocent question, but I couldn't handle it. I broke into tears and ran into the girls' bathroom. I knew I left Todd standing there with no clue what was going on, but the hurt was too deep, too fresh, the anger too raw.

How's it going? I'll tell you how it's going. My parents just told us the "good" news—they're splitting up. Yep, after 23 years of marriage, they decided to call it quits. They've "moved apart," "don't share the same values," "don't love each other anymore." And you know what's the biggest joke? They actually said, "This is for the best."

The best? The best for *who*? I wish you could have seen my younger brother's face. I wish *they* could feel just a tiny bit of the hurt, betrayal and rejection that I feel right now. Best for *us*? Who are they kidding?!

But that's not the worst part. My dad already moved out. And they're already talking about where my brother and I are going to spend Thanksgiving and Christmas and who will get us which weeks of the summer. What are we? A couple of pieces of luggage? That's what it feels like.

I don't understand it. I don't want to understand it. How could my parents do this? How could God allow this to happen to my brother and me? What's going to happen to us?

For more on divorce, go to
www.TrueImagesBible.com

broken families in focus

The sad statistic is that about half of all marriages in the United States end in divorce. To deal with the shock of such horrible news . . .

» *Turn* to *God, not away from him* (see Psalm 55:22, page 707). Sometimes we're tempted to turn away from God during tough times, but that's when we need him most. God hates divorce, too (see Malachi 2:16, page 1282). Tell him all your thoughts and feelings. He's strong enough to handle it.

» *Talk about it.* Don't keep your feelings bottled up inside. Tell your parents what you're feeling (note: *tell*, not attack). Talk to a pastor or a Christian counselor. Talk to a close friend. Just talk.

» *Spend time with your family.* Yes, your family is changing, but it's not the end of your relationship with your parents. They may not love each other any more, but they will *always* love you.

For more on this topic, see the index on page 1656.

---

the distinction between the righteous and the wicked, between those who serve God and those who do not.

The Day of the LORD

4 "Surely the day is coming; it will burn like a furnace. All the arrogant and every evildoer will be stubble, and that day that is coming will set them on fire," says the LORD Almighty. "Not a root or a branch will be left to them. ²But for you who revere my name,

truth *or dare*

Do you like watching previews? Even though there's a four hundred year gap between Malachi and the next great prophet, John the Baptist (who was like Elijah), these verses give a sneak peek at coming attractions.

4:5–6

the sun of righteousness will rise with healing in its wings. And you will go out and leap like calves released from the stall. ³Then you will trample down the wicked; they will be ashes under the soles of your feet on the day when I do these things," says the LORD Almighty.

⁴"Remember the law of my servant Moses, the decrees and laws I gave him at Horeb for all Israel.

⁵"See, I will send you the prophet Elijah before that great and dreadful day of the LORD comes. ⁶He will turn the hearts of the fathers to their children, and the hearts of the children to their fathers; or else I will come and strike the land with a curse."

» new testament

at a glance ⌄

author:	Matthew, also called Levi.
date:	Probably between A.D. 60 and 70.
setting:	Matthew most likely wrote from Israel, though some believe he wrote from Syrian Antioch.
verse to remember:	Simon Peter answered, "You are the Christ, the Son of the living God" (16:16).
theme to consider:	Matthew's message is clear: Jesus is the long-awaited Messiah, the King of kings and Lord of lords. Examine the evidence and accept Jesus as Lord of your life.

unchanging truth

What was the last piece of info that caused you to move heaven and earth (if you could) to determine whether or not it was absolutely, 100 percent true? The effort you put into searching is usually equal to the importance of the information. You probably wouldn't put a lot of effort into finding out whether the latest rumor about a celebrity is true. But if the information were critical to your life in some way, you would keep on searching until you found the answers you needed.

Matthew discovered an important piece of life-saving information: Jesus was the Savior God promised long ago to send. This piece of information changed Matthew's life. He willingly gave up his high-paying job as a Roman tax collector to become one of Jesus' unpaid disciples. During Matthew's three years with Jesus, he saw the miracles Jesus performed. He noticed how all of the Old Testament prophecies concerning the Savior were fulfilled in Jesus' life. But the biggest piece of evidence, besides the miracles, was Jesus' death and resurrection. Matthew was willing to stake his life on the truth of this information.

As you read through this book, consider the evidence presented to show that Jesus *is* the ultimate Savior. Like Matthew, are you willing to stake your life on the truth?

matthew

life lessons

3

1. Jesus used the Word of God to avoid giving in to temptation. God gives us the equipment—his Word—to resist temptation (4:1–11).

2. Jesus gave the Sermon on the Mount to help people understand how to obey God. God wants us to follow his rules for living in order to live godly lives (5:1—7:29).

3. Jesus warned his listeners that obedience comes with a price. God requires our complete commitment to Jesus (10:37–39; 16:24–27).

⌃

The Genealogy of Jesus

1 A record of the genealogy of Jesus Christ the son of David, the son of Abraham:

² Abraham was the father of Isaac,
Isaac the father of Jacob,
Jacob the father of Judah and his brothers,
³ Judah the father of Perez and Zerah, whose mother was Tamar,
Perez the father of Hezron,
Hezron the father of Ram,
⁴ Ram the father of Amminadab,
Amminadab the father of Nahshon,
Nahshon the father of Salmon,
⁵ Salmon the father of Boaz, whose mother was Rahab,
Boaz the father of Obed, whose mother was Ruth,
Obed the father of Jesse,
⁶ and Jesse the father of King David.

David was the father of Solomon, whose mother had been Uriah's wife,
⁷ Solomon the father of Rehoboam,
Rehoboam the father of Abijah,
Abijah the father of Asa,
⁸ Asa the father of Jehoshaphat,
Jehoshaphat the father of Jehoram,
Jehoram the father of Uzziah,
⁹ Uzziah the father of Jotham,
Jotham the father of Ahaz,
Ahaz the father of Hezekiah,
¹⁰ Hezekiah the father of Manasseh,
Manasseh the father of Amon,
Amon the father of Josiah,
¹¹ and Josiah the father of Jeconiah*ᵃ* and his brothers at the time of the exile to Babylon.

¹² After the exile to Babylon:
Jeconiah was the father of Shealtiel,
Shealtiel the father of Zerubbabel,
¹³ Zerubbabel the father of Abiud,
Abiud the father of Eliakim,
Eliakim the father of Azor,
¹⁴ Azor the father of Zadok,
Zadok the father of Akim,
Akim the father of Eliud,
¹⁵ Eliud the father of Eleazar,
Eleazar the father of Matthan,
Matthan the father of Jacob,
¹⁶ and Jacob the father of Joseph, the husband of Mary, of whom was born Jesus, who is called Christ.

¹⁷ Thus there were fourteen generations in all from Abraham to David, fourteen from David to the exile to Babylon, and fourteen from the exile to the Christ.*ᵇ*

genuine

life »» 1:3,5-6

Tamar—a widow who tricked her father-in-law into sleeping with her. Rahab—a foreign prostitute who helped the Israelites. Ruth—a penniless, immigrant widow who cared for her mother-in-law. Uriah's wife, Bathsheba—King David's partner in adultery. Why are these sketchy women named in Jesus' genealogy? Maybe in part to show that Jesus came to save sinners, and also because these were ordinary women whose lives made an extraordinary difference. They never knew that, in spite of their shortcomings, they were in the Messianic line. You may never see all the difference your life makes; it's probably more than you'll ever know.

a 11 That is, Jehoiachin; also in verse 12   *b 17* Or *Messiah*. "The Christ" (Greek) and "the Messiah" (Hebrew) both mean "the Anointed One."

The Birth of Jesus Christ

¹⁸This is how the birth of Jesus Christ came about: His mother Mary was pledged to be married to Joseph, but before they came together, she was found to be with child through the Holy Spirit. ¹⁹Because Joseph her husband was a righteous man and did not want to expose her to public disgrace, he had in mind to divorce her quietly.

²⁰But after he had considered this, an angel of the Lord appeared to him in a dream and said, "Joseph son of David, do not be afraid to take Mary home as your wife, because what is conceived in her is from the Holy Spirit. ²¹She will give birth to a son, and you are to give him the name Jesus,ᵃ because he will save his people from their sins."

²²All this took place to fulfill what the Lord had said through the prophet: ²³"The virgin will be with child and will give birth to a son, and they will call him Immanuel"ᵇ—which means, "God with us."

²⁴When Joseph woke up, he did what the angel of the Lord had commanded him and took Mary home as his wife. ²⁵But he had no union with her until she gave birth to a son. And he gave him the name Jesus.

truth or dare

In order for us to get with it, God needed to get with us . . . literally. So scratch that picture of a God far, far away. He's already come as your Immanuel.

1:23

genuine

evangelism » 2:1-12

The Magi were surprise guests at Jesus' house. No one would have expected these foreign dignitaries to know who Jesus was—much less come to worship him. But God specializes in the unexpected. Celebrities and the homeless, prostitutes and socialites, little old ladies and tiny children, the cool and the hopelessly out-of-touch—Jesus reveals himself to people from *all* walks of life. The Magi remind us of that. Do you tend to share the gospel only with certain kinds of people—the ones you think are most likely to accept it? Branch out! You'll be surprised at who comes to worship Jesus.

The Visit of the Magi

2 After Jesus was born in Bethlehem in Judea, during the time of King Herod, Magiᶜ from the east came to Jerusalem ²and asked, "Where is the one who has been born king of the Jews? We saw his star in the eastᵈ and have come to worship him."

³When King Herod heard this he was disturbed, and all Jerusalem with him. ⁴When he had called together all the people's chief priests and teachers of the law, he asked them where the Christᵉ was to be born. ⁵"In Bethlehem in Judea," they replied, "for this is what the prophet has written:

⁶ " 'But you, Bethlehem, in the land of Judah,
　　are by no means least among
　　　　the rulers of Judah;
for out of you will come a ruler
　who will be the shepherd of
　　my people Israel.'ᶠ"

⁷Then Herod called the Magi secretly and found out from them the exact time the star had appeared. ⁸He sent them to Bethlehem and said, "Go and make a careful search for the child. As soon as you find him, report to me, so that I too may go and worship him."

⁹After they had heard the king, they went on their way, and the star they had seen in the eastᵍ went ahead of them until it stopped over the place where the child was. ¹⁰When they saw the star, they were overjoyed. ¹¹On coming to the house, they saw the child with his mother Mary, and they bowed down and worshiped him. Then they opened their treasures and presented him with gifts

ᵃ 21 *Jesus* is the Greek form of *Joshua*, which means *the Lᴏʀᴅ saves.*　　ᵇ 23 Isaiah 7:14　　ᶜ 1 Traditionally *Wise Men*
ᵈ 2 Or *star when it rose*　　ᵉ 4 Or *Messiah*　　ᶠ 6 Micah 5:2　　ᵍ 9 Or *seen when it rose*

of gold and of incense and of myrrh. [12]And having been warned in a dream not to go back to Herod, they returned to their country by another route.

The Escape to Egypt

[13]When they had gone, an angel of the Lord appeared to Joseph in a dream. "Get up," he said, "take the child and his mother and escape to Egypt. Stay there until I tell you, for Herod is going to search for the child to kill him."

[14]So he got up, took the child and his mother during the night and left for Egypt, [15]where he stayed until the death of Herod. And so was fulfilled what the Lord had said through the prophet: "Out of Egypt I called my son." [a]

[16]When Herod realized that he had been outwitted by the Magi, he was furious, and he gave orders to kill all the boys in Bethlehem and its vicinity who were two years old and under, in accordance with the time he had learned from the Magi. [17]Then what was said through the prophet Jeremiah was fulfilled:

> [18]"A voice is heard in Ramah,
>   weeping and great mourning,
> Rachel weeping for her children
>   and refusing to be comforted,
> because they are no more." [b]

The Return to Nazareth

[19]After Herod died, an angel of the Lord appeared in a dream to Joseph in Egypt [20]and said, "Get up, take the child and his mother and go to the land of Israel, for those who were trying to take the child's life are dead."

[21]So he got up, took the child and his mother and went to the land of Israel. [22]But when he heard that Archelaus was reigning in Judea in place of his father Herod, he was afraid to go there. Having been warned in a dream, he withdrew to the district of Galilee, [23]and he went and lived in a town called Nazareth. So was fulfilled what was said through the prophets: "He will be called a Nazarene."

John the Baptist Prepares the Way

3 In those days John the Baptist came, preaching in the Desert of Judea [2]and saying, "Repent, for the kingdom of heaven is near." [3]This is he who was spoken of through the prophet Isaiah:

> "A voice of one calling in the desert,
> 'Prepare the way for the Lord,
>   make straight paths for him.' " [c]

[4]John's clothes were made of camel's hair, and he had a leather belt around his waist. His food was locusts and wild honey. [5]People went out to him from Jerusalem and all Judea and the whole region of the Jordan. [6]Confessing their sins, they were baptized by him in the Jordan River.

[7]But when he saw many of the Pharisees and Sadducees coming to where he was baptizing, he said to them: "You brood of vipers! Who warned you to flee from the coming wrath? [8]Produce fruit in keeping with repentance. [9]And do not think you can say to yourselves, 'We have Abraham as our father.' I tell you that out of these stones God can raise up children for Abraham. [10]The ax is already at the root of the trees, and every tree that does not produce good fruit will be cut down and thrown into the fire.

[11]"I baptize you with [d] water for repentance. But after me will come one who is more powerful than I, whose sandals I am not fit to carry. He will baptize you with the Holy Spirit and with

truth or dare

Baptism is a public declaration. Although Jesus wasn't confessing sin, he *was* openly committing himself to God's work.

3:13–15

a 15 Hosea 11:1   *b* 18 Jer. 31:15   *c* 3 Isaiah 40:3   *d* 11 Or *in*

A Better Body?

focus Profile: **Fran**

I wish I could change the way I look. I find myself glued to the mirror every day, even though I keep telling myself not to look. I'm really self-conscious about my body. My weight's okay, I guess. (Well, my thighs could be thinner.) But sometimes I feel, well, *ugly*. My Mom's always telling me I'm not, but moms are supposed to say stuff like that. Some days my nose feels ten inches long. And my hair looks like dishwater.

I wish the image I see in the mirror could magically change somehow. I feel so . . . average-looking. I'm not asking to look like a supermodel (although I wouldn't complain). I just wish I at least looked like this girl Stephanie at my school. She's the most popular girl in our class. All the girls hate her (I'm trying not to), because the guys flirt with her nonstop. Our eyes are the same color (green), but they don't look the same. Boys never notice my eyes.

Sometimes I wish I looked like a combination of the women in *Teen People* or *Cosmo Girl*. They're all gorgeous. I've tried using the same makeup and wearing the same clothes. (Well, some of them. Some stuff I'd feel too self-conscious wearing.) I still look like me. If only I had like Jennifer Lopez's body or maybe Jennifer Aniston's. I don't know sometimes. Maybe all girls feel like this. I wish I could stop feeling this way. But I can't.

For more ideas on how to deal with body image, check out the link on www.TrueImagesBible.com

body image in focus

Every day we're bombarded with society's views of "the perfect body." Maybe that's why more than half of 13-year-old girls are dissatisfied with their bodies, and that ratio increases to more than 3/4 by age 17. Do you feel dissatisfied with some aspect of your body?

»Replace the mental tapes of "I'm so ugly" with the message of Psalm 139:13–14 (page 791). God made you as you are, which makes you pretty cool. This doesn't mean that you skip trying to look your best. It does mean you skip trying to look like someone you're not.

»Realize that some of what you see in magazines isn't real. Thanks to technology, magazines can now make imperfect people appear perfect.

»Don't obsess about your body and beauty. Instead, focus on your relationship with Jesus (see Matthew 6:25–34, page 1298).

For more on this topic, see the index on page 1656.

fire. [12]His winnowing fork is in his hand, and he will clear his threshing floor, gathering his wheat into the barn and burning up the chaff with unquenchable fire."

The Baptism of Jesus

[13]Then Jesus came from Galilee to the Jordan to be baptized by John. [14]But John tried to deter him, saying, "I need to be baptized by you, and do you come to me?"

[15]Jesus replied, "Let it be so now; it is proper for us to do this to fulfill all righteousness." Then John consented.

[16]As soon as Jesus was baptized, he went up out of the water. At that moment heaven was

opened, and he saw the Spirit of God descending like a dove and lighting on him. [17]And a voice from heaven said, "This is my Son, whom I love; with him I am well pleased."

The Temptation of Jesus

4 Then Jesus was led by the Spirit into the desert to be tempted by the devil. [2]After fasting forty days and forty nights, he was hungry. [3]The tempter came to him and said, "If you are the Son of God, tell these stones to become bread."

[4]Jesus answered, "It is written: 'Man does not live on bread alone, but on every word that comes from the mouth of God.'[a]"

[5]Then the devil took him to the holy city and had him stand on the highest point of the temple. [6]"If you are the Son of God," he said, "throw yourself down. For it is written:

> " 'He will command his angels
>   concerning you,
>   and they will lift you up in their
>   hands,
> so that you will not strike your
>   foot against a stone.'[b]"

[7]Jesus answered him, "It is also written: 'Do not put the Lord your God to the test.'[c]"

[8]Again, the devil took him to a very high mountain and showed him all the kingdoms of the world and their splendor. [9]"All this I will give you," he said, "if you will bow down and worship me."

[10]Jesus said to him, "Away from me, Satan! For it is written: 'Worship the Lord your God, and serve him only.'[d]"

[11]Then the devil left him, and angels came and attended him.

truth or dare

Looking to wage war on temptation? When Satan attacked, Jesus already had an arsenal of God's Word *memorized* to fight against temptation. How prepared are you?

4:4,7,10

---

genuine devotion » 4:18-22

Did you catch that? Jesus called Simon and Andrew to follow him, and they left their nets *at once*. He called James and John to follow, and they left their boat *immediately*. No delays, no excuses, no asking for just a little more time to do their own thing. They knew Jesus was the Messiah (see John 1:41), so when he called, they didn't hesitate to give up everything to follow him. They knew what Jesus offered was worth so much more than what they already had. Do you know that, too? Are you willing to give up everything to follow Jesus?

Jesus Begins to Preach

[12]When Jesus heard that John had been put in prison, he returned to Galilee. [13]Leaving Nazareth, he went and lived in Capernaum, which was by the lake in the area of Zebulun and Naphtali— [14]to fulfill what was said through the prophet Isaiah:

[15] "Land of Zebulun and land of Naphtali,
>   the way to the sea, along the
>   Jordan,
> Galilee of the Gentiles—
[16] the people living in darkness
>   have seen a great light;
> on those living in the land of the
>   shadow of death
> a light has dawned."[e]

[17]From that time on Jesus began to preach, "Repent, for the kingdom of heaven is near."

The Calling of the First Disciples

[18]As Jesus was walking beside the Sea of Galilee, he saw two brothers, Simon called

a 4 Deut. 8:3   *b 6* Psalm 91:11,12
c 7 Deut. 6:16   *d 10* Deut. 6:13
e 16 Isaiah 9:1,2

Peter and his brother Andrew. They were casting a net into the lake, for they were fishermen. [19]"Come, follow me," Jesus said, "and I will make you fishers of men." [20]At once they left their nets and followed him.

[21]Going on from there, he saw two other brothers, James son of Zebedee and his brother John. They were in a boat with their father Zebedee, preparing their nets. Jesus called them, [22]and immediately they left the boat and their father and followed him.

Jesus Heals the Sick

[23]Jesus went throughout Galilee, teaching in their synagogues, preaching the good news of the kingdom, and healing every disease and sickness among the people. [24]News about him spread all over Syria, and people brought to him all who were ill with various diseases, those suffering severe pain, the demon-possessed, those having seizures, and the paralyzed, and he healed them. [25]Large crowds from Galilee, the Decapolis,[a] Jerusalem, Judea and the region across the Jordan followed him.

The Beatitudes

5 Now when he saw the crowds, he went up on a mountainside and sat down. His disciples came to him, [2]and he began to teach them, saying:

genuine

character » 5:3-12

Have you noticed there's a new kind of female character taking over movies and TV? She's sort of a female Rambo who shows no mercy and takes no prisoners in her attempt to accomplish her mission. And while she's got some admirable qualities, you'd better pause before making her your hero. You see, God's kind of girl is humble, sorrowful over sin, strong but ruled by gentleness, hungry for purity rather than power, willing to be insulted and persecuted, and peace-loving. *That's* the kind of girl who will be a hero in the kingdom of God.

[3]"Blessed are the poor in spirit,
  for theirs is the kingdom of
    heaven.
[4]Blessed are those who mourn,
  for they will be comforted.
[5]Blessed are the meek,
  for they will inherit the earth.
[6]Blessed are those who hunger and
    thirst for righteousness,
  for they will be filled.
[7]Blessed are the merciful,
  for they will be shown mercy.
[8]Blessed are the pure in heart,
  for they will see God.
[9]Blessed are the peacemakers,
  for they will be called sons of
    God.
[10]Blessed are those who are
    persecuted because of
    righteousness,
  for theirs is the kingdom of
    heaven.

[11]"Blessed are you when people insult you, persecute you and falsely say all kinds of evil against you because of me. [12]Rejoice and be glad, because great is your reward in heaven, for in the same way they persecuted the prophets who were before you.

Salt and Light

[13]"You are the salt of the earth. But if the salt loses its saltiness, how can it be made salty again? It is no longer good for anything, except to be thrown out and trampled by men.

[14]"You are the light of the world. A city on a hill cannot be hidden. [15]Neither do people light a lamp and put it under a bowl. Instead they put it on its stand, and it gives light to everyone in the house. [16]In the same way, let your light shine before men, that they may see your good deeds and praise your Father in heaven.

[a] 25 That is, the Ten Cities

The Fulfillment of the Law

¹⁷"Do not think that I have come to abolish the Law or the Prophets; I have not come to abolish them but to fulfill them. ¹⁸I tell you the truth, until heaven and earth disappear, not the smallest letter, not the least stroke of a pen, will by any means disappear from the Law until everything is accomplished. ¹⁹Anyone who breaks one of the least of these commandments and teaches others to do the same will be called least in the kingdom of heaven, but whoever practices and teaches these commands will be called great in the kingdom of heaven. ²⁰For I tell you that unless your righteousness surpasses that of the Pharisees and the teachers of the law, you will certainly not enter the kingdom of heaven.

Murder

²¹"You have heard that it was said to the people long ago, 'Do not murder,^a and anyone who murders will be subject to judgment.' ²²But I tell you that anyone who is angry with his brother^b will be subject to judgment. Again, anyone who says to his brother, 'Raca,^c' is answerable to the Sanhedrin. But anyone who says, 'You fool!' will be in danger of the fire of hell.

²³"Therefore, if you are offering your gift at the altar and there remember that your brother has something against you, ²⁴leave your gift there in front of the altar. First go and be reconciled to your brother; then come and offer your gift.

²⁵"Settle matters quickly with your adversary who is taking you to court. Do it while you are still with him on the way, or he may hand you over to the judge, and the judge may hand you over to the officer, and you may be thrown into prison. ²⁶I tell you the truth, you will not get out until you have paid the last penny.^d

truth or dare

It's so important to God that you live at peace with others (even with that pesky little brother of yours!) that he wants you to drop everything—even the offering plate—to go make peace *first*.

5:23–24

Adultery

²⁷"You have heard that it was said, 'Do not commit adultery.'^e ²⁸But I tell you that anyone who looks at a woman lustfully has already committed adultery with her in his heart. ²⁹If your right eye causes you to sin, gouge it out and throw it away. It is better for you to lose one part of your body than for your whole body to be thrown into hell. ³⁰And if your right hand causes you to sin, cut it off and throw it away. It is better for you to lose one part of your body than for your whole body to go into hell.

Divorce

³¹"It has been said, 'Anyone who divorces his wife must give her a certificate of divorce.'^f ³²But I tell you that anyone who divorces his wife, except for marital unfaithfulness, causes her to become an adulteress, and anyone who marries the divorced woman commits adultery.

Oaths

³³"Again, you have heard that it was said to the people long ago, 'Do not break your oath, but keep the oaths you have made to the Lord.' ³⁴But I tell you, Do not swear at all: either by heaven, for it is God's throne; ³⁵or by the earth, for it is his footstool; or by Jerusalem, for it is the city of the Great King. ³⁶And do not swear by your head, for you cannot make even one hair white or black. ³⁷Simply let your 'Yes' be 'Yes,' and your 'No,' 'No'; anything beyond this comes from the evil one.

An Eye for an Eye

³⁸"You have heard that it was said, 'Eye for eye, and tooth for tooth.'^g ³⁹But I tell you, Do not resist an evil person. If someone strikes you on the right cheek, turn to him the other also. ⁴⁰And if someone wants to sue you and take your tunic, let him have your cloak as well. ⁴¹If someone forc-

---

a 21 Exodus 20:13   *b 22* Some manuscripts *brother without cause*   *c 22* An Aramaic term of contempt
d 26 Greek *kodrantes*   *e 27* Exodus 20:14   *f 31* Deut. 24:1   *g 38* Exodus 21:24; Lev. 24:20; Deut. 19:21

es you to go one mile, go with him two miles. [42]Give to the one who asks you, and do not turn away from the one who wants to borrow from you.

Love for Enemies

[43]"You have heard that it was said, 'Love your neighbor[a] and hate your enemy.' [44]But I tell you: Love your enemies[b] and pray for those who persecute you, [45]that you may be sons of your Father in heaven. He causes his sun to rise on the evil and the good, and sends rain on the righteous and the unrighteous. [46]If you love those who love you, what reward will you get? Are not even the tax collectors doing that? [47]And if you greet only your brothers, what are you doing more than others? Do not even pagans do that? [48]Be perfect, therefore, as your heavenly Father is perfect.

Giving to the Needy

6 "Be careful not to do your 'acts of righteousness' before men, to be seen by them. If you do, you will have no reward from your Father in heaven.

[2]"So when you give to the needy, do not announce it with trumpets, as the hypocrites do in the synagogues and on the streets, to be honored by men. I tell you the truth, they have received their reward in full. [3]But when you give to the needy, do not let your left hand know what your right hand is doing, [4]so that your giving may be in secret. Then your Father, who sees what is done in secret, will reward you.

Prayer

[5]"And when you pray, do not be like the hypocrites, for they love to pray standing in the synagogues and on the street corners to be seen by men. I tell you the truth, they have received their reward in full. [6]But when you pray, go into your room, close the door and pray to your Father, who is unseen. Then your Father, who sees what is done in secret, will reward you. [7]And when you pray, do not keep on babbling like pagans, for they think they will be heard because of their many words. [8]Do not be like them, for your Father knows what you need before you ask him.

[9]"This, then, is how you should pray:

" 'Our Father in heaven,
hallowed be your name,
[10]your kingdom come,
your will be done
on earth as it is in heaven.
[11]Give us today our daily bread.
[12]Forgive us our debts,
as we also have forgiven our debtors.

genuine
love » 5:43-48

Say what?! There must be some mistake! Jesus wants me to love my enemies and pray for those who persecute me? Does he know what he's asking? Actually, yes, he does. The Bible says that, as sinners, we were God's enemies—and that while we were still his enemies, Jesus loved us so much he died for us (see Romans 5:8–10). On the cross, he prayed for those who crucified him (Luke 23:34). Is there someone who's always getting in your face and making your life difficult? Remember what Jesus did for his enemies, and follow his example of love and prayer.

truth or dare

What were you expecting—an elaborate, mystical chant? God's prayer model is short, sweet and to the point. After all, prayer is communicating *directly* with God. Make your words meaningful and sincere.

6:9–13

[a] 43 Lev. 19:18   [b] 44 Some late manuscripts *enemies, bless those who curse you, do good to those who hate you*

[13] And lead us not into temptation,
but deliver us from the evil one. *ᵃ*

[14] For if you forgive men when they sin against you, your heavenly Father will also forgive you. [15] But if you do not forgive men their sins, your Father will not forgive your sins.

Fasting

[16] "When you fast, do not look somber as the hypocrites do, for they disfigure their faces to show men they are fasting. I tell you the truth, they have received their reward in full. [17] But when you fast, put oil on your head and wash your face, [18] so that it will not be obvious to men that you are fasting, but only to your Father, who is unseen; and your Father, who sees what is done in secret, will reward you.

Treasures in Heaven

[19] "Do not store up for yourselves treasures on earth, where moth and rust destroy, and where thieves break in and steal. [20] But store up for yourselves treasures in heaven, where moth and rust do not destroy, and where thieves do not break in and steal. [21] For where your treasure is, there your heart will be also.

[22] "The eye is the lamp of the body. If your eyes are good, your whole body will be full of light. [23] But if your eyes are bad, your whole body will be full of darkness. If then the light within you is darkness, how great is that darkness!

[24] "No one can serve two masters. Either he will hate the one and love the other, or he will be devoted to the one and despise the other. You cannot serve both God and Money.

Do Not Worry

[25] "Therefore I tell you, do not worry about your life, what you will eat or drink; or about your body, what you will wear. Is not life more important than food, and the body more important than clothes? [26] Look at the birds of the air; they do not sow or reap or store away in barns, and yet your heavenly Father feeds them. Are you not much more valuable than they? [27] Who of you by worrying can add a single hour to his life *ᵇ*?

[28] "And why do you worry about clothes? See how the lilies of the field grow. They do not labor or spin. [29] Yet I tell you that not even Solomon in all his splendor was dressed like one of these. [30] If that is how God clothes the grass of the field, which is here today and tomorrow is thrown into the fire, will he not much more clothe you, O you of little faith? [31] So do not worry, saying, 'What shall we eat?' or 'What shall we drink?' or 'What shall we wear?' [32] For the pagans run after all these things, and your heavenly Father knows that you need them. [33] But seek first his kingdom and his righteousness, and all these things will be given to you as well. [34] Therefore do not worry about tomorrow, for tomorrow will worry about itself. Each day has enough trouble of its own.

genuine
character » 6:19-21

What is your most prized possession? The diamond earrings that were your grandmother's? That top-of-the-line pocket PC with the built-in cell phone? The black leather jacket you bought with your own money? No matter how great that thing is, it's not gonna last forever. Diamonds get stolen, PC's become obsolete, and leather gets worn and goes out of style. That's why it's important to value the things you can't see—like love and obedience to God—because they do last forever. Invest your time, money and energy into those things, and you'll find yourself with everlasting treasure.

ᵃ 13 Or *from evil*; some late manuscripts *one, / for yours is the kingdom and the power and the glory forever. Amen.*
ᵇ 27 Or *single cubit to his height*

Judging Others

7 "Do not judge, or you too will be judged. ²For in the same way you judge others, you will be judged, and with the measure you use, it will be measured to you.

³"Why do you look at the speck of sawdust in your brother's eye and pay no attention to the plank in your own eye? ⁴How can you say to your brother, 'Let me take the speck out of your eye,' when all the time there is a plank in your own eye? ⁵You hypocrite, first take the plank out of your own eye, and then you will see clearly to remove the speck from your brother's eye.

⁶"Do not give dogs what is sacred; do not throw your pearls to pigs. If you do, they may trample them under their feet, and then turn and tear you to pieces.

Ask, Seek, Knock

⁷"Ask and it will be given to you; seek and you will find; knock and the door will be opened to you. ⁸For everyone who asks receives; he who seeks finds; and to him who knocks, the door will be opened.

⁹"Which of you, if his son asks for bread, will give him a stone? ¹⁰Or if he asks for a fish, will give him a snake? ¹¹If you, then, though you are evil, know how to give good gifts to your children, how much more will your Father in heaven give good gifts to those who ask him! ¹²So in everything, do to others what you would have them do to you, for this sums up the Law and the Prophets.

The Narrow and Wide Gates

¹³"Enter through the narrow gate. For wide is the gate and broad is the road that leads to destruction, and many enter through it. ¹⁴But small is the gate and narrow the road that leads to life, and only a few find it.

A Tree and Its Fruit

¹⁵"Watch out for false prophets. They come to you in sheep's clothing, but inwardly they are ferocious wolves. ¹⁶By their fruit you will recognize them. Do people pick grapes from thornbushes, or figs from thistles? ¹⁷Likewise every good tree bears good fruit, but a bad tree bears bad fruit. ¹⁸A good tree cannot bear bad fruit, and a bad tree cannot bear good fruit. ¹⁹Every tree that does not bear good fruit is cut down and thrown into the fire. ²⁰Thus, by their fruit you will recognize them.

²¹"Not everyone who says to me, 'Lord, Lord,' will enter the kingdom of heaven, but only he who does the will of my Father who is in heaven. ²²Many will say to me on that day, 'Lord, Lord, did we not prophesy in your name, and in your name drive out demons and perform many miracles?' ²³Then I will tell them plainly, 'I never knew you. Away from me, you evildoers!'

The Wise and Foolish Builders

²⁴"Therefore everyone who hears these words of mine and puts them into practice is like a wise man who built his house on the rock. ²⁵The rain came down, the streams rose, and the winds blew and beat against that house; yet it did not fall, because it had its foundation on the rock. ²⁶But everyone who hears these words of mine and does not put them into practice is like a foolish man who built his house on sand. ²⁷The rain came down, the streams rose, and the winds blew and beat against that house, and it fell with a great crash."

genuine

righteousness » 7:1-5

Let's face it: We constantly measure ourselves against other people. We think, *I'm not so bad. At least I don't swear like Haley.* Or, *I'm better than Ashley because I read my Bible.* But Jesus says not to get caught up in "comparative righteousness." Your righteousness before God isn't based on how good you are compared to someone else—it's based on whether or not you've placed your faith in Christ's perfect righteousness and his forgiveness. For every speck in someone else's eye, there's likely a log in your own. So quit pointing the finger, and deal with your own issues instead.

²⁸When Jesus had finished saying these things, the crowds were amazed at his teaching, ²⁹because he taught as one who had authority, and not as their teachers of the law.

The Man With Leprosy

8 When he came down from the mountainside, large crowds followed him. ²A man with leprosy^a came and knelt before him and said, "Lord, if you are willing, you can make me clean." ³Jesus reached out his hand and touched the man. "I am willing," he said. "Be clean!" Immediately he was cured^b of his leprosy. ⁴Then Jesus said to him, "See that you don't tell anyone. But go, show yourself to the priest and offer the gift Moses commanded, as a testimony to them."

The Faith of the Centurion

⁵When Jesus had entered Capernaum, a centurion came to him, asking for help. ⁶"Lord," he said, "my servant lies at home paralyzed and in terrible suffering."

⁷Jesus said to him, "I will go and heal him."

⁸The centurion replied, "Lord, I do not deserve to have you come under my roof. But just say the word, and my servant will be healed. ⁹For I myself am a man under authority, with soldiers under me. I tell this one, 'Go,' and he goes; and that one, 'Come,' and he comes. I say to my servant, 'Do this,' and he does it."

¹⁰When Jesus heard this, he was astonished and said to those following him, "I tell you the truth, I have not found anyone in Israel with such great faith. ¹¹I say to you that many will come from the east and the west, and will take their places at the feast with Abraham, Isaac and Jacob in the kingdom of heaven. ¹²But the subjects of the kingdom will be thrown outside, into the darkness, where there will be weeping and gnashing of teeth."

¹³Then Jesus said to the centurion, "Go! It will be done just as you believed it would." And his servant was healed at that very hour.

Jesus Heals Many

¹⁴When Jesus came into Peter's house, he saw Peter's mother-in-law lying in bed with a fever. ¹⁵He touched her hand and the fever left her, and she got up and began to wait on him.

¹⁶When evening came, many who were demon-possessed were brought to him, and he drove out the spirits with a word and healed all the sick. ¹⁷This was to fulfill what was spoken through the prophet Isaiah:

"He took up our infirmities
and carried our diseases."^c

The Cost of Following Jesus

¹⁸When Jesus saw the crowd around him, he gave orders to cross to the other side of the lake. ¹⁹Then a teacher of the law came to him and said, "Teacher, I will follow you wherever you go."

²⁰Jesus replied, "Foxes have holes and birds of the air have nests, but the Son of Man has no place to lay his head."

²¹Another disciple said to him, "Lord, first let me go and bury my father."

²²But Jesus told him, "Follow me, and let the dead bury their own dead."

Jesus Calms the Storm

²³Then he got into the boat and his disciples followed him. ²⁴Without warning, a furious storm came up on the lake, so that the waves swept over the boat. But Jesus was sleeping. ²⁵The disciples went and woke him, saying, "Lord, save us! We're going to drown!"

²⁶He replied, "You of little faith, why are you so afraid?" Then he got up and rebuked the winds and the waves, and it was completely calm.

²⁷The men were amazed and asked, "What kind of man is this? Even the winds and the waves obey him!"

---

^a 2 The Greek word was used for various diseases affecting the skin—not necessarily leprosy.   ^b 3 Greek *made clean*
^c 17 Isaiah 53:4

A Prayer for Mama T.

Mama T.'s dead. That's my grandmama. I miss her so much. Mama T.'s the only mama I ever knew. She's the one who raised me after my mama went to jail. That happened when I was four years old. I'm fifteen now. I never even knew my father.

I'm staying with my auntie now. She's okay, but she's not like Mama T.

Mama T. taught me about God. She said that as long as I lived in her house, I had to go to church—no excuses. I gave her a hard time about it when I was younger, but I really liked to go.

She's the one who told me that God answers prayers. She always said stuff like, "He's faithful." I believed her because he always seemed to answer her prayers.

The whole time she had breast cancer, I prayed and prayed, asking God to please heal Mama T. Everybody at our church prayed for months while she was on chemo. For a while there, she seemed to be doing better. She started eating again. (She said she didn't have much of an appetite while she was on chemo.) We all thought she would make it. But during her second round of chemo, she got worse and then died on a Saturday.

Were our prayers just not good enough for God? I don't think I prayed selfishly. I wanted Mama T. to be well. She was in a lot of pain. I believed that God could heal Mama T. He just . . . didn't.

I don't understand God. Why didn't he heal her? Why would he take away the only person who really seemed to care about me? How can I trust him if he ignores my important prayers?

For more on prayer, go to www.TrueImagesBible.com

unanswered prayer in focus

Have you memorized Matthew 7:7 yet (page 1299)? It's the verse where Jesus invites you to ask, seek and knock. In other words—*pray*. Like Spring, have you ever wondered if God's simply forgotten about your prayer or is ignoring you?

» God answers all prayers in some way—either "yes," "no" or "wait." We'd all like the yes vote, but occasionally God exercises his right to say no or wait. No matter what the answer is, he will use it for your good if you love him (see Romans 8:28, page 1494).

» God uses tough, unexplainable situations to make us more like Jesus (see Romans 8:18, page 1493; James 1:2–4, page 1602).

» God never stops caring for us. It's impossible for him to stop caring. God totally knows the best way to answer our prayers, and he wants us to trust him.

For more on this topic, see the index on page 1656.

The Healing of Two Demon-possessed Men

²⁸When he arrived at the other side in the region of the Gadarenes, ᵃ two demon-possessed men coming from the tombs met him. They were so violent that no one could pass that way. ²⁹"What

ᵃ *28* Some manuscripts *Gergesenes*; others *Gerasenes*

do you want with us, Son of God?" they shouted. "Have you come here to torture us before the appointed time?"

[30]Some distance from them a large herd of pigs was feeding. [31]The demons begged Jesus, "If you drive us out, send us into the herd of pigs."

[32]He said to them, "Go!" So they came out and went into the pigs, and the whole herd rushed down the steep bank into the lake and died in the water. [33]Those tending the pigs ran off, went into the town and reported all this, including what had happened to the demon-possessed men. [34]Then the whole town went out to meet Jesus. And when they saw him, they pleaded with him to leave their region.

Jesus Heals a Paralytic

9 Jesus stepped into a boat, crossed over and came to his own town. [2]Some men brought to him a paralytic, lying on a mat. When Jesus saw their faith, he said to the paralytic, "Take heart, son; your sins are forgiven."

[3]At this, some of the teachers of the law said to themselves, "This fellow is blaspheming!"

[4]Knowing their thoughts, Jesus said, "Why do you entertain evil thoughts in your hearts? [5]Which is easier: to say, 'Your sins are forgiven,' or to say, 'Get up and walk'? [6]But so that you may know that the Son of Man has authority on earth to forgive sins . . . ." Then he said to the paralytic, "Get up, take your mat and go home." [7]And the man got up and went home. [8]When the crowd saw this, they were filled with awe; and they praised God, who had given such authority to men.

The Calling of Matthew

[9]As Jesus went on from there, he saw a man named Matthew sitting at the tax collector's booth. "Follow me," he told him, and Matthew got up and followed him.

[10]While Jesus was having dinner at Matthew's house, many tax collectors and "sinners" came and ate with him and his disciples. [11]When the Pharisees saw this, they asked his disciples, "Why does your teacher eat with tax collectors and 'sinners'?"

[12]On hearing this, Jesus said, "It is not the healthy who need a doctor, but the sick. [13]But go and learn what this means: 'I desire mercy, not sacrifice.'[a] For I have not come to call the righteous, but sinners."

Jesus Questioned About Fasting

[14]Then John's disciples came and asked him, "How is it that we and the Pharisees fast, but your disciples do not fast?"

[15]Jesus answered, "How can the guests of the bridegroom mourn while he is with them? The time will come when the bridegroom will be taken from them; then they will fast.

[16]"No one sews a patch of unshrunk cloth on an old garment, for the patch will pull away from the garment, making the tear worse. [17]Neither do men pour new wine into old wineskins. If they do, the skins will burst, the wine will run out and the wineskins will be ruined. No, they pour new wine into new wineskins, and both are preserved."

A Dead Girl and a Sick Woman

[18]While he was saying this, a ruler came and knelt before him and said, "My daughter has just died. But come and put your hand on her, and she will live." [19]Jesus got up and went with him, and so did his disciples.

[20]Just then a woman who had been subject to bleeding for twelve years came up behind him and touched the edge of his cloak. [21]She said to herself, "If I only touch his cloak, I will be healed." [22]Jesus turned and saw her. "Take heart, daughter," he said, "your faith has healed you." And the woman was healed from that moment.

[23]When Jesus entered the ruler's house and saw the flute players and the noisy crowd, [24]he said, "Go away. The girl is not dead but asleep." But they laughed at him. [25]After the crowd had been put outside, he went in and took the girl by the hand, and she got up. [26]News of this spread through all that region.

a 13 Hosea 6:6

Jesus Heals the Blind and Mute

²⁷As Jesus went on from there, two blind men followed him, calling out, "Have mercy on us, Son of David!"

²⁸When he had gone indoors, the blind men came to him, and he asked them, "Do you believe that I am able to do this?"

"Yes, Lord," they replied.

²⁹Then he touched their eyes and said, "According to your faith will it be done to you"; ³⁰and their sight was restored. Jesus warned them sternly, "See that no one knows about this." ³¹But they went out and spread the news about him all over that region.

³²While they were going out, a man who was demon-possessed and could not talk was brought to Jesus. ³³And when the demon was driven out, the man who had been mute spoke. The crowd was amazed and said, "Nothing like this has ever been seen in Israel."

³⁴But the Pharisees said, "It is by the prince of demons that he drives out demons."

The Workers Are Few

³⁵Jesus went through all the towns and villages, teaching in their synagogues, preaching the good news of the kingdom and healing every disease and sickness. ³⁶When he saw the crowds, he had compassion on them, because they were harassed and helpless, like sheep without a shepherd. ³⁷Then he said to his disciples, "The harvest is plentiful but the workers are few. ³⁸Ask the Lord of the harvest, therefore, to send out workers into his harvest field."

Jesus Sends Out the Twelve

10 He called his twelve disciples to him and gave them authority to drive out evil*ᵃ* spirits and to heal every disease and sickness.

²These are the names of the twelve apostles: first, Simon (who is called Peter) and his brother Andrew; James son of Zebedee, and his brother John; ³Philip and Bartholomew; Thomas and Matthew the tax collector; James son of Alphaeus, and Thaddaeus; ⁴Simon the Zealot and Judas Iscariot, who betrayed him.

⁵These twelve Jesus sent out with the following instructions: "Do not go among the Gentiles or enter any town of the Samaritans. ⁶Go rather to the lost sheep of Israel. ⁷As you go, preach this message: 'The kingdom of heaven is near.' ⁸Heal the sick, raise the dead, cleanse those who have leprosy,*ᵇ* drive out demons. Freely you have received, freely give. ⁹Do not take along any gold or silver or copper in your belts; ¹⁰take no bag for the journey, or extra tunic, or sandals or a staff; for the worker is worth his keep.

¹¹"Whatever town or village you enter, search for some worthy person there and stay at his house until you leave. ¹²As you enter the home, give it your greeting. ¹³If the home is deserving, let your peace rest on it; if it is not, let your peace return to you. ¹⁴If anyone will not welcome you or listen to your words, shake the dust off your feet when you leave that home or town. ¹⁵I tell you the truth, it will be more bearable for Sodom and Gomorrah on the day of judgment than for that town. ¹⁶I am sending you out like sheep among wolves. Therefore be as shrewd as snakes and as innocent as doves.

¹⁷"Be on your guard against men; they will hand you over to the local councils and flog you in their synagogues. ¹⁸On my account you will be brought before governors and kings as witnesses to them and to the Gentiles. ¹⁹But when they arrest you, do not worry about what to say or how to say it. At that time you will be given what to say, ²⁰for it will not be you speaking, but the Spirit of your Father speaking through you.

²¹"Brother will betray brother to death, and a father his child; children will rebel against their parents and have them put to death. ²²All men will hate you because of me, but he who stands firm to the end will be saved. ²³When you are persecuted in one place, flee to another. I tell you the truth, you will not finish going through the cities of Israel before the Son of Man comes.

²⁴"A student is not above his teacher, nor a servant above his master. ²⁵It is enough for the student to be like his teacher, and the servant like his master. If the head of the house has been called Beelzebub,*ᶜ* how much more the members of his household!

---

a 1 Greek *unclean*   *b 8* The Greek word was used for various diseases affecting the skin—not necessarily leprosy.
c 25 Greek *Beezeboul* or *Beelzeboul*

²⁶"So do not be afraid of them. There is nothing concealed that will not be disclosed, or hidden that will not be made known. ²⁷What I tell you in the dark, speak in the daylight; what is whispered in your ear, proclaim from the roofs. ²⁸Do not be afraid of those who kill the body but cannot kill the soul. Rather, be afraid of the One who can destroy both soul and body in hell. ²⁹Are not two sparrows sold for a penny*ᵃ*? Yet not one of them will fall to the ground apart from the will of your Father. ³⁰And even the very hairs of your head are all numbered. ³¹So don't be afraid; you are worth more than many sparrows.

³²"Whoever acknowledges me before men, I will also acknowledge him before my Father in heaven. ³³But whoever disowns me before men, I will disown him before my Father in heaven.

³⁴"Do not suppose that I have come to bring peace to the earth. I did not come to bring peace, but a sword. ³⁵For I have come to turn

" 'a man against his father,
a daughter against her mother,
a daughter-in-law against her
mother-in-law—
³⁶a man's enemies will be the
members of his own
household.'ᵇ

³⁷"Anyone who loves his father or mother more than me is not worthy of me; anyone who loves his son or daughter more than me is not worthy of me; ³⁸and anyone who does not take his cross and follow me is not worthy of me. ³⁹Whoever finds his life will lose it, and whoever loses his life for my sake will find it.

⁴⁰"He who receives you receives me, and he who receives me receives the one who sent me. ⁴¹Anyone who receives a prophet because he is a prophet will receive a prophet's reward, and anyone who receives a righteous man because he is a righteous man will receive a righteous man's reward. ⁴²And if anyone gives even a cup of cold water to one of these little ones because he is my disciple, I tell you the truth, he will certainly not lose his reward."

Jesus and John the Baptist

11 After Jesus had finished instructing his twelve disciples, he went on from there to teach and preach in the towns of Galilee.ᶜ

²When John heard in prison what Christ was doing, he sent his disciples ³to ask him, "Are you the one who was to come, or should we expect someone else?"

⁴Jesus replied, "Go back and report to John what you hear and see: ⁵The blind receive sight, the lame walk, those who have leprosyᵈ are cured, the deaf hear, the dead

love ♥ notes

10:29–31

My valuable daughter,

If I know the second a sparrow falls, trust me that I know what's happening with you. I know the exact number of hairs on your head—that's how completely I know everything that's going on in your life. Trust me to care for you.

—Your Father

Reflect on what it means to you that
God knows you so completely.

ᵃ 29 Greek *an assarion*   ᵇ 36 Micah 7:6
ᶜ 1 Greek *in their towns*   ᵈ 5 The Greek word was used for various diseases affecting the skin—not necessarily leprosy.

are raised, and the good news is preached to the poor. [6]Blessed is the man who does not fall away on account of me."

[7]As John's disciples were leaving, Jesus began to speak to the crowd about John: "What did you go out into the desert to see? A reed swayed by the wind? [8]If not, what did you go out to see? A man dressed in fine clothes? No, those who wear fine clothes are in kings' palaces. [9]Then what did you go out to see? A prophet? Yes, I tell you, and more than a prophet. [10]This is the one about whom it is written:

> " 'I will send my messenger ahead of you,
> who will prepare your way before you.'[a]

[11]I tell you the truth: Among those born of women there has not risen anyone greater than John the Baptist; yet he who is least in the kingdom of heaven is greater than he. [12]From the days of John the Baptist until now, the kingdom of heaven has been forcefully advancing, and forceful men lay hold of it. [13]For all the Prophets and the Law prophesied until John. [14]And if you are willing to accept it, he is the Elijah who was to come. [15]He who has ears, let him hear.

[16]"To what can I compare this generation? They are like children sitting in the marketplaces and calling out to others:

> [17] " 'We played the flute for you,
> and you did not dance;
> we sang a dirge,
> and you did not mourn.'

[18]For John came neither eating nor drinking, and they say, 'He has a demon.' [19]The Son of Man came eating and drinking, and they say, 'Here is a glutton and a drunkard, a friend of tax collectors and "sinners." ' But wisdom is proved right by her actions."

Woe on Unrepentant Cities

[20]Then Jesus began to denounce the cities in which most of his miracles had been performed, because they did not repent. [21]"Woe to you, Korazin! Woe to you, Bethsaida! If the miracles that were performed in you had been performed in Tyre and Sidon, they would have repented long ago in sackcloth and ashes. [22]But I tell you, it will be more bearable for Tyre and Sidon on the day of judgment than for you. [23]And you, Capernaum, will you be lifted up to the skies? No, you will go down to the depths.[b] If the miracles that were performed in you had been performed in Sodom, it would have remained to this day. [24]But I tell you that it will be more bearable for Sodom on the day of judgment than for you."

Rest for the Weary

[25]At that time Jesus said, "I praise you, Father, Lord of heaven and earth, because you have hidden these things from the wise and learned, and revealed them to little children. [26]Yes, Father, for this was your good pleasure.

[27]"All things have been committed to me by my Father. No one knows the Son except the Father, and no one knows the Father except the Son and those to whom the Son chooses to reveal him.

[28]"Come to me, all you who are weary and burdened, and I will give you rest. [29]Take my yoke upon you and learn from me, for I am gentle and humble in heart, and you will find rest for your souls. [30]For my yoke is easy and my burden is light."

Lord of the Sabbath

12 At that time Jesus went through the grainfields on the Sabbath. His disciples were hungry and began to pick some heads of grain and eat them. [2]When the Pharisees saw this, they said to him, "Look! Your disciples are doing what is unlawful on the Sabbath."

[3]He answered, "Haven't you read what David did when he and his companions were hungry? [4]He entered the house of God, and he and his companions ate the consecrated bread—which was not lawful for them to do, but only for the priests. [5]Or haven't you read in the Law that on the Sab-

a 10 Mal. 3:1 b 23 Greek *Hades*

bath the priests in the temple desecrate the day and yet are innocent? [6]I tell you that one[a] greater than the temple is here. [7]If you had known what these words mean, 'I desire mercy, not sacrifice,'[b] you would not have condemned the innocent. [8]For the Son of Man is Lord of the Sabbath."

[9]Going on from that place, he went into their synagogue, [10]and a man with a shriveled hand was there. Looking for a reason to accuse Jesus, they asked him, "Is it lawful to heal on the Sabbath?"

[11]He said to them, "If any of you has a sheep and it falls into a pit on the Sabbath, will you not take hold of it and lift it out? [12]How much more valuable is a man than a sheep! Therefore it is lawful to do good on the Sabbath."

[13]Then he said to the man, "Stretch out your hand." So he stretched it out and it was completely restored, just as sound as the other. [14]But the Pharisees went out and plotted how they might kill Jesus.

love notes

11:28–30

Child,

Are you plain worn-out and tired from the daily routine and constant demands on you? Come, learn from me and receive rest. I will reenergize you. In me, you will find purpose and meaning to all you do.

—The One who gives you rest

What's wearing you down right now? Lift it up to the Lord, and ask him to carry your burdens.

_____

_____

_____

_____

_____

_____

God's Chosen Servant

[15]Aware of this, Jesus withdrew from that place. Many followed him, and he healed all their sick, [16]warning them not to tell who he was. [17]This was to fulfill what was spoken through the prophet Isaiah:

[18]"Here is my servant whom I have chosen,
    the one I love, in whom I delight;
I will put my Spirit on him,
    and he will proclaim justice to
      the nations.
[19]He will not quarrel or cry out;
    no one will hear his voice in
      the streets.
[20]A bruised reed he will not break,
    and a smoldering wick he will
      not snuff out,
    till he leads justice to victory.
[21]In his name the nations will
      put their hope."[c]

Jesus and Beelzebub

[22]Then they brought him a demon-possessed man who was blind and mute, and Jesus healed him, so that he could both talk and see. [23]All the people were astonished and said, "Could this be the Son of David?"

[24]But when the Pharisees heard this, they said, "It is only by Beelzebub,[d] the prince of demons, that this fellow drives out demons."

[25]Jesus knew their thoughts and said to them, "Every kingdom divided against itself will be ruined, and every city or household divided against itself will not stand. [26]If Satan drives out Satan, he is divided against himself. How then can his kingdom stand? [27]And if I drive out demons by Beelzebub, by

---

[a] 6 Or *something*; also in verses 41 and 42
[b] 7 Hosea 6:6   [c] 21 Isaiah 42:1-4   [d] 24 Greek *Beezeboul* or *Beelzeboul*; also in verse 27

whom do your people drive them out? So then, they will be your judges. ²⁸But if I drive out demons by the Spirit of God, then the kingdom of God has come upon you.

²⁹"Or again, how can anyone enter a strong man's house and carry off his possessions unless he first ties up the strong man? Then he can rob his house.

³⁰"He who is not with me is against me, and he who does not gather with me scatters. ³¹And so I tell you, every sin and blasphemy will be forgiven men, but the blasphemy against the Spirit will not be forgiven. ³²Anyone who speaks a word against the Son of Man will be forgiven, but anyone who speaks against the Holy Spirit will not be forgiven, either in this age or in the age to come.

³³"Make a tree good and its fruit will be good, or make a tree bad and its fruit will be bad, for a tree is recognized by its fruit. ³⁴You brood of vipers, how can you who are evil say anything good? For out of the overflow of the heart the mouth speaks. ³⁵The good man brings good things out of the good stored up in him, and the evil man brings evil things out of the evil stored up in him. ³⁶But I tell you that men will have to give account on the day of judgment for every careless word they have spoken. ³⁷For by your words you will be acquitted, and by your words you will be condemned."

The Sign of Jonah

³⁸Then some of the Pharisees and teachers of the law said to him, "Teacher, we want to see a miraculous sign from you."

³⁹He answered, "A wicked and adulterous generation asks for a miraculous sign! But none will be given it except the sign of the prophet Jonah. ⁴⁰For as Jonah was three days and three nights in the belly of a huge fish, so the Son of Man will be three days and three nights in the heart of the earth. ⁴¹The men of Nineveh will stand up at the judgment with this generation and condemn it; for they repented at the preaching of Jonah, and now one*ᵃ* greater than Jonah is here. ⁴²The Queen of the South will rise at the judgment with this generation and condemn it; for she came from the ends of the earth to listen to Solomon's wisdom, and now one greater than Solomon is here.

⁴³"When an evil*ᵇ* spirit comes out of a man, it goes through arid places seeking rest and does not find it. ⁴⁴Then it says, 'I will return to the house I left.' When it arrives, it finds the house unoccupied, swept clean and put in order. ⁴⁵Then it goes and takes with it seven other spirits more wicked than itself, and they go in and live there. And the final condition of that man is worse than the first. That is how it will be with this wicked generation."

Jesus' Mother and Brothers

⁴⁶While Jesus was still talking to the crowd, his mother and brothers stood outside, wanting to speak to him. ⁴⁷Someone told him, "Your mother and brothers are standing outside, wanting to speak to you."*ᶜ*

⁴⁸He replied to him, "Who is my mother, and who are my brothers?" ⁴⁹Pointing to his disciples, he said, "Here are my mother and my brothers. ⁵⁰For whoever does the will of my Father in heaven is my brother and sister and mother."

ᵃ 41 Or *something*; also in verse 42   *ᵇ 43* Greek *unclean*   *ᶜ 47* Some manuscripts do not have verse 47.

The Parable of the Sower

13 That same day Jesus went out of the house and sat by the lake. [2]Such large crowds gathered around him that he got into a boat and sat in it, while all the people stood on the shore. [3]Then he told them many things in parables, saying: "A farmer went out to sow his seed. [4]As he was scattering the seed, some fell along the path, and the birds came and ate it up. [5]Some fell on rocky places, where it did not have much soil. It sprang up quickly, because the soil was shallow. [6]But when the sun came up, the plants were scorched, and they withered because they had no root. [7]Other seed fell among thorns, which grew up and choked the plants. [8]Still other seed fell on good soil, where it produced a crop—a hundred, sixty or thirty times what was sown. [9]He who has ears, let him hear."

[10]The disciples came to him and asked, "Why do you speak to the people in parables?"

[11]He replied, "The knowledge of the secrets of the kingdom of heaven has been given to you, but not to them. [12]Whoever has will be given more, and he will have an abundance. Whoever does not have, even what he has will be taken from him. [13]This is why I speak to them in parables:

"Though seeing, they do not see;
   though hearing, they do not hear or understand.

[14]In them is fulfilled the prophecy of Isaiah:

" 'You will be ever hearing but never understanding;
   you will be ever seeing but never perceiving.
[15]For this people's heart has become calloused;
   they hardly hear with their ears,
   and they have closed their eyes.
Otherwise they might see with their eyes,
   hear with their ears,
   understand with their hearts
and turn, and I would heal them.' [a]

[16]But blessed are your eyes because they see, and your ears because they hear. [17]For I tell you the truth, many prophets and righteous men longed to see what you see but did not see it, and to hear what you hear but did not hear it.

[18]"Listen then to what the parable of the sower means: [19]When anyone hears the message about the kingdom and does not understand it, the evil one comes and snatches away what was sown in his heart. This is the seed sown along the path. [20]The one who received the seed that fell on rocky places is the man who hears the word and at once receives it with joy. [21]But since he has no root, he lasts only a short time. When trouble or persecution comes because of the word, he quickly falls away. [22]The one who received the seed that fell among the thorns is the man who hears the word, but the worries of this life and the deceitfulness of wealth choke it, making it unfruitful. [23]But the one who received the seed that fell on good soil is the man who hears the word and understands it. He produces a crop, yielding a hundred, sixty or thirty times what was sown."

truth or dare

Don't let this be you! Fretting over life and chasing after the stuff of this world distract you from God. Have you let worries and wealth choke your relationship with God?

13:22

The Parable of the Weeds

[24]Jesus told them another parable: "The kingdom of heaven is like a man who sowed good seed in his field. [25]But while everyone was sleeping, his enemy came and sowed weeds among the wheat, and went away. [26]When the wheat sprouted and formed heads, then the weeds also appeared.

[27]"The owner's servants came to him and said, 'Sir, didn't you sow good seed in your field? Where then did the weeds come from?'

a 15 Isaiah 6:9,10

[28]" 'An enemy did this,' he replied.

"The servants asked him, 'Do you want us to go and pull them up?'

[29]" 'No,' he answered, 'because while you are pulling the weeds, you may root up the wheat with them. [30]Let both grow together until the harvest. At that time I will tell the harvesters: First collect the weeds and tie them in bundles to be burned; then gather the wheat and bring it into my barn.' "

The Parables of the Mustard Seed and the Yeast

[31]He told them another parable: "The kingdom of heaven is like a mustard seed, which a man took and planted in his field. [32]Though it is the smallest of all your seeds, yet when it grows, it is the largest of garden plants and becomes a tree, so that the birds of the air come and perch in its branches."

[33]He told them still another parable: "The kingdom of heaven is like yeast that a woman took and mixed into a large amount[a] of flour until it worked all through the dough."

[34]Jesus spoke all these things to the crowd in parables; he did not say anything to them without using a parable. [35]So was fulfilled what was spoken through the prophet:

"I will open my mouth in parables,
I will utter things hidden since the creation of the world."[b]

The Parable of the Weeds Explained

[36]Then he left the crowd and went into the house. His disciples came to him and said, "Explain to us the parable of the weeds in the field."

[37]He answered, "The one who sowed the good seed is the Son of Man. [38]The field is the world, and the good seed stands for the sons of the kingdom. The weeds are the sons of the evil one, [39]and the enemy who sows them is the devil. The harvest is the end of the age, and the harvesters are angels.

[40]"As the weeds are pulled up and burned in the fire, so it will be at the end of the age. [41]The Son of Man will send out his angels, and they will weed out of his kingdom everything that causes sin and all who do evil. [42]They will throw them into the fiery furnace, where there will be weeping and gnashing of teeth. [43]Then the righteous will shine like the sun in the kingdom of their Father. He who has ears, let him hear.

The Parables of the Hidden Treasure and the Pearl

[44]"The kingdom of heaven is like treasure hidden in a field. When a man found it, he hid it again, and then in his joy went and sold all he had and bought that field.

[45]"Again, the kingdom of heaven is like a merchant looking for fine pearls. [46]When he found one of great value, he went away and sold everything he had and bought it.

The Parable of the Net

[47]"Once again, the kingdom of heaven is like a net that was let down into the lake and caught all kinds of fish. [48]When it was full, the fishermen pulled it up on the shore. Then they sat down and collected the good fish in baskets, but threw the bad away. [49]This is how it will be at the end of the age. The angels will come and separate the wicked from the righteous [50]and throw them into the fiery furnace, where there will be weeping and gnashing of teeth.

[51]"Have you understood all these things?" Jesus asked.

"Yes," they replied.

[52]He said to them, "Therefore every teacher of the law who has been instructed about the kingdom of heaven is like the owner of a house who brings out of his storeroom new treasures as well as old."

truth or dare

Any pearl lovers out there? Picture the most dazzling pearl in the world. The kingdom of heaven is worth way more than that! Give up everything else in life to get it.

13:45–46

---

[a] 33 Greek three satas (probably about 1/2 bushel or 22 liters)   [b] 35 Psalm 78:2

A Prophet Without Honor

[53]When Jesus had finished these parables, he moved on from there. [54]Coming to his hometown, he began teaching the people in their synagogue, and they were amazed. "Where did this man get this wisdom and these miraculous powers?" they asked. [55]"Isn't this the carpenter's son? Isn't his mother's name Mary, and aren't his brothers James, Joseph, Simon and Judas? [56]Aren't all his sisters with us? Where then did this man get all these things?" [57]And they took offense at him.

But Jesus said to them, "Only in his hometown and in his own house is a prophet without honor." [58]And he did not do many miracles there because of their lack of faith.

John the Baptist Beheaded

14

At that time Herod the tetrarch heard the reports about Jesus, [2]and he said to his attendants, "This is John the Baptist; he has risen from the dead! That is why miraculous powers are at work in him."

[3]Now Herod had arrested John and bound him and put him in prison because of Herodias, his brother Philip's wife, [4]for John had been saying to him: "It is not lawful for you to have her." [5]Herod wanted to kill John, but he was afraid of the people, because they considered him a prophet.

[6]On Herod's birthday the daughter of Herodias danced for them and pleased Herod so much [7]that he promised with an oath to give her whatever she asked. [8]Prompted by her mother, she said, "Give me here on a platter the head of John the Baptist." [9]The king was distressed, but because of his oaths and his dinner guests, he ordered that her request be granted [10]and had John beheaded in the prison. [11]His head was brought in on a platter and given to the girl, who carried it to her mother. [12]John's disciples came and took his body and buried it. Then they went and told Jesus.

Jesus Feeds the Five Thousand

[13]When Jesus heard what had happened, he withdrew by boat privately to a solitary place. Hearing of this, the crowds followed him on foot from the towns. [14]When Jesus landed and saw a large crowd, he had compassion on them and healed their sick.

[15]As evening approached, the disciples came to him and said, "This is a remote place, and it's already getting late. Send the crowds away, so they can go to the villages and buy themselves some food."

[16]Jesus replied, "They do not need to go away. You give them something to eat."

[17]"We have here only five loaves of bread and two fish," they answered.

[18]"Bring them here to me," he said. [19]And he directed the people to sit down on the grass. Taking the five loaves and the two fish and looking up to heaven, he gave thanks and broke the loaves. Then he gave them to the disciples, and the disciples gave them to the people. [20]They all ate and were satisfied, and the disciples picked up twelve basketfuls of broken pieces that were left over. [21]The number of those who ate was about five thousand men, besides women and children.

Jesus Walks on the Water

[22]Immediately Jesus made the disciples get into the boat and go on ahead of him to the other side, while he dismissed the crowd. [23]After he had dismissed them, he went up on a mountainside by himself to pray. When evening came, he was there alone, [24]but the boat was already a considerable distance[a] from land, buffeted by the waves because the wind was against it.

[25]During the fourth watch of the night Jesus went out to them, walking on the lake. [26]When the disciples saw him walking on the lake, they were terrified. "It's a ghost," they said, and cried out in fear.

[27]But Jesus immediately said to them: "Take courage! It is I. Don't be afraid."

[28]"Lord, if it's you," Peter replied, "tell me to come to you on the water."

[29]"Come," he said.

Then Peter got down out of the boat, walked on the water and came toward Jesus. [30]But when he saw the wind, he was afraid and, beginning to sink, cried out, "Lord, save me!"

[31]Immediately Jesus reached out his hand and caught him. "You of little faith," he said, "why did you doubt?"

[32]And when they climbed into the boat, the wind died down. [33]Then those who were in the boat

a 24 Greek many stadia

worshiped him, saying, "Truly you are the Son of God."

[34]When they had crossed over, they landed at Gennesaret. [35]And when the men of that place recognized Jesus, they sent word to all the surrounding country. People brought all their sick to him [36]and begged him to let the sick just touch the edge of his cloak, and all who touched him were healed.

Clean and Unclean

15 Then some Pharisees and teachers of the law came to Jesus from Jerusalem and asked, [2]"Why do your disciples break the tradition of the elders? They don't wash their hands before they eat!"

[3]Jesus replied, "And why do you break the command of God for the sake of your tradition? [4]For God said, 'Honor your father and mother'[a] and 'Anyone who curses his father or mother must be put to death.'[b] [5]But you say that if a man says to his father or mother, 'Whatever help you might otherwise have received from me is a gift devoted to God,' [6]he is not to 'honor his father'[c] with it. Thus you nullify the word of God for the sake of your tradition. [7]You hypocrites! Isaiah was right when he prophesied about you:

[8]" 'These people honor me with their lips,
    but their hearts are far from me.
[9]They worship me in vain;
    their teachings are but rules taught by men.'[d]"

[10]Jesus called the crowd to him and said, "Listen and understand. [11]What goes into a man's mouth does not make him 'unclean,' but what comes out of his mouth, that is what makes him 'unclean.' "

[12]Then the disciples came to him and asked, "Do you know that the Pharisees were offended when they heard this?"

[13]He replied, "Every plant that my heavenly Father has not planted will be pulled up by the roots. [14]Leave them; they are blind guides.[e] If a blind man leads a blind man, both will fall into a pit."

[15]Peter said, "Explain the parable to us."

[16]"Are you still so dull?" Jesus asked them. [17]"Don't you see that whatever enters the mouth goes into the stomach and then out of the body? [18]But the things that come out of the mouth come from the heart, and these make a man 'unclean.' [19]For out of the heart come evil thoughts, murder, adultery, sexual immorality, theft, false testimony, slander. [20]These are what make a man 'unclean'; but eating with unwashed hands does not make him 'unclean.' "

The Faith of the Canaanite Woman

[21]Leaving that place, Jesus withdrew to the region of Tyre and Sidon. [22]A Canaanite woman from that vicinity came to him, crying out, "Lord, Son of David, have mercy on me! My daughter is suffering terribly from demon-possession."

[a] 4 Exodus 20:12; Deut. 5:16   [b] 4 Exodus 21:17; Lev. 20:9   [c] 6 Some manuscripts *father or his mother*
[d] 9 Isaiah 29:13   [e] 14 Some manuscripts *guides of the blind*

mirror images

He appeared first to Mary Magdalene, out of whom he had driven seven demons. Mark 16:9

Mary Magdalene—Undying Gratitude

How would you feel if you had been brought from death to life? What if you were really sick, at the point of death, and then suddenly you were healed? What would you do with your life after that? Would the experience change you?

Mary Magdalene experienced a life transformation when she met Jesus. She was tormented by seven demons, an outcast from society. But then she met one man who didn't see her that way. Jesus cast out her demons, healing her from the inside out—bringing her from death to life. So what do you think Mary did with her life after that?

Mary must have realized the remarkable chance she had at a new life. So she chose to spend her days faithfully following and serving Jesus for the next three years. Even when all but one of the twelve disciples deserted Jesus' crucifixion in fear, she stood near the cross, mourning the loss of her Savior.

Three days later, she was still faithful. She went to the tomb and discovered that Jesus' body was missing. Confused and upset, she didn't recognize Jesus when he approached. Then he said her name, "Mary." She knew that voice, the words of the one who had set her free. The risen Savior could have appeared to his twelve disciples, but instead he chose Mary Magdalene, the woman who showed him undying gratitude. She ran to spread the good news, "I have seen the Lord!"

Remember the last time you were so thankful you had to shout? Good news about a sick relative, a first date or a college acceptance letter. All are reasons to rejoice. But how about being grateful for life in Christ? If you've trusted Jesus Christ to save you from your sins, you've been given the promise of eternal life in heaven. You are loved by the heavenly Father, who promises you life to the full in him. So don't just stand there! Show your undying gratitude to your Savior by telling others what Jesus has done for you.

Dear Jesus, I am eternally grateful for what you've done for me. Help me to love you more each day and to tell others of my undying grattude. Amen.

To read the next Mirror Images profile, go to page 1329.

➤➤ **Read more in Matthew 27–28 (pages 1330–1333); Mark 15–16 (pages 1358–1361); John 19–20 (pages 1439–1442).**

²³Jesus did not answer a word. So his disciples came to him and urged him, "Send her away, for she keeps crying out after us."

²⁴He answered, "I was sent only to the lost sheep of Israel."

²⁵The woman came and knelt before him. "Lord, help me!" she said.

²⁶He replied, "It is not right to take the children's bread and toss it to their dogs."

²⁷"Yes, Lord," she said, "but even the dogs eat the crumbs that fall from their masters' table."

²⁸Then Jesus answered, "Woman, you have great faith! Your request is granted." And her daughter was healed from that very hour.

Jesus Feeds the Four Thousand

²⁹Jesus left there and went along the Sea of Galilee. Then he went up on a mountainside and sat down. ³⁰Great crowds came to him, bringing the lame, the blind, the crippled, the mute and many others, and laid them at his feet; and he healed them. ³¹The people were amazed when they saw the mute speaking, the crippled made well, the lame walking and the blind seeing. And they praised the God of Israel.

³²Jesus called his disciples to him and said, "I have compassion for these people; they have already been with me three days and have nothing to eat. I do not want to send them away hungry, or they may collapse on the way."

³³His disciples answered, "Where could we get enough bread in this remote place to feed such a crowd?"

³⁴"How many loaves do you have?" Jesus asked.

"Seven," they replied, "and a few small fish."

³⁵He told the crowd to sit down on the ground. ³⁶Then he took the seven loaves and the fish, and when he had given thanks, he broke them and gave them to the disciples, and they in turn to the people. ³⁷They all ate and were satisfied. Afterward the disciples picked up seven basketfuls of broken pieces that were left over. ³⁸The number of those who ate was four thousand, besides women and children. ³⁹After Jesus had sent the crowd away, he got into the boat and went to the vicinity of Magadan.

The Demand for a Sign

16 The Pharisees and Sadducees came to Jesus and tested him by asking him to show them a sign from heaven.

²He replied,ᵃ "When evening comes, you say, 'It will be fair weather, for the sky is red,' ³and in the morning, 'Today it will be stormy, for the sky is red and overcast.' You know how to interpret the appearance of the sky, but you cannot interpret the signs of the times. ⁴A wicked and adulterous generation looks for a miraculous sign, but none will be given it except the sign of Jonah." Jesus then left them and went away.

The Yeast of the Pharisees and Sadducees

⁵When they went across the lake, the disciples forgot to take bread. ⁶"Be careful," Jesus said to them. "Be on your guard against the yeast of the Pharisees and Sadducees."

⁷They discussed this among themselves and said, "It is because we didn't bring any bread."

⁸Aware of their discussion, Jesus asked, "You of little faith, why are you talking among yourselves about having no bread? ⁹Do you still not understand? Don't you remember the five loaves for the five thousand, and how many basketfuls you gathered? ¹⁰Or the seven loaves for the four thousand, and how many basketfuls you gathered? ¹¹How is it you don't understand that I was not talking to you about bread? But be on your guard against the yeast of the Pharisees and Sadducees." ¹²Then they understood that he was not telling them to guard against the yeast used in bread, but against the teaching of the Pharisees and Sadducees.

Peter's Confession of Christ

¹³When Jesus came to the region of Caesarea Philippi, he asked his disciples, "Who do people say the Son of Man is?"

ᵃ 2 Some early manuscripts do not have the rest of verse 2 and all of verse 3.

¹⁴They replied, "Some say John the Baptist; others say Elijah; and still others, Jeremiah or one of the prophets."

¹⁵"But what about you?" he asked. "Who do you say I am?"

¹⁶Simon Peter answered, "You are the Christ,ᵃ the Son of the living God."

¹⁷Jesus replied, "Blessed are you, Simon son of Jonah, for this was not revealed to you by man, but by my Father in heaven. ¹⁸And I tell you that you are Peter,ᵇ and on this rock I will build my church, and the gates of Hadesᶜ will not overcome it.ᵈ ¹⁹I will give you the keys of the kingdom of heaven; whatever you bind on earth will beᵉ bound in heaven, and whatever you loose on earth will beᵉ loosed in heaven." ²⁰Then he warned his disciples not to tell anyone that he was the Christ.

truth or dare

Peter wasn't low-key about his faith. When Jesus asked the disciples what they believed about him, Peter spoke up and gave a bold confession. Will you speak boldly for Christ?

16:13–16

Jesus Predicts His Death

²¹From that time on Jesus began to explain to his disciples that he must go to Jerusalem and suffer many things at the hands of the elders, chief priests and teachers of the law, and that he must be killed and on the third day be raised to life.

²²Peter took him aside and began to rebuke him. "Never, Lord!" he said. "This shall never happen to you!"

²³Jesus turned and said to Peter, "Get behind me, Satan! You are a stumbling block to me; you do not have in mind the things of God, but the things of men."

²⁴Then Jesus said to his disciples, "If anyone would come after me, he must deny himself and take up his cross and follow me. ²⁵For whoever wants to save his lifeᶠ will lose it, but whoever loses his life for me will find it. ²⁶What good will it be for a man if he gains the whole world, yet forfeits his soul? Or what can a man give in exchange for his soul? ²⁷For the Son of Man is going to come in his Father's glory with his angels, and then he will reward each person according to what he has done. ²⁸I tell you the truth, some who are standing here will not taste death before they see the Son of Man coming in his kingdom."

The Transfiguration

17 After six days Jesus took with him Peter, James and John the brother of James, and led them up a high mountain by themselves. ²There he was transfigured before them. His face shone like the sun, and his clothes became as white as the light. ³Just then there appeared before them Moses and Elijah, talking with Jesus.

⁴Peter said to Jesus, "Lord, it is good for us to be here. If you wish, I will put up three shelters—one for you, one for Moses and one for Elijah."

⁵While he was still speaking, a bright cloud enveloped them, and a voice from the cloud said, "This is my Son, whom I love; with him I am well pleased. Listen to him!"

⁶When the disciples heard this, they fell facedown to the ground, terrified. ⁷But Jesus came and touched them. "Get up," he said. "Don't be afraid." ⁸When they looked up, they saw no one except Jesus.

⁹As they were coming down the mountain, Jesus instructed them, "Don't tell anyone what you have seen, until the Son of Man has been raised from the dead."

¹⁰The disciples asked him, "Why then do the teachers of the law say that Elijah must come first?"

¹¹Jesus replied, "To be sure, Elijah comes and will restore all things. ¹²But I tell you, Elijah has already come, and they did not recognize him, but have done to him everything they wished. In the same way the Son of Man is going to suffer at their hands." ¹³Then the disciples understood that he was talking to them about John the Baptist.

ᵃ 16 Or *Messiah*; also in verse 20   ᵇ 18 *Peter* means *rock*.   ᶜ 18 Or *hell*   ᵈ 18 Or *not prove stronger than it*
ᵉ 19 Or *have been*   ᶠ 25 The Greek word means either *life* or *soul*; also in verse 26.

The Healing of a Boy With a Demon

[14]When they came to the crowd, a man approached Jesus and knelt before him. [15]"Lord, have mercy on my son," he said. "He has seizures and is suffering greatly. He often falls into the fire or into the water. [16]I brought him to your disciples, but they could not heal him."

[17]"O unbelieving and perverse generation," Jesus replied, "how long shall I stay with you? How long shall I put up with you? Bring the boy here to me." [18]Jesus rebuked the demon, and it came out of the boy, and he was healed from that moment.

[19]Then the disciples came to Jesus in private and asked, "Why couldn't we drive it out?"

[20]He replied, "Because you have so little faith. I tell you the truth, if you have faith as small as a mustard seed, you can say to this mountain, 'Move from here to there' and it will move. Nothing will be impossible for you.[a]"

[22]When they came together in Galilee, he said to them, "The Son of Man is going to be betrayed into the hands of men. [23]They will kill him, and on the third day he will be raised to life." And the disciples were filled with grief.

truth or dare

Want success in prayer, ministry or life? You've gotta have faith. You don't have to be the model of perfection in order to see God's power—you just need that mustard seed of pure faith.

17:20

The Temple Tax

[24]After Jesus and his disciples arrived in Capernaum, the collectors of the two-drachma tax came to Peter and asked, "Doesn't your teacher pay the temple tax[b]?"

[25]"Yes, he does," he replied.

When Peter came into the house, Jesus was the first to speak. "What do you think, Simon?" he asked. "From whom do the kings of the earth collect duty and taxes—from their own sons or from others?"

[26]"From others," Peter answered.

"Then the sons are exempt," Jesus said to him. [27]"But so that we may not offend them, go to the lake and throw out your line. Take the first fish you catch; open its mouth and you will find a four-drachma coin. Take it and give it to them for my tax and yours."

The Greatest in the Kingdom of Heaven

18 At that time the disciples came to Jesus and asked, "Who is the greatest in the kingdom of heaven?"

[2]He called a little child and had him stand among them. [3]And he said: "I tell you the truth, unless you change and become like little children, you will never enter the kingdom of heaven. [4]Therefore, whoever humbles himself like this child is the greatest in the kingdom of heaven.

[5]"And whoever welcomes a little child like this in my name welcomes me. [6]But if

genuine

humility » 18:1-4

Ever get sick of being treated like a child? Wish your parents would talk to you like an adult? Hey, don't knock being a kid. Jesus said there's a lot to be learned from them. Children are humble and honest and trusting. They're open and unassuming. And in order to enter God's kingdom, you have to have that kind of heart. So, as you grow up into adulthood, don't leave all of childhood behind. Keep a childlike heart as you trust in Jesus.

---

[a] 20 Some manuscripts *you.* [21]*But this kind does not go out except by prayer and fasting.*   [b] 24 Greek *the two drachmas*

anyone causes one of these little ones who believe in me to sin, it would be better for him to have a large millstone hung around his neck and to be drowned in the depths of the sea.

[7]"Woe to the world because of the things that cause people to sin! Such things must come, but woe to the man through whom they come! [8]If your hand or your foot causes you to sin, cut it off and throw it away. It is better for you to enter life maimed or crippled than to have two hands or two feet and be thrown into eternal fire. [9]And if your eye causes you to sin, gouge it out and throw it away. It is better for you to enter life with one eye than to have two eyes and be thrown into the fire of hell.

The Parable of the Lost Sheep

[10]"See that you do not look down on one of these little ones. For I tell you that their angels in heaven always see the face of my Father in heaven. [a]

[12]"What do you think? If a man owns a hundred sheep, and one of them wanders away, will he not leave the ninety-nine on the hills and go to look for the one that wandered off? [13]And if he finds it, I tell you the truth, he is happier about that one sheep than about the ninety-nine that did not wander off. [14]In the same way your Father in heaven is not willing that any of these little ones should be lost.

A Brother Who Sins Against You

[15]"If your brother sins against you, [b] go and show him his fault, just between the two of you. If he listens to you, you have won your brother over. [16]But if he will not listen, take one or two others along, so that 'every matter may be established by the testimony of two or three witnesses.' [c] [17]If he refuses to listen to them, tell it to the church; and if he refuses to listen even to the church, treat him as you would a pagan or a tax collector.

[18]"I tell you the truth, whatever you bind on earth will be [d] bound in heaven, and whatever you loose on earth will be [d] loosed in heaven.

[19]"Again, I tell you that if two of you on earth agree about anything you ask for, it will be done for you by my Father in heaven. [20]For where two or three come together in my name, there am I with them."

The Parable of the Unmerciful Servant

[21]Then Peter came to Jesus and asked, "Lord, how many times shall I forgive my brother when he sins against me? Up to seven times?"

[22]Jesus answered, "I tell you, not seven times, but seventy-seven times. [e]

[23]"Therefore, the kingdom of heaven is like a king who wanted to settle accounts with his servants. [24]As he began the settlement, a man who owed him ten thousand talents [f] was brought to him. [25]Since he was not able to pay, the master ordered that he and his wife and his children and all that he had be sold to repay the debt.

[26]"The servant fell on his knees before him. 'Be patient with me,' he begged, 'and I will pay back everything.' [27]The servant's master took pity on him, canceled the debt and let him go.

[28]"But when that servant went out, he found one of his fellow servants who owed him a hundred denarii. [g] He grabbed him and began to choke him. 'Pay back what you owe me!' he demanded.

[29]"His fellow servant fell to his knees and begged him, 'Be patient with me, and I will pay you back.'

[30]"But he refused. Instead, he went off and had the man thrown into prison until he could pay the debt. [31]When the other servants saw what had happened, they were greatly distressed and went and told their master everything that had happened.

truth or dare

What an amazing promise from God! If you team up in prayer, he's going to be there. So, don't miss out. Take time each week to pray with your friends.

18:19–20

---

[a] 10 Some manuscripts heaven. [11]The Son of Man came to save what was lost. [b] 15 Some manuscripts do not have against you. [c] 16 Deut. 19:15 [d] 18 Or have been [e] 22 Or seventy times seven [f] 24 That is, millions of dollars [g] 28 That is, a few dollars

³²"Then the master called the servant in. 'You wicked servant,' he said, 'I canceled all that debt of yours because you begged me to. ³³Shouldn't you have had mercy on your fellow servant just as I had on you?' ³⁴In anger his master turned him over to the jailers to be tortured, until he should pay back all he owed.

³⁵"This is how my heavenly Father will treat each of you unless you forgive your brother from your heart."

Divorce

19 When Jesus had finished saying these things, he left Galilee and went into the region of Judea to the other side of the Jordan. ²Large crowds followed him, and he healed them there.

³Some Pharisees came to him to test him. They asked, "Is it lawful for a man to divorce his wife for any and every reason?"

⁴"Haven't you read," he replied, "that at the beginning the Creator 'made them male and female,'ᵃ ⁵and said, 'For this reason a man will leave his father and mother and be united to his wife, and the two will become one flesh'ᵇ? ⁶So they are no longer two, but one. Therefore what God has joined together, let man not separate."

⁷"Why then," they asked, "did Moses command that a man give his wife a certificate of divorce and send her away?"

⁸Jesus replied, "Moses permitted you to divorce your wives because your hearts were hard. But it was not this way from the beginning. ⁹I tell you that anyone who divorces his wife, except for marital unfaithfulness, and marries another woman commits adultery."

¹⁰The disciples said to him, "If this is the situation between a husband and wife, it is better not to marry."

¹¹Jesus replied, "Not everyone can accept this word, but only those to whom it has been given. ¹²For some are eunuchs because they were born that way; others were made that way by men; and others have renounced marriageᶜ because of the kingdom of heaven. The one who can accept this should accept it."

The Little Children and Jesus

¹³Then little children were brought to Jesus for him to place his hands on them and pray for them. But the disciples rebuked those who brought them.

¹⁴Jesus said, "Let the little children come to me, and do not hinder them, for the kingdom of heaven belongs to such as these." ¹⁵When he had placed his hands on them, he went on from there.

The Rich Young Man

¹⁶Now a man came up to Jesus and asked, "Teacher, what good thing must I do to get eternal life?"

¹⁷"Why do you ask me about what is good?" Jesus replied. "There is only One who is good. If you want to enter life, obey the commandments."

¹⁸"Which ones?" the man inquired.

Jesus replied, " 'Do not murder, do not commit adultery, do not steal, do not give false testimony, ¹⁹honor your father and mother,'ᵈ and 'love your neighbor as yourself.'ᵉ"

²⁰"All these I have kept," the young man said. "What do I still lack?"

²¹Jesus answered, "If you want to be perfect, go, sell your possessions and give to the poor, and you will have treasure in heaven. Then come, follow me."

²²When the young man heard this, he went away sad, because he had great wealth.

truth or dare

Being wealthy isn't a bad thing. But Jesus did want to give us a big warning: Don't let your $$$ distract you from the true treasure—Jesus.

19:21–24

ᵃ 4 Gen. 1:27   ᵇ 5 Gen. 2:24   ᶜ 12 Or *have made themselves eunuchs*   ᵈ 19 Exodus 20:12-16; Deut. 5:16-20
ᵉ 19 Lev. 19:18

²³Then Jesus said to his disciples, "I tell you the truth, it is hard for a rich man to enter the kingdom of heaven. ²⁴Again I tell you, it is easier for a camel to go through the eye of a needle than for a rich man to enter the kingdom of God."

²⁵When the disciples heard this, they were greatly astonished and asked, "Who then can be saved?"

²⁶Jesus looked at them and said, "With man this is impossible, but with God all things are possible."

²⁷Peter answered him, "We have left everything to follow you! What then will there be for us?"

²⁸Jesus said to them, "I tell you the truth, at the renewal of all things, when the Son of Man sits on his glorious throne, you who have followed me will also sit on twelve thrones, judging the twelve tribes of Israel. ²⁹And everyone who has left houses or brothers or sisters or father or mother *ᵃ* or children or fields for my sake will receive a hundred times as much and will inherit eternal life. ³⁰But many who are first will be last, and many who are last will be first.

The Parable of the Workers in the Vineyard

20 "For the kingdom of heaven is like a landowner who went out early in the morning to hire men to work in his vineyard. ²He agreed to pay them a denarius for the day and sent them into his vineyard.

³"About the third hour he went out and saw others standing in the marketplace doing nothing. ⁴He told them, 'You also go and work in my vineyard, and I will pay you whatever is right.' ⁵So they went.

"He went out again about the sixth hour and the ninth hour and did the same thing. ⁶About the eleventh hour he went out and found still others standing around. He asked them, 'Why have you been standing here all day long doing nothing?'

⁷"'Because no one has hired us,' they answered.

"He said to them, 'You also go and work in my vineyard.'

⁸"When evening came, the owner of the vineyard said to his foreman, 'Call the workers and pay them their wages, beginning with the last ones hired and going on to the first.'

⁹"The workers who were hired about the eleventh hour came and each received a denarius. ¹⁰So when those came who were hired first, they expected to receive more. But each one of them also received a denarius. ¹¹When they received it, they began to grumble against the landowner. ¹²'These men who were hired last worked only one hour,' they said, 'and you have made them equal to us who have borne the burden of the work and the heat of the day.'

¹³"But he answered one of them, 'Friend, I am not being unfair to you. Didn't you agree to work for a denarius? ¹⁴Take your pay and go. I want to give the man who was hired last the same as I gave you. ¹⁵Don't I have the right to do what I want with my own money? Or are you envious because I am generous?'

¹⁶"So the last will be first, and the first will be last."

Jesus Again Predicts His Death

¹⁷Now as Jesus was going up to Jerusalem, he took the twelve disciples aside and said to them, ¹⁸"We are going up to Jerusalem, and the Son of Man will be betrayed to the chief priests and the teachers of the law. They will condemn him to death ¹⁹and will turn him over to the Gentiles to be mocked and flogged and crucified. On the third day he will be raised to life!"

A Mother's Request

²⁰Then the mother of Zebedee's sons came to Jesus with her sons and, kneeling down, asked a favor of him.

²¹"What is it you want?" he asked.

She said, "Grant that one of these two sons of mine may sit at your right and the other at your left in your kingdom."

²²"You don't know what you are asking," Jesus said to them. "Can you drink the cup I am going to drink?"

"We can," they answered.

ᵃ 29 Some manuscripts *mother or wife*

[23]Jesus said to them, "You will indeed drink from my cup, but to sit at my right or left is not for me to grant. These places belong to those for whom they have been prepared by my Father."

[24]When the ten heard about this, they were indignant with the two brothers. [25]Jesus called them together and said, "You know that the rulers of the Gentiles lord it over them, and their high officials exercise authority over them. [26]Not so with you. Instead, whoever wants to become great among you must be your servant, [27]and whoever wants to be first must be your slave— [28]just as the Son of Man did not come to be served, but to serve, and to give his life as a ransom for many."

Two Blind Men Receive Sight

[29]As Jesus and his disciples were leaving Jericho, a large crowd followed him. [30]Two blind men were sitting by the roadside, and when they heard that Jesus was going by, they shouted, "Lord, Son of David, have mercy on us!"

[31]The crowd rebuked them and told them to be quiet, but they shouted all the louder, "Lord, Son of David, have mercy on us!"

[32]Jesus stopped and called them. "What do you want me to do for you?" he asked.

[33]"Lord," they answered, "we want our sight."

[34]Jesus had compassion on them and touched their eyes. Immediately they received their sight and followed him.

The Triumphal Entry

21 As they approached Jerusalem and came to Bethphage on the Mount of Olives, Jesus sent two disciples, [2]saying to them, "Go to the village ahead of you, and at once you will find a donkey tied there, with her colt by her. Untie them and bring them to me. [3]If anyone says anything to you, tell him that the Lord needs them, and he will send them right away."

[4]This took place to fulfill what was spoken through the prophet:

[5]"Say to the Daughter of Zion,
'See, your king comes to you,
gentle and riding on a donkey,
on a colt, the foal of a donkey.' "[a]

[6]The disciples went and did as Jesus had instructed them. [7]They brought the donkey and the colt, placed their cloaks on them, and Jesus sat on them. [8]A very large crowd spread their cloaks on the road, while others cut branches from the trees and spread them on the road. [9]The crowds that went ahead of him and those that followed shouted,

"Hosanna[b] to the Son of David!"

"Blessed is he who comes in the name of the Lord!"[c]

"Hosanna[b] in the highest!"

[10]When Jesus entered Jerusalem, the whole city was stirred and asked, "Who is this?"

[11]The crowds answered, "This is Jesus, the prophet from Nazareth in Galilee."

Jesus at the Temple

[12]Jesus entered the temple area and drove out all who were buying and selling there. He overturned the tables of the money changers and the benches of those selling doves. [13]"It is written," he said to them, " 'My house will be called a house of prayer,'[d] but you are making it a 'den of robbers.'[e]"

[14]The blind and the lame came to him at the temple, and he healed them. [15]But when the chief priests and the teachers of the law saw the wonderful things he did and the children shouting in the temple area, "Hosanna to the Son of David," they were indignant.

[16]"Do you hear what these children are saying?" they asked him.

"Yes," replied Jesus, "have you never read,

a 5 Zech. 9:9   *b 9* A Hebrew expression meaning "Save!" which became an exclamation of praise; also in verse 15
c 9 Psalm 118:26   *d 13* Isaiah 56:7   *e 13* Jer. 7:11

" 'From the lips of children and infants
you have ordained praise'[a]?"

[17]And he left them and went out of the city to Bethany, where he spent the night.

The Fig Tree Withers

[18]Early in the morning, as he was on his way back to the city, he was hungry. [19]Seeing a fig tree by the road, he went up to it but found nothing on it except leaves. Then he said to it, "May you never bear fruit again!" Immediately the tree withered.

[20]When the disciples saw this, they were amazed. "How did the fig tree wither so quickly?" they asked.

[21]Jesus replied, "I tell you the truth, if you have faith and do not doubt, not only can you do what was done to the fig tree, but also you can say to this mountain, 'Go, throw yourself into the sea,' and it will be done. [22]If you believe, you will receive whatever you ask for in prayer."

truth or dare

These verses don't mean you'll win the lottery if you pray. The more you believe, the more God will shape your will—and your prayers—to be in line with his.

21:21–22

The Authority of Jesus Questioned

[23]Jesus entered the temple courts, and, while he was teaching, the chief priests and the elders of the people came to him. "By what authority are you doing these things?" they asked. "And who gave you this authority?"

[24]Jesus replied, "I will also ask you one question. If you answer me, I will tell you by what authority I am doing these things. [25]John's baptism—where did it come from? Was it from heaven, or from men?"

They discussed it among themselves and said, "If we say, 'From heaven,' he will ask, 'Then why didn't you believe him?' [26]But if we say, 'From men'—we are afraid of the people, for they all hold that John was a prophet."

[27]So they answered Jesus, "We don't know."

Then he said, "Neither will I tell you by what authority I am doing these things.

The Parable of the Two Sons

[28]"What do you think? There was a man who had two sons. He went to the first and said, 'Son, go and work today in the vineyard.'

[29]" 'I will not,' he answered, but later he changed his mind and went.

[30]"Then the father went to the other son and said the same thing. He answered, 'I will, sir,' but he did not go.

[31]"Which of the two did what his father wanted?"

"The first," they answered.

Jesus said to them, "I tell you the truth, the tax collectors and the prostitutes are entering the kingdom of God ahead of you. [32]For John came to you to show you the way of righteousness, and you did not believe him, but the tax collectors and the prostitutes did. And even after you saw this, you did not repent and believe him.

The Parable of the Tenants

[33]"Listen to another parable: There was a landowner who planted a vineyard. He put a wall around it, dug a winepress in it and built a watchtower. Then he rented the vineyard to some farmers and went away on a journey. [34]When the harvest time approached, he sent his servants to the tenants to collect his fruit.

[35]"The tenants seized his servants; they beat one, killed another, and stoned a third. [36]Then he sent other servants to them, more than the first time, and the tenants treated them the same way. [37]Last of all, he sent his son to them. 'They will respect my son,' he said.

[38]"But when the tenants saw the son, they said to each other, 'This is the heir. Come, let's kill him and take his inheritance.' [39]So they took him and threw him out of the vineyard and killed him.

a 16 Psalm 8:2

⁴⁰"Therefore, when the owner of the vineyard comes, what will he do to those tenants?"

⁴¹"He will bring those wretches to a wretched end," they replied, "and he will rent the vineyard to other tenants, who will give him his share of the crop at harvest time."

⁴²Jesus said to them, "Have you never read in the Scriptures:

> " 'The stone the builders rejected
> has become the capstone *a*;
> the Lord has done this,
> and it is marvelous in our eyes' *b*?

⁴³"Therefore I tell you that the kingdom of God will be taken away from you and given to a people who will produce its fruit. ⁴⁴He who falls on this stone will be broken to pieces, but he on whom it falls will be crushed." *c*

⁴⁵When the chief priests and the Pharisees heard Jesus' parables, they knew he was talking about them. ⁴⁶They looked for a way to arrest him, but they were afraid of the crowd because the people held that he was a prophet.

The Parable of the Wedding Banquet

22 Jesus spoke to them again in parables, saying: ²"The kingdom of heaven is like a king who prepared a wedding banquet for his son. ³He sent his servants to those who had been invited to the banquet to tell them to come, but they refused to come.

⁴"Then he sent some more servants and said, 'Tell those who have been invited that I have prepared my dinner: My oxen and fattened cattle have been butchered, and everything is ready. Come to the wedding banquet.'

⁵"But they paid no attention and went off—one to his field, another to his business. ⁶The rest seized his servants, mistreated them and killed them. ⁷The king was enraged. He sent his army and destroyed those murderers and burned their city.

⁸"Then he said to his servants, 'The wedding banquet is ready, but those I invited did not deserve to come. ⁹Go to the street corners and invite to the banquet anyone you find.' ¹⁰So the servants went out into the streets and gathered all the people they could find, both good and bad, and the wedding hall was filled with guests.

¹¹"But when the king came in to see the guests, he noticed a man there who was not wearing wedding clothes. ¹²'Friend,' he asked, 'how did you get in here without wedding clothes?' The man was speechless.

¹³"Then the king told the attendants, 'Tie him hand and foot, and throw him outside, into the darkness, where there will be weeping and gnashing of teeth.'

¹⁴"For many are invited, but few are chosen."

Paying Taxes to Caesar

¹⁵Then the Pharisees went out and laid plans to trap him in his words. ¹⁶They sent their disciples to him along with the Herodians. "Teacher," they said, "we know you are a man of integrity and that you teach the way of God in accordance with the truth. You aren't swayed by men, because you pay no attention to who they are. ¹⁷Tell us then, what is your opinion? Is it right to pay taxes to Caesar or not?"

¹⁸But Jesus, knowing their evil intent, said, "You hypocrites, why are you trying to trap me? ¹⁹Show me the coin used for paying the tax." They brought him a denarius, ²⁰and he asked them, "Whose portrait is this? And whose inscription?"

²¹"Caesar's," they replied.

Then he said to them, "Give to Caesar what is Caesar's, and to God what is God's."

²²When they heard this, they were amazed. So they left him and went away.

Marriage at the Resurrection

²³That same day the Sadducees, who say there is no resurrection, came to him with a question. ²⁴"Teacher," they said, "Moses told us that if a man dies without having children, his brother must marry the widow and have children for him. ²⁵Now there were seven brothers among us. The

a 42 Or *cornerstone*   *b 42* Psalm 118:22,23   *c 44* Some manuscripts do not have verse 44.

Backstabber

"Oh. My. Word. I love your new tattoo, Shari!" Suzie said with enthusiasm in that familiar voice of hers.

"Thanks, Suz! I got it this weekend," Shari said as she entered the stall in the girl's restroom.

"Very cool. Hey, did you see what Bailey was wearing today?" Suzie asked as she carefully applied lip liner in the mirror, waiting on Shari.

"I wouldn't be caught *dead* in that outfit," Shari said over the flushing sound as she opened the door and fastened her belt.

Suzie laughed and said, "Maybe her grandma bought it for her or something."

"Or it *belonged* to her grandma . . ." Shari's voice dropped off as they left the girls restroom, laughing hysterically as if they'd just heard the best joke.

Only it wasn't a joke they were laughing at. It was *me*. They didn't know I was in the last stall, listening to their whole conversation. I felt sick to my stomach, and my face was flushed. These were supposed to be my friends? Wasn't that *Shari* making fun of *Suzie* just the other day after Suzie walked away? And didn't Suzie just confide in me her true feelings about Shari's new ankle tattoo? That she thought it looked like a stick-on from the dollar store?

I wanted to scream. Or cry. I had thought I looked nice. Now I wanted to call my mom to bring me a different outfit. Actually, I wanted her to take me out of this stupid school forever. ✦

True, I'm just as bad—saying things about people behind their backs. I just never realized how much it hurt . . . till now.

gossip in focus

Think your words are no big deal? Read Matthew 12:36 (page 1307). Remember . . .

»Gossip is addicting. We can't wait to hear the scoop on someone else. However, how does it feel to imagine *yourself* as the hot topic of conversation? What goes around comes around (see Galatians 6:7, page 1540).

»The Bible says our mouths get us into more trouble than anything else. See James 3:6–8 (page 1604) for James's choice words about choosing our words.

»When your friends start to gossip about someone, walk away. Listening to it is just as bad as spreading it. If you can't walk away, then change the subject or throw in something nice about that person.

For more on this topic, see the index on page 1656.

gossip

first one married and died, and since he had no children, he left his wife to his brother. ²⁶The same thing happened to the second and third brother, right on down to the seventh. ²⁷Finally, the woman died. ²⁸Now then, at the resurrection, whose wife will she be of the seven, since all of them were married to her?"

[29]Jesus replied, "You are in error because you do not know the Scriptures or the power of God. [30]At the resurrection people will neither marry nor be given in marriage; they will be like the angels in heaven. [31]But about the resurrection of the dead—have you not read what God said to you, [32]'I am the God of Abraham, the God of Isaac, and the God of Jacob'[a]? He is not the God of the dead but of the living."

[33]When the crowds heard this, they were astonished at his teaching.

The Greatest Commandment

[34]Hearing that Jesus had silenced the Sadducees, the Pharisees got together. [35]One of them, an expert in the law, tested him with this question: [36]"Teacher, which is the greatest commandment in the Law?"

[37]Jesus replied: " 'Love the Lord your God with all your heart and with all your soul and with all your mind.'[b] [38]This is the first and greatest commandment. [39]And the second is like it: 'Love your neighbor as yourself.'[c] [40]All the Law and the Prophets hang on these two commandments."

Whose Son Is the Christ?

[41]While the Pharisees were gathered together, Jesus asked them, [42]"What do you think about the Christ[d]? Whose son is he?"

"The son of David," they replied.

[43]He said to them, "How is it then that David, speaking by the Spirit, calls him 'Lord'? For he says,

[44]" 'The Lord said to my Lord:
  "Sit at my right hand
  until I put your enemies
    under your feet." '[e]

[45]If then David calls him 'Lord,' how can he be his son?" [46]No one could say a word in reply, and from that day on no one dared to ask him any more questions.

Seven Woes

23 Then Jesus said to the crowds and to his disciples: [2]"The teachers of the law and the Pharisees sit in Moses' seat. [3]So you must obey them and do everything they tell you. But do not do what they do, for they do not practice what they preach. [4]They tie up heavy loads and put them on men's shoulders, but they themselves are not willing to lift a finger to move them.

[5]"Everything they do is done for men to see: They make their phylacteries[f] wide and the tassels on their garments long; [6]they love the place of honor at banquets and the most important seats in the synagogues; [7]they love to be greeted in the marketplaces and to have men call them 'Rabbi.'

[8]"But you are not to be called 'Rabbi,' for you have only one Master and you are all brothers. [9]And do not call anyone on earth 'father,' for you have one Father, and he is in heaven. [10]Nor are you to be called 'teacher,' for you have one Teacher, the Christ.[d] [11]The greatest among you will be your servant. [12]For whoever exalts himself will be humbled, and whoever humbles himself will be exalted.

[13]"Woe to you, teachers of the law and Pharisees, you hypocrites! You shut the kingdom of heaven in men's faces. You yourselves do not enter, nor will you let those enter who are trying to.[g]

[15]"Woe to you, teachers of the law and Pharisees, you hypocrites! You travel over land and sea to win a single convert, and when he becomes one, you make him twice as much a son of hell as you are.

[16]"Woe to you, blind guides! You say, 'If anyone swears by the temple, it means nothing; but if anyone swears by the gold of the temple, he is bound by his oath.' [17]You blind fools! Which is greater: the gold, or the temple that makes the gold sacred? [18]You also say, 'If anyone swears by the altar, it means nothing; but if anyone swears by the gift on it, he is bound by his oath.' [19]You blind men! Which is greater: the gift, or the altar that makes the gift sacred? [20]Therefore, he who swears by the altar swears by it and by everything on it. [21]And he who swears by the temple swears by it

---

[a] 32 Exodus 3:6   [b] 37 Deut. 6:5   [c] 39 Lev. 19:18   [d] 42,10 Or Messiah   [e] 44 Psalm 110:1   [f] 5 That is, boxes containing Scripture verses, worn on forehead and arm   [g] 13 Some manuscripts to. [14]Woe to you, teachers of the law and Pharisees, you hypocrites! You devour widows' houses and for a show make lengthy prayers. Therefore you will be punished more severely.

and by the one who dwells in it. ²²And he who swears by heaven swears by God's throne and by the one who sits on it.

²³"Woe to you, teachers of the law and Pharisees, you hypocrites! You give a tenth of your spices—mint, dill and cummin. But you have neglected the more important matters of the law—justice, mercy and faithfulness. You should have practiced the latter, without neglecting the former. ²⁴You blind guides! You strain out a gnat but swallow a camel.

²⁵"Woe to you, teachers of the law and Pharisees, you hypocrites! You clean the outside of the cup and dish, but inside they are full of greed and self-indulgence. ²⁶Blind Pharisee! First clean the inside of the cup and dish, and then the outside also will be clean.

²⁷"Woe to you, teachers of the law and Pharisees, you hypocrites! You are like whitewashed tombs, which look beautiful on the outside but on the inside are full of dead men's bones and everything unclean. ²⁸In the same way, on the outside you appear to people as righteous but on the inside you are full of hypocrisy and wickedness.

²⁹"Woe to you, teachers of the law and Pharisees, you hypocrites! You build tombs for the prophets and decorate the graves of the righteous. ³⁰And you say, 'If we had lived in the days of our forefathers, we would not have taken part with them in shedding the blood of the prophets.' ³¹So you testify against yourselves that you are the descendants of those who murdered the prophets. ³²Fill up, then, the measure of the sin of your forefathers!

³³"You snakes! You brood of vipers! How will you escape being condemned to hell? ³⁴Therefore I am sending you prophets and wise men and teachers. Some of them you will kill and crucify; others you will flog in your synagogues and pursue from town to town. ³⁵And so upon you will come all the righteous blood that has been shed on earth, from the blood of righteous Abel to the blood of Zechariah son of Berekiah, whom you murdered between the temple and the altar. ³⁶I tell you the truth, all this will come upon this generation.

³⁷"O Jerusalem, Jerusalem, you who kill the prophets and stone those sent to you, how often I have longed to gather your children together, as a hen gathers her chicks under her wings, but you were not willing. ³⁸Look, your house is left to you desolate. ³⁹For I tell you, you will not see me again until you say, 'Blessed is he who comes in the name of the Lord.' ᵃ"

Signs of the End of the Age

24 Jesus left the temple and was walking away when his disciples came up to him to call his attention to its buildings. ²"Do you see all these things?" he asked. "I tell you the truth, not one stone here will be left on another; every one will be thrown down."

³As Jesus was sitting on the Mount of Olives, the disciples came to him privately. "Tell us," they said, "when will this happen, and what will be the sign of your coming and of the end of the age?"

⁴Jesus answered: "Watch out that no one deceives you. ⁵For many will come in my name, claiming, 'I am the Christ,' ᵇ and will deceive many. ⁶You will hear of wars and rumors of wars, but see to it that you are not alarmed. Such things must happen, but the end is still to come. ⁷Nation will rise against nation, and kingdom against kingdom. There will be famines and earthquakes in various places. ⁸All these are the beginning of birth pains.

⁹"Then you will be handed over to be persecuted and put to death, and you will be hated by all nations because of me. ¹⁰At that time many will turn away from the faith and will betray and hate each other, ¹¹and many false prophets will appear and deceive many people. ¹²Because of the increase of wickedness, the love of most will grow cold, ¹³but he who stands firm to the end will be saved. ¹⁴And this gospel of the kingdom will be preached in the whole world as a testimony to all nations, and then the end will come.

¹⁵"So when you see standing in the holy place 'the abomination that causes desolation,' ᶜ spo-

truth *or dare*

Following Christ isn't just about starting the race (though that's important). It's about finishing—sticking with Jesus and loving him your whole life, to the very end.

24:12–13

ᵃ 39 Psalm 118:26   ᵇ 5 Or *Messiah*; also in verse 23   ᶜ 15 Daniel 9:27; 11:31; 12:11

ken of through the prophet Daniel—let the reader understand— ¹⁶then let those who are in Judea flee to the mountains. ¹⁷Let no one on the roof of his house go down to take anything out of the house. ¹⁸Let no one in the field go back to get his cloak. ¹⁹How dreadful it will be in those days for pregnant women and nursing mothers! ²⁰Pray that your flight will not take place in winter or on the Sabbath. ²¹For then there will be great distress, unequaled from the beginning of the world until now—and never to be equaled again. ²²If those days had not been cut short, no one would survive, but for the sake of the elect those days will be shortened. ²³At that time if anyone says to you, 'Look, here is the Christ!' or, 'There he is!' do not believe it. ²⁴For false Christs and false prophets will appear and perform great signs and miracles to deceive even the elect—if that were possible. ²⁵See, I have told you ahead of time.

²⁶"So if anyone tells you, 'There he is, out in the desert,' do not go out; or, 'Here he is, in the inner rooms,' do not believe it. ²⁷For as lightning that comes from the east is visible even in the west, so will be the coming of the Son of Man. ²⁸Wherever there is a carcass, there the vultures will gather.

²⁹"Immediately after the distress of those days

> " 'the sun will be darkened,
>   and the moon will not give its light;
>   the stars will fall from the sky,
>   and the heavenly bodies will be shaken.' ᵃ

³⁰"At that time the sign of the Son of Man will appear in the sky, and all the nations of the earth will mourn. They will see the Son of Man coming on the clouds of the sky, with power and great glory. ³¹And he will send his angels with a loud trumpet call, and they will gather his elect from the four winds, from one end of the heavens to the other.

³²"Now learn this lesson from the fig tree: As soon as its twigs get tender and its leaves come out, you know that summer is near. ³³Even so, when you see all these things, you know that it ᵇ is near, right at the door. ³⁴I tell you the truth, this generation ᶜ will certainly not pass away until all these things have happened. ³⁵Heaven and earth will pass away, but my words will never pass away.

The Day and Hour Unknown

³⁶"No one knows about that day or hour, not even the angels in heaven, nor the Son, ᵈ but only the Father. ³⁷As it was in the days of Noah, so it will be at the coming of the Son of Man. ³⁸For in the days before the flood, people were eating and drinking, marrying and giving in marriage, up to the day Noah entered the ark; ³⁹and they knew nothing about what would happen until the flood came and took them all away. That is how it will be at the coming of the Son of Man. ⁴⁰Two men will be in the field; one will be taken and the other left. ⁴¹Two women will be grinding with a hand mill; one will be taken and the other left.

⁴²"Therefore keep watch, because you do not know on what day your Lord will come. ⁴³But understand this: If the owner of the house had known at what time of night the thief was coming, he would have kept watch and would not have let his house be broken into. ⁴⁴So you also must be ready, because the Son of Man will come at an hour when you do not expect him.

⁴⁵"Who then is the faithful and wise servant, whom the master has put in charge of the servants in his household to give them their food at the proper time? ⁴⁶It will be good for that servant whose master finds him doing so when he returns. ⁴⁷I tell you the truth, he will put him in charge of all his possessions. ⁴⁸But suppose that servant is wicked and says to himself, 'My master is staying away a long time,' ⁴⁹and he then begins to beat his fellow servants and to eat and drink with drunkards. ⁵⁰The master of that servant will come on a day when he does not expect him and at an hour he is not aware of. ⁵¹He will cut him to pieces and assign him a place with the hypocrites, where there will be weeping and gnashing of teeth.

The Parable of the Ten Virgins

25 "At that time the kingdom of heaven will be like ten virgins who took their lamps and went out to meet the bridegroom. ²Five of them were foolish and five were wise. ³The foolish ones took their lamps but did not take any oil with them. ⁴The wise, however,

---

ᵃ 29 Isaiah 13:10; 34:4   ᵇ 33 Or he   ᶜ 34 Or race   ᵈ 36 Some manuscripts do not have nor the Son.

took oil in jars along with their lamps. [5]The bridegroom was a long time in coming, and they all became drowsy and fell asleep.

[6]"At midnight the cry rang out: 'Here's the bridegroom! Come out to meet him!'

[7]"Then all the virgins woke up and trimmed their lamps. [8]The foolish ones said to the wise, 'Give us some of your oil; our lamps are going out.'

[9]" 'No,' they replied, 'there may not be enough for both us and you. Instead, go to those who sell oil and buy some for yourselves.'

[10]"But while they were on their way to buy the oil, the bridegroom arrived. The virgins who were ready went in with him to the wedding banquet. And the door was shut.

[11]"Later the others also came. 'Sir! Sir!' they said. 'Open the door for us!'

[12]"But he replied, 'I tell you the truth, I don't know you.'

[13]"Therefore keep watch, because you do not know the day or the hour.

truth or dare

God's giving us a huge heads-up in this verse: Christ is coming soon, and we don't know what day or time. We've gotta be ready now.

25:13

The Parable of the Talents

[14]"Again, it will be like a man going on a journey, who called his servants and entrusted his property to them. [15]To one he gave five talents[a] of money, to another two talents, and to another one talent, each according to his ability. Then he went on his journey. [16]The man who had received the five talents went at once and put his money to work and gained five more. [17]So also, the one with the two talents gained two more. [18]But the man who had received the one talent went off, dug a hole in the ground and hid his master's money.

[19]"After a long time the master of those servants returned and settled accounts with them. [20]The man who had received the five talents brought the other five. 'Master,' he said, 'you entrusted me with five talents. See, I have gained five more.'

[21]"His master replied, 'Well done, good and faithful servant! You have been faithful with a few things; I will put you in charge of many things. Come and share your master's happiness!'

[22]"The man with the two talents also came. 'Master,' he said, 'you entrusted me with two talents; see, I have gained two more.'

[23]"His master replied, 'Well done, good and faithful servant! You have been faithful with a few things; I will put you in charge of many things. Come and share your master's happiness!'

[24]"Then the man who had received the one talent came. 'Master,' he said, 'I knew that you are a hard man, harvesting where you have not sown and gathering where you have not scattered seed. [25]So I was afraid and went out and hid your talent in the ground. See, here is what belongs to you.'

[26]"His master replied, 'You wicked, lazy servant! So you knew that I harvest where I have not sown and gather where I have not scattered seed? [27]Well then, you should have put my money on deposit with the bankers, so that when I returned I would have received it back with interest.

[28]" 'Take the talent from him and give it to the one who has the ten talents. [29]For everyone who has will be given more, and he will have an abundance. Whoever does not have, even what he has will be taken from him. [30]And throw that worthless servant outside, into the darkness, where there will be weeping and gnashing of teeth.'

The Sheep and the Goats

[31]"When the Son of Man comes in his glory, and all the angels with him, he will sit on his throne in heavenly glory. [32]All the nations will be gathered before him, and he will separate the people one from another as a shepherd separates the sheep from the goats. [33]He will put the sheep on his right and the goats on his left.

[34]"Then the King will say to those on his right, 'Come, you who are blessed by my Father; take your inheritance, the kingdom prepared for you since the creation of the world. [35]For I was hungry

[a] 15 A talent was worth more than a thousand dollars.

and you gave me something to eat, I was thirsty and you gave me something to drink, I was a stranger and you invited me in, [36]I needed clothes and you clothed me, I was sick and you looked after me, I was in prison and you came to visit me.'

[37]"Then the righteous will answer him, 'Lord, when did we see you hungry and feed you, or thirsty and give you something to drink? [38]When did we see you a stranger and invite you in, or needing clothes and clothe you? [39]When did we see you sick or in prison and go to visit you?'

[40]"The King will reply, 'I tell you the truth, whatever you did for one of the least of these brothers of mine, you did for me.'

[41]"Then he will say to those on his left, 'Depart from me, you who are cursed, into the eternal fire prepared for the devil and his angels. [42]For I was hungry and you gave me nothing to eat, I was thirsty and you gave me nothing to drink, [43]I was a stranger and you did not invite me in, I needed clothes and you did not clothe me, I was sick and in prison and you did not look after me.'

[44]"They also will answer, 'Lord, when did we see you hungry or thirsty or a stranger or needing clothes or sick or in prison, and did not help you?'

[45]"He will reply, 'I tell you the truth, whatever you did not do for one of the least of these, you did not do for me.'

[46]"Then they will go away to eternal punishment, but the righteous to eternal life."

The Plot Against Jesus

26 When Jesus had finished saying all these things, he said to his disciples, [2]"As you know, the Passover is two days away—and the Son of Man will be handed over to be crucified."

[3]Then the chief priests and the elders of the people assembled in the palace of the high priest, whose name was Caiaphas, [4]and they plotted to arrest Jesus in some sly way and kill him. [5]"But not during the Feast," they said, "or there may be a riot among the people."

Jesus Anointed at Bethany

[6]While Jesus was in Bethany in the home of a man known as Simon the Leper, [7]a woman came to him with an alabaster jar of very expensive perfume, which she poured on his head as he was reclining at the table.

[8]When the disciples saw this, they were indignant. "Why this waste?" they asked. [9]"This perfume could have been sold at a high price and the money given to the poor."

[10]Aware of this, Jesus said to them, "Why are you bothering this woman? She has done a beautiful thing to me. [11]The poor you will always have with you, but you will not always have me. [12]When she poured this perfume on my body, she did it to prepare me for burial. [13]I tell you the truth, wherever this gospel is preached throughout the world, what she has done will also be told, in memory of her."

Judas Agrees to Betray Jesus

[14]Then one of the Twelve—the one called Judas Iscariot—went to the chief priests [15]and asked, "What are you willing to give me if I hand him over to you?" So they counted out for him thirty silver coins. [16]From then on Judas watched for an opportunity to hand him over.

The Lord's Supper

[17]On the first day of the Feast of Unleavened Bread, the disciples came to Jesus and asked, "Where do you want us to make preparations for you to eat the Passover?"

[18]He replied, "Go into the city to a certain man and tell him, 'The Teacher says: My appointed time is near. I am going to celebrate the Passover with my disciples at your house.' " [19]So the disciples did as Jesus had directed them and prepared the Passover.

[20]When evening came, Jesus was reclining at the table with the Twelve. [21]And while they were eating, he said, "I tell you the truth, one of you will betray me."

[22]They were very sad and began to say to him one after the other, "Surely not I, Lord?"

[23]Jesus replied, "The one who has dipped his hand into the bowl with me will betray me. [24]The Son of Man will go just as it is written about him. But woe to that man who betrays the Son of Man! It would be better for him if he had not been born."

[25]Then Judas, the one who would betray him, said, "Surely not I, Rabbi?"

Jesus answered, "Yes, it is you." [a]

[26]While they were eating, Jesus took bread, gave thanks and broke it, and gave it to his disciples, saying, "Take and eat; this is my body."

[27]Then he took the cup, gave thanks and offered it to them, saying, "Drink from it, all of you. [28]This is my blood of the [b] covenant, which is poured out for many for the forgiveness of sins. [29]I tell you, I will not drink of this fruit of the vine from now on until that day when I drink it anew with you in my Father's kingdom."

[30]When they had sung a hymn, they went out to the Mount of Olives.

Jesus Predicts Peter's Denial

[31]Then Jesus told them, "This very night you will all fall away on account of me, for it is written:

" 'I will strike the shepherd,
    and the sheep of the flock will be scattered.' [c]

[32]But after I have risen, I will go ahead of you into Galilee."

[33]Peter replied, "Even if all fall away on account of you, I never will."

[34]"I tell you the truth," Jesus answered, "this very night, before the rooster crows, you will disown me three times."

[35]But Peter declared, "Even if I have to die with you, I will never disown you." And all the other disciples said the same.

Gethsemane

[36]Then Jesus went with his disciples to a place called Gethsemane, and he said to them, "Sit here while I go over there and pray." [37]He took Peter and the two sons of Zebedee along with him, and he began to be sorrowful and troubled. [38]Then he said to them, "My soul is overwhelmed with sorrow to the point of death. Stay here and keep watch with me."

[39]Going a little farther, he fell with his face to the ground and prayed, "My Father, if it is possible, may this cup be taken from me. Yet not as I will, but as you will."

[40]Then he returned to his disciples and found them sleeping. "Could you men not keep watch with me for one hour?" he asked Peter. [41]"Watch and pray so that you will not fall into temptation. The spirit is willing, but the body is weak."

[42]He went away a second time and prayed, "My Father, if it is not possible for this cup to be taken away unless I drink it, may your will be done."

[43]When he came back, he again found them sleeping, because their eyes were heavy. [44]So he left them and went away once more and prayed the third time, saying the same thing.

[45]Then he returned to the disciples and said to them, "Are you still sleeping and resting? Look, the hour is near, and the Son of Man is betrayed into the hands of sinners. [46]Rise, let us go! Here comes my betrayer!"

Jesus Arrested

[47]While he was still speaking, Judas, one of the Twelve, arrived. With him was a large crowd armed with swords and clubs, sent from the chief priests and the elders of the people. [48]Now the betrayer had arranged a signal with them: "The one I kiss is the man; arrest him." [49]Going at once to Jesus, Judas said, "Greetings, Rabbi!" and kissed him.

[50]Jesus replied, "Friend, do what you came for." [d]

Then the men stepped forward, seized Jesus and arrested him. [51]With that, one of Jesus' companions reached for his sword, drew it out and struck the servant of the high priest, cutting off his ear.

[52]"Put your sword back in its place," Jesus said to him, "for all who draw the sword will die by the sword. [53]Do you think I cannot call on my Father, and he will at once put at my disposal more than twelve legions of angels? [54]But how then would the Scriptures be fulfilled that say it must happen in this way?"

[55]At that time Jesus said to the crowd, "Am I leading a rebellion, that you have come out with

a 25 Or "You yourself have said it"   b 28 Some manuscripts the new   c 31 Zech. 13:7   d 50 Or "Friend, why have you come?"

mirror images

Jesus said to them, "Why are you bothering this woman? She has done a beautiful thing to me." Matthew 26:10

Mary of Bethany—An Uncommon Love

I f Mary took a "test your love quotient" quiz, she'd score off the charts. And she'd let her love be known—no matter what anyone said.

Matthew 26 says Mary entered the home where Jesus was visiting (see also John 11:2). She boldly stood beside him and broke a jar of expensive perfume, pouring it on her Savior's head. Imagine how shocked Jesus' followers were! And the complaining started right away. "That perfume cost more than a year's wages!" "We could have sold that stuff and given the money to the poor!"

Yet as the beautiful scent filled the home, Jesus was far from shocked or uncomfortable. He was pleased. "Stop bothering her," he scolded the whiners. "You'll always have poor people with you, but you won't always have me. Mary's done a beautiful thing in getting me ready for my death. And whenever anyone hears the truth of my gospel, her story of extravagant love will be told, too." Mary's gesture of love so impressed her Lord that he promised that her story would become a part of history.

Think of the wonder on Mary's face when she heard Jesus' words of approval. He saw straight into her heart—and he was pleased. When Jesus peers into your heart, what does he see? A girl who's stingy with her money and love? Or a girl who follows Mary's example and lavishes love on her Lord? Maybe you can't picture yourself pouring your favorite bottle of Ralph Lauren on Jesus' head, but through Mary's story, Jesus shows us that he wants our hearts most of all. How can you show Mary's brand of extravagant love to your Lord?

To read the next Mirror Images profile, go to page 1343.

Dear Jesus, when it comes to giving you my heart, sometimes I give you only part. Help me to give you my best, as Mary did, and show me how to live out an uncommon love. Amen.

dear Jesus

» Read more about Mary in Mark 14:3–9 (page 1355); Luke 10:38–42 (page 1383); John 11:17–45 and 12:1–11 (pages 1429–1430).

swords and clubs to capture me? Every day I sat in the temple courts teaching, and you did not arrest me. [56]But this has all taken place that the writings of the prophets might be fulfilled." Then all the disciples deserted him and fled.

Before the Sanhedrin

[57]Those who had arrested Jesus took him to Caiaphas, the high priest, where the teachers of the law and the elders had assembled. [58]But Peter followed him at a distance, right up to the courtyard of the high priest. He entered and sat down with the guards to see the outcome.

[59]The chief priests and the whole Sanhedrin were looking for false evidence against Jesus so that they could put him to death. [60]But they did not find any, though many false witnesses came forward.

Finally two came forward [61]and declared, "This fellow said, 'I am able to destroy the temple of God and rebuild it in three days.' "

[62]Then the high priest stood up and said to Jesus, "Are you not going to answer? What is this testimony that these men are bringing against you?" [63]But Jesus remained silent.

The high priest said to him, "I charge you under oath by the living God: Tell us if you are the Christ,[a] the Son of God."

[64]"Yes, it is as you say," Jesus replied. "But I say to all of you: In the future you will see the Son of Man sitting at the right hand of the Mighty One and coming on the clouds of heaven."

[65]Then the high priest tore his clothes and said, "He has spoken blasphemy! Why do we need any more witnesses? Look, now you have heard the blasphemy. [66]What do you think?"

"He is worthy of death," they answered.

[67]Then they spit in his face and struck him with their fists. Others slapped him [68]and said, "Prophesy to us, Christ. Who hit you?"

Peter Disowns Jesus

[69]Now Peter was sitting out in the courtyard, and a servant girl came to him. "You also were with Jesus of Galilee," she said.

[70]But he denied it before them all. "I don't know what you're talking about," he said.

[71]Then he went out to the gateway, where another girl saw him and said to the people there, "This fellow was with Jesus of Nazareth."

[72]He denied it again, with an oath: "I don't know the man!"

[73]After a little while, those standing there went up to Peter and said, "Surely you are one of them, for your accent gives you away."

[74]Then he began to call down curses on himself and he swore to them, "I don't know the man!"

Immediately a rooster crowed. [75]Then Peter remembered the word Jesus had spoken: "Before the rooster crows, you will disown me three times." And he went outside and wept bitterly.

Judas Hangs Himself

27 Early in the morning, all the chief priests and the elders of the people came to the decision to put Jesus to death. [2]They bound him, led him away and handed him over to Pilate, the governor.

[3]When Judas, who had betrayed him, saw that Jesus was condemned, he was seized with remorse and returned the thirty silver coins to the chief priests and the elders. [4]"I have sinned," he said, "for I have betrayed innocent blood."

"What is that to us?" they replied. "That's your responsibility."

[5]So Judas threw the money into the temple and left. Then he went away and hanged himself.

[6]The chief priests picked up the coins and said, "It is against the law to put this into the treasury, since it is blood money." [7]So they decided to use the money to buy the potter's field as a burial place for foreigners. [8]That is why it has been called the Field of Blood to this day. [9]Then what was spoken by Jeremiah the prophet was fulfilled: "They took the thirty silver coins, the price set on him by the people of Israel, [10]and they used them to buy the potter's field, as the Lord commanded me."[b]

---

a 63 Or *Messiah*; also in verse 68   b 10 See Zech. 11:12,13; Jer. 19:1-13; 32:6-9.

Jesus Before Pilate

[11]Meanwhile Jesus stood before the governor, and the governor asked him, "Are you the king of the Jews?"

"Yes, it is as you say," Jesus replied.

[12]When he was accused by the chief priests and the elders, he gave no answer. [13]Then Pilate asked him, "Don't you hear the testimony they are bringing against you?" [14]But Jesus made no reply, not even to a single charge—to the great amazement of the governor.

[15]Now it was the governor's custom at the Feast to release a prisoner chosen by the crowd. [16]At that time they had a notorious prisoner, called Barabbas. [17]So when the crowd had gathered, Pilate asked them, "Which one do you want me to release to you: Barabbas, or Jesus who is called Christ?" [18]For he knew it was out of envy that they had handed Jesus over to him.

[19]While Pilate was sitting on the judge's seat, his wife sent him this message: "Don't have anything to do with that innocent man, for I have suffered a great deal today in a dream because of him."

[20]But the chief priests and the elders persuaded the crowd to ask for Barabbas and to have Jesus executed.

[21]"Which of the two do you want me to release to you?" asked the governor.

"Barabbas," they answered.

[22]"What shall I do, then, with Jesus who is called Christ?" Pilate asked.

They all answered, "Crucify him!"

[23]"Why? What crime has he committed?" asked Pilate.

But they shouted all the louder, "Crucify him!"

[24]When Pilate saw that he was getting nowhere, but that instead an uproar was starting, he took water and washed his hands in front of the crowd. "I am innocent of this man's blood," he said. "It is your responsibility!"

[25]All the people answered, "Let his blood be on us and on our children!"

[26]Then he released Barabbas to them. But he had Jesus flogged, and handed him over to be crucified.

The Soldiers Mock Jesus

[27]Then the governor's soldiers took Jesus into the Praetorium and gathered the whole company of soldiers around him. [28]They stripped him and put a scarlet robe on him, [29]and then twisted together a crown of thorns and set it on his head. They put a staff in his right hand and knelt in front of him and mocked him. "Hail, king of the Jews!" they said. [30]They spit on him, and took the staff and struck him on the head again and again. [31]After they had mocked him, they took off the robe and put his own clothes on him. Then they led him away to crucify him.

The Crucifixion

[32]As they were going out, they met a man from Cyrene, named Simon, and they forced him to carry the cross. [33]They came to a place called Golgotha (which means The Place of the Skull). [34]There they offered Jesus wine to drink, mixed with gall; but after tasting it, he refused to drink it. [35]When they had crucified him, they divided up his clothes by casting lots. [a] [36]And sitting down, they kept watch over him there. [37]Above his head they placed the written charge against him: THIS IS JESUS, THE KING OF THE JEWS. [38]Two robbers were crucified with him, one on his right and one on his left. [39]Those who passed by hurled insults at him, shaking their heads [40]and saying, "You who are going to destroy the temple and build it in three days, save yourself! Come down from the cross, if you are the Son of God!"

[41]In the same way the chief priests, the teachers of the law and the elders mocked him. [42]"He

truth or dare

Crucifixion was bad enough. But Jesus also went through public humiliation, beating, nakedness and being spit on and laughed at—for you. Are you ashamed to openly admit that you know him?

27:26–31

---

[a] 35 A few late manuscripts *lots that the word spoken by the prophet might be fulfilled: "They divided my garments among themselves and cast lots for my clothing"* (Psalm 22:18)

saved others," they said, "but he can't save himself! He's the King of Israel! Let him come down now from the cross, and we will believe in him. [43]He trusts in God. Let God rescue him now if he wants him, for he said, 'I am the Son of God.' " [44]In the same way the robbers who were crucified with him also heaped insults on him.

The Death of Jesus

[45]From the sixth hour until the ninth hour darkness came over all the land. [46]About the ninth hour Jesus cried out in a loud voice, *"Eloi, Eloi,[a] lama sabachthani?"*—which means, "My God, my God, why have you forsaken me?"[b]

[47]When some of those standing there heard this, they said, "He's calling Elijah."

[48]Immediately one of them ran and got a sponge. He filled it with wine vinegar, put it on a stick, and offered it to Jesus to drink. [49]The rest said, "Now leave him alone. Let's see if Elijah comes to save him."

[50]And when Jesus had cried out again in a loud voice, he gave up his spirit.

[51]At that moment the curtain of the temple was torn in two from top to bottom. The earth shook and the rocks split. [52]The tombs broke open and the bodies of many holy people who had died were raised to life. [53]They came out of the tombs, and after Jesus' resurrection they went into the holy city and appeared to many people.

[54]When the centurion and those with him who were guarding Jesus saw the earthquake and all that had happened, they were terrified, and exclaimed, "Surely he was the Son[c] of God!"

[55]Many women were there, watching from a distance. They had followed Jesus from Galilee to care for his needs. [56]Among them were Mary Magdalene, Mary the mother of James and Joses, and the mother of Zebedee's sons.

The Burial of Jesus

[57]As evening approached, there came a rich man from Arimathea, named Joseph, who had himself become a disciple of Jesus. [58]Going to Pilate, he asked for Jesus' body, and Pilate ordered that it be given to him. [59]Joseph took the body, wrapped it in a clean linen cloth, [60]and placed it in his own new tomb that he had cut out of the rock. He rolled a big stone in front of the entrance to the tomb and went away. [61]Mary Magdalene and the other Mary were sitting there opposite the tomb.

The Guard at the Tomb

[62]The next day, the one after Preparation Day, the chief priests and the Pharisees went to Pilate. [63]"Sir," they said, "we remember that while he was still alive that deceiver said, 'After three days I will rise again.' [64]So give the order for the tomb to be made secure until the third day. Otherwise, his disciples may come and steal the body and tell the people that he has been raised from the dead. This last deception will be worse than the first."

[65]"Take a guard," Pilate answered. "Go, make the tomb as secure as you know how." [66]So they went and made the tomb secure by putting a seal on the stone and posting the guard.

The Resurrection

28 After the Sabbath, at dawn on the first day of the week, Mary Magdalene and the other Mary went to look at the tomb.

[2]There was a violent earthquake, for an angel of the Lord came down from heaven and, going to the tomb, rolled back the stone and sat on it. [3]His appearance was like lightning, and his clothes were white as snow. [4]The guards were so afraid of him that they shook and became like dead men.

[5]The angel said to the women, "Do not be afraid, for I know that you are looking for Jesus, who was crucified. [6]He is not here; he has risen, just as he said. Come and see the place where he lay. [7]Then go quickly and tell his disciples: 'He has risen from the dead and is going ahead of you into Galilee. There you will see him.' Now I have told you."

[8]So the women hurried away from the tomb, afraid yet filled with joy, and ran to tell his disciples. [9]Suddenly Jesus met them. "Greetings," he said. They came to him, clasped his feet and wor-

a 46 Some manuscripts *Eli, Eli*   *b 46* Psalm 22:1   *c 54* Or *a son* shiped him. ¹⁰Then Jesus said to them, "Do not be afraid. Go and tell my brothers to go to Galilee; there they will see me."

The Guards' Report

¹¹While the women were on their way, some of the guards went into the city and reported to the chief priests everything that had happened. ¹²When the chief priests had met with the elders and devised a plan, they gave the soldiers a large sum of money, ¹³telling them, "You are to say, 'His disciples came during the night and stole him away while we were asleep.' ¹⁴If this report gets to the governor, we will satisfy him and keep you out of trouble." ¹⁵So the soldiers took the money and did as they were instructed. And this story has been widely circulated among the Jews to this very day.

The Great Commission

¹⁶Then the eleven disciples went to Galilee, to the mountain where Jesus had told them to go. ¹⁷When they saw him, they worshiped him; but some doubted. ¹⁸Then Jesus came to them and said, "All authority in heaven and on earth has been given to me. ¹⁹Therefore go and make disciples of all nations, baptizing them in[a] the name of the Father and of the Son and of the Holy Spirit, ²⁰and teaching them to obey everything I have commanded you. And surely I am with you always, to the very end of the age."

love notes

28:20

Beloved,

Wherever this life may take you—college, the mission field, marriage, a career—I am with you always. I send my Spirit with you everywhere you go. I'll never leave you or forget about you.

—The risen Lord

Do you ever feel like Jesus is far away? He isn't! Thank him that he is with you at all times.

a 19 Or *into*; see Acts 8:16; 19:5; Romans 6:3; 1 Cor. 1:13; 10:2 and Gal. 3:27.

author:	John Mark.
date:	Probably between A.D. 55 and 65.
setting:	Mark most likely wrote from Rome, where he received—according to early church sources—the information for his Gospel from the apostle Peter.
verse to remember:	"For even the Son of Man did not come to be served, but to serve, and to give his life as a ransom for many" (10:45).
theme to consider:	The book of Mark is a quick-paced, rapid-fire picture of Jesus on earth—healing, teaching, serving and saving.

mark

unchanging truth

What was the last book or movie that you really loved? What really grabbed you about it? The plot? The actors? The romance? The excitement? The theme song? Some stories have the power to inspire you or even to change your life. Is there anything about *your* story that would inspire others? You might be surprised at what others would find interesting about your life. Maybe your faith or your determination to keep going through tough times would inspire someone else to do the same.

Mark believed that the story of Jesus' life would inspire others. Although he wasn't part of "the Twelve"—Jesus' core group of followers—he became a believer early on. He also was a friend of the apostles Peter and Paul and a cousin of Barnabas, Paul's missionary companion. Although Mark had some setbacks early on (see Acts 15:37–40), he continued in the faith (see 2 Timothy 4:11). His Gospel points to the power of Jesus to change a life.

Mark's Gospel is like an action movie from start to finish. Bam! John the Baptist prepares the way by preaching about the need for sorrow over sin. Pow! The first disciples are chosen. Zing! Jesus continually does the impossible by healing the sick and casting out demons. And that's just the first chapter! Get the picture? That's actually Mark's goal—for you to get the picture of the perfect Savior.

life lessons

1. The compassion of our active Savior should inspire us to show the same compassion toward others (1:29–42).

2. When "storms" (hard times) arise in our lives, we don't have to fear (4:35–41). Instead, like Jesus' disciples, we can learn to trust that Jesus is in complete control.

3. The sad story of the rich young man teaches us to value Jesus above anyone or anything else (10:17–22).

John the Baptist Prepares the Way

1 The beginning of the gospel about Jesus Christ, the Son of God.[a]

²It is written in Isaiah the prophet:

> "I will send my messenger ahead of you,
>   who will prepare your way"[b]—
> ³ "a voice of one calling in the desert,
> 'Prepare the way for the Lord,
>   make straight paths for him.' "[c]

⁴And so John came, baptizing in the desert region and preaching a baptism of repentance for the forgiveness of sins. ⁵The whole Judean countryside and all the people of Jerusalem went out to him. Confessing their sins, they were baptized by him in the Jordan River. ⁶John wore clothing made of camel's hair, with a leather belt around his waist, and he ate locusts and wild honey. ⁷And this was his message: "After me will come one more powerful than I, the thongs of whose sandals I am not worthy to stoop down and untie. ⁸I baptize you with[d] water, but he will baptize you with the Holy Spirit."

The Baptism and Temptation of Jesus

⁹At that time Jesus came from Nazareth in Galilee and was baptized by John in the Jordan. ¹⁰As Jesus was coming up out of the water, he saw heaven being torn open and the Spirit descending on him like a dove. ¹¹And a voice came from heaven: "You are my Son, whom I love; with you I am well pleased."

¹²At once the Spirit sent him out into the desert, ¹³and he was in the desert forty days, being tempted by Satan. He was with the wild animals, and angels attended him.

The Calling of the First Disciples

¹⁴After John was put in prison, Jesus went into Galilee, proclaiming the good news of God. ¹⁵"The time has come," he said. "The kingdom of God is near. Repent and believe the good news!"

¹⁶As Jesus walked beside the Sea of Galilee, he saw Simon and his brother Andrew casting a net into the lake, for they were fishermen. ¹⁷"Come, follow me," Jesus said, "and I will make you fishers of men." ¹⁸At once they left their nets and followed him.

¹⁹When he had gone a little farther, he saw James son of Zebedee and his brother John in a boat, preparing their nets. ²⁰Without delay he called them, and they left their father Zebedee in the boat with the hired men and followed him.

Jesus Drives Out an Evil Spirit

²¹They went to Capernaum, and when the Sabbath came, Jesus went into the synagogue and began to teach. ²²The people were amazed at his teaching, because he taught them as one who had authority, not as the teachers of the law. ²³Just then a man in their synagogue who was possessed by an evil[e] spirit cried out, ²⁴"What do you want with us, Jesus of Nazareth? Have you come to destroy us? I know who you are—the Holy One of God!"

²⁵"Be quiet!" said Jesus sternly. "Come out of him!" ²⁶The evil spirit shook the man violently and came out of him with a shriek.

²⁷The people were all so amazed that they asked each other, "What is this? A new teaching—and with authority! He even gives orders to evil spirits and they obey him." ²⁸News about him spread quickly over the whole region of Galilee.

truth or dare

Can you imagine yourself in this situation? Jesus walks up and simply invites you to follow him. Would you, like Simon and Andrew, immediately drop everything to follow him?

1:16–18

---

[a] 1 Some manuscripts do not have *the Son of God*.   [b] 2 Mal. 3:1   [c] 3 Isaiah 40:3   [d] 8 Or *in*   [e] 23 Greek *unclean*; also in verses 26 and 27

Jesus Heals Many

²⁹As soon as they left the synagogue, they went with James and John to the home of Simon and Andrew. ³⁰Simon's mother-in-law was in bed with a fever, and they told Jesus about her. ³¹So he went to her, took her hand and helped her up. The fever left her and she began to wait on them.

³²That evening after sunset the people brought to Jesus all the sick and demon-possessed. ³³The whole town gathered at the door, ³⁴and Jesus healed many who had various diseases. He also drove out many demons, but he would not let the demons speak because they knew who he was.

Jesus Prays in a Solitary Place

³⁵Very early in the morning, while it was still dark, Jesus got up, left the house and went off to a solitary place, where he prayed. ³⁶Simon and his companions went to look for him, ³⁷and when they found him, they exclaimed: "Everyone is looking for you!"

³⁸Jesus replied, "Let us go somewhere else—to the nearby villages—so I can preach there also. That is why I have come." ³⁹So he traveled throughout Galilee, preaching in their synagogues and driving out demons.

genuine love » 1:40-42

Nobody touched lepers. No one ever hugged them, shook their hands or even brushed against them in a crowd. Lepers had a skin disease and lived separate from everyone else. Nobody went near a leper, much less touched one willingly. Except Jesus. Jesus could have cured the man with a word or a look—but he didn't. Jesus went the extra mile to love the leper by healing him with a touch—the one thing the man craved more than anything else. Do you know people who are treated like lepers—isolated and left out? How will you go the extra mile to show them love?

A Man With Leprosy

⁴⁰A man with leprosy*a* came to him and begged him on his knees, "If you are willing, you can make me clean."

⁴¹Filled with compassion, Jesus reached out his hand and touched the man. "I am willing," he said. "Be clean!" ⁴²Immediately the leprosy left him and he was cured.

⁴³Jesus sent him away at once with a strong warning: ⁴⁴"See that you don't tell this to anyone. But go, show yourself to the priest and offer the sacrifices that Moses commanded for your cleansing, as a testimony to them." ⁴⁵Instead he went out and began to talk freely, spreading the news. As a result, Jesus could no longer enter a town openly but stayed outside in lonely places. Yet the people still came to him from everywhere.

Jesus Heals a Paralytic

2 A few days later, when Jesus again entered Capernaum, the people heard that he had come home. ²So many gathered that there was no room left, not even outside the door, and he preached the word to them. ³Some men came, bringing to him a paralytic, carried by four of them. ⁴Since they could not get him to Jesus because of the crowd, they made an opening in the roof above Jesus and, after digging through it, lowered the mat the paralyzed man was lying on. ⁵When Jesus saw their faith, he said to the paralytic, "Son, your sins are forgiven."

⁶Now some teachers of the law were sitting there, thinking to themselves, ⁷"Why does this fellow talk like that? He's blaspheming! Who can forgive sins but God alone?"

⁸Immediately Jesus knew in his spirit that this was what they were thinking in their hearts, and he said to them, "Why are you thinking these things? ⁹Which is easier: to say to the paralytic, 'Your sins are forgiven,' or to say, 'Get up, take your mat and walk'? ¹⁰But that you may know that the Son of Man has authority on earth to forgive sins . . ." He said to the paralytic, ¹¹"I tell you, get up, take your mat and go home." ¹²He got up, took his mat and walked out in full view of them all. This amazed everyone and they praised God, saying, "We have never seen anything like this!"

---

a 40 The Greek word was used for various diseases affecting the skin—not necessarily leprosy.

The Calling of Levi

¹³Once again Jesus went out beside the lake. A large crowd came to him, and he began to teach them. ¹⁴As he walked along, he saw Levi son of Alphaeus sitting at the tax collector's booth. "Follow me," Jesus told him, and Levi got up and followed him.

¹⁵While Jesus was having dinner at Levi's house, many tax collectors and "sinners" were eating with him and his disciples, for there were many who followed him. ¹⁶When the teachers of the law who were Pharisees saw him eating with the "sinners" and tax collectors, they asked his disciples: "Why does he eat with tax collectors and 'sinners'?"

¹⁷On hearing this, Jesus said to them, "It is not the healthy who need a doctor, but the sick. I have not come to call the righteous, but sinners."

Jesus Questioned About Fasting

¹⁸Now John's disciples and the Pharisees were fasting. Some people came and asked Jesus, "How is it that John's disciples and the disciples of the Pharisees are fasting, but yours are not?"

¹⁹Jesus answered, "How can the guests of the bridegroom fast while he is with them? They cannot, so long as they have him with them. ²⁰But the time will come when the bridegroom will be taken from them, and on that day they will fast.

²¹"No one sews a patch of unshrunk cloth on an old garment. If he does, the new piece will pull away from the old, making the tear worse. ²²And no one pours new wine into old wineskins. If he does, the wine will burst the skins, and both the wine and the wineskins will be ruined. No, he pours new wine into new wineskins."

Lord of the Sabbath

²³One Sabbath Jesus was going through the grainfields, and as his disciples walked along, they began to pick some heads of grain. ²⁴The Pharisees said to him, "Look, why are they doing what is unlawful on the Sabbath?"

²⁵He answered, "Have you never read what David did when he and his companions were hungry and in need? ²⁶In the days of Abiathar the high priest, he entered the house of God and ate the consecrated bread, which is lawful only for priests to eat. And he also gave some to his companions."

²⁷Then he said to them, "The Sabbath was made for man, not man for the Sabbath. ²⁸So the Son of Man is Lord even of the Sabbath."

3 Another time he went into the synagogue, and a man with a shriveled hand was there. ²Some of them were looking for a reason to accuse Jesus, so they watched him closely to see if he would heal him on the Sabbath. ³Jesus said to the man with the shriveled hand, "Stand up in front of everyone."

⁴Then Jesus asked them, "Which is lawful on the Sabbath: to do good or to do evil, to save life or to kill?" But they remained silent.

⁵He looked around at them in anger and, deeply distressed at their stubborn hearts, said to the man, "Stretch out your hand." He stretched it out, and his hand was completely restored. ⁶Then the Pharisees went out and began to plot with the Herodians how they might kill Jesus.

Crowds Follow Jesus

⁷Jesus withdrew with his disciples to the lake, and a large crowd from Galilee followed. ⁸When they heard all he was doing, many people came to him from Judea, Jerusalem, Idumea, and the regions across the Jordan and around Tyre and Sidon. ⁹Because of the crowd he told his disciples to have a small boat ready for him, to keep the people from crowding him. ¹⁰For he had healed many, so that those with diseases were pushing forward to touch him. ¹¹Whenever the evil*a* spirits saw him, they fell down before him and cried out, "You are the Son of God." ¹²But he gave them strict orders not to tell who he was.

The Appointing of the Twelve Apostles

¹³Jesus went up on a mountainside and called to him those he wanted, and they came to him. ¹⁴He appointed twelve—designating them apostles*b*—that they might be with him and that he might send them out to preach ¹⁵and to have authority to drive out demons. ¹⁶These are the twelve

a 11 Greek *unclean*; also in verse 30   *b 14* Some manuscripts do not have *designating them apostles*.

he appointed: Simon (to whom he gave the name Peter); ¹⁷James son of Zebedee and his brother John (to them he gave the name Boanerges, which means Sons of Thunder); ¹⁸Andrew, Philip, Bartholomew, Matthew, Thomas, James son of Alphaeus, Thaddaeus, Simon the Zealot ¹⁹and Judas Iscariot, who betrayed him.

Jesus and Beelzebub

²⁰Then Jesus entered a house, and again a crowd gathered, so that he and his disciples were not even able to eat. ²¹When his family heard about this, they went to take charge of him, for they said, "He is out of his mind."

²²And the teachers of the law who came down from Jerusalem said, "He is possessed by Beelzebub ᵃ! By the prince of demons he is driving out demons."

²³So Jesus called them and spoke to them in parables: "How can Satan drive out Satan? ²⁴If a kingdom is divided against itself, that kingdom cannot stand. ²⁵If a house is divided against itself, that house cannot stand. ²⁶And if Satan opposes himself and is divided, he cannot stand; his end has come. ²⁷In fact, no one can enter a strong man's house and carry off his possessions unless he first ties up the strong man. Then he can rob his house. ²⁸I tell you the truth, all the sins and blasphemies of men will be forgiven them. ²⁹But whoever blasphemes against the Holy Spirit will never be forgiven; he is guilty of an eternal sin."

³⁰He said this because they were saying, "He has an evil spirit."

Jesus' Mother and Brothers

³¹Then Jesus' mother and brothers arrived. Standing outside, they sent someone in to call him. ³²A crowd was sitting around him, and they told him, "Your mother and brothers are outside looking for you."

³³"Who are my mother and my brothers?" he asked.

³⁴Then he looked at those seated in a circle around him and said, "Here are my mother and my brothers! ³⁵Whoever does God's will is my brother and sister and mother."

truth *or dare*

Jesus wasn't trying to disrespect his family. But he *was* making an important point: being in God's family is about obeying God, not about your spiritual pedigree.

3:31–35

The Parable of the Sower

4 Again Jesus began to teach by the lake. The crowd that gathered around him was so large that he got into a boat and sat in it out on the lake, while all the people were along the shore at the water's edge. ²He taught them many things by parables, and in his teaching said: ³"Listen! A farmer went out to sow his seed. ⁴As he was scattering the seed, some fell along the path, and the birds came and ate it up. ⁵Some fell on rocky places, where it did not have much soil. It sprang up quickly, because the soil was shallow. ⁶But when the sun came up, the plants were scorched, and they withered because they had no root. ⁷Other seed fell among thorns, which grew up and choked the plants, so that they did not bear grain. ⁸Still other seed fell on good soil. It came up, grew and produced a crop, multiplying thirty, sixty, or even a hundred times."

⁹Then Jesus said, "He who has ears to hear, let him hear."

¹⁰When he was alone, the Twelve and the others around him asked him about the parables. ¹¹He told them, "The secret of the kingdom of God has been given to you. But to those on the outside everything is said in parables ¹²so that,

" 'they may be ever seeing but never perceiving,
    and ever hearing but never understanding;
otherwise they might turn and be forgiven!' ᵇ

¹³Then Jesus said to them, "Don't you understand this parable? How then will you understand any parable? ¹⁴The farmer sows the word. ¹⁵Some people are like seed along the path, where the word is sown. As soon as they hear it, Satan comes and takes away the word that was sown in them.

ᵃ 22 Greek *Beezeboul* or *Beelzeboul*   ᵇ 12 Isaiah 6:9,10

¹⁶Others, like seed sown on rocky places, hear the word and at once receive it with joy. ¹⁷But since they have no root, they last only a short time. When trouble or persecution comes because of the word, they quickly fall away. ¹⁸Still others, like seed sown among thorns, hear the word; ¹⁹but the worries of this life, the deceitfulness of wealth and the desires for other things come in and choke the word, making it unfruitful. ²⁰Others, like seed sown on good soil, hear the word, accept it, and produce a crop—thirty, sixty or even a hundred times what was sown."

A Lamp on a Stand

²¹He said to them, "Do you bring in a lamp to put it under a bowl or a bed? Instead, don't you put it on its stand? ²²For whatever is hidden is meant to be disclosed, and whatever is concealed is meant to be brought out into the open. ²³If anyone has ears to hear, let him hear."

²⁴"Consider carefully what you hear," he continued. "With the measure you use, it will be measured to you—and even more. ²⁵Whoever has will be given more; whoever does not have, even what he has will be taken from him."

The Parable of the Growing Seed

²⁶He also said, "This is what the kingdom of God is like. A man scatters seed on the ground. ²⁷Night and day, whether he sleeps or gets up, the seed sprouts and grows, though he does not know how. ²⁸All by itself the soil produces grain—first the stalk, then the head, then the full kernel in the head. ²⁹As soon as the grain is ripe, he puts the sickle to it, because the harvest has come."

truth or dare

If you feel like you're the only believer around, don't get discouraged. Planting just one seed—telling one friend about Christ— can help the kingdom of God explode in size.

4:30–32

genuine

comfort »

Life can get pretty stormy sometimes—fights with friends, problems with parents, pressure to be the best in sports and school and music, fear of being left out or not liked, decisions about the future. When life hits you full in the face like a 90 mph wind, it can be awfully scary. That's when you've got to hold on tight to the one who made the wind and the waves. The same power that Jesus used to calm the seas for the disciples will help you weather the storms that assault you each day.

4:35–41

The Parable of the Mustard Seed

³⁰Again he said, "What shall we say the kingdom of God is like, or what parable shall we use to describe it? ³¹It is like a mustard seed, which is the smallest seed you plant in the ground. ³²Yet when planted, it grows and becomes the largest of all garden plants, with such big branches that the birds of the air can perch in its shade."

³³With many similar parables Jesus spoke the word to them, as much as they could understand. ³⁴He did not say anything to them without using a parable. But when he was alone with his own disciples, he explained everything.

Jesus Calms the Storm

³⁵That day when evening came, he said to his disciples, "Let us go over to the other side." ³⁶Leaving the crowd behind, they took him along, just as he was, in the boat. There were also other boats with him. ³⁷A furious squall came up, and the waves broke over the boat, so that it was nearly swamped. ³⁸Jesus was in the stern, sleeping on a cushion. The disciples woke him and said to him, "Teacher, don't you care if we drown?"

³⁹He got up, rebuked the wind and said to the waves, "Quiet! Be still!" Then the wind died down and it was completely calm.

⁴⁰He said to his disciples, "Why are you so afraid? Do you still have no faith?"

⁴¹They were terrified and asked each other, "Who is this? Even the wind and the waves obey him!"

The Healing of a Demon-possessed Man

5 They went across the lake to the region of the Gerasenes.ᵃ ²When Jesus got out of the boat, a man with an evilᵇ spirit came from the tombs to meet him. ³This man lived in the tombs, and no one could bind him any more, not even with a chain. ⁴For he had often been chained hand and foot, but he tore the chains apart and broke the irons on his feet. No one was strong enough to subdue him. ⁵Night and day among the tombs and in the hills he would cry out and cut himself with stones.

⁶When he saw Jesus from a distance, he ran and fell on his knees in front of him. ⁷He shouted at the top of his voice, "What do you want with me, Jesus, Son of the Most High God? Swear to God that you won't torture me!" ⁸For Jesus had said to him, "Come out of this man, you evil spirit!"

⁹Then Jesus asked him, "What is your name?"

"My name is Legion," he replied, "for we are many." ¹⁰And he begged Jesus again and again not to send them out of the area.

¹¹A large herd of pigs was feeding on the nearby hillside. ¹²The demons begged Jesus, "Send us among the pigs; allow us to go into them." ¹³He gave them permission, and the evil spirits came out and went into the pigs. The herd, about two thousand in number, rushed down the steep bank into the lake and were drowned.

¹⁴Those tending the pigs ran off and reported this in the town and countryside, and the people went out to see what had happened. ¹⁵When they came to Jesus, they saw the man who had been possessed by the legion of demons, sitting there, dressed and in his right mind; and they were afraid. ¹⁶Those who had seen it told the people what had happened to the demon-possessed man—and told about the pigs as well. ¹⁷Then the people began to plead with Jesus to leave their region.

¹⁸As Jesus was getting into the boat, the man who had been demon-possessed begged to go with him. ¹⁹Jesus did not let him, but said, "Go home to your family and tell them how much the Lord has done for you, and how he has had mercy on you." ²⁰So the man went away and began to tell in the Decapolisᶜ how much Jesus had done for him. And all the people were amazed.

ᵃ 1 Some manuscripts Gadarenes; other manuscripts Gergesenes   ᵇ 2 Greek unclean; also in verses 8 and 13   ᶜ 20 That is, the Ten Cities

love ♥ notes

5:34

My daughter,

Just as I brought healing to this frightened, lonely woman, I freely open my arms to you. Whether you are hurting physically, emotionally or mentally, reach out to me in faith. You will find healing.

—Jesus, the healer

How are you hurting right now? Reach out to Jesus for healing.

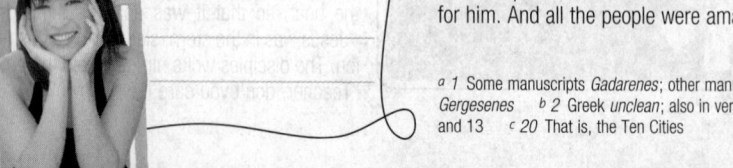

A Dead Girl and a Sick Woman

²¹When Jesus had again crossed over by boat to the other side of the lake, a large crowd gathered around him while he was by the lake. ²²Then one of the synagogue rulers, named Jairus, came there. Seeing Jesus, he fell at his feet ²³and pleaded earnestly with him, "My little daughter is dying. Please come and put your hands on her so that she will be healed and live." ²⁴So Jesus went with him.

A large crowd followed and pressed around him. ²⁵And a woman was there who had been subject to bleeding for twelve years. ²⁶She had suffered a great deal under the care of many doctors and had spent all she had, yet instead of getting better she grew worse. ²⁷When she heard about Jesus, she came up behind him in the crowd and touched his cloak, ²⁸because she thought, "If I just touch his clothes, I will be healed." ²⁹Immediately her bleeding stopped and she felt in her body that she was freed from her suffering.

³⁰At once Jesus realized that power had gone out from him. He turned around in the crowd and asked, "Who touched my clothes?"

³¹"You see the people crowding against you," his disciples answered, "and yet you can ask, 'Who touched me?' "

³²But Jesus kept looking around to see who had done it. ³³Then the woman, knowing what had happened to her, came and fell at his feet and, trembling with fear, told him the whole truth. ³⁴He said to her, "Daughter, your faith has healed you. Go in peace and be freed from your suffering."

³⁵While Jesus was still speaking, some men came from the house of Jairus, the synagogue ruler. "Your daughter is dead," they said. "Why bother the teacher any more?"

³⁶Ignoring what they said, Jesus told the synagogue ruler, "Don't be afraid; just believe."

³⁷He did not let anyone follow him except Peter, James and John the brother of James. ³⁸When they came to the home of the synagogue ruler, Jesus saw a commotion, with people crying and wailing loudly. ³⁹He went in and said to them, "Why all this commotion and wailing? The child is not dead but asleep." ⁴⁰But they laughed at him.

After he put them all out, he took the child's father and mother and the disciples who were with him, and went in where the child was. ⁴¹He took her by the hand and said to her, *"Talitha koum!"* (which means, "Little girl, I say to you, get up!"). ⁴²Immediately the girl stood up and walked around (she was twelve years old). At this they were completely astonished. ⁴³He gave strict orders not to let anyone know about this, and told them to give her something to eat.

A Prophet Without Honor

6 Jesus left there and went to his hometown, accompanied by his disciples. ²When the Sabbath came, he began to teach in the synagogue, and many who heard him were amazed.

"Where did this man get these things?" they asked. "What's this wisdom that has been given him, that he even does miracles! ³Isn't this the carpenter? Isn't this Mary's son and the brother of James, Joseph,^a Judas and Simon? Aren't his sisters here with us?" And they took offense at him.

⁴Jesus said to them, "Only in his hometown, among his relatives and in his own house is a prophet without honor." ⁵He could not do any miracles there, except lay his hands on a few sick people and heal them. ⁶And he was amazed at their lack of faith.

Jesus Sends Out the Twelve

Then Jesus went around teaching from village to village. ⁷Calling the Twelve to him, he sent them out two by two and gave them authority over evil^b spirits.

⁸These were his instructions: "Take nothing for the journey except a staff—no bread, no bag, no money in your belts. ⁹Wear sandals but not an extra tunic. ¹⁰Whenever you enter a house, stay there until you leave that town. ¹¹And if any place will not welcome you or listen to you, shake the dust off your feet when you leave, as a testimony against them."

¹²They went out and preached that people should repent. ¹³They drove out many demons and anointed many sick people with oil and healed them.

John the Baptist Beheaded

¹⁴King Herod heard about this, for Jesus' name had become well known. Some were saying,^c "John the Baptist has been raised from the dead, and that is why miraculous powers are at work in him."

^a 3 Greek *Joses*, a variant of *Joseph*   ^b 7 Greek *unclean*   ^c 14 Some early manuscripts *He was saying*

¹⁵Others said, "He is Elijah."

And still others claimed, "He is a prophet, like one of the prophets of long ago."

¹⁶But when Herod heard this, he said, "John, the man I beheaded, has been raised from the dead!"

¹⁷For Herod himself had given orders to have John arrested, and he had him bound and put in prison. He did this because of Herodias, his brother Philip's wife, whom he had married. ¹⁸For John had been saying to Herod, "It is not lawful for you to have your brother's wife." ¹⁹So Herodias nursed a grudge against John and wanted to kill him. But she was not able to, ²⁰because Herod feared John and protected him, knowing him to be a righteous and holy man. When Herod heard John, he was greatly puzzled*; yet he liked to listen to him.

²¹Finally the opportune time came. On his birthday Herod gave a banquet for his high officials and military commanders and the leading men of Galilee. ²²When the daughter of Herodias came in and danced, she pleased Herod and his dinner guests.

The king said to the girl, "Ask me for anything you want, and I'll give it to you." ²³And he promised her with an oath, "Whatever you ask I will give you, up to half my kingdom."

²⁴She went out and said to her mother, "What shall I ask for?"

"The head of John the Baptist," she answered.

²⁵At once the girl hurried in to the king with the request: "I want you to give me right now the head of John the Baptist on a platter."

²⁶The king was greatly distressed, but because of his oaths and his dinner guests, he did not want to refuse her. ²⁷So he immediately sent an executioner with orders to bring John's head. The man went, beheaded John in the prison, ²⁸and brought back his head on a platter. He presented it to the girl, and she gave it to her mother. ²⁹On hearing of this, John's disciples came and took his body and laid it in a tomb.

Jesus Feeds the Five Thousand

³⁰The apostles gathered around Jesus and reported to him all they had done and taught. ³¹Then, because so many people were coming and going that they did not even have a chance to eat, he said to them, "Come with me by yourselves to a quiet place and get some rest."

³²So they went away by themselves in a boat to a solitary place. ³³But many who saw them leaving recognized them and ran on foot from all the towns and got there ahead of them. ³⁴When Jesus landed and saw a large crowd, he had compassion on them, because they were like sheep without a shepherd. So he began teaching them many things.

³⁵By this time it was late in the day, so his disciples came to him. "This is a remote place," they said, "and it's already very late. ³⁶Send the people away so they can go to the surrounding countryside and villages and buy themselves something to eat."

³⁷But he answered, "You give them something to eat."

They said to him, "That would take eight months of a man's wages*! Are we to go and spend that much on bread and give it to them to eat?"

³⁸"How many loaves do you have?" he asked. "Go and see."

When they found out, they said, "Five—and two fish."

³⁹Then Jesus directed them to have all the people sit down in groups on the green grass. ⁴⁰So they sat down in groups of hundreds and fifties. ⁴¹Taking the five loaves and the two fish and looking up to heaven, he gave thanks and broke the loaves. Then he gave them to his disciples to set before the people. He also divided the two fish among them all. ⁴²They all ate and were satisfied, ⁴³and the disciples picked up twelve basketfuls of broken pieces of bread and fish. ⁴⁴The number of the men who had eaten was five thousand.

Jesus Walks on the Water

⁴⁵Immediately Jesus made his disciples get into the boat and go on ahead of him to Bethsaida, while he dismissed the crowd. ⁴⁶After leaving them, he went up on a mountainside to pray.

⁴⁷When evening came, the boat was in the middle of the lake, and he was alone on land. ⁴⁸He saw the disciples straining at the oars, because the wind was against them. About the fourth watch of the night he went out to them, walking on the lake. He was about to pass by them, ⁴⁹but when

a 20 Some early manuscripts *he did many things*   *b 37* Greek *take two hundred denarii*

mirror images

When she heard about Jesus, she came up behind him in the crowd and touched his cloak, because she thought, "If I just touch his clothes, I will be healed." Immediately her bleeding stopped and she felt in her body that she was freed from her suffering. Mark 5:27–29

Suffering Woman—Free Indeed

Pssst . . . what's with the social outcast? You know, the girl who stutters, has hair that's out of control or maybe lives out her lonely days with a physical or mental disability. Always on the outside, looking in. Maybe you know a girl like that—or maybe, like the suffering woman, you've been there yourself.

The Bible doesn't tell us what her name was or even what she looked like. Drop-dead gorgeous or as plain as vanilla ice cream? It hardly matters because she had a disease that made her an outcast from society. This woman suffered from menstrual bleeding for 12 years straight. Since women of the day were considered "unclean" whenever they got their period, she was constantly alone, untouchable, unwanted. And since no doctor could help, she had probably given up all hope, until . . . .

Jesus came to her hometown. How long did she follow him in the crowd, trying to get up the courage to touch him? *What if he rejects me, just like everyone else does?* she must have wondered. She took the chance. Pressing in, she reached for his hem, and instantly healing flooded her body.

"Who touched my clothes?" Jesus demanded. She shrank back in horror. *Oh no! What if he takes back the healing? What if he rebukes or rejects me? Not again!*

She took another chance. Falling at his feet, she confessed the truth.

Jesus spoke to her gently, calling her "daughter." No rebuke. No indignation or outrage. Just tenderness, healing and a freedom that would change everything.

It's a promise of hope that extends to each of us. "Daughter," Jesus says, "I don't base my feelings for you on the latest popularity poll. I love you no matter what. Trust me with your pain, whatever it is, and let me show you how to be free."

To read the next Mirror Images profile, go to page 1371.

Dear Jesus, thank you for loving me with no strings attached. Thanks for caring for me like you did for the suffering woman, and help me to treat others with that same tenderness. Amen.

▶▶ Read more about the suffering woman in Matthew 9:20–22 (page 1302); Mark 5:25–34 (page 1341) and Luke 8:43–48 (page 1379).

they saw him walking on the lake, they thought he was a ghost. They cried out, [50]because they all saw him and were terrified.

Immediately he spoke to them and said, "Take courage! It is I. Don't be afraid." [51]Then he climbed into the boat with them, and the wind died down. They were completely amazed, [52]for they had not understood about the loaves; their hearts were hardened.

[53]When they had crossed over, they landed at Gennesaret and anchored there. [54]As soon as they got out of the boat, people recognized Jesus. [55]They ran throughout that whole region and carried the sick on mats to wherever they heard he was. [56]And wherever he went—into villages, towns or countryside—they placed the sick in the marketplaces. They begged him to let them touch even the edge of his cloak, and all who touched him were healed.

Clean and Unclean

7 The Pharisees and some of the teachers of the law who had come from Jerusalem gathered around Jesus and [2]saw some of his disciples eating food with hands that were "unclean," that is, unwashed. [3](The Pharisees and all the Jews do not eat unless they give their hands a ceremonial washing, holding to the tradition of the elders. [4]When they come from the marketplace they do not eat unless they wash. And they observe many other traditions, such as the washing of cups, pitchers and kettles.[a])

[5]So the Pharisees and teachers of the law asked Jesus, "Why don't your disciples live according to the tradition of the elders instead of eating their food with 'unclean' hands?"

[6]He replied, "Isaiah was right when he prophesied about you hypocrites; as it is written:

> " 'These people honor me with their lips,
>   but their hearts are far from me.
> [7]They worship me in vain;
>   their teachings are but rules taught by men.'[b]

[8]You have let go of the commands of God and are holding on to the traditions of men."

[9]And he said to them: "You have a fine way of setting aside the commands of God in order to observe[c] your own traditions! [10]For Moses said, 'Honor your father and your mother,'[d] and, 'Anyone who curses his father or mother must be put to death.'[e] [11]But you say that if a man says to his father or mother: 'Whatever help you might otherwise have received from me is Corban' (that is, a gift devoted to God), [12]then you no longer let him do anything for his father or mother. [13]Thus you nullify the word of God by your tradition that you have handed down. And you do many things like that."

[14]Again Jesus called the crowd to him and said, "Listen to me, everyone, and understand this. [15]Nothing outside a man can make him 'unclean' by going into him. Rather, it is what comes out of a man that makes him 'unclean.'[f]"

[17]After he had left the crowd and entered the house, his disciples asked him about this parable. [18]"Are you so dull?" he asked. "Don't you see that nothing that enters a man from the outside can make him 'unclean'? [19]For it doesn't go into his heart but into his stomach, and then out of his body." (In saying this, Jesus declared all foods "clean.")

[20]He went on: "What comes out of a man is what makes him 'unclean.' [21]For from within, out of men's hearts, come evil thoughts, sexual immorality, theft, murder, adultery, [22]greed, malice, deceit, lewdness, envy, slander, arrogance and folly. [23]All these evils come from inside and make a man 'unclean.' "

The Faith of a Syrophoenician Woman

[24]Jesus left that place and went to the vicinity of Tyre.[g] He entered a house and did not want anyone to know it; yet he could not keep his presence secret. [25]In fact, as soon as she heard about him, a woman whose little daughter was possessed by an evil[h] spirit came and fell at his feet. [26]The woman was a Greek, born in Syrian Phoenicia. She begged Jesus to drive the demon out of her daughter.

a 4 Some early manuscripts *pitchers, kettles and dining couches*   *b 6,7* Isaiah 29:13   *c 9* Some manuscripts *set up*
d 10 Exodus 20:12; Deut. 5:16   *e 10* Exodus 21:17; Lev. 20:9   *f 15* Some early manuscripts *'unclean.' 16If anyone has ears to hear, let him hear.*   *g 24* Many early manuscripts *Tyre and Sidon*   *h 25* Greek *unclean*

²⁷"First let the children eat all they want," he told her, "for it is not right to take the children's bread and toss it to their dogs."

²⁸"Yes, Lord," she replied, "but even the dogs under the table eat the children's crumbs."

²⁹Then he told her, "For such a reply, you may go; the demon has left your daughter."

³⁰She went home and found her child lying on the bed, and the demon gone.

The Healing of a Deaf and Mute Man

³¹Then Jesus left the vicinity of Tyre and went through Sidon, down to the Sea of Galilee and into the region of the Decapolis. ᵃ ³²There some people brought to him a man who was deaf and could hardly talk, and they begged him to place his hand on the man.

³³After he took him aside, away from the crowd, Jesus put his fingers into the man's ears. Then he spit and touched the man's tongue. ³⁴He looked up to heaven and with a deep sigh said to him, *"Ephphatha!"* (which means, "Be opened!"). ³⁵At this, the man's ears were opened, his tongue was loosened and he began to speak plainly.

³⁶Jesus commanded them not to tell anyone. But the more he did so, the more they kept talking about it. ³⁷People were overwhelmed with amazement. "He has done everything well," they said. "He even makes the deaf hear and the mute speak."

truth or dare

From his humble birth to his hush-hush healings, Jesus kept his whole ministry on the DL. Why? Jesus wanted status as Savior, not celebrity.

7:36–37

Jesus Feeds the Four Thousand

8 During those days another large crowd gathered. Since they had nothing to eat, Jesus called his disciples to him and said, ²"I have compassion for these people; they have already been with me three days and have nothing to eat. ³If I send them home hungry, they will collapse on the way, because some of them have come a long distance."

⁴His disciples answered, "But where in this remote place can anyone get enough bread to feed them?"

⁵"How many loaves do you have?" Jesus asked.

"Seven," they replied.

⁶He told the crowd to sit down on the ground. When he had taken the seven loaves and given thanks, he broke them and gave them to his disciples to set before the people, and they did so. ⁷They had a few small fish as well; he gave thanks for them also and told the disciples to distribute them. ⁸The people ate and were satisfied. Afterward the disciples picked up seven basketfuls of broken pieces that were left over. ⁹About four thousand men were present. And having sent them away, ¹⁰he got into the boat with his disciples and went to the region of Dalmanutha.

¹¹The Pharisees came and began to question Jesus. To test him, they asked him for a sign from heaven. ¹²He sighed deeply and said, "Why does this generation ask for a miraculous sign? I tell you the truth, no sign will be given to it." ¹³Then he left them, got back into the boat and crossed to the other side.

The Yeast of the Pharisees and Herod

¹⁴The disciples had forgotten to bring bread, except for one loaf they had with them in the boat. ¹⁵"Be careful," Jesus warned them. "Watch out for the yeast of the Pharisees and that of Herod."

¹⁶They discussed this with one another and said, "It is because we have no bread."

¹⁷Aware of their discussion, Jesus asked them: "Why are you talking about having no bread? Do you still not see or understand? Are your hearts hardened? ¹⁸Do you have eyes but fail to see, and ears but fail to hear? And don't you remember? ¹⁹When I broke the five loaves for the five thousand, how many basketfuls of pieces did you pick up?"

"Twelve," they replied.

a 31 That is, the Ten Cities

²⁰"And when I broke the seven loaves for the four thousand, how many basketfuls of pieces did you pick up?"

They answered, "Seven."

²¹He said to them, "Do you still not understand?"

The Healing of a Blind Man at Bethsaida

²²They came to Bethsaida, and some people brought a blind man and begged Jesus to touch him. ²³He took the blind man by the hand and led him outside the village. When he had spit on the man's eyes and put his hands on him, Jesus asked, "Do you see anything?"

²⁴He looked up and said, "I see people; they look like trees walking around."

²⁵Once more Jesus put his hands on the man's eyes. Then his eyes were opened, his sight was restored, and he saw everything clearly. ²⁶Jesus sent him home, saying, "Don't go into the village. ᵃ"

Peter's Confession of Christ

²⁷Jesus and his disciples went on to the villages around Caesarea Philippi. On the way he asked them, "Who do people say I am?"

²⁸They replied, "Some say John the Baptist; others say Elijah; and still others, one of the prophets."

²⁹"But what about you?" he asked. "Who do you say I am?"

Peter answered, "You are the Christ. ᵇ"

³⁰Jesus warned them not to tell anyone about him.

Jesus Predicts His Death

³¹He then began to teach them that the Son of Man must suffer many things and be rejected by the elders, chief priests and teachers of the law, and that he must be killed and after three days rise again. ³²He spoke plainly about this, and Peter took him aside and began to rebuke him.

³³But when Jesus turned and looked at his disciples, he rebuked Peter. "Get behind me, Satan!" he said. "You do not have in mind the things of God, but the things of men."

³⁴Then he called the crowd to him along with his disciples and said: "If anyone would come after me, he must deny himself and take up his cross and follow me. ³⁵For whoever wants to save his life ᶜ will lose it, but whoever loses his life for me and for the gospel will save it. ³⁶What good is it for a man to gain the whole world, yet forfeit his soul? ³⁷Or what can a man give in exchange for his soul? ³⁸If anyone is ashamed of me and my words in this adulterous and sinful generation, the Son of Man will be ashamed of him when he comes in his Father's glory with the holy angels."

truth or dare

Peter had good intentions—he was trying to protect Jesus. But Jesus' whole purpose in life was to die, and he wouldn't let Peter or anyone else stand in his way.

8:31–33

9 And he said to them, "I tell you the truth, some who are standing here will not taste death before they see the kingdom of God come with power."

The Transfiguration

²After six days Jesus took Peter, James and John with him and led them up a high mountain, where they were all alone. There he was transfigured before them. ³His clothes became dazzling white, whiter than anyone in the world could bleach them. ⁴And there appeared before them Elijah and Moses, who were talking with Jesus.

⁵Peter said to Jesus, "Rabbi, it is good for us to be here. Let us put up three shelters—one for you, one for Moses and one for Elijah." ⁶(He did not know what to say, they were so frightened.)

ᵃ 26 Some manuscripts Don't go and tell anyone in the village   ᵇ 29 Or Messiah. "The Christ" (Greek) and "the Messiah" (Hebrew) both mean "the Anointed One."   ᶜ 35 The Greek word means either life or soul; also in verse 36.

[7]Then a cloud appeared and enveloped them, and a voice came from the cloud: "This is my Son, whom I love. Listen to him!"

[8]Suddenly, when they looked around, they no longer saw anyone with them except Jesus.

[9]As they were coming down the mountain, Jesus gave them orders not to tell anyone what they had seen until the Son of Man had risen from the dead. [10]They kept the matter to themselves, discussing what "rising from the dead" meant.

[11]And they asked him, "Why do the teachers of the law say that Elijah must come first?"

[12]Jesus replied, "To be sure, Elijah does come first, and restores all things. Why then is it written that the Son of Man must suffer much and be rejected? [13]But I tell you, Elijah has come, and they have done to him everything they wished, just as it is written about him."

The Healing of a Boy With an Evil Spirit

[14]When they came to the other disciples, they saw a large crowd around them and the teachers of the law arguing with them. [15]As soon as all the people saw Jesus, they were overwhelmed with wonder and ran to greet him.

[16]"What are you arguing with them about?" he asked.

[17]A man in the crowd answered, "Teacher, I brought you my son, who is possessed by a spirit that has robbed him of speech. [18]Whenever it seizes him, it throws him to the ground. He foams at the mouth, gnashes his teeth and becomes rigid. I asked your disciples to drive out the spirit, but they could not."

[19]"O unbelieving generation," Jesus replied, "how long shall I stay with you? How long shall I put up with you? Bring the boy to me."

[20]So they brought him. When the spirit saw Jesus, it immediately threw the boy into a convulsion. He fell to the ground and rolled around, foaming at the mouth.

[21]Jesus asked the boy's father, "How long has he been like this?"

"From childhood," he answered. [22]"It has often thrown him into fire or water to kill him. But if you can do anything, take pity on us and help us."

[23]" 'If you can'?" said Jesus. "Everything is possible for him who believes."

[24]Immediately the boy's father exclaimed, "I do believe; help me overcome my unbelief!"

[25]When Jesus saw that a crowd was running to the scene, he rebuked the evil[a] spirit. "You deaf and mute spirit," he said, "I command you, come out of him and never enter him again."

[26]The spirit shrieked, convulsed him violently and came out. The boy looked so much like a corpse that many said, "He's dead." [27]But Jesus took him by the hand and lifted him to his feet, and he stood up.

[28]After Jesus had gone indoors, his disciples asked him privately, "Why couldn't we drive it out?"

[29]He replied, "This kind can come out only by prayer.[b]"

[30]They left that place and passed through Galilee. Jesus did not want anyone to know where they were, [31]because he was teaching his disciples. He said to them, "The Son of Man is going to be betrayed into the hands of men. They will kill him, and after three days he will rise." [32]But they did not understand what he meant and were afraid to ask him about it.

genuine

honesty » 9:23-24

Ever feel like you're the only one who doesn't have it all together? Well, you're not. Take a lesson from this man. He saw how much he needed to believe—and he wanted to believe—but he knew he didn't believe like he ought to. So did he put on an act? Pretend to be more than he was? No! He was honest with Jesus and himself. It's okay to pray, "God, I love you—help me love you more. I trust you—help me trust you more. I believe in you—help me believe you more." He will.

---

a 25 Greek *unclean* *b 29* Some manuscripts *prayer and fasting*

Who Is the Greatest?

[33]They came to Capernaum. When he was in the house, he asked them, "What were you arguing about on the road?" [34]But they kept quiet because on the way they had argued about who was the greatest.

[35]Sitting down, Jesus called the Twelve and said, "If anyone wants to be first, he must be the very last, and the servant of all."

[36]He took a little child and had him stand among them. Taking him in his arms, he said to them, [37]"Whoever welcomes one of these little children in my name welcomes me; and whoever welcomes me does not welcome me but the one who sent me."

Whoever Is Not Against Us Is for Us

[38]"Teacher," said John, "we saw a man driving out demons in your name and we told him to stop, because he was not one of us."

[39]"Do not stop him," Jesus said. "No one who does a miracle in my name can in the next moment say anything bad about me, [40]for whoever is not against us is for us. [41]I tell you the truth, anyone who gives you a cup of water in my name because you belong to Christ will certainly not lose his reward.

Causing to Sin

[42]"And if anyone causes one of these little ones who believe in me to sin, it would be better for him to be thrown into the sea with a large millstone tied around his neck. [43]If your hand causes you to sin, cut it off. It is better for you to enter life maimed than with two hands to go into hell, where the fire never goes out. [a] [45]And if your foot causes you to sin, cut it off. It is better for you to enter life crippled than to have two feet and be thrown into hell. [b] [47]And if your eye causes you to sin, pluck it out. It is better for you to enter the kingdom of God with one eye than to have two eyes and be thrown into hell, [48]where

" 'their worm does not die,
and the fire is not quenched.' [c]

[49]Everyone will be salted with fire.

[50]"Salt is good, but if it loses its saltiness, how can you make it salty again? Have salt in yourselves, and be at peace with each other."

Divorce

10 Jesus then left that place and went into the region of Judea and across the Jordan. Again crowds of people came to him, and as was his custom, he taught them.

[2]Some Pharisees came and tested him by asking, "Is it lawful for a man to divorce his wife?"

[3]"What did Moses command you?" he replied.

[4]They said, "Moses permitted a man to write a certificate of divorce and send her away."

[5]"It was because your hearts were hard that Moses wrote you this law," Jesus replied. [6]"But at the beginning of creation God 'made them male and female.' [d] [7]'For this reason a man will leave his father and mother and be united to his wife, [e] [8]and the two will become one flesh.' [f] So they are no longer two, but one. [9]Therefore what God has joined together, let man not separate."

[10]When they were in the house again, the disciples asked Jesus about this. [11]He answered, "Anyone who divorces his wife and marries another woman commits adultery against her. [12]And if she divorces her husband and marries another man, she commits adultery."

truth or dare

God didn't create marriage to be like clothes—worn a couple times and then trashed. It's not a casual commitment. Check out God's view on marriage.

10:2–9

[a] 43 Some manuscripts out, [44]where / " 'their worm does not die, / and the fire is not quenched.' [b] 45 Some manuscripts hell, [46]where / " 'their worm does not die, / and the fire is not quenched.' [c] 48 Isaiah 66:24 [d] 6 Gen. 1:27 [e] 7 Some early manuscripts do not have and be united to his wife. [f] 8 Gen. 2:24

The Little Children and Jesus

¹³People were bringing little children to Jesus to have him touch them, but the disciples rebuked them. ¹⁴When Jesus saw this, he was indignant. He said to them, "Let the little children come to me, and do not hinder them, for the kingdom of God belongs to such as these. ¹⁵I tell you the truth, anyone who will not receive the kingdom of God like a little child will never enter it." ¹⁶And he took the children in his arms, put his hands on them and blessed them.

The Rich Young Man

¹⁷As Jesus started on his way, a man ran up to him and fell on his knees before him. "Good teacher," he asked, "what must I do to inherit eternal life?"

¹⁸"Why do you call me good?" Jesus answered. "No one is good—except God alone. ¹⁹You know the commandments: 'Do not murder, do not commit adultery, do not steal, do not give false testimony, do not defraud, honor your father and mother.'ᵃ"

²⁰"Teacher," he declared, "all these I have kept since I was a boy."

²¹Jesus looked at him and loved him. "One thing you lack," he said. "Go, sell everything you have and give to the poor, and you will have treasure in heaven. Then come, follow me."

²²At this the man's face fell. He went away sad, because he had great wealth.

²³Jesus looked around and said to his disciples, "How hard it is for the rich to enter the kingdom of God!"

²⁴The disciples were amazed at his words. But Jesus said again, "Children, how hard it isᵇ to enter the kingdom of God! ²⁵It is easier for a camel to go through the eye of a needle than for a rich man to enter the kingdom of God."

²⁶The disciples were even more amazed, and said to each other, "Who then can be saved?"

²⁷Jesus looked at them and said, "With man this is impossible, but not with God; all things are possible with God."

²⁸Peter said to him, "We have left everything to follow you!"

²⁹"I tell you the truth," Jesus replied, "no one who has left home or brothers or sisters or mother or father or children or fields for me and the gospel ³⁰will fail to receive a hundred times as much in this present age (homes, brothers, sisters, mothers, children and fields—and with them, persecutions) and in the age to come, eternal life. ³¹But many who are first will be last, and the last first."

Jesus Again Predicts His Death

³²They were on their way up to Jerusalem, with Jesus leading the way, and the

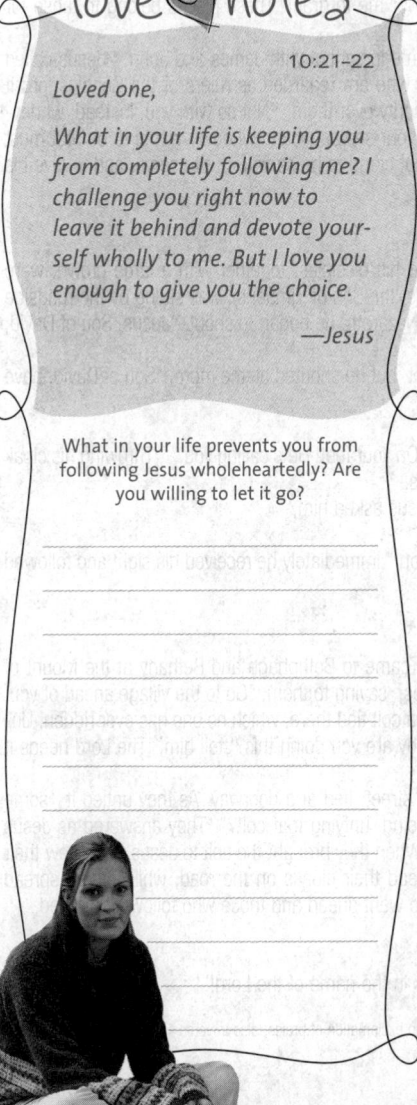

love ♥ notes

10:21-22

Loved one,

What in your life is keeping you from completely following me? I challenge you right now to leave it behind and devote yourself wholly to me. But I love you enough to give you the choice.

—Jesus

What in your life prevents you from following Jesus wholeheartedly? Are you willing to let it go?

_____

_____

_____

_____

_____

_____

_____

_____

_____

_____

ᵃ 19 Exodus 20:12-16; Deut. 5:16-20   ᵇ 24 Some manuscripts *is for those who trust in riches* disciples were astonished, while those who followed were afraid. Again he took the Twelve aside and told them what was going to happen to him. ³³"We are going up to Jerusalem," he said, "and the Son of Man will be betrayed to the chief priests and teachers of the law. They will condemn him to death and will hand him over to the Gentiles, ³⁴who will mock him and spit on him, flog him and kill him. Three days later he will rise."

The Request of James and John

³⁵Then James and John, the sons of Zebedee, came to him. "Teacher," they said, "we want you to do for us whatever we ask."

³⁶"What do you want me to do for you?" he asked.

³⁷They replied, "Let one of us sit at your right and the other at your left in your glory."

³⁸"You don't know what you are asking," Jesus said. "Can you drink the cup I drink or be baptized with the baptism I am baptized with?"

³⁹"We can," they answered.

Jesus said to them, "You will drink the cup I drink and be baptized with the baptism I am baptized with, ⁴⁰but to sit at my right or left is not for me to grant. These places belong to those for whom they have been prepared."

⁴¹When the ten heard about this, they became indignant with James and John. ⁴²Jesus called them together and said, "You know that those who are regarded as rulers of the Gentiles lord it over them, and their high officials exercise authority over them. ⁴³Not so with you. Instead, whoever wants to become great among you must be your servant, ⁴⁴and whoever wants to be first must be slave of all. ⁴⁵For even the Son of Man did not come to be served, but to serve, and to give his life as a ransom for many."

Blind Bartimaeus Receives His Sight

⁴⁶Then they came to Jericho. As Jesus and his disciples, together with a large crowd, were leaving the city, a blind man, Bartimaeus (that is, the Son of Timaeus), was sitting by the roadside begging. ⁴⁷When he heard that it was Jesus of Nazareth, he began to shout, "Jesus, Son of David, have mercy on me!"

⁴⁸Many rebuked him and told him to be quiet, but he shouted all the more, "Son of David, have mercy on me!"

⁴⁹Jesus stopped and said, "Call him."

So they called to the blind man, "Cheer up! On your feet! He's calling you." ⁵⁰Throwing his cloak aside, he jumped to his feet and came to Jesus.

⁵¹"What do you want me to do for you?" Jesus asked him.

The blind man said, "Rabbi, I want to see."

⁵²"Go," said Jesus, "your faith has healed you." Immediately he received his sight and followed Jesus along the road.

The Triumphal Entry

11 As they approached Jerusalem and came to Bethphage and Bethany at the Mount of Olives, Jesus sent two of his disciples, ²saying to them, "Go to the village ahead of you, and just as you enter it, you will find a colt tied there, which no one has ever ridden. Untie it and bring it here. ³If anyone asks you, 'Why are you doing this?' tell him, 'The Lord needs it and will send it back here shortly.' "

⁴They went and found a colt outside in the street, tied at a doorway. As they untied it, ⁵some people standing there asked, "What are you doing, untying that colt?" ⁶They answered as Jesus had told them to, and the people let them go. ⁷When they brought the colt to Jesus and threw their cloaks over it, he sat on it. ⁸Many people spread their cloaks on the road, while others spread branches they had cut in the fields. ⁹Those who went ahead and those who followed shouted,

"Hosanna!ᵃ"

"Blessed is he who comes in the name of the Lord!"ᵇ

ᵃ 9 A Hebrew expression meaning "Save!" which became an exclamation of praise; also in verse 10
ᵇ 9 Psalm 118:25,26

¹⁰"Blessed is the coming kingdom of our father David!"

"Hosanna in the highest!"

¹¹Jesus entered Jerusalem and went to the temple. He looked around at everything, but since it was already late, he went out to Bethany with the Twelve.

Jesus Clears the Temple

¹²The next day as they were leaving Bethany, Jesus was hungry. ¹³Seeing in the distance a fig tree in leaf, he went to find out if it had any fruit. When he reached it, he found nothing but leaves, because it was not the season for figs. ¹⁴Then he said to the tree, "May no one ever eat fruit from you again." And his disciples heard him say it.

¹⁵On reaching Jerusalem, Jesus entered the temple area and began driving out those who were buying and selling there. He overturned the tables of the money changers and the benches of those selling doves, ¹⁶and would not allow anyone to carry merchandise through the temple courts. ¹⁷And as he taught them, he said, "Is it not written:

" 'My house will be called
a house of prayer for all nations'ᵃ?

But you have made it 'a den of robbers.'ᵇ"

¹⁸The chief priests and the teachers of the law heard this and began looking for a way to kill him, for they feared him, because the whole crowd was amazed at his teaching.

¹⁹When evening came, theyᶜ went out of the city.

The Withered Fig Tree

²⁰In the morning, as they went along, they saw the fig tree withered from the roots. ²¹Peter remembered and said to Jesus, "Rabbi, look! The fig tree you cursed has withered!"

²²"Haveᵈ faith in God," Jesus answered. ²³"I tell you the truth, if anyone says to this mountain, 'Go, throw yourself into the sea,' and does not doubt in his heart but believes that what he says will happen, it will be done for him. ²⁴Therefore I tell you, whatever you ask for in prayer, believe that you have received it, and it will be yours. ²⁵And when you stand praying, if you hold anything against anyone, forgive him, so that your Father in heaven may forgive you your sins.ᵉ"

The Authority of Jesus Questioned

²⁷They arrived again in Jerusalem, and while Jesus was walking in the temple courts, the chief priests, the teachers of the law and the elders came to him. ²⁸"By what authority are you doing these things?" they asked. "And who gave you authority to do this?"

²⁹Jesus replied, "I will ask you one question. Answer me, and I will tell you by what authority I am doing these things. ³⁰John's baptism—was it from heaven, or from men? Tell me!"

³¹They discussed it among themselves and said, "If we say, 'From heaven,' he will ask, 'Then why didn't you believe him?' ³²But if we say, 'From men' . . ." (They feared the people, for everyone held that John really was a prophet.)

³³So they answered Jesus, "We don't know."

Jesus said, "Neither will I tell you by what authority I am doing these things."

The Parable of the Tenants

12 He then began to speak to them in parables: "A man planted a vineyard. He put a wall around it, dug a pit for the winepress and built a watchtower. Then he rented the vineyard to some farmers and went away on a journey. ²At harvest time he sent a servant to the tenants to collect from them some of the fruit of the vineyard. ³But they seized him, beat him and sent him away empty-handed. ⁴Then he sent another servant to them; they struck this man on the head and treated him shamefully. ⁵He sent still another, and that one they killed. He sent many others; some of them they beat, others they killed.

ᵃ 17 Isaiah 56:7   ᵇ 17 Jer. 7:11   ᶜ 19 Some early manuscripts he   ᵈ 22 Some early manuscripts If you have
ᵉ 25 Some manuscripts sins. ²⁶But if you do not forgive, neither will your Father who is in heaven forgive your sins.

⁶"He had one left to send, a son, whom he loved. He sent him last of all, saying, 'They will respect my son.'

⁷"But the tenants said to one another, 'This is the heir. Come, let's kill him, and the inheritance will be ours.' ⁸So they took him and killed him, and threw him out of the vineyard.

⁹"What then will the owner of the vineyard do? He will come and kill those tenants and give the vineyard to others. ¹⁰Haven't you read this scripture:

> " 'The stone the builders rejected
>   has become the capstone*ᵃ*;
> ¹¹ the Lord has done this,
>   and it is marvelous in our eyes'*ᵇ*?"

¹²Then they looked for a way to arrest him because they knew he had spoken the parable against them. But they were afraid of the crowd; so they left him and went away.

Paying Taxes to Caesar

¹³Later they sent some of the Pharisees and Herodians to Jesus to catch him in his words. ¹⁴They came to him and said, "Teacher, we know you are a man of integrity. You aren't swayed by men, because you pay no attention to who they are; but you teach the way of God in accordance with the truth. Is it right to pay taxes to Caesar or not? ¹⁵Should we pay or shouldn't we?"

But Jesus knew their hypocrisy. "Why are you trying to trap me?" he asked. "Bring me a denarius and let me look at it." ¹⁶They brought the coin, and he asked them, "Whose portrait is this? And whose inscription?"

"Caesar's," they replied.

¹⁷Then Jesus said to them, "Give to Caesar what is Caesar's and to God what is God's."

And they were amazed at him.

Marriage at the Resurrection

¹⁸Then the Sadducees, who say there is no resurrection, came to him with a question. ¹⁹"Teacher," they said, "Moses wrote for us that if a man's brother dies and leaves a wife but no children, the man must marry the widow and have children for his brother. ²⁰Now there were seven brothers. The first one married and died without leaving any children. ²¹The second one married the widow, but he also died, leaving no child. It was the same with the third. ²²In fact, none of the seven left any children. Last of all, the woman died too. ²³At the resurrection*ᶜ* whose wife will she be, since the seven were married to her?"

²⁴Jesus replied, "Are you not in error because you do not know the Scriptures or the power of God? ²⁵When the dead rise, they will neither marry nor be given in marriage; they will be like the angels in heaven. ²⁶Now about the dead rising—have you not read in the book of Moses, in the account of the bush, how God said to him, 'I am the God of Abraham, the God of Isaac, and the God of Jacob'*ᵈ*? ²⁷He is not the God of the dead, but of the living. You are badly mistaken!"

The Greatest Commandment

²⁸One of the teachers of the law came and heard them debating. Noticing that Jesus had given them a good answer, he asked him, "Of all the commandments, which is the most important?"

²⁹"The most important one," answered Jesus, "is this: 'Hear, O Israel, the Lord our God, the Lord is one.*ᵉ* ³⁰Love the Lord your God with all your heart and with all your soul and with all your mind and with all your strength.'*ᶠ* ³¹The second is this: 'Love your neighbor as yourself.'*ᵍ* There is no commandment greater than these."

³²"Well said, teacher," the man replied. "You are right in saying that God is one and there is no other but him. ³³To love him with all your heart, with all your understanding and with all your strength, and to love your neighbor as yourself is more important than all burnt offerings and sacrifices."

³⁴When Jesus saw that he had answered wisely, he said to him, "You are not far from the kingdom of God." And from then on no one dared ask him any more questions.

---

a 10 Or *cornerstone*   *b 11* Psalm 118:22,23   *c 23* Some manuscripts *resurrection, when men rise from the dead,*
d 26 Exodus 3:6   *e 29* Or *the Lord our God is one Lord*   *f 30* Deut. 6:4,5   *g 31* Lev. 19:18

Some Words About Weed

Profile: Addie

I'm not going to lie. I've been tempted to smoke pot. I was at a party on Friday when someone lit a joint. My friend Nicole tried it. She tried to get me to do it. I don't know . . . I just couldn't do it. Something inside of me kept saying no. Maybe that was God or something.

But I was the only one there who didn't try it. Everyone looked at me like I was a big loser or something. Nicole was like, "Addie, why didn't you try it? You don't have to inhale." I didn't know what to tell her.

Most of my friends have tried pot at some point. They all claim they're not addicted. "It's just like smoking cigarettes," one of them said. "It's just something to try, that's all. It helps you relax."

My little sister overheard us talking about it and went ballistic. She threatened to tell Mom. She's a big tattler—always trying to get someone in trouble. She kept telling me that drugs are bad. Like I need advice from a twelve-year-old. I know Mom would completely freak.

I've never really done anything wild in my life. Nicole says I'm entitled to try at least one wild thing so I'll have something to tell my kids someday. "At least do it to be social," she advised me.

I'm starting to wonder . . . *why not?*

For more information on the dangers of drugs, check out the link on www.TrueImagesBible.com

drugs in focus

"Everybody's doin' it." That's a common argument you'll hear about marijuana. The fact is that *not everyone* is doing it. About one in five teens try it. Many who try it become addicted. Some facts to consider:

» Short-term use of marijuana can affect coordination and memory. Prolonged smoking of marijuana can actually lower your IQ.

» The Bible prohibits getting drunk, and you can also apply this advice to anything that potentially impairs your judgment (like getting high on marijuana). See Isaiah 28:7; 1 Corinthians 5:11; Ephesians 5:18 (pages 923, 1510, 1546).

» A friend who tries to get you to take drugs is not a friend who cares about you. Say no.

» Marijuana is considered a "gateway" drug because it crosses an emotional threshold. Once you say "yes" to pot, its easier to try the next drug offered.

For more on this topic, see the index on page 1656.

Whose Son Is the Christ?

[35]While Jesus was teaching in the temple courts, he asked, "How is it that the teachers of the law say that the Christ[a] is the son of David? [36]David himself, speaking by the Holy Spirit, declared:

" 'The Lord said to my Lord:
"Sit at my right hand
until I put your enemies
under your feet." '[b]

[a] 35 Or *Messiah*   [b] 36 Psalm 110:1

³⁷David himself calls him 'Lord.' How then can he be his son?"

The large crowd listened to him with delight.

³⁸As he taught, Jesus said, "Watch out for the teachers of the law. They like to walk around in flowing robes and be greeted in the marketplaces, ³⁹and have the most important seats in the synagogues and the places of honor at banquets. ⁴⁰They devour widows' houses and for a show make lengthy prayers. Such men will be punished most severely."

The Widow's Offering

⁴¹Jesus sat down opposite the place where the offerings were put and watched the crowd putting their money into the temple treasury. Many rich people threw in large amounts. ⁴²But a poor widow came and put in two very small copper coins,ᵃ worth only a fraction of a penny.ᵇ

⁴³Calling his disciples to him, Jesus said, "I tell you the truth, this poor widow has put more into the treasury than all the others. ⁴⁴They all gave out of their wealth; but she, out of her poverty, put in everything—all she had to live on."

Signs of the End of the Age

13 As he was leaving the temple, one of his disciples said to him, "Look, Teacher! What massive stones! What magnificent buildings!"

²"Do you see all these great buildings?" replied Jesus. "Not one stone here will be left on another; every one will be thrown down."

³As Jesus was sitting on the Mount of Olives opposite the temple, Peter, James, John and Andrew asked him privately, ⁴"Tell us, when will these things happen? And what will be the sign that they are all about to be fulfilled?"

⁵Jesus said to them: "Watch out that no one deceives you. ⁶Many will come in my name, claiming, 'I am he,' and will deceive many. ⁷When you hear of wars and rumors of wars, do not be alarmed. Such things must happen, but the end is still to come. ⁸Nation will rise against nation, and kingdom against kingdom. There will be earthquakes in various places, and famines. These are the beginning of birth pains.

⁹"You must be on your guard. You will be handed over to the local councils and flogged in the synagogues. On account of me you will stand before governors and kings as witnesses to them. ¹⁰And the gospel must first be preached to all nations. ¹¹Whenever you are arrested and brought to trial, do not worry beforehand about what to say. Just say whatever is given you at the time, for it is not you speaking, but the Holy Spirit.

¹²"Brother will betray brother to death, and a father his child. Children will rebel against their parents and have them put to death. ¹³All men will hate you because of me, but he who stands firm to the end will be saved.

¹⁴"When you see 'the abomination that causes desolation'ᶜ standing where itᵈ does not belong—let the reader understand—then let those who are in Judea flee to the mountains. ¹⁵Let no one on the roof of his house go down or enter the house to take anything out. ¹⁶Let no one in the field go back to get his cloak. ¹⁷How dreadful it will be in those days for pregnant women and nursing mothers! ¹⁸Pray that this will not take place in winter, ¹⁹because those will be days of distress unequaled from the beginning, when God created the world, until now—and never to be equaled again. ²⁰If the Lord had not cut short those days, no one would survive. But for the sake of the elect, whom he has chosen, he has shortened them. ²¹At that time if anyone says to you, 'Look, here is the Christᵉ!' or, 'Look, there he is!' do not believe it. ²²For false Christs and false prophets will appear and perform signs and miracles to deceive the elect—if that were possible. ²³So be on your guard; I have told you everything ahead of time.

truth or dare

Ever have someone argue with you or attack you about your faith? Be ready to explain your faith, but rely on the Holy Spirit to provide the right words.

13:11

ᵃ 42 Greek *two lepta*   ᵇ 42 Greek *kodrantes*   ᶜ 14 Daniel 9:27; 11:31; 12:11   ᵈ 14 Or *he*; also in verse 29
ᵉ 21 Or *Messiah*

²⁴"But in those days, following that distress,

" 'the sun will be darkened,
and the moon will not give its light;
²⁵the stars will fall from the sky,
and the heavenly bodies will be shaken.'^a

²⁶"At that time men will see the Son of Man coming in clouds with great power and glory. ²⁷And he will send his angels and gather his elect from the four winds, from the ends of the earth to the ends of the heavens.

²⁸"Now learn this lesson from the fig tree: As soon as its twigs get tender and its leaves come out, you know that summer is near. ²⁹Even so, when you see these things happening, you know that it is near, right at the door. ³⁰I tell you the truth, this generation^b will certainly not pass away until all these things have happened. ³¹Heaven and earth will pass away, but my words will never pass away.

The Day and Hour Unknown

³²"No one knows about that day or hour, not even the angels in heaven, nor the Son, but only the Father. ³³Be on guard! Be alert^c! You do not know when that time will come. ³⁴It's like a man going away: He leaves his house and puts his servants in charge, each with his assigned task, and tells the one at the door to keep watch.

³⁵"Therefore keep watch because you do not know when the owner of the house will come back—whether in the evening, or at midnight, or when the rooster crows, or at dawn. ³⁶If he comes suddenly, do not let him find you sleeping. ³⁷What I say to you, I say to everyone: 'Watch!' "

Jesus Anointed at Bethany

14 Now the Passover and the Feast of Unleavened Bread were only two days away, and the chief priests and the teachers of the law were looking for some sly way to arrest Jesus and kill him. ²"But not during the Feast," they said, "or the people may riot."

³While he was in Bethany, reclining at the table in the home of a man known as Simon the Leper, a woman came with an alabaster jar of very expensive perfume, made of pure nard. She broke the jar and poured the perfume on his head.

⁴Some of those present were saying indignantly to one another, "Why this waste of perfume? ⁵It could have been sold for more than a year's wages^d and the money given to the poor." And they rebuked her harshly.

⁶"Leave her alone," said Jesus. "Why are you bothering her? She has done a beautiful thing to me. ⁷The poor you will always have with you, and you can help them any time you want. But you will not always have me. ⁸She did what she could. She poured perfume on my body beforehand to prepare for my burial. ⁹I tell you the truth, wherever the gospel is preached throughout the world, what she has done will also be told, in memory of her."

¹⁰Then Judas Iscariot, one of the Twelve, went to the chief priests to betray Jesus to them.

ξenuine devotion » 14:3-9

Mary wasn't an apostle or anyone particularly significant in the world's eyes, but she sat at Jesus' feet and really listened to him, giving her a deeper understanding of his teachings. You may not be a pastor or a well-known intellectual, but you too can know Jesus in a deeper way. Sit at his feet, spend time listening to him through his Word and see what you discover.

^a 25 Isaiah 13:10; 34:4   ^b 30 Or *race*   ^c 33 Some manuscripts *alert and pray*   ^d 5 Greek *than three hundred denarii*

[11]They were delighted to hear this and promised to give him money. So he watched for an opportunity to hand him over.

The Lord's Supper

[12]On the first day of the Feast of Unleavened Bread, when it was customary to sacrifice the Passover lamb, Jesus' disciples asked him, "Where do you want us to go and make preparations for you to eat the Passover?"

[13]So he sent two of his disciples, telling them, "Go into the city, and a man carrying a jar of water will meet you. Follow him. [14]Say to the owner of the house he enters, 'The Teacher asks: Where is my guest room, where I may eat the Passover with my disciples?' [15]He will show you a large upper room, furnished and ready. Make preparations for us there."

[16]The disciples left, went into the city and found things just as Jesus had told them. So they prepared the Passover.

[17]When evening came, Jesus arrived with the Twelve. [18]While they were reclining at the table eating, he said, "I tell you the truth, one of you will betray me—one who is eating with me."

[19]They were saddened, and one by one they said to him, "Surely not I?"

[20]"It is one of the Twelve," he replied, "one who dips bread into the bowl with me. [21]The Son of Man will go just as it is written about him. But woe to that man who betrays the Son of Man! It would be better for him if he had not been born."

[22]While they were eating, Jesus took bread, gave thanks and broke it, and gave it to his disciples, saying, "Take it; this is my body."

[23]Then he took the cup, gave thanks and offered it to them, and they all drank from it.

[24]"This is my blood of the[a] covenant, which is poured out for many," he said to them. [25]"I tell you the truth, I will not drink again of the fruit of the vine until that day when I drink it anew in the kingdom of God."

[26]When they had sung a hymn, they went out to the Mount of Olives.

Jesus Predicts Peter's Denial

[27]"You will all fall away," Jesus told them, "for it is written:

" 'I will strike the shepherd,
    and the sheep will be scattered.'[b]

[28]But after I have risen, I will go ahead of you into Galilee."

[29]Peter declared, "Even if all fall away, I will not."

[30]"I tell you the truth," Jesus answered, "today—yes, tonight—before the rooster crows twice[c] you yourself will disown me three times."

[31]But Peter insisted emphatically, "Even if I have to die with you, I will never disown you." And all the others said the same.

Gethsemane

[32]They went to a place called Gethsemane, and Jesus said to his disciples, "Sit here while I pray." [33]He took Peter, James and John along with him, and he began to be deeply distressed and troubled. [34]"My soul is overwhelmed with sorrow to the point of death," he said to them. "Stay here and keep watch."

[35]Going a little farther, he fell to the ground and prayed that if possible the hour might pass from him. [36]"Abba,[d] Father," he said, "everything is possible for you. Take this cup from me. Yet not what I will, but what you will."

[37]Then he returned to his disciples and found them sleeping. "Simon," he said to Peter, "are you asleep? Could you not keep watch for one hour? [38]Watch and pray so that you will not fall into temptation. The spirit is willing, but the body is weak."

[39]Once more he went away and prayed the same thing. [40]When he came back, he again found them sleeping, because their eyes were heavy. They did not know what to say to him.

[41]Returning the third time, he said to them, "Are you still sleeping and resting? Enough! The

a 24 Some manuscripts the new   b 27 Zech. 13:7   c 30 Some early manuscripts do not have twice.   d 36 Aramaic for Father hour has come. Look, the Son of Man is betrayed into the hands of sinners. ⁴²Rise! Let us go! Here comes my betrayer!"

Jesus Arrested

⁴³Just as he was speaking, Judas, one of the Twelve, appeared. With him was a crowd armed with swords and clubs, sent from the chief priests, the teachers of the law, and the elders.

⁴⁴Now the betrayer had arranged a signal with them: "The one I kiss is the man; arrest him and lead him away under guard." ⁴⁵Going at once to Jesus, Judas said, "Rabbi!" and kissed him. ⁴⁶The men seized Jesus and arrested him. ⁴⁷Then one of those standing near drew his sword and struck the servant of the high priest, cutting off his ear.

⁴⁸"Am I leading a rebellion," said Jesus, "that you have come out with swords and clubs to capture me? ⁴⁹Every day I was with you, teaching in the temple courts, and you did not arrest me. But the Scriptures must be fulfilled." ⁵⁰Then everyone deserted him and fled.

⁵¹A young man, wearing nothing but a linen garment, was following Jesus. When they seized him, ⁵²he fled naked, leaving his garment behind.

Before the Sanhedrin

⁵³They took Jesus to the high priest, and all the chief priests, elders and teachers of the law came together. ⁵⁴Peter followed him at a distance, right into the courtyard of the high priest. There he sat with the guards and warmed himself at the fire.

⁵⁵The chief priests and the whole Sanhedrin were looking for evidence against Jesus so that they could put him to death, but they did not find any. ⁵⁶Many testified falsely against him, but their statements did not agree.

⁵⁷Then some stood up and gave this false testimony against him: ⁵⁸"We heard him say, 'I will destroy this man-made temple and in three days will build another, not made by man.' " ⁵⁹Yet even then their testimony did not agree.

⁶⁰Then the high priest stood up before them and asked Jesus, "Are you not going to answer? What is this testimony that these men are bringing against you?" ⁶¹But Jesus remained silent and gave no answer.

Again the high priest asked him, "Are you the Christ,ᵃ the Son of the Blessed One?"

⁶²"I am," said Jesus. "And you will see the Son of Man sitting at the right hand of the Mighty One and coming on the clouds of heaven."

⁶³The high priest tore his clothes. "Why do we need any more witnesses?" he asked. ⁶⁴"You have heard the blasphemy. What do you think?"

They all condemned him as worthy of death. ⁶⁵Then some began to spit at him; they blindfolded him, struck him with their fists, and said, "Prophesy!" And the guards took him and beat him.

Peter Disowns Jesus

⁶⁶While Peter was below in the courtyard, one of the servant girls of the high priest came by. ⁶⁷When she saw Peter warming himself, she looked closely at him.

"You also were with that Nazarene, Jesus," she said.

⁶⁸But he denied it. "I don't know or understand what you're talking about," he said, and went out into the entryway.ᵇ

⁶⁹When the servant girl saw him there, she said again to those standing around, "This fellow is one of them." ⁷⁰Again he denied it.

After a little while, those standing near said to Peter, "Surely you are one of them, for you are a Galilean."

truth or dare

Just when Jesus needed his friends' support the most, he found them sleeping on the job. When your girlfriends experience major stress, what kind of friend are you?

14:32–41

ᵃ 61 Or *Messiah*   ᵇ 68 Some early manuscripts *entryway and the rooster crowed*

⁷¹He began to call down curses on himself, and he swore to them, "I don't know this man you're talking about."

⁷²Immediately the rooster crowed the second time. ª Then Peter remembered the word Jesus had spoken to him: "Before the rooster crows twice ᵇ you will disown me three times." And he broke down and wept.

Jesus Before Pilate

15 Very early in the morning, the chief priests, with the elders, the teachers of the law and the whole Sanhedrin, reached a decision. They bound Jesus, led him away and handed him over to Pilate.

²"Are you the king of the Jews?" asked Pilate.

"Yes, it is as you say," Jesus replied.

³The chief priests accused him of many things. ⁴So again Pilate asked him, "Aren't you going to answer? See how many things they are accusing you of."

⁵But Jesus still made no reply, and Pilate was amazed.

⁶Now it was the custom at the Feast to release a prisoner whom the people requested. ⁷A man called Barabbas was in prison with the insurrectionists who had committed murder in the uprising. ⁸The crowd came up and asked Pilate to do for them what he usually did.

⁹"Do you want me to release to you the king of the Jews?" asked Pilate, ¹⁰knowing it was out of envy that the chief priests had handed Jesus over to him. ¹¹But the chief priests stirred up the crowd to have Pilate release Barabbas instead.

¹²"What shall I do, then, with the one you call the king of the Jews?" Pilate asked them.

¹³"Crucify him!" they shouted.

¹⁴"Why? What crime has he committed?" asked Pilate.

But they shouted all the louder, "Crucify him!"

¹⁵Wanting to satisfy the crowd, Pilate released Barabbas to them. He had Jesus flogged, and handed him over to be crucified.

The Soldiers Mock Jesus

¹⁶The soldiers led Jesus away into the palace (that is, the Praetorium) and called together the whole company of soldiers. ¹⁷They put a purple robe on him, then twisted together a crown of thorns and set it on him. ¹⁸And they began to call out to him, "Hail, king of the Jews!" ¹⁹Again and again they struck him on the head with a staff and spit on him. Falling on their knees, they paid homage to him. ²⁰And when they had mocked him, they took off the purple robe and put his own clothes on him. Then they led him out to crucify him.

The Crucifixion

²¹A certain man from Cyrene, Simon, the father of Alexander and Rufus, was passing by on his way in from the country, and they forced him to carry the cross. ²²They brought Jesus to the place called Golgotha (which means The Place of the Skull). ²³Then they offered him wine mixed with myrrh, but he did not take it. ²⁴And they crucified him. Dividing up his clothes, they cast lots to see what each would get.

genuine integrity » 15:15

Wanting to satisfy the crowd . . . Pilate could see that Jesus was being framed, that he was innocent of the charges being brought against him. So did he stand up and do the right thing, even though it was hard? Noooooooooo. He caved in to the pressure placed on him by the crowd and his own shaky standing as a leader in Judea. He chose to satisfy the crowd instead of doing what was right. How about you? When the pressure's on and the crowd's shouting at you to do the wrong thing— what will you do?

ª 72 Some early manuscripts do not have *the second time.*   ᵇ 72 Some early manuscripts do not have *twice.*

²⁵It was the third hour when they crucified him. ²⁶The written notice of the charge against him read: THE KING OF THE JEWS. ²⁷They crucified two robbers with him, one on his right and one on his left. ᵃ ²⁹Those who passed by hurled insults at him, shaking their heads and saying, "So! You who are going to destroy the temple and build it in three days, ³⁰come down from the cross and save yourself!"

³¹In the same way the chief priests and the teachers of the law mocked him among themselves. "He saved others," they said, "but he can't save himself! ³²Let this Christ, ᵇ this King of Israel, come down now from the cross, that we may see and believe." Those crucified with him also heaped insults on him.

The Death of Jesus

³³At the sixth hour darkness came over the whole land until the ninth hour. ³⁴And at the ninth hour Jesus cried out in a loud voice, *"Eloi, Eloi, lama sabachthani?"*—which means, "My God, my God, why have you forsaken me?" ᶜ

³⁵When some of those standing near heard this, they said, "Listen, he's calling Elijah."

³⁶One man ran, filled a sponge with wine vinegar, put it on a stick, and offered it to Jesus to drink. "Now leave him alone. Let's see if Elijah comes to take him down," he said.

³⁷With a loud cry, Jesus breathed his last.

³⁸The curtain of the temple was torn in two from top to bottom. ³⁹And when the centurion, who stood there in front of Jesus, heard his cry andᵈ saw how he died, he said, "Surely this man was the Sonᵉ of God!"

⁴⁰Some women were watching from a distance. Among them were Mary Magdalene, Mary the mother of James the younger and of Joses, and Salome. ⁴¹In Galilee these women had followed him and cared for his needs. Many other women who had come up with him to Jerusalem were also there.

truth or dare

Forsaking someone means abandoning or disowning them. The Son of God was temporarily separated and forsaken by his Father so you would never have to experience this same abandonment.

15:34

The Burial of Jesus

⁴²It was Preparation Day (that is, the day before the Sabbath). So as evening approached, ⁴³Joseph of Arimathea, a prominent member of the Council, who was himself waiting for the kingdom of God, went boldly to Pilate and asked for Jesus' body. ⁴⁴Pilate was surprised to hear that he was already dead. Summoning the centurion, he asked him if Jesus had already died. ⁴⁵When he learned from the centurion that it was so, he gave the body to Joseph. ⁴⁶So Joseph bought some linen cloth, took down the body, wrapped it in the linen, and placed it in a tomb cut out of rock. Then he rolled a stone against the entrance of the tomb. ⁴⁷Mary Magdalene and Mary the mother of Joses saw where he was laid.

The Resurrection

16 When the Sabbath was over, Mary Magdalene, Mary the mother of James, and Salome bought spices so that they might go to anoint Jesus' body. ²Very early on the first day of the week, just after sunrise, they were on their way to the tomb ³and they asked each other, "Who will roll the stone away from the entrance of the tomb?"

⁴But when they looked up, they saw that the stone, which was very large, had been rolled away. ⁵As they entered the tomb, they saw a young man dressed in a white robe sitting on the right side, and they were alarmed.

⁶"Don't be alarmed," he said. "You are looking for Jesus the Nazarene, who was crucified. He

ᵃ 27 Some manuscripts left, ²⁸and the scripture was fulfilled which says, "He was counted with the lawless ones" (Isaiah 53:12)   ᵇ 32 Or Messiah   ᶜ 34 Psalm 22:1   ᵈ 39 Some manuscripts do not have heard his cry and   ᵉ 39 Or a son

The Great Omission

Dawn. Patrick. Devin. Anthony. Cara. They're all my friends. I've known Dawn and Patrick since we were in fifth grade. Devin, Anthony and Cara became my good friends in eighth grade. We're freshmen now. We like hanging out together.

None of them is a Christian. I am, though.

I know what I need to do—tell them about Jesus. I just can't seem to do it. I feel like . . . I don't know . . . like a dork, I guess, because I'm not sure what to say. How do you tell someone, "Hey, you need Jesus!" when you're talking about TV shows or whether or not to go to homecoming? It's so awkward!

I've also heard some of them make fun of Bible-bangers—those TV evangelists. That made me uncomfortable. But it's funny. They all know I'm a Christian, and they've never made fun of *me* for what I believe. They're great friends. I just wish they knew the truth about Jesus.

Actually, I don't know that they *don't* believe. Maybe they're curious about it. Like when Devin asked me if I go to church every Sunday. I said, "Yeah," but then changed the subject right away. It's not that I'm ashamed or anything. (At least, I don't *think* I am.) I just feel uncomfortable talking about my beliefs. Half the time I'm not sure I've got it all straight anyway.

My friend Bianca, who's also a Christian, suggested that I get some tracts. No way! Tracts are *not* my thing.

I feel so guilty!

witnessing in focus

Before he left the earth, Jesus told his disciples, "Go into all the world and preach the good news to all creation" (Mark 16:15, page 1361). This is known as the Great Commission. Does that command scare you? Is the Great Commission a big omission in your life? Here are some ways you can live it out:

»*Be a witness by your friendship.* Your love and acceptance can be a better open door for Christ than a tract hastily thrown at someone.

»*Ask God for opportunities to speak for him.* He might show you a verse you can use. He'll definitely give you the courage to speak when you need to.

»*Rely on the Holy Spirit.* You can't talk someone into becoming a Christian. Remember that it's the Holy Spirit who draws people to Christ—not *you*. Trust the Holy Spirit to work in the person's heart (see John 15:26; 16:7–11, page 1436).

For more on this topic, see the index on page 1656.

has risen! He is not here. See the place where they laid him. [7]But go, tell his disciples and Peter, 'He is going ahead of you into Galilee. There you will see him, just as he told you.' "

[8]Trembling and bewildered, the women went out and fled from the tomb. They said nothing to anyone, because they were afraid.

[The earliest manuscripts and some other ancient witnesses do not have Mark 16:9–20.]

[9]When Jesus rose early on the first day of the week, he appeared first to Mary Magdalene, out of whom he had driven seven demons. [10]She went and told those who had been with him and who were mourning and weeping. [11]When they heard that Jesus was alive and that she had seen him, they did not believe it.

[12]Afterward Jesus appeared in a different form to two of them while they were walking in the country. [13]These returned and reported it to the rest; but they did not believe them either.

[14]Later Jesus appeared to the Eleven as they were eating; he rebuked them for their lack of faith and their stubborn refusal to believe those who had seen him after he had risen.

[15]He said to them, "Go into all the world and preach the good news to all creation. [16]Whoever believes and is baptized will be saved, but whoever does not believe will be condemned. [17]And these signs will accompany those who believe: In my name they will drive out demons; they will speak in new tongues; [18]they will pick up snakes with their hands; and when they drink deadly poison, it will not hurt them at all; they will place their hands on sick people, and they will get well."

[19]After the Lord Jesus had spoken to them, he was taken up into heaven and he sat at the right hand of God. [20]Then the disciples went out and preached everywhere, and the Lord worked with them and confirmed his word by the signs that accompanied it.

at a glance

author: Luke, a doctor and Gentile Christian.

date: Probably about A.D. 60.

setting: Luke probably wrote from Rome, or perhaps from Caesarea. He wanted the Gentiles to hear the true details about the life of Jesus.

verse to remember: "For the Son of Man came to seek and to save what was lost" (19:10).

theme to consider: Dr. Luke presents a carefully documented biography of Jesus, the perfect Son of Man, who came to save *all* who are lost. Look for the emphasis on Jesus' relationships with others, and in particular, the prominence given to women in this book.

luke

unchanging truth

Think about what you treasure the most. Many people value relationships above all else. It's great to make new ones and hold on to old ones, isn't it? Consider how much better your life is because of your friends and family. Which relationships do you especially treasure? Who do you spend the most time with?

Look throughout the Gospel of Luke, and what do you find? People. The Gospel of Luke is like the *People* magazine of the Bible (but in a non-gossipy way!). It zeroes in on relationships. Of course, the main story is Jesus and how his story weaves into the fabric of others' lives—including yours.

Throughout the Gospel are several stories within a story—the parables Jesus told. Since Jesus was so social, it's only fitting that he would use stories in order to explain deep, spiritual truths. His stories were for a wide range of people. Even small children could understand them.

What's also fitting is the fact that Luke wrote to a friend of his in order to explain the story of the most influential person who ever lived. As a doctor and missionary, Luke met and became friends with a lot of people. He especially wanted his friend Theophilus to know the truth about Jesus. Is that your hope for the people in your life? How do you use what you know about Jesus to influence your friends and family for good?

life lessons

1 Jesus acknowledged the task that God had given him: to preach the gospel and save the world (4:16–21). God wants you to be willing to take on whatever task he has for you.

2 Back in a time when women were considered second class, Jesus gave them an important place in his ministry. Many women provided for Jesus' earthly needs (8:1–3). We can give our time, money and resources to further Jesus' work today.

3 Like Martha, we're often distracted by what we have to do. However, like Mary, we can choose to spend time with Jesus (10:38–42).

Introduction

Many have undertaken to draw up an account of the things that have been fulfilled[a] among us, [2]just as they were handed down to us by those who from the first were eyewitnesses and servants of the word. [3]Therefore, since I myself have carefully investigated everything from the beginning, it seemed good also to me to write an orderly account for you, most excellent Theophilus, [4]so that you may know the certainty of the things you have been taught.

The Birth of John the Baptist Foretold

[5]In the time of Herod king of Judea there was a priest named Zechariah, who belonged to the priestly division of Abijah; his wife Elizabeth was also a descendant of Aaron. [6]Both of them were upright in the sight of God, observing all the Lord's commandments and regulations blamelessly. [7]But they had no children, because Elizabeth was barren; and they were both well along in years.

[8]Once when Zechariah's division was on duty and he was serving as priest before God, [9]he was chosen by lot, according to the custom of the priesthood, to go into the temple of the Lord and burn incense. [10]And when the time for the burning of incense came, all the assembled worshipers were praying outside.

[11]Then an angel of the Lord appeared to him, standing at the right side of the altar of incense. [12]When Zechariah saw him, he was startled and was gripped with fear. [13]But the angel said to him: "Do not be afraid, Zechariah; your prayer has been heard. Your wife Elizabeth will bear you a son, and you are to give him the name John. [14]He will be a joy and delight to you, and many will rejoice because of his birth, [15]for he will be great in the sight of the Lord. He is never to take wine or other fermented drink, and he will be filled with the Holy Spirit even from birth.[b] [16]Many of the people of Israel will he bring back to the Lord their God. [17]And he will go on before the Lord, in the spirit and power of Elijah, to turn the hearts of the fathers to their children and the disobedient to the wisdom of the righteous—to make ready a people prepared for the Lord."

[18]Zechariah asked the angel, "How can I be sure of this? I am an old man and my wife is well along in years."

[19]The angel answered, "I am Gabriel. I stand in the presence of God, and I have been sent to speak to you and to tell you this good news. [20]And now you will be silent and not able to speak until the day this happens, because you did not believe my words, which will come true at their proper time."

[21]Meanwhile, the people were waiting for Zechariah and wondering why he stayed so long in the temple. [22]When he came out, he could not speak to them. They realized he had seen a vision in the temple, for he kept making signs to them but remained unable to speak.

[23]When his time of service was completed, he returned home. [24]After this his wife Elizabeth became pregnant and for five months remained in seclusion. [25]"The Lord has done this for me," she said. "In these days he has shown his favor and taken away my disgrace among the people."

The Birth of Jesus Foretold

[26]In the sixth month, God sent the angel Gabriel to Nazareth, a town in Galilee, [27]to a virgin pledged to be married to a man named Joseph, a descendant of David. The virgin's name was Mary. [28]The angel went to her and said, "Greetings, you who are highly favored! The Lord is with you."

[29]Mary was greatly troubled at his words and wondered what kind of greeting this might be. [30]But the angel said to her, "Do not be afraid, Mary, you have found favor with God. [31]You will be with child and give birth to a son, and you are to give him the name Jesus. [32]He will be great and will be called the Son of the Most High. The Lord God will give him the throne of his father David, [33]and he will reign over the house of Jacob forever; his kingdom will never end."

truth or dare

Can you imagine questioning an angel?! Zechariah gives a perfect example of how we sometimes doubt God's Word, even after he's done amazing things in our lives.

1:18–20

[a] 1 Or *been surely believed*   [b] 15 Or *from his mother's womb*

³⁴"How will this be," Mary asked the angel, "since I am a virgin?"

³⁵The angel answered, "The Holy Spirit will come upon you, and the power of the Most High will overshadow you. So the holy one to be born will be called ᵃ the Son of God. ³⁶Even Elizabeth your relative is going to have a child in her old age, and she who was said to be barren is in her sixth month. ³⁷For nothing is impossible with God."

³⁸"I am the Lord's servant," Mary answered. "May it be to me as you have said." Then the angel left her.

Mary Visits Elizabeth

³⁹At that time Mary got ready and hurried to a town in the hill country of Judea, ⁴⁰where she entered Zechariah's home and greeted Elizabeth. ⁴¹When Elizabeth heard Mary's greeting, the baby leaped in her womb, and Elizabeth was filled with the Holy Spirit. ⁴²In a loud voice she exclaimed: "Blessed are you among women, and blessed is the child you will bear! ⁴³But why am I so favored, that the mother of my Lord should come to me? ⁴⁴As soon as the sound of your greeting reached my ears, the baby in my womb leaped for joy. ⁴⁵Blessed is she who has believed that what the Lord has said to her will be accomplished!"

Mary's Song

⁴⁶And Mary said:

"My soul glorifies the Lord
⁴⁷   and my spirit rejoices in God my Savior,
⁴⁸for he has been mindful
        of the humble state of his servant.
    From now on all generations will call me blessed,
⁴⁹   for the Mighty One has done great things for me—
        holy is his name.
⁵⁰His mercy extends to those who fear him,
        from generation to generation.
⁵¹He has performed mighty deeds with his arm;
        he has scattered those who are proud in their inmost thoughts.
⁵²He has brought down rulers from their thrones
        but has lifted up the humble.
⁵³He has filled the hungry with good things
        but has sent the rich away empty.
⁵⁴He has helped his servant Israel,
        remembering to be merciful
⁵⁵to Abraham and his descendants forever,
        even as he said to our fathers."

⁵⁶Mary stayed with Elizabeth for about three months and then returned home.

ᵃ 35 Or *So the child to be born will be called holy,*

genuine obedience » 1:38

Put yourself in Mary's shoes. She was probably about your age. She was poor. And she lived in a culture where being pregnant and unmarried meant total ruin. She was engaged and had plans for her future—when God suddenly turned her life upside down. Do you think she freaked out? Told the angel, "No stinkin' way!"? Not at all. Because she saw herself as God's servant, she willingly accepted whatever God had for her. How about you? When God brings you opportunities to serve him—even ones that don't fit with *your* plans— how will you respond? (Read more about Mary in the Mirror Images profile, page 897.)

The Birth of John the Baptist

⁵⁷When it was time for Elizabeth to have her baby, she gave birth to a son. ⁵⁸Her neighbors and relatives heard that the Lord had shown her great mercy, and they shared her joy.

⁵⁹On the eighth day they came to circumcise the child, and they were going to name him after his father Zechariah, ⁶⁰but his mother spoke up and said, "No! He is to be called John."

⁶¹They said to her, "There is no one among your relatives who has that name."

⁶²Then they made signs to his father, to find out what he would like to name the child. ⁶³He asked for a writing tablet, and to everyone's astonishment he wrote, "His name is John." ⁶⁴Immediately his mouth was opened and his tongue was loosed, and he began to speak, praising God. ⁶⁵The neighbors were all filled with awe, and throughout the hill country of Judea people were talking about all these things. ⁶⁶Everyone who heard this wondered about it, asking, "What then is this child going to be?" For the Lord's hand was with him.

Zechariah's Song

⁶⁷His father Zechariah was filled with the Holy Spirit and prophesied:

> ⁶⁸"Praise be to the Lord, the God of Israel,
>   because he has come and has redeemed his people.
> ⁶⁹He has raised up a horn ᵃ of salvation for us
>   in the house of his servant David
> ⁷⁰(as he said through his holy prophets of long ago),
> ⁷¹salvation from our enemies
>   and from the hand of all who hate us—
> ⁷²to show mercy to our fathers
>   and to remember his holy covenant,
> ⁷³   the oath he swore to our father Abraham:
> ⁷⁴to rescue us from the hand of our enemies,
>   and to enable us to serve him without fear
> ⁷⁵   in holiness and righteousness before him all our days.
>
> ⁷⁶And you, my child, will be called a prophet of the Most High;
>   for you will go on before the Lord to prepare the way for him,
> ⁷⁷to give his people the knowledge of salvation
>   through the forgiveness of their sins,
> ⁷⁸because of the tender mercy of our God,
>   by which the rising sun will come to us from heaven
> ⁷⁹to shine on those living in darkness
>   and in the shadow of death,
>   to guide our feet into the path of peace."

⁸⁰And the child grew and became strong in spirit; and he lived in the desert until he appeared publicly to Israel.

The Birth of Jesus

2 In those days Caesar Augustus issued a decree that a census should be taken of the entire Roman world. ²(This was the first census that took place while Quirinius was governor of Syria.) ³And everyone went to his own town to register.

⁴So Joseph also went up from the town of Nazareth in Galilee to Judea, to Bethlehem the town of David, because he belonged to the house and line of David. ⁵He went there to register with Mary, who was pledged to be married to him and was expecting a child. ⁶While they were there, the time came for the baby to be born, ⁷and she gave birth to her firstborn, a son. She wrapped him in cloths and placed him in a manger, because there was no room for them in the inn.

ᵃ 69 Horn here symbolizes strength.

The Shepherds and the Angels

[8]And there were shepherds living out in the fields nearby, keeping watch over their flocks at night. [9]An angel of the Lord appeared to them, and the glory of the Lord shone around them, and they were terrified. [10]But the angel said to them, "Do not be afraid. I bring you good news of great joy that will be for all the people. [11]Today in the town of David a Savior has been born to you; he is Christ[a] the Lord. [12]This will be a sign to you: You will find a baby wrapped in cloths and lying in a manger."

[13]Suddenly a great company of the heavenly host appeared with the angel, praising God and saying,

[14]"Glory to God in the highest,
and on earth peace to men on whom his
favor rests."

[15]When the angels had left them and gone into heaven, the shepherds said to one another, "Let's go to Bethlehem and see this thing that has happened, which the Lord has told us about."

[16]So they hurried off and found Mary and Joseph, and the baby, who was lying in the manger. [17]When they had seen him, they spread the word concerning what had been told them about this child, [18]and all who heard it were amazed at what the shepherds said to them. [19]But Mary treasured up all these things and pondered them in her heart. [20]The shepherds returned, glorifying and praising God for all the things they had heard and seen, which were just as they had been told.

truth or dare

Can you picture the one who created the universe—atoms, planets, humans, etc.—squeezing himself into the body of a helpless baby lying in a dirty horse trough?

2:7

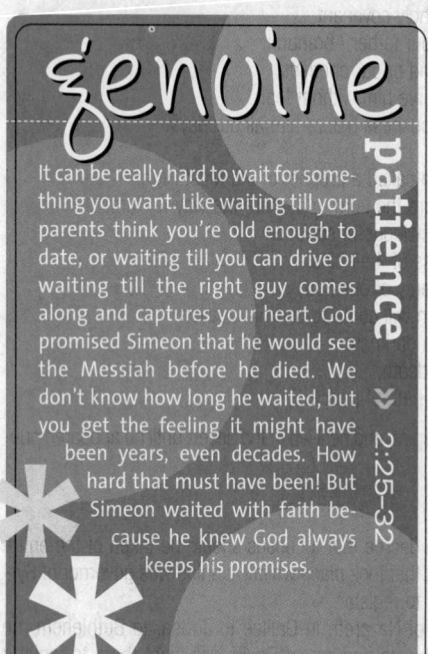

genuine patience

It can be really hard to wait for something you want. Like waiting till your parents think you're old enough to date, or waiting till you can drive or waiting till the right guy comes along and captures your heart. God promised Simeon that he would see the Messiah before he died. We don't know how long he waited, but you get the feeling it might have been years, even decades. How hard that must have been! But Simeon waited with faith because he knew God always keeps his promises.

» 2:25-32

Jesus Presented in the Temple

[21]On the eighth day, when it was time to circumcise him, he was named Jesus, the name the angel had given him before he had been conceived.

[22]When the time of their purification according to the Law of Moses had been completed, Joseph and Mary took him to Jerusalem to present him to the Lord [23](as it is written in the Law of the Lord, "Every firstborn male is to be consecrated to the Lord"[b]), [24]and to offer a sacrifice in keeping with what is said in the Law of the Lord: "a pair of doves or two young pigeons."[c]

[25]Now there was a man in Jerusalem called Simeon, who was righteous and devout. He was waiting for the consolation of Israel, and the Holy Spirit was upon him. [26]It had been revealed to him by the Holy Spirit that he would not die before he had seen the Lord's Christ. [27]Moved by the Spirit, he went into the temple courts. When the parents brought in the child Jesus to do for him what the custom of the Law required, [28]Simeon took him in his arms and praised God, saying:

[29]"Sovereign Lord, as you have
promised,

[a] 11 Or *Messiah*. "The Christ" (Greek) and "the Messiah" (Hebrew) both mean "the Anointed One"; also in verse 26.
[b] 23 Exodus 13:2,12   [c] 24 Lev. 12:8

you now dismiss[a] your servant in peace.
30 For my eyes have seen your salvation,
31   which you have prepared in the sight of all people,
32 a light for revelation to the Gentiles
    and for glory to your people Israel."

33 The child's father and mother marveled at what was said about him. 34 Then Simeon blessed them and said to Mary, his mother: "This child is destined to cause the falling and rising of many in Israel, and to be a sign that will be spoken against, 35 so that the thoughts of many hearts will be revealed. And a sword will pierce your own soul too."

36 There was also a prophetess, Anna, the daughter of Phanuel, of the tribe of Asher. She was very old; she had lived with her husband seven years after her marriage, 37 and then was a widow until she was eighty-four.[b] She never left the temple but worshiped night and day, fasting and praying. 38 Coming up to them at that very moment, she gave thanks to God and spoke about the child to all who were looking forward to the redemption of Jerusalem.

39 When Joseph and Mary had done everything required by the Law of the Lord, they returned to Galilee to their own town of Nazareth. 40 And the child grew and became strong; he was filled with wisdom, and the grace of God was upon him.

The Boy Jesus at the Temple

41 Every year his parents went to Jerusalem for the Feast of the Passover. 42 When he was twelve years old, they went up to the Feast, according to the custom. 43 After the Feast was over, while his parents were returning home, the boy Jesus stayed behind in Jerusalem, but they were unaware of it. 44 Thinking he was in their company, they traveled on for a day. Then they began looking for him among their relatives and friends. 45 When they did not find him, they went back to Jerusalem to look for him. 46 After three days they found him in the temple courts, sitting among the teachers, listening to them and asking them questions. 47 Everyone who heard him was amazed at his understanding and his answers. 48 When his parents saw him, they were astonished. His mother said to him, "Son, why have you treated us like this? Your father and I have been anxiously searching for you."

49 "Why were you searching for me?" he asked. "Didn't you know I had to be in my Father's house?" 50 But they did not understand what he was saying to them.

51 Then he went down to Nazareth with them and was obedient to them. But his mother treasured all these things in her heart. 52 And Jesus grew in wisdom and stature, and in favor with God and men.

John the Baptist Prepares the Way

3 In the fifteenth year of the reign of Tiberius Caesar—when Pontius Pilate was governor of Judea, Herod tetrarch of Galilee, his brother Philip tetrarch of Iturea and Traconitis, and Lysanias tetrarch of Abilene— 2 during the high priesthood of Annas and Caiaphas, the word of God came to John son of Zechariah in the desert. 3 He went into all the country around the Jordan, preaching a baptism of repentance for the forgiveness of sins. 4 As is written in the book of the words of Isaiah the prophet:

"A voice of one calling in the desert,
'Prepare the way for the Lord,
    make straight paths for him.
5 Every valley shall be filled in,
    every mountain and hill made low.
The crooked roads shall become straight,
    the rough ways smooth.
6 And all mankind will see God's salvation.' "[c]

7 John said to the crowds coming out to be baptized by him, "You brood of vipers! Who warned you to flee from the coming wrath? 8 Produce fruit in keeping with repentance. And do not begin to say to yourselves, 'We have Abraham as our father.' For I tell you that out of these stones God can

a 29 Or promised, / now dismiss   b 37 Or widow for eighty-four years   c 6 Isaiah 40:3-5 raise up children for Abraham. [9]The ax is already at the root of the trees, and every tree that does not produce good fruit will be cut down and thrown into the fire."

[10]"What should we do then?" the crowd asked.

[11]John answered, "The man with two tunics should share with him who has none, and the one who has food should do the same."

[12]Tax collectors also came to be baptized. "Teacher," they asked, "what should we do?"

[13]"Don't collect any more than you are required to," he told them.

[14]Then some soldiers asked him, "And what should we do?"

He replied, "Don't extort money and don't accuse people falsely—be content with your pay."

[15]The people were waiting expectantly and were all wondering in their hearts if John might possibly be the Christ.[a] [16]John answered them all, "I baptize you with[b] water. But one more powerful than I will come, the thongs of whose sandals I am not worthy to untie. He will baptize you with the Holy Spirit and with fire. [17]His winnowing fork is in his hand to clear his threshing floor and to gather the wheat into his barn, but he will burn up the chaff with unquenchable fire." [18]And with many other words John exhorted the people and preached the good news to them.

[19]But when John rebuked Herod the tetrarch because of Herodias, his brother's wife, and all the other evil things he had done, [20]Herod added this to them all: He locked John up in prison.

The Baptism and Genealogy of Jesus

[21]When all the people were being baptized, Jesus was baptized too. And as he was praying, heaven was opened [22]and the Holy Spirit descended on him in bodily form like a dove. And a voice came from heaven: "You are my Son, whom I love; with you I am well pleased."

[23]Now Jesus himself was about thirty years old when he began his ministry. He was the son, so it was thought, of Joseph,

the son of Heli, [24]the son of Matthat,
the son of Levi, the son of Melki,
the son of Jannai, the son of Joseph,
[25]the son of Mattathias, the son of Amos,
the son of Nahum, the son of Esli,
the son of Naggai, [26]the son of Maath,
the son of Mattathias, the son of Semein,
the son of Josech, the son of Joda,
[27]the son of Joanan, the son of Rhesa,
the son of Zerubbabel, the son of Shealtiel,
the son of Neri, [28]the son of Melki,
the son of Addi, the son of Cosam,
the son of Elmadam, the son of Er,
[29]the son of Joshua, the son of Eliezer,
the son of Jorim, the son of Matthat,

genuine relationships » 3:7-9

God doesn't offer a "package deal" or a "group rate" to heaven. The people John was talking to didn't understand this. They figured that since Abraham had an "in" with God, and they were his descendants, then they were cool with God, too. John said salvation isn't about your *family's* relationship with God—it's about *your* relationship with God. Being part of a "Christian family" doesn't automatically make you a Christian. Leaning on your family's faith won't cut it. Only your own faith in Jesus counts.

a 15 Or *Messiah*   *b* 16 Or *in*

the son of Levi, ³⁰the son of Simeon,
the son of Judah, the son of Joseph,
the son of Jonam, the son of Eliakim,
³¹the son of Melea, the son of Menna,
the son of Mattatha, the son of Nathan,
the son of David, ³²the son of Jesse,
the son of Obed, the son of Boaz,
the son of Salmon, ᵃ the son of Nahshon,
³³the son of Amminadab, the son of Ram, ᵇ
the son of Hezron, the son of Perez,
the son of Judah, ³⁴the son of Jacob,
the son of Isaac, the son of Abraham,
the son of Terah, the son of Nahor,
³⁵the son of Serug, the son of Reu,
the son of Peleg, the son of Eber,
the son of Shelah, ³⁶the son of Cainan,
the son of Arphaxad, the son of Shem,
the son of Noah, the son of Lamech,
³⁷the son of Methuselah, the son of Enoch,
the son of Jared, the son of Mahalalel,
the son of Kenan, ³⁸the son of Enosh,
the son of Seth, the son of Adam,
the son of God.

truth or dare

Wait! Don't skip the genealogy! This important family tree *proves* Jesus' royal birth line all the way from King David to Judah. He was purebred Jewish royalty.

3:31–33

The Temptation of Jesus

4 Jesus, full of the Holy Spirit, returned from the Jordan and was led by the Spirit in the desert, ²where for forty days he was tempted by the devil. He ate nothing during those days, and at the end of them he was hungry.

³The devil said to him, "If you are the Son of God, tell this stone to become bread."

⁴Jesus answered, "It is written: 'Man does not live on bread alone.'ᶜ"

⁵The devil led him up to a high place and showed him in an instant all the kingdoms of the world. ⁶And he said to him, "I will give you all their authority and splendor, for it has been given to me, and I can give it to anyone I want to. ⁷So if you worship me, it will all be yours."

⁸Jesus answered, "It is written: 'Worship the Lord your God and serve him only.'ᵈ"

⁹The devil led him to Jerusalem and had him stand on the highest point of the temple. "If you are the Son of God," he said, "throw yourself down from here. ¹⁰For it is written:

> " 'He will command his angels concerning you
>   to guard you carefully;
> ¹¹they will lift you up in their hands,
>   so that you will not strike your foot against a stone.'ᵉ"

¹²Jesus answered, "It says: 'Do not put the Lord your God to the test.'ᶠ"

¹³When the devil had finished all this tempting, he left him until an opportune time.

Jesus Rejected at Nazareth

¹⁴Jesus returned to Galilee in the power of the Spirit, and news about him spread through the whole countryside. ¹⁵He taught in their synagogues, and everyone praised him.

¹⁶He went to Nazareth, where he had been brought up, and on the Sabbath day he went into the synagogue, as was his custom. And he stood up to read. ¹⁷The scroll of the prophet Isaiah was handed to him. Unrolling it, he found the place where it is written:

> ¹⁸"The Spirit of the Lord is on me,
>   because he has anointed me
>   to preach good news to the poor.

ᵃ *32* Some early manuscripts *Sala*   ᵇ *33* Some manuscripts *Amminadab, the son of Admin, the son of Arni*; other manuscripts vary widely.   ᶜ *4* Deut. 8:3   ᵈ *8* Deut. 6:13   ᵉ *11* Psalm 91:11,12   ᶠ *12* Deut. 6:16

He has sent me to proclaim freedom for the prisoners
and recovery of sight for the blind,
to release the oppressed,
[19] to proclaim the year of the Lord's favor."[a]

[20]Then he rolled up the scroll, gave it back to the attendant and sat down. The eyes of everyone in the synagogue were fastened on him, [21]and he began by saying to them, "Today this scripture is fulfilled in your hearing."

[22]All spoke well of him and were amazed at the gracious words that came from his lips. "Isn't this Joseph's son?" they asked.

[23]Jesus said to them, "Surely you will quote this proverb to me: 'Physician, heal yourself! Do here in your hometown what we have heard that you did in Capernaum.' "

[24]"I tell you the truth," he continued, "no prophet is accepted in his hometown. [25]I assure you that there were many widows in Israel in Elijah's time, when the sky was shut for three and a half years and there was a severe famine throughout the land. [26]Yet Elijah was not sent to any of them, but to a widow in Zarephath in the region of Sidon. [27]And there were many in Israel with leprosy[b] in the time of Elisha the prophet, yet not one of them was cleansed—only Naaman the Syrian."

[28]All the people in the synagogue were furious when they heard this. [29]They got up, drove him out of the town, and took him to the brow of the hill on which the town was built, in order to throw him down the cliff. [30]But he walked right through the crowd and went on his way.

Jesus Drives Out an Evil Spirit

[31]Then he went down to Capernaum, a town in Galilee, and on the Sabbath began to teach the people. [32]They were amazed at his teaching, because his message had authority.

[33]In the synagogue there was a man possessed by a demon, an evil[c] spirit. He cried out at the top of his voice, [34]"Ha! What do you want with us, Jesus of Nazareth? Have you come to destroy us? I know who you are—the Holy One of God!"

[35]"Be quiet!" Jesus said sternly. "Come out of him!" Then the demon threw the man down before them all and came out without injuring him.

[36]All the people were amazed and said to each other, "What is this teaching? With authority and power he gives orders to evil spirits and they come out!" [37]And the news about him spread throughout the surrounding area.

Jesus Heals Many

[38]Jesus left the synagogue and went to the home of Simon. Now Simon's mother-in-law was suffering from a high fever, and they asked Jesus to help her. [39]So he bent over her and rebuked the fever, and it left her. She got up at once and began to wait on them.

[40]When the sun was setting, the people brought to Jesus all who had various kinds of sickness, and laying his hands on each one, he healed them. [41]Moreover, demons came out of many people, shouting, "You are the Son of God!" But he rebuked them and would not allow them to speak, because they knew he was the Christ.[d]

[42]At daybreak Jesus went out to a solitary place. The people were looking for him and when they came to where he was, they tried to keep him from leaving them. [43]But he said, "I must preach the good news of the kingdom of God to the other towns also, because that is why I was sent." [44]And he kept on preaching in the synagogues of Judea.[e]

The Calling of the First Disciples

5 One day as Jesus was standing by the Lake of Gennesaret,[f] with the people crowding around him and listening to the word of God, [2]he saw at the water's edge two boats, left there by the fishermen, who were washing their nets. [3]He got into one of the boats, the one belonging to Simon, and asked him to put out a little from shore. Then he sat down and taught the people from the boat.

---

[a] 19 Isaiah 61:1,2   [b] 27 The Greek word was used for various diseases affecting the skin—not necessarily leprosy.
[c] 33 Greek unclean; also in verse 36   [d] 41 Or Messiah   [e] 44 Or the land of the Jews; some manuscripts Galilee
[f] 1 That is, Sea of Galilee

mirror images

Anna—Amazing Patience

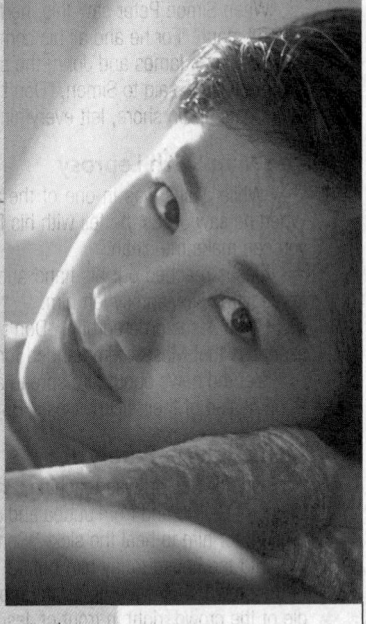

Anna wasn't the type of woman who had a problem with time management—and it's not because she owned a digital planner. Since she had no job or family, her schedule was virtually clear. And that freed her to do the most important things.

Back in that day, you'd find Anna in the temple of Jerusalem. In fact, you wouldn't bother looking anywhere else. The temple became her home, and for most of her life, prayer was her occupation. Each day she would faithfully pray that God's kingdom would come and that the Messiah would come to Jerusalem.

Anna became a widow at a young age, so she took up worship, prayer and fasting inside the temple walls. She prayed for 10 years, then 20 . . . before she knew it she had prayed for 30 and then 40 years . . . then 50 and perhaps 60 . . . still she waited for the Messiah.

At the ripe old age of 84, Anna was in the temple court when she heard a joyful announcement. A man named Simeon was holding up a tiny baby (Jesus), proclaiming that the salvation of Israel had come. At last, her prayers were answered! Anna gave thanks and told all who would listen about the Messiah.

Her amazing patience may leave you dumbfounded. Think of the times you've prayed and asked God for something—expecting an immediate answer, hoping for a quick fix. Why is it God would let Anna wait so long for an answer, and why does it seem he sometimes doesn't answer our prayers?

One thing Anna teaches us is to pray for God's will, not ours. She knew God had already promised a Messiah—and while she was praying, God was teaching her to trust him even with what she couldn't see. Do you pray for relationships to be mended, friends and family to come to Jesus and God to be first in your life? From the Bible we know those are the things God desires, too. Be faithful in prayer—and discover, as Anna did, what patience can do.

> Dear Jesus, to be honest, I'd prefer a "quick fix" instead of a "long haul." Help me to be like Anna, praying with patience and growing to trust you more each day.

To read the next Mirror Images profile, go to page 1385.

» You can read more about Anna in Luke 2:22–38 (pages 1366–1367).

⁴When he had finished speaking, he said to Simon, "Put out into deep water, and let down*ᵃ* the nets for a catch."

⁵Simon answered, "Master, we've worked hard all night and haven't caught anything. But because you say so, I will let down the nets."

⁶When they had done so, they caught such a large number of fish that their nets began to break. ⁷So they signaled their partners in the other boat to come and help them, and they came and filled both boats so full that they began to sink.

⁸When Simon Peter saw this, he fell at Jesus' knees and said, "Go away from me, Lord; I am a sinful man!" ⁹For he and all his companions were astonished at the catch of fish they had taken, ¹⁰and so were James and John, the sons of Zebedee, Simon's partners.

Then Jesus said to Simon, "Don't be afraid; from now on you will catch men." ¹¹So they pulled their boats up on shore, left everything and followed him.

The Man With Leprosy

¹²While Jesus was in one of the towns, a man came along who was covered with leprosy.*ᵇ* When he saw Jesus, he fell with his face to the ground and begged him, "Lord, if you are willing, you can make me clean."

¹³Jesus reached out his hand and touched the man. "I am willing," he said. "Be clean!" And immediately the leprosy left him.

¹⁴Then Jesus ordered him, "Don't tell anyone, but go, show yourself to the priest and offer the sacrifices that Moses commanded for your cleansing, as a testimony to them."

¹⁵Yet the news about him spread all the more, so that crowds of people came to hear him and to be healed of their sicknesses. ¹⁶But Jesus often withdrew to lonely places and prayed.

Jesus Heals a Paralytic

¹⁷One day as he was teaching, Pharisees and teachers of the law, who had come from every village of Galilee and from Judea and Jerusalem, were sitting there. And the power of the Lord was present for him to heal the sick. ¹⁸Some men came carrying a paralytic on a mat and tried to take him into the house to lay him before Jesus. ¹⁹When they could not find a way to do this because of the crowd, they went up on the roof and lowered him on his mat through the tiles into the middle of the crowd, right in front of Jesus.

²⁰When Jesus saw their faith, he said, "Friend, your sins are forgiven."

²¹The Pharisees and the teachers of the law began thinking to themselves, "Who is this fellow who speaks blasphemy? Who can forgive sins but God alone?"

²²Jesus knew what they were thinking and asked, "Why are you thinking these things in your hearts? ²³Which is easier: to say, 'Your sins are forgiven,' or to say, 'Get up and walk'? ²⁴But that you may know that the Son of Man has authority on earth to forgive sins . . ." He said to the paralyzed man, "I tell you, get up, take your mat and go home." ²⁵Immediately he stood up in front of them, took what he had been lying on and went home praising God. ²⁶Everyone was amazed and gave praise to God. They were filled with awe and said, "We have seen remarkable things today."

The Calling of Levi

²⁷After this, Jesus went out and saw a tax collector by the name of Levi sitting at his tax booth. "Follow me," Jesus said to him, ²⁸and Levi got up, left everything and followed him.

²⁹Then Levi held a great banquet for Jesus at his house, and a large crowd of tax collectors and others were eating with them. ³⁰But the Pharisees and the teachers of the law who belonged to their sect complained to his disciples, "Why do you eat and drink with tax collectors and 'sinners'?"

³¹Jesus answered them, "It is not the healthy who need a doctor, but the sick. ³²I have not come to call the righteous, but sinners to repentance."

Jesus Questioned About Fasting

³³They said to him, "John's disciples often fast and pray, and so do the disciples of the Pharisees, but yours go on eating and drinking."

ᵃ 4 The Greek verb is plural.   *ᵇ 12* The Greek word was used for various diseases affecting the skin—not necessarily leprosy.

³⁴Jesus answered, "Can you make the guests of the bridegroom fast while he is with them? ³⁵But the time will come when the bridegroom will be taken from them; in those days they will fast."

³⁶He told them this parable: "No one tears a patch from a new garment and sews it on an old one. If he does, he will have torn the new garment, and the patch from the new will not match the old. ³⁷And no one pours new wine into old wineskins. If he does, the new wine will burst the skins, the wine will run out and the wineskins will be ruined. ³⁸No, new wine must be poured into new wineskins. ³⁹And no one after drinking old wine wants the new, for he says, 'The old is better.' "

Lord of the Sabbath

6 One Sabbath Jesus was going through the grainfields, and his disciples began to pick some heads of grain, rub them in their hands and eat the kernels. ²Some of the Pharisees asked, "Why are you doing what is unlawful on the Sabbath?"

³Jesus answered them, "Have you never read what David did when he and his companions were hungry? ⁴He entered the house of God, and taking the consecrated bread, he ate what is lawful only for priests to eat. And he also gave some to his companions." ⁵Then Jesus said to them, "The Son of Man is Lord of the Sabbath."

⁶On another Sabbath he went into the synagogue and was teaching, and a man was there whose right hand was shriveled. ⁷The Pharisees and the teachers of the law were looking for a reason to accuse Jesus, so they watched him closely to see if he would heal on the Sabbath. ⁸But Jesus knew what they were thinking and said to the man with the shriveled hand, "Get up and stand in front of everyone." So he got up and stood there.

⁹Then Jesus said to them, "I ask you, which is lawful on the Sabbath: to do good or to do evil, to save life or to destroy it?"

¹⁰He looked around at them all, and then said to the man, "Stretch out your hand." He did so, and his hand was completely restored. ¹¹But they were furious and began to discuss with one another what they might do to Jesus.

The Twelve Apostles

¹²One of those days Jesus went out to a mountainside to pray, and spent the night praying to God. ¹³When morning came, he called his disciples to him and chose twelve of them, whom he also designated apostles: ¹⁴Simon (whom he named Peter), his brother Andrew, James, John, Philip, Bartholomew, ¹⁵Matthew, Thomas, James son of Alphaeus, Simon who was called the Zealot, ¹⁶Judas son of James, and Judas Iscariot, who became a traitor.

Blessings and Woes

¹⁷He went down with them and stood on a level place. A large crowd of his disciples was there and a great number of people from all over Judea, from Jerusalem, and from the coast of Tyre and Sidon, ¹⁸who had come to hear him and to be healed of their diseases. Those troubled by evil[a] spirits were cured, ¹⁹and the people all tried to touch him, because power was coming from him and healing them all.

²⁰Looking at his disciples, he said:

"Blessed are you who are poor,
for yours is the kingdom of God.
²¹ Blessed are you who hunger now,
for you will be satisfied.
Blessed are you who weep now,
for you will laugh.
²² Blessed are you when men hate you,

truth or dare

Ever blow off your prayer time, thinking it's no big deal? Even Jesus prayed. And not just a quick chat; it was an intense conversation with his best friend, the heavenly Father.

6:12

a 18 Greek *unclean*

when they exclude you and insult you
and reject your name as evil,
because of the Son of Man.

²³"Rejoice in that day and leap for joy, because great is your reward in heaven. For that is how their fathers treated the prophets.

²⁴ "But woe to you who are rich,
for you have already received your comfort.
²⁵ Woe to you who are well fed now,
for you will go hungry.
Woe to you who laugh now,
for you will mourn and weep.
²⁶ Woe to you when all men speak well of you,
for that is how their fathers treated the false prophets.

Love for Enemies

²⁷"But I tell you who hear me: Love your enemies, do good to those who hate you, ²⁸bless those who curse you, pray for those who mistreat you. ²⁹If someone strikes you on one cheek, turn to him the other also. If someone takes your cloak, do not stop him from taking your tunic. ³⁰Give to everyone who asks you, and if anyone takes what belongs to you, do not demand it back. ³¹Do to others as you would have them do to you.

³²"If you love those who love you, what credit is that to you? Even 'sinners' love those who love them. ³³And if you do good to those who are good to you, what credit is that to you? Even 'sinners' do that. ³⁴And if you lend to those from whom you expect repayment, what credit is that to you? Even 'sinners' lend to 'sinners,' expecting to be repaid in full. ³⁵But love your enemies, do good to them, and lend to them without expecting to get anything back. Then your reward will be great, and you will be sons of the Most High, because he is kind to the ungrateful and wicked. ³⁶Be merciful, just as your Father is merciful.

Judging Others

³⁷"Do not judge, and you will not be judged. Do not condemn, and you will not be condemned. Forgive, and you will be forgiven. ³⁸Give, and it will be given to you. A good measure, pressed down, shaken together and running over, will be poured into your lap. For with the measure you use, it will be measured to you."

³⁹He also told them this parable: "Can a blind man lead a blind man? Will they not both fall into a pit? ⁴⁰A student is not above his teacher, but everyone who is fully trained will be like his teacher.

⁴¹"Why do you look at the speck of sawdust in your brother's eye and pay no attention to the plank in your own eye? ⁴²How can you say to your brother, 'Brother, let me take the speck out of your eye,' when you yourself fail to see the plank in your own eye? You hypocrite, first take the plank out of your eye, and then you will see clearly to remove the speck from your brother's eye.

truth or dare

Ever heard of a matching fund? When we freely forgive others, God promises to "match" our generosity by blessing us in return. 6:37–38

A Tree and Its Fruit

⁴³"No good tree bears bad fruit, nor does a bad tree bear good fruit. ⁴⁴Each tree is recognized by its own fruit. People do not pick figs from thornbushes, or grapes from briers. ⁴⁵The good man brings good things out of the good stored up in his heart, and the evil man brings evil things out of the evil stored up in his heart. For out of the overflow of his heart his mouth speaks.

The Wise and Foolish Builders

⁴⁶"Why do you call me, 'Lord, Lord,' and do not do what I say? ⁴⁷I will show you what he is like who comes to me and hears my words and puts them into practice. ⁴⁸He is like a man building a house, who dug down deep and laid the foundation on rock. When a flood came, the torrent struck

that house but could not shake it, because it was well built. ⁴⁹But the one who hears my words and does not put them into practice is like a man who built a house on the ground without a foundation. The moment the torrent struck that house, it collapsed and its destruction was complete."

The Faith of the Centurion

7When Jesus had finished saying all this in the hearing of the people, he entered Capernaum. ²There a centurion's servant, whom his master valued highly, was sick and about to die. ³The centurion heard of Jesus and sent some elders of the Jews to him, asking him to come and heal his servant. ⁴When they came to Jesus, they pleaded earnestly with him, "This man deserves to have you do this, ⁵because he loves our nation and has built our synagogue." ⁶So Jesus went with them.

He was not far from the house when the centurion sent friends to say to him: "Lord, don't trouble yourself, for I do not deserve to have you come under my roof. ⁷That is why I did not even consider myself worthy to come to you. But say the word, and my servant will be healed. ⁸For I myself am a man under authority, with soldiers under me. I tell this one, 'Go,' and he goes; and that one, 'Come,' and he comes. I say to my servant, 'Do this,' and he does it."

⁹When Jesus heard this, he was amazed at him, and turning to the crowd following him, he said, "I tell you, I have not found such great faith even in Israel." ¹⁰Then the men who had been sent returned to the house and found the servant well.

Jesus Raises a Widow's Son

¹¹Soon afterward, Jesus went to a town called Nain, and his disciples and a large crowd went along with him. ¹²As he approached the town gate, a dead person was being carried out—the only son of his mother, and she was a widow. And a large crowd from the town was with her. ¹³When the Lord saw her, his heart went out to her and he said, "Don't cry."

¹⁴Then he went up and touched the coffin, and those carrying it stood still. He said, "Young man, I say to you, get up!" ¹⁵The dead man sat up and began to talk, and Jesus gave him back to his mother.

¹⁶They were all filled with awe and praised God. "A great prophet has appeared among us," they said. "God has come to help his people." ¹⁷This news about Jesus spread throughout Judea*a* and the surrounding country.

Jesus and John the Baptist

¹⁸John's disciples told him about all these things. Calling two of them, ¹⁹he sent them to the Lord to ask, "Are you the one who was to come, or should we expect someone else?"

²⁰When the men came to Jesus, they said, "John the Baptist sent us to you to ask, 'Are you the one who was to come, or should we expect someone else?' "

²¹At that very time Jesus cured many who had diseases, sicknesses and evil spirits, and gave sight to many who were blind. ²²So he replied to the messengers, "Go back and report to John what you have seen and heard: The blind receive sight, the lame walk, those who have leprosy*b* are cured, the deaf hear, the dead are raised, and the good news is preached to the poor. ²³Blessed is the man who does not fall away on account of me."

²⁴After John's messengers left, Jesus began to speak to the crowd about John: "What did you go out into the desert to see? A reed swayed by the wind? ²⁵If not, what did you go out to see? A man dressed in fine clothes? No, those who wear expensive clothes and indulge in luxury are in palaces. ²⁶But what did you go out to see? A prophet? Yes, I tell you, and more than a prophet. ²⁷This is the one about whom it is written:

> " 'I will send my messenger ahead of you,
>   who will prepare your way before you.'*c*

²⁸I tell you, among those born of women there is no one greater than John; yet the one who is least in the kingdom of God is greater than he."

²⁹(All the people, even the tax collectors, when they heard Jesus' words, acknowledged that

a 17 Or *the land of the Jews*   *b 22* The Greek word was used for various diseases affecting the skin—not necessarily leprosy.   *c 27* Mal. 3:1

No Respect

Profile: Daria

"Daria. Daria! Daaaaarriiiiiaaaaa!" my mom yelled up the stairs. I could hear her screaming, but I didn't care. I was listening to my new CD and lip-synching in front of the mirror.

"Daria!" my mom yelled as she burst through my door and whipped the volume control down on my stereo.

"What!?" I said, startled by her interruption. I felt my lips twitch as I struggled to keep from smiling—my mom looks so funny when she's mad! Her eyebrows arch and she does this jaw-clenching thing that makes her look so ridiculous.

"Daria, you're supposed to be watching your brother so I can finish my report. You know I have class tonight," my mom said in a pleading voice. "Honey, how many times do I have to tell you I need your help while I'm in school?"

"I dunno, Mom, maybe a million times? I'll be down in a minute," I said sarcastically, rolling my eyes as if she was imposing on my personal time and space.

"And you still haven't taken out the trash from this . . . " my mom began.

"Alright!" I interrupted. "I *said* I'd do it, okay? I'm just going to finish this song," I snapped back, turning up my CD player at the same time.

"Daria, I wish you wouldn't talk to me that way," my mom said as she turned to go.

"What? I can't hear you!" I mouthed with fake sincerity as my eyes glared at her.

parents in focus

Sometimes we treat our parents like dirt (especially our moms). We treat them as if they're not human and have no life or feelings of their own. It's a very selfish attitude. Even though we'd never treat our friends like that, we do it to our parents. Consider this:

»Jesus was obedient to his own parents (see Luke 2:51–52, page 1367).
»The Bible has a lot to say about our attitudes when it comes to obedience. See Ephesians 6:1–3 (page 1548), for starters. He requires wholehearted obedience to our parents—no stalling, no sarcasm, no complaining. See Colossians 3:20 (page 1559).
»Choose to make your house a no-grumbling zone (see James 5:9, page 1606).
»Sometimes we mistakenly feel we have to reject our parents in order to "be ourselves." Growing up doesn't have to come at the expense of our relationship to our parents.

For more on this topic, see the index on page 1656.

God's way was right, because they had been baptized by John. ³⁰But the Pharisees and experts in the law rejected God's purpose for themselves, because they had not been baptized by John.)

³¹"To what, then, can I compare the people of this generation? What are they like? ³²They are like children sitting in the marketplace and calling out to each other:

" 'We played the flute for you,
and you did not dance;

> we sang a dirge,
>> and you did not cry.'

[33]For John the Baptist came neither eating bread nor drinking wine, and you say, 'He has a demon.' [34]The Son of Man came eating and drinking, and you say, 'Here is a glutton and a drunkard, a friend of tax collectors and "sinners." ' [35]But wisdom is proved right by all her children."

Jesus Anointed by a Sinful Woman

[36]Now one of the Pharisees invited Jesus to have dinner with him, so he went to the Pharisee's house and reclined at the table. [37]When a woman who had lived a sinful life in that town learned that Jesus was eating at the Pharisee's house, she brought an alabaster jar of perfume, [38]and as she stood behind him at his feet weeping, she began to wet his feet with her tears. Then she wiped them with her hair, kissed them and poured perfume on them.

[39]When the Pharisee who had invited him saw this, he said to himself, "If this man were a prophet, he would know who is touching him and what kind of woman she is—that she is a sinner."

[40]Jesus answered him, "Simon, I have something to tell you."

"Tell me, teacher," he said.

[41]"Two men owed money to a certain moneylender. One owed him five hundred denarii,[a] and the other fifty. [42]Neither of them had the money to pay him back, so he canceled the debts of both. Now which of them will love him more?"

[43]Simon replied, "I suppose the one who had the bigger debt canceled."

"You have judged correctly," Jesus said.

[44]Then he turned toward the woman and said to Simon, "Do you see this woman? I came into your house. You did not give me any water for my feet, but she wet my feet with her tears and wiped them with her hair. [45]You did not give me a kiss, but this woman, from the time I entered, has not stopped kissing my feet. [46]You did not put oil on my head, but she has poured perfume on my feet. [47]Therefore, I tell you, her many sins have been forgiven—for she loved much. But he who has been forgiven little loves little."

[48]Then Jesus said to her, "Your sins are forgiven."

[49]The other guests began to say among themselves, "Who is this who even forgives sins?"

[50]Jesus said to the woman, "Your faith has saved you; go in peace."

The Parable of the Sower

8 After this, Jesus traveled about from one town and village to another, proclaiming the good news of the kingdom of God. The Twelve were with him, [2]and also some women who had been cured of evil spirits and diseases: Mary (called Magdalene) from whom seven demons had come out; [3]Joanna the wife of Cuza, the manager of Herod's household; Susanna; and many others. These women were helping to support them out of their own means.

[4]While a large crowd was gathering and people were coming to Jesus from town after town, he told this parable: [5]"A farmer went out to sow his seed. As he was scattering the seed, some fell along the path; it was trampled on, and the birds of the air ate it up. [6]Some fell on rock, and when it came up, the plants withered because they had no moisture. [7]Other seed fell among thorns, which grew up with it and choked the plants. [8]Still other seed fell on good soil. It came up and yielded a crop, a hundred times more than was sown."

When he said this, he called out, "He who has ears to hear, let him hear."

[9]His disciples asked him what this parable meant. [10]He said, "The knowledge of the secrets of the kingdom of God has been given to you, but to others I speak in parables, so that,

> " 'though seeing, they may not see;
>> though hearing, they may not understand.'[b]

[11]"This is the meaning of the parable: The seed is the word of God. [12]Those along the path are the ones who hear, and then the devil comes and takes away the word from their hearts, so that they may not believe and be saved. [13]Those on the rock are the ones who receive the word with joy when they hear it, but they have no root. They believe for a while, but in the time of testing they fall away. [14]The seed that fell among thorns stands for those who hear, but as they go on their way

a 41 A denarius was a coin worth about a day's wages.   b 10 Isaiah 6:9

they are choked by life's worries, riches and pleasures, and they do not mature. ¹⁵But the seed on good soil stands for those with a noble and good heart, who hear the word, retain it, and by persevering produce a crop.

A Lamp on a Stand

¹⁶"No one lights a lamp and hides it in a jar or puts it under a bed. Instead, he puts it on a stand, so that those who come in can see the light. ¹⁷For there is nothing hidden that will not be disclosed, and nothing concealed that will not be known or brought out into the open. ¹⁸Therefore consider carefully how you listen. Whoever has will be given more; whoever does not have, even what he thinks he has will be taken from him."

Jesus' Mother and Brothers

¹⁹Now Jesus' mother and brothers came to see him, but they were not able to get near him because of the crowd. ²⁰Someone told him, "Your mother and brothers are standing outside, wanting to see you."

²¹He replied, "My mother and brothers are those who hear God's word and put it into practice."

Jesus Calms the Storm

²²One day Jesus said to his disciples, "Let's go over to the other side of the lake." So they got into a boat and set out. ²³As they sailed, he fell asleep. A squall came down on the lake, so that the boat was being swamped, and they were in great danger.

²⁴The disciples went and woke him, saying, "Master, Master, we're going to drown!"

He got up and rebuked the wind and the raging waters; the storm subsided, and all was calm. ²⁵"Where is your faith?" he asked his disciples.

In fear and amazement they asked one another, "Who is this? He commands even the winds and the water, and they obey him."

truth or dare

In the middle of the worst storms in your life, trust Jesus. He has power even over nature, over fear, over problems, over everything. He's Lord of all.

8:22–25

The Healing of a Demon-possessed Man

²⁶They sailed to the region of the Gerasenes,ᵃ which is across the lake from Galilee. ²⁷When Jesus stepped ashore, he was met by a demon-possessed man from the town. For a long time this man had not worn clothes or lived in a house, but had lived in the tombs. ²⁸When he saw Jesus, he cried out and fell at his feet, shouting at the top of his voice, "What do you want with me, Jesus, Son of the Most High God? I beg you, don't torture me!" ²⁹For Jesus had commanded the evilᵇ spirit to come out of the man. Many times it had seized him, and though he was chained hand and foot and kept under guard, he had broken his chains and had been driven by the demon into solitary places.

³⁰Jesus asked him, "What is your name?"

"Legion," he replied, because many demons had gone into him. ³¹And they begged him repeatedly not to order them to go into the Abyss.

³²A large herd of pigs was feeding there on the hillside. The demons begged Jesus to let them go into them, and he gave them permission. ³³When the demons came out of the man, they went into the pigs, and the herd rushed down the steep bank into the lake and was drowned.

³⁴When those tending the pigs saw what had happened, they ran off and reported this in the town and countryside, ³⁵and the people went out to see what had happened. When they came to Jesus, they found the man from whom the demons had gone out, sitting at Jesus' feet, dressed and in his right mind; and they were afraid. ³⁶Those who had seen it told the people how the demon-possessed man had been cured. ³⁷Then all the people of the region of the Gerasenes asked Jesus to leave them, because they were overcome with fear. So he got into the boat and left.

³⁸The man from whom the demons had gone out begged to go with him, but Jesus sent him

ᵃ 26 Some manuscripts *Gadarenes*; other manuscripts *Gergesenes*; also in verse 37   ᵇ 29 Greek *unclean* away, saying, [39]"Return home and tell how much God has done for you." So the man went away and told all over town how much Jesus had done for him.

A Dead Girl and a Sick Woman

[40]Now when Jesus returned, a crowd welcomed him, for they were all expecting him. [41]Then a man named Jairus, a ruler of the synagogue, came and fell at Jesus' feet, pleading with him to come to his house [42]because his only daughter, a girl of about twelve, was dying.

As Jesus was on his way, the crowds almost crushed him. [43]And a woman was there who had been subject to bleeding for twelve years,[a] but no one could heal her. [44]She came up behind him and touched the edge of his cloak, and immediately her bleeding stopped.

[45]"Who touched me?" Jesus asked.

When they all denied it, Peter said, "Master, the people are crowding and pressing against you."

[46]But Jesus said, "Someone touched me; I know that power has gone out from me."

[47]Then the woman, seeing that she could not go unnoticed, came trembling and fell at his feet. In the presence of all the people, she told why she had touched him and how she had been instantly healed. [48]Then he said to her, "Daughter, your faith has healed you. Go in peace."

[49]While Jesus was still speaking, someone came from the house of Jairus, the synagogue ruler. "Your daughter is dead," he said. "Don't bother the teacher any more."

[50]Hearing this, Jesus said to Jairus, "Don't be afraid; just believe, and she will be healed."

[51]When he arrived at the house of Jairus, he did not let anyone go in with him except Peter, John and James, and the child's father and mother. [52]Meanwhile, all the people were wailing and mourning for her. "Stop wailing," Jesus said. "She is not dead but asleep."

[53]They laughed at him, knowing that she was dead. [54]But he took her by the hand and said, "My child, get up!" [55]Her spirit returned, and at once she stood up. Then Jesus told them to give her something to eat. [56]Her parents were astonished, but he ordered them not to tell anyone what had happened.

Jesus Sends Out the Twelve

9 When Jesus had called the Twelve together, he gave them power and authority to drive out all demons and to cure diseases, [2]and he sent them out to preach the kingdom of God and to heal the sick. [3]He told them: "Take nothing for the journey—no staff, no bag, no bread, no money, no extra tunic. [4]Whatever house you enter, stay there until you leave that town. [5]If people do not welcome you, shake the dust off your feet when you leave their town, as a testimony against them." [6]So they set out and went from village to village, preaching the gospel and healing people everywhere.

[7]Now Herod the tetrarch heard about all that was going on. And he was perplexed, because some were saying that John had been raised from the dead, [8]others that Elijah had appeared, and still others that one of the prophets of long ago had come back to life. [9]But Herod said, "I beheaded John. Who, then, is this I hear such things about?" And he tried to see him.

Jesus Feeds the Five Thousand

[10]When the apostles returned, they reported to Jesus what they had done. Then he took them with him and they withdrew by themselves to a town called Bethsaida, [11]but the crowds learned about it and followed him. He welcomed them and spoke to them about the kingdom of God, and healed those who needed healing.

[12]Late in the afternoon the Twelve came to him and said, "Send the crowd away so they can go to the surrounding villages and countryside and find food and lodging, because we are in a remote place here."

[13]He replied, "You give them something to eat."

They answered, "We have only five loaves of bread and two fish—unless we go and buy food for all this crowd." [14](About five thousand men were there.)

But he said to his disciples, "Have them sit down in groups of about fifty each." [15]The disciples did so, and everybody sat down. [16]Taking the five loaves and the two fish and looking up to heav-

a 43 Many manuscripts *years, and she had spent all she had on doctors* en, he gave thanks and broke them. Then he gave them to the disciples to set before the people. ¹⁷They all ate and were satisfied, and the disciples picked up twelve basketfuls of broken pieces that were left over.

Peter's Confession of Christ

¹⁸Once when Jesus was praying in private and his disciples were with him, he asked them, "Who do the crowds say I am?"

¹⁹They replied, "Some say John the Baptist; others say Elijah; and still others, that one of the prophets of long ago has come back to life."

²⁰"But what about you?" he asked. "Who do you say I am?"

Peter answered, "The Christ*ᵃ* of God."

²¹Jesus strictly warned them not to tell this to anyone. ²²And he said, "The Son of Man must suffer many things and be rejected by the elders, chief priests and teachers of the law, and he must be killed and on the third day be raised to life."

²³Then he said to them all: "If anyone would come after me, he must deny himself and take up his cross daily and follow me. ²⁴For whoever wants to save his life will lose it, but whoever loses his life for me will save it. ²⁵What good is it for a man to gain the whole world, and yet lose or forfeit his very self? ²⁶If anyone is ashamed of me and my words, the Son of Man will be ashamed of him when he comes in his glory and in the glory of the Father and of the holy angels. ²⁷I tell you the truth, some who are standing here will not taste death before they see the kingdom of God."

The Transfiguration

²⁸About eight days after Jesus said this, he took Peter, John and James with him and went up onto a mountain to pray. ²⁹As he was praying, the appearance of his face changed, and his clothes became as bright as a flash of lightning. ³⁰Two men, Moses and Elijah, ³¹appeared in glorious splendor, talking with Jesus. They spoke about his departure, which he was about to bring to fulfillment at Jerusalem. ³²Peter and his companions were very sleepy, but when they became fully awake, they saw his glory and the two men standing with him. ³³As the men were leaving Jesus, Peter said to him, "Master, it is good for us to be here. Let us put up three shelters—one for you, one for Moses and one for Elijah." (He did not know what he was saying.)

³⁴While he was speaking, a cloud appeared and enveloped them, and they were afraid as they entered the cloud. ³⁵A voice came from the cloud, saying, "This is my Son, whom I have chosen; listen to him." ³⁶When the voice had spoken, they found that Jesus was alone. The disciples kept this to themselves, and told no one at that time what they had seen.

genuine purpose ≫ 9:25

Picture yourself at the end of your life: a self-made millionaire, married to a handsome movie star, with celebrities as your closest friends and three happy, successful children. Was it a good life? No regrets? Only if you'd spent your years walking with Jesus, willing to make whatever sacrifice he asked you to make in order to love and obey him. Otherwise, you'd find you had gained the world but forfeited your soul. As you make goals for the future and choices for today, remember what's really important, and be willing to give up everything in this world to follow Christ.

The Healing of a Boy With an Evil Spirit

³⁷The next day, when they came down from the mountain, a large crowd met him. ³⁸A man in the crowd called out, "Teacher, I beg you to look at my son, for he is my only child. ³⁹A spirit seizes him and he suddenly screams; it throws him into convulsions so that he foams at the mouth. It

ᵃ 20 Or Messiah

scarcely ever leaves him and is destroying him. [40]I begged your disciples to drive it out, but they could not."

[41]"O unbelieving and perverse generation," Jesus replied, "how long shall I stay with you and put up with you? Bring your son here."

[42]Even while the boy was coming, the demon threw him to the ground in a convulsion. But Jesus rebuked the evil[a] spirit, healed the boy and gave him back to his father. [43]And they were all amazed at the greatness of God.

While everyone was marveling at all that Jesus did, he said to his disciples, [44]"Listen carefully to what I am about to tell you: The Son of Man is going to be betrayed into the hands of men." [45]But they did not understand what this meant. It was hidden from them, so that they did not grasp it, and they were afraid to ask him about it.

Who Will Be the Greatest?

[46]An argument started among the disciples as to which of them would be the greatest. [47]Jesus, knowing their thoughts, took a little child and had him stand beside him. [48]Then he said to them, "Whoever welcomes this little child in my name welcomes me; and whoever welcomes me welcomes the one who sent me. For he who is least among you all—he is the greatest."

[49]"Master," said John, "we saw a man driving out demons in your name and we tried to stop him, because he is not one of us."

[50]"Do not stop him," Jesus said, "for whoever is not against you is for you."

Samaritan Opposition

[51]As the time approached for him to be taken up to heaven, Jesus resolutely set out for Jerusalem. [52]And he sent messengers on ahead, who went into a Samaritan village to get things ready for him; [53]but the people there did not welcome him, because he was heading for Jerusalem. [54]When the disciples James and John saw this, they asked, "Lord, do you want us to call fire down from heaven to destroy them[b]?" [55]But Jesus turned and rebuked them, [56]and[c] they went to another village.

The Cost of Following Jesus

[57]As they were walking along the road, a man said to him, "I will follow you wherever you go."

[58]Jesus replied, "Foxes have holes and birds of the air have nests, but the Son of Man has no place to lay his head."

[59]He said to another man, "Follow me."

But the man replied, "Lord, first let me go and bury my father."

[60]Jesus said to him, "Let the dead bury their own dead, but you go and proclaim the kingdom of God."

[61]Still another said, "I will follow you, Lord; but first let me go back and say good-by to my family."

[62]Jesus replied, "No one who puts his hand to the plow and looks back is fit for service in the kingdom of God."

Jesus Sends Out the Seventy-two

10 After this the Lord appointed seventy-two[d] others and sent them two by two ahead of him to every town and place where he was about to go. [2]He told them, "The harvest is plentiful, but the workers are few. Ask the Lord of the harvest, therefore, to send out workers into his harvest field. [3]Go! I am sending you out like lambs among wolves. [4]Do not take a purse or bag or sandals; and do not greet anyone on the road.

[5]"When you enter a house, first say, 'Peace to this house.' [6]If a man of peace is there, your peace will rest on him; if not, it will return to you. [7]Stay in that house, eating and drinking whatever they give you, for the worker deserves his wages. Do not move around from house to house.

[8]"When you enter a town and are welcomed, eat what is set before you. [9]Heal the sick who are

a 42 Greek unclean   b 54 Some manuscripts them, even as Elijah did   c 55,56 Some manuscripts them. And he said, "You do not know what kind of spirit you are of, for the Son of Man did not come to destroy men's lives, but to save them." 56And   d 1 Some manuscripts seventy; also in verse 17 there and tell them, 'The kingdom of God is near you.' [10]But when you enter a town and are not welcomed, go into its streets and say, [11]'Even the dust of your town that sticks to our feet we wipe off against you. Yet be sure of this: The kingdom of God is near.' [12]I tell you, it will be more bearable on that day for Sodom than for that town.

[13]"Woe to you, Korazin! Woe to you, Bethsaida! For if the miracles that were performed in you had been performed in Tyre and Sidon, they would have repented long ago, sitting in sackcloth and ashes. [14]But it will be more bearable for Tyre and Sidon at the judgment than for you. [15]And you, Capernaum, will you be lifted up to the skies? No, you will go down to the depths. [a]

[16]"He who listens to you listens to me; he who rejects you rejects me; but he who rejects me rejects him who sent me."

[17]The seventy-two returned with joy and said, "Lord, even the demons submit to us in your name."

[18]He replied, "I saw Satan fall like lightning from heaven. [19]I have given you authority to trample on snakes and scorpions and to overcome all the power of the enemy; nothing will harm you. [20]However, do not rejoice that the spirits submit to you, but rejoice that your names are written in heaven."

[21]At that time Jesus, full of joy through the Holy Spirit, said, "I praise you, Father, Lord of heaven and earth, because you have hidden these things from the wise and learned, and revealed them to little children. Yes, Father, for this was your good pleasure.

[22]"All things have been committed to me by my Father. No one knows who the Son is except the Father, and no one knows who the Father is except the Son and those to whom the Son chooses to reveal him."

[23]Then he turned to his disciples and said privately, "Blessed are the eyes that see what you see. [24]For I tell you that many prophets and kings wanted to see what you see but did not see it, and to hear what you hear but did not hear it."

The Parable of the Good Samaritan

[25]On one occasion an expert in the law stood up to test Jesus. "Teacher," he asked, "what must I do to inherit eternal life?"

[26]"What is written in the Law?" he replied. "How do you read it?"

[27]He answered: " 'Love the Lord your God with all your heart and with all your soul and with all your strength and with all your mind' [b]; and, 'Love your neighbor as yourself.' [c]"

[28]"You have answered correctly," Jesus replied. "Do this and you will live."

[29]But he wanted to justify himself, so he asked Jesus, "And who is my neighbor?"

[30]In reply Jesus said: "A man was going down from Jerusalem to Jericho, when he fell into the hands of robbers. They stripped him of his clothes, beat him and went away, leaving him half dead. [31]A priest happened to be going down the same road, and when he saw the man, he passed by on the other side. [32]So too, a Levite, when he came to the place and saw him, passed by on the other side. [33]But a Samaritan, as he traveled, came where the man was; and when he saw him, he took pity on him. [34]He went to him and bandaged his wounds, pouring on oil and wine. Then he put the man on his own donkey, took him to an inn and took care of him. [35]The next day he took out two silver coins [d] and gave them to the innkeeper. 'Look after him,' he said, 'and when I return, I will reimburse you for any extra expense you may have.'

genuine love » 10:29-37

This is the well-known parable of the "Good Samaritan." What was it that made the Samaritan so good? Well, he went out of his way to show kindness to someone who would normally have looked down on him. He loved without holding back or expecting anything in return. Now what does it mean for you to be a "good Samaritan"? How can you go out of your way to love someone who isn't expecting it? Do you have a rival or know someone who's always mean to you? Loving your neighbor means looking for opportunities to love even that person, too.

---

[a] 15 Greek *Hades*   [b] 27 Deut. 6:5   [c] 27 Lev. 19:18   [d] 35 Greek *two denarii*

³⁶"Which of these three do you think was a neighbor to the man who fell into the hands of robbers?"

³⁷The expert in the law replied, "The one who had mercy on him."

Jesus told him, "Go and do likewise."

At the Home of Martha and Mary

³⁸As Jesus and his disciples were on their way, he came to a village where a woman named Martha opened her home to him. ³⁹She had a sister called Mary, who sat at the Lord's feet listening to what he said. ⁴⁰But Martha was distracted by all the preparations that had to be made. She came to him and asked, "Lord, don't you care that my sister has left me to do the work by myself? Tell her to help me!"

⁴¹"Martha, Martha," the Lord answered, "you are worried and upset about many things, ⁴²but only one thing is needed. ª Mary has chosen what is better, and it will not be taken away from her."

love notes

10:41–42

Child,

What's distracting you today? An overloaded schedule? A to-do list that you have no hope of completing? Sit down and choose, as Mary did, "what is better"—time with me. The benefits of that choice will not be taken from you.

—Jesus

Are you making time with Jesus a top priority? How can you change your schedule to spend more time with him?

Jesus' Teaching on Prayer

11 One day Jesus was praying in a certain place. When he finished, one of his disciples said to him, "Lord, teach us to pray, just as John taught his disciples."

²He said to them, "When you pray, say:

" 'Father, ᵇ
hallowed be your name,
your kingdom come. ᶜ
³Give us each day our daily bread.
⁴Forgive us our sins,
for we also forgive everyone
who sins against us. ᵈ
And lead us not into temptation. ᵉ' "

⁵Then he said to them, "Suppose one of you has a friend, and he goes to him at midnight and says, 'Friend, lend me three loaves of bread, ⁶because a friend of mine on a journey has come to me, and I have nothing to set before him.'

⁷"Then the one inside answers, 'Don't bother me. The door is already locked, and my children are with me in bed. I can't get up and give you anything.' ⁸I tell you, though he will not get up and give him the bread because he is his friend, yet because of the man's boldnessᶠ he will get up and give him as much as he needs.

⁹"So I say to you: Ask and it will be given to you; seek and you will find; knock and the door will be opened to you. ¹⁰For everyone who asks receives; he who seeks finds; and to him who knocks, the door will be opened.

ª 42 Some manuscripts *but few things are needed—or only one*   ᵇ 2 Some manuscripts *Our Father in heaven*   ᶜ 2 Some manuscripts *come. May your will be done on earth as it is in heaven.*   ᵈ 4 Greek *everyone who is indebted to us*   ᵉ 4 Some manuscripts *temptation but deliver us from the evil one*   ᶠ 8 Or *persistence*

¹¹"Which of you fathers, if your son asks for* a fish, will give him a snake instead? ¹²Or if he asks for an egg, will give him a scorpion? ¹³If you then, though you are evil, know how to give good gifts to your children, how much more will your Father in heaven give the Holy Spirit to those who ask him!"

Jesus and Beelzebub

¹⁴Jesus was driving out a demon that was mute. When the demon left, the man who had been mute spoke, and the crowd was amazed. ¹⁵But some of them said, "By Beelzebub,ᵇ the prince of demons, he is driving out demons." ¹⁶Others tested him by asking for a sign from heaven.

¹⁷Jesus knew their thoughts and said to them: "Any kingdom divided against itself will be ruined, and a house divided against itself will fall. ¹⁸If Satan is divided against himself, how can his kingdom stand? I say this because you claim that I drive out demons by Beelzebub. ¹⁹Now if I drive out demons by Beelzebub, by whom do your followers drive them out? So then, they will be your judges. ²⁰But if I drive out demons by the finger of God, then the kingdom of God has come to you.

²¹"When a strong man, fully armed, guards his own house, his possessions are safe. ²²But when someone stronger attacks and overpowers him, he takes away the armor in which the man trusted and divides up the spoils.

²³"He who is not with me is against me, and he who does not gather with me, scatters.

²⁴"When an evilᶜ spirit comes out of a man, it goes through arid places seeking rest and does not find it. Then it says, 'I will return to the house I left.' ²⁵When it arrives, it finds the house swept clean and put in order. ²⁶Then it goes and takes seven other spirits more wicked than itself, and they go in and live there. And the final condition of that man is worse than the first."

²⁷As Jesus was saying these things, a woman in the crowd called out, "Blessed is the mother who gave you birth and nursed you."

²⁸He replied, "Blessed rather are those who hear the word of God and obey it."

The Sign of Jonah

²⁹As the crowds increased, Jesus said, "This is a wicked generation. It asks for a miraculous sign, but none will be given it except the sign of Jonah. ³⁰For as Jonah was a sign to the Ninevites, so also will the Son of Man be to this generation. ³¹The Queen of the South will rise at the judgment with the men of this generation and condemn them; for she came from the ends of the earth to listen to Solomon's wisdom, and now oneᵈ greater than Solomon is here. ³²The men of Nineveh will stand up at the judgment with this generation and condemn it; for they repented at the preaching of Jonah, and now one greater than Jonah is here.

The Lamp of the Body

³³"No one lights a lamp and puts it in a place where it will be hidden, or under a bowl. Instead he puts it on its stand, so that those who come in may see the light. ³⁴Your eye is the lamp of your body. When your eyes are good, your whole body also is full of light. But when they are bad, your body also is full of darkness. ³⁵See to it, then, that the light within you is not darkness. ³⁶Therefore, if your whole body is full of light, and no part of it dark, it will be completely lighted, as when the light of a lamp shines on you."

Six Woes

³⁷When Jesus had finished speaking, a Pharisee invited him to eat with him; so he went in and reclined at the table. ³⁸But the Pharisee, noticing that Jesus did not first wash before the meal, was surprised.

³⁹Then the Lord said to him, "Now then, you Pharisees clean the outside of the cup and dish, but inside you are full of greed and wickedness. ⁴⁰You foolish people! Did not the one who made the outside make the inside also? ⁴¹But give what is inside ⌊the dish⌋ᵉ to the poor, and everything will be clean for you.

⁴²"Woe to you Pharisees, because you give God a tenth of your mint, rue and all other kinds of

a 11 Some manuscripts *for bread, will give him a stone; or if he asks for*   *b 15* Greek *Beezeboul* or *Beelzeboul*; also in verses 18 and 19   *c 24* Greek *unclean*   *d 31* Or *something*; also in verse 32   *e 41* Or *what you have*

Martha—The Busiest Girl on the Planet

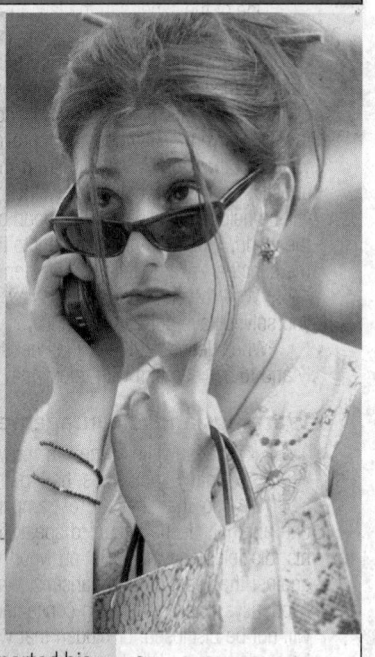

You'd know Martha if you saw her at school. She's the girl scribbling a growing to-do list on the back of her hand, running between classes. Her pager is beeping, and her cell phone is ringing. She wants to please everyone. Her coach wants her to play basketball this season, while her mom really wishes she'd practice piano. Her schedule is full—school, band practice, homework, part-time job at the mall. She falls asleep with *To Kill a Mockingbird* half finished on her pillow and wakes up with the sinking feeling that the book report is due today. She knows she should be having quiet time alone with God, but how can she? It just seems like one more thing on her never-ending list.

In the Bible, we see Martha busy doing many good things. She was a noble girl who loved to serve. Martha, her sister, Mary, and her brother, Lazarus, were some of Jesus' best friends. They supported his ministry and were friends with the disciples. Jesus would stay at their home when he was in the area. Martha saw Jesus bring Lazarus back from the dead. Yet, even though these good things filled up her schedule, sometimes she missed God's best. The one thing she needed most was missing from her busy life: time alone with Jesus.

Many times we open our lives to Jesus, just like Martha opened her home. Jesus settles down in a comfortable chair, ready to spend time with us, talking and reading his Word. "I'll be right there, Jesus!" we say in a rush. Yet we soon forget about him. After all, there is so much to do! When you look in the mirror, do you see reflections of Martha, the busiest girl on the planet? Racing around trying to get everything done? Take a deep breath. Slow down. You'll never have time for God unless you make time for him. When will you make a "date" to spend time with God?

Dear Jesus, some days I feel like the busiest girl on the planet. If I don't have time for you, then help me make time instead. Maybe a little. Maybe a lot. Either way, I just can't go another day missing you. Amen.

To read the next Mirror Images profile, go to page 1415.

Read more about Martha in Luke 10:38–42 (page 1383) and John 11:17–45 (page 1429).

garden herbs, but you neglect justice and the love of God. You should have practiced the latter without leaving the former undone.

[43]"Woe to you Pharisees, because you love the most important seats in the synagogues and greetings in the marketplaces.

[44]"Woe to you, because you are like unmarked graves, which men walk over without knowing it."

[45]One of the experts in the law answered him, "Teacher, when you say these things, you insult us also."

[46]Jesus replied, "And you experts in the law, woe to you, because you load people down with burdens they can hardly carry, and you yourselves will not lift one finger to help them.

[47]"Woe to you, because you build tombs for the prophets, and it was your forefathers who killed them. [48]So you testify that you approve of what your forefathers did; they killed the prophets, and you build their tombs. [49]Because of this, God in his wisdom said, 'I will send them prophets and apostles, some of whom they will kill and others they will persecute.' [50]Therefore this generation will be held responsible for the blood of all the prophets that has been shed since the beginning of the world, [51]from the blood of Abel to the blood of Zechariah, who was killed between the altar and the sanctuary. Yes, I tell you, this generation will be held responsible for it all.

[52]"Woe to you experts in the law, because you have taken away the key to knowledge. You yourselves have not entered, and you have hindered those who were entering."

[53]When Jesus left there, the Pharisees and the teachers of the law began to oppose him fiercely and to besiege him with questions, [54]waiting to catch him in something he might say.

Warnings and Encouragements

12 Meanwhile, when a crowd of many thousands had gathered, so that they were trampling on one another, Jesus began to speak first to his disciples, saying: "Be on your guard against the yeast of the Pharisees, which is hypocrisy. [2]There is nothing concealed that will not be disclosed, or hidden that will not be made known. [3]What you have said in the dark will be heard in the daylight, and what you have whispered in the ear in the inner rooms will be proclaimed from the roofs.

[4]"I tell you, my friends, do not be afraid of those who kill the body and after that can do no more. [5]But I will show you whom you should fear: Fear him who, after the killing of the body, has power to throw you into hell. Yes, I tell you, fear him. [6]Are not five sparrows sold for two pennies[a]? Yet not one of them is forgotten by God. [7]Indeed, the very hairs of your head are all numbered. Don't be afraid; you are worth more than many sparrows.

[8]"I tell you, whoever acknowledges me before men, the Son of Man will also acknowledge him before the angels of God. [9]But he who disowns me before men will be disowned before the angels of God. [10]And everyone who speaks a word against the Son of Man will be forgiven, but anyone who blasphemes against the Holy Spirit will not be forgiven.

[11]"When you are brought before synagogues, rulers and authorities, do not worry about how you will defend yourselves or what you will say, [12]for the Holy Spirit will teach you at that time what you should say."

genuine courage » 12:4-5

Have you ever done something you shouldn't have done because you were afraid? Maybe you smoked or drank because you were scared your friends would think less of you if you didn't. Maybe you slept with your boyfriend because you were afraid of losing him to another girl. Maybe you let a guy cheat off your test because you were afraid he'd mock you if you didn't. Don't ever let fear of what other people might think or do overshadow doing what God wants you to do. He is the only one we are to fear, revere and trust. He's stronger and more important than any person.

[a] 6 Greek two assaria

The Parable of the Rich Fool

¹³Someone in the crowd said to him, "Teacher, tell my brother to divide the inheritance with me."

¹⁴Jesus replied, "Man, who appointed me a judge or an arbiter between you?" ¹⁵Then he said to them, "Watch out! Be on your guard against all kinds of greed; a man's life does not consist in the abundance of his possessions."

¹⁶And he told them this parable: "The ground of a certain rich man produced a good crop. ¹⁷He thought to himself, 'What shall I do? I have no place to store my crops.'

¹⁸"Then he said, 'This is what I'll do. I will tear down my barns and build bigger ones, and there I will store all my grain and my goods. ¹⁹And I'll say to myself, "You have plenty of good things laid up for many years. Take life easy; eat, drink and be merry." '

²⁰"But God said to him, 'You fool! This very night your life will be demanded from you. Then who will get what you have prepared for yourself?'

²¹"This is how it will be with anyone who stores up things for himself but is not rich toward God."

Do Not Worry

²²Then Jesus said to his disciples: "Therefore I tell you, do not worry about your life, what you will eat; or about your body, what you will wear. ²³Life is more than food, and the body more than clothes. ²⁴Consider the ravens: They do not sow or reap, they have no storeroom or barn; yet God feeds them. And how much more valuable you are than birds! ²⁵Who of you by worrying can add a single hour to his life*? ²⁶Since you cannot do this very little thing, why do you worry about the rest?

genuine riches » 12:15-21

"Cute shirt. Is it from The Gap?" "Great cell. Can it take pictures, too?" "Cool car. Is it yours or your parents'?" It's so easy to be defined by your possessions, isn't it? You gain a certain level of respect and popularity from people when you have nice things—and lots of them. But your life is meant to be about so much more than your stuff. *You* are meant to be about so much more than your stuff. Make sure that, above all else, you have a rich relationship with God. That's all that really counts.

²⁷"Consider how the lilies grow. They do not labor or spin. Yet I tell you, not even Solomon in all his splendor was dressed like one of these. ²⁸If that is how God clothes the grass of the field, which is here today, and tomorrow is thrown into the fire, how much more will he clothe you, O you of little faith! ²⁹And do not set your heart on what you will eat or drink; do not worry about it. ³⁰For the pagan world runs after all such things, and your Father knows that you need them. ³¹But seek his kingdom, and these things will be given to you as well.

³²"Do not be afraid, little flock, for your Father has been pleased to give you the kingdom. ³³Sell your possessions and give to the poor. Provide purses for yourselves that will not wear out, a treasure in heaven that will not be exhausted, where no thief comes near and no moth destroys. ³⁴For where your treasure is, there your heart will be also.

Watchfulness

³⁵"Be dressed ready for service and keep your lamps burning, ³⁶like men waiting for their master to return from a wedding banquet, so that when he comes and knocks they can immediately open the door for him. ³⁷It will be good for those servants whose master finds them watching when he comes. I tell you the truth, he will dress himself to serve, will have them recline at the table and will come and wait on them. ³⁸It will be good for those servants whose master finds them ready, even if he comes in the second or third watch of the night. ³⁹But understand this: If the owner of

a 25 Or single cubit to his height

the house had known at what hour the thief was coming, he would not have let his house be broken into. [40]You also must be ready, because the Son of Man will come at an hour when you do not expect him."

[41]Peter asked, "Lord, are you telling this parable to us, or to everyone?"

[42]The Lord answered, "Who then is the faithful and wise manager, whom the master puts in charge of his servants to give them their food allowance at the proper time? [43]It will be good for that servant whom the master finds doing so when he returns. [44]I tell you the truth, he will put him in charge of all his possessions. [45]But suppose the servant says to himself, 'My master is taking a long time in coming,' and he then begins to beat the menservants and maidservants and to eat and drink and get drunk. [46]The master of that servant will come on a day when he does not expect him and at an hour he is not aware of. He will cut him to pieces and assign him a place with the unbelievers.

[47]"That servant who knows his master's will and does not get ready or does not do what his master wants will be beaten with many blows. [48]But the one who does not know and does things deserving punishment will be beaten with few blows. From everyone who has been given much, much will be demanded; and from the one who has been entrusted with much, much more will be asked.

Not Peace but Division

[49]"I have come to bring fire on the earth, and how I wish it were already kindled! [50]But I have a baptism to undergo, and how distressed I am until it is completed! [51]Do you think I came to bring peace on earth? No, I tell you, but division. [52]From now on there will be five in one family divided against each other, three against two and two against three. [53]They will be divided, father against son and son against father, mother against daughter and daughter against mother, mother-in-law against daughter-in-law and daughter-in-law against mother-in-law."

Interpreting the Times

[54]He said to the crowd: "When you see a cloud rising in the west, immediately you say, 'It's going to rain,' and it does. [55]And when the south wind blows, you say, 'It's going to be hot,' and it is. [56]Hypocrites! You know how to interpret the appearance of the earth and the sky. How is it that you don't know how to interpret this present time?

[57]"Why don't you judge for yourselves what is right? [58]As you are going with your adversary to the magistrate, try hard to be reconciled to him on the way, or he may drag you off to the judge, and the judge turn you over to the officer, and the officer throw you into prison. [59]I tell you, you will not get out until you have paid the last penny.[a]"

_a 59_ Greek _lepton_

love ❤ notes

12:22–31

Dear one,

Why do you worry? I feed the birds and all my creatures. I clothe the flowers in glorious colors. But life is far more than what you eat or wear. Don't worry about such things, my child. I know what you need.

—_Father God_

Write down what is worrying you right now. Commit it to God in prayer.

_____

_____

_____

_____

_____

_____

_____

_____

_____

Repent or Perish

13

Now there were some present at that time who told Jesus about the Galileans whose blood Pilate had mixed with their sacrifices. [2]Jesus answered, "Do you think that these Galileans were worse sinners than all the other Galileans because they suffered this way? [3]I tell you, no! But unless you repent, you too will all perish. [4]Or those eighteen who died when the tower in Siloam fell on them—do you think they were more guilty than all the others living in Jerusalem? [5]I tell you, no! But unless you repent, you too will all perish."

[6]Then he told this parable: "A man had a fig tree, planted in his vineyard, and he went to look for fruit on it, but did not find any. [7]So he said to the man who took care of the vineyard, 'For three years now I've been coming to look for fruit on this fig tree and haven't found any. Cut it down! Why should it use up the soil?'

[8]" 'Sir,' the man replied, 'leave it alone for one more year, and I'll dig around it and fertilize it. [9]If it bears fruit next year, fine! If not, then cut it down.' "

A Crippled Woman Healed on the Sabbath

[10]On a Sabbath Jesus was teaching in one of the synagogues, [11]and a woman was there who had been crippled by a spirit for eighteen years. She was bent over and could not straighten up at all. [12]When Jesus saw her, he called her forward and said to her, "Woman, you are set free from your infirmity." [13]Then he put his hands on her, and immediately she straightened up and praised God.

[14]Indignant because Jesus had healed on the Sabbath, the synagogue ruler said to the people, "There are six days for work. So come and be healed on those days, not on the Sabbath."

[15]The Lord answered him, "You hypocrites! Doesn't each of you on the Sabbath untie his ox or donkey from the stall and lead it out to give it water? [16]Then should not this woman, a daughter of Abraham, whom Satan has kept bound for eighteen long years, be set free on the Sabbath day from what bound her?"

[17]When he said this, all his opponents were humiliated, but the people were delighted with all the wonderful things he was doing.

truth *or dare*

Many of the Jewish religious leaders had forgotten the real purpose, or *spirit*, of the law. They cared more about picky rules than someone's healing. Don't let the rules kill your love.

13:10–16

The Parables of the Mustard Seed and the Yeast

[18]Then Jesus asked, "What is the kingdom of God like? What shall I compare it to? [19]It is like a mustard seed, which a man took and planted in his garden. It grew and became a tree, and the birds of the air perched in its branches."

[20]Again he asked, "What shall I compare the kingdom of God to? [21]It is like yeast that a woman took and mixed into a large amount[a] of flour until it worked all through the dough."

The Narrow Door

[22]Then Jesus went through the towns and villages, teaching as he made his way to Jerusalem. [23]Someone asked him, "Lord, are only a few people going to be saved?"

He said to them, [24]"Make every effort to enter through the narrow door, because many, I tell you, will try to enter and will not be able to. [25]Once the owner of the house gets up and closes the door, you will stand outside knocking and pleading, 'Sir, open the door for us.'

"But he will answer, 'I don't know you or where you come from.'

[26]"Then you will say, 'We ate and drank with you, and you taught in our streets.'

[27]"But he will reply, 'I don't know you or where you come from. Away from me, all you evildoers!'

[28]"There will be weeping there, and gnashing of teeth, when you see Abraham, Isaac and Jacob and all the prophets in the kingdom of God, but you yourselves thrown out. [29]People will come from east and west and north and south, and will take their places at the feast in the kingdom of God. [30]Indeed there are those who are last who will be first, and first who will be last."

a 21 Greek *three satas* (probably about 1/2 bushel or 22 liters)

Jesus' Sorrow for Jerusalem

³¹At that time some Pharisees came to Jesus and said to him, "Leave this place and go somewhere else. Herod wants to kill you."

³²He replied, "Go tell that fox, 'I will drive out demons and heal people today and tomorrow, and on the third day I will reach my goal.' ³³In any case, I must keep going today and tomorrow and the next day—for surely no prophet can die outside Jerusalem!

³⁴"O Jerusalem, Jerusalem, you who kill the prophets and stone those sent to you, how often I have longed to gather your children together, as a hen gathers her chicks under her wings, but you were not willing! ³⁵Look, your house is left to you desolate. I tell you, you will not see me again until you say, 'Blessed is he who comes in the name of the Lord.'ᵃ"

Jesus at a Pharisee's House

14 One Sabbath, when Jesus went to eat in the house of a prominent Pharisee, he was being carefully watched. ²There in front of him was a man suffering from dropsy. ³Jesus asked the Pharisees and experts in the law, "Is it lawful to heal on the Sabbath or not?" ⁴But they remained silent. So taking hold of the man, he healed him and sent him away.

⁵Then he asked them, "If one of you has a sonᵇ or an ox that falls into a well on the Sabbath day, will you not immediately pull him out?" ⁶And they had nothing to say.

⁷When he noticed how the guests picked the places of honor at the table, he told them this parable: ⁸"When someone invites you to a wedding feast, do not take the place of honor, for a person more distinguished than you may have been invited. ⁹If so, the host who invited both of you will come and say to you, 'Give this man your seat.' Then, humiliated, you will have to take the least important place. ¹⁰But when you are invited, take the lowest place, so that when your host comes, he will say to you, 'Friend, move up to a better place.' Then you will be honored in the presence of all your fellow guests. ¹¹For everyone who exalts himself will be humbled, and he who humbles himself will be exalted."

¹²Then Jesus said to his host, "When you give a luncheon or dinner, do not invite your friends, your brothers or relatives, or your rich neighbors; if you do, they may invite you back and so you will be repaid. ¹³But when you give a banquet, invite the poor, the crippled, the lame, the blind, ¹⁴and you will be blessed. Although they cannot repay you, you will be repaid at the resurrection of the righteous."

The Parable of the Great Banquet

¹⁵When one of those at the table with him heard this, he said to Jesus, "Blessed is the man who will eat at the feast in the kingdom of God."

¹⁶Jesus replied: "A certain man was preparing a great banquet and invited many guests. ¹⁷At the time of the banquet he sent his servant to tell those who had been invited, 'Come, for everything is now ready.'

¹⁸"But they all alike began to make excuses. The first said, 'I have just bought a field, and I must go and see it. Please excuse me.'

¹⁹"Another said, 'I have just bought five yoke of oxen, and I'm on my way to try them out. Please excuse me.'

²⁰"Still another said, 'I just got married, so I can't come.'

²¹"The servant came back and reported this to his master. Then the owner of the house became angry and ordered his servant, 'Go out quickly into the streets and alleys of the town and bring in the poor, the crippled, the blind and the lame.'

²²"'Sir,' the servant said, 'what you ordered has been done, but there is still room.'

²³"Then the master told his servant, 'Go out to the roads and country lanes and make them come in, so that my house will be full. ²⁴I tell you, not one of those men who were invited will get a taste of my banquet.' "

The Cost of Being a Disciple

²⁵Large crowds were traveling with Jesus, and turning to them he said: ²⁶"If anyone comes to me and does not hate his father and mother, his wife and children, his brothers and sisters—yes,

ᵃ 35 Psalm 118:26   ᵇ 5 Some manuscripts *donkey*

She's All That

focus   Profile: **Lauren**

"Whatever. She's just jealous."

That was my first reaction when Akasha told me what Jamie had said about me. Jamie told all the girls in gym class how I'm stuck on myself. "Miss Thang," she called me, saying I'm not half as good on the court as I think I am. I'm sorry, but if I'm not that good, why am I sporting the athlete-of-the-month title at school? Hello! Does she not notice the moves I put on the court each week? Or does she just not know talent when she sees it? No one's going to offer *Jamie* any scholarships next year—unless it's for debate team or the chess club. I'm already hearing from some scouts, and I'm not even a junior yet.

She's just jealous because Coach gives me way more PT (playing time, duh) than she gets. You know why? Because I'm better than she is, that's why. And she can't handle that. I've been working hard playing ball since I was a kid. Up before dawn, shooting hoops with my dad. Conditioning. Staying up late watching the college playoffs. I always dreamed of the day when other people would be saying my name when they talked about the greatest athletes in the sport. And now they're saying it when I walk the halls at school. It's "Lauren this" and "Lauren that." This is my moment. This is my time. And no one's going to take it from me.

pride in focus

There's nothing wrong with ambition and hard work. However, while you're pursuing your dreams, keep this in mind:

» The Bible tells us to work at things with our whole heart. However, the Bible does warn against "selfish ambition" (Philippians 2:3, page 1551), which is trying to get ahead at someone else's expense.

» Pride (see Proverbs 8:13, page 814) means we credit ourselves with our successes and have an inflated sense of our own worth. Jesus says that if we lift ourselves up, we'll be humbled, but if we humble ourselves, he'll lift us up (see Luke 14:11, page 1390).

» Taking ourselves too seriously leads to being "lonely at the top." Pride and arrogance will leave you in isolation from your friends.

For more on this topic, see the index on page 1656.

even his own life—he cannot be my disciple. 27And anyone who does not carry his cross and follow me cannot be my disciple.

28"Suppose one of you wants to build a tower. Will he not first sit down and estimate the cost to see if he has enough money to complete it? 29For if he lays the foundation and is not able to finish it, everyone who sees it will ridicule him, 30saying, 'This fellow began to build and was not able to finish.'

31"Or suppose a king is about to go to war against another king. Will he not first sit down and consider whether he is able with ten thousand men to oppose the one coming against him with twenty thousand? 32If he is not able, he will send a delegation while the other is still a long way off and will ask for terms of peace. ³³In the same way, any of you who does not give up everything he has cannot be my disciple.

³⁴"Salt is good, but if it loses its saltiness, how can it be made salty again? ³⁵It is fit neither for the soil nor for the manure pile; it is thrown out.

"He who has ears to hear, let him hear."

The Parable of the Lost Sheep

15 Now the tax collectors and "sinners" were all gathering around to hear him. ²But the Pharisees and the teachers of the law muttered, "This man welcomes sinners and eats with them."

³Then Jesus told them this parable: ⁴"Suppose one of you has a hundred sheep and loses one of them. Does he not leave the ninety-nine in the open country and go after the lost sheep until he finds it? ⁵And when he finds it, he joyfully puts it on his shoulders ⁶and goes home. Then he calls his friends and neighbors together and says, 'Rejoice with me; I have found my lost sheep.' ⁷I tell you that in the same way there will be more rejoicing in heaven over one sinner who repents than over ninety-nine righteous persons who do not need to repent.

The Parable of the Lost Coin

⁸"Or suppose a woman has ten silver coins*ᵃ* and loses one. Does she not light a lamp, sweep the house and search carefully until she finds it? ⁹And when she finds it, she calls her friends and neighbors together and says, 'Rejoice with me; I have found my lost coin.' ¹⁰In the same way, I tell you, there is rejoicing in the presence of the angels of God over one sinner who repents."

The Parable of the Lost Son

¹¹Jesus continued: "There was a man who had two sons. ¹²The younger one said to his father, 'Father, give me my share of the estate.' So he divided his property between them.

¹³"Not long after that, the younger son got together all he had, set off for a distant country and there squandered his wealth in wild living. ¹⁴After he had spent everything, there was a severe famine in that whole country, and he began to be in need. ¹⁵So he went and hired himself out to a citizen of that country, who sent him to his fields to feed pigs. ¹⁶He longed to fill his stomach with the pods that the pigs were eating, but no one gave him anything.

¹⁷"When he came to his senses, he said, 'How many of my father's hired men have food to spare, and here I am starving to death! ¹⁸I will set out and go back to my father and say to him: Father, I have sinned against heaven and against you. ¹⁹I am no longer worthy to be called your son; make me like one of your hired men.' ²⁰So he got up and went to his father.

"But while he was still a long way off, his father saw him and was filled with compassion for him; he ran to his son, threw his arms around him and kissed him.

²¹"The son said to him, 'Father, I have sinned against heaven and against you. I am no longer worthy to be called your son.*ᵇ*'

²²"But the father said to his servants, 'Quick! Bring the best robe and put it on him. Put a ring on his finger and sandals on his feet. ²³Bring the fattened calf and kill it. Let's have a feast and celebrate. ²⁴For this son of mine was dead and is alive again; he was lost and is found.' So they began to celebrate.

²⁵"Meanwhile, the older son was in the field. When he came near the house, he heard music and dancing. ²⁶So he called one of the servants and asked him what was going on. ²⁷'Your brother has come,' he replied, 'and your father has killed the fattened calf because he has him back safe and sound.'

truth or dare

Who would have guessed that angels are such party animals? Don't deprive heaven of a party! Share the good news of Jesus with others today.

15:10

ᵃ 8 Greek *ten drachmas,* each worth about a day's wages   *ᵇ 21* Some early manuscripts *son. Make me like one of your hired men.*

28"The older brother became angry and refused to go in. So his father went out and pleaded with him. 29But he answered his father, 'Look! All these years I've been slaving for you and never disobeyed your orders. Yet you never gave me even a young goat so I could celebrate with my friends. 30But when this son of yours who has squandered your property with prostitutes comes home, you kill the fattened calf for him!'

31" 'My son,' the father said, 'you are always with me, and everything I have is yours. 32But we had to celebrate and be glad, because this brother of yours was dead and is alive again; he was lost and is found.' "

The Parable of the Shrewd Manager

16 Jesus told his disciples: "There was a rich man whose manager was accused of wasting his possessions. 2So he called him in and asked him, 'What is this I hear about you? Give an account of your management, because you cannot be manager any longer.'

3"The manager said to himself, 'What shall I do now? My master is taking away my job. I'm not strong enough to dig, and I'm ashamed to beg— 4I know what I'll do so that, when I lose my job here, people will welcome me into their houses.'

5"So he called in each one of his master's debtors. He asked the first, 'How much do you owe my master?'

6" 'Eight hundred gallons*a* of olive oil,' he replied.

"The manager told him, 'Take your bill, sit down quickly, and make it four hundred.'

7"Then he asked the second, 'And how much do you owe?'

" 'A thousand bushels*b* of wheat,' he replied.

"He told him, 'Take your bill and make it eight hundred.'

8"The master commended the dishonest manager because he had acted shrewdly. For the people of this world are more shrewd in dealing with their own kind than are the people of the light. 9I tell you, use worldly wealth to gain friends for yourselves, so that when it is gone, you will be welcomed into eternal dwellings.

10"Whoever can be trusted with very little can also be trusted with much, and whoever is dishonest with very little will also be dishonest with much. 11So if you have not been trustworthy in handling worldly wealth, who will trust you with true riches? 12And if you have not been trustworthy with someone else's property, who will give you property of your own?

13"No servant can serve two masters. Either he will hate the one and love the other,

love ♥ notes

15:17–20

Daughter,

It doesn't matter how far you wander from me in this world, what detours you take, how many mistakes you make or how badly you mess up. When you return, I run to you with open arms, ready to welcome you home.

—Your Father

What does it mean to you to know that God longs for you to turn away from sin and come home to him?

a 6 Greek *one hundred batous* (probably about 3 kiloliters)   *b 7* Greek *one hundred korous* (probably about 35 kiloliters) or he will be devoted to the one and despise the other. You cannot serve both God and Money."

[14]The Pharisees, who loved money, heard all this and were sneering at Jesus. [15]He said to them, "You are the ones who justify yourselves in the eyes of men, but God knows your hearts. What is highly valued among men is detestable in God's sight.

Additional Teachings

[16]"The Law and the Prophets were proclaimed until John. Since that time, the good news of the kingdom of God is being preached, and everyone is forcing his way into it. [17]It is easier for heaven and earth to disappear than for the least stroke of a pen to drop out of the Law.

[18]"Anyone who divorces his wife and marries another woman commits adultery, and the man who marries a divorced woman commits adultery.

truth or dare

Being a servant isn't optional. You *will* serve something with your life. Whether it's God or money is your choice.

16:13

The Rich Man and Lazarus

[19]"There was a rich man who was dressed in purple and fine linen and lived in luxury every day. [20]At his gate was laid a beggar named Lazarus, covered with sores [21]and longing to eat what fell from the rich man's table. Even the dogs came and licked his sores.

[22]"The time came when the beggar died and the angels carried him to Abraham's side. The rich man also died and was buried. [23]In hell,[a] where he was in torment, he looked up and saw Abraham far away, with Lazarus by his side. [24]So he called to him, 'Father Abraham, have pity on me and send Lazarus to dip the tip of his finger in water and cool my tongue, because I am in agony in this fire.'

[25]"But Abraham replied, 'Son, remember that in your lifetime you received your good things, while Lazarus received bad things, but now he is comforted here and you are in agony. [26]And besides all this, between us and you a great chasm has been fixed, so that those who want to go from here to you cannot, nor can anyone cross over from there to us.'

[27]"He answered, 'Then I beg you, father, send Lazarus to my father's house, [28]for I have five brothers. Let him warn them, so that they will not also come to this place of torment.'

[29]"Abraham replied, 'They have Moses and the Prophets; let them listen to them.'

[30]" 'No, father Abraham,' he said, 'but if someone from the dead goes to them, they will repent.'

[31]"He said to him, 'If they do not listen to Moses and the Prophets, they will not be convinced even if someone rises from the dead.' "

Sin, Faith, Duty

17 Jesus said to his disciples: "Things that cause people to sin are bound to come, but woe to that person through whom they come. [2]It would be better for him to be thrown into the sea with a millstone tied around his neck than for him to cause one of these little ones to sin. [3]So watch yourselves.

"If your brother sins, rebuke him, and if he repents, forgive him. [4]If he sins against you seven times in a day, and seven times comes back to you and says, 'I repent,' forgive him."

[5]The apostles said to the Lord, "Increase our faith!"

[6]He replied, "If you have faith as small as a mustard seed, you can say to this mulberry tree, 'Be uprooted and planted in the sea,' and it will obey you.

[7]"Suppose one of you had a servant plowing or looking after the sheep. Would he say to the servant when he comes in from the field, 'Come along now and sit down to eat'? [8]Would he not rather say, 'Prepare my supper, get yourself ready and wait on me while I eat and drink; after that you may eat and drink'? [9]Would he thank the servant because he did what he was told to do? [10]So you also, when you have done everything you were told to do, should say, 'We are unworthy servants; we have only done our duty.' "

a 23 Greek *Hades*

Ten Healed of Leprosy

¹¹Now on his way to Jerusalem, Jesus traveled along the border between Samaria and Galilee. ¹²As he was going into a village, ten men who had leprosy^a met him. They stood at a distance ¹³and called out in a loud voice, "Jesus, Master, have pity on us!"

¹⁴When he saw them, he said, "Go, show yourselves to the priests." And as they went, they were cleansed.

¹⁵One of them, when he saw he was healed, came back, praising God in a loud voice. ¹⁶He threw himself at Jesus' feet and thanked him—and he was a Samaritan.

¹⁷Jesus asked, "Were not all ten cleansed? Where are the other nine? ¹⁸Was no one found to return and give praise to God except this foreigner?" ¹⁹Then he said to him, "Rise and go; your faith has made you well."

The Coming of the Kingdom of God

²⁰Once, having been asked by the Pharisees when the kingdom of God would come, Jesus replied, "The kingdom of God does not come with your careful observation, ²¹nor will people say, 'Here it is,' or 'There it is,' because the kingdom of God is within^b you."

genuine gratitude » 17:11-19

Ingrates. Unappreciative jerks. Losers. Jesus healed ten lepers, and nine of them didn't even have the decency to come back and say thank you. How dare they?! Of course, *you'd* be the one who came back to say thanks. Wouldn't you? Because of course you've thanked God lately—really thanked him with all your heart—for sending Jesus to die on the cross, for forgiving your sins, for continuing to love and forgive you each time you fail him, for giving you strength and joy to face each day, for the hope of heaven . . . Haven't you?

²²Then he said to his disciples, "The time is coming when you will long to see one of the days of the Son of Man, but you will not see it. ²³Men will tell you, 'There he is!' or 'Here he is!' Do not go running off after them. ²⁴For the Son of Man in his day^c will be like the lightning, which flashes and lights up the sky from one end to the other. ²⁵But first he must suffer many things and be rejected by this generation.

²⁶"Just as it was in the days of Noah, so also will it be in the days of the Son of Man. ²⁷People were eating, drinking, marrying and being given in marriage up to the day Noah entered the ark. Then the flood came and destroyed them all.

²⁸"It was the same in the days of Lot. People were eating and drinking, buying and selling, planting and building. ²⁹But the day Lot left Sodom, fire and sulfur rained down from heaven and destroyed them all.

³⁰"It will be just like this on the day the Son of Man is revealed. ³¹On that day no one who is on the roof of his house, with his goods inside, should go down to get them. Likewise, no one in the field should go back for anything. ³²Remember Lot's wife! ³³Whoever tries to keep his life will lose it, and whoever loses his life will preserve it. ³⁴I tell you, on that night two people will be in one bed; one will be taken and the other left. ³⁵Two women will be grinding grain together; one will be taken and the other left.^d"

³⁷"Where, Lord?" they asked.

He replied, "Where there is a dead body, there the vultures will gather."

The Parable of the Persistent Widow

18 Then Jesus told his disciples a parable to show them that they should always pray and not give up. ²He said: "In a certain town there was a judge who neither feared God nor cared about men. ³And there was a widow in that town who kept coming to him with the plea, 'Grant me justice against my adversary.'

---

^a 12 The Greek word was used for various diseases affecting the skin—not necessarily leprosy.   ^b 21 Or *among*
^c 24 Some manuscripts do not have *in his day.*   ^d 35 Some manuscripts *left. 36Two men will be in the field; one will be taken and the other left.*

⁴"For some time he refused. But finally he said to himself, 'Even though I don't fear God or care about men, ⁵yet because this widow keeps bothering me, I will see that she gets justice, so that she won't eventually wear me out with her coming!' "

⁶And the Lord said, "Listen to what the unjust judge says. ⁷And will not God bring about justice for his chosen ones, who cry out to him day and night? Will he keep putting them off? ⁸I tell you, he will see that they get justice, and quickly. However, when the Son of Man comes, will he find faith on the earth?"

The Parable of the Pharisee and the Tax Collector

⁹To some who were confident of their own righteousness and looked down on everybody else, Jesus told this parable: ¹⁰"Two men went up to the temple to pray, one a Pharisee and the other a tax collector. ¹¹The Pharisee stood up and prayed about[a] himself: 'God, I thank you that I am not like other men—robbers, evildoers, adulterers—or even like this tax collector. ¹²I fast twice a week and give a tenth of all I get.'

¹³"But the tax collector stood at a distance. He would not even look up to heaven, but beat his breast and said, 'God, have mercy on me, a sinner.'

¹⁴"I tell you that this man, rather than the other, went home justified before God. For everyone who exalts himself will be humbled, and he who humbles himself will be exalted."

The Little Children and Jesus

¹⁵People were also bringing babies to Jesus to have him touch them. When the disciples saw this, they rebuked them. ¹⁶But Jesus called the children to him and said, "Let the little children come to me, and do not hinder them, for the kingdom of God belongs to such as these. ¹⁷I tell you the truth, anyone who will not receive the kingdom of God like a little child will never enter it."

The Rich Ruler

¹⁸A certain ruler asked him, "Good teacher, what must I do to inherit eternal life?"

¹⁹"Why do you call me good?" Jesus answered. "No one is good—except God alone. ²⁰You know the commandments: 'Do not commit adultery, do not murder, do not steal, do not give false testimony, honor your father and mother.'[b]"

²¹"All these I have kept since I was a boy," he said.

²²When Jesus heard this, he said to him, "You still lack one thing. Sell everything you have and give to the poor, and you will have treasure in heaven. Then come, follow me."

²³When he heard this, he became very sad, because he was a man of great wealth. ²⁴Jesus looked at him and said, "How hard it is for the rich to enter the kingdom of God! ²⁵Indeed, it is easier for a camel to go through the eye of a needle than for a rich man to enter the kingdom of God."

²⁶Those who heard this asked, "Who then can be saved?"

²⁷Jesus replied, "What is impossible with men is possible with God."

²⁸Peter said to him, "We have left all we had to follow you!"

²⁹"I tell you the truth," Jesus said to them,

genuine humility » 18:9-14

Picture this: A "good" Christian girl stands in church and prays, "God, thank you that I'm not like other girls who sleep around, party, smoke, drink and swear—like that tattoo-covered girl over who'd probably hook up with anyone. What's *she* doing here?!" Meanwhile, the other girl, who was indeed guilty of all those things, prays tearfully, "God, have mercy on me, a sinner." Now, guess which one makes God smile. Here's a hint: It's not the "good" Christian. It's the one with the humble, repentant heart. That's more important to God than anything else. So which one are you?

a 11 Or *to*   *b* 20 Exodus 20:12-16; Deut. 5:16-20

"no one who has left home or wife or brothers or parents or children for the sake of the kingdom of God ³⁰will fail to receive many times as much in this age and, in the age to come, eternal life."

Jesus Again Predicts His Death

³¹Jesus took the Twelve aside and told them, "We are going up to Jerusalem, and everything that is written by the prophets about the Son of Man will be fulfilled. ³²He will be handed over to the Gentiles. They will mock him, insult him, spit on him, flog him and kill him. ³³On the third day he will rise again."

³⁴The disciples did not understand any of this. Its meaning was hidden from them, and they did not know what he was talking about.

A Blind Beggar Receives His Sight

³⁵As Jesus approached Jericho, a blind man was sitting by the roadside begging. ³⁶When he heard the crowd going by, he asked what was happening. ³⁷They told him, "Jesus of Nazareth is passing by."

³⁸He called out, "Jesus, Son of David, have mercy on me!"

³⁹Those who led the way rebuked him and told him to be quiet, but he shouted all the more, "Son of David, have mercy on me!"

⁴⁰Jesus stopped and ordered the man to be brought to him. When he came near, Jesus asked him, ⁴¹"What do you want me to do for you?"

"Lord, I want to see," he replied.

⁴²Jesus said to him, "Receive your sight; your faith has healed you." ⁴³Immediately he received his sight and followed Jesus, praising God. When all the people saw it, they also praised God.

Zacchaeus the Tax Collector

19 Jesus entered Jericho and was passing through. ²A man was there by the name of Zacchaeus; he was a chief tax collector and was wealthy. ³He wanted to see who Jesus was, but being a short man he could not, because of the crowd. ⁴So he ran ahead and climbed a sycamore-fig tree to see him, since Jesus was coming that way.

⁵When Jesus reached the spot, he looked up and said to him, "Zacchaeus, come down immediately. I must stay at your house today." ⁶So he came down at once and welcomed him gladly.

⁷All the people saw this and began to mutter, "He has gone to be the guest of a 'sinner.' "

⁸But Zacchaeus stood up and said to the Lord, "Look, Lord! Here and now I give half of my possessions to the poor, and if I have cheated anybody out of anything, I will pay back four times the amount."

⁹Jesus said to him, "Today salvation has come to this house, because this man, too, is a son of Abraham. ¹⁰For the Son of Man came to seek and to save what was lost."

The Parable of the Ten Minas

¹¹While they were listening to this, he went on to tell them a parable, because he was near Jerusalem and the people thought that the kingdom of God was going to appear at once. ¹²He said: "A man of noble birth went to a distant country to have himself appointed king and then to return. ¹³So he called ten of his servants and gave them ten minas. ᵃ 'Put this money to work,' he said, 'until I come back.'

¹⁴"But his subjects hated him and sent a delegation after him to say, 'We don't want this man to be our king.'

¹⁵"He was made king, however, and returned home. Then he sent for the servants to whom he had given the money, in order to find out what they had gained with it.

¹⁶"The first one came and said, 'Sir, your mina has earned ten more.'

¹⁷" 'Well done, my good servant!' his master replied. 'Because you have been trustworthy in a very small matter, take charge of ten cities.'

¹⁸"The second came and said, 'Sir, your mina has earned five more.'

¹⁹"His master answered, 'You take charge of five cities.'

²⁰"Then another servant came and said, 'Sir, here is your mina; I have kept it laid away in a

---

ᵃ 13 A mina was about three months' wages.

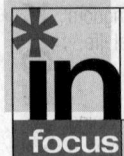

Fallen Friend

I've got this friend, Amanda. Lately, whenever she wants to hang around me, I just cringe. And she's my best friend. Or was. Well, she still is. But I wonder for how long.

Lately, she's always in whine-mode. When she's not doing that, she's in total attitude-mode. That's all I see—*attitude*. It's gotten so that none of our other friends wants to be around her. And she gossips constantly now. Some of what she says isn't true.

I've even caught her in some lies. Like the time she was supposed to meet me at the mall. Well, she never showed. I called her house. There she was. She came up with some lame story about losing track of time because her cousin Rhonda stopped by. I *knew* she was lying because I saw her cousin at the mall.

My friends are like, "El, how can you stand her? You don't need her! Move on with life." But how can I ditch her? I've known her since third grade. She hasn't always been like this. She used to be a total blast. She's the one who first took me to church. But ever since the start of our freshman year, I've never known what to expect from her. She's so moody. We're almost sophomores now, and she's still in this "phase," or whatever it is. My mom says it's hormones or something. I don't know.

Is it just time out for our friendship? I've heard that friends sometimes grow apart. Maybe I've outgrown Amanda.

For more on friendship, go to www.TrueImagesBible.com

friendship in focus

A great friend is a great gift. Friends not only chase away the blues, but they can also build one another up. "As iron sharpens iron, so one man sharpens another" (Proverbs 27:17, page 843). But what happens when one friend seems to change in negative ways? Is it time to pull up anchor and sail away, bidding a fond farewell to your friend? Or should you stay loyal to the end? If you're in the same boat as Ellie:

»Pray for your friend. Ask God for wisdom to know how to deal with her. He can also help you know when it's time to let go.

»Getting the attitude alert? What's the root cause? Sometimes divorce, drugs or disillusionment plays a part in turning someone sour. Look before you leap completely out of a friendship. Your friend's mood might be a cry for help.

For more on this topic, see the index on page 1656.

piece of cloth. [21]I was afraid of you, because you are a hard man. You take out what you did not put in and reap what you did not sow.'

[22]"His master replied, 'I will judge you by your own words, you wicked servant! You knew, did you, that I am a hard man, taking out what I did not put in, and reaping what I did not sow? [23]Why then didn't you put my money on deposit, so that when I came back, I could have collected it with interest?'

[24]"Then he said to those standing by, 'Take his mina away from him and give it to the one who has ten minas.'

25" 'Sir,' they said, 'he already has ten!'

26"He replied, 'I tell you that to everyone who has, more will be given, but as for the one who has nothing, even what he has will be taken away. 27But those enemies of mine who did not want me to be king over them—bring them here and kill them in front of me.' "

The Triumphal Entry

28After Jesus had said this, he went on ahead, going up to Jerusalem. 29As he approached Bethphage and Bethany at the hill called the Mount of Olives, he sent two of his disciples, saying to them, 30"Go to the village ahead of you, and as you enter it, you will find a colt tied there, which no one has ever ridden. Untie it and bring it here. 31If anyone asks you, 'Why are you untying it?' tell him, 'The Lord needs it.' "

32Those who were sent ahead went and found it just as he had told them. 33As they were untying the colt, its owners asked them, "Why are you untying the colt?"

34They replied, "The Lord needs it."

35They brought it to Jesus, threw their cloaks on the colt and put Jesus on it. 36As he went along, people spread their cloaks on the road.

37When he came near the place where the road goes down the Mount of Olives, the whole crowd of disciples began joyfully to praise God in loud voices for all the miracles they had seen:

38 "Blessed is the king who comes in the name of the Lord!" *a*

"Peace in heaven and glory in the highest!"

39Some of the Pharisees in the crowd said to Jesus, "Teacher, rebuke your disciples!"

40"I tell you," he replied, "if they keep quiet, the stones will cry out."

41As he approached Jerusalem and saw the city, he wept over it 42and said, "If you, even you, had only known on this day what would bring you peace—but now it is hidden from your eyes. 43The days will come upon you when your enemies will build an embankment against you and encircle you and hem you in on every side. 44They will dash you to the ground, you and the children within your walls. They will not leave one stone on another, because you did not recognize the time of God's coming to you."

Jesus at the Temple

45Then he entered the temple area and began driving out those who were selling. 46"It is written," he said to them, " 'My house will be a house of prayer' *b*; but you have made it 'a den of robbers.' *c*"

47Every day he was teaching at the temple. But the chief priests, the teachers of the law and the leaders among the people were trying to kill him. 48Yet they could not find any way to do it, because all the people hung on his words.

The Authority of Jesus Questioned

20 One day as he was teaching the people in the temple courts and preaching the gospel, the chief priests and the teachers of the law, together with the elders, came up to him. 2"Tell us by what authority you are doing these things," they said. "Who gave you this authority?"

3He replied, "I will also ask you a question. Tell me, 4John's baptism—was it from heaven, or from men?"

5They discussed it among themselves and said, "If we say, 'From heaven,' he will ask, 'Why didn't you believe him?' 6But if we say, 'From men,' all the people will stone us, because they are persuaded that John was a prophet."

7So they answered, "We don't know where it was from."

8Jesus said, "Neither will I tell you by what authority I am doing these things."

The Parable of the Tenants

9He went on to tell the people this parable: "A man planted a vineyard, rented it to some farmers and went away for a long time. 10At harvest time he sent a servant to the tenants so they would

a 38 Psalm 118:26   *b 46* Isaiah 56:7   *c 46* Jer. 7:11

give him some of the fruit of the vineyard. But the tenants beat him and sent him away empty-handed. [11]He sent another servant, but that one also they beat and treated shamefully and sent away empty-handed. [12]He sent still a third, and they wounded him and threw him out.

[13]"Then the owner of the vineyard said, 'What shall I do? I will send my son, whom I love; perhaps they will respect him.'

[14]"But when the tenants saw him, they talked the matter over. 'This is the heir,' they said. 'Let's kill him, and the inheritance will be ours.' [15]So they threw him out of the vineyard and killed him.

"What then will the owner of the vineyard do to them? [16]He will come and kill those tenants and give the vineyard to others."

When the people heard this, they said, "May this never be!"

[17]Jesus looked directly at them and asked, "Then what is the meaning of that which is written:

" 'The stone the builders rejected
has become the capstone[a]'[b]?

[18]Everyone who falls on that stone will be broken to pieces, but he on whom it falls will be crushed."

[19]The teachers of the law and the chief priests looked for a way to arrest him immediately, because they knew he had spoken this parable against them. But they were afraid of the people.

Paying Taxes to Caesar

[20]Keeping a close watch on him, they sent spies, who pretended to be honest. They hoped to catch Jesus in something he said so that they might hand him over to the power and authority of the governor. [21]So the spies questioned him: "Teacher, we know that you speak and teach what is right, and that you do not show partiality but teach the way of God in accordance with the truth. [22]Is it right for us to pay taxes to Caesar or not?"

[23]He saw through their duplicity and said to them, [24]"Show me a denarius. Whose portrait and inscription are on it?"

[25]"Caesar's," they replied.

He said to them, "Then give to Caesar what is Caesar's, and to God what is God's."

[26]They were unable to trap him in what he had said there in public. And astonished by his answer, they became silent.

The Resurrection and Marriage

[27]Some of the Sadducees, who say there is no resurrection, came to Jesus with a question. [28]"Teacher," they said, "Moses wrote for us that if a man's brother dies and leaves a wife but no children, the man must marry the widow and have children for his brother. [29]Now there were seven brothers. The first one married a woman and died childless. [30]The second [31]and then the third married her, and in the same way the seven died, leaving no children. [32]Finally, the woman died too. [33]Now then, at the resurrection whose wife will she be, since the seven were married to her?"

[34]Jesus replied, "The people of this age marry and are given in marriage. [35]But those who are considered worthy of taking part in that age and in the resurrection from the dead will neither marry nor be given in marriage, [36]and they can no longer die; for they are like the angels. They are God's children, since they are children of the resurrection. [37]But in the account of the bush, even Moses showed that the dead rise, for he calls the Lord 'the God of Abraham, and the God of Isaac, and the God of Jacob.'[c] [38]He is not the God of the dead, but of the living, for to him all are alive."

[39]Some of the teachers of the law responded, "Well said, teacher!" [40]And no one dared to ask him any more questions.

Whose Son Is the Christ?

[41]Then Jesus said to them, "How is it that they say the Christ[d] is the Son of David? [42]David himself declares in the Book of Psalms:

" 'The Lord said to my Lord:
"Sit at my right hand
[43]until I make your enemies
a footstool for your feet." '[e]

a 17 Or cornerstone   b 17 Psalm 118:22   c 37 Exodus 3:6   d 41 Or Messiah   e 43 Psalm 110:1

⁴⁴"David calls him 'Lord.' How then can he be his son?"

⁴⁵While all the people were listening, Jesus said to his disciples, ⁴⁶"Beware of the teachers of the law. They like to walk around in flowing robes and love to be greeted in the marketplaces and have the most important seats in the synagogues and the places of honor at banquets. ⁴⁷They devour widows' houses and for a show make lengthy prayers. Such men will be punished most severely."

The Widow's Offering

21 As he looked up, Jesus saw the rich putting their gifts into the temple treasury. ²He also saw a poor widow put in two very small copper coins. ᵃ ³"I tell you the truth," he said, "this poor widow has put in more than all the others. ⁴All these people gave their gifts out of their wealth; but she out of her poverty put in all she had to live on."

Signs of the End of the Age

⁵Some of his disciples were remarking about how the temple was adorned with beautiful stones and with gifts dedicated to God. But Jesus said, ⁶"As for what you see here, the time will come when not one stone will be left on another; every one of them will be thrown down."

⁷"Teacher," they asked, "when will these things happen? And what will be the sign that they are about to take place?"

⁸He replied: "Watch out that you are not deceived. For many will come in my name, claiming, 'I am he,' and, 'The time is near.' Do not follow them. ⁹When you hear of wars and revolutions, do not be frightened. These things must happen first, but the end will not come right away."

¹⁰Then he said to them: "Nation will rise against nation, and kingdom against kingdom. ¹¹There will be great earthquakes, famines and pestilences in various places, and fearful events and great signs from heaven.

¹²"But before all this, they will lay hands on you and persecute you. They will deliver you to synagogues and prisons, and you will be brought before kings and governors, and all on account of my name. ¹³This will result in your being witnesses to them. ¹⁴But make up your mind not to worry beforehand how you will defend yourselves. ¹⁵For I will give you words and wisdom that none of your adversaries will be able to resist or contradict. ¹⁶You will be betrayed even by parents, brothers, relatives and friends, and they will put some of you to death. ¹⁷All men will hate you because of me. ¹⁸But not a hair of your head will perish. ¹⁹By standing firm you will gain life.

²⁰"When you see Jerusalem being surrounded by armies, you will know that its desolation is near. ²¹Then let those who are in Judea flee to the mountains, let those in the city get out, and let those in the country not enter the city. ²²For this is the time of punishment in fulfillment of all that has been written. ²³How dreadful it will be in those days for pregnant women and nursing mothers! There will be great distress in the land and wrath against this people. ²⁴They will fall by the sword and will be taken as prisoners to all the nations. Jerusalem will be trampled on by the Gentiles until the times of the Gentiles are fulfilled.

²⁵"There will be signs in the sun, moon and stars. On the earth, nations will be in anguish and perplexity at the roaring and tossing of the sea. ²⁶Men will faint from terror, apprehensive of what is coming on the world, for the heavenly bodies will be shaken. ²⁷At that time they will see the Son of Man coming in a cloud with power and great glory. ²⁸When these things begin to take place, stand up and lift up your heads, because your redemption is drawing near."

²⁹He told them this parable: "Look at the fig tree and all the trees. ³⁰When they sprout leaves, you can see for yourselves and know that summer is near. ³¹Even so, when you see these things happening, you know that the kingdom of God is near.

³²"I tell you the truth, this generationᵇ will certainly not pass away until all these things have happened. ³³Heaven and earth will pass away, but my words will never pass away.

³⁴"Be careful, or your hearts will be weighed down with dissipation, drunkenness and the anxieties of life, and that day will close on you unexpectedly like a trap. ³⁵For it will come upon all those who live on the face of the whole earth. ³⁶Be always on the watch, and pray that you may be able to escape all that is about to happen, and that you may be able to stand before the Son of Man."

³⁷Each day Jesus was teaching at the temple, and each evening he went out to spend the night

---

ᵃ 2 Greek *two lepta*   *ᵇ 32* Or *race*

on the hill called the Mount of Olives, ³⁸and all the people came early in the morning to hear him at the temple.

Judas Agrees to Betray Jesus

22 Now the Feast of Unleavened Bread, called the Passover, was approaching, ²and the chief priests and the teachers of the law were looking for some way to get rid of Jesus, for they were afraid of the people. ³Then Satan entered Judas, called Iscariot, one of the Twelve. ⁴And Judas went to the chief priests and the officers of the temple guard and discussed with them how he might betray Jesus. ⁵They were delighted and agreed to give him money. ⁶He consented, and watched for an opportunity to hand Jesus over to them when no crowd was present.

The Last Supper

⁷Then came the day of Unleavened Bread on which the Passover lamb had to be sacrificed. ⁸Jesus sent Peter and John, saying, "Go and make preparations for us to eat the Passover."

⁹"Where do you want us to prepare for it?" they asked.

¹⁰He replied, "As you enter the city, a man carrying a jar of water will meet you. Follow him to the house that he enters, ¹¹and say to the owner of the house, 'The Teacher asks: Where is the guest room, where I may eat the Passover with my disciples?' ¹²He will show you a large upper room, all furnished. Make preparations there."

¹³They left and found things just as Jesus had told them. So they prepared the Passover.

¹⁴When the hour came, Jesus and his apostles reclined at the table. ¹⁵And he said to them, "I have eagerly desired to eat this Passover with you before I suffer. ¹⁶For I tell you, I will not eat it again until it finds fulfillment in the kingdom of God."

¹⁷After taking the cup, he gave thanks and said, "Take this and divide it among you. ¹⁸For I tell you I will not drink again of the fruit of the vine until the kingdom of God comes."

¹⁹And he took bread, gave thanks and broke it, and gave it to them, saying, "This is my body given for you; do this in remembrance of me."

²⁰In the same way, after the supper he took the cup, saying, "This cup is the new covenant in my blood, which is poured out for you. ²¹But the hand of him who is going to betray me is with mine on the table. ²²The Son of Man will go as it has been decreed, but woe to that man who betrays him." ²³They began to question among themselves which of them it might be who would do this.

²⁴Also a dispute arose among them as to which of them was considered to be greatest. ²⁵Jesus said to them, "The kings of the Gentiles lord it over them; and those who exercise authority over them call themselves Benefactors. ²⁶But you are not to be like that. Instead, the greatest among you should be like the youngest, and the one who rules like the one who serves. ²⁷For who is greater, the one who is at the table or the one who serves? Is it not the one who is at the table? But I am among you as one who serves. ²⁸You are those who have stood by me in my trials. ²⁹And I confer on you a kingdom, just as my Father conferred one on me, ³⁰so that you may eat and drink at my table in my kingdom and sit on thrones, judging the twelve tribes of Israel.

³¹"Simon, Simon, Satan has asked to sift you*ᵃ* as wheat. ³²But I have prayed for you, Simon, that your faith may not fail. And when you have turned back, strengthen your brothers."

ᵃ 31 The Greek is plural.

truth or dare

Getting drunk, living for self-indulgent pleasures (dissipation) and worrying—that pretty much sums up our society's values. Don't let these things distract you. Keep watching for Jesus.

21:34

truth or dare

Peter *thought* his faith was strong, but he was ripe for a fall. Still, Jesus promised to restore him. Recently fail a test of faith? God will restore you, too.

22:31–34

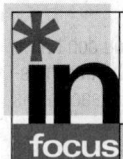

A Little Spin Goes a Long Way

I wouldn't call it outright *lying*—let's just say I know how to put some spin on the truth. If my parents want to know where I'm going on Friday nights, I tell them I'm going to the movies. This is the absolute truth. With that said, I usually get out the door without too many other questions. After all, what trouble can I get into at the movies, right? They feel good about their parental duty to monitor their only child, and I get away without having to lie to their face. Why ruin it by telling them I'm only meeting up with friends at the movies *then* going to Darrell's party from there?

Sometimes it's just plain easier to tell them a half-truth. If I boldfaced lied to them (which I'd never get away with anyway), I would feel so guilty about it I'd be miserable. And telling them the outright truth is just as unrealistic.

"Honey, where are you going tonight?"

"Oh, Mom, I'm going to the party at Darrell's . . . Remember his parents are out of town this weekend?"

"That's right, sweetie. I forgot. Well, have a good time."

"Thanks, Mom! Don't wait up!"

Right, like that conversation's ever going to happen! It's just not convenient or comfortable to tell the truth all the time. As long as I get away with it, nobody gets hurt. They can't worry about what they don't know about. I'm always careful. I usually make curfew. So, what's the harm?

honesty in focus

Read more concerning the truth about lying at www.TrueImagesBible.com

Seville's right about one thing—the truth isn't always convenient, cool or comfortable. In fact, lying comes second nature to us. It's the first thing that often pops into our head to get out of a sticky situation. However, consider this:

» No one really gets away with anything dishonest or untrue. "Do not be deceived: God cannot be mocked. A man reaps what he sows" (Galatians 6:7, page 1540).

» Lying brings consequences we often don't think about, like losing someone's trust—maybe forever. We also lose self-respect, and we compromise our character.

» Not only that, but we also allow the devil, the father of lies (see John 8:44, page 1424) to get a firm footing in our lives (see Ephesians 4:27, page 1545).

For more on this topic, see the index on page 1656.

---

³³But he replied, "Lord, I am ready to go with you to prison and to death."

³⁴Jesus answered, "I tell you, Peter, before the rooster crows today, you will deny three times that you know me."

³⁵Then Jesus asked them, "When I sent you without purse, bag or sandals, did you lack anything?"

"Nothing," they answered.

[36]He said to them, "But now if you have a purse, take it, and also a bag; and if you don't have a sword, sell your cloak and buy one. [37]It is written: 'And he was numbered with the transgressors'[a]; and I tell you that this must be fulfilled in me. Yes, what is written about me is reaching its fulfillment."

[38]The disciples said, "See, Lord, here are two swords."

"That is enough," he replied.

Jesus Prays on the Mount of Olives

[39]Jesus went out as usual to the Mount of Olives, and his disciples followed him. [40]On reaching the place, he said to them, "Pray that you will not fall into temptation." [41]He withdrew about a stone's throw beyond them, knelt down and prayed, [42]"Father, if you are willing, take this cup from me; yet not my will, but yours be done." [43]An angel from heaven appeared to him and strengthened him. [44]And being in anguish, he prayed more earnestly, and his sweat was like drops of blood falling to the ground.[b]

[45]When he rose from prayer and went back to the disciples, he found them asleep, exhausted from sorrow. [46]"Why are you sleeping?" he asked them. "Get up and pray so that you will not fall into temptation."

Jesus Arrested

[47]While he was still speaking a crowd came up, and the man who was called Judas, one of the Twelve, was leading them. He approached Jesus to kiss him, [48]but Jesus asked him, "Judas, are you betraying the Son of Man with a kiss?"

[49]When Jesus' followers saw what was going to happen, they said, "Lord, should we strike with our swords?" [50]And one of them struck the servant of the high priest, cutting off his right ear.

[51]But Jesus answered, "No more of this!" And he touched the man's ear and healed him.

[52]Then Jesus said to the chief priests, the officers of the temple guard, and the elders, who had come for him, "Am I leading a rebellion, that you have come with swords and clubs? [53]Every day I was with you in the temple courts, and you did not lay a hand on me. But this is your hour—when darkness reigns."

Peter Disowns Jesus

[54]Then seizing him, they led him away and took him into the house of the high priest. Peter followed at a distance. [55]But when they had kindled a fire in the middle of the courtyard and had sat down together, Peter sat down with them. [56]A servant girl saw him seated there in the firelight. She looked closely at him and said, "This man was with him."

[57]But he denied it. "Woman, I don't know him," he said.

[58]A little later someone else saw him and said, "You also are one of them."

"Man, I am not!" Peter replied.

[59]About an hour later another asserted, "Certainly this fellow was with him, for he is a Galilean."

[60]Peter replied, "Man, I don't know what you're talking about!" Just as he was speaking, the rooster crowed. [61]The Lord turned and looked straight at Peter. Then Peter remembered the word the Lord had spoken to him: "Before the rooster crows today, you will disown me three times." [62]And he went outside and wept bitterly.

The Guards Mock Jesus

[63]The men who were guarding Jesus began mocking and beating him. [64]They blindfolded him and demanded, "Prophesy! Who hit you?" [65]And they said many other insulting things to him.

Jesus Before Pilate and Herod

[66]At daybreak the council of the elders of the people, both the chief priests and teachers of the law, met together, and Jesus was led before them. [67]"If you are the Christ,[c]" they said, "tell us."

Jesus answered, "If I tell you, you will not believe me, [68]and if I asked you, you would not answer. [69]But from now on, the Son of Man will be seated at the right hand of the mighty God."

---

[a] 37 Isaiah 53:12   [b] 44 Some early manuscripts do not have verses 43 and 44.   [c] 67 Or *Messiah*

⁷⁰They all asked, "Are you then the Son of God?"

He replied, "You are right in saying I am."

⁷¹Then they said, "Why do we need any more testimony? We have heard it from his own lips."

23 Then the whole assembly rose and led him off to Pilate. ²And they began to accuse him, saying, "We have found this man subverting our nation. He opposes payment of taxes to Caesar and claims to be Christ,ᵃ a king."

³So Pilate asked Jesus, "Are you the king of the Jews?"

"Yes, it is as you say," Jesus replied.

⁴Then Pilate announced to the chief priests and the crowd, "I find no basis for a charge against this man."

⁵But they insisted, "He stirs up the people all over Judeaᵇ by his teaching. He started in Galilee and has come all the way here."

⁶On hearing this, Pilate asked if the man was a Galilean. ⁷When he learned that Jesus was under Herod's jurisdiction, he sent him to Herod, who was also in Jerusalem at that time.

⁸When Herod saw Jesus, he was greatly pleased, because for a long time he had been wanting to see him. From what he had heard about him, he hoped to see him perform some miracle. ⁹He plied him with many questions, but Jesus gave him no answer. ¹⁰The chief priests and the teachers of the law were standing there, vehemently accusing him. ¹¹Then Herod and his soldiers ridiculed and mocked him. Dressing him in an elegant robe, they sent him back to Pilate. ¹²That day Herod and Pilate became friends—before this they had been enemies.

¹³Pilate called together the chief priests, the rulers and the people, ¹⁴and said to them, "You brought me this man as one who was inciting the people to rebellion. I have examined him in your presence and have found no basis for your charges against him. ¹⁵Neither has Herod, for he sent him back to us; as you can see, he has done nothing to deserve death. ¹⁶Therefore, I will punish him and then release him.ᶜ"

¹⁸With one voice they cried out, "Away with this man! Release Barabbas to us!" ¹⁹(Barabbas had been thrown into prison for an insurrection in the city, and for murder.)

²⁰Wanting to release Jesus, Pilate appealed to them again. ²¹But they kept shouting, "Crucify him! Crucify him!"

²²For the third time he spoke to them: "Why? What crime has this man committed? I have found in him no grounds for the death penalty. Therefore I will have him punished and then release him."

²³But with loud shouts they insistently demanded that he be crucified, and their shouts prevailed. ²⁴So Pilate decided to grant their demand. ²⁵He released the man who had been thrown into prison for insurrection and murder, the one they asked for, and surrendered Jesus to their will.

The Crucifixion

²⁶As they led him away, they seized Simon from Cyrene, who was on his way in from the country, and put the cross on him and made him carry it behind Jesus. ²⁷A large number of people followed him, including women who mourned and wailed for him. ²⁸Jesus turned and said to them, "Daughters of Jerusalem, do not weep for me; weep for yourselves and for your children. ²⁹For the time will come when you will say, 'Blessed are the barren women, the wombs that never bore and the breasts that never nursed!' ³⁰Then

" 'they will say to the mountains, "Fall on us!"
and to the hills, "Cover us!" 'ᵈ

³¹For if men do these things when the tree is green, what will happen when it is dry?"

³²Two other men, both criminals, were also led out with him to be executed. ³³When they came to the place called the Skull, there they crucified him, along with the criminals—one on his right, the other on his left. ³⁴Jesus said, "Father, forgive them, for they do not know what they are doing."ᵉ And they divided up his clothes by casting lots.

³⁵The people stood watching, and the rulers even sneered at him. They said, "He saved others; let him save himself if he is the Christ of God, the Chosen One."

ᵃ 2 Or *Messiah*; also in verses 35 and 39   ᵇ 5 Or *over the land of the Jews*   ᶜ 16 Some manuscripts *him." ¹⁷Now he was obliged to release one man to them at the Feast.*   ᵈ 30 Hosea 10:8   ᵉ 34 Some early manuscripts do not have this sentence.

[36]The soldiers also came up and mocked him. They offered him wine vinegar [37]and said, "If you are the king of the Jews, save yourself."

[38]There was a written notice above him, which read: THIS IS THE KING OF THE JEWS.

[39]One of the criminals who hung there hurled insults at him: "Aren't you the Christ? Save yourself and us!"

[40]But the other criminal rebuked him. "Don't you fear God," he said, "since you are under the same sentence? [41]We are punished justly, for we are getting what our deeds deserve. But this man has done nothing wrong."

[42]Then he said, "Jesus, remember me when you come into your kingdom.[a]"

[43]Jesus answered him, "I tell you the truth, today you will be with me in paradise."

Jesus' Death

[44]It was now about the sixth hour, and darkness came over the whole land until the ninth hour, [45]for the sun stopped shining. And the curtain of the temple was torn in two. [46]Jesus called out with a loud voice, "Father, into your hands I commit my spirit." When he had said this, he breathed his last.

[47]The centurion, seeing what had happened, praised God and said, "Surely this was a righteous man." [48]When all the people who had gathered to witness this sight saw what took place, they beat their breasts and went away. [49]But all those who knew him, including the women who had followed him from Galilee, stood at a distance, watching these things.

Jesus' Burial

[50]Now there was a man named Joseph, a member of the Council, a good and upright man, [51]who had not consented to their decision and action. He came from the Judean town of Arimathea and he was waiting for the kingdom of God. [52]Going to Pilate, he asked for Jesus' body. [53]Then he took it down, wrapped it in linen cloth and placed it in a tomb cut in the rock, one in which no one had yet been laid. [54]It was Preparation Day, and the Sabbath was about to begin.

[55]The women who had come with Jesus from Galilee followed Joseph and saw the tomb and how his body was laid in it. [56]Then they went home and prepared spices and perfumes. But they rested on the Sabbath in obedience to the commandment.

The Resurrection

24 On the first day of the week, very early in the morning, the women took the spices they had prepared and went to the tomb. [2]They found the

love♥notes

23:33

Beloved,

If you're ever tempted to doubt my love for you, remember this: I loved you so much that I stretched out my arms upon a wooden cross, had my hands and feet nailed down and gave up my life just for you.

—Your Lord and Savior

Write a prayer of response, thanking Jesus for his wonderful sacrifice of love.

a 42 Some manuscripts come with your kingly power

truth or dare

As this criminal was in the process of being executed, Jesus handed him a spiritual pardon. It's never too late to come to Jesus and ask for forgiveness.

23:39–43

stone rolled away from the tomb, ³but when they entered, they did not find the body of the Lord Jesus. ⁴While they were wondering about this, suddenly two men in clothes that gleamed like lightning stood beside them. ⁵In their fright the women bowed down with their faces to the ground, but the men said to them, "Why do you look for the living among the dead? ⁶He is not here; he has risen! Remember how he told you, while he was still with you in Galilee: ⁷'The Son of Man must be delivered into the hands of sinful men, be crucified and on the third day be raised again.'" ⁸Then they remembered his words.

⁹When they came back from the tomb, they told all these things to the Eleven and to all the others. ¹⁰It was Mary Magdalene, Joanna, Mary the mother of James, and the others with them who told this to the apostles. ¹¹But they did not believe the women, because their words seemed to them like nonsense. ¹²Peter, however, got up and ran to the tomb. Bending over, he saw the strips of linen lying by themselves, and he went away, wondering to himself what had happened.

On the Road to Emmaus

¹³Now that same day two of them were going to a village called Emmaus, about seven miles* from Jerusalem. ¹⁴They were talking with each other about everything that had happened. ¹⁵As they talked and discussed these things with each other, Jesus himself came up and walked along with them; ¹⁶but they were kept from recognizing him.

¹⁷He asked them, "What are you discussing together as you walk along?"

They stood still, their faces downcast. ¹⁸One of them, named Cleopas, asked him, "Are you only a visitor to Jerusalem and do not know the things that have happened there in these days?"

¹⁹"What things?" he asked.

"About Jesus of Nazareth," they replied. "He was a prophet, powerful in word and deed before God and all the people. ²⁰The chief priests and our rulers handed him over to be sentenced to death, and they crucified him; ²¹but we had hoped that he was the one who was going to redeem Israel. And what is more, it is the third day since all this took place. ²²In addition, some of our women amazed us. They went to the tomb early this morning ²³but didn't find his body. They came and told us that they had seen a vision of angels, who said he was alive. ²⁴Then some of our companions went to the tomb and found it just as the women had said, but him they did not see."

²⁵He said to them, "How foolish you are, and how slow of heart to believe all that the prophets have spoken! ²⁶Did not the Christ* have to suffer these things and then enter his glory?" ²⁷And beginning with Moses and all the Prophets, he explained to them what was said in all the Scriptures concerning himself.

²⁸As they approached the village to which they were going, Jesus acted as if he were going farther. ²⁹But they urged him strongly, "Stay with us, for it is nearly evening; the day is almost over." So he went in to stay with them.

³⁰When he was at the table with them, he took bread, gave thanks, broke it and began to give it to them. ³¹Then their eyes were opened and they recognized him, and he disappeared from their sight. ³²They asked each other, "Were not our hearts burning within us while he talked with us on the road and opened the Scriptures to us?"

³³They got up and returned at once to Jerusalem. There they found the Eleven and those with them, assembled together ³⁴and saying, "It is true! The Lord has risen and has appeared to Simon." ³⁵Then the two told what had happened on the way, and how Jesus was recognized by them when he broke the bread.

---

a 13 Greek *sixty stadia* (about 11 kilometers)   *b 26* Or *Messiah*; also in verse 46

Jesus Appears to the Disciples

³⁶While they were still talking about this, Jesus himself stood among them and said to them, "Peace be with you."

³⁷They were startled and frightened, thinking they saw a ghost. ³⁸He said to them, "Why are you troubled, and why do doubts rise in your minds? ³⁹Look at my hands and my feet. It is I myself! Touch me and see; a ghost does not have flesh and bones, as you see I have."

⁴⁰When he had said this, he showed them his hands and feet. ⁴¹And while they still did not believe it because of joy and amazement, he asked them, "Do you have anything here to eat?" ⁴²They gave him a piece of broiled fish, ⁴³and he took it and ate it in their presence.

⁴⁴He said to them, "This is what I told you while I was still with you: Everything must be fulfilled that is written about me in the Law of Moses, the Prophets and the Psalms."

⁴⁵Then he opened their minds so they could understand the Scriptures. ⁴⁶He told them, "This is what is written: The Christ will suffer and rise from the dead on the third day, ⁴⁷and repentance and forgiveness of sins will be preached in his name to all nations, beginning at Jerusalem. ⁴⁸You are witnesses of these things. ⁴⁹I am going to send you what my Father has promised; but stay in the city until you have been clothed with power from on high."

The Ascension

⁵⁰When he had led them out to the vicinity of Bethany, he lifted up his hands and blessed them. ⁵¹While he was blessing them, he left them and was taken up into heaven. ⁵²Then they worshiped him and returned to Jerusalem with great joy. ⁵³And they stayed continually at the temple, praising God.

truth or dare

Jesus' sacrifice on the cross took care of your sin. Jesus' resurrection from the dead sealed your salvation! If you believe, death no longer has any hold on you.

24:45–47

author: John, the apostle.

date: Probably A.D. 85–90.

setting: It's assumed that John's eyewitness account was the last Gospel written, sometime before John was exiled to the island of Patmos.

verse to remember: But these are written that you may believe that Jesus is the Christ, the Son of God, and that by believing you may have life in his name (20:31).

theme to consider: John's Gospel is not just a record of Jesus' life; it is a powerful argument that Jesus *is* the heaven-sent Son of God and the only source of eternal life. Believe and be saved!

unchanging truth

When you need information, you have a variety of sources to choose from—the Internet, books, a friend, the newspaper, maybe even the well-connected gossip at school. You choose your source based on what kind of info you need, right? For example, if you wanted advice on which shirt looks good on you, you probably wouldn't go to your local library. You'd need someone standing there looking at you. (And someone with good taste.)

Not every source of information can be considered reliable or believable. For example, would you be more likely to believe a story in a supermarket tabloid or a story in the *New York Times?* The source makes all the difference.

A reliable source usually provides the best information. As one of Jesus' twelve disciples, John was considered a reliable source of information about Jesus. He was one of Jesus' closest friends, even among the Twelve. He didn't have to rely on hearsay; he had seen with his own eyes what Jesus could do. He was convinced that Jesus was fully God and fully man.

John wrote his Gospel for one reason: to help people believe in Jesus—the source of all wisdom and eternal life (see 20:31). He wanted to present evidence that would make people get off the fence of doubt and into believer territory. To John, the facts were clear. Can you say the same?

life lessons

1 The fact that Jesus is both God and human is the foundation of all Christian beliefs (1:14). We cannot hold on to this truth and unbelief at the same time.

2 The truth of the gospel can free us from our sinful habits (8:32).

3 When we fail Jesus, we don't need to waste time wallowing in guilt. Instead, we can seek his forgiveness and move on (13:37–38; 18:15–18,25–27; 21:15–19).

⌃

The Word Became Flesh

1 In the beginning was the Word, and the Word was with God, and the Word was God. ²He was with God in the beginning.

³Through him all things were made; without him nothing was made that has been made. ⁴In him was life, and that life was the light of men. ⁵The light shines in the darkness, but the darkness has not understood[a] it.

⁶There came a man who was sent from God; his name was John. ⁷He came as a witness to testify concerning that light, so that through him all men might believe. ⁸He himself was not the light; he came only as a witness to the light. ⁹The true light that gives light to every man was coming into the world.[b]

¹⁰He was in the world, and though the world was made through him, the world did not recognize him. ¹¹He came to that which was his own, but his own did not receive him. ¹²Yet to all who received him, to those who believed in his name, he gave the right to become children of God— ¹³children born not of natural descent,[c] nor of human decision or a husband's will, but born of God.

¹⁴The Word became flesh and made his dwelling among us. We have seen his glory, the glory of the One and Only,[d] who came from the Father, full of grace and truth.

¹⁵John testifies concerning him. He cries out, saying, "This was he of whom I said, 'He who comes after me has surpassed me because he was before me.'" ¹⁶From the fullness of his grace we have all received one blessing after another. ¹⁷For the law was given through Moses; grace and truth came through Jesus Christ. ¹⁸No one has ever seen God, but God the One and Only,[d,e] who is at the Father's side, has made him known.

love notes

1:12–13

Daughter,

You are my child, accepted into my family, not because of anything you did or deserved or merited. You are my child simply because you believe in the one I sent, and it is my desire that you are part of my family. Welcome!

—Your heavenly Dad

Write out your testimony about how you became part of God's family; then share it with someone you know.

truth or dare

Want to know who Jesus really is? This verse confirms that Jesus is the eternal Word of God—he is God!

1:1

ᵃ 5 Or *darkness, and the darkness has not overcome* ᵇ 9 Or *This was the true light that gives light to every man who comes into the world* ᶜ 13 Greek *of bloods* ᵈ 14,18 Or *the Only Begotten* ᵉ 18 Some manuscripts *but the only (or only begotten) Son*

John the Baptist Denies Being the Christ

¹⁹Now this was John's testimony when the Jews of Jerusalem sent priests and Levites to ask him who he was. ²⁰He did not fail to confess, but confessed freely, "I am not the Christ.ᵃ"

²¹They asked him, "Then who are you? Are you Elijah?"

He said, "I am not."

"Are you the Prophet?"

He answered, "No."

²²Finally they said, "Who are you? Give us an answer to take back to those who sent us. What do you say about yourself?"

²³John replied in the words of Isaiah the prophet, "I am the voice of one calling in the desert, 'Make straight the way for the Lord.' "ᵇ

²⁴Now some Pharisees who had been sent ²⁵questioned him, "Why then do you baptize if you are not the Christ, nor Elijah, nor the Prophet?"

²⁶"I baptize withᶜ water," John replied, "but among you stands one you do not know. ²⁷He is the one who comes after me, the thongs of whose sandals I am not worthy to untie."

²⁸This all happened at Bethany on the other side of the Jordan, where John was baptizing.

Jesus the Lamb of God

²⁹The next day John saw Jesus coming toward him and said, "Look, the Lamb of God, who takes away the sin of the world! ³⁰This is the one I meant when I said, 'A man who comes after me has surpassed me because he was before me.' ³¹I myself did not know him, but the reason I came baptizing with water was that he might be revealed to Israel."

³²Then John gave this testimony: "I saw the Spirit come down from heaven as a dove and remain on him. ³³I would not have known him, except that the one who sent me to baptize with water told me, 'The man on whom you see the Spirit come down and remain is he who will baptize with the Holy Spirit.' ³⁴I have seen and I testify that this is the Son of God."

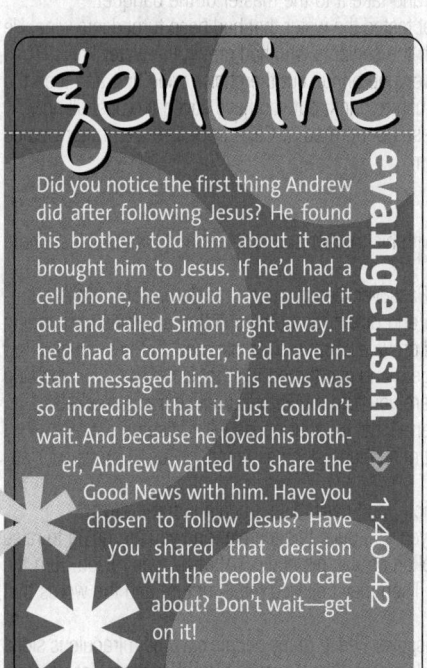

genuine

evangelism » 1:40-42

Did you notice the first thing Andrew did after following Jesus? He found his brother, told him about it and brought him to Jesus. If he'd had a cell phone, he would have pulled it out and called Simon right away. If he'd had a computer, he'd have instant messaged him. This news was so incredible that it just couldn't wait. And because he loved his brother, Andrew wanted to share the Good News with him. Have you chosen to follow Jesus? Have you shared that decision with the people you care about? Don't wait—get on it!

Jesus' First Disciples

³⁵The next day John was there again with two of his disciples. ³⁶When he saw Jesus passing by, he said, "Look, the Lamb of God!"

³⁷When the two disciples heard him say this, they followed Jesus. ³⁸Turning around, Jesus saw them following and asked, "What do you want?"

They said, "Rabbi" (which means Teacher), "where are you staying?"

³⁹"Come," he replied, "and you will see."

So they went and saw where he was staying, and spent that day with him. It was about the tenth hour.

⁴⁰Andrew, Simon Peter's brother, was one of the two who heard what John had said and who had followed Jesus. ⁴¹The first thing Andrew did was to find his brother Simon and tell him, "We have found the Messiah" (that is, the Christ). ⁴²And he brought him to Jesus.

Jesus looked at him and said, "You are Simon son of John. You will be called Cephas" (which, when translated, is Peterᵈ).

ᵃ 20 Or Messiah. "The Christ" (Greek) and "the Messiah" (Hebrew) both mean "the Anointed One"; also in verse 25.
ᵇ 23 Isaiah 40:3   ᶜ 26 Or in; also in verses 31 and 33   ᵈ 42 Both Cephas (Aramaic) and Peter (Greek) mean rock.

Jesus Calls Philip and Nathanael

⁴³The next day Jesus decided to leave for Galilee. Finding Philip, he said to him, "Follow me."

⁴⁴Philip, like Andrew and Peter, was from the town of Bethsaida. ⁴⁵Philip found Nathanael and told him, "We have found the one Moses wrote about in the Law, and about whom the prophets also wrote—Jesus of Nazareth, the son of Joseph."

⁴⁶"Nazareth! Can anything good come from there?" Nathanael asked.

"Come and see," said Philip.

⁴⁷When Jesus saw Nathanael approaching, he said of him, "Here is a true Israelite, in whom there is nothing false."

⁴⁸"How do you know me?" Nathanael asked.

Jesus answered, "I saw you while you were still under the fig tree before Philip called you."

⁴⁹Then Nathanael declared, "Rabbi, you are the Son of God; you are the King of Israel."

⁵⁰Jesus said, "You believe *ᵃ* because I told you I saw you under the fig tree. You shall see greater things than that." ⁵¹He then added, "I tell you *ᵇ* the truth, you *ᵇ* shall see heaven open, and the angels of God ascending and descending on the Son of Man."

Jesus Changes Water to Wine

2 On the third day a wedding took place at Cana in Galilee. Jesus' mother was there, ²and Jesus and his disciples had also been invited to the wedding. ³When the wine was gone, Jesus' mother said to him, "They have no more wine."

⁴"Dear woman, why do you involve me?" Jesus replied. "My time has not yet come."

⁵His mother said to the servants, "Do whatever he tells you."

⁶Nearby stood six stone water jars, the kind used by the Jews for ceremonial washing, each holding from twenty to thirty gallons. *ᶜ*

⁷Jesus said to the servants, "Fill the jars with water"; so they filled them to the brim.

⁸Then he told them, "Now draw some out and take it to the master of the banquet."

They did so, ⁹and the master of the banquet tasted the water that had been turned into wine. He did not realize where it had come from, though the servants who had drawn the water knew. Then he called the bridegroom aside ¹⁰and said, "Everyone brings out the choice wine first and then the cheaper wine after the guests have had too much to drink; but you have saved the best till now."

¹¹This, the first of his miraculous signs, Jesus performed at Cana in Galilee. He thus revealed his glory, and his disciples put their faith in him.

Jesus Clears the Temple

¹²After this he went down to Capernaum with his mother and brothers and his disciples. There they stayed for a few days.

¹³When it was almost time for the Jewish Passover, Jesus went up to Jerusalem. ¹⁴In the temple courts he found men selling cattle, sheep and doves, and others sitting at tables exchanging money. ¹⁵So he made a whip out of cords, and drove all from the temple area, both sheep and cattle; he scattered the coins of the money changers and overturned their tables. ¹⁶To those who sold doves he said, "Get these out of here! How dare you turn my Father's house into a market!"

¹⁷His disciples remembered that it is written: "Zeal for your house will consume me." *ᵈ*

¹⁸Then the Jews demanded of him, "What miraculous sign can you show us to prove your authority to do all this?"

¹⁹Jesus answered them, "Destroy this temple, and I will raise it again in three days."

²⁰The Jews replied, "It has taken forty-six years to build this temple, and you are going to raise it in three days?" ²¹But the temple he had spoken of was his body. ²²After he was raised from the dead, his disciples recalled what he had said. Then they believed the Scripture and the words that Jesus had spoken.

²³Now while he was in Jerusalem at the Passover Feast, many people saw the miraculous signs he was doing and believed in his name. *ᵉ* ²⁴But Jesus would not entrust himself to them, for he knew all men. ²⁵He did not need man's testimony about man, for he knew what was in a man.

ᵃ 50 Or *Do you believe . . . ?*   *ᵇ 51* The Greek is plural.   *ᶜ 6* Greek *two to three metretes* (probably about 75 to 115 liters)   *ᵈ 17* Psalm 69:9   *ᵉ 23* Or *and believed in him*

Jesus Teaches Nicodemus

3 Now there was a man of the Pharisees named Nicodemus, a member of the Jewish ruling council. ²He came to Jesus at night and said, "Rabbi, we know you are a teacher who has come from God. For no one could perform the miraculous signs you are doing if God were not with him."

³In reply Jesus declared, "I tell you the truth, no one can see the kingdom of God unless he is born again.ᵃ"

⁴"How can a man be born when he is old?" Nicodemus asked. "Surely he cannot enter a second time into his mother's womb to be born!"

⁵Jesus answered, "I tell you the truth, no one can enter the kingdom of God unless he is born of water and the Spirit. ⁶Flesh gives birth to flesh, but the Spiritᵇ gives birth to spirit. ⁷You should not be surprised at my saying, 'Youᶜ must be born again.' ⁸The wind blows wherever it pleases. You hear its sound, but you cannot tell where it comes from or where it is going. So it is with everyone born of the Spirit."

⁹"How can this be?" Nicodemus asked.

¹⁰"You are Israel's teacher," said Jesus, "and do you not understand these things? ¹¹I tell you the truth, we speak of what we know, and we testify to what we have seen, but still you people do not accept our testimony. ¹²I have spoken to you of earthly things and you do not believe; how then will you believe if I speak of heavenly things? ¹³No one has ever gone into heaven except the one who came from heaven—the Son of Man.ᵈ ¹⁴Just as Moses lifted up the snake in the desert, so the Son of Man must be lifted up, ¹⁵that everyone who believes in him may have eternal life.ᵉ

¹⁶"For God so loved the world that he gave his one and only Son,ᶠ that whoever believes in him shall not perish but have eternal life. ¹⁷For God did not send his Son

love notes

3:16

Loved one,

Because of my great love for you, I planned from the beginning to give you the best, most wonderful gift imaginable—no matter the cost. So I sent you my Son, who lovingly and willingly died for you so that you might live.

—God

Reflect on this familiar verse and what it means that Jesus died for *you*.

truth or dare

Ever heard the phrase "born again"? It means a *spiritual* rebirth. You can't get into heaven just by living a good life. You have to be spiritually reborn through faith in Christ.

3:3

ᵃ 3 Or *born from above*; also in verse 7   ᵇ 6 Or *but spirit*   ᶜ 7 The Greek is plural.   ᵈ 13 Some manuscripts *Man, who is in heaven*
ᵉ 15 Or *believes may have eternal life in him*
ᶠ 16 Or *his only begotten Son*

john 3:17

» 1413

into the world to condemn the world, but to save the world through him. [18]Whoever believes in him is not condemned, but whoever does not believe stands condemned already because he has not believed in the name of God's one and only Son.[a] [19]This is the verdict: Light has come into the world, but men loved darkness instead of light because their deeds were evil. [20]Everyone who does evil hates the light, and will not come into the light for fear that his deeds will be exposed. [21]But whoever lives by the truth comes into the light, so that it may be seen plainly that what he has done has been done through God."[b]

John the Baptist's Testimony About Jesus

[22]After this, Jesus and his disciples went out into the Judean countryside, where he spent some time with them, and baptized. [23]Now John also was baptizing at Aenon near Salim, because there was plenty of water, and people were constantly coming to be baptized. [24](This was before John was put in prison.) [25]An argument developed between some of John's disciples and a certain Jew[c] over the matter of ceremonial washing. [26]They came to John and said to him, "Rabbi, that man who was with you on the other side of the Jordan—the one you testified about—well, he is baptizing, and everyone is going to him."

[27]To this John replied, "A man can receive only what is given him from heaven. [28]You yourselves can testify that I said, 'I am not the Christ[d] but am sent ahead of him.' [29]The bride belongs to the bridegroom. The friend who attends the bridegroom waits and listens for him, and is full of joy when he hears the bridegroom's voice. That joy is mine, and it is now complete. [30]He must become greater; I must become less.

[31]"The one who comes from above is above all; the one who is from the earth belongs to the earth, and speaks as one from the earth. The one who comes from heaven is above all. [32]He testifies to what he has seen and heard, but no one accepts his testimony. [33]The man who has accepted it has certified that God is truthful. [34]For the one whom God has sent speaks the words of God, for God[e] gives the Spirit without limit. [35]The Father loves the Son and has placed everything in his hands. [36]Whoever believes in the Son has eternal life, but whoever rejects the Son will not see life, for God's wrath remains on him."[f]

Jesus Talks With a Samaritan Woman

4 The Pharisees heard that Jesus was gaining and baptizing more disciples than John, [2]although in fact it was not Jesus who baptized, but his disciples. [3]When the Lord learned of this, he left Judea and went back once more to Galilee.

[4]Now he had to go through Samaria. [5]So he came to a town in Samaria called Sychar, near the plot of ground Jacob had given to his son Joseph. [6]Jacob's well was there, and Jesus, tired as he was from the journey, sat down by the well. It was about the sixth hour.

[7]When a Samaritan woman came to draw water, Jesus said to her, "Will you give me a drink?" [8](His disciples had gone into the town to buy food.)

[9]The Samaritan woman said to him, "You are a Jew and I am a Samaritan woman. How can you ask me for a drink?" (For Jews do not associate with Samaritans.[g])

[10]Jesus answered her, "If you knew the gift of God and who it is that asks you for a drink, you would have asked him and he would have given you living water."

[11]"Sir," the woman said, "you have nothing to draw with and the well is deep. Where can you get this living water? [12]Are you greater than our father Jacob, who gave us the well and drank from it himself, as did also his sons and his flocks and herds?"

[13]Jesus answered, "Everyone who drinks this water will be thirsty again, [14]but whoever drinks the water I give him will never thirst. Indeed, the water I give him will become in him a spring of water welling up to eternal life."

[15]The woman said to him, "Sir, give me this water so that I won't get thirsty and have to keep coming here to draw water."

[16]He told her, "Go, call your husband and come back."

[17]"I have no husband," she replied.

---

[a] 18 Or *God's only begotten Son* [b] 21 Some interpreters end the quotation after verse 15. [c] 25 Some manuscripts *and certain Jews* [d] 28 Or *Messiah* [e] 34 Greek *he* [f] 36 Some interpreters end the quotation after verse 30. [g] 9 Or *do not use dishes Samaritans have used*

mirror images

Jesus answered her, "If you knew the gift of God and who it is that asks you for a drink, you would have asked him and he would have given you living water." John 4:10

The Samaritan Woman—Plenty Thirsty

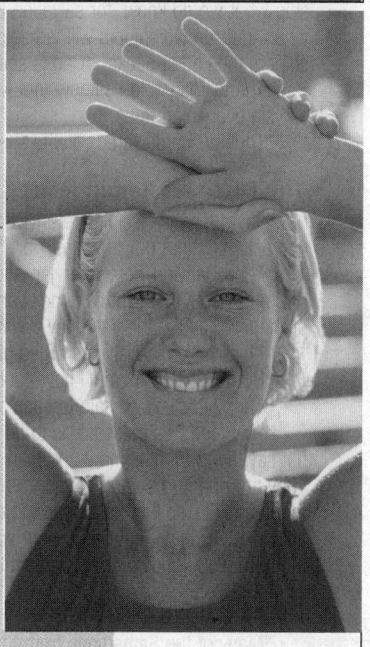

Aaaaaahhh. Go all day without a drink of water, and you'll be amazed at how refreshing the wet stuff can be. Since our bodies crave water so often, wouldn't it be great if we could find some that satisfies our thirst forever?

The Samaritan woman was also looking for the ultimate thirst quencher. Carrying her water pot to the town well, she was surprised when a Jewish man at the water hole called out to her. *Doesn't he know that Jews don't talk to Samaritans?* she thought.

When Jesus asked for a drink, the woman resisted—until he offered her living water. Jesus skipped the small talk and cut straight to the heart of the matter—to her heart and her past, a string of broken marriages and unhappiness. Amazed at this man's insight, she began to realize just how thirsty her soul was. Could this living water really quench the deepest, unfulfilled desires of her heart? Could this man's promises be true? And could he really be who he said he was—the Messiah?

Quickly she dropped her water pot and ran into town. Instead of carrying her filled water pot as usual, this time she carried living water, the good news of the Savior, to her fellow Samaritans. "Come, see a man who told me everything I ever did. Could this be the Christ?" When Jesus chose to reveal his identity to a group of Samaritans, he selected an unlikely candidate to bear the news. He chose the thirstiest girl in town.

Imagine Jesus today, sitting by a drinking fountain. "What are you really thirsty for?" he asks. No matter where you've tried to satisfy your desires in the past, his living water is the only thing that can quench your spiritual thirst. Ask him to turn your struggles with sin into moments that make you thirstier for him.

To read the next Mirror Images profile, go to page 1453.

Dear Jesus, sometimes I forget that your living water satisfies, and I turn to other things to quench the thirst inside of me. Please help me to turn only to you to quench my thirst. Amen.

dear Jesus

» Read more about the Samaritan woman in John 4:1–42 (pages 1414–1416).

Jesus said to her, "You are right when you say you have no husband. ¹⁸The fact is, you have had five husbands, and the man you now have is not your husband. What you have just said is quite true."

¹⁹"Sir," the woman said, "I can see that you are a prophet. ²⁰Our fathers worshiped on this mountain, but you Jews claim that the place where we must worship is in Jerusalem."

²¹Jesus declared, "Believe me, woman, a time is coming when you will worship the Father neither on this mountain nor in Jerusalem. ²²You Samaritans worship what you do not know; we worship what we do know, for salvation is from the Jews. ²³Yet a time is coming and has now come when the true worshipers will worship the Father in spirit and truth, for they are the kind of worshipers the Father seeks. ²⁴God is spirit, and his worshipers must worship in spirit and in truth."

²⁵The woman said, "I know that Messiah" (called Christ) "is coming. When he comes, he will explain everything to us."

²⁶Then Jesus declared, "I who speak to you am he."

The Disciples Rejoin Jesus

²⁷Just then his disciples returned and were surprised to find him talking with a woman. But no one asked, "What do you want?" or "Why are you talking with her?"

²⁸Then, leaving her water jar, the woman went back to the town and said to the people, ²⁹"Come, see a man who told me everything I ever did. Could this be the Christ*?" ³⁰They came out of the town and made their way toward him.

³¹Meanwhile his disciples urged him, "Rabbi, eat something."

³²But he said to them, "I have food to eat that you know nothing about."

³³Then his disciples said to each other, "Could someone have brought him food?"

³⁴"My food," said Jesus, "is to do the will of him who sent me and to finish his work. ³⁵Do you not say, 'Four months more and then the harvest'? I tell you, open your eyes and look at the fields! They are ripe for harvest. ³⁶Even now the reaper draws his wages, even now he harvests the crop for eternal life, so that the sower and the reaper may be glad together. ³⁷Thus the saying 'One sows and another reaps' is true. ³⁸I sent you to reap what you have not worked for. Others have done the hard work, and you have reaped the benefits of their labor."

Many Samaritans Believe

³⁹Many of the Samaritans from that town believed in him because of the woman's testimony, "He told me everything I ever did." ⁴⁰So when the Samaritans came to him, they urged him to stay with them, and he stayed two days. ⁴¹And because of his words many more became believers.

⁴²They said to the woman, "We no longer believe just because of what you said; now we have heard for ourselves, and we know that this man really is the Savior of the world."

Jesus Heals the Official's Son

⁴³After the two days he left for Galilee. ⁴⁴(Now Jesus himself had pointed out that a prophet has no honor in his own country.) ⁴⁵When he arrived in Galilee, the Galileans welcomed him. They had seen all that he had done in Jerusalem at the Passover Feast, for they also had been there.

⁴⁶Once more he visited Cana in Galilee, where he had turned the water into wine. And there was a certain royal official whose son lay sick at Capernaum. ⁴⁷When this man heard that Jesus had arrived in Galilee from Judea, he went to him and begged him to come and heal his son, who was close to death.

⁴⁸"Unless you people see miraculous signs and wonders," Jesus told him, "you will never believe."

⁴⁹The royal official said, "Sir, come down before my child dies."

⁵⁰Jesus replied, "You may go. Your son will live."

The man took Jesus at his word and departed. ⁵¹While he was still on the way, his servants met him with the news that his boy was living. ⁵²When he inquired as to the time when his son got better, they said to him, "The fever left him yesterday at the seventh hour."

⁵³Then the father realized that this was the exact time at which Jesus had said to him, "Your son will live." So he and all his household believed.

⁵⁴This was the second miraculous sign that Jesus performed, having come from Judea to Galilee.

a 29 Or *Messiah*

The Healing at the Pool

5 Some time later, Jesus went up to Jerusalem for a feast of the Jews. [2]Now there is in Jerusalem near the Sheep Gate a pool, which in Aramaic is called Bethesda[a] and which is surrounded by five covered colonnades. [3]Here a great number of disabled people used to lie—the blind, the lame, the paralyzed.[b] [5]One who was there had been an invalid for thirty-eight years. [6]When Jesus saw him lying there and learned that he had been in this condition for a long time, he asked him, "Do you want to get well?"

[7]"Sir," the invalid replied, "I have no one to help me into the pool when the water is stirred. While I am trying to get in, someone else goes down ahead of me."

[8]Then Jesus said to him, "Get up! Pick up your mat and walk." [9]At once the man was cured; he picked up his mat and walked.

The day on which this took place was a Sabbath, [10]and so the Jews said to the man who had been healed, "It is the Sabbath; the law forbids you to carry your mat."

[11]But he replied, "The man who made me well said to me, 'Pick up your mat and walk.' "

[12]So they asked him, "Who is this fellow who told you to pick it up and walk?"

[13]The man who was healed had no idea who it was, for Jesus had slipped away into the crowd that was there.

[14]Later Jesus found him at the temple and said to him, "See, you are well again. Stop sinning or something worse may happen to you." [15]The man went away and told the Jews that it was Jesus who had made him well.

Life Through the Son

[16]So, because Jesus was doing these things on the Sabbath, the Jews persecuted him. [17]Jesus said to them, "My Father is always at his work to this very day, and I, too, am working." [18]For this reason the Jews tried all the harder to kill him; not only was he breaking the Sabbath, but he was even calling God his own Father, making himself equal with God.

[19]Jesus gave them this answer: "I tell you the truth, the Son can do nothing by himself; he can do only what he sees his Father doing, because whatever the Father does the Son also does. [20]For the Father loves the Son and shows him all he does. Yes, to your amazement he will show him even greater things than these. [21]For just as the Father raises the dead and gives them life, even so the Son gives life to whom he is pleased to give it. [22]Moreover, the Father judges no one, but has entrusted all judgment to the Son, [23]that all may honor the Son just as they honor the Father. He who does not honor the Son does not honor the Father, who sent him.

[24]"I tell you the truth, whoever hears my word and believes him who sent me has eternal life and will not be condemned; he has crossed over from death to life. [25]I tell you the truth, a time is coming and has now come when the dead will hear the voice of the Son of God and those who hear will live. [26]For as the Father has life in himself, so he has granted the Son to have life in himself. [27]And he has given him authority to judge because he is the Son of Man.

[28]"Do not be amazed at this, for a time is coming when all who are in their graves will hear his voice [29]and come out—those who have done good will rise to live, and those who have done evil will rise to be condemned. [30]By myself I can do nothing; I judge only as I hear, and my judgment is just, for I seek not to please myself but him who sent me.

Testimonies About Jesus

[31]"If I testify about myself, my testimony is not valid. [32]There is another who testifies in my favor, and I know that his testimony about me is valid.

[33]"You have sent to John and he has testified to the truth. [34]Not that I accept human testimony; but I mention it that you may be saved. [35]John was a lamp that burned and gave light, and you chose for a time to enjoy his light.

[36]"I have testimony weightier than that of John. For the very work that the Father has given me to finish, and which I am doing, testifies that the Father has sent me. [37]And the Father who sent me has himself testified concerning me. You have never heard his voice nor seen his form, [38]nor

---

a 2 Some manuscripts *Bethzatha*; other manuscripts *Bethsaida*   b 3 Some less important manuscripts *paralyzed—and they waited for the moving of the waters. 4From time to time an angel of the Lord would come down and stir up the waters. The first one into the pool after each such disturbance would be cured of whatever disease he had.*

does his word dwell in you, for you do not believe the one he sent. ³⁹You diligently study*ᵃ* the Scriptures because you think that by them you possess eternal life. These are the Scriptures that testify about me, ⁴⁰yet you refuse to come to me to have life.

⁴¹"I do not accept praise from men, ⁴²but I know you. I know that you do not have the love of God in your hearts. ⁴³I have come in my Father's name, and you do not accept me; but if someone else comes in his own name, you will accept him. ⁴⁴How can you believe if you accept praise from one another, yet make no effort to obtain the praise that comes from the only God*ᵇ*?

⁴⁵"But do not think I will accuse you before the Father. Your accuser is Moses, on whom your hopes are set. ⁴⁶If you believed Moses, you would believe me, for he wrote about me. ⁴⁷But since you do not believe what he wrote, how are you going to believe what I say?"

Jesus Feeds the Five Thousand

6 Some time after this, Jesus crossed to the far shore of the Sea of Galilee (that is, the Sea of Tiberias), ²and a great crowd of people followed him because they saw the miraculous signs he had performed on the sick. ³Then Jesus went up on a mountainside and sat down with his disciples. ⁴The Jewish Passover Feast was near.

⁵When Jesus looked up and saw a great crowd coming toward him, he said to Philip, "Where shall we buy bread for these people to eat?" ⁶He asked this only to test him, for he already had in mind what he was going to do.

⁷Philip answered him, "Eight months' wages*ᶜ* would not buy enough bread for each one to have a bite!"

⁸Another of his disciples, Andrew, Simon Peter's brother, spoke up, ⁹"Here is a boy with five small barley loaves and two small fish, but how far will they go among so many?"

¹⁰Jesus said, "Have the people sit down." There was plenty of grass in that place, and the men sat down, about five thousand of them. ¹¹Jesus then took the loaves, gave thanks, and distributed to those who were seated as much as they wanted. He did the same with the fish.

¹²When they had all had enough to eat, he said to his disciples, "Gather the pieces that are left over. Let nothing be wasted." ¹³So they gathered them and filled twelve baskets with the pieces of the five barley loaves left over by those who had eaten.

¹⁴After the people saw the miraculous sign that Jesus did, they began to say, "Surely this is the Prophet who is to come into the world." ¹⁵Jesus, knowing that they intended to come and make him king by force, withdrew again to a mountain by himself.

Jesus Walks on the Water

¹⁶When evening came, his disciples went down to the lake, ¹⁷where they got into a boat and set off across the lake for Capernaum. By now it was dark, and Jesus had not yet joined them. ¹⁸A strong wind was blowing and the waters grew rough. ¹⁹When they had rowed three or three and a half miles,*ᵈ* they saw Jesus approaching the boat, walking on the water; and they were terrified. ²⁰But he said to them, "It is I; don't be afraid." ²¹Then they were willing to take him into the boat, and immediately the boat reached the shore where they were heading.

genuine faith »» 6:5-13

Ever feel like you don't have much to offer God? Maybe you're not especially smart, or strong, or outgoing or talented—certainly not the kind of person who does great things for God. But you'd be surprised. Just look at what God did with one boy's lunch. He multiplied those loaves and fish until they fed thousands of people—with leftovers! That's God's way. He loves to take the little we bring and work miracles. So don't hold back because you feel like you don't have much to give. Offer what you have, and watch how God multiplies it.

ᵃ 39 Or *Study diligently* (the imperative)   *ᵇ 44* Some early manuscripts *the Only One*   *ᶜ 7* Greek *two hundred denarii*
ᵈ 19 Greek *rowed twenty-five or thirty stadia* (about 5 or 6 kilometers)

[22]The next day the crowd that had stayed on the opposite shore of the lake realized that only one boat had been there, and that Jesus had not entered it with his disciples, but that they had gone away alone. [23]Then some boats from Tiberias landed near the place where the people had eaten the bread after the Lord had given thanks. [24]Once the crowd realized that neither Jesus nor his disciples were there, they got into the boats and went to Capernaum in search of Jesus.

Jesus the Bread of Life

[25]When they found him on the other side of the lake, they asked him, "Rabbi, when did you get here?"

[26]Jesus answered, "I tell you the truth, you are looking for me, not because you saw miraculous signs but because you ate the loaves and had your fill. [27]Do not work for food that spoils, but for food that endures to eternal life, which the Son of Man will give you. On him God the Father has placed his seal of approval."

[28]Then they asked him, "What must we do to do the works God requires?"

[29]Jesus answered, "The work of God is this: to believe in the one he has sent."

[30]So they asked him, "What miraculous sign then will you give that we may see it and believe you? What will you do? [31]Our forefathers ate the manna in the desert; as it is written: 'He gave them bread from heaven to eat.'[a]"

[32]Jesus said to them, "I tell you the truth, it is not Moses who has given you the bread from heaven, but it is my Father who gives you the true bread from heaven. [33]For the bread of God is he who comes down from heaven and gives life to the world."

[34]"Sir," they said, "from now on give us this bread."

[35]Then Jesus declared, "I am the bread of life. He who comes to me will never go hungry, and he who believes in me will never be thirsty. [36]But as I told you, you have seen me and still you do not believe. [37]All that the Father gives me will come to me, and whoever comes to me I will never drive away. [38]For I have come down from heaven not to do my will but to do the will of him who sent me. [39]And this is the will of him who sent me, that I shall lose none of all that he has given me, but raise them up at the last day. [40]For my Father's will is that everyone who looks to the Son and believes in him shall have eternal life, and I will raise him up at the last day."

truth or dare

Eating is a big part of life. You *have* to eat for your body to survive. Jesus is food for your spirit. If you don't have him, you're spiritually starving.

6:35

[41]At this the Jews began to grumble about him because he said, "I am the bread that came down from heaven." [42]They said, "Is this not Jesus, the son of Joseph, whose father and mother we know? How can he now say, 'I came down from heaven'?"

[43]"Stop grumbling among yourselves," Jesus answered. [44]"No one can come to me unless the Father who sent me draws him, and I will raise him up at the last day. [45]It is written in the Prophets: 'They will all be taught by God.'[b] Everyone who listens to the Father and learns from him comes to me. [46]No one has seen the Father except the one who is from God; only he has seen the Father. [47]I tell you the truth, he who believes has everlasting life. [48]I am the bread of life. [49]Your forefathers ate the manna in the desert, yet they died. [50]But here is the bread that comes down from heaven, which a man may eat and not die. [51]I am the living bread that came down from heaven. If anyone eats of this bread, he will live forever. This bread is my flesh, which I will give for the life of the world."

[52]Then the Jews began to argue sharply among themselves, "How can this man give us his flesh to eat?"

[53]Jesus said to them, "I tell you the truth, unless you eat the flesh of the Son of Man and drink his blood, you have no life in you. [54]Whoever eats my flesh and drinks my blood has eternal life, and I will raise him up at the last day. [55]For my flesh is real food and my blood is real drink. [56]Whoever eats my flesh and drinks my blood remains in me, and I in him. [57]Just as the living Father sent me and I live because of the Father, so the one who feeds on me will live because of me. [58]This is

a 31 Exodus 16:4; Neh. 9:15; Psalm 78:24,25   *b 45* Isaiah 54:13

the bread that came down from heaven. Your forefathers ate manna and died, but he who feeds on this bread will live forever." ⁵⁹He said this while teaching in the synagogue in Capernaum.

Many Disciples Desert Jesus

⁶⁰On hearing it, many of his disciples said, "This is a hard teaching. Who can accept it?"

⁶¹Aware that his disciples were grumbling about this, Jesus said to them, "Does this offend you? ⁶²What if you see the Son of Man ascend to where he was before! ⁶³The Spirit gives life; the flesh counts for nothing. The words I have spoken to you are spirit^a and they are life. ⁶⁴Yet there are some of you who do not believe." For Jesus had known from the beginning which of them did not believe and who would betray him. ⁶⁵He went on to say, "This is why I told you that no one can come to me unless the Father has enabled him."

⁶⁶From this time many of his disciples turned back and no longer followed him.

⁶⁷"You do not want to leave too, do you?" Jesus asked the Twelve.

⁶⁸Simon Peter answered him, "Lord, to whom shall we go? You have the words of eternal life. ⁶⁹We believe and know that you are the Holy One of God."

⁷⁰Then Jesus replied, "Have I not chosen you, the Twelve? Yet one of you is a devil!" ⁷¹(He meant Judas, the son of Simon Iscariot, who, though one of the Twelve, was later to betray him.)

genuine life » 6:66-69

You can look for it in friends. You can look for it in family. You can look for it in money, clothes and nice things. You can look for it in beauty and in having others admire you. You can look for it in the success of being the best. You can look for it in sex, drinking and drugs. You can look for a purpose in life that goes beyond today and reaches into the future and only find it in one place: Jesus. He alone has the words of eternal life. Look for it in him.

Jesus Goes to the Feast of Tabernacles

7 After this, Jesus went around in Galilee, purposely staying away from Judea because the Jews there were waiting to take his life. ²But when the Jewish Feast of Tabernacles was near, ³Jesus' brothers said to him, "You ought to leave here and go to Judea, so that your disciples may see the miracles you do. ⁴No one who wants to become a public figure acts in secret. Since you are doing these things, show yourself to the world." ⁵For even his own brothers did not believe in him.

⁶Therefore Jesus told them, "The right time for me has not yet come; for you any time is right. ⁷The world cannot hate you, but it hates me because I testify that what it does is evil. ⁸You go to the Feast. I am not yet^b going up to this Feast, because for me the right time has not yet come." ⁹Having said this, he stayed in Galilee.

¹⁰However, after his brothers had left for the Feast, he went also, not publicly, but in secret. ¹¹Now at the Feast the Jews were watching for him and asking, "Where is that man?"

¹²Among the crowds there was widespread whispering about him. Some said, "He is a good man."

Others replied, "No, he deceives the people." ¹³But no one would say anything publicly about him for fear of the Jews.

Jesus Teaches at the Feast

¹⁴Not until halfway through the Feast did Jesus go up to the temple courts and begin to teach. ¹⁵The Jews were amazed and asked, "How did this man get such learning without having studied?"

¹⁶Jesus answered, "My teaching is not my own. It comes from him who sent me. ¹⁷If anyone

^a 63 Or Spirit   ^b 8 Some early manuscripts do not have yet.

A Major Loss

My name is Avery, and I'm no longer a virgin. I'm not trying to sound like one of those support group people. I'm trying to admit to something I've felt awful about for a while.

Last year, when I was fifteen, I slept with my boyfriend Scott. That was the biggest mistake of my life. I was just living for the moment then. I didn't even think about the fact that I might later regret losing my virginity. I thought I loved Scott and that we'd be together forever—like in fairy tales. "Forever" lasted about six months.

Now all I feel is regret—regret that I'm no longer a virgin and regret for what I did to my relationship with God. When I was with Scott, I wasn't into church much, even though I believed in God. But after we broke up, I guess God finally got my full attention. My heart was so broken. I started going to my aunt's church and got involved in the youth group. I learned that God's the only one who will really love me forever.

But even though I'm back with God, I still wonder if he could ever forgive me for what I did. Did I totally blow it forever? Could I ever get back what I gave away?

You know how people say, "If I could do it all over again, I'd do things differently"? That's how I feel.

For more information, check out the Loss of Virginity Link on www.TrueImagesBible.com

loss of virginity in focus

You've probably heard the statistics about teens and sex. "Who's doing it" isn't the issue here. The real issue is this: Can someone who was once a virgin ever experience sexual purity again?

»Maybe you or someone you know has asked this question. The answer is *yes*. Regaining sexual purity starts with the knowledge that you've been forgiven. God can make you clean and new inside (see Isaiah 1:18, page 882). But, as Jesus once reminded a woman he rescued from a stoning, you are forgiven so you can leave that life behind (see John 8:11, page 1423).

»You can't change the past, but guilt doesn't have to be part of your future. Have you asked for forgiveness? Then accept it and walk in freedom.

»Shame is one of Satan's best tools. If he can convince us we are terrible, then we think, "why change? I'm a lost cause." But Jesus sets us free from shame. Talk to him!

For more on this topic, see the index on page 1656.

chooses to do God's will, he will find out whether my teaching comes from God or whether I speak on my own. [18]He who speaks on his own does so to gain honor for himself, but he who works for the honor of the one who sent him is a man of truth; there is nothing false about him. [19]Has not Moses given you the law? Yet not one of you keeps the law. Why are you trying to kill me?"

[20]"You are demon-possessed," the crowd answered. "Who is trying to kill you?"

[21]Jesus said to them, "I did one miracle, and you are all astonished. [22]Yet, because Moses gave you circumcision (though actually it did not come from Moses, but from the patriarchs), you circumcise a child on the Sabbath. [23]Now if a child can be circumcised on the Sabbath so that the law of Moses may not be broken, why are you angry with me for healing the whole man on the Sabbath? [24]Stop judging by mere appearances, and make a right judgment."

Is Jesus the Christ?

[25]At that point some of the people of Jerusalem began to ask, "Isn't this the man they are trying to kill? [26]Here he is, speaking publicly, and they are not saying a word to him. Have the authorities really concluded that he is the Christ[a]? [27]But we know where this man is from; when the Christ comes, no one will know where he is from."

[28]Then Jesus, still teaching in the temple courts, cried out, "Yes, you know me, and you know where I am from. I am not here on my own, but he who sent me is true. You do not know him, [29]but I know him because I am from him and he sent me."

[30]At this they tried to seize him, but no one laid a hand on him, because his time had not yet come. [31]Still, many in the crowd put their faith in him. They said, "When the Christ comes, will he do more miraculous signs than this man?"

[32]The Pharisees heard the crowd whispering such things about him. Then the chief priests and the Pharisees sent temple guards to arrest him.

[33]Jesus said, "I am with you for only a short time, and then I go to the one who sent me. [34]You will look for me, but you will not find me; and where I am, you cannot come."

[35]The Jews said to one another, "Where does this man intend to go that we cannot find him? Will he go where our people live scattered among the Greeks, and teach the Greeks? [36]What did he mean when he said, 'You will look for me, but you will not find me,' and 'Where I am, you cannot come'?"

[37]On the last and greatest day of the Feast, Jesus stood and said in a loud voice, "If anyone is thirsty, let him come to me and drink. [38]Whoever believes in me, as[b] the Scripture has said, streams of living water will flow from within him." [39]By this he meant the Spirit, whom those who believed in him were later to receive. Up to that time the Spirit had not been given, since Jesus had not yet been glorified.

[40]On hearing his words, some of the people said, "Surely this man is the Prophet."

[41]Others said, "He is the Christ."

Still others asked, "How can the Christ come from Galilee? [42]Does not the Scripture say that the Christ will come from David's family[c] and from Bethlehem, the town where David lived?" [43]Thus the people were divided because of Jesus. [44]Some wanted to seize him, but no one laid a hand on him.

Unbelief of the Jewish Leaders

[45]Finally the temple guards went back to the chief priests and Pharisees, who asked them, "Why didn't you bring him in?"

[46]"No one ever spoke the way this man does," the guards declared.

[47]"You mean he has deceived you also?" the Pharisees retorted. [48]"Has any of the rulers or of the Pharisees believed in him? [49]No! But this mob that knows nothing of the law—there is a curse on them."

[50]Nicodemus, who had gone to Jesus earlier and who was one of their own number, asked, [51]"Does our law condemn anyone without first hearing him to find out what he is doing?"

[52]They replied, "Are you from Galilee, too? Look into it, and you will find that a prophet[d] does not come out of Galilee."

[The earliest manuscripts and many other ancient witnesses do not have John 7:53–8:11.]

[53]Then each went to his own home.

8 But Jesus went to the Mount of Olives. [2]At dawn he appeared again in the temple courts, where all the people gathered around him, and he sat down to teach them. [3]The teachers of the law and the Pharisees brought in a woman caught in adultery. They made her stand before the group [4]and said to Jesus, "Teacher, this woman was caught in the act of adultery. [5]In the Law Moses commanded us to stone such women. Now what do you say?" [6]They were using this question as a trap, in order to have a basis for accusing him.

a 26 Or *Messiah*; also in verses 27, 31, 41 and 42   *b 37,38* Or / *If anyone is thirsty, let him come to me. / And let him drink, 38who believes in me. / As*   *c 42* Greek *seed*   *d 52* Two early manuscripts *the Prophet*

But Jesus bent down and started to write on the ground with his finger. ⁷When they kept on questioning him, he straightened up and said to them, "If any one of you is without sin, let him be the first to throw a stone at her." ⁸Again he stooped down and wrote on the ground.

⁹At this, those who heard began to go away one at a time, the older ones first, until only Jesus was left, with the woman still standing there. ¹⁰Jesus straightened up and asked her, "Woman, where are they? Has no one condemned you?"

¹¹"No one, sir," she said.

"Then neither do I condemn you," Jesus declared. "Go now and leave your life of sin."

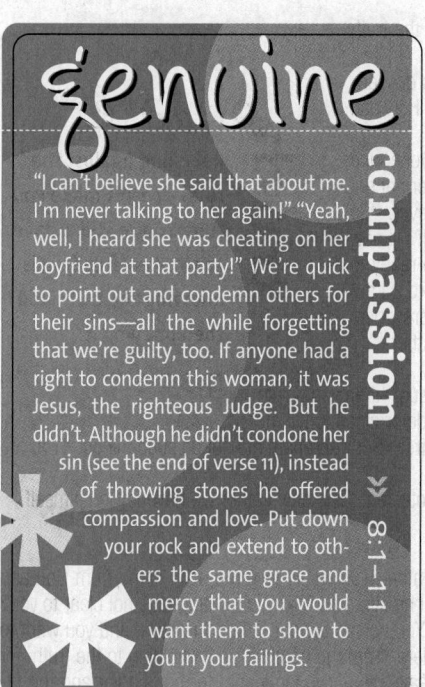

genuine

compassion

"I can't believe she said that about me. I'm never talking to her again!" "Yeah, well, I heard she was cheating on her boyfriend at that party!" We're quick to point out and condemn others for their sins—all the while forgetting that we're guilty, too. If anyone had a right to condemn this woman, it was Jesus, the righteous Judge. But he didn't. Although he didn't condone her sin (see the end of verse 11), instead of throwing stones he offered compassion and love. Put down your rock and extend to others the same grace and mercy that you would want them to show to you in your failings.

8:1-11

The Validity of Jesus' Testimony

¹²When Jesus spoke again to the people, he said, "I am the light of the world. Whoever follows me will never walk in darkness, but will have the light of life."

¹³The Pharisees challenged him, "Here you are, appearing as your own witness; your testimony is not valid."

¹⁴Jesus answered, "Even if I testify on my own behalf, my testimony is valid, for I know where I came from and where I am going. But you have no idea where I come from or where I am going. ¹⁵You judge by human standards; I pass judgment on no one. ¹⁶But if I do judge, my decisions are right, because I am not alone. I stand with the Father, who sent me. ¹⁷In your own Law it is written that the testimony of two men is valid. ¹⁸I am one who testifies for myself; my other witness is the Father, who sent me."

¹⁹Then they asked him, "Where is your father?"

"You do not know me or my Father," Jesus replied. "If you knew me, you would know my Father also." ²⁰He spoke these words while teaching in the temple area near the place where the offerings were put. Yet no one seized him, because his time had not yet come.

²¹Once more Jesus said to them, "I am going away, and you will look for me, and you will die in your sin. Where I go, you cannot come."

²²This made the Jews ask, "Will he kill himself? Is that why he says, 'Where I go, you cannot come'?"

²³But he continued, "You are from below; I am from above. You are of this world; I am not of this world. ²⁴I told you that you would die in your sins; if you do not believe that I am ˌthe one I claim to beˌ,ᵃ you will indeed die in your sins."

²⁵"Who are you?" they asked.

"Just what I have been claiming all along," Jesus replied. ²⁶"I have much to say in judgment of you. But he who sent me is reliable, and what I have heard from him I tell the world."

²⁷They did not understand that he was telling them about his Father. ²⁸So Jesus said, "When you have lifted up the Son of Man, then you will know that I am ˌthe one I claim to beˌ and that I do nothing on my own but speak just what the Father has taught me. ²⁹The one who sent me is with me; he has not left me alone, for I always do what pleases him." ³⁰Even as he spoke, many put their faith in him.

The Children of Abraham

³¹To the Jews who had believed him, Jesus said, "If you hold to my teaching, you are really my

ᵃ 24 Or I am he; also in verse 28

disciples. ³²Then you will know the truth, and the truth will set you free."

³³They answered him, "We are Abraham's descendants[a] and have never been slaves of anyone. How can you say that we shall be set free?"

³⁴Jesus replied, "I tell you the truth, everyone who sins is a slave to sin. ³⁵Now a slave has no permanent place in the family, but a son belongs to it forever. ³⁶So if the Son sets you free, you will be free indeed. ³⁷I know you are Abraham's descendants. Yet you are ready to kill me, because you have no room for my word. ³⁸I am telling you what I have seen in the Father's presence, and you do what you have heard from your father.[b]"

³⁹"Abraham is our father," they answered.

"If you were Abraham's children," said Jesus, "then you would[c] do the things Abraham did. ⁴⁰As it is, you are determined to kill me, a man who has told you the truth that I heard from God. Abraham did not do such things. ⁴¹You are doing the things your own father does."

"We are not illegitimate children," they protested. "The only Father we have is God himself."

truth or dare

Rebelling against the rules doesn't make you free. You're still a slave to sin. *Real* freedom is knowing the truth and then obeying it.

8:31–36

The Children of the Devil

⁴²Jesus said to them, "If God were your Father, you would love me, for I came from God and now am here. I have not come on my own; but he sent me. ⁴³Why is my language not clear to you? Because you are unable to hear what I say. ⁴⁴You belong to your father, the devil, and you want to carry out your father's desire. He was a murderer from the beginning, not holding to the truth, for there is no truth in him. When he lies, he speaks his native language, for he is a liar and the father of lies. ⁴⁵Yet because I tell the truth, you do not believe me! ⁴⁶Can any of you prove me guilty of sin? If I am telling the truth, why don't you believe me? ⁴⁷He who belongs to God hears what God says. The reason you do not hear is that you do not belong to God."

The Claims of Jesus About Himself

⁴⁸The Jews answered him, "Aren't we right in saying that you are a Samaritan and demon-possessed?"

⁴⁹"I am not possessed by a demon," said Jesus, "but I honor my Father and you dishonor me. ⁵⁰I am not seeking glory for myself; but there is one who seeks it, and he is the judge. ⁵¹I tell you the truth, if anyone keeps my word, he will never see death."

⁵²At this the Jews exclaimed, "Now we know that you are demon-possessed! Abraham died and so did the prophets, yet you say that if anyone keeps your word, he will never taste death. ⁵³Are you greater than our father Abraham? He died, and so did the prophets. Who do you think you are?"

⁵⁴Jesus replied, "If I glorify myself, my glory means nothing. My Father, whom you claim as your God, is the one who glorifies me. ⁵⁵Though you do not know him, I know him. If I said I did not, I would be a liar like you, but I do know him and keep his word. ⁵⁶Your father Abraham rejoiced at the thought of seeing my day; he saw it and was glad."

truth or dare

When Jesus said, "I am," he was intentionally calling himself God (see Exodus 3:14). Don't let anyone tell you that Jesus was just a prophet or a good teacher. He is God.

8:58

⁵⁷"You are not yet fifty years old," the Jews said to him, "and you have seen Abraham!"

⁵⁸"I tell you the truth," Jesus answered, "before Abraham was born, I am!" ⁵⁹At this, they picked up stones to stone him, but Jesus hid himself, slipping away from the temple grounds.

a 33 Greek seed; also in verse 37   *b 38 Or presence. Therefore do what you have heard from the Father.*
c 39 Some early manuscripts "If you are Abraham's children," said Jesus, "then

Jesus Heals a Man Born Blind

9 As he went along, he saw a man blind from birth. [2]His disciples asked him, "Rabbi, who sinned, this man or his parents, that he was born blind?"

[3]"Neither this man nor his parents sinned," said Jesus, "but this happened so that the work of God might be displayed in his life. [4]As long as it is day, we must do the work of him who sent me. Night is coming, when no one can work. [5]While I am in the world, I am the light of the world."

[6]Having said this, he spit on the ground, made some mud with the saliva, and put it on the man's eyes. [7]"Go," he told him, "wash in the Pool of Siloam" (this word means Sent). So the man went and washed, and came home seeing.

[8]His neighbors and those who had formerly seen him begging asked, "Isn't this the same man who used to sit and beg?" [9]Some claimed that he was.

Others said, "No, he only looks like him."

But he himself insisted, "I am the man."

[10]"How then were your eyes opened?" they demanded.

[11]He replied, "The man they call Jesus made some mud and put it on my eyes. He told me to go to Siloam and wash. So I went and washed, and then I could see."

[12]"Where is this man?" they asked him.

"I don't know," he said.

The Pharisees Investigate the Healing

[13]They brought to the Pharisees the man who had been blind. [14]Now the day on which Jesus had made the mud and opened the man's eyes was a Sabbath. [15]Therefore the Pharisees also asked him how he had received his sight. "He put mud on my eyes," the man replied, "and I washed, and now I see."

[16]Some of the Pharisees said, "This man is not from God, for he does not keep the Sabbath."

But others asked, "How can a sinner do such miraculous signs?" So they were divided.

[17]Finally they turned again to the blind man, "What have you to say about him? It was your eyes he opened."

The man replied, "He is a prophet."

[18]The Jews still did not believe that he had been blind and had received his sight until they sent for the man's parents. [19]"Is this your son?" they asked. "Is this the one you say was born blind? How is it that now he can see?"

[20]"We know he is our son," the parents answered, "and we know he was born blind. [21]But how he can see now, or who opened his eyes, we don't know. Ask him. He is of age; he will speak for himself." [22]His parents said this because they were afraid of the Jews, for already the Jews had decided that anyone who acknowledged that Jesus was the Christ[a] would be put out of the synagogue. [23]That was why his parents said, "He is of age; ask him."

[24]A second time they summoned the man who had been blind. "Give glory to God,[b]" they said. "We know this man is a sinner."

[25]He replied, "Whether he is a sinner or not, I don't know. One thing I do know. I was blind but now I see!"

[26]Then they asked him, "What did he do to you? How did he open your eyes?"

[27]He answered, "I have told you already and you did not listen. Why do you want to hear it again? Do you want to become his disciples, too?"

[28]Then they hurled insults at him and said, "You are this fellow's disciple! We are disciples of Moses! [29]We know that God spoke to Moses, but as for this fellow, we don't even know where he comes from."

[30]The man answered, "Now that is remarkable! You don't know where he comes from, yet he opened my eyes. [31]We know that God

truth or dare

This man wasn't a Bible scholar. He was just a normal guy who met Jesus and simply testified about his experience. However God has touched your life, that's *your* personal testimony.

9:24–33

a 22 Or *Messiah*   *b 24* A solemn charge to tell the truth (see Joshua 7:19) does not listen to sinners. He listens to the godly man who does his will. ³²Nobody has ever heard of opening the eyes of a man born blind. ³³If this man were not from God, he could do nothing."

³⁴To this they replied, "You were steeped in sin at birth; how dare you lecture us!" And they threw him out.

Spiritual Blindness

³⁵Jesus heard that they had thrown him out, and when he found him, he said, "Do you believe in the Son of Man?"

³⁶"Who is he, sir?" the man asked. "Tell me so that I may believe in him."

³⁷Jesus said, "You have now seen him; in fact, he is the one speaking with you."

³⁸Then the man said, "Lord, I believe," and he worshiped him.

³⁹Jesus said, "For judgment I have come into this world, so that the blind will see and those who see will become blind."

⁴⁰Some Pharisees who were with him heard him say this and asked, "What? Are we blind too?"

⁴¹Jesus said, "If you were blind, you would not be guilty of sin; but now that you claim you can see, your guilt remains.

The Shepherd and His Flock

10 "I tell you the truth, the man who does not enter the sheep pen by the gate, but climbs in by some other way, is a thief and a robber. ²The man who enters by the gate is the shepherd of his sheep. ³The watchman opens the gate for him, and the sheep listen to his voice. He calls his own sheep by name and leads them out. ⁴When he has brought out all his own, he goes on ahead of them, and his sheep follow him because they know his voice. ⁵But they will never follow a stranger; in fact, they will run away from him because they do not recognize a stranger's voice." ⁶Jesus used this figure of speech, but they did not understand what he was telling them.

⁷Therefore Jesus said again, "I tell you the truth, I am the gate for the sheep. ⁸All who ever came before me were thieves and robbers, but the sheep did not listen to them. ⁹I am the gate; whoever enters through me will be saved.ᵃ He will come in and go out, and find pasture. ¹⁰The thief comes only to steal and kill and destroy; I have come that they may have life, and have it to the full.

¹¹"I am the good shepherd. The good shepherd lays down his life for the sheep. ¹²The hired hand is not the shepherd who owns the sheep. So when he sees the wolf coming, he abandons the sheep and runs away. Then the wolf attacks the flock and scatters it. ¹³The man runs away because he is a hired hand and cares nothing for the sheep.

¹⁴"I am the good shepherd; I know my sheep and my sheep know me— ¹⁵just as the Father knows me and I know the Father—and I lay down my life for the sheep. ¹⁶I have other sheep that are not of this sheep pen. I must bring them also. They too will listen to my voice, and there shall be one flock and one shepherd. ¹⁷The reason my Father loves me is that I lay down my life— only to take it up again. ¹⁸No one takes it

genuine life » 10:10

Many people think of God as basically a big party pooper. He's the big guy in the sky who wants to ruin all their fun. But they believe a lie. Jesus said that thieves, or spiritual counterfeits, come to ruin the lives of people here on Earth, while God has come to give us life, and life to the fullest. You were created to glorify God—to know him and love him. And that's why Jesus came—so you could do that and experience the most abundant life imaginable. Don't fall for the lie.

ᵃ 9 Or *kept safe*

Just One Question

Most people think of me as a good Christian girl. I guess that's why I got voted secretary of FCA (Fellowship of Christian Athletes) this year. I'm really involved in my youth group, and I read my Bible more often than not. I talk to God throughout the day . . . but I still have just one question. *How do I know if I'm really saved?* You'd think I'd have that one taken care of—but lately I'm just not sure. I mean, I remember praying with my mom one night when I was little and asking Jesus to come into my heart. But that moment seems so long ago.

Plus, this guy gave his testimony at church a few weeks ago. He had such an incredible story. He used to be wild, dealing and doing drugs, and then he met Jesus. Some street evangelist shared the plan of salvation with him one day, and he prayed "the sinner's prayer." Now he travels all over the country sharing his testimony. I don't have a dramatic story like that. I don't even remember *not* being a Christian—I was practically born in church. Did I really accept Jesus . . . or did I just take him for granted?

salvation in focus

Every Christian deals with doubts at some point. Doubts can be good— leading you to explore your beliefs. Doubts can be bad, though—they can keep you from being effective in God's kingdom. Remember . . .

»Just because you don't have a dramatic testimony doesn't mean you're not saved. Every testimony is powerful—not because of you, but because of Jesus.
»It is possible to go through the motions of Christianity without knowing Jesus. Actions without true faith are worthless. (Read Matthew 7:21–23, page 1299.)
»There's a difference between conviction (the work of the Holy Spirit) and condemnation (the work of Satan). Satan wants you to think there's no hope for you, to feel like you're so guilty you're beyond God's reach. That's a lie.
»If you doubt your salvation, talk about it with someone you trust.
»If you're truly saved, you can't lose that. Read John 10:28–29 (page 1428).

For more on this topic, see the index on page 1656.

What does it mean to be saved? Fortunately, the plan of salvation is clear and simple. Read it online at www.TrueImagesBible.com

from me, but I lay it down of my own accord. I have authority to lay it down and authority to take it up again. This command I received from my Father."

[19]At these words the Jews were again divided. [20]Many of them said, "He is demon-possessed and raving mad. Why listen to him?"

[21]But others said, "These are not the sayings of a man possessed by a demon. Can a demon open the eyes of the blind?"

The Unbelief of the Jews

[22]Then came the Feast of Dedication[a] at Jerusalem. It was winter, [23]and Jesus was in the temple area walking in Solomon's Colonnade. [24]The Jews gathered around him, saying, "How long will you keep us in suspense? If you are the Christ,[b] tell us plainly."

---

[a] 22 That is, Hanukkah   [b] 24 Or *Messiah*

²⁵Jesus answered, "I did tell you, but you do not believe. The miracles I do in my Father's name speak for me, ²⁶but you do not believe because you are not my sheep. ²⁷My sheep listen to my voice; I know them, and they follow me. ²⁸I give them eternal life, and they shall never perish; no one can snatch them out of my hand. ²⁹My Father, who has given them to me, is greater than all[a]; no one can snatch them out of my Father's hand. ³⁰I and the Father are one."

³¹Again the Jews picked up stones to stone him, ³²but Jesus said to them, "I have shown you many great miracles from the Father. For which of these do you stone me?"

³³"We are not stoning you for any of these," replied the Jews, "but for blasphemy, because you, a mere man, claim to be God."

³⁴Jesus answered them, "Is it not written in your Law, 'I have said you are gods'[b]? ³⁵If he called them 'gods,' to whom the word of God came—and the Scripture cannot be broken— ³⁶what about the one whom the Father set apart as his very own and sent into the world? Why then do you accuse me of blasphemy because I said, 'I am God's Son'? ³⁷Do not believe me unless I do what my Father does. ³⁸But if I do it, even though you do not believe me, believe the miracles, that you may know and understand that the Father is in me, and I in the Father." ³⁹Again they tried to seize him, but he escaped their grasp.

⁴⁰Then Jesus went back across the Jordan to the place where John had been baptizing in the early days. Here he stayed ⁴¹and many people came to him. They said, "Though John never performed a miraculous sign, all that John said about this man was true." ⁴²And in that place many believed in Jesus.

The Death of Lazarus

11 Now a man named Lazarus was sick. He was from Bethany, the village of Mary and her sister Martha. ²This Mary, whose brother Lazarus now lay sick, was the same one who poured perfume on the Lord and wiped his feet with her hair. ³So the sisters sent word to Jesus, "Lord, the one you love is sick."

⁴When he heard this, Jesus said, "This sickness will not end in death. No, it is for God's glory so that God's Son may be glorified through it." ⁵Jesus loved Martha and her sister and Lazarus. ⁶Yet when he heard that Lazarus was sick, he stayed where he was two more days.

⁷Then he said to his disciples, "Let us go back to Judea."

⁸"But Rabbi," they said, "a short while ago the Jews tried to stone you, and yet you are going back there?"

⁹Jesus answered, "Are there not twelve hours of daylight? A man who walks by day will not stumble, for he sees by this world's light. ¹⁰It is when he walks by night that he stumbles, for he has no light."

¹¹After he had said this, he went on to tell them, "Our friend Lazarus has fallen asleep; but I am going there to wake him up."

¹²His disciples replied, "Lord, if he sleeps, he will get better." ¹³Jesus had been speaking of his death, but his disciples thought he meant natural sleep.

¹⁴So then he told them plainly, "Lazarus is dead, ¹⁵and for your sake I am glad I was not there, so that you may believe. But let us go to him."

genuine faith » 11:1-21,32

Your parents get divorced, someone you love dies, your dad loses his job . . . . When bad things happen, you struggle to understand why. *If God loved me, why would he let this happen?* Mary and Martha felt that way. They didn't understand why Jesus let Lazarus die. But in verse 4 Jesus tells us why: It happened so that God would be glorified. No matter how bad things get, you can trust God to work even the painful things in your life for your good and his glory—which is what life's all about.

---

a 29 Many early manuscripts *What my Father has given me is greater than all*   *b 34* Psalm 82:6

[16]Then Thomas (called Didymus) said to the rest of the disciples, "Let us also go, that we may die with him."

Jesus Comforts the Sisters

[17]On his arrival, Jesus found that Lazarus had already been in the tomb for four days. [18]Bethany was less than two miles[a] from Jerusalem, [19]and many Jews had come to Martha and Mary to comfort them in the loss of their brother. [20]When Martha heard that Jesus was coming, she went out to meet him, but Mary stayed at home.

[21]"Lord," Martha said to Jesus, "if you had been here, my brother would not have died. [22]But I know that even now God will give you whatever you ask."

[23]Jesus said to her, "Your brother will rise again."

[24]Martha answered, "I know he will rise again in the resurrection at the last day."

[25]Jesus said to her, "I am the resurrection and the life. He who believes in me will live, even though he dies; [26]and whoever lives and believes in me will never die. Do you believe this?"

[27]"Yes, Lord," she told him, "I believe that you are the Christ,[b] the Son of God, who was to come into the world."

[28]And after she had said this, she went back and called her sister Mary aside. "The Teacher is here," she said, "and is asking for you." [29]When Mary heard this, she got up quickly and went to him. [30]Now Jesus had not yet entered the village, but was still at the place where Martha had met him. [31]When the Jews who had been with Mary in the house, comforting her, noticed how quickly she got up and went out, they followed her, supposing she was going to the tomb to mourn there.

[32]When Mary reached the place where Jesus was and saw him, she fell at his feet and said, "Lord, if you had been here, my brother would not have died."

[33]When Jesus saw her weeping, and the Jews who had come along with her also weeping, he was deeply moved in spirit and troubled. [34]"Where have you laid him?" he asked.

"Come and see, Lord," they replied.

[35]Jesus wept.

[36]Then the Jews said, "See how he loved him!"

[37]But some of them said, "Could not he who opened the eyes of the blind man have kept this man from dying?"

truth or dare

Crying doesn't mean you're weak. Even Jesus, God in the flesh, wept when his friend died. Jesus isn't embarrassed by your pain or sadness, either. Don't be afraid to share your hurts with him.

11:35

Jesus Raises Lazarus From the Dead

[38]Jesus, once more deeply moved, came to the tomb. It was a cave with a stone laid across the entrance. [39]"Take away the stone," he said.

"But, Lord," said Martha, the sister of the dead man, "by this time there is a bad odor, for he has been there four days."

[40]Then Jesus said, "Did I not tell you that if you believed, you would see the glory of God?"

[41]So they took away the stone. Then Jesus looked up and said, "Father, I thank you that you have heard me. [42]I knew that you always hear me, but I said this for the benefit of the people standing here, that they may believe that you sent me."

[43]When he had said this, Jesus called in a loud voice, "Lazarus, come out!" [44]The dead man came out, his hands and feet wrapped with strips of linen, and a cloth around his face.

Jesus said to them, "Take off the grave clothes and let him go."

The Plot to Kill Jesus

[45]Therefore many of the Jews who had come to visit Mary, and had seen what Jesus did, put their faith in him. [46]But some of them went to the Pharisees and told them what Jesus had done. [47]Then the chief priests and the Pharisees called a meeting of the Sanhedrin.

a 18 Greek *fifteen stadia* (about 3 kilometers)   *b 27* Or *Messiah*

"What are we accomplishing?" they asked. "Here is this man performing many miraculous signs. [48]If we let him go on like this, everyone will believe in him, and then the Romans will come and take away both our place[a] and our nation."

[49]Then one of them, named Caiaphas, who was high priest that year, spoke up, "You know nothing at all! [50]You do not realize that it is better for you that one man die for the people than that the whole nation perish."

[51]He did not say this on his own, but as high priest that year he prophesied that Jesus would die for the Jewish nation, [52]and not only for that nation but also for the scattered children of God, to bring them together and make them one. [53]So from that day on they plotted to take his life.

[54]Therefore Jesus no longer moved about publicly among the Jews. Instead he withdrew to a region near the desert, to a village called Ephraim, where he stayed with his disciples.

[55]When it was almost time for the Jewish Passover, many went up from the country to Jerusalem for their ceremonial cleansing before the Passover. [56]They kept looking for Jesus, and as they stood in the temple area they asked one another, "What do you think? Isn't he coming to the Feast at all?" [57]But the chief priests and Pharisees had given orders that if anyone found out where Jesus was, he should report it so that they might arrest him.

Jesus Anointed at Bethany

12 Six days before the Passover, Jesus arrived at Bethany, where Lazarus lived, whom Jesus had raised from the dead. [2]Here a dinner was given in Jesus' honor. Martha served, while Lazarus was among those reclining at the table with him. [3]Then Mary took about a pint[b] of pure nard, an expensive perfume; she poured it on Jesus' feet and wiped his feet with her hair. And the house was filled with the fragrance of the perfume.

[4]But one of his disciples, Judas Iscariot, who was later to betray him, objected, [5]"Why wasn't this perfume sold and the money given to the poor? It was worth a year's wages.[c]" [6]He did not say this because he cared about the poor but because he was a thief; as keeper of the money bag, he used to help himself to what was put into it.

[7]"Leave her alone," Jesus replied. "It was intended that she should save this perfume for the day of my burial. [8]You will always have the poor among you, but you will not always have me."

[9]Meanwhile a large crowd of Jews found out that Jesus was there and came, not only because of him but also to see Lazarus, whom he had raised from the dead. [10]So the chief priests made plans to kill Lazarus as well, [11]for on account of him many of the Jews were going over to Jesus and putting their faith in him.

The Triumphal Entry

[12]The next day the great crowd that had come for the Feast heard that Jesus was on his way to Jerusalem. [13]They took palm branches and went out to meet him, shouting,

"Hosanna![d]"

"Blessed is he who comes in the name of the Lord!"[e]

"Blessed is the King of Israel!"

[14]Jesus found a young donkey and sat upon it, as it is written,

[15]"Do not be afraid, O Daughter of Zion;
see, your king is coming,
seated on a donkey's colt."[f]

[16]At first his disciples did not understand all this. Only after Jesus was glorified did they realize that these things had been written about him and that they had done these things to him.

[17]Now the crowd that was with him when he called Lazarus from the tomb and raised him from the dead continued to spread the word. [18]Many people, because they had heard that he had given this miraculous sign, went out to meet him. [19]So the Pharisees said to one another, "See, this is getting us nowhere. Look how the whole world has gone after him!"

a 48 Or *temple*   *b 3* Greek *a litra* (probably about 0.5 liter)   *c 5* Greek *three hundred denarii*   *d 13* A Hebrew expression meaning "Save!" which became an exclamation of praise   *e 13* Psalm 118:25,26   *f 15* Zech. 9:9

Jesus Predicts His Death

[20]Now there were some Greeks among those who went up to worship at the Feast. [21]They came to Philip, who was from Bethsaida in Galilee, with a request. "Sir," they said, "we would like to see Jesus." [22]Philip went to tell Andrew; Andrew and Philip in turn told Jesus.

[23]Jesus replied, "The hour has come for the Son of Man to be glorified. [24]I tell you the truth, unless a kernel of wheat falls to the ground and dies, it remains only a single seed. But if it dies, it produces many seeds. [25]The man who loves his life will lose it, while the man who hates his life in this world will keep it for eternal life. [26]Whoever serves me must follow me; and where I am, my servant also will be. My Father will honor the one who serves me.

[27]"Now my heart is troubled, and what shall I say? 'Father, save me from this hour'? No, it was for this very reason I came to this hour. [28]Father, glorify your name!"

Then a voice came from heaven, "I have glorified it, and will glorify it again." [29]The crowd that was there and heard it said it had thundered; others said an angel had spoken to him.

[30]Jesus said, "This voice was for your benefit, not mine. [31]Now is the time for judgment on this world; now the prince of this world will be driven out. [32]But I, when I am lifted up from the earth, will draw all men to myself." [33]He said this to show the kind of death he was going to die.

[34]The crowd spoke up, "We have heard from the Law that the Christ[a] will remain forever, so how can you say, 'The Son of Man must be lifted up'? Who is this 'Son of Man'?"

[35]Then Jesus told them, "You are going to have the light just a little while longer. Walk while you have the light, before darkness overtakes you. The man who walks in the dark does not know where he is going. [36]Put your trust in the light while you have it, so that you may become sons of light." When he had finished speaking, Jesus left and hid himself from them.

The Jews Continue in Their Unbelief

[37]Even after Jesus had done all these miraculous signs in their presence, they still would not believe in him. [38]This was to fulfill the word of Isaiah the prophet:

> "Lord, who has believed our message
> and to whom has the arm of the Lord been revealed?"[b]

[39]For this reason they could not believe, because, as Isaiah says elsewhere:

> [40]"He has blinded their eyes
> and deadened their hearts,
> so they can neither see with their eyes,
> nor understand with their hearts,
> nor turn—and I would heal them."[c]

[41]Isaiah said this because he saw Jesus' glory and spoke about him.

[42]Yet at the same time many even among the leaders believed in him. But because of the Pharisees they would not confess their faith for fear they would be put out of the synagogue; [43]for they loved praise from men more than praise from God.

[44]Then Jesus cried out, "When a man believes in me, he does not believe in me only, but in the one who sent me. [45]When he looks at me, he sees the one who sent me. [46]I have come into the world as a light, so that no one who believes in me should stay in darkness.

[47]"As for the person who hears my words but does not keep them, I do not judge him. For I did not come to judge the world, but to save it. [48]There is a judge for the one who rejects me and does not accept my words; that very word which I spoke will condemn him at the last day. [49]For I did not speak of my own accord, but the Father who sent me commanded me what to say and how to say it. [50]I know that his command leads to eternal life. So whatever I say is just what the Father has told me to say."

Jesus Washes His Disciples' Feet

13 It was just before the Passover Feast. Jesus knew that the time had come for him to leave this world and go to the Father. Having loved his own who were in the world, he now showed them the full extent of his love.[d]

a 34 Or *Messiah*   *b 38* Isaiah 53:1   *c 40* Isaiah 6:10   *d 1* Or *he loved them to the last*

²The evening meal was being served, and the devil had already prompted Judas Iscariot, son of Simon, to betray Jesus. ³Jesus knew that the Father had put all things under his power, and that he had come from God and was returning to God; ⁴so he got up from the meal, took off his outer clothing, and wrapped a towel around his waist. ⁵After that, he poured water into a basin and began to wash his disciples' feet, drying them with the towel that was wrapped around him.

⁶He came to Simon Peter, who said to him, "Lord, are you going to wash my feet?"

⁷Jesus replied, "You do not realize now what I am doing, but later you will understand."

⁸"No," said Peter, "you shall never wash my feet."

Jesus answered, "Unless I wash you, you have no part with me."

⁹"Then, Lord," Simon Peter replied, "not just my feet but my hands and my head as well!"

¹⁰Jesus answered, "A person who has had a bath needs only to wash his feet; his whole body is clean. And you are clean, though not every one of you." ¹¹For he knew who was going to betray him, and that was why he said not every one was clean.

¹²When he had finished washing their feet, he put on his clothes and returned to his place. "Do you understand what I have done for you?" he asked them. ¹³"You call me 'Teacher' and 'Lord,' and rightly so, for that is what I am. ¹⁴Now that I, your Lord and Teacher, have washed your feet, you also should wash one another's feet. ¹⁵I have set you an example that you should do as I have done for you. ¹⁶I tell you the truth, no servant is greater than his master, nor is a messenger greater than the one who sent him. ¹⁷Now that you know these things, you will be blessed if you do them.

Jesus Predicts His Betrayal

¹⁸"I am not referring to all of you; I know those I have chosen. But this is to fulfill the scripture: 'He who shares my bread has lifted up his heel against me.'ᵃ

¹⁹"I am telling you now before it happens, so that when it does happen you will believe that I am He. ²⁰I tell you the truth, whoever accepts anyone I send accepts me; and whoever accepts me accepts the one who sent me."

²¹After he had said this, Jesus was troubled in spirit and testified, "I tell you the truth, one of you is going to betray me."

²²His disciples stared at one another, at a loss to know which of them he meant. ²³One of them, the disciple whom Jesus loved, was reclining next to him. ²⁴Simon Peter motioned to this disciple and said, "Ask him which one he means."

²⁵Leaning back against Jesus, he asked him, "Lord, who is it?"

²⁶Jesus answered, "It is the one to whom I will give this piece of bread when I have dipped it in the dish." Then, dipping the piece of bread, he gave it to Judas Iscariot, son of Simon. ²⁷As soon as Judas took the bread, Satan entered into him.

"What you are about to do, do quickly," Jesus told him, ²⁸but no one at the meal understood why Jesus said this to him. ²⁹Since Judas had charge of the money, some thought Jesus was telling him to buy what was needed for the Feast, or to give something to the poor. ³⁰As soon as Judas had taken the bread, he went out. And it was night.

genuine humility » 13:2-17

So was foot washing some kind of Jewish party game? Ummmmmm, no. In this culture of dusty roads and sandaled feet, it was customary for a servant to wash the guests' feet when they arrived. It was a dirty, gross, lowly job—you know, sweaty feet generally aren't very attractive! So when Jesus wrapped the towel around his waist and began to perform this menial task for his disciples, he sent a message to them and to us. If the Son of God himself could serve like that, surely none of us is too good to serve others in whatever way we can.

ᵃ 18 Psalm 41:9

Jesus Predicts Peter's Denial

³¹When he was gone, Jesus said, "Now is the Son of Man glorified and God is glorified in him. ³²If God is glorified in him,ᵃ God will glorify the Son in himself, and will glorify him at once.

³³"My children, I will be with you only a little longer. You will look for me, and just as I told the Jews, so I tell you now: Where I am going, you cannot come.

³⁴"A new command I give you: Love one another. As I have loved you, so you must love one another. ³⁵By this all men will know that you are my disciples, if you love one another."

³⁶Simon Peter asked him, "Lord, where are you going?"

Jesus replied, "Where I am going, you cannot follow now, but you will follow later."

³⁷Peter asked, "Lord, why can't I follow you now? I will lay down my life for you."

³⁸Then Jesus answered, "Will you really lay down your life for me? I tell you the truth, before the rooster crows, you will disown me three times!

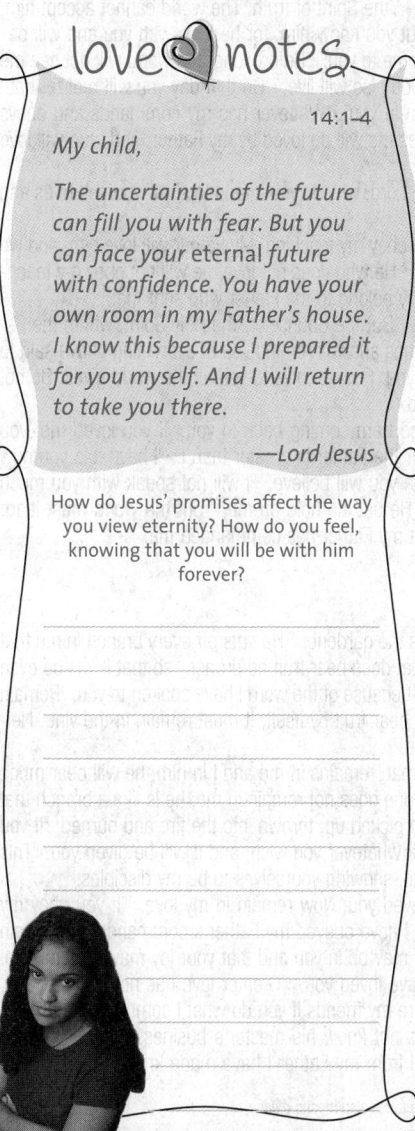

love notes

14:1–4

My child,

The uncertainties of the future can fill you with fear. But you can face your eternal future with confidence. You have your own room in my Father's house. I know this because I prepared it for you myself. And I will return to take you there.

—Lord Jesus

How do Jesus' promises affect the way you view eternity? How do you feel, knowing that you will be with him forever?

Jesus Comforts His Disciples

14 "Do not let your hearts be troubled. Trust in God ᵇ; trust also in me. ²In my Father's house are many rooms; if it were not so, I would have told you. I am going there to prepare a place for you. ³And if I go and prepare a place for you, I will come back and take you to be with me that you also may be where I am. ⁴You know the way to the place where I am going."

Jesus the Way to the Father

⁵Thomas said to him, "Lord, we don't know where you are going, so how can we know the way?"

⁶Jesus answered, "I am the way and the truth and the life. No one comes to the Father except through me. ⁷If you really knew me, you would know ᶜ my Father as well. From now on, you do know him and have seen him."

truth or dare

Telling people there's only one way to God can seem offensive. But Jesus wasn't worried about being PC when he made this statement. Are you as bold as Jesus with the truth?

14:6

ᵃ 32 Many early manuscripts do not have *If God is glorified in him.*   ᵇ 1 Or *You trust in God*
ᶜ 7 Some early manuscripts *If you really have known me, you will know*

[8]Philip said, "Lord, show us the Father and that will be enough for us."

[9]Jesus answered: "Don't you know me, Philip, even after I have been among you such a long time? Anyone who has seen me has seen the Father. How can you say, 'Show us the Father'? [10]Don't you believe that I am in the Father, and that the Father is in me? The words I say to you are not just my own. Rather, it is the Father, living in me, who is doing his work. [11]Believe me when I say that I am in the Father and the Father is in me; or at least believe on the evidence of the miracles themselves. [12]I tell you the truth, anyone who has faith in me will do what I have been doing. He will do even greater things than these, because I am going to the Father. [13]And I will do whatever you ask in my name, so that the Son may bring glory to the Father. [14]You may ask me for anything in my name, and I will do it.

Jesus Promises the Holy Spirit

[15]"If you love me, you will obey what I command. [16]And I will ask the Father, and he will give you another Counselor to be with you forever— [17]the Spirit of truth. The world cannot accept him, because it neither sees him nor knows him. But you know him, for he lives with you and will be[a] in you. [18]I will not leave you as orphans; I will come to you. [19]Before long, the world will not see me anymore, but you will see me. Because I live, you also will live. [20]On that day you will realize that I am in my Father, and you are in me, and I am in you. [21]Whoever has my commands and obeys them, he is the one who loves me. He who loves me will be loved by my Father, and I too will love him and show myself to him."

[22]Then Judas (not Judas Iscariot) said, "But, Lord, why do you intend to show yourself to us and not to the world?"

[23]Jesus replied, "If anyone loves me, he will obey my teaching. My Father will love him, and we will come to him and make our home with him. [24]He who does not love me will not obey my teaching. These words you hear are not my own; they belong to the Father who sent me.

[25]"All this I have spoken while still with you. [26]But the Counselor, the Holy Spirit, whom the Father will send in my name, will teach you all things and will remind you of everything I have said to you. [27]Peace I leave with you; my peace I give you. I do not give to you as the world gives. Do not let your hearts be troubled and do not be afraid.

[28]"You heard me say, 'I am going away and I am coming back to you.' If you loved me, you would be glad that I am going to the Father, for the Father is greater than I. [29]I have told you now before it happens, so that when it does happen you will believe. [30]I will not speak with you much longer, for the prince of this world is coming. He has no hold on me, [31]but the world must learn that I love the Father and that I do exactly what my Father has commanded me.

"Come now; let us leave.

The Vine and the Branches

15 "I am the true vine, and my Father is the gardener. [2]He cuts off every branch in me that bears no fruit, while every branch that does bear fruit he prunes[b] so that it will be even more fruitful. [3]You are already clean because of the word I have spoken to you. [4]Remain in me, and I will remain in you. No branch can bear fruit by itself; it must remain in the vine. Neither can you bear fruit unless you remain in me.

[5]"I am the vine; you are the branches. If a man remains in me and I in him, he will bear much fruit; apart from me you can do nothing. [6]If anyone does not remain in me, he is like a branch that is thrown away and withers; such branches are picked up, thrown into the fire and burned. [7]If you remain in me and my words remain in you, ask whatever you wish, and it will be given you. [8]This is to my Father's glory, that you bear much fruit, showing yourselves to be my disciples.

[9]"As the Father has loved me, so have I loved you. Now remain in my love. [10]If you obey my commands, you will remain in my love, just as I have obeyed my Father's commands and remain in his love. [11]I have told you this so that my joy may be in you and that your joy may be complete. [12]My command is this: Love each other as I have loved you. [13]Greater love has no one than this, that he lay down his life for his friends. [14]You are my friends if you do what I command. [15]I no longer call you servants, because a servant does not know his master's business. Instead, I have called you friends, for everything that I learned from my Father I have made known to you. [16]You

---

[a] 17 Some early manuscripts *and is*   [b] 2 The Greek for *prunes* also means *cleans*.

Only One Way?

"So you're saying if I don't believe in Jesus I'm going to hell?" When Lyla point-blank asked me that question, I didn't know what to say. I'd felt really excited at the start of our conversation that day. I had just come back from a week at church camp and felt so close to God. I couldn't wait to come home and tell Lyla about Jesus. I knew it would be difficult to talk to her about it, since she's a Muslim, but I wasn't prepared for her question. Suddenly, I lost all my confidence.

Lyla's my best friend in the whole world. She trusts me. I trust her. So, how could I look her in the face and tell her God would send her to hell for not believing the way I do? On the other hand, how could I afford *not* to tell her the truth? That is, if believing Jesus is the only way to God *really is* the truth.

I was starting to have my doubts. It's like these little voices creep inside my head at moments like these, and I start to wonder.

Who's to say I'm right and she's wrong?

Maybe Allah is God, or just another name for him.

What kind of God would send someone as sweet as Lyla to hell anyway?

I stared at Lyla for a long, uncomfortable moment, not sure whether to say something else or just change the subject . . .

truth in focus

Some people claim Christianity is unjustly intolerant toward other religions. Yet Jesus himself said he was the *only way* to God (John 14:6, page 1433). Either Jesus is who he claimed to be OR he was crazy, OR, worse yet, a liar who fooled his closest companions. There aren't any other alternatives. Consider this:

> »Truth is truth whether we choose to believe it or not. Why? Because God is truth (see John 1:14,17, page 1410)—and he doesn't change (see Hebrews 13:8, page 1599).

> »Non-Christians aren't going to hell for believing in Mohammed, Buddha or some other religion. Lost people are going to hell because they are sinners (see Romans 3:23; 6:23, pages 1489,1492). Sin—not a faulty religion—is what separates our lost friends from God.

For more on this topic, see the index on page 1656.

did not choose me, but I chose you and appointed you to go and bear fruit—fruit that will last. Then the Father will give you whatever you ask in my name. [17]This is my command: Love each other.

The World Hates the Disciples

[18]"If the world hates you, keep in mind that it hated me first. [19]If you belonged to the world, it would love you as its own. As it is, you do not belong to the world, but I have chosen you out of the world. That is why the world hates you. [20]Remember the words I spoke to you: 'No servant is

greater than his master.'ᵃ If they persecuted me, they will persecute you also. If they obeyed my teaching, they will obey yours also. ²¹They will treat you this way because of my name, for they do not know the One who sent me. ²²If I had not come and spoken to them, they would not be guilty of sin. Now, however, they have no excuse for their sin. ²³He who hates me hates my Father as well. ²⁴If I had not done among them what no one else did, they would not be guilty of sin. But now they have seen these miracles, and yet they have hated both me and my Father. ²⁵But this is to fulfill what is written in their Law: 'They hated me without reason.'ᵇ

²⁶"When the Counselor comes, whom I will send to you from the Father, the Spirit of truth who goes out from the Father, he will testify about me. ²⁷And you also must testify, for you have been with me from the beginning.

16 "All this I have told you so that you will not go astray. ²They will put you out of the synagogue; in fact, a time is coming when anyone who kills you will think he is offering a service to God. ³They will do such things because they have not known the Father or me. ⁴I have told you this, so that when the time comes you will remember that I warned you. I did not tell you this at first because I was with you.

The Work of the Holy Spirit

⁵"Now I am going to him who sent me, yet none of you asks me, 'Where are you going?' ⁶Because I have said these things, you are filled with grief. ⁷But I tell you the truth: It is for your good that I am going away. Unless I go away, the Counselor will not come to you; but if I go, I will send him to you. ⁸When he comes, he will convict the world of guiltᶜ in regard to sin and righteousness and judgment: ⁹in regard to sin, because men do not believe in me; ¹⁰in regard to righteousness, because I am going to the Father, where you can see me no longer; ¹¹and in regard to judgment, because the prince of this world now stands condemned.

¹²"I have much more to say to you, more than you can now bear. ¹³But when he, the Spirit of truth, comes, he will guide you into all truth. He will not speak on his own; he will speak only what he hears, and he will tell you what is yet to come. ¹⁴He will bring glory to me by taking from what is mine and making it known to you. ¹⁵All that belongs to the Father is mine. That is why I said the Spirit will take from what is mine and make it known to you.

¹⁶"In a little while you will see me no more, and then after a little while you will see me."

The Disciples' Grief Will Turn to Joy

¹⁷Some of his disciples said to one another, "What does he mean by saying, 'In a little while you will see me no more, and then after a little while you will see me,' and 'Because I am going to the Father'?" ¹⁸They kept asking, "What does he mean by 'a little while'? We don't understand what he is saying."

¹⁹Jesus saw that they wanted to ask him about this, so he said to them, "Are you asking one another what I meant when I said, 'In a little while you will see me no more, and then after a little while you will see me'? ²⁰I tell you the truth, you will weep and mourn while the world rejoices. You will grieve, but your grief will turn to joy. ²¹A woman giving birth to a child has pain because her time has come; but when her baby is born she forgets the anguish because of her joy that a child is born into the world. ²²So with you: Now is your time of grief, but I will see you again and you will rejoice, and no one will take away your joy. ²³In that day you will no longer ask me anything. I tell you the truth, my Father will give you whatever you ask in my name. ²⁴Until now you have not asked for anything in my name. Ask and you will receive, and your joy will be complete.

²⁵"Though I have been speaking figuratively, a time is coming when I will no longer use this kind of language but will tell you plainly about my Father. ²⁶In that day you will ask in my name. I am not saying that I will ask the Father on your behalf. ²⁷No, the Father himself loves you because you have loved me and have believed that I came from God. ²⁸I came from the Father and entered the world; now I am leaving the world and going back to the Father."

²⁹Then Jesus' disciples said, "Now you are speaking clearly and without figures of speech. ³⁰Now we can see that you know all things and that you do not even need to have anyone ask you questions. This makes us believe that you came from God."

ᵃ 20 John 13:16   ᵇ 25 Psalms 35:19; 69:4   ᶜ 8 Or *will expose the guilt of the world*

³¹"You believe at last!" ᵃ Jesus answered. ³²"But a time is coming, and has come, when you will be scattered, each to his own home. You will leave me all alone. Yet I am not alone, for my Father is with me.

³³"I have told you these things, so that in me you may have peace. In this world you will have trouble. But take heart! I have overcome the world."

Jesus Prays for Himself

17 After Jesus said this, he looked toward heaven and prayed:

"Father, the time has come. Glorify your Son, that your Son may glorify you. ²For you granted him authority over all people that he might give eternal life to all those you have given him. ³Now this is eternal life: that they may know you, the only true God, and Jesus Christ, whom you have sent. ⁴I have brought you glory on earth by completing the work you gave me to do. ⁵And now, Father, glorify me in your presence with the glory I had with you before the world began.

truth or dare

Think having peace means being free from trouble? Think again! Jesus guarantees you'll experience pain. But in the midst of craziness, you can also have peace knowing God's in control.

16:33

genuine life » 17:3

You're sitting at a spa, fuzzy robe on, shoulders relaxed from a massage, face freshly steamed and nails newly manicured . . . you lean your head back and sigh, "Aaaaaaahhhhh, this is the life." Sounds good, doesn't it? Well, what's *eternal* life? Jesus said it's knowing him and the Father who sent him. So if you're a believer, your eternal life has already started. It's only going to get better when you get to heaven, but you don't have to wait until then to start enjoying it! Get to know Jesus, and you'll say, "Aaaahhh, this is eternal life."

Jesus Prays for His Disciples

⁶"I have revealed you ᵇ to those whom you gave me out of the world. They were yours; you gave them to me and they have obeyed your word. ⁷Now they know that everything you have given me comes from you. ⁸For I gave them the words you gave me and they accepted them. They knew with certainty that I came from you, and they believed that you sent me. ⁹I pray for them. I am not praying for the world, but for those you have given me, for they are yours. ¹⁰All I have is yours, and all you have is mine. And glory has come to me through them. ¹¹I will remain in the world no longer, but they are still in the world, and I am coming to you. Holy Father, protect them by the power of your name—the name you gave me—so that they may be one as we are one. ¹²While I was with them, I protected them and kept them safe by that name you gave me. None has been lost except the one doomed to destruction so that Scripture would be fulfilled.

¹³"I am coming to you now, but I say these things while I am still in the world, so that they may have the full measure of my joy within them. ¹⁴I have given them your word and the world has hated them, for they are not of the world any more than I am of the world. ¹⁵My prayer is not that you take them out of the world but that you protect them from the evil one. ¹⁶They are not of the world, even as I am not of it. ¹⁷Sanctify ᶜ them by the truth; your word is truth. ¹⁸As you sent me into the world, I have sent them into the world. ¹⁹For

ᵃ 31 Or "Do you now believe?" ᵇ 6 Greek your name; also in verse 26 ᶜ 17 Greek hagiazo (set apart for sacred use or make holy); also in verse 19 them I sanctify myself, that they too may be truly sanctified.

Jesus Prays for All Believers

²⁰"My prayer is not for them alone. I pray also for those who will believe in me through their message, ²¹that all of them may be one, Father, just as you are in me and I am in you. May they also be in us so that the world may believe that you have sent me. ²²I have given them the glory that you gave me, that they may be one as we are one: ²³I in them and you in me. May they be brought to complete unity to let the world know that you sent me and have loved them even as you loved me.

²⁴"Father, I want those you have given me to be with me where I am, and to see my glory, the glory you have given me because you loved me before the creation of the world.

²⁵"Righteous Father, though the world does not know you, I know you, and they know that you have sent me. ²⁶I have made you known to them, and will continue to make you known in order that the love you have for me may be in them and that I myself may be in them."

Jesus Arrested

18 When he had finished praying, Jesus left with his disciples and crossed the Kidron Valley. On the other side there was an olive grove, and he and his disciples went into it. ²Now Judas, who betrayed him, knew the place, because Jesus had often met there with his disciples. ³So Judas came to the grove, guiding a detachment of soldiers and some officials from the chief priests and Pharisees. They were carrying torches, lanterns and weapons.

⁴Jesus, knowing all that was going to happen to him, went out and asked them, "Who is it you want?"

⁵"Jesus of Nazareth," they replied.

"I am he," Jesus said. (And Judas the traitor was standing there with them.) ⁶When Jesus said, "I am he," they drew back and fell to the ground.

⁷Again he asked them, "Who is it you want?"

And they said, "Jesus of Nazareth."

⁸"I told you that I am he," Jesus answered. "If you are looking for me, then let these men go." ⁹This happened so that the words he had spoken would be fulfilled: "I have not lost one of those you gave me." ᵃ

¹⁰Then Simon Peter, who had a sword, drew it and struck the high priest's servant, cutting off his right ear. (The servant's name was Malchus.)

¹¹Jesus commanded Peter, "Put your sword away! Shall I not drink the cup the Father has given me?"

Jesus Taken to Annas

¹²Then the detachment of soldiers with its commander and the Jewish officials arrested Jesus. They bound him ¹³and brought him first to Annas, who was the father-in-law of Caiaphas, the high priest that year. ¹⁴Caiaphas was the one who had advised the Jews that it would be good if one man died for the people.

Peter's First Denial

¹⁵Simon Peter and another disciple were following Jesus. Because this disciple was known to the high priest, he went with Jesus into the high priest's courtyard, ¹⁶but Peter had to wait outside at the door. The other disciple, who was known to the high priest, came back, spoke to the girl on duty there and brought Peter in.

ᵃ 9 John 6:39

¹⁷"You are not one of his disciples, are you?" the girl at the door asked Peter. He replied, "I am not."

¹⁸It was cold, and the servants and officials stood around a fire they had made to keep warm. Peter also was standing with them, warming himself.

The High Priest Questions Jesus

¹⁹Meanwhile, the high priest questioned Jesus about his disciples and his teaching.

²⁰"I have spoken openly to the world," Jesus replied. "I always taught in synagogues or at the temple, where all the Jews come together. I said nothing in secret. ²¹Why question me? Ask those who heard me. Surely they know what I said."

²²When Jesus said this, one of the officials nearby struck him in the face. "Is this the way you answer the high priest?" he demanded.

²³"If I said something wrong," Jesus replied, "testify as to what is wrong. But if I spoke the truth, why did you strike me?" ²⁴Then Annas sent him, still bound, to Caiaphas the high priest.ᵃ

Peter's Second and Third Denials

²⁵As Simon Peter stood warming himself, he was asked, "You are not one of his disciples, are you?" He denied it, saying, "I am not."

²⁶One of the high priest's servants, a relative of the man whose ear Peter had cut off, challenged him, "Didn't I see you with him in the olive grove?" ²⁷Again Peter denied it, and at that moment a rooster began to crow.

Jesus Before Pilate

²⁸Then the Jews led Jesus from Caiaphas to the palace of the Roman governor. By now it was early morning, and to avoid ceremonial uncleanness the Jews did not enter the palace; they wanted to be able to eat the Passover. ²⁹So Pilate came out to them and asked, "What charges are you bringing against this man?"

³⁰"If he were not a criminal," they replied, "we would not have handed him over to you."

³¹Pilate said, "Take him yourselves and judge him by your own law."

"But we have no right to execute anyone," the Jews objected. ³²This happened so that the words Jesus had spoken indicating the kind of death he was going to die would be fulfilled.

³³Pilate then went back inside the palace, summoned Jesus and asked him, "Are you the king of the Jews?"

³⁴"Is that your own idea," Jesus asked, "or did others talk to you about me?"

³⁵"Am I a Jew?" Pilate replied. "It was your people and your chief priests who handed you over to me. What is it you have done?"

³⁶Jesus said, "My kingdom is not of this world. If it were, my servants would fight to prevent my arrest by the Jews. But now my kingdom is from another place."

³⁷"You are a king, then!" said Pilate.

Jesus answered, "You are right in saying I am a king. In fact, for this reason I was born, and for this I came into the world, to testify to the truth. Everyone on the side of truth listens to me."

³⁸"What is truth?" Pilate asked. With this he went out again to the Jews and said, "I find no basis for a charge against him. ³⁹But it is your custom for me to release to you one prisoner at the time of the Passover. Do you want me to release 'the king of the Jews'?"

⁴⁰They shouted back, "No, not him! Give us Barabbas!" Now Barabbas had taken part in a rebellion.

Jesus Sentenced to Be Crucified

19 Then Pilate took Jesus and had him flogged. ²The soldiers twisted together a crown of thorns and put it on his head. They clothed him in a purple robe ³and went up to him again and again, saying, "Hail, king of the Jews!" And they struck him in the face.

⁴Once more Pilate came out and said to the Jews, "Look, I am bringing him out to you to let you know that I find no basis for a charge against him." ⁵When Jesus came out wearing the crown of thorns and the purple robe, Pilate said to them, "Here is the man!"

ᵃ 24 Or (Now Annas had sent him, still bound, to Caiaphas the high priest.)

⁶As soon as the chief priests and their officials saw him, they shouted, "Crucify! Crucify!"

But Pilate answered, "You take him and crucify him. As for me, I find no basis for a charge against him."

⁷The Jews insisted, "We have a law, and according to that law he must die, because he claimed to be the Son of God."

⁸When Pilate heard this, he was even more afraid, ⁹and he went back inside the palace. "Where do you come from?" he asked Jesus, but Jesus gave him no answer. ¹⁰"Do you refuse to speak to me?" Pilate said. "Don't you realize I have power either to free you or to crucify you?"

¹¹Jesus answered, "You would have no power over me if it were not given to you from above. Therefore the one who handed me over to you is guilty of a greater sin."

¹²From then on, Pilate tried to set Jesus free, but the Jews kept shouting, "If you let this man go, you are no friend of Caesar. Anyone who claims to be a king opposes Caesar."

¹³When Pilate heard this, he brought Jesus out and sat down on the judge's seat at a place known as the Stone Pavement (which in Aramaic is Gabbatha). ¹⁴It was the day of Preparation of Passover Week, about the sixth hour.

"Here is your king," Pilate said to the Jews.

¹⁵But they shouted, "Take him away! Take him away! Crucify him!"

"Shall I crucify your king?" Pilate asked.

"We have no king but Caesar," the chief priests answered.

¹⁶Finally Pilate handed him over to them to be crucified.

The Crucifixion

So the soldiers took charge of Jesus. ¹⁷Carrying his own cross, he went out to the place of the Skull (which in Aramaic is called Golgotha). ¹⁸Here they crucified him, and with him two others— one on each side and Jesus in the middle.

¹⁹Pilate had a notice prepared and fastened to the cross. It read: JESUS OF NAZARETH, THE KING OF THE JEWS. ²⁰Many of the Jews read this sign, for the place where Jesus was crucified was near the city, and the sign was written in Aramaic, Latin and Greek. ²¹The chief priests of the Jews protested to Pilate, "Do not write 'The King of the Jews,' but that this man claimed to be king of the Jews."

²²Pilate answered, "What I have written, I have written."

²³When the soldiers crucified Jesus, they took his clothes, dividing them into four shares, one for each of them, with the undergarment remaining. This garment was seamless, woven in one piece from top to bottom.

²⁴"Let's not tear it," they said to one another. "Let's decide by lot who will get it."

This happened that the scripture might be fulfilled which said,

> "They divided my garments among them
> and cast lots for my clothing."ᵃ

So this is what the soldiers did.

²⁵Near the cross of Jesus stood his mother, his mother's sister, Mary the wife of Clopas, and Mary Magdalene. ²⁶When Jesus saw his mother there, and the disciple whom he loved standing nearby, he said to his mother, "Dear woman, here is your son," ²⁷and to the disciple, "Here is your mother." From that time on, this disciple took her into his home.

The Death of Jesus

²⁸Later, knowing that all was now completed, and so that the Scripture would be fulfilled, Jesus said, "I am thirsty." ²⁹A jar of wine vinegar was there, so they soaked a sponge in it, put the sponge on a stalk of the hyssop plant, and lifted it to Jesus' lips. ³⁰When he had received the drink, Jesus said, "It is finished." With that, he bowed his head and gave up his spirit.

³¹Now it was the day of Preparation, and the next day was to be a special Sabbath. Because the Jews did not want the bodies left on the crosses during the Sabbath, they asked Pilate to have the legs broken and the bodies taken down. ³²The soldiers therefore came and broke the legs of the first man who had been crucified with Jesus, and then those of the other. ³³But when they came to Jesus and found that he was already dead, they did not break his legs. ³⁴Instead, one of the sol-

ᵃ 24 Psalm 22:18

genuine

Finals are coming up, you need to memorize lines for the play and you have extra practices before basketball play-offs. Your parents expect you to keep up with chores, babysit your little sister and be there for "family time." You can barely juggle all your own commitments, let alone help out anybody else! You think *you've* got a lot going on—check out Jesus. On the cross, Jesus looked beyond his own pain and his own issues to make sure that his mom was taken care of. Let's just say it's a matter of priorities sometimes.

character » 19:26-27

diers pierced Jesus' side with a spear, bringing a sudden flow of blood and water. [35]The man who saw it has given testimony, and his testimony is true. He knows that he tells the truth, and he testifies so that you also may believe. [36]These things happened so that the scripture would be fulfilled: "Not one of his bones will be broken," [a] [37]and, as another scripture says, "They will look on the one they have pierced." [b]

The Burial of Jesus

[38]Later, Joseph of Arimathea asked Pilate for the body of Jesus. Now Joseph was a disciple of Jesus, but secretly because he feared the Jews. With Pilate's permission, he came and took the body away. [39]He was accompanied by Nicodemus, the man who earlier had visited Jesus at night. Nicodemus brought a mixture of myrrh and aloes, about seventy-five pounds. [c] [40]Taking Jesus' body, the two of them wrapped it, with the spices, in strips of linen. This was in accordance with Jewish burial customs. [41]At the place where Jesus was crucified, there was a garden, and in the garden a new tomb, in which no one had ever been laid. [42]Because it was the Jewish day of Preparation and since the tomb was nearby, they laid Jesus there.

The Empty Tomb

20 Early on the first day of the week, while it was still dark, Mary Magdalene went to the tomb and saw that the stone had been removed from the entrance. [2]So she came running to Simon Peter and the other disciple, the one Jesus loved, and said, "They have taken the Lord out of the tomb, and we don't know where they have put him!"

[3]So Peter and the other disciple started for the tomb. [4]Both were running, but the other disciple outran Peter and reached the tomb first. [5]He bent over and looked in at the strips of linen lying there but did not go in. [6]Then Simon Peter, who was behind him, arrived and went into the tomb. He saw the strips of linen lying there, [7]as well as the burial cloth that had been around Jesus' head. The cloth was folded up by itself, separate from the linen. [8]Finally the other disciple, who had reached the tomb first, also went inside. He saw and believed. [9](They still did not understand from Scripture that Jesus had to rise from the dead.)

Jesus Appears to Mary Magdalene

[10]Then the disciples went back to their homes, [11]but Mary stood outside the tomb crying. As she wept, she bent over to look into the tomb [12]and saw two angels in white, seated where Jesus' body had been, one at the head and the other at the foot.

[13]They asked her, "Woman, why are you crying?"

"They have taken my Lord away," she said, "and I don't know where they have put him." [14]At this, she turned around and saw Jesus standing there, but she did not realize that it was Jesus.

[15]"Woman," he said, "why are you crying? Who is it you are looking for?"

Thinking he was the gardener, she said, "Sir, if you have carried him away, tell me where you have put him, and I will get him."

[16]Jesus said to her, "Mary."

She turned toward him and cried out in Aramaic, "Rabboni!" (which means Teacher).

---

[a] 36 Exodus 12:46; Num. 9:12; Psalm 34:20   [b] 37 Zech. 12:10   [c] 39 Greek *a hundred litrai* (about 34 kilograms)

[17]Jesus said, "Do not hold on to me, for I have not yet returned to the Father. Go instead to my brothers and tell them, 'I am returning to my Father and your Father, to my God and your God.' "
[18]Mary Magdalene went to the disciples with the news: "I have seen the Lord!" And she told them that he had said these things to her.

Jesus Appears to His Disciples

[19]On the evening of that first day of the week, when the disciples were together, with the doors locked for fear of the Jews, Jesus came and stood among them and said, "Peace be with you!" [20]After he said this, he showed them his hands and side. The disciples were overjoyed when they saw the Lord.

[21]Again Jesus said, "Peace be with you! As the Father has sent me, I am sending you." [22]And with that he breathed on them and said, "Receive the Holy Spirit. [23]If you forgive anyone his sins, they are forgiven; if you do not forgive them, they are not forgiven."

Jesus Appears to Thomas

[24]Now Thomas (called Didymus), one of the Twelve, was not with the disciples when Jesus came. [25]So the other disciples told him, "We have seen the Lord!"

But he said to them, "Unless I see the nail marks in his hands and put my finger where the nails were, and put my hand into his side, I will not believe it."

[26]A week later his disciples were in the house again, and Thomas was with them. Though the doors were locked, Jesus came and stood among them and said, "Peace be with you!" [27]Then he said to Thomas, "Put your finger here; see my hands. Reach out your hand and put it into my side. Stop doubting and believe."

[28]Thomas said to him, "My Lord and my God!"

[29]Then Jesus told him, "Because you have seen me, you have believed; blessed are those who have not seen and yet have believed."

[30]Jesus did many other miraculous signs in the presence of his disciples, which are not recorded in this book. [31]But these are written that you may[a] believe that Jesus is the Christ, the Son of God, and that by believing you may have life in his name.

truth or dare

Hey! That's *us* he's talking about here! We haven't seen Jesus, yet we believe in him. That kind of faith really pleases the Lord.

20:29

Jesus and the Miraculous Catch of Fish

21 Afterward Jesus appeared again to his disciples, by the Sea of Tiberias.[b] It happened this way: [2]Simon Peter, Thomas (called Didymus), Nathanael from Cana in Galilee, the sons of Zebedee, and two other disciples were together. [3]"I'm going out to fish," Simon Peter told them, and they said, "We'll go with you." So they went out and got into the boat, but that night they caught nothing.

[4]Early in the morning, Jesus stood on the shore, but the disciples did not realize that it was Jesus.

[5]He called out to them, "Friends, haven't you any fish?"

"No," they answered.

[6]He said, "Throw your net on the right side of the boat and you will find some." When they did, they were unable to haul the net in because of the large number of fish.

[7]Then the disciple whom Jesus loved said to Peter, "It is the Lord!" As soon as Simon Peter heard him say, "It is the Lord," he wrapped his outer garment around him (for he had taken it off) and jumped into the water. [8]The other disciples followed in the boat, towing the net full of fish, for they were not far from shore, about a hundred yards.[c] [9]When they landed, they saw a fire of burning coals there with fish on it, and some bread.

[10]Jesus said to them, "Bring some of the fish you have just caught."

---

[a] 31 Some manuscripts *may continue to*   [b] 1 That is, Sea of Galilee   [c] 8 Greek *about two hundred cubits* (about 90 meters)

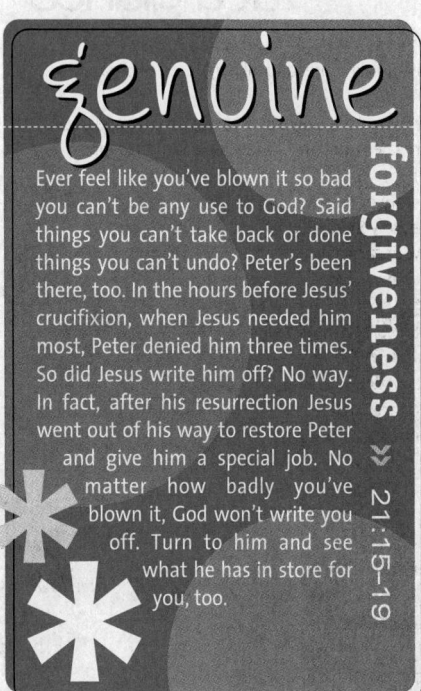

genuine

forgiveness » 21:15–19

Ever feel like you've blown it so bad you can't be any use to God? Said things you can't take back or done things you can't undo? Peter's been there, too. In the hours before Jesus' crucifixion, when Jesus needed him most, Peter denied him three times. So did Jesus write him off? No way. In fact, after his resurrection Jesus went out of his way to restore Peter and give him a special job. No matter how badly you've blown it, God won't write you off. Turn to him and see what he has in store for you, too.

[11] Simon Peter climbed aboard and dragged the net ashore. It was full of large fish, 153, but even with so many the net was not torn. [12] Jesus said to them, "Come and have breakfast." None of the disciples dared ask him, "Who are you?" They knew it was the Lord. [13] Jesus came, took the bread and gave it to them, and did the same with the fish. [14] This was now the third time Jesus appeared to his disciples after he was raised from the dead.

Jesus Reinstates Peter

[15] When they had finished eating, Jesus said to Simon Peter, "Simon son of John, do you truly love me more than these?"

"Yes, Lord," he said, "you know that I love you."

Jesus said, "Feed my lambs."

[16] Again Jesus said, "Simon son of John, do you truly love me?"

He answered, "Yes, Lord, you know that I love you."

Jesus said, "Take care of my sheep."

[17] The third time he said to him, "Simon son of John, do you love me?"

Peter was hurt because Jesus asked him the third time, "Do you love me?" He said, "Lord, you know all things; you know that I love you."

Jesus said, "Feed my sheep. [18] I tell you the truth, when you were younger you dressed yourself and went where you wanted; but when you are old you will stretch out your hands, and someone else will dress you and lead you where you do not want to go." [19] Jesus said this to indicate the kind of death by which Peter would glorify God. Then he said to him, "Follow me!"

[20] Peter turned and saw that the disciple whom Jesus loved was following them. (This was the one who had leaned back against Jesus at the supper and had said, "Lord, who is going to betray you?") [21] When Peter saw him, he asked, "Lord, what about him?"

[22] Jesus answered, "If I want him to remain alive until I return, what is that to you? You must follow me." [23] Because of this, the rumor spread among the brothers that this disciple would not die. But Jesus did not say that he would not die; he only said, "If I want him to remain alive until I return, what is that to you?"

[24] This is the disciple who testifies to these things and who wrote them down. We know that his testimony is true.

[25] Jesus did many other things as well. If every one of them were written down, I suppose that even the whole world would not have room for the books that would be written.

truth or dare

In just three years of ministry, Jesus accomplished so much that John couldn't even write it all down. Fortunately, the most amazing thing he did didn't stay a secret.

21:25

author:	Luke.
date:	Probably about A.D. 63.
setting:	The message of Jesus Christ quickly spread to all parts of the Roman Empire.
verse to remember:	"But you will receive power when the Holy Spirit comes on you; and you will be my witnesses in Jerusalem, and in all Judea and Samaria, and to the ends of the earth" (1:8).
theme to consider:	The book of Acts tells the story of men and women who spread the gospel with the help of the Holy Spirit. Read it and allow the Spirit to move you to boldly share your faith with others.

acts

unchanging truth

You'd had enough of just playing church. It was time to get serious about God. "Let's start a Bible study at school," you decided at the campfire on the last night of church camp one summer. "Who knows what might happen?"

No one could have guessed then how God was going to use you and your group of friends.

At first, people wondered what you were doing. Sitting in a group in the courtyard during lunch. Laughing. Talking. Praying together. Reading God's Word. Then some of those people started hanging around. Listening in. Taking a seat.

Before you knew it, something special was taking place. God was there! People accepted Christ. A couple of kids brought their guitars and played praise choruses. It was awesome! God was doing his thing, and no one and nothing could stop it.

This is exactly what happened in the book of Acts—a small group of people got serious about God, and God blew them away with his power. What started as a meeting on the second story of a small building grew to thousands of people as God used the disciples and others to start the very first church. The message of Jesus Christ spread from city to city and eventually spread across the world.

And it all started with one small group who, empowered by God's Holy Spirit, decided to change the world by beginning in their own backyard.

life lessons

1 Being a witness for Jesus starts in your own backyard—in your school, with your friends, even in your own home (1:8).

2 The Christian life isn't meant to be lived alone. When you're committed to Jesus, you also have to be committed to his church. Do you genuinely love and support the church (2:42–47; 4:32–37)?

3 Living for Jesus is risky business. Are you willing to risk everything—your reputation, your image, even your life—for him (5:12–42; 6:8—7:60)?

Jesus Taken Up Into Heaven

In my former book, Theophilus, I wrote about all that Jesus began to do and to teach ²until the day he was taken up to heaven, after giving instructions through the Holy Spirit to the apostles he had chosen. ³After his suffering, he showed himself to these men and gave many convincing proofs that he was alive. He appeared to them over a period of forty days and spoke about the kingdom of God. ⁴On one occasion, while he was eating with them, he gave them this command: "Do not leave Jerusalem, but wait for the gift my Father promised, which you have heard me speak about. ⁵For John baptized with ᵃ water, but in a few days you will be baptized with the Holy Spirit."

⁶So when they met together, they asked him, "Lord, are you at this time going to restore the kingdom to Israel?"

⁷He said to them: "It is not for you to know the times or dates the Father has set by his own authority. ⁸But you will receive power when the Holy Spirit comes on you; and you will be my witnesses in Jerusalem, and in all Judea and Samaria, and to the ends of the earth."

⁹After he said this, he was taken up before their very eyes, and a cloud hid him from their sight.

¹⁰They were looking intently up into the sky as he was going, when suddenly two men dressed in white stood beside them. ¹¹"Men of Galilee," they said, "why do you stand here looking into the sky? This same Jesus, who has been taken from you into heaven, will come back in the same way you have seen him go into heaven."

truth or dare

No mysterious Big Foot-like "sightings" of Jesus after his resurrection. For 40 days he openly appeared to people. The evidence is clear, and many witnesses confirmed it: Jesus is alive!

1:3

Matthias Chosen to Replace Judas

¹²Then they returned to Jerusalem from the hill called the Mount of Olives, a Sabbath day's walk ᵇ from the city. ¹³When they arrived, they went upstairs to the room where they were staying. Those present were Peter, John, James and Andrew; Philip and Thomas, Bartholomew and Matthew; James son of Alphaeus and Simon the Zealot, and Judas son of James. ¹⁴They all joined together constantly in prayer, along with the women and Mary the mother of Jesus, and with his brothers.

¹⁵In those days Peter stood up among the believers ᶜ (a group numbering about a hundred and twenty) ¹⁶and said, "Brothers, the Scripture had to be fulfilled which the Holy Spirit spoke long ago through the mouth of David concerning Judas, who served as guide for those who arrested Jesus— ¹⁷he was one of our number and shared in this ministry."

¹⁸(With the reward he got for his wickedness, Judas bought a field; there he fell headlong, his body burst open and all his intestines spilled out. ¹⁹Everyone in Jerusalem heard about this, so they called that field in their language Akeldama, that is, Field of Blood.)

²⁰"For," said Peter, "it is written in the book of Psalms,

" 'May his place be deserted;
let there be no one to dwell in it,' ᵈ

and,

" 'May another take his place of leadership.' ᵉ

²¹Therefore it is necessary to choose one of the men who have been with us the whole time the Lord Jesus went in and out among us, ²²beginning from John's baptism to the time when Jesus was taken up from us. For one of these must become a witness with us of his resurrection."

²³So they proposed two men: Joseph called Barsabbas (also known as Justus) and Matthias. ²⁴Then they prayed, "Lord, you know everyone's heart. Show us which of these two you have chosen ²⁵to take over this apostolic ministry, which Judas left to go where he belongs." ²⁶Then they cast lots, and the lot fell to Matthias; so he was added to the eleven apostles.

ᵃ 5 Or *in*   ᵇ 12 That is, about 3/4 mile (about 1,100 meters)   ᶜ 15 Greek *brothers*   ᵈ 20 Psalm 69:25
ᵉ 20 Psalm 109:8

The Holy Spirit Comes at Pentecost

2 When the day of Pentecost came, they were all together in one place. ²Suddenly a sound like the blowing of a violent wind came from heaven and filled the whole house where they were sitting. ³They saw what seemed to be tongues of fire that separated and came to rest on each of them. ⁴All of them were filled with the Holy Spirit and began to speak in other tongues*ᵃ* as the Spirit enabled them.

⁵Now there were staying in Jerusalem God-fearing Jews from every nation under heaven. ⁶When they heard this sound, a crowd came together in bewilderment, because each one heard them speaking in his own language. ⁷Utterly amazed, they asked: "Are not all these men who are speaking Galileans? ⁸Then how is it that each of us hears them in his own native language? ⁹Parthians, Medes and Elamites; residents of Mesopotamia, Judea and Cappadocia, Pontus and Asia, ¹⁰Phrygia and Pamphylia, Egypt and the parts of Libya near Cyrene; visitors from Rome ¹¹(both Jews and converts to Judaism); Cretans and Arabs—we hear them declaring the wonders of God in our own tongues!" ¹²Amazed and perplexed, they asked one another, "What does this mean?"

¹³Some, however, made fun of them and said, "They have had too much wine.*ᵇ*"

truth or dare

The Holy Spirit's arrival on the scene made a big impact. In fact, God's presence always creates a commotion in hearts and lives. Are you filled with his Spirit?
2:1–4

Peter Addresses the Crowd

¹⁴Then Peter stood up with the Eleven, raised his voice and addressed the crowd: "Fellow Jews and all of you who live in Jerusalem, let me explain this to you; listen carefully to what I say. ¹⁵These men are not drunk, as you suppose. It's only nine in the morning! ¹⁶No, this is what was spoken by the prophet Joel:

¹⁷" 'In the last days, God says,
    I will pour out my Spirit on all people.
Your sons and daughters will prophesy,
    your young men will see visions,
    your old men will dream dreams.
¹⁸Even on my servants, both men and women,
    I will pour out my Spirit in those days,
    and they will prophesy.
¹⁹I will show wonders in the heaven above
    and signs on the earth below,
    blood and fire and billows of smoke.
²⁰The sun will be turned to darkness
    and the moon to blood
    before the coming of the great and glorious day of the Lord.
²¹And everyone who calls
    on the name of the Lord will be saved.'*ᶜ*

²²"Men of Israel, listen to this: Jesus of Nazareth was a man accredited by God to you by miracles, wonders and signs, which God did among you through him, as you yourselves know. ²³This man was handed over to you by God's set purpose and foreknowledge; and you, with the help of wicked men,*ᵈ* put him to death by nailing him to the cross. ²⁴But God raised him from the dead, freeing him from the agony of death, because it was impossible for death to keep its hold on him. ²⁵David said about him:

" 'I saw the Lord always before me.
    Because he is at my right hand,

---

a 4 Or *languages*; also in verse 11   *b 13* Or *sweet wine*   *c 21* Joel 2:28-32   *d 23* Or *of those not having the law* (that is, Gentiles)

truth or dare

Sometimes we make salvation seem overly complex, like a "50-Step Method to Being Saved." It's actually simple, though—just call out to Jesus in faith.

2:21

I will not be shaken.
²⁶ Therefore my heart is glad and
my tongue rejoices;
my body also will live in hope,
²⁷ because you will not abandon me
to the grave,
nor will you let your Holy One
see decay.
²⁸ You have made known to me the
paths of life;
you will fill me with joy in your
presence.'ᵃ

²⁹"Brothers, I can tell you confidently that the patriarch David died and was buried, and his tomb is here to this day. ³⁰But he was a prophet and knew that God had promised him on oath that he would place one of his descendants on his throne. ³¹Seeing what was ahead, he spoke of the resurrection of the Christ,ᵇ that he was not abandoned to the grave, nor did his body see decay. ³²God has raised this Jesus to life, and we are all witnesses of the fact. ³³Exalted to the right hand of God, he has received from the Father the promised Holy Spirit and has poured out what you now see and hear. ³⁴For David did not ascend to heaven, and yet he said,

" 'The Lord said to my Lord:
"Sit at my right hand
³⁵ until I make your enemies
a footstool for your feet." ' ᶜ

genuine relationships

Okay, moment of truth: Why do you *really* go to church? Because your parents make you? To see that hot guy in your youth group? Back in Acts when the church first started, the early Christians had a clear purpose in mind—teaching, fellowship, communion ("breaking bread") and prayer. God's plan for church involvement isn't just getting together and shootin' the breeze; it's challenging each other and keeping our eyes focused on God. How pure is *your* motivation?

2:42-43

³⁶"Therefore let all Israel be assured of this: God has made this Jesus, whom you crucified, both Lord and Christ."

³⁷When the people heard this, they were cut to the heart and said to Peter and the other apostles, "Brothers, what shall we do?"

³⁸Peter replied, "Repent and be baptized, every one of you, in the name of Jesus Christ for the forgiveness of your sins. And you will receive the gift of the Holy Spirit. ³⁹The promise is for you and your children and for all who are far off—for all whom the Lord our God will call."

⁴⁰With many other words he warned them; and he pleaded with them, "Save yourselves from this corrupt generation." ⁴¹Those who accepted his message were baptized, and about three thousand were added to their number that day.

The Fellowship of the Believers

⁴²They devoted themselves to the apostles' teaching and to the fellowship, to the breaking of bread and to prayer. ⁴³Everyone was filled with awe, and many wonders and miraculous signs were done by the apostles. ⁴⁴All the believers were together and had ev-

ᵃ 28 Psalm 16:8-11   ᵇ 31 Or *Messiah*. "The Christ" (Greek) and "the Messiah" (Hebrew) both mean "the Anointed One"; also in verse 36.   ᶜ 35 Psalm 110:1

erything in common. [45]Selling their possessions and goods, they gave to anyone as he had need. [46]Every day they continued to meet together in the temple courts. They broke bread in their homes and ate together with glad and sincere hearts, [47]praising God and enjoying the favor of all the people. And the Lord added to their number daily those who were being saved.

Peter Heals the Crippled Beggar

3 One day Peter and John were going up to the temple at the time of prayer—at three in the afternoon. [2]Now a man crippled from birth was being carried to the temple gate called Beautiful, where he was put every day to beg from those going into the temple courts. [3]When he saw Peter and John about to enter, he asked them for money. [4]Peter looked straight at him, as did John. Then Peter said, "Look at us!" [5]So the man gave them his attention, expecting to get something from them.

[6]Then Peter said, "Silver or gold I do not have, but what I have I give you. In the name of Jesus Christ of Nazareth, walk." [7]Taking him by the right hand, he helped him up, and instantly the man's feet and ankles became strong. [8]He jumped to his feet and began to walk. Then he went with them into the temple courts, walking and jumping, and praising God. [9]When all the people saw him walking and praising God, [10]they recognized him as the same man who used to sit begging at the temple gate called Beautiful, and they were filled with wonder and amazement at what had happened to him.

truth or dare

In life, we often ask for too little. Catching a few coins would've made this man's day. But he didn't dare ask for what he *really* needed. Have big faith.

3:1–8

Peter Speaks to the Onlookers

[11]While the beggar held on to Peter and John, all the people were astonished and came running to them in the place called Solomon's Colonnade. [12]When Peter saw this, he said to them: "Men of Israel, why does this surprise you? Why do you stare at us as if by our own power or godliness we had made this man walk? [13]The God of Abraham, Isaac and Jacob, the God of our fathers, has glorified his servant Jesus. You handed him over to be killed, and you disowned him before Pilate, though he had decided to let him go. [14]You disowned the Holy and Righteous One and asked that a murderer be released to you. [15]You killed the author of life, but God raised him from the dead. We are witnesses of this. [16]By faith in the name of Jesus, this man whom you see and know was made strong. It is Jesus' name and the faith that comes through him that has given this complete healing to him, as you can all see.

[17]"Now, brothers, I know that you acted in ignorance, as did your leaders. [18]But this is how God fulfilled what he had foretold through all the prophets, saying that his Christ[a] would suffer. [19]Repent, then, and turn to God, so that your sins may be wiped out, that times of refreshing may come from the Lord, [20]and that he may send the Christ, who has been appointed for you—even Jesus. [21]He must remain in heaven until the time comes for God to restore everything, as he promised long ago through his holy prophets. [22]For Moses said, 'The Lord your God will raise up for you a prophet like me from among your own people; you must listen to everything he tells you. [23]Anyone who does not listen to him will be completely cut off from among his people.'[b]

[24]"Indeed, all the prophets from Samuel on, as many as have spoken, have foretold these days. [25]And you are heirs of the prophets and of the covenant God made with your fathers. He said to Abraham, 'Through your offspring all peoples on earth will be blessed.'[c] [26]When God raised up his servant, he sent him first to you to bless you by turning each of you from your wicked ways."

Peter and John Before the Sanhedrin

4 The priests and the captain of the temple guard and the Sadducees came up to Peter and John while they were speaking to the people. [2]They were greatly disturbed because the apostles were teaching the people and proclaiming in Jesus the resurrection of the dead. [3]They

a 18 Or *Messiah*; also in verse 20   *b 23* Deut. 18:15,18,19   *c 25* Gen. 22:18; 26:4

seized Peter and John, and because it was evening, they put them in jail until the next day. [4]But many who heard the message believed, and the number of men grew to about five thousand.

[5]The next day the rulers, elders and teachers of the law met in Jerusalem. [6]Annas the high priest was there, and so were Caiaphas, John, Alexander and the other men of the high priest's family. [7]They had Peter and John brought before them and began to question them: "By what power or what name did you do this?"

[8]Then Peter, filled with the Holy Spirit, said to them: "Rulers and elders of the people! [9]If we are being called to account today for an act of kindness shown to a cripple and are asked how he was healed, [10]then know this, you and all the people of Israel: It is by the name of Jesus Christ of Nazareth, whom you crucified but whom God raised from the dead, that this man stands before you healed. [11]He is

" 'the stone you builders rejected,
which has become the capstone.[a][b]

[12]Salvation is found in no one else, for there is no other name under heaven given to men by which we must be saved."

[13]When they saw the courage of Peter and John and realized that they were unschooled, ordinary men, they were astonished and they took note that these men had been with Jesus. [14]But since they could see the man who had been healed standing there with them, there was nothing they could say. [15]So they ordered them to withdraw from the Sanhedrin and then conferred together. [16]"What are we going to do with these men?" they asked. "Everybody living in Jerusalem knows they have done an outstanding miracle, and we cannot deny it. [17]But to stop this thing from spreading any further among the people, we must warn these men to speak no longer to anyone in this name."

truth or dare

Truth (with a capital T) isn't like the flavor of the day. Tomorrow and forever, Jesus will *still* be the only one who saves.

4:12

[18]Then they called them in again and commanded them not to speak or teach at all in the name of Jesus. [19]But Peter and John replied, "Judge for yourselves whether it is right in God's sight to obey you rather than God. [20]For we cannot help speaking about what we have seen and heard."

[21]After further threats they let them go. They could not decide how to punish them, because all the people were praising God for what had happened. [22]For the man who was miraculously healed was over forty years old.

The Believers' Prayer

[23]On their release, Peter and John went back to their own people and reported all that the chief priests and elders had said to them. [24]When they heard this, they raised their voices together in prayer to God. "Sovereign Lord," they said, "you made the heaven and the earth and the sea, and everything in them. [25]You spoke by the Holy Spirit through the mouth of your servant, our father David:

" 'Why do the nations rage
and the peoples plot in vain?
[26]The kings of the earth take their stand
and the rulers gather together
against the Lord
and against his Anointed One.[c][d]

[27]Indeed Herod and Pontius Pilate met together with the Gentiles and the people[e] of Israel in this city to conspire against your holy servant Jesus, whom you anointed. [28]They did what your power and will had decided beforehand should happen. [29]Now, Lord, consider their threats and enable

a 11 Or *cornerstone*   *b 11* Psalm 118:22   *c 26* That is, Christ or Messiah   *d 26* Psalm 2:1,2   *e 27* The Greek is plural.

your servants to speak your word with great boldness. ³⁰Stretch out your hand to heal and perform miraculous signs and wonders through the name of your holy servant Jesus."

³¹After they prayed, the place where they were meeting was shaken. And they were all filled with the Holy Spirit and spoke the word of God boldly.

The Believers Share Their Possessions

³²All the believers were one in heart and mind. No one claimed that any of his possessions was his own, but they shared everything they had. ³³With great power the apostles continued to testify to the resurrection of the Lord Jesus, and much grace was upon them all. ³⁴There were no needy persons among them. For from time to time those who owned lands or houses sold them, brought the money from the sales ³⁵and put it at the apostles' feet, and it was distributed to anyone as he had need.

³⁶Joseph, a Levite from Cyprus, whom the apostles called Barnabas (which means Son of Encouragement), ³⁷sold a field he owned and brought the money and put it at the apostles' feet.

Ananias and Sapphira

5 Now a man named Ananias, together with his wife Sapphira, also sold a piece of property. ²With his wife's full knowledge he kept back part of the money for himself, but brought the rest and put it at the apostles' feet.

³Then Peter said, "Ananias, how is it that Satan has so filled your heart that you have lied to the Holy Spirit and have kept for yourself some of the money you received for the land? ⁴Didn't it belong to you before it was sold? And after it was sold, wasn't the money at your disposal? What made you think of doing such a thing? You have not lied to men but to God."

⁵When Ananias heard this, he fell down and died. And great fear seized all who heard what had happened. ⁶Then the young men came forward, wrapped up his body, and carried him out and buried him.

⁷About three hours later his wife came in, not knowing what had happened. ⁸Peter asked her, "Tell me, is this the price you and Ananias got for the land?"

"Yes," she said, "that is the price."

⁹Peter said to her, "How could you agree to test the Spirit of the Lord? Look! The feet of the men who buried your husband are at the door, and they will carry you out also."

¹⁰At that moment she fell down at his feet and died. Then the young men came in and, finding her dead, carried her out and buried her beside her husband. ¹¹Great fear seized the whole church and all who heard about these events.

The Apostles Heal Many

¹²The apostles performed many miraculous signs and wonders among the people. And all the believers used to meet together in Solomon's Colonnade. ¹³No one else dared join them, even though they were highly regarded by the people. ¹⁴Nevertheless, more and more men and women believed in the Lord and were added to their number. ¹⁵As a result, people brought the sick into the streets and laid them on beds and mats so that at least Peter's shadow might fall on some of

genuine confidence » 4:29

When the going got tough, these believers got . . . bolder?! Their lives were threatened, so, naturally, they prayed. But do you notice what they *didn't* pray for? They *didn't* ask God to miraculously intervene and change their enemies' hearts. They *didn't* pray for God to make their lives easy and comfortable. Instead, they asked God for great boldness so they could continue to speak out in spite of any fear. When you're on the hot seat for your faith, what are you praying for? An easier life? Or the boldness to speak out?

them as he passed by. ¹⁶Crowds gathered also from the towns around Jerusalem, bringing their sick and those tormented by evil ᵃ spirits, and all of them were healed.

The Apostles Persecuted

¹⁷Then the high priest and all his associates, who were members of the party of the Sadducees, were filled with jealousy. ¹⁸They arrested the apostles and put them in the public jail. ¹⁹But during the night an angel of the Lord opened the doors of the jail and brought them out. ²⁰"Go, stand in the temple courts," he said, "and tell the people the full message of this new life."

²¹At daybreak they entered the temple courts, as they had been told, and began to teach the people.

When the high priest and his associates arrived, they called together the Sanhedrin—the full assembly of the elders of Israel—and sent to the jail for the apostles. ²²But on arriving at the jail, the officers did not find them there. So they went back and reported, ²³"We found the jail securely locked, with the guards standing at the doors; but when we opened them, we found no one inside." ²⁴On hearing this report, the captain of the temple guard and the chief priests were puzzled, wondering what would come of this.

²⁵Then someone came and said, "Look! The men you put in jail are standing in the temple courts teaching the people." ²⁶At that, the captain went with his officers and brought the apostles. They did not use force, because they feared that the people would stone them.

²⁷Having brought the apostles, they made them appear before the Sanhedrin to be questioned by the high priest. ²⁸"We gave you strict orders not to teach in this name," he said. "Yet you have filled Jerusalem with your teaching and are determined to make us guilty of this man's blood."

²⁹Peter and the other apostles replied: "We must obey God rather than men! ³⁰The God of our fathers raised Jesus from the dead—whom you had killed by hanging him on a tree. ³¹God exalted him to his own right hand as Prince and Savior that he might give repentance and forgiveness of sins to Israel. ³²We are witnesses of these things, and so is the Holy Spirit, whom God has given to those who obey him."

³³When they heard this, they were furious and wanted to put them to death. ³⁴But a Pharisee named Gamaliel, a teacher of the law, who was honored by all the people, stood up in the Sanhedrin and ordered that the men be put outside for a little while. ³⁵Then he addressed them: "Men of Israel, consider carefully what you intend to do to these men. ³⁶Some time ago Theudas appeared, claiming to be somebody, and about four hundred men rallied to him. He was killed, all his followers were dispersed, and it all came to nothing. ³⁷After him, Judas the Galilean appeared in the days of the census and led a band of people in revolt. He too was killed, and all his followers were scattered. ³⁸Therefore, in the present case I advise you: Leave these men alone! Let them go! For if their purpose or activity is of human origin, it will fail. ³⁹But if it is from God, you will not be able to stop these men; you will only find yourselves fighting against God."

⁴⁰His speech persuaded them. They called the apostles in and had them flogged. Then they ordered them not to speak in the name of Jesus, and let them go.

⁴¹The apostles left the Sanhedrin, rejoicing because they had been counted worthy of suffering disgrace for the Name. ⁴²Day af-

genuine

honor »» 5:41

Wait a minute! These guys just got flogged! That's a severe, bloody beating. Yet they waltzed out of there rejoicing? Were these guys award-winning actors, or did they take some morbid delight in getting beat up? Actually, they realized that suffering for Jesus was a great honor. He chose *them* to represent him before the skeptics, and that seemed like a privilege. When you get laughed at or treated unfairly because of your faith, consider the fact that Jesus chose you to represent him, and that's worth celebrating. He counted *you* worthy of his name.

ᵃ 16 Greek *unclean*

ter day, in the temple courts and from house to house, they never stopped teaching and proclaiming the good news that Jesus is the Christ.[a]

The Choosing of the Seven

6 In those days when the number of disciples was increasing, the Grecian Jews among them complained against the Hebraic Jews because their widows were being overlooked in the daily distribution of food. [2]So the Twelve gathered all the disciples together and said, "It would not be right for us to neglect the ministry of the word of God in order to wait on tables. [3]Brothers, choose seven men from among you who are known to be full of the Spirit and wisdom. We will turn this responsibility over to them [4]and will give our attention to prayer and the ministry of the word."

[5]This proposal pleased the whole group. They chose Stephen, a man full of faith and of the Holy Spirit; also Philip, Procorus, Nicanor, Timon, Parmenas, and Nicolas from Antioch, a convert to Judaism. [6]They presented these men to the apostles, who prayed and laid their hands on them.

[7]So the word of God spread. The number of disciples in Jerusalem increased rapidly, and a large number of priests became obedient to the faith.

Stephen Seized

[8]Now Stephen, a man full of God's grace and power, did great wonders and miraculous signs among the people. [9]Opposition arose, however, from members of the Synagogue of the Freedmen (as it was called)—Jews of Cyrene and Alexandria as well as the provinces of Cilicia and Asia. These men began to argue with Stephen, [10]but they could not stand up against his wisdom or the Spirit by whom he spoke.

[11]Then they secretly persuaded some men to say, "We have heard Stephen speak words of blasphemy against Moses and against God."

[12]So they stirred up the people and the elders and the teachers of the law. They seized Stephen and brought him before the Sanhedrin. [13]They produced false witnesses, who testified, "This fellow never stops speaking against this holy place and against the law. [14]For we have heard him say that this Jesus of Nazareth will destroy this place and change the customs Moses handed down to us."

[15]All who were sitting in the Sanhedrin looked intently at Stephen, and they saw that his face was like the face of an angel.

Stephen's Speech to the Sanhedrin

7 Then the high priest asked him, "Are these charges true?"

[2]To this he replied: "Brothers and fathers, listen to me! The God of glory appeared to our father Abraham while he was still in Mesopotamia, before he lived in Haran. [3]'Leave your country and your people,' God said, 'and go to the land I will show you.'[b]

[4]"So he left the land of the Chaldeans and settled in Haran. After the death of his father, God sent him to this land where you are now living. [5]He gave him no inheritance here, not even a foot of ground. But God promised him that he and his descendants after him would possess the land, even though at that time Abraham had no child. [6]God spoke to him in this way: 'Your descendants will be strangers in a country not their own, and they will be enslaved and mistreated four hundred years. [7]But I will punish the nation they serve as slaves,' God said, 'and afterward they will come out of that country and worship me in this place.'[c] [8]Then he gave Abraham the covenant of circumcision. And Abraham became the father of Isaac and circumcised him eight days after his birth. Later Isaac became the father of Jacob, and Jacob became the father of the twelve patriarchs.

[9]"Because the patriarchs were jealous of Joseph, they sold him as a slave into Egypt. But God was with him [10]and rescued him from all his troubles. He gave Joseph wisdom and enabled him to gain the goodwill of Pharaoh king of Egypt; so he made him ruler over Egypt and all his palace.

[11]"Then a famine struck all Egypt and Canaan, bringing great suffering, and our fathers could not find food. [12]When Jacob heard that there was grain in Egypt, he sent our fathers on their first visit. [13]On their second visit, Joseph told his brothers who he was, and Pharaoh learned about Joseph's family. [14]After this, Joseph sent for his father Jacob and his whole family, seventy-five in all. [15]Then Jacob went down to Egypt, where he and our fathers died. [16]Their bodies were brought

a 42 Or Messiah   b 3 Gen. 12:1   c 7 Gen. 15:13,14

mirror images

Sapphira—Deadly Deception

Can you spot a hypocrite? Someone who says one thing and does the opposite? Maybe it's the "Just Say No" supermodel who's arrested for drug use. Or the teen employee on the lookout for shoplifters—only to stuff clothes into her backpack after work. We call them fakes, frauds and phonies. And in the Bible, people called one of them . . . *Sapphira*.

Even though her name actually meant "beautiful," the sin in her heart was ugly. Sapphira and her husband Ananias were proud members of the early church. On the outside, they appeared to have a good thing going. They attended church services, fellowshipped with other believers and even sold some property—giving "all" the money to the church.

What's the big deal? we may wonder. *They kept a little back for spending money. So?* The problem wasn't the gift; it was the deception—conniving to keep some cash for themselves while telling everyone else they were giving it all. The apostle Peter called their bluff. But they didn't get busted just for lying to Peter. They were severely punished for lying to the Holy Spirit.

In an instant, the church learned a powerful lesson—no one gets away with lying to God. And while it's easy to call Sapphira a two-faced liar, our hearts can often hold some of the same ugliness. Have you ever prayed in public and said something you really didn't mean? Or sung a worship song while thinking about the girl you hate at school? Maybe you've told all your friends you're a Christian, but you've found ways to hold on to your "secret sins."

Ananias and Sapphira allowed Satan to fill them with lying and hypocrisy, and he'd love to do the same to you. Take a stand against his deception. Find a friend who keeps you accountable for your sins. And most importantly, ask God to help you live a life of complete honesty.

To read the next Mirror Images profile, go to page 1458.

Read more about Sapphira in Acts 5:1–10 (page 1450).

dear Jesus

Dear Jesus, I can learn a lot from Sapphira's example. Give me the courage and strength to resist Satan, and help me to "tell the truth" through what I say and do. Amen.

1453

back to Shechem and placed in the tomb that Abraham had bought from the sons of Hamor at Shechem for a certain sum of money.

[17]"As the time drew near for God to fulfill his promise to Abraham, the number of our people in Egypt greatly increased. [18]Then another king, who knew nothing about Joseph, became ruler of Egypt. [19]He dealt treacherously with our people and oppressed our forefathers by forcing them to throw out their newborn babies so that they would die.

[20]"At that time Moses was born, and he was no ordinary child.[a] For three months he was cared for in his father's house. [21]When he was placed outside, Pharaoh's daughter took him and brought him up as her own son. [22]Moses was educated in all the wisdom of the Egyptians and was powerful in speech and action.

[23]"When Moses was forty years old, he decided to visit his fellow Israelites. [24]He saw one of them being mistreated by an Egyptian, so he went to his defense and avenged him by killing the Egyptian. [25]Moses thought that his own people would realize that God was using him to rescue them, but they did not. [26]The next day Moses came upon two Israelites who were fighting. He tried to reconcile them by saying, 'Men, you are brothers; why do you want to hurt each other?'

[27]"But the man who was mistreating the other pushed Moses aside and said, 'Who made you ruler and judge over us? [28]Do you want to kill me as you killed the Egyptian yesterday?'[b] [29]When Moses heard this, he fled to Midian, where he settled as a foreigner and had two sons.

[30]"After forty years had passed, an angel appeared to Moses in the flames of a burning bush in the desert near Mount Sinai. [31]When he saw this, he was amazed at the sight. As he went over to look more closely, he heard the Lord's voice: [32]'I am the God of your fathers, the God of Abraham, Isaac and Jacob.'[c] Moses trembled with fear and did not dare to look.

[33]"Then the Lord said to him, 'Take off your sandals; the place where you are standing is holy ground. [34]I have indeed seen the oppression of my people in Egypt. I have heard their groaning and have come down to set them free. Now come, I will send you back to Egypt.'[d]

[35]"This is the same Moses whom they had rejected with the words, 'Who made you ruler and judge?' He was sent to be their ruler and deliverer by God himself, through the angel who appeared to him in the bush. [36]He led them out of Egypt and did wonders and miraculous signs in Egypt, at the Red Sea[e] and for forty years in the desert.

[37]"This is that Moses who told the Israelites, 'God will send you a prophet like me from your own people.'[f] [38]He was in the assembly in the desert, with the angel who spoke to him on Mount Sinai, and with our fathers; and he received living words to pass on to us.

[39]"But our fathers refused to obey him. Instead, they rejected him and in their hearts turned back to Egypt. [40]They told Aaron, 'Make us gods who will go before us. As for this fellow Moses who led us out of Egypt—we don't know what has happened to him!'[g] [41]That was the time they made an idol in the form of a calf. They brought sacrifices to it and held a celebration in honor of what their hands had made. [42]But God turned away and gave them over to the worship of the heavenly bodies. This agrees with what is written in the book of the prophets:

genuine forgiveness » 7:59-60

Put yourself in Stephen's place. He looked up into the angry faces of the mob that hated him. He locked eyes with his murderers as they pummeled his body with stones. Yet he asked God to forgive them. How is that humanly possible, to forgive someone for something so heinous? It's only possible through Jesus, the one who did it first. Even in dying, Stephen followed his Savior's example (see Luke 23:34). God can transform your heart and your attitudes in ways that might seem impossible to you now. Radical forgiveness is the mark of a follower of Jesus.

---

a 20 Or *was fair in the sight of God*   *b 28* Exodus 2:14   *c 32* Exodus 3:6   *d 34* Exodus 3:5,7,8,10   *e 36* That is, Sea of Reeds   *f 37* Deut. 18:15   *g 40* Exodus 32:1

" 'Did you bring me sacrifices and offerings
    forty years in the desert, O house of Israel?
[43] You have lifted up the shrine of Molech
    and the star of your god Rephan,
    the idols you made to worship.
Therefore I will send you into exile' [a] beyond Babylon.

[44]"Our forefathers had the tabernacle of the Testimony with them in the desert. It had been made as God directed Moses, according to the pattern he had seen. [45]Having received the tabernacle, our fathers under Joshua brought it with them when they took the land from the nations God drove out before them. It remained in the land until the time of David, [46]who enjoyed God's favor and asked that he might provide a dwelling place for the God of Jacob. [b] [47]But it was Solomon who built the house for him.

[48]"However, the Most High does not live in houses made by men. As the prophet says:

[49]" 'Heaven is my throne,
    and the earth is my footstool.
What kind of house will you build for me?
                   says the Lord.
Or where will my resting place be?
[50] Has not my hand made all these things?' [c]

[51]"You stiff-necked people, with uncircumcised hearts and ears! You are just like your fathers: You always resist the Holy Spirit! [52]Was there ever a prophet your fathers did not persecute? They even killed those who predicted the coming of the Righteous One. And now you have betrayed and murdered him— [53]you who have received the law that was put into effect through angels but have not obeyed it."

The Stoning of Stephen

[54]When they heard this, they were furious and gnashed their teeth at him. [55]But Stephen, full of the Holy Spirit, looked up to heaven and saw the glory of God, and Jesus standing at the right hand of God. [56]"Look," he said, "I see heaven open and the Son of Man standing at the right hand of God."

[57]At this they covered their ears and, yelling at the top of their voices, they all rushed at him, [58]dragged him out of the city and began to stone him. Meanwhile, the witnesses laid their clothes at the feet of a young man named Saul.

[59]While they were stoning him, Stephen prayed, "Lord Jesus, receive my spirit." [60]Then he fell on his knees and cried out, "Lord, do not hold this sin against them." When he had said this, he fell asleep.

8 And Saul was there, giving approval to his death.

The Church Persecuted and Scattered

On that day a great persecution broke out against the church at Jerusalem, and all except the apostles were scattered throughout Judea and Samaria. [2]Godly men buried Stephen and mourned deeply for him. [3]But Saul began to destroy the church. Going from house to house, he dragged off men and women and put them in prison.

Philip in Samaria

[4]Those who had been scattered preached the word wherever they went. [5]Philip went down to a city in Samaria and proclaimed the Christ [d] there. [6]When the crowds heard Philip and saw the miraculous signs he did, they all paid

truth *or dare*

Could persecution actually be a *good* thing? Yup. These believers faced massive harassment, got scattered and spread the Word everywhere. It was God's plan to mobilize the message.

8:1,4

---

[a] 43 Amos 5:25-27   [b] 46 Some early manuscripts *the house of Jacob*   [c] 50 Isaiah 66:1,2   [d] 5 Or *Messiah*

close attention to what he said. [7]With shrieks, evil[a] spirits came out of many, and many paralytics and cripples were healed. [8]So there was great joy in that city.

Simon the Sorcerer

[9]Now for some time a man named Simon had practiced sorcery in the city and amazed all the people of Samaria. He boasted that he was someone great, [10]and all the people, both high and low, gave him their attention and exclaimed, "This man is the divine power known as the Great Power." [11]They followed him because he had amazed them for a long time with his magic. [12]But when they believed Philip as he preached the good news of the kingdom of God and the name of Jesus Christ, they were baptized, both men and women. [13]Simon himself believed and was baptized. And he followed Philip everywhere, astonished by the great signs and miracles he saw.

[14]When the apostles in Jerusalem heard that Samaria had accepted the word of God, they sent Peter and John to them. [15]When they arrived, they prayed for them that they might receive the Holy Spirit, [16]because the Holy Spirit had not yet come upon any of them; they had simply been baptized into[b] the name of the Lord Jesus. [17]Then Peter and John placed their hands on them, and they received the Holy Spirit.

[18]When Simon saw that the Spirit was given at the laying on of the apostles' hands, he offered them money [19]and said, "Give me also this ability so that everyone on whom I lay my hands may receive the Holy Spirit."

[20]Peter answered: "May your money perish with you, because you thought you could buy the gift of God with money! [21]You have no part or share in this ministry, because your heart is not right before God. [22]Repent of this wickedness and pray to the Lord. Perhaps he will forgive you for having such a thought in your heart. [23]For I see that you are full of bitterness and captive to sin."

[24]Then Simon answered, "Pray to the Lord for me so that nothing you have said may happen to me."

[25]When they had testified and proclaimed the word of the Lord, Peter and John returned to Jerusalem, preaching the gospel in many Samaritan villages.

Philip and the Ethiopian

[26]Now an angel of the Lord said to Philip, "Go south to the road—the desert road—that goes down from Jerusalem to Gaza." [27]So he started out, and on his way he met an Ethiopian[c] eunuch, an important official in charge of all the treasury of Candace, queen of the Ethiopians. This man had gone to Jerusalem to worship, [28]and on his way home was sitting in his chariot reading the book of Isaiah the prophet. [29]The Spirit told Philip, "Go to that chariot and stay near it."

[30]Then Philip ran up to the chariot and heard the man reading Isaiah the prophet. "Do you understand what you are reading?" Philip asked.

[31]"How can I," he said, "unless someone explains it to me?" So he invited Philip to come up and sit with him.

[32]The eunuch was reading this passage of Scripture:

> "He was led like a sheep to the
>   slaughter,
> and as a lamb before the
>   shearer is silent,
> so he did not open his mouth.
> [33]In his humiliation he was deprived of justice.
>   Who can speak of his descendants?
>   For his life was taken from the earth."[d]

[34]The eunuch asked Philip, "Tell me, please, who is the prophet talking about, himself or someone else?" [35]Then Philip began with that very passage of Scripture and told him the good news about Jesus.

truth or dare

There's no magic formula for leading someone to Christ. Want to share God's love with your friends? Start where *they* are—appealing to their unique experiences, as Philip did.

8:29–35

a 7 Greek *unclean*   *b* 16 Or *in*   *c* 27 That is, from the upper Nile region   *d* 33 Isaiah 53:7,8

Are You a Good Friend?

1. Your bud's failing a class. You say . . .
- A. "Oh yeah, my brother failed a class once. That was tough."
- B. "How 'bout I come over and help you study?"
- C. "Oh, that's not good . . . So anyways—what do you think of my new jeans?"

2. What would your best friend say about you?
- A. "She's fun to hang out with, but I wouldn't go to her with any major problems."
- B. "I really like her, but I don't feel like she knows me that well yet."
- C. "She's always there for me—I can tell her anything, anytime."

3. Someone's bad-mouthin' your bud. You . . .
- A. Stick up for her—don't go messin' with my sista!
- B. Fidget nervously and try to change the subject.
- C. Laugh along with them—now is not the time to pick a fight.

4. Your best friend's crush starts grilling you about her. You . . .
- A. Tell him she's not interested and start flirting with him.
- B. Start describing her, but you can't keep your eyes off him. He's such a hottie!
- C. Talk her up and give him her #.

5. Your best friend is having a bad day and snaps at you. How do you react?
- A. Blow her off and give her some space for a couple days.
- B. Forgive and forget—you've had your off days, too.
- C. Want an argument? Bring it on!

6. Your bud is captain of the soccer team, and you're pretty good at keeping the bench warm. She just scored the game-winning goal. You . . .
- A. Run out and hug her—you're genuinely happy for her!
- B. Downplay it—you could have done the same thing if you were in the game.
- C. Slap her five in the locker room—sometimes you wish you could share in the glory.

7. It's been three months since your friend moved away (sad!). You . . .
- A. Called her two weeks ago, and she was doing okay then.
- B. Totally lost her address (whoops!). Was it North Carolina or South Carolina?
- C. IM her every day 'cause you know she must be lonely.

8. You're starting to become friends with some cooler girls, and they asked you to sit with them at lunch.
- A. You say "no thanks"—you know where your loyalties lie.
- B. You say "Sure, great!" and invite your friend to join you (knowing she won't have the guts to come).
- C. You say, "Good-bye, anonymity; hello, popularity!" Suddenly your best friend doesn't seem so cool anymore.

(A) (B) (C) (?)

1. A=1; B=2; C=0
2. A=0; B=1; C=2
3. A=2; B=1; C=0
4. A=0; B=1; C=2
5. A=1; B=2; C=0
6. A=2; B=0; C=1
7. A=1; B=0; C=2
8. A=2; B=1; C=0

Add up your points for each question and see what kind of friend you are.

Best Bud (13–16)

When it comes to friends, you're one of the best! Your friends value your loyalty and can come to you anytime. Remember, though, that you can never coast through friendships. You have to keep investing in them to make them work, so don't get too comfortable.

Fair-weather Friend (9–12)

You're a decent friend, but you have some work to do. Sometimes you get distracted by selfish motives and don't look out for your buds. Solid friendships are worth the effort, so start working, sista!

Convenient Companion (0–8)

Girl, you have some major work to do in the friendship department! Remember—in order to *have* a good friend, you first have to *be* a good friend. It starts by taking your focus off yourself and showing some interest in your girlfriends. If you don't work at it, you're gonna be very lonely someday soon.

What makes a good friend?

Loyalty, honesty, listening, caring, looking out for her interests, being happy for her success, overlooking faults, being encouraging. Does that describe you?

Friendship 101

Check out these classic friendships for some tips on how to take your friendships from good to great!

» Ruth and Naomi (Ruth 1:11–18)
» Jonathan and David (1 Samuel 18:1–4, 19:1–7, 20:1–42)
» Jesus and his disciples (John 13:1–17)

GIRLFRIEND TIP:

Don't take your buds for granted! Look for ways to keep building and growing your friendships!

What's Your Image?

4 What's on those lips of yours?
- A. Lipliner for definition, matte color and a dot of gloss on the lower lip for added fullness.
- B. Carmex or Blistex—whatever happens to be in your pocket at the time.
- C. Hard Candy lip gloss in your favorite shade.

5 What outfit makes you feel the most like *you*?
- A. A stylish black dress.
- B. Flannel pants, J. Crew shirt and a hoodie.
- C. That great t-ball shirt, retro jeans and a striped belt.

6 The 'do—do tell.
- A. Straightened and pulled back in matching little clips.
- B. Baseball cap with a messy ponytail.
- C. Long and natural (but you might get it all braided soon).

7 You'd most like to be known as . . .
- A. A beautiful girl.
- B. A talented athlete.
- C. A unique individual.

8 Your worst enemies would accuse you of being . . .
- A. Snotty and prissy.
- B. Tomboy-ish and sloppy.
- C. Weird and artsy.

9 Your most-worn pair of shoes is . . .
- A. Stylish sandals.
- B. Those comfy running shoes.
- C. Funky clogs you found at the thrift store.

10 When you're getting dressed in the morning, this thought runs through your head:
- A. I wonder what my friends are wearing today.
- B. Long day ahead . . . I've gotta grab my favorite jeans out of the laundry.
- C. I bought this whole outfit for less than $20!

1 In the bottom of your backpack, what would you find?
- A. First of all, you wouldn't be carrying a backpack—try "messenger bag." Inside would be one of your favorite catalogs.
- B. Workout clothes—you never know when the urge will hit.
- C. This great album you just found at the resale shop.

2 Your morning routine consists of . . .
- A. Straightening your hair, applying make-up perfectly and touching up your nails.
- B. Quick shower (or at least washing your face) and a granola bar for the road.
- C. Routine? What routine? I just roll out of bed and go to school.

3 A generous aunt gave you $50 for your birthday. How ya gonna spend it?
- A. The latest M.A.C. essentials, of course. You should see this season's new shades!
- B. On this awesome new Adidas gear—it will be great for training camp this summer!
- C. Tickets to a concert by your favorite underground band. Yes!

A B C ?

Mostly A 's—*Trendy Girl*

Style is your middle name. You always keep up with the latest fashions and coolest brands. You have this aura of beauty about you, and you have fun with it! Remember, there's nothing wrong with having fun with make-up, hair and clothes, as long as you don't obsess over them.

> *Tip:* Others may perceive you as a high-maintenance girl who spends a lot of time on her appearance. Be careful not to get too engrossed in your looks. Beauty is a gift that must be carried gracefully, and true beauty always begins on the inside.

Mostly B 's—*Sporty Girl*

Even if you're not a killer athlete, you enjoy the comfort of the casual, sporty look. Sweats, sneakers, pajama pants, t-shirts, baseball caps, old jeans, cotton shorts—you could happily live in your favorite clothes 24/7. You'd much rather keep it simple and enjoy life than stress about your make-up supply and shoe collection.

> *Tip:* Don't get stuck in a rut or judge others who are a bit more done-up than you. You may want to branch out and try another look every now and then.

Mostly C 's—*Alternative Girl*

You pride yourself on bucking the old status quo and being an individual. You're willing to try new styles and aren't locked into one standard look. You enjoy discovering new stores, new brands, new music. You view clothing as an outward expression of the inner you.

> *Tip:* There's no harm in being or looking different, but don't get so consumed with being an individual that you miss the joy of connecting with others. Build friendships with girls who are nothing like you. You might be surprised what you can learn from each other.

All mixed up—*Schizo Girl*

Okay, let's be honest here: We're dealing with stereotypes, and you obviously don't fit into any of 'em! You wear what you want and don't get stereotyped with one crowd. When it comes to style, you're just plain *you*—whatever you're in the mood for, that's what you throw on. And the beauty of it is that you have the multi-faceted personality to pull it off!

> *Tip:* Having friends of all kinds will help you become a well-rounded person. Use your personal style to reach out to girls you don't know. Remember, variety is the spice of life!

reflections from the other side

question:
What do you first notice about a girl's style?

answer:
I tend to like girls who have strong personalities, real outgoing girls, and don't care as much about their style. You know how you can tell when a girl's trying to be something she's not? Like she's working so hard at looking a certain way that she can barely hold a conversation? Definitely not relationship material.

"The LORD does not look at the things man looks at. Man looks at the outward appearance, but the LORD looks at the heart" (1 Samuel 16:7).

"**Charm is deceptive, and beauty is fleeting; but a woman who fears the LORD is to be praised**" (Proverbs 31:30).

[36]As they traveled along the road, they came to some water and the eunuch said, "Look, here is water. Why shouldn't I be baptized?"[a] [38]And he gave orders to stop the chariot. Then both Philip and the eunuch went down into the water and Philip baptized him. [39]When they came up out of the water, the Spirit of the Lord suddenly took Philip away, and the eunuch did not see him again, but went on his way rejoicing. [40]Philip, however, appeared at Azotus and traveled about, preaching the gospel in all the towns until he reached Caesarea.

Saul's Conversion

9 Meanwhile, Saul was still breathing out murderous threats against the Lord's disciples. He went to the high priest [2]and asked him for letters to the synagogues in Damascus, so that if he found any there who belonged to the Way, whether men or women, he might take them as prisoners to Jerusalem. [3]As he neared Damascus on his journey, suddenly a light from heaven flashed around him. [4]He fell to the ground and heard a voice say to him, "Saul, Saul, why do you persecute me?"

[5]"Who are you, Lord?" Saul asked.

"I am Jesus, whom you are persecuting," he replied. [6]"Now get up and go into the city, and you will be told what you must do."

[7]The men traveling with Saul stood there speechless; they heard the sound but did not see anyone. [8]Saul got up from the ground, but when he opened his eyes he could see nothing. So they led him by the hand into Damascus. [9]For three days he was blind, and did not eat or drink anything.

[10]In Damascus there was a disciple named Ananias. The Lord called to him in a vision, "Ananias!"

"Yes, Lord," he answered.

[11]The Lord told him, "Go to the house of Judas on Straight Street and ask for a man from Tarsus named Saul, for he is praying. [12]In a vision he has seen a man named Ananias come and place his hands on him to restore his sight."

[13]"Lord," Ananias answered, "I have heard many reports about this man and all the harm he has done to your saints in Jerusalem. [14]And he has come here with authority from the chief priests to arrest all who call on your name."

[15]But the Lord said to Ananias, "Go! This man is my chosen instrument to carry my name before the Gentiles and their kings and before the people of Israel. [16]I will show him how much he must suffer for my name."

[17]Then Ananias went to the house and entered it. Placing his hands on Saul, he said, "Brother Saul, the Lord—Jesus, who appeared to you on the road as you were coming here—has sent me so that you may see again and be filled with the Holy Spirit." [18]Immediately, something like scales fell from Saul's eyes, and he could see again. He got up and was baptized, [19]and after taking some food, he regained his strength.

Saul in Damascus and Jerusalem

Saul spent several days with the disciples in Damascus. [20]At once he began to preach in the synagogues that Jesus is the Son of God. [21]All those who heard him were astonished and asked, "Isn't he the man who raised havoc in Jerusalem among those who call on this name? And hasn't he come here to take them as prisoners to the chief priests?" [22]Yet Saul grew more and more powerful and baffled the Jews living in Damascus by proving that Jesus is the Christ.[b]

[23]After many days had gone by, the Jews conspired to kill him, [24]but Saul learned of their plan. Day and night they kept close watch on the city gates in order to kill him. [25]But his followers took him by night and lowered him in a basket through an opening in the wall.

[26]When he came to Jerusalem, he tried to join the disciples, but they were all afraid of him, not believing that he really was a disciple. [27]But Barnabas took him and brought him to the apostles. He told them how Saul on his journey had seen the Lord and that the Lord had spoken to him, and how in Damascus he had preached fearlessly in the name of Jesus. [28]So Saul stayed with them and moved about freely in Jerusalem, speaking boldly in the name of the Lord. [29]He talked and de-

a 36 Some late manuscripts baptized?" [37]Philip said, "If you believe with all your heart, you may." The eunuch answered, "I believe that Jesus Christ is the Son of God."   b 22 Or Messiah

mirror images

Dorcas—Behind the Scenes

Have you ever been accused of being a Dorcas? No, not a *dork*, a *Dorcas*. Seriously, this is no insult. It's actually quite a compliment! A girl like Dorcas serves others, volunteers her time for a ministry and takes care of needs before people even realize they have them. Steady, dependable and caring, she's no "high-maintenance" friend. Dorcas is a treasure.

In the Bible, we know many women followed Jesus and learned from him. But Dorcas was the only one mentioned as a "disciple." Not only did she listen to Jesus' teaching, but she also took on his lifestyle, serving others with abandon. Someone need an outfit for a new baby? Could an elderly woman use a friend to talk to? Was there a family in desperate need of food? Dorcas had it covered.

When Dorcas became sick and died, the people she had served called the apostle Peter into her room. They held up clothes she had made them and mourned the loss of this caring servant. Peter took Dorcas's limp hand and raised her to life. And the miracle done to this humble, servant-hearted woman became the big news in town, bringing many to believe in Jesus Christ.

Dorcas shows us that serving Jesus isn't about doing something people would call "big." It's about doing whatever you can to help others around you—quietly, unselfishly and lovingly—just like Jesus did. It may not win you any awards, but it will help you make relationships that matter for eternity.

To read the next Mirror Images profile, go to page 1504.

Dear Jesus, with your help, I'd like to choose the attitude Dorcas had. Keep my eyes peeled for needy people around me, and give me an opportunity to serve them today. Amen.

>> Read more about Dorcas in Acts 9:36–42 (page 1459).

bated with the Grecian Jews, but they tried to kill him. [30]When the brothers learned of this, they took him down to Caesarea and sent him off to Tarsus.

[31]Then the church throughout Judea, Galilee and Samaria enjoyed a time of peace. It was strengthened; and encouraged by the Holy Spirit, it grew in numbers, living in the fear of the Lord.

Aeneas and Dorcas

[32]As Peter traveled about the country, he went to visit the saints in Lydda. [33]There he found a man named Aeneas, a paralytic who had been bedridden for eight years. [34]"Aeneas," Peter said to him, "Jesus Christ heals you. Get up and take care of your mat." Immediately Aeneas got up. [35]All those who lived in Lydda and Sharon saw him and turned to the Lord.

[36]In Joppa there was a disciple named Tabitha (which, when translated, is Dorcas[a]), who was always doing good and helping the poor. [37]About that time she became sick and died, and her body was washed and placed in an upstairs room. [38]Lydda was near Joppa; so when the disciples heard that Peter was in Lydda, they sent two men to him and urged him, "Please come at once!"

[39]Peter went with them, and when he arrived he was taken upstairs to the room. All the widows stood around him, crying and showing him the robes and other clothing that Dorcas had made while she was still with them.

[40]Peter sent them all out of the room; then he got down on his knees and prayed. Turning toward the dead woman, he said, "Tabitha, get up." She opened her eyes, and seeing Peter she sat up. [41]He took her by the hand and helped her to her feet. Then he called the believers and the widows and presented her to them alive. [42]This became known all over Joppa, and many people believed in the Lord. [43]Peter stayed in Joppa for some time with a tanner named Simon.

Cornelius Calls for Peter

10 At Caesarea there was a man named Cornelius, a centurion in what was known as the Italian Regiment. [2]He and all his family were devout and God-fearing; he gave generously to those in need and prayed to God regularly. [3]One day at about three in the afternoon he had a vision. He distinctly saw an angel of God, who came to him and said, "Cornelius!"

[4]Cornelius stared at him in fear. "What is it, Lord?" he asked.

The angel answered, "Your prayers and gifts to the poor have come up as a memorial offering before God. [5]Now send men to Joppa to bring back a man named Simon who is called Peter. [6]He is staying with Simon the tanner, whose house is by the sea."

[7]When the angel who spoke to him had gone, Cornelius called two of his servants and a devout soldier who was one of his attendants. [8]He told them everything that had happened and sent them to Joppa.

Peter's Vision

[9]About noon the following day as they were on their journey and approaching the city, Peter went up on the roof to pray. [10]He became hungry and wanted something to eat, and while the meal was being prepared, he fell into a trance. [11]He saw heaven opened and something like a large sheet being let down to earth by its four corners. [12]It contained all kinds of four-footed animals, as well as reptiles of the earth and birds of the air. [13]Then a voice told him, "Get up, Peter. Kill and eat."

[14]"Surely not, Lord!" Peter replied. "I have never eaten anything impure or unclean."

[15]The voice spoke to him a second time, "Do not call anything impure that God has made clean."

[16]This happened three times, and immediately the sheet was taken back to heaven.

[17]While Peter was wondering about the meaning of the vision, the men sent by Cornelius found out where Simon's house was and stopped at the gate. [18]They called out, asking if Simon who was known as Peter was staying there.

[19]While Peter was still thinking about the vision, the Spirit said to him, "Simon, three[b] men are looking for you. [20]So get up and go downstairs. Do not hesitate to go with them, for I have sent them."

[21]Peter went down and said to the men, "I'm the one you're looking for. Why have you come?"

---

a 36 Both *Tabitha* (Aramaic) and *Dorcas* (Greek) mean *gazelle.*   *b 19* One early manuscript *two*; other manuscripts do not have the number.

²²The men replied, "We have come from Cornelius the centurion. He is a righteous and God-fearing man, who is respected by all the Jewish people. A holy angel told him to have you come to his house so that he could hear what you have to say." ²³Then Peter invited the men into the house to be his guests.

Peter at Cornelius's House

The next day Peter started out with them, and some of the brothers from Joppa went along. ²⁴The following day he arrived in Caesarea. Cornelius was expecting them and had called together his relatives and close friends. ²⁵As Peter entered the house, Cornelius met him and fell at his feet in reverence. ²⁶But Peter made him get up. "Stand up," he said, "I am only a man myself."

²⁷Talking with him, Peter went inside and found a large gathering of people. ²⁸He said to them: "You are well aware that it is against our law for a Jew to associate with a Gentile or visit him. But God has shown me that I should not call any man impure or unclean. ²⁹So when I was sent for, I came without raising any objection. May I ask why you sent for me?"

³⁰Cornelius answered: "Four days ago I was in my house praying at this hour, at three in the afternoon. Suddenly a man in shining clothes stood before me ³¹and said, 'Cornelius, God has heard your prayer and remembered your gifts to the poor. ³²Send to Joppa for Simon who is called Peter. He is a guest in the home of Simon the tanner, who lives by the sea.' ³³So I sent for you immediately, and it was good of you to come. Now we are all here in the presence of God to listen to everything the Lord has commanded you to tell us."

³⁴Then Peter began to speak: "I now realize how true it is that God does not show favoritism ³⁵but accepts men from every nation who fear him and do what is right. ³⁶You know the message God sent to the people of Israel, telling the good news of peace through Jesus Christ, who is Lord of all. ³⁷You know what has happened throughout Judea, beginning in Galilee after the baptism that John preached— ³⁸how God anointed Jesus of Nazareth with the Holy Spirit and power, and how he went around doing good and healing all who were under the power of the devil, because God was with him.

³⁹"We are witnesses of everything he did in the country of the Jews and in Jerusalem. They killed him by hanging him on a tree, ⁴⁰but God raised him from the dead on the third day and caused him to be seen. ⁴¹He was not seen by all the people, but by witnesses whom God had already chosen—by us who ate and drank with him after he rose from the dead. ⁴²He commanded us to preach to the people and to testify that he is the one whom God appointed as judge of the living and the dead. ⁴³All the prophets testify about him that everyone who believes in him receives forgiveness of sins through his name."

⁴⁴While Peter was still speaking these words, the Holy Spirit came on all who heard the message. ⁴⁵The circumcised believers who had come with Peter were astonished that the gift of the Holy Spirit had been poured out even on the Gentiles. ⁴⁶For they heard them speaking in tongues*ᵃ* and praising God.

Then Peter said, ⁴⁷"Can anyone keep these people from being baptized with water? They have received the Holy Spirit just as we have." ⁴⁸So he ordered that they be baptized in the name of Jesus Christ. Then they asked Peter to stay with them for a few days.

truth or dare

Have you labeled certain people as "Never Gonna Get Saved" and others as "Seems Like She's Already Saved"? Regardless of background, God doesn't play favorites.

10:34–35

Peter Explains His Actions

11 The apostles and the brothers throughout Judea heard that the Gentiles also had received the word of God. ²So when Peter went up to Jerusalem, the circumcised believers criticized him ³and said, "You went into the house of uncircumcised men and ate with them." ⁴Peter began and explained everything to them precisely as it had happened: ⁵"I was in the city

ᵃ 46 Or *other languages*

of Joppa praying, and in a trance I saw a vision. I saw something like a large sheet being let down from heaven by its four corners, and it came down to where I was. ⁶I looked into it and saw four-footed animals of the earth, wild beasts, reptiles, and birds of the air. ⁷Then I heard a voice telling me, 'Get up, Peter. Kill and eat.'

⁸"I replied, 'Surely not, Lord! Nothing impure or unclean has ever entered my mouth.'

⁹"The voice spoke from heaven a second time, 'Do not call anything impure that God has made clean.' ¹⁰This happened three times, and then it was all pulled up to heaven again.

¹¹"Right then three men who had been sent to me from Caesarea stopped at the house where I was staying. ¹²The Spirit told me to have no hesitation about going with them. These six brothers also went with me, and we entered the man's house. ¹³He told us how he had seen an angel appear in his house and say, 'Send to Joppa for Simon who is called Peter. ¹⁴He will bring you a message through which you and all your household will be saved.'

¹⁵"As I began to speak, the Holy Spirit came on them as he had come on us at the beginning. ¹⁶Then I remembered what the Lord had said: 'John baptized with ᵃ water, but you will be baptized with the Holy Spirit.' ¹⁷So if God gave them the same gift as he gave us, who believed in the Lord Jesus Christ, who was I to think that I could oppose God?"

¹⁸When they heard this, they had no further objections and praised God, saying, "So then, God has granted even the Gentiles repentance unto life."

The Church in Antioch

¹⁹Now those who had been scattered by the persecution in connection with Stephen traveled as far as Phoenicia, Cyprus and Antioch, telling the message only to Jews. ²⁰Some of them, however, men from Cyprus and Cyrene, went to Antioch and began to speak to Greeks also, telling them the good news about the Lord Jesus. ²¹The Lord's hand was with them, and a great number of people believed and turned to the Lord.

²²News of this reached the ears of the church at Jerusalem, and they sent Barnabas to Antioch. ²³When he arrived and saw the evidence of the grace of God, he was glad and encouraged them all to remain true to the Lord with all their hearts. ²⁴He was a good man, full of the Holy Spirit and faith, and a great number of people were brought to the Lord.

²⁵Then Barnabas went to Tarsus to look for Saul, ²⁶and when he found him, he brought him to Antioch. So for a whole year Barnabas and Saul met with the church and taught great numbers of people. The disciples were called Christians first at Antioch.

²⁷During this time some prophets came down from Jerusalem to Antioch. ²⁸One of them, named Agabus, stood up and through the Spirit predicted that a severe famine would spread over the entire Roman world. (This happened during the reign of Claudius.) ²⁹The disciples, each according to his ability, decided to provide help for the brothers living in Judea. ³⁰This they did, sending their gift to the elders by Barnabas and Saul.

Peter's Miraculous Escape From Prison

12 It was about this time that King Herod arrested some who belonged to the church, intending to persecute them. ²He had James, the brother of John, put to death with the sword. ³When he saw that this pleased the Jews, he proceeded to seize Peter also. This happened during the Feast of Unleavened Bread. ⁴After arresting him, he put him in prison, handing him over to be guarded by four squads of four soldiers each. Herod intended to bring him out for public trial after the Passover.

⁵So Peter was kept in prison, but the church was earnestly praying to God for him.

⁶The night before Herod was to bring him to trial, Peter was sleeping between two soldiers, bound with two chains, and sentries stood guard at the entrance. ⁷Suddenly an angel of the Lord appeared and a light shone in the cell. He struck Peter on the side and woke him up. "Quick, get up!" he said, and the chains fell off Peter's wrists.

⁸Then the angel said to him, "Put on your clothes and sandals." And Peter did so. "Wrap your cloak around you and follow me," the angel told him. ⁹Peter followed him out of the prison, but he had no idea that what the angel was doing was really happening; he thought he was seeing a vision. ¹⁰They passed the first and second guards and came to the iron gate leading to the city. It

a 16 Or in

opened for them by itself, and they went through it. When they had walked the length of one street, suddenly the angel left him.

¹¹Then Peter came to himself and said, "Now I know without a doubt that the Lord sent his angel and rescued me from Herod's clutches and from everything the Jewish people were anticipating."

¹²When this had dawned on him, he went to the house of Mary the mother of John, also called Mark, where many people had gathered and were praying. ¹³Peter knocked at the outer entrance, and a servant girl named Rhoda came to answer the door. ¹⁴When she recognized Peter's voice, she was so overjoyed she ran back without opening it and exclaimed, "Peter is at the door!"

¹⁵"You're out of your mind," they told her. When she kept insisting that it was so, they said, "It must be his angel."

¹⁶But Peter kept on knocking, and when they opened the door and saw him, they were astonished. ¹⁷Peter motioned with his hand for them to be quiet and described how the Lord had brought him out of prison. "Tell James and the brothers about this," he said, and then he left for another place.

¹⁸In the morning, there was no small commotion among the soldiers as to what had become of Peter. ¹⁹After Herod had a thorough search made for him and did not find him, he cross-examined the guards and ordered that they be executed.

Herod's Death

Then Herod went from Judea to Caesarea and stayed there a while. ²⁰He had been quarreling with the people of Tyre and Sidon; they now joined together and sought an audience with him. Having secured the support of Blastus, a trusted personal servant of the king, they asked for peace, because they depended on the king's country for their food supply.

²¹On the appointed day Herod, wearing his royal robes, sat on his throne and delivered a public address to the people. ²²They shouted, "This is the voice of a god, not of a man." ²³Immediately, because Herod did not give praise to God, an angel of the Lord struck him down, and he was eaten by worms and died.

²⁴But the word of God continued to increase and spread.

²⁵When Barnabas and Saul had finished their mission, they returned from*ᵃ* Jerusalem, taking with them John, also called Mark.

Barnabas and Saul Sent Off

13 In the church at Antioch there were prophets and teachers: Barnabas, Simeon called Niger, Lucius of Cyrene, Manaen (who had been brought up with Herod the tetrarch) and Saul. ²While they were worshiping the Lord and fasting, the Holy Spirit said, "Set apart for me Barnabas and Saul for the work to which I have called them." ³So after they had fasted and prayed, they placed their hands on them and sent them off.

On Cyprus

⁴The two of them, sent on their way by the Holy Spirit, went down to Seleucia and sailed from there to Cyprus. ⁵When they arrived at Salamis, they proclaimed the word of God in the Jewish synagogues. John was with them as their helper.

⁶They traveled through the whole island until they came to Paphos. There they met a Jewish sorcerer and false prophet named Bar-Jesus, ⁷who was an attendant of the proconsul, Sergius Paulus. The proconsul, an intelligent man, sent for Barnabas and Saul because he wanted to hear the word of God. ⁸But Elymas the sorcerer (for that is what his name means) opposed them and tried to turn the proconsul from the faith. ⁹Then Saul, who was also called Paul, filled with the Holy Spirit, looked straight at Elymas and said, ¹⁰"You are a child of the devil and an enemy of everything that is right! You are full of all kinds of deceit and trickery. Will you never stop perverting the right ways of the Lord? ¹¹Now the hand of the Lord is against you. You are going to be blind, and for a time you will be unable to see the light of the sun."

Immediately mist and darkness came over him, and he groped about, seeking someone to lead him by the hand. ¹²When the proconsul saw what had happened, he believed, for he was amazed at the teaching about the Lord.

ᵃ 25 Some manuscripts to

In Pisidian Antioch

[13]From Paphos, Paul and his companions sailed to Perga in Pamphylia, where John left them to return to Jerusalem. [14]From Perga they went on to Pisidian Antioch. On the Sabbath they entered the synagogue and sat down. [15]After the reading from the Law and the Prophets, the synagogue rulers sent word to them, saying, "Brothers, if you have a message of encouragement for the people, please speak."

genuine devotion » 13:22

"A girl after God's own heart." Wouldn't it be flattering if the God of the universe called you that? It doesn't mean you have to be perfect—David certainly wasn't. It simply means that you diligently seek after God throughout your life. You desire to serve and obey him. And if you mess up, you learn your lesson and run back to him for forgiveness. To be a girl after God's own heart means to walk with him today and tomorrow and every day after that for as long as you live.

[16]Standing up, Paul motioned with his hand and said: "Men of Israel and you Gentiles who worship God, listen to me! [17]The God of the people of Israel chose our fathers; he made the people prosper during their stay in Egypt, with mighty power he led them out of that country, [18]he endured their conduct[a] for about forty years in the desert, [19]he overthrew seven nations in Canaan and gave their land to his people as their inheritance. [20]All this took about 450 years.

"After this, God gave them judges until the time of Samuel the prophet. [21]Then the people asked for a king, and he gave them Saul son of Kish, of the tribe of Benjamin, who ruled forty years. [22]After removing Saul, he made David their king. He testified concerning him: 'I have found David son of Jesse a man after my own heart; he will do everything I want him to do.'

[23]"From this man's descendants God has brought to Israel the Savior Jesus, as he promised. [24]Before the coming of Jesus, John preached repentance and baptism to all the people of Israel. [25]As John was completing his work, he said: 'Who do you think I am? I am not that one. No, but he is coming after me, whose sandals I am not worthy to untie.'

[26]"Brothers, children of Abraham, and you God-fearing Gentiles, it is to us that this message of salvation has been sent. [27]The people of Jerusalem and their rulers did not recognize Jesus, yet in condemning him they fulfilled the words of the prophets that are read every Sabbath. [28]Though they found no proper ground for a death sentence, they asked Pilate to have him executed. [29]When they had carried out all that was written about him, they took him down from the tree and laid him in a tomb. [30]But God raised him from the dead, [31]and for many days he was seen by those who had traveled with him from Galilee to Jerusalem. They are now his witnesses to our people.

[32]"We tell you the good news: What God promised our fathers [33]he has fulfilled for us, their children, by raising up Jesus. As it is written in the second Psalm:

" 'You are my Son;
today I have become your Father.'[b][c]

[34]The fact that God raised him from the dead, never to decay, is stated in these words:

" 'I will give you the holy and sure blessings promised to David.'[d]

[35]So it is stated elsewhere:

" 'You will not let your Holy One see decay.'[e]

---

[a] 18 Some manuscripts *and cared for them*   [b] 33 Or *have begotten you*   [c] 33 Psalm 2:7   [d] 34 Isaiah 55:3
[e] 35 Psalm 16:10

[36]"For when David had served God's purpose in his own generation, he fell asleep; he was buried with his fathers and his body decayed. [37]But the one whom God raised from the dead did not see decay.

[38]"Therefore, my brothers, I want you to know that through Jesus the forgiveness of sins is proclaimed to you. [39]Through him everyone who believes is justified from everything you could not be justified from by the law of Moses. [40]Take care that what the prophets have said does not happen to you:

[41]" 'Look, you scoffers,
wonder and perish,
for I am going to do something in your days
that you would never believe,
even if someone told you.' [a]"

love notes

13:36

Daughter,

Imagine yourself five years from now. How about ten years? At times, it's hard to imagine what's going to happen next year. But I know. I have a purpose for your life, just as I did for King David's. Trust me with your future.

—Father God

Imagine what you will be doing five years from now. How does God figure into your plans?

[42]As Paul and Barnabas were leaving the synagogue, the people invited them to speak further about these things on the next Sabbath. [43]When the congregation was dismissed, many of the Jews and devout converts to Judaism followed Paul and Barnabas, who talked with them and urged them to continue in the grace of God.

[44]On the next Sabbath almost the whole city gathered to hear the word of the Lord. [45]When the Jews saw the crowds, they were filled with jealousy and talked abusively against what Paul was saying.

[46]Then Paul and Barnabas answered them boldly: "We had to speak the word of God to you first. Since you reject it and do not consider yourselves worthy of eternal life, we now turn to the Gentiles. [47]For this is what the Lord has commanded us:

" 'I have made you [b] a light for
the Gentiles,
that you [b] may bring salvation
to the ends of the
earth.' [c]"

[48]When the Gentiles heard this, they were glad and honored the word of the Lord; and all who were appointed for eternal life believed.

[49]The word of the Lord spread through the whole region. [50]But the Jews incited the God-fearing women of high standing and the leading men of the city. They stirred up persecution against Paul and Barnabas, and expelled them from their region. [51]So they shook the dust from their feet in protest against them and went to Iconium. [52]And the disciples were filled with joy and with the Holy Spirit.

a 41 Hab. 1:5   *b 47* The Greek is singular.
c 47 Isaiah 49:6

In Iconium

14

At Iconium Paul and Barnabas went as usual into the Jewish synagogue. There they spoke so effectively that a great number of Jews and Gentiles believed. [2]But the Jews who refused to believe stirred up the Gentiles and poisoned their minds against the brothers. [3]So Paul and Barnabas spent considerable time there, speaking boldly for the Lord, who confirmed the message of his grace by enabling them to do miraculous signs and wonders. [4]The people of the city were divided; some sided with the Jews, others with the apostles. [5]There was a plot afoot among the Gentiles and Jews, together with their leaders, to mistreat them and stone them. [6]But they found out about it and fled to the Lycaonian cities of Lystra and Derbe and to the surrounding country, [7]where they continued to preach the good news.

In Lystra and Derbe

[8]In Lystra there sat a man crippled in his feet, who was lame from birth and had never walked. [9]He listened to Paul as he was speaking. Paul looked directly at him, saw that he had faith to be healed [10]and called out, "Stand up on your feet!" At that, the man jumped up and began to walk.

[11]When the crowd saw what Paul had done, they shouted in the Lycaonian language, "The gods have come down to us in human form!" [12]Barnabas they called Zeus, and Paul they called Hermes because he was the chief speaker. [13]The priest of Zeus, whose temple was just outside the city, brought bulls and wreaths to the city gates because he and the crowd wanted to offer sacrifices to them.

[14]But when the apostles Barnabas and Paul heard of this, they tore their clothes and rushed out into the crowd, shouting: [15]"Men, why are you doing this? We too are only men, human like you. We are bringing you good news, telling you to turn from these worthless things to the living God, who made heaven and earth and sea and everything in them. [16]In the past, he let all nations go their own way. [17]Yet he has not left himself without testimony: He has shown kindness by giving you rain from heaven and crops in their seasons; he provides you with plenty of food and fills your hearts with joy." [18]Even with these words, they had difficulty keeping the crowd from sacrificing to them.

[19]Then some Jews came from Antioch and Iconium and won the crowd over. They stoned Paul and dragged him outside the city, thinking he was dead. [20]But after the disciples had gathered around him, he got up and went back into the city. The next day he and Barnabas left for Derbe.

The Return to Antioch in Syria

[21]They preached the good news in that city and won a large number of disciples. Then they returned to Lystra, Iconium and Antioch, [22]strengthening the disciples and encouraging them to remain true to the faith. "We must go through many hardships to enter the kingdom of God," they said. [23]Paul and Barnabas appointed elders[a] for them in each church and, with prayer and fasting, committed them to the Lord, in whom they had put their trust. [24]After going through Pisidia, they came into Pamphylia, [25]and when they had preached the word in Perga, they went down to Attalia.

[26]From Attalia they sailed back to Antioch, where they had been committed to the grace of God for the work they had now completed. [27]On arriving there, they gathered the church together and reported all that God had done through them and how he had opened the door of faith to the Gentiles. [28]And they stayed there a long time with the disciples.

The Council at Jerusalem

15

Some men came down from Judea to Antioch and were teaching the brothers: "Unless you are circumcised, according to the custom taught by Moses, you cannot be saved." [2]This brought Paul and Barnabas into sharp dispute and debate with them. So Paul and Barnabas were appointed, along with some other believers, to go up to Jerusalem to see the apostles and elders about this question. [3]The church sent them on their way, and as they traveled through Phoenicia and Samaria, they told how the Gentiles had been converted. This news made all the brothers very glad. [4]When they came to Jerusalem, they were welcomed by the church and the apostles and elders, to whom they reported everything God had done through them.

a 23 Or *Barnabas ordained elders*; or *Barnabas had elders elected*

in focus

On My Own

Profile: Crisanna

I feel like I'm ready to hurl every time I see those Hallmark commercials with the happy families all hugging each other. Give me a break. That's definitely not *my* family.

My mom barely pays attention to me. She's always at work or with her friends or her boyfriend. And my dad? Well, I haven't seen him since I was seven. After he and Mom got divorced, he moved somewhere out west. I remember hearing him tell my mom that he never wanted kids anyway.

Great. Thanks for sharing, Dad.

Half the time Mom acts like she doesn't want me around either. She goes out of her way to avoid spending time with me. I was in day care as soon as my mom could dump me off on someone. I stayed there till I was old enough to go to school.

When I was in grade school, I think Mom showed up to like one thing I was in—a Christmas play. Since then, she's never come to any of my volleyball games—not even the championship game that I played in. (We won, too.) Mom always says, "I can't. I have to work. Somebody has to earn money around here."

Right, Mom.

I don't know what it's like to have parents who want me. It hurts, so I try not to think about it very much. When I was younger, I used to cry about it a lot. I've been on my own ever since I can remember.

abandonment in focus

Unwanted. Abandoned. Are there sadder words in the English language? Many girls feel unwanted or abandoned in one way or another—many times by family members.

Feeling abandoned? That's a king-sized problem that only a king-sized God can solve. Nothing can ever separate you from God's incredible love (see Romans 8:38–39, page 1494). He offers hope and permanence. Check out these words of comfort:

» "Though my father and mother forsake me, the LORD will receive me" (Psalm 27:10, page 679).

» "And surely I am with you always, to the very end of the age" (Matthew 28:20, page 1333).

» "Never will I leave you; never will I forsake you" (Hebrews 13:5, page 1599).

For more on this topic, see the index on page 1656.

⁵Then some of the believers who belonged to the party of the Pharisees stood up and said, "The Gentiles must be circumcised and required to obey the law of Moses."

⁶The apostles and elders met to consider this question. ⁷After much discussion, Peter got up and addressed them: "Brothers, you know that some time ago God made a choice among you that the Gentiles might hear from my lips the message of the gospel and believe. ⁸God, who knows the heart, showed that he accepted them by giving the Holy Spirit to them, just as he did to us. ⁹He made no distinction between us and them, for he purified their hearts by faith. ¹⁰Now then, why do you try to test God by putting on the necks of the disciples a yoke that neither we nor our fathers

have been able to bear? ¹¹No! We believe it is through the grace of our Lord Jesus that we are saved, just as they are."

¹²The whole assembly became silent as they listened to Barnabas and Paul telling about the miraculous signs and wonders God had done among the Gentiles through them. ¹³When they finished, James spoke up: "Brothers, listen to me. ¹⁴Simon[a] has described to us how God at first showed his concern by taking from the Gentiles a people for himself. ¹⁵The words of the prophets are in agreement with this, as it is written:

> ¹⁶" 'After this I will return
>   and rebuild David's fallen tent.
> Its ruins I will rebuild,
>   and I will restore it,
> ¹⁷that the remnant of men may seek the Lord,
>   and all the Gentiles who bear my name,
>   says the Lord, who does these things'[b]
> ¹⁸   that have been known for ages.[c]

¹⁹"It is my judgment, therefore, that we should not make it difficult for the Gentiles who are turning to God. ²⁰Instead we should write to them, telling them to abstain from food polluted by idols, from sexual immorality, from the meat of strangled animals and from blood. ²¹For Moses has been preached in every city from the earliest times and is read in the synagogues on every Sabbath."

The Council's Letter to Gentile Believers

²²Then the apostles and elders, with the whole church, decided to choose some of their own men and send them to Antioch with Paul and Barnabas. They chose Judas (called Barsabbas) and Silas, two men who were leaders among the brothers. ²³With them they sent the following letter:

The apostles and elders, your brothers,

To the Gentile believers in Antioch, Syria and Cilicia:

Greetings.

²⁴We have heard that some went out from us without our authorization and disturbed you, troubling your minds by what they said. ²⁵So we all agreed to choose some men and send them to you with our dear friends Barnabas and Paul— ²⁶men who have risked their lives for the name of our Lord Jesus Christ. ²⁷Therefore we are sending Judas and Silas to confirm by word of mouth what we are writing. ²⁸It seemed good to the Holy Spirit and to us not to burden you with anything beyond the following requirements: ²⁹You are to abstain from food sacrificed to idols, from blood, from the meat of strangled animals and from sexual immorality. You will do well to avoid these things.

Farewell.

³⁰The men were sent off and went down to Antioch, where they gathered the church together and delivered the letter. ³¹The people read it and were glad for its encouraging message. ³²Judas and Silas, who themselves were prophets, said much to encourage and strengthen the brothers. ³³After spending some time there, they were sent off by the brothers with the blessing of peace to return to those who had sent them.[d] ³⁵But Paul and Barnabas remained in Antioch, where they and many others taught and preached the word of the Lord.

Disagreement Between Paul and Barnabas

³⁶Some time later Paul said to Barnabas, "Let us go back and visit the brothers in all the towns where we preached the word of the Lord and see how they are doing." ³⁷Barnabas wanted to take John, also called Mark, with them, ³⁸but Paul did not think it wise to take him, because he had deserted them in Pamphylia and had not continued with them in the work. ³⁹They had such a sharp

a 14 Greek *Simeon*, a variant of *Simon*; that is, Peter   *b 17* Amos 9:11,12   *c 17,18* Some manuscripts *things'— /*
18known to the Lord for ages is his work   d 33 Some manuscripts *them, 34but Silas decided to remain there*

disagreement that they parted company. Barnabas took Mark and sailed for Cyprus, ⁴⁰but Paul chose Silas and left, commended by the brothers to the grace of the Lord. ⁴¹He went through Syria and Cilicia, strengthening the churches.

Timothy Joins Paul and Silas

16 He came to Derbe and then to Lystra, where a disciple named Timothy lived, whose mother was a Jewess and a believer, but whose father was a Greek. ²The brothers at Lystra and Iconium spoke well of him. ³Paul wanted to take him along on the journey, so he circumcised him because of the Jews who lived in that area, for they all knew that his father was a Greek. ⁴As they traveled from town to town, they delivered the decisions reached by the apostles and elders in Jerusalem for the people to obey. ⁵So the churches were strengthened in the faith and grew daily in numbers.

Paul's Vision of the Man of Macedonia

⁶Paul and his companions traveled throughout the region of Phrygia and Galatia, having been kept by the Holy Spirit from preaching the word in the province of Asia. ⁷When they came to the border of Mysia, they tried to enter Bithynia, but the Spirit of Jesus would not allow them to. ⁸So they passed by Mysia and went down to Troas. ⁹During the night Paul had a vision of a man of Macedonia standing and begging him, "Come over to Macedonia and help us." ¹⁰After Paul had seen the vision, we got ready at once to leave for Macedonia, concluding that God had called us to preach the gospel to them.

Lydia's Conversion in Philippi

¹¹From Troas we put out to sea and sailed straight for Samothrace, and the next day on to Neapolis. ¹²From there we traveled to Philippi, a Roman colony and the leading city of that district of Macedonia. And we stayed there several days.

¹³On the Sabbath we went outside the city gate to the river, where we expected to find a place of prayer. We sat down and began to speak to the women who had gathered there. ¹⁴One of those listening was a woman named Lydia, a dealer in purple cloth from the city of Thyatira, who was a worshiper of God. The Lord opened her heart to respond to Paul's message. ¹⁵When she and the members of her household were baptized, she invited us to her home. "If you consider me a believer in the Lord," she said, "come and stay at my house." And she persuaded us.

Paul and Silas in Prison

¹⁶Once when we were going to the place of prayer, we were met by a slave girl who had a spirit by which she predicted the future. She earned a great deal of money for her owners by fortune-telling. ¹⁷This girl followed Paul and the rest of us, shouting, "These men are servants of the Most High God, who are telling you the way to be saved." ¹⁸She kept this up for many days. Finally Paul became so troubled that he turned around and said to the spirit, "In the name of Jesus Christ I command you to come out of her!" At that moment the spirit left her.

¹⁹When the owners of the slave girl realized that their hope of making money was gone, they seized Paul and Silas and dragged them into the marketplace to face the authorities. ²⁰They brought

genuine

hospitality »» 16:11-15

Ever gone on a long road trip? Just when you think everyone's ready to kill each other from being cooped up in the car, you pull up to Grandma's house. Ahhhhh, finally—a comfortable couch and a home-cooked meal. Thank goodness for good old-fashioned hospitality. Imagine how relieved Paul's group was to arrive at Lydia's house for a good night's sleep and a warm meal after walking for miles and miles and being away from home for so long. Hospitality—making others feel comfortable at your home—is a gift. How can you offer others a refreshing stop along their way?

them before the magistrates and said, "These men are Jews, and are throwing our city into an uproar [21]by advocating customs unlawful for us Romans to accept or practice."

[22]The crowd joined in the attack against Paul and Silas, and the magistrates ordered them to be stripped and beaten. [23]After they had been severely flogged, they were thrown into prison, and the jailer was commanded to guard them carefully. [24]Upon receiving such orders, he put them in the inner cell and fastened their feet in the stocks.

[25]About midnight Paul and Silas were praying and singing hymns to God, and the other prisoners were listening to them. [26]Suddenly there was such a violent earthquake that the foundations of the prison were shaken. At once all the prison doors flew open, and everybody's chains came loose. [27]The jailer woke up, and when he saw the prison doors open, he drew his sword and was about to kill himself because he thought the prisoners had escaped. [28]But Paul shouted, "Don't harm yourself! We are all here!"

[29]The jailer called for lights, rushed in and fell trembling before Paul and Silas. [30]He then brought them out and asked, "Sirs, what must I do to be saved?"

[31]They replied, "Believe in the Lord Jesus, and you will be saved—you and your household." [32]Then they spoke the word of the Lord to him and to all the others in his house. [33]At that hour of the night the jailer took them and washed their wounds; then immediately he and all his family were baptized. [34]The jailer brought them into his house and set a meal before them; he was filled with joy because he had come to believe in God—he and his whole family.

[35]When it was daylight, the magistrates sent their officers to the jailer with the order: "Release those men." [36]The jailer told Paul, "The magistrates have ordered that you and Silas be released. Now you can leave. Go in peace."

[37]But Paul said to the officers: "They beat us publicly without a trial, even though we are Roman citizens, and threw us into prison. And now do they want to get rid of us quietly? No! Let them come themselves and escort us out."

[38]The officers reported this to the magistrates, and when they heard that Paul and Silas were Roman citizens, they were alarmed. [39]They came to appease them and escorted them from the prison, requesting them to leave the city. [40]After Paul and Silas came out of the prison, they went to Lydia's house, where they met with the brothers and encouraged them. Then they left.

In Thessalonica

17 When they had passed through Amphipolis and Apollonia, they came to Thessalonica, where there was a Jewish synagogue. [2]As his custom was, Paul went into the synagogue, and on three Sabbath days he reasoned with them from the Scriptures, [3]explaining and proving that the Christ[a] had to suffer and rise from the dead. "This Jesus I am proclaiming to you is the Christ,[a]" he said. [4]Some of the Jews were persuaded and joined Paul and Silas, as did a large number of God-fearing Greeks and not a few prominent women.

[5]But the Jews were jealous; so they rounded up some bad characters from the marketplace, formed a mob and started a riot in the city. They rushed to Jason's house in search of Paul and Silas in order to bring them out to the crowd.[b] [6]But when they did not find them, they dragged Jason and some other brothers before the city officials, shouting: "These men who have caused trouble all over the world have now come here, [7]and Jason has welcomed them into his house. They are all defying Caesar's decrees, saying that there is another king, one called Jesus." [8]When they heard this, the crowd and the city officials were thrown into turmoil. [9]Then they made Jason and the others post bond and let them go.

In Berea

[10]As soon as it was night, the brothers sent Paul and Silas away to Berea. On arriving there, they went to the Jewish synagogue. [11]Now the Bereans were of more noble character than the Thessalonians, for they received the message with great eagerness and examined the Scriptures every day to see if what Paul said was true. [12]Many of the Jews believed, as did also a number of prominent Greek women and many Greek men.

[13]When the Jews in Thessalonica learned that Paul was preaching the word of God at Berea, they went there too, agitating the crowds and stirring them up. [14]The brothers immediately sent

a 3 Or *Messiah*   *b 5* Or *the assembly of the people*

Paul to the coast, but Silas and Timothy stayed at Berea. ¹⁵The men who escorted Paul brought him to Athens and then left with instructions for Silas and Timothy to join him as soon as possible.

In Athens

¹⁶While Paul was waiting for them in Athens, he was greatly distressed to see that the city was full of idols. ¹⁷So he reasoned in the synagogue with the Jews and the God-fearing Greeks, as well as in the marketplace day by day with those who happened to be there. ¹⁸A group of Epicurean and Stoic philosophers began to dispute with him. Some of them asked, "What is this babbler trying to say?" Others remarked, "He seems to be advocating foreign gods." They said this because Paul was preaching the good news about Jesus and the resurrection. ¹⁹Then they took him and brought him to a meeting of the Areopagus, where they said to him, "May we know what this new teaching is that you are presenting? ²⁰You are bringing some strange ideas to our ears, and we want to know what they mean." ²¹(All the Athenians and the foreigners who lived there spent their time doing nothing but talking about and listening to the latest ideas.)

²²Paul then stood up in the meeting of the Areopagus and said: "Men of Athens! I see that in every way you are very religious. ²³For as I walked around and looked carefully at your objects of worship, I even found an altar with this inscription: TO AN UNKNOWN GOD. Now what you worship as something unknown I am going to proclaim to you.

²⁴"The God who made the world and everything in it is the Lord of heaven and earth and does not live in temples built by hands. ²⁵And he is not served by human hands, as if he needed anything, because he himself gives all men life and breath and everything else. ²⁶From one man he made every nation of men, that they should inhabit the whole earth; and he determined the times set for them and the exact places where they should live. ²⁷God did this so that men would seek him and perhaps reach out for him and find him, though he is not far from each one of us. ²⁸'For in him we live and move and have our being.' As some of your own poets have said, 'We are his offspring.'

²⁹"Therefore since we are God's offspring, we should not think that the divine being is like gold or silver or stone—an image made by man's design and skill. ³⁰In the past God overlooked such ignorance, but now he commands all people everywhere to repent. ³¹For he has set a day when he will judge the world with justice by the man he has appointed. He has given proof of this to all men by raising him from the dead."

³²When they heard about the resurrection of the dead, some of them sneered, but others said, "We want to hear you again on this subject." ³³At that, Paul left the Council. ³⁴A few men became followers of Paul and believed. Among them was Dionysius, a member of the Areopagus, also a woman named Damaris, and a number of others.

love ♥ notes

17:26–28

My child,

I hold all of history in my hand, and you can be sure that includes you. Nothing about your life is a coincidence—not the time or the place. I'm never far from you. Reach out and find me. I'm right here.

—Your heavenly Father

Write down what it means to you to "live and move and have your being" in God.

Home Sweet Home?

focus Profile: **Toni**

"Leave me alone!" my little brother Skip yelled as he pounded up the basement stairs.

My friends and I turned in shock just in time to see my big brother skid around the corner and drill Skip with a football. It bounced off his head, crashed into a lamp and sent the lamp smashing to the floor, shattering in pieces. *So much for having friends over at my house*, I thought.

"Whoa! Your house is *wild!*" my friend Shawna said. *This is nothing*, I thought. Shawna's an only child. She lives in peace and total quiet every day, with no one to harass her and no screaming.

Dad stormed around the corner and shouted, "What's going on here?!" He lunged straight for my brothers, oblivious of us girls. "You two are paying for this! Say goodbye to your allowance for the next month!"

Before Dad scared my friends away forever, I decided to try cutting off his rampage. "Dad? This is Shawna and Kali." He grumbled a greeting and stomped out. A door slammed. My brothers argued their way downstairs to the basement. Shawna's face was still frozen in shock. I'm sure she'd never seen anything like this before in her life.

"Oh, that's nothing," Kali said, "You should've seen how my parents fought before their divorce. Now it's quiet *all* the time." We sat there quietly for a minute. I wondered how family fighting could cross the line from rudeness to violence. What kind of fighting would it take to break our family forever?

For more on family conflict, go to www.TrueImagesBible.com

family conflict in focus

Sometimes family fighting can be intense, embarrassing and even frightening. Families can get into destructive patterns of yelling and verbal abuse instead of finding peaceful ways to solve their conflicts. So what can *you* do if your home's a war zone?

»Don't yell back. Yelling only fuels the fire. Check out the great advice in Proverbs 15:1 (page 824).

»Whenever possible, be a peacemaker (see Matthew 5:9, page 1295). Stay calm. Don't take sides.

»If you, a parent or your siblings are ever in physical danger at home, don't be afraid to get help. Talk to a counselor at school, a pastor or a youth leader.

»If the situation involves violence, call 911, a local abuse hotline, or a "safehouse" shelter. Don't stay in a dangerous situation.

For more on this topic, see the index on page 1656.

In Corinth

18 After this, Paul left Athens and went to Corinth. ²There he met a Jew named Aquila, a native of Pontus, who had recently come from Italy with his wife Priscilla, because Claudius had ordered all the Jews to leave Rome. Paul went to see them, ³and because he was a tentmaker as they were, he stayed and worked with them. ⁴Every Sabbath he reasoned in the synagogue, trying to persuade Jews and Greeks.

⁵When Silas and Timothy came from Macedonia, Paul devoted himself exclusively to preaching, testifying to the Jews that Jesus was the Christ.ᵃ ⁶But when the Jews opposed Paul and became abusive, he shook out his clothes in protest and said to them, "Your blood be on your own heads! I am clear of my responsibility. From now on I will go to the Gentiles."

⁷Then Paul left the synagogue and went next door to the house of Titius Justus, a worshiper of God. ⁸Crispus, the synagogue ruler, and his entire household believed in the Lord; and many of the Corinthians who heard him believed and were baptized.

⁹One night the Lord spoke to Paul in a vision: "Do not be afraid; keep on speaking, do not be silent. ¹⁰For I am with you, and no one is going to attack and harm you, because I have many people in this city." ¹¹So Paul stayed for a year and a half, teaching them the word of God.

¹²While Gallio was proconsul of Achaia, the Jews made a united attack on Paul and brought him into court. ¹³"This man," they charged, "is persuading the people to worship God in ways contrary to the law."

¹⁴Just as Paul was about to speak, Gallio said to the Jews, "If you Jews were making a complaint about some misdemeanor or serious crime, it would be reasonable for me to listen to you. ¹⁵But since it involves questions about words and names and your own law—settle the matter yourselves. I will not be a judge of such things." ¹⁶So he had them ejected from the court. ¹⁷Then they all turned on Sosthenes the synagogue ruler and beat him in front of the court. But Gallio showed no concern whatever.

Priscilla, Aquila and Apollos

¹⁸Paul stayed on in Corinth for some time. Then he left the brothers and sailed for Syria, accompanied by Priscilla and Aquila. Before he sailed, he had his hair cut off at Cenchrea because of a vow he had taken. ¹⁹They arrived at Ephesus, where Paul left Priscilla and Aquila. He himself went into the synagogue and reasoned with the Jews. ²⁰When they asked him to spend more time with them, he declined. ²¹But as he left, he promised, "I will come back if it is God's will." Then he set sail from Ephesus. ²²When he landed at Caesarea, he went up and greeted the church and then went down to Antioch.

²³After spending some time in Antioch, Paul set out from there and traveled from place to place throughout the region of Galatia and Phrygia, strengthening all the disciples.

²⁴Meanwhile a Jew named Apollos, a native of Alexandria, came to Ephesus. He was a learned man, with a thorough knowledge of the Scriptures. ²⁵He had been instructed in the way of the Lord, and he spoke with great fervorᵇ and taught about Jesus accurately, though he knew only the baptism of John. ²⁶He began to speak boldly in the synagogue. When Priscilla and Aquila heard him, they invited him to their home and explained to him the way of God more adequately.

²⁷When Apollos wanted to go to Achaia, the brothers encouraged him and wrote to the disciples there to welcome him. On arriving, he was a great help to those who by grace had believed. ²⁸For he vigorously refuted the Jews in public debate, proving from the Scriptures that Jesus was the Christ.

Paul in Ephesus

19 While Apollos was at Corinth, Paul took the road through the interior and arrived at Ephesus. There he found some disciples ²and asked them, "Did you receive the Holy Spirit whenᶜ you believed?"

They answered, "No, we have not even heard that there is a Holy Spirit."

³So Paul asked, "Then what baptism did you receive?"

"John's baptism," they replied.

⁴Paul said, "John's baptism was a baptism of repentance. He told the people to believe in the one coming after him, that is, in Jesus." ⁵On hearing this, they were baptized intoᵈ the name of the Lord Jesus. ⁶When Paul placed his hands on them, the Holy Spirit came on them, and they spoke in tonguesᵉ and prophesied. ⁷There were about twelve men in all.

⁸Paul entered the synagogue and spoke boldly there for three months, arguing persuasively about the kingdom of God. ⁹But some of them became obstinate; they refused to believe and pub-

a 5 Or *Messiah;* also in verse 28   *b 25* Or *with fervor in the Spirit*   *c 2* Or *after*   *d 5* Or *in*   *e 6* Or *other languages* licly maligned the Way. So Paul left them. He took the disciples with him and had discussions daily in the lecture hall of Tyrannus. ¹⁰This went on for two years, so that all the Jews and Greeks who lived in the province of Asia heard the word of the Lord.

¹¹God did extraordinary miracles through Paul, ¹²so that even handkerchiefs and aprons that had touched him were taken to the sick, and their illnesses were cured and the evil spirits left them.

¹³Some Jews who went around driving out evil spirits tried to invoke the name of the Lord Jesus over those who were demon-possessed. They would say, "In the name of Jesus, whom Paul preaches, I command you to come out." ¹⁴Seven sons of Sceva, a Jewish chief priest, were doing this. ¹⁵One day the evil spirit answered them, "Jesus I know, and I know about Paul, but who are you?" ¹⁶Then the man who had the evil spirit jumped on them and overpowered them all. He gave them such a beating that they ran out of the house naked and bleeding.

¹⁷When this became known to the Jews and Greeks living in Ephesus, they were all seized with fear, and the name of the Lord Jesus was held in high honor. ¹⁸Many of those who believed now came and openly confessed their evil deeds. ¹⁹A number who had practiced sorcery brought their scrolls together and burned them publicly. When they calculated the value of the scrolls, the total came to fifty thousand drachmas. ᵃ ²⁰In this way the word of the Lord spread widely and grew in power.

²¹After all this had happened, Paul decided to go to Jerusalem, passing through Macedonia and Achaia. "After I have been there," he said, "I must visit Rome also." ²²He sent two of his helpers, Timothy and Erastus, to Macedonia, while he stayed in the province of Asia a little longer.

The Riot in Ephesus

²³About that time there arose a great disturbance about the Way. ²⁴A silversmith named Demetrius, who made silver shrines of Artemis, brought in no little business for the craftsmen. ²⁵He called them together, along with the workmen in related trades, and said: "Men, you know we receive a good income from this business. ²⁶And you see and hear how this fellow Paul has convinced and led astray large numbers of people here in Ephesus and in practically the whole province of Asia. He says that man-made gods are no gods at all. ²⁷There is danger not only that our trade will lose its good name, but also that the temple of the great goddess Artemis will be discredited, and the goddess herself, who is worshiped throughout the province of Asia and the world, will be robbed of her divine majesty."

²⁸When they heard this, they were furious and began shouting: "Great is Artemis of the Ephesians!" ²⁹Soon the whole city was in an uproar. The people seized Gaius and Aristarchus, Paul's traveling companions from Macedonia, and rushed as one man into the theater. ³⁰Paul wanted to appear before the crowd, but the disciples would not let him. ³¹Even some of the officials of the province, friends of Paul, sent him a message begging him not to venture into the theater.

³²The assembly was in confusion: Some were shouting one thing, some another. Most of the people did not even know why they were there. ³³The Jews pushed Alexander to the front, and some of the crowd shouted instructions to him. He motioned for silence in order to make a defense before the people. ³⁴But when they realized he was a Jew, they all shouted in unison for about two hours: "Great is Artemis of the Ephesians!"

³⁵The city clerk quieted the crowd and said: "Men of Ephesus, doesn't all the world know that the city of Ephesus is the guardian of the temple of the great Artemis and of her image, which fell from heaven? ³⁶Therefore, since these facts are undeniable, you ought to be quiet and not do anything rash. ³⁷You have brought these men here, though they have neither robbed temples nor blasphemed our goddess. ³⁸If, then, Demetrius and his fellow craftsmen have a grievance against anybody, the courts are open and there are proconsuls. They can press charges. ³⁹If there is anything further you want to bring up, it must be settled in a legal assembly. ⁴⁰As it is, we are in danger of being charged with rioting because of today's events. In that case we would not be able to account for this commotion, since there is no reason for it." ⁴¹After he had said this, he dismissed the assembly.

Through Macedonia and Greece

20 When the uproar had ended, Paul sent for the disciples and, after encouraging them, said good-by and set out for Macedonia. ²He traveled through that area, speaking many words of encouragement to the people, and finally arrived in Greece, ³where he stayed

ᵃ 19 A drachma was a silver coin worth about a day's wages.

three months. Because the Jews made a plot against him just as he was about to sail for Syria, he decided to go back through Macedonia. ⁴He was accompanied by Sopater son of Pyrrhus from Berea, Aristarchus and Secundus from Thessalonica, Gaius from Derbe, Timothy also, and Tychicus and Trophimus from the province of Asia. ⁵These men went on ahead and waited for us at Troas. ⁶But we sailed from Philippi after the Feast of Unleavened Bread, and five days later joined the others at Troas, where we stayed seven days.

Eutychus Raised From the Dead at Troas

⁷On the first day of the week we came together to break bread. Paul spoke to the people and, because he intended to leave the next day, kept on talking until midnight. ⁸There were many lamps in the upstairs room where we were meeting. ⁹Seated in a window was a young man named Eutychus, who was sinking into a deep sleep as Paul talked on and on. When he was sound asleep, he fell to the ground from the third story and was picked up dead. ¹⁰Paul went down, threw himself on the young man and put his arms around him. "Don't be alarmed," he said. "He's alive!" ¹¹Then he went upstairs again and broke bread and ate. After talking until daylight, he left. ¹²The people took the young man home alive and were greatly comforted.

Paul's Farewell to the Ephesian Elders

¹³We went on ahead to the ship and sailed for Assos, where we were going to take Paul aboard. He had made this arrangement because he was going there on foot. ¹⁴When he met us at Assos, we took him aboard and went on to Mitylene. ¹⁵The next day we set sail from there and arrived off Kios. The day after that we crossed over to Samos, and on the following day arrived at Miletus. ¹⁶Paul had decided to sail past Ephesus to avoid spending time in the province of Asia, for he was in a hurry to reach Jerusalem, if possible, by the day of Pentecost.

¹⁷From Miletus, Paul sent to Ephesus for the elders of the church. ¹⁸When they arrived, he said to them: "You know how I lived the whole time I was with you, from the first day I came into the province of Asia. ¹⁹I served the Lord with great humility and with tears, although I was severely tested by the plots of the Jews. ²⁰You know that I have not hesitated to preach anything that would be helpful to you but have taught you publicly and from house to house. ²¹I have declared to both Jews and Greeks that they must turn to God in repentance and have faith in our Lord Jesus.

²²"And now, compelled by the Spirit, I am going to Jerusalem, not knowing what will happen to me there. ²³I only know that in every city the Holy Spirit warns me that prison and hardships are facing me. ²⁴However, I consider my life worth nothing to me, if only I may finish the race and complete the task the Lord Jesus has given me—the task of testifying to the gospel of God's grace.

²⁵"Now I know that none of you among whom I have gone about preaching the kingdom will

truth or dare

Ever get caught snoozing in class? This young guy's drowsiness had some pretty harsh consequences. How hardcore (and attentive) are you in your search for God?

20:7–12

genuine faith » 20:24

Whoooooaaaa. Paul said his life was "worth nothing"? Was he severely depressed? Not at all. You see, Paul was referring to his priorities. At this time, he was headed to Jerusalem, where he thought he might be killed. So he told his friends not to worry about him because he believed that serving God was far more important than trying to save his own skin. Is the same true for you? When you think about your life, are you focused on serving God fully or on milking your years on earth to the fullest? If you focus on serving God, he'll take care of your lifespan.

ever see me again. ²⁶Therefore, I declare to you today that I am innocent of the blood of all men. ²⁷For I have not hesitated to proclaim to you the whole will of God. ²⁸Keep watch over yourselves and all the flock of which the Holy Spirit has made you overseers. *ᵃ* Be shepherds of the church of God,*ᵇ* which he bought with his own blood. ²⁹I know that after I leave, savage wolves will come in among you and will not spare the flock. ³⁰Even from your own number men will arise and distort the truth in order to draw away disciples after them. ³¹So be on your guard! Remember that for three years I never stopped warning each of you night and day with tears.

³²"Now I commit you to God and to the word of his grace, which can build you up and give you an inheritance among all those who are sanctified. ³³I have not coveted anyone's silver or gold or clothing. ³⁴You yourselves know that these hands of mine have supplied my own needs and the needs of my companions. ³⁵In everything I did, I showed you that by this kind of hard work we must help the weak, remembering the words the Lord Jesus himself said: 'It is more blessed to give than to receive.' "

³⁶When he had said this, he knelt down with all of them and prayed. ³⁷They all wept as they embraced him and kissed him. ³⁸What grieved them most was his statement that they would never see his face again. Then they accompanied him to the ship.

On to Jerusalem

21 After we had torn ourselves away from them, we put out to sea and sailed straight to Cos. The next day we went to Rhodes and from there to Patara. ²We found a ship crossing over to Phoenicia, went on board and set sail. ³After sighting Cyprus and passing to the south of it, we sailed on to Syria. We landed at Tyre, where our ship was to unload its cargo. ⁴Finding the disciples there, we stayed with them seven days. Through the Spirit they urged Paul not to go on to Jerusalem. ⁵But when our time was up, we left and continued on our way. All the disciples and their wives and children accompanied us out of the city, and there on the beach we knelt to pray. ⁶After saying good-by to each other, we went aboard the ship, and they returned home.

⁷We continued our voyage from Tyre and landed at Ptolemais, where we greeted the brothers and stayed with them for a day. ⁸Leaving the next day, we reached Caesarea and stayed at the house of Philip the evangelist, one of the Seven. ⁹He had four unmarried daughters who prophesied.

¹⁰After we had been there a number of days, a prophet named Agabus came down from Judea. ¹¹Coming over to us, he took Paul's belt, tied his own hands and feet with it and said, "The Holy Spirit says, 'In this way the Jews of Jerusalem will bind the owner of this belt and will hand him over to the Gentiles.' "

¹²When we heard this, we and the people there pleaded with Paul not to go up to Jerusalem. ¹³Then Paul answered, "Why are you weeping and breaking my heart? I am ready not only to be bound, but also to die in Jerusalem for the name of the Lord Jesus." ¹⁴When he would not be dissuaded, we gave up and said, "The Lord's will be done."

¹⁵After this, we got ready and went up to Jerusalem. ¹⁶Some of the disciples from Caesarea accompanied us and brought us to the home of Mnason, where we were to stay. He was a man from Cyprus and one of the early disciples.

Paul's Arrival at Jerusalem

¹⁷When we arrived at Jerusalem, the brothers received us warmly. ¹⁸The next day Paul and the rest of us went to see James, and all the elders were present. ¹⁹Paul greeted them and reported in detail what God had done among the Gentiles through his ministry.

²⁰When they heard this, they praised God. Then they said to Paul: "You see, brother, how many thousands of Jews have believed, and all of them are zealous for the law. ²¹They have been informed that you teach all the Jews who live among the Gentiles to turn away from Moses, telling them not to circumcise their children or live according to our customs. ²²What shall we do? They will certainly hear that you have come, ²³so do what we tell you. There are four men with us who have made a vow. ²⁴Take these men, join in their purification rites and pay their expenses, so that they can have their heads shaved. Then everybody will know there is no truth in these reports about

---

ᵃ 28 Traditionally *bishops*   *ᵇ 28* Many manuscripts *of the Lord* you, but that you yourself are living in obedience to the law. ²⁵As for the Gentile believers, we have written to them our decision that they should abstain from food sacrificed to idols, from blood, from the meat of strangled animals and from sexual immorality."

²⁶The next day Paul took the men and purified himself along with them. Then he went to the temple to give notice of the date when the days of purification would end and the offering would be made for each of them.

Paul Arrested

²⁷When the seven days were nearly over, some Jews from the province of Asia saw Paul at the temple. They stirred up the whole crowd and seized him, ²⁸shouting, "Men of Israel, help us! This is the man who teaches all men everywhere against our people and our law and this place. And besides, he has brought Greeks into the temple area and defiled this holy place." ²⁹(They had previously seen Trophimus the Ephesian in the city with Paul and assumed that Paul had brought him into the temple area.)

³⁰The whole city was aroused, and the people came running from all directions. Seizing Paul, they dragged him from the temple, and immediately the gates were shut. ³¹While they were trying to kill him, news reached the commander of the Roman troops that the whole city of Jerusalem was in an uproar. ³²He at once took some officers and soldiers and ran down to the crowd. When the rioters saw the commander and his soldiers, they stopped beating Paul.

³³The commander came up and arrested him and ordered him to be bound with two chains. Then he asked who he was and what he had done. ³⁴Some in the crowd shouted one thing and some another, and since the commander could not get at the truth because of the uproar, he ordered that Paul be taken into the barracks. ³⁵When Paul reached the steps, the violence of the mob was so great he had to be carried by the soldiers. ³⁶The crowd that followed kept shouting, "Away with him!"

Paul Speaks to the Crowd

³⁷As the soldiers were about to take Paul into the barracks, he asked the commander, "May I say something to you?"

"Do you speak Greek?" he replied. ³⁸"Aren't you the Egyptian who started a revolt and led four thousand terrorists out into the desert some time ago?"

³⁹Paul answered, "I am a Jew, from Tarsus in Cilicia, a citizen of no ordinary city. Please let me speak to the people."

⁴⁰Having received the commander's permission, Paul stood on the steps and motioned to the crowd. When they were all silent, he said to them in Aramaic*: ¹"Brothers and fathers, listen now to my defense."

22 ²When they heard him speak to them in Aramaic, they became very quiet.

Then Paul said: ³"I am a Jew, born in Tarsus of Cilicia, but brought up in this city. Under Gamaliel I was thoroughly trained in the law of our fathers and was just as zealous for God as any of you are today. ⁴I persecuted the followers of this Way to their death, arresting both men and women and throwing them into prison, ⁵as also the high priest and all the Council can testify. I even obtained letters from them to their brothers in Damascus, and went there to bring these people as prisoners to Jerusalem to be punished.

⁶"About noon as I came near Damascus, suddenly a bright light from heaven flashed around me. ⁷I fell to the ground and heard a voice say to me, 'Saul! Saul! Why do you persecute me?'

⁸" 'Who are you, Lord?' I asked.

" 'I am Jesus of Nazareth, whom you are persecuting,' he replied. ⁹My companions saw the light, but they did not understand the voice of him who was speaking to me.

¹⁰" 'What shall I do, Lord?' I asked.

" 'Get up,' the Lord said, 'and go into Damascus. There you will be told all that you have been assigned to do.' ¹¹My companions led me by the hand into Damascus, because the brilliance of the light had blinded me.

¹²"A man named Ananias came to see me. He was a devout observer of the law and highly respected by all the Jews living there. ¹³He stood beside me and said, 'Brother Saul, receive your sight!' And at that very moment I was able to see him.

a 40 Or possibly *Hebrew*; also in 22:2

Intolerant About Tolerance?

My high school just celebrated Diversity Week. We're supposed to "embrace" the differences among us—different races, religions, genders, sexual preferences, etc.

I'm not sure how to react to all of that. I mean, racial differences are cool and all. Some of my best friends (seriously) are not Latina like me. I think it's great that we're not all the same race. That would be *aburrido* (boring).

Some differences deserve tolerance. Like I tolerate my friend Ryan's need to say stupid things sometimes. Or, I tolerate people who don't speak any Spanish whatsoever. But I'm not so sure about the different religions or sexual preferences thing. See, I'm a Christian. I've been taught that homosexuality is wrong and that Jesus is the only way to God and stuff. But am I just like some kind of bigot if I can't accept other religions or think that homosexuals should be straight?

For Diversity Week, my language arts teacher (Mrs. Archer; we call her Torture, sometimes) wants us to write an essay defending a person's right to determine his or her own path in life. This could include being gay, getting an abortion, being a Buddhist—whatever. I'll bet that won't include being a Christian. She once made fun of my friend Jake when he said he believed in Creationism. Guess she's not all that tolerant of Christians.

Ugh! This would happen to me! If I don't get a good grade on this paper, I could ruin my grade in the class. It doesn't seem fair that people can be intolerant of Christianity but then call Christians intolerant.

tolerance in focus

Seems like "truth" is an ever-evolving concept in society. But the truth of the Bible never changes. Here's some unchanging truth about tolerance:

» Ever heard the old saying, "Love the sinner, hate the sin"? God doesn't need us to judge or punish others for their sins. We have enough of our own sins to deal with! But he does want us to take a firm stand for truth.

» Approach everything you hear about tolerance with wisdom. Be wise about what's good and innocent about what's evil (see Romans 16:19, page 1505).

» Some things are always flat-out wrong, like homosexuality or worshiping other gods. Yet treating others unfairly or inhumanely because of their sexual or religious preference is also wrong. Those who are desperately seeking hope or peace need your compasion, love and prayers.

For more on this topic, see the index on page 1656.

14"Then he said: 'The God of our fathers has chosen you to know his will and to see the Righteous One and to hear words from his mouth. 15You will be his witness to all men of what you have seen and heard. 16And now what are you waiting for? Get up, be baptized and wash your sins away, calling on his name.'

17"When I returned to Jerusalem and was praying at the temple, I fell into a trance 18and saw the Lord speaking. 'Quick!' he said to me. 'Leave Jerusalem immediately, because they will not accept your testimony about me.'

[19] "'Lord,' I replied, 'these men know that I went from one synagogue to another to imprison and beat those who believe in you. [20]And when the blood of your martyr[a] Stephen was shed, I stood there giving my approval and guarding the clothes of those who were killing him.'

[21]"Then the Lord said to me, 'Go; I will send you far away to the Gentiles.' "

Paul the Roman Citizen

[22]The crowd listened to Paul until he said this. Then they raised their voices and shouted, "Rid the earth of him! He's not fit to live!"

[23]As they were shouting and throwing off their cloaks and flinging dust into the air, [24]the commander ordered Paul to be taken into the barracks. He directed that he be flogged and questioned in order to find out why the people were shouting at him like this. [25]As they stretched him out to flog him, Paul said to the centurion standing there, "Is it legal for you to flog a Roman citizen who hasn't even been found guilty?"

[26]When the centurion heard this, he went to the commander and reported it. "What are you going to do?" he asked. "This man is a Roman citizen."

[27]The commander went to Paul and asked, "Tell me, are you a Roman citizen?"

"Yes, I am," he answered.

[28]Then the commander said, "I had to pay a big price for my citizenship."

"But I was born a citizen," Paul replied.

[29]Those who were about to question him withdrew immediately. The commander himself was alarmed when he realized that he had put Paul, a Roman citizen, in chains.

Before the Sanhedrin

[30]The next day, since the commander wanted to find out exactly why Paul was being accused by the Jews, he released him and ordered the chief priests and all the Sanhedrin to assemble. Then he brought Paul and had him stand before them.

23 Paul looked straight at the Sanhedrin and said, "My brothers, I have fulfilled my duty to God in all good conscience to this day." [2]At this the high priest Ananias ordered those standing near Paul to strike him on the mouth. [3]Then Paul said to him, "God will strike you, you whitewashed wall! You sit there to judge me according to the law, yet you yourself violate the law by commanding that I be struck!"

[4]Those who were standing near Paul said, "You dare to insult God's high priest?"

[5]Paul replied, "Brothers, I did not realize that he was the high priest; for it is written: 'Do not speak evil about the ruler of your people.'[b]"

[6]Then Paul, knowing that some of them were Sadducees and the others Pharisees, called out in the Sanhedrin, "My brothers, I am a Pharisee, the son of a Pharisee. I stand on trial because of my hope in the resurrection of the dead." [7]When he said this, a dispute broke out between the Pharisees and the Sadducees, and the assembly was divided. [8](The Sadducees say that there is no resurrection, and that there are neither angels nor spirits, but the Pharisees acknowledge them all.)

[9]There was a great uproar, and some of the teachers of the law who were Pharisees stood up and argued vigorously. "We find nothing wrong with this man," they said. "What if a spirit or an angel has spoken to him?" [10]The dispute became so violent that the commander was afraid Paul would be torn to pieces by them. He ordered the troops to go down and take him away from them by force and bring him into the barracks.

[11]The following night the Lord stood near Paul and said, "Take courage! As you have testified about me in Jerusalem, so you must also testify in Rome."

The Plot to Kill Paul

[12]The next morning the Jews formed a conspiracy and bound themselves with an oath not to eat or drink until they had killed Paul. [13]More than forty men were involved in this plot. [14]They went to the chief priests and elders and said, "We have taken a solemn oath not to eat anything until we have killed Paul. [15]Now then, you and the Sanhedrin petition the commander to bring him before

you on the pretext of wanting more accurate information about his case. We are ready to kill him before he gets here."

¹⁶But when the son of Paul's sister heard of this plot, he went into the barracks and told Paul.

¹⁷Then Paul called one of the centurions and said, "Take this young man to the commander; he has something to tell him." ¹⁸So he took him to the commander.

The centurion said, "Paul, the prisoner, sent for me and asked me to bring this young man to you because he has something to tell you."

¹⁹The commander took the young man by the hand, drew him aside and asked, "What is it you want to tell me?"

²⁰He said: "The Jews have agreed to ask you to bring Paul before the Sanhedrin tomorrow on the pretext of wanting more accurate information about him. ²¹Don't give in to them, because more than forty of them are waiting in ambush for him. They have taken an oath not to eat or drink until they have killed him. They are ready now, waiting for your consent to their request."

²²The commander dismissed the young man and cautioned him, "Don't tell anyone that you have reported this to me."

Paul Transferred to Caesarea

²³Then he called two of his centurions and ordered them, "Get ready a detachment of two hundred soldiers, seventy horsemen and two hundred spearmen[a] to go to Caesarea at nine tonight. ²⁴Provide mounts for Paul so that he may be taken safely to Governor Felix."

²⁵He wrote a letter as follows:

²⁶Claudius Lysias,

To His Excellency, Governor Felix:

Greetings.

²⁷This man was seized by the Jews and they were about to kill him, but I came with my troops and rescued him, for I had learned that he is a Roman citizen. ²⁸I wanted to know why they were accusing him, so I brought him to their Sanhedrin. ²⁹I found that the accusation had to do with questions about their law, but there was no charge against him that deserved death or imprisonment. ³⁰When I was informed of a plot to be carried out against the man, I sent him to you at once. I also ordered his accusers to present to you their case against him.

³¹So the soldiers, carrying out their orders, took Paul with them during the night and brought him as far as Antipatris. ³²The next day they let the cavalry go on with him, while they returned to the barracks. ³³When the cavalry arrived in Caesarea, they delivered the letter to the governor and handed Paul over to him. ³⁴The governor read the letter and asked what province he was from. Learning that he was from Cilicia, ³⁵he said, "I will hear your case when your accusers get here." Then he ordered that Paul be kept under guard in Herod's palace.

The Trial Before Felix

24 Five days later the high priest Ananias went down to Caesarea with some of the elders and a lawyer named Tertullus, and they brought their charges against Paul before the governor. ²When Paul was called in, Tertullus presented his case before Felix: "We have enjoyed a long period of peace under you, and your foresight has brought about reforms in this nation. ³Everywhere and in every way, most excellent Felix, we acknowledge this with profound gratitude. ⁴But in order not to weary you further, I would request that you be kind enough to hear us briefly.

⁵"We have found this man to be a troublemaker, stirring up riots among the Jews all over the world. He is a ringleader of the Nazarene sect ⁶and even tried to desecrate the temple; so we seized him. ⁸By[b] examining him yourself you will be able to learn the truth about all these charges we are bringing against him."

a 23 The meaning of the Greek for this word is uncertain.   b 6-8 Some manuscripts him and wanted to judge him according to our law. 7But the commander, Lysias, came and with the use of much force snatched him from our hands 8and ordered his accusers to come before you. By

⁹The Jews joined in the accusation, asserting that these things were true.

¹⁰When the governor motioned for him to speak, Paul replied: "I know that for a number of years you have been a judge over this nation; so I gladly make my defense. ¹¹You can easily verify that no more than twelve days ago I went up to Jerusalem to worship. ¹²My accusers did not find me arguing with anyone at the temple, or stirring up a crowd in the synagogues or anywhere else in the city. ¹³And they cannot prove to you the charges they are now making against me. ¹⁴However, I admit that I worship the God of our fathers as a follower of the Way, which they call a sect. I believe everything that agrees with the Law and that is written in the Prophets, ¹⁵and I have the same hope in God as these men, that there will be a resurrection of both the righteous and the wicked. ¹⁶So I strive always to keep my conscience clear before God and man.

¹⁷"After an absence of several years, I came to Jerusalem to bring my people gifts for the poor and to present offerings. ¹⁸I was ceremonially clean when they found me in the temple courts doing this. There was no crowd with me, nor was I involved in any disturbance. ¹⁹But there are some Jews from the province of Asia, who ought to be here before you and bring charges if they have anything against me. ²⁰Or these who are here should state what crime they found in me when I stood before the Sanhedrin— ²¹unless it was this one thing I shouted as I stood in their presence: 'It is concerning the resurrection of the dead that I am on trial before you today.' "

²²Then Felix, who was well acquainted with the Way, adjourned the proceedings. "When Lysias the commander comes," he said, "I will decide your case." ²³He ordered the centurion to keep Paul under guard but to give him some freedom and permit his friends to take care of his needs.

²⁴Several days later Felix came with his wife Drusilla, who was a Jewess. He sent for Paul and listened to him as he spoke about faith in Christ Jesus. ²⁵As Paul discoursed on righteousness, self-control and the judgment to come, Felix was afraid and said, "That's enough for now! You may leave. When I find it convenient, I will send for you." ²⁶At the same time he was hoping that Paul would offer him a bribe, so he sent for him frequently and talked with him.

²⁷When two years had passed, Felix was succeeded by Porcius Festus, but because Felix wanted to grant a favor to the Jews, he left Paul in prison.

The Trial Before Festus

25 Three days after arriving in the province, Festus went up from Caesarea to Jerusalem, ²where the chief priests and Jewish leaders appeared before him and presented the charges against Paul. ³They urgently requested Festus, as a favor to them, to have Paul transferred to Jerusalem, for they were preparing an ambush to kill him along the way. ⁴Festus answered, "Paul is being held at Caesarea, and I myself am going there soon. ⁵Let some of your leaders come with me and press charges against the man there, if he has done anything wrong."

⁶After spending eight or ten days with them, he went down to Caesarea, and the next day he convened the court and ordered that Paul be brought before him. ⁷When Paul appeared, the Jews who had come down from Jerusalem stood around him, bringing many serious charges against him, which they could not prove.

⁸Then Paul made his defense: "I have done nothing wrong against the law of the Jews or against the temple or against Caesar."

⁹Festus, wishing to do the Jews a favor, said to Paul, "Are you willing to go up to Jerusalem and stand trial before me there on these charges?"

¹⁰Paul answered: "I am now standing before Caesar's court, where I ought to be tried. I have not done any wrong to the Jews, as you yourself know very well. ¹¹If, however, I am guilty of doing anything deserving death, I do not refuse to die. But if the charges brought against me by these Jews are not true, no one has the right to hand me over to them. I appeal to Caesar!"

¹²After Festus had conferred with his council, he declared: "You have appealed to Caesar. To Caesar you will go!"

Festus Consults King Agrippa

¹³A few days later King Agrippa and Bernice arrived at Caesarea to pay their respects to Festus. ¹⁴Since they were spending many days there, Festus discussed Paul's case with the king. He said: "There is a man here whom Felix left as a prisoner. ¹⁵When I went to Jerusalem, the chief priests and elders of the Jews brought charges against him and asked that he be condemned.

¹⁶"I told them that it is not the Roman custom to hand over any man before he has faced his accusers and has had an opportunity to defend himself against their charges. ¹⁷When they came here with me, I did not delay the case, but convened the court the next day and ordered the man to be brought in. ¹⁸When his accusers got up to speak, they did not charge him with any of the crimes I had expected. ¹⁹Instead, they had some points of dispute with him about their own religion and about a dead man named Jesus who Paul claimed was alive. ²⁰I was at a loss how to investigate such matters; so I asked if he would be willing to go to Jerusalem and stand trial there on these charges. ²¹When Paul made his appeal to be held over for the Emperor's decision, I ordered him held until I could send him to Caesar."

²²Then Agrippa said to Festus, "I would like to hear this man myself."

He replied, "Tomorrow you will hear him."

Paul Before Agrippa

²³The next day Agrippa and Bernice came with great pomp and entered the audience room with the high ranking officers and the leading men of the city. At the command of Festus, Paul was brought in. ²⁴Festus said: "King Agrippa, and all who are present with us, you see this man! The whole Jewish community has petitioned me about him in Jerusalem and here in Caesarea, shouting that he ought not to live any longer. ²⁵I found he had done nothing deserving of death, but because he made his appeal to the Emperor I decided to send him to Rome. ²⁶But I have nothing definite to write to His Majesty about him. Therefore I have brought him before all of you, and especially before you, King Agrippa, so that as a result of this investigation I may have something to write. ²⁷For I think it is unreasonable to send on a prisoner without specifying the charges against him."

26 Then Agrippa said to Paul, "You have permission to speak for yourself."

So Paul motioned with his hand and began his defense: ²"King Agrippa, I consider myself fortunate to stand before you today as I make my defense against all the accusations of the Jews, ³and especially so because you are well acquainted with all the Jewish customs and controversies. Therefore, I beg you to listen to me patiently.

⁴"The Jews all know the way I have lived ever since I was a child, from the beginning of my life in my own country, and also in Jerusalem. ⁵They have known me for a long time and can testify, if they are willing, that according to the strictest sect of our religion, I lived as a Pharisee. ⁶And now it is because of my hope in what God has promised our fathers that I am on trial today. ⁷This is the promise our twelve tribes are hoping to see fulfilled as they earnestly serve God day and night. O king, it is because of this hope that the Jews are accusing me. ⁸Why should any of you consider it incredible that God raises the dead?

⁹"I too was convinced that I ought to do all that was possible to oppose the name of Jesus of Nazareth. ¹⁰And that is just what I did in Jerusalem. On the authority of the chief priests I put many of the saints in prison, and when they were put to death, I cast my vote against them. ¹¹Many a time I went from one synagogue to another to have them punished, and I tried to force them to blaspheme. In my obsession against them, I even went to foreign cities to persecute them.

¹²"On one of these journeys I was going to Damascus with the authority and commission of the chief priests. ¹³About noon, O king, as I was on the road, I saw a light from heaven, brighter than the sun, blazing around me and my companions. ¹⁴We all fell to the ground, and I heard a voice

saying to me in Aramaic,ᵃ 'Saul, Saul, why do you persecute me? It is hard for you to kick against the goads.'

¹⁵"Then I asked, 'Who are you, Lord?'

" 'I am Jesus, whom you are persecuting,' the Lord replied. ¹⁶'Now get up and stand on your feet. I have appeared to you to appoint you as a servant and as a witness of what you have seen of me and what I will show you. ¹⁷I will rescue you from your own people and from the Gentiles. I am sending you to them ¹⁸to open their eyes and turn them from darkness to light, and from the power of Satan to God, so that they may receive forgiveness of sins and a place among those who are sanctified by faith in me.'

¹⁹"So then, King Agrippa, I was not disobedient to the vision from heaven. ²⁰First to those in Damascus, then to those in Jerusalem and in all Judea, and to the Gentiles also, I preached that they should repent and turn to God and prove their repentance by their deeds. ²¹That is why the Jews seized me in the temple courts and tried to kill me. ²²But I have had God's help to this very day, and so I stand here and testify to small and great alike. I am saying nothing beyond what the prophets and Moses said would happen— ²³that the Christᵇ would suffer and, as the first to rise from the dead, would proclaim light to his own people and to the Gentiles."

²⁴At this point Festus interrupted Paul's defense. "You are out of your mind, Paul!" he shouted. "Your great learning is driving you insane."

²⁵"I am not insane, most excellent Festus," Paul replied. "What I am saying is true and reasonable. ²⁶The king is familiar with these things, and I can speak freely to him. I am convinced that none of this has escaped his notice, because it was not done in a corner. ²⁷King Agrippa, do you believe the prophets? I know you do."

²⁸Then Agrippa said to Paul, "Do you think that in such a short time you can persuade me to be a Christian?"

²⁹Paul replied, "Short time or long—I pray God that not only you but all who are listening to me today may become what I am, except for these chains."

³⁰The king rose, and with him the governor and Bernice and those sitting with them. ³¹They left the room, and while talking with one another, they said, "This man is not doing anything that deserves death or imprisonment."

³²Agrippa said to Festus, "This man could have been set free if he had not appealed to Caesar."

Paul Sails for Rome

27 When it was decided that we would sail for Italy, Paul and some other prisoners were handed over to a centurion named Julius, who belonged to the Imperial Regiment. ²We boarded a ship from Adramyttium about to sail for ports along the coast of the province of Asia, and we put out to sea. Aristarchus, a Macedonian from Thessalonica, was with us.

³The next day we landed at Sidon; and Julius, in kindness to Paul, allowed him to go to his friends so they might provide for his needs. ⁴From there we put out to sea again and passed to the lee of Cyprus because the winds were against us. ⁵When we had sailed across the open sea off the coast of Cilicia and Pamphylia, we landed at Myra in Lycia. ⁶There the centurion found an Alexandrian ship sailing for Italy and put us on board. ⁷We made slow headway for many days and had difficulty arriving off Cnidus. When the wind did not allow us to hold our course, we sailed to the lee of Crete, opposite Salmone. ⁸We moved along the coast with difficulty and came to a place called Fair Havens, near the town of Lasea.

⁹Much time had been lost, and sailing had already become dangerous because by now it was after the Fast.ᶜ So Paul warned them, ¹⁰"Men, I can see that our voyage is going to be disastrous and bring great loss to ship and cargo, and to our own lives also." ¹¹But the centurion, instead of listening to what Paul said, followed the advice of the pilot and of the owner of the ship. ¹²Since the harbor was unsuitable to winter in, the majority decided that we should sail on, hoping to reach Phoenix and winter there. This was a harbor in Crete, facing both southwest and northwest.

The Storm

¹³When a gentle south wind began to blow, they thought they had obtained what they wanted; so they weighed anchor and sailed along the shore of Crete. ¹⁴Before very long, a wind of hurri-

ᵃ 14 Or Hebrew   ᵇ 23 Or Messiah   ᶜ 9 That is, the Day of Atonement (Yom Kippur)

Too Much Talk

focus Profile: **Chloe**

It all started on Monday morning. On the way into English class, Jenna whispered to me that Lian Schiller had hooked up with Troy Cooper at a party over the weekend. How's that for the Monday morning news! I've always felt a little jealous of Lian. That girl's got it all—the perfect body, the rich parents, the new car and the perfect boyfriend, Chad. And now she gets Troy, too?

When Mr. Hillen gave us an extended reading time, my friend Mallory leaned over and asked me about my weekend. Mr. Hillen wandered out in the hall, oblivious to the fact that very few students were reading.

I couldn't resist. "Did you hear about Lian and Troy?" I asked Mallory. I felt a twinge of guilt—I knew I was gossiping—but I couldn't keep this to myself.

Mallory looked at me with this intense look in her eyes. And then I remembered.

Oh no. No, no, no! How could I make a slip like this?! Mallory and Chad are old friends. She's never liked Lian. She'd like nothing more than to ruin their relationship.

"Oh nothing, I mean, um, I heard something, that's all, I have no idea if it's true, it's no big deal, I'm sure." Shoot. There was no way out of this. Mallory arched her eyebrow and gave me a skeptical look. The damage was done.

Imagine how I felt at the end of the day when I found out that Troy had made it all up.

gossip in focus

Sometimes life feels like a reality TV show—alliances, gossip, intrigue and lies. We often forget that gossip is a sin. "Do not let any unwholesome talk come out of your mouths" (Ephesians 4:29, page 1546). So how do you put that into practice?

»Pause before you speak. Ask yourself, "Is what I'm about to say going to help or hurt someone?"

»If you feel that little twinge of guilt, don't say it. That's the Holy Spirit warning you not to gossip. Obey him.

»Memorize some verses and ask the Lord to bring these to your mind throughout the day. Check out Psalm 15:1–3 (page 666), Psalm 34:13 (page 686), Proverbs 11:13; 16:28 (page 818,827) and 2 Corinthians 12:20 (page 1533).

For more on this topic, see the index on page 1656.

For the full scoop on gossip and its damage, go to www.TrueImagesBible.com

---

cane force, called the "northeaster," swept down from the island. [15]The ship was caught by the storm and could not head into the wind; so we gave way to it and were driven along. [16]As we passed to the lee of a small island called Cauda, we were hardly able to make the lifeboat secure. [17]When the men had hoisted it aboard, they passed ropes under the ship itself to hold it together. Fearing that they would run aground on the sandbars of Syrtis, they lowered the sea anchor and let the ship be driven along. [18]We took such a violent battering from the storm that the next day they began to throw the cargo overboard. [19]On the third day, they threw the ship's tackle overboard with their own hands. ²⁰When neither sun nor stars appeared for many days and the storm continued raging, we finally gave up all hope of being saved.

²¹After the men had gone a long time without food, Paul stood up before them and said: "Men, you should have taken my advice not to sail from Crete; then you would have spared yourselves this damage and loss. ²²But now I urge you to keep up your courage, because not one of you will be lost; only the ship will be destroyed. ²³Last night an angel of the God whose I am and whom I serve stood beside me ²⁴and said, 'Do not be afraid, Paul. You must stand trial before Caesar; and God has graciously given you the lives of all who sail with you.' ²⁵So keep up your courage, men, for I have faith in God that it will happen just as he told me. ²⁶Nevertheless, we must run aground on some island."

The Shipwreck

²⁷On the fourteenth night we were still being driven across the Adriatic [a] Sea, when about midnight the sailors sensed they were approaching land. ²⁸They took soundings and found that the water was a hundred and twenty feet [b] deep. A short time later they took soundings again and found it was ninety feet [c] deep. ²⁹Fearing that we would be dashed against the rocks, they dropped four anchors from the stern and prayed for daylight. ³⁰In an attempt to escape from the ship, the sailors let the lifeboat down into the sea, pretending they were going to lower some anchors from the bow. ³¹Then Paul said to the centurion and the soldiers, "Unless these men stay with the ship, you cannot be saved." ³²So the soldiers cut the ropes that held the lifeboat and let it fall away.

³³Just before dawn Paul urged them all to eat. "For the last fourteen days," he said, "you have been in constant suspense and have gone without food—you haven't eaten anything. ³⁴Now I urge you to take some food. You need it to survive. Not one of you will lose a single hair from his head." ³⁵After he said this, he took some bread and gave thanks to God in front of them all. Then he broke it and began to eat. ³⁶They were all encouraged and ate some food themselves. ³⁷Altogether there were 276 of us on board. ³⁸When they had eaten as much as they wanted, they lightened the ship by throwing the grain into the sea.

³⁹When daylight came, they did not recognize the land, but they saw a bay with a sandy beach, where they decided to run the ship aground if they could. ⁴⁰Cutting loose the anchors, they left them in the sea and at the same time untied the ropes that held the rudders. Then they hoisted the foresail to the wind and made for the beach. ⁴¹But the ship struck a sandbar and ran aground. The bow stuck fast and would not move, and the stern was broken to pieces by the pounding of the surf.

⁴²The soldiers planned to kill the prisoners to prevent any of them from swimming away and escaping. ⁴³But the centurion wanted to spare Paul's life and kept them from carrying out their plan. He ordered those who could swim to jump overboard first and get to land. ⁴⁴The rest were to get there on planks or on pieces of the ship. In this way everyone reached land in safety.

Ashore on Malta

28 Once safely on shore, we found out that the island was called Malta. ²The islanders showed us unusual kindness. They built a fire and welcomed us all because it was raining and cold. ³Paul gathered a pile of brushwood and, as he put it on the fire, a viper, driven out by the heat, fastened itself on his hand. ⁴When the islanders saw the snake hanging from his hand, they said to each other, "This man must be a murderer; for though he escaped from the sea, Justice has not allowed him to live." ⁵But Paul shook the snake off into the fire and suffered no ill effects. ⁶The people expected him to swell up or suddenly fall dead, but after waiting a long time and seeing nothing unusual happen to him, they changed their minds and said he was a god.

⁷There was an estate nearby that belonged to Publius, the chief official of the island. He welcomed us to his home and for three days entertained us hospitably. ⁸His father was sick in bed, suffering from fever and dysentery. Paul went in to see him and, after prayer, placed his hands on him and healed him. ⁹When this had happened, the rest of the sick on the island came and were cured. ¹⁰They honored us in many ways and when we were ready to sail, they furnished us with the supplies we needed.

---

a 27 In ancient times the name referred to an area extending well south of Italy.   *b 28* Greek *twenty orguias* (about 37 meters)   *c 28* Greek *fifteen orguias* (about 27 meters)

Arrival at Rome

[11]After three months we put out to sea in a ship that had wintered in the island. It was an Alexandrian ship with the figurehead of the twin gods Castor and Pollux. [12]We put in at Syracuse and stayed there three days. [13]From there we set sail and arrived at Rhegium. The next day the south wind came up, and on the following day we reached Puteoli. [14]There we found some brothers who invited us to spend a week with them. And so we came to Rome. [15]The brothers there had heard that we were coming, and they traveled as far as the Forum of Appius and the Three Taverns to meet us. At the sight of these men Paul thanked God and was encouraged. [16]When we got to Rome, Paul was allowed to live by himself, with a soldier to guard him.

Paul Preaches at Rome Under Guard

[17]Three days later he called together the leaders of the Jews. When they had assembled, Paul said to them: "My brothers, although I have done nothing against our people or against the customs of our ancestors, I was arrested in Jerusalem and handed over to the Romans. [18]They examined me and wanted to release me, because I was not guilty of any crime deserving death. [19]But when the Jews objected, I was compelled to appeal to Caesar—not that I had any charge to bring against my own people. [20]For this reason I have asked to see you and talk with you. It is because of the hope of Israel that I am bound with this chain."

[21]They replied, "We have not received any letters from Judea concerning you, and none of the brothers who have come from there has reported or said anything bad about you. [22]But we want to hear what your views are, for we know that people everywhere are talking against this sect."

[23]They arranged to meet Paul on a certain day, and came in even larger numbers to the place where he was staying. From morning till evening he explained and declared to them the kingdom of God and tried to convince them about Jesus from the Law of Moses and from the Prophets. [24]Some were convinced by what he said, but others would not believe. [25]They disagreed among themselves and began to leave after Paul had made this final statement: "The Holy Spirit spoke the truth to your forefathers when he said through Isaiah the prophet:

[26]" 'Go to this people and say,
    "You will be ever hearing but never understanding;
        you will be ever seeing but
            never perceiving."
[27]For this people's heart has
            become calloused;
        they hardly hear with their
            ears,
        and they have closed their
            eyes.
    Otherwise they might see with
            their eyes,
        hear with their ears,
        understand with their hearts
        and turn, and I would heal
            them.'[a]

[28]"Therefore I want you to know that God's salvation has been sent to the Gentiles, and they will listen!"[b]

[30]For two whole years Paul stayed there in his own rented house and welcomed all who came to see him. [31]Boldly and without hindrance he preached the kingdom of God and taught about the Lord Jesus Christ.

truth or dare

You have easy access to spiritual resources, like Bibles and devotionals. But the best materials won't help you if they're only collecting dust. Open your eyes, ears and heart.

28:23–28

---

[a] 27 Isaiah 6:9,10   [b] 28 Some manuscripts *listen!"* [29]*After he said this, the Jews left, arguing vigorously among themselves.*

at a glance

author: The apostle Paul.

date: About A.D. 57.

setting: Paul, who was in Corinth, was about to visit Rome after making a stop in Jerusalem.

verse to remember: I am not ashamed of the gospel, because it is the power of God for the salvation of everyone who believes (1:16).

theme to consider: The book of Romans is a handbook on the Christian faith: All of us are sinners; Christ died to forgive sin; we are made right with God through faith; and this faith comes through a relationship with Jesus.

romans

unchanging truth

It's easy to freeze up when your friends challenge your faith. When they wonder why you go to church. When they ask why you have a Bible in your locker. What do you say in response? Where do you begin?

Sometimes we're unprepared for a witnessing opportunity. We don't know what to say, so we don't say anything at all. Sometimes we're confused. We end up throwing out spiritual mumbo-jumbo instead of giving our friends truth they can understand.

The book of Romans teaches us the bottom line, the basics of Christianity. If you want to be able to share your faith in a way that will help your friends understand what you believe, start with this book. Want to understand why some people don't even want to hear what you have to say about Jesus? Find out in Romans. Want to know why we got into this mess with sin in the first place? Read Romans. Did Jesus really have to die? Wasn't there some other way he could save us? Check out what Romans has to say about that.

Paul wrote this book for people like you—people who had questions about what to believe and how to explain it to others. When what's in your heart becomes clear in your mind, it's easier to share your faith with your friends.

life lessons

1. Who needs Jesus? Everyone does. We've all blown it when it comes to meeting God's standard for righteousness (1:18—3:24).

2. However, God made a way for us to be right with him again through a faith relationship with Jesus Christ (6:1–23).

3. Once we're saved, we learn how to really live. Paul shows us how to act, talk and think like Jesus (12:1—15:13).

1 Paul, a servant of Christ Jesus, called to be an apostle and set apart for the gospel of God—²the gospel he promised beforehand through his prophets in the Holy Scriptures ³regarding his Son, who as to his human nature was a descendant of David, ⁴and who through the Spirit*ᵃ of holiness was declared with power to be the Son of God*ᵇ by his resurrection from the dead: Jesus Christ our Lord. ⁵Through him and for his name's sake, we received grace and apostleship to call people from among all the Gentiles to the obedience that comes from faith. ⁶And you also are among those who are called to belong to Jesus Christ.

⁷To all in Rome who are loved by God and called to be saints:

Grace and peace to you from God our Father and from the Lord Jesus Christ.

Paul's Longing to Visit Rome

⁸First, I thank my God through Jesus Christ for all of you, because your faith is being reported all over the world. ⁹God, whom I serve with my whole heart in preaching the gospel of his Son, is my witness how constantly I remember you ¹⁰in my prayers at all times; and I pray that now at last by God's will the way may be opened for me to come to you.

¹¹I long to see you so that I may impart to you some spiritual gift to make you strong— ¹²that is, that you and I may be mutually encouraged by each other's faith. ¹³I do not want you to be unaware, brothers, that I planned many times to come to you (but have been prevented from doing so until now) in order that I might have a harvest among you, just as I have had among the other Gentiles.

¹⁴I am obligated both to Greeks and non-Greeks, both to the wise and the foolish. ¹⁵That is why I am so eager to preach the gospel also to you who are at Rome.

¹⁶I am not ashamed of the gospel, because it is the power of God for the salvation of everyone who believes: first for the Jew, then for the Gentile. ¹⁷For in the gospel a righteousness from God is revealed, a righteousness that is by faith from first to last,*ᶜ just as it is written: "The righteous will live by faith."*ᵈ

God's Wrath Against Mankind

¹⁸The wrath of God is being revealed from heaven against all the godlessness and wickedness of men who suppress the truth by their wickedness, ¹⁹since what may be known about God is plain to them, because God has made it plain to them. ²⁰For since the creation of the world God's invisible qualities—his eternal power and divine nature—have been clearly seen, being understood from what has been made, so that men are without excuse.

²¹For although they knew God, they neither glorified him as God nor gave thanks to him, but their thinking became futile and their foolish hearts were darkened. ²²Although they claimed to be wise, they became fools ²³and exchanged the glory of the immortal God for images made to look like mortal man and birds and animals and reptiles.

²⁴Therefore God gave them over in the sinful desires of their hearts to sexual impurity for the degrading of their bodies with one another. ²⁵They exchanged the truth of God for a lie, and worshiped and served created things rather than the Creator—who is forever praised. Amen.

²⁶Because of this, God gave them over to shameful lusts. Even their women exchanged natural relations for unnatural ones. ²⁷In the same way the men also abandoned natural relations with women and were inflamed with lust for one another. Men committed indecent acts with other men, and received in themselves the due penalty for their perversion.

²⁸Furthermore, since they did not think it worthwhile to retain the knowledge of God, he gave them over to a depraved mind, to do what ought not to be done. ²⁹They have become filled with every kind of wickedness, evil, greed and depravity. They are full of envy, murder, strife, deceit and malice. They are gossips, ³⁰slanderers, God-haters, insolent, arrogant and boastful; they invent ways of doing evil; they disobey their parents; ³¹they are senseless, faithless, heartless, ruthless. ³²Although they know God's righteous decree that those who do such things deserve death, they not only continue to do these very things but also approve of those who practice them.

a 4 Or *who as to his spirit*　　*b 4* Or *was appointed to be the Son of God with power*　　*c 17* Or *is from faith to faith*
d 17 Hab. 2:4

God's Righteous Judgment

2 You, therefore, have no excuse, you who pass judgment on someone else, for at whatever point you judge the other, you are condemning yourself, because you who pass judgment do the same things. ²Now we know that God's judgment against those who do such things is based on truth. ³So when you, a mere man, pass judgment on them and yet do the same things, do you think you will escape God's judgment? ⁴Or do you show contempt for the riches of his kindness, tolerance and patience, not realizing that God's kindness leads you toward repentance?

⁵But because of your stubbornness and your unrepentant heart, you are storing up wrath against yourself for the day of God's wrath, when his righteous judgment will be revealed. ⁶God "will give to each person according to what he has done." *a* ⁷To those who by persistence in doing good seek glory, honor and immortality, he will give eternal life. ⁸But for those who are self-seeking and who reject the truth and follow evil, there will be wrath and anger. ⁹There will be trouble and distress for every human being who does evil: first for the Jew, then for the Gentile; ¹⁰but glory, honor and peace for everyone who does good: first for the Jew, then for the Gentile. ¹¹For God does not show favoritism.

¹²All who sin apart from the law will also perish apart from the law, and all who sin under the law will be judged by the law. ¹³For it is not those who hear the law who are righteous in God's sight, but it is those who obey the law who will be declared righteous. ¹⁴(Indeed, when Gentiles, who do not have the law, do by nature things required by the law, they are a law for themselves, even though they do not have the law, ¹⁵since they show that the requirements of the law are written on their hearts, their consciences also bearing witness, and their thoughts now accusing, now even defending them.) ¹⁶This will take place on the day when God will judge men's secrets through Jesus Christ, as my gospel declares.

The Jews and the Law

¹⁷Now you, if you call yourself a Jew; if you rely on the law and brag about your relationship to God; ¹⁸if you know his will and approve of what is superior because you are instructed by the law; ¹⁹if you are convinced that you are a guide for the blind, a light for those who are in the dark, ²⁰an instructor of the foolish, a teacher of infants, because you have in the law the embodiment of knowledge and truth— ²¹you, then, who teach others, do you not teach yourself? You who preach against stealing, do you steal? ²²You who say that people should not commit adultery, do you commit adultery? You who abhor idols, do you rob temples? ²³You who brag about the law, do you dishonor God by breaking the law? ²⁴As it is written: "God's name is blasphemed among the Gentiles because of you." *b*

²⁵Circumcision has value if you observe the law, but if you break the law, you have become as though you had not been circumcised. ²⁶If those who are not circumcised keep the law's requirements, will they not be regarded as though they were circumcised? ²⁷The one who is not circumcised physically and yet obeys the law will condemn you who, even though you have the *c* written code and circumcision, are a lawbreaker.

²⁸A man is not a Jew if he is only one outwardly, nor is circumcision merely outward and physical. ²⁹No, a man is a Jew if he is one inwardly; and circumcision is circumcision of the heart, by the Spirit, not by the written code. Such a man's praise is not from men, but from God.

God's Faithfulness

3 What advantage, then, is there in being a Jew, or what value is there in circumcision? ²Much in every way! First of all, they have been entrusted with the very words of God.
³What if some did not have faith? Will their lack of faith nullify God's faithfulness? ⁴Not at all! Let God be true, and every man a liar. As it is written:

> "So that you may be proved right when you speak
> and prevail when you judge." *d*

⁵But if our unrighteousness brings out God's righteousness more clearly, what shall we say? That God is unjust in bringing his wrath on us? (I am using a human argument.) ⁶Certainly not! If that were so, how could God judge the world? ⁷Someone might argue, "If my falsehood enhances

a 6 Psalm 62:12; Prov. 24:12   *b 24* Isaiah 52:5; Ezek. 36:22   *c 27* Or *who, by means of a*   *d 4* Psalm 51:4

God's truthfulness and so increases his glory, why am I still condemned as a sinner?" [8]Why not say—as we are being slanderously reported as saying and as some claim that we say—"Let us do evil that good may result"? Their condemnation is deserved.

No One Is Righteous

[9]What shall we conclude then? Are we any better[a]? Not at all! We have already made the charge that Jews and Gentiles alike are all under sin. [10]As it is written:

> "There is no one righteous, not even one;
> [11]   there is no one who understands,
>   no one who seeks God.
> [12]All have turned away,
>   they have together become worthless;
>   there is no one who does good,
>   not even one."[b]
> [13]"Their throats are open graves;
>   their tongues practice deceit."[c]
>   "The poison of vipers is on their lips."[d]
> [14]   "Their mouths are full of cursing and bitterness."[e]
> [15]"Their feet are swift to shed blood;
> [16]   ruin and misery mark their ways,
> [17]and the way of peace they do not know."[f]
> [18]   "There is no fear of God before their eyes."[g]

[19]Now we know that whatever the law says, it says to those who are under the law, so that every mouth may be silenced and the whole world held accountable to God. [20]Therefore no one will be declared righteous in his sight by observing the law; rather, through the law we become conscious of sin.

Righteousness Through Faith

[21]But now a righteousness from God, apart from law, has been made known, to which the Law and the Prophets testify. [22]This righteousness from God comes through faith in Jesus Christ to all who believe. There is no difference, [23]for all have sinned and fall short of the glory of God, [24]and are justified freely by his grace through the redemption that came by Christ Jesus. [25]God presented him as a sacrifice of atonement,[h] through faith in his blood. He did this to demonstrate his justice, because in his forbearance he had left the sins committed beforehand unpunished— [26]he did it to demonstrate his justice at the present time, so as to be just and the one who justifies those who have faith in Jesus.

[27]Where, then, is boasting? It is excluded. On what principle? On that of observing the law? No, but on that of faith. [28]For we maintain that a man is justified by faith apart from observing the law. [29]Is God the God of Jews only? Is he not the God of Gentiles too? Yes, of Gentiles too, [30]since there is only one God, who will justify the circumcised by faith and the uncircumcised through that same faith. [31]Do we, then, nullify the law by this faith? Not at all! Rather, we uphold the law.

Abraham Justified by Faith

4 What then shall we say that Abraham, our forefather, discovered in this matter? [2]If, in fact, Abraham was justified by works, he had something to boast about—but not before God. [3]What does the Scripture say? "Abraham believed God, and it was credited to him as righteousness."[i]

truth or dare

When it comes to perfection, we're in way over our heads. Starting to have that *sinking* feeling? The first step to salvation is realizing you *need* saving.

3:23

romans 4:3

---

[a] 9 Or *worse*   [b] 12 Psalms 14:1-3; 53:1-3; Eccles. 7:20   [c] 13 Psalm 5:9   [d] 13 Psalm 140:3   [e] 14 Psalm 10:7
[f] 17 Isaiah 59:7,8   [g] 18 Psalm 36:1   [h] 25 Or *as the one who would turn aside his wrath, taking away sin*
[i] 3 Gen. 15:6; also in verse 22

[4]Now when a man works, his wages are not credited to him as a gift, but as an obligation. [5]However, to the man who does not work but trusts God who justifies the wicked, his faith is credited as righteousness. [6]David says the same thing when he speaks of the blessedness of the man to whom God credits righteousness apart from works:

[7]"Blessed are they
    whose transgressions are forgiven,
    whose sins are covered.
[8]Blessed is the man
    whose sin the Lord will never count against him." [a]

[9]Is this blessedness only for the circumcised, or also for the uncircumcised? We have been saying that Abraham's faith was credited to him as righteousness. [10]Under what circumstances was it credited? Was it after he was circumcised, or before? It was not after, but before! [11]And he received the sign of circumcision, a seal of the righteousness that he had by faith while he was still uncircumcised. So then, he is the father of all who believe but have not been circumcised, in order that righteousness might be credited to them. [12]And he is also the father of the circumcised who not only are circumcised but who also walk in the footsteps of the faith that our father Abraham had before he was circumcised.

[13]It was not through law that Abraham and his offspring received the promise that he would be heir of the world, but through the righteousness that comes by faith. [14]For if those who live by law are heirs, faith has no value and the promise is worthless, [15]because law brings wrath. And where there is no law there is no transgression.

[16]Therefore, the promise comes by faith, so that it may be by grace and may be guaranteed to all Abraham's offspring—not only to those who are of the law but also to those who are of the faith of Abraham. He is the father of us all. [17]As it is written: "I have made you a father of many nations." [b] He is our father in the sight of God, in whom he believed—the God who gives life to the dead and calls things that are not as though they were.

[18]Against all hope, Abraham in hope believed and so became the father of many nations, just as it had been said to him, "So shall your offspring be." [c] [19]Without weakening in his faith, he faced the fact that his body was as good as dead—since he was about a hundred years old—and that Sarah's womb was also dead. [20]Yet he did not waver through unbelief regarding the promise of God, but was strengthened in his faith and gave glory to God, [21]being fully persuaded that God had power to do what he had promised. [22]This is why "it was credited to him as righteousness." [23]The words "it was credited to him" were written not for him alone, [24]but also for us, to whom God will credit righteousness—for us who believe in him who raised Jesus our Lord from the dead. [25]He was delivered over to death for our sins and was raised to life for our justification.

Peace and Joy

5 Therefore, since we have been justified through faith, we[d] have peace with God through our Lord Jesus Christ, [2]through whom we have gained access by faith into this grace in which we now stand. And we[d] rejoice in the hope of the glory of God. [3]Not only so, but we[d] also rejoice in our sufferings, because we know that suffering produces perseverance; [4]perseverance, character; and character, hope. [5]And hope does not disappoint us, because God has poured out his love into our hearts by the Holy Spirit, whom he has given us.

[6]You see, at just the right time, when we were still powerless, Christ died for the ungodly. [7]Very rarely will anyone die for a righteous man, though for a good man someone might possibly dare to die. [8]But God demonstrates his own love for us in this: While we were still sinners, Christ died for us.

truth or dare

While you might think that roses, quality time or a heartfelt talk is the ultimate display of love, think again. Jesus' love expression can never be equaled.

5:8

a 8 Psalm 32:1,2   *b 17* Gen. 17:5   *c 18* Gen. 15:5   *d 1,2,3* Or *let us*

[9]Since we have now been justified by his blood, how much more shall we be saved from God's wrath through him! [10]For if, when we were God's enemies, we were reconciled to him through the death of his Son, how much more, having been reconciled, shall we be saved through his life! [11]Not only is this so, but we also rejoice in God through our Lord Jesus Christ, through whom we have now received reconciliation.

Death Through Adam, Life Through Christ

[12]Therefore, just as sin entered the world through one man, and death through sin, and in this way death came to all men, because all sinned— [13]for before the law was given, sin was in the world. But sin is not taken into account when there is no law. [14]Nevertheless, death reigned from the time of Adam to the time of Moses, even over those who did not sin by breaking a command, as did Adam, who was a pattern of the one to come.

[15]But the gift is not like the trespass. For if the many died by the trespass of the one man, how much more did God's grace and the gift that came by the grace of the one man, Jesus Christ, overflow to the many! [16]Again, the gift of God is not like the result of the one man's sin: The judgment followed one sin and brought condemnation, but the gift followed many trespasses and brought justification. [17]For if, by the trespass of the one man, death reigned through that one man, how much more will those who receive God's abundant provision of grace and of the gift of righteousness reign in life through the one man, Jesus Christ.

[18]Consequently, just as the result of one trespass was condemnation for all men, so also the result of one act of righteousness was justification that brings life for all men. [19]For just as through the disobedience of the one man the many were made sinners, so also through the obedience of the one man the many will be made righteous.

[20]The law was added so that the trespass might increase. But where sin increased, grace increased all the more, [21]so that, just as sin reigned in death, so also grace might reign through righteousness to bring eternal life through Jesus Christ our Lord.

Dead to Sin, Alive in Christ

6 What shall we say, then? Shall we go on sinning so that grace may increase? [2]By no means! We died to sin; how can we live in it any longer? [3]Or don't you know that all of us who were baptized into Christ Jesus were baptized into his death? [4]We were therefore buried with him through baptism into death in order that, just as Christ was raised from the dead through the glory of the Father, we too may live a new life.

[5]If we have been united with him like this in his death, we will certainly also be united with him in his resurrection. [6]For we know that our old self was crucified with him so that the body of sin might be done away with, *a* that we should no longer be slaves to sin— [7]because anyone who has died has been freed from sin.

[8]Now if we died with Christ, we believe that we will also live with him. [9]For we know that since Christ was raised from the dead, he cannot die again; death no longer has mastery over him. [10]The death he died, he died to sin once for all; but the life he lives, he lives to God.

a 6 Or be rendered powerless

¹¹In the same way, count yourselves dead to sin but alive to God in Christ Jesus. ¹²Therefore do not let sin reign in your mortal body so that you obey its evil desires. ¹³Do not offer the parts of your body to sin, as instruments of wickedness, but rather offer yourselves to God, as those who have been brought from death to life; and offer the parts of your body to him as instruments of righteousness. ¹⁴For sin shall not be your master, because you are not under law, but under grace.

Slaves to Righteousness

¹⁵What then? Shall we sin because we are not under law but under grace? By no means! ¹⁶Don't you know that when you offer yourselves to someone to obey him as slaves, you are slaves to the one whom you obey—whether you are slaves to sin, which leads to death, or to obedience, which leads to righteousness? ¹⁷But thanks be to God that, though you used to be slaves to sin, you wholeheartedly obeyed the form of teaching to which you were entrusted. ¹⁸You have been set free from sin and have become slaves to righteousness.

¹⁹I put this in human terms because you are weak in your natural selves. Just as you used to offer the parts of your body in slavery to impurity and to ever-increasing wickedness, so now offer them in slavery to righteousness leading to holiness. ²⁰When you were slaves to sin, you were free from the control of righteousness. ²¹What benefit did you reap at that time from the things you are now ashamed of? Those things result in death! ²²But now that you have been set free from sin and have become slaves to God, the benefit you reap leads to holiness, and the result is eternal life. ²³For the wages of sin is death, but the gift of God is eternal life in ᵃ Christ Jesus our Lord.

truth or dare

Wages are what you rightfully earn for your work. This verse tells exactly what you deserve for your sin . . . and what's free for the taking.

6:23

An Illustration From Marriage

7 Do you not know, brothers—for I am speaking to men who know the law—that the law has authority over a man only as long as he lives? ²For example, by law a married woman is bound to her husband as long as he is alive, but if her husband dies, she is released from the law of marriage. ³So then, if she marries another man while her husband is still alive, she is called an adulteress. But if her husband dies, she is released from that law and is not an adulteress, even though she marries another man.

⁴So, my brothers, you also died to the law through the body of Christ, that you might belong to another, to him who was raised from the dead, in order that we might bear fruit to God. ⁵For when we were controlled by the sinful nature, ᵇ the sinful passions aroused by the law were at work in our bodies, so that we bore fruit for death. ⁶But now, by dying to what once bound us, we have been released from the law so that we serve in the new way of the Spirit, and not in the old way of the written code.

Struggling With Sin

⁷What shall we say, then? Is the law sin? Certainly not! Indeed I would not have known what sin was except through the law. For I would not have known what coveting really was if the law had not said, "Do not covet." ᶜ ⁸But sin, seizing the opportunity afforded by the commandment, produced in me every kind of covetous desire. For apart from law, sin is dead. ⁹Once I was alive apart from law; but when the commandment came, sin sprang to life and I died. ¹⁰I found that the very commandment that was intended to bring life actually brought death. ¹¹For sin, seizing the opportunity afforded by the commandment, deceived me, and through the commandment put me to death. ¹²So then, the law is holy, and the commandment is holy, righteous and good.

¹³Did that which is good, then, become death to me? By no means! But in order that sin might be recognized as sin, it produced death in me through what was good, so that through the commandment sin might become utterly sinful.

ᵃ 23 Or *through*   ᵇ 5 Or *the flesh*; also in verse 25   ᶜ 7 Exodus 20:17; Deut. 5:21

¹⁴We know that the law is spiritual; but I am unspiritual, sold as a slave to sin. ¹⁵I do not understand what I do. For what I want to do I do not do, but what I hate I do. ¹⁶And if I do what I do not want to do, I agree that the law is good. ¹⁷As it is, it is no longer I myself who do it, but it is sin living in me. ¹⁸I know that nothing good lives in me, that is, in my sinful nature.ᵃ For I have the desire to do what is good, but I cannot carry it out. ¹⁹For what I do is not the good I want to do; no, the evil I do not want to do—this I keep on doing. ²⁰Now if I do what I do not want to do, it is no longer I who do it, but it is sin living in me that does it.

²¹So I find this law at work: When I want to do good, evil is right there with me. ²²For in my inner being I delight in God's law; ²³but I see another law at work in the members of my body, waging war against the law of my mind and making me a prisoner of the law of sin at work within my members. ²⁴What a wretched man I am! Who will rescue me from this body of death? ²⁵Thanks be to God—through Jesus Christ our Lord!

So then, I myself in my mind am a slave to God's law, but in the sinful nature a slave to the law of sin.

truth or dare

Isn't it crazy how you can know what's right but keep doing what's wrong?! As long as we're alive we'll struggle with sin. Thank God that Jesus rescues us!

7:15–25

Life Through the Spirit

8 Therefore, there is now no condemnation for those who are in Christ Jesus,ᵇ ²because through Christ Jesus the law of the Spirit of life set me free from the law of sin and death. ³For what the law was powerless to do in that it was weakened by the sinful nature,ᶜ God did by sending his own Son in the likeness of sinful man to be a sin offering.ᵈ And so he condemned sin in sinful man,ᵉ ⁴in order that the righteous requirements of the law might be fully met in us, who do not live according to the sinful nature but according to the Spirit.

⁵Those who live according to the sinful nature have their minds set on what that nature desires; but those who live in accordance with the Spirit have their minds set on what the Spirit desires. ⁶The mind of sinful manᶠ is death, but the mind controlled by the Spirit is life and peace; ⁷the sinful mindᵍ is hostile to God. It does not submit to God's law, nor can it do so. ⁸Those controlled by the sinful nature cannot please God.

⁹You, however, are controlled not by the sinful nature but by the Spirit, if the Spirit of God lives in you. And if anyone does not have the Spirit of Christ, he does not belong to Christ. ¹⁰But if Christ is in you, your body is dead because of sin, yet your spirit is alive because of righteousness. ¹¹And if the Spirit of him who raised Jesus from the dead is living in you, he who raised Christ from the dead will also give life to your mortal bodies through his Spirit, who lives in you.

¹²Therefore, brothers, we have an obligation—but it is not to the sinful nature, to live according to it. ¹³For if you live according to the sinful nature, you will die; but if by the Spirit you put to death the misdeeds of the body, you will live, ¹⁴because those who are led by the Spirit of God are sons of God. ¹⁵For you did not receive a spirit that makes you a slave again to fear, but you received the Spirit of sonship.ʰ And by him we cry, "Abba,ⁱ Father." ¹⁶The Spirit himself testifies with our spirit that we are God's children. ¹⁷Now if we are children, then we are heirs—heirs of God and co-heirs with Christ, if indeed we share in his sufferings in order that we may also share in his glory.

Future Glory

¹⁸I consider that our present sufferings are not worth comparing with the glory that will be revealed in us. ¹⁹The creation waits in eager expectation for the sons of God to be revealed. ²⁰For the creation was subjected to frustration, not by its own choice, but by the will of the one who subject-

---

a 18 Or *my flesh*   *b 1* Some later manuscripts *Jesus, who do not live according to the sinful nature but according to the Spirit,*   *c 3* Or *the flesh*; also in verses 4, 5, 8, 9, 12 and 13   *d 3* Or *man, for sin*   *e 3* Or *in the flesh*
f 6 Or *mind set on the flesh*   *g 7* Or *the mind set on the flesh*   *h 15* Or *adoption*   *i 15* Aramaic for *Father*

ed it, in hope ²¹that ª the creation itself will be liberated from its bondage to decay and brought into the glorious freedom of the children of God.

²²We know that the whole creation has been groaning as in the pains of childbirth right up to the present time. ²³Not only so, but we ourselves, who have the firstfruits of the Spirit, groan inwardly as we wait eagerly for our adoption as sons, the redemption of our bodies. ²⁴For in this hope we were saved. But hope that is seen is no hope at all. Who hopes for what he already has? ²⁵But if we hope for what we do not yet have, we wait for it patiently.

²⁶In the same way, the Spirit helps us in our weakness. We do not know what we ought to pray for, but the Spirit himself intercedes for us with groans that words cannot express. ²⁷And he who searches our hearts knows the mind of the Spirit, because the Spirit intercedes for the saints in accordance with God's will.

More Than Conquerors

²⁸And we know that in all things God works for the good of those who love him, ᵇ who ᶜ have been called according to his purpose. ²⁹For those God foreknew he also predestined to be conformed to the likeness of his Son, that he might be the firstborn among many brothers. ³⁰And those he predestined, he also called; those he called, he also justified; those he justified, he also glorified.

³¹What, then, shall we say in response to this? If God is for us, who can be against us? ³²He who did not spare his own Son, but gave him up for us all—how will he not also, along with him, graciously give us all things? ³³Who will bring any charge against those whom God has chosen? It is God who justifies. ³⁴Who is he that condemns? Christ Jesus, who died—more than that, who was raised to life—is at the right hand of God and is also interceding for us. ³⁵Who shall separate us from the love of Christ? Shall trouble or hardship or persecution or famine or nakedness or danger or sword? ³⁶As it is written:

genuine prayer » 8:26-27

Sometimes you're hurting so much that you don't even know what to pray or how to pray. Sometimes a situation feels so painful that you're at a total loss for words. So you get down on your knees, and all you can do is cry. You know what? That's a prayer to God. These verses promise that the Holy Spirit knows what's going on in your life, and he'll intercede for you with God. When you have no words to say, let the Spirit turn your sighs into prayers to God. He promises to hear.

"For your sake we face death all day long;
we are considered as sheep to be slaughtered." ᵈ

³⁷No, in all these things we are more than conquerors through him who loved us. ³⁸For I am convinced that neither death nor life, neither angels nor demons, ᵉ neither the present nor the future, nor any powers, ³⁹neither height nor depth, nor anything else in all creation, will be able to separate us from the love of God that is in Christ Jesus our Lord.

God's Sovereign Choice

9 I speak the truth in Christ—I am not lying, my conscience confirms it in the Holy Spirit— ²I have great sorrow and unceasing anguish in my heart. ³For I could wish that I myself were cursed and cut off from Christ for the sake of my brothers, those of my own race, ⁴the people of Israel. Theirs is the adoption as sons; theirs the divine glory, the covenants, the receiving of

ª 20,21 Or subjected it in hope. 21For   ᵇ 28 Some manuscripts And we know that all things work together for good to those who love God   ᶜ 28 Or works together with those who love him to bring about what is good—with those who   ᵈ 36 Psalm 44:22   ᵉ 38 Or nor heavenly rulers the law, the temple worship and the promises. [5]Theirs are the patriarchs, and from them is traced the human ancestry of Christ, who is God over all, forever praised![a] Amen.

[6]It is not as though God's word had failed. For not all who are descended from Israel are Israel. [7]Nor because they are his descendants are they all Abraham's children. On the contrary, "It is through Isaac that your offspring will be reckoned."[b] [8]In other words, it is not the natural children who are God's children, but it is the children of the promise who are regarded as Abraham's offspring. [9]For this was how the promise was stated: "At the appointed time I will return, and Sarah will have a son."[c]

[10]Not only that, but Rebekah's children had one and the same father, our father Isaac. [11]Yet, before the twins were born or had done anything good or bad—in order that God's purpose in election might stand: [12]not by works but by him who calls—she was told, "The older will serve the younger."[d] [13]Just as it is written: "Jacob I loved, but Esau I hated."[e]

[14]What then shall we say? Is God unjust? Not at all! [15]For he says to Moses,

"I will have mercy on whom I
    have mercy,
and I will have compassion on
    whom I have
    compassion."[f]

[16]It does not, therefore, depend on man's desire or effort, but on God's mercy. [17]For the Scripture says to Pharaoh: "I raised you up for this very purpose, that I might display my power in you and that my name might be proclaimed in all the earth."[g] [18]Therefore God has mercy on whom he wants to have mercy, and he hardens whom he wants to harden.

[19]One of you will say to me: "Then why does God still blame us? For who resists his will?" [20]But who are you, O man, to talk back to God? "Shall what is formed say to him who formed it, 'Why did you make me like this?' "[h] [21]Does not the potter have the right to make out of the same lump of clay some pottery for noble purposes and some for common use?

[22]What if God, choosing to show his wrath and make his power known, bore with great patience the objects of his wrath—prepared for destruction? [23]What if he did this to make the riches of his glory known to the objects of his mercy, whom he prepared in advance for glory— [24]even us, whom he also called, not only from the Jews but also from the Gentiles? [25]As he says in Hosea:

"I will call them 'my people' who
    are not my people;
and I will call her 'my loved
    one' who is not my
    loved one,"[i]

love notes

8:35–39

Beloved,

There is absolutely nothing in this world that can take my love away from you. Nothing! Not hardship, not persecution, not Satan, not even death itself. My love for you overcomes anything—and everything—in this world.

—Your loving Father

What in your life—attitudes, thoughts, behaviors, circumstances—make you feel separated from God's love? How do these verses comfort you?

_____

_____

_____

_____

_____

_____

_____

a 5 Or Christ, who is over all. God be forever praised! Or Christ. God who is over all be forever praised!
b 7 Gen. 21:12   c 9 Gen. 18:10,14
d 12 Gen. 25:23   e 13 Mal. 1:2,3
f 15 Exodus 33:19   g 17 Exodus 9:16
h 20 Isaiah 29:16; 45:9   i 25 Hosea 2:23

The Big Payback

focus | Profile: **Stacey**

It's payback time. Or is it? I'm not sure anymore.

I've got the scoop of a lifetime on my ex-friend Nadine—a backstabber if ever there was one. Some friend. I trusted her with my secrets. The biggest one I had was that I went out with Tyler one time after Carlos and I had a fight. Okay, I shouldn't have gone out with Tyler. I regretted it. But not half as much as I regretted telling Nadine. She went and blabbed to Carlos, who is now my *ex*, just so she could try to steal him for herself. And sure enough, after Carlos and I broke up, he started going out with Nadine. Well, that ended my friendship with both of them. I could hardly believe that Nadine would betray me like that.

Well, they quickly became Couple of the Year at school. That was a horrible year. But I never would've thought that I'd catch *her* cheating on Carlos. (Surprise, surprise.) But I did! While I was at the movies near my cousin's house, I caught her with . . . Tyler! (He is so low, raking in everyone's girlfriends.) She didn't see me, though. I even heard her planning another date with Tyler.

I have the perfect opportunity to get even with her. I should just go to Carlos and let him know where he can find Nadine and Tyler. Nadine totally deserves what's coming to her.

Now I have to decide: Should I do it?

revenge in focus

Payback seems mighty sweet when you see it in movies or in classic books like *The Count of Monte Cristo* and *The Odyssey*. But when it comes to revenge, God expects you to just say no.

»God reserves revenge for himself alone (see Romans 12:19, page 1500). Only he has the perfect judgment and thoroughness to do it properly and mercifully.

»Need further convincing? Check out these Scriptures: Genesis 50:15–21 (pages 67–68), Leviticus 19:18 (page 142), Deuteronomy 32:35 (page 248) and Proverbs 20:22 (page 833).

»Instead of taking revenge, we're commanded to forgive. (See Matthew 18:15–35, pages 1316–1317.) Not asked to—*commanded to*. Impossible, you say? It sure is. But not with God.

For more on this topic, see the index on page 1656.

²⁶and,

> "It will happen that in the very place where it was said to them,
>   'You are not my people,'
>   they will be called 'sons of the living God.' " ᵃ

²⁷Isaiah cries out concerning Israel:

ᵃ 26 Hosea 1:10

"Though the number of the Israelites be like the sand by the sea,
only the remnant will be saved.
[28] For the Lord will carry out
his sentence on earth with speed and finality." [a]

[29] It is just as Isaiah said previously:

"Unless the Lord Almighty
had left us descendants,
we would have become like Sodom,
we would have been like Gomorrah." [b]

Israel's Unbelief

[30] What then shall we say? That the Gentiles, who did not pursue righteousness, have obtained it, a righteousness that is by faith; [31] but Israel, who pursued a law of righteousness, has not attained it. [32] Why not? Because they pursued it not by faith but as if it were by works. They stumbled over the "stumbling stone." [33] As it is written:

"See, I lay in Zion a stone that causes men to stumble
and a rock that makes them fall,
and the one who trusts in him will never be put to shame." [c]

10 Brothers, my heart's desire and prayer to God for the Israelites is that they may be saved. [2] For I can testify about them that they are zealous for God, but their zeal is not based on knowledge. [3] Since they did not know the righteousness that comes from God and sought to establish their own, they did not submit to God's righteousness. [4] Christ is the end of the law so that there may be righteousness for everyone who believes.

[5] Moses describes in this way the righteousness that is by the law: "The man who does these things will live by them." [d] [6] But the righteousness that is by faith says: "Do not say in your heart, 'Who will ascend into heaven?' [e]" (that is, to bring Christ down) [7] "or 'Who will descend into the deep?' [f]" (that is, to bring Christ up from the dead). [8] But what does it say? "The word is near you; it is in your mouth and in your heart," [g] that is, the word of faith we are proclaiming: [9] That if you confess with your mouth, "Jesus is Lord," and believe in your heart that God raised him from the dead, you will be saved. [10] For it is with your heart that you believe and are justified, and it is with your mouth that you confess and are saved. [11] As the Scripture says, "Anyone who trusts in him will never be put to shame." [h] [12] For there is no difference between Jew and Gentile—the same Lord is Lord of all and richly blesses all who call on him, [13] for, "Everyone who calls on the name of the Lord will be saved." [i]

[14] How, then, can they call on the one they have not believed in? And how can they believe in the one of whom they have not heard? And how can they hear without someone preaching to them? [15] And how can they preach unless they are sent? As it is written, "How beautiful are the feet of those who bring good news!" [j]

[16] But not all the Israelites accepted the good news. For Isaiah says, "Lord, who has believed our message?" [k] [17] Consequently, faith comes from hearing the message, and the message is heard through the word of Christ. [18] But I ask: Did they not hear? Of course they did:

"Their voice has gone out into all the earth,
their words to the ends of the world." [l]

truth or dare

God doesn't want closet Christians. Speak up! When you publicly announce, "Jesus is my Lord (my master)," you confirm that your inner belief is the real deal.

10:9

---

a 28 Isaiah 10:22,23   *b 29* Isaiah 1:9   *c 33* Isaiah 8:14; 28:16   *d 5* Lev. 18:5   *e 6* Deut. 30:12
f 7 Deut. 30:13   *g 8* Deut. 30:14   *h 11* Isaiah 28:16   *i 13* Joel 2:32   *j 15* Isaiah 52:7   *k 16* Isaiah 53:1
l 18 Psalm 19:4

[19]Again I ask: Did Israel not understand? First, Moses says,

> "I will make you envious by those who are not a nation;
> I will make you angry by a nation that has no understanding."[a]

[20]And Isaiah boldly says,

> "I was found by those who did not seek me;
> I revealed myself to those who did not ask for me."[b]

[21]But concerning Israel he says,

> "All day long I have held out my hands
> to a disobedient and obstinate people."[c]

The Remnant of Israel

11 I ask then: Did God reject his people? By no means! I am an Israelite myself, a descendant of Abraham, from the tribe of Benjamin. [2]God did not reject his people, whom he foreknew. Don't you know what the Scripture says in the passage about Elijah—how he appealed to God against Israel: [3]"Lord, they have killed your prophets and torn down your altars; I am the only one left, and they are trying to kill me"[d]? [4]And what was God's answer to him? "I have reserved for myself seven thousand who have not bowed the knee to Baal."[e] [5]So too, at the present time there is a remnant chosen by grace. [6]And if by grace, then it is no longer by works; if it were, grace would no longer be grace.[f]

[7]What then? What Israel sought so earnestly it did not obtain, but the elect did. The others were hardened, [8]as it is written:

> "God gave them a spirit of stupor,
>   eyes so that they could not see
>   and ears so that they could not hear,
> to this very day."[g]

[9]And David says:

> "May their table become a snare and a trap,
>   a stumbling block and a retribution for them.
> [10]May their eyes be darkened so they cannot see,
>   and their backs be bent forever."[h]

Ingrafted Branches

[11]Again I ask: Did they stumble so as to fall beyond recovery? Not at all! Rather, because of their transgression, salvation has come to the Gentiles to make Israel envious. [12]But if their transgression means riches for the world, and their loss means riches for the Gentiles, how much greater riches will their fullness bring!

[13]I am talking to you Gentiles. Inasmuch as I am the apostle to the Gentiles, I make much of my ministry [14]in the hope that I may somehow arouse my own people to envy and save some of them. [15]For if their rejection is the reconciliation of the world, what will their acceptance be but life from the dead? [16]If the part of the dough offered as firstfruits is holy, then the whole batch is holy; if the root is holy, so are the branches.

[17]If some of the branches have been broken off, and you, though a wild olive shoot, have been grafted in among the others and now share in the nourishing sap from the olive root, [18]do not boast over those branches. If you do, consider this: You do not support the root, but the root supports you. [19]You will say then, "Branches were broken off so that I could be grafted in." [20]Granted. But they were broken off because of unbelief, and you stand by faith. Do not be arrogant, but be afraid. [21]For if God did not spare the natural branches, he will not spare you either.

[22]Consider therefore the kindness and sternness of God: sternness to those who fell, but kind-

---

a 19 Deut. 32:21   *b 20* Isaiah 65:1   *c 21* Isaiah 65:2   *d 3* 1 Kings 19:10,14   *e 4* 1 Kings 19:18   *f 6* Some manuscripts *be grace. But if by works, then it is no longer grace; if it were, work would no longer be work.*   *g 8* Deut. 29:4; Isaiah 29:10   *h 10* Psalm 69:22,23 ness to you, provided that you continue in his kindness. Otherwise, you also will be cut off. [23]And if they do not persist in unbelief, they will be grafted in, for God is able to graft them in again. [24]After all, if you were cut out of an olive tree that is wild by nature, and contrary to nature were grafted into a cultivated olive tree, how much more readily will these, the natural branches, be grafted into their own olive tree!

All Israel Will Be Saved

[25]I do not want you to be ignorant of this mystery, brothers, so that you may not be conceited: Israel has experienced a hardening in part until the full number of the Gentiles has come in. [26]And so all Israel will be saved, as it is written:

> "The deliverer will come from Zion;
>   he will turn godlessness away from Jacob.
> [27]And this is[a] my covenant with them
>   when I take away their sins."[b]

[28]As far as the gospel is concerned, they are enemies on your account; but as far as election is concerned, they are loved on account of the patriarchs, [29]for God's gifts and his call are irrevocable. [30]Just as you who were at one time disobedient to God have now received mercy as a result of their disobedience, [31]so they too have now become disobedient in order that they too may now[c] receive mercy as a result of God's mercy to you. [32]For God has bound all men over to disobedience so that he may have mercy on them all.

Doxology

> [33]Oh, the depth of the riches of the wisdom and[d] knowledge of God!
>   How unsearchable his judgments,
>   and his paths beyond tracing out!
> [34]"Who has known the mind of the Lord?
>   Or who has been his counselor?"[e]
> [35]"Who has ever given to God,
>   that God should repay him?"[f]
> [36]For from him and through him and to him are all things.
>   To him be the glory forever! Amen.

Living Sacrifices

12 Therefore, I urge you, brothers, in view of God's mercy, to offer your bodies as living sacrifices, holy and pleasing to God—this is your spiritual[g] act of worship. [2]Do not conform any longer to the pattern of this world, but be transformed by the renewing of your mind. Then you will be able to test and approve what God's will is—his good, pleasing and perfect will.

[3]For by the grace given me I say to every one of you: Do not think of yourself more highly than you ought, but rather think of yourself with sober judgment, in accordance with the measure of faith God has given you. [4]Just as each of us has one body with many members, and these members do not all have the same function, [5]so in Christ we who are many form one body, and each member belongs to all the others. [6]We have different gifts, according to the grace given us. If a man's gift is prophesying, let him use it in proportion to his[h] faith. [7]If it is serving, let him serve; if it is teaching, let him teach; [8]if it is encouraging, let him encourage;

truth or dare

Don't sacrifices always involve death? Yes. Being a *living* sacrifice means dying to yourself and living for Christ. Dare you to take that step of faith.

12:1–2

---

[a] 27 Or *will be*   [b] 27 Isaiah 59:20,21; 27:9; Jer. 31:33,34   [c] 31 Some manuscripts do not have *now*.   [d] 33 Or *riches and the wisdom and the*   [e] 34 Isaiah 40:13   [f] 35 Job 41:11   [g] 1 Or *reasonable*   [h] 6 Or in *agreement with the*

genuine friendship »
12:9-13

Friendships go through seasons—times when you're close, other times when you seem to drift apart. You may feel close to someone, and then you don't hear from her for a while. Or she hurts your feelings, intentionally or not. Then a few months later, you're best friends again. Perhaps you notice that pattern in your friendships. Want some surefire tips on keeping close with others? Be sincere. Honor others above yourself. Be joyful and patient. Share. Be hospitable. Others may be inconsistent with you, but you can be consistent in how you treat your friends—and that pleases God.

if it is contributing to the needs of others, let him give generously; if it is leadership, let him govern diligently; if it is showing mercy, let him do it cheerfully.

Love

⁹Love must be sincere. Hate what is evil; cling to what is good. ¹⁰Be devoted to one another in brotherly love. Honor one another above yourselves. ¹¹Never be lacking in zeal, but keep your spiritual fervor, serving the Lord. ¹²Be joyful in hope, patient in affliction, faithful in prayer. ¹³Share with God's people who are in need. Practice hospitality.

¹⁴Bless those who persecute you; bless and do not curse. ¹⁵Rejoice with those who rejoice; mourn with those who mourn. ¹⁶Live in harmony with one another. Do not be proud, but be willing to associate with people of low position.ᵃ Do not be conceited.

¹⁷Do not repay anyone evil for evil. Be careful to do what is right in the eyes of everybody. ¹⁸If it is possible, as far as it depends on you, live at peace with everyone. ¹⁹Do not take revenge, my friends, but leave room for God's wrath, for it is written: "It is mine to avenge; I will repay,"ᵇ says the Lord.

²⁰On the contrary:

"If your enemy is hungry, feed him;
   if he is thirsty, give him something to drink.
In doing this, you will heap burning coals on his head."ᶜ

²¹Do not be overcome by evil, but overcome evil with good.

Submission to the Authorities

13 Everyone must submit himself to the governing authorities, for there is no authority except that which God has established. The authorities that exist have been established by God. ²Consequently, he who rebels against the authority is rebelling against what God has instituted, and those who do so will bring judgment on themselves. ³For rulers hold no terror for those who do right, but for those who do wrong. Do you want to be free from fear of the one in authority? Then do what is right and he will commend you. ⁴For he is God's servant to do you good. But if you do wrong, be afraid, for he does not bear the sword for nothing. He is God's servant, an agent of wrath to bring punishment on the wrongdoer. ⁵Therefore, it is necessary to submit to the authorities, not only because of possible punishment but also because of conscience.

⁶This is also why you pay taxes, for the authorities are God's servants, who give their full time to governing. ⁷Give everyone what you owe him: If you owe taxes, pay taxes; if revenue, then revenue; if respect, then respect; if honor, then honor.

Love, for the Day Is Near

⁸Let no debt remain outstanding, except the continuing debt to love one another, for he who loves his fellowman has fulfilled the law. ⁹The commandments, "Do not commit adultery," "Do not murder," "Do not steal," "Do not covet,"ᵈ and whatever other commandment there may be, are summed up in this one rule: "Love your neighbor as yourself."ᵉ ¹⁰Love does no harm to its neigh-

---

ᵃ 16 Or willing to do menial work   ᵇ 19 Deut. 32:35   ᶜ 20 Prov. 25:21,22   ᵈ 9 Exodus 20:13-15,17; Deut. 5:17-19,21   ᵉ 9 Lev. 19:18

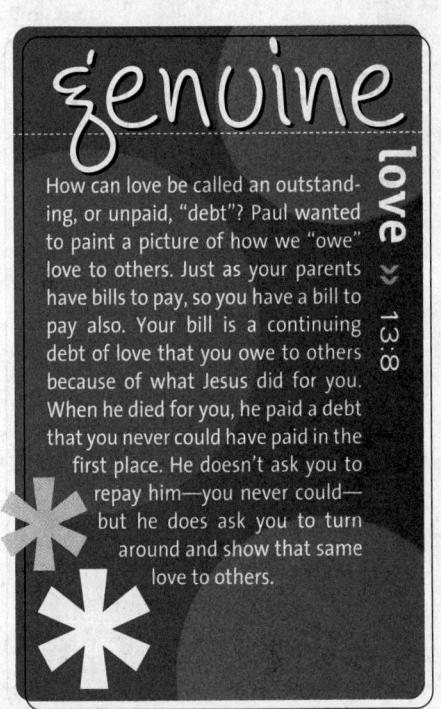

genuine

love » 13:8

How can love be called an outstanding, or unpaid, "debt"? Paul wanted to paint a picture of how we "owe" love to others. Just as your parents have bills to pay, so you have a bill to pay also. Your bill is a continuing debt of love that you owe to others because of what Jesus did for you. When he died for you, he paid a debt that you never could have paid in the first place. He doesn't ask you to repay him—you never could—but he does ask you to turn around and show that same love to others.

bor. Therefore love is the fulfillment of the law.

[11] And do this, understanding the present time. The hour has come for you to wake up from your slumber, because our salvation is nearer now than when we first believed. [12] The night is nearly over; the day is almost here. So let us put aside the deeds of darkness and put on the armor of light. [13] Let us behave decently, as in the daytime, not in orgies and drunkenness, not in sexual immorality and debauchery, not in dissension and jealousy. [14] Rather, clothe yourselves with the Lord Jesus Christ, and do not think about how to gratify the desires of the sinful nature. [a]

The Weak and the Strong

14 Accept him whose faith is weak, without passing judgment on disputable matters. [2] One man's faith allows him to eat everything, but another man, whose faith is weak, eats only vegetables. [3] The man who eats everything must not look down on him who does not, and the man who does not eat everything must not condemn the man who does, for God has accepted him. [4] Who are you to judge someone else's servant? To his own master he stands or falls. And he will stand, for the Lord is able to make him stand.

[5] One man considers one day more sacred than another; another man considers every day alike. Each one should be fully convinced in his own mind. [6] He who regards one day as special, does so to the Lord. He who eats meat, eats to the Lord, for he gives thanks to God; and he who abstains, does so to the Lord and gives thanks to God. [7] For none of us lives to himself alone and none of us dies to himself alone. [8] If we live, we live to the Lord; and if we die, we die to the Lord. So, whether we live or die, we belong to the Lord.

[9] For this very reason, Christ died and returned to life so that he might be the Lord of both the dead and the living. [10] You, then, why do you judge your brother? Or why do you look down on your brother? For we will all stand before God's judgment seat. [11] It is written:

" 'As surely as I live,' says the Lord,
'every knee will bow before me;
every tongue will confess to God.' " [b]

[12] So then, each of us will give an account of himself to God.

[13] Therefore let us stop passing judgment on one another. Instead, make up your mind not to put any stumbling block or obstacle in your brother's way. [14] As one who is in the Lord Jesus, I am fully convinced that no food [c] is unclean in itself. But if anyone regards something as unclean, then for him it is unclean. [15] If your brother is distressed because of what you eat, you are no longer acting in love. Do not by your eating destroy your brother for whom Christ died. [16] Do not allow what you consider good to be spoken of as evil. [17] For the kingdom of God is not a matter of eating and drinking, but of righteousness, peace and joy in the Holy Spirit, [18] because anyone who serves Christ in this way is pleasing to God and approved by men.

[19] Let us therefore make every effort to do what leads to peace and to mutual edification. [20] Do not destroy the work of God for the sake of food. All food is clean, but it is wrong for a man to eat anything that causes someone else to stumble. [21] It is better not to eat meat or drink wine or to do

a 14 Or *the flesh*   *b 11* Isaiah 45:23   *c 14* Or *that nothing* anything else that will cause your brother to fall.

22So whatever you believe about these things keep between yourself and God. Blessed is the man who does not condemn himself by what he approves. 23But the man who has doubts is condemned if he eats, because his eating is not from faith; and everything that does not come from faith is sin.

15 We who are strong ought to bear with the failings of the weak and not to please ourselves. 2Each of us should please his neighbor for his good, to build him up. 3For even Christ did not please himself but, as it is written: "The insults of those who insult you have fallen on me."*a* 4For everything that was written in the past was written to teach us, so that through endurance and the encouragement of the Scriptures we might have hope.

5May the God who gives endurance and encouragement give you a spirit of unity among yourselves as you follow Christ Jesus, 6so that with one heart and mouth you may glorify the God and Father of our Lord Jesus Christ.

genuine *unity* » 15:5-7

True unity doesn't magically happen; you've gotta work at it. If you've ever seen a church split or Christians arguing over something, then you know exactly how elusive unity can be. Throughout life you're gonna find that Christians will disagree about many things—and that's not necessarily bad, if they're getting to the truth in love (see Ephesians 4:15). But arguments just for the sake of arguing are pointless. The bottom line is that those of us who follow Jesus may disagree on the little stuff, but we're to be united on what's truly important—Jesus and what he's done for us.

7Accept one another, then, just as Christ accepted you, in order to bring praise to God. 8For I tell you that Christ has become a servant of the Jews*b* on behalf of God's truth, to confirm the promises made to the patriarchs 9so that the Gentiles may glorify God for his mercy, as it is written:

"Therefore I will praise you among the Gentiles;
    I will sing hymns to your name."*c*

10Again, it says,

"Rejoice, O Gentiles, with his people."*d*

11And again,

"Praise the Lord, all you Gentiles,
    and sing praises to him, all you peoples."*e*

12And again, Isaiah says,

"The Root of Jesse will spring up,
    one who will arise to rule over the nations;
    the Gentiles will hope in him."*f*

13May the God of hope fill you with all joy and peace as you trust in him, so that you may overflow with hope by the power of the Holy Spirit.

Paul the Minister to the Gentiles

14I myself am convinced, my brothers, that you yourselves are full of goodness, complete in knowledge and competent to instruct one another. 15I have written you quite boldly on some points, as if to remind you of them again, because of the grace God gave me 16to be a minister of Christ

a 3 Psalm 69:9   *b 8* Greek *circumcision*   *c 9* 2 Samuel 22:50; Psalm 18:49   *d 10* Deut. 32:43
e 11 Psalm 117:1   *f 12* Isaiah 11:10

Jesus to the Gentiles with the priestly duty of proclaiming the gospel of God, so that the Gentiles might become an offering acceptable to God, sanctified by the Holy Spirit.

[17]Therefore I glory in Christ Jesus in my service to God. [18]I will not venture to speak of anything except what Christ has accomplished through me in leading the Gentiles to obey God by what I have said and done— [19]by the power of signs and miracles, through the power of the Spirit. So from Jerusalem all the way around to Illyricum, I have fully proclaimed the gospel of Christ. [20]It has always been my ambition to preach the gospel where Christ was not known, so that I would not be building on someone else's foundation. [21]Rather, as it is written:

> "Those who were not told about him will see,
>   and those who have not heard will understand." [a]

[22]This is why I have often been hindered from coming to you.

Paul's Plan to Visit Rome

[23]But now that there is no more place for me to work in these regions, and since I have been longing for many years to see you, [24]I plan to do so when I go to Spain. I hope to visit you while passing through and to have you assist me on my journey there, after I have enjoyed your company for a while. [25]Now, however, I am on my way to Jerusalem in the service of the saints there. [26]For Macedonia and Achaia were pleased to make a contribution for the poor among the saints in Jerusalem. [27]They were pleased to do it, and indeed they owe it to them. For if the Gentiles have shared in the Jews' spiritual blessings, they owe it to the Jews to share with them their material blessings. [28]So after I have completed this task and have made sure that they have received this fruit, I will go to Spain and visit you on the way. [29]I know that when I come to you, I will come in the full measure of the blessing of Christ.

[30]I urge you, brothers, by our Lord Jesus Christ and by the love of the Spirit, to join me in my struggle by praying to God for me. [31]Pray that I may be rescued from the unbelievers in Judea and that my service in Jerusalem may be acceptable to the saints there, [32]so that by God's will I may come to you with joy and together with you be refreshed. [33]The God of peace be with you all. Amen.

Personal Greetings

16 I commend to you our sister Phoebe, a servant[b] of the church in Cenchrea. [2]I ask you to receive her in the Lord in a way worthy of the saints and to give her any help she may need from you, for she has been a great help to many people, including me.

[3]Greet Priscilla[c] and Aquila, my fellow workers in Christ Jesus. [4]They risked their lives for me. Not only I but all the churches of the Gentiles are grateful to them.

[5]Greet also the church that meets at their house.

Greet my dear friend Epenetus, who was the first convert to Christ in the province of Asia.

[6]Greet Mary, who worked very hard for you.

[7]Greet Andronicus and Junias, my relatives who have been in prison with me. They are outstanding among the apostles, and they were in Christ before I was.

[8]Greet Ampliatus, whom I love in the Lord.

[9]Greet Urbanus, our fellow worker in Christ, and my dear friend Stachys.

[10]Greet Apelles, tested and approved in Christ.

Greet those who belong to the household of Aristobulus.

[11]Greet Herodion, my relative.

Greet those in the household of Narcissus who are in the Lord.

[12]Greet Tryphena and Tryphosa, those women who work hard in the Lord.

Greet my dear friend Persis, another woman who has worked very hard in the Lord.

[13]Greet Rufus, chosen in the Lord, and his mother, who has been a mother to me, too.

[14]Greet Asyncritus, Phlegon, Hermes, Patrobas, Hermas and the brothers with them.

[15]Greet Philologus, Julia, Nereus and his sister, and Olympas and all the saints with them.

[16]Greet one another with a holy kiss.

All the churches of Christ send greetings.

a 21 Isaiah 52:15   *b* 1 Or *deaconess*   *c* 3 Greek *Prisca*, a variant of *Priscilla*

I commend to you our sister Phoebe, a servant of the church in Cenchrea. Romans 16:1

Phoebe—A Trustworthy Disciple

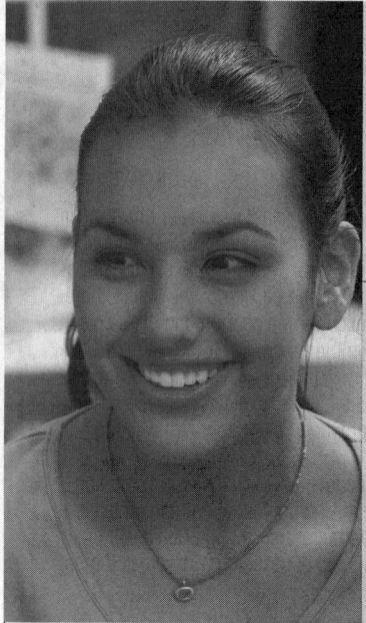

Hey, girl—how would you like to travel 1200 miles? Sorry, no cars or planes available. You'll spend days on foot and weeks in a boat. But in the end, your tiring journey will be worth it all. That is, if you can deliver the only copy of an important letter to the appropriate destination. So tell me—can we count on you?

Phoebe's mission was to personally carry the book of Romans from Corinth to Rome—and like never before, the apostle Paul was counting on her. Faithfully completing the long journey, Phoebe found herself among friends. The apostle Paul's letter asked the believers in Rome to welcome this "servant of the church," a trustworthy disciple who had helped many of the less fortunate, including Paul. It was a recommendation she had earned through her many acts of service.

And although Phoebe may not have realized it, the delivery of the book of Romans would play a key part in history. In its precious pages, Paul explained that salvation through Jesus is available to all—regardless of who we are or the sins we've done. Think of how many people have read and believed this trusted message, delivered by a trustworthy servant!

Do you wish others would trust you with something that big? Test your "trustworthiness quotient" by listening to how your friends and authority figures describe you. Do they make comments about your good character, as Paul did of Phoebe's? If not, you can earn their trust by being faithful and keeping your promises, showing others you're the kind of girl they can depend on.

To read the next Mirror Images profile, go to page 1518.

Dear Jesus, I want to be a trustworthy disciple you can count on. And with your help I'd like to show others I can be trusted like Phoebe was, in both big and small things. Amen.

>> Read more about Phoebe in Romans 16:1–2 (page 1503).

¹⁷I urge you, brothers, to watch out for those who cause divisions and put obstacles in your way that are contrary to the teaching you have learned. Keep away from them. ¹⁸For such people are not serving our Lord Christ, but their own appetites. By smooth talk and flattery they deceive the minds of naive people. ¹⁹Everyone has heard about your obedience, so I am full of joy over you; but I want you to be wise about what is good, and innocent about what is evil.

²⁰The God of peace will soon crush Satan under your feet.

The grace of our Lord Jesus be with you.

²¹Timothy, my fellow worker, sends his greetings to you, as do Lucius, Jason and Sosipater, my relatives.

²²I, Tertius, who wrote down this letter, greet you in the Lord.

²³Gaius, whose hospitality I and the whole church here enjoy, sends you his greetings.

Erastus, who is the city's director of public works, and our brother Quartus send you their greetings. ^a

²⁵Now to him who is able to establish you by my gospel and the proclamation of Jesus Christ, according to the revelation of the mystery hidden for long ages past, ²⁶but now revealed and made known through the prophetic writings by the command of the eternal God, so that all nations might believe and obey him— ²⁷to the only wise God be glory forever through Jesus Christ! Amen.

---

a 23 Some manuscripts *their greetings. 24May the grace of our Lord Jesus Christ be with all of you. Amen.*

author: The apostle Paul.

date: About A.D. 55.

setting: Paul started the church in Corinth, a city in Greece, during his second missionary journey.

verse to remember: Do you not know that your body is a temple of the Holy Spirit, who is in you, whom you have received from God? You are not your own; you were bought at a price. Therefore honor God with your body (6:19–20).

theme to consider: As Christians, we need to think and act differently than the world.

1 corinthians

unchanging truth

Jesus doesn't come into your life to improve your old way of living. He comes to radically change it. He turns it upside down and right side up again.

You used to gossip about your friends at the lunch table. Now you're learning your palm fits perfectly over the size of your mouth.

You used to fly into a rage whenever your little brother borrowed a CD from your room. Now you may be upset, but the rage is gone.

You used to get jealous every time you saw that new girl with your ex-boyfriend. Now you pray about it when those feelings come around. And those feelings don't last for long.

You used to think sex was something everyone was doing. Now you see the importance of saving it for marriage.

Paul wrote to the church in Corinth about how they were supposed to be different from the world. Now that they had a personal relationship with Jesus and his Spirit lived inside of them, they shouldn't live the way they used to live. For example, sex was no longer "no big deal"—they were learning to set it aside as God's special gift. Because of Christ, they were now different people. Christ was working in their lives to help them grow into the kind of people God intended them to be.

If you are in Christ, you don't talk, walk or live like you used to. You have been changed.

life lessons

1. When it comes to sex, Christians don't settle for anything less than the best: one partner, for life (6:12–20).

2. Paul reminds us we're all in this together. Use the gifts God has given you to encourage others and keep your fellow Christians on the right path (12:4–31).

3. The world has a totally different definition of love than God does. *True* love is God's kind of love (13:1–13).

1

Paul, called to be an apostle of Christ Jesus by the will of God, and our brother Sosthenes,

[2]To the church of God in Corinth, to those sanctified in Christ Jesus and called to be holy, together with all those everywhere who call on the name of our Lord Jesus Christ—their Lord and ours:

[3]Grace and peace to you from God our Father and the Lord Jesus Christ.

Thanksgiving

[4]I always thank God for you because of his grace given you in Christ Jesus. [5]For in him you have been enriched in every way—in all your speaking and in all your knowledge— [6]because our testimony about Christ was confirmed in you. [7]Therefore you do not lack any spiritual gift as you eagerly wait for our Lord Jesus Christ to be revealed. [8]He will keep you strong to the end, so that you will be blameless on the day of our Lord Jesus Christ. [9]God, who has called you into fellowship with his Son Jesus Christ our Lord, is faithful.

Divisions in the Church

[10]I appeal to you, brothers, in the name of our Lord Jesus Christ, that all of you agree with one another so that there may be no divisions among you and that you may be perfectly united in mind and thought. [11]My brothers, some from Chloe's household have informed me that there are quarrels among you. [12]What I mean is this: One of you says, "I follow Paul"; another, "I follow Apollos"; another, "I follow Cephas[a]"; still another, "I follow Christ."

[13]Is Christ divided? Was Paul crucified for you? Were you baptized into[b] the name of Paul? [14]I am thankful that I did not baptize any of you except Crispus and Gaius, [15]so no one can say that you were baptized into my name. [16](Yes, I also baptized the household of Stephanas; beyond that, I don't remember if I baptized anyone else.) [17]For Christ did not send me to baptize, but to preach the gospel—not with words of human wisdom, lest the cross of Christ be emptied of its power.

Christ the Wisdom and Power of God

[18]For the message of the cross is foolishness to those who are perishing, but to us who are being saved it is the power of God. [19]For it is written:

> "I will destroy the wisdom of the wise;
> the intelligence of the intelligent I will frustrate."[c]

[20]Where is the wise man? Where is the scholar? Where is the philosopher of this age? Has not God made foolish the wisdom of the world? [21]For since in the wisdom of God the world through its wisdom did not know him, God was pleased through the foolishness of what was preached to save those who believe. [22]Jews demand miraculous signs and Greeks look for wisdom, [23]but we preach Christ crucified: a stumbling block to Jews and foolishness to Gentiles, [24]but to those whom God has called, both Jews and Greeks, Christ the power of God and the wisdom of God. [25]For the foolishness of God is wiser than man's wisdom, and the weakness of God is stronger than man's strength.

[26]Brothers, think of what you were when you were called. Not many of you were wise by human standards; not many were influential; not many were of noble birth. [27]But God chose the foolish things of the world to shame the wise; God chose the weak things of the world to shame the strong. [28]He chose the lowly things of this world and the despised things—and the things that are not—to nullify the things that are, [29]so that no one may boast before him. [30]It is because of him that you are in Christ Jesus, who has become for us wisdom from God—that is, our righteousness, holiness and redemption. [31]Therefore, as it is written: "Let him who boasts boast in the Lord."[d]

truth or dare

The smartest person on earth can't follow God's train of thought. The gospel doesn't make sense to skeptics' blinded hearts; you gotta first have *faith*, not reason.

1:18–25

---

a 12 That is, Peter   *b 13* Or *in*; also in verse 15   *c 19* Isaiah 29:14   *d 31* Jer. 9:24

2 When I came to you, brothers, I did not come with eloquence or superior wisdom as I proclaimed to you the testimony about God.[a] [2]For I resolved to know nothing while I was with you except Jesus Christ and him crucified. [3]I came to you in weakness and fear, and with much trembling. [4]My message and my preaching were not with wise and persuasive words, but with a demonstration of the Spirit's power, [5]so that your faith might not rest on men's wisdom, but on God's power.

Wisdom From the Spirit

[6]We do, however, speak a message of wisdom among the mature, but not the wisdom of this age or of the rulers of this age, who are coming to nothing. [7]No, we speak of God's secret wisdom, a wisdom that has been hidden and that God destined for our glory before time began. [8]None of the rulers of this age understood it, for if they had, they would not have crucified the Lord of glory. [9]However, as it is written:

> "No eye has seen,
> no ear has heard,
> no mind has conceived
> what God has prepared for those who love him"[b]—

[10]but God has revealed it to us by his Spirit.

The Spirit searches all things, even the deep things of God. [11]For who among men knows the thoughts of a man except the man's spirit within him? In the same way no one knows the thoughts of God except the Spirit of God. [12]We have not received the spirit of the world but the Spirit who is from God, that we may understand what God has freely given us. [13]This is what we speak, not in words taught us by human wisdom but in words taught by the Spirit, expressing spiritual truths in spiritual words.[c] [14]The man without the Spirit does not accept the things that come from the Spirit of God, for they are foolishness to him, and he cannot understand them, because they are spiritually discerned. [15]The spiritual man makes judgments about all things, but he himself is not subject to any man's judgment:

> [16]"For who has known the mind of the Lord
> that he may instruct him?"[d]

But we have the mind of Christ.

On Divisions in the Church

3 Brothers, I could not address you as spiritual but as worldly—mere infants in Christ. [2]I gave you milk, not solid food, for you were not yet ready for it. Indeed, you are still not ready. [3]You are still worldly. For since there is jealousy and quarreling among you, are you not worldly? Are you not acting like mere men? [4]For when one says, "I follow Paul," and another, "I follow Apollos," are you not mere men?

[5]What, after all, is Apollos? And what is Paul? Only servants, through whom you came to believe—as the Lord has assigned to each his task. [6]I planted the seed, Apollos watered it, but God made it grow. [7]So neither he who plants nor he who waters is anything, but only God, who makes things grow. [8]The man who plants and the man who waters have one purpose, and each will be rewarded according to his own labor. [9]For we are God's fellow workers; you are God's field, God's building.

[10]By the grace God has given me, I laid a foundation as an expert builder, and someone else is building on it. But each one should be careful how he builds. [11]For no one can lay any foundation other than the one already laid, which is Jesus Christ. [12]If any man builds on this foundation using gold, silver, costly stones, wood, hay or straw, [13]his work will be shown for what it is, because the Day will bring it to light. It will be revealed with fire, and the fire will test the quality of each man's work. [14]If what he has built survives, he will receive his reward. [15]If it is burned up, he will suffer loss; he himself will be saved, but only as one escaping through the flames.

[16]Don't you know that you yourselves are God's temple and that God's Spirit lives in you? [17]If anyone destroys God's temple, God will destroy him; for God's temple is sacred, and you are that temple.

---

a 1 Some manuscripts *as I proclaimed to you God's mystery*   *b 9* Isaiah 64:4   *c 13* Or *Spirit, interpreting spiritual truths to spiritual men*   *d 16* Isaiah 40:13

[18]Do not deceive yourselves. If any one of you thinks he is wise by the standards of this age, he should become a "fool" so that he may become wise. [19]For the wisdom of this world is foolishness in God's sight. As it is written: "He catches the wise in their craftiness"[a]; [20]and again, "The Lord knows that the thoughts of the wise are futile."[b] [21]So then, no more boasting about men! All things are yours, [22]whether Paul or Apollos or Cephas[c] or the world or life or death or the present or the future—all are yours, [23]and you are of Christ, and Christ is of God.

Apostles of Christ

4 So then, men ought to regard us as servants of Christ and as those entrusted with the secret things of God. [2]Now it is required that those who have been given a trust must prove faithful. [3]I care very little if I am judged by you or by any human court; indeed, I do not even judge myself. [4]My conscience is clear, but that does not make me innocent. It is the Lord who judges me. [5]Therefore judge nothing before the appointed time; wait till the Lord comes. He will bring to light what is hidden in darkness and will expose the motives of men's hearts. At that time each will receive his praise from God.

[6]Now, brothers, I have applied these things to myself and Apollos for your benefit, so that you may learn from us the meaning of the saying, "Do not go beyond what is written." Then you will not take pride in one man over against another. [7]For who makes you different from anyone else? What do you have that you did not receive? And if you did receive it, why do you boast as though you did not?

[8]Already you have all you want! Already you have become rich! You have become kings—and that without us! How I wish that you really had become kings so that we might be kings with you! [9]For it seems to me that God has put us apostles on display at the end of the procession, like men condemned to die in the arena. We have been made a spectacle to the whole universe, to angels as well as to men. [10]We are fools for Christ, but you are so wise in Christ! We are weak, but you are strong! You are honored, we are dishonored! [11]To this very hour we go hungry and thirsty, we are in rags, we are brutally treated, we are homeless. [12]We work hard with our own hands. When we are cursed, we bless; when we are persecuted, we endure it; [13]when we are slandered, we answer kindly. Up to this moment we have become the scum of the earth, the refuse of the world.

[14]I am not writing this to shame you, but to warn you, as my dear children. [15]Even though you have ten thousand guardians in Christ, you do not have many fathers, for in Christ Jesus I became your father through the gospel. [16]Therefore I urge you to imitate me. [17]For this reason I am sending to you Timothy, my son whom I love, who is faithful in the Lord. He will remind you of my way of life in Christ Jesus, which agrees with what I teach everywhere in every church.

[18]Some of you have become arrogant, as if I were not coming to you. [19]But I will come to you very soon, if the Lord is willing, and then I will find out not only how these arrogant people are talking, but what power they have. [20]For the kingdom of God is not a matter of talk but of power. [21]What do you prefer? Shall I come to you with a whip, or in love and with a gentle spirit?

Expel the Immoral Brother!

5 It is actually reported that there is sexual immorality among you, and of a kind that does not occur even among pagans: A man has his father's wife. [2]And you are proud! Shouldn't you rather have been filled with grief and have put out of your fellowship the man who did this? [3]Even though I am not physically present, I am with you in spirit. And I have already passed judgment on the one who did this, just as if I were present. [4]When you are assembled in the name of our Lord Jesus and I am with you in spirit, and the power of our Lord Jesus is present, [5]hand this man over to Satan, so that the sinful nature[d] may be destroyed and his spirit saved on the day of the Lord.

[6]Your boasting is not good. Don't you know that a little yeast works through the whole batch of dough? [7]Get rid of the old yeast that you may be a new batch without yeast—as you really are. For Christ, our Passover lamb, has been sacrificed. [8]Therefore let us keep the Festival, not with the old yeast, the yeast of malice and wickedness, but with bread without yeast, the bread of sincerity and truth.

[9]I have written you in my letter not to associate with sexually immoral people— [10]not at all

---

[a] 19 Job 5:13   [b] 20 Psalm 94:11   [c] 22 That is, Peter   [d] 5 Or *that his body*; or *that the flesh*

A Close-up of Death

I was afraid I wouldn't make it there in time, that I wouldn't get to see her, that I would be too late. Everything felt so surreal. Just moments ago, my mom had received the call on her cell phone as she was watching my softball game. My best friend Laine had been in an accident, and they didn't think she was going to make it. We left the game and drove to the hospital as fast as we could.

As we walked to her room, everything felt like it was moving in slow motion. I saw Laine's feet peeking out from under the hospital blanket. They looked swollen and strange. When my eyes moved up toward her face, I saw it was covered in tubes and a mask. It didn't even look like her. Her mom was stroking her hand, but Laine showed no signs of life. *Was she in pain? Could she hear us? Was she already dead? What's happening?* The questions floated through my mind as if I were in a dream.

"Can she . . ." I tried to speak but my throat closed around the words. "Can she hear me?"

"We're not sure," said Laine's dad softly. "Go ahead. I know she'd want to hear your voice." I made my way to her side and noticed her ear had bits of dried blood inside. *Is this what it's like to die?* I remember thinking as I stared at my best friend and strained for words.

death in focus

It hurts so badly when a loved one dies. It's so final. All the things we wanted to say and do with that person, we'll never have a chance to do. Or will we?

» There is life after death, a reunion with other believers who have gone to heaven before us. Even though we miss them terribly during this life, we have hope— the certainty that we'll see them again.

» Even though we can't escape death, we don't have to fear it, because Jesus has conquered death, and he will raise to life those who belong to him (see 1 Corinthians 15:20–26,55–57, pages 1521–1522)!

» Could death possibly be a good thing, a relief from evil? Read Isaiah 57:1–2 (page 974) for a unique perspective on death.

For more on this topic, see the index on page 1656.

Struggling with the issue of death or the loss of a loved one? Read more online at www.TrueImagesBible.com

meaning the people of this world who are immoral, or the greedy and swindlers, or idolaters. In that case you would have to leave this world. [11]But now I am writing you that you must not associate with anyone who calls himself a brother but is sexually immoral or greedy, an idolater or a slanderer, a drunkard or a swindler. With such a man do not even eat.

[12]What business is it of mine to judge those outside the church? Are you not to judge those inside? [13]God will judge those outside. "Expel the wicked man from among you."[a]

a 13 Deut. 17:7; 19:19; 21:21; 22:21,24; 24:7

Lawsuits Among Believers

6 If any of you has a dispute with another, dare he take it before the ungodly for judgment instead of before the saints? [2]Do you not know that the saints will judge the world? And if you are to judge the world, are you not competent to judge trivial cases? [3]Do you not know that we will judge angels? How much more the things of this life! [4]Therefore, if you have disputes about such matters, appoint as judges even men of little account in the church![a] [5]I say this to shame you. Is it possible that there is nobody among you wise enough to judge a dispute between believers? [6]But instead, one brother goes to law against another—and this in front of unbelievers!

[7]The very fact that you have lawsuits among you means you have been completely defeated already. Why not rather be wronged? Why not rather be cheated? [8]Instead, you yourselves cheat and do wrong, and you do this to your brothers.

[9]Do you not know that the wicked will not inherit the kingdom of God? Do not be deceived: Neither the sexually immoral nor idolaters nor adulterers nor male prostitutes nor homosexual offenders [10]nor thieves nor the greedy nor drunkards nor slanderers nor swindlers will inherit the kingdom of God. [11]And that is what some of you were. But you were washed, you were sanctified, you were justified in the name of the Lord Jesus Christ and by the Spirit of our God.

Sexual Immorality

[12]"Everything is permissible for me"—but not everything is beneficial. "Everything is permissible for me"—but I will not be mastered by anything. [13]"Food for the stomach and the stomach for food"—but God will destroy them both. The body is not meant for sexual immorality, but for the Lord, and the Lord for the body. [14]By his power God raised the Lord from the dead, and he will raise us also. [15]Do you not know that your bodies are members of Christ himself? Shall I then take the members of Christ and unite them with a prostitute? Never! [16]Do you not know that he who unites himself with a prostitute is one with her in body? For it is said, "The two will become one flesh."[b] [17]But he who unites himself with the Lord is one with him in spirit.

[18]Flee from sexual immorality. All other sins a man commits are outside his body, but he who sins sexually sins against his own body. [19]Do you not know that your body is a temple of the Holy Spirit, who is in you, whom you have received from God? You are not your own; [20]you were bought at a price. Therefore honor God with your body.

truth or dare

You can't expect non-Christians to act like Christians—they don't have the same morals. You need to reach out to them. But don't even associate with someone who claims to be a believer but is immoral.

5:9–11

genuine

purity » 6:18-20

When you look in the mirror, what do you see? A temple? That's what *God* sees when he looks at you. Because his Spirit lives in you, that makes you God's temple. Perhaps you don't think very highly of your body, but God does. He's not obsessed with its shape or size. He's not concerned with how trendy your clothes and makeup are. What he does want is for you to take good care of yourself—for example, staying sexually pure and keeping harmful substances out of your body. That's the least you can do for God's home.

---

a 4 Or *matters, do you appoint as judges men of little account in the church?*   *b 16* Gen. 2:24

7 Now for the matters you wrote about: It is good for a man not to marry. [a] ²But since there is so much immorality, each man should have his own wife, and each woman her own husband. ³The husband should fulfill his marital duty to his wife, and likewise the wife to her husband. ⁴The wife's body does not belong to her alone but also to her husband. In the same way, the husband's body does not belong to him alone but also to his wife. ⁵Do not deprive each other except by mutual consent and for a time, so that you may devote yourselves to prayer. Then come together again so that Satan will not tempt you because of your lack of self-control. ⁶I say this as a concession, not as a command. ⁷I wish that all men were as I am. But each man has his own gift from God; one has this gift, another has that.

⁸Now to the unmarried and the widows I say: It is good for them to stay unmarried, as I am. ⁹But if they cannot control themselves, they should marry, for it is better to marry than to burn with passion.

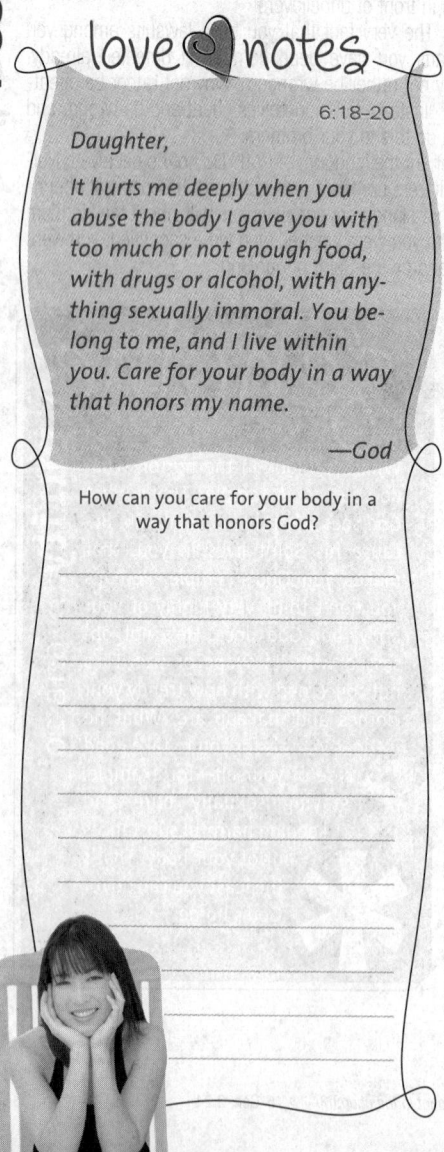

love ♥ notes

6:18–20

Daughter,

It hurts me deeply when you abuse the body I gave you with too much or not enough food, with drugs or alcohol, with anything sexually immoral. You belong to me, and I live within you. Care for your body in a way that honors my name.

—God

How can you care for your body in a way that honors God?

_____

_____

_____

_____

_____

_____

_____

_____

_____

_____

_____

¹⁰To the married I give this command (not I, but the Lord): A wife must not separate from her husband. ¹¹But if she does, she must remain unmarried or else be reconciled to her husband. And a husband must not divorce his wife.

¹²To the rest I say this (I, not the Lord): If any brother has a wife who is not a believer and she is willing to live with him, he must not divorce her. ¹³And if a woman has a husband who is not a believer and he is willing to live with her, she must not divorce him. ¹⁴For the unbelieving husband has been sanctified through his wife, and the unbelieving wife has been sanctified through her believing husband. Otherwise your children would be unclean, but as it is, they are holy.

¹⁵But if the unbeliever leaves, let him do so. A believing man or woman is not bound in such circumstances; God has called us to live in peace. ¹⁶How do you know, wife, whether you will save your husband? Or, how do you know, husband, whether you will save your wife?

¹⁷Nevertheless, each one should retain the place in life that the Lord assigned to him and to which God has called him. This is the rule I lay down in all the churches. ¹⁸Was a man already circumcised when he was called? He should not become uncircumcised. Was a man uncircumcised when he was called? He should not be circumcised. ¹⁹Circumcision is nothing and uncircumcision is nothing. Keeping God's commands is what counts. ²⁰Each one should remain in the situation which he was in when God called him. ²¹Were you a slave when you were called? Don't let it trouble you—although if you can gain your freedom, do so. ²²For he who was a slave when he was called by the Lord is the

a 1 Or "It is good for a man not to have sexual relations with a woman."

Lord's freedman; similarly, he who was a free man when he was called is Christ's slave. ²³You were bought at a price; do not become slaves of men. ²⁴Brothers, each man, as responsible to God, should remain in the situation God called him to.

²⁵Now about virgins: I have no command from the Lord, but I give a judgment as one who by the Lord's mercy is trustworthy. ²⁶Because of the present crisis, I think that it is good for you to remain as you are. ²⁷Are you married? Do not seek a divorce. Are you unmarried? Do not look for a wife. ²⁸But if you do marry, you have not sinned; and if a virgin marries, she has not sinned. But those who marry will face many troubles in this life, and I want to spare you this.

²⁹What I mean, brothers, is that the time is short. From now on those who have wives should live as if they had none; ³⁰those who mourn, as if they did not; those who are happy, as if they were not; those who buy something, as if it were not theirs to keep; ³¹those who use the things of the world, as if not engrossed in them. For this world in its present form is passing away.

³²I would like you to be free from concern. An unmarried man is concerned about the Lord's affairs—how he can please the Lord. ³³But a married man is concerned about the affairs of this world—how he can please his wife— ³⁴and his interests are divided. An unmarried woman or virgin is concerned about the Lord's affairs: Her aim is to be devoted to the Lord in both body and spirit. But a married woman is concerned about the affairs of this world—how she can please her husband. ³⁵I am saying this for your own good, not to restrict you, but that you may live in a right way in undivided devotion to the Lord.

³⁶If anyone thinks he is acting improperly toward the virgin he is engaged to, and if she is getting along in years and he feels he ought to marry, he should do as he wants. He is not sinning. They should get married. ³⁷But the man who has settled the matter in his own mind, who is under no compulsion but has control over his own will, and who has made up his mind not to marry the virgin—this man also does the right thing. ³⁸So then, he who marries the virgin does right, but he who does not marry her does even better. ᵃ

³⁹A woman is bound to her husband as long as he lives. But if her husband dies, she is free to marry anyone she wishes, but he must belong to the Lord. ⁴⁰In my judgment, she is happier if she stays as she is—and I think that I too have the Spirit of God.

Food Sacrificed to Idols

8 Now about food sacrificed to idols: We know that we all possess knowledge. ᵇ Knowledge puffs up, but love builds up. ²The man who thinks he knows something does not yet know as he ought to know. ³But the man who loves God is known by God.

⁴So then, about eating food sacrificed to idols: We know that an idol is nothing at all in the world and that there is no God but one. ⁵For even if there are so-called gods, whether in heaven or on earth (as indeed there are many "gods" and many "lords"), ⁶yet for us there is but one God, the Father, from whom all things came and for whom we live; and

genuine love » 8:1-3

Ever run across someone who acts like she knows everything? Some girls are pretty smart and have impressive memory banks, but if they act like know-it-alls, they annoy everyone around them. They're "puffed up," to use Paul's words. And the more puffed up they get, the less everyone else wants to be around them. Love has the opposite effect. It's a powerful force that builds others up. It transforms lives. God has no patience for arrogant knowledge. In fact, before you can really get to know God, you have to first start by loving him.

ᵃ 36-38 Or ³⁶If anyone thinks he is not treating his daughter properly, and if she is getting along in years, and he feels she ought to marry, he should do as he wants. He is not sinning. He should let her get married. ³⁷But the man who has settled the matter in his own mind, who is under no compulsion but has control over his own will, and who has made up his mind to keep the virgin unmarried—this man also does the right thing. ³⁸So then, he who gives his virgin in marriage does right, but he who does not give her in marriage does even better.   ᵇ 1 Or "We all possess knowledge," as you say there is but one Lord, Jesus Christ, through whom all things came and through whom we live.

[7]But not everyone knows this. Some people are still so accustomed to idols that when they eat such food they think of it as having been sacrificed to an idol, and since their conscience is weak, it is defiled. [8]But food does not bring us near to God; we are no worse if we do not eat, and no better if we do.

[9]Be careful, however, that the exercise of your freedom does not become a stumbling block to the weak. [10]For if anyone with a weak conscience sees you who have this knowledge eating in an idol's temple, won't he be emboldened to eat what has been sacrificed to idols? [11]So this weak brother, for whom Christ died, is destroyed by your knowledge. [12]When you sin against your brothers in this way and wound their weak conscience, you sin against Christ. [13]Therefore, if what I eat causes my brother to fall into sin, I will never eat meat again, so that I will not cause him to fall.

The Rights of an Apostle

9 Am I not free? Am I not an apostle? Have I not seen Jesus our Lord? Are you not the result of my work in the Lord? [2]Even though I may not be an apostle to others, surely I am to you! For you are the seal of my apostleship in the Lord.

[3]This is my defense to those who sit in judgment on me. [4]Don't we have the right to food and drink? [5]Don't we have the right to take a believing wife along with us, as do the other apostles and the Lord's brothers and Cephas[a]? [6]Or is it only I and Barnabas who must work for a living?

[7]Who serves as a soldier at his own expense? Who plants a vineyard and does not eat of its grapes? Who tends a flock and does not drink of the milk? [8]Do I say this merely from a human point of view? Doesn't the Law say the same thing? [9]For it is written in the Law of Moses: "Do not muzzle an ox while it is treading out the grain."[b] Is it about oxen that God is concerned? [10]Surely he says this for us, doesn't he? Yes, this was written for us, because when the plowman plows and the thresher threshes, they ought to do so in the hope of sharing in the harvest. [11]If we have sown spiritual seed among you, is it too much if we reap a material harvest from you? [12]If others have this right of support from you, shouldn't we have it all the more?

But we did not use this right. On the contrary, we put up with anything rather than hinder the gospel of Christ. [13]Don't you know that those who work in the temple get their food from the temple, and those who serve at the altar share in what is offered on the altar? [14]In the same way, the Lord has commanded that those who preach the gospel should receive their living from the gospel.

[15]But I have not used any of these rights. And I am not writing this in the hope that you

truth or dare

Careful! Some stuff isn't for the weak at heart ... or conscience. Make sure that your choices—even if they're technically okay—don't make others question the faith.

8:9–12

genuine evangelism » 9:19–23

Paul had a single goal in life—to share the gospel. So he took the message to others, wherever they happened to be. That doesn't mean he compromised his identity or his message to please his listeners. It means he appealed to their common ground. Have a friend who loves sports like you do? Start there. Know someone who's never been to church? Start simple. Have a friend who has a broken family like yours? You can relate. Know a girl who enjoys the same hobbies? Huh, you just found more common ground! Take the message to others—wherever they may be.

a 5 That is, Peter   *b 9* Deut. 25:4

will do such things for me. I would rather die than have anyone deprive me of this boast. ¹⁶Yet when I preach the gospel, I cannot boast, for I am compelled to preach. Woe to me if I do not preach the gospel! ¹⁷If I preach voluntarily, I have a reward; if not voluntarily, I am simply discharging the trust committed to me. ¹⁸What then is my reward? Just this: that in preaching the gospel I may offer it free of charge, and so not make use of my rights in preaching it.

¹⁹Though I am free and belong to no man, I make myself a slave to everyone, to win as many as possible. ²⁰To the Jews I became like a Jew, to win the Jews. To those under the law I became like one under the law (though I myself am not under the law), so as to win those under the law. ²¹To those not having the law I became like one not having the law (though I am not free from God's law but am under Christ's law), so as to win those not having the law. ²²To the weak I became weak, to win the weak. I have become all things to all men so that by all possible means I might save some. ²³I do all this for the sake of the gospel, that I may share in its blessings.

²⁴Do you not know that in a race all the runners run, but only one gets the prize? Run in such a way as to get the prize. ²⁵Everyone who competes in the games goes into strict training. They do it to get a crown that will not last; but we do it to get a crown that will last forever. ²⁶Therefore I do not run like a man running aimlessly; I do not fight like a man beating the air. ²⁷No, I beat my body and make it my slave so that after I have preached to others, I myself will not be disqualified for the prize.

truth *or dare*

In a race, would you ever *try* to come in last? Then why start a relationship with Christ only to do your very *least* to keep it alive? Run to win!

9:24–27

Warnings From Israel's History

10 For I do not want you to be ignorant of the fact, brothers, that our forefathers were all under the cloud and that they all passed through the sea. ²They were all baptized into Moses in the cloud and in the sea. ³They all ate the same spiritual food ⁴and drank the same spiritual drink; for they drank from the spiritual rock that accompanied them, and that rock was Christ. ⁵Nevertheless, God was not pleased with most of them; their bodies were scattered over the desert.

⁶Now these things occurred as examples *ᵃ* to keep us from setting our hearts on evil things as they did. ⁷Do not be idolaters, as some of them were; as it is written: "The people sat down to eat and drink and got up to indulge in pagan revelry." *ᵇ* ⁸We should not commit sexual immorality, as some of them did—and in one day twenty-three thousand of them died. ⁹We should not test the Lord, as some of them did—and were killed by snakes. ¹⁰And do not grumble, as some of them did—and were killed by the destroying angel.

¹¹These things happened to them as examples and were written down as warnings for us, on whom the fulfillment of the ages has come. ¹²So, if you think you are standing firm, be careful that you don't fall! ¹³No temptation has seized you except what is common to man. And God is faithful; he will not let you be tempted beyond what you can bear. But when you are tempted, he will also provide a way out so that you can stand up under it.

truth *or dare*

Being tempted to have sex, lie, get wasted, etc. isn't new. *Everyone* faces temptation. *Not everyone fights against it. Are you a fighter?*

10:13

Idol Feasts and the Lord's Supper

¹⁴Therefore, my dear friends, flee from idolatry. ¹⁵I speak to sensible people; judge for yourselves what I say. ¹⁶Is not the cup of thanksgiving for which we give thanks a participation in the

ᵃ 6 Or *types*; also in verse 11   *ᵇ 7* Exodus 32:6

blood of Christ? And is not the bread that we break a participation in the body of Christ? [17]Because there is one loaf, we, who are many, are one body, for we all partake of the one loaf.

[18]Consider the people of Israel: Do not those who eat the sacrifices participate in the altar? [19]Do I mean then that a sacrifice offered to an idol is anything, or that an idol is anything? [20]No, but the sacrifices of pagans are offered to demons, not to God, and I do not want you to be participants with demons. [21]You cannot drink the cup of the Lord and the cup of demons too; you cannot have a part in both the Lord's table and the table of demons. [22]Are we trying to arouse the Lord's jealousy? Are we stronger than he?

The Believer's Freedom

[23]"Everything is permissible"—but not everything is beneficial. "Everything is permissible"—but not everything is constructive. [24]Nobody should seek his own good, but the good of others.

[25]Eat anything sold in the meat market without raising questions of conscience, [26]for, "The earth is the Lord's, and everything in it." [a]

[27]If some unbeliever invites you to a meal and you want to go, eat whatever is put before you without raising questions of conscience. [28]But if anyone says to you, "This has been offered in sacrifice," then do not eat it, both for the sake of the man who told you and for conscience' sake [b]— [29]the other man's conscience, I mean, not yours. For why should my freedom be judged by another's conscience? [30]If I take part in the meal with thankfulness, why am I denounced because of something I thank God for?

[31]So whether you eat or drink or whatever you do, do it all for the glory of God. [32]Do not cause anyone to stumble, whether Jews, Greeks or the church of God— [33]even as I try to please everybody in every way. For I am not seeking my own good but the good of many, so that they may be saved.

11

[1]Follow my example, as I follow the example of Christ.

Propriety in Worship

[2]I praise you for remembering me in everything and for holding to the teachings, [c] just as I passed them on to you.

[3]Now I want you to realize that the head of every man is Christ, and the head of the woman is man, and the head of Christ is God. [4]Every man who prays or prophesies with his head covered dishonors his head. [5]And every woman who prays or prophesies with her head uncovered dishonors her head—it is just as though her head were shaved. [6]If a woman does not cover her head, she should have her hair cut off; and if it is a disgrace for a woman to have her hair cut or shaved off, she should cover her head. [7]A man ought not to cover his head, [d] since he is the image and glory of God; but the woman is the glory of man. [8]For man did not come from woman, but woman from man; [9]neither was man created for woman, but woman for man. [10]For this reason, and because of the angels, the woman ought to have a sign of authority on her head.

[11]In the Lord, however, woman is not independent of man, nor is man independent of woman. [12]For as woman came from man, so also man is born of woman. But everything comes from God. [13]Judge for yourselves: Is it proper for a woman to pray to God with her head uncovered? [14]Does not the very nature of things teach you that if a man has long hair, it is a disgrace to him, [15]but that if a woman has long hair, it is her glory? For long hair is given to her as a covering. [16]If anyone wants to be contentious about this, we have no other practice—nor do the churches of God.

The Lord's Supper

[17]In the following directives I have no praise for you, for your meetings do more harm than good. [18]In the first place, I hear that when you come together as a church, there are divisions among you, and to some extent I believe it. [19]No doubt there have to be differences among you to show which of you have God's approval. [20]When you come together, it is not the Lord's Supper you eat, [21]for as

---

a 26 Psalm 24:1   b 28 Some manuscripts conscience' sake, for "the earth is the Lord's and everything in it"
c 2 Or traditions   d 4-7 Or 4Every man who prays or prophesies with long hair dishonors his head. 5And every woman who prays or prophesies with no covering of hair, on her head dishonors her head—she is just like one of the "shorn women." 6If a woman has no covering, let her be for now with short hair, but since it is a disgrace for a woman to have her hair shorn or shaved, she should grow it again. 7A man ought not to have long hair

you eat, each of you goes ahead without waiting for anybody else. One remains hungry, another gets drunk. ²²Don't you have homes to eat and drink in? Or do you despise the church of God and humiliate those who have nothing? What shall I say to you? Shall I praise you for this? Certainly not!

²³For I received from the Lord what I also passed on to you: The Lord Jesus, on the night he was betrayed, took bread, ²⁴and when he had given thanks, he broke it and said, "This is my body, which is for you; do this in remembrance of me." ²⁵In the same way, after supper he took the cup, saying, "This cup is the new covenant in my blood; do this, whenever you drink it, in remembrance of me." ²⁶For whenever you eat this bread and drink this cup, you proclaim the Lord's death until he comes.

²⁷Therefore, whoever eats the bread or drinks the cup of the Lord in an unworthy manner will be guilty of sinning against the body and blood of the Lord. ²⁸A man ought to examine himself before he eats of the bread and drinks of the cup. ²⁹For anyone who eats and drinks without recognizing the body of the Lord eats and drinks judgment on himself. ³⁰That is why many among you are weak and sick, and a number of you have fallen asleep. ³¹But if we judged ourselves, we would not come under judgment. ³²When we are judged by the Lord, we are being disciplined so that we will not be condemned with the world.

³³So then, my brothers, when you come together to eat, wait for each other. ³⁴If anyone is hungry, he should eat at home, so that when you meet together it may not result in judgment.

And when I come I will give further directions.

Spiritual Gifts

12 Now about spiritual gifts, brothers, I do not want you to be ignorant. ²You know that when you were pagans, somehow or other you were influenced and led astray to mute idols. ³Therefore I tell you that no one who is speaking by the Spirit of God says, "Jesus be cursed," and no one can say, "Jesus is Lord," except by the Holy Spirit.

⁴There are different kinds of gifts, but the same Spirit. ⁵There are different kinds of service, but the same Lord. ⁶There are different kinds of working, but the same God works all of them in all men.

⁷Now to each one the manifestation of the Spirit is given for the common good. ⁸To one there is given through the Spirit the message of wisdom, to another the message of knowledge by means of the same Spirit, ⁹to another faith by the same Spirit, to another gifts of healing by that one Spirit, ¹⁰to another miraculous powers, to another prophecy, to another distinguishing between spirits, to another speaking in different kinds of tongues,ᵃ and to still another the interpretation of tongues.ᵃ ¹¹All these are the work of one and the same Spirit, and he gives them to each one, just as he determines.

One Body, Many Parts

¹²The body is a unit, though it is made up of many parts; and though all its parts are many, they form one body. So it is with Christ. ¹³For we were all baptized byᵇ one Spirit into one body—whether Jews or Greeks, slave or free—and we were all given the one Spirit to drink.

¹⁴Now the body is not made up of one part but of many. ¹⁵If the foot should say, "Because I am not a hand, I do not belong to the body," it would not for that reason cease to be part of the body. ¹⁶And if the ear should say, "Because I am not an eye, I do not belong to the body," it would not for that reason cease to be part of the body. ¹⁷If the whole body were an eye, where would the sense of hearing be? If the whole body were an ear, where would the sense of smell be? ¹⁸But in fact God has arranged the parts in the body, every one of them, just as he wanted them to be. ¹⁹If they were all one part, where would the body be? ²⁰As it is, there are many parts, but one body.

²¹The eye cannot say to the hand, "I don't need you!" And the head cannot say to the feet, "I don't need you!" ²²On the contrary, those parts of the body that seem to be weaker are indispensable, ²³and the parts that we think are less honorable we treat with special honor. And the parts that are unpresentable are treated with special modesty, ²⁴while our presentable parts need no special treatment. But God has combined the members of the body and has given greater honor to the parts that lacked it, ²⁵so that there should be no division in the body, but that its parts should have equal concern for each other. ²⁶If one part suffers, every part suffers with it; if one part is honored, every part rejoices with it.

²⁷Now you are the body of Christ, and each one of you is a part of it. ²⁸And in the church God

ᵃ 10 Or languages; also in verse 28   ᵇ 13 Or with; or in

mirror images

One of those listening was a woman named Lydia, a dealer in purple cloth from the city of Thyatira, who was a worshiper of God. The Lord opened her heart to respond to Paul's message. Acts 16:14

Lydia—A Woman of Influence

Dear Jesus, sometimes I forget that people are watching me—people who need you. Show me how to live a life like Lydia's, leading others to know you, too. Amen.

Think about the women you know who have found "success"—athletes, entertainers and CEOs. You naturally look up to them, don't you? These women are role models for many people—they are women who have used their gifts to get ahead in their field.

It's possible that to the people of Philippi, Lydia was a role model. She was a successful businesswoman, a seller of purple. Cloth dyed this color gave the wearer a sign of nobility, and Lydia knew the ins and outs of making and selling purple garments for a tidy profit. But amidst her busy schedule, this woman of influence found time to seek God.

As Lydia walked to a Jewish prayer meeting, she was unaware she would soon find much more than a life of success. She would find Jesus. When a small group of women gathered at the river's edge, the apostle Paul stopped to talk with them about Jesus. Lydia had already been following the one true God; she was only too happy to accept his Son into her heart.

Not one to waste an opportunity, Lydia shared the good news with her whole family, encouraging them to accept Christ as well. And she immediately invited Paul and Silas to stay in her home as distinguished guests. From that time on, her home became a sanctuary for God's servants. As the first person in Europe to accept Christ, Lydia was a role model in more ways than one.

How about you? Are you a role model for others? Do you use your time, stuff and opportunities to share Jesus' message? You may be influencing others in many ways, but one way that will last for eternity is to share what Christ has done for you.

To read the next Mirror Images profile, go to page 1579.

»» **Read more about Lydia in Acts 16:12–15,40 (pages 1468–1469).**

has appointed first of all apostles, second prophets, third teachers, then workers of miracles, also those having gifts of healing, those able to help others, those with gifts of administration, and those speaking in different kinds of tongues. [29]Are all apostles? Are all prophets? Are all teachers? Do all work miracles? [30]Do all have gifts of healing? Do all speak in tongues[a]? Do all interpret? [31]But eagerly desire[b] the greater gifts.

Love

And now I will show you the most excellent way.

13 If I speak in the tongues[c] of men and of angels, but have not love, I am only a resounding gong or a clanging cymbal. [2]If I have the gift of prophecy and can fathom all mysteries and all knowledge, and if I have a faith that can move mountains, but have not love, I am nothing. [3]If I give all I possess to the poor and surrender my body to the flames,[d] but have not love, I gain nothing.

[4]Love is patient, love is kind. It does not envy, it does not boast, it is not proud. [5]It is not rude, it is not self-seeking, it is not easily angered, it keeps no record of wrongs. [6]Love does not delight in evil but rejoices with the truth. [7]It always protects, always trusts, always hopes, always perseveres.

[8]Love never fails. But where there are prophecies, they will cease; where there are tongues, they will be stilled; where there is knowledge, it will pass away. [9]For we know in part and we prophesy in part, [10]but when perfection comes, the imperfect disappears.

[11]When I was a child, I talked like a child, I thought like a child, I reasoned like a child. When I became a man, I put childish ways behind me. [12]Now we see but a poor reflection as in a mirror; then we shall see face to face. Now I know in part; then I shall know fully, even as I am fully known.

[13]And now these three remain: faith, hope and love. But the greatest of these is love.

Gifts of Prophecy and Tongues

14 Follow the way of love and eagerly desire spiritual gifts, especially the gift of prophecy. [2]For anyone who speaks in a tongue[e] does not speak to men but to God. Indeed, no one understands him; he utters mysteries with his spirit.[f] [3]But everyone who prophesies speaks to men for their strengthening, encouragement and comfort. [4]He who speaks in a tongue edifies himself, but he who prophesies edifies the church. [5]I would like every one of you to speak in tongues,[g] but I would rather have you prophesy. He who prophesies is greater than one who speaks in tongues,[g] unless he interprets, so that the church may be edified.

[6]Now, brothers, if I come to you and speak in tongues, what good will I be to you, unless I bring you some revelation or knowledge or prophecy or word of instruction? [7]Even in the case of lifeless things that make sounds, such as the flute or harp, how will anyone know what tune is being played unless there is a distinction in the notes? [8]Again, if the trumpet does not sound a clear call, who will get ready for battle? [9]So it is with you. Unless you speak intelligible words with your tongue, how will anyone know what you are saying? You will just be speaking into the air. [10]Undoubtedly there are all sorts of languages in the world, yet none of them is without meaning. [11]If then I do not grasp the meaning of what someone is saying, I am a foreigner to the speaker, and he is a for-

---

a 30 Or *other languages*   *b 31* Or *But you are eagerly desiring*   *c 1* Or *languages*   *d 3* Some early manuscripts *body that I may boast*   *e 2* Or *another language*; also in verses 4, 13, 14, 19, 26 and 27   *f 2* Or *by the Spirit*   *g 5* Or *other languages*; also in verses 6, 18, 22, 23 and 39 eigner to me. ¹²So it is with you. Since you are eager to have spiritual gifts, try to excel in gifts that build up the church.

¹³For this reason anyone who speaks in a tongue should pray that he may interpret what he says. ¹⁴For if I pray in a tongue, my spirit prays, but my mind is unfruitful. ¹⁵So what shall I do? I will pray with my spirit, but I will also pray with my mind; I will sing with my spirit, but I will also sing with my mind. ¹⁶If you are praising God with your spirit, how can one who finds himself among those who do not understand* say "Amen" to your thanksgiving, since he does not know what you are saying? ¹⁷You may be giving thanks well enough, but the other man is not edified.

¹⁸I thank God that I speak in tongues more than all of you. ¹⁹But in the church I would rather speak five intelligible words to instruct others than ten thousand words in a tongue.

²⁰Brothers, stop thinking like children. In regard to evil be infants, but in your thinking be adults. ²¹In the Law it is written:

> "Through men of strange tongues
>   and through the lips of foreigners
> I will speak to this people,
>   but even then they will not listen to me," *ᵇ*
>
>   says the Lord.

²²Tongues, then, are a sign, not for believers but for unbelievers; prophecy, however, is for believers, not for unbelievers. ²³So if the whole church comes together and everyone speaks in tongues, and some who do not understand *ᶜ* or some unbelievers come in, will they not say that you are out of your mind? ²⁴But if an unbeliever or someone who does not understand *ᵈ* comes in while everybody is prophesying, he will be convinced by all that he is a sinner and will be judged by all, ²⁵and the secrets of his heart will be laid bare. So he will fall down and worship God, exclaiming, "God is really among you!"

Orderly Worship

²⁶What then shall we say, brothers? When you come together, everyone has a hymn, or a word of instruction, a revelation, a tongue or an interpretation. All of these must be done for the strengthening of the church. ²⁷If anyone speaks in a tongue, two—or at the most three—should speak, one at a time, and someone must interpret. ²⁸If there is no interpreter, the speaker should keep quiet in the church and speak to himself and God.

²⁹Two or three prophets should speak, and the others should weigh carefully what is said. ³⁰And if a revelation comes to someone who is sitting down, the first speaker should stop. ³¹For you can all prophesy in turn so that everyone may be instructed and encouraged. ³²The spirits of prophets are subject to the control of prophets. ³³For God is not a God of disorder but of peace.

As in all the congregations of the saints, ³⁴women should remain silent in the churches. They are not allowed to speak, but must be in submission, as the Law says. ³⁵If they want to inquire about something, they should ask their own husbands at home; for it is disgraceful for a woman to speak in the church.

³⁶Did the word of God originate with you? Or are you the only people it has reached? ³⁷If anybody thinks he is a prophet or spiritually gifted, let him acknowledge that what I am writing to you is the Lord's command. ³⁸If he ignores this, he himself will be ignored. *ᵉ*

³⁹Therefore, my brothers, be eager to prophesy, and do not forbid speaking in tongues. ⁴⁰But everything should be done in a fitting and orderly way.

The Resurrection of Christ

15 Now, brothers, I want to remind you of the gospel I preached to you, which you received and on which you have taken your stand. ²By this gospel you are saved, if you hold firmly to the word I preached to you. Otherwise, you have believed in vain.

³For what I received I passed on to you as of first importance *ᶠ*: that Christ died for our sins according to the Scriptures, ⁴that he was buried, that he was raised on the third day according to the Scriptures, ⁵and that he appeared to Peter, *ᵍ* and then to the Twelve. ⁶After that, he appeared to more than five hundred of the brothers at the same time, most of whom are still living, though some

---

a 16 Or *among the inquirers*   *b 21* Isaiah 28:11,12   *c 23* Or *some inquirers*   *d 24* Or *or some inquirer*
e 38 Some manuscripts *If he is ignorant of this, let him be ignorant*   *f 3* Or *you at the first*   *g 5* Greek *Cephas*

have fallen asleep. [7]Then he appeared to James, then to all the apostles, [8]and last of all he appeared to me also, as to one abnormally born.

[9]For I am the least of the apostles and do not even deserve to be called an apostle, because I persecuted the church of God. [10]But by the grace of God I am what I am, and his grace to me was not without effect. No, I worked harder than all of them—yet not I, but the grace of God that was with me. [11]Whether, then, it was I or they, this is what we preach, and this is what you believed.

The Resurrection of the Dead

[12]But if it is preached that Christ has been raised from the dead, how can some of you say that there is no resurrection of the dead? [13]If there is no resurrection of the dead, then not even Christ has been raised. [14]And if Christ has not been raised, our preaching is useless and so is your faith. [15]More than that, we are then found to be false witnesses about God, for we have testified about God that he raised Christ from the dead. But he did not raise him if in fact the dead are not raised. [16]For if the dead are not raised, then Christ has not been raised either. [17]And if Christ has not been raised, your faith is futile; you are still in your sins. [18]Then those also who have fallen asleep in Christ are lost. [19]If only for this life we have hope in Christ, we are to be pitied more than all men.

[20]But Christ has indeed been raised from the dead, the firstfruits of those who have fallen asleep. [21]For since death came through a man, the resurrection of the dead comes also through a man. [22]For as in Adam all die, so in Christ all will be made alive. [23]But each in his own turn: Christ, the firstfruits; then, when he comes, those who belong to him. [24]Then the end will come, when he hands over the kingdom to God the Father after he has destroyed all dominion, authority and power. [25]For he must reign until he has put all his enemies under his feet. [26]The last enemy to be destroyed is death. [27]For he "has put everything under his feet."[a] Now when it says that "everything" has been put under him, it is clear that this does not include God himself, who put everything under Christ. [28]When he has done this, then the Son himself will be made subject to him who put everything under him, so that God may be all in all.

[29]Now if there is no resurrection, what will those do who are baptized for the dead? If the dead are not raised at all, why are people baptized for them? [30]And as for us, why do we endanger ourselves every hour? [31]I die every day—I mean that, brothers—just as surely as I glory over you in Christ Jesus our Lord. [32]If I fought wild beasts in Ephesus for merely human reasons, what have I gained? If the dead are not raised,

> "Let us eat and drink,
>   for tomorrow we die."[b]

[33]Do not be misled: "Bad company corrupts good character." [34]Come back to your senses as you ought, and stop sinning; for there are some who are ignorant of God—I say this to your shame.

The Resurrection Body

[35]But someone may ask, "How are the dead raised? With what kind of body will they come?" [36]How foolish! What you sow does not come to life unless it dies. [37]When you sow, you do not plant the body that will be, but just a seed, perhaps of wheat or of something else. [38]But God gives it a body as he has determined, and to each kind of seed he gives its own body. [39]All flesh is not the same: Men have one kind of flesh, animals have another, birds another and fish another. [40]There are also heavenly bodies and there are earthly bodies; but the splendor of the heavenly bodies is one kind, and the splendor of the earthly bodies is another. [41]The sun has one kind of splendor, the moon another and the stars another; and star differs from star in splendor.

[42]So will it be with the resurrection of the dead. The body that is sown is perishable, it is raised imperishable; [43]it is sown in dishonor, it is raised in glory; it is sown in weakness, it is raised in power; [44]it is sown a natural body, it is raised a spiritual body.

If there is a natural body, there is also a spiritual body. [45]So it is written: "The first man Adam became a living being"[c]; the last Adam, a life-giving spirit. [46]The spiritual did not come first, but the natural, and after that the spiritual. [47]The first man was of the dust of the earth, the second man from heaven. [48]As was the earthly man, so are those who are of the earth; and as is the man from heaven, so also are those who are of heaven. [49]And just as we have borne the likeness of the

a 27 Psalm 8:6   b 32 Isaiah 22:13   c 45 Gen. 2:7

earthly man, so shall we[a] bear the likeness of the man from heaven.

[50]I declare to you, brothers, that flesh and blood cannot inherit the kingdom of God, nor does the perishable inherit the imperishable. [51]Listen, I tell you a mystery: We will not all sleep, but we will all be changed— [52]in a flash, in the twinkling of an eye, at the last trumpet. For the trumpet will sound, the dead will be raised imperishable, and we will be changed. [53]For the perishable must clothe itself with the imperishable, and the mortal with immortality. [54]When the perishable has been clothed with the imperishable, and the mortal with immortality, then the saying that is written will come true: "Death has been swallowed up in victory."[b]

> [55]"Where, O death, is your victory?
> Where, O death, is your sting?"[c]

[56]The sting of death is sin, and the power of sin is the law. [57]But thanks be to God! He gives us the victory through our Lord Jesus Christ.

[58]Therefore, my dear brothers, stand firm. Let nothing move you. Always give yourselves fully to the work of the Lord, because you know that your labor in the Lord is not in vain.

truth or dare

If wasps couldn't sting, would you still have to avoid them? Of course not! Check out what else you don't have to fear, now that it's lost its sting.

15:55–57

The Collection for God's People

16 Now about the collection for God's people: Do what I told the Galatian churches to do. [2]On the first day of every week, each one of you should set aside a sum of money in keeping with his income, saving it up, so that when I come no collections will have to be made. [3]Then, when I arrive, I will give letters of introduction to the men you approve and send them with your gift to Jerusalem. [4]If it seems advisable for me to go also, they will accompany me.

Personal Requests

[5]After I go through Macedonia, I will come to you—for I will be going through Macedonia. [6]Perhaps I will stay with you awhile, or even spend the winter, so that you can help me on my journey, wherever I go. [7]I do not want to see you now and make only a passing visit; I hope to spend some time with you, if the Lord permits. [8]But I will stay on at Ephesus until Pentecost, [9]because a great door for effective work has opened to me, and there are many who oppose me.

[10]If Timothy comes, see to it that he has nothing to fear while he is with you, for he is carrying on the work of the Lord, just as I am. [11]No one, then, should refuse to accept him. Send him on his way in peace so that he may return to me. I am expecting him along with the brothers.

[12]Now about our brother Apollos: I strongly urged him to go to you with the brothers. He was quite unwilling to go now, but he will go when he has the opportunity.

[13]Be on your guard; stand firm in the faith; be men of courage; be strong. [14]Do everything in love.

[15]You know that the household of Stephanas were the first converts in Achaia, and they have devoted themselves to the service of the saints. I urge you, brothers, [16]to submit to such as these and to everyone who joins in the work, and labors at it. [17]I was glad when Stephanas, Fortunatus and Achaicus arrived, because they have supplied what was lacking from you. [18]For they refreshed my spirit and yours also. Such men deserve recognition.

Final Greetings

[19]The churches in the province of Asia send you greetings. Aquila and Priscilla[d] greet you warmly in the Lord, and so does the church that meets at their house. [20]All the brothers here send you greetings. Greet one another with a holy kiss.

[21]I, Paul, write this greeting in my own hand.

[22]If anyone does not love the Lord—a curse be on him. Come, O Lord[e]!

[23]The grace of the Lord Jesus be with you.

[24]My love to all of you in Christ Jesus. Amen.[f]

---

a 49 Some early manuscripts *so let us*   b 54 Isaiah 25:8   c 55 Hosea 13:14   d 19 Greek *Prisca*, a variant of *Priscilla*   e 22 In Aramaic the expression *Come, O Lord* is *Marana tha.*   f 24 Some manuscripts do not have *Amen.*

author: The apostle Paul.

date: About A.D. 55.

setting: False teachers in the church in Corinth were denying Paul's authority over them as an apostle.

verse to remember: Therefore, if anyone is in Christ, he is a new creation; the old has gone, the new has come (5:17)!

theme to consider: Paul speaks out against false teachers and defends his own character, conduct and calling as an apostle of Jesus Christ. Do you live with that kind of personal integrity?

unchanging truth

2 corinthians

You didn't know how hard living for Jesus was going to be. Until the people at school called you a hypocrite. Until they shredded your reputation to pieces and started rumors behind your back.

Why do some people hate Christians so much? Why do they pounce on someone whose morals are higher than their own? The world tries so hard to discredit those who are trying to live for Jesus, confusing them with false teaching and persecuting them at every turn. We may be tempted to tell ourselves, "It shouldn't be this hard to be a Christian." Or should it?

If you haven't yet encountered persecution for Jesus' sake, take note. Maybe you're not living out your faith so others can see. Because if everyone sees your faith, you're bound to take some heat for it. However, Paul's second letter to the Corinthians reminds us that trouble can make our beliefs stronger. It helps us see what's really important and teaches us to lean on Jesus for strength. Paul also shows us how to firm up our grip on what we believe by telling the difference between who is teaching the truth and who's just out to confuse others.

God is always at work to strengthen your faith in him. He can use anything—even difficulties—to your advantage.

life lessons

1 As Christians, we're not exempt from problems. However, God can turn trouble around and use it to our advantage (4:7–18), as well as to help others (1:3–11).

2 Beware of people who use smooth-talking and confusing teachings to tear down your faith in Christ (11:1–4,13–15).

3 Paul knew the secret of living for Jesus even when he felt like giving up. When he was at his weakest, Jesus made him strong (12:7–10).

1

Paul, an apostle of Christ Jesus by the will of God, and Timothy our brother,

To the church of God in Corinth, together with all the saints throughout Achaia:

²Grace and peace to you from God our Father and the Lord Jesus Christ.

The God of All Comfort

³Praise be to the God and Father of our Lord Jesus Christ, the Father of compassion and the God of all comfort, ⁴who comforts us in all our troubles, so that we can comfort those in any trouble with the comfort we ourselves have received from God. ⁵For just as the sufferings of Christ flow over into our lives, so also through Christ our comfort overflows. ⁶If we are distressed, it is for your comfort and salvation; if we are comforted, it is for your comfort, which produces in you patient endurance of the same sufferings we suffer. ⁷And our hope for you is firm, because we know that just as you share in our sufferings, so also you share in our comfort.

⁸We do not want you to be uninformed, brothers, about the hardships we suffered in the province of Asia. We were under great pressure, far beyond our ability to endure, so that we despaired even of life. ⁹Indeed, in our hearts we felt the sentence of death. But this happened that we might not rely on ourselves but on God, who raises the dead. ¹⁰He has delivered us from such a deadly peril, and he will deliver us. On him we have set our hope that he will continue to deliver us, ¹¹as you help us by your prayers. Then many will give thanks on our[a] behalf for the gracious favor granted us in answer to the prayers of many.

genuine

comfort « 1:3-5

You may wonder why God has allowed certain difficulties into your life. Instead of asking why, ask him to comfort you. God comforts us in our troubles so that we can, in turn, comfort others. Think about it. It's the people who've been through the same pain who can really comfort us when we go through something similar. What hard times has God allowed you to go through? Your parents' divorce? A problem at school? A poor self-image? Get comfort and strength from God, then share that with someone else who's in a similar situation.

Paul's Change of Plans

¹²Now this is our boast: Our conscience testifies that we have conducted ourselves in the world, and especially in our relations with you, in the holiness and sincerity that are from God. We have done so not according to worldly wisdom but according to God's grace. ¹³For we do not write you anything you cannot read or understand. And I hope that, ¹⁴as you have understood us in part, you will come to understand fully that you can boast of us just as we will boast of you in the day of the Lord Jesus.

¹⁵Because I was confident of this, I planned to visit you first so that you might benefit twice. ¹⁶I planned to visit you on my way to Macedonia and to come back to you from Macedonia, and then to have you send me on my way to Judea. ¹⁷When I planned this, did I do it lightly? Or do I make my plans in a worldly manner so that in the same breath I say, "Yes, yes" and "No, no"?

¹⁸But as surely as God is faithful, our message to you is not "Yes" and "No." ¹⁹For the Son of God, Jesus Christ, who was preached among you by me and Silas[b] and Timothy, was not "Yes" and "No," but in him it has always been "Yes." ²⁰For no matter how many promises God has made, they are "Yes" in Christ. And so through him the "Amen" is spoken by us to the glory of God. ²¹Now it is God who makes both us and you stand firm in Christ. He anointed us, ²²set his seal of ownership on us, and put his Spirit in our hearts as a deposit, guaranteeing what is to come.

²³I call God as my witness that it was in order to spare you that I did not return to Corinth. ²⁴Not that we lord it over your faith, but we work with you for your joy, because it is by faith you stand firm.

a 11 Many manuscripts *your*   *b 19* Greek *Silvanus*, a variant of *Silas*

2 ¹So I made up my mind that I would not make another painful visit to you. ²For if I grieve you, who is left to make me glad but you whom I have grieved? ³I wrote as I did so that when I came I should not be distressed by those who ought to make me rejoice. I had confidence in all of you, that you would all share my joy. ⁴For I wrote you out of great distress and anguish of heart and with many tears, not to grieve you but to let you know the depth of my love for you.

Forgiveness for the Sinner

⁵If anyone has caused grief, he has not so much grieved me as he has grieved all of you, to some extent—not to put it too severely. ⁶The punishment inflicted on him by the majority is sufficient for him. ⁷Now instead, you ought to forgive and comfort him, so that he will not be overwhelmed by excessive sorrow. ⁸I urge you, therefore, to reaffirm your love for him. ⁹The reason I wrote you was to see if you would stand the test and be obedient in everything. ¹⁰If you forgive anyone, I also forgive him. And what I have forgiven—if there was anything to forgive—I have forgiven in the sight of Christ for your sake, ¹¹in order that Satan might not outwit us. For we are not unaware of his schemes.

Ministers of the New Covenant

¹²Now when I went to Troas to preach the gospel of Christ and found that the Lord had opened a door for me, ¹³I still had no peace of mind, because I did not find my brother Titus there. So I said good-by to them and went on to Macedonia.

¹⁴But thanks be to God, who always leads us in triumphal procession in Christ and through us spreads everywhere the fragrance of the knowledge of him. ¹⁵For we are to God the aroma of Christ among those who are being saved and those who are perishing. ¹⁶To the one we are the smell of death; to the other, the fragrance of life. And who is equal to such a task? ¹⁷Unlike so many, we do not peddle the word of God for profit. On the contrary, in Christ we speak before God with sincerity, like men sent from God.

love ♥ notes

1:21-22

Cherished one,

It has been said that in this life there are no guarantees. Well, here's one—my absolute guarantee that you belong to me. The Holy Spirit is my down payment on all the benefits you will enjoy with me one day in heaven. Bank on it.

—*Your Father in Heaven*

How can you find comfort and security in this promise?

truth or dare

Move over, aromatherapy! The power of certain scents was known *way* before the 21st century. But just like any scent, this one gets mixed reactions.

2:14-16

3 Are we beginning to commend ourselves again? Or do we need, like some people, letters of recommendation to you or from you? ²You yourselves are our letter, written on our hearts, known and read by everybody. ³You show that you are a letter from Christ, the result of our ministry, written not with ink but with the Spirit of the living God, not on tablets of stone but on tablets of human hearts.

⁴Such confidence as this is ours through Christ before God. ⁵Not that we are competent in ourselves to claim anything for ourselves, but our competence comes from God. ⁶He has made us competent as ministers of a new covenant—not of the letter but of the Spirit; for the letter kills, but the Spirit gives life.

The Glory of the New Covenant

⁷Now if the ministry that brought death, which was engraved in letters on stone, came with glory, so that the Israelites could not look steadily at the face of Moses because of its glory, fading though it was, ⁸will not the ministry of the Spirit be even more glorious? ⁹If the ministry that condemns men is glorious, how much more glorious is the ministry that brings righteousness! ¹⁰For what was glorious has no glory now in comparison with the surpassing glory. ¹¹And if what was fading away came with glory, how much greater is the glory of that which lasts!

¹²Therefore, since we have such a hope, we are very bold. ¹³We are not like Moses, who would put a veil over his face to keep the Israelites from gazing at it while the radiance was fading away. ¹⁴But their minds were made dull, for to this day the same veil remains when the old covenant is read. It has not been removed, because only in Christ is it taken away. ¹⁵Even to this day when Moses is read, a veil covers their hearts. ¹⁶But whenever anyone turns to the Lord, the veil is taken away. ¹⁷Now the Lord is the Spirit, and where the Spirit of the Lord is, there is freedom. ¹⁸And we, who with unveiled faces all reflect*ᵃ* the Lord's glory, are being transformed into his likeness with ever-increasing glory, which comes from the Lord, who is the Spirit.

Treasures in Jars of Clay

4 Therefore, since through God's mercy we have this ministry, we do not lose heart. ²Rather, we have renounced secret and shameful ways; we do not use deception, nor do we distort the word of God. On the contrary, by setting forth the truth plainly we commend ourselves to every man's conscience in the sight of God. ³And even if our gospel is veiled, it is veiled to those who are perishing. ⁴The god of this age has blinded the minds of unbelievers, so that they cannot see the light of the gospel of the glory of Christ, who is the image of God. ⁵For we do not preach ourselves, but Jesus Christ as Lord, and ourselves as your servants for Jesus' sake. ⁶For God, who said, "Let light shine out of darkness,"*ᵇ* made his light shine in our hearts to give us the light of the knowledge of the glory of God in the face of Christ.

⁷But we have this treasure in jars of clay to show that this all-surpassing power is from God and not from us. ⁸We are hard pressed on every side, but not crushed; perplexed, but not in despair; ⁹persecuted, but not abandoned; struck down, but not destroyed. ¹⁰We always carry around in our body the death of Jesus, so that the life of Jesus may also be revealed in our body. ¹¹For we who are alive are always being given over to death for Jesus' sake, so that his life may be revealed in our mortal body. ¹²So then, death is at work in us, but life is at work in you.

¹³It is written: "I believed; therefore I have spoken."*ᶜ* With that same spirit of faith we also believe and therefore speak, ¹⁴because we know that the one who raised the Lord Jesus from the dead will also raise us with Jesus and present us with you in his presence. ¹⁵All this is for your benefit, so that the grace that is reaching more and more people may cause thanksgiving to overflow to the glory of God.

¹⁶Therefore we do not lose heart. Though outwardly we are wasting away, yet inwardly we are being renewed day by day. ¹⁷For our light and momentary troubles are achieving for us an eternal glory that far outweighs them all. ¹⁸So we fix our eyes not on what is seen, but on what is unseen. For what is seen is temporary, but what is unseen is eternal.

a 18 Or *contemplate*   *b 6* Gen. 1:3   *c 13* Psalm 116:10

Our Heavenly Dwelling

5 Now we know that if the earthly tent we live in is destroyed, we have a building from God, an eternal house in heaven, not built by human hands. [2]Meanwhile we groan, longing to be clothed with our heavenly dwelling, [3]because when we are clothed, we will not be found naked. [4]For while we are in this tent, we groan and are burdened, because we do not wish to be unclothed but to be clothed with our heavenly dwelling, so that what is mortal may be swallowed up by life. [5]Now it is God who has made us for this very purpose and has given us the Spirit as a deposit, guaranteeing what is to come.

[6]Therefore we are always confident and know that as long as we are at home in the body we are away from the Lord. [7]We live by faith, not by sight. [8]We are confident, I say, and would prefer to be away from the body and at home with the Lord. [9]So we make it our goal to please him, whether we are at home in the body or away from it. [10]For we must all appear before the judgment seat of Christ, that each one may receive what is due him for the things done while in the body, whether good or bad.

The Ministry of Reconciliation

[11]Since, then, we know what it is to fear the Lord, we try to persuade men. What we are is plain to God, and I hope it is also plain to your conscience. [12]We are not trying to commend ourselves to you again, but are giving you an opportunity to take pride in us, so that you can answer those who take pride in what is seen rather than in what is in the heart. [13]If we are out of our mind, it is for the sake of God; if we are in our right mind, it is for you. [14]For Christ's love compels us, because we are convinced that one died for all, and therefore all died. [15]And he died for all, that those who live should no longer live for themselves but for him who died for them and was raised again.

[16]So from now on we regard no one from a worldly point of view. Though we once regarded Christ in this way, we do so no longer. [17]Therefore, if anyone is in Christ, he is a new creation; the old has gone, the new has come! [18]All this is from God, who reconciled us to himself through Christ and gave us the ministry of reconciliation: [19]that God was reconciling the world to himself in Christ, not counting men's sins against them. And he has committed to us the message of reconciliation. [20]We are therefore Christ's ambassadors, as though God were making his appeal through us. We implore you on Christ's behalf: Be reconciled to God. [21]God made him who had no sin to be sin[a] for us, so that in him we might become the righteousness of God.

6 As God's fellow workers we urge you not to receive God's grace in vain. [2]For he says,

> "In the time of my favor I heard you,
> and in the day of salvation I helped you."[b]

I tell you, now is the time of God's favor, now is the day of salvation.

Paul's Hardships

[3]We put no stumbling block in anyone's path, so that our ministry will not be discredited. [4]Rather, as servants of God we commend ourselves in every way: in great endurance; in troubles, hardships and distresses; [5]in beatings, imprisonments and riots; in hard work, sleepless nights and hunger; [6]in purity, understanding, patience and kindness; in the Holy Spirit and in sincere love; [7]in truthful speech and in the power of God; with weapons of righteousness in the right hand and in the left; [8]through glory and dishonor, bad report and good report; genuine, yet regarded as impostors; [9]known, yet regarded as unknown; dying, and yet we live on; beaten, and yet not killed; [10]sorrowful, yet always rejoicing; poor, yet making many rich; having nothing, and yet possessing everything.

[11]We have spoken freely to you, Corinthians, and opened wide our hearts to you. [12]We are not withholding our affection from you, but you are withholding yours from us. [13]As a fair exchange—I speak as to my children—open wide your hearts also.

Do Not Be Yoked With Unbelievers

[14]Do not be yoked together with unbelievers. For what do righteousness and wickedness have in common? Or what fellowship can light have with darkness? [15]What harmony is there between Christ

a 21 Or *be a sin offering* *b 2* Isaiah 49:8

An Inconvenient Rule

"It does *not* say *that*," I said indignantly. "Here, give it to me," I said, trying to grab the book from her hands. My best friend, Ginnie, and I were reading a book together on Christian dating. She'd just gotten to the part about dating a non-Christian.

"Not so fast! I'm not finished reading yet . . ." Ginnie laughed and jumped out of reach. She read aloud as if she were performing a soliloquy from *Hamlet* or something.

"'Do not be yoked together with unbelievers. For what do righteousness and wickedness have in common? Or what fellowship can light have with darkness? . . . What does a believer have in common with an unbeliever?' Right here in 2 Corinthians 6:14–15—a Christian shouldn't date a non-Christian!"

"Even if he happens to be the resident hottie at school?" I asked. She and I both knew who I was talking about: Eric McGuire. Gorgeous. Smart. Popular. Hilarious. He was everything I ever wanted in a boyfriend—only he was missing just one thing. He wasn't a Christian.

I knew what the author was going to say even before Ginnie read it. Just this week, my mom and even my youth pastor had commented on my growing relationship with Eric. I wasn't sure what to do—I mean, you don't just go off and break up with the almost-perfect guy, do you? Who knows—maybe God put me in Eric's life so he could be saved, too.

For more on healthy guidelines for Christian dating, go to www.TrueImagesBible.com

dating in focus

What's the big deal about dating a non-Christian? Well, consider this:

» When your heart's involved, things get complicated fast. You may have feelings you can't control for someone who's not right for you. Proverbs 4:23 (page 808) tells us to guard our hearts.

» God knows that if you fall for someone who doesn't share your convictions—and it's easy to do—you'll face all kinds of trouble and temptation. Sexually. Emotionally. Spiritually. And it's harder than ever to pull out of a relationship once you realize you're in trouble because your heart's already involved.

» Would it make sense for God to make an exception to his rules in order for you to do a little evangelistic dating—dating a non-Christian in order to lead him to Christ? God doesn't need (or want) you to break one of his commands so you can lead someone to Christ. If God's going to win this guy's heart, he'll do it—without putting you at risk.

For more on this topic, see the index on page 1656.

and Belial[a]? What does a believer have in common with an unbeliever? ¹⁶What agreement is there between the temple of God and idols? For we are the temple of the living God. As God has said: "I will live with them and walk among them, and I will be their God, and they will be my people."[b]

¹⁷"Therefore come out from them
    and be separate,

                        says the Lord.

a 15 Greek *Beliar*, a variant of *Belial*   *b 16* Lev. 26:12; Jer. 32:38; Ezek. 37:27

genuine

riches » 6:10

Who wants to marry a millionaire? Who wants to always have enough money for clothes, trips around the world and a beautiful home? Silly questions! However, without Christ, life is ultimately empty. With him, you have all the riches of heaven. You can indeed have nothing and possess everything. You can also have it all and really have nothing. Don't focus on material things or a life of ease. Focus on doing what God calls you to do. Then no matter how much or little you have on this earth, you have it all because you have God.

Touch no unclean thing,
and I will receive you." [a]
[18] "I will be a Father to you,
and you will be my sons and
daughters,
says the Lord
Almighty." [b]

7 Since we have these promises, dear friends, let us purify ourselves from everything that contaminates body and spirit, perfecting holiness out of reverence for God.

Paul's Joy

[2] Make room for us in your hearts. We have wronged no one, we have corrupted no one, we have exploited no one. [3] I do not say this to condemn you; I have said before that you have such a place in our hearts that we would live or die with you. [4] I have great confidence in you; I take great pride in you. I am greatly encouraged; in all our troubles my joy knows no bounds.

[5] For when we came into Macedonia, this body of ours had no rest, but we were harassed at every turn—conflicts on the outside, fears within. [6] But God, who comforts the downcast, comforted us by the coming of Titus, [7] and not only by his coming but also by the comfort you had given him. He told us about your longing for me, your deep sorrow, your ardent concern for me, so that my joy was greater than ever.

[8] Even if I caused you sorrow by my letter, I do not regret it. Though I did regret it—I see that my letter hurt you, but only for a little while— [9] yet now I am happy, not because you were made sorry, but because your sorrow led you to repentance. For you became sorrowful as God intended and so were not harmed in any way by us. [10] Godly sorrow brings repentance that leads to salvation and leaves no regret, but worldly sorrow brings death. [11] See what this godly sorrow has produced in you: what earnestness, what eagerness to clear yourselves, what indignation, what alarm, what longing, what concern, what readiness to see justice done. At every point you have proved yourselves to be innocent in this matter. [12] So even though I wrote to you, it was not on account of the one who did the wrong or of the injured party, but rather that before God you could see for yourselves how devoted to us you are. [13] By all this we are encouraged.

In addition to our own encouragement, we were especially delighted to see how happy Titus was, because his spirit has been refreshed by all of you. [14] I had boasted to him about you, and you have not embarrassed me. But just as everything we said to you was true, so our boasting about you to Titus has proved to be true as well. [15] And his affection for you is all the greater when he remembers that you were all obedient, receiving him with fear and trembling. [16] I am glad I can have complete confidence in you.

truth or dare

Mental torture and depression for messing up isn't the right response to sin. Godly sorrow moves you *through* forgiveness (both from God and yourself!) into change and freedom from guilt.

7:10

a 17 Isaiah 52:11; Ezek. 20:34,41   *b 18* 2 Samuel 7:14; 7:8

Generosity Encouraged

8 And now, brothers, we want you to know about the grace that God has given the Macedonian churches. [2]Out of the most severe trial, their overflowing joy and their extreme poverty welled up in rich generosity. [3]For I testify that they gave as much as they were able, and even beyond their ability. Entirely on their own, [4]they urgently pleaded with us for the privilege of sharing in this service to the saints. [5]And they did not do as we expected, but they gave themselves first to the Lord and then to us in keeping with God's will. [6]So we urged Titus, since he had earlier made a beginning, to bring also to completion this act of grace on your part. [7]But just as you excel in everything—in faith, in speech, in knowledge, in complete earnestness and in your love for us[a]—see that you also excel in this grace of giving.

[8]I am not commanding you, but I want to test the sincerity of your love by comparing it with the earnestness of others. [9]For you know the grace of our Lord Jesus Christ, that though he was rich, yet for your sakes he became poor, so that you through his poverty might become rich.

[10]And here is my advice about what is best for you in this matter: Last year you were the first not only to give but also to have the desire to do so. [11]Now finish the work, so that your eager willingness to do it may be matched by your completion of it, according to your means. [12]For if the willingness is there, the gift is acceptable according to what one has, not according to what he does not have.

[13]Our desire is not that others might be relieved while you are hard pressed, but that there might be equality. [14]At the present time your plenty will supply what they need, so that in turn their plenty will supply what you need. Then there will be equality, [15]as it is written: "He who gathered much did not have too much, and he who gathered little did not have too little." [b]

Titus Sent to Corinth

[16]I thank God, who put into the heart of Titus the same concern I have for you. [17]For Titus not only welcomed our appeal, but he is coming to you with much enthusiasm and on his own initiative. [18]And we are sending along with him the brother who is praised by all the churches for his service to the gospel. [19]What is more, he was chosen by the churches to accompany us as we carry the offering, which we administer in order to honor the Lord himself and to show our eagerness to help. [20]We want to avoid any criticism of the way we administer this liberal gift. [21]For we are taking pains to do what is right, not only in the eyes of the Lord but also in the eyes of men.

[22]In addition, we are sending with them our brother who has often proved to us in many ways that he is zealous, and now even more so because of his great confidence in you. [23]As for Titus, he is my partner and fellow worker among you; as for our brothers, they are representatives of the churches and an honor to Christ. [24]Therefore show these men the proof of your love and the reason for our pride in you, so that the churches can see it.

9 There is no need for me to write to you about this service to the saints. [2]For I know your eagerness to help, and I have been boasting about it to the Macedonians, telling them that since last year you in Achaia were ready to give; and your enthusiasm has stirred most of them to action. [3]But I am sending the brothers in order that our boasting about you in this matter should not prove hollow, but that you may be ready, as I said you would be. [4]For if any Macedonians come with me and find you unprepared, we—not to say anything about you—would be ashamed of having been so confident. [5]So I thought it necessary to urge the brothers to visit you in advance and finish the arrangements for the generous gift you had promised. Then it will be ready as a generous gift, not as one grudgingly given.

Sowing Generously

[6]Remember this: Whoever sows sparingly will also reap sparingly, and whoever sows generously will also reap generously. [7]Each man should give what he has decided in his heart to give, not reluctantly or under compulsion, for God loves a cheerful

truth or dare

Farmers spend money on seed because they know they'll get a crop at harvest time. Give like someone expecting a huge future harvest.

9:6–7

---

a 7 Some manuscripts *in our love for you*   *b 15* Exodus 16:18

giver. [8]And God is able to make all grace abound to you, so that in all things at all times, having all that you need, you will abound in every good work. [9]As it is written:

> "He has scattered abroad his gifts to the poor;
> his righteousness endures forever." [a]

[10]Now he who supplies seed to the sower and bread for food will also supply and increase your store of seed and will enlarge the harvest of your righteousness. [11]You will be made rich in every way so that you can be generous on every occasion, and through us your generosity will result in thanksgiving to God.

[12]This service that you perform is not only supplying the needs of God's people but is also overflowing in many expressions of thanks to God. [13]Because of the service by which you have proved yourselves, men will praise God for the obedience that accompanies your confession of the gospel of Christ, and for your generosity in sharing with them and with everyone else. [14]And in their prayers for you their hearts will go out to you, because of the surpassing grace God has given you. [15]Thanks be to God for his indescribable gift!

Paul's Defense of His Ministry

10 By the meekness and gentleness of Christ, I appeal to you—I, Paul, who am "timid" when face to face with you, but "bold" when away! [2]I beg you that when I come I may not have to be as bold as I expect to be toward some people who think that we live by the standards of this world. [3]For though we live in the world, we do not wage war as the world does. [4]The weapons we fight with are not the weapons of the world. On the contrary, they have divine power to demolish strongholds. [5]We demolish arguments and every pretension that sets itself up against the knowledge of God, and we take captive every thought to make it obedient to Christ. [6]And we will be ready to punish every act of disobedience, once your obedience is complete.

[7]You are looking only on the surface of things. [b] If anyone is confident that he belongs to Christ, he should consider again that we belong to Christ just as much as he. [8]For even if I boast somewhat freely about the authority the Lord gave us for building you up rather than pulling you down, I will not be ashamed of it. [9]I do not want to seem to be trying to frighten you with my letters. [10]For some say, "His letters are weighty and forceful, but in person he is unimpressive and his speaking amounts to nothing." [11]Such people should realize that what we are in our letters when we are absent, we will be in our actions when we are present.

[12]We do not dare to classify or compare ourselves with some who commend themselves. When they measure themselves by themselves and compare themselves with themselves, they are not wise. [13]We, however, will not boast beyond proper limits, but will confine our boasting to the field God has assigned to us, a field that reaches even to you. [14]We are not going too far in our boasting, as would be the case if we had not come to you, for we did get as far as you with the gospel of Christ. [15]Neither do we go beyond our limits by boasting of work done by others. [c] Our hope is that, as your faith continues to grow, our area of activity among you will greatly expand, [16]so that we can preach the gospel in the regions beyond you. For we do not want to boast about work already done in another man's territory. [17]But, "Let him who boasts boast in the Lord." [d] [18]For it is not the one who commends himself who is approved, but the one whom the Lord commends.

Paul and the False Apostles

11 I hope you will put up with a little of my foolishness; but you are already doing that. [2]I am jealous for you with a godly jealousy. I promised you to one husband, to Christ, so that I might present you as a pure virgin to him. [3]But I am afraid that just as Eve was deceived by the serpent's cunning, your minds may somehow be led astray from your sincere and pure devotion to Christ. [4]For if someone comes to you and preaches a Jesus other than the Jesus we preached, or if you receive a different spirit from the one you received, or a different gospel from the one you accepted, you put up with it easily enough. [5]But I do not think I am in the least

---

a 9 Psalm 112:9   *b* 7 Or *Look at the obvious facts*   *c* 13-15 Or [13]*We, however, will not boast about things that cannot be measured, but we will boast according to the standard of measurement that the God of measure has assigned us—a measurement that relates even to you.* 14 . . . . [15]*Neither do we boast about things that cannot be measured in regard to the work done by others.*   *d* 17 Jer. 9:24

3

inferior to those "super-apostles." ⁶I may not be a trained speaker, but I do have knowledge. We have made this perfectly clear to you in every way.

⁷Was it a sin for me to lower myself in order to elevate you by preaching the gospel of God to you free of charge? ⁸I robbed other churches by receiving support from them so as to serve you. ⁹And when I was with you and needed something, I was not a burden to anyone, for the brothers who came from Macedonia supplied what I needed. I have kept myself from being a burden to you in any way, and will continue to do so. ¹⁰As surely as the truth of Christ is in me, nobody in the regions of Achaia will stop this boasting of mine. ¹¹Why? Because I do not love you? God knows I do! ¹²And I will keep on doing what I am doing in order to cut the ground from under those who want an opportunity to be considered equal with us in the things they boast about.

¹³For such men are false apostles, deceitful workmen, masquerading as apostles of Christ. ¹⁴And no wonder, for Satan himself masquerades as an angel of light. ¹⁵It is not surprising, then, if his servants masquerade as servants of righteousness. Their end will be what their actions deserve.

Paul Boasts About His Sufferings

¹⁶I repeat: Let no one take me for a fool. But if you do, then receive me just as you would a fool, so that I may do a little boasting. ¹⁷In this self-confident boasting I am not talking as the Lord would, but as a fool. ¹⁸Since many are boasting in the way the world does, I too will boast. ¹⁹You gladly put up with fools since you are so wise! ²⁰In fact, you even put up with anyone who enslaves you or exploits you or takes advantage of you or pushes himself forward or slaps you in the face. ²¹To my shame I admit that we were too weak for that!

What anyone else dares to boast about—I am speaking as a fool—I also dare to boast about. ²²Are they Hebrews? So am I. Are they Israelites? So am I. Are they Abraham's descendants? So am I. ²³Are they servants of Christ? (I am out of my mind to talk like this.) I am more. I have worked much harder, been in prison more frequently, been flogged more severely, and been exposed to death again and again. ²⁴Five times I received from the Jews the forty lashes minus one. ²⁵Three times I was beaten with rods, once I was stoned, three times I was shipwrecked, I spent a night and a day in the open sea, ²⁶I have been constantly on the move. I have been in danger from rivers, in danger from bandits, in danger from my own countrymen, in danger from Gentiles; in danger in the city, in danger in the country, in danger at sea; and in danger from false brothers. ²⁷I have labored and toiled and have often gone without sleep; I have known hunger and thirst and have often gone without food; I have been cold and naked. ²⁸Besides everything else, I face daily the pressure of my concern for all the churches. ²⁹Who is weak, and I do not feel weak? Who is led into sin, and I do not inwardly burn?

³⁰If I must boast, I will boast of the things that show my weakness. ³¹The God and Father of the Lord Jesus, who is to be praised forever, knows that I am not lying. ³²In Damascus the governor under King Aretas had the city of the Damascenes guarded in order to arrest me. ³³But I was lowered in a basket from a window in the wall and slipped through his hands.

Paul's Vision and His Thorn

12 I must go on boasting. Although there is nothing to be gained, I will go on to visions and revelations from the Lord. ²I know a man in Christ who fourteen years ago was caught up to the third heaven. Whether it was in the body or out of the body I do not know— God knows. ³And I know that this man—whether in the body or apart from the body I do not know, but God knows— ⁴was caught up to paradise. He heard inexpressible things, things that man is not permitted to tell. ⁵I will boast about a man like that, but I will not boast about myself, except about my weaknesses. ⁶Even if I should choose to boast, I would not be a fool, because I would be speaking the truth. But I refrain, so no one will think more of me than is warranted by what I do or say.

⁷To keep me from becoming conceited because of these surpassingly great revelations, there was given me a thorn in my flesh, a messenger of Satan, to torment me. ⁸Three times I pleaded with the Lord to take it away from me. ⁹But he said to me, "My grace is sufficient for you, for my power is made perfect in weakness." Therefore I will boast all the more gladly about my weaknesses, so that Christ's power may rest on me. ¹⁰That is why, for Christ's sake, I delight in weaknesses, in insults, in hardships, in persecutions, in difficulties. For when I am weak, then I am strong.

Paul's Concern for the Corinthians

[11]I have made a fool of myself, but you drove me to it. I ought to have been commended by you, for I am not in the least inferior to the "super-apostles," even though I am nothing. [12]The things that mark an apostle—signs, wonders and miracles—were done among you with great perseverance. [13]How were you inferior to the other churches, except that I was never a burden to you? Forgive me this wrong!

[14]Now I am ready to visit you for the third time, and I will not be a burden to you, because what I want is not your possessions but you. After all, children should not have to save up for their parents, but parents for their children. [15]So I will very gladly spend for you everything I have and expend myself as well. If I love you more, will you love me less? [16]Be that as it may, I have not been a burden to you. Yet, crafty fellow that I am, I caught you by trickery! [17]Did I exploit you through any of the men I sent you? [18]I urged Titus to go to you and I sent our brother with him. Titus did not exploit you, did he? Did we not act in the same spirit and follow the same course?

[19]Have you been thinking all along that we have been defending ourselves to you? We have been speaking in the sight of God as those in Christ; and everything we do, dear friends, is for your strengthening. [20]For I am afraid that when I come I may not find you as I want you to be, and you may not find me as you want me to be. I fear that there may be quarreling, jealousy, outbursts of anger, factions, slander, gossip, arrogance and disorder. [21]I am afraid that when I come again my God will humble me before you, and I will be grieved over many who have sinned earlier and have not repented of the impurity, sexual sin and debauchery in which they have indulged.

Final Warnings

13 This will be my third visit to you. "Every matter must be established by the testimony of two or three witnesses."[a] [2]I already gave you a warning when I was with you the second time. I now repeat it while absent: On my return I will not spare those who sinned earlier or any of the others, [3]since you are demanding proof that Christ is speaking through me. He is not weak in dealing with you, but is powerful among you. [4]For to be sure, he was crucified in weakness, yet he lives by God's power. Likewise, we are weak in him, yet by God's power we will live with him to serve you.

[5]Examine yourselves to see whether you are in the faith; test yourselves. Do you not realize that Christ Jesus is in you—unless, of course, you fail the test? [6]And I trust that you will discover that we have not failed the test. [7]Now we pray to God that you will not do anything wrong. Not that people will see that we have stood the test but that you will do what

love notes

12:9–10

Dear one,

Don't get down on yourself because of your weaknesses. It's when you realize that you can't do everything on your own that you turn to me, and that's when my power and grace really shine through. Let me be your strength.

—Lord Jesus

In what areas of your life do you need God's strength? Tell him about it.

is right even though we may seem to have failed. [8]For we cannot do anything against the truth, but only for the truth. [9]We are glad whenever we are weak but you are strong; and our prayer is for your perfection. [10]This is why I write these things when I am absent, that when I come I may not have to be harsh in my use of authority—the authority the Lord gave me for building you up, not for tearing you down.

Final Greetings

[11]Finally, brothers, good-by. Aim for perfection, listen to my appeal, be of one mind, live in peace. And the God of love and peace will be with you.

[12]Greet one another with a holy kiss. [13]All the saints send their greetings.

[14]May the grace of the Lord Jesus Christ, and the love of God, and the fellowship of the Holy Spirit be with you all.

author: The apostle Paul.

date: About A.D. 50.

setting: People called *Judaizers* were teaching that Gentiles had to obey the Jewish laws in order to be saved.

verse to remember: I have been crucified with Christ and I no longer live, but Christ lives in me. The life I live in the body, I live by faith in the Son of God, who loved me and gave himself for me (2:20)!

theme to consider: We can never earn God's salvation by what we do or how well we obey the rules. It is by God's grace alone.

galatians

unchanging truth

Remember playing tag on the playground and trying not to be caught by whoever's "it"? Remember the rush of running to home base where you'd be safe from the evil grasp of your friend's "tag" on your shoulder? Being almost-safe was a long way from being safe. And that's when we figured it out: *almost* doesn't count.

Nope, being *almost* perfect isn't the same as being perfect. One little mistake, one slip-up, and it's all over because God's standard is perfection.

So what's up with trying to be good enough for God? It can't be done. Our good deeds can only get us so far. Listening to Christian music is good, but it can't save you. Going to church is great, but that alone doesn't cut it with God. Face it. You couldn't obey your parents, look after your baby brother without complaining or take out the trash enough times to get you off the hook with God. Even if you went to church youth camp every summer for the rest of your life, that couldn't save you.

Paul wrote the book of Galatians to tell us that being almost good enough for God doesn't count when it comes to salvation. In fact, even our best attempt at being good is a joke compared to what our holy God requires. That's why we need Jesus. Only Jesus satisfies God's standard of perfection. He alone is "home base"—the place where we are safe and secure in God's love.

life lessons

1 Salvation is by God's grace through faith in Jesus Christ—period. End of story (1:1–9).

2 If you're free in Christ, don't wear yourself out trying to impress God or other people with your spirituality. That will get you nowhere fast (3:1–14).

3 If we try to be good on our own, we're like plastic fruit—nice to look at but fake on the inside. However, the Holy Spirit creates the sweet-tasting spiritual fruit of Jesus' character (5:16–26).

1 Paul, an apostle—sent not from men nor by man, but by Jesus Christ and God the Father, who raised him from the dead— ²and all the brothers with me,

To the churches in Galatia:

³Grace and peace to you from God our Father and the Lord Jesus Christ, ⁴who gave himself for our sins to rescue us from the present evil age, according to the will of our God and Father, ⁵to whom be glory for ever and ever. Amen.

No Other Gospel

⁶I am astonished that you are so quickly deserting the one who called you by the grace of Christ and are turning to a different gospel— ⁷which is really no gospel at all. Evidently some people are throwing you into confusion and are trying to pervert the gospel of Christ. ⁸But even if we or an angel from heaven should preach a gospel other than the one we preached to you, let him be eternally condemned! ⁹As we have already said, so now I say again: If anybody is preaching to you a gospel other than what you accepted, let him be eternally condemned!

¹⁰Am I now trying to win the approval of men, or of God? Or am I trying to please men? If I were still trying to please men, I would not be a servant of Christ.

Paul Called by God

¹¹I want you to know, brothers, that the gospel I preached is not something that man made up. ¹²I did not receive it from any man, nor was I taught it; rather, I received it by revelation from Jesus Christ.

¹³For you have heard of my previous way of life in Judaism, how intensely I persecuted the church of God and tried to destroy it. ¹⁴I was advancing in Judaism beyond many Jews of my own age and was extremely zealous for the traditions of my fathers. ¹⁵But when God, who set me apart from birth*ᵃ* and called me by his grace, was pleased ¹⁶to reveal his Son in me so that I might preach him among the Gentiles, I did not consult any man, ¹⁷nor did I go up to Jerusalem to see those who were apostles before I was, but I went immediately into Arabia and later returned to Damascus.

¹⁸Then after three years, I went up to Jerusalem to get acquainted with Peter*ᵇ* and stayed with him fifteen days. ¹⁹I saw none of the other apostles—only James, the Lord's brother. ²⁰I assure you before God that what I am writing you is no lie. ²¹Later I went to Syria and Cilicia. ²²I was personally unknown to the churches of Judea that are in Christ. ²³They only heard the report: "The man who formerly persecuted us is now preaching the faith he once tried to destroy." ²⁴And they praised God because of me.

Paul Accepted by the Apostles

2 Fourteen years later I went up again to Jerusalem, this time with Barnabas. I took Titus along also. ²I went in response to a revelation and set before them the gospel that I preach among the Gentiles. But I did this privately to those who seemed to be leaders, for fear that I was running or had run my race in vain. ³Yet not even Titus, who was with me, was compelled to be circumcised, even though he was a Greek. ⁴ʟThis matter aroseᴶ because some false brothers had infiltrated our ranks to spy on the freedom we have in Christ Jesus and to make us slaves. ⁵We did not give in to them for a moment, so that the truth of the gospel might remain with you.

⁶As for those who seemed to be important—whatever they were makes no difference to me; God does not judge by external appearance—those men added nothing to my message. ⁷On the contrary, they saw that I had been entrusted with the task of preaching the gospel to the Gentiles,*ᶜ* just as Peter had been to the Jews.*ᵈ* ⁸For God, who was at work in the ministry of Peter as an apostle to the Jews, was also at work in my ministry as an apostle to the Gentiles. ⁹James, Peter*ᵉ* and John, those reputed to be pillars, gave me and Barnabas the right hand of fellowship when they recognized the grace given to me. They agreed that we should go to the Gentiles, and they to the Jews. ¹⁰All they asked was that we should continue to remember the poor, the very thing I was eager to do.

---

a 15 Or *from my mother's womb*   *b 18* Greek *Cephas*   *c 7* Greek *uncircumcised*   *d 7* Greek *circumcised*; also in verses 8 and 9   *e 9* Greek *Cephas*; also in verses 11 and 14

Paul Opposes Peter

[11] When Peter came to Antioch, I opposed him to his face, because he was clearly in the wrong. [12] Before certain men came from James, he used to eat with the Gentiles. But when they arrived, he began to draw back and separate himself from the Gentiles because he was afraid of those who belonged to the circumcision group. [13] The other Jews joined him in his hypocrisy, so that by their hypocrisy even Barnabas was led astray.

[14] When I saw that they were not acting in line with the truth of the gospel, I said to Peter in front of them all, "You are a Jew, yet you live like a Gentile and not like a Jew. How is it, then, that you force Gentiles to follow Jewish customs?

[15] "We who are Jews by birth and not 'Gentile sinners' [16] know that a man is not justified by observing the law, but by faith in Jesus Christ. So we, too, have put our faith in Christ Jesus that we may be justified by faith in Christ and not by observing the law, because by observing the law no one will be justified.

[17] "If, while we seek to be justified in Christ, it becomes evident that we ourselves are sinners, does that mean that Christ promotes sin? Absolutely not! [18] If I rebuild what I destroyed, I prove that I am a lawbreaker. [19] For through the law I died to the law so that I might live for God. [20] I have been crucified with Christ and I no longer live, but Christ lives in me. The life I live in the body, I live by faith in the Son of God, who loved me and gave himself for me. [21] I do not set aside the grace of God, for if righteousness could be gained through the law, Christ died for nothing!" [a]

truth or dare

If you're dead, you can't run the show anymore. Do you claim you've "given your life to Jesus" but still grip the reins? Jesus loves you— let him take control.

2:20

Faith or Observance of the Law

3 You foolish Galatians! Who has bewitched you? Before your very eyes Jesus Christ was clearly portrayed as crucified. [2] I would like to learn just one thing from you: Did you receive the Spirit by observing the law, or by believing what you heard? [3] Are you so foolish? After beginning with the Spirit, are you now trying to attain your goal by human effort? [4] Have you suffered so much for nothing—if it really was for nothing? [5] Does God give you his Spirit and work miracles among you because you observe the law, or because you believe what you heard?

[6] Consider Abraham: "He believed God, and it was credited to him as righteousness." [b] [7] Understand, then, that those who believe are children of Abraham. [8] The Scripture foresaw that God would justify the Gentiles by faith, and announced the gospel in advance to Abraham: "All nations will be blessed through you." [c] [9] So those who have faith are blessed along with Abraham, the man of faith.

[10] All who rely on observing the law are under a curse, for it is written: "Cursed is everyone who does not continue to do everything written in the Book of the Law." [d] [11] Clearly no one is justified before God by the law, because, "The righteous will live by faith." [e] [12] The law is not based on faith; on the contrary, "The man who does these things will live by them." [f] [13] Christ redeemed us from the curse of the law by becoming a curse for us, for it is written: "Cursed is everyone who is hung on a tree." [g] [14] He redeemed us in order that the blessing given to Abraham might come to the Gentiles through Christ Jesus, so that by faith we might receive the promise of the Spirit.

The Law and the Promise

[15] Brothers, let me take an example from everyday life. Just as no one can set aside or add to a human covenant that has been duly established, so it is in this case. [16] The promises were spoken to Abraham and to his seed. The Scripture does not say "and to seeds," meaning many people, but "and to your seed," [h] meaning one person, who is Christ. [17] What I mean is this: The law, introduced 430 years later, does not set aside the covenant previously established by God and thus do away with the promise. [18] For if the inheritance depends on the law, then it no longer depends on a promise; but God in his grace gave it to Abraham through a promise.

a 21 Some interpreters end the quotation after verse 14.   *b* 6 Gen. 15:6   *c* 8 Gen. 12:3; 18:18; 22:18   *d* 10 Deut. 27:26   *e* 11 Hab. 2:4   *f* 12 Lev. 18:5   *g* 13 Deut. 21:23   *h* 16 Gen. 12:7; 13:15; 24:7

¹⁹What, then, was the purpose of the law? It was added because of transgressions until the Seed to whom the promise referred had come. The law was put into effect through angels by a mediator. ²⁰A mediator, however, does not represent just one party; but God is one.

²¹Is the law, therefore, opposed to the promises of God? Absolutely not! For if a law had been given that could impart life, then righteousness would certainly have come by the law. ²²But the Scripture declares that the whole world is a prisoner of sin, so that what was promised, being given through faith in Jesus Christ, might be given to those who believe.

²³Before this faith came, we were held prisoners by the law, locked up until faith should be revealed. ²⁴So the law was put in charge to lead us to Christ*ᵃ* that we might be justified by faith. ²⁵Now that faith has come, we are no longer under the supervision of the law.

Sons of God

²⁶You are all sons of God through faith in Christ Jesus, ²⁷for all of you who were baptized into Christ have clothed yourselves with Christ. ²⁸There is neither Jew nor Greek, slave nor free, male nor female, for you are all one in Christ Jesus. ²⁹If you belong to Christ, then you are Abraham's seed, and heirs according to the promise.

4 What I am saying is that as long as the heir is a child, he is no different from a slave, although he owns the whole estate. ²He is subject to guardians and trustees until the time set by his father. ³So also, when we were children, we were in slavery under the basic principles of the world. ⁴But when the time had fully come, God sent his Son, born of a woman, born under law, ⁵to redeem those under law, that we might receive the full rights of sons. ⁶Because you are sons, God sent the Spirit of his Son into our hearts, the Spirit who calls out, *"Abba,ᵇ* Father." ⁷So you are no longer a slave, but a son; and since you are a son, God has made you also an heir.

Paul's Concern for the Galatians

⁸Formerly, when you did not know God, you were slaves to those who by nature are not gods. ⁹But now that you know God—or rather are known by God—how is it that you are turning back to those weak and miserable principles? Do you wish to be enslaved by them all over again? ¹⁰You are observing special days and months and seasons and years! ¹¹I fear for you, that somehow I have wasted my efforts on you.

¹²I plead with you, brothers, become like me, for I became like you. You have done me no wrong. ¹³As you know, it was because of an illness that I first preached the gospel to you. ¹⁴Even though my illness was a trial to you, you did not treat me with contempt or scorn. Instead, you welcomed me as if I were an angel of God, as if I were Christ Jesus himself. ¹⁵What has happened to all your joy? I can testify that, if you could have done so, you would have torn out your eyes and given them to me. ¹⁶Have I now become your enemy by telling you the truth?

¹⁷Those people are zealous to win you over, but for no good. What they want is to alienate you ⌊from us⌋, so that you may be zealous for them. ¹⁸It is fine to be zealous, provided the purpose is good, and to be so always and not just when I am with you. ¹⁹My dear children, for whom I am again in the pains of childbirth until Christ is formed in you, ²⁰how I wish I could be with you now and change my tone, because I am perplexed about you!

Hagar and Sarah

²¹Tell me, you who want to be under the law, are you not aware of what the law says? ²²For it is written that Abraham had two sons, one by the slave woman and the other by the free woman. ²³His son by the slave woman was born in the ordinary way; but his son by the free woman was born as the result of a promise.

²⁴These things may be taken figuratively, for the women represent two covenants. One cov-

truth *or dare*

"The Battle of the Sexes" is like "The Battle of the Denominations"— neither belongs in the body of Christ. Make an effort to *unite* with other believers.

3:28

a 24 Or *charge until Christ came*   *b* 6 Aramaic for *Father* enant is from Mount Sinai and bears children who are to be slaves: This is Hagar. ²⁵Now Hagar stands for Mount Sinai in Arabia and corresponds to the present city of Jerusalem, because she is in slavery with her children. ²⁶But the Jerusalem that is above is free, and she is our mother. ²⁷For it is written:

"Be glad, O barren woman,
　who bears no children;
break forth and cry aloud,
　you who have no labor pains;
because more are the children of the desolate woman
　than of her who has a husband." ᵃ

²⁸Now you, brothers, like Isaac, are children of promise. ²⁹At that time the son born in the ordinary way persecuted the son born by the power of the Spirit. It is the same now. ³⁰But what does the Scripture say? "Get rid of the slave woman and her son, for the slave woman's son will never share in the inheritance with the free woman's son." ᵇ ³¹Therefore, brothers, we are not children of the slave woman, but of the free woman.

Freedom in Christ

5 It is for freedom that Christ has set us free. Stand firm, then, and do not let yourselves be burdened again by a yoke of slavery.

²Mark my words! I, Paul, tell you that if you let yourselves be circumcised, Christ will be of no value to you at all. ³Again I declare to every man who lets himself be circumcised that he is obligated to obey the whole law. ⁴You who are trying to be justified by law have been alienated from Christ; you have fallen away from grace. ⁵But by faith we eagerly await through the Spirit the righteousness for which we hope. ⁶For in Christ Jesus neither circumcision nor uncircumcision has any value. The only thing that counts is faith expressing itself through love.

⁷You were running a good race. Who cut in on you and kept you from obeying the truth? ⁸That kind of persuasion does not come from the one who calls you. ⁹"A little yeast works through the whole batch of dough." ¹⁰I am confident in the Lord that you will take no other view. The one who is throwing you into confusion will pay the penalty, whoever he may be. ¹¹Brothers, if I am still preaching circumcision, why am I still being persecuted? In that case the offense of the cross has been abolished. ¹²As for those agitators, I wish they would go the whole way and emasculate themselves!

¹³You, my brothers, were called to be free. But do not use your freedom to indulge

love ♥ notes

4:4-7

Child,

You are my daughter, adopted into my eternal family. There is nothing within my power and my possession that I will withhold from you. All my resources—power, forgiveness, grace and love—belong to you.

—Abba, Daddy

Write down in your own words what it means to be God's heir.

_____
_____
_____
_____
_____
_____
_____
_____
_____

the sinful nature[a]; rather, serve one another in love. [14]The entire law is summed up in a single command: "Love your neighbor as yourself."[b] [15]If you keep on biting and devouring each other, watch out or you will be destroyed by each other.

Life by the Spirit

[16]So I say, live by the Spirit, and you will not gratify the desires of the sinful nature. [17]For the sinful nature desires what is contrary to the Spirit, and the Spirit what is contrary to the sinful nature. They are in conflict with each other, so that you do not do what you want. [18]But if you are led by the Spirit, you are not under law.

[19]The acts of the sinful nature are obvious: sexual immorality, impurity and debauchery; [20]idolatry and witchcraft; hatred, discord, jealousy, fits of rage, selfish ambition, dissensions, factions [21]and envy; drunkenness, orgies, and the like. I warn you, as I did before, that those who live like this will not inherit the kingdom of God.

[22]But the fruit of the Spirit is love, joy, peace, patience, kindness, goodness, faithfulness, [23]gentleness and self-control. Against such things there is no law. [24]Those who belong to Christ Jesus have crucified the sinful nature with its passions and desires. [25]Since we live by the Spirit, let us keep in step with the Spirit. [26]Let us not become conceited, provoking and envying each other.

genuine

growth » 5:22–23

These verses aren't a to-do list. "I was kind today. I'll check that off. Tomorrow I'll work on self-control." You know from experience that tomorrow you might not be very kind at all.

The Spirit is the one who produces fruit in your life, like grapes on a grape vine (see John 15:4–5). The branch doesn't *decide* to grow grapes; it just does because it's connected to the vine. As long as you're connected to God, he'll keep growing more fruit in you.

Doing Good to All

6 Brothers, if someone is caught in a sin, you who are spiritual should restore him gently. But watch yourself, or you also may be tempted. [2]Carry each other's burdens, and in this way you will fulfill the law of Christ. [3]If anyone thinks he is something when he is nothing, he deceives himself. [4]Each one should test his own actions. Then he can take pride in himself, without comparing himself to somebody else, [5]for each one should carry his own load.

[6]Anyone who receives instruction in the word must share all good things with his instructor.

[7]Do not be deceived: God cannot be mocked. A man reaps what he sows. [8]The one who sows to please his sinful nature, from that nature[c] will reap destruction; the one who sows to please the Spirit, from the Spirit will reap eternal life. [9]Let us not become weary in doing good, for at the proper time we will reap a harvest if we do not give up. [10]Therefore, as we have opportunity, let us do good to all people, especially to those who belong to the family of believers.

Not Circumcision but a New Creation

[11]See what large letters I use as I write to you with my own hand!

[12]Those who want to make a good impression out-

truth **or dare**

Always getting ragged on for being the "good girl"? Going against the flow *can* get tiring. Now's not the time to give up, though—the harvest is just ahead.

6:9

a 13 Or the flesh; also in verses 16, 17, 19 and 24   *b 14 Lev. 19:18*   *c 8 Or his flesh, from the flesh* wardly are trying to compel you to be circumcised. The only reason they do this is to avoid being persecuted for the cross of Christ. [13]Not even those who are circumcised obey the law, yet they want you to be circumcised that they may boast about your flesh. [14]May I never boast except in the cross of our Lord Jesus Christ, through which[a] the world has been crucified to me, and I to the world. [15]Neither circumcision nor uncircumcision means anything; what counts is a new creation. [16]Peace and mercy to all who follow this rule, even to the Israel of God.

[17]Finally, let no one cause me trouble, for I bear on my body the marks of Jesus.

[18]The grace of our Lord Jesus Christ be with your spirit, brothers. Amen.

a 14 Or whom

at a glance

author: The apostle Paul.

date: About A.D. 60.

setting: Paul wrote this letter from Rome while he was in prison. He probably intended this to be a circular letter, to be passed on from the believers in Ephesus to other Christians in the area.

verse to remember: There is one body and one Spirit—just as you were called to one hope when you were called—one Lord, one faith, one baptism; one God and Father of all, who is over all and through all and in all (4:4–6).

theme to consider: As believers, we are united in Jesus Christ. We should do all we can to live in unity with other believers.

ephesians

unchanging truth

What the youth leaders planned to be a weekend youth retreat of mountain air, togetherness and spiritual encouragement instead turned into something else altogether. A jealousy-fest broke out among the sophomore girls over who was shamelessly flirting with whom. There were more backstabbings than pillow fights in the junior high cabin. And kids came to the worship services with attitudes that were as bitter as the camp food.

Sound familiar? If you've been around the church much, you may feel like you've seen it all. Sometimes it's hard to tell the difference between a church youth group and a gang of rowdies who don't know any better. *This* is what the church is supposed to be like?! Hardly.

Paul's message to the Ephesians about the importance of unity among Christians could have been addressed to any modern-day youth group. "Enough!" he says. "It's time for you to grow up!" We've wasted far too much time being spiritual babies and insisting everything go our way. We have to start looking out for other people instead of for "number one."

The message of the book of Ephesians is this: If we're going to call ourselves Christians, then we're going to have to start acting like Christ. Paul reminds us that with the help of the Spirit, we will be able to do that.

life lessons

1 Christians are the body of Christ, and the world is looking to us to get a picture of what Jesus is like (4:1–13).

2 It's time for us to grow up and mature in our Christian faith—the old way of living just won't do anymore (4:14–32).

3 Good and evil are at war, and the battle lines are drawn across our souls (6:10–18).

1

Paul, an apostle of Christ Jesus by the will of God,

To the saints in Ephesus,*a* the faithful*b* in Christ Jesus:

²Grace and peace to you from God our Father and the Lord Jesus Christ.

Spiritual Blessings in Christ

³Praise be to the God and Father of our Lord Jesus Christ, who has blessed us in the heavenly realms with every spiritual blessing in Christ. ⁴For he chose us in him before the creation of the world to be holy and blameless in his sight. In love ⁵he*c* predestined us to be adopted as his sons through Jesus Christ, in accordance with his pleasure and will— ⁶to the praise of his glorious grace, which he has freely given us in the One he loves. ⁷In him we have redemption through his blood, the forgiveness of sins, in accordance with the riches of God's grace ⁸that he lavished on us with all wisdom and understanding. ⁹And he*d* made known to us the mystery of his will according to his good pleasure, which he purposed in Christ, ¹⁰to be put into effect when the times will have reached their fulfillment—to bring all things in heaven and on earth together under one head, even Christ.

¹¹In him we were also chosen,*e* having been predestined according to the plan of him who works out everything in conformity with the purpose of his will, ¹²in order that we, who were the first to hope in Christ, might be for the praise of his glory. ¹³And you also were included in Christ when you heard the word of truth, the gospel of your salvation. Having believed, you were marked in him with a seal, the promised Holy Spirit, ¹⁴who is a deposit guaranteeing our inheritance until the redemption of those who are God's possession—to the praise of his glory.

Thanksgiving and Prayer

¹⁵For this reason, ever since I heard about your faith in the Lord Jesus and your love for all the saints, ¹⁶I have not stopped giving thanks for you, remembering you in my prayers. ¹⁷I keep asking that the God of our Lord Jesus Christ, the glorious Father, may give you the Spirit*f* of wisdom and revelation, so that you may know him better. ¹⁸I pray also that the eyes of your heart may be enlightened in order that you may know the hope to which he has called you, the riches of his glorious inheritance in the saints, ¹⁹and his incomparably great power for us who believe. That power is like the working of his mighty strength, ²⁰which he exerted in Christ when he raised him from the dead and seated him at his right hand in the heavenly realms, ²¹far above all rule and authority, power and dominion, and every title that can be given, not only in the present age but also in the one to come. ²²And God placed all things under his feet and appointed him to be head over everything for the church, ²³which is his body, the fullness of him who fills everything in every way.

Made Alive in Christ

2

As for you, you were dead in your transgressions and sins, ²in which you used to live when you followed the ways of this world and of the ruler of the kingdom of the air, the spirit who is now at work in those who are disobedient. ³All of us also lived among them at one time, gratifying the cravings of our sinful nature*g* and following its desires and thoughts. Like the rest, we were by nature objects of wrath. ⁴But because of his great love for us, God, who is rich in mercy, ⁵made us alive with Christ even when we were dead in transgressions—it is by grace you have been saved. ⁶And God raised us up with Christ and seated us with him in the heavenly realms in Christ Jesus, ⁷in order that in the coming ages he might show the incomparable riches of his grace, expressed in his kindness to us in Christ Jesus. ⁸For it is by grace you have been saved, through faith—and this not from yourselves, it is the gift of God— ⁹not by works, so that no one can boast. ¹⁰For we are God's

truth or dare

It doesn't get any clearer than this. Being a "good person" won't win you a ticket to heaven. Salvation is not a reward; it's a gift.

2:8–9

---

a 1 Some early manuscripts do not have *in Ephesus.*   *b 1* Or *believers who are*   *c 4,5* Or *sight in love. ⁵He*   *d 8,9* Or *us. With all wisdom and understanding, ⁹he*   *e 11* Or *were made heirs*   *f 17* Or *a spirit*   *g 3* Or *our flesh* workmanship, created in Christ Jesus to do good works, which God prepared in advance for us to do.

One in Christ

[11]Therefore, remember that formerly you who are Gentiles by birth and called "uncircumcised" by those who call themselves "the circumcision" (that done in the body by the hands of men)— [12]remember that at that time you were separate from Christ, excluded from citizenship in Israel and foreigners to the covenants of the promise, without hope and without God in the world. [13]But now in Christ Jesus you who once were far away have been brought near through the blood of Christ.

[14]For he himself is our peace, who has made the two one and has destroyed the barrier, the dividing wall of hostility, [15]by abolishing in his flesh the law with its commandments and regulations. His purpose was to create in himself one new man out of the two, thus making peace, [16]and in this one body to reconcile both of them to God through the cross, by which he put to death their hostility. [17]He came and preached peace to you who were far away and peace to those who were near. [18]For through him we both have access to the Father by one Spirit.

[19]Consequently, you are no longer foreigners and aliens, but fellow citizens with God's people and members of God's household, [20]built on the foundation of the apostles and prophets, with Christ Jesus himself as the chief cornerstone. [21]In him the whole building is joined together and rises to become a holy temple in the Lord. [22]And in him you too are being built together to become a dwelling in which God lives by his Spirit.

Paul the Preacher to the Gentiles

3 For this reason I, Paul, the prisoner of Christ Jesus for the sake of you Gentiles— [2]Surely you have heard about the administration of God's grace that was given to me for you, [3]that is, the mystery made known to me by revelation, as I have already written briefly. [4]In reading this, then, you will be able to understand my insight into the mystery of Christ, [5]which was not made known to men in other generations as it has now been revealed by the Spirit to God's holy apostles and prophets. [6]This mystery is that through the gospel the Gentiles are heirs together with Israel, members together of one body, and sharers together in the promise in Christ Jesus.

[7]I became a servant of this gospel by the gift of God's grace given me through the working of his power. [8]Although I am less than the least of all God's people, this grace was given me: to preach to the Gentiles the unsearchable riches of Christ, [9]and to make plain to everyone the administration of this mystery, which for ages past was kept hidden in God, who created all things. [10]His intent was that now, through the church, the manifold wisdom of God should be made known to the rulers and authorities in the heavenly realms, [11]according to his eternal purpose which he accomplished in Christ Jesus our Lord. [12]In him and through faith in him we may approach God with freedom and confidence. [13]I ask you, therefore, not to be discouraged because of my sufferings for you, which are your glory.

A Prayer for the Ephesians

[14]For this reason I kneel before the Father, [15]from whom his whole family[a] in heaven and on earth derives its name. [16]I pray that out of his glorious riches he may strengthen you with power through his Spirit in your inner being, [17]so that Christ may dwell in your hearts through faith. And I pray that you, being rooted and established in love, [18]may have power, together with all the saints, to grasp how wide and long and high and deep is the love of Christ, [19]and to know this love that surpasses knowledge—that you may be filled to the measure of all the fullness of God.

[20]Now to him who is able to do immeasurably more than all we ask or imagine, according to his power that is at work within us, [21]to him be glory in the church and in Christ Jesus throughout all generations, for ever and ever! Amen.

Unity in the Body of Christ

4 As a prisoner for the Lord, then, I urge you to live a life worthy of the calling you have received. [2]Be completely humble and gentle; be patient, bearing with one another in love. [3]Make every effort to keep the unity of the Spirit through the bond of peace. [4]There is one

a 15 Or *whom all fatherhood*

body and one Spirit—just as you were called to one hope when you were called— [5]one Lord, one faith, one baptism; [6]one God and Father of all, who is over all and through all and in all.

[7]But to each one of us grace has been given as Christ apportioned it. [8]This is why it[a] says:

> "When he ascended on high,
> he led captives in his train
> and gave gifts to men."[b]

[9](What does "he ascended" mean except that he also descended to the lower, earthly regions[c]? [10]He who descended is the very one who ascended higher than all the heavens, in order to fill the whole universe.) [11]It was he who gave some to be apostles, some to be prophets, some to be evangelists, and some to be pastors and teachers, [12]to prepare God's people for works of service, so that the body of Christ may be built up [13]until we all reach unity in the faith and in the knowledge of the Son of God and become mature, attaining to the whole measure of the fullness of Christ.

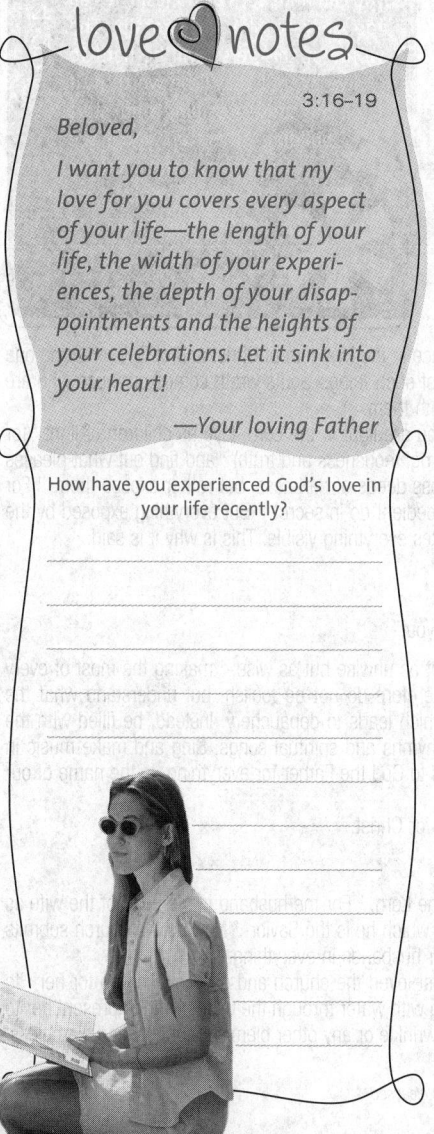

love ♥ notes

3:16–19

Beloved,

I want you to know that my love for you covers every aspect of your life—the length of your life, the width of your experiences, the depth of your disappointments and the heights of your celebrations. Let it sink into your heart!

—Your loving Father

How have you experienced God's love in your life recently?

[14]Then we will no longer be infants, tossed back and forth by the waves, and blown here and there by every wind of teaching and by the cunning and craftiness of men in their deceitful scheming. [15]Instead, speaking the truth in love, we will in all things grow up into him who is the Head, that is, Christ. [16]From him the whole body, joined and held together by every supporting ligament, grows and builds itself up in love, as each part does its work.

Living as Children of Light

[17]So I tell you this, and insist on it in the Lord, that you must no longer live as the Gentiles do, in the futility of their thinking. [18]They are darkened in their understanding and separated from the life of God because of the ignorance that is in them due to the hardening of their hearts. [19]Having lost all sensitivity, they have given themselves over to sensuality so as to indulge in every kind of impurity, with a continual lust for more.

[20]You, however, did not come to know Christ that way. [21]Surely you heard of him and were taught in him in accordance with the truth that is in Jesus. [22]You were taught, with regard to your former way of life, to put off your old self, which is being corrupted by its deceitful desires; [23]to be made new in the attitude of your minds; [24]and to put on the new self, created to be like God in true righteousness and holiness.

[25]Therefore each of you must put off falsehood and speak truthfully to his neighbor, for we are all members of one body. [26]"In your anger do not sin"[d]: Do not let the sun go down while you are still angry, [27]and do not give the devil a foothold. [28]He who has been stealing must steal no longer, but

---

a 8 Or God   b 8 Psalm 68:18   c 9 Or the depths of the earth   d 26 Psalm 4:4 must work, doing something useful with his own hands, that he may have something to share with those in need.

²⁹Do not let any unwholesome talk come out of your mouths, but only what is helpful for building others up according to their needs, that it may benefit those who listen. ³⁰And do not grieve the Holy Spirit of God, with whom you were sealed for the day of redemption. ³¹Get rid of all bitterness, rage and anger, brawling and slander, along with every form of malice. ³²Be kind and compassionate to one another, forgiving each other, just as in Christ God forgave you.

5 Be imitators of God, therefore, as dearly loved children ²and live a life of love, just as Christ loved us and gave himself up for us as a fragrant offering and sacrifice to God.

³But among you there must not be even a hint of sexual immorality, or of any kind of impurity, or of greed, because these are improper for God's holy people. ⁴Nor should there be obscenity, foolish talk or coarse joking, which are out of place, but rather thanksgiving. ⁵For of this you can be sure: No immoral, impure or greedy person— such a man is an idolater—has any inheritance in the kingdom of Christ and of God.ᵃ ⁶Let no one deceive you with empty words, for because of such things God's wrath comes on those who are disobedient. ⁷Therefore do not be partners with them.

⁸For you were once darkness, but now you are light in the Lord. Live as children of light ⁹(for the fruit of the light consists in all goodness, righteousness and truth) ¹⁰and find out what pleases the Lord. ¹¹Have nothing to do with the fruitless deeds of darkness, but rather expose them. ¹²For it is shameful even to mention what the disobedient do in secret. ¹³But everything exposed by the light becomes visible, ¹⁴for it is light that makes everything visible. This is why it is said:

> "Wake up, O sleeper,
>   rise from the dead,
>   and Christ will shine on you."

¹⁵Be very careful, then, how you live—not as unwise but as wise, ¹⁶making the most of every opportunity, because the days are evil. ¹⁷Therefore do not be foolish, but understand what the Lord's will is. ¹⁸Do not get drunk on wine, which leads to debauchery. Instead, be filled with the Spirit. ¹⁹Speak to one another with psalms, hymns and spiritual songs. Sing and make music in your heart to the Lord, ²⁰always giving thanks to God the Father for everything, in the name of our Lord Jesus Christ.

²¹Submit to one another out of reverence for Christ.

Wives and Husbands

²²Wives, submit to your husbands as to the Lord. ²³For the husband is the head of the wife as Christ is the head of the church, his body, of which he is the Savior. ²⁴Now as the church submits to Christ, so also wives should submit to their husbands in everything.

²⁵Husbands, love your wives, just as Christ loved the church and gave himself up for her ²⁶to make her holy, cleansingᵇ her by the washing with water through the word, ²⁷and to present her to himself as a radiant church, without stain or wrinkle or any other blemish, but holy and blameless.

---

genuine speech » 4:29

When you get together with your friends, what do you talk about? When the conversation turns to other people, is it focused on how wonderful they are? Or does your group usually put others down, gossip about them and point out every fault you can find? Let's be honest—it's all too easy to slip into gossip. The words of this verse will be hard to live by, but they'll be worth it. If you stop gossiping and start building others up, you'll see a transformation in others and in yourself. Let your words be only kind and true.

ᵃ 5 Or *kingdom of the Christ and God*   ᵇ 26 Or *having cleansed*

At the Click of a Mouse

focus | Profile: **Trina**

What do I do when I'm not online? Eat and sleep. Talk on the phone. Other than that, I'm surfing the Web. It's addicting, for sure! There's always more to do, see, look up, send, copy and chat about. My friends IM each other all the time, even when we're supposed to be asleep. It's so easy, and I don't have to worry about my mom eavesdropping.

When I was younger, my mom kept the computer in the living room like she was the Internet Police. Now I have my own computer in my room. She trusts me not to look at anything hardcore (like I'd even want to), and we have parental controls on all our computers anyway.

It's the little things that I sometimes feel guilty about—free music, school reports for sale and all that. It's just so easy to get, and everyone does it. If it's illegal, then it shouldn't be so available. Honestly, anyone with half a brain can find unlimited free stuff online. Like anyone really cares what some girl in Ohio downloads.

I've gotten into chat rooms a lot lately, too. Yeah, I've heard all the freaky stories about kids who meet up with people they've met online. Someone pretends to be a teenager and then turns out to be mass murderer or kidnapper or something. But that wouldn't happen to me—everyone I talk to in chat rooms seems really nice, and I know enough to protect myself.

---

internet in focus

For more info, check out the Internet Link on www.TrueImagesBible.com

The Internet is one of the coolest things going—it's changed our world forever. Keep this in mind as you're clicking away:

»Parental controls only go so far, as you've probably already discovered. Visiting sites you know your parents wouldn't allow falls under the "stupid" rule. "If it's stupid, don't do it." This includes Internet plagiarism—downloading school reports and submitting them as your own work (hello, lying+stealing).

»How about those "free" music downloads? Some artists release their music online free of charge. Other music gets ripped off, which cuts into artists' profits. Regardless of whether or not you decide they can afford it, that's still stealing (see Ephesians 4:28, page 1545).

»Practice safe surfing! Never give personal information to someone you meet in a chatroom, including your last name, phone number or other private information.

For more on this topic, see the index on page 1656.

---

[28]In this same way, husbands ought to love their wives as their own bodies. He who loves his wife loves himself. [29]After all, no one ever hated his own body, but he feeds and cares for it, just as Christ does the church— [30]for we are members of his body. [31]"For this reason a man will leave his father and mother and be united to his wife, and the two will become one flesh." [a] [32]This is a profound mystery—but I am talking about Christ and the church. [33]However, each one of you also must love his wife as he loves himself, and the wife must respect her husband.

a 31 Gen. 2:24

Children and Parents

6 Children, obey your parents in the Lord, for this is right. ²"Honor your father and mother"—which is the first commandment with a promise— ³"that it may go well with you and that you may enjoy long life on the earth."ᵃ

⁴Fathers, do not exasperate your children; instead, bring them up in the training and instruction of the Lord.

Slaves and Masters

⁵Slaves, obey your earthly masters with respect and fear, and with sincerity of heart, just as you would obey Christ. ⁶Obey them not only to win their favor when their eye is on you, but like slaves of Christ, doing the will of God from your heart. ⁷Serve wholeheartedly, as if you were serving the Lord, not men, ⁸because you know that the Lord will reward everyone for whatever good he does, whether he is slave or free.

⁹And masters, treat your slaves in the same way. Do not threaten them, since you know that he who is both their Master and yours is in heaven, and there is no favoritism with him.

The Armor of God

¹⁰Finally, be strong in the Lord and in his mighty power. ¹¹Put on the full armor of God so that you can take your stand against the devil's schemes. ¹²For our struggle is not against flesh and blood, but against the rulers, against the authorities, against the powers of this dark world and against the spiritual forces of evil in the heavenly realms. ¹³Therefore put on the full armor of God, so that when the day of evil comes, you may be able to stand your ground, and after you have done everything, to stand. ¹⁴Stand firm then, with the belt of truth buckled around your waist, with the breastplate of righteousness in place, ¹⁵and with your feet fitted with the readiness that comes from the gospel of peace. ¹⁶In addition to all this, take up the shield of faith, with which you can extinguish all the flaming arrows of the evil one. ¹⁷Take the helmet of salvation and the sword of the Spirit, which is the word of God. ¹⁸And pray in the Spirit on all occasions with all kinds of prayers and requests. With this in mind, be alert and always keep on praying for all the saints.

truth or dare

The battle for your heart is fierce. God's taken ground in your life, and the cost was Christ's blood. Don't retreat. Put on your armor and stand your ground, soldier.

6:13

¹⁹Pray also for me, that whenever I open my mouth, words may be given me so that I will fearlessly make known the mystery of the gospel, ²⁰for which I am an ambassador in chains. Pray that I may declare it fearlessly, as I should.

Final Greetings

²¹Tychicus, the dear brother and faithful servant in the Lord, will tell you everything, so that you also may know how I am and what I am doing. ²²I am sending him to you for this very purpose, that you may know how we are, and that he may encourage you.

²³Peace to the brothers, and love with faith from God the Father and the Lord Jesus Christ. ²⁴Grace to all who love our Lord Jesus Christ with an undying love.

ᵃ 3 Deut. 5:16

at a glance ⌄

author:	The apostle Paul.
date:	About A.D. 61.
setting:	Paul had started the church at Philippi, the first church on the continent of Europe, during his second missionary journey. He wrote this letter from prison in Rome.
verse to remember:	Rejoice in the Lord always. I will say it again: Rejoice (4:4)!
theme to consider:	Joy has nothing to do with our circumstances. According to Paul, if you belong to Christ, then you can have joy in suffering, joy in serving, joy in believing and joy in giving. That's reason to rejoice!

unchanging truth

Raise your hand if you thought life would get easier once you became a Christian. Now, raise your hand if you know that's not true. The truth is, bad things happen to everyone—and Christians are no exception. One thing is different for Christians, however, when it comes to tough times. It's called *attitude*.

The same storms in life come to Christians and non-Christians—how we handle those trials is what makes us different. We can choose to be joyful despite the pain (see 4:12–13), or we can choose to let our circumstances get the best of us. Notice that we're not talking about feeling happy. That comes and goes. We may be up one day and down the next. Yet our joy—what Jesus gives deep down inside of us—is unmovable. Unshakeable.

Paul knew that what happens to us in life is not what determines our outcome. We determine our outcome by having the right attitude *despite* what happens to us. For Paul, that meant writing letters of encouragement to the church in Philippi despite being imprisoned in Rome. He chose to remain joyful. Our parents may get divorced, a teacher may hate us without reason and a guy may break our hearts more than once. However, that doesn't have to mean life is over for us. No way. No one and nothing can take away our joy without our consent. Just look at Paul's letter to the Philippians—joy is all over the place.

life lessons

1 Joy is a choice we make despite our less-than-happy circumstances (1:12–30).

2 If you're going through a tough time right now, Jesus knows how you feel, so follow his lead (2:1–18).

3 Under the circumstances, we may not have a reason for joy. But what is a Christian doing "under" the circumstances anyway, when we can be on top of our troubles (4:4–13)?

1

Paul and Timothy, servants of Christ Jesus,

To all the saints in Christ Jesus at Philippi, together with the overseers[a] and deacons:

[2]Grace and peace to you from God our Father and the Lord Jesus Christ.

Thanksgiving and Prayer

[3]I thank my God every time I remember you. [4]In all my prayers for all of you, I always pray with joy [5]because of your partnership in the gospel from the first day until now, [6]being confident of this, that he who began a good work in you will carry it on to completion until the day of Christ Jesus.

[7]It is right for me to feel this way about all of you, since I have you in my heart; for whether I am in chains or defending and confirming the gospel, all of you share in God's grace with me. [8]God can testify how I long for all of you with the affection of Christ Jesus.

[9]And this is my prayer: that your love may abound more and more in knowledge and depth of insight, [10]so that you may be able to discern what is best and may be pure and blameless until the day of Christ, [11]filled with the fruit of righteousness that comes through Jesus Christ—to the glory and praise of God.

Paul's Chains Advance the Gospel

[12]Now I want you to know, brothers, that what has happened to me has really served to advance the gospel. [13]As a result, it has become clear throughout the whole palace guard[b] and to everyone else that I am in chains for Christ. [14]Because of my chains, most of the brothers in the Lord have been encouraged to speak the word of God more courageously and fearlessly.

[15]It is true that some preach Christ out of envy and rivalry, but others out of goodwill. [16]The latter do so in love, knowing that I am put here for the defense of the gospel. [17]The former preach Christ out of selfish ambition, not sincerely, supposing that they can stir up trouble for me while I am in chains.[c] [18]But what does it matter? The important thing is that in every way, whether from false motives or true, Christ is preached. And because of this I rejoice.

Yes, and I will continue to rejoice, [19]for I know that through your prayers and the help given by the Spirit of Jesus Christ, what has happened to me will turn out for my deliverance.[d] [20]I eagerly expect and hope that I will in no way be ashamed, but will have sufficient courage so that now as always Christ will be exalted in my body, whether by life or by death. [21]For to me, to live is Christ and to die is gain. [22]If I am to go on living in the body, this will mean fruitful labor for me. Yet what shall I choose? I do not know! [23]I am torn between the two: I desire to depart and be with Christ, which is better by far; [24]but it is more necessary for you that I remain in the body. [25]Convinced of this, I know that I will remain, and I will continue with all of you for your progress and joy in the faith, [26]so that through my being with you again your joy in Christ Jesus will overflow on account of me.

[27]Whatever happens, conduct yourselves in a manner worthy of the gospel of Christ. Then, whether I come and see you or only hear about you in my absence, I will know that you stand firm in one spirit, contending as one man for the faith of the gospel [28]without being frightened in any way by those who oppose you. This is a sign to them that they will be destroyed, but that you will be saved—and that by God. [29]For it has been granted to you on behalf of Christ not only to believe on him, but also to suffer for him, [30]since you are going through the same struggle you saw I had, and now hear that I still have.

truth or dare

What a revolutionary perspective! If you set your eyes on eternity and realize that life is short, then you're prepared to accept whatever comes. Live or die, you win.

1:21

---

[a] 1 Traditionally *bishops*   [b] 13 Or *whole palace*   [c] 16,17 Some late manuscripts have verses 16 and 17 in reverse order.   [d] 19 Or *salvation*

Imitating Christ's Humility

2 If you have any encouragement from being united with Christ, if any comfort from his love, if any fellowship with the Spirit, if any tenderness and compassion, [2]then make my joy complete by being like-minded, having the same love, being one in spirit and purpose. [3]Do nothing out of selfish ambition or vain conceit, but in humility consider others better than yourselves. [4]Each of you should look not only to your own interests, but also to the interests of others.

[5]Your attitude should be the same as that of Christ Jesus:

[6]Who, being in very nature[a] God,
  did not consider equality with God something to be grasped,
[7]but made himself nothing,
  taking the very nature[b] of a servant,
  being made in human likeness.

[8]And being found in appearance
    as a man,
  he humbled himself
  and became obedient to death—
    even death on a cross!
[9]Therefore God exalted him to the
    highest place
  and gave him the name that
    is above every name,
[10]that at the name of Jesus every
    knee should bow,
  in heaven and on earth and
    under the earth,
[11]and every tongue confess that
    Jesus Christ is Lord,
  to the glory of God the Father.

Shining as Stars

[12]Therefore, my dear friends, as you have always obeyed—not only in my presence, but now much more in my absence—

---

love notes

1:6

My dear child,

Don't despair when you struggle with your faults—whether it's a short temper or trouble staying organized. Know this: I am at work within you, and you are my good work. I will complete what I have started in you.

—Your heavenly Father

What qualities would you like to see God develop in your life?

_____

_____

_____

_____

_____

---

truth or dare

"Work out your salvation"?! That doesn't mean you *earn* salvation, but it does mean that you take your faith seriously and invest your best efforts into your relationship with God.

2:12-13

---

[a] 6 Or *in the form of*   [b] 7 Or *the form*

continue to work out your salvation with fear and trembling, ¹³for it is God who works in you to will and to act according to his good purpose.

¹⁴Do everything without complaining or arguing, ¹⁵so that you may become blameless and pure, children of God without fault in a crooked and depraved generation, in which you shine like stars in the universe ¹⁶as you hold out*ᵃ* the word of life—in order that I may boast on the day of Christ that I did not run or labor for nothing. ¹⁷But even if I am being poured out like a drink offering on the sacrifice and service coming from your faith, I am glad and rejoice with all of you. ¹⁸So you too should be glad and rejoice with me.

Timothy and Epaphroditus

¹⁹I hope in the Lord Jesus to send Timothy to you soon, that I also may be cheered when I receive news about you. ²⁰I have no one else like him, who takes a genuine interest in your welfare. ²¹For everyone looks out for his own interests, not those of Jesus Christ. ²²But you know that Timothy has proved himself, because as a son with his father he has served with me in the work of the gospel. ²³I hope, therefore, to send him as soon as I see how things go with me. ²⁴And I am confident in the Lord that I myself will come soon.

²⁵But I think it is necessary to send back to you Epaphroditus, my brother, fellow worker and fellow soldier, who is also your messenger, whom you sent to take care of my needs. ²⁶For he longs for all of you and is distressed because you heard he was ill. ²⁷Indeed he was ill, and almost died. But God had mercy on him, and not on him only but also on me, to spare me sorrow upon sorrow. ²⁸Therefore I am all the more eager to send him, so that when you see him again you may be glad and I may have less anxiety. ²⁹Welcome him in the Lord with great joy, and honor men like him, ³⁰because he almost died for the work of Christ, risking his life to make up for the help you could not give me.

No Confidence in the Flesh

3 Finally, my brothers, rejoice in the Lord! It is no trouble for me to write the same things to you again, and it is a safeguard for you. ²Watch out for those dogs, those men who do evil, those mutilators of the flesh. ³For it is we who are the circumcision, we who worship by the Spirit of God, who glory in Christ Jesus, and who put no confidence in the flesh— ⁴though I myself have reasons for such confidence.

If anyone else thinks he has reasons to put confidence in the flesh, I have more: ⁵circumcised on the eighth day, of the people of Israel, of the tribe of Benjamin, a Hebrew of Hebrews; in regard to the law, a Pharisee; ⁶as for zeal, persecuting the church; as for legalistic righteousness, faultless.

⁷But whatever was to my profit I now consider loss for the sake of Christ. ⁸What is more, I consider everything a loss compared to the surpassing greatness of knowing Christ Jesus my Lord, for whose sake I have lost all things. I consider them rubbish, that I may gain Christ ⁹and be found in him, not having a righteousness of my own that comes from the law, but that which is through faith in Christ—the righteousness that comes from God and is by faith. ¹⁰I want to know Christ and the power of his resurrection and the fellowship of sharing in his sufferings, becoming like him in his death, ¹¹and so, somehow, to attain to the resurrection from the dead.

genuine character » 2:14-15

Maybe you know someone whose chief purpose in life is to complain. "Whine" is her official language. Nothing is ever right; nothing is good enough for her. Basically, people like that are not fun to hang out with. God says there is a better way—to do everything without grumbling. (Did you catch that? *Everything.*) Why is that so important? Because when our lives are characterized by a peace-loving, positive and patient outlook, we stand out from the rest of the crowd. Our lives shine like stars! How are you shining for God today?

ᵃ 16 Or *hold on to*

Pressing on Toward the Goal

¹²Not that I have already obtained all this, or have already been made perfect, but I press on to take hold of that for which Christ Jesus took hold of me. ¹³Brothers, I do not consider myself yet to have taken hold of it. But one thing I do: Forgetting what is behind and straining toward what is ahead, ¹⁴I press on toward the goal to win the prize for which God has called me heavenward in Christ Jesus.

¹⁵All of us who are mature should take such a view of things. And if on some point you think differently, that too God will make clear to you. ¹⁶Only let us live up to what we have already attained.

¹⁷Join with others in following my example, brothers, and take note of those who live according to the pattern we gave you. ¹⁸For, as I have often told you before and now say again even with tears, many live as enemies of the cross of Christ. ¹⁹Their destiny is destruction, their god is their stomach, and their glory is in their shame. Their mind is on earthly things. ²⁰But our citizenship is in heaven. And we eagerly await a Savior from there, the Lord Jesus Christ, ²¹who, by the power that enables him to bring everything under his control, will transform our lowly bodies so that they will be like his glorious body.

4 Therefore, my brothers, you whom I love and long for, my joy and crown, that is how you should stand firm in the Lord, dear friends!

Exhortations

²I plead with Euodia and I plead with Syntyche to agree with each other in the Lord. ³Yes, and I ask you, loyal yokefellow, *a* help these women who have contended at my side in the cause of the gospel, along with Clement and the rest of my fellow workers, whose names are in the book of life.

⁴Rejoice in the Lord always. I will say it again: Rejoice! ⁵Let your gentleness be evident to all. The Lord is near. ⁶Do not be anxious about anything, but in everything, by prayer and petition, with thanksgiving, present your requests to God. ⁷And the peace of God, which transcends all understanding, will guard your hearts and your minds in Christ Jesus.

⁸Finally, brothers, whatever is true, whatever is noble, whatever is right, whatever is pure, whatever is lovely, whatever is admirable—if anything is excellent or praiseworthy—think about such things. ⁹Whatever you have learned or received or heard from me, or seen in me—put it into practice. And the God of peace will be with you.

Thanks for Their Gifts

¹⁰I rejoice greatly in the Lord that at last you have renewed your concern for me. Indeed, you have been concerned, but you had no opportunity to show it. ¹¹I am not saying this because I am in need, for I have learned to be content whatever the circumstances. ¹²I know what it is to be in need, and I know what it is to have plenty. I have learned the secret of being content in any and every situation, whether well fed or hungry, whether living in plenty or in want. ¹³I can do everything through him who gives me strength.

¹⁴Yet it was good of you to share in my

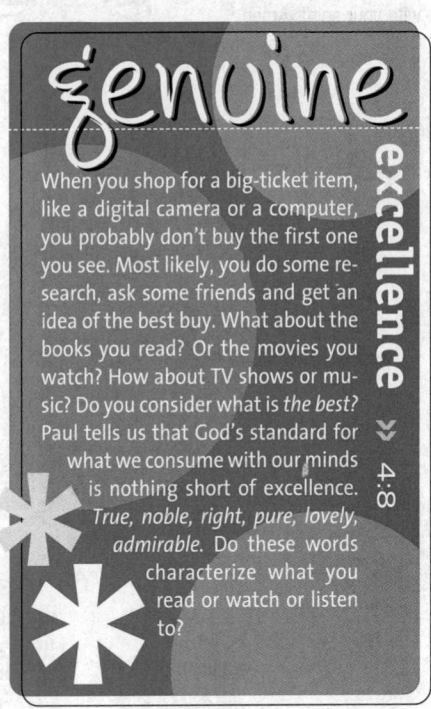

genuine excellence

When you shop for a big-ticket item, like a digital camera or a computer, you probably don't buy the first one you see. Most likely, you do some research, ask some friends and get an idea of the best buy. What about the books you read? Or the movies you watch? How about TV shows or music? Do you consider what is *the best?* Paul tells us that God's standard for what we consume with our minds is nothing short of excellence. *True, noble, right, pure, lovely, admirable.* Do these words characterize what you read or watch or listen to?

» 4:8

---

a 3 Or loyal *Syzygus*

troubles. ¹⁵Moreover, as you Philippians know, in the early days of your acquaintance with the gospel, when I set out from Macedonia, not one church shared with me in the matter of giving and receiving, except you only; ¹⁶for even when I was in Thessalonica, you sent me aid again and again when I was in need. ¹⁷Not that I am looking for a gift, but I am looking for what may be credited to your account. ¹⁸I have received full payment and even more; I am amply supplied, now that I have received from Epaphroditus the gifts you sent. They are a fragrant offering, an acceptable sacrifice, pleasing to God. ¹⁹And my God will meet all your needs according to his glorious riches in Christ Jesus.

²⁰To our God and Father be glory for ever and ever. Amen.

Final Greetings

²¹Greet all the saints in Christ Jesus. The brothers who are with me send greetings. ²²All the saints send you greetings, especially those who belong to Caesar's household.

²³The grace of the Lord Jesus Christ be with your spirit. Amen.ᵃ

genuine

contentment » 4:10-13

If only I had straight hair . . . if only I were ten pounds thinner . . . if only that guy in English class would notice me. If only. Sometimes our lives are ruled by the "if onlys" and the "what ifs" and the "I wishes." Paul taught that true contentment doesn't come from our circumstances. Rather, it is found in Jesus—knowing him, trusting him and depending on his power for each day. When you focus on Jesus' priorities and what he wants you to do rather than on what you wish you had, you will find genuine contentment.

ᵃ 23 Some manuscripts do not have *Amen.*

author:	The apostle Paul.
date:	About A.D. 60.
setting:	Although Paul had never been to Colosse, a city in Asia Minor (modern-day Turkey), he had heard from prison in Rome that false teachers were at work in the church.
verse to remember:	Since, then, you have been raised with Christ, set your hearts on things above, where Christ is seated at the right hand of God. Set your minds on things above, not on earthly things (3:1–2).
theme to consider:	We have everything we could possibly need in Christ.

unchanging truth

Getting ready for school in the morning is a chore. Get up. Iron a shirt (or maybe not) and get dressed. Wash your hair. Dry it. Shovel down some breakfast. Grab your homework, backpack, house key and oh yeah, don't forget your lunch. It's a wonder you manage to get to school on time at all with all you need to do to get ready to go.

The good thing is that when it comes to being ready in life, Jesus is all you need. Forget having to iron out your issues. Never mind your "dirty" laundry. You don't need a backpack full of all your good intentions and failed promises. Come as you are and leave that baggage all behind. Jesus is all you need to live a successful Christian life—and he doesn't mind if you have bed-head. He alone can get you ready for what he has called you to do. He is your source, your power and your strength for living.

Paul wrote this letter to the church at Colosse because they'd forgotten that Christ was their essential connection. While it may be tempting to start relying on our own power to live the Christian life, it's not very smart. In fact, it's downright dumb. Paul warned the Colossians not to fall into that trap. Staying connected to Jesus is the only way to live a life that is pleasing to God. Period. He alone can empower us to live day to day, and he alone can get us ready to meet the Father one day.

life lessons

1 Worried you don't have what it takes to live for God? You're right. You don't have it. But Jesus does (1:15–23)!

2 Want to know what Christian living looks like? Christ provides the blueprint—and the power (3:1–17).

3 Stay connected to Jesus throughout your day by constantly communicating with him in prayer (4:2–4).

⌃

1

Paul, an apostle of Christ Jesus by the will of God, and Timothy our brother,

²To the holy and faithful *ᵃ* brothers in Christ at Colosse:

Grace and peace to you from God our Father. *ᵇ*

Thanksgiving and Prayer

³We always thank God, the Father of our Lord Jesus Christ, when we pray for you, ⁴because we have heard of your faith in Christ Jesus and of the love you have for all the saints— ⁵the faith and love that spring from the hope that is stored up for you in heaven and that you have already heard about in the word of truth, the gospel ⁶that has come to you. All over the world this gospel is bearing fruit and growing, just as it has been doing among you since the day you heard it and understood God's grace in all its truth. ⁷You learned it from Epaphras, our dear fellow servant, who is a faithful minister of Christ on our *ᶜ* behalf, ⁸and who also told us of your love in the Spirit.

⁹For this reason, since the day we heard about you, we have not stopped praying for you and asking God to fill you with the knowledge of his will through all spiritual wisdom and understanding. ¹⁰And we pray this in order that you may live a life worthy of the Lord and may please him in every way: bearing fruit in every good work, growing in the knowledge of God, ¹¹being strengthened with all power according to his glorious might so that you may have great endurance and patience, and joyfully ¹²giving thanks to the Father, who has qualified you *ᵈ* to share in the inheritance of the saints in the kingdom of light. ¹³For he has rescued us from the dominion of darkness and brought us into the kingdom of the Son he loves, ¹⁴in whom we have redemption, *ᵉ* the forgiveness of sins.

The Supremacy of Christ

¹⁵He is the image of the invisible God, the firstborn over all creation. ¹⁶For by him all things were created: things in heaven and on earth, visible and invisible, whether thrones or powers or rulers or authorities; all things were created by him and for him. ¹⁷He is before all things, and in him all things hold together. ¹⁸And he is the head of the body, the church; he is the beginning and the firstborn from among the dead, so that in everything he might have the supremacy. ¹⁹For God was pleased to have all his fullness dwell in him, ²⁰and through him to reconcile to himself all things, whether things on earth or things in heaven, by making peace through his blood, shed on the cross.

²¹Once you were alienated from God and were enemies in your minds because of *ᶠ* your evil behavior. ²²But now he has reconciled you by Christ's physical body through death to present you holy in his sight, without blemish and free from accusation— ²³if you continue in your faith, established and firm, not moved from the hope held out in the gospel. This is the gospel that you heard and that has been proclaimed to every creature under heaven, and of which I, Paul, have become a servant.

truth or dare

If mirrors didn't exist, would you know what your face looked like? Even though God is invisible, Jesus reflects/reveals God to us. Know what God's like by looking at Jesus.

1:15

Paul's Labor for the Church

²⁴Now I rejoice in what was suffered for you, and I fill up in my flesh what is still lacking in regard to Christ's afflictions, for the sake of his body, which is the church. ²⁵I have become its servant by the commission God gave me to present to you the word of God in its fullness— ²⁶the mystery that has been kept hidden for ages and generations, but is now disclosed to the saints. ²⁷To them God has chosen to make known among the Gentiles the glorious riches of this mystery, which is Christ in you, the hope of glory.

²⁸We proclaim him, admonishing and teaching everyone with all wisdom, so that we may pre-

---

ᵃ 2 Or *believing*   *ᵇ* 2 Some manuscripts *Father and the Lord Jesus Christ*   *ᶜ* 7 Some manuscripts *your*   *ᵈ* 12 Some manuscripts *us*   *ᵉ* 14 A few late manuscripts *redemption through his blood*   *ᶠ* 21 Or *minds, as shown by*

Unspoken

I'm shaking like a leaf. Why should I be afraid to tell my own mother? Afraid to talk about the sexual abuse I suffered five years ago. Afraid to tell her that my skin crawls whenever a guy touches me. Afraid to even think about what he used to do to me. I'm 16 years old. I can't keep this nightmare to myself anymore.

It took every ounce of courage I had to tell my sister, Elise. I was amazed when she said, "Why didn't you tell me before? He did it to me, too . . ." Her voice trailed off, and we stared at each other in disbelief.

Why *didn't* I say anything before? Why have I kept this awful secret to myself for so many years? Would Mom even believe me? What if she thought it was the power of suggestion, with so many stories of abuse in the news? What if she didn't believe me and sided with Uncle Tim? What if she thought it was my fault? She thought Tim walked on water. He was her little brother, and he'd been the "man in our lives" since Dad left us ten years ago. Uncle Tim came to our house for dinner every Thursday. He stayed with us when Mom went out of town. He came to every game, every concert, every birthday party. In fact, he's coming over any minute now.

I can't put it off any longer. I have to tell her.

For more on sexual abuse, go to
www.TrueImagesBible.com

sexual abuse in focus

Sexual abuse is devastating, and the pain is magnified by the fact that many girls keep it a secret. Sometimes feelings of fear, shame or misplaced guilt cause victims to remain quiet and not seek help or healing.

If you or someone you know has been sexually abused . . .

»Tell someone *today*. Talk to a parent, a school counselor, a pastor or another trusted Christian adult. Don't wait.

»It's not your fault. Sexual abuse is a sin against you; you are not to blame.

»Keep in mind that sexual abuse is completely against God's plan for sex (see 1 Corinthians 6:13, page 1511 and Hebrews 13:4, page 1599). Sexual abusers will have to answer to God for what they've done (see Galatians 6:7, page 1540).

»God has a plan for healing in your life and wants to set you free from the fear, false shame and bitterness.

For more on this topic, see the index on page 1656.

---

sent everyone perfect in Christ. [29]To this end I labor, struggling with all his energy, which so powerfully works in me.

2 I want you to know how much I am struggling for you and for those at Laodicea, and for all who have not met me personally. [2]My purpose is that they may be encouraged in heart and united in love, so that they may have the full riches of complete understanding, in order that they may know the mystery of God, namely, Christ, [3]in whom are hidden all the treasures of wisdom and knowledge. [4]I tell you this so that no one may deceive you by fine-sounding arguments. [5]For though I am absent from you in body, I am present with you in spirit and delight to see how orderly you are and how firm your faith in Christ is.

Freedom From Human Regulations Through Life With Christ

[6]So then, just as you received Christ Jesus as Lord, continue to live in him, [7]rooted and built up in him, strengthened in the faith as you were taught, and overflowing with thankfulness.

[8]See to it that no one takes you captive through hollow and deceptive philosophy, which depends on human tradition and the basic principles of this world rather than on Christ.

[9]For in Christ all the fullness of the Deity lives in bodily form, [10]and you have been given fullness in Christ, who is the head over every power and authority. [11]In him you were also circumcised, in the putting off of the sinful nature,[a] not with a circumcision done by the hands of men but with the circumcision done by Christ, [12]having been buried with him in baptism and raised with him through your faith in the power of God, who raised him from the dead.

[13]When you were dead in your sins and in the uncircumcision of your sinful nature,[b] God made you[c] alive with Christ. He forgave us all our sins, [14]having canceled the written code, with its regulations, that was against us and that stood opposed to us; he took it away, nailing it to the cross. [15]And having disarmed the powers and authorities, he made a public spectacle of them, triumphing over them by the cross.[d]

[16]Therefore do not let anyone judge you by what you eat or drink, or with regard to a religious festival, a New Moon celebration or a Sabbath day. [17]These are a shadow of the things that were to come; the reality, however, is found in Christ. [18]Do not let anyone who delights in false humility and the worship of angels disqualify you for the prize. Such a person goes into great detail about what he has seen, and his unspiritual mind puffs him up with idle notions. [19]He has lost connection with the Head, from whom the whole body, supported and held together by its ligaments and sinews, grows as God causes it to grow.

[20]Since you died with Christ to the basic principles of this world, why, as though you still belonged to it, do you submit to its rules: [21]"Do not handle! Do not taste! Do not touch!"? [22]These are all destined to perish with use, because they are based on human commands and teachings. [23]Such regulations indeed have an appearance of wisdom, with their self-imposed worship, their false humility and their harsh treatment of the body, but they lack any value in restraining sensual indulgence.

Rules for Holy Living

3 Since, then, you have been raised with Christ, set your hearts on things above, where Christ is seated at the right hand of God. [2]Set your minds on things above, not on earthly things. [3]For you died, and your life is now hidden with Christ in God. [4]When Christ, who is your[e] life, appears, then you also will appear with him in glory.

[5]Put to death, therefore, whatever belongs to your earthly nature: sexual immorality, impurity, lust, evil desires and greed, which is idolatry. [6]Because of these, the wrath of God is coming.[f] [7]You used to walk in these ways, in the life you once lived. [8]But now you must rid yourselves of all such things as these: anger, rage, malice, slander, and filthy language from your lips. [9]Do not lie to each other, since you have taken off your old self with its practices [10]and have put on the new self, which is being renewed in knowledge in the image of its Creator. [11]Here there is no Greek or Jew, circumcised or uncircumcised, barbarian, Scythian, slave or free, but Christ is all, and is in all.

[12]Therefore, as God's chosen people, holy and dearly loved, clothe yourselves with compassion, kindness, humility, gentleness and patience. [13]Bear with each other and forgive whatever grievances you may have against one another. Forgive as the Lord forgave you. [14]And over all these virtues put on love, which binds them all together in perfect unity.

[15]Let the peace of Christ rule in your hearts, since as members of one body you were called to peace. And be thankful. [16]Let the word of Christ dwell in you richly as you teach and admonish one another with all wisdom, and as you sing psalms, hymns and spiritual songs with gratitude in your hearts to God. [17]And whatever you do, whether in word or deed, do it all in the name of the Lord Jesus, giving thanks to God the Father through him.

Rules for Christian Households

[18]Wives, submit to your husbands, as is fitting in the Lord.

[19]Husbands, love your wives and do not be harsh with them.

---

a 11 Or *the flesh*   *b 13* Or *your flesh*   *c 13* Some manuscripts *us*   *d 15* Or *them in him*   *e 4* Some manuscripts *our*   *f 6* Some early manuscripts *coming on those who are disobedient*

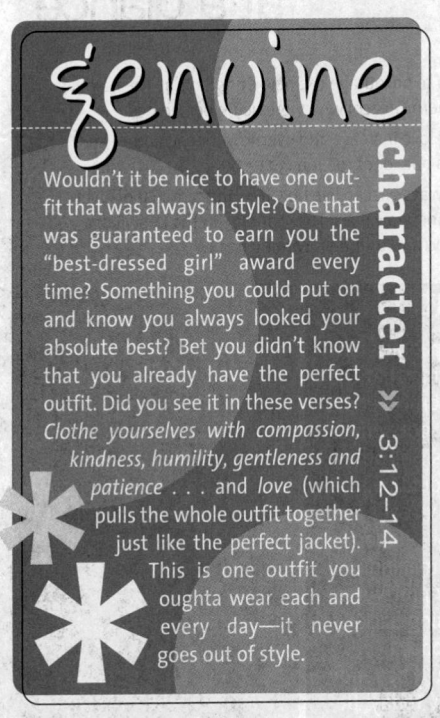

character » 3:12-14

genuine

Wouldn't it be nice to have one outfit that was always in style? One that was guaranteed to earn you the "best-dressed girl" award every time? Something you could put on and know you always looked your absolute best? Bet you didn't know that you already have the perfect outfit. Did you see it in these verses? *Clothe yourselves with compassion, kindness, humility, gentleness and patience . . . and love* (which pulls the whole outfit together just like the perfect jacket). This is one outfit you oughta wear each and every day—it never goes out of style.

²⁰Children, obey your parents in everything, for this pleases the Lord. ²¹Fathers, do not embitter your children, or they will become discouraged. ²²Slaves, obey your earthly masters in everything; and do it, not only when their eye is on you and to win their favor, but with sincerity of heart and reverence for the Lord. ²³Whatever you do, work at it with all your heart, as working for the Lord, not for men, ²⁴since you know that you will receive an inheritance from the Lord as a reward. It is the Lord Christ you are serving. ²⁵Anyone who does wrong will be repaid for his wrong, and there is no favoritism.

4 Masters, provide your slaves with what is right and fair, because you know that you also have a Master in heaven.

Further Instructions

²Devote yourselves to prayer, being watchful and thankful. ³And pray for us, too, that God may open a door for our message, so that we may proclaim the mystery of Christ, for which I am in chains. ⁴Pray that I may proclaim it clearly, as I should. ⁵Be wise in the way you act toward outsiders; make the most of every opportunity. ⁶Let your conversation be always full of grace, seasoned with salt, so that you may know how to answer everyone.

Final Greetings

⁷Tychicus will tell you all the news about me. He is a dear brother, a faithful minister and fellow servant in the Lord. ⁸I am sending him to you for the express purpose that you may know about our*a* circumstances and that he may encourage your hearts. ⁹He is coming with Onesimus, our faithful and dear brother, who is one of you. They will tell you everything that is happening here.

¹⁰My fellow prisoner Aristarchus sends you his greetings, as does Mark, the cousin of Barnabas. (You have received instructions about him; if he comes to you, welcome him.) ¹¹Jesus, who is called Justus, also sends greetings. These are the only Jews among my fellow workers for the kingdom of God, and they have proved a comfort to me. ¹²Epaphras, who is one of you and a servant of Christ Jesus, sends greetings. He is always wrestling in prayer for you, that you may stand firm in all the will of God, mature and fully assured. ¹³I vouch for him that he is working hard for you and for those at Laodicea and Hierapolis. ¹⁴Our dear friend Luke, the doctor, and Demas send greetings. ¹⁵Give my greetings to the brothers at Laodicea, and to Nympha and the church in her house.

¹⁶After this letter has been read to you, see that it is also read in the church of the Laodiceans and that you in turn read the letter from Laodicea.

¹⁷Tell Archippus: "See to it that you complete the work you have received in the Lord."

¹⁸I, Paul, write this greeting in my own hand. Remember my chains. Grace be with you.

a 8 Some manuscripts that he may know about your

author: The apostle Paul.

date: About A.D. 51.

setting: Paul wrote from Corinth to encourage the new Christians at Thessalonica (in modern-day northern Greece) who were being persecuted.

verse to remember: May the Lord make your love increase and overflow for each other and for everyone else, just as ours does for you (3:12–13).

theme to consider: Watch for the practical ways we can live holy lives in the midst of a culture that is hostile to Christian values. Take courage in the knowledge that Christ is with us now and that he *is* coming again.

1 thessalonians

unchanging truth

When the year 2000 drew near, people started doing some weird things, thinking that the end of the world was at hand. Some people loaded up on canned food. Others got serious about digging underground shelters. Still others holed away on a hilltop so Jesus would be sure to see them in case he returned New Year's Eve. While some people went through elaborate preparations for the approaching millennium, preparing for Jesus' return is really pretty simple. If you believe that Jesus is coming back tomorrow, just live like he's coming today.

In other words, the only way you'll be ready for him tomorrow is if you're ready today. Being ready for Jesus' return doesn't mean stuffing soup cans and water jugs under your bed. It means living expectantly—keeping your eyes on him every day so that when the last day comes, you'll be ready to go.

Sure, you may not feel like you're ready to leave this life and move on to the next one. It's hard enough to let someone we love leave this life and go on to heaven without thinking how we'll all have to make that same journey one day—unless Jesus comes back before then. The people in Thessalonica could relate to that feeling. However, Paul reminded them that this world is not our home. Ready or not, we'll all leave it behind one day. And knowing what's coming tomorrow makes all the difference in how we choose to live today.

life lessons

1 Living for Jesus today means we're prepared for his return tomorrow (4:1–12).

2 There is more to life than living and dying. The best is yet to come (4:13–18)!

3 Knowing Jesus is returning soon should motivate us to live for God and look out for each other (5:1–24).

1

Paul, Silas[a] and Timothy,

To the church of the Thessalonians in God the Father and the Lord Jesus Christ:

Grace and peace to you.[b]

Thanksgiving for the Thessalonians' Faith

[2]We always thank God for all of you, mentioning you in our prayers. [3]We continually remember before our God and Father your work produced by faith, your labor prompted by love, and your endurance inspired by hope in our Lord Jesus Christ.

[4]For we know, brothers loved by God, that he has chosen you, [5]because our gospel came to you not simply with words, but also with power, with the Holy Spirit and with deep conviction. You know how we lived among you for your sake. [6]You became imitators of us and of the Lord; in spite of severe suffering, you welcomed the message with the joy given by the Holy Spirit. [7]And so you became a model to all the believers in Macedonia and Achaia. [8]The Lord's message rang out from you not only in Macedonia and Achaia—your faith in God has become known everywhere. Therefore we do not need to say anything about it, [9]for they themselves report what kind of reception you gave us. They tell how you turned to God from idols to serve the living and true God, [10]and to wait for his Son from heaven, whom he raised from the dead—Jesus, who rescues us from the coming wrath.

Paul's Ministry in Thessalonica

2

You know, brothers, that our visit to you was not a failure. [2]We had previously suffered and been insulted in Philippi, as you know, but with the help of our God we dared to tell you his gospel in spite of strong opposition. [3]For the appeal we make does not spring from error or impure motives, nor are we trying to trick you. [4]On the contrary, we speak as men approved by God to be entrusted with the gospel. We are not trying to please men but God, who tests our hearts. [5]You know we never used flattery, nor did we put on a mask to cover up greed—God is our witness. [6]We were not looking for praise from men, not from you or anyone else.

As apostles of Christ we could have been a burden to you, [7]but we were gentle among you, like a mother caring for her little children. [8]We loved you so much that we were delighted to share with you not only the gospel of God but our lives as well, because you had become so dear to us. [9]Surely you remember, brothers, our toil and hardship; we worked night and day in order not to be a burden to anyone while we preached the gospel of God to you.

[10]You are witnesses, and so is God, of how holy, righteous and blameless we were among you who believed. [11]For you know that we dealt with each of you as a father deals with his own children, [12]encouraging, comforting and urging you to live lives worthy of God, who calls you into his kingdom and glory.

[13]And we also thank God continually because, when you received the word of God, which you heard from us, you accepted it not as the word of men, but as it actually is, the word of God, which is at work in you who believe. [14]For you, brothers, became imitators of God's churches in Judea, which are in Christ Jesus: You suffered from your own countrymen the same things those churches suffered from the Jews, [15]who killed the Lord Jesus and the prophets and also drove us out. They displease God and are hostile to all men [16]in their effort to keep us from speaking to the Gentiles so that they may be saved. In this way they always heap up their sins to the limit. The wrath of God has come upon them at last.[c]

Paul's Longing to See the Thessalonians

[17]But, brothers, when we were torn away from you for a short time (in person, not in thought), out of our intense longing we made every effort to see you. [18]For we wanted to come to you—certainly I, Paul, did, again and again—but Satan stopped us. [19]For what is our hope, our joy, or the crown in which we will glory in the presence of our Lord Jesus when he comes? Is it not you? [20]Indeed, you are our glory and joy.

---

[a] 1 Greek *Silvanus*, a variant of *Silas*   [b] 1 Some early manuscripts *you from God our Father and the Lord Jesus Christ*   [c] 16 Or *them fully*

3 So when we could stand it no longer, we thought it best to be left by ourselves in Athens. [2]We sent Timothy, who is our brother and God's fellow worker[a] in spreading the gospel of Christ, to strengthen and encourage you in your faith, [3]so that no one would be unsettled by these trials. You know quite well that we were destined for them. [4]In fact, when we were with you, we kept telling you that we would be persecuted. And it turned out that way, as you well know. [5]For this reason, when I could stand it no longer, I sent to find out about your faith. I was afraid that in some way the tempter might have tempted you and our efforts might have been useless.

Timothy's Encouraging Report

[6]But Timothy has just now come to us from you and has brought good news about your faith and love. He has told us that you always have pleasant memories of us and that you long to see us, just as we also long to see you. [7]Therefore, brothers, in all our distress and persecution we were encouraged about you because of your faith. [8]For now we really live, since you are standing firm in the Lord. [9]How can we thank God enough for you in return for all the joy we have in the presence of our God because of you? [10]Night and day we pray most earnestly that we may see you again and supply what is lacking in your faith.

[11]Now may our God and Father himself and our Lord Jesus clear the way for us to come to you. [12]May the Lord make your love increase and overflow for each other and for everyone else, just as ours does for you. [13]May he strengthen your hearts so that you will be blameless and holy in the presence of our God and Father when our Lord Jesus comes with all his holy ones.

Living to Please God

4 Finally, brothers, we instructed you how to live in order to please God, as in fact you are living. Now we ask you and urge you in the Lord Jesus to do this more and more. [2]For you know what instructions we gave you by the authority of the Lord Jesus.

[3]It is God's will that you should be sanctified: that you should avoid sexual immorality; [4]that each of you should learn to control his own body[b] in a way that is holy and honorable, [5]not in passionate lust like the heathen, who do not know God; [6]and that in this matter no one should wrong his brother or take advantage of him. The Lord will punish men for all such sins, as we have already told you and warned you. [7]For God did not call us to be impure, but to live a holy life. [8]Therefore, he who rejects this instruction does not reject man but God, who gives you his Holy Spirit.

[9]Now about brotherly love we do not need to write to you, for you yourselves have been taught by God to love each other. [10]And in fact, you do love all the brothers throughout Macedonia. Yet we urge you, brothers, to do so more and more.

[11]Make it your ambition to lead a quiet life, to mind your own business and to work with your hands, just as we told you, [12]so that your daily life may win the respect of outsiders and so that you will not be dependent on anybody.

genuine love » 3:12

Have you ever seen what happens when you shake a can of soda really, really hard, then open it up fast? The soda sprays out all over the person holding the can and probably even covers the people nearby, too. Did you know God wants you to be like that can? God wants your life to be so full of love that it overflows and spills out onto everyone around you. God has poured his love into you so that you can share it with others. So go ahead—shake it up and spray it out!

---

a 2 Some manuscripts *brother and fellow worker*; other manuscripts *brother and God's servant*   b 4 Or *learn to live with his own wife*; or *learn to acquire a wife*

The Coming of the Lord

[13]Brothers, we do not want you to be ignorant about those who fall asleep, or to grieve like the rest of men, who have no hope. [14]We believe that Jesus died and rose again and so we believe that God will bring with Jesus those who have fallen asleep in him. [15]According to the Lord's own word, we tell you that we who are still alive, who are left till the coming of the Lord, will certainly not precede those who have fallen asleep. [16]For the Lord himself will come down from heaven, with a loud command, with the voice of the archangel and with the trumpet call of God, and the dead in Christ will rise first. [17]After that, we who are still alive and are left will be caught up together with them in the clouds to meet the Lord in the air. And so we will be with the Lord forever. [18]Therefore encourage each other with these words.

5 Now, brothers, about times and dates we do not need to write to you, [2]for you know very well that the day of the Lord will come like a thief in the night. [3]While people are saying, "Peace and safety," destruction will come on them suddenly, as labor pains on a pregnant woman, and they will not escape.

[4]But you, brothers, are not in darkness so that this day should surprise you like a thief. [5]You are all sons of the light and sons of the day. We do not belong to the night or to the darkness. [6]So then, let us not be like others, who are asleep, but let us be alert and self-controlled. [7]For those who sleep, sleep at night, and those who get drunk, get drunk at night. [8]But since we belong to the day, let us be self-controlled, putting on faith and love as a breastplate, and the hope of salvation as a helmet. [9]For God did not appoint us to suffer wrath but to receive salvation through our Lord Jesus Christ. [10]He died for us so that, whether we are awake or asleep, we may live together with him. [11]Therefore encourage one another and build each other up, just as in fact you are doing.

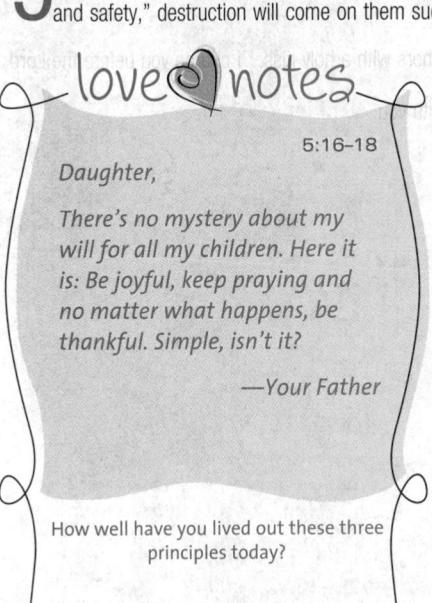

love notes

5:16–18

Daughter,

There's no mystery about my will for all my children. Here it is: Be joyful, keep praying and no matter what happens, be thankful. Simple, isn't it?

—Your Father

How well have you lived out these three principles today?

_____

_____

_____

_____

_____

_____

_____

_____

_____

_____

truth or dare

You shouldn't obsess over unbelievers' opinions of you. Neither should you *try* to be an outcast. A Christian who lives with integrity and consistency will gain others' respect and a voice to share Christ with them.

4:11–12

Final Instructions

¹²Now we ask you, brothers, to respect those who work hard among you, who are over you in the Lord and who admonish you. ¹³Hold them in the highest regard in love because of their work. Live in peace with each other. ¹⁴And we urge you, brothers, warn those who are idle, encourage the timid, help the weak, be patient with everyone. ¹⁵Make sure that nobody pays back wrong for wrong, but always try to be kind to each other and to everyone else.

¹⁶Be joyful always; ¹⁷pray continually; ¹⁸give thanks in all circumstances, for this is God's will for you in Christ Jesus.

¹⁹Do not put out the Spirit's fire; ²⁰do not treat prophecies with contempt. ²¹Test everything. Hold on to the good. ²²Avoid every kind of evil.

²³May God himself, the God of peace, sanctify you through and through. May your whole spirit, soul and body be kept blameless at the coming of our Lord Jesus Christ. ²⁴The one who calls you is faithful and he will do it.

²⁵Brothers, pray for us. ²⁶Greet all the brothers with a holy kiss. ²⁷I charge you before the Lord to have this letter read to all the brothers.

²⁸The grace of our Lord Jesus Christ be with you.

author: The apostle Paul.

date: About A.D. 51 or 52.

setting: Paul wrote this letter from Corinth to correct the Christians in Thessalonica. They thought the second coming of Christ would happen at any moment. As a result, many became lazy and quit working.

verse to remember: Don't let anyone deceive you in any way, for that day will not come until the rebellion occurs and the man of lawlessness is revealed, the man doomed to destruction (2:3).

theme to consider: As we wait for Jesus' return, we should heed Paul's advice to the Thessalonians—live purely, use our time well and work for God's kingdom.

2 thessalonians

unchanging truth

Will I still be alive when Jesus comes back? When exactly is he coming anyway? How can I know for sure he'll keep his promise?

If you've ever wondered these things, you're not alone. A whole church in Thessalonica wondered the same things. It was a confusing time for them as they tried to figure it all out. Think about it—it hadn't been that long since Jesus' resurrection. Jesus had promised to return soon (but keep in mind, God's timing is way different than ours!). So, wouldn't it make sense to think Jesus would return in their lifetime? Well, yes and no. Yes, Jesus was still planning to return. But no, he obviously didn't come back in their lifetime.

So, did they waste their time waiting for him? It depends. If some of them waited around with nothing to do (which some did), then that definitely would have been a waste of time. However, Paul, as their spiritual leader, instructed them to do just the opposite. "Get busy!" he said to his fellow Christians. "There's work to be done!"

No one knows when Jesus will return, but he is returning. The question is not, "When will he return?" but, "What will he find you busy doing?" Napping? Blowing off church? Backstabbing a friend? Sleeping with your boyfriend? It's possible for him to return at any hour. What will he find you doing?

3 life lessons

1. Jesus' return is no accident—we can count on it happening soon (2:1–6).

2. We can't be wishy-washy about his return. He wants us to stand firm for him and his truth (2:13–17).

3. There's no time to waste blowing off your commitment to the Lord. Ask yourself, "Do I want to be doing [this activity] when Jesus comes back?" If not, change your course (3:6–15).

1

Paul, Silas[a] and Timothy,

To the church of the Thessalonians in God our Father and the Lord Jesus Christ:

[2]Grace and peace to you from God the Father and the Lord Jesus Christ.

Thanksgiving and Prayer

[3]We ought always to thank God for you, brothers, and rightly so, because your faith is growing more and more, and the love every one of you has for each other is increasing. [4]Therefore, among God's churches we boast about your perseverance and faith in all the persecutions and trials you are enduring.

[5]All this is evidence that God's judgment is right, and as a result you will be counted worthy of the kingdom of God, for which you are suffering. [6]God is just: He will pay back trouble to those who trouble you [7]and give relief to you who are troubled, and to us as well. This will happen when the Lord Jesus is revealed from heaven in blazing fire with his powerful angels. [8]He will punish those who do not know God and do not obey the gospel of our Lord Jesus. [9]They will be punished with everlasting destruction and shut out from the presence of the Lord and from the majesty of his power [10]on the day he comes to be glorified in his holy people and to be marveled at among all those who have believed. This includes you, because you believed our testimony to you.

[11]With this in mind, we constantly pray for you, that our God may count you worthy of his calling, and that by his power he may fulfill every good purpose of yours and every act prompted by your faith. [12]We pray this so that the name of our Lord Jesus may be glorified in you, and you in him, according to the grace of our God and the Lord Jesus Christ.[b]

The Man of Lawlessness

2

Concerning the coming of our Lord Jesus Christ and our being gathered to him, we ask you, brothers, [2]not to become easily unsettled or alarmed by some prophecy, report or letter supposed to have come from us, saying that the day of the Lord has already come. [3]Don't let anyone deceive you in any way, for that day will not come until the rebellion occurs and the man of lawlessness[c] is revealed, the man doomed to destruction. [4]He will oppose and will exalt himself over everything that is called God or is worshiped, so that he sets himself up in God's temple, proclaiming himself to be God.

[5]Don't you remember that when I was with you I used to tell you these things? [6]And now you know what is holding him back, so that he may be revealed at the proper time. [7]For the secret power of lawlessness is already at work; but the one who now holds it back will continue to do so till he is taken out of the way. [8]And then the lawless one will be revealed, whom the Lord Jesus will overthrow with the breath of his mouth and destroy by the splendor of his coming. [9]The coming of the lawless one will be in accordance with the work of Satan displayed in all kinds of counterfeit miracles, signs and wonders, [10]and in every sort of evil that deceives those who are perishing. They perish because they refused to love the truth and so be saved. [11]For this reason God sends them a powerful delusion so that they will believe the lie [12]and so that all will be condemned who have not believed the truth but have delighted in wickedness.

truth or dare

You can bet there'll *always* be "end of the world" hype. Knowing your facts helps you spot the phonies and prepare for the real thing.

2:1–4

Stand Firm

[13]But we ought always to thank God for you, brothers loved by the Lord, because from the beginning God chose you[d] to be saved through the sanctifying work of the Spirit and through belief in the truth. [14]He called you to this through our gospel, that you might share in the glory of our Lord

a 1 Greek *Silvanus,* a variant of *Silas*   *b 12* Or *God and Lord, Jesus Christ*   *c 3* Some manuscripts *sin*   *d 13* Some manuscripts *because God chose you as his firstfruits*

genuine encouragement >> 2:16-17

Are you feelin' down? Discouraged about life? Wondering if maybe you'll never really amount to much of anything, never really make a difference? Wondering if doing the right thing is worth all the effort? When you're feeling discouraged, there are lots of ways you can search for encouragement: seeking out friends, distracting yourself with music or movies, losing yourself in sports or school or work. But those things can't compare with what you'll find in God. He's the source of "eternal encouragement and good hope." When you're having a low day, look to him for new strength.

Jesus Christ. [15]So then, brothers, stand firm and hold to the teachings[a] we passed on to you, whether by word of mouth or by letter.

[16]May our Lord Jesus Christ himself and God our Father, who loved us and by his grace gave us eternal encouragement and good hope, [17]encourage your hearts and strengthen you in every good deed and word.

Request for Prayer

3 Finally, brothers, pray for us that the message of the Lord may spread rapidly and be honored, just as it was with you. [2]And pray that we may be delivered from wicked and evil men, for not everyone has faith. [3]But the Lord is faithful, and he will strengthen and protect you from the evil one. [4]We have confidence in the Lord that you are doing and will continue to do the things we command. [5]May the Lord direct your hearts into God's love and Christ's perseverance.

Warning Against Idleness

[6]In the name of the Lord Jesus Christ, we command you, brothers, to keep away from every brother who is idle and does not live according to the teaching[b] you received from us. [7]For you yourselves know how you ought to follow our example. We were not idle when we were with you, [8]nor did we eat anyone's food without paying for it. On the contrary, we worked night and day, laboring and toiling so that we would not be a burden to any of you. [9]We did this, not because we do not have the right to such help, but in order to make ourselves a model for you to follow. [10]For even when we were with you, we gave you this rule: "If a man will not work, he shall not eat."

[11]We hear that some among you are idle. They are not busy; they are busybodies. [12]Such people we command and urge in the Lord Jesus Christ to settle down and earn the bread they eat. [13]And as for you, brothers, never tire of doing what is right.

[14]If anyone does not obey our instruction in this letter, take special note of him. Do not associate with him, in order that he may feel ashamed. [15]Yet do not regard him as an enemy, but warn him as a brother.

Final Greetings

[16]Now may the Lord of peace himself give you peace at all times and in every way. The Lord be with all of you.

[17]I, Paul, write this greeting in my own hand, which is the distinguishing mark in all my letters. This is how I write.

[18]The grace of our Lord Jesus Christ be with you all.

a 15 Or traditions   b 6 Or tradition

at a glance

author: The apostle Paul.

date: About A.D. 64, probably between Paul's first and second imprisonments in Rome.

setting: Paul had previously directed Timothy to lead the church in Ephesus; now he writes with advice on how to manage the church.

verse to remember: Don't let anyone look down on you because you are young, but set an example for the believers in speech, in life, in love, in faith and in purity (4:12).

theme to consider: Ever feel you are too young to serve? Then you will want to carefully read Paul's advice to his young friend, Timothy.

1 timothy

unchanging truth

Guess who was behind some of the most significant revivals the church has ever seen. Stuffy old preachers? Sunday school teachers? Seminary professors? No, no and no. It was young people like you. Some of the most significant players in the revivals that have swept the world have been students who caught a fresh vision of faith.

So where is God moving today? You got it—students. Students are riding the wave of excitement when it comes to worshiping God. Student-led Bible studies are cropping up on campuses everywhere!

All it takes is one person to make a difference. Ask Paul. He realized early on that Timothy was the real deal—a true believer who, in spite of some apparent shyness (see 2 Timothy 1:6–8), was willing to stand up for Christ. Timothy was a young leader who accompanied Paul on some missionary journeys. Paul didn't overlook Timothy because he was young. Who knows? Maybe Paul put Timothy in the game *because* he was young. He had twice the energy and enthusiasm of the older believers.

So, why are you waiting around for God to use the "grown-ups" in your church? Do you think that only professional youth ministers can reach your school for Christ? Check out the book of 1 Timothy and think again.

life lessons

1. It helps to have an older "Paul" to encourage us when we're young in our faith (1:1–2). Sometimes we find them. And sometimes they find us.

2. Listening to advice is crucial—don't shipwreck your faith (1:18–19).

3. God can use anyone at any age for his purposes—as long as she's devoted to him (4:11–16).

1

¹Paul, an apostle of Christ Jesus by the command of God our Savior and of Christ Jesus our hope,

²To Timothy my true son in the faith:

Grace, mercy and peace from God the Father and Christ Jesus our Lord.

Warning Against False Teachers of the Law

³As I urged you when I went into Macedonia, stay there in Ephesus so that you may command certain men not to teach false doctrines any longer ⁴nor to devote themselves to myths and endless genealogies. These promote controversies rather than God's work—which is by faith. ⁵The goal of this command is love, which comes from a pure heart and a good conscience and a sincere faith. ⁶Some have wandered away from these and turned to meaningless talk. ⁷They want to be teachers of the law, but they do not know what they are talking about or what they so confidently affirm.

⁸We know that the law is good if one uses it properly. ⁹We also know that law*ᵃ* is made not for the righteous but for lawbreakers and rebels, the ungodly and sinful, the unholy and irreligious; for those who kill their fathers or mothers, for murderers, ¹⁰for adulterers and perverts, for slave traders and liars and perjurers—and for whatever else is contrary to the sound doctrine ¹¹that conforms to the glorious gospel of the blessed God, which he entrusted to me.

The Lord's Grace to Paul

¹²I thank Christ Jesus our Lord, who has given me strength, that he considered me faithful, appointing me to his service. ¹³Even though I was once a blasphemer and a persecutor and a violent man, I was shown mercy because I acted in ignorance and unbelief. ¹⁴The grace of our Lord was poured out on me abundantly, along with the faith and love that are in Christ Jesus.

¹⁵Here is a trustworthy saying that deserves full acceptance: Christ Jesus came into the world to save sinners—of whom I am the worst. ¹⁶But for that very reason I was shown mercy so that in me, the worst of sinners, Christ Jesus might display his unlimited patience as an example for those who would believe on him and receive eternal life. ¹⁷Now to the King eternal, immortal, invisible, the only God, be honor and glory for ever and ever. Amen.

¹⁸Timothy, my son, I give you this instruction in keeping with the prophecies once made about you, so that by following them you may fight the good fight, ¹⁹holding on to faith and a good conscience. Some have rejected these and so have shipwrecked their faith. ²⁰Among them are Hymenaeus and Alexander, whom I have handed over to Satan to be taught not to blaspheme.

truth or dare

Ever met someone who thought her sin was beyond Jesus' forgiveness? Impossible! Jesus came to save the worst of sinners—those like Paul, the former but forgiven persecutor of Christians.

1:15

Instructions on Worship

2

¹I urge, then, first of all, that requests, prayers, intercession and thanksgiving be made for everyone— ²for kings and all those in authority, that we may live peaceful and quiet lives in all godliness and holiness. ³This is good, and pleases God our Savior, ⁴who wants all men to be saved and to come to a knowledge of the truth. ⁵For there is one God and one mediator between God and men, the man Christ Jesus, ⁶who gave himself as a ransom for all men—the testimony given in its proper time. ⁷And for this purpose I was appointed a herald and an apostle—I am telling the truth, I am not lying—and a teacher of the true faith to the Gentiles.

⁸I want men everywhere to lift up holy hands in prayer, without anger or disputing.

⁹I also want women to dress modestly, with decency and propriety, not with braided hair or gold or pearls or expensive clothes, ¹⁰but with good deeds, appropriate for women who profess to worship God.

ᵃ 9 Or that the law

¹¹A woman should learn in quietness and full submission. ¹²I do not permit a woman to teach or to have authority over a man; she must be silent. ¹³For Adam was formed first, then Eve. ¹⁴And Adam was not the one deceived; it was the woman who was deceived and became a sinner. ¹⁵But women*ª* will be saved*ᵇ* through childbearing—if they continue in faith, love and holiness with propriety.

Overseers and Deacons

3 Here is a trustworthy saying: If anyone sets his heart on being an overseer,*ᶜ* he desires a noble task. ²Now the overseer must be above reproach, the husband of but one wife, temperate, self-controlled, respectable, hospitable, able to teach, ³not given to drunkenness, not violent but gentle, not quarrelsome, not a lover of money. ⁴He must manage his own family well and see that his children obey him with proper respect. ⁵(If anyone does not know how to manage his own family, how can he take care of God's church?) ⁶He must not be a recent convert, or he may become conceited and fall under the same judgment as the devil. ⁷He must also have a good reputation with outsiders, so that he will not fall into disgrace and into the devil's trap.

⁸Deacons, likewise, are to be men worthy of respect, sincere, not indulging in much wine, and not pursuing dishonest gain. ⁹They must keep hold of the deep truths of the faith with a clear conscience. ¹⁰They must first be tested; and then if there is nothing against them, let them serve as deacons.

¹¹In the same way, their wives*ᵈ* are to be women worthy of respect, not malicious talkers but temperate and trustworthy in everything.

¹²A deacon must be the husband of but one wife and must manage his children and his household well. ¹³Those who have served well gain an excellent standing and great assurance in their faith in Christ Jesus.

¹⁴Although I hope to come to you soon, I am writing you these instructions so that, ¹⁵if I am delayed, you will know how people ought to conduct themselves in God's household, which is the church of the living God, the pillar and foundation of the truth. ¹⁶Beyond all question, the mystery of godliness is great:

> He*ᵉ* appeared in a body,*ᶠ*
>   was vindicated by the Spirit,
> was seen by angels,
>   was preached among the nations,
> was believed on in the world,
>   was taken up in glory.

Instructions to Timothy

4 The Spirit clearly says that in later times some will abandon the faith and follow deceiving spirits and things taught by demons. ²Such teachings come through hypocritical liars, whose consciences have been seared as with a hot iron. ³They forbid people to marry and order

genuine beauty » 2:9-10

Does this mean I should trash my hair clips, sell my jewelry and start shopping for clothes at the dollar store? Well, that's not really the point here. So what is? Paul's point is that what gets you noticed shouldn't be your outward appearance; it should be your heart and how that shows through in the things you do for others. In other words, if you have a choice between being known as the best-dressed girl in school or being known as a girl who's tight with God— Paul's telling you which one you should go for.

---

a 15 Greek *she*   *b 15* Or *restored*   *c 1* Traditionally *bishop*; also in verse 2   *d 11* Or *way, deaconesses*
e 16 Some manuscripts *God*   *f 16* Or *in the flesh*

Worn Thin

"Remember, your research papers are due on *Friday*," our English teacher said as the bell rang. She had this sick gloating tone in her voice, like she enjoyed making us suffer.

"That's if I'm still alive by that point," I muttered to Sabrina as we gathered our books.

"Yeah. You and me both," she sighed. "Do the teachers have a conspiracy or something? Why is everything due this week?!"

"Yeah, worst week ever," I agreed. "Get this. My manager scheduled me to close—again—so I can't even start on that awful paper till tomorrow. And tomorrow morning we have an early swim practice." Sabrina nodded in sympathy. I felt like I was already behind. And it was only Monday!

This has been the hardest year of my life so far—between school and work, I hardly have any time to relax. What ever happened to those peaceful days of summer I used to look forward to as a kid? This year, I didn't even get a break. I just worked and went to summer school.

Some days I feel like I could just sleep forever. Maybe a few solid weeks of hibernation and then I'd be okay. But I'm up late every night just trying to get my physics and calc homework done. I'm afraid I won't get into a good college unless I keep up the pace. But I'm not sure how long I can keep going like this.

For more information about stress and overcommitment, go online at www.TrueImagesBible.com

overcommitment in focus

The busiest people on earth are teenagers. Work. School. Extra-curricular activities. Friends. How can we experience God's peace when our lives are in constant motion? Keep in mind . . .

»God's peace comes when we focus on *him* instead of our problems (see Isaiah 26:3, page 919). We usually get it mixed up—focusing on our problems first and then coming to God when we're already overwhelmed.

»Sometimes we rob ourselves of peace—overcommitting ourselves, jamming our schedules, trying to do more than we should and then suffering the consequences. Take a long, hard look at your schedule. Which things are absolutely necessary, and which things can you live without? How can you shift your priorities?

»Give your worries to God in prayer, and his peace will guard your thoughts (see Philippians 4:6–7, page 1553).

For more on this topic, see the index on page 1656.

them to abstain from certain foods, which God created to be received with thanksgiving by those who believe and who know the truth. [4]For everything God created is good, and nothing is to be rejected if it is received with thanksgiving, [5]because it is consecrated by the word of God and prayer.

[6]If you point these things out to the brothers, you will be a good minister of Christ Jesus, brought up in the truths of the faith and of the good teaching that you have followed. [7]Have nothing to do with godless myths and old wives' tales; rather, train yourself to be godly. [8]For physical training is of some value, but godliness has value for all things, holding promise for both the present life and the life to come.

⁹This is a trustworthy saying that deserves full acceptance ¹⁰(and for this we labor and strive), that we have put our hope in the living God, who is the Savior of all men, and especially of those who believe.

¹¹Command and teach these things. ¹²Don't let anyone look down on you because you are young, but set an example for the believers in speech, in life, in love, in faith and in purity. ¹³Until I come, devote yourself to the public reading of Scripture, to preaching and to teaching. ¹⁴Do not neglect your gift, which was given you through a prophetic message when the body of elders laid their hands on you.

¹⁵Be diligent in these matters; give yourself wholly to them, so that everyone may see your progress. ¹⁶Watch your life and doctrine closely. Persevere in them, because if you do, you will save both yourself and your hearers.

Advice About Widows, Elders and Slaves

5 Do not rebuke an older man harshly, but exhort him as if he were your father. Treat younger men as brothers, ²older women as mothers, and younger women as sisters, with absolute purity.

³Give proper recognition to those widows who are really in need. ⁴But if a widow has children or grandchildren, these should learn first of all to put their religion into practice by caring for their own family and so repaying their parents and grandparents, for this is pleasing to God. ⁵The widow who is really in need and left all alone puts her hope in God and continues night and day to pray and to ask God for help. ⁶But the widow who lives for pleasure is dead even while she lives. ⁷Give the people these instructions, too, so that no one may be open to blame. ⁸If anyone does not provide for his relatives, and especially for his immediate family, he has denied the faith and is worse than an unbeliever.

⁹No widow may be put on the list of widows unless she is over sixty, has been faithful to her husband,ᵃ ¹⁰and is well known for her good deeds, such as bringing up children, showing hospitality, washing the feet of the saints, helping those in trouble and devoting herself to all kinds of good deeds.

¹¹As for younger widows, do not put them on such a list. For when their sensual desires overcome their dedication to Christ, they want to marry. ¹²Thus they bring judgment on themselves, because they have broken their first pledge. ¹³Besides, they get into the habit of being idle and going about from house to house. And not only do they become idlers, but also gossips and busybodies, saying things they ought not to. ¹⁴So I counsel younger widows to marry, to have children, to manage their homes and to give the enemy no opportunity for slander. ¹⁵Some have in fact already turned away to follow Satan.

¹⁶If any woman who is a believer has widows in her family, she should help them and not let the church be burdened with them, so that the church can help those widows who are really in need.

¹⁷The elders who direct the affairs of the church well are worthy of double honor, especially those whose work is preaching and teaching. ¹⁸For the Scripture says, "Do not muzzle the ox while it is treading out the grain,"ᵇ and "The worker deserves his wages."ᶜ ¹⁹Do not entertain an accusation against an elder unless it is brought by two or three witnesses. ²⁰Those who sin are to be rebuked publicly, so that the others may take warning.

genuine faith » 4:7-8

Are you really faithful about working out (or wish you were)? Maybe you take a spin class or do Pilates or like to run. Maybe you're on a sports team and always work hard at practice. Paul says that's great, because there's real value in training your body. But—and that's a key word!—it has limited value compared to training yourself spiritually. Working hard at growing in your faith will benefit you not only for the next 70 years or so that you live on earth but for all eternity. So, how can you start getting more "spiritually fit"?

ᵃ 9 Or has had but one husband   ᵇ 18 Deut. 25:4   ᶜ 18 Luke 10:7

²¹I charge you, in the sight of God and Christ Jesus and the elect angels, to keep these instructions without partiality, and to do nothing out of favoritism. ²²Do not be hasty in the laying on of hands, and do not share in the sins of others. Keep yourself pure.

²³Stop drinking only water, and use a little wine because of your stomach and your frequent illnesses.

²⁴The sins of some men are obvious, reaching the place of judgment ahead of them; the sins of others trail behind them. ²⁵In the same way, good deeds are obvious, and even those that are not cannot be hidden.

6 All who are under the yoke of slavery should consider their masters worthy of full respect, so that God's name and our teaching may not be slandered. ²Those who have believing masters are not to show less respect for them because they are brothers. Instead, they are to serve them even better, because those who benefit from their service are believers, and dear to them. These are the things you are to teach and urge on them.

Love of Money

³If anyone teaches false doctrines and does not agree to the sound instruction of our Lord Jesus Christ and to godly teaching, ⁴he is conceited and understands nothing. He has an unhealthy interest in controversies and quarrels about words that result in envy, strife, malicious talk, evil suspicions ⁵and constant friction between men of corrupt mind, who have been robbed of the truth and who think that godliness is a means to financial gain.

⁶But godliness with contentment is great gain. ⁷For we brought nothing into the world, and we can take nothing out of it. ⁸But if we have food and clothing, we will be content with that. ⁹People who want to get rich fall into temptation and a trap and into many foolish and harmful desires that plunge men into ruin and destruction. ¹⁰For the love of money is a root of all kinds of evil. Some people, eager for money, have wandered from the faith and pierced themselves with many griefs.

love notes

4:12

Loved one,

There are no age requirements for being my effective witness. Right now, today, you can be an example through the way you live and what you say; through your love for others, your faith in me and through your purity.

—Father God

How have you been an effective witness for God this week?

truth or dare

Catch that? Money's not evil. Lovin' it is. Completely root out this poisonous weed from your heart.

6:10

Paul's Charge to Timothy

[11]But you, man of God, flee from all this, and pursue righteousness, godliness, faith, love, endurance and gentleness. [12]Fight the good fight of the faith. Take hold of the eternal life to which you were called when you made your good confession in the presence of many witnesses. [13]In the sight of God, who gives life to everything, and of Christ Jesus, who while testifying before Pontius Pilate made the good confession, I charge you [14]to keep this command without spot or blame until the appearing of our Lord Jesus Christ, [15]which God will bring about in his own time—God, the blessed and only Ruler, the King of kings and Lord of lords, [16]who alone is immortal and who lives in unapproachable light, whom no one has seen or can see. To him be honor and might forever. Amen.

[17]Command those who are rich in this present world not to be arrogant nor to put their hope in wealth, which is so uncertain, but to put their hope in God, who richly provides us with everything for our enjoyment. [18]Command them to do good, to be rich in good deeds, and to be generous and willing to share. [19]In this way they will lay up treasure for themselves as a firm foundation for the coming age, so that they may take hold of the life that is truly life.

[20]Timothy, guard what has been entrusted to your care. Turn away from godless chatter and the opposing ideas of what is falsely called knowledge, [21]which some have professed and in so doing have wandered from the faith.

Grace be with you.

author: The apostle Paul.

date: About A.D. 66 or 67.

setting: Paul wrote this, his last letter, from a cold dungeon in Rome shortly before he was executed for his faith. He had left Timothy in Ephesus to supervise the church there.

verse to remember: Endure hardship with us like a good soldier of Christ Jesus (2:3).

theme to consider: Like Paul, when we serve Christ, we will likely face persecution and suffering. Like Paul, we will consider it all worthwhile when we achieve our goal of honoring Jesus in all that we do.

2 timothy

unchanging truth

Will I find myself taking some heat if I stand up for Christ?

That's an easy question to answer—yes. Let's look at some tougher ones.

Will I be left off the invitation list of some parties if I get serious about my faith?

Definitely.

Are some days going to be easier than others when it comes to being persecuted?

No doubt.

Does this mean I'll have to spend some Friday nights alone if I keep my dating standards high?

Uh-huh.

There's no way living out my faith is going to affect my popularity, is there?

Yes way.

The Bible says in 2 Timothy 3:12, "In fact, everyone who wants to live a godly life in Christ Jesus will be persecuted." Sounds like there are no exceptions to that rule. If we live for Christ, we can count on persecution. However, we can also count on something else. It's worth it. Every bit of it. Every snide remark, every snub, every overlooked invitation to a party—we'll agree with God that every bit of it was worth it.

That was Paul's message to Timothy in this second letter to him. Hang in there. Don't give up. Stay true to what you believe. Keep the faith.

life lessons

1 The world will try to loosen our grip on our faith—don't let it (1:6–8)!

2 We can't chalk up our mistakes to being young—God calls us to be better than that (2:22–24).

3 Jesus, waiting for us with open arms at the finish line, makes it all worth it (4:6–8).

1 Paul, an apostle of Christ Jesus by the will of God, according to the promise of life that is in Christ Jesus,

²To Timothy, my dear son:

Grace, mercy and peace from God the Father and Christ Jesus our Lord.

Encouragement to Be Faithful

³I thank God, whom I serve, as my forefathers did, with a clear conscience, as night and day I constantly remember you in my prayers. ⁴Recalling your tears, I long to see you, so that I may be filled with joy. ⁵I have been reminded of your sincere faith, which first lived in your grandmother Lois and in your mother Eunice and, I am persuaded, now lives in you also. ⁶For this reason I remind you to fan into flame the gift of God, which is in you through the laying on of my hands. ⁷For God did not give us a spirit of timidity, but a spirit of power, of love and of self-discipline.

⁸So do not be ashamed to testify about our Lord, or ashamed of me his prisoner. But join with me in suffering for the gospel, by the power of God, ⁹who has saved us and called us to a holy life—not because of anything we have done but because of his own purpose and grace. This grace was given us in Christ Jesus before the beginning of time, ¹⁰but it has now been revealed through the appearing of our Savior, Christ Jesus, who has destroyed death and has brought life and immortality to light through the gospel. ¹¹And of this gospel I was appointed a herald and an apostle and a teacher. ¹²That is why I am suffering as I am. Yet I am not ashamed, because I know whom I have believed, and am convinced that he is able to guard what I have entrusted to him for that day.

¹³What you heard from me, keep as the pattern of sound teaching, with faith and love in Christ Jesus. ¹⁴Guard the good deposit that was entrusted to you—guard it with the help of the Holy Spirit who lives in us.

¹⁵You know that everyone in the province of Asia has deserted me, including Phygelus and Hermogenes.

¹⁶May the Lord show mercy to the household of Onesiphorus, because he often refreshed me and was not ashamed of my chains. ¹⁷On the contrary, when he was in Rome, he searched hard for me until he found me. ¹⁸May the Lord grant that he will find mercy from the Lord on that day! You know very well in how many ways he helped me in Ephesus.

genuine

courage ≫ 1:7–8

Your teacher says the Bible is just a good work of fiction. Are you afraid to challenge that opinion? People at school think it's narrow-minded and arrogant to believe there's only way to God. Are you reluctant to tell them what you believe? Your youth group leader asks you to share with the group how you became a Christ-follower. Are you too scared to do it? Don't back down in these situations! You've been given a spirit of power, love and self-discipline that will help you overcome your natural tendencies so that you will "not be ashamed to testify about our Lord."

2 You then, my son, be strong in the grace that is in Christ Jesus. ²And the things you have heard me say in the presence of many witnesses entrust to reliable men who will also be qualified to teach others. ³Endure hardship with us like a good soldier of Christ Jesus. ⁴No one serving as a soldier gets involved in civilian affairs—he wants to please his commanding officer. ⁵Similarly, if anyone competes as an athlete, he does not receive the victor's crown unless he competes according to the rules. ⁶The hardworking farmer should be the first to receive a share of the crops. ⁷Reflect on what I am saying, for the Lord will give you insight into all this.

⁸Remember Jesus Christ, raised from the dead, descended from David. This is my gospel, ⁹for which I am suffering even to the point of being chained like a criminal. But God's word is not chained. ¹⁰Therefore I endure everything for the sake of the elect, that they too may obtain the salvation that is in Christ Jesus, with eternal glory.

¹¹Here is a trustworthy saying:

If we died with him,
we will also live with him;
¹²if we endure,
we will also reign with him.
If we disown him,
he will also disown us;
¹³if we are faithless,
he will remain faithful,
for he cannot disown himself.

A Workman Approved by God

¹⁴Keep reminding them of these things. Warn them before God against quarreling about words; it is of no value, and only ruins those who listen. ¹⁵Do your best to present yourself to God as one approved, a workman who does not need to be ashamed and who correctly handles the word of truth. ¹⁶Avoid godless chatter, because those who indulge in it will become more and more ungodly. ¹⁷Their teaching will spread like gangrene. Among them are Hymenaeus and Philetus, ¹⁸who have wandered away from the truth. They say that the resurrection has already taken place, and they destroy the faith of some. ¹⁹Nevertheless, God's solid foundation stands firm, sealed with this inscription: "The Lord knows those who are his," ᵃ and, "Everyone who confesses the name of the Lord must turn away from wickedness."

²⁰In a large house there are articles not only of gold and silver, but also of wood and clay; some are for noble purposes and some for ignoble. ²¹If a man cleanses himself from the latter, he will be an instrument for noble purposes, made holy, useful to the Master and prepared to do any good work.

²²Flee the evil desires of youth, and pursue righteousness, faith, love and peace, along with those who call on the Lord out of a pure heart. ²³Don't have anything to do with foolish and stupid arguments, because you know they produce quarrels. ²⁴And the Lord's servant must not quarrel; instead, he must be kind to everyone, able to teach, not resentful. ²⁵Those who oppose him he must gently instruct, in the hope that God will grant them repentance leading them to a knowledge of the truth, ²⁶and that they will come to their senses and escape from the trap of the devil, who has taken them captive to do his will.

Godlessness in the Last Days

3 But mark this: There will be terrible times in the last days. ²People will be lovers of themselves, lovers of money,

boastful, proud, abusive, disobedient to their parents, ungrateful, unholy, ³without love, unforgiving, slanderous, without self-control, brutal, not lovers of the good, ⁴treacherous, rash, conceited, lovers of pleasure rather than lovers of God— ⁵having a form of godliness but denying its power. Have nothing to do with them.

⁶They are the kind who worm their way into homes and gain control over weak-willed women, who are loaded down with sins and are swayed by all kinds of evil desires, ⁷always learning but

genuine life » 2:22

Picture this for Nike's next commercial: Before leaving for school, a girl puts on some sweet new running shoes. Watching her throughout the day, you see she's running, always running. Running fast *away* from something and running hard *to* something. What's she running from? "The evil desires of youth"— the temptations she faces every day to pursue popularity rather than purity, to be more concerned about herself than others, to doubt God's promises . . . And what's she running hard after? Righteousness. Faith. Love. Peace. Might make for a weird commercial—but makes for a great life! So put your shoes on.

ᵃ 19 Num. 16:5 (see Septuagint)

never able to acknowledge the truth. [8]Just as Jannes and Jambres opposed Moses, so also these men oppose the truth—men of depraved minds, who, as far as the faith is concerned, are rejected. [9]But they will not get very far because, as in the case of those men, their folly will be clear to everyone.

Paul's Charge to Timothy

[10]You, however, know all about my teaching, my way of life, my purpose, faith, patience, love, endurance, [11]persecutions, sufferings—what kinds of things happened to me in Antioch, Iconium and Lystra, the persecutions I endured. Yet the Lord rescued me from all of them. [12]In fact, everyone who wants to live a godly life in Christ Jesus will be persecuted, [13]while evil men and impostors will go from bad to worse, deceiving and being deceived. [14]But as for you, continue in what you have learned and have become convinced of, because you know those from whom you learned it, [15]and how from infancy you have known the holy Scriptures, which are able to make you wise for salvation through faith in Christ Jesus. [16]All Scripture is God-breathed and is useful for teaching, rebuking, correcting and training in righteousness, [17]so that the man of God may be thoroughly equipped for every good work.

truth or dare

Ever skip sections or books of the Bible in favor of others? Don't stunt your growth. Since God inspired it all, give your spiritual health a boost—get a balanced reading of God's *whole* Word.

3:16–17

4 In the presence of God and of Christ Jesus, who will judge the living and the dead, and in view of his appearing and his kingdom, I give you this charge: [2]Preach the Word; be prepared in season and out of season; correct, rebuke and encourage—with great patience and careful instruction. [3]For the time will come when men will not put up with sound doctrine. Instead, to suit their own desires, they will gather around them a great number of teachers to say what their itching ears want to hear. [4]They will turn their ears away from the truth and turn aside to myths. [5]But you, keep your head in all situations, endure hardship, do the work of an evangelist, discharge all the duties of your ministry.

[6]For I am already being poured out like a drink offering, and the time has come for my departure. [7]I have fought the good fight, I have finished the race, I have kept the faith. [8]Now there is in store for me the crown of righteousness, which the Lord, the righteous Judge, will award to me on that day—and not only to me, but also to all who have longed for his appearing.

Personal Remarks

[9]Do your best to come to me quickly, [10]for Demas, because he loved this world, has deserted me and has gone to Thessalonica. Crescens has gone to Galatia, and Titus to Dalmatia. [11]Only Luke is with me. Get Mark and bring him with you, because he is helpful to me in my ministry. [12]I sent Tychicus to Ephesus. [13]When you come, bring the cloak that I left with Carpus at Troas, and my scrolls, especially the parchments.

[14]Alexander the metalworker did me a great deal of harm. The Lord will repay him for what he has done. [15]You too should be on your guard against him, because he strongly opposed our message.

[16]At my first defense, no one came to my support, but everyone deserted me. May it not be held against them. [17]But the Lord stood at my side and gave me strength, so that through me the message might be fully proclaimed and all the Gentiles might hear it. And I was delivered from the lion's mouth. [18]The Lord will rescue me from every evil attack and will bring me safely to his heavenly kingdom. To him be glory for ever and ever. Amen.

Final Greetings

[19]Greet Priscilla[a] and Aquila and the household of Onesiphorus. [20]Erastus stayed in Corinth, and I left Trophimus sick in Miletus. [21]Do your best to get here before winter. Eubulus greets you, and so do Pudens, Linus, Claudia and all the brothers.

[22]The Lord be with your spirit. Grace be with you.

a 19 Greek *Prisca*, a variant of *Priscilla*

mirror images

I have been reminded of your sincere faith, which first lived in your grandmother Lois and in your mother Eunice and, I am persuaded, now lives in you also. 2 Timothy 1:5

Eunice—Passing on the Faith

"Yes, Jesus loves me. The Bible tells me sooooo!" If you grew up going to church, you probably sang "Jesus Loves Me." And if you have parents who love Jesus, you may have learned more about God and his love from them.

Timothy sure did—and what a difference his mom's faith made in his life! Eunice was a Jewish woman who became a Christian. She was married to a Greek man who apparently didn't share her faith in the Lord, but that didn't stop her from teaching her son about God. With the help of Timothy's grandmother, Lois, Eunice taught tiny Tim everything she knew about God's Word.

We know this for a fact because the apostle Paul says that since Timothy was a little child, he knew the Scriptures (see 2 Timothy 3:15). And you can be sure that Eunice also communicated God's love in everyday ways. Little Timothy probably listened to her pray and watched his mom care for others with a kind word or a helpful deed. And Eunice's careful instruction prepared Timothy to teach others the truth about what God had done for them. Timothy grew up to become one of the most famous pastors in the New Testament.

When you look at Timothy's life, you have to wonder what a "Eunice" could do for you. Not every girl has Christian parents. But all of us can be on the lookout for a mentor who can show us everything it means to be a Jesus-follower.

Know someone whose faith affects everything she does? The best way to become more like this woman is to get to know her better. Be on the lookout for your own "Eunice," and ask if you can spend time with her, talking about what God wants for you and what he's doing in your life. As this special person helps you grow in Christ, you may discover that you're ready to be a Eunice, too—showing others everything it means to follow Jesus.

To read the next Mirror Images profile, go to page 1589.

Dear Jesus, I'd like to be a girl whose faith shines brightly like Timothy's. Help me to find someone like Eunice, who can show me the way to becoming more like you. Amen.

dear Jesus

>> Read more about Eunice in Acts 16:1–3 (page 1468) and 2 Timothy 1:5; 3:14–15 (pages 1576,1578).

>> 1579

author: The apostle Paul.

date: About A.D. 64.

setting: After visiting the Mediterranean island of Crete, Paul left Titus there to lead the churches.

verse to remember: This is a trustworthy saying. And I want you to stress these things, so that those who have trusted in God may be careful to devote themselves to doing what is good. These things are excellent and profitable for everyone (3:8).

theme to consider: In order to be effective leaders for Christ, we first must be self-disciplined, responsible, living examples of our faith.

titus

unchanging truth

"Do as I say, not as I do." Ever heard that one? It's something adults sometimes say when what they do falls short of what they tell you to do. It's the opposite of leading by example. The only problem is that *saying* what's right is no substitute for *doing* what's right.

Before you go off on others for being hypocrites, be honest—how many times have you done it yourself? You say Christians aren't supposed to cheat. But what about when you didn't study for that test and your eyes veered over to that smart kid's paper? Or maybe your hypocrisy is more blatant. How about telling your little brother not to smoke, yet you light up with your friends when he's not around?

Think about it. What makes more of a statement to you about Christianity—someone who talks about it or someone who lives it? Paul wanted his friend Titus, as the leader of the churches in Crete, to understand the importance of living out his faith (see 2:7–8). After all, what good is the church if the people in it don't back up what they say by how they live? That includes you. To a watching world, your life is the only "Bible" some will ever read. And you're the only "sermon" some will ever hear. Will what you say match up with what you do when the world looks your way?

life lessons

1. We can claim to know God but actually deny him by our actions (1:16).

2. God's "rules" for the church show that he cares more about shaping our character than about our keeping a list of do's and don'ts (2:1–15).

3. When God saved us, he provided a way for our walk to match our talk—the power of Jesus Christ living inside us (3:3–8).

1 Paul, a servant of God and an apostle of Jesus Christ for the faith of God's elect and the knowledge of the truth that leads to godliness— ²a faith and knowledge resting on the hope of eternal life, which God, who does not lie, promised before the beginning of time, ³and at his appointed season he brought his word to light through the preaching entrusted to me by the command of God our Savior,

⁴To Titus, my true son in our common faith:

Grace and peace from God the Father and Christ Jesus our Savior.

Titus's Task on Crete

⁵The reason I left you in Crete was that you might straighten out what was left unfinished and appoint*ᵃ* elders in every town, as I directed you. ⁶An elder must be blameless, the husband of but one wife, a man whose children believe and are not open to the charge of being wild and disobedient. ⁷Since an overseer*ᵇ* is entrusted with God's work, he must be blameless—not overbearing, not quick-tempered, not given to drunkenness, not violent, not pursuing dishonest gain. ⁸Rather he must be hospitable, one who loves what is good, who is self-controlled, upright, holy and disciplined. ⁹He must hold firmly to the trustworthy message as it has been taught, so that he can encourage others by sound doctrine and refute those who oppose it.

¹⁰For there are many rebellious people, mere talkers and deceivers, especially those of the circumcision group. ¹¹They must be silenced, because they are ruining whole households by teaching things they ought not to teach—and that for the sake of dishonest gain. ¹²Even one of their own prophets has said, "Cretans are always liars, evil brutes, lazy gluttons." ¹³This testimony is true. Therefore, rebuke them sharply, so that they will be sound in the faith ¹⁴and will pay no attention to Jewish myths or to the commands of those who reject the truth. ¹⁵To the pure, all things are pure, but to those who are corrupted and do not believe, nothing is pure. In fact, both their minds and consciences are corrupted. ¹⁶They claim to know God, but by their actions they deny him. They are detestable, disobedient and unfit for doing anything good.

What Must Be Taught to Various Groups

2 You must teach what is in accord with sound doctrine. ²Teach the older men to be temperate, worthy of respect, self-controlled, and sound in faith, in love and in endurance.
³Likewise, teach the older women to be reverent in the way they live, not to be slanderers or addicted to much wine, but to teach what is good. ⁴Then they can train the younger women to love their husbands and children, ⁵to be self-controlled and pure, to be busy at home, to be kind, and to be subject to their husbands, so that no one will malign the word of God.

⁶Similarly, encourage the young men to be self-controlled. ⁷In everything set them an example by doing what is good. In your teaching show integrity, seriousness ⁸and soundness of speech that cannot be condemned, so that those who oppose you may be ashamed because they have nothing bad to say about us.

⁹Teach slaves to be subject to their masters in everything, to try to please them, not to talk back to them, ¹⁰and not to steal from them, but to show that they can be fully trusted, so that in every way they will make the teaching about God our Savior attractive.

¹¹For the grace of God that brings salvation has appeared to all men. ¹²It teaches us to say "No" to ungodliness and worldly passions, and to live self-controlled, upright and godly lives in this present age, ¹³while we wait for the blessed hope—the glorious appearing of our great God and Savior, Jesus Christ, ¹⁴who gave himself for us to redeem us from all wickedness and to purify for himself a people that are his very own, eager to do what is good.

truth or dare

Need an objective listener and good advice? Sometimes you need to talk to someone other than your friends or parents. Find a mature Christian woman to mentor you.

2:3–5

ᵃ 5 Or ordain   ᵇ 7 Traditionally *bishop*

[15]These, then, are the things you should teach. Encourage and rebuke with all authority. Do not let anyone despise you.

Doing What Is Good

3 Remind the people to be subject to rulers and authorities, to be obedient, to be ready to do whatever is good, [2]to slander no one, to be peaceable and considerate, and to show true humility toward all men.

[3]At one time we too were foolish, disobedient, deceived and enslaved by all kinds of passions and pleasures. We lived in malice and envy, being hated and hating one another. [4]But when the kindness and love of God our Savior appeared, [5]he saved us, not because of righteous things we had done, but because of his mercy. He saved us through the washing of rebirth and renewal by the Holy Spirit, [6]whom he poured out on us generously through Jesus Christ our Savior, [7]so that, having been justified by his grace, we might become heirs having the hope of eternal life. [8]This is a trustworthy saying. And I want you to stress these things, so that those who have trusted in God may be careful to devote themselves to doing what is good. These things are excellent and profitable for everyone.

[9]But avoid foolish controversies and genealogies and arguments and quarrels about the law, because these are unprofitable and useless. [10]Warn a divisive person once, and then warn him a second time. After that, have nothing to do with him. [11]You may be sure that such a man is warped and sinful; he is self-condemned.

Final Remarks

[12]As soon as I send Artemas or Tychicus to you, do your best to come to me at Nicopolis, because I have decided to winter there. [13]Do everything you can to help Zenas the lawyer and Apollos on their way and see that they have everything they need. [14]Our people must learn to devote themselves to doing what is good, in order that they may provide for daily necessities and not live unproductive lives.

[15]Everyone with me sends you greetings. Greet those who love us in the faith.

Grace be with you all.

genuine growth » 2:11-14

Do you look at certain people—like your pastor or the kid at school who leads a Bible study—and think they've got something that you don't, something that just automatically makes them more spiritual? Do you think, "I could never be a Christian like that"? If so, my friend, you are badly mistaken. You see, the grace of God that appeared to *all* people—including you—is the same grace that will help you grow in godliness. Your pastor ain't got nothin' that you don't got! You've just got to keep growing!

author: The apostle Paul.

date: About A.D. 60.

setting: Paul wrote this letter to Philemon to ask him to forgive and accept his runaway slave, Onesimus.

verse to remember: Perhaps the reason he was separated from you for a little while was that you might have him back for good—no longer as a slave, but better than a slave, as a dear brother. He is very dear to me but even dearer to you (15–16).

theme to consider: What barriers separate you from other believers? We are called to remove those barriers and accept our sisters and brothers in Christ.

philemon

unchanging truth

Some walked the earth, wearing robes and sandals; others traveled in cars, dressed in jeans. Some were kings and queens, while others were dirt poor. Every race, every economic class—we all will be together one day in heaven under the family name "Christian." Despite our obvious outward differences while here on earth, we share one thing in common with our spiritual family—Jesus lives inside each of one of us.

So, if we will be together with him in heaven someday, what's keeping us apart here in the world today? Pride. Misunderstanding. Bias.

Paul's letter to Philemon, a wealthy slave owner in the Colossian church, addressed these issues when he tried to convince Philemon to accept back a repentant runaway slave named Onesimus. Only Philemon wouldn't be receiving a slave—he would be receiving a brother in Christ because Onesimus had accepted Christ while he was on the run. Could Philemon get past all the differences and accept Onesimus as part of the family now?

We need to ask ourselves the same question. Think of a student who is the most different from you in every way—the way she dresses, talks and acts. You're total opposites in every way. What if she were your sister in Christ? How would you treat her? If you would do anything less than accept her with willing and open arms, then this letter's for you.

life lessons

1 No one can make us accept another person—it's something that comes from the heart (8–10).

2 Christians are more than teammates or acquaintances; we're family (15–16).

3 Paul models true friendship with Onesimus when he offers to pay for his friend's mistakes (17–19).

⌃

¹Paul, a prisoner of Christ Jesus, and Timothy our brother,

To Philemon our dear friend and fellow worker, ²to Apphia our sister, to Archippus our fellow soldier and to the church that meets in your home:

³Grace to you and peace from God our Father and the Lord Jesus Christ.

Thanksgiving and Prayer

⁴I always thank my God as I remember you in my prayers, ⁵because I hear about your faith in the Lord Jesus and your love for all the saints. ⁶I pray that you may be active in sharing your faith, so that you will have a full understanding of every good thing we have in Christ. ⁷Your love has given me great joy and encouragement, because you, brother, have refreshed the hearts of the saints.

Paul's Plea for Onesimus

⁸Therefore, although in Christ I could be bold and order you to do what you ought to do, ⁹yet I appeal to you on the basis of love. I then, as Paul—an old man and now also a prisoner of Christ Jesus— ¹⁰I appeal to you for my son Onesimus,ᵃ who became my son while I was in chains. ¹¹Formerly he was useless to you, but now he has become useful both to you and to me.

¹²I am sending him—who is my very heart—back to you. ¹³I would have liked to keep him with me so that he could take your place in helping me while I am in chains for the gospel. ¹⁴But I did not want to do anything without your consent, so that any favor you do will be spontaneous and not forced. ¹⁵Perhaps the reason he was separated from you for a little while was that you might have him back for good— ¹⁶no longer as a slave, but better than a slave, as a dear brother. He is very dear to me but even dearer to you, both as a man and as a brother in the Lord.

genuine evangelism » 6

Maybe you've read in a magazine or heard people on the news talking about the "benefits of an active lifestyle." It seems there are a lot of drawbacks to spending all your time sitting in front of the TV or the computer, and there's a lot to be gained from putting forth some energy on a regular basis. Looks like the same thing is true spiritually. Paul says that when you're active in sharing your faith, you're rewarded with a greater understanding of all the awesome things you've already been given in Christ. That's one major benefit!

¹⁷So if you consider me a partner, welcome him as you would welcome me. ¹⁸If he has done you any wrong or owes you anything, charge it to me. ¹⁹I, Paul, am writing this with my own hand. I will pay it back—not to mention that you owe me your very self. ²⁰I do wish, brother, that I may have some benefit from you in the Lord; refresh my heart in Christ. ²¹Confident of your obedience, I write to you, knowing that you will do even more than I ask.

²²And one thing more: Prepare a guest room for me, because I hope to be restored to you in answer to your prayers.

²³Epaphras, my fellow prisoner in Christ Jesus, sends you greetings. ²⁴And so do Mark, Aristarchus, Demas and Luke, my fellow workers.

²⁵The grace of the Lord Jesus Christ be with your spirit.

truth or dare

Paul could've thrown his weight around and screamed out orders. Instead, he gently guided his friend Philemon to make a godly decision. Harsh words, however true, are hardest to hear.

8–10

ᵃ 10 Onesimus means useful.

author:	Unknown.
date:	Sometime before the destruction of the temple in Jerusalem in A.D. 70.
setting:	These Jewish Christians were being persecuted, probably by both Jews and Romans.
verse to remember:	Let us fix our eyes on Jesus, the author and perfecter of our faith, who for the joy set before him endured the cross, scorning its shame, and sat down at the right hand of the throne of God (12:2).
theme to consider:	The message of the book of Hebrews is clear: Jesus is better; Christianity is superior; and Christ is sufficient for salvation.

unchanging truth

Here it is—the question you've been dying to ask. The one that sneaks into your head at night. The doubt that pops up in your mind when you least expect it and causes you to question everything.

Is Jesus for real?

You want only the truth. Is he really everything people say he is? Or will he end up disappointing you? Is he more than you've dreamed he would be? Or is he less than what you expected? Is he going to stay forever and never leave you, or will he turn out to be as unstable as everyone else? You're not the only one who wants to know the answer. And you're certainly not the first to wonder if Jesus is for real.

In fact, the Jewish Christians who received this letter had the very same questions. They figured if they were going to sell out wholeheartedly to this Jesus, then he had better be for real. They weren't going to be able to withstand the pressure from persecution unless they knew without a doubt that Jesus was exactly who he said he was. If he was anything less than that, then why go through with the tough work of following him? It wouldn't be worth it.

Have you ever asked yourself these same questions? The answers are all right here in the book of Hebrews—a foundation for the faith.

hebrews

life lessons

1 If Jesus is everything he says he is, then why risk ignoring him? He deserves our highest devotion (2:1–4; 3:7–19).

2 Jesus is exalted above everyone and everything (1:3), yet the King of the universe is also a friend to us. He can relate to us and gladly welcomes us into his arms (4:14–16).

3 God loves us so much that he cares about our choices. Just as parents discipline their children in love, so God will also discipline our poor choices (12:4–11).

The Son Superior to Angels

1 In the past God spoke to our forefathers through the prophets at many times and in various ways, [2]but in these last days he has spoken to us by his Son, whom he appointed heir of all things, and through whom he made the universe. [3]The Son is the radiance of God's glory and the exact representation of his being, sustaining all things by his powerful word. After he had provided purification for sins, he sat down at the right hand of the Majesty in heaven. [4]So he became as much superior to the angels as the name he has inherited is superior to theirs.

[5]For to which of the angels did God ever say,

"You are my Son;
today I have become your Father[a]"[b]?

Or again,

"I will be his Father,
and he will be my Son"[c]?

[6]And again, when God brings his firstborn into the world, he says,

"Let all God's angels worship him."[d]

[7]In speaking of the angels he says,

"He makes his angels winds,
his servants flames of fire."[e]

[8]But about the Son he says,

"Your throne, O God, will last for ever and ever,
and righteousness will be the scepter of your kingdom.
[9]You have loved righteousness and hated wickedness;
therefore God, your God, has set you above your companions
by anointing you with the oil of joy."[f]

[10]He also says,

"In the beginning, O Lord, you laid the foundations of the earth,
and the heavens are the work of your hands.
[11]They will perish, but you remain;
they will all wear out like a garment.
[12]You will roll them up like a robe;
like a garment they will be changed.
But you remain the same,
and your years will never end."[g]

[13]To which of the angels did God ever say,

"Sit at my right hand
until I make your enemies
a footstool for your feet"[h]?

[14]Are not all angels ministering spirits sent to serve those who will inherit salvation?

Warning to Pay Attention

2 We must pay more careful attention, therefore, to what we have heard, so that we do not drift away. [2]For if the message spoken by angels was binding, and every violation and disobedience received its just punishment, [3]how shall we escape if we ignore such a great salvation? This salvation, which was first announced by the Lord, was confirmed to us by those who heard him. [4]God also testified to it by signs, wonders and various miracles, and gifts of the Holy Spirit distributed according to his will.

[a] 5 Or *have begotten you*   [b] 5 Psalm 2:7   [c] 5 2 Samuel 7:14; 1 Chron. 17:13   [d] 6 Deut. 32:43 (see Dead Sea Scrolls and Septuagint)   [e] 7 Psalm 104:4   [f] 9 Psalm 45:6,7   [g] 12 Psalm 102:25-27   [h] 13 Psalm 110:1

Jesus Made Like His Brothers

⁵It is not to angels that he has subjected the world to come, about which we are speaking. ⁶But there is a place where someone has testified:

"What is man that you are mindful of him,
the son of man that you care for him?
⁷You made him a little*ᵃ* lower than the angels;
you crowned him with glory and honor
⁸ and put everything under his feet."*ᵇ*

In putting everything under him, God left nothing that is not subject to him. Yet at present we do not see everything subject to him. ⁹But we see Jesus, who was made a little lower than the angels, now crowned with glory and honor because he suffered death, so that by the grace of God he might taste death for everyone.

¹⁰In bringing many sons to glory, it was fitting that God, for whom and through whom everything exists, should make the author of their salvation perfect through suffering. ¹¹Both the one who makes men holy and those who are made holy are of the same family. So Jesus is not ashamed to call them brothers. ¹²He says,

"I will declare your name to my
brothers;
in the presence of the
congregation I will sing
your praises."*ᶜ*

¹³And again,

"I will put my trust in him."*ᵈ*

And again he says,

"Here am I, and the children God has given me."*ᵉ*

truth or dare

Are you afraid of dying? Most people are. But when Jesus died, he defeated the devil, who held the power of death. So now you have nothin' to fear.

2:14–15

¹⁴Since the children have flesh and blood, he too shared in their humanity so that by his death he might destroy him who holds the power of death—that is, the devil— ¹⁵and free those who all their lives were held in slavery by their fear of death. ¹⁶For surely it is not angels he helps, but Abraham's descendants. ¹⁷For this reason he had to be made like his brothers in every way, in order that he might become a merciful and faithful high priest in service to God, and that he might make atonement for*ᶠ* the sins of the people. ¹⁸Because he himself suffered when he was tempted, he is able to help those who are being tempted.

Jesus Greater Than Moses

3 Therefore, holy brothers, who share in the heavenly calling, fix your thoughts on Jesus, the apostle and high priest whom we confess. ²He was faithful to the one who appointed him, just as Moses was faithful in all God's house. ³Jesus has been found worthy of greater honor than Moses, just as the builder of a house has greater honor than the house itself. ⁴For every house is built by someone, but God is the builder of everything. ⁵Moses was faithful as a servant in all God's house, testifying to what would be said in the future. ⁶But Christ is faithful as a son over God's house. And we are his house, if we hold on to our courage and the hope of which we boast.

Warning Against Unbelief

⁷So, as the Holy Spirit says:

"Today, if you hear his voice,
⁸ do not harden your hearts

ᵃ 7 Or him for a little while; also in verse 9   ᵇ 8 Psalm 8:4-6   ᶜ 12 Psalm 22:22   ᵈ 13 Isaiah 8:17
ᵉ 13 Isaiah 8:18   ᶠ 17 Or and that he might turn aside God's wrath, taking away

as you did in the rebellion,
　during the time of testing in the desert,
⁹where your fathers tested and tried me
　and for forty years saw what I did.
¹⁰That is why I was angry with that generation,
　and I said, 'Their hearts are always going astray,
　and they have not known my ways.'
¹¹So I declared on oath in my anger,
　'They shall never enter my rest.' "ᵃ

¹²See to it, brothers, that none of you has a sinful, unbelieving heart that turns away from the living God. ¹³But encourage one another daily, as long as it is called Today, so that none of you may be hardened by sin's deceitfulness. ¹⁴We have come to share in Christ if we hold firmly till the end the confidence we had at first. ¹⁵As has just been said:

"Today, if you hear his voice,
　do not harden your hearts
　as you did in the rebellion."ᵇ

¹⁶Who were they who heard and rebelled? Were they not all those Moses led out of Egypt? ¹⁷And with whom was he angry for forty years? Was it not with those who sinned, whose bodies fell in the desert? ¹⁸And to whom did God swear that they would never enter his rest if not to those who disobeyedᶜ? ¹⁹So we see that they were not able to enter, because of their unbelief.

A Sabbath-Rest for the People of God

4 Therefore, since the promise of entering his rest still stands, let us be careful that none of you be found to have fallen short of it. ²For we also have had the gospel preached to us, just as they did; but the message they heard was of no value to them, because those who heard did not combine it with faith.ᵈ ³Now we who have believed enter that rest, just as God has said,

"So I declared on oath in my anger,
　'They shall never enter my rest.' "ᵉ

And yet his work has been finished since the creation of the world. ⁴For somewhere he has spoken about the seventh day in these words: "And on the seventh day God rested from all his work."ᶠ ⁵And again in the passage above he says, "They shall never enter my rest."

⁶It still remains that some will enter that rest, and those who formerly had the gospel preached to them did not go in, because of their disobedience. ⁷Therefore God again set a certain day, calling it Today, when a long time later he spoke through David, as was said before:

"Today, if you hear his voice,
　do not harden your hearts."ᵇ

⁸For if Joshua had given them rest, God would not have spoken later about another day. ⁹There remains, then, a Sabbath-rest for the people of God; ¹⁰for anyone who enters God's rest also rests from his own work, just as God did from his. ¹¹Let us, therefore, make every effort to enter that rest, so that no one will fall by following their example of disobedience.

¹²For the word of God is living and active. Sharper than any double-edged sword, it penetrates even to dividing soul and spirit, joints and marrow; it judges the thoughts and attitudes of the heart. ¹³Nothing in all creation is hidden from God's sight. Everything is uncovered and laid bare before the eyes of him to whom we must give account.

Jesus the Great High Priest

¹⁴Therefore, since we have a great high priest who has gone through the heavens,ᵍ Jesus the Son of God, let us hold firmly to the faith we profess. ¹⁵For we do not have a high priest who is unable to sympathize with our weaknesses, but we have one who has been tempted in every way, just as we

ᵃ 11 Psalm 95:7-11　ᵇ 15,7 Psalm 95:7,8　ᶜ 18 Or disbelieved　ᵈ 2 Many manuscripts because they did not share in the faith of those who obeyed　ᵉ 3 Psalm 95:11; also in verse 5　ᶠ 4 Gen. 2:2　ᵍ 14 Or gone into heaven

mirror images

The king rose, and with him the governor and Bernice and those sitting with them . . . and while talking with one another, they said, "This man is not doing anything that deserves death or imprisonment." Acts 26:30–31

Bernice—Lost Opportunity

A t first glance, Bernice might remind you of one of Cinderella's stepsisters. Showy and selfish. Like the stepsisters when they approached the prince, she had a golden opportunity—and she blew it.

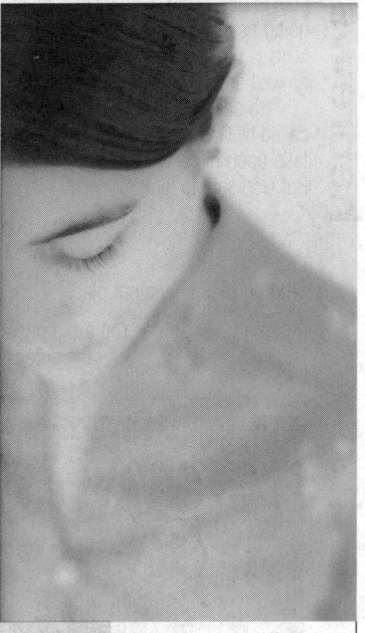

According to history, Bernice was engaged to one man but then married her own uncle when she was 13. When he died, she went to live with her brother, King Agrippa. To silence rumors that they had a sexual relationship, Bernice married the king of Cilicia, but soon left him to go back to Agrippa. Later she became the mistress of the Roman emperor's son. Her immoral lifestyle was so well-known that she deserves to go down in Rome's "hall of shame."

Serving as her brother's companion, Bernice accompanied him with "great pomp" to hear the case of the famous apostle Paul. As Paul spoke, he told Agrippa and Bernice the story of how Jesus had rescued him from a life of sin. No doubt Bernice had heard of Jesus, but now she knew what this Messiah did for Paul . . . and what he wanted to do for her.

Maybe Bernice forgot to clean her ears. Although she heard every word of Paul's testimony, she ignored the only message that could save her from a life of sin. And while she and Agrippa agreed that Paul was innocent, Bernice put the story of this Christian behind her. Her opportunity to find new life and hope in Christ passed by, and we know from history that Bernice continued in her evil deeds.

Not only did she die in shame, but Bernice also went down in history as a "bad girl of the Bible." Still, her story deserves to be remembered. Look what happens when you harden your heart against God and follow your own evil desires. If you don't know Jesus, take the opportunity to talk with someone who does about getting to know him personally. Allow God to speak to you through his Word, the Bible. And when he does speak, open your ears and your heart to listen, even if it means giving up your own desires.

To read the next Mirror Images profile, go to page 1641.

Dear Jesus, I don't want to miss out like Bernice did. Forgive my sins, and teach me to listen and obey, growing to know you more each day. Amen.

dear Jesus

Read more about Bernice in Acts 25:13—26:32 (pages 1481–1482).

are—yet was without sin. ¹⁶Let us then approach the throne of grace with confidence, so that we may receive mercy and find grace to help us in our time of need.

5 Every high priest is selected from among men and is appointed to represent them in matters related to God, to offer gifts and sacrifices for sins. ²He is able to deal gently with those who are ignorant and are going astray, since he himself is subject to weakness. ³This is why he has to offer sacrifices for his own sins, as well as for the sins of the people.

⁴No one takes this honor upon himself; he must be called by God, just as Aaron was. ⁵So Christ also did not take upon himself the glory of becoming a high priest. But God said to him,

> "You are my Son;
> today I have become your Father."[a] [b]

⁶And he says in another place,

> "You are a priest forever,
> in the order of Melchizedek."[c]

truth or dare

Sex, alcohol, cheating . . . has anyone ever had to face so much temptation? Yep—Jesus. He faced every kind of temptation. So now we can go to him for help when we're tempted.

4:14–16

⁷During the days of Jesus' life on earth, he offered up prayers and petitions with loud cries and tears to the one who could save him from death, and he was heard because of his reverent submission. ⁸Although he was a son, he learned obedience from what he suffered ⁹and, once made perfect, he became the source of eternal salvation for all who obey him ¹⁰and was designated by God to be high priest in the order of Melchizedek.

Warning Against Falling Away

¹¹We have much to say about this, but it is hard to explain because you are slow to learn. ¹²In fact, though by this time you ought to be teachers, you need someone to teach you the elementary truths of God's word all over again. You need milk, not solid food! ¹³Anyone who lives on milk, being still an infant, is not acquainted with the teaching about righteousness. ¹⁴But solid food is for the mature, who by constant use have trained themselves to distinguish good from evil.

genuine

As a baby you lived off milk; it was all that you needed. But now that you've grown, it's important that you have more solid food, such as fruits, veggies, meats, cheeses and breads. When someone first becomes a Christian, she too needs to live off "just milk" spiritually—just the basics of Christianity. But there comes a time to grow up and move on to more solid food as a follower of Christ—to become a deep learner who uses her spiritual gifts, not just a spiritual baby. How about you? Is it time for you to grow up?

growth » 5:11–14

6 Therefore let us leave the elementary teachings about Christ and go on to maturity, not laying again the foundation of repentance from acts that lead to death,[d] and of faith in God, ²instruction about baptisms, the laying on of hands, the resurrection of the dead, and eternal judgment. ³And God permitting, we will do so.

⁴It is impossible for those who have once been enlightened, who have tasted the heavenly gift, who have shared in the Holy Spirit, ⁵who have tasted the goodness of the word of God and the powers of the coming age, ⁶if they fall away, to be brought back to repentance, because[e] to their loss they are

a 5 Or have begotten you   b 5 Psalm 2:7   c 6 Psalm 110:4   d 1 Or from useless rituals   e 6 Or repentance while

genuine

Do you sometimes feel like you're a little boat, drifting all alone on the sea of life? Tossed about by the winds and the waves of friends, teachers, parents, teammates and life in general? Do you wonder if you're doomed to go under or crash against the rocks? What you need is an anchor! And there's only one that's strong enough and secure enough to hold you. Place your faith in Christ, and you'll discover you have a hope that will anchor your soul—no matter how stormy life gets.

hope »» 6:19-20

crucifying the Son of God all over again and subjecting him to public disgrace.

⁷Land that drinks in the rain often falling on it and that produces a crop useful to those for whom it is farmed receives the blessing of God. ⁸But land that produces thorns and thistles is worthless and is in danger of being cursed. In the end it will be burned.

⁹Even though we speak like this, dear friends, we are confident of better things in your case—things that accompany salvation. ¹⁰God is not unjust; he will not forget your work and the love you have shown him as you have helped his people and continue to help them. ¹¹We want each of you to show this same diligence to the very end, in order to make your hope sure. ¹²We do not want you to become lazy, but to imitate those who through faith and patience inherit what has been promised.

The Certainty of God's Promise

¹³When God made his promise to Abraham, since there was no one greater for him to swear by, he swore by himself, ¹⁴saying, "I will surely bless you and give you many descendants."[a] ¹⁵And so after waiting patiently, Abraham received what was promised.

¹⁶Men swear by someone greater than themselves, and the oath confirms what is said and puts an end to all argument. ¹⁷Because God wanted to make the unchanging nature of his purpose very clear to the heirs of what was promised, he confirmed it with an oath. ¹⁸God did this so that, by two unchangeable things in which it is impossible for God to lie, we who have fled to take hold of the hope offered to us may be greatly encouraged. ¹⁹We have this hope as an anchor for the soul, firm and secure. It enters the inner sanctuary behind the curtain, ²⁰where Jesus, who went before us, has entered on our behalf. He has become a high priest forever, in the order of Melchizedek.

Melchizedek the Priest

7 This Melchizedek was king of Salem and priest of God Most High. He met Abraham returning from the defeat of the kings and blessed him, ²and Abraham gave him a tenth of everything. First, his name means "king of righteousness"; then also, "king of Salem" means "king of peace." ³Without father or mother, without genealogy, without beginning of days or end of life, like the Son of God he remains a priest forever.

⁴Just think how great he was: Even the patriarch Abraham gave him a tenth of the plunder! ⁵Now the law requires the descendants of Levi who become priests to collect a tenth from the people—that is, their brothers—even though their brothers are descended from Abraham. ⁶This man, however, did not trace his descent from Levi, yet he collected a tenth from Abraham and blessed him who had the promises. ⁷And without doubt the lesser person is blessed by the greater. ⁸In the one case, the tenth is collected by men who die; but in the other case, by him who is declared to be living. ⁹One might even say that Levi, who collects the tenth, paid the tenth through Abraham, ¹⁰because when Melchizedek met Abraham, Levi was still in the body of his ancestor.

Jesus Like Melchizedek

¹¹If perfection could have been attained through the Levitical priesthood (for on the basis of it the law was given to the people), why was there still need for another priest to come—one in the

a 14 Gen. 22:17

order of Melchizedek, not in the order of Aaron? [12]For when there is a change of the priesthood, there must also be a change of the law. [13]He of whom these things are said belonged to a different tribe, and no one from that tribe has ever served at the altar. [14]For it is clear that our Lord descended from Judah, and in regard to that tribe Moses said nothing about priests. [15]And what we have said is even more clear if another priest like Melchizedek appears, [16]one who has become a priest not on the basis of a regulation as to his ancestry but on the basis of the power of an indestructible life. [17]For it is declared:

> "You are a priest forever,
>> in the order of Melchizedek." [a]

[18]The former regulation is set aside because it was weak and useless [19](for the law made nothing perfect), and a better hope is introduced, by which we draw near to God.

[20]And it was not without an oath! Others became priests without any oath, [21]but he became a priest with an oath when God said to him:

> "The Lord has sworn
>> and will not change his mind:
>> 'You are a priest forever.' " [a]

[22]Because of this oath, Jesus has become the guarantee of a better covenant.

[23]Now there have been many of those priests, since death prevented them from continuing in office; [24]but because Jesus lives forever, he has a permanent priesthood. [25]Therefore he is able to save completely [b] those who come to God through him, because he always lives to intercede for them.

[26]Such a high priest meets our need—one who is holy, blameless, pure, set apart from sinners, exalted above the heavens. [27]Unlike the other high priests, he does not need to offer sacrifices day after day, first for his own sins, and then for the sins of the people. He sacrificed for their sins once for all when he offered himself. [28]For the law appoints as high priests men who are weak; but the oath, which came after the law, appointed the Son, who has been made perfect forever.

The High Priest of a New Covenant

8 The point of what we are saying is this: We do have such a high priest, who sat down at the right hand of the throne of the Majesty in heaven, [2]and who serves in the sanctuary, the true tabernacle set up by the Lord, not by man.

[3]Every high priest is appointed to offer both gifts and sacrifices, and so it was necessary for this one also to have something to offer. [4]If he were on earth, he would not be a priest, for there are already men who offer the gifts prescribed by the law. [5]They serve at a sanctuary that is a copy and shadow of what is in heaven. This is why Moses was warned when he was about to build the tabernacle: "See to it that you make everything according to the pattern shown you on the mountain." [c] [6]But the ministry Jesus has received is as superior to theirs as the covenant of which he is mediator is superior to the old one, and it is founded on better promises.

[7]For if there had been nothing wrong with that first covenant, no place would have been sought for another. [8]But God found fault with the people and said [d]:

> "The time is coming, declares the Lord,
>> when I will make a new covenant
> with the house of Israel
>> and with the house of Judah.
> [9]It will not be like the covenant
>> I made with their forefathers
> when I took them by the hand
>> to lead them out of Egypt,
> because they did not remain faithful to my covenant,
>> and I turned away from them,
>>>>>> declares the Lord.

a 17,21 Psalm 110:4   *b 25 Or forever*   *c 5 Exodus 25:40*   *d 8 Some manuscripts may be translated fault and said to the people.*

¹⁰This is the covenant I will make with the house of Israel
    after that time, declares the Lord.
I will put my laws in their minds
    and write them on their hearts.
I will be their God,
    and they will be my people.
¹¹No longer will a man teach his neighbor,
    or a man his brother, saying, 'Know the Lord,'
because they will all know me,
    from the least of them to the greatest.
¹²For I will forgive their wickedness
    and will remember their sins no more." ᵃ

¹³By calling this covenant "new," he has made the first one obsolete; and what is obsolete and aging will soon disappear.

Worship in the Earthly Tabernacle

9 Now the first covenant had regulations for worship and also an earthly sanctuary. ²A tabernacle was set up. In its first room were the lampstand, the table and the consecrated bread; this was called the Holy Place. ³Behind the second curtain was a room called the Most Holy Place, ⁴which had the golden altar of incense and the gold-covered ark of the covenant. This ark contained the gold jar of manna, Aaron's staff that had budded, and the stone tablets of the covenant. ⁵Above the ark were the cherubim of the Glory, overshadowing the atonement cover.ᵇ But we cannot discuss these things in detail now.

⁶When everything had been arranged like this, the priests entered regularly into the outer room to carry on their ministry. ⁷But only the high priest entered the inner room, and that only once a year, and never without blood, which he offered for himself and for the sins the people had committed in ignorance. ⁸The Holy Spirit was showing by this that the way into the Most Holy Place had not yet been disclosed as long as the first tabernacle was still standing. ⁹This is an illustration for the present time, indicating that the gifts and sacrifices being offered were not able to clear the conscience of the worshiper. ¹⁰They are only a matter of food and drink and various ceremonial washings—external regulations applying until the time of the new order.

The Blood of Christ

¹¹When Christ came as high priest of the good things that are already here,ᶜ he went through the greater and more perfect tabernacle that is not man-made, that is to say, not a part of this creation. ¹²He did not enter by means of the blood of goats and calves; but he entered the Most Holy Place once for all by his own blood, having obtained eternal redemption. ¹³The blood of goats and bulls and the ashes of a heifer sprinkled on those who are ceremonially unclean sanctify them so that they are outwardly clean. ¹⁴How much more, then, will the blood of Christ, who through the eternal Spirit offered himself unblemished to God, cleanse our consciences from acts that lead to death,ᵈ so that we may serve the living God!

¹⁵For this reason Christ is the mediator of a new covenant, that those who are called may receive the promised eternal inheritance—now that he has died as a ransom to set them free from the sins committed under the first covenant.

¹⁶In the case of a will,ᵉ it is necessary to prove the death of the one who made it, ¹⁷because a will is in force only when somebody has died; it never takes effect while the one who made it is living. ¹⁸This is why even the first covenant was not put into effect without blood. ¹⁹When Moses had proclaimed every commandment of the law to all the people, he took the blood of calves, together with water, scarlet wool and branches of hyssop, and sprinkled the scroll and all the people. ²⁰He said, "This is the blood of the covenant, which God has commanded you to keep."ᶠ ²¹In the same way, he sprinkled with the blood both the tabernacle and everything used in its ceremonies. ²²In fact, the law requires that nearly everything be cleansed with blood, and without the shedding of blood there is no forgiveness.

ᵃ 12 Jer. 31:31-34   ᵇ 5 Traditionally *the mercy seat*   ᶜ 11 Some early manuscripts *are to come*   ᵈ 14 Or *from useless rituals*   ᵉ 16 Same Greek word as *covenant*; also in verse 17   ᶠ 20 Exodus 24:8

Hard Lessons

"Oh, come on, Dreena, don't be so dumb!" Tricia said, throwing a wrapper across the lunch table at me. "How could you not know your reading class is for slow kids?"

"Because," I said, "my teacher said all the reading classes are mixed."

"Yeah, right," Sarah said, "like anyone else believes that. That means you're for sure in the dumb class. Besides, don't you know that Mrs. Riggs is a special ed teacher? Nobody sees her except the LD kids."

Aimee coughed loudly and deliberately tried to change the subject. "So how about that killer chemistry quiz?"

The other girls groaned and started complaining about chem. I stared down at my half-eaten sandwich, realizing that Sarah was right. Everyone in my class is really slow at reading out loud. I thought they were just nervous, like me. Do I have a learning disorder? I pretended like I was paying attention to the other girls, but that was all I could think about.

That night, I asked my mom if I was LD. She said it doesn't matter and it labels people. After I asked her again, she finally admitted that she thinks I have a learning disability. She said the school called about it last week and wants to test me. Wonder when she was going to tell me. ∗

How can I face those girls again? They all knew about me even before I did. I must be really dumb . . .

learning disabilities in focus

Having a learning disability is nothing to be ashamed of. Yet when you're the one who has it, sometimes you can't help but feel inferior. Keep in mind . . .

» Having an LD doesn't mean you're dumb. In fact, many LD students are highly intelligent and work even harder than other students.

» Many "disabilities" are really just *differences* in the way you learn. Testing from a trained professional can help clarify the situation and give guidance on how to be most successful in school.

» Don't build your identity on just your GPA. If that's all there is to you, then you're pretty shallow. *What you can do* has nothing to do with *who you are*. God didn't make a mistake when he custom-designed you (see Psalm 139:13–14, page 791).

» In 1 Corinthians 12:12–27 (page 1517) God reminds us that we're all unique and that no part of the body of Christ is less important than any other.

For more on this topic, see the index on page 1656.

[23]It was necessary, then, for the copies of the heavenly things to be purified with these sacrifices, but the heavenly things themselves with better sacrifices than these. [24]For Christ did not enter a man-made sanctuary that was only a copy of the true one; he entered heaven itself, now to appear for us in God's presence. [25]Nor did he enter heaven to offer himself again and again, the way the high priest enters the Most Holy Place every year with blood that is not his own. [26]Then Christ would have had to suffer many times since the creation of the world. But now he has appeared once for all at the end of the ages to do away with sin by the sacrifice of himself. [27]Just as

man is destined to die once, and after that to face judgment, [28]so Christ was sacrificed once to take away the sins of many people; and he will appear a second time, not to bear sin, but to bring salvation to those who are waiting for him.

Christ's Sacrifice Once for All

10 The law is only a shadow of the good things that are coming—not the realities themselves. For this reason it can never, by the same sacrifices repeated endlessly year after year, make perfect those who draw near to worship. [2]If it could, would they not have stopped being offered? For the worshipers would have been cleansed once for all, and would no longer have felt guilty for their sins. [3]But those sacrifices are an annual reminder of sins, [4]because it is impossible for the blood of bulls and goats to take away sins.

[5]Therefore, when Christ came into the world, he said:

> "Sacrifice and offering you did not desire,
>   but a body you prepared for me;
> [6]with burnt offerings and sin offerings
>   you were not pleased.
> [7]Then I said, 'Here I am—it is written about me in the scroll—
>   I have come to do your will, O God.' "[a]

[8]First he said, "Sacrifices and offerings, burnt offerings and sin offerings you did not desire, nor were you pleased with them" (although the law required them to be made). [9]Then he said, "Here I am, I have come to do your will." He sets aside the first to establish the second. [10]And by that will, we have been made holy through the sacrifice of the body of Jesus Christ once for all.

[11]Day after day every priest stands and performs his religious duties; again and again he offers the same sacrifices, which can never take away sins. [12]But when this priest had offered for all time one sacrifice for sins, he sat down at the right hand of God. [13]Since that time he waits for his enemies to be made his footstool, [14]because by one sacrifice he has made perfect forever those who are being made holy.

[15]The Holy Spirit also testifies to us about this. First he says:

> [16]"This is the covenant I will make with them
>   after that time, says the Lord.
> I will put my laws in their hearts,
>   and I will write them on their minds."[b]

[17]Then he adds:

> "Their sins and lawless acts
>   I will remember no more."[c]

[18]And where these have been forgiven, there is no longer any sacrifice for sin.

A Call to Persevere

[19]Therefore, brothers, since we have confidence to enter the Most Holy Place by the blood of Jesus, [20]by a new and living way opened for us through the curtain, that is, his body, [21]and since we have a great priest over the house of God, [22]let us draw near to God with a sincere heart in full assurance of faith, having our hearts sprinkled to cleanse us from a guilty conscience and having our bodies washed with pure water. [23]Let us hold unswervingly to the hope we profess, for he who promised is faithful. [24]And let us consider how we may spur one another on toward love and good deeds. [25]Let us not give up meeting together, as some are in the habit of doing, but let us encourage one another—and all the more as you see the Day approaching.

[26]If we deliberately keep on sinning after we have received the knowledge of the truth, no sacrifice for sins is left, [27]but only a fearful expectation of judgment and of raging fire that will consume the enemies of God. [28]Anyone who rejected the law of Moses died without mercy on the testimony of two or three witnesses. [29]How much more severely do you think a man deserves to be punished who has trampled the Son of God under foot, who has treated as an unholy thing the

a 7 Psalm 40:6-8 (see Septuagint)   *b 16* Jer. 31:33   *c 17* Jer. 31:34

blood of the covenant that sanctified him, and who has insulted the Spirit of grace? [30]For we know him who said, "It is mine to avenge; I will repay,"[a] and again, "The Lord will judge his people."[b] [31]It is a dreadful thing to fall into the hands of the living God.

[32]Remember those earlier days after you had received the light, when you stood your ground in a great contest in the face of suffering. [33]Sometimes you were publicly exposed to insult and persecution; at other times you stood side by side with those who were so treated. [34]You sympathized with those in prison and joyfully accepted the confiscation of your property, because you knew that you yourselves had better and lasting possessions.

[35]So do not throw away your confidence; it will be richly rewarded. [36]You need to persevere so that when you have done the will of God, you will receive what he has promised. [37]For in just a very little while,

> "He who is coming will
> come and
> will not delay.
> [38]   But my righteous
> one[c] will live
> by faith.
> And if he shrinks back,
> I will not be pleased with him."[d]

genuine commitment » 10:25

"I get paid extra for working on Sundays. It's hard to pass up the cash to go to church." "Churches are full of hypocrites. I've been hurt by them enough. I can get along just fine without going to church." "Sunday's my day to relax. I'll just have my own church at home." Whoa there—hold up, everyone! Sometimes it's hard to stay committed to going to church, and it can be pretty tempting to not make it a priority. But God designed us so that we need to meet together and encourage each other. So don't give up on it!

[39]But we are not of those who shrink back and are destroyed, but of those who believe and are saved.

By Faith

11 Now faith is being sure of what we hope for and certain of what we do not see. [2]This is what the ancients were commended for.
[3]By faith we understand that the universe was formed at God's command, so that what is seen was not made out of what was visible.

[4]By faith Abel offered God a better sacrifice than Cain did. By faith he was commended as a righteous man, when God spoke well of his offerings. And by faith he still speaks, even though he is dead.

[5]By faith Enoch was taken from this life, so that he did not experience death; he could not be found, because God had taken him away. For before he was taken, he was commended as one who pleased God. [6]And without faith it is impossible to please God, because anyone who comes to him must believe that he exists and that he rewards those who earnestly seek him.

[7]By faith Noah, when warned about things not yet seen, in holy fear built an ark to save his family. By his faith he condemned the world and became heir of the righteousness that comes by faith.

[8]By faith Abraham, when called to go to a place he would later receive as his inheritance, obeyed and went, even though he did not know where he was going. [9]By faith he made his home in the promised land like a stranger in a foreign country; he lived in tents, as did Isaac and Jacob, who were heirs with him of the same promise. [10]For he was looking forward to the city with foundations, whose architect and builder is God.

a 30 Deut. 32:35   *b 30* Deut. 32:36; Psalm 135:14   *c 38* One early manuscript *But the righteous*   *d 38* Hab. 2:3,4

[11]By faith Abraham, even though he was past age—and Sarah herself was barren—was enabled to become a father because he[a] considered him faithful who had made the promise. [12]And so from this one man, and he as good as dead, came descendants as numerous as the stars in the sky and as countless as the sand on the seashore.

[13]All these people were still living by faith when they died. They did not receive the things promised; they only saw them and welcomed them from a distance. And they admitted that they were aliens and strangers on earth. [14]People who say such things show that they are looking for a country of their own. [15]If they had been thinking of the country they had left, they would have had opportunity to return. [16]Instead, they were longing for a better country—a heavenly one. Therefore God is not ashamed to be called their God, for he has prepared a city for them.

[17]By faith Abraham, when God tested him, offered Isaac as a sacrifice. He who had received the promises was about to sacrifice his one and only son, [18]even though God had said to him, "It is through Isaac that your offspring[b] will be reckoned."[c] [19]Abraham reasoned that God could raise the dead, and figuratively speaking, he did receive Isaac back from death.

[20]By faith Isaac blessed Jacob and Esau in regard to their future.

[21]By faith Jacob, when he was dying, blessed each of Joseph's sons, and worshiped as he leaned on the top of his staff.

[22]By faith Joseph, when his end was near, spoke about the exodus of the Israelites from Egypt and gave instructions about his bones.

[23]By faith Moses' parents hid him for three months after he was born, because they saw he was no ordinary child, and they were not afraid of the king's edict.

[24]By faith Moses, when he had grown up, refused to be known as the son of Pharaoh's daughter. [25]He chose to be mistreated along with the people of God rather than to enjoy the pleasures of sin for a short time. [26]He regarded disgrace for the sake of Christ as of greater value than the treasures of Egypt, because he was looking ahead to his reward. [27]By faith he left Egypt, not fearing the king's anger; he persevered because he saw him who is invisible. [28]By faith he kept the Passover and the sprinkling of blood, so that the destroyer of the firstborn would not touch the firstborn of Israel.

[29]By faith the people passed through the Red Sea[d] as on dry land; but when the Egyptians tried to do so, they were drowned.

[30]By faith the walls of Jericho fell, after the people had marched around them for seven days.

[31]By faith the prostitute Rahab, because she welcomed the spies, was not killed with those who were disobedient.[e]

[32]And what more shall I say? I do not

love notes

11:16

My treasured one,

There is a better place. At times, it's hard to conceive of any place other than this world you live in. But I promise that one day I will take you to live with me in my heavenly home. Have faith.

—Your Father in Heaven

Describe what you imagine heaven will be like.

_____

_____

_____

_____

_____

_____

_____

_____

_____

_____

_____

_____

_____

_____

_____

a 11 Or By faith even Sarah, who was past age, was enabled to bear children because she   b 18 Greek seed   c 18 Gen. 21:12   d 29 That is, Sea of Reeds   e 31 Or unbelieving have time to tell about Gideon, Barak, Samson, Jephthah, David, Samuel and the prophets, [33]who through faith conquered kingdoms, administered justice, and gained what was promised; who shut the mouths of lions, [34]quenched the fury of the flames, and escaped the edge of the sword; whose weakness was turned to strength; and who became powerful in battle and routed foreign armies. [35]Women received back their dead, raised to life again. Others were tortured and refused to be released, so that they might gain a better resurrection. [36]Some faced jeers and flogging, while still others were chained and put in prison. [37]They were stoned[a]; they were sawed in two; they were put to death by the sword. They went about in sheepskins and goatskins, destitute, persecuted and mistreated— [38]the world was not worthy of them. They wandered in deserts and mountains, and in caves and holes in the ground.

[39]These were all commended for their faith, yet none of them received what had been promised. [40]God had planned something better for us so that only together with us would they be made perfect.

God Disciplines His Sons

12 Therefore, since we are surrounded by such a great cloud of witnesses, let us throw off everything that hinders and the sin that so easily entangles, and let us run with perseverance the race marked out for us. [2]Let us fix our eyes on Jesus, the author and perfecter of our faith, who for the joy set before him endured the cross, scorning its shame, and sat down at the right hand of the throne of God. [3]Consider him who endured such opposition from sinful men, so that you will not grow weary and lose heart.

[4]In your struggle against sin, you have not yet resisted to the point of shedding your blood. [5]And you have forgotten that word of encouragement that addresses you as sons:

> "My son, do not make light of the Lord's discipline,
> and do not lose heart when he rebukes you,
> [6]because the Lord disciplines those he loves,
> and he punishes everyone he accepts as a son."[b]

[7]Endure hardship as discipline; God is treating you as sons. For what son is not disciplined by his father? [8]If you are not disciplined (and everyone undergoes discipline), then you are illegitimate children and not true sons. [9]Moreover, we have all had human fathers who disciplined us and we respected them for it. How much more should we submit to the Father of our spirits and live! [10]Our fathers disciplined us for a little while as they thought best; but God disciplines us for our good, that we may share in his holiness. [11]No discipline seems pleasant at the time, but painful. Later on, however, it produces a harvest of righteousness and peace for those who have been trained by it.

[12]Therefore, strengthen your feeble arms and weak knees. [13]"Make level paths for your feet,"[c] so that the lame may not be disabled, but rather healed.

Warning Against Refusing God

[14]Make every effort to live in peace with all men and to be holy; without holiness no one will see the Lord. [15]See to it that no one misses the grace of God and that no bitter root grows up to cause trouble and defile many. [16]See that no one is sexually immoral, or is godless like Esau, who for a single meal sold his inheritance rights as the oldest son. [17]Afterward, as you know, when he wanted to inherit this blessing, he was rejected. He could bring about no change of mind, though he sought the blessing with tears.

[18]You have not come to a mountain that can be touched and that is burning with fire; to dark-

truth or dare

In a competition, the roar of the crowd can give you that final push to finish strong. Right now, the faithful example of the spiritual heroes of the past is cheering *you* on. Keep going, girl!

12:1–2

---

a 37 Some early manuscripts *stoned; they were put to the test;*   *b 6* Prov. 3:11,12   *c 13* Prov. 4:26

ness, gloom and storm; [19]to a trumpet blast or to such a voice speaking words that those who heard it begged that no further word be spoken to them, [20]because they could not bear what was commanded: "If even an animal touches the mountain, it must be stoned." [a] [21]The sight was so terrifying that Moses said, "I am trembling with fear." [b]

[22]But you have come to Mount Zion, to the heavenly Jerusalem, the city of the living God. You have come to thousands upon thousands of angels in joyful assembly, [23]to the church of the firstborn, whose names are written in heaven. You have come to God, the judge of all men, to the spirits of righteous men made perfect, [24]to Jesus the mediator of a new covenant, and to the sprinkled blood that speaks a better word than the blood of Abel.

[25]See to it that you do not refuse him who speaks. If they did not escape when they refused him who warned them on earth, how much less will we, if we turn away from him who warns us from heaven? [26]At that time his voice shook the earth, but now he has promised, "Once more I will shake not only the earth but also the heavens." [c] [27]The words "once more" indicate the removing of what can be shaken—that is, created things—so that what cannot be shaken may remain.

[28]Therefore, since we are receiving a kingdom that cannot be shaken, let us be thankful, and so worship God acceptably with reverence and awe, [29]for our "God is a consuming fire." [d]

Concluding Exhortations

13 Keep on loving each other as brothers. [2]Do not forget to entertain strangers, for by so doing some people have entertained angels without knowing it. [3]Remember those in prison as if you were their fellow prisoners, and those who are mistreated as if you yourselves were suffering.

[4]Marriage should be honored by all, and the marriage bed kept pure, for God will judge the adulterer and all the sexually immoral. [5]Keep your lives free from the love of money and be content with what you have, because God has said,

"Never will I leave you;
never will I forsake you." [e]

[6]So we say with confidence,

"The Lord is my helper; I will not be afraid.
What can man do to me?" [f]

[7]Remember your leaders, who spoke the word of God to you. Consider the outcome of their way of life and imitate their faith. [8]Jesus Christ is the same yesterday and today and forever.

[9]Do not be carried away by all kinds of strange teachings. It is good for our hearts to be strengthened by grace, not by ceremonial foods, which are of no value to those who eat them. [10]We have an altar from which those who minister at the tabernacle have no right to eat.

[11]The high priest carries the blood of animals into the Most Holy Place as a sin offering, but the bodies are burned outside the camp. [12]And so Jesus also suffered outside the city gate to make the people holy through his own blood. [13]Let us, then, go to him outside the camp, bearing the disgrace he bore. [14]For here we do not have an enduring city, but we are looking for the city that is to come.

[15]Through Jesus, therefore, let us continually offer to God a sacrifice of praise—the fruit of lips that confess his name. [16]And do not forget to do good and to share with others, for with such sacrifices God is pleased.

[17]Obey your leaders and submit to their authority. They keep watch over you as men who must

truth or dare

As a teen girl, you naturally go through a daily roller coaster of feelings about school, guys and life in general. That's okay. Unlike us, Jesus never changes.

13:8

a 20 Exodus 19:12,13   *b 21* Deut. 9:19   *c 26* Haggai 2:6   *d 29* Deut. 4:24   *e 5* Deut. 31:6
f 6 Psalm 118:6,7

give an account. Obey them so that their work will be a joy, not a burden, for that would be of no advantage to you.

¹⁸Pray for us. We are sure that we have a clear conscience and desire to live honorably in every way. ¹⁹I particularly urge you to pray so that I may be restored to you soon.

²⁰May the God of peace, who through the blood of the eternal covenant brought back from the dead our Lord Jesus, that great Shepherd of the sheep, ²¹equip you with everything good for doing his will, and may he work in us what is pleasing to him, through Jesus Christ, to whom be glory for ever and ever. Amen.

²²Brothers, I urge you to bear with my word of exhortation, for I have written you only a short letter.

²³I want you to know that our brother Timothy has been released. If he arrives soon, I will come with him to see you.

²⁴Greet all your leaders and all God's people. Those from Italy send you their greetings.

²⁵Grace be with you all.

genuine
respect » 13:17

You may not enjoy submitting to the authorities in your life. When your parents tell you to clean your room, you roll your eyes and complain. When your coach asks you to play a different position, you give her a major attitude in response. When your youth pastor wants you to work out your differences with another girl at church, you try hard to avoid it. Did you know you're only making things harder on yourself? God put these people in your life for a reason, and it's in *your* best interests to obey them.

author:	James, the brother of Jesus.
date:	Probably about A.D. 49.
setting:	James was likely writing to believers who had been part of the early church in Jerusalem and had been scattered to various places because of persecution.
verse to remember:	Therefore, get rid of all moral filth and the evil that is so prevalent and humbly accept the word planted in you, which can save you. Do not merely listen to the word, and so deceive yourselves. Do what it says (1:21–22).
theme to consider:	Our faith determines our attitudes and actions.

unchanging truth

Here's an equation that's easy to remember: Faith = Belief + Actions.

It's not enough to have a set of Christian beliefs in our minds. Everything we may have learned in church is good—but it is not good enough. How will people know what we really believe if we don't act on our faith? If we say we believe we ought to befriend the friendless, then we can't blow off the girl who's sitting by herself at lunch. If we believe God wants us to tell others about Christ, then we can't keep our mouths shut when we hear others use his name in vain.

It takes a bold person to sit by the lonely girl in the cafeteria. It takes courage to confront blasphemy. However, it's worth every ounce of courage it takes to put our beliefs into action . . . or else our beliefs are worthless. You see, faith "works" only when it goes to work. When we believe it and live it, then we show that our faith is real.

James didn't beat around the bush in his letter. He had seen enough hypocrisy, and now he was calling the church on it. As Jesus' brother, he was serious about getting serious for Jesus. He didn't try to sugarcoat his words. He didn't attempt to smooth things over. He told it like it was when he said to the church, "It's time for a little less talk and a lot more action." What is he saying to you?

life lessons

1 Faith is not something you merely "have"; it's something you "live" (2:14–26).

2 Sometimes what you *don't* say is as important as what you *do* say (3:1–12).

3 What we often do as a last resort is actually what does the most good—prayer (5:13–18).

⌃

1

James, a servant of God and of the Lord Jesus Christ,

To the twelve tribes scattered among the nations:

Greetings.

Trials and Temptations

²Consider it pure joy, my brothers, whenever you face trials of many kinds, ³because you know that the testing of your faith develops perseverance. ⁴Perseverance must finish its work so that you may be mature and complete, not lacking anything. ⁵If any of you lacks wisdom, he should ask God, who gives generously to all without finding fault, and it will be given to him. ⁶But when he asks, he must believe and not doubt, because he who doubts is like a wave of the sea, blown and tossed by the wind. ⁷That man should not think he will receive anything from the Lord; ⁸he is a double-minded man, unstable in all he does.

⁹The brother in humble circumstances ought to take pride in his high position. ¹⁰But the one who is rich should take pride in his low position, because he will pass away like a wild flower. ¹¹For the sun rises with scorching heat and withers the plant; its blossom falls and its beauty is destroyed. In the same way, the rich man will fade away even while he goes about his business.

genuine faith » 1:2-4

The last thing you want to be known as is *immature*. You want others to see you as the mature person you consider yourself to be, right? The Bible's method to maturity may seem odd, but it's true: trials. When you face hard things in life, you can still have joy because you know that God will use them to make your faith mature. Most of us go out of our way to avoid trials. But no matter how hard we try, they find us. And when they do, how you respond shows your true level of maturity.

¹²Blessed is the man who perseveres under trial, because when he has stood the test, he will receive the crown of life that God has promised to those who love him.

¹³When tempted, no one should say, "God is tempting me." For God cannot be tempted by evil, nor does he tempt anyone; ¹⁴but each one is tempted when, by his own evil desire, he is dragged away and enticed. ¹⁵Then, after desire has conceived, it gives birth to sin; and sin, when it is full-grown, gives birth to death.

¹⁶Don't be deceived, my dear brothers. ¹⁷Every good and perfect gift is from above, coming down from the Father of the heavenly lights, who does not change like shifting shadows. ¹⁸He chose to give us birth through the word of truth, that we might be a kind of firstfruits of all he created.

Listening and Doing

¹⁹My dear brothers, take note of this: Everyone should be quick to listen, slow to speak and slow to become angry, ²⁰for man's anger does not bring about the righteous life that God desires. ²¹Therefore, get rid of all moral filth and the evil that is so prevalent and humbly accept the word planted in you, which can save you.

²²Do not merely listen to the word, and so deceive yourselves. Do what it says. ²³Anyone who listens to the word but does not do what it says is like a man who looks at his face in a mirror ²⁴and, after looking at himself, goes away and immediately forgets what he looks like. ²⁵But the man who looks intently into the perfect law that gives freedom, and continues to do this, not forgetting what he has heard, but doing it—he will be blessed in what he does.

²⁶If anyone considers himself religious and yet does not keep a tight rein on his tongue, he deceives himself and his religion is worthless. ²⁷Religion that God our Father accepts as pure and faultless is this: to look after orphans and widows in their distress and to keep oneself from being polluted by the world.

Favoritism Forbidden

2 My brothers, as believers in our glorious Lord Jesus Christ, don't show favoritism. ²Suppose a man comes into your meeting wearing a gold ring and fine clothes, and a poor man in shabby clothes also comes in. ³If you show special attention to the man wearing fine clothes and say, "Here's a good seat for you," but say to the poor man, "You stand there" or "Sit on the floor by my feet," ⁴have you not discriminated among yourselves and become judges with evil thoughts?

⁵Listen, my dear brothers: Has not God chosen those who are poor in the eyes of the world to be rich in faith and to inherit the kingdom he promised those who love him? ⁶But you have insulted the poor. Is it not the rich who are exploiting you? Are they not the ones who are dragging you into court? ⁷Are they not the ones who are slandering the noble name of him to whom you belong?

⁸If you really keep the royal law found in Scripture, "Love your neighbor as yourself," ᵃ you are doing right. ⁹But if you show favoritism, you sin and are convicted by the law as lawbreakers. ¹⁰For whoever keeps the whole law and yet stumbles at just one point is guilty of breaking all of it. ¹¹For he who said, "Do not commit adultery," ᵇ also said, "Do not murder." ᶜ If you do not commit adultery but do commit murder, you have become a lawbreaker.

¹²Speak and act as those who are going to be judged by the law that gives freedom, ¹³because judgment without mercy will be shown to anyone who has not been merciful. Mercy triumphs over judgment!

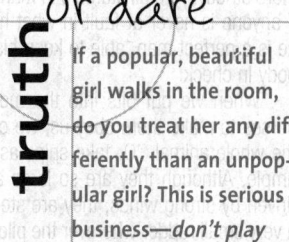

truth or dare

If a popular, beautiful girl walks in the room, do you treat her any differently than an unpopular girl? This is serious business—*don't play favorites.*

2:1–4

truth or dare

You can't *see* the difference between a good battery and a dead one. You've got to *use* it to prove that it works. Same goes for faith. Does yours work?

2:14–17

Faith and Deeds

¹⁴What good is it, my brothers, if a man claims to have faith but has no deeds? Can such faith save him? ¹⁵Suppose a brother or sister is without clothes and daily food. ¹⁶If one of you says to him, "Go, I wish you well; keep warm and well fed," but does nothing about his physical needs, what good is it? ¹⁷In the same way, faith by itself, if it is not accompanied by action, is dead.

¹⁸But someone will say, "You have faith; I have deeds."

Show me your faith without deeds, and I will show you my faith by what I do. ¹⁹You believe that there is one God. Good! Even the demons believe that—and shudder.

²⁰You foolish man, do you want evidence that faith without deeds is useless ᵈ? ²¹Was not our ancestor Abraham considered righteous for what he did when he offered his son Isaac on the altar? ²²You see that his faith and his actions were working together, and his faith was made complete by what he did. ²³And the scripture was fulfilled that says, "Abraham believed God, and it was credited to him as righteousness," ᵉ and he was called God's friend. ²⁴You see that a person is justified by what he does and not by faith alone.

²⁵In the same way, was not even Rahab the prostitute considered righteous for what she did when she gave lodging to the spies and sent them off in a different direction? ²⁶As the body without the spirit is dead, so faith without deeds is dead.

ᵃ *8* Lev. 19:18   ᵇ *11* Exodus 20:14; Deut. 5:18   ᶜ *11* Exodus 20:13; Deut. 5:17   ᵈ *20* Some early manuscripts *dead*   ᵉ *23* Gen. 15:6

Taming the Tongue

3 Not many of you should presume to be teachers, my brothers, because you know that we who teach will be judged more strictly. ²We all stumble in many ways. If anyone is never at fault in what he says, he is a perfect man, able to keep his whole body in check.

³When we put bits into the mouths of horses to make them obey us, we can turn the whole animal. ⁴Or take ships as an example. Although they are so large and are driven by strong winds, they are steered by a very small rudder wherever the pilot wants to go. ⁵Likewise the tongue is a small part of the body, but it makes great boasts. Consider what a great forest is set on fire by a small spark. ⁶The tongue also is a fire, a world of evil among the parts of the body. It corrupts the whole person, sets the whole course of his life on fire, and is itself set on fire by hell.

⁷All kinds of animals, birds, reptiles and creatures of the sea are being tamed and have been tamed by man, ⁸but no man can tame the tongue. It is a restless evil, full of deadly poison.

⁹With the tongue we praise our Lord and Father, and with it we curse men, who have been made in God's likeness. ¹⁰Out of the same mouth come praise and cursing. My brothers, this should not be. ¹¹Can both fresh water and salt*ᵃ* water flow from the same spring? ¹²My brothers, can a fig tree bear olives, or a grapevine bear figs? Neither can a salt spring produce fresh water.

Two Kinds of Wisdom

¹³Who is wise and understanding among you? Let him show it by his good life, by deeds done in the humility that comes from wisdom. ¹⁴But if you harbor bitter envy and selfish ambition in your hearts, do not boast about it or deny the truth. ¹⁵Such "wisdom" does not come down from heaven but is earthly, unspiritual, of the devil. ¹⁶For where you have envy and selfish ambition, there you find disorder and every evil practice.

¹⁷But the wisdom that comes from heaven is first of all pure; then peace-loving, considerate, submissive, full of mercy and good fruit, impartial and sincere. ¹⁸Peacemakers who sow in peace raise a harvest of righteousness.

Submit Yourselves to God

4 What causes fights and quarrels among you? Don't they come from your desires that battle within you? ²You want something but don't get it. You kill and covet, but you cannot have what you want. You quarrel and fight. You do not have, because you do not ask God. ³When you ask, you do not receive, because you ask with wrong motives, that you may spend what you get on your pleasures.

⁴You adulterous people, don't you know that friendship with the world is hatred toward God? Anyone who chooses to be a friend of the world becomes an enemy of God. ⁵Or do you think Scripture says without reason that the spirit he caused to live in us envies intensely?*ᵇ* ⁶But he gives us more grace. That is why Scripture says:

genuine speech » 3:1-12

Like the tiny computer chip that accesses the Internet . . . like the steering wheel of a car that maneuvers two tons of steel . . . like the small dusting of poison that can kill an individual . . . your tongue is little compared to the rest of your body, but oh-so-very powerful. It has the power to shake another person's confidence, reputation or joy—to do more evil than you can imagine. *Or* it has the power to build others up, point them to Jesus and praise God. Will you use this power for good or for evil?

a 11 Greek *bitter* (see also verse 14)   *b 5* Or *that God jealously longs for the spirit that he made to live in us;* or *that the Spirit he caused to live in us longs jealously*

in focus

Forgiving the Unforgivable

Profile: Jacqueline

"This is *who?*" I asked.

"It's . . . it's your dad, Jacqueline," said the voice on the other end of the line. "I was hoping we could talk. I know it's been a long time, but . . . I'd like to see you. I feel like I've missed so many years of your life, and I don't want that to continue." I stood there, frozen. I had no idea what to say. Why is he calling me after all this time? Seven years ago, he left my mom and our family—for another guy.

"No thanks, *Jack,*" I said coldly and hung up the phone. I hated even thinking of him as my father. Honestly, from his voice you'd never know he had turned our whole world upside down. He sounded so normal.

This was the third time he'd called me. When I told my mom he called again today, I was sure she'd be on my side and tell me to ignore him. Instead, Mom told me I should at least talk to him because he's still my dad. It's like she was saying that because so much time has passed, we can just pretend like nothing happened. How can my mom be cool with it now, after what he did to her? Why should I forgive him? He's still sinning with no hint of changing. I'll never be able to accept seeing him with some guy or imagining them living together. It seems like some sins are just too big to forgive.

forgiveness in focus

Have you subconsciously decided that some sins just can't be forgiven? We often "weigh" sins differently, but in God's eyes, we're all sinners in need of forgiveness.

If you're struggling to forgive someone who has failed you, keep in mind . . .

»Sometimes we hold others to a standard of perfection—especially someone close to us who's hurt us deeply. Yet all human beings fall short of this standard.

»Forgiveness is a command, not an option (see Ephesians 4:32, page 1546).

»Forgiveness is a choice. You might not *feel* like forgiving someone; you have to *choose* to forgive.

»Forgiveness is a process. You may have to forgive that person over and over. Sometimes even after we've forgiven someone, new feelings of hurt or resentment come up, and we have to forgive the person all over again (Matthew 18:21–22, page 1316).

For more on this topic, see the index on page 1656.

"God opposes the proud
but gives grace to the humble." [a]

[7]Submit yourselves, then, to God. Resist the devil, and he will flee from you. [8]Come near to God and he will come near to you. Wash your hands, you sinners, and purify your hearts, you double-minded. [9]Grieve, mourn and wail. Change your laughter to mourning and your joy to gloom. [10]Humble yourselves before the Lord, and he will lift you up.

[11]Brothers, do not slander one another. Anyone who speaks against his brother or judges him

[a] 6 Prov. 3:34

speaks against the law and judges it. When you judge the law, you are not keeping it, but sitting in judgment on it. [12]There is only one Lawgiver and Judge, the one who is able to save and destroy. But you—who are you to judge your neighbor?

Boasting About Tomorrow

[13]Now listen, you who say, "Today or tomorrow we will go to this or that city, spend a year there, carry on business and make money." [14]Why, you do not even know what will happen tomorrow. What is your life? You are a mist that appears for a little while and then vanishes. [15]Instead, you ought to say, "If it is the Lord's will, we will live and do this or that." [16]As it is, you boast and brag. All such boasting is evil. [17]Anyone, then, who knows the good he ought to do and doesn't do it, sins.

Warning to Rich Oppressors

5 Now listen, you rich people, weep and wail because of the misery that is coming upon you. [2]Your wealth has rotted, and moths have eaten your clothes. [3]Your gold and silver are corroded. Their corrosion will testify against you and eat your flesh like fire. You have hoarded wealth in the last days. [4]Look! The wages you failed to pay the workmen who mowed your fields are crying out against you. The cries of the harvesters have reached the ears of the Lord Almighty. [5]You have lived on earth in luxury and self-indulgence. You have fattened yourselves in the day of slaughter.[a] [6]You have condemned and murdered innocent men, who were not opposing you.

Patience in Suffering

[7]Be patient, then, brothers, until the Lord's coming. See how the farmer waits for the land to yield its valuable crop and how patient he is for the autumn and spring rains. [8]You too, be patient and stand firm, because the Lord's coming is near. [9]Don't grumble against each other, brothers, or you will be judged. The Judge is standing at the door!

[10]Brothers, as an example of patience in the face of suffering, take the prophets who spoke in the name of the Lord. [11]As you know, we consider blessed those who have persevered. You have heard of Job's perseverance and have seen what the Lord finally brought about. The Lord is full of compassion and mercy.

[12]Above all, my brothers, do not swear—not by heaven or by earth or by anything else. Let your "Yes" be yes, and your "No," no, or you will be condemned.

The Prayer of Faith

[13]Is any one of you in trouble? He should pray. Is anyone happy? Let him sing songs of praise. [14]Is any one of you sick? He should call the elders of the church to pray over him and anoint him with oil in the name of the Lord. [15]And the prayer offered in faith will make the sick person well; the Lord will raise him up. If he has sinned, he will be forgiven. [16]Therefore confess your sins to each other and pray for each other so that you may be healed. The prayer of a righteous man is powerful and effective.

[17]Elijah was a man just like us. He prayed earnestly that it would not rain, and it did not rain on the land for three and a half years. [18]Again he prayed, and the heavens gave rain, and the earth produced its crops.

[19]My brothers, if one of you should wander from the truth and someone should bring him back, [20]remember this: Whoever turns a sinner from the error of his way will save him from death and cover over a multitude of sins.

» *a* 5 Or *yourselves as in a day of feasting*

at a glance ⌄

author:	The apostle Peter.
date:	About A.D. 62–64, possibly written from Rome.
setting:	Christians were being tortured and killed under Emperor Nero, and the church in Jerusalem was being scattered.
verse to remember:	Dear friends, do not be surprised at the painful trial you are suffering, as though something strange were happening to you. But rejoice that you participate in the sufferings of Christ (4:12–13).
theme to consider:	No one likes to go through hard times. But as you read this book, you'll be reminded that God will use those times to strengthen your faith.

1 peter

unchanging truth

What would Jesus do? It's an easy enough question to help us make the right choice at the right time. But have you ever thought about what Jesus *wouldn't* do? That's the message of 1 Peter—a letter Peter wrote to people who suffered for Jesus on a daily basis. Peter wanted them to know what Jesus wouldn't do when times got tough. When life got to him. Even when his life was at stake.

Jesus wouldn't give up. He would keep going despite the pain, knowing that God would honor his obedience.

Jesus wouldn't complain. He wouldn't throw up his hands in disgust and accuse his Father of giving him a raw deal. He knew suffering was part of God's greater plan, and God would somehow use it for his good purposes.

Jesus wouldn't give in. Although he wouldn't retaliate when he was attacked, he also wouldn't back down when people challenged his beliefs. He wouldn't compromise. He wouldn't walk away from what he knew to be true—God and God's plan are real. More real than suffering.

What will you do when you suffer for his sake? Cry? Sure, that's understandable. Hurt? Undoubtedly—people can be cruel. But think about this—what *won't* you do? If you're going to follow Jesus' example, then you won't give up. You won't complain. And you won't give in. Not now. Not ever.

life lessons

1 We should follow in the steps of Jesus, wherever they may lead (2:19–23).

2 The time to get serious about our faith is *now*. We've wasted enough time in the past, and the clock's ticking (4:1–11).

3 Suffering for Jesus' sake is part of growing in your faith. When you do suffer, cast your anxiety on him and receive his strength (5:6–11).

⌃

1 Peter, an apostle of Jesus Christ,

To God's elect, strangers in the world, scattered throughout Pontus, Galatia, Cappadocia, Asia and Bithynia, ²who have been chosen according to the foreknowledge of God the Father, through the sanctifying work of the Spirit, for obedience to Jesus Christ and sprinkling by his blood:

Grace and peace be yours in abundance.

Praise to God for a Living Hope

³Praise be to the God and Father of our Lord Jesus Christ! In his great mercy he has given us new birth into a living hope through the resurrection of Jesus Christ from the dead, ⁴and into an inheritance that can never perish, spoil or fade—kept in heaven for you, ⁵who through faith are shielded by God's power until the coming of the salvation that is ready to be revealed in the last time. ⁶In this you greatly rejoice, though now for a little while you may have had to suffer grief in all kinds of trials. ⁷These have come so that your faith—of greater worth than gold, which perishes even though refined by fire—may be proved genuine and may result in praise, glory and honor when Jesus Christ is revealed. ⁸Though you have not seen him, you love him; and even though you do not see him now, you believe in him and are filled with an inexpressible and glorious joy, ⁹for you are receiving the goal of your faith, the salvation of your souls.

¹⁰Concerning this salvation, the prophets, who spoke of the grace that was to come to you, searched intently and with the greatest care, ¹¹trying to find out the time and circumstances to which the Spirit of Christ in them was pointing when he predicted the sufferings of Christ and the glories that would follow. ¹²It was revealed to them that they were not serving themselves but you, when they spoke of the things that have now been told you by those who have preached the gospel to you by the Holy Spirit sent from heaven. Even angels long to look into these things.

Be Holy

¹³Therefore, prepare your minds for action; be self-controlled; set your hope fully on the grace to be given you when Jesus Christ is revealed. ¹⁴As obedient children, do not conform to the evil desires you had when you lived in ignorance. ¹⁵But just as he who called you is holy, so be holy in all you do; ¹⁶for it is written: "Be holy, because I am holy." [a]

¹⁷Since you call on a Father who judges each man's work impartially, live your lives as strangers here in reverent fear. ¹⁸For you know that it was not with perishable things such as silver or gold that you were redeemed from the empty way of life handed down to you from your forefathers, ¹⁹but with the precious blood of Christ, a lamb without blemish or defect. ²⁰He was chosen before the creation of the world, but was revealed in these last times for your sake. ²¹Through him you believe in God, who raised him from the dead and glorified him, and so your faith and hope are in God.

²²Now that you have purified yourselves by obeying the truth so that you have sincere love for your brothers, love one another deeply, from the heart. [b] ²³For you have been born again, not of perishable seed, but of imperishable, through the living and enduring word of God. ²⁴For,

> "All men are like grass,
>   and all their glory is like the flowers of the field;
> the grass withers and the flowers fall,
> ²⁵   but the word of the Lord stands forever." [c]

And this is the word that was preached to you.

2 Therefore, rid yourselves of all malice and all deceit, hypocrisy, envy, and slander of every kind. ²Like newborn babies, crave pure spiritual milk, so that by it you may grow up in your salvation, ³now that you have tasted that the Lord is good.

The Living Stone and a Chosen People

⁴As you come to him, the living Stone—rejected by men but chosen by God and precious to him— ⁵you also, like living stones, are being built into a spiritual house to be a holy priesthood, offering spiritual sacrifices acceptable to God through Jesus Christ. ⁶For in Scripture it says:

a 16 Lev. 11:44,45; 19:2   b 22 Some early manuscripts *from a pure heart*   c 25 Isaiah 40:6-8

"See, I lay a stone in Zion,
    a chosen and precious cornerstone,
and the one who trusts in him
    will never be put to shame." [a]

[7]Now to you who believe, this stone is precious. But to those who do not believe,

"The stone the builders rejected
    has become the capstone," [b] [c]

[8]and,

"A stone that causes men to stumble
    and a rock that makes them fall." [d]

They stumble because they disobey the message—which is also what they were destined for.

[9]But you are a chosen people, a royal priesthood, a holy nation, a people belonging to God, that you may declare the praises of him who called you out of darkness into his wonderful light. [10]Once you were not a people, but now you are the people of God; once you had not received mercy, but now you have received mercy.

[11]Dear friends, I urge you, as aliens and strangers in the world, to abstain from sinful desires, which war against your soul. [12]Live such good lives among the pagans that, though they accuse you of doing wrong, they may see your good deeds and glorify God on the day he visits us.

Submission to Rulers and Masters

[13]Submit yourselves for the Lord's sake to every authority instituted among men: whether to the king, as the supreme authority, [14]or to governors, who are sent by him to punish those who do wrong and to commend those who do right. [15]For it is God's will that by doing good you should silence the ignorant talk of foolish men. [16]Live as free men, but do not use your freedom as a cover-up for evil; live as servants of God. [17]Show proper respect to everyone: Love the brotherhood of believers, fear God, honor the king.

[18]Slaves, submit yourselves to your masters with all respect, not only to those who are good and considerate, but also to those who are harsh. [19]For it is commendable if a man bears up under the pain of unjust suffering because he is conscious of God. [20]But how is it to your credit if you receive a beating for doing wrong and endure it? But if you suffer for doing good and you endure it, this is commendable before God. [21]To this you were called, because Christ suffered for you, leaving you an example, that you should follow in his steps.

[22]"He committed no sin,
    and no deceit was found in his mouth." [e]

[23]When they hurled their insults at him, he did not retaliate; when he suffered, he made no threats. Instead, he entrusted himself to him who judges justly. [24]He himself bore our sins in his body on the tree, so that we might die to sins and live for righteousness; by his wounds you have been healed. [25]For you were like sheep going astray, but now you have returned to the Shepherd and Overseer of your souls.

Wives and Husbands

3 Wives, in the same way be submissive to your husbands so that, if any of them do not believe the word, they may be won over without words by the behavior of their wives, [2]when they see the purity and reverence of your lives. [3]Your beauty should not come from outward adornment, such as braided hair and the wearing of gold jewelry and fine clothes. [4]Instead, it should be that of your inner self, the unfading beauty of a gentle and quiet spirit, which is of great worth in God's sight. [5]For this is the way the holy women of the past who put their hope in God used to make themselves beautiful. They were submissive to their own husbands, [6]like Sarah, who obeyed Abraham and called him her master. You are her daughters if you do what is right and do not give way to fear.

[7]Husbands, in the same way be considerate as you live with your wives, and treat them with

a 6 Isaiah 28:16   *b 7* Or *cornerstone*   *c 7* Psalm 118:22   *d 8* Isaiah 8:14   *e 22* Isaiah 53:9

respect as the weaker partner and as heirs with you of the gracious gift of life, so that nothing will hinder your prayers.

Suffering for Doing Good

⁸Finally, all of you, live in harmony with one another; be sympathetic, love as brothers, be compassionate and humble. ⁹Do not repay evil with evil or insult with insult, but with blessing, because to this you were called so that you may inherit a blessing. ¹⁰For,

> "Whoever would love life
> and see good days
> must keep his tongue from evil
> and his lips from deceitful speech.
> ¹¹He must turn from evil and do good;
> he must seek peace and pursue it.
> ¹²For the eyes of the Lord are on the righteous
> and his ears are attentive to their prayer,
> but the face of the Lord is against those who do evil." *ᵃ*

¹³Who is going to harm you if you are eager to do good? ¹⁴But even if you should suffer for what is right, you are blessed. "Do not fear what they fear *ᵇ*; do not be frightened." *ᶜ* ¹⁵But in your hearts set apart Christ as Lord. Always be prepared to give an answer to everyone who asks you to give the reason for the hope that you have. But do this with gentleness and respect, ¹⁶keeping a clear conscience, so that those who speak maliciously against your good behavior in Christ may be ashamed of their slander. ¹⁷It is better, if it is God's will, to suffer for doing good than for doing evil. ¹⁸For Christ died for sins once for all, the righteous for the unrighteous, to bring you to God. He was put to death in the body but made alive by the Spirit, ¹⁹through whom *ᵈ* also he went and preached to the spirits in prison ²⁰who disobeyed long ago when God waited patiently in the days of Noah while the ark was being built. In it only a few people, eight in all, were saved through water, ²¹and this water symbolizes baptism that now saves you also—not the removal of dirt from the body but the pledge *ᵉ* of a good conscience toward God. It saves you by the resurrection of Jesus Christ, ²²who has gone into heaven and is at God's right hand—with angels, authorities and powers in submission to him.

Living for God

4 Therefore, since Christ suffered in his body, arm yourselves also with the same attitude, because he who has suffered in his body is done with sin. ²As a result, he does not live the rest of his earthly life for evil human desires, but rather for the will of God. ³For you have spent enough

truth or dare

So you might not be able to recite the Bible by memory or debate theology with famous gurus. Okay. Just be ready to share your faith when you get an opportunity.

3:15–16

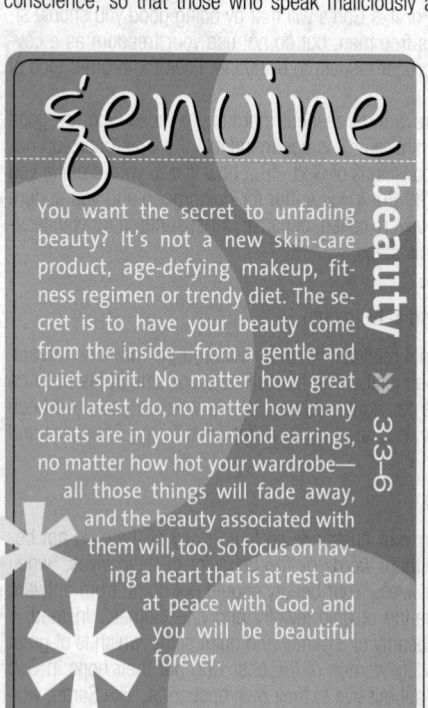

genuine beauty ≫ 3:3-6

You want the secret to unfading beauty? It's not a new skin-care product, age-defying makeup, fitness regimen or trendy diet. The secret is to have your beauty come from the inside—from a gentle and quiet spirit. No matter how great your latest 'do, no matter how many carats are in your diamond earrings, no matter how hot your wardrobe—all those things will fade away, and the beauty associated with them will, too. So focus on having a heart that is at rest and at peace with God, and you will be beautiful forever.

ᵃ 12 Psalm 34:12-16   *ᵇ 14* Or *not fear their threats*   *ᶜ 14* Isaiah 8:12   *ᵈ 18,19* Or *alive in the spirit,* ¹⁹*through which*   *ᵉ 21* Or *response*

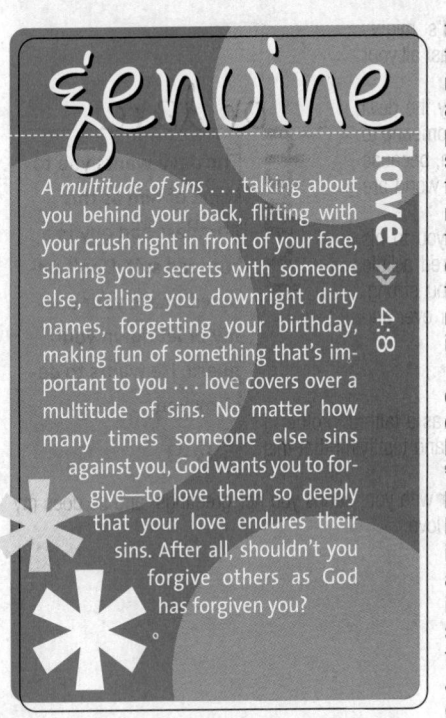

genuine
love ≫ 4:8

A multitude of sins . . . talking about you behind your back, flirting with your crush right in front of your face, sharing your secrets with someone else, calling you downright dirty names, forgetting your birthday, making fun of something that's important to you . . . love covers over a multitude of sins. No matter how many times someone else sins against you, God wants you to forgive—to love them so deeply that your love endures their sins. After all, shouldn't you forgive others as God has forgiven you?

time in the past doing what pagans choose to do—living in debauchery, lust, drunkenness, orgies, carousing and detestable idolatry. [4]They think it strange that you do not plunge with them into the same flood of dissipation, and they heap abuse on you. [5]But they will have to give account to him who is ready to judge the living and the dead. [6]For this is the reason the gospel was preached even to those who are now dead, so that they might be judged according to men in regard to the body, but live according to God in regard to the spirit.

[7]The end of all things is near. Therefore be clear minded and self-controlled so that you can pray. [8]Above all, love each other deeply, because love covers over a multitude of sins. [9]Offer hospitality to one another without grumbling. [10]Each one should use whatever gift he has received to serve others, faithfully administering God's grace in its various forms. [11]If anyone speaks, he should do it as one speaking the very words of God. If anyone serves, he should do it with the strength God provides, so that in all things God may be praised through Jesus Christ. To him be the glory and the power for ever and ever. Amen.

Suffering for Being a Christian

[12]Dear friends, do not be surprised at the painful trial you are suffering, as though something strange were happening to you. [13]But rejoice that you participate in the sufferings of Christ, so that you may be overjoyed when his glory is revealed. [14]If you are insulted because of the name of Christ, you are blessed, for the Spirit of glory and of God rests on you. [15]If you suffer, it should not be as a murderer or thief or any other kind of criminal, or even as a meddler. [16]However, if you suffer as a Christian, do not be ashamed, but praise God that you bear that name. [17]For it is time for judgment to begin with the family of God; and if it begins with us, what will the outcome be for those who do not obey the gospel of God? [18]And,

> "If it is hard for the righteous to be saved,
> what will become of the ungodly and the sinner?" [a]

[19]So then, those who suffer according to God's will should commit themselves to their faithful Creator and continue to do good.

To Elders and Young Men

5 To the elders among you, I appeal as a fellow elder, a witness of Christ's sufferings and one who also will share in the glory to be revealed: [2]Be shepherds of God's flock that is under your care, serving as overseers—not because you must, but because you are willing, as God wants you to be; not greedy for money, but eager to serve; [3]not lording it over those entrusted to you, but being examples to the flock. [4]And when the Chief Shepherd appears, you will receive the crown of glory that will never fade away.

[5]Young men, in the same way be submissive to those who are older. All of you, clothe yourselves with humility toward one another, because,

> "God opposes the proud
> but gives grace to the humble." [b]

a 18 Prov. 11:31   b 5 Prov. 3:34

⁶Humble yourselves, therefore, under God's mighty hand, that he may lift you up in due time. ⁷Cast all your anxiety on him because he cares for you.

⁸Be self-controlled and alert. Your enemy the devil prowls around like a roaring lion looking for someone to devour. ⁹Resist him, standing firm in the faith, because you know that your brothers throughout the world are undergoing the same kind of sufferings.

¹⁰And the God of all grace, who called you to his eternal glory in Christ, after you have suffered a little while, will himself restore you and make you strong, firm and steadfast. ¹¹To him be the power for ever and ever. Amen.

Final Greetings

¹²With the help of Silas,ᵃ whom I regard as a faithful brother, I have written to you briefly, encouraging you and testifying that this is the true grace of God. Stand fast in it.

¹³She who is in Babylon, chosen together with you, sends you her greetings, and so does my son Mark. ¹⁴Greet one another with a kiss of love.

Peace to all of you who are in Christ.

truth or dare

The devil wants you to think of him as this harmless bad guy in a cute red suit. Don't underestimate your enemy or let down your guard. He wants to destroy you.

5:8–9

ᵃ 12 Greek Silvanus, a variant of Silas

at a glance ⌄

author:	The apostle Peter.
date:	About A.D. 67.
setting:	Peter wrote this letter shortly before his death to warn believers about false teachers.
verse to remember:	His divine power has given us everything we need for life and godliness through our knowledge of him who called us by his own glory and goodness (1:3).
theme to consider:	How can we defend against falling prey to wrong teachings and false teachers? In this book, we learn that the answer is to continually grow in our relationship with Christ.

unchanging truth

2 peter

Let's say you hear a nasty rumor floating around school about your best friend. You'd probably go directly to your friend to find out the facts, right?

What if your history teacher asked you to find out a slew of facts about the War of 1812? Where would you turn? Probably an encyclopedia, right?

Now what do you do when you hear something confusing about your faith? Maybe it sounds reasonable but just slightly "off" from what you've always heard. Where do you go to find out if it's true? There's only one source for ultimate truth: God's Word.

Peter wrote his second letter both as a warning against false teachers and as a reminder about the bedrock truth of Scripture. He wanted to warn Christians about false teachers—these bold fiends who'll do anything to twist the truth about God. Then he also reminded Christians that the only surefire way to know whether or not something's true is to test it against Scripture. If it agrees with God's Word—it's true. If it contradicts God's Word—it's false. Period.

That was good advice then; it's still good advice for us today. When you hear false messages floating around—that there are many ways to God, that there's no absolute truth, that God's something that he's not—test them against God's Word and see how they compare.

life lessons

1 False teachers are alive and well. Watch out for their schemes (2:1–3).

2 False teaching is a high crime in God's court—he will punish it severely (2:10–22).

3 If you ever wonder if something's true, compare it to God's Word—the ultimate authority (1:16–21; 3:14–18).

1

Simon Peter, a servant and apostle of Jesus Christ,

To those who through the righteousness of our God and Savior Jesus Christ have received a faith as precious as ours:

[2]Grace and peace be yours in abundance through the knowledge of God and of Jesus our Lord.

Making One's Calling and Election Sure

[3]His divine power has given us everything we need for life and godliness through our knowledge of him who called us by his own glory and goodness. [4]Through these he has given us his very great and precious promises, so that through them you may participate in the divine nature and escape the corruption in the world caused by evil desires.

[5]For this very reason, make every effort to add to your faith goodness; and to goodness, knowledge; [6]and to knowledge, self-control; and to self-control, perseverance; and to perseverance, godliness; [7]and to godliness, brotherly kindness; and to brotherly kindness, love. [8]For if you possess these qualities in increasing measure, they will keep you from being ineffective and unproductive in your knowledge of our Lord Jesus Christ. [9]But if anyone does not have them, he is nearsighted and blind, and has forgotten that he has been cleansed from his past sins.

[10]Therefore, my brothers, be all the more eager to make your calling and election sure. For if you do these things, you will never fall, [11]and you will receive a rich welcome into the eternal kingdom of our Lord and Savior Jesus Christ.

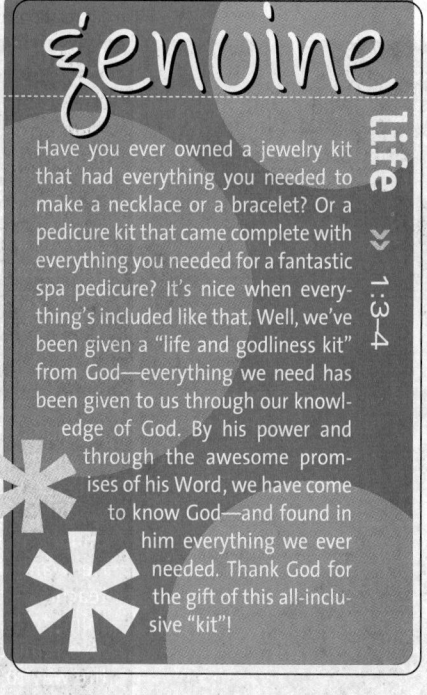

genuine life » 1:3-4

Have you ever owned a jewelry kit that had everything you needed to make a necklace or a bracelet? Or a pedicure kit that came complete with everything you needed for a fantastic spa pedicure? It's nice when everything's included like that. Well, we've been given a "life and godliness kit" from God—everything we need has been given to us through our knowledge of God. By his power and through the awesome promises of his Word, we have come to know God—and found in him everything we ever needed. Thank God for the gift of this all-inclusive "kit"!

Prophecy of Scripture

[12]So I will always remind you of these things, even though you know them and are firmly established in the truth you now have. [13]I think it is right to refresh your memory as long as I live in the tent of this body, [14]because I know that I will soon put it aside, as our Lord Jesus Christ has made clear to me. [15]And I will make every effort to see that after my departure you will always be able to remember these things.

[16]We did not follow cleverly invented stories when we told you about the power and coming of our Lord Jesus Christ, but we were eyewitnesses of his majesty. [17]For he received honor and glory from God the Father when the voice came to him from the Majestic Glory, saying, "This is my Son, whom I love; with him I am well pleased."[a] [18]We ourselves heard this voice that came from heaven when we were with him on the sacred mountain.

[19]And we have the word of the prophets made more certain, and you will do well to pay attention to it, as to a light shining in a dark place, until the day dawns and the morning star rises in your hearts. [20]Above all, you must understand that no prophecy of Scripture came about by the prophet's own interpretation. [21]For prophecy never had its origin in the will of man, but men spoke from God as they were carried along by the Holy Spirit.

a 17 Matt. 17:5; Mark 9:7; Luke 9:35

False Teachers and Their Destruction

2 But there were also false prophets among the people, just as there will be false teachers among you. They will secretly introduce destructive heresies, even denying the sovereign Lord who bought them—bringing swift destruction on themselves. [2]Many will follow their shameful ways and will bring the way of truth into disrepute. [3]In their greed these teachers will exploit you with stories they have made up. Their condemnation has long been hanging over them, and their destruction has not been sleeping.

[4]For if God did not spare angels when they sinned, but sent them to hell,[a] putting them into gloomy dungeons[b] to be held for judgment; [5]if he did not spare the ancient world when he brought the flood on its ungodly people, but protected Noah, a preacher of righteousness, and seven others; [6]if he condemned the cities of Sodom and Gomorrah by burning them to ashes, and made them an example of what is going to happen to the ungodly; [7]and if he rescued Lot, a righteous man, who was distressed by the filthy lives of lawless men [8](for that righteous man, living among them day after day, was tormented in his righteous soul by the lawless deeds he saw and heard)— [9]if this is so, then the Lord knows how to rescue godly men from trials and to hold the unrighteous for the day of judgment, while continuing their punishment.[c] [10]This is especially true of those who follow the corrupt desire of the sinful nature[d] and despise authority.

Bold and arrogant, these men are not afraid to slander celestial beings; [11]yet even angels, although they are stronger and more powerful, do not bring slanderous accusations against such beings in the presence of the Lord. [12]But these men blaspheme in matters they do not understand. They are like brute beasts, creatures of instinct, born only to be caught and destroyed, and like beasts they too will perish.

[13]They will be paid back with harm for the harm they have done. Their idea of pleasure is to carouse in broad daylight. They are blots and blemishes, reveling in their pleasures while they feast with you.[e] [14]With eyes full of adultery, they never stop sinning; they seduce the unstable; they are experts in greed—an accursed brood! [15]They have left the straight way and wandered off to follow the way of Balaam son of Beor, who loved the wages of wickedness. [16]But he was rebuked for his wrongdoing by a donkey—a beast without speech—who spoke with a man's voice and restrained the prophet's madness.

[17]These men are springs without water and mists driven by a storm. Blackest darkness is reserved for them. [18]For they mouth empty, boastful words and, by appealing to the lustful desires of sinful human nature, they entice people who are just escaping from those who live in error. [19]They promise them freedom, while they themselves are slaves of depravity—for a man is a slave to whatever has mastered him. [20]If they have escaped the corruption of the world by knowing our Lord and Savior Jesus Christ and are again entangled in it and overcome, they are worse off at the end than they were at the beginning. [21]It would have been better for them not to have known the way of righteousness, than to have known it and then to turn their backs on the sacred command that was passed on to them. [22]Of them the proverbs are true: "A dog returns to its vomit,"[f] and, "A sow that is washed goes back to her wallowing in the mud."

The Day of the Lord

3 Dear friends, this is now my second letter to you. I have written both of them as reminders to stimulate you to wholesome thinking. [2]I want you to recall the words spoken in the past by the holy prophets and the command given by our Lord and Savior through your apostles.

[3]First of all, you must understand that in the last days scoffers will come, scoffing and following their own evil desires. [4]They will say, "Where is this 'coming' he promised? Ever since our fathers died, everything goes on as it has since the beginning of creation." [5]But they deliberately forget that long ago by God's word the heavens existed and the earth was formed out of water and by water. [6]By these waters also the world of that time was deluged and destroyed. [7]By the same word the present heavens and earth are reserved for fire, being kept for the day of judgment and destruction of ungodly men.

[8]But do not forget this one thing, dear friends: With the Lord a day is like a thousand years, and a thousand years are like a day. [9]The Lord is not slow in keeping his promise, as some understand

---

a 4 Greek *Tartarus*   *b 4* Some manuscripts *into chains of darkness*   *c 9* Or *unrighteous for punishment until the day of judgment*   *d 10* Or *the flesh*   *e 13* Some manuscripts *in their love feasts*   *f 22* Prov. 26:11

slowness. He is patient with you, not wanting anyone to perish, but everyone to come to repentance.

¹⁰But the day of the Lord will come like a thief. The heavens will disappear with a roar; the elements will be destroyed by fire, and the earth and everything in it will be laid bare.ᵃ

¹¹Since everything will be destroyed in this way, what kind of people ought you to be? You ought to live holy and godly lives ¹²as you look forward to the day of God and speed its coming.ᵇ That day will bring about the destruction of the heavens by fire, and the elements will melt in the heat. ¹³But in keeping with his promise we are looking forward to a new heaven and a new earth, the home of righteousness.

¹⁴So then, dear friends, since you are looking forward to this, make every effort to be found spotless, blameless and at peace with him. ¹⁵Bear in mind that our Lord's patience means salvation, just as our dear brother Paul also wrote you with the wisdom that God gave him. ¹⁶He writes the same way in all his letters, speaking in them of these matters. His letters contain some things that are hard to understand, which ignorant and unstable people distort, as they do the other Scriptures, to their own destruction.

¹⁷Therefore, dear friends, since you already know this, be on your guard so that you may not be carried away by the error of lawless men and fall from your secure position. ¹⁸But grow in the grace and knowledge of our Lord and Savior Jesus Christ. To him be glory both now and forever! Amen.

truth or dare

Do you ever feel like God's schedule is *way* different than yours? Well . . . it is! But his timeframe is always right—especially when it comes to patience for sinners.

3:8–9

ᵃ 10 Some manuscripts *be burned up*   ᵇ 12 Or *as you wait eagerly for the day of God to come*

at a glance ⌄

author:	The apostle John.
date:	Between A.D. 85–95.
setting:	John, who was an eyewitness and close friend of Christ, wrote to encourage Christians to have confidence in God and in their faith.
verse to remember:	I write these things to you who believe in the name of the Son of God so that you may know that you have eternal life (5:13).
theme to consider:	When doubts about faith creep in, read the book of 1 John. It will help you understand the reality of God in your life, assure you of your eternal life and encourage you to remain in fellowship with God.

unchanging truth

It's okay to have doubts. That happens to every Christian. What's not okay is getting comfortable with them and letting them linger. You see, doubts do one of two things to our faith. They either motivate us to find out the truth and become sure of what we believe, or they drown out the voice of faith and cause us to become weak.

This book uses the word "know" more than 30 times. Count 'em. God wants us to *know* beyond a doubt that he is real and that he loves us. If we just *think* that's true, then we open ourselves up to all kinds of doubts. For example, if you're never 100 percent certain God loves you unconditionally, then you're more likely to believe that anything you do or say wrong is a potential threat to your relationship with him. Majorly mess up? You're outta there. Forget your quiet time for a few days? You're history. Fortunately, God doesn't work that way. He wants us to know we're loved and that we're safe and secure in that love.

The human heart is a tricky thing. It can tell us that we're no good and that God has abandoned us. When we sin, our hearts can race with worry that God doesn't love us anymore. However, God holds our hearts in his hands and sets them at rest. He says, "Don't worry. It's okay. I still love you just as much." For "God is greater than our hearts," and his love reminds us of the truth (3:19–20).

1 john

life lessons

1 Obedience is the only real proof that we love God and are saved (2:3–6).

2 The one who invented love and is love itself will always love us (4:7–18).

3 Love others. It's not an option; it's a command. If you don't love others, how can you really love God (2:9–11; 4:7–12,19–21)?!

⌃

The Word of Life

1 That which was from the beginning, which we have heard, which we have seen with our eyes, which we have looked at and our hands have touched—this we proclaim concerning the Word of life. ²The life appeared; we have seen it and testify to it, and we proclaim to you the eternal life, which was with the Father and has appeared to us. ³We proclaim to you what we have seen and heard, so that you also may have fellowship with us. And our fellowship is with the Father and with his Son, Jesus Christ. ⁴We write this to make our*ᵃ* joy complete.

Walking in the Light

⁵This is the message we have heard from him and declare to you: God is light; in him there is no darkness at all. ⁶If we claim to have fellowship with him yet walk in the darkness, we lie and do not live by the truth. ⁷But if we walk in the light, as he is in the light, we have fellowship with one another, and the blood of Jesus, his Son, purifies us from all*ᵇ* sin.

⁸If we claim to be without sin, we deceive ourselves and the truth is not in us. ⁹If we confess our sins, he is faithful and just and will forgive us our sins and purify us from all unrighteousness. ¹⁰If we claim we have not sinned, we make him out to be a liar and his word has no place in our lives.

2 My dear children, I write this to you so that you will not sin. But if anybody does sin, we have one who speaks to the Father in our defense—Jesus Christ, the Righteous One. ²He is the atoning sacrifice for our sins, and not only for ours but also for*ᶜ* the sins of the whole world.

³We know that we have come to know him if we obey his commands. ⁴The man who says, "I know him," but does not do what he commands is a liar, and the truth is not in him. ⁵But if anyone obeys his word, God's love*ᵈ* is truly made complete in him. This is how we know we are in him: ⁶Whoever claims to live in him must walk as Jesus did.

⁷Dear friends, I am not writing you a new command but an old one, which you have had since the beginning. This old command is the message you have heard. ⁸Yet I am writing you a new command; its truth is seen in him and you, because the darkness is passing and the true light is already shining.

⁹Anyone who claims to be in the light but hates his brother is still in the darkness. ¹⁰Whoever loves his brother lives in the light, and there is nothing in him*ᵉ* to make him stumble. ¹¹But whoever hates his brother is in the darkness and walks around in the darkness; he does not know where he is going, because the darkness has blinded him.

truth or dare

Since God loves everyone, what does it say about *your* love for him when you totally dismiss someone he sent his Son to die for?

2:9

¹²I write to you, dear children,
    because your sins have been forgiven on account of his name.
¹³I write to you, fathers,
    because you have known him who is from the beginning.
I write to you, young men,
    because you have overcome the evil one.
I write to you, dear children,
    because you have known the Father.
¹⁴I write to you, fathers,
    because you have known him who is from the beginning.
I write to you, young men,
    because you are strong,
    and the word of God lives in you,
    and you have overcome the evil one.

ᵃ 4 Some manuscripts your   ᵇ 7 Or every   ᶜ 2 Or He is the one who turns aside God's wrath, taking away our sins, and not only ours but also   ᵈ 5 Or word, love for God   ᵉ 10 Or it

Do Not Love the World

[15]Do not love the world or anything in the world. If anyone loves the world, the love of the Father is not in him. [16]For everything in the world—the cravings of sinful man, the lust of his eyes and the boasting of what he has and does—comes not from the Father but from the world. [17]The world and its desires pass away, but the man who does the will of God lives forever.

Warning Against Antichrists

[18]Dear children, this is the last hour; and as you have heard that the antichrist is coming, even now many antichrists have come. This is how we know it is the last hour. [19]They went out from us, but they did not really belong to us. For if they had belonged to us, they would have remained with us; but their going showed that none of them belonged to us.

[20]But you have an anointing from the Holy One, and all of you know the truth.[a] [21]I do not write to you because you do not know the truth, but because you do know it and because no lie comes from the truth. [22]Who is the liar? It is the man who denies that Jesus is the Christ. Such a man is the antichrist—he denies the Father and the Son. [23]No one who denies the Son has the Father; whoever acknowledges the Son has the Father also.

[24]See that what you have heard from the beginning remains in you. If it does, you also will remain in the Son and in the Father. [25]And this is what he promised us—even eternal life.

[26]I am writing these things to you about those who are trying to lead you astray. [27]As for you, the anointing you received from him remains in you, and you do not need anyone to teach you. But as his anointing teaches you about all things and as that anointing is real, not counterfeit—just as it has taught you, remain in him.

Children of God

[28]And now, dear children, continue in him, so that when he appears we may be confident and unashamed before him at his coming.

[29]If you know that he is righteous, you know that everyone who does what is right has been born of him.

3 How great is the love the Father has lavished on us, that we should be called children of God! And that is what we are! The reason the world does not know us is that it did not know him. [2]Dear friends, now we are children of God, and what we will be has not yet been made known. But we know that when he appears,[b] we shall be like him, for we shall see him as he is. [3]Everyone who has this hope in him purifies himself, just as he is pure.

[4]Everyone who sins breaks the law; in fact, sin is lawlessness. [5]But you know that he appeared so that he might take away our sins. And in him is no sin. [6]No one who lives in him keeps on sinning. No one who continues to sin has either seen him or known him.

[7]Dear children, do not let anyone lead you astray. He who does what is right is righteous, just as he is righteous. [8]He who does what is sinful is of the devil, because the devil has been sinning from the beginning. The reason the Son of God appeared was to destroy the devil's work. [9]No one who is born of God will continue to sin, because God's seed remains in him; he cannot go on sinning, because he has been born of God. [10]This is how we know who the children of God are and who the children of the devil are: Anyone who does not do what is right is not a child of God; nor is anyone who does not love his brother.

Love One Another

[11]This is the message you heard from the beginning: We should love one another. [12]Do not be like Cain, who belonged to the evil one and murdered his brother. And why did he murder him? Because his own actions were evil and his brother's were righteous. [13]Do not be surprised, my brothers, if the world hates you. [14]We know that we have passed from death to life, because we love our brothers. Anyone who does not love remains in death. [15]Anyone who hates his brother is a murderer, and you know that no murderer has eternal life in him.

[16]This is how we know what love is: Jesus Christ laid down his life for us. And we ought to lay down our lives for our brothers. [17]If anyone has material possessions and sees his brother in need but has no pity on him, how can the love of God be in him? [18]Dear children, let us not love with

---

I Want It All

"I have to pay for the *car insurance?*" I asked.

"Four hundred dollars," Dad said, as he underlined the number twice on his notepad.

My jaw dropped. Why did Dad have to be a stingy accountant anyway? "Dad!" I pleaded. "None of my friends pay for insurance. Or drive the family minivan!" I was supposed to be excited about driving *that?* Whoo-hoo.

"Sorry, Jill." Dad's mind was already made up. "We're not getting a new car anytime soon. And if you want to drive, you'll have to help pay for gas and insurance."

I was seething. Just then the doorbell rang. I walked to the front door and opened it to find my best friend, Vanya, swinging a set of keys. In my driveway sat a brand new red Jeep. "Hey! Wanna come for a ride?" Vanya asked. She pointed to the Jeep and said, "Isn't it sweet?! It's my birthday present."

I forced a smile. "Okay, sure," I said flatly. What did she do to deserve her good fortune? But the truth was, I couldn't hate Vanya, even if I wanted to. She was always really generous toward me. Her family took me on their vacation to California and paid for everything. Vanya always said to me, "Don't worry. When I get my license, I'll drive you to school, so you won't have to take the bus ever again."

As we climbed into the Jeep, I felt sick with envy. If only we had enough money for things like this . . .

For more on materialism, check out
www.TrueImagesBible.com

materialism in focus

The struggle against materialism is a tough battle in our culture. Every day we're bombarded with messages and advertisements about possessions and the "happiness" that they supposedly bring. We feel like if we could just have that one thing, then we'd be happy. But the truth is that our deepest, heartfelt needs are ultimately never met by material things.

»God whispers a very different message in the midst of this material world, telling us not to look to things to provide comfort. The secret to contentment, he says, is in looking to Jesus to meet our deepest needs. Check out Philippians 3:8; 4:11–13,19 (pages 1552–1554).

»The stuff of this world won't last. And it won't satisfy you. Don't set your heart on it (see 1 John 2:15–17, page 1619).

For more on this topic, see the index on page 1656.

words or tongue but with actions and in truth. [19]This then is how we know that we belong to the truth, and how we set our hearts at rest in his presence [20]whenever our hearts condemn us. For God is greater than our hearts, and he knows everything.

[21]Dear friends, if our hearts do not condemn us, we have confidence before God [22]and receive from him anything we ask, because we obey his commands and do what pleases him. [23]And this is his command: to believe in the name of his Son, Jesus Christ, and to love one another as he commanded us. [24]Those who obey his commands live in him, and he in them. And this is how we know that he lives in us: We know it by the Spirit he gave us.

Test the Spirits

4 Dear friends, do not believe every spirit, but test the spirits to see whether they are from God, because many false prophets have gone out into the world. ²This is how you can recognize the Spirit of God: Every spirit that acknowledges that Jesus Christ has come in the flesh is from God, ³but every spirit that does not acknowledge Jesus is not from God. This is the spirit of the antichrist, which you have heard is coming and even now is already in the world.

⁴You, dear children, are from God and have overcome them, because the one who is in you is greater than the one who is in the world. ⁵They are from the world and therefore speak from the viewpoint of the world, and the world listens to them. ⁶We are from God, and whoever knows God listens to us; but whoever is not from God does not listen to us. This is how we recognize the Spirit*ᵃ* of truth and the spirit of falsehood.

God's Love and Ours

⁷Dear friends, let us love one another, for love comes from God. Everyone who loves has been born of God and knows God. ⁸Whoever does not love does not know God, because God is love. ⁹This is how God showed his love among us: He sent his one and only Son*ᵇ* into the world that we might live through him. ¹⁰This is love: not that we loved God, but that he loved us and sent his Son as an atoning sacrifice for*ᶜ* our sins. ¹¹Dear friends, since God so loved us, we also ought to love one another. ¹²No one has ever seen God; but if we love one another, God lives in us and his love is made complete in us.

¹³We know that we live in him and he in us, because he has given us of his Spirit. ¹⁴And we have seen and testify that the Father has sent his Son to be the Savior of the world. ¹⁵If anyone acknowledges that Jesus is the Son of God, God lives in him and he in God. ¹⁶And so we know and rely on the love God has for us.

God is love. Whoever lives in love lives in God, and God in him. ¹⁷In this way, love is made complete among us so that we will have confidence on the day of judgment, because in this world we are like him. ¹⁸There is no fear in love. But perfect love drives out fear, because fear has to do with punishment. The one who fears is not made perfect in love.

¹⁹We love because he first loved us. ²⁰If anyone says, "I love God," yet hates his brother, he is a liar. For anyone who does not love his brother, whom he has seen, cannot love God, whom he has not seen. ²¹And he has given us this command: Whoever loves God must also love his brother.

genuine

love » 4:7-12

School attendance is generally mandatory. Extra credit on the test is optional. Helping out around your house is probably mandatory, while scrubbing the floor with a toothbrush is usually optional. Some things in life you *have* to do—and some things you don't. Well, loving others isn't one of those things you can get away with just doing when you feel like it. It's not optional. Because God loved us so incredibly, he requires us to love one another. Whether we feel like it or not. When it's easy and when it's hard. Loving others isn't optional—it's mandatory.

Faith in the Son of God

5 Everyone who believes that Jesus is the Christ is born of God, and everyone who loves the father loves his child as well. ²This is how we know that we love the children of God: by loving God and carrying out his commands. ³This is love for God: to obey his commands. And his commands are not burdensome, ⁴for everyone born of God overcomes the world. This is the victory that has overcome the world, even our faith. ⁵Who is it that overcomes the world? Only he who believes that Jesus is the Son of God.

⁶This is the one who came by water and blood—Jesus Christ. He did not come by water only, but by water and blood. And it is the Spirit who testifies, because the Spirit is the truth. ⁷For there

---

ᵃ 6 Or spirit   ᵇ 9 Or his only begotten Son   ᶜ 10 Or as the one who would turn aside his wrath, taking away are three that testify: [8]the[a] Spirit, the water and the blood; and the three are in agreement. [9]We accept man's testimony, but God's testimony is greater because it is the testimony of God, which he has given about his Son. [10]Anyone who believes in the Son of God has this testimony in his heart. Anyone who does not believe God has made him out to be a liar, because he has not believed the testimony God has given about his Son. [11]And this is the testimony: God has given us eternal life, and this life is in his Son. [12]He who has the Son has life; he who does not have the Son of God does not have life.

Concluding Remarks

[13]I write these things to you who believe in the name of the Son of God so that you may know that you have eternal life. [14]This is the confidence we have in approaching God: that if we ask anything according to his will, he hears us. [15]And if we know that he hears us—whatever we ask—we know that we have what we asked of him.

[16]If anyone sees his brother commit a sin that does not lead to death, he should pray and God will give him life. I refer to those whose sin does not lead to death. There is a sin that leads to death. I am not saying that he should pray about that. [17]All wrongdoing is sin, and there is sin that does not lead to death.

[18]We know that anyone born of God does not continue to sin; the one who was born of God keeps him safe, and the evil one cannot harm him. [19]We know that we are children of God, and that the whole world is under the control of the evil one. [20]We know also that the Son of God has come and has given us understanding, so that we may know him who is true. And we are in him who is true—even in his Son Jesus Christ. He is the true God and eternal life.

[21]Dear children, keep yourselves from idols.

[a] 7,8 Late manuscripts of the Vulgate *testify in heaven: the Father, the Word and the Holy Spirit, and these three are one.* [8]*And there are three that testify on earth: the* (not found in any Greek manuscript before the fourteenth century)

at a glance ⌄

author:	The apostle John.
date:	Between A.D. 85–95.
setting:	"The chosen lady and her children" may have been actual friends of the apostle John, or "the chosen lady" may have been a figure of speech for a church and "her children" were the members.
verse to remember:	Anyone who runs ahead and does not continue in the teaching of Christ does not have God; whoever continues in the teaching has both the Father and the Son. If anyone comes to you and does not bring this teaching, do not take him into your house or welcome him (9–10).
theme to consider:	Truth and love go hand-in-hand for believers.

2 john

unchanging truth

Are you going along in life hand-in-hand with someone who is not following the truth? It's a tough question, but let's ask it another way. Let's say you're currently head over heels for a cute guy at school. He seems perfect in every way—except he's not a Christian. If truth and love must go hand-in-hand for believers, then what are you doing holding hands with someone who doesn't follow the truth? Ouch! Or maybe your best friend in life, the girl you share everything with, doesn't know and love Jesus like you do. How can you truly be soul mates if you don't share the thing that's most important in life? Ouch again!

In this letter, John warns believers during the vulnerable early days of Christianity not to welcome false teachers who were committed to opposing the truth and destroying their faith. Although you probably won't face that exact situation, it's an important principle to keep in mind. Don't welcome into your life those who directly oppose Jesus and his Word.

It's not that having friends who are outside the faith is wrong. How else are you going to share your faith with them if you're not involved in their lives? It's just that the place for our closest friends, and certainly for our love interests, should be reserved for those who follow the truth.

life lessons

1 Love should be the focus of our lives—especially love toward believers (4–6).

2 Guard your heart against compromise in your life (7–11).

¹The elder,

To the chosen lady and her children, whom I love in the truth—and not I only, but also all who know the truth— ²because of the truth, which lives in us and will be with us forever:

³Grace, mercy and peace from God the Father and from Jesus Christ, the Father's Son, will be with us in truth and love.

⁴It has given me great joy to find some of your children walking in the truth, just as the Father commanded us. ⁵And now, dear lady, I am not writing you a new command but one we have had from the beginning. I ask that we love one another. ⁶And this is love: that we walk in obedience to his commands. As you have heard from the beginning, his command is that you walk in love.

⁷Many deceivers, who do not acknowledge Jesus Christ as coming in the flesh, have gone out into the world. Any such person is the deceiver and the antichrist. ⁸Watch out that you do not lose what you have worked for, but that you may be rewarded fully. ⁹Anyone who runs ahead and does not continue in the teaching of Christ does not have God; whoever continues in the teaching has both the Father and the Son. ¹⁰If anyone comes to you and does not bring this teaching, do not take him into your house or welcome him. ¹¹Anyone who welcomes him shares in his wicked work.

¹²I have much to write to you, but I do not want to use paper and ink. Instead, I hope to visit you and talk with you face to face, so that our joy may be complete.

¹³The children of your chosen sister send their greetings.

author:	The apostle John.
date:	Between A.D. 85–95.
setting:	Church leaders traveled from town to town starting new churches. They depended on the hospitality of Christians when they traveled.
verse to remember:	Dear friend, you are faithful in what you are doing for the brothers, even though they are strangers to you (5).
theme to consider:	One of the most effective ways to demonstrate God's values and Jesus' love to our sisters and brothers in Christ is to welcome them into our homes and lives.

3 john

unchanging truth

What do you do when you're going through heartache? Scarf down cookies and ice cream and eat your way into a self-induced coma? Torture yourself by hitting "repeat" on a sappy, sad love song? Bawl like a baby in your mom's lap? Prank call his house when everyone else is asleep?

When we're hurting, we do a lot of crazy things to try to make ourselves feel better. However, there's one thing that's sure to lift us up when we're feeling low—being with a best friend. Ever been there when someone really needed you? Ever comforted a friend who didn't make the team? Who failed a test? Who lost a pet? Ever cried with someone—not saying a word of advice, just crying alongside her? Being with a friend who knows us and understands us is the best. In the same way, that feeling you have when you know how much your friend needs you is beyond compare.

In the last of his three letters found in the New Testament, John once again emphasizes loving and caring for fellow believers. It's like a P.S. on his message to the church.

P.S. Did I mention that I want you to love each other?

P.P.S. Oh yeah, don't forget to love each other.

It's as if he can't say it enough. If Christians are not there for each other, who will be?

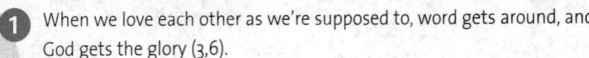

life lessons

1 When we love each other as we're supposed to, word gets around, and God gets the glory (3,6).

2 We need to realize how much other Christians need our support and love (5–8).

¹The elder,

To my dear friend Gaius, whom I love in the truth.

²Dear friend, I pray that you may enjoy good health and that all may go well with you, even as your soul is getting along well. ³It gave me great joy to have some brothers come and tell about your faithfulness to the truth and how you continue to walk in the truth. ⁴I have no greater joy than to hear that my children are walking in the truth.

⁵Dear friend, you are faithful in what you are doing for the brothers, even though they are strangers to you. ⁶They have told the church about your love. You will do well to send them on their way in a manner worthy of God. ⁷It was for the sake of the Name that they went out, receiving no help from the pagans. ⁸We ought therefore to show hospitality to such men so that we may work together for the truth.

⁹I wrote to the church, but Diotrephes, who loves to be first, will have nothing to do with us. ¹⁰So if I come, I will call attention to what he is doing, gossiping maliciously about us. Not satisfied with that, he refuses to welcome the brothers. He also stops those who want to do so and puts them out of the church.

¹¹Dear friend, do not imitate what is evil but what is good. Anyone who does what is good is from God. Anyone who does what is evil has not seen God. ¹²Demetrius is well spoken of by everyone—and even by the truth itself. We also speak well of him, and you know that our testimony is true.

¹³I have much to write you, but I do not want to do so with pen and ink. ¹⁴I hope to see you soon, and we will talk face to face.

Peace to you. The friends here send their greetings. Greet the friends there by name.

truth or dare

Having trouble plugging up your endless stream of gossip? Don't just focus on the symptoms. Research the motive of Diotrephes's malicious gossip (see verse 9).

9–10

genuine character » 11

Have you noticed that when you hang out with someone, after a while you start to become alike? You might use the same phrases, develop some of the same mannerisms, maybe dress alike or do your hair the same. Without even meaning to, we tend to imitate others. Sometimes it's girls at school; sometimes it's celebrities or models. We imitate their attitudes, their look, their way of talking. So God issues a warning: don't imitate what is evil but what is good. Take stock of who you try to be like, and ask yourself, "Am I imitating what is good?"

author: Jude, the brother of James and Jesus.

date: About A.D. 65.

setting: Jude's original plan was to write about the subject of salvation. But because false teachers were infiltrating the church, Jude shifted his letter to one of warning.

verse to remember: Dear friends, although I was very eager to write to you about the salvation we share, I felt I had to write and urge you to contend for the faith that was once for all entrusted to the saints (3).

theme to consider: As believers, we have been given an awesome responsibility—to carry God's truth to others and defend it against false teachers.

unchanging truth

jude

The human body is an amazing machine. Even if you're not a science buff, it's pretty incredible to learn how the body fights against infection. White blood cells race to the scene of an infection and go to work, literally fighting to the death against the intruder virus. If the virus gets the upper hand, it begins multiplying and attacking the body's health. So, the body starts an all-out war against its foe—as you well know if you'll recall your latest bout with a cold or flu.

For centuries, with the same ferocity as a virus, evil has attacked the church on every side in an attempt to overthrow it. False teachers and preachers with their ridiculous ideas have come and gone. Dangerous heresy has multiplied and spread. Yet the church has withstood adversity after adversity because Christians were ready to fight for what they believed.

Is your faith that important to you? Are you willing to go to "war" against what is wrong so that right will prevail? That's what Jude wanted to know from believers everywhere. His letter is a call to arms and a wake-up call for slumbering saints. "Get with it!" he cries. In your schools. In your clubs. On your sports teams. In your neighborhood. There's a battle going on for your beliefs—so stand up and fight!

life lessons

1 False teachers mean business, and they can ruin your faith if you let them (3–16).

2 Fighting for the faith is not an option—it's the duty of every Christian (17–23).

⌃

¹Jude, a servant of Jesus Christ and a brother of James,

To those who have been called, who are loved by God the Father and kept by*ᵃ* Jesus Christ:

²Mercy, peace and love be yours in abundance.

The Sin and Doom of Godless Men

³Dear friends, although I was very eager to write to you about the salvation we share, I felt I had to write and urge you to contend for the faith that was once for all entrusted to the saints. ⁴For certain men whose condemnation was written about*ᵇ* long ago have secretly slipped in among you. They are godless men, who change the grace of our God into a license for immorality and deny Jesus Christ our only Sovereign and Lord.

⁵Though you already know all this, I want to remind you that the Lord*ᶜ* delivered his people out of Egypt, but later destroyed those who did not believe. ⁶And the angels who did not keep their positions of authority but abandoned their own home—these he has kept in darkness, bound with everlasting chains for judgment on the great Day. ⁷In a similar way, Sodom and Gomorrah and the surrounding towns gave themselves up to sexual immorality and perversion. They serve as an example of those who suffer the punishment of eternal fire.

⁸In the very same way, these dreamers pollute their own bodies, reject authority and slander celestial beings. ⁹But even the archangel Michael, when he was disputing with the devil about the body of Moses, did not dare to bring a slanderous accusation against him, but said, "The Lord rebuke you!" ¹⁰Yet these men speak abusively against whatever they do not understand; and what things they do understand by instinct, like unreasoning animals—these are the very things that destroy them.

¹¹Woe to them! They have taken the way of Cain; they have rushed for profit into Balaam's error; they have been destroyed in Korah's rebellion.

¹²These men are blemishes at your love feasts, eating with you without the slightest qualm—shepherds who feed only themselves. They are clouds without rain, blown along by the wind; autumn trees, without fruit and uprooted—twice dead. ¹³They are wild waves of the sea, foaming up their shame; wandering stars, for whom blackest darkness has been reserved forever.

¹⁴Enoch, the seventh from Adam, prophesied about these men: "See, the Lord is coming with thousands upon thousands of his holy ones ¹⁵to judge everyone, and to convict all the ungodly of all the ungodly acts they have done in the ungodly way, and of all the harsh words ungodly sinners have spoken against him." ¹⁶These men are grumblers and faultfinders; they follow their own evil desires; they boast about themselves and flatter others for their own advantage.

A Call to Persevere

¹⁷But, dear friends, remember what the apostles of our Lord Jesus Christ foretold. ¹⁸They said to you, "In the last times there will be scoffers who will follow their own ungodly desires." ¹⁹These are the men who divide you, who follow mere natural instincts and do not have the Spirit.

²⁰But you, dear friends, build yourselves up in your most holy faith and pray in the Holy Spirit. ²¹Keep yourselves in God's love as you wait for the mercy of our Lord Jesus Christ to bring you to eternal life.

²²Be merciful to those who doubt; ²³snatch others from the fire and save them; to others show mercy, mixed with fear—hating even the clothing stained by corrupted flesh.

Doxology

²⁴To him who is able to keep you from falling and to present you before his glorious presence without fault and with great joy— ²⁵to the only God our Savior be glory, majesty, power and authority, through Jesus Christ our Lord, before all ages, now and forevermore! Amen.

ᵃ *1* Or *for; or in*   ᵇ *4* Or *men who were marked out for condemnation*   ᶜ *5* Some early manuscripts *Jesus*

author:	The apostle John.
date:	About A.D. 95.
setting:	John wrote the book of Revelation while exiled on the island of Patmos.
verse to remember:	"Only hold on to what you have until I come. To him who overcomes and does my will to the end, I will give authority over the nations" (2:25–26).
theme to consider:	Revelation is a book of warning, but it is also a book of hope: God is in control; Christ's return and absolute victory are assured; and all who trust in him will be saved! "Amen. Come, Lord Jesus" (22:20).

revelation

unchanging truth

If you love sci-fi, you'll love the book of Revelation. Only this letter isn't the product of an overactive imagination—it's God's truth. Before you get too caught up in and confused by the ominous horses and riders, the freaky beast out of the sea and that weird woman and dragon thing, take a step back and remember the point of the book. It's a book about hope. It's a book about triumph.

See, this book is not necessarily a good read if you read it one chapter at a time. You can't stop midway, put down the book and say you've got the gist of it. If you do, you're likely to worry and fret about all kinds of questions. *What's going to happen in our world? Is Satan in control? Is he going to pin down all the Christians to the mat?* Only when you get to the end of the book, and thus the end of time as we know it, will you see the big picture. No matter what else happens between chapters one and twenty-two, God wins in the end.

John's fantastic vision from God should encourage us about the big picture—not confuse and divide us about the details of when and where it's all going to happen. The point is that God pulls off an everlasting victory over evil—a one-two punch for all time. Everything that happens between now and then is necessary to lead up to the most incredible showdown between good and evil the world has ever seen. Are you ready?

life lessons

1. The opposite of loving Jesus is not necessarily hating him—it may be indifference toward him. Don't grow apathetic in your relationship with him (3:15–16).

2. Judgment is real. God will hold everyone who has ever lived accountable for his or her actions. The only way to escape is through faith in Jesus Christ (20:11–15).

3. Heaven is better than our wildest imagination. We will be there with Jesus forever (21:3–4,21–27; 22:14).

Prologue

1 The revelation of Jesus Christ, which God gave him to show his servants what must soon take place. He made it known by sending his angel to his servant John, [2]who testifies to everything he saw—that is, the word of God and the testimony of Jesus Christ. [3]Blessed is the one who reads the words of this prophecy, and blessed are those who hear it and take to heart what is written in it, because the time is near.

Greetings and Doxology

[4]John,

To the seven churches in the province of Asia:

Grace and peace to you from him who is, and who was, and who is to come, and from the seven spirits[a] before his throne, [5]and from Jesus Christ, who is the faithful witness, the firstborn from the dead, and the ruler of the kings of the earth.

To him who loves us and has freed us from our sins by his blood, [6]and has made us to be a kingdom and priests to serve his God and Father—to him be glory and power for ever and ever! Amen.

> [7]Look, he is coming with the clouds,
> and every eye will see him,
> even those who pierced him;
> and all the peoples of the earth will mourn because of him.
>
> So shall it be! Amen.

[8]"I am the Alpha and the Omega," says the Lord God, "who is, and who was, and who is to come, the Almighty."

One Like a Son of Man

[9]I, John, your brother and companion in the suffering and kingdom and patient endurance that are ours in Jesus, was on the island of Patmos because of the word of God and the testimony of Jesus. [10]On the Lord's Day I was in the Spirit, and I heard behind me a loud voice like a trumpet, [11]which said: "Write on a scroll what you see and send it to the seven churches: to Ephesus, Smyrna, Pergamum, Thyatira, Sardis, Philadelphia and Laodicea."

[12]I turned around to see the voice that was speaking to me. And when I turned I saw seven golden lampstands, [13]and among the lampstands was someone "like a son of man,"[b] dressed in a robe reaching down to his feet and with a golden sash around his chest.

truth *or dare*

Nope, the Lord isn't using code names. *Alpha* and *Omega* are the first and last letters in the Greek alphabet. What's the point? He's got things covered from A to Z.

1:8

[14]His head and hair were white like wool, as white as snow, and his eyes were like blazing fire. [15]His feet were like bronze glowing in a furnace, and his voice was like the sound of rushing waters. [16]In his right hand he held seven stars, and out of his mouth came a sharp double-edged sword. His face was like the sun shining in all its brilliance.

[17]When I saw him, I fell at his feet as though dead. Then he placed his right hand on me and said: "Do not be afraid. I am the First and the Last. [18]I am the Living One; I was dead, and behold I am alive for ever and ever! And I hold the keys of death and Hades.

[19]"Write, therefore, what you have seen, what is now and what will take place later. [20]The mystery of the seven stars that you saw in my right hand and of the seven golden lampstands is this: The seven stars are the angels[c] of the seven churches, and the seven lampstands are the seven churches.

a 4 Or the sevenfold Spirit   b 13 Daniel 7:13   c 20 Or messengers

To the Church in Ephesus

2 "To the angel[a] of the church in Ephesus write:

These are the words of him who holds the seven stars in his right hand and walks among the seven golden lampstands: [2]I know your deeds, your hard work and your perseverance. I know that you cannot tolerate wicked men, that you have tested those who claim to be apostles but are not, and have found them false. [3]You have persevered and have endured hardships for my name, and have not grown weary.

[4]Yet I hold this against you: You have forsaken your first love. [5]Remember the height from which you have fallen! Repent and do the things you did at first. If you do not repent, I will come to you and remove your lampstand from its place. [6]But you have this in your favor: You hate the practices of the Nicolaitans, which I also hate.

[7]He who has an ear, let him hear what the Spirit says to the churches. To him who overcomes, I will give the right to eat from the tree of life, which is in the paradise of God.

To the Church in Smyrna

[8]"To the angel of the church in Smyrna write:

These are the words of him who is the First and the Last, who died and came to life again. [9]I know your afflictions and your poverty—yet you are rich! I know the slander of those who say they are Jews and are not, but are a synagogue of Satan. [10]Do not be afraid of what you are about to suffer. I tell you, the devil will put some of you in prison to test you, and you will suffer persecution for ten days. Be faithful, even to the point of death, and I will give you the crown of life.

[11]He who has an ear, let him hear what the Spirit says to the churches. He who overcomes will not be hurt at all by the second death.

To the Church in Pergamum

[12]"To the angel of the church in Pergamum write:

These are the words of him who has the sharp, double-edged sword. [13]I know where you live—where Satan has his throne. Yet you remain true to my name. You did not renounce your faith in me, even in the days of Antipas, my faithful witness, who was put to death in your city—where Satan lives.

genuine relationships

When a couple first falls in love, they put a lot into their relationship. Sometimes after the "newness" wears off, they get lazy about doing the things they once did to show how much they care, and they let other stuff crowd in. That's a critical point in the relationship. Jesus rebukes the church in Ephesus for forsaking their first love for him (and probably for each other). And he tells them to do the things they used to do when they first started their relationship with him. What about you? Do you take your relationship with Jesus for granted? How can you refresh your love for him?

» 2:4-5

[14]Nevertheless, I have a few things against you: You have people there who hold to the teaching of Balaam, who taught Balak to entice the Israelites to sin by eating food sacrificed to idols and by committing sexual immorality. [15]Likewise you also have those who hold to the teaching of the Nicolaitans. [16]Repent therefore! Otherwise, I will soon come to you and will fight against them with the sword of my mouth.

[17]He who has an ear, let him hear what the Spirit says to the churches. To him who overcomes, I will give some of the hidden manna. I will also give him a white stone with a new name written on it, known only to him who receives it.

a 1 Or *messenger*; also in verses 8, 12 and 18

To the Church in Thyatira

18"To the angel of the church in Thyatira write:

These are the words of the Son of God, whose eyes are like blazing fire and whose feet are like burnished bronze. 19I know your deeds, your love and faith, your service and perseverance, and that you are now doing more than you did at first.

20Nevertheless, I have this against you: You tolerate that woman Jezebel, who calls herself a prophetess. By her teaching she misleads my servants into sexual immorality and the eating of food sacrificed to idols. 21I have given her time to repent of her immorality, but she is unwilling. 22So I will cast her on a bed of suffering, and I will make those who commit adultery with her suffer intensely, unless they repent of her ways. 23I will strike her children dead. Then all the churches will know that I am he who searches hearts and minds, and I will repay each of you according to your deeds. 24Now I say to the rest of you in Thyatira, to you who do not hold to her teaching and have not learned Satan's so-called deep secrets (I will not impose any other burden on you): 25Only hold on to what you have until I come.

26To him who overcomes and does my will to the end, I will give authority over the nations—

27 'He will rule them with an iron scepter;
he will dash them to pieces like pottery' *a*—

just as I have received authority from my Father. 28I will also give him the morning star. 29He who has an ear, let him hear what the Spirit says to the churches.

To the Church in Sardis

3 "To the angel *b* of the church in Sardis write:

These are the words of him who holds the seven spirits *c* of God and the seven stars. I know your deeds; you have a reputation of being alive, but you are dead. 2Wake up! Strengthen what remains and is about to die, for I have not found your deeds complete in the sight of my God. 3Remember, therefore, what you have received and heard; obey it, and repent. But if you do not wake up, I will come like a thief, and you will not know at what time I will come to you.

4Yet you have a few people in Sardis who have not soiled their clothes. They will walk with me, dressed in white, for they are worthy. 5He who overcomes will, like them, be dressed in white. I will never blot out his name from the book of life, but will acknowledge his name before my Father and his angels. 6He who has an ear, let him hear what the Spirit says to the churches.

To the Church in Philadelphia

7"To the angel of the church in Philadelphia write:

These are the words of him who is holy and true, who holds the key of David. What he opens no one can shut, and what he shuts no one can open. 8I know your deeds. See, I have placed before you an open door that no one can shut. I know that you have little strength, yet you have kept my word and have not denied my name. 9I will make those who are of the synagogue of Satan, who claim to be Jews though they are not, but are liars— I will make them come and fall down at your feet and acknowledge that I have loved you. 10Since you have kept my command to endure patiently, I will also keep you from the hour of trial that is going to come upon the whole world to test those who live on the earth.

11I am coming soon. Hold on to what you have, so that no one will take your crown. 12Him who overcomes I will make a pillar in the temple of my God. Never again will he leave it. I will write on him the name of my God and the name of the city of my God, the new Jerusalem, which is coming down out of heaven from my God; and I will also write on him my new name. 13He who has an ear, let him hear what the Spirit says to the churches.

a 27 Psalm 2:9   *b 1* Or *messenger;* also in verses 7 and 14   *c 1* Or *the sevenfold Spirit*

genuine

integrity » 3:15-16

Let's say you go to Starbucks and order a decaf latte. Anticipating the piping hot warmth of your favorite drink, you take a sip and find out it's not hot—it's lukewarm. Yuck! You're sending that one right back! Or you order a frappuccino, looking forward to the icy smoothness of the frosty drink, but your first taste reveals that it's also lukewarm. Gross! Totally unappealing, right? Well, it's also totally unappealing to be lukewarm in your walk with God—to be without convictions, indifferent, not really giving a rip about much of anything spiritually. So turn up the heat, girl!

To the Church in Laodicea

¹⁴"To the angel of the church in Laodicea write:

These are the words of the Amen, the faithful and true witness, the ruler of God's creation. ¹⁵I know your deeds, that you are neither cold nor hot. I wish you were either one or the other! ¹⁶So, because you are lukewarm—neither hot nor cold—I am about to spit you out of my mouth. ¹⁷You say, 'I am rich; I have acquired wealth and do not need a thing.' But you do not realize that you are wretched, pitiful, poor, blind and naked. ¹⁸I counsel you to buy from me gold refined in the fire, so you can become rich; and white clothes to wear, so you can cover your shameful nakedness; and salve to put on your eyes, so you can see.

¹⁹Those whom I love I rebuke and discipline. So be earnest, and repent. ²⁰Here I am! I stand at the door and knock. If anyone hears my voice and opens the door, I will come in and eat with him, and he with me.

²¹To him who overcomes, I will give the right to sit with me on my throne, just as I overcame and sat down with my Father on his throne. ²²He who has an ear, let him hear what the Spirit says to the churches."

The Throne in Heaven

4 After this I looked, and there before me was a door standing open in heaven. And the voice I had first heard speaking to me like a trumpet said, "Come up here, and I will show you what must take place after this." ²At once I was in the Spirit, and there before me was a throne in heaven with someone sitting on it. ³And the one who sat there had the appearance of jasper and carnelian. A rainbow, resembling an emerald, encircled the throne. ⁴Surrounding the throne were twenty-four other thrones, and seated on them were twenty-four elders. They were dressed in white and had crowns of gold on their heads. ⁵From the throne came flashes of lightning, rumblings and peals of thunder. Before the throne, seven lamps were blazing. These are the seven spirits*a* of God. ⁶Also before the throne there was what looked like a sea of glass, clear as crystal.

In the center, around the throne, were four living creatures, and they were covered with eyes, in front and in back. ⁷The first living creature was like a lion, the second was like an ox, the third had a face like a man, the fourth was like a flying eagle. ⁸Each of the four living creatures had six wings and was covered with eyes all around, even under his wings. Day and night they never stop saying:

"Holy, holy, holy
is the Lord God Almighty,
who was, and is, and is to come."

⁹Whenever the living creatures give glory, honor and thanks to him who sits on the throne and who lives for ever and ever, ¹⁰the twenty-four elders fall down before him who sits on the throne, and worship him who lives for ever and ever. They lay their crowns before the throne and say:

a 5 Or the sevenfold Spirit

¹¹"You are worthy, our Lord and God,
   to receive glory and honor and power,
for you created all things,
   and by your will they were created
   and have their being."

The Scroll and the Lamb

5 Then I saw in the right hand of him who sat on the throne a scroll with writing on both sides and sealed with seven seals. ²And I saw a mighty angel proclaiming in a loud voice, "Who is worthy to break the seals and open the scroll?" ³But no one in heaven or on earth or under the earth could open the scroll or even look inside it. ⁴I wept and wept because no one was found who was worthy to open the scroll or look inside. ⁵Then one of the elders said to me, "Do not weep! See, the Lion of the tribe of Judah, the Root of David, has triumphed. He is able to open the scroll and its seven seals."

⁶Then I saw a Lamb, looking as if it had been slain, standing in the center of the throne, encircled by the four living creatures and the elders. He had seven horns and seven eyes, which are the seven spirits*ᵃ* of God sent out into all the earth. ⁷He came and took the scroll from the right hand of him who sat on the throne. ⁸And when he had taken it, the four living creatures and the twenty-four elders fell down before the Lamb. Each one had a harp and they were holding golden bowls full of incense, which are the prayers of the saints. ⁹And they sang a new song:

truth *or dare*

You've probably heard of incenses like sandal-wood, sage or vanilla . . . but *prayer*-scented? This passage gives proof that heaven is one sweet-smelling place.

5:8

"You are worthy to take the scroll
   and to open its seals,
because you were slain,
   and with your blood you purchased men
      for God
   from every tribe and language and people and nation.
¹⁰You have made them to be a kingdom and priests to serve our God,
   and they will reign on the earth."

¹¹Then I looked and heard the voice of many angels, numbering thousands upon thousands, and ten thousand times ten thousand. They encircled the throne and the living creatures and the elders. ¹²In a loud voice they sang:

"Worthy is the Lamb, who was slain,
   to receive power and wealth and wisdom and strength
   and honor and glory and praise!"

¹³Then I heard every creature in heaven and on earth and under the earth and on the sea, and all that is in them, singing:

"To him who sits on the throne and to the Lamb
   be praise and honor and glory and power,
      for ever and ever!"

¹⁴The four living creatures said, "Amen," and the elders fell down and worshiped.

The Seals

6 I watched as the Lamb opened the first of the seven seals. Then I heard one of the four living creatures say in a voice like thunder, "Come!" ²I looked, and there before me was a white horse! Its rider held a bow, and he was given a crown, and he rode out as a conqueror bent on conquest.

ᵃ 6 Or *the sevenfold Spirit*

³When the Lamb opened the second seal, I heard the second living creature say, "Come!" ⁴Then another horse came out, a fiery red one. Its rider was given power to take peace from the earth and to make men slay each other. To him was given a large sword.

⁵When the Lamb opened the third seal, I heard the third living creature say, "Come!" I looked, and there before me was a black horse! Its rider was holding a pair of scales in his hand. ⁶Then I heard what sounded like a voice among the four living creatures, saying, "A quart*ᵃ* of wheat for a day's wages,*ᵇ* and three quarts of barley for a day's wages,*ᵇ* and do not damage the oil and the wine!"

⁷When the Lamb opened the fourth seal, I heard the voice of the fourth living creature say, "Come!" ⁸I looked, and there before me was a pale horse! Its rider was named Death, and Hades was following close behind him. They were given power over a fourth of the earth to kill by sword, famine and plague, and by the wild beasts of the earth.

⁹When he opened the fifth seal, I saw under the altar the souls of those who had been slain because of the word of God and the testimony they had maintained. ¹⁰They called out in a loud voice, "How long, Sovereign Lord, holy and true, until you judge the inhabitants of the earth and avenge our blood?" ¹¹Then each of them was given a white robe, and they were told to wait a little longer, until the number of their fellow servants and brothers who were to be killed as they had been was completed.

¹²I watched as he opened the sixth seal. There was a great earthquake. The sun turned black like sackcloth made of goat hair, the whole moon turned blood red, ¹³and the stars in the sky fell to earth, as late figs drop from a fig tree when shaken by a strong wind. ¹⁴The sky receded like a scroll, rolling up, and every mountain and island was removed from its place.

¹⁵Then the kings of the earth, the princes, the generals, the rich, the mighty, and every slave and every free man hid in caves and among the rocks of the mountains. ¹⁶They called to the mountains and the rocks, "Fall on us and hide us from the face of him who sits on the throne and from the wrath of the Lamb! ¹⁷For the great day of their wrath has come, and who can stand?"

144,000 Sealed

7 After this I saw four angels standing at the four corners of the earth, holding back the four winds of the earth to prevent any wind from blowing on the land or on the sea or on any tree. ²Then I saw another angel coming up from the east, having the seal of the living God. He called out in a loud voice to the four angels who had been given power to harm the land and the sea: ³"Do not harm the land or the sea or the trees until we put a seal on the foreheads of the servants of our God." ⁴Then I heard the number of those who were sealed: 144,000 from all the tribes of Israel.

⁵From the tribe of Judah 12,000 were sealed,
 from the tribe of Reuben 12,000,
 from the tribe of Gad 12,000,
⁶from the tribe of Asher 12,000,
 from the tribe of Naphtali 12,000,
 from the tribe of Manasseh 12,000,
⁷from the tribe of Simeon 12,000,
 from the tribe of Levi 12,000,
 from the tribe of Issachar 12,000,
⁸from the tribe of Zebulun 12,000,
 from the tribe of Joseph 12,000,
 from the tribe of Benjamin 12,000.

The Great Multitude in White Robes

⁹After this I looked and there before me was a great multitude that no one could count, from every nation, tribe, people and language, standing before the throne and in front of the Lamb. They were wearing white robes and were holding palm branches in their hands. ¹⁰And they cried out in a loud voice:

ᵃ 6 Greek *a choinix* (probably about a liter)   *ᵇ 6* Greek *a denarius*

Living a Lie

Pastor Faust was pacing across the front of the church, his face red, little drops of spit flying out the side of his mouth, preaching like it was the end of the world. He always does. I've gotten so used to his voice that I can completely tune him out.

I sighed. Mom glanced over at me, so I sat up straighter to show how closely I was paying attention (yeah right). Mom smiled at me and looked away. She's clueless.

For all she knows, I'm the perfect daughter. The good student, obedient, respectful, the model Christian girl who knows all the answers in Sunday school.

Then there's the real Mandie. Sometimes I feel like I'm two totally different people trapped in the same body. On the outside I keep up the good Mandie façade, and on the inside, I have all these wild thoughts running through my head. I didn't win the lead in the school play by being a weak actress. No, I can play the good girl role perfectly.

While Pastor Faust was working up for the finale, all I could think about was the party at Kelsey's house last Friday (her parents were out of town), and my date with Delaine last night. Technically I didn't lie to my parents—I did go to the cast party—but I "forgot" to mention to them that I slipped out early to meet Delaine. Since I was home by curfew, my mom had no idea.

No one does.

For more on hypocrisy, go to www.TrueImagesBible.com

hypocrisy in focus

Ever feel like you're living a lie? Being one person at church and at home and someone completely different at school? Hypocrisy is pretending to be something you're not. And while it might hold up for a while, it can't last forever.

»God knows everything about you—even your thoughts (see Psalm 139:1–12, page 791; Hebrews 4:12–13, page 1588). You may be able to fool everyone else around you, but you can't fool God.

»Torn between two different lifestyles? Check out how Jesus feels about half-hearted faith (see Revelation 3:15–16, page 1633).

»The choice is yours. You can't live two lives forever. If you're struggling with hypocrisy, talk and pray with a trusted Christian adult, like a youth leader or pastor. God loves it when we're sold out for him.

For more on this topic, see the index on page 1656.

"Salvation belongs to our God,
who sits on the throne,
and to the Lamb."

[11]All the angels were standing around the throne and around the elders and the four living creatures. They fell down on their faces before the throne and worshiped God, [12]saying:

"Amen!
Praise and glory
and wisdom and thanks and honor

and power and strength
be to our God for ever and ever.
Amen!"

¹³Then one of the elders asked me, "These in white robes—who are they, and where did they come from?"

¹⁴I answered, "Sir, you know."

And he said, "These are they who have come out of the great tribulation; they have washed their robes and made them white in the blood of the Lamb. ¹⁵Therefore,

"they are before the throne of God
and serve him day and night in his temple;
and he who sits on the throne will spread his tent over them.
¹⁶Never again will they hunger;
never again will they thirst.
The sun will not beat upon them,
nor any scorching heat.
¹⁷For the Lamb at the center of the throne will be their shepherd;
he will lead them to springs of living water.
And God will wipe away every tear from their eyes."

The Seventh Seal and the Golden Censer

8 When he opened the seventh seal, there was silence in heaven for about half an hour.
²And I saw the seven angels who stand before God, and to them were given seven trumpets.

³Another angel, who had a golden censer, came and stood at the altar. He was given much incense to offer, with the prayers of all the saints, on the golden altar before the throne. ⁴The smoke of the incense, together with the prayers of the saints, went up before God from the angel's hand. ⁵Then the angel took the censer, filled it with fire from the altar, and hurled it on the earth; and there came peals of thunder, rumblings, flashes of lightning and an earthquake.

The Trumpets

⁶Then the seven angels who had the seven trumpets prepared to sound them.

⁷The first angel sounded his trumpet, and there came hail and fire mixed with blood, and it was hurled down upon the earth. A third of the earth was burned up, a third of the trees were burned up, and all the green grass was burned up.

⁸The second angel sounded his trumpet, and something like a huge mountain, all ablaze, was thrown into the sea. A third of the sea turned into blood, ⁹a third of the living creatures in the sea died, and a third of the ships were destroyed.

¹⁰The third angel sounded his trumpet, and a great star, blazing like a torch, fell from the sky on a third of the rivers and on the springs of water— ¹¹the name of the star is Wormwood. ᵃ A third of the waters turned bitter, and many people died from the waters that had become bitter.

¹²The fourth angel sounded his trumpet, and a third of the sun was struck, a third of the moon, and a third of the stars, so that a third of them turned dark. A third of the day was without light, and also a third of the night.

¹³As I watched, I heard an eagle that was flying in midair call out in a loud voice: "Woe! Woe! Woe to the inhabitants of the earth, because of the trumpet blasts about to be sounded by the other three angels!"

9 The fifth angel sounded his trumpet, and I saw a star that had fallen from the sky to the earth. The star was given the key to the shaft of the Abyss. ²When he opened the Abyss, smoke rose from it like the smoke from a gigantic furnace. The sun and sky were darkened by the smoke from the Abyss. ³And out of the smoke locusts came down upon the earth and were given power like that of scorpions of the earth. ⁴They were told not to harm the grass of the earth or any plant or tree, but only those people who did not have the seal of God on their foreheads. ⁵They were not given power to kill them, but only to torture them for five months. And the agony they suffered

ᵃ 11 That is, Bitterness

was like that of the sting of a scorpion when it strikes a man. ⁶During those days men will seek death, but will not find it; they will long to die, but death will elude them.

⁷The locusts looked like horses prepared for battle. On their heads they wore something like crowns of gold, and their faces resembled human faces. ⁸Their hair was like women's hair, and their teeth were like lions' teeth. ⁹They had breastplates like breastplates of iron, and the sound of their wings was like the thundering of many horses and chariots rushing into battle. ¹⁰They had tails and stings like scorpions, and in their tails they had power to torment people for five months. ¹¹They had as king over them the angel of the Abyss, whose name in Hebrew is Abaddon, and in Greek, Apollyon. ᵃ

¹²The first woe is past; two other woes are yet to come.

¹³The sixth angel sounded his trumpet, and I heard a voice coming from the horns ᵇ of the golden altar that is before God. ¹⁴It said to the sixth angel who had the trumpet, "Release the four angels who are bound at the great river Euphrates." ¹⁵And the four angels who had been kept ready for this very hour and day and month and year were released to kill a third of mankind. ¹⁶The number of the mounted troops was two hundred million. I heard their number.

¹⁷The horses and riders I saw in my vision looked like this: Their breastplates were fiery red, dark blue, and yellow as sulfur. The heads of the horses resembled the heads of lions, and out of their mouths came fire, smoke and sulfur. ¹⁸A third of mankind was killed by the three plagues of fire, smoke and sulfur that came out of their mouths. ¹⁹The power of the horses was in their mouths and in their tails; for their tails were like snakes, having heads with which they inflict injury.

²⁰The rest of mankind that were not killed by these plagues still did not repent of the work of their hands; they did not stop worshiping demons, and idols of gold, silver, bronze, stone and wood—idols that cannot see or hear or walk. ²¹Nor did they repent of their murders, their magic arts, their sexual immorality or their thefts.

truth *or dare*

These hard-hearted villains went through terrifying plagues yet *still* refused to repent of their sins. Don't choose the same fate—get right with God before it's too late.

9:20–21

The Angel and the Little Scroll

10 Then I saw another mighty angel coming down from heaven. He was robed in a cloud, with a rainbow above his head; his face was like the sun, and his legs were like fiery pillars. ²He was holding a little scroll, which lay open in his hand. He planted his right foot on the sea and his left foot on the land, ³and he gave a loud shout like the roar of a lion. When he shouted, the voices of the seven thunders spoke. ⁴And when the seven thunders spoke, I was about to write; but I heard a voice from heaven say, "Seal up what the seven thunders have said and do not write it down."

⁵Then the angel I had seen standing on the sea and on the land raised his right hand to heaven. ⁶And he swore by him who lives for ever and ever, who created the heavens and all that is in them, the earth and all that is in it, and the sea and all that is in it, and said, "There will be no more delay! ⁷But in the days when the seventh angel is about to sound his trumpet, the mystery of God will be accomplished, just as he announced to his servants the prophets."

⁸Then the voice that I had heard from heaven spoke to me once more: "Go, take the scroll that lies open in the hand of the angel who is standing on the sea and on the land."

⁹So I went to the angel and asked him to give me the little scroll. He said to me, "Take it and eat it. It will turn your stomach sour, but in your mouth it will be as sweet as honey." ¹⁰I took the little scroll from the angel's hand and ate it. It tasted as sweet as honey in my mouth, but when I had eaten it, my stomach turned sour. ¹¹Then I was told, "You must prophesy again about many peoples, nations, languages and kings."

ᵃ 11 *Abaddon* and *Apollyon* mean *Destroyer.*   ᵇ 13 That is, projections

The Two Witnesses

11 I was given a reed like a measuring rod and was told, "Go and measure the temple of God and the altar, and count the worshipers there. ²But exclude the outer court; do not measure it, because it has been given to the Gentiles. They will trample on the holy city for 42 months. ³And I will give power to my two witnesses, and they will prophesy for 1,260 days, clothed in sackcloth." ⁴These are the two olive trees and the two lampstands that stand before the Lord of the earth. ⁵If anyone tries to harm them, fire comes from their mouths and devours their enemies. This is how anyone who wants to harm them must die. ⁶These men have power to shut up the sky so that it will not rain during the time they are prophesying; and they have power to turn the waters into blood and to strike the earth with every kind of plague as often as they want.

truth or dare

Sweet and sour? God's Word is both sweet, with the good news of salvation for believers, and sour, with the message of judgment for unbelievers.

10:9–11

⁷Now when they have finished their testimony, the beast that comes up from the Abyss will attack them, and overpower and kill them. ⁸Their bodies will lie in the street of the great city, which is figuratively called Sodom and Egypt, where also their Lord was crucified. ⁹For three and a half days men from every people, tribe, language and nation will gaze on their bodies and refuse them burial. ¹⁰The inhabitants of the earth will gloat over them and will celebrate by sending each other gifts, because these two prophets had tormented those who live on the earth.

¹¹But after the three and a half days a breath of life from God entered them, and they stood on their feet, and terror struck those who saw them. ¹²Then they heard a loud voice from heaven saying to them, "Come up here." And they went up to heaven in a cloud, while their enemies looked on.

¹³At that very hour there was a severe earthquake and a tenth of the city collapsed. Seven thousand people were killed in the earthquake, and the survivors were terrified and gave glory to the God of heaven.

¹⁴The second woe has passed; the third woe is coming soon.

The Seventh Trumpet

¹⁵The seventh angel sounded his trumpet, and there were loud voices in heaven, which said:

"The kingdom of the world has become the kingdom of our Lord and of
his Christ,
and he will reign for ever and ever."

¹⁶And the twenty-four elders, who were seated on their thrones before God, fell on their faces and worshiped God, ¹⁷saying:

"We give thanks to you, Lord God Almighty,
the One who is and who was,
because you have taken your great power
and have begun to reign.
¹⁸The nations were angry;
and your wrath has come.
The time has come for judging the dead,
and for rewarding your servants the prophets
and your saints and those who reverence your name,
both small and great—
and for destroying those who destroy the earth."

¹⁹Then God's temple in heaven was opened, and within his temple was seen the ark of his covenant. And there came flashes of lightning, rumblings, peals of thunder, an earthquake and a great hailstorm.

The Woman and the Dragon

12 A great and wondrous sign appeared in heaven: a woman clothed with the sun, with the moon under her feet and a crown of twelve stars on her head. ²She was pregnant and cried out in pain as she was about to give birth. ³Then another sign appeared in heaven: an enormous red dragon with seven heads and ten horns and seven crowns on his heads. ⁴His tail swept a third of the stars out of the sky and flung them to the earth. The dragon stood in front of the woman who was about to give birth, so that he might devour her child the moment it was born. ⁵She gave birth to a son, a male child, who will rule all the nations with an iron scepter. And her child was snatched up to God and to his throne. ⁶The woman fled into the desert to a place prepared for her by God, where she might be taken care of for 1,260 days.

⁷And there was war in heaven. Michael and his angels fought against the dragon, and the dragon and his angels fought back. ⁸But he was not strong enough, and they lost their place in heaven. ⁹The great dragon was hurled down—that ancient serpent called the devil, or Satan, who leads the whole world astray. He was hurled to the earth, and his angels with him.

¹⁰Then I heard a loud voice in heaven say:

> "Now have come the salvation and the power and the kingdom
> of our God,
> and the authority of his Christ.
> For the accuser of our brothers,
> who accuses them before our God day and night,
> has been hurled down.
> ¹¹They overcame him
> by the blood of the Lamb
> and by the word of their testimony;
> they did not love their lives so much
> as to shrink from death.
> ¹²Therefore rejoice, you heavens
> and you who dwell in them!
> But woe to the earth and the sea,
> because the devil has gone down to you!
> He is filled with fury,
> because he knows that his time is short."

¹³When the dragon saw that he had been hurled to the earth, he pursued the woman who had given birth to the male child. ¹⁴The woman was given the two wings of a great eagle, so that she might fly to the place prepared for her in the desert, where she would be taken care of for a time, times and half a time, out of the serpent's reach. ¹⁵Then from his mouth the serpent spewed water like a river, to overtake the woman and sweep her away with the torrent. ¹⁶But the earth helped the woman by opening its mouth and swallowing the river that the dragon had spewed out of his mouth. ¹⁷Then the dragon was enraged at the woman and went off to make war against the rest of her offspring—those who obey God's commandments and hold to the testimony of Jesus.

13 ¹And the dragon *ᵃ* stood on the shore of the sea.

The Beast out of the Sea

And I saw a beast coming out of the sea. He had ten horns and seven heads, with ten crowns on his horns, and on each head a blasphemous name. ²The beast I saw resembled a leopard, but had feet like those of a bear and a mouth like that of a lion. The dragon gave the beast his power and his throne and great authority. ³One of the heads of the beast seemed to have had a fatal wound, but the fatal wound had been healed. The whole world was astonished and followed the beast. ⁴Men worshiped the dragon because he had given authority to the beast, and they also worshiped the beast and asked, "Who is like the beast? Who can make war against him?"

⁵The beast was given a mouth to utter proud words and blasphemies and to exercise his au-

ᵃ 1 Some late manuscripts And I

mirror images

> Greet Priscilla and Aquila, my fellow workers in Christ Jesus. They risked their lives for me. Romans 16:3–4

Priscilla—A Leader in Love

How many couples do you know who stick together like glue? And that isn't a reference to their kissing abilities! We're talking *soul mates*—a couple who shares everything and stands by each other through thick and thin. Not your typical romance.

Then again, Priscilla and Aquila were hardly typical. In the Bible, you won't see Priscilla's name mentioned without also reading about her husband Aquila. A faithful husband and wife team, they fled from religious persecution in Rome and established their home in the city of Corinth. Soon they became well known as tentmakers—sewing and building tents together, side by side.

But as much as Priscilla and Aquila thrived on togetherness, they still shared their lives with others. They welcomed the apostle Paul into their home, providing him refuge, friendship and work. They helped Paul get a church started in Corinth, and then went with him to Ephesus and started a church there. And when push came to shove, they put their lives on the line for Paul, God's servant and their friend.

No matter the cost, no matter the danger, no matter the inconvenience, this couple used their teamwork to spread the Good News about Jesus. That makes them leaders worthy to be followed.

Today it's rare to find a couple like this—lifelong lovers who give everything to their marriage and their Lord. Sometimes commitment is difficult, and it would be easier to just give up. But that same devotion that kept Priscilla and Aquila together through thick and thin also fueled their commitment to Jesus, regardless of the cost.

When you think about what it means to really be in love, think about Priscilla's example. Devoted follower of Jesus. Devoted wife. The two go hand in hand. And when you stick to your commitments, your life becomes an incredible example of the joy and love that come from living God's way.

Dear Jesus, in this world it's so easy to give up on our commitments. Help me to be a girl who sticks to my commitment to you and to my future husband someday—through thick and thin. Amen.

To read the next Mirror Images profile, go to page 7.

» Read more about Priscilla (and Aquila) in Acts 18 (pages 1471–1472); Romans 16:3–5 (page 1503); 1 Corinthians 16:19 (page 1522) and 2 Timothy 4:19 (page 1578).

thority for forty-two months. [6]He opened his mouth to blaspheme God, and to slander his name and his dwelling place and those who live in heaven. [7]He was given power to make war against the saints and to conquer them. And he was given authority over every tribe, people, language and nation. [8]All inhabitants of the earth will worship the beast—all whose names have not been written in the book of life belonging to the Lamb that was slain from the creation of the world. [a]

[9]He who has an ear, let him hear.

> [10]If anyone is to go into captivity,
>   into captivity he will go.
> If anyone is to be killed [b] with the sword,
>   with the sword he will be killed.

This calls for patient endurance and faithfulness on the part of the saints.

The Beast out of the Earth

[11]Then I saw another beast, coming out of the earth. He had two horns like a lamb, but he spoke like a dragon. [12]He exercised all the authority of the first beast on his behalf, and made the earth and its inhabitants worship the first beast, whose fatal wound had been healed. [13]And he performed great and miraculous signs, even causing fire to come down from heaven to earth in full view of men. [14]Because of the signs he was given power to do on behalf of the first beast, he deceived the inhabitants of the earth. He ordered them to set up an image in honor of the beast who was wounded by the sword and yet lived. [15]He was given power to give breath to the image of the first beast, so that it could speak and cause all who refused to worship the image to be killed. [16]He also forced everyone, small and great, rich and poor, free and slave, to receive a mark on his right hand or on his forehead, [17]so that no one could buy or sell unless he had the mark, which is the name of the beast or the number of his name.

[18]This calls for wisdom. If anyone has insight, let him calculate the number of the beast, for it is man's number. His number is 666.

The Lamb and the 144,000

14 Then I looked, and there before me was the Lamb, standing on Mount Zion, and with him 144,000 who had his name and his Father's name written on their foreheads. [2]And I heard a sound from heaven like the roar of rushing waters and like a loud peal of thunder. The sound I heard was like that of harpists playing their harps. [3]And they sang a new song before the throne and before the four living creatures and the elders. No one could learn the song except the 144,000 who had been redeemed from the earth. [4]These are those who did not defile themselves with women, for they kept themselves pure. They follow the Lamb wherever he goes. They were purchased from among men and offered as firstfruits to God and the Lamb. [5]No lie was found in their mouths; they are blameless.

The Three Angels

[6]Then I saw another angel flying in midair, and he had the eternal gospel to proclaim to those who live on the earth—to every nation, tribe, language and people. [7]He said in a loud voice, "Fear God and give him glory, because the hour of his judgment has come. Worship him who made the heavens, the earth, the sea and the springs of water."

[8]A second angel followed and said, "Fallen! Fallen is Babylon the Great, which made all the nations drink the maddening wine of her adulteries."

[9]A third angel followed them and said in a loud voice: "If anyone worships the beast and his image and receives his mark on the forehead or on the hand, [10]he, too, will drink of the wine of God's fury, which has been poured full strength into the cup of his wrath. He will be tormented with burning sulfur in the presence of the holy angels and of the Lamb. [11]And the smoke of their torment rises for ever and ever. There is no rest day or night for those who worship the beast and his image, or for anyone who receives the mark of his name." [12]This calls for patient endurance on the part of the saints who obey God's commandments and remain faithful to Jesus.

---

a 8 Or written from the creation of the world in the book of life belonging to the Lamb that was slain   *b 10 Some manuscripts anyone kills*

[13]Then I heard a voice from heaven say, "Write: Blessed are the dead who die in the Lord from now on."

"Yes," says the Spirit, "they will rest from their labor, for their deeds will follow them."

The Harvest of the Earth

[14]I looked, and there before me was a white cloud, and seated on the cloud was one "like a son of man"[a] with a crown of gold on his head and a sharp sickle in his hand. [15]Then another angel came out of the temple and called in a loud voice to him who was sitting on the cloud, "Take your sickle and reap, because the time to reap has come, for the harvest of the earth is ripe." [16]So he who was seated on the cloud swung his sickle over the earth, and the earth was harvested.

[17]Another angel came out of the temple in heaven, and he too had a sharp sickle. [18]Still another angel, who had charge of the fire, came from the altar and called in a loud voice to him who had the sharp sickle, "Take your sharp sickle and gather the clusters of grapes from the earth's vine, because its grapes are ripe." [19]The angel swung his sickle on the earth, gathered its grapes and threw them into the great winepress of God's wrath. [20]They were trampled in the winepress outside the city, and blood flowed out of the press, rising as high as the horses' bridles for a distance of 1,600 stadia.[b]

Seven Angels With Seven Plagues

15 I saw in heaven another great and marvelous sign: seven angels with the seven last plagues—last, because with them God's wrath is completed. [2]And I saw what looked like a sea of glass mixed with fire and, standing beside the sea, those who had been victorious over the beast and his image and over the number of his name. They held harps given them by God [3]and sang the song of Moses the servant of God and the song of the Lamb:

> "Great and marvelous are your deeds,
>   Lord God Almighty.
> Just and true are your ways,
>   King of the ages.
> [4]Who will not fear you, O Lord,
>   and bring glory to your name?
> For you alone are holy.
> All nations will come
>   and worship before you,
>   for your righteous acts have been revealed."

[5]After this I looked and in heaven the temple, that is, the tabernacle of the Testimony, was opened. [6]Out of the temple came the seven angels with the seven plagues. They were dressed in clean, shining linen and wore golden sashes around their chests. [7]Then one of the four living creatures gave to the seven angels seven golden bowls filled with the wrath of God, who lives for ever and ever. [8]And the temple was filled with smoke from the glory of God and from his power, and no one could enter the temple until the seven plagues of the seven angels were completed.

The Seven Bowls of God's Wrath

16 Then I heard a loud voice from the temple saying to the seven angels, "Go, pour out the seven bowls of God's wrath on the earth."

[2]The first angel went and poured out his bowl on the land, and ugly and painful sores broke out on the people who had the mark of the beast and worshiped his image.

[3]The second angel poured out his bowl on the sea, and it turned into blood like that of a dead man, and every living thing in the sea died.

[4]The third angel poured out his bowl on the rivers and springs of water, and they became blood. [5]Then I heard the angel in charge of the waters say:

> "You are just in these judgments,
>   you who are and who were, the Holy One,
>   because you have so judged;

a 14 Daniel 7:13   b 20 That is, about 180 miles (about 300 kilometers)

High Stakes

My brother made me swear not to tell anyone. He said he'd go through with it for real if I said anything to Mom or Dad. I can't tell if he's kidding or what—either way, suicide isn't funny. I'm so worried. What if I come home some afternoon and find him *dead*? It would be *my* fault because I knew what was going on and didn't say anything.

Earlier this afternoon I was looking in his room for his jacket. I wanted to wear it to the game tonight. I found it wadded up on the floor, and when I leaned down to grab it, something fell out of the sleeve—a gun!

I caught up with him later at the game. He was with these guys I know are potheads and dropouts. I pulled him aside and demanded, "David, what are you doing with a gun? And why are you with these losers?!"

"What are you doing snooping around in my room?" he said angrily.

"I borrowed your jacket for tonight," I replied.

"Just mind your own business—and keep the stupid jacket," he blurted in a sharp tone. I could smell alcohol on his breath. David never drank before this year. In fact, David never used to do the stuff he's into now. Every day he locks himself in his room and blares his music. He never laughs anymore. He sleeps constantly.

"David, I don't want to come home one day and find you dead or something," I pleaded.

"I'll just make sure you don't find me, then," he said with a strange tone in his voice. Then he walked away.

suicide in focus

Suicide is a permanent solution to a temporary problem. Teens are especially susceptible to emotional depression. Only time can help us mature emotionally so we learn to weather the highs and lows of life.

»There are certain warning signs you might notice with someone who is contemplating suicide, such as sudden changes in eating or sleeping habits, giving away possessions, sudden mood swings, use of drugs or alcohol, etc.

»Threatening suicide is one secret you can't afford to keep. Tell a responsible adult in your life—a youth pastor, parent, teacher or coach—if you or someone you know is contemplating suicide. Trust them; they'll know what to do to help.

»God wants us to choose life. See Deuteronomy 30:19 (page 243); John 10:10 (1426).

»Professional Christian couseling can help. Encourage your friend to take this wise course of action.

For more on this topic, see the index on page 1656.

For a complete list of warning signs and more info on helping a friend who seems suicidal, go to www.TrueImagesBible.com

⁶for they have shed the blood of your saints and prophets,
    and you have given them blood to drink as they deserve."

⁷And I heard the altar respond:

"Yes, Lord God Almighty,
    true and just are your judgments."

⁸The fourth angel poured out his bowl on the sun, and the sun was given power to scorch people with fire. ⁹They were seared by the intense heat and they cursed the name of God, who had control over these plagues, but they refused to repent and glorify him.

¹⁰The fifth angel poured out his bowl on the throne of the beast, and his kingdom was plunged into darkness. Men gnawed their tongues in agony ¹¹and cursed the God of heaven because of their pains and their sores, but they refused to repent of what they had done.

¹²The sixth angel poured out his bowl on the great river Euphrates, and its water was dried up to prepare the way for the kings from the East. ¹³Then I saw three evil ᵃ spirits that looked like frogs; they came out of the mouth of the dragon, out of the mouth of the beast and out of the mouth of the false prophet. ¹⁴They are spirits of demons performing miraculous signs, and they go out to the kings of the whole world, to gather them for the battle on the great day of God Almighty.

¹⁵"Behold, I come like a thief! Blessed is he who stays awake and keeps his clothes with him, so that he may not go naked and be shamefully exposed."

¹⁶Then they gathered the kings together to the place that in Hebrew is called Armageddon.

¹⁷The seventh angel poured out his bowl into the air, and out of the temple came a loud voice from the throne, saying, "It is done!" ¹⁸Then there came flashes of lightning, rumblings, peals of thunder and a severe earthquake. No earthquake like it has ever occurred since man has been on earth, so tremendous was the quake. ¹⁹The great city split into three parts, and the cities of the nations collapsed. God remembered Babylon the Great and gave her the cup filled with the wine of the fury of his wrath. ²⁰Every island fled away and the mountains could not be found. ²¹From the sky huge hailstones of about a hundred pounds each fell upon men. And they cursed God on account of the plague of hail, because the plague was so terrible.

The Woman on the Beast

17 One of the seven angels who had the seven bowls came and said to me, "Come, I will show you the punishment of the great prostitute, who sits on many waters. ²With her the kings of the earth committed adultery and the inhabitants of the earth were intoxicated with the wine of her adulteries."

³Then the angel carried me away in the Spirit into a desert. There I saw a woman sitting on a scarlet beast that was covered with blasphemous names and had seven heads and ten horns. ⁴The woman was dressed in purple and scarlet, and was glittering with gold, precious stones and pearls. She held a golden cup in her hand, filled with abominable things and the filth of her adulteries. ⁵This title was written on her forehead:

MYSTERY
BABYLON THE GREAT
THE MOTHER OF PROSTITUTES
AND OF THE ABOMINATIONS OF THE EARTH.

⁶I saw that the woman was drunk with the blood of the saints, the blood of those who bore testimony to Jesus.

When I saw her, I was greatly astonished. ⁷Then the angel said to me: "Why are you astonished? I will explain to you the mystery of the woman and of the beast she rides, which has the seven heads and ten horns. ⁸The beast, which you saw, once was, now is not, and will come up out of the Abyss and go to his destruction. The inhabitants of the earth whose names have not been written in the book of life from the creation of the world will be astonished when they see the beast, because he once was, now is not, and yet will come.

⁹"This calls for a mind with wisdom. The seven heads are seven hills on which the woman sits. ¹⁰They are also seven kings. Five have fallen, one is, the other has not yet come; but when he does come, he must remain for a little while. ¹¹The beast who once was, and now is not, is an eighth king. He belongs to the seven and is going to his destruction.

¹²"The ten horns you saw are ten kings who have not yet received a kingdom, but who for one hour will receive authority as kings along with the beast. ¹³They have one purpose and will give their power and authority to the beast. ¹⁴They will make war against the Lamb, but the Lamb will over-

ᵃ 13 Greek *unclean*

come them because he is Lord of lords and King of kings—and with him will be his called, chosen and faithful followers."

¹⁵Then the angel said to me, "The waters you saw, where the prostitute sits, are peoples, multitudes, nations and languages. ¹⁶The beast and the ten horns you saw will hate the prostitute. They will bring her to ruin and leave her naked; they will eat her flesh and burn her with fire. ¹⁷For God has put it into their hearts to accomplish his purpose by agreeing to give the beast their power to rule, until God's words are fulfilled. ¹⁸The woman you saw is the great city that rules over the kings of the earth."

The Fall of Babylon

18 After this I saw another angel coming down from heaven. He had great authority, and the earth was illuminated by his splendor. ²With a mighty voice he shouted:

"Fallen! Fallen is Babylon the Great!
    She has become a home for demons
and a haunt for every evil* spirit,
    a haunt for every unclean and detestable bird.
³For all the nations have drunk
    the maddening wine of her adulteries.
The kings of the earth committed adultery with her,
    and the merchants of the earth grew rich from her excessive
        luxuries."

⁴Then I heard another voice from heaven say:

"Come out of her, my people,
    so that you will not share in her sins,
    so that you will not receive any of her plagues;
⁵for her sins are piled up to heaven,
    and God has remembered her crimes.
⁶Give back to her as she has given;
    pay her back double for what she has done.
    Mix her a double portion from her own cup.
⁷Give her as much torture and grief
    as the glory and luxury she gave herself.
In her heart she boasts,
    'I sit as queen; I am not a widow,
    and I will never mourn.'
⁸Therefore in one day her plagues will overtake her:
    death, mourning and famine.
She will be consumed by fire,
    for mighty is the Lord God who judges her.

⁹"When the kings of the earth who committed adultery with her and shared her luxury see the smoke of her burning, they will weep and mourn over her. ¹⁰Terrified at her torment, they will stand far off and cry:

" 'Woe! Woe, O great city,
    O Babylon, city of power!
    In one hour your doom has come!'

¹¹"The merchants of the earth will weep and mourn over her because no one buys their car-

truth or dare

If you feel in the minority as a Christian, don't worry. God uses even evil people to make things happen. In the end, nothing can prevent God's will.

17:17

a 2 Greek unclean

goes any more— [12]cargoes of gold, silver, precious stones and pearls; fine linen, purple, silk and scarlet cloth; every sort of citron wood, and articles of every kind made of ivory, costly wood, bronze, iron and marble; [13]cargoes of cinnamon and spice, of incense, myrrh and frankincense, of wine and olive oil, of fine flour and wheat; cattle and sheep; horses and carriages; and bodies and souls of men.

[14]"They will say, 'The fruit you longed for is gone from you. All your riches and splendor have vanished, never to be recovered.' [15]The merchants who sold these things and gained their wealth from her will stand far off, terrified at her torment. They will weep and mourn [16]and cry out:

> " 'Woe! Woe, O great city,
>   dressed in fine linen, purple and scarlet,
>   and glittering with gold, precious stones and pearls!
> [17]In one hour such great wealth has been brought to ruin!'

"Every sea captain, and all who travel by ship, the sailors, and all who earn their living from the sea, will stand far off. [18]When they see the smoke of her burning, they will exclaim, 'Was there ever a city like this great city?' [19]They will throw dust on their heads, and with weeping and mourning cry out:

> " 'Woe! Woe, O great city,
>   where all who had ships on the sea
>   became rich through her wealth!
> In one hour she has been brought to ruin!
> [20]Rejoice over her, O heaven!
>   Rejoice, saints and apostles and prophets!
> God has judged her for the way she treated you.' "

[21]Then a mighty angel picked up a boulder the size of a large millstone and threw it into the sea, and said:

> "With such violence
>   the great city of Babylon will be thrown down,
>   never to be found again.
> [22]The music of harpists and musicians, flute players and trumpeters,
>   will never be heard in you again.
> No workman of any trade
>   will ever be found in you again.
> The sound of a millstone
>   will never be heard in you again.
> [23]The light of a lamp
>   will never shine in you again.
> The voice of bridegroom and bride
>   will never be heard in you again.
> Your merchants were the world's great men.
>   By your magic spell all the nations were led astray.
> [24]In her was found the blood of prophets and of the saints,
>   and of all who have been killed on the earth."

Hallelujah!

19

After this I heard what sounded like the roar of a great multitude in heaven shouting:

> "Hallelujah!
> Salvation and glory and power belong to our God,
> [2]   for true and just are his judgments.
> He has condemned the great prostitute
>   who corrupted the earth by her adulteries.
> He has avenged on her the blood of his servants."

[3]And again they shouted:

"Hallelujah!
The smoke from her goes up for ever and ever."

⁴The twenty-four elders and the four living creatures fell down and worshiped God, who was seated on the throne. And they cried:

"Amen, Hallelujah!"

⁵Then a voice came from the throne, saying:

"Praise our God,
all you his servants,
you who fear him,
both small and great!"

⁶Then I heard what sounded like a great multitude, like the roar of rushing waters and like loud peals of thunder, shouting:

"Hallelujah!
For our Lord God Almighty
reigns.
⁷Let us rejoice and be glad
and give him glory!
For the wedding of the Lamb has
come,
and his bride has made herself ready.
⁸Fine linen, bright and clean,
was given her to wear."
(Fine linen stands for the righteous acts of the saints.)

truth or dare

While you may dream about getting married someday, did you know you're already a bride? The church (all faithful believers) is Jesus' bride. Be pure and spotless for him.

19:7–8

⁹Then the angel said to me, "Write: 'Blessed are those who are invited to the wedding supper of the Lamb!'" And he added, "These are the true words of God."

¹⁰At this I fell at his feet to worship him. But he said to me, "Do not do it! I am a fellow servant with you and with your brothers who hold to the testimony of Jesus. Worship God! For the testimony of Jesus is the spirit of prophecy."

The Rider on the White Horse

¹¹I saw heaven standing open and there before me was a white horse, whose rider is called Faithful and True. With justice he judges and makes war. ¹²His eyes are like blazing fire, and on his head are many crowns. He has a name written on him that no one knows but he himself. ¹³He is dressed in a robe dipped in blood, and his name is the Word of God. ¹⁴The armies of heaven were following him, riding on white horses and dressed in fine linen, white and clean. ¹⁵Out of his mouth comes a sharp sword with which to strike down the nations. "He will rule them with an iron scepter." ᵃ He treads the winepress of the fury of the wrath of God Almighty. ¹⁶On his robe and on his thigh he has this name written:

KING OF KINGS AND LORD OF LORDS.

¹⁷And I saw an angel standing in the sun, who cried in a loud voice to all the birds flying in midair, "Come, gather together for the great supper of God, ¹⁸so that you may eat the flesh of kings, generals, and mighty men, of horses and their riders, and the flesh of all people, free and slave, small and great."

¹⁹Then I saw the beast and the kings of the earth and their armies gathered together to make war against the rider on the horse and his army. ²⁰But the beast was captured, and with him the false prophet who had performed the miraculous signs on his behalf. With these signs he had deluded those who had received the mark of the beast and worshiped his image. The two of them were thrown alive into the fiery lake of burning sulfur. ²¹The rest of them were killed with the sword

ᵃ 15 Psalm 2:9

that came out of the mouth of the rider on the horse, and all the birds gorged themselves on their flesh.

The Thousand Years

20 And I saw an angel coming down out of heaven, having the key to the Abyss and holding in his hand a great chain. ²He seized the dragon, that ancient serpent, who is the devil, or Satan, and bound him for a thousand years. ³He threw him into the Abyss, and locked and sealed it over him, to keep him from deceiving the nations anymore until the thousand years were ended. After that, he must be set free for a short time.

⁴I saw thrones on which were seated those who had been given authority to judge. And I saw the souls of those who had been beheaded because of their testimony for Jesus and because of the word of God. They had not worshiped the beast or his image and had not received his mark on their foreheads or their hands. They came to life and reigned with Christ a thousand years. ⁵(The rest of the dead did not come to life until the thousand years were ended.) This is the first resurrection. ⁶Blessed and holy are those who have part in the first resurrection. The second death has no power over them, but they will be priests of God and of Christ and will reign with him for a thousand years.

Satan's Doom

⁷When the thousand years are over, Satan will be released from his prison ⁸and will go out to deceive the nations in the four corners of the earth—Gog and Magog—to gather them for battle. In number they are like the sand on the seashore. ⁹They marched across the breadth of the earth and surrounded the camp of God's people, the city he loves. But fire came down from heaven and devoured them. ¹⁰And the devil, who deceived them, was thrown into the lake of burning sulfur, where the beast and the false prophet had been thrown. They will be tormented day and night for ever and ever.

The Dead Are Judged

¹¹Then I saw a great white throne and him who was seated on it. Earth and sky fled from his presence, and there was no place for them. ¹²And I saw the dead, great and small, standing before the throne, and books were opened. Another book was opened, which is the book of life. The dead were judged according to what they had done as recorded in the books. ¹³The sea gave up the dead that were in it, and death and Hades gave up the dead that were in them, and each person was judged according to what he had done. ¹⁴Then death and Hades were thrown into the lake of fire. The lake of fire is the second death. ¹⁵If anyone's name was not found written in the book of life, he was thrown into the lake of fire.

The New Jerusalem

21 Then I saw a new heaven and a new earth, for the first heaven and the first earth had passed away, and there was no longer any sea. ²I saw the Holy City, the new Jerusalem, coming down out of heaven from God, prepared as a bride beautifully dressed for her husband. ³And I heard a loud voice from the throne saying, "Now the dwelling of God is with men, and he will live with them. They will be his people, and God himself will be with them and be their God. ⁴He will wipe every tear from their eyes. There will be no more death or mourning or crying or pain, for the old order of things has passed away."

⁵He who was seated on the throne said, "I am making everything new!" Then he said, "Write this down, for these words are trustworthy and true."

⁶He said to me: "It is done. I am the Alpha and the Omega, the Beginning and the End. To him who is thirsty I will give to drink without cost from the spring of the water of life. ⁷He who overcomes will inherit all this, and I will be his God and he will be my son. ⁸But the cowardly, the unbelieving, the vile, the murderers, the sexually immoral, those who practice magic arts, the idolaters and all liars—their place will be in the fiery lake of burning sulfur. This is the second death."

⁹One of the seven angels who had the seven bowls full of the seven last plagues came and said to me, "Come, I will show you the bride, the wife of the Lamb." ¹⁰And he carried me away in the Spirit to a mountain great and high, and showed me the Holy City, Jerusalem, coming down out of heaven from God. ¹¹It shone with the glory of God, and its brilliance was like that of a very precious

jewel, like a jasper, clear as crystal. [12]It had a great, high wall with twelve gates, and with twelve angels at the gates. On the gates were written the names of the twelve tribes of Israel. [13]There were three gates on the east, three on the north, three on the south and three on the west. [14]The wall of the city had twelve foundations, and on them were the names of the twelve apostles of the Lamb.

[15]The angel who talked with me had a measuring rod of gold to measure the city, its gates and its walls. [16]The city was laid out like a square, as long as it was wide. He measured the city with the rod and found it to be 12,000 stadia[a] in length, and as wide and high as it is long. [17]He measured its wall and it was 144 cubits[b] thick,[c] by man's measurement, which the angel was using. [18]The wall was made of jasper, and the city of pure gold, as pure as glass. [19]The foundations of the city walls were decorated with every kind of precious stone. The first foundation was jasper, the second sapphire, the third chalcedony, the fourth emerald, [20]the fifth sardonyx, the sixth carnelian, the seventh chrysolite, the eighth beryl, the ninth topaz, the tenth chrysoprase, the eleventh jacinth, and the twelfth amethyst.[d] [21]The twelve gates were twelve pearls, each gate made of a single pearl. The great street of the city was of pure gold, like transparent glass.

[22]I did not see a temple in the city, because the Lord God Almighty and the Lamb are its temple. [23]The city does not need the sun or the moon to shine on it, for the glory of God gives it light, and the Lamb is its lamp. [24]The nations will walk by its light, and the kings of the earth will bring their splendor into it. [25]On no day will its gates ever be shut, for there will be no night there. [26]The glory and honor of the nations will be brought into it. [27]Nothing impure will ever enter it, nor will anyone who does what is shameful or deceitful, but only those whose names are written in the Lamb's book of life.

The River of Life

22 Then the angel showed me the river of the water of life, as clear as crystal, flowing from the throne of God and of the Lamb [2]down the middle of the great street of the city. On each side of the river stood the tree of life, bearing twelve crops of fruit, yielding its fruit every month. And the leaves of the tree are for the healing of the nations. [3]No longer will there be any curse. The throne of God and of the Lamb will be in the city, and his servants will serve him. [4]They will see his face, and his name will be on their foreheads. [5]There will be no more night. They will not need the light of a lamp or the light of the sun, for the Lord God will give them light. And they will reign for ever and ever.

love ❤ notes

21:3–4

Beloved,

No more tears. No more pain or grief or death. All of it will be removed, wiped out completely. And you will be with me, and I with you. Forever.

Eternally yours,

—God

What is causing you pain right now? Imagine a time when you will no longer experience that. Thank God for his promises.

a 16 That is, about 1,400 miles (about 2,200 kilometers)   b 17 That is, about 200 feet (about 65 meters)   c 17 Or high   d 20 The precise identification of some of these precious stones is uncertain.

⁶The angel said to me, "These words are trustworthy and true. The Lord, the God of the spirits of the prophets, sent his angel to show his servants the things that must soon take place."

Jesus Is Coming

⁷"Behold, I am coming soon! Blessed is he who keeps the words of the prophecy in this book."

⁸I, John, am the one who heard and saw these things. And when I had heard and seen them, I fell down to worship at the feet of the angel who had been showing them to me. ⁹But he said to me, "Do not do it! I am a fellow servant with you and with your brothers the prophets and of all who keep the words of this book. Worship God!"

¹⁰Then he told me, "Do not seal up the words of the prophecy of this book, because the time is near. ¹¹Let him who does wrong continue to do wrong; let him who is vile continue to be vile; let him who does right continue to do right; and let him who is holy continue to be holy."

¹²"Behold, I am coming soon! My reward is with me, and I will give to everyone according to what he has done. ¹³I am the Alpha and the Omega, the First and the Last, the Beginning and the End.

¹⁴"Blessed are those who wash their robes, that they may have the right to the tree of life and may go through the gates into the city. ¹⁵Outside are the dogs, those who practice magic arts, the sexually immoral, the murderers, the idolaters and everyone who loves and practices falsehood.

¹⁶"I, Jesus, have sent my angel to give you*ᵃ* this testimony for the churches. I am the Root and the Offspring of David, and the bright Morning Star."

¹⁷The Spirit and the bride say, "Come!" And let him who hears say, "Come!" Whoever is thirsty, let him come; and whoever wishes, let him take the free gift of the water of life.

¹⁸I warn everyone who hears the words of the prophecy of this book: If anyone adds anything to them, God will add to him the plagues described in this book. ¹⁹And if anyone takes words away from this book of prophecy, God will take away from him his share in the tree of life and in the holy city, which are described in this book.

²⁰He who testifies to these things says, "Yes, I am coming soon."

Amen. Come, Lord Jesus.

²¹The grace of the Lord Jesus be with God's people. Amen.

---

genuine

hope » 22:20

They're making a sequel to your favorite movie, and you can't wait for it to come "to a theater near you." It's April, school's winding down for the year and summer can't come fast enough for you. Graduation, college, driving, dating, finding the love of your life—all things that you wish would come soon. Something far better than all those things is coming: Jesus is coming back to earth to bring an end to sin and establish his perfect kingdom forever. Are you looking forward to that? Can you say with John, "Amen. Come, Lord Jesus"?

---

a 16 The Greek is plural.

weights & measures

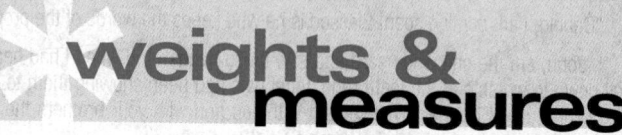

	BIBLICAL UNIT	APPROXIMATE AMERICAN EQUIVALENT		APPROXIMATE METRIC EQUIVALENT	
weights	talent (60 minas)	75	pounds	34	kilograms
	mina (50 shekels)	1¼	pounds	0.6	kilogram
	shekel (2 bekas)	²/₅	ounce	11.5	grams
	pim (²/₃ shekel)	¹/₃	ounce	7.6	grams
	beka (10 gerahs)	¹/₅	ounce	5.5	grams
	gerah	¹/₅₀	ounce	0.6	gram
length	cubit	18	inches	0.5	meter
	span	9	inches	23	centimeters
	handbreadth	3	inches	8	centimeters
capacity					
dry measure	cor [homer] (10 ephahs)	6	bushels	220	liters
	lethek (5 ephahs)	3	bushels	110	liters
	ephah (10 omers)	³/₅	bushel	22	liters
	seah (¹/₃ ephah)	7	quarts	7.3	liters
	omer (¹/₁₀ ephah)	2	quarts	2	liters
	cab (¹/₁₈ ephah)	1	quart	1	liter
liquid measure	bath (1 ephah)	6	gallons	22	liters
	hin (¹/₆ bath)	4	quarts	4	liters
	log (¹/₇₂ bath)	¹/₃	quart	0.3	liter

The figures of the table are calculated on the basis of a shekel equaling 11.5 grams, a cubit equaling 18 inches and an ephah equaling 22 liters. The quart referred to is either a dry quart (slightly larger than a liter) or a liquid quart (slightly smaller than a liter), whichever is applicable. The ton referred to in the footnotes is the American ton of 2,000 pounds.

This table is based upon the best available information, but it is not intended to be mathematically precise; like the measurement equivalents in the footnotes, it merely gives approximate amounts and distances. Weights and measures differed somewhat at various times and places in the ancient world. There is uncertainty particularly about the ephah and the bath; further discoveries may shed more light on these units of capacity.

:contents

❖ christianity 101

Perhaps the greatest mystery of life is that the Creator of the universe loves you. He spins the galaxies and directs the course of history, yet he also wants to have a personal relationship with you. He wants to be closer to you than your parents, a best friend or even a boyfriend.

First, some bad news.

Not only does God exist, but he's also holy. That means he's perfect. He's never made a mistake or done something he's regretted. He's never been guilty of a crime or broken a law. In short, God is free from any hint of sin. He's so holy and perfect that someone who sins can't even stand in his presence. Even worse news for us is that sin must be paid for—and the price is high. God said that the "wages of sin is death" (Romans 6:23) and that "without the shedding of blood there is no forgiveness" (Hebrews 9:22). Sin is serious. The Old Testament describes how the Hebrew people offered sacrifices of lambs and goats to make payment for their sins (see Leviticus 1–7).

Second, some good news.

After thousands of years of sacrifices, God provided a better way. God sent his Son, Jesus Christ, as the perfect Lamb. Jesus was both fully God and fully human. As God, he's perfect in every way. As a human, he knows what it's like to be us. He experienced the same temptations we experience, and he represents us before God at all times. He died on the cross for us (see Matthew 27:32–61). Proving he had power over all sin and death, he didn't stay dead. After three days he was raised to life again (see Matthew 28). Because he was without fault and sin, he was the perfect sacrifice—a sacrifice so complete that it's powerful enough to forgive all your sins—past, present and future (see Hebrews 10:17–18).

Jesus paid the penalty we deserve for our sins. In exchange, he gives us his righteousness. In other words, when God sees us, he doesn't see our sin any more; he sees Jesus' holiness, which has been given to us (see 2 Corinthians 5:17–21).

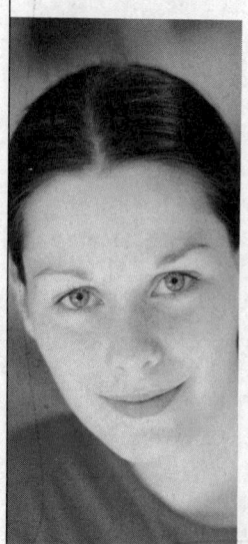

So, what's Christianity?

Simply put, Christianity is aligning yourself with Christ.

* It's admitting that you have sinned and that your sin is really offensive to God (see Psalm 53:3).

* It's recognizing that there's nothing you can do to pay for your sins (see Romans 3:23).

* It's confessing your sins to God. Even though he already knows them, he wants you to confess them—to come to grips with them (see 1 John 1:9).

* It's following him—getting to know him, reading his Word and doing your best to follow him daily (see Romans 12:1–2).

So, what's next?

If you'd like to become a follower of Christ and enjoy friendship with God, here's a great way to get started . . .

Pray.

Here's a prayer that can help you give your life to Jesus:

"God, I believe in you. I know that I am a sinner. Thank you for sending your Son, Jesus, to die for my sins and make me right with you. Please come into my life. I give it to you. I want to live for you from now on."

Read.

Spend some regular time getting to know God better. Start with the 30 Days for New Christians reading plan on page 1668. Read some of God's Word each day. Spend some time thinking about what you read and talking with God. Tell him about your day, the things you're learning, the things that frustrate you and the things that you're excited about. As a true friend, he cares about you and your life.

Don't go it alone.

The Christian life isn't meant to be lived alone. Spend time with other Christians. Get involved in a church or youth group that loves God and wants you to know him better.

Remember . . .

Above all else, remember that God's friendship with you is permanent. Sure, there will be times when you make mistakes. You'll fail, you'll sin and you'll even feel guilty. There will be times when you disappoint yourself and others. In those moments, though, remember that God is your constant companion. He remains your proud friend, loving Father and faithful Savior. He'll never leave you; he'll never forsake you. He promises you that (see Romans 8:28–39).

 If you've recently become a Christian, we'd love to hear your story. Log on to www.TrueImagesBible.com, click on the "Tell Us Your Story" link and tell us when and how you decided to follow Christ.

subject index

This subject index will help you find information about a particular topic. Look through the list; you'll probably find something you want to read about!

:a tour of the Bible

A 90-day reading plan to give you an overview of the Bible.

old testament

Day	Event/Theme/Person	Reading
1	The Universe Is Created	Genesis 1-2
2	Adam, Eve and a Slimy Serpent	Genesis 3-4
3	Noah and the Flood	Genesis 6-9
		Genesis 11:1-8
4	Job: Faithful in Affliction	Job 1-2
		Job 42
5	Abraham: Father of a Nation	Genesis 12:1-8
		Genesis 15-16
		Genesis 18:1-15
6	Isaac: A Promise Come True	Genesis 21-22
7	Jacob: A Man on the Move	Genesis 25:19-34
		Genesis 27-30:1-24
		Genesis 32:22-31
8	Joseph: Dreamer Turned King	Genesis 37
		Genesis 39-41
9	A Family Reunited	Genesis 42-45
10	Israel in Egypt	Genesis 46-47
		Exodus 1
11	Moses: A Born Leader	Exodus 2-4
12	The Passover & the Exodus	Exodus 11-12
		Exodus 13:17-14
13	The Israelites Covenant With God	Exodus 19-20
		Exodus 24
14	Instructions for the Tabernacle	Exodus 25-27
15	Numbering & Shortcomings of Israel	Numbers 1
		Numbers 11-14
16	Moses' Farewell Speech	Deuteronomy 1:1-2:23
17	Reminders to the People	Deuteronomy 4-7
18	The Golden Calf	Deuteronomy 8-10
19	Instructions on Worship	Deuteronomy 11-16
20	Laws for Living	Deuteronomy 17-20
21		Deuteronomy 21-25
22	Moses' Final Words	Deuteronomy 28-31
23	Joshua	Joshua 1-4

» 1664

reading plan

:a tour of the Bible

new testament

reading plan

30 Days for New Christians

:•30 Days With Jesus

reading plan

30 Days in the Psalms

∴30 Days of Genuine Living

Day	Theme	Passage
1	Beauty	Proverbs 11:22
2	Character	Leviticus 18:3
3	Comfort	Zephaniah 2:5
4	Confidence	Isaiah 32:17
5	Courage	Esther 4:15-16
6	Faith	Psalm 138:8
7	Forgiveness	Acts 7:59-60
8	Friendship	Genesis 14:14-16
9	Generosity	Exodus 35:21-22
10	Gratitude	Deuteronomy 8:10-18
11	Honor	Genesis 31:38-42
12	Hope	Hebrews 6:19-20
13	Humility	Job 1:20-22
14	Integrity	Job 2:7-10
15	Joy	Ecclesiastes 2:24-26
16	Life	John 6:66-69
17	Love	1 Corinthians 13:4-7
18	Obedience	Jeremiah 7:22-23
19	Patience	Psalm 40:1-3
20	Peace	Psalm 34:14
21	Persistence	2 Chronicles 8:14-15
22	Purity	Song of Songs 4:9-15
23	Purpose	Judges 3:12-30
24	Relationships	Revelation 2:4-5
25	Repentance	2 Chronicles 30:9
26	Security	Isaiah 49:15-16
27	Speech	1 Chronicles 16:23-24
28	Success	Hosea 14:9
29	Trust	Daniel 3:13-30
30	Wisdom	Proverbs 2:1-9

reading plan

:30 Stories You've Probably Never Heard

Day	Theme	Passage
1	Fire and Birds: God Lays Down the Law	Numbers 11
2	Miriam: Leprous as Snow	Numbers 12
3	Korah, Dathan and Abiran: Gulp!	Numbers 16
4	Aaron: A Budding Leader	Numbers 17
5	Moses Strikes Out	Numbers 20:1-13
6	Afraid of Snakes?	Numbers 21:4-9
7	Balaam's . . . er, Donkey	Numbers 22
8		Numbers 23-24
9	Laws for a Special People in a Special Time	Deuteronomy 21
10	Moses: End of an Era	Deuteronomy 31
11		Deuteronomy 32:44-52; 34
12	Solar Stand Still	Joshua 10:1-15
13	Ehud: Left Handed Wonder	Judges 3:12-30
14	Deborah and Jael: Girl Power	Judges 4
15	Jephthah: A Hero's Vow	Judges 11
16	A Levite: The Wickedness of Israel	Judges 19
17	David and Abigail: The Good Guy Wins	1 Samuel 25
18	Mephibosheth: Rags to Riches	2 Samuel 9
19	Elisha: Miracle Man	2 Kings 2:23-25; 4:8-37
20		2 Kings 6:1-23
21	Asa: But if You Forsake Him . . .	2 Chronicles 15
22		2 Chronicles 16
23	Joash: Kindness Forgotten	2 Chronicles 22:10-23:21
24		2 Chronicles 24
25	Josiah: Youthful Ruler	2 Chronicles 34
26		2 Chronicles 35
27	Nehemiah: Homesickness	Nehemiah 1
28		Nehemiah 2
29	Jerusalem Falls: Judgment Arrives	Jeremiah 52
30	The Writing on the Wall	Daniel 5

:·30 Stories of Love and Friendship

»reading plan

:prayer log

request

_____

date

God's response

_____

_____

request

_____

date

God's response

_____

_____

:prayer log

request
_____

_____

_____

date
God's response
_____

_____

_____

_____

request
_____

_____

_____

date
God's response
_____

_____

_____

:prayer log

request

date

God's response

request

date

God's response

:prayer log

request
_____

_____

_____

date
_____

God's response
_____

_____

_____

_____

_____

request
_____

_____

_____

date
_____

God's response
_____

_____

_____

_____

_____

:prayer log

request

date

God's response

request

date

God's response

:true images

Project Management and Editorial
Shari TeSlaa

Editorial Assistance
Julie Zahm

Katie Whitcomb

Theological Review
Andrew Sloan, M.Div., Oral Roberts University

Professional Consulting
Jeffrey Gorter, M.S.W., CAC-1 (certified addiction counselor)
Outpatient Therapist, Pine Rest Christian Mental Health Services

Production Management
Phil Herich

Art Direction
Jamie DeBruyn

Cover Design
Jamie DeBruyn

Interior Design
Kirk Luttrell, The Livingstone Corporation

Gayle Raymer

Proofreading
Peachtree Editorial and Proofreading Service, Peachtree, GA

Interior Typesetting
Blue Heron Bookcraft, Battle Ground, WA

covenant

of a True Images girl

What does it mean to be a True Images girl?

✳ *A True Images girl knows what she wants.* She's willing to give up what the world has to offer since it will never make her truly happy. Because God designed her, only he can make her complete and her life full (see John 10:10).

✳ *A True Images girl guards her mind.* She protects her mental purity from destructive images in the media and commits to filling her mind with what is pure and true (see Philippians 4:8).

✳ *A True Images girl is willing to wait.* She values her sexual purity, trusting that God's plan is best and that he will bless those who are obedient to him (see Psalm 1:1–3).

✳ *A True Images girl has genuine beauty.* She doesn't seek shallow outer beauty; she desires a deep, inner, lasting beauty (see Proverbs 31:30).

✳ *A True Images girl is true to herself.* She develops qualities of genuine character, such as love, contentment, kindness, self-control, integrity and purity (see Galatians 5:22–23).

✳ *A True Images girl looks for leaders.* She models her life after the women of God, those in the Bible and those in her own church (see Hebrews 13:7).

✳ *A True Images girl knows her worth.* She knows that her personal value is not based on her appearance, performance, popularity or accomplishments but on who she is in God's eyes (see Psalm 139:13–16).

✳ *A True Images girl's first love is Jesus.* Knowing he passionately and deeply loves her changes how she lives her life (see 1 John 3:1).

✳ *A True Images girl is a girl of the Word.* She stays connected to God through reading the Bible and growing her roots deep into Christ (see Colossians 2:6–7).

✳ *A True Images girl gives away her faith.* She knows the secret to eternal life, and she shares that freely with others who need God (see Galatians 6:9).

✳ *A True Images girl is never alone.* She knows that there are other girls out there who are striving to live for Christ just as she is (see Romans 12:4–5).

A True Images girl makes a statement—not about what she does or does not do—but about who she is.

If you want to be a True Images girl,

Take your stand
Embrace the covenant
Be true.